# Unit Conversions (Equivalents)

## Length

1 in. = 2.54 cm
1 cm = 0.3937 in.
1 ft = 30.48 cm
1 m = 39.37 in. = 3.281 ft
1 mi = 5280 ft = 1.609 km
1 km = 0.6214 mi
1 nautical mile (U.S.) = 1.151 mi = 6076 ft = 1.852 km
1 fermi = 1 femtometer (fm) = $10^{-15}$ m
1 angstrom (Å) = $10^{-10}$ m = 0.1 nm
1 light-year (ly) = $9.461 \times 10^{15}$ m
1 parsec = 3.26 ly = $3.09 \times 10^{16}$ m

## Volume

1 liter (L) = 1000 mL = 1000 $cm^3$ = $1.0 \times 10^{-3}\ m^3$ = 1.057 qt (U.S.) = 61.02 $in.^3$
1 gal (U.S.) = 4 qt (U.S.) = 231 $in.^3$ = 3.785 L = 0.8327 gal (British)
1 quart (U.S.) = 2 pints (U.S.) = 946 mL
1 pint (British) = 1.20 pints (U.S.) = 568 mL
1 $m^3$ = 35.31 $ft^3$

## Speed

1 mi/h = 1.467 ft/s = 1.609 km/h = 0.447 m/s
1 km/h = 0.278 m/s = 0.621 mi/h
1 ft/s = 0.305 m/s = 0.682 mi/h
1 m/s = 3.281 ft/s = 3.600 km/h = 2.237 mi/h
1 knot ≐ 1.151 mi/h = 0.5144 m/s

## Angle

1 radian (rad) = 57.30° = 57°18′
1° = 0.01745 rad
1 rev/min (rpm) = 0.1047 rad/s

## Time

1 day = $8.64 \times 10^4$ s
1 year = $3.156 \times 10^7$ s

## Mass

1 atomic mass unit (u) = $1.6605 \times 10^{-27}$ kg
1 kg = 0.0685 slug
[1 kg has a weight of 2.20 lb where $g = 9.80\ m/s^2$.]

## Force

1 lb = 4.45 N
1 N = $10^5$ dyne = 0.225 lb

## Energy and Work

1 J = $10^7$ ergs = 0.738 ft·lb
1 ft·lb = 1.36 J = $1.29 \times 10^{-3}$ Btu = $3.24 \times 10^{-4}$ kcal
1 kcal = $4.186 \times 10^3$ J = 3.97 Btu
1 eV = $1.602 \times 10^{-19}$ J
1 kWh = $3.60 \times 10^6$ J = 860 kcal

## Power

1 W = 1 J/s = 0.738 ft·lb/s = 3.42 Btu/h
1 hp = 550 ft·lb/s = 746 W

## Pressure

1 atm = 1.013 bar = $1.013 \times 10^5\ N/m^2$ = 14.7 $lb/in.^2$ = 760 torr
1 $lb/in.^2$ = $6.90 \times 10^3\ N/m^2$
1 Pa = 1 $N/m^2$ = $1.45 \times 10^{-4}\ lb/in.^2$

# SI Derived Units and Their Abbreviations

| Quantity | Unit | Abbreviation | In Terms of Base Units† |
|---|---|---|---|
| Force | newton | N | $kg \cdot m/s^2$ |
| Energy and work | joule | J | $kg \cdot m^2/s^2$ |
| Power | watt | W | $kg \cdot m^2/s^3$ |
| Pressure | pascal | Pa | $kg/(m \cdot s^2)$ |
| Frequency | hertz | Hz | $s^{-1}$ |
| Electric charge | coulomb | C | $A \cdot s$ |
| Electric potential | volt | V | $kg \cdot m^2/(A \cdot s^3)$ |
| Electric resistance | ohm | Ω | $kg \cdot m^2/(A^2 \cdot s^3)$ |
| Capacitance | farad | F | $A^2 \cdot s^4/(kg \cdot m^2)$ |
| Magnetic field | tesla | T | $kg/(A \cdot s^2)$ |
| Magnetic flux | weber | Wb | $kg \cdot m^2/(A \cdot s^2)$ |
| Inductance | henry | H | $kg \cdot m^2/(s^2 \cdot A^2)$ |

† kg = kilogram (mass), m = meter (length), s = second (time), A = ampere (electric current).

# Metric (SI) Multipliers

| Prefix | Abbreviation | Value |
|---|---|---|
| yotta | Y | $10^{24}$ |
| zeta | Z | $10^{21}$ |
| exa | E | $10^{18}$ |
| peta | P | $10^{15}$ |
| tera | T | $10^{12}$ |
| giga | G | $10^{9}$ |
| mega | M | $10^{6}$ |
| kilo | k | $10^{3}$ |
| hecto | h | $10^{2}$ |
| deka | da | $10^{1}$ |
| deci | d | $10^{-1}$ |
| centi | c | $10^{-2}$ |
| milli | m | $10^{-3}$ |
| micro | $\mu$ | $10^{-6}$ |
| nano | n | $10^{-9}$ |
| pico | p | $10^{-12}$ |
| femto | f | $10^{-15}$ |
| atto | a | $10^{-18}$ |
| zepto | z | $10^{-21}$ |
| yocto | y | $10^{-24}$ |

**Dear Student:**
In this course you will be using MasteringPhysics, an online tutorial and homework companion to your textbook.

## What You Need:

- ✓ **A valid email address**
- ✓ **A student access code** (packaged with your text or available for purchase at http://www.masteringphysics.com/).
- ✓ **The zip code for the University of Oregon is 97403.**

In addition, your instructor will provide you with:

- ✓ **A "Course ID"**: ______________________

## Student Registration:

- Go to http://www.masteringphysics.com/ and select the **textbook** for your course (if you do not see the text for your course, select "MasteringPhysics Stand Alone").
- If you have your new student access code, click **Register.** (*Don't have a new access code?* You can purchase access by clicking Buy Now and following those steps to register).
- Read the **License Agreement** and **Privacy Policy** and click "**I Accept**."
- Leave "**No, I am a New User**" selected, then type in your **Access Code** in the fields provided. (Enter one "word" per box, without the dashes.)
- Enter your School **Zip Code**, select your **Country** and click **Next.**
- Enter your **Name** and **Email** and select **Your School.**
- Create a personal **Login Name** and **Password**, answer the **Security Question** and click **Next**.

If successful, you will receive a **Confirmation Screen** with your registration information (this information will also be emailed to you).

## Enrolling in Your Course:

You will need to "enroll" in your MasteringPhysics course to be included in your instructor's gradebook.

- Go to www.masteringphysics.com and select the textbook for your course (or Stand Alone version).
- Under "Established User," enter the **login name and password** you created and click **Log In**.
- When prompted, enter your **Course ID.** Your instructor may also provide you with a unique **student ID** specific to this course: Be sure to enter this information EXACTLY as instructed.

Congratulations! You now have access to the powerful resources of MasteringPhysics. To access your course from now on, simply go to www.masteringphysics.com, click on your textbook, and enter the login name and password you just created.

## System Requirements & Technical Support:

- ✓ Check the "Minimum System Requirements" to make sure you have everything you need to run Mastering Physics.
- ✓ View the "Navigating Mastering Physics" page to practice using the Mastering Physics navigation.
- ✓ Go to http://www.masteringsupport.com and click "MasteringPhysics" for Frequently Asked Questions, minimum requirements, and extensive online help resources.

# PHYSICS

## Principles with Applications

**CUSTOM EDITION FOR THE UNIVERSITY OF OREGON**


**DOUGLAS C. GIANCOLI**


Taken from:

*Physics: Principles with Applications,* Sixth Edition
by Douglas C. Giancoli


**Custom Publishing**

New York Boston San Francisco
London Toronto Sydney Tokyo Singapore Madrid
Mexico City Munich Paris Cape Town Hong Kong Montreal

Cover credit: Courtesy of PhotoDisc/Getty Images, Corbis

Taken from:

*Physics: Principles with Applications,* Sixth Edition
by Douglas C. Giancoli

Published by Prentice Hall
Upper Saddle River, New Jersey 07458



This special edition published in cooperation with Pearson Custom Publishing.



Printed in the United States of America

10 9 8 7 6 5 4 3 2

2008460110

DM

**Pearson Custom Publishing** is a division of

PEARSON

www.pearsonhighered.com

ISBN 10: 0-558-02734-2
ISBN 13: 978-0-558-02734-6

# CONTENTS

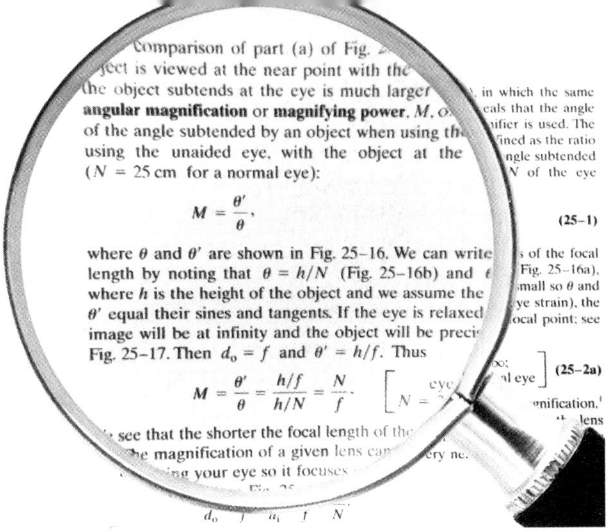

angular magnification or magnifying power
where θ and θ′ are shown in Fig. 25–16. We can write
length by noting that θ = h/N (Fig. 25–16b) and
where h is the height of the object and we assume the
θ′ equal their sines and tangents. If the eye is relaxed
image will be at infinity and the object will be preci
Fig. 25–17. Then d₀ = f and θ′ = h/f. Thus
(25–1)
(25–2a)

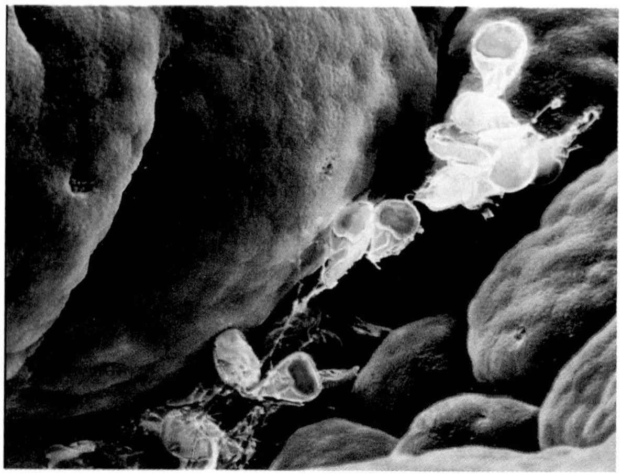

# APPLICATIONS TO BIOLOGY AND MEDICINE



# APPLICATIONS TO OTHER FIELDS AND EVERYDAY LIFE

# Problem Solving Boxes

# PREFACE

## See the World through Eyes that Know Physics

This book is written for students. It has been written to give students a thorough understanding of the basic concepts of physics in all its aspects, from mechanics to modern physics. It aims to explain physics in a readable and interesting manner that is accessible and clear, and to teach students by anticipating their needs and difficulties without oversimplifying. A second objective is to show students how useful physics is in their own lives and future professions by means of interesting applications. In addition, much effort has gone into techniques and approaches for solving problems.

This textbook is especially suited for students taking a one-year introductory course in physics that uses algebra and trigonometry but not calculus. Many of these students are majoring in biology or (pre)medicine, and others may be in architecture, technology, or the earth or environmental sciences. Many applications to these fields are intended to answer that common student query: "Why must I study physics?" The answer is that physics is fundamental to a full understanding of these fields, and here they can see how. Physics is all about us in the everyday world. It is the goal of this book to help students "see the world through eyes that know physics."

NEW ▶ Some of the new features in this sixth edition include: (1) in-text Exercises for students to check their understanding; (2) new Approach paragraphs for worked-out Examples; (3) new Examples that step-by-step follow each Problem Solving Box; (4) new physics such as a rigorously updated Chapter 33 on cosmology and astrophysics to reflect the latest results in today's "Cosmological Revolution"; and (5) new applications such as detailed physics-based descriptions of liquid crystal screens (LCD), digital cameras (with CCD), and expanded coverage of electrical safety and devices. These and other new aspects are highlighted below.

## Physics and How to Understand It

I have avoided the common, dry, dogmatic approach of treating topics formally and abstractly first, and only later relating the material to the students' own experience. My approach is to recognize that physics is a description of reality and thus to start each topic with concrete observations and experiences that students can directly relate to. Then we move on to the generalizations and more formal treatment of the topic. Not only does this make the material more interesting and easier to understand, but it is closer to the way physics is actually practiced.

A major effort has been made to not throw too much at students reading the first few chapters. The basics have to be learned first; many aspects can come later, when the students are more prepared. If we don't overwhelm students with too much detail, especially at the start, maybe they can find physics interesting, fun, and helpful—and those who were afraid may lose their fear.

The *great laws of physics* are emphasized by giving them a tan-colored screen and a marginal note in capital letters enclosed in a rectangle. All important equations are given a number to distinguish them from less useful ones. To help make clear which equations are general and which are not, the limitations of important equations are given in brackets next to the equation, such as

$$x = x_0 + v_0 t + \tfrac{1}{2}at^2. \qquad \text{[constant acceleration]}$$

*Mathematics* can be an obstacle to student understanding. I have aimed at including all steps in a derivation. Important mathematical tools, such as addition of vectors and trigonometry, are incorporated in the text where first needed, so they come with a context rather than in a scary introductory Chapter. Appendices contain a review of algebra and geometry (plus a few advanced topics: rotating reference frames, inertial forces, Coriolis effect; heat capacities of gases and equipartition of energy; Lorentz transformations). Système International (SI) units are used throughout. Other metric and British units are defined for informational purposes.

Chapter 1 is not a throwaway. It is fundamental to physics to realize that every measurement has an *uncertainty*, and how significant figures are used to reflect that. Converting units and being able to make rapid *estimates* are also basic. The cultural aspects at the start of Chapter 1 broaden a person's understanding of the world but do not have to be covered in class.

The many *applications* sometimes serve only as examples of physical principles. Others are treated in depth. They have been carefully chosen and integrated into the text so as not to interfere with the development of the physics, but rather to illuminate it. To make it easy to spot the applications, a Physics Applied marginal note is placed in the margin.

*Color* is used pedagogically to bring out the physics. Different types of vectors are given different colors (see the chart on page xxv). This book has been printed in 5 colors (5 passes through the presses) to provide better variety and definition for illustrating vectors and other concepts such as fields and rays. The photographs opening each Chapter, some of which have vectors superimposed on them, have been chosen so that the accompanying caption can be a sort of summary of the Chapter.

Some of the **new** aspects of physics and pedagogy in this sixth edition are:

***Cosmological Revolution:*** The latest results in cosmology and astrophysics are presented with the generous help of top experts in the field. We give readers the latest results and interpretations from the present, ongoing "Golden Age of Cosmology."

***Greater clarity:*** No topic, no paragraph in this book was overlooked in the search to improve the clarity of the presentation. Many changes and clarifications have been made, both small and not so small. One goal has been to eliminate phrases and sentences that may slow down the principle argument: keep to the essentials at first, give the elaborations later.

***Vector notation, arrows:*** The symbols for vector quantities in the text and Figures now have a tiny arrow over them, so they are similar to what a professor writes by hand in lecture. The letters are still the traditional boldface: thus $\vec{\mathbf{v}}$ for velocity, $\vec{\mathbf{F}}$ for force. ◀ NEW

***Exercises*** within the text, for students to check their understanding. Answers are given at the end of the Chapter. ◀ NEW

***Step-by Step Examples***, after a Problem Solving Box, as discussed on page xvii. ◀ NEW

***Conceptual Examples*** are not a new feature, but there are some new ones.

***Examples modified:*** more math steps are spelled out, and many new Examples added: see page xvii.

***Page layout:*** Complete Derivations. Even more than in the previous edition, serious attention has been paid to how each page is formatted. Great effort has been made to keep important derivations and arguments on facing pages. Students then don't have to turn back and forth. Throughout the book readers see before them, on two facing pages, an important slice of physics.

***Subheads:*** Many of the Sections within a Chapter are now divided into subsections, thus breaking up the topics into more manageable "bites." They allow "pauses" for the students to rest or catch their breath. ◀ NEW

NEW ▶ ***Marginal notes: Caution.*** Margin notes, in blue, point out main topics acting as a sort of outline and as an aid to find topics in review. They also point out applications and problem-solving hints. A new type, labeled CAUTION, points out possible misunderstandings discussed in the adjacent text.

***Deletions.*** To keep the book from being too long, and also to reduce the burden on students in more advanced topics, many topics have been shortened or streamlined, and a few dropped.

## New Physics Topics and Major Revisions

Here is a list of major changes or additions, but there are many others:

Symmetry used more, including for solving Problems
NEW ▶ Dimensional analysis, optional (Ch. 1)
More graphs in kinematics (Ch. 2)
Engine efficiency (Chs. 6, 15)
Work-energy principle, and conservation of energy: new subsection (Ch. 6); carried through in thermodynamics (Ch. 15) and electricity (Ch. 17)
NEW ▶ Force on tennis ball by racket (Ch. 7)
NEW ▶ Airplane wings, curve balls, sailboats, and other applications of Bernoulli's principle: improved and clarified with new material (Ch. 10)
Distinguish wave interference in space and in time (beats) (Ch. 11)
Doppler shift for light (Ch. 12 now, as well as Ch. 33)
NEW ▶ Giant star radius (Ch. 14)
First law of thermodynamics rewritten and extended, connected better to work-energy principle and energy conservation (Ch. 15)
Energy resources shortened (Ch. 15)
NEW ▶ SEER rating (Ch. 15)
NEW ▶ Separation of charge in nonconductors (Ch. 16)
NEW ▶ Gauss's law, optional (Ch. 16)
NEW ▶ Photocopiers and computer printers (Ch. 16)
Electric force and field directions emphasized more (Chs. 16, 17)
Electric potential related better to work, more detail (Ch. 17)
NEW ▶ Dielectric effect on capacitor with and without connection to voltage plus other details (Ch. 17)
NEW ▶ Parallel-plate capacitor derivation, optional (Ch. 17)
NEW ▶ Electric hazards, grounding, safety, current interrupters: expanded with much new material (Chs. 17, 18, 19 especially, 20, 21)
NEW ▶ Electric current, misconceptions discussed in Chapter 18
Superconductivity updated (Ch. 18)
Terminal voltage and emf reorganized, with more detail (Ch. 19)
Magnetic materials shortened (Ch. 20)
NEW ▶ Right-hand rules summarized in a Table (Ch. 20)
Faraday's and Lenz's laws expanded (Ch. 21)
AC circuits shortened (Ch. 21), displacement current downplayed (Ch. 22)
NEW ▶ Radiation pressure and momentum of EM waves (Ch. 22)
NEW ▶ Where to see yourself in a mirror; where you can actually *see* a lens image (Ch. 23)
NEW ▶ Liquid crystal displays (LCD) (Ch. 24)
NEW ▶ Physics behind digital cameras and CCD (Ch. 25)
NEW ▶ Seeing under water (Ch. 25)
Relativistic mass redone (Ch. 26)
NEW ▶ Revolutionary results in cosmology: flatness and age of universe, WMAP, SDSS, dark matter, and dark energy (Ch. 33)
NEW ▶ Specific heats of gases, equipartition of energy (Appendix)

## Problem Solving, with New and Improved Approaches

Being able to solve problems is a valuable technique in general. Solving problems is also an effective way to understand the physics more deeply. Here are some of the ways this book uses to help students become effective problem solvers.

***Problem Solving Boxes,*** about 20 of them, are found throughout the book (there is a list on p. xiii.). Each one outlines a step-by-step approach to solving problems in general, or specifically for the material being covered. The best students may find these "boxes" unnecessary (they can skip them), but many students may find it helpful to be reminded of the general approach and of steps they can take to get started. The general Problem Solving Box in Section 4–9 is placed there, after students have had some experience wrestling with problems, so they may be motivated to read it with close attention. Section 4–9 can be covered earlier if desired. Problem Solving Boxes are not intended to be a prescription, but rather a guide. Hence they sometimes follow the Examples to serve as a summary for future use.

***Problem Solving Sections*** (such as Sections 2–6, 3–6, 4–7, 6–7, 8–6, and 13–8) are intended to provide extra drill in areas where solving problems is especially important.

***Examples:*** Worked-out Examples, each with a title for easy reference, fall into four categories:

(1) The majority are regular worked-out Examples that serve as "practice problems." New ones have been added, a few old ones have been dropped, and many have been reworked to provide greater clarity, more math steps, more of "why we do it this way," and with the new Approach paragraph more discussion of the reasoning and approach. The aim is to "think aloud" with the students, leading them to develop insight. The level of the worked-out Examples for most topics increases gradually, with the more complicated ones being on a par with the most difficult Problems at the end of each Chapter. Many Examples provide relevant applications to various fields and to everyday life.

(2) ***Step-by-step Examples:*** After many of the Problem Solving Boxes, the next Example is done step-by-step following the steps of the preceding Box, just to show students how the Box can be used. Such solutions are long and can be redundant, so only one of each type is done in this manner. ◀ NEW

(3) ***Estimating Examples,*** roughly 10% of the total, are intended to develop the skills for making order-of-magnitude estimates, even when the data are scarce, and even when you might never have guessed that any result was possible at all. See, for example, Section 1–7, Examples 1–6 to 1–9.

(4) ***Conceptual Examples:*** Each is a brief Socratic question intended to stimulate student response before reading the Response given.

***APPROACH paragraph:*** Worked-out numerical Examples now all have a short introductory paragraph before the Solution, outlining an approach and the steps we can take to solve the given problem. ◀ NEW

***NOTE:*** Many Examples now have a brief "note" after the Solution, sometimes remarking on the Solution itself, sometimes mentioning an application, sometimes giving an alternate approach to solving the problem. These new Note paragraphs let the student know the Solution is finished, and now we mention a related issue(s). ◀ NEW

***Additional Examples:*** Some physics subjects require many different worked-out Examples to clarify the issues. But so many Examples in a row can be overwhelming to some students. In those places, a subhead "Additional Example(s)" is meant to suggest to students that they could skip these in a first reading. When students include them during a second reading of the Chapter, they can give power to solve a greater range of Problems. ◀ NEW

***Exercises*** within the text, after an Example or a derivation, which give students a chance to see if they have understood enough to answer a simple question or do a simple calculation. Answers are given at the bottom of the last page of each Chapter. ◀ NEW

***Problems*** at the end of each Chapter have been increased in quality and quantity. Some old ones have been replaced or rewritten to make them clearer, and/or have had their numerical values changed. Each Chapter contains a large group of Problems arranged by Section and graded according to (approximate) difficulty: level I Problems are simple, designed to give students confidence; level II are "normal" Problems, providing more of a challenge and often the combination of two different concepts; level III are the most complex and are intended as "extra credit" Problems that will challenge even superior students. The arrangement by Section number is to help the instructors choose which material they want to emphasize, and means that those Problems depend on material up to and including that Section: earlier material may also be relied upon.
***General Problems*** are unranked and grouped together at the end of each Chapter, accounting for perhaps 30% of all Problems. These are not necessarily more difficult, but they may be more likely to call on material from earlier Chapters. They are useful for instructors who want to give students a few Problems without the clue as to what Section must be referred to or how hard they are.
***Questions,*** also at the end of each Chapter, are conceptual. They help students to use and apply the principles and concepts, and thus deepen their understanding (or let them know they need to study more).

## Assigning Problems

I suggest that instructors assign a significant number of the level I and level II Problems, as well as a small number of General Problems, and reserve level III Problems only as "extra credit" to stimulate the best students. Although most level I problems may seem easy, they help to build self-confidence—an important part of learning, especially in physics. Answers to odd-numbered Problems are given in the back of the book.

## Organization

The general outline of this new edition retains a traditional order of topics: mechanics (Chapters 1 to 9); fluids, vibrations, waves, and sound (Chapters 10 to 12); kinetic theory and thermodynamics (Chapters 13 to 15); electricity and magnetism (Chapters 16 to 22); light (Chapters 23 to 25); and modern physics (Chapters 26 to 33). Nearly all topics customarily taught in introductory physics courses are included here.

The tradition of beginning with mechanics is sensible because it was developed first, historically, and because so much else in physics depends on it. Within mechanics, there are various ways to order topics, and this book allows for considerable flexibility. I prefer to cover statics after dynamics, partly because many students have trouble with the concept of force without motion. Furthermore, statics is a special case of dynamics—we study statics so that we can prevent structures from becoming dynamic (falling down). Nonetheless, statics (Chapter 9) could be covered earlier after a brief introduction to vectors. Another option is light, which I have placed after electricity and magnetism and EM waves. But light could be treated immediately after waves (Chapter 11). Special relativity (Chapter 26) could be treated along with mechanics, if desired—say, after Chapter 7.

Not every Chapter need be given equal weight. Whereas Chapter 4 or Chapter 21 might require $1\frac{1}{2}$ to 2 weeks of coverage, Chapter 12 or 22 may need only $\frac{1}{2}$ week or less. Because Chapter 11 covers standing waves, Chapter 12 could be left to the students to read on their own if little class time is available.

The book contains more material than can be covered in most one-year courses. Yet there is great flexibility in choice of topics. Sections marked with a star (*) are considered optional. They contain slightly more advanced physics material (perhaps material not usually covered in typical courses) and/or interesting applications. They contain no material needed in later Chapters, except perhaps in later optional Sections. Not all unstarred Sections must be covered; there remains considerable flexibility in the choice of material. For a brief course, all optional material could be dropped, as well as major parts of Chapters 10, 12, 19, 22, 28, 29, 32, and 33, and perhaps selected parts of Chapters 7, 8, 9, 15, 21, 24, 25, and 31. Topics not covered in class can be a resource to students for later study.

## New Applications

Relevant applications of physics to biology and medicine, as well as to architecture, other fields, and everyday life, have always been a strong feature of this book, and continue to be. Applications are interesting in themselves, plus they answer the students' question, "Why must I study physics?" New applications have been added. Here are a few of the new ones (see list after Table of Contents, pages xii and xiii).

◀ ALL ARE NEW

- Digital cameras, charge coupled devices (CCD) (Ch. 25)
- Liquid Crystal Displays (LCD) (Ch. 24)
- Electric safety, hazards, and various types of current interrupters and circuit breakers (Chs. 17, 18, 19, 20, 21)
- Photocopy machines (Ch. 16)
- Inkjet and Laser printers (Ch. 16)
- World's tallest peaks (unit conversion, Ch. 1)
- Airport metal detectors (Ch. 21)
- Capacitor uses (Ch. 17)
- Underwater vision (Ch. 25)
- SEER rating (Ch. 15)
- Curve ball (Ch. 10)
- Jump starting a car (Ch. 19)
- *RC* circuits in pacemakers, turn signals, wipers (Ch. 19)
- Digital voltmeters (Ch. 19)

## Thanks

Over 50 physics professors provided input and direct feedback on every aspect of the text: organization, content, figures, and suggestions for new Examples and Problems. The reviewers for this sixth edition are listed below. I owe each of them a debt of gratitude:

Zaven Altounian (McGill University)
David Amadio (Cypress Falls Senior High School)
Andrew Bacher (Indiana University)
Rama Bansil (Boston University)
Mitchell C. Begelman (University of Colorado)
Cornelius Bennhold (George Washington University)
Mike Berger (Indiana University)
George W. Brandenburg (Harvard University)
Robert Coakley (University of Southern Maine)
Renee D. Diehl (Penn State University)
Kathryn Dimiduk (University of New Mexico)
Leroy W. Dubeck (Temple University)
Andrew Duffy (Boston University)
John J. Dykla (Loyola University Chicago)
John Essick (Reed College)
David Faust (Mt. Hood Community College)
Gerald Feldman (George Washington University)
Frank A. Ferrone (Drexel University)
Alex Filippenko (University of California, Berkeley)
Richard Firestone (Lawrence Berkeley Lab)
Theodore Gotis (Oakton Community College)
J. Erik Hendrickson (University of Wisconsin, Eau Claire)
Laurent Hodges (Iowa State University)
Brian Houser (Eastern Washington University)
Brad Johnson (Western Washington University)
Randall S. Jones (Loyola College of Maryland)
Joseph A. Keane (St. Thomas Aquinas College)
Arthur Kosowsky (Rutgers University)
Amitabh Lath (Rutgers University)
Paul L. Lee (California State University, Northridge)
Jerome R. Long (Virginia Tech)
Mark Lucas (Ohio University)
Dan MacIsaac (Northern Arizona University)
William W. McNairy (Duke University)
Laszlo Mihaly (SUNY Stony Brook)
Peter J. Mohr (NIST)
Lisa K. Morris (Washington State University)
Paul Morris (Abilene Christian University)
Hon-Kie Ng (Florida State University)
Mark Oreglia (University of Chicago)
Lyman Page (Princeton University)
Bruce Partridge (Haverford College)
R. Daryl Pedigo (University of Washington)
Robert Pelcovits (Brown University)
Alan Pepper (Campbell School, Adelaide, Australia)
Kevin T. Pitts (University of Illinois)
Steven Pollock (University of Colorado, Boulder)
W. Steve Quon (Ventura College)
Michele Rallis (Ohio State University)
James J. Rhyne (University of Missouri, Columbia)
Paul L. Richards (University of California, Berkeley)
Dennis Rioux (University of Wisconsin, Oshkosh)
Robert Ross (University of Detroit, Mercy)
Roy S. Rubins (University of Texas, Arlington)
Wolfgang Rueckner (Harvard University Extension)
Randall J. Scalise (Southern Methodist University)
Arthur G. Schmidt (Northwestern University)
Cindy Schwarz (Vassar College)

Bartlett M. Sheinberg (Houston Community College)
J. L. Shinpaugh (East Carolina University)
Ross L. Spencer (Brigham Young University)
Mark Sprague (East Carolina University)
Michael G. Strauss (University of Oklahoma)
Chun Fu Su (Mississippi State University)
Ronald G. Taback (Youngstown State University)
Leo H. Takahashi (Pennsylvania State University, Beaver)
Ed Tryon (Hunter College, NYC)
Raymond C. Turner (Clemson University)
Robert C. Webb (Texas A&M University)
Arthur Wiggins (Oakland Community College)
Stanley Wojcicki (Stanford University)
Edward L. Wright (University of California, Los Angeles)
Andrzej Zieminski (Indiana University)

I am grateful also to those other physicist reviewers of earlier editions:

David B. Aaron (South Dakota State University)
Narahari Achar (Memphis State University)
William T. Achor (Western Maryland College)
Arthur Alt (College of Great Falls)
John Anderson (University of Pittsburgh)
Subhash Antani (Edgewood College)
Atam P. Arya (West Virginia University)
Sirus Aryainejad (Eastern Illinois University)
Charles R. Bacon (Ferris State University)
Arthur Ballato (Brookhaven National Laboratory)
David E. Bannon (Chemeketa Community College)
Gene Barnes (California State University, Sacramento)
Jacob Becher (Old Dominion University)
Paul A. Bender (Washington State University)
Michael S. Berger (Indiana University)
Donald E. Bowen (Stephen F. Austin University)
Joseph Boyle (Miami-Dade Community College)
Peter Brancazio (Brooklyn College, CUNY)
Michael E. Browne (University of Idaho)
Michael Broyles (Collin County Community College)
Anthony Buffa (California Polytechnic State University)
David Bushnell (Northern Illinois University)
Neal M. Cason (University of Notre Dame)
H. R. Chandrasekhar (University of Missouri)
Ram D. Chaudhari (SUNY, Oswego)
K. Kelvin Cheng (Texas Tech University)
Lowell O. Christensen (American River College)
Mark W. Plano Clark (Doane College)
Irvine G. Clator (UNC, Wilmington)
Albert C. Claus (Loyola University of Chicago)
Scott Cohen (Portland State University)
Lawrence Coleman (University of California, Davis)
Lattie Collins (East Tennessee State University)
Eugene Commins (University of California, Berkeley)
Sally Daniels (Oakland University)
Jack E. Denson (Mississippi State University)
Waren Deshotels (Marquette University)
Eric Dietz (California State University, Chico)
Frank Drake (University of California, Santa Cruz)
Paul Draper (University of Texas, Arlington)
Miles J. Dresser (Washington State University)
Ryan Droste (The College of Charleston)
F. Eugene Dunnam (University of Florida)
Len Feuerhelm (Oklahoma Christian University)
Donald Foster (Wichita State University)
Gregory E. Francis (Montana State University)
Philip Gash (California State University, Chico)
J. David Gavenda (University of Texas, Austin)
Simon George (California State University, Long Beach)
James Gerhart (University of Washington)
Bernard Gerstman (Florida International University)
Charles Glashausser (Rutgers University)
Grant W. Hart (Brigham Young University)
Hershel J. Hausman (Ohio State University)
Melissa Hill (Marquette University)
Mark Hillery (Hunter College)
Hans Hochheimer (Colorado State University)
Joseph M. Hoffman (Frostburg State University)
Peter Hoffman-Pinther (University of Houston, Downtown)
Alex Holloway (University of Nebraska, Omaha)
Fred W. Inman (Mankato State University)
M. Azad Islan (SUNY, Potsdam)
James P. Jacobs (University of Montana)
Larry D. Johnson (Northeast Louisiana University)
Gordon Jones (Mississippi State University)
Rex Joyner (Indiana Institute of Technology)
Sina David Kaviani (El Camino College)
Kirby W. Kemper (Florida State University)
Sanford Kern (Colorado State University)
James E. Kettler (Ohio University, Eastern Campus)
James R. Kirk (Edinboro University of Pennsylvania)
Alok Kuman (SUNY, Oswego)
Sung Kyu Kim (Macalester College)
Amer Lahamer (Berea College)
Clement Y. Lam (North Harris College)
David Lamp (Texas Tech University)
Peter Landry (McGill University)
Michael Lieber (University of Arkansas)
Bryan H. Long (Columbia State College)
Michael C. LoPresto (Henry Ford Community College)
James Madsen (University of Wisconsin, River Falls)
Ponn Mahes (Winthrop University)
Robert H. March (University of Wisconsin, Madison)
David Markowitz (University of Connecticut)
Daniel J. McLaughlin (University of Hartford)
E. R. Menzel (Texas Tech University)
Robert Messina
David Mills (College of the Redwoods)
George K. Miner (University of Dayton)
Victor Montemeyer (Middle Tennessee State University)
Marina Morrow (Lansing Community College)
Ed Nelson (University of Iowa)
Dennis Nemeschansky (USC)
Gregor Novak (Indiana University/Purdue University)
Roy J. Peterson (University of Colorado, Boulder)
Frederick M. Phelps (Central Michigan University)
Brian L. Pickering (Laney College)
T. A. K. Pillai (University of Wisconsin, La Crosse)
John Polo (Edinboro University of Pennsylvania)
Michael Ram (University of Buffalo)
John Reading (Texas A&M University)
David Reid (Eastern Michigan University)
Charles Richardson (University of Arkansas)
William Riley (Ohio State University)
Larry Rowan (University of North Carolina)
D. Lee Rutledge (Oklahoma State University)
Hajime Sakai (University of Massachusetts, Amherst)
Thomas Sayetta (East Carolina University)
Neil Schiller (Ocean County College)
Ann Schmiedekamp (Pennsylvania State University, Ogontz)
Juergen Schroeer (Illinois State University)
Mark Semon (Bates College)
James P. Sheerin (Eastern Michigan University)
Eric Sheldon (University of Massachusetts, Lowell)
K. Y. Shen (California State University, Long Beach)
Marc Sher (College of William and Mary)

Joseph Shinar (Iowa State University)
Thomas W. Sills (Wilbur Wright College)
Anthony A. Siluidi (Kent State University)
Michael A. Simon (Housatonic Community College)
Upindranath Singh (Embry-Riddle)
Michael I. Sobel (Brooklyn College)
Donald Sparks (Los Angeles Pierce College)
Thor F. Stromberg (New Mexico State University)
James F. Sullivan (University of Cincinnati)
Kenneth Swinney (Bevill State Community College)
Harold E. Taylor (Stockton State University)
John E. Teggins (Auburn University at Montgomery)
Colin Terry (Ventura College)
Michael Thoennessen (Michigan State University)
Kwok Yeung Tsang (Georgia Institute of Technology)
Jagdish K. Tuli (Brookhaven National Laboratory)
Paul Urone (CSU, Sacramento)
Linn D. Van Woerkom (Ohio State University)
S. L. Varghese (University of South Alabama)
Jearl Walker (Cleveland State University)
Robert A. Walking (University of Southern Maine)
Jai-Ching Wang (Alabama A&M University)
Thomas A. Weber (Iowa State University)
John C. Wells (Tennessee Technological)
Gareth Williams (San Jose State University)
Wendall S. Williams (Case Western Reserve University)
Jerry Wilson (Metropolitan State College at Denver)
Lowell Wood (University of Houston)
David Wright (Tidewater Community College)
Peter Zimmerman (Louisiana State University)

I owe special thanks to Profs. Bob Davis and J. Erik Hendrickson for much valuable input, and especially for working out all the Problems and producing the Solutions Manual with solutions to all Problems and Questions, as well as for providing the answers to odd-numbered Problems at the end of this book. Thanks as well to the team they managed (Profs. David Curott, Bryan Long, and Richard Louie) who also worked out all the Problems and Questions, each checking the others.

I am grateful to Profs. Robert Coakley, Lisa Morris, Kathryn Dimiduk, Robert Pelcovits, Raymond Turner, Cornelius Bennhold, Gerald Feldman, Alan Pepper, Michael Strauss, and Zaven Altounian, who inspired many of the Examples, Questions, Problems, and significant clarifications.

Chapter 33 on Cosmology and Astrophysics absorbed more time by far than any other Chapter because of the very recent, and ongoing, "revolutionary" results that I wanted to present. I was fortunate to receive generous input from some of the top experts in the field, to whom I owe a debt of gratitude: Paul Richards and Alex Filippenko (U.C. Berkeley), Lyman Page (Princeton and WMAP), Edward Wright (U.C.L.A. and WMAP), Mitchell Begelman (U. Colorado), Bruce Partridge (Haverford College), Arthur Kosowsky (Rutgers), and Michael Strauss (Princeton and SDSS).

I especially wish to thank Profs. Howard Shugart, Chris McKee, and many others at the University of California, Berkeley, Physics Department for helpful discussions, and for hospitality. Thanks also to Prof. Tito Arecchi and others at the Istituto Nazionale di Ottica, Florence, Italy.

Finally, I am most grateful to the many people at Prentice Hall with whom I worked on this project, especially to the highly professional and wonderfully dedicated Paul Corey, Karen Karlin, and Susan Fisher. The final responsibility for all errors lies with me. I welcome comments, corrections, and suggestions as soon as possible to benefit students for the next reprint.

D.C.G.

# Available Supplements and Media

**MasteringPhysics™ (www.masteringphysics.com)**
is a sophisticated online tutoring and homework system developed for physics courses. Originally developed by David Pritchard and collaborators at MIT, MasteringPhysics provides **students** with individualized online tutoring by responding to their wrong answers and providing hints for solving multi-step problems when they get stuck. It gives them immediate and up-to-date assessment of their progress, and shows where they need to practice more. MasteringPhysics provides **instructors** with a fast and effective way to assign tried-and-tested online homework assignments that comprise a range of problem types. The powerful post-assignment diagnostics allow instructors to assess the progress of their class as a whole as well as individual students, and quickly identify areas of difficulty.

## Supplements for the Student

**Student Study Guide with Selected Solutions**
**(Volume I: 0-13-035239-X, Volume II: 0-13-146557-0)**
by Joseph Boyle (Miami-Dade Community College)
This study guide contains overviews, exercises, key phrases and terms, self-study exams, questions for review, answers and solutions to selected end-of-Chapter Questions and Problems for each Chapter of this textbook.

**Student Pocket Companion (0-13-035249-7)**
by Biman Das (SUNY–Potsdam)
This 5"×7" paperback book contains a summary of *Physics: Principles with Applications*, Sixth Edition, including key concepts, equations, and tips and hints.

**Mathematics for College Physics (0-13-141427-5)**
by Biman Das (SUNY–Potsdam)
This text, for students who need help with the necessary mathematical tools, shows how mathematics is directly applied to physics, and discusses how to overcome math anxiety.

**Ranking Task Exercises in Physics, Student Edition (0-13-144851-X)**
by Thomas L. O'Kuma, David P. Maloney, and Curtis J. Hieggelke
Ranking Tasks are an innovative type of conceptual exercise that ask students to make comparative judgments about variations on a particular physical situation. This supplement includes over 200 Ranking Task Exercises covering all of classical physics except optics.

**E&M TIPERs: Electricity & Magnetism Tasks Inspired by Physics Education Research (0-13-185499-2)** by Curtis J. Hieggelke, David P. Maloney, Stephen E. Kanim, and Thomas L. O'Kuma
E&M TIPERs is a comprehensive set of conceptual exercises for electricity and magnetism based on the results of education research into how students learn physics. This workbook contains over 300 tasks in eleven different task formats.

**Interactive Physics Workbook, Second Edition (0-13-067108-8)**
by Cindy Schwarz (Vassar College), John Ertel (Naval Academy), MSC.Software
This workbook and hybrid CD-ROM package is designed to help students visualize and work with specific physics problems by means of simulations created from Interactive Physics files. The accompanying workbook/study guide provides instructions, a physics review, hints, and questions. The CD-ROM contains everything students need to run the simulations.

**Physlet® Physics (0-13-101969-4)**
by Wolfgang Christian and Mario Belloni (Davidson College)
This CD-ROM and text package has over 800 ready-to-run interactive Java applets which have been widely adopted by physics instructors. No web-server or Internet connection is required.

**MCAT Physics Study Guide (0-13-627951-1)**
by Joseph Boone (California Polytechnic State University–San Luis Obispo)
This MCAT study guide includes in-depth review, practice problems, and review questions.

## Supplements for the Instructor

**Test Item File (0-13-047311-1)**
Revised by Delena Bell Gatch (Georgia Southern University)
This test bank contains approximately 2800 multiple choice, true or false, short answer, and essay questions, of which about 25% are conceptual. All questions are ranked by level of difficulty and referenced to the corresponding text Section of this book. The *Test Item File* is also available in electronic format on the *Instructor Resource Center on CD-ROM*.

**Instructor's Solutions Manual**
**(Volume I: 0-13-035237-3, Volume II: 0-13-141545-X)**
by Bob Davis (Taylor University) and J. Erik Hendrickson (University of Wisconsin-Eau Claire)
The Solutions Manual contains detailed worked solutions to every end-of-Chapter Problem in this textbook, as well as answers to the Questions. Electronic versions are available on the *Instructor Resource Center on CD-ROM* for instructors with Microsoft Word or Word-compatible software.

**Instructor's Resource Manual and Instructor Notes on ConcepTest Questions (0-13-035251-9)**
Prepared by Katherine Whatley and Judith Beck (both of the University of North Carolina, Asheville), the IRM contains lecture outlines, notes, demonstration suggestions, readings, and other teaching resources. The Instructor Notes, prepared by Cornelius Bennhold and Gerald Feldman (both of The George Washington University), contains an overview of the development and implementation of ConcepTests, as well as instructor notes for each ConcepTest found on the *Instructor Resource Center on CD-ROM*.

**Instructor Resource Center on CD-ROM (0-13-035246-2)**
This three-CD set contains all text illustrations and tables in JPEG, Microsoft PowerPoint™, and Adobe PDF formats. Instructors can preview and sequence images, perform key-word searches, add lecture notes, and incorporate their own digital resources. Also contained is TestGenerator, an easy-to-use networkable program for creating quizzes and tests. The CD-ROMs also contain the instructor's version of *Physlet® Physics*, the *Physics You Can See* demonstration videos, additional Powerpoint Presentations, electronic versions of the *Test Item File*, the *Instructor's Solutions Manual*, the *Instructor's Resource Manual*, and the end-of-chapter Questions and Problems from *Physics: Principles with Applications, sixth edition.*

**Transparency Pack (0-13-035245-4)**
The pack includes approximately 400 full-color transparencies of images and Tables from this book.

**"Physics You Can See" Video (0-205-12393-7)**
This video contains eleven classic physics demonstrations, each 2 to 5 minutes long.

## OneKey Course Management Systems

WebCT, BlackBoard, and CourseCompass allow instructors to assign and grade homework online, manage their roster and grade book, and post course-related documents.

The content cartridges for WebCT, BlackBoard, and CourseCompass are text-specific and include:

*Just-in-Time Teaching* tools: Warm-Ups, Puzzles, and Applications, by Gregor Novak and Andrew Gavrin (Indiana University–Purdue University, Indianapolis)

*Ranking Task Exercises* by Thomas L. O'Kuma (Lee College), David P. Maloney (Indiana–Purdue Universities, Fort Wayne), and Curtis J. Hieggelke (Joliet JC)

*Physlet® Problems* by Wolfgang Christian and Mario Belloni (Davidson College)

*Algorithmic Practice Problems* by Carl Adler (East Carolina University)

*MCAT Study Guide* with questions from "Kaplan Test Prep and Admissions"

**Companion Website (http://physics.prenhall.com/giancolippa)**
This site contains Practice Objectives, Problems, Practice Questions, Destinations (links to related sites), and Applications with links to related sites. Practice Problems and Questions are scored by computer, and results can be automatically e-mailed to the instructor.

## Online Homework Systems

**WebAssign (www.webassign.net)**
WebAssign is a nationally hosted online homework system that allows instructors to create, post, collect, grade, and record assignments from a ready-to-use database of Problems and Questions from this textbook.

**CAPA and LON-CAPA**
Computer Assisted Personalized Approach (CAPA) is a locally hosted online homework system that allows instructors to create, post, collect, grade, and record assignments from a ready-to-use database of Problems and Questions from this textbook. The Learning Online Network with a Computer Assisted Personalized Approach (LON-CAPA) is an integrated system for online learning and assessment. It consists of a course management system, an individualized homework and automatic grading system, a data collection and data mining system, and a content delivery system that will provide gateways to and from NSF's National STEM Digital Library.

## NOTES TO STUDENTS (AND INSTRUCTORS) ON THE FORMAT

1. Sections marked with a star (*) are considered optional. They can be omitted without interrupting the main flow of topics. No later material depends on them except possibly later starred Sections. They may be fun to read.
2. The customary conventions are used: symbols for quantities (such as $m$ for mass) are italicized, whereas units (such as m for meter) are not italicized. Symbols for vectors are shown in boldface with a small arrow above: $\vec{\mathbf{F}}$.
3. Few equations are valid in all situations. Where practical, the limitations of important equations are stated in square brackets next to the equation. The equations that represent the great laws of physics are displayed with a tan background, as are a few other indispensable equations.
4. The number of significant figures (Section 1–4) should not be assumed to be greater or less than given: if a number is stated as (say) 6, with its units, it is meant to be 6 and not 6.0 or 6.00.
5. At the end of each Chapter is a set of Questions that students should attempt to answer (to themselves at least). These are followed by Problems which are ranked as level I, II, or III, according to estimated difficulty, with level I Problems being the easiest. Level II are normal Problems, and level III are for "extra credit." These ranked Problems are arranged by Section, but Problems for a given Section may depend on earlier material as well. There follows a group of General Problems, which are not arranged by Section nor ranked as to difficulty. Questions and Problems that relate to optional Sections are starred (*). Answers to odd-numbered Problems are given at the end of the book.
6. Being able to solve problems is a crucial part of learning physics, and provides a powerful means for understanding the concepts and principles. This book contains many aids to problem solving: (a) worked-out Examples and their solutions in the text (set off with a vertical blue line in the margin) which should be studied as an integral part of the text; (b) some of the worked-out Examples are Estimation Examples, which show how rough or approximate results can be obtained even if the given data are sparse (see Section 1–7); (c) special "Problem Solving Boxes" placed throughout the text to suggest a step-by-step approach to problem solving for a particular topic—but don't get the idea that every topic has its own "techniques," because the basics remain the same; some of these "Boxes" are followed by an Example that is solved by explicitly following the suggested steps; (d) special problem-solving Sections; (e) "Problem Solving" marginal notes (see point 9 below) which refer to hints for solving problems within the text; (f) Exercises within the text that you should work out immediately, and then check your response against the answer given at the bottom of the last page of that Chapter; (g) the Problems themselves at the end of each Chapter (point 5 above).
7. Conceptual Examples are conceptual rather than numerical. Each poses a question or two, which hopefully starts you to think and come up with a response. Give yourself a little time to come up with your own response before reading the Response given.
8. "Additional Examples" subheadings contain Examples that you could skip on a first reading, in case you are feeling overwhelmed. But a day or two later, when you read the Chapter a second time, try to work through these Examples too because they can give you more power in doing a wide range of Problems.
9. Margin notes: brief notes in the margin of almost every page are printed in blue and are of five types: (a) ordinary notes (the majority) that serve as a sort of outline of the text and can help you later locate important concepts and equations; (b) notes that refer to the great laws and principles of physics, and these are in capital letters and in a box for emphasis; (c) notes that refer to a problem-solving hint or technique treated in the text, and these say "Problem Solving"; (d) notes that refer to an application of physics in the text or an Example, and these say "Physics Applied"; (e) "Caution" notes that point out a possible misconception spelled out in the adjacent text.
10. This book is printed in full color—but not simply to make it more attractive. The color is used above all in the Figures, to give them greater clarity for our analysis. The Table on the next page is a summary of which colors are used for the different kinds of vectors, for field lines, and for other symbols and objects. These colors are used consistently throughout the book.
11. Math review, plus some additional topics, are found in Appendices. Useful data, conversion factors, and math formulas are found inside the front and back covers.

# USE OF COLOR

## Vectors

A general vector

resultant vector (sum) is slightly thicker

components of any vector are dashed

Displacement ($\vec{\mathbf{D}}, \vec{\mathbf{r}}$)

Velocity ($\vec{\mathbf{v}}$)

Acceleration ($\vec{\mathbf{a}}$)

Force ($\vec{\mathbf{F}}$)

Force on second or third object in same figure

Momentum ($\vec{\mathbf{p}}$ or $m\vec{\mathbf{v}}$)

Angular momentum ($\vec{\mathbf{L}}$)

Angular velocity ($\vec{\boldsymbol{\omega}}$)

Torque ($\vec{\boldsymbol{\tau}}$)

Electric field ($\vec{\mathbf{E}}$)

Magnetic field ($\vec{\mathbf{B}}$)

## Electricity and magnetism

Electric field lines

Equipotential lines

Magnetic field lines

Electric charge (+) — (+) or ● +

Electric charge (–) — (–) or ● –

## Electric circuit symbols

Wire

Resistor

Capacitor

Inductor

Battery

## Optics

Light rays

Object

Real image (dashed)

Virtual image (dashed and paler)

## Other

Energy level (atom, etc.)

Measurement lines — |←1.0 m→|

Path of a moving object

Direction of motion or current

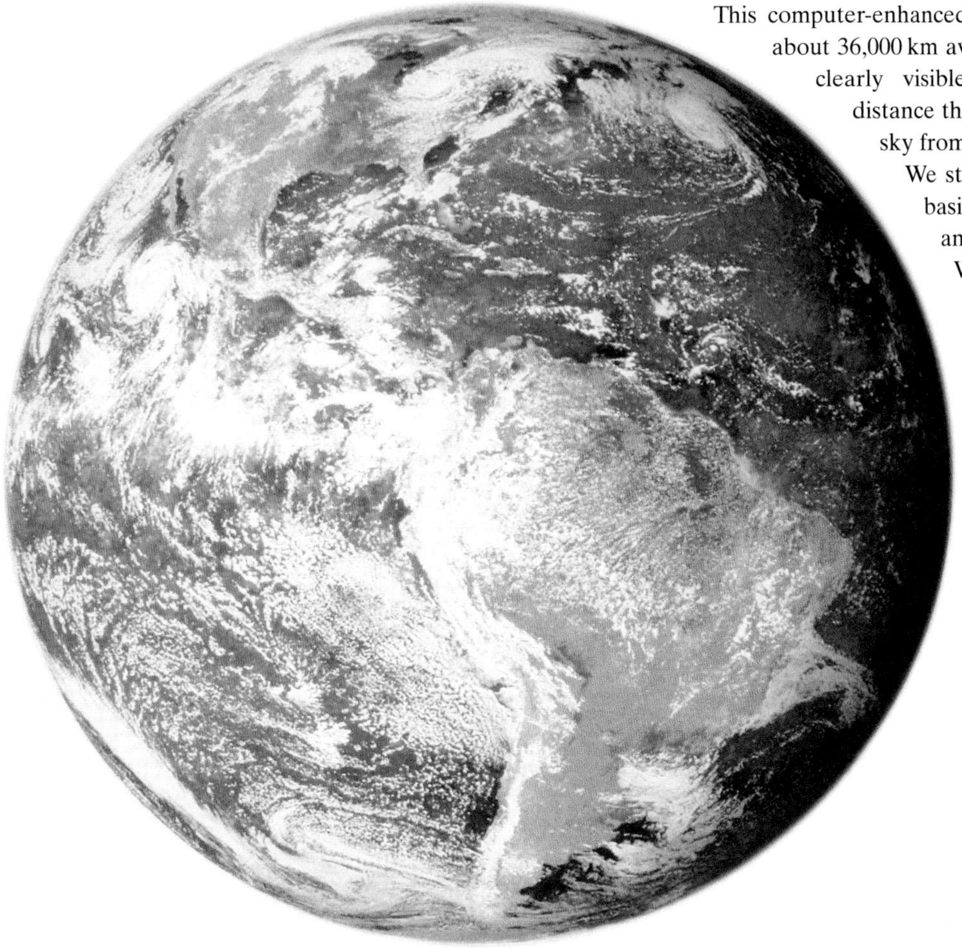

This computer-enhanced photo of Earth was taken from about 36,000 km away. North and South America are clearly visible below the clouds. From this distance the "sky" is black. (Why we see blue sky from Earth is discussed in Chapter 24.) We start this Chapter by learning some basics about science and its theories, and about measurement and units. We also learn how to make quick estimates.

CHAPTER 1

# Introduction, Measurement, Estimating

Physics is the most basic of the sciences. It deals with the behavior and structure of matter. The field of physics is usually divided into *classical physics* which includes motion, fluids, heat, sound, light, electricity, and magnetism; and *modern physics* which includes the topics of relativity, atomic structure, condensed matter, nuclear physics, elementary particles, and cosmology and astrophysics. We will cover all these topics in this book, beginning with motion (or mechanics, as it is often called). But before we begin on the physics itself, we take a brief look at how this overall activity called "science," including physics, is actually practiced.

## 1–1 The Nature of Science

The principal aim of all sciences, including physics, is generally considered to be the search for order in our observations of the world around us. Many people think that science is a mechanical process of collecting facts and devising theories. But it is not so simple. Science is a creative activity that in many respects resembles other creative activities of the human mind.

**FIGURE 1–1** Aristotle is the central figure (dressed in blue) at the top of the stairs (the figure next to him is Plato) in this famous Renaissance portrayal of *The School of Athens*, painted by Raphael around 1510. Also in this painting, considered one of the great masterpieces in art, are Euclid (drawing a circle at the lower right), Ptolemy (extreme right with globe), Pythagoras, Socrates, and Diogenes.

*Observation and experiment*

One important aspect of science is **observation** of events, which includes the design and carrying out of experiments. But observation requires imagination, for scientists can never include everything in a description of what they observe. Hence, scientists must make judgments about what is relevant in their observations and experiments. Consider, for example, how two great minds, Aristotle (384–322 B.C.; Fig. 1–1) and Galileo (1564–1642; Fig. 2–17), interpreted motion along a horizontal surface. Aristotle noted that objects given an initial push along the ground (or on a tabletop) always slow down and stop. Consequently, Aristotle argued that the natural state of an object is at rest. Galileo, in his reexamination of horizontal motion in the early 1600s, imagined that if friction could be eliminated, an object given an initial push along a horizontal surface would continue to move indefinitely without stopping. He concluded that for an object to be in motion was just as natural as for it to be at rest. By inventing a new approach, Galileo founded our modern view of motion (Chapters 2, 3, and 4). Galileo made this intellectual leap conceptually, without actually eliminating friction.

*Motion is as natural as rest*

Observation, with careful experimentation and measurement, is one side of the scientific process. The other side is the invention or creation of **theories** to explain and order the observations. Theories are never derived directly from observations. Observations may help inspire a theory, and theories are accepted or rejected based on observation and experiment.

*Theories*

Theories are inspirations that come from the minds of human beings. For example, the idea that matter is made up of atoms (the atomic theory) was not arrived at by direct observation of atoms—we can't see atoms directly. Rather, the idea sprang from creative minds. The theory of relativity, the electromagnetic theory of light, and Newton's law of universal gravitation were likewise the result of human imagination.

The great theories of science may be compared, as creative achievements, with great works of art or literature. But how does science differ from these other creative activities? One important difference is that science requires **testing** of its ideas or theories to see if their predictions are borne out by experiment. But theories are not "proved" by testing. First of all, no measuring instrument is perfect, so exact confirmation cannot be possible. Furthermore, it is not possible to test a theory for every possible set of circumstances. Hence a theory can never be absolutely "proved." Indeed, the history of science tells us that long-held theories are sometimes replaced by new ones.

*Testing a theory*

*Theory acceptance*

A new theory is accepted by scientists in some cases because its predictions are quantitatively in better agreement with experiment than those of the older

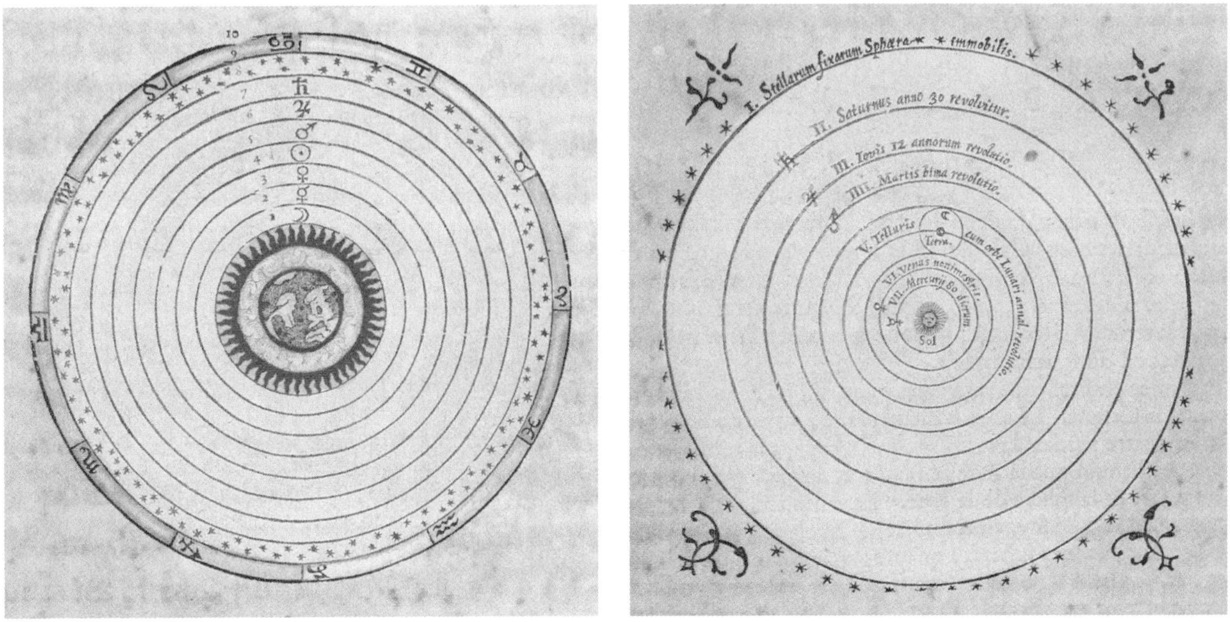

(a) (b)

**FIGURE 1–2** (a) Ptolemy's geocentric view of the universe. Note at the center the four elements of the ancients: Earth, water, air (clouds around the Earth), and fire; then the circles, with symbols, for the Moon, Mercury, Venus, Sun, Mars, Jupiter, Saturn, the fixed stars, and the signs of the zodiac. (b) An early representation of Copernicus's heliocentric view of the universe with the Sun at the center. (See Chapter 5.)

theory. But in many cases, a new theory is accepted only if it explains a greater *range* of phenomena than does the older one. Copernicus's Sun-centered theory of the universe (Fig. 1–2b), for example, was originally no more accurate than Ptolemy's Earth-centered theory (Fig. 1–2a) for predicting the motion of heavenly bodies (Sun, Moon, planets). But Copernicus's theory had consequences that Ptolemy's did not, such as predicting the moonlike phases of Venus. A simpler and richer theory, one which unifies and explains a greater variety of phenomena, is more useful and beautiful to a scientist. And this aspect, as well as quantitative agreement, plays a major role in the acceptance of a theory.

An important aspect of any theory is how well it can quantitatively predict phenomena, and from this point of view a new theory may often seem to be only a minor advance over the old one. For example, Einstein's theory of relativity gives predictions that differ very little from the older theories of Galileo and Newton in nearly all everyday situations. Its predictions are better mainly in the extreme case of very high speeds close to the speed of light. But quantitative prediction is not the only important outcome of a theory. Our view of the world is affected as well. As a result of Einstein's theory of relativity, for example, our concepts of space and time have been completely altered, and we have come to see mass and energy as a single entity (via the famous equation $E = mc^2$).

**FIGURE 1–3** Studies on the forces in structures by Leonardo da Vinci (1452–1519).

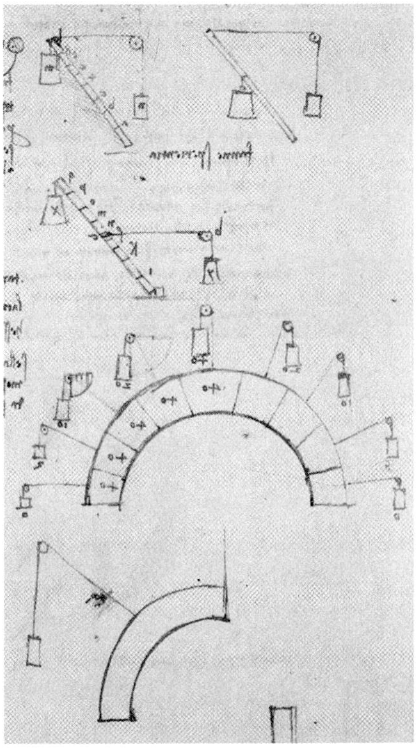

## 1–2 Physics and its Relation to Other Fields

For a long time science was more or less a united whole known as natural philosophy. Not until a century or two ago did the distinctions between physics and chemistry and even the life sciences become prominent. Indeed, the sharp distinction we now see between the arts and the sciences is itself but a few centuries old. It is no wonder then that the development of physics has both influenced and been influenced by other fields. For example, the notebooks (Fig. 1–3) of Leonardo da Vinci, the great Renaissance artist, researcher, and engineer, contain the first references to the forces acting within a structure, a subject we consider as physics today; but then, as now, it has great relevance to architecture and building.

(a) (b)

**FIGURE 1–4** (a) This Roman aqueduct was built 2000 years ago and still stands. (b) Collapse of the Hartford Civic Center in 1978, just two years after it was built.

Early work in electricity that led to the discovery of the electric battery and electric current was done by an eighteenth-century physiologist, Luigi Galvani (1737–1798). He noticed the twitching of frogs' legs in response to an electric spark and later that the muscles twitched when in contact with two dissimilar metals (Chapter 18). At first this phenomenon was known as "animal electricity," but it shortly became clear that electric current itself could exist in the absence of an animal.

*Physics applies to many fields*

Physics is used in many fields. A zoologist, for example, may find physics useful in understanding how prairie dogs and other animals can live underground without suffocating. A physical therapist will do a more effective job if aware of the principles of center of gravity and the action of forces within the human body. A knowledge of the operating principles of optical and electronic equipment is helpful in a variety of fields. Life scientists and architects alike will be interested in the nature of heat loss and gain in human beings and the resulting comfort or discomfort. Architects themselves may not have to calculate, for example, the dimensions of the pipes in a heating system or the forces involved in a given structure to determine if it will remain standing (Fig. 1–4). But architects must know the principles behind these analyses in order to make realistic designs and to communicate effectively with engineering consultants and other specialists. From the aesthetic or psychological point of view, too, architects must be aware of the forces involved in a structure—for instability, even if only illusory, can be discomforting to those who must live or work in the structure.

The list of ways in which physics relates to other fields is extensive. In the Chapters that follow we will discuss many such applications as we carry out our principal aim of explaining basic physics.

## 1–3 Models, Theories, and Laws

*Models*

When scientists are trying to understand a particular set of phenomena, they often make use of a **model**. A model, in the scientific sense, is a kind of analogy or mental image of the phenomena in terms of something else we are already familiar with. One example is the wave model of light. We cannot see waves of light as we can water waves. But it is valuable to think of light as if it were made up of waves, because experiments indicate that light behaves in many respects as water waves do.

The purpose of a model is to give us an approximate mental or visual picture—something to hold onto—when we cannot see or understand what actually is happening. Models often give us a deeper understanding: the analogy to a known system (for instance, water waves in the above example) can suggest new experiments to perform and can provide ideas about what other related phenomena might occur.

*Theories (vs. models)*

You may wonder what the difference is between a theory and a model. Usually, a model is relatively simple and provides a structural similarity to the phenomena being studied. A **theory** is broader, more detailed, and can give quantitatively testable predictions, often with great precision. It is important, however, not to confuse a model or a theory with the real system or the phenomena themselves.

*Laws and principles*

Scientists give the title **law** to certain concise but general statements about how nature behaves (that energy is conserved, for example). Sometimes the statement takes the form of a relationship or equation between quantities (such as Newton's second law, $F = ma$).

To be called a law, a statement must be found experimentally valid over a wide range of observed phenomena. For less general statements, the term **principle** is often used (such as Archimedes' principle).

Scientific laws are different from political laws in that the latter are *prescriptive*: they tell us how we ought to behave. Scientific laws are *descriptive*: they do not say how nature *should* behave, but rather are meant to describe how nature *does* behave. As with theories, laws cannot be tested in the infinite variety of cases possible. So we cannot be sure that any law is absolutely true. We use the term "law" when its validity has been tested over a wide range of cases, and when any limitations and the range of validity are clearly understood.

Scientists normally do their work as if the accepted laws and theories were true. But they are obliged to keep an open mind in case new information should alter the validity of any given law or theory.

## 1–4 Measurement and Uncertainty; Significant Figures

In the quest to understand the world around us, scientists try to work out relationships among physical quantities that can be measured.

### Uncertainty

*Every measurement has an uncertainty*

Accurate, precise measurements are an important part of physics. But no measurement is absolutely precise. There is an uncertainty associated with every measurement. Among the most important sources of uncertainty, other than blunders, are the limited accuracy of every measuring instrument and the inability to read an instrument beyond some fraction of the smallest division shown. For example, if you were to use a centimeter ruler to measure the width of a board (Fig. 1–5), the result could be claimed to be precise to about 0.1 cm (1 mm), the smallest division on the ruler, although half of this value might be a valid claim as well. The reason for this is that it is difficult for the observer to estimate between the smallest divisions. Furthermore, the ruler itself may not have been manufactured to an accuracy any better than this.[†]

**FIGURE 1–5** Measuring the width of a board with a centimeter ruler. Accuracy is about ± 1 mm.

[†]There is a technical difference between "precision" and "accuracy." **Precision** in a strict sense refers to the repeatability of the measurement using a given instrument. For example, if you measure the width of a board many times, getting results like 8.81 cm, 8.85 cm, 8.78 cm, 8.82 cm (estimating between the 0.1-cm marks as best as possible each time), you could say the measurements give a *precision* a bit better than 0.1 cm. **Accuracy** refers to how close a measurement is to the true value. For example, if the ruler shown in Fig. 1–5 was manufactured with a 2% error, the accuracy of its measurement of the board's width (about 8.8 cm) would be about 2% of 8.8 cm, or about ± 0.2 cm. Estimated uncertainty is meant to take both accuracy and precision into account.

*Stating the uncertainty*

When giving the result of a measurement, it is important to state the **estimated uncertainty** in the measurement. For example, the width of a board might be written as $8.8 \pm 0.1$ cm. The $\pm 0.1$ cm ("plus or minus 0.1 cm") represents the estimated uncertainty in the measurement, so that the actual width most likely lies between 8.7 and 8.9 cm. The **percent uncertainty** is simply the ratio of the uncertainty to the measured value, multiplied by 100. For example, if the measurement is 8.8 and the uncertainty about 0.1 cm, the percent uncertainty is

$$\frac{0.1}{8.8} \times 100\% \approx 1\%$$

where $\approx$ means "is roughly equal to."

*Assumed uncertainty*

Often the uncertainty in a measured value is not specified explicitly. In such cases, the uncertainty is generally assumed to be one or a few units in the last digit specified. For example, if a length is given as 8.8 cm, the uncertainty is assumed to be about 0.1 cm or 0.2 cm. It is important in this case that you do not write 8.80 cm, for this implies an uncertainty on the order of 0.01 cm; it assumes that the length is probably between 8.79 cm and 8.81 cm, when actually you believe it is between 8.7 and 8.9 cm.

CONCEPTUAL EXAMPLE 1–1 **Is the diamond yours?** A friend asks to borrow your precious diamond for a day to show her family. You are a bit worried, so you carefully have your diamond weighed on a scale which reads 8.17 grams. The scale's accuracy is claimed to be $\pm 0.05$ gram. The next day you weigh the returned diamond again, getting 8.09 grams. Is this your diamond?

**RESPONSE** The scale readings are measurements and do not necessarily give the "true" value of the mass. Each measurement could have been high or low by up to 0.05 gram or so. The actual mass of your diamond lies most likely between 8.12 grams and 8.22 grams. The actual mass of the returned diamond is most likely between 8.04 grams and 8.14 grams. These two ranges overlap, so there is not a strong reason to doubt that the returned diamond is yours, at least based on the scale readings.

## Significant Figures

*Which digits are significant?*

The number of reliably known digits in a number is called the number of **significant figures**. Thus there are four significant figures in the number 23.21 cm and two in the number 0.062 cm (the zeros in the latter are merely place holders that show where the decimal point goes). The number of significant figures may not always be clear. Take, for example, the number 80. Are there one or two significant figures? If we say it is *about* 80 km between two cities, there is only one significant figure (the 8) since the zero is merely a place holder. If it is *exactly* 80 km within an accuracy of 1 or 2 km, then the 80 has two significant figures.[†] If it is precisely 80 km, to within $\pm 0.1$ km, then we write 80.0 km.

When making measurements, or when doing calculations, you should avoid the temptation to keep more digits in the final answer than is justified. For example, to calculate the area of a rectangle 11.3 cm by 6.8 cm, the result of multiplication would be 76.84 cm$^2$. But this answer is clearly not accurate to 0.01 cm$^2$, since (using the outer limits of the assumed uncertainty for each measurement) the result could be between $11.2\text{ cm} \times 6.7\text{ cm} = 75.04\text{ cm}^2$ and $11.4\text{ cm} \times 6.9\text{ cm} = 78.66\text{ cm}^2$. At best, we can quote the answer as 77 cm$^2$, which implies an uncertainty of about 1 or 2 cm$^2$. The other two digits (in the number 76.84 cm$^2$) must be dropped since they are not significant. As a rough general rule (i.e., in the absence of a detailed consideration of uncertainties), we can say that *the final result of a multiplication or division should have only as many digits as the number with the least number of significant figures used in the calculation*. In our example, 6.8 cm has the least number of significant figures, namely two. Thus the result 76.84 cm$^2$ needs to be rounded off to 77 cm$^2$.

**PROBLEM SOLVING**

*Number of significant figures in final result should be same as least significant input value*

[†]If the 80 has two significant figures, some people prefer to write it 80., with a decimal point. This is not usually done, so the number of significant figures in 80 can be ambiguous unless something is said about it such as "about" (meaning $80 \pm 10$), or "very nearly" or "precisely" (meaning $80 \pm 1$).

**EXERCISE A** The area of a rectangle 4.5 cm by 3.25 cm is correctly given by (*a*) 14.625 $\text{cm}^2$; (*b*) 14.63 $\text{cm}^2$; (*c*) 14.6 $\text{cm}^2$; (*d*) 15 $\text{cm}^2$.

When adding or subtracting numbers, the final result is no more accurate than the least accurate number used. For example, the result of subtracting 0.57 from 3.6 is 3.0 (and not 3.03).

**CAUTION**

*Calculators err with significant figures*

Keep in mind when you use a calculator that all the digits it produces may not be significant. When you divide 2.0 by 3.0, the proper answer is 0.67, and not some such thing as 0.666666666. Digits should not be quoted in a result, unless they are truly significant figures. However, to obtain the most accurate result, you should normally *keep one or more extra significant figures throughout a calculation, and round off only in the final result.* (With a calculator, you can keep all its digits in intermediate results.) Note also that calculators sometimes give too few significant figures. For example, when you multiply $2.5 \times 3.2$, a calculator may give the answer as simply 8. But the answer is good to two significant figures, so the proper answer is 8.0. See Fig. 1–6.

**PROBLEM SOLVING**

*Report only the proper number of significant figures in the final result. Keep extra digits during the calculation.*

(a) (b)

**FIGURE 1–6** These two calculators show the wrong number of significant figures. In (a), 2.0 was divided by 3.0. The correct final result would be 0.67. In (b), 2.5 was multiplied by 3.2. The correct result is 8.0.

**EXERCISE B** Do 0.00324 and 0.00056 have the same number of significant figures?

Be careful not to confuse significant figures with the number of decimal places.

**EXERCISE C** For each of the following numbers, state the number of significant figures and the number of decimal places: (*a*) 1.23; (*b*) 0.123; (*c*) 0.0123.

CONCEPTUAL EXAMPLE 1–2 **Significant figures.** Using a protractor (Fig. 1–7), you measure an angle to be 30°. (*a*) How many significant figures should you quote in this measurement? (*b*) Use a calculator to find the cosine of the angle you measured.

**RESPONSE** (*a*) If you look at a protractor, you will see that the precision with which you can measure an angle is about one degree (certainly not 0.1°). So you can quote two significant figures, namely, 30° (not 30.0°). (*b*) If you enter cos 30° in your calculator, you will get a number like 0.866025403. However, the angle you entered is known only to two significant figures, so its cosine is correctly given by 0.87; i.e., you must round your answer to two significant figures.

**NOTE** We discuss trigonometric functions like cosine in Chapter 3.

**FIGURE 1–7** Example 1–2. A protractor used to measure an angle.

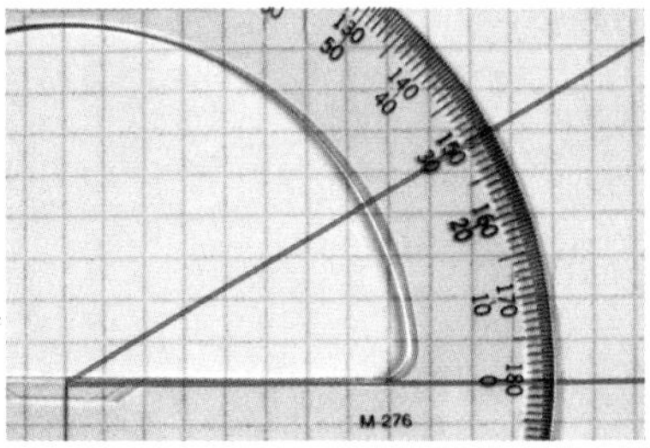

## Scientific Notation

We commonly write numbers in "powers of ten," or "scientific" notation—for instance 36,900 as $3.69 \times 10^4$, or 0.0021 as $2.1 \times 10^{-3}$. One advantage of scientific notation (discussed in Appendix A) is that it allows the number of significant figures to be clearly expressed. For example, it is not clear whether 36,900 has three, four, or five significant figures. With powers of ten notation the ambiguity can be avoided: if the number is known to an accuracy of three significant figures, we write $3.69 \times 10^4$, but if it is known to four, we write $3.690 \times 10^4$.

## * Percent Error

The significant figures rule is only approximate, and in some cases may underestimate the precision of the answer. Suppose for example we divide 97 by 92:

$$\frac{97}{92} = 1.05 \approx 1.1.$$

Both 97 and 92 have two significant figures, so the rule says to give the answer as 1.1. Yet the numbers 97 and 92 both imply an uncertainty of $\pm 1$ if no other uncertainty is stated. Now $92 \pm 1$ and $97 \pm 1$ both imply an accuracy of about 1% ($1/92 \approx 0.01 = 1\%$). But the final result to two significant figures is 1.1, with an implied uncertainty of $\pm 0.1$, which is an uncertainty of $0.1/1.1 \approx 0.1 \approx 10\%$. In this case it is better to give the answer as 1.05 (which is three significant figures). Why? Because 1.05 implies an uncertainty of $\pm 0.01$ which is $0.01/1.05 \approx 0.01 \approx 1\%$, just like the uncertainty in the original numbers 92 and 97.

SUGGESTION: Use the significant figures rule, but consider the % uncertainty too, and add an extra digit if it gives a more realistic estimate of uncertainty.

## 1–5 Units, Standards, and the SI System

The measurement of any quantity is made relative to a particular standard or **unit**, and this unit must be specified along with the numerical value of the quantity. For example, we can measure length in units such as inches, feet, or miles, or in the metric system in centimeters, meters, or kilometers. To specify that the length of a particular object is 18.6 is meaningless. The unit *must* be given; for clearly, 18.6 meters is very different from 18.6 inches or 18.6 millimeters.

For any unit we use, such as the meter for distance or the second for time, we need to define a **standard** which defines exactly how long one meter or one second is. It is important that standards be chosen that are readily reproducible so that anyone needing to make a very accurate measurement can refer to the standard in the laboratory.

### Length

*Standard of length (meter)*

The first truly international standard was the **meter** (abbreviated m) established as the standard of **length** by the French Academy of Sciences in the 1790s. The standard meter was originally chosen to be one ten-millionth of the distance from the Earth's equator to either pole,† and a platinum rod to represent this length was made. (One meter is, very roughly, the distance from the tip of your nose to the tip of your finger, with arm and hand stretched out to the side.) In 1889, the meter was defined more precisely as the distance between two finely engraved marks on a particular bar of platinum–iridium alloy. In 1960, to provide greater precision and reproducibility, the meter was redefined as 1,650,763.73 wavelengths of a particular orange light emitted by the gas krypton-86. In 1983 the meter was again redefined, this time in terms of the speed of light (whose best measured value in terms of the older definition of the meter was 299,792,458 m/s, with an uncertainty of 1 m/s). The new definition reads: "The meter is the length of path traveled by light in vacuum during a time interval of 1/299,792,458 of a second." ‡

British units of length (inch, foot, mile) are now defined in terms of the meter. The inch (in.) is defined as precisely 2.54 centimeters (cm; 1 cm = 0.01 m). Other conversion factors are given in the Table on the inside of the front cover of this book. Table 1–1 presents some typical lengths, from very small to very large, rounded off to the nearest power of ten. See also Fig. 1–8. [Note that the abbreviation for inches (in.) is the only one with a period, to distinguish it from the word "in".]

**FIGURE 1–8** Some lengths: (a) viruses (about $10^{-7}$ m long) attacking a cell; (b) Mt. Everest's height is on the order of $10^4$ m (8850 m, to be precise).

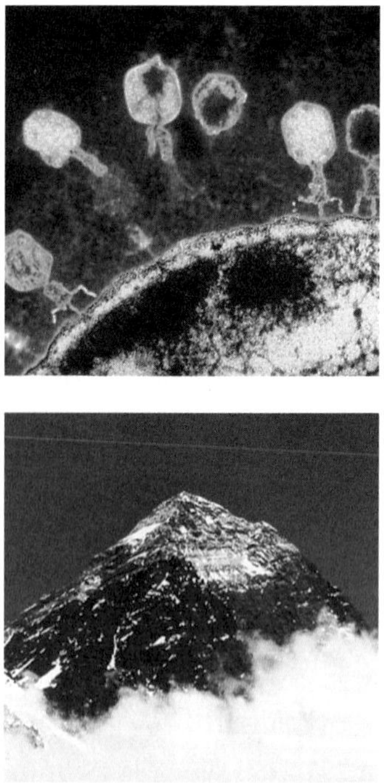

(a)

(b)

**TABLE 1–1 Some Typical Lengths or Distances (order of magnitude)**

| Length (or Distance) | Meters (approximate) |
|---|---|
| Neutron or proton (radius) | $10^{-15}$ m |
| Atom | $10^{-10}$ m |
| Virus [see Fig. 1–8a] | $10^{-7}$ m |
| Sheet of paper (thickness) | $10^{-4}$ m |
| Finger width | $10^{-2}$ m |
| Football field length | $10^{2}$ m |
| Height of Mt. Everest [see Fig. 1–8b] | $10^{4}$ m |
| Earth diameter | $10^{7}$ m |
| Earth to Sun | $10^{11}$ m |
| Earth to nearest star | $10^{16}$ m |
| Earth to nearest galaxy | $10^{22}$ m |
| Earth to farthest galaxy visible | $10^{26}$ m |

†Modern measurements of the Earth's circumference reveal that the intended length is off by about one-fiftieth of 1%. Not bad!

‡The new definition of the meter has the effect of giving the speed of light the exact value of 299,792,458 m/s.

**TABLE 1–2 Some Typical Time Intervals**

| Time Interval | Seconds (approximate) |
|---|---|
| Lifetime of very unstable subatomic particle | $10^{-23}$ s |
| Lifetime of radioactive elements | $10^{-22}$ s to $10^{28}$ s |
| Lifetime of muon | $10^{-6}$ s |
| Time between human heartbeats | $10^{0}$ s (= 1 s) |
| One day | $10^{5}$ s |
| One year | $3 \times 10^{7}$ s |
| Human life span | $2 \times 10^{9}$ s |
| Length of recorded history | $10^{11}$ s |
| Humans on Earth | $10^{14}$ s |
| Life on Earth | $10^{17}$ s |
| Age of Universe | $10^{18}$ s |

**TABLE 1–3 Some Masses**

| Object | Kilograms (approximate) |
|---|---|
| Electron | $10^{-30}$ kg |
| Proton, neutron | $10^{-27}$ kg |
| DNA molecule | $10^{-17}$ kg |
| Bacterium | $10^{-15}$ kg |
| Mosquito | $10^{-5}$ kg |
| Plum | $10^{-1}$ kg |
| Human | $10^{2}$ kg |
| Ship | $10^{8}$ kg |
| Earth | $6 \times 10^{24}$ kg |
| Sun | $2 \times 10^{30}$ kg |
| Galaxy | $10^{41}$ kg |

## Time

The standard unit of **time** is the **second** (s). For many years, the second was defined as 1/86,400 of a mean solar day. The standard second is now defined more precisely in terms of the frequency of radiation emitted by cesium atoms when they pass between two particular states. [Specifically, one second is defined as the time required for 9,192,631,770 periods of this radiation.] There are, by definition, 60 s in one minute (min) and 60 minutes in one hour (h). Table 1–2 presents a range of measured time intervals, rounded off to the nearest power of ten.

## Mass

The standard unit of **mass** is the **kilogram** (kg). The standard mass is a particular platinum–iridium cylinder, kept at the International Bureau of Weights and Measures near Paris, France, whose mass is defined as exactly 1 kg. A range of masses is presented in Table 1–3. [For practical purposes, 1 kg weighs about 2.2 pounds on Earth.]

When dealing with atoms and molecules, we usually use the **unified atomic mass unit** (u). In terms of the kilogram,

$$1\text{ u} = 1.6605 \times 10^{-27}\text{ kg}.$$

The definitions of other standard units for other quantities will be given as we encounter them in later Chapters.

**TABLE 1–4 Metric (SI) Prefixes**

| Prefix | Abbreviation | Value |
|---|---|---|
| yotta | Y | $10^{24}$ |
| zetta | Z | $10^{21}$ |
| exa | E | $10^{18}$ |
| peta | P | $10^{15}$ |
| tera | T | $10^{12}$ |
| giga | G | $10^{9}$ |
| mega | M | $10^{6}$ |
| kilo | k | $10^{3}$ |
| hecto | h | $10^{2}$ |
| deka | da | $10^{1}$ |
| deci | d | $10^{-1}$ |
| centi | c | $10^{-2}$ |
| milli | m | $10^{-3}$ |
| micro† | $\mu$ | $10^{-6}$ |
| nano | n | $10^{-9}$ |
| pico | p | $10^{-12}$ |
| femto | f | $10^{-15}$ |
| atto | a | $10^{-18}$ |
| zepto | z | $10^{-21}$ |
| yocto | y | $10^{-24}$ |

† $\mu$ is the Greek letter "mu."

## Unit Prefixes

In the metric system, the larger and smaller units are defined in multiples of 10 from the standard unit, and this makes calculation particularly easy. Thus 1 kilometer (km) is 1000 m, 1 centimeter is $\frac{1}{100}$ m, 1 millimeter (mm) is $\frac{1}{1000}$ m or $\frac{1}{10}$ cm, and so on. The prefixes "centi-," "kilo-," and others are listed in Table 1–4 and can be applied not only to units of length, but to units of volume, mass, or any other metric unit. For example, a centiliter (cL) is $\frac{1}{100}$ liter (L), and a kilogram (kg) is 1000 grams (g).

## Systems of Units

**PROBLEM SOLVING**

*Always use a consistent set of units*

When dealing with the laws and equations of physics it is very important to use a consistent set of units. Several systems of units have been in use over the years. Today the most important is the **Système International** (French for International System), which is abbreviated SI. In SI units, the standard of length is the meter, the standard for time is the second, and the standard for mass is the kilogram. This system used to be called the MKS (meter-kilogram-second) system.

*SI units*

A second metric system is the **cgs system**, in which the centimeter, gram, and second are the standard units of length, mass, and time, as abbreviated in the title. The **British engineering system** takes as its standards the foot for length, the pound for force, and the second for time.

**TABLE 1–5 SI Base Quantities and Units**

| Quantity | Unit | Unit Abbreviation |
|---|---|---|
| Length | meter | m |
| Time | second | s |
| Mass | kilogram | kg |
| Electric current | ampere | A |
| Temperature | kelvin | K |
| Amount of substance | mole | mol |
| Luminous intensity | candela | cd |

SI units are the principal ones used today in scientific work. We will therefore use SI units almost exclusively in this book, although we will give the cgs and British units for various quantities when introduced.

### Base vs. Derived Quantities

Physical quantities can be divided into two categories: *base quantities* and *derived quantities*. The corresponding units for these quantities are called *base units* and *derived units*. A **base quantity** must be defined in terms of a standard. Scientists, in the interest of simplicity, want the smallest number of base quantities possible consistent with a full description of the physical world. This number turns out to be seven, and those used in the SI are given in Table 1–5. All other quantities can be defined in terms of these seven base quantities,† and hence are referred to as **derived quantities**. An example of a derived quantity is speed, which is defined as distance divided by the time it takes to travel that distance. A Table inside the front cover lists many derived quantities and their units in terms of base units. To define any quantity, whether base or derived, we can specify a rule or procedure, and this is called an **operational definition**.

## 1–6 Converting Units

Any quantity we measure, such as a length, a speed, or an electric current, consists of a number *and* a unit. Often we are given a quantity in one set of units, but we want it expressed in another set of units. For example, suppose we measure that a table is 21.5 inches wide, and we want to express this in centimeters. We must use a **conversion factor**, which in this case is

$$1 \text{ in.} = 2.54 \text{ cm}$$

or, written another way,

$$1 = 2.54 \text{ cm/in.}$$

Since multiplying by one does not change anything, the width of our table, in cm, is

$$21.5 \text{ inches} = (21.5 \cancel{\text{in.}}) \times \left(2.54 \frac{\text{cm}}{\cancel{\text{in.}}}\right) = 54.6 \text{ cm}.$$

Note how the units (inches in this case) cancelled out. A Table containing many unit conversions is found inside the front cover of this book. Let's take some Examples.

**FIGURE 1–9** The world's second highest peak, K2, whose summit is considered the most difficult of the 8,000-ers. K2 is seen here from the north (China). Our cover shows K2 from the south (Pakistan). Example 1–3.

PHYSICS APPLIED
*The world's tallest peaks*

**EXAMPLE 1–3 The 8000-m peaks.** The fourteen tallest peaks in the world (Fig. 1–9 and Table 1–6) are referred to as "eight-thousanders," meaning their summits are over 8000 m above sea level. What is the elevation, in feet, of an elevation of 8000 m?

**APPROACH** We need simply to convert meters to feet, and we can start with the conversion factor 1 in. = 2.54 cm, which is exact. That is, 1 in. = 2.5400 cm to any number of significant figures.

**SOLUTION** One foot is 12 in., so we can write

$$1 \text{ ft} = (12 \cancel{\text{in.}})\left(2.54 \frac{\text{cm}}{\cancel{\text{in.}}}\right) = 30.48 \text{ cm} = 0.3048 \text{ m}.$$

The units cancel (colored slashes), and our result is exact. We can rewrite this

†The only exceptions are for angle (radians—see Chapter 8) and solid angle (steradian). No general agreement has been reached as to whether these are base or derived quantities.

equation to find the number of feet in 1 meter:

$$1\text{ m} = \frac{1\text{ ft}}{0.3048} = 3.28084\text{ ft}.$$

We multiply this equation by 8,000.0 (to have five significant figures):

$$8{,}000.0\text{ m} = (8{,}000.0\,\cancel{\text{m}})\left(3.28084\,\frac{\text{ft}}{\cancel{\text{m}}}\right) = 26{,}247\text{ ft}.$$

An elevation of 8000 m is 26,247 ft above sea level.

**NOTE** We could have done the conversion all in one line:

$$8000\text{ m} = (8000\,\cancel{\text{m}})\left(\frac{100\,\cancel{\text{cm}}}{1\,\cancel{\text{m}}}\right)\left(\frac{1\,\cancel{\text{in.}}}{2.54\,\cancel{\text{cm}}}\right)\left(\frac{1\text{ ft}}{12\,\cancel{\text{in.}}}\right) = 26{,}247\text{ ft}.$$

The key is to multiply conversion factors, each equal to one (= 1.0000), and to make sure the units cancel.

**EXERCISE D** There are only 14 eight-thousand-meter peaks in the world (see Example 1–3) and their names and elevations are given in Table 1–6. They are all in the Himalaya mountain range in India, Pakistan, Tibet, and China. Determine the elevation of the world's three highest peaks in feet.

**TABLE 1–6 The 8000-m Peaks**

| Peak | Height (m) |
|---|---|
| Mt. Everest | 8850 |
| K2 | 8611 |
| Kangchenjunga | 8586 |
| Lhotse | 8516 |
| Makalu | 8462 |
| Cho Oyu | 8201 |
| Dhaulagiri | 8167 |
| Manaslu | 8156 |
| Nanga Parbat | 8125 |
| Annapurna | 8091 |
| Gasherbrum I | 8068 |
| Broad Peak | 8047 |
| Gasherbrum II | 8035 |
| Shisha Pangma | 8013 |

**EXAMPLE 1–4** **Area of a semiconductor chip.** A silicon chip has an area of 1.25 square inches. Express this in square centimeters.

**APPROACH** We use the same conversion factor, $1\text{ in.} = 2.54\text{ cm}$, but this time we have to use it twice.

**SOLUTION** Because $1\text{ in.} = 2.54\text{ cm}$, then $1\text{ in.}^2 = (2.54\text{ cm})^2 = 6.45\text{ cm}^2$. So

$$1.25\text{ in.}^2 = (1.25\text{ in.}^2)\left(2.54\,\frac{\text{cm}}{\text{in.}}\right)^2 = (1.25\,\cancel{\text{in.}}^2)\left(6.45\,\frac{\text{cm}^2}{\cancel{\text{in.}}^2}\right) = 8.06\text{ cm}^2.$$

**EXAMPLE 1–5** **Speeds.** Where the posted speed limit is 55 miles per hour (mi/h or mph), what is this speed (*a*) in meters per second (m/s) and (*b*) in kilometers per hour (km/h)?

**APPROACH** We again use the conversion factor $1\text{ in.} = 2.54\text{ cm}$, and we recall that there are 5280 ft in a mile and 12 inches in a foot; also, one hour contains $(60\text{ min/h}) \times (60\text{ s/min}) = 3600\text{ s/h}$.

**SOLUTION** (*a*) We can write 1 mile as

$$1\text{ mi} = (5280\,\cancel{\text{ft}})\left(12\,\frac{\cancel{\text{in.}}}{\cancel{\text{ft}}}\right)\left(2.54\,\frac{\cancel{\text{cm}}}{\cancel{\text{in.}}}\right)\left(\frac{1\text{ m}}{100\,\cancel{\text{cm}}}\right) = 1609\text{ m}.$$

Note that each conversion factor is equal to one. We also know that 1 hour contains 3600 s, so

*Conversion factors = 1*

$$55\,\frac{\text{mi}}{\text{h}} = \left(55\,\frac{\cancel{\text{mi}}}{\cancel{\text{h}}}\right)\left(1609\,\frac{\text{m}}{\cancel{\text{mi}}}\right)\left(\frac{1\,\cancel{\text{h}}}{3600\text{ s}}\right) = 25\,\frac{\text{m}}{\text{s}},$$

where we rounded off to two significant figures.

(*b*) Now we use $1\text{ mi} = 1609\text{ m} = 1.609\text{ km}$; then

$$55\,\frac{\text{mi}}{\text{h}} = \left(55\,\frac{\cancel{\text{mi}}}{\text{h}}\right)\left(1.609\,\frac{\text{km}}{\cancel{\text{mi}}}\right) = 88\,\frac{\text{km}}{\text{h}}.$$

**NOTE** These unit conversions are very handy. You can always look them up in the Table inside the front cover.

**EXERCISE E** Would a driver traveling at 15 m/s in a 35 mi/h zone be exceeding the speed limit?

When changing units, you can avoid making an error in the use of conversion factors by checking that units cancel out properly. For example, in our conversion of 1 mi to 1609 m in Example 1–5(*a*), if we had incorrectly used the factor $\left(\frac{100\text{ cm}}{1\text{ m}}\right)$ instead of $\left(\frac{1\text{ m}}{100\text{ cm}}\right)$, the centimeter units would not have cancelled out; we would not have ended up with meters.

**➡ PROBLEM SOLVING**
*Unit conversion is wrong if units do not cancel*

## 1–7 Order of Magnitude: Rapid Estimating

We are sometimes interested only in an approximate value for a quantity. This might be because an accurate calculation would take more time than it is worth or would require additional data that are not available. In other cases, we may want to make a rough estimate in order to check an accurate calculation made on a calculator, to make sure that no blunders were made when the numbers were entered.

**PROBLEM SOLVING**
*How to make a rough estimate*

A rough estimate is made by rounding off all numbers to one significant figure and its power of 10, and after the calculation is made, again only one significant figure is kept. Such an estimate is called an **order-of-magnitude estimate** and can be accurate within a factor of 10, and often better. In fact, the phrase "order of magnitude" is sometimes used to refer simply to the power of 10.

To give you some idea of how useful and powerful rough estimates can be, let us do a few "worked-out Examples."

**PHYSICS APPLIED**
*Estimating the volume (or mass) of a lake; see also Fig. 1–10*

**EXAMPLE 1–6 ESTIMATE Volume of a lake.** Estimate how much water there is in a particular lake, Fig. 1–10a, which is roughly circular, about 1 km across, and you guess it has an average depth of about 10 m.

**APPROACH** No lake is a perfect circle, nor can lakes be expected to have a perfectly flat bottom. We are only estimating here. To estimate the volume, we can use a simple model of the lake as a cylinder: we multiply the average depth of the lake times its roughly circular surface area, as if the lake were a cylinder (Fig. 1–10b).

**SOLUTION** The volume $V$ of a cylinder is the product of its height $h$ times the area of its base: $V = h\pi r^2$, where $r$ is the radius of the circular base.† The radius $r$ is $\frac{1}{2}$ km $= 500$ m, so the volume is approximately

$$V = h\pi r^2 \approx (10\,\text{m}) \times (3) \times \left(5 \times 10^2\,\text{m}\right)^2 \approx 8 \times 10^6\,\text{m}^3 \approx 10^7\,\text{m}^3,$$

where $\pi$ was rounded off to 3. So the volume is on the order of $10^7\,\text{m}^3$, ten million cubic meters. Because of all the estimates that went into this calculation, the order-of-magnitude estimate $\left(10^7\,\text{m}^3\right)$ is probably better to quote than the $8 \times 10^6\,\text{m}^3$ figure.

†Formulas like this for volume, area, etc., are found inside the back cover of this book.

(a)

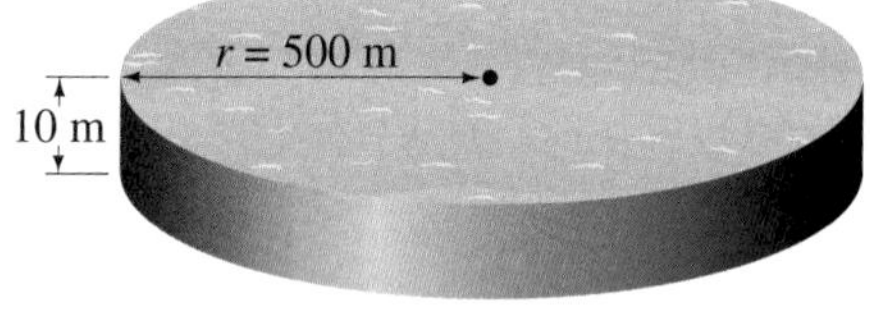


(b)

**FIGURE 1–10** Example 1–6. (a) How much water is in this lake? (Photo is of one of the Rae Lakes in the Sierra Nevada of California.) (b) Model of the lake as a cylinder. [We could go one step further and estimate the mass or weight of this lake. We will see later that water has a density of $1000\,\text{kg/m}^3$, so this lake has a mass of about $\left(10^3\,\text{kg/m}^3\right)\left(10^7\,\text{m}^3\right) \approx 10^{10}$ kg, which is about 10 billion kg or 10 million metric tons. (A metric ton is 1000 kg, about 2200 lbs, slightly larger than a British ton, 2000 lbs.)]

**NOTE** To express our result in U.S. gallons, we see in the Table on the inside front cover that $1\text{ liter} = 10^{-3}\,\text{m}^3 \approx \frac{1}{4}\,\text{gallon}$. Hence, the lake contains $(10^7\,\text{m}^3)(1\text{ gallon}/4 \times 10^{-3}\,\text{m}^3) \approx 2 \times 10^9$ gallons of water.

**EXAMPLE 1–7 ESTIMATE** **Thickness of a page.** Estimate the thickness of a page of this book.

➡ **PROBLEM SOLVING**
*Use symmetry when possible*

**APPROACH** At first you might think that a special measuring device, a micrometer (Fig. 1–11), is needed to measure the thickness of one page since an ordinary ruler clearly won't do. But we can use a trick or, to put it in physics terms, make use of a *symmetry*: we can make the reasonable assumption that all the pages of this book are equal in thickness.

**SOLUTION** We can use a ruler to measure hundreds of pages at once. If you measure the thickness of the first 500 pages of this book (page 1 to page 500), you might get something like 1.5 cm. Note that 500 pages counted front and back is 250 separate pieces of paper. So one page must have a thickness of about

$$\frac{1.5\text{ cm}}{250\text{ pages}} \approx 6 \times 10^{-3}\,\text{cm} = 6 \times 10^{-2}\,\text{mm},$$

or less than a tenth of a millimeter (0.1 mm).

**FIGURE 1–11** Example 1–7. A micrometer, which is used for measuring small thicknesses.

**EXAMPLE 1–8 ESTIMATE** **Total number of heartbeats.** Estimate the total number of beats a typical human heart makes in a lifetime.

**APPROACH** A typical resting heart rate is 70 beats/min. But during exercise it can be a lot higher. A reasonable average might be 80 beats/min.

**SOLUTION** If an average person lives $70\text{ years} \approx 2 \times 10^9\,\text{s}$ (see Table 1–2),

$$\left(80\,\frac{\text{beats}}{\text{min}}\right)\left(\frac{1\text{ min}}{60\text{ s}}\right)(2 \times 10^9\,\text{s}) \approx 3 \times 10^9,$$

or 3 trillion.

Now let's take a simple Example of how a diagram can be useful for making an estimate. It cannot be emphasized enough how important it is to draw a diagram when trying to solve a physics problem.

**EXAMPLE 1–9 ESTIMATE** **Height by triangulation.** Estimate the height of the building shown in Fig. 1–12, by "triangulation," with the help of a bus-stop pole and a friend.

**APPROACH** By standing your friend next to the pole, you estimate the height of the pole to be 3 m. You next step away from the pole until the top of the pole is in line with the top of the building, Fig. 1–12a. You are 5 ft 6 in. tall, so your eyes are about 1.5 m above the ground. Your friend is taller, and when she stretches out her arms, one hand touches you, and the other touches the pole, so you estimate that distance as 2 m (Fig. 1–12a). You then pace off the distance from the pole to the base of the building with big, 1-m-long, steps, and you get a total of 16 steps or 16 m.

**SOLUTION** Now you draw, to scale, the diagram shown in Fig. 1–12b using these measurements. You can measure, right on the diagram, the last side of the triangle to be about $x = 13\,\text{m}$. Alternatively, you can use similar triangles to obtain the height $x$:

$$\frac{1.5\text{ m}}{2\text{ m}} = \frac{x}{18\text{ m}}, \quad \text{so} \quad x \approx 13\tfrac{1}{2}\,\text{m}.$$

Finally you add in your eye height of 1.5 m above the ground to get your final result: the building is about 15 m tall.

**FIGURE 1–12** Example 1–9. Diagrams are really useful!

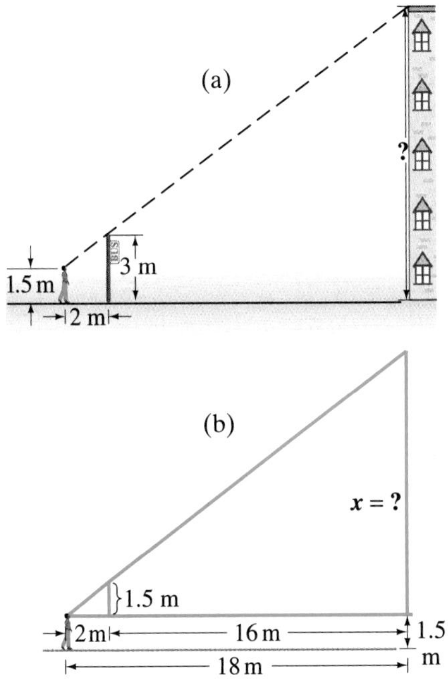

Another technique for estimating, this one made famous by Enrico Fermi to his physics students, is to estimate the number of piano tuners in a city, say, Chicago or San Francisco. To get a rough order-of-magnitude estimate of the number of piano tuners today in San Francisco, a city of about 700,000 inhabitants, we can proceed by estimating the number of functioning pianos, how often each piano is tuned, and how many pianos each tuner can tune. To estimate the number of pianos in San Francisco, we note that certainly not everyone has a piano. A guess of 1 family in 3 having a piano would correspond to 1 piano per 12 persons, assuming an average family of 4 persons. As an order of magnitude, let's say 1 piano per 10 people. This is certainly more reasonable than 1 per 100 people, or 1 per every person, so let's proceed with the estimate that 1 person in 10 has a piano, or about 70,000 pianos in San Francisco. Now a piano tuner needs an hour or two to tune a piano. So let's estimate that a tuner can tune 4 or 5 pianos a day. A piano ought to be tuned every 6 months or a year—let's say once each year. A piano tuner tuning 4 pianos a day, 5 days a week, 50 weeks a year can tune about 1000 pianos a year. So San Francisco, with its (very) roughly 70,000 pianos, needs about 70 piano tuners. This is, of course, only a rough estimate.† It tells us that there must be many more than 10 piano tuners, and surely not as many as 1000. If you were estimating the number of car mechanics, on the other hand, your estimate would be rather different!

**PROBLEM SOLVING**
*Estimating how many piano tuners there are in a city*

## * 1–8 Dimensions and Dimensional Analysis‡

When we speak of the **dimensions** of a quantity, we are referring to the type of units or base quantities that make it up. The dimensions of area, for example, are always length squared, abbreviated $[L^2]$, using square brackets; the units can be square meters, square feet, $cm^2$, and so on. Velocity, on the other hand, can be measured in units of km/h, m/s, or mi/h, but the dimensions are always a length $[L]$ divided by a time $[T]$; that is, $[L/T]$.

The formula for a quantity may be different in different cases, but the dimensions remain the same. For example, the area of a triangle of base $b$ and height $h$ is $A = \frac{1}{2}bh$, whereas the area of a circle of radius $r$ is $A = \pi r^2$. The formulas are different in the two cases, but the dimensions of area in both cases are the same: $[L^2]$.

When we specify the dimensions of a quantity, we usually do so in terms of base quantities, not derived quantities. For example, force, which we will see later has the same units as mass $[M]$ times acceleration $[L/T^2]$, has dimensions of $[ML/T^2]$.

Dimensions can be used as a help in working out relationships, and such a procedure is referred to as **dimensional analysis**.§ One useful technique is the use of dimensions to check if a relationship is *incorrect*. A simple rule applies here: we add or subtract quantities only if they have the same dimensions (we don't add centimeters and hours). This implies that the quantities on each side of an equals sign must have the same dimensions. (In numerical calculations, the units must also be the same on both sides of an equation.)

*Dimensional analysis*

For example, suppose you derived the equation $v = v_0 + \frac{1}{2}at^2$, where $v$ is the speed of an object after a time $t$, $v_0$ is the object's initial speed, and the object undergoes an acceleration $a$. Let's do a dimensional check to see if this equation is correct; note that numerical factors, like the $\frac{1}{2}$ here, do not affect

†A check of the San Francisco Yellow Pages (done after this calculation) reveals about 50 listings. Each of these listings may employ more than one tuner, but on the other hand, each may also do repairs as well as tuning. In any case, our estimate is reasonable.

‡Some Sections of this book, such as this one, may be considered *optional* at the discretion of the instructor. See the Preface for more details.

§The techniques described in the next few paragraphs may seem more meaningful after you have studied a few Chapters of this book. Reading this Section now will give you an overview of the subject, and you can then return to it later as needed.

dimensional checks. We write a dimensional equation as follows, remembering that the dimensions of speed are $[L/T]$ and (as we shall see in Chapter 2) the dimensions of acceleration are $[L/T^2]$:

$$\left[\frac{L}{T}\right] \stackrel{?}{=} \left[\frac{L}{T}\right] + \left[\frac{L}{T^2}\right][T^2]$$

$$\stackrel{?}{=} \left[\frac{L}{T}\right] + [L].$$

The dimensions are incorrect: on the right side, we have the sum of quantities whose dimensions are not the same. Thus we conclude that an error was made in the derivation of the original equation.

If such a dimensional check does come out correct, it does not prove that the equation is correct. For example, a dimensionless numerical factor (such as $\frac{1}{2}$ or $2\pi$) could be wrong. Thus a dimensional check can only tell you when a relationship is wrong. It can't tell you if it is completely right.

Dimensional analysis can also be used as a quick check on an equation you are not sure about. For example, suppose that you can't remember whether the equation for the period $T$ (the time to make one back-and-forth swing) of a simple pendulum of length $l$ is $T = 2\pi\sqrt{l/g}$ or $T = 2\pi\sqrt{g/l}$, where $g$ is the acceleration due to gravity and, like all accelerations, has dimensions $[L/T^2]$. (Do not worry about these formulas—the correct one will be derived in Chapter 11; what we are concerned about here is a person's forgetting whether it contains $l/g$ or $g/l$.) A dimensional check shows that the former $(l/g)$ is correct:

$$[T] = \sqrt{\frac{[L]}{[L/T^2]}} = \sqrt{[T^2]} = [T],$$

whereas the latter $(g/l)$ is not:

$$[T] \neq \sqrt{\frac{[L/T^2]}{[L]}} = \sqrt{\frac{1}{[T^2]}} = \frac{1}{[T]}.$$

Note that the constant $2\pi$ has no dimensions and so can't be checked using dimensions.

## Summary

[The Summary that appears at the end of each Chapter in this book gives a brief overview of the main ideas of the Chapter. The Summary *cannot* serve to give an understanding of the material, which can be accomplished only by a detailed reading of the Chapter.]

Physics, like other sciences, is a creative endeavor. It is not simply a collection of facts. Important **theories** are created with the idea of explaining **observations**. To be accepted, theories are "tested" by comparing their predictions with the results of actual experiments. Note that, in general, a theory cannot be "proved" in an absolute sense.

Scientists often devise models of physical phenomena. A **model** is a kind of picture or analogy that helps to describe the phenomena in terms of something we already know. A **theory**, often developed from a model, is usually deeper and more complex than a simple model.

A scientific **law** is a concise statement, often expressed in the form of an equation, which quantitatively describes a wide range of phenomena.

**Measurements** play a crucial role in physics, but can never be perfectly precise. It is important to specify the **uncertainty** of a measurement either by stating it directly using the ± notation, and/or by keeping only the correct number of **significant figures**.

Physical quantities are always specified relative to a particular standard or **unit**, and the unit used should always be stated. The commonly accepted set of units today is the **Système International** (SI), in which the standard units of length, mass, and time are the **meter**, **kilogram**, and **second**.

When converting units, check all **conversion factors** for correct cancellation of units.

Making rough, **order-of-magnitude estimates** is a very useful technique in science as well as in everyday life.

[*The **dimensions** of a quantity refer to the combination of base quantities that comprise it. Velocity, for example, has dimensions of [length/time] or $[L/T]$. Working with only the dimensions of the various quantities in a given relationship (this technique is called **dimensional analysis**) make it possible to check a relationship for correct form.]

## Questions

1. What are the merits and drawbacks of using a person's foot as a standard? Consider both (*a*) a particular person's foot, and (*b*) any person's foot. Keep in mind that it is advantagous that fundamental standards be accessible (easy to compare to), invariable (do not change), indestructible, and reproducible.
2. When traveling a highway in the mountains, you may see elevation signs that read "914 m (3000 ft)." Critics of the metric system claim that such numbers show the metric system is more complicated. How would you alter such signs to be more consistent with a switch to the metric system?
3. Why is it incorrect to think that the more digits you represent in your answer, the more accurate it is?
4. What is wrong with this road sign:
   Memphis 7 mi (11.263 km)?
5. For an answer to be complete, the units need to be specified. Why?
6. Discuss how the notion of symmetry could be used to estimate the number of marbles in a 1-liter jar.
7. You measure the radius of a wheel to be 4.16 cm. If you multiply by 2 to get the diameter, should you write the result as 8 cm or as 8.32 cm? Justify your answer.
8. Express the sine of 30.0° with the correct number of significant figures.
9. A recipe for a soufflé specifies that the measured ingredients must be exact, or the soufflé will not rise. The recipe calls for 6 large eggs. The size of "large" eggs can vary by 10%, according to the USDA specifications. What does this tell you about how exactly you need to measure the other ingredients?
10. List assumptions useful to estimate the number of car mechanics in (*a*) San Francisco, (*b*) your hometown, and then make the estimates.

## Problems

[The Problems at the end of each Chapter are ranked I, II, or III according to estimated difficulty, with (I) Problems being easiest. Level (III) Problems are meant mainly as a challenge for the best students, for "extra credit." The Problems are arranged by Sections, meaning that the reader should have read up to and including that Section, but not only that Section—Problems often depend on earlier material. Each Chapter also has a group of General Problems that are not arranged by Section and not ranked.]

### 1–4 Measurement, Uncertainty, Significant Figures

(*Note:* In Problems, assume a number like 6.4 is accurate to $\pm 0.1$; and 950 is $\pm 10$ unless 950 is said to be "precisely" or "very nearly" 950, in which case assume $950 \pm 1$.)

1. (I) The age of the universe is thought to be about 14 billion years. Assuming two significant figures, write this in powers of ten in (*a*) years, (*b*) seconds.
2. (I) How many significant figures do each of the following numbers have: (*a*) 214, (*b*) 81.60, (*c*) 7.03, (*d*) 0.03, (*e*) 0.0086, (*f*) 3236, and (*g*) 8700?
3. (I) Write the following numbers in powers of ten notation: (*a*) 1.156, (*b*) 21.8, (*c*) 0.0068, (*d*) 27.635, (*e*) 0.219, and (*f*) 444.
4. (I) Write out the following numbers in full with the correct number of zeros: (*a*) $8.69 \times 10^4$, (*b*) $9.1 \times 10^3$, (*c*) $8.8 \times 10^{-1}$, (*d*) $4.76 \times 10^2$, and (*e*) $3.62 \times 10^{-5}$.
5. (II) What, approximately, is the percent uncertainty for the measurement given as $1.57\ \mathrm{m}^2$?
6. (II) What is the percent uncertainty in the measurement $3.76 \pm 0.25$ m?
7. (II) Time intervals measured with a stopwatch typically have an uncertainty of about 0.2 s, due to human reaction time at the start and stop moments. What is the percent uncertainty of a handtimed measurement of (*a*) 5 s, (*b*) 50 s, (*c*) 5 min?
8. (II) Add $(9.2 \times 10^3\ \mathrm{s}) + (8.3 \times 10^4\ \mathrm{s}) + (0.008 \times 10^6\ \mathrm{s})$.
9. (II) Multiply $2.079 \times 10^2$ m by $0.082 \times 10^{-1}$, taking into account significant figures.
10. (III) What is the area, and its approximate uncertainty, of a circle of radius $3.8 \times 10^4$ cm?
11. (III) What, roughly, is the percent uncertainty in the volume of a spherical beach ball whose radius is $r = 2.86 \pm 0.09$ m?

### 1–5 and 1–6 Units, Standards, SI, Converting Units

12. (I) Write the following as full (decimal) numbers with standard units: (*a*) 286.6 mm, (*b*) 85 $\mu$V, (*c*) 760 mg, (*d*) 60.0 ps, (*e*) 22.5 fm, (*f*) 2.50 gigavolts.
13. (I) Express the following using the prefixes of Table 1–4: (*a*) $1 \times 10^6$ volts, (*b*) $2 \times 10^{-6}$ meters, (*c*) $6 \times 10^3$ days, (*d*) $18 \times 10^2$ bucks, and (*e*) $8 \times 10^{-9}$ pieces.
14. (I) Determine your own height in meters, and your mass in kg.
15. (I) The Sun, on average, is 93 million miles from Earth. How many meters is this? Express (*a*) using powers of ten, and (*b*) using a metric prefix.
16. (II) What is the conversion factor between (*a*) $\mathrm{ft}^2$ and $\mathrm{yd}^2$, (*b*) $\mathrm{m}^2$ and $\mathrm{ft}^2$?
17. (II) An airplane travels at 950 km/h. How long does it take to travel 1.00 km?
18. (II) A typical atom has a diameter of about $1.0 \times 10^{-10}$ m. (*a*) What is this in inches? (*b*) Approximately how many atoms are there along a 1.0-cm line?
19. (II) Express the following sum with the correct number of significant figures: $1.80\ \mathrm{m} + 142.5\ \mathrm{cm} + 5.34 \times 10^5\ \mu\mathrm{m}$.
20. (II) Determine the conversion factor between (*a*) km/h and mi/h, (*b*) m/s and ft/s, and (*c*) km/h and m/s.
21. (II) How much longer (percentage) is a one-mile race than a 1500-m race ("the metric mile")?
22. (II) A *light-year* is the distance light travels in one year (at speed $= 2.998 \times 10^8$ m/s). (*a*) How many meters are there in 1.00 light-year? (*b*) An astronomical unit (AU) is the average distance from the Sun to Earth, $1.50 \times 10^8$ km. How many AU are there in 1.00 light-year? (*c*) What is the speed of light in AU/h?
23. (III) The diameter of the Moon is 3480 km. (*a*) What is the surface area of the Moon? (*b*) How many times larger is the surface area of the Earth?

### 1–7 Order of Magnitude Estimating

(*Note:* Remember that for rough estimates, only round numbers are needed both as input to calculations and as final results.)

24. (I) Estimate the order of magnitude (power of ten) of: (*a*) 2800, (*b*) $86.30 \times 10^2$, (*c*) 0.0076, and (*d*) $15.0 \times 10^8$.
25. (II) Estimate how many books can be shelved in a college library with 3500 square meters of floor space. Assume 8 shelves high, having books on both sides, with corridors 1.5 m wide. Assume books are about the size of this one, on average.
26. (II) Estimate how many hours it would take a runner to run (at 10 km/h) across the United States from New York to California.
27. (II) Estimate how long it would take one person to mow a football field using an ordinary home lawn mower (Fig. 1–13). Assume the mower moves with a 1 km/h speed, and has a 0.5 m width.

**FIGURE 1–13** Problem 27.

28. (II) Estimate the number of liters of water a human drinks in a lifetime.
29. (II) Make a rough estimate of the volume of your body (in $cm^3$).
30. (II) Make a rough estimate, for a typical suburban house, of the % of its outside wall area that consists of window area.
31. (III) The rubber worn from tires mostly enters the atmosphere as particulate pollution. Estimate how much rubber (in kg) is put into the air in the United States every year. To get started, a good estimate for a tire tread's depth is 1 cm when new, and the density of rubber is about $1200\ kg/m^3$.

### * 1–8 Dimensions

* 32. (II) The speed, $v$, of an object is given by the equation $v = At^3 - Bt$, where $t$ refers to time. What are the dimensions of $A$ and $B$?

* 33. (II) Three students derive the following equations in which $x$ refers to distance traveled, $v$ the speed, $a$ the acceleration $(m/s^2)$, and $t$ the time, and the subscript $(_0)$ means a quantity at time $t = 0$: (*a*) $x = vt^2 + 2at$, (*b*) $x = v_0 t + \frac{1}{2}at^2$, and (*c*) $x = v_0 t + 2at^2$. Which of these could possibly be correct according to a dimensional check?

## General Problems

34. **Global positioning satellites (GPS)** can be used to determine positions with great accuracy. The system works by determining the distance between the observer and each of several satellites orbiting Earth. If one of the satellites is at a distance of 20,000 km from you, what percent accuracy in the distance is required if we desire a 2-meter uncertainty? How many significant figures do we need to have in the distance?
35. Computer chips (Fig. 1–14) are etched on circular silicon wafers of thickness 0.60 mm that are sliced from a solid cylindrical silicon crystal of length 30 cm. If each wafer can hold 100 chips, what is the maximum number of chips that can be produced from one entire cylinder?

**FIGURE 1–14** Problem 35. The wafer held by the hand (above) is shown below, enlarged and illuminated by colored light. Visible are rows of integrated circuits (chips).

36. (*a*) How many seconds are there in 1.00 year? (*b*) How many nanoseconds are there in 1.00 year? (*c*) How many years are there in 1.00 second?
37. A typical adult human lung contains about 300 million tiny cavities called alveoli. Estimate the average diameter of a single alveolus.
38. One hectare is defined as $10^4\ m^2$. One acre is $4 \times 10^4\ ft^2$. How many acres are in one hectare?
39. Use Table 1–3 to estimate the total number of protons or neutrons in (*a*) a bacterium, (*b*) a DNA molecule, (*c*) the human body, (*d*) our Galaxy.
40. Estimate the number of gallons of gasoline consumed by the total of all automobile drivers in the United States, per year.
41. Estimate the number of gumballs in the machine of Fig. 1–15.

**FIGURE 1–15** Problem 41. Estimate the number of gumballs in the machine.

42. An average family of four uses roughly 1200 liters (about 300 gallons) of water per day. (One liter = $1000\ \mathrm{cm}^3$.) How much depth would a lake lose per year if it uniformly covered an area of 50 square kilometers and supplied a local town with a population of 40,000 people? Consider only population uses, and neglect evaporation and so on.

43. How big is a ton? That is, what is the volume of something that weighs a ton? To be specific, estimate the diameter of a 1-ton rock, but first make a wild guess: will it be 1 ft across, 3 ft, or the size of a car? [*Hint*: Rock has mass per volume about 3 times that of water, which is 1 kg per liter ($10^3\ \mathrm{cm}^3$) or 62 lb per cubic foot.]

44. A heavy rainstorm dumps 1.0 cm of rain on a city 5 km wide and 8 km long in a 2-h period. How many metric tons (1 metric ton = $10^3$ kg) of water fell on the city? [$1\ \mathrm{cm}^3$ of water has a mass of 1 gram = $10^{-3}$ kg.] How many gallons of water was this?

45. Hold a pencil in front of your eye at a position where its blunt end just blocks out the Moon (Fig. 1–16). Make appropriate measurements to estimate the diameter of the Moon, given that the Earth–Moon distance is $3.8 \times 10^5$ km.

**FIGURE 1–16** Problem 45. How big is the Moon?

46. Estimate how many days it would take to walk around the world, assuming 10 h walking per day at 4 km/h.

47. Noah's ark was ordered to be 300 cubits long, 50 cubits wide, and 30 cubits high. The cubit was a unit of measure equal to the length of a human forearm, elbow to the tip of the longest finger. Express the dimensions of Noah's ark in meters, and estimate its volume ($\mathrm{m}^3$).

48. One liter ($1000\ \mathrm{cm}^3$) of oil is spilled onto a smooth lake. If the oil spreads out uniformly until it makes an oil slick just one molecule thick, with adjacent molecules just touching, estimate the diameter of the oil slick. Assume the oil molecules have a diameter of $2 \times 10^{-10}$ m.

49. Jean camps beside a wide river and wonders how wide it is. She spots a large rock on the bank directly across from her. She then walks upstream until she judges that the angle between her and the rock, which she can still see clearly, is now at an angle of 30° downstream (Fig. 1–17). Jean measures her stride to be about one yard long. The distance back to her camp is 120 strides. About how far across, both in yards and in meters, is the river?

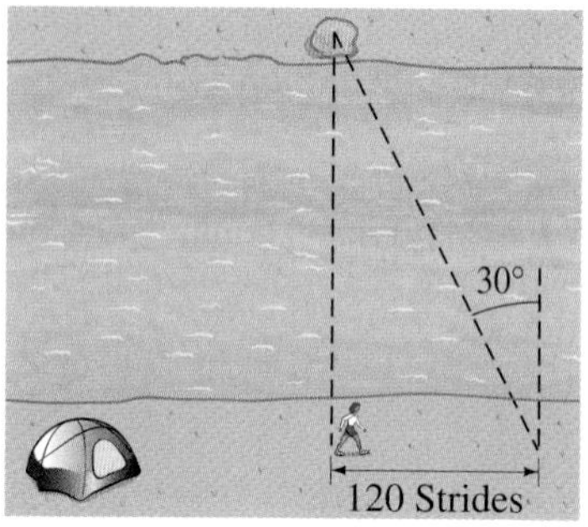


**FIGURE 1–17** Problem 49.

50. A watch manufacturer claims that its watches gain or lose no more than 8 seconds in a year. How accurate is this watch, expressed as a percentage?

51. The diameter of the Moon is 3480 km. What is the volume of the Moon? How many Moons would be needed to create a volume equal to that of Earth?

52. An angstrom (symbol Å) is a unit of length, defined as $10^{-10}$ m, which is on the order of the diameter of an atom. (*a*) How many nanometers are in 1.0 angstrom? (*b*) How many femtometers or fermis (the common unit of length in nuclear physics) are in 1.0 angstrom? (*c*) How many angstroms are in 1.0 meter? (*d*) How many angstroms are in 1.0 light-year (see Problem 22)?

53. Determine the percent uncertainty in $\theta$, and in $\sin\theta$, when (*a*) $\theta = 15.0° \pm 0.5°$, (*b*) $\theta = 75.0° \pm 0.5°$.

54. If you began walking along one of Earth's lines of longitude and walked until you had changed latitude by 1 minute of arc (there are 60 minutes per degree), how far would you have walked (in miles)? This distance is called a "nautical mile."

## Answers to Exercises

**A:** (d).
**B:** No: 3, 2.
**C:** All three have three significant figures, although the number of decimal places is (*a*) 2, (*b*) 3, (*c*) 4.
**D:** Mt. Everest, 29,035 ft; K2, 28,251 ft; Kangchenjunga, 28,169 ft.
**E:** No: 15 m/s ≈ 34 mi/h.

A high-speed car has released a parachute to reduce its speed quickly. The directions of the car's velocity and acceleration are shown by the green ($\vec{\mathbf{v}}$) and gold ($\vec{\mathbf{a}}$) arrows. Motion is described using the concepts of velocity and acceleration. We see here that the acceleration $\vec{\mathbf{a}}$ can sometimes be in the opposite direction from the velocity $\vec{\mathbf{v}}$. We will also examine in detail motion with constant acceleration, including the vertical motion of objects falling under gravity.

CHAPTER 2

# Describing Motion: Kinematics in One Dimension

The motion of objects—baseballs, automobiles, joggers, and even the Sun and Moon—is an obvious part of everyday life. It was not until the sixteenth and seventeenth centuries that our modern understanding of motion was established. Many individuals contributed to this understanding, particularly Galileo Galilei (1564–1642) and Isaac Newton (1642–1727).

The study of the motion of objects, and the related concepts of force and energy, form the field called **mechanics**. Mechanics is customarily divided into two parts: **kinematics**, which is the description of how objects move, and **dynamics**, which deals with force and why objects move as they do. This Chapter and the next deal with kinematics.

For now we only discuss objects that move without rotating (Fig. 2–1a). Such motion is called **translational motion**. In this Chapter we will be concerned with describing an object that moves along a straight-line path, which is one-dimensional translational motion. In Chapter 3 we will describe translational motion in two (or three) dimensions along paths that are not straight. (We discuss rotation, as in Fig. 2–1b, in Chapter 8.)

We will often use the concept, or *model*, of an idealized **particle** which is considered to be a mathematical point and to have no spatial extent (no size). A particle can undergo only translational motion. The particle model is useful in many real situations where we are interested only in translational motion and the object's size is not so significant. For example, we might consider a billiard ball, or even a spacecraft traveling toward the Moon, as a particle for many purposes.

(a) (b)

**FIGURE 2–1** The pinecone in (a) undergoes pure translation as it falls, whereas in (b) it is rotating as well as translating.

## 2–1 Reference Frames and Displacement

*All measurements are made relative to a frame of reference*

Any measurement of position, distance, or speed must be made with respect to a **reference frame**, or **frame of reference**. For example, while you are on a train traveling at 80 km/h, suppose a person walks past you toward the front of the train at a speed of, say, 5 km/h (Fig. 2–2). This 5 km/h is the person's speed with respect to the train as frame of reference. With respect to the ground, that person is moving at a speed of $80\,\text{km/h} + 5\,\text{km/h} = 85\,\text{km/h}$. It is always important to specify the frame of reference when stating a speed. In everyday life, we usually mean "with respect to the Earth" without even thinking about it, but the reference frame must be specified whenever there might be confusion.

**FIGURE 2–2** A person walks toward the front of a train at 5 km/h. The train is moving 80 km/h with respect to the ground, so the walking person's speed, relative to the ground, is 85 km/h.

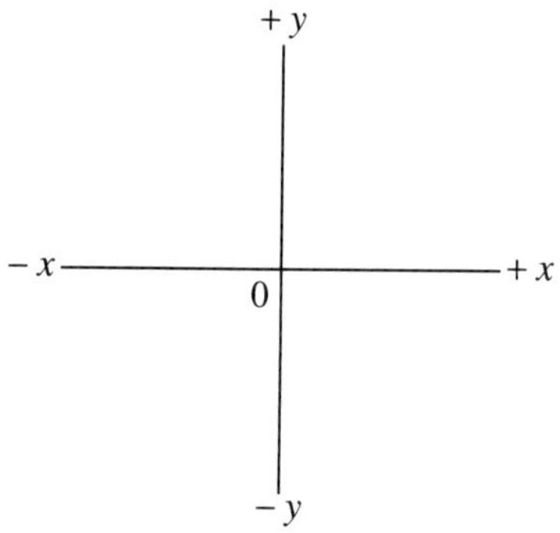


**FIGURE 2–3** Standard set of *xy* coordinate axes.

When specifying the motion of an object, it is important to specify not only the speed but also the direction of motion. Often we can specify a direction by using north, east, south, and west, and by "up" and "down." In physics, we often draw a set of **coordinate axes**, as shown in Fig. 2–3, to represent a frame of reference. We can always place the origin 0, and the directions of the $x$ and $y$ axes, as we like for convenience. The $x$ and $y$ axes are always perpendicular to each other. Objects positioned to the right of the origin of coordinates (0) on the $x$ axis have an $x$ coordinate which we usually choose to be positive; objects to the left of 0 then have a negative $x$ coordinate. The position along the $y$ axis is usually considered positive when above 0, and negative when below 0, although the reverse convention can be used if convenient. Any point on the plane can be specified by giving its $x$ and $y$ coordinates. In three dimensions, a $z$ axis perpendicular to the $x$ and $y$ axes is added.

For one-dimensional motion, we often choose the $x$ axis as the line along which the motion takes place. Then the **position** of an object at any moment is given by its $x$ coordinate. If the motion is vertical, as for a dropped object, we usually use the $y$ axis.

*Displacement*

We need to make a distinction between the *distance* an object has traveled and its **displacement**, which is defined as the *change in position* of the object. That is, *displacement is how far the object is from its starting point*. To see the distinction between total distance and displacement, imagine a person walking 70 m to the east and then turning around and walking back (west) a distance of 30 m (see Fig. 2–4). The total *distance* traveled is 100 m, but the *displacement* is only 40 m since the person is now only 40 m from the starting point.

**CAUTION**
*The displacement may not equal the total distance traveled*

**FIGURE 2–4** A person walks 70 m east, then 30 m west. The total distance traveled is 100 m (path is shown dashed in black); but the displacement, shown as a blue arrow, is 40 m to the east.

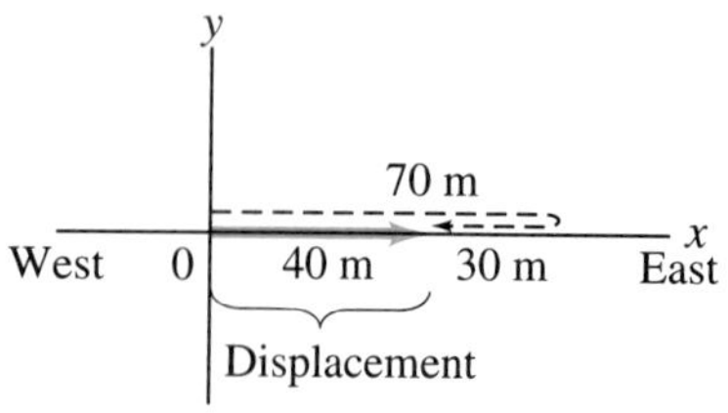


Displacement is a quantity that has both magnitude and direction. Such quantities are called **vectors**, and are represented by arrows in diagrams. For example, in Fig. 2–4, the blue arrow represents the displacement whose magnitude is 40 m and whose direction is to the right (east).

We will deal with vectors more fully in Chapter 3. For now, we deal only with motion in one dimension, along a line. In this case, vectors which point in one direction will have a positive sign, whereas vectors that point in the opposite direction will have a negative sign, along with their magnitude.

Consider the motion of an object over a particular time interval. Suppose that at some initial time, call it $t_1$, the object is on the $x$ axis at the position $x_1$ in the coordinate system shown in Fig. 2–5. At some later time, $t_2$, suppose the object has moved to position $x_2$. The displacement of our object is $x_2 - x_1$, and is represented by the arrow pointing to the right in Fig. 2–5. It is convenient to write

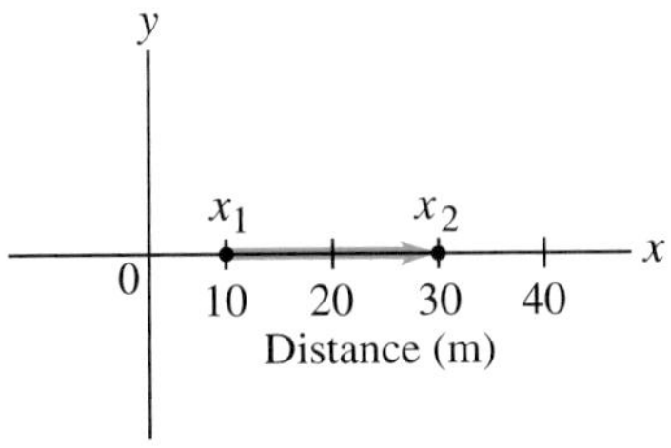


**FIGURE 2–5** The arrow represents the displacement $x_2 - x_1$. Distances are in meters.

$$\Delta x = x_2 - x_1,$$

where the symbol $\Delta$ (Greek letter delta) means "change in." Then $\Delta x$ means "the change in $x$," or "change in position," which is the displacement. Note that the "change in" any quantity means the final value of that quantity, minus the initial value.

*$\Delta$ means final value minus initial value*

Suppose $x_1 = 10.0\,\text{m}$ and $x_2 = 30.0\,\text{m}$. Then

$$\Delta x = x_2 - x_1 = 30.0\,\text{m} - 10.0\,\text{m} = 20.0\,\text{m},$$

so the displacement is 20.0 m in the positive direction, as in Fig. 2–5.

Now consider an object moving to the left as shown in Fig. 2–6. Here the object, say, a person, starts at $x_1 = 30.0\,\text{m}$ and walks to the left to the point $x_2 = 10.0\,\text{m}$. In this case

**FIGURE 2–6** For the displacement $\Delta x = x_2 - x_1 = 10.0\,\text{m} - 30.0\,\text{m}$, the displacement vector points to the left.

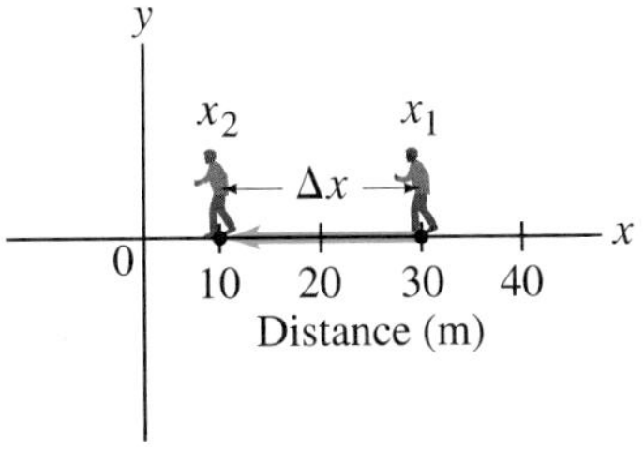


$$\Delta x = x_2 - x_1 = 10.0\,\text{m} - 30.0\,\text{m} = -20.0\,\text{m},$$

and the blue arrow representing the vector displacement points to the left. The displacement is 20.0 m in the negative direction. This example illustrates that for one-dimensional motion along the $x$ axis, a vector pointing to the right has a positive sign, whereas a vector pointing to the left has a negative sign.

## 2–2 Average Velocity

Consider a racing sprinter, a galloping horse, a speeding Ferrari, or a rocket shot off into space. The most obvious aspect of their motion is how fast they are moving, which brings us to the idea of speed and velocity.

The term "speed" refers to how far an object travels in a given time interval, regardless of direction. If a car travels 240 kilometers (km) in 3 hours (h), we say its average speed was 80 km/h. In general, the **average speed** of an object is defined as *the total distance traveled along its path divided by the time it takes to travel this distance*:

$$\text{average speed} = \frac{\text{distance traveled}}{\text{time elapsed}}. \tag{2–1}$$

*Average speed*

The terms "velocity" and "speed" are often used interchangeably in ordinary language. But in physics we make a distinction between the two. Speed is simply a positive number, with units. **Velocity**, on the other hand, is used to signify both the *magnitude* (numerical value) of how fast an object is moving and also the *direction* in which it is moving. (Velocity is therefore a vector.) There is a second difference between speed and velocity: namely, the **average velocity** is defined in terms of *displacement*, rather than total distance traveled:

*Velocity*

$$\text{average velocity} = \frac{\text{displacement}}{\text{time elapsed}} = \frac{\text{final position} - \text{initial position}}{\text{time elapsed}}.$$

*Average velocity*

**CAUTION**
*Average speed is not necessarily equal to the magnitude of the average velocity*

Average speed and average velocity have the same magnitude when the motion is all in one direction. In other cases, they may differ: recall the walk we described earlier, in Fig. 2–4, where a person walked 70 m east and then 30 m west. The total distance traveled was $70\text{ m} + 30\text{ m} = 100\text{ m}$, but the displacement was 40 m. Suppose this walk took 70 s to complete. Then the average speed was:

$$\frac{\text{distance}}{\text{time elapsed}} = \frac{100\text{ m}}{70\text{ s}} = 1.4\text{ m/s}.$$

The magnitude of the average velocity, on the other hand, was:

$$\frac{\text{displacement}}{\text{time elapsed}} = \frac{40\text{ m}}{70\text{ s}} = 0.57\text{ m/s}.$$

This difference between the speed and the magnitude of the velocity can occur when we calculate *average* values.

To discuss one-dimensional motion of an object in general, suppose that at some moment in time, call it $t_1$, the object is on the $x$ axis at position $x_1$ in a coordinate system, and at some later time, $t_2$, suppose it is at position $x_2$. The elapsed time is $t_2 - t_1$; during this time interval the displacement of our object is $\Delta x = x_2 - x_1$. Then the average velocity, defined as *the displacement divided by the elapsed time*, can be written

*Average velocity*

$$\bar{v} = \frac{x_2 - x_1}{t_2 - t_1} = \frac{\Delta x}{\Delta t}, \qquad \textbf{(2–2)}$$

where $v$ stands for velocity and the bar ($^-$) over the $v$ is a standard symbol meaning "average."

The **elapsed time**, or **time interval**, $t_2 - t_1$, is the time that has passed during our chosen period of observation.

**PROBLEM SOLVING**
*+ or − sign can signify the direction for linear motion*

For the usual case of the $+x$ axis to the right, note that if $x_2$ is less than $x_1$, the object is moving to the left, and then $\Delta x = x_2 - x_1$ is less than zero. The sign of the displacement, and thus of the average velocity, indicates the direction: the average velocity is positive for an object moving to the right along the $+x$ axis and negative when the object moves to the left. The direction of the average velocity is always the same as the direction of the displacement.

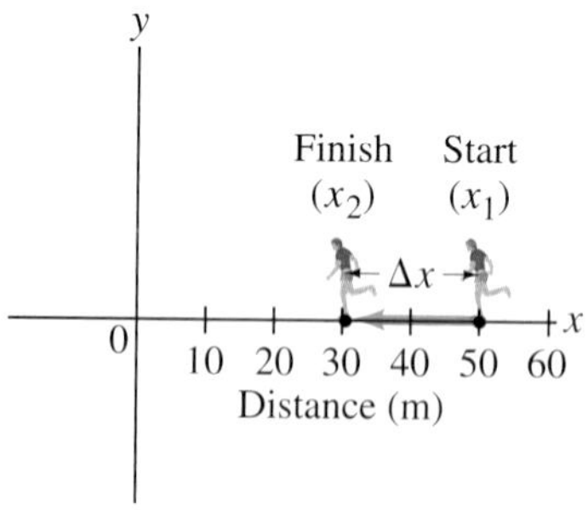


**FIGURE 2–7** Example 2–1. A person runs from $x_1 = 50.0$ m to $x_2 = 30.5$ m. The displacement is $-19.5$ m.

**EXAMPLE 2–1 Runner's average velocity.** The position of a runner as a function of time is plotted as moving along the $x$ axis of a coordinate system. During a 3.00-s time interval, the runner's position changes from $x_1 = 50.0$ m to $x_2 = 30.5$ m, as shown in Fig. 2–7. What was the runner's average velocity?

**APPROACH** We want to find the average velocity, which is the displacement divided by the elapsed time.

**SOLUTION** The displacement is $\Delta x = x_2 - x_1 = 30.5\text{ m} - 50.0\text{ m} = -19.5\text{ m}$. The elapsed time, or time interval, is $\Delta t = 3.00\text{ s}$. The average velocity is

$$\bar{v} = \frac{\Delta x}{\Delta t} = \frac{-19.5\text{ m}}{3.00\text{ s}} = -6.50\text{ m/s}.$$

The displacement and average velocity are negative, which tells us that the runner is moving to the left along the $x$ axis, as indicated by the arrow in Fig. 2–7. Thus we can say that the runner's average velocity is 6.50 m/s to the left.

**EXAMPLE 2–2 Distance a cyclist travels.** How far can a cyclist travel in 2.5 h along a straight road if her average velocity is 18 km/h?

**APPROACH** We are given the average velocity and the time interval (= 2.5 h). We want to find the distance traveled, so we solve Eq. 2–2 for $\Delta x$.

**SOLUTION** We rewrite Eq. 2–2 as $\Delta x = \bar{v}\,\Delta t$, and find

$$\Delta x = \bar{v}\,\Delta t = (18\text{ km/h})(2.5\text{ h}) = 45\text{ km}.$$

## 2–3 Instantaneous Velocity

If you drive a car 150 km along a straight road in one direction for 2.0 h, the magnitude of your average velocity is 75 km/h. It is unlikely, though, that you were moving at precisely 75 km/h at every instant. To deal with this situation we need the concept of *instantaneous velocity*, which is the velocity at any instant of time. (Its magnitude is the number, with units, indicated by a speedometer; Fig. 2–8.) More precisely, the **instantaneous velocity** at any moment is defined as *the average velocity during an infinitesimally short time interval*. That is, starting with Eq. 2–2,

$$\bar{v} = \frac{\Delta x}{\Delta t},$$

**FIGURE 2–8** Car speedometer showing mi/h in white, and km/h in orange.

we define instantaneous velocity as the average velocity as we let $\Delta t$ become extremely small, approaching zero. We can write the definition of instantaneous velocity, $v$, for one-dimensional motion as

$$v = \lim_{\Delta t \to 0} \frac{\Delta x}{\Delta t}. \tag{2–3}$$

*Instantaneous velocity*

The notation $\lim_{\Delta t \to 0}$ means the ratio $\Delta x/\Delta t$ is to be evaluated in the limit of $\Delta t$ approaching zero.

For instantaneous velocity we use the symbol $v$, whereas for average velocity we use $\bar{v}$, with a bar. In the rest of this book, when we use the term "velocity," it will refer to instantaneous velocity. When we want to speak of the average velocity, we will make this clear by including the word "average."

Note that the *instantaneous* speed always equals the magnitude of the instantaneous velocity. Why? Because the distance and the magnitude of the displacement become the same when they become infinitesimally small.

If an object moves at a uniform (that is, constant) velocity during a particular time interval, then its instantaneous velocity at any instant is the same as its average velocity (see Fig. 2–9a). But in many situations this is not the case. For example, a car may start from rest, speed up to 50 km/h, remain at that velocity for a time, then slow down to 20 km/h in a traffic jam, and finally stop at its destination after traveling a total of 15 km in 30 min. This trip is plotted on the graph of Fig. 2–9b. Also shown on the graph is the average velocity (dashed line), which is $\bar{v} = \Delta x/\Delta t = 15\text{ km}/0.50\text{ h} = 30\text{ km/h}$.

**FIGURE 2–9** Velocity of a car as a function of time: (a) at constant velocity; (b) with varying velocity.

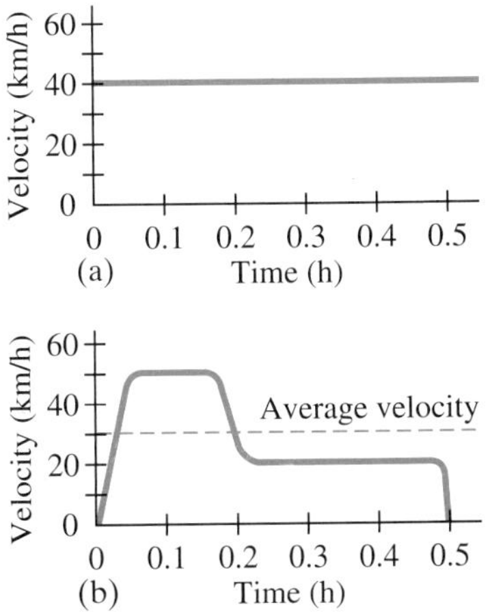


## 2–4 Acceleration

An object whose velocity is changing is said to be accelerating. For instance, a car whose velocity increases in magnitude from zero to 80 km/h is accelerating. Acceleration specifies how rapidly the velocity of an object is changing.

**Average acceleration** is defined as the change in velocity divided by the time taken to make this change:

$$\text{average acceleration} = \frac{\text{change of velocity}}{\text{time elapsed}}.$$

In symbols, the average acceleration, $\bar{a}$, during a time interval $\Delta t = t_2 - t_1$ over which the velocity changes by $\Delta v = v_2 - v_1$, is defined as

$$\bar{a} = \frac{v_2 - v_1}{t_2 - t_1} = \frac{\Delta v}{\Delta t}. \tag{2–4}$$

*Average acceleration*

Acceleration is also a vector, but for one-dimensional motion, we need only use a plus or minus sign to indicate direction relative to a chosen coordinate system.

The **instantaneous acceleration**, $a$, can be defined in analogy to instantaneous velocity, for any specific instant:

*Instantaneous acceleration*

$$a = \lim_{\Delta t \to 0} \frac{\Delta v}{\Delta t}. \qquad \textbf{(2–5)}$$

Here $\Delta v$ is the very small change in velocity during the very short time interval $\Delta t$.

**EXAMPLE 2–3** **Average acceleration.** A car accelerates along a straight road from rest to 75 km/h in 5.0 s, Fig. 2–10. What is the magnitude of its average acceleration?

**APPROACH** Average acceleration is the change in velocity divided by elapsed time, 5.0 s. The car starts from rest, so $v_1 = 0$. The final velocity is $v_2 = 75\,\text{km/h}$.

*At rest means $v = 0$*

**SOLUTION** From Eq. 2–4, the average acceleration is

$$\bar{a} = \frac{v_2 - v_1}{t_2 - t_1} = \frac{75\,\text{km/h} - 0\,\text{km/h}}{5.0\,\text{s}} = 15\,\frac{\text{km/h}}{\text{s}}.$$

This is read as "fifteen kilometers per hour per second" and means that, on average, the velocity changed by 15 km/h during each second. That is, assuming the acceleration was constant, during the first second the car's velocity increased from zero to 15 km/h. During the next second its velocity increased by another 15 km/h, reaching a velocity of 30 km/h at $t = 2.0\,\text{s}$, and so on. See Fig. 2–10.

**NOTE** Our result contains two different time units: hours and seconds. We usually prefer to use only seconds. To do so we can change km/h to m/s (see Section 1–6, and Example 1–5):

$$75\,\text{km/h} = \left(75\,\frac{\cancel{\text{km}}}{\cancel{\text{h}}}\right)\left(\frac{1000\,\text{m}}{1\,\cancel{\text{km}}}\right)\left(\frac{1\,\cancel{\text{h}}}{3600\,\text{s}}\right) = 21\,\text{m/s}.$$

Then

$$\bar{a} = \frac{21\,\text{m/s} - 0.0\,\text{m/s}}{5.0\,\text{s}} = 4.2\,\frac{\text{m/s}}{\text{s}} = 4.2\,\frac{\text{m}}{\text{s}^2}.$$

We almost always write the units for acceleration as $\text{m/s}^2$ (meters per second squared), as we just did, instead of m/s/s. This is possible because:

$$\frac{\text{m/s}}{\text{s}} = \frac{\text{m}}{\text{s}\cdot\text{s}} = \frac{\text{m}}{\text{s}^2}.$$

According to the calculation in Example 2–3, the velocity changed on the average by 4.2 m/s during each second, for a total change of 21 m/s over the 5.0 s.

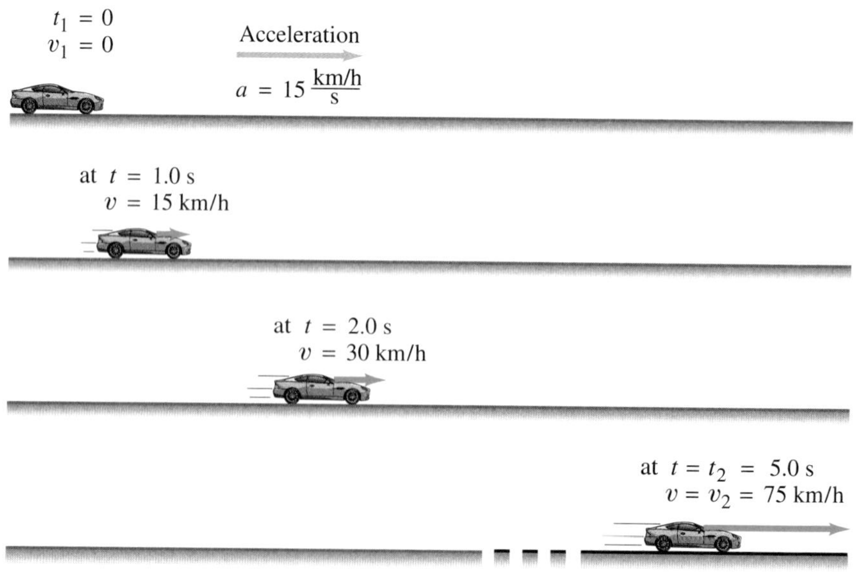


**FIGURE 2–10** Example 2–3. The car is shown at the start with $v_1 = 0$ at $t_1 = 0$. The car is shown three more times, at $t = 1.0\,\text{s}$, $t = 2.0\,\text{s}$, and at the end of our time interval, $t_2 = 5.0\,\text{s}$. We assume the acceleration is constant and equals 15 km/h/s. The green arrows represent the velocity vectors; the length of each arrow represents the magnitude of the velocity at that moment. The acceleration vector is the orange arrow. Distances are not to scale.

Note that *acceleration tells us how quickly the velocity changes*, whereas *velocity tells us how quickly the position changes*.

**CAUTION**
*Distinguish velocity from acceleration*

**CONCEPTUAL EXAMPLE 2–4** **Velocity and acceleration.** (*a*) If the velocity of an object is zero, does it mean that the acceleration is zero? (*b*) If the acceleration is zero, does it mean that the velocity is zero? Think of some examples.

**CAUTION**
*If $v$ or $a$ is zero, is the other zero too?*

**RESPONSE** A zero velocity does not necessarily mean that the acceleration is zero, nor does a zero acceleration mean that the velocity is zero. (*a*) For example, when you put your foot on the gas pedal of your car which is at rest, the velocity starts from zero but the acceleration is not zero since the velocity of the car changes. (How else could your car start forward if its velocity weren't changing—that is, accelerating?) (*b*) As you cruise along a straight highway at a constant velocity of 100 km/h, your acceleration is zero: $a = 0, v \neq 0$.

**EXERCISE A** A car is advertised to go from zero to 60 mi/h in 6.0 s. What does this say about the car: (*a*) it is fast (high speed); or (*b*) it accelerates well?

**EXAMPLE 2–5** **Car slowing down.** An automobile is moving to the right along a straight highway, which we choose to be the positive $x$ axis (Fig. 2–11). Then the driver puts on the brakes. If the initial velocity (when the driver hits the brakes) is $v_1 = 15.0\,\mathrm{m/s}$, and it takes 5.0 s to slow down to $v_2 = 5.0\,\mathrm{m/s}$, what was the car's average acceleration?

**APPROACH** We are given the initial and final velocities and the elapsed time, so we can calculate $\bar{a}$ using Eq. 2–4.

**SOLUTION** We use Eq. 2–4 and call the initial time $t_1 = 0$; then $t_2 = 5.0\,\mathrm{s}$. (Note that our choice of $t_1 = 0$ doesn't affect the calculation of $\bar{a}$ because only $\Delta t = t_2 - t_1$ appears in Eq. 2–4.) Then

$$\bar{a} = \frac{5.0\,\mathrm{m/s} - 15.0\,\mathrm{m/s}}{5.0\,\mathrm{s}} = -2.0\,\mathrm{m/s^2}.$$

The negative sign appears because the final velocity is less than the initial velocity. In this case the direction of the acceleration is to the left (in the negative $x$ direction)—even though the velocity is always pointing to the right. We say that the acceleration is $2.0\,\mathrm{m/s^2}$ to the left, and it is shown in Fig. 2–11 as an orange arrow.

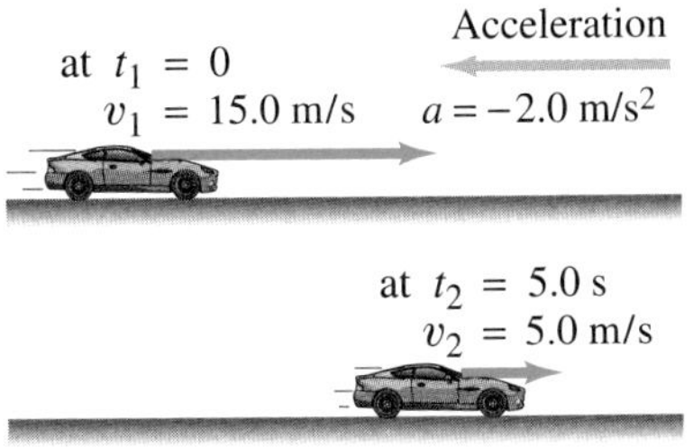


**FIGURE 2–11** Example 2–5, showing the position of the car at times $t_1$ and $t_2$, as well as the car's velocity represented by the green arrows. The acceleration vector (orange) points to the left as the car slows down while moving to the right.

## Deceleration

When an object is slowing down, we sometimes say it is **decelerating**. But be careful: deceleration does *not* mean that the acceleration is necessarily negative. For an object moving to the right along the positive $x$ axis and slowing down (as in Fig. 2–11), the acceleration *is* negative. But the same car moving to the left (decreasing $x$), and slowing down, has positive acceleration that points to the right, as shown in Fig. 2–12. We have a deceleration whenever the magnitude of the velocity is decreasing, and then the velocity and acceleration point in opposite directions.

**CAUTION**
*Deceleration means the magnitude of the velocity is decreasing; it does* not *necessarily mean $a$ is negative*

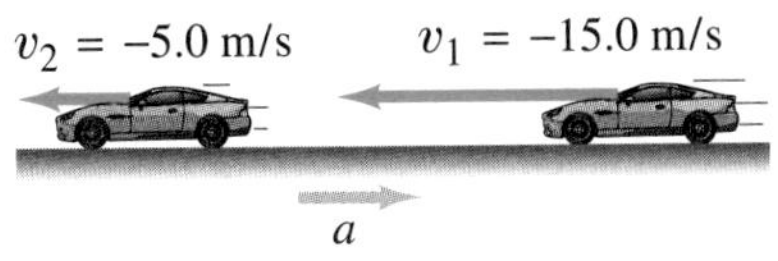


**FIGURE 2–12** The car of Example 2–5, now moving to the *left* and decelerating. The acceleration is

$$a = \frac{v_2 - v_1}{\Delta t} = \frac{-5.0\,\mathrm{m/s} - (-15.0\,\mathrm{m/s})}{5.0\,\mathrm{s}} = \frac{-5.0\,\mathrm{m/s} + 15.0\,\mathrm{m/s}}{5.0\,\mathrm{s}} = +2.0\,\mathrm{m/s}.$$

**EXERCISE B** A car moves along the $x$ axis. What is the sign of the car's acceleration if it is moving in the positive $x$ direction with (*a*) increasing speed or (*b*) decreasing speed? What is the sign of the acceleration if the car moves in the negative direction with (*c*) increasing speed or (*d*) decreasing speed?

## 2–5 Motion at Constant Acceleration

*Let $a$ = constant*

Many practical situations occur in which the acceleration is constant or nearly constant. We now examine this situation when the magnitude of the acceleration is constant and the motion is in a straight line. In this case, the instantaneous and average accelerations are equal.

We now use our definitions of velocity and acceleration to derive a set of extremely useful equations that relate $x$, $v$, $a$, and $t$ when $a$ is constant, allowing us to determine any one of these variables if we know the others.

*$x$ (at $t = 0$) $= x_0$*
*$v$ (at $t = 0$) $= v_0$*
*$t$ = elapsed time*

To simplify our notation, let us take the initial time in any discussion to be zero, and we call it $t_0$: $t_1 = t_0 = 0$. (This is effectively starting a stopwatch at $t_0$.) We can then let $t_2 = t$ be the elapsed time. The initial position $(x_1)$ and the initial velocity $(v_1)$ of an object will now be represented by $x_0$ and $v_0$, since they represent $x$ and $v$ at $t = 0$. At time $t$ the position and velocity will be called $x$ and $v$ (rather than $x_2$ and $v_2$). The average velocity during the time interval $t - t_0$ will be (Eq. 2–2)

$$\bar{v} = \frac{x - x_0}{t - t_0} = \frac{x - x_0}{t}$$

since we chose $t_0 = 0$. The acceleration, assumed constant in time, is (Eq. 2–4)

$$a = \frac{v - v_0}{t}.$$

A common problem is to determine the velocity of an object after any elapsed time $t$, when we are given the object's constant acceleration. We can solve such problems by solving for $v$ in the last equation to obtain:

*$v$ related to $a$ and $t$ ($a$ = constant, $t$ = elapsed time)*

$$v = v_0 + at. \qquad \text{[constant acceleration]} \quad \textbf{(2–6)}$$

For example, it may be known that the acceleration of a particular motorcycle is $4.0\,\text{m/s}^2$, and we wish to determine how fast it will be going after an elapsed time $t = 6.0\,\text{s}$ when it starts from rest ($v_0 = 0$ at $t_0 = 0$). At $t = 6.0\,\text{s}$, the velocity will be $v = at = (4.0\,\text{m/s}^2)(6.0\,\text{s}) = 24\,\text{m/s}$.

Next, let us see how to calculate the position of an object after a time $t$ when it is undergoing constant acceleration. The definition of average velocity (Eq. 2–2) is $\bar{v} = (x - x_0)/t$, which we can rewrite as

$$x = x_0 + \bar{v}t. \qquad \textbf{(2–7)}$$

Because the velocity increases at a uniform rate, the average velocity, $\bar{v}$, will be midway between the initial and final velocities:

**CAUTION**
*Average velocity, but only if $a$ = constant*

$$\bar{v} = \frac{v_0 + v}{2}. \qquad \text{[constant acceleration]} \quad \textbf{(2–8)}$$

(Careful: Eq. 2–8 is not necessarily valid if the acceleration is not constant.) We combine the last two Equations with Eq. 2–6 and find

$$x = x_0 + \bar{v}t = x_0 + \left(\frac{v_0 + v}{2}\right)t$$
$$= x_0 + \left(\frac{v_0 + v_0 + at}{2}\right)t$$

or

*$x$ related to $a$ and $t$ ($a$ = constant)*

$$x = x_0 + v_0 t + \tfrac{1}{2}at^2. \qquad \text{[constant acceleration]} \quad \textbf{(2–9)}$$

Equations 2–6, 2–8, and 2–9 are three of the four most useful equations for motion at constant acceleration. We now derive the fourth equation, which is useful in situations where the time $t$ is not known. We begin with Eq. 2–7 and substitute in Eq. 2–8:

$$x = x_0 + \bar{v}t = x_0 + \left(\frac{v + v_0}{2}\right)t.$$

Next we solve Eq. 2–6 for $t$, obtaining

$$t = \frac{v - v_0}{a},$$

and substituting this into the previous equation we have

$$x = x_0 + \left(\frac{v + v_0}{2}\right)\left(\frac{v - v_0}{a}\right) = x_0 + \frac{v^2 - v_0^2}{2a}.$$

We solve this for $v^2$ and obtain

$$v^2 = v_0^2 + 2a(x - x_0), \qquad \text{[constant acceleration]} \quad \textbf{(2–10)}$$

*$v$ related to $a$ and $x$ ($a$ = constant)*

which is the useful equation we sought.

We now have four equations relating position, velocity, acceleration, and time, when the acceleration $a$ is constant. We collect these kinematic equations here in one place for future reference (the tan background screen emphasizes their usefulness):

$$v = v_0 + at \qquad [a = \text{constant}] \quad \textbf{(2–11a)}$$

$$x = x_0 + v_0 t + \tfrac{1}{2}at^2 \qquad [a = \text{constant}] \quad \textbf{(2–11b)}$$

$$v^2 = v_0^2 + 2a(x - x_0) \qquad [a = \text{constant}] \quad \textbf{(2–11c)}$$

$$\bar{v} = \frac{v + v_0}{2}. \qquad [a = \text{constant}] \quad \textbf{(2–11d)}$$

*Kinematic equations for constant acceleration (we'll use them a lot)*

These useful equations are not valid unless $a$ is a constant. In many cases we can set $x_0 = 0$, and this simplifies the above equations a bit. Note that $x$ represents position, not distance, that $x - x_0$ is the displacement, and that $t$ is the elapsed time.

**EXAMPLE 2–6** **Runway design.** You are designing an airport for small planes. One kind of airplane that might use this airfield must reach a speed before takeoff of at least 27.8 m/s (100 km/h), and can accelerate at 2.00 m/s². (*a*) If the runway is 150 m long, can this airplane reach the required speed for take off? (*b*) If not, what minimum length must the runway have?

PHYSICS APPLIED
*Airport design*

**APPROACH** The plane's acceleration is given as constant ($a = 2.00\ \text{m/s}^2$), so we can use the kinematic equations for constant acceleration. In (*a*), we are given that the plane can travel a distance of 150 m. The plane starts from rest, so $v_0 = 0$ and we take $x_0 = 0$. We want to find its velocity, to determine if it will be at least 27.8 m/s. We want to find $v$ when we are given:

| Known | Wanted |
|---|---|
| $x_0 = 0$ | $v$ |
| $v_0 = 0$ | |
| $x = 150\ \text{m}$ | |
| $a = 2.00\ \text{m/s}^2$ | |

**SOLUTION** (*a*) Of the above four equations, Eq. 2–11c will give us $v$ when we know $v_0$, $a$, $x$, and $x_0$:

$$\begin{aligned} v^2 &= v_0^2 + 2a(x - x_0) \\ &= 0 + 2(2.0\ \text{m/s}^2)(150\ \text{m}) = 600\ \text{m}^2/\text{s}^2 \\ v &= \sqrt{600\ \text{m}^2/\text{s}^2} = 24.5\ \text{m/s}. \end{aligned}$$

PROBLEM SOLVING
*Equations 2–11 are valid only when the acceleration is constant, which we assume in this Example*

This runway length is *not* sufficient.

(*b*) Now we want to find the minimum length of runway, $x - x_0$, given $v = 27.8\ \text{m/s}$ and $a = 2.00\ \text{m/s}^2$. So we again use Eq. 2–11c, but rewritten as

$$(x - x_0) = \frac{v^2 - v_0^2}{2a} = \frac{(27.8\ \text{m/s})^2 - 0}{2(2.0\ \text{m/s}^2)} = 193\ \text{m}.$$

A 200-m runway is more appropriate for this plane.

## 2–6 Solving Problems

Before doing more worked-out Examples, let us look at how to approach problem solving. First, it is important to note that physics is *not* a collection of equations to be memorized. (In fact, rather than memorizing the very useful Eqs. 2–11, it is better to understand how to derive them from the definitions of velocity and acceleration as we did above.) Simply searching for an equation that might work can lead you to a wrong result and will surely not help you understand physics. A better approach is to use the following (rough) procedure, which we put in a special "Box." (Other such Problem Solving Boxes, as an aid, will be found throughout the book.)

### PROBLEM SOLVING

1. Read and **reread** the whole problem carefully before trying to solve it.
2. Decide what **object** (or objects) you are going to study, and for what **time interval**. You can often choose the initial time to be $t = 0$.
3. **Draw** a **diagram** or picture of the situation, with coordinate axes wherever applicable. [You can place the origin of coordinates and the axes wherever you like to make your calculations easier. You also choose which direction is positive and which is negative. Usually we choose the $x$ axis to the right as positive.]
4. Write down what quantities are "**known**" or "given," and then what you *want* to know. Consider quantities both at the beginning and at the end of the chosen time interval. You may need to "translate" stated language into physical terms, such as "starts from rest" means $v_0 = 0$.
5. Think about which **principles of physics** apply in this problem. Use common sense and your own experiences. Then plan an approach.
6. Consider which **equations** (and/or definitions) relate the quantities involved. Before using them, be sure their **range of validity** includes your problem (for example, Eqs. 2–11 are valid only when the acceleration is constant). If you find an applicable equation that involves only known quantities and one desired unknown, **solve** the equation algebraically for the unknown. In many instances several sequential calculations, or a combination of equations, may be needed. It is often preferable to solve algebraically for the desired unknown before putting in numerical values.
7. Carry out the **calculation** if it is a numerical problem. Keep one or two extra digits during the calculations, but round off the final answer(s) to the correct number of significant figures (Section 1–4).
8. Think carefully about the result you obtain: Is it **reasonable**? Does it make sense according to your own intuition and experience? A good check is to do a rough **estimate** using only powers of ten, as discussed in Section 1–7. Often it is preferable to do a rough estimate at the *start* of a numerical problem because it can help you focus your attention on finding a path toward a solution.
9. A very important aspect of doing problems is keeping track of **units**. An equals sign implies the units on each side must be the same, just as the numbers must. If the units do not balance, a mistake has no doubt been made. This can serve as a **check** on your solution (but it only tells you if you're wrong, not if you're right). And: always use a consistent set of units.

➡ PROBLEM SOLVING

*"Starting from rest" means $v = 0$ at $t = 0$ [i.e., $v_0 = 0$]*

**FIGURE 2–13** Example 2–7.

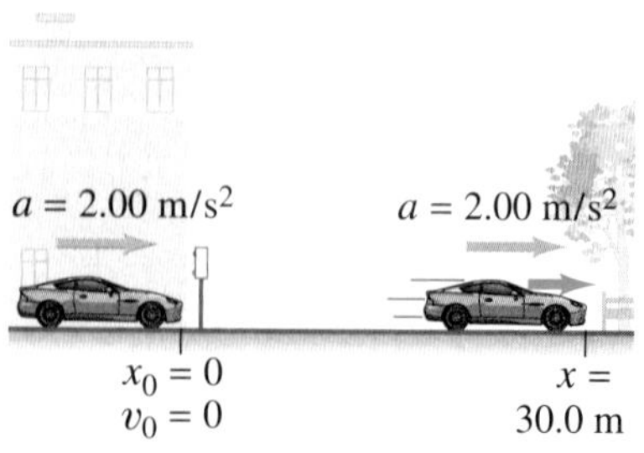


**EXAMPLE 2–7 Acceleration of a car.** How long does it take a car to cross a 30.0-m-wide intersection after the light turns green, if the car accelerates from rest at a constant $2.00\ \text{m/s}^2$?

**APPROACH** We follow the Problem Solving Box, step by step.

**SOLUTION**

1. **Reread** the problem. Be sure you understand what it asks for (here, a time period).
2. The **object** under study is the car. We need to choose the **time interval** during which we look at the car's motion: we choose $t = 0$, the initial time, to be the moment the car starts to accelerate from rest ($v_0 = 0$); the time $t$ is the instant the car has traveled the full 30.0-m width of the intersection.
3. **Draw** a **diagram**: the situation is shown in Fig. 2–13, where the car is shown moving along the positive $x$ axis. We choose $x_0 = 0$ at the front bumper of the car before it starts to move.

4. The "**knowns**" and the "wanted" are shown in the Table in the margin, and we choose $x_0 = 0$. Note that "starting from rest" means $v = 0$ at $t = 0$; that is, $v_0 = 0$.
5. The **physics**: the motion takes place at constant acceleration, so we can use the kinematic equations, Eqs. 2–11.
6. **Equations**: we want to find the time, given the distance and acceleration; Eq. 2–11b is perfect since the only unknown quantity is $t$. Setting $v_0 = 0$ and $x_0 = 0$ in Eq. 2–11b $\left(x = x_0 + v_0 t + \frac{1}{2}at^2\right)$, we can solve for $t$:

$$x = \tfrac{1}{2}at^2,$$

$$t^2 = \frac{2x}{a},$$

so

$$t = \sqrt{\frac{2x}{a}}.$$

7. The **calculation**:

$$t = \sqrt{\frac{2x}{a}} = \sqrt{\frac{2(30.0\text{ m})}{2.00\text{ m/s}^2}} = 5.48\text{ s}.$$

This is our answer. Note that the units come out correctly.
8. We can check the **reasonableness** of the answer by calculating the final velocity $v = at = (2.00\text{ m/s}^2)(5.48\text{ s}) = 10.96\text{ m/s}$, and then finding $x = x_0 + \bar{v}t = 0 + \frac{1}{2}(10.96\text{ m/s} + 0)(5.48\text{ s}) = 30.0\text{ m}$, which is our given distance.
9. We checked the **units**, and they came out perfectly (seconds).

**NOTE** In steps 6 and 7, when we took the square root, we should have written $t = \pm\sqrt{2x/a} = \pm 5.48\text{ s}$. Mathematically there are two solutions. But the second solution, $t = -5.48\text{ s}$, is a time *before* our chosen time interval and makes no sense physically. We say it is "unphysical" and ignore it.

| Known | Wanted |
|---|---|
| $x_0 = 0$ | $t$ |
| $x = 30.0\text{ m}$ | |
| $a = 2.00\text{ m/s}^2$ | |
| $v_0 = 0$ | |

PROBLEM SOLVING
*Check your answer*

We explicitly followed the steps of the Problem Solving Box in Example 2–7. In upcoming Examples, we will use our usual "approach" and "solution" to avoid being wordy.

**EXAMPLE 2–8 ESTIMATE** **Air bags.** Suppose you want to design an air-bag system that can protect the driver in a head-on collision at a speed of 100 km/h (60 mph). Estimate how fast the air bag must inflate (Fig. 2–14) to effectively protect the driver. How does the use of a seat belt help the driver?

PHYSICS APPLIED
*Car safety—air bags*

**APPROACH** We assume the acceleration is roughly constant, so we can use Eqs. 2–11. Both Eqs. 2–11a and 2–11b contain $t$, our desired unknown. They both contain $a$, so we must first find $a$, which we can do using Eq. 2–11c if we know the distance $x$ over which the car crumples. A rough estimate might be about 1 meter. We choose the time interval to start at the instant of impact with the car moving at $v_0 = 100\text{ km/h}$, and to end when the car comes to rest $(v = 0)$ after traveling 1 m.

**SOLUTION** We convert the given initial speed to SI units: $100\text{ km/h} = 100 \times 10^3\text{ m}/3600\text{ s} = 28\text{ m/s}$. We then find the acceleration from Eq. 2–11c:

$$a = -\frac{v_0^2}{2x} = -\frac{(28\text{ m/s})^2}{2.0\text{ m}} = -390\text{ m/s}^2.$$

This enormous acceleration takes place in a time given by (Eq. 2–11a):

$$t = \frac{v - v_0}{a} = \frac{0 - 28\text{ m/s}}{-390\text{ m/s}^2} = 0.07\text{ s}.$$

To be effective, the air bag would need to inflate faster than this.

What does the air bag do? It spreads the force over a large area of the chest (to avoid puncture of the chest by the steering wheel). The seat belt keeps the person in a stable position against the expanding air bag.

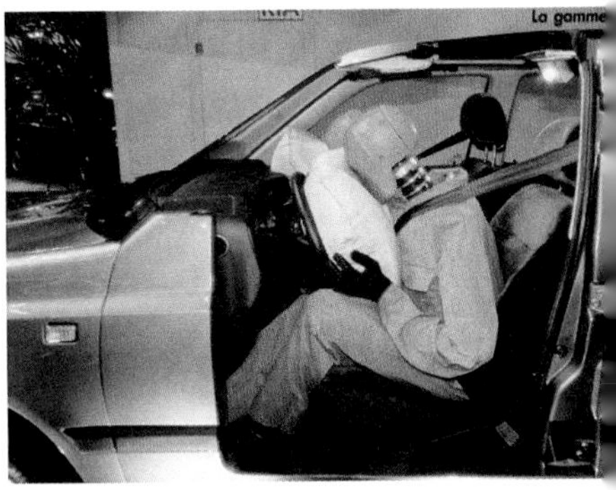


**FIGURE 2–14** An air bag deploying on impact. Example 2–8.

FIGURE 2–15 Example 2–9: stopping distance for a braking car.

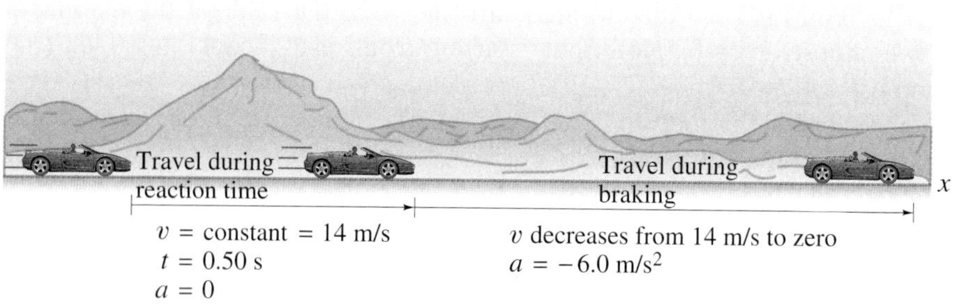


PHYSICS APPLIED
*Braking distances*

**EXAMPLE 2–9 ESTIMATE Braking distances.** Estimate the minimum stopping distance for a car, which is important for traffic safety and traffic design. The problem is best dealt with in two parts, two separate time intervals. (1) The first time interval begins when the driver decides to hit the brakes, and ends when the foot touches the brake pedal. This is the "reaction time" during which the speed is constant, so $a = 0$. (2) The second time interval is the actual braking period when the vehicle slows down ($a \neq 0$) and comes to a stop. The stopping distance depends on the reaction time of the driver, the initial speed of the car (the final speed is zero), and the acceleration of the car. For a dry road and good tires, good brakes can decelerate a car at a rate of about $5\ \mathrm{m/s^2}$ to $8\ \mathrm{m/s^2}$. Calculate the total stopping distance for an initial velocity of 50 km/h ($14\ \mathrm{m/s} \approx 31\ \mathrm{mi/h}$) and assume the acceleration of the car is $-6.0\ \mathrm{m/s^2}$ (the minus sign appears because the velocity is taken to be in the positive $x$ direction and its magnitude is decreasing). Reaction time for normal drivers varies from perhaps 0.3 s to about 1.0 s; take it to be 0.50 s.

**APPROACH** During the "reaction time," part (1), the car moves at constant speed of 14 m/s, so $a = 0$. Once the brakes are applied, part (2), the acceleration is $a = -6.0\ \mathrm{m/s^2}$ and is constant over this time interval. For both parts $a$ is constant, so we can use Eqs. 2–11.

*Part 1: Reaction time*

| Known | Wanted |
|---|---|
| $t = 0.50\ \mathrm{s}$ | $x$ |
| $v_0 = 14\ \mathrm{m/s}$ | |
| $v = 14\ \mathrm{m/s}$ | |
| $a = 0$ | |
| $x_0 = 0$ | |

**SOLUTION** Part (1). We take $x_0 = 0$ for the first part of the problem, in which the car travels at a constant speed of 14 m/s during the time interval when the driver is reacting (0.50 s). See Fig. 2–15 and the Table in the margin. To find $x$, the position of the car at $t = 0.50\ \mathrm{s}$ (when the brakes are applied), we cannot use Eq. 2–11c because $x$ is multiplied by $a$, which is zero. But Eq. 2–11b works:

$$x = v_0 t + 0 = (14\ \mathrm{m/s})(0.50\ \mathrm{s}) = 7.0\ \mathrm{m}.$$

Thus the car travels 7.0 m during the driver's reaction time, until the moment the brakes are applied. We will use this result as input to part (2).

*Part 2: Braking*

| Known | Wanted |
|---|---|
| $x_0 = 7.0\ \mathrm{m}$ | $x$ |
| $v_0 = 14\ \mathrm{m/s}$ | |
| $v = 0$ | |
| $a = -6.0\ \mathrm{m/s^2}$ | |

Part (2). Now we consider the second time interval, during which the brakes are applied and the car is brought to rest. We have an initial position $x_0 = 7.0\ \mathrm{m}$ (result of part (1)), and other variables are shown in the Table in the margin. Equation 2–11a doesn't contain $x$; Eq. 2–11b contains $x$ but also the unknown $t$. Equation 2–11c, $v^2 - v_0^2 = 2a(x - x_0)$, is what we want; after setting $x_0 = 7.0\ \mathrm{m}$, we solve for $x$, the final position of the car (when it stops):

$$x = x_0 + \frac{v^2 - v_0^2}{2a}$$

$$= 7.0\ \mathrm{m} + \frac{0 - (14\ \mathrm{m/s})^2}{2(-6.0\ \mathrm{m/s^2})} = 7.0\ \mathrm{m} + \frac{-196\ \mathrm{m^2/s^2}}{-12\ \mathrm{m/s^2}}$$

$$= 7.0\ \mathrm{m} + 16\ \mathrm{m} = 23\ \mathrm{m}.$$

The car traveled 7.0 m while the driver was reacting and another 16 m during the braking period before coming to a stop. The total distance traveled was then 23 m. Figure 2–16 shows a graph of $v$ vs. $t$: $v$ is constant from $t = 0$ to $t = 0.50\ \mathrm{s}$ and decreases linearly, to zero, after $t = 0.50\ \mathrm{s}$.

FIGURE 2–16 Example 2–9. Graph of $v$ vs. $t$.

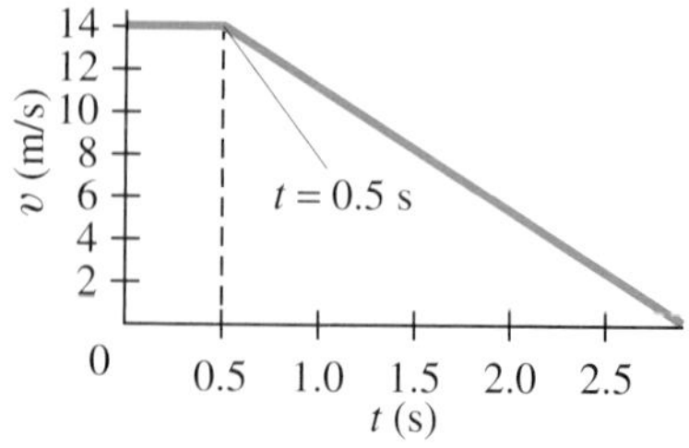


**NOTE** From the equation above for $x$, we see that the stopping distance after you hit the brakes ($= x - x_0$) increases with the *square* of the initial speed, not just linearly with speed. If you are traveling twice as fast, it takes four times the distance to stop.

The analysis of motion we have been discussing in this Chapter is basically algebraic. It is sometimes helpful to use a graphical interpretation as well; see the optional Section 2–8.

## 2–7 Falling Objects

One of the most common examples of uniformly accelerated motion is that of an object allowed to fall freely near the Earth's surface. That a falling object is accelerating may not be obvious at first. And beware of thinking, as was widely believed until the time of Galileo (Fig. 2–17), that heavier objects fall faster than lighter objects and that the speed of fall is proportional to how heavy the object is.

**FIGURE 2–17** Galileo Galilei (1564–1642).

**CAUTION**
*The speed of a falling object is NOT proportional to its mass or weight*

Galileo's analysis of falling objects made use of his new and creative technique of imagining what would happen in idealized (simplified) cases. For free fall, he postulated that all objects would fall with the *same constant acceleration* in the absence of air or other resistance. He showed that this postulate predicts that for an object falling from rest, the distance traveled will be proportional to the square of the time (Fig. 2–18); that is, $d \propto t^2$. We can see this from Eq. 2–11b, but Galileo was the first to derive this mathematical relation. [Among Galileo's great contributions to science was to establish such mathematical relations, and to insist on specific experimental consequences that could be quantitatively checked, such as $d \propto t^2$.]

**FIGURE 2–18** Multiflash photograph of a falling apple, at equal time intervals. The apple falls farther during each successive interval, which means it is accelerating.

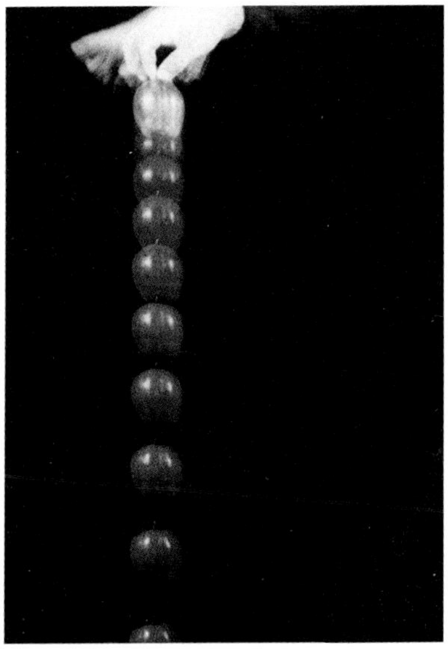

To support his claim that falling objects increase in speed as they fall, Galileo made use of a clever argument: a heavy stone dropped from a height of 2 m will drive a stake into the ground much further than will the same stone dropped from a height of only 0.2 m. Clearly, the stone must be moving faster in the former case.

As we saw, Galileo also claimed that *all* objects, light or heavy, fall with the *same* acceleration, at least in the absence of air. If you hold a piece of paper horizontally in one hand and a heavier object—say, a baseball—in the other, and release them at the same time as in Fig. 2–19a, the heavier object will reach the ground first. But if you repeat the experiment, this time crumpling the paper into a small wad (see Fig. 2–19b), you will find that the two objects reach the floor at nearly the same time.

Galileo was sure that air acts as a resistance to very light objects that have a large surface area. But in many circumstances this air resistance is negligible. In a chamber from which the air has been removed, even light objects like a feather or a horizontally held piece of paper will fall with the same acceleration as any other object (see Fig. 2–20). Such a demonstration in vacuum was not possible in Galileo's time, which makes Galileo's achievement all the greater. Galileo is often called the "father of modern science," not only for the content of his science (astronomical discoveries, inertia, free fall), but also for his style or approach to science (idealization and simplification, mathematization of theory, theories that have testable consequences, experiments to test theoretical predictions).

(a) (b)

**FIGURE 2–19** (a) A ball and a light piece of paper are dropped at the same time. (b) Repeated, with the paper wadded up.

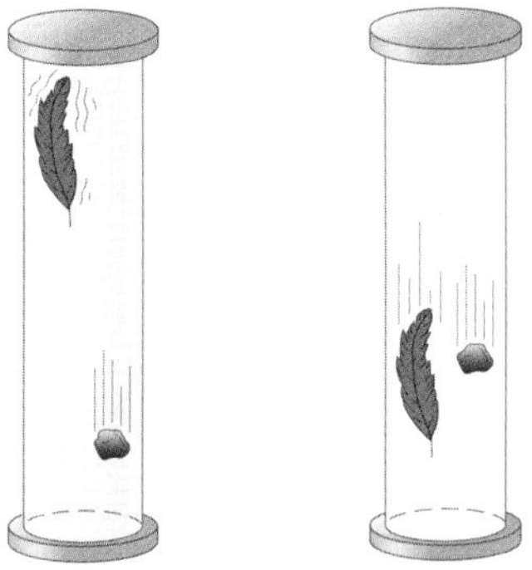


**FIGURE 2–20** A rock and a feather are dropped simultaneously (a) in air, (b) in a vacuum.

Galileo's specific contribution to our understanding of the motion of falling objects can be summarized as follows:

*Galileo's hypothesis: free fall is at constant acceleration g*

**at a given location on the Earth and in the absence of air resistance, all objects fall with the same constant acceleration.**

We call this acceleration the **acceleration due to gravity** on the Earth, and we give it the symbol $g$. Its magnitude is approximately

*Acceleration due to gravity*

$$g = 9.80\ \mathrm{m/s^2}. \qquad \text{[at surface of Earth]}$$

In British units $g$ is about $32\ \mathrm{ft/s^2}$. Actually, $g$ varies slightly according to latitude and elevation, but these variations are so small that we will ignore them for most purposes. The effects of air resistance are often small, and we will neglect them for the most part. However, air resistance will be noticeable even on a reasonably heavy object if the velocity becomes large.† Acceleration due to gravity is a vector, as is any acceleration, and its direction is toward the center of the Earth.

When dealing with freely falling objects we can make use of Eqs. 2–11, where for $a$ we use the value of $g$ given above. Also, since the motion is vertical we will substitute $y$ in place of $x$, and $y_0$ in place of $x_0$. We take $y_0 = 0$ unless otherwise specified. *It is arbitrary whether we choose y to be positive in the upward direction or in the downward direction; but we must be consistent about it throughout a problem's solution.*

**PROBLEM SOLVING**
*You choose y to be positive either up or down*

*"Drop" means $v_0 = 0$*

**EXAMPLE 2–10** **Falling from a tower.** Suppose that a ball is dropped $(v_0 = 0)$ from a tower 70.0 m high. How far will the ball have fallen after a time $t_1 = 1.00\ \mathrm{s}$, $t_2 = 2.00\ \mathrm{s}$, and $t_3 = 3.00\ \mathrm{s}$?

**APPROACH** Let us take $y$ as positive downward. We neglect any air resistance. Thus the acceleration is $a = g = +9.80\ \mathrm{m/s^2}$, which is positive because we have chosen downward as positive. We set $v_0 = 0$ and $y_0 = 0$. We want to find the position $y$ of the ball after three different time intervals. Equation 2–11b, with $x$ replaced by $y$, relates the given quantities ($t$, $a$, and $v_0$) to the unknown $y$.

**SOLUTION** We set $t = t_1 = 1.00\ \mathrm{s}$ in Eq. 2–11b:

$$\begin{aligned} y_1 &= v_0 t_1 + \tfrac{1}{2} a t_1^2 \\ &= 0 + \tfrac{1}{2} a t_1^2 = \tfrac{1}{2}(9.80\ \mathrm{m/s^2})(1.00\ \mathrm{s})^2 = 4.90\ \mathrm{m}. \end{aligned}$$

The ball has fallen a distance of 4.90 m during the time interval $t = 0$ to $t_1 = 1.00\ \mathrm{s}$. Similarly, after 2.00 s ($= t_2$), the ball's position is

$$y_2 = \tfrac{1}{2} a t_2^2 = \tfrac{1}{2}(9.80\ \mathrm{m/s^2})(2.00\ \mathrm{s})^2 = 19.6\ \mathrm{m}.$$

Finally, after 3.00 s ($= t_3$), the ball's position is (see Fig. 2–21)

$$y_3 = \tfrac{1}{2} a t_3^2 = \tfrac{1}{2}(9.80\ \mathrm{m/s^2})(3.00\ \mathrm{s})^2 = 44.1\ \mathrm{m}.$$

**NOTE** Whenever we say "dropped," we mean $v_0 = 0$.

**FIGURE 2–21** Example 2–10. (a) An object dropped from a tower falls with progressively greater speed and covers greater distance with each successive second. (See also Fig. 2–18.) (b) Graph of $y$ vs. $t$.

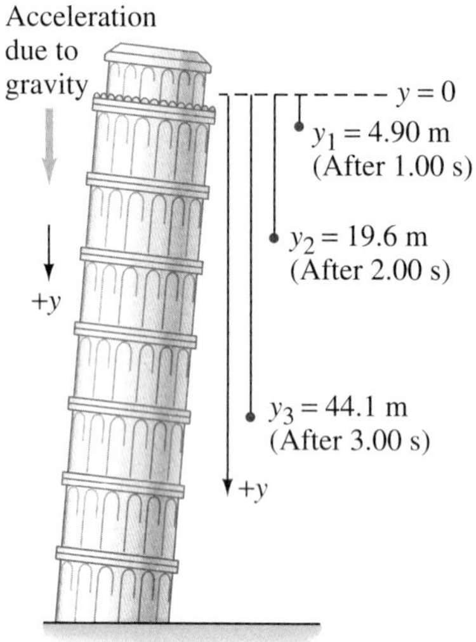

(a)

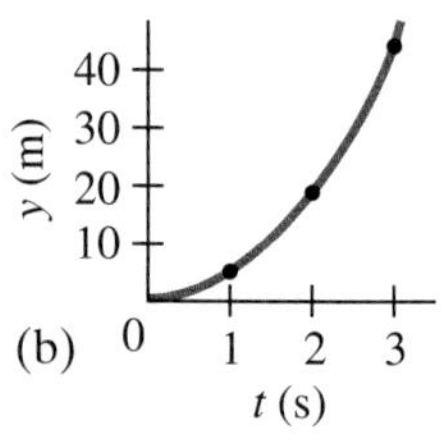

(b)

**EXAMPLE 2–11** **Thrown down from a tower.** Suppose the ball in Example 2–10 is *thrown* downward with an initial velocity of 3.00 m/s, instead of being dropped. (*a*) What then would be its position after 1.00 s and 2.00 s? (*b*) What would its speed be after 1.00 s and 2.00 s? Compare with the speeds of a dropped ball.

**APPROACH** We can approach this in the same way as in Example 2–10. Again we use Eq. 2–11b, but now $v_0$ is not zero, it is $v_0 = 3.00\ \mathrm{m/s}$.

**SOLUTION** (*a*) At $t = 1.00\ \mathrm{s}$, the position of the ball as given by Eq. 2–11b is

$$y = v_0 t + \tfrac{1}{2} a t^2 = (3.00\ \mathrm{m/s})(1.00\ \mathrm{s}) + \tfrac{1}{2}(9.80\ \mathrm{m/s^2})(1.00\ \mathrm{s})^2 = 7.90\ \mathrm{m}.$$

At $t = 2.00\ \mathrm{s}$, (time interval $t = 0$ to $t = 2.00\ \mathrm{s}$), the position is

$$y = v_0 t + \tfrac{1}{2} a t^2 = (3.00\ \mathrm{m/s})(2.00\ \mathrm{s}) + \tfrac{1}{2}(9.80\ \mathrm{m/s^2})(2.00\ \mathrm{s})^2 = 25.6\ \mathrm{m}.$$

As expected, the ball falls farther each second than if it were dropped with $v_0 = 0$.

†The speed of an object falling in air (or other fluid) does not increase indefinitely. If the object falls far enough, it will reach a maximum velocity called the **terminal velocity** due to air resistance.

(*b*) The velocity is obtained from Eq. 2–11a:

$$v = v_0 + at$$
$$= 3.00\,\text{m/s} + (9.80\,\text{m/s}^2)(1.00\,\text{s}) = 12.8\,\text{m/s} \qquad [\text{at } t_1 = 1.00\,\text{s}]$$
$$= 3.00\,\text{m/s} + (9.80\,\text{m/s}^2)(2.00\,\text{s}) = 22.6\,\text{m/s}. \qquad [\text{at } t_2 = 2.00\,\text{s}]$$

In Example 2–10, when the ball was dropped $(v_0 = 0)$, the first term $(v_0)$ in these equations was zero, so

$$v = 0 + at$$
$$= (9.80\,\text{m/s}^2)(1.00\,\text{s}) = 9.80\,\text{m/s} \qquad [\text{at } t_1 = 1.00\,\text{s}]$$
$$= (9.80\,\text{m/s}^2)(2.00\,\text{s}) = 19.6\,\text{m/s}. \qquad [\text{at } t_2 = 2.00\,\text{s}]$$

**NOTE** For both Examples 2–10 and 2–11, the speed increases linearly in time by 9.80 m/s during each second. But the speed of the downwardly thrown ball at any moment is always 3.00 m/s (its initial speed) higher than that of a dropped ball.

**EXAMPLE 2–12 Ball thrown upward, I.** A person throws a ball *upward* into the air with an initial velocity of 15.0 m/s. Calculate (*a*) how high it goes, and (*b*) how long the ball is in the air before it comes back to his hand.

**APPROACH** We are not concerned here with the throwing action, but only with the motion of the ball *after* it leaves the thrower's hand (Fig. 2–22) and until it comes back to his hand again. Let us choose $y$ to be positive in the upward direction and negative in the downward direction. (This is a different convention from that used in Examples 2–10 and 2–11, and so illustrates our options.) The acceleration due to gravity will have a negative sign, $a = -g = -9.80\,\text{m/s}^2$. As the ball rises, its speed decreases until it reaches the highest point (B in Fig. 2–22), where its speed is zero for an instant; then it descends, with increasing speed.

**SOLUTION** (*a*) We consider the time interval from when the ball leaves the thrower's hand until the ball reaches the highest point. To determine the maximum height, we calculate the position of the ball when its velocity equals zero ($v = 0$ at the highest point). At $t = 0$ (point A in Fig. 2–22) we have $y_0 = 0$, $v_0 = 15.0\,\text{m/s}$, and $a = -9.80\,\text{m/s}^2$. At time $t$ (maximum height), $v = 0$, $a = -9.80\,\text{m/s}^2$, and we wish to find $y$. We use Eq. 2–11c, replacing $x$ with $y$: $v^2 = v_0^2 + 2ay$. We solve this equation for $y$:

$$y = \frac{v^2 - v_0^2}{2a} = \frac{0 - (15.0\,\text{m/s})^2}{2(-9.80\,\text{m/s}^2)} = 11.5\,\text{m}.$$

The ball reaches a height of 11.5 m above the hand.

(*b*) Now we need to choose a different time interval to calculate how long the ball is in the air before it returns to his hand. We could do this calculation in two parts by first determining the time required for the ball to reach its highest point, and then determining the time it takes to fall back down. However, it is simpler to consider the time interval for the entire motion from A to B to C (Fig. 2–22) in one step and use Eq. 2–11b. We can do this because $y$ (or $x$) represents position or displacement, and not the total distance traveled. Thus, at both points A and C, $y = 0$. We use Eq. 2–11b with $a = -9.80\,\text{m/s}^2$ and find

$$y = v_0 t + \tfrac{1}{2}at^2$$
$$0 = (15.0\,\text{m/s})t + \tfrac{1}{2}(-9.80\,\text{m/s}^2)t^2.$$

This equation is readily factored (we factor out one $t$):

$$(15.0\,\text{m/s} - 4.90\,\text{m/s}^2\,t)\,t = 0.$$

There are two solutions:

$$t = 0 \qquad \text{and} \qquad t = \frac{15.0\,\text{m/s}}{4.90\,\text{m/s}^2} = 3.06\,\text{s}.$$

The first solution ($t = 0$) corresponds to the initial point (A) in Fig. 2–22, when the ball was first thrown from $y = 0$. The second solution, $t = 3.06\,\text{s}$, corresponds to point C, when the ball has returned to $y = 0$. Thus the ball is in the air 3.06 s.

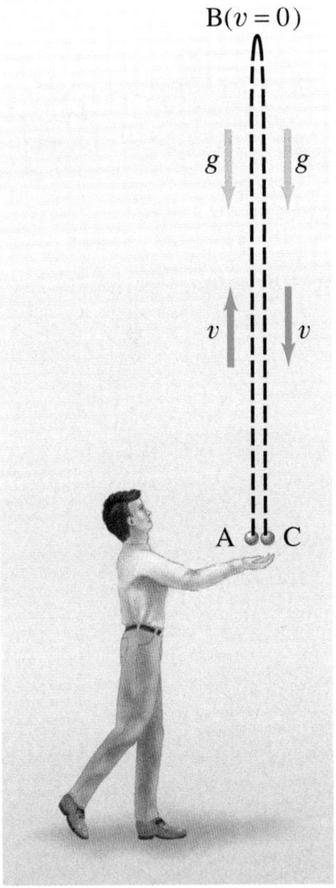


**FIGURE 2–22** An object thrown into the air leaves the thrower's hand at A, reaches its maximum height at B, and returns to the original position at C. Examples 2–12, 2–13, 2–14, and 2–15.

We did not consider the throwing action in this Example. Why? Because during the throw, the thrower's hand is touching the ball and accelerating the ball at a rate unknown to us—the acceleration is *not* $g$. We consider only the time when the ball is in the air and the acceleration is equal to $g$.

**CAUTION** *Quadratic equations have two solutions. Sometimes only one corresponds to reality, sometimes both*

Every quadratic equation (where the variable is squared) mathematically produces two solutions. In physics, sometimes only one solution corresponds to the real situation, as in Example 2–7, in which case we ignore the "unphysical" solution. But in Example 2–12, both solutions to our equation in $t^2$ are physically meaningful: $t = 0$ and $t = 3.06$ s.

**CONCEPTUAL EXAMPLE 2–13** **Two possible misconceptions.** Give examples to show the error in these two common misconceptions: (1) that acceleration and velocity are always in the same direction, and (2) that an object thrown upward has zero acceleration at the highest point (B in Fig. 2–22).

**CAUTION** *(1) Velocity and acceleration are not always in the same direction; the acceleration (of gravity) always points down* *(2) $a \neq 0$ even at the highest point of a trajectory*

**RESPONSE** Both are wrong. (1) Velocity and acceleration are *not* necessarily in the same direction. When the ball in Example 2–12 is moving upward, its velocity is positive (upward), whereas the acceleration is negative (downward). (2) At the highest point (B in Fig. 2–22), the ball has zero velocity for an instant. Is the acceleration also zero at this point? No. The velocity near the top of the arc points upward, then becomes zero (for zero time) at the highest point, and then points downward. Gravity does not stop acting, so $a = -g = -9.80\ \text{m/s}^2$ even there. Thinking that $a = 0$ at point B would lead to the conclusion that upon reaching point B, the ball would stay there: if the acceleration (= rate of change of velocity) were zero, the velocity would stay zero at the highest point, and the ball would stay up there without falling. In sum, the acceleration of gravity always points down toward the Earth, even when the object is moving up.

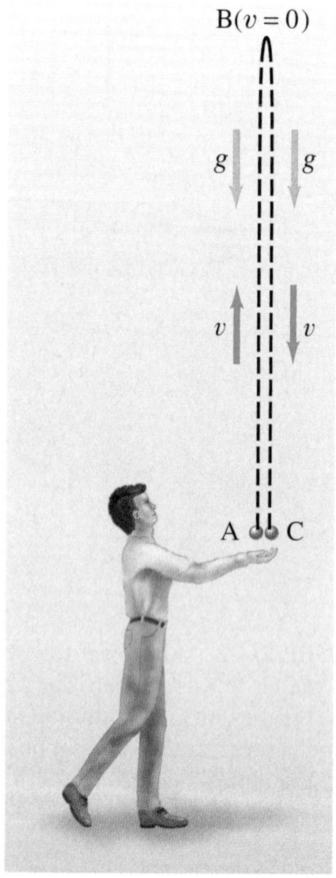


**FIGURE 2–22** (Repeated for Examples 2–13, 2–14, and 2–15.)

**EXAMPLE 2–14** **Ball thrown upward, II.** Let us consider again the ball thrown upward of Example 2–12, and make more calculations. Calculate (*a*) how much time it takes for the ball to reach the maximum height (point B in Fig. 2–22), and (*b*) the velocity of the ball when it returns to the thrower's hand (point C).

**APPROACH** Again we assume the acceleration is constant, so Eqs. 2–11 are valid. We have the height of 11.5 m from Example 2–12. Again we take $y$ as positive upward.

**SOLUTION** (*a*) We consider the time interval between the throw $(t = 0, v_0 = 15.0\ \text{m/s})$ and the top of the path (where $y = +11.5$ m and $v = 0$), and we want to find $t$ for this highest point. The acceleration is constant at $a = -g = -9.80\ \text{m/s}^2$. Both Eqs. 2–11a and 2–11b contain the time $t$ with other quantities known. Let us use Eq. 2–11a with $a = -9.80\ \text{m/s}^2$, $v_0 = 15.0$ m/s, and $v = 0$:

$$v = v_0 + at;$$

setting $v = 0$ and solving for $t$ gives

$$t = -\frac{v_0}{a} = -\frac{15.0\ \text{m/s}}{-9.80\ \text{m/s}^2} = 1.53\ \text{s}.$$

This is just half the time it takes the ball to go up and fall back to its original position [3.06 s, calculated in part (*b*) of Example 2–12]. Thus it takes the same time to reach the maximum height as to fall back to the starting point.

(*b*) Now we consider the time interval from the throw $(t = 0, v_0 = 15.0\ \text{m/s})$ until the ball's return to the hand, which occurs at $t = 3.06$ s (as calculated in Example 2–12), and we want to find $v$ when $t = 3.06$ s:

$$v = v_0 + at = 15.0\ \text{m/s} - (9.80\ \text{m/s}^2)(3.06\ \text{s}) = -15.0\ \text{m/s}.$$

*Note the symmetry: the speed at any height is the same when going up as when coming down (but the direction is opposite)*

**NOTE** The ball has the same magnitude of velocity when it returns to the starting point as it did initially, but in the opposite direction (this is the meaning of the negative sign). Thus, as we gathered from part (*a*), the motion is symmetrical about the maximum height.

**EXERCISE C** Two balls are thrown from a cliff. One is thrown directly up, the other directly down. Both balls have the same initial speed, and both hit the ground below the cliff. Which ball hits the ground at the greater speed: (*a*) the ball thrown upward, (*b*) the ball thrown downward, or (*c*) both the same? Ignore air resistance. [*Hint*: See the result of Example 2–14, part (*b*).]

The acceleration of objects such as rockets and fast airplanes is often given as a multiple of $g = 9.80\,\mathrm{m/s^2}$. For example, a plane pulling out of a dive and undergoing 3.00 $g$'s would have an acceleration of $(3.00)(9.80\,\mathrm{m/s^2}) = 29.4\,\mathrm{m/s^2}$.

*Acceleration expressed in g's*

**EXERCISE D** If a car is said to accelerate at $0.50\,g$, what is its acceleration in $\mathrm{m/s^2}$?

## Additional Example—Using the Quadratic Formula

**EXAMPLE 2–15** **Ball thrown upward, III.** For the ball in Example 2–14, calculate at what time $t$ the ball passes a point 8.00 m above the person's hand.

**APPROACH** We choose the time interval from the throw ($t = 0$, $v_0 = 15.0\,\mathrm{m/s}$) until the time $t$ (to be determined) when the ball is at position $y = 8.00\,\mathrm{m}$, using Eq. 2–11b.

**SOLUTION** We want $t$, given $y = 8.00\,\mathrm{m}$, $y_0 = 0$, $v_0 = 15.0\,\mathrm{m/s}$, and $a = -9.80\,\mathrm{m/s^2}$. We use Eq. 2–11b:

$$y = y_0 + v_0 t + \tfrac{1}{2}at^2$$

$$8.00\,\mathrm{m} = 0 + (15.0\,\mathrm{m/s})\,t + \tfrac{1}{2}(-9.80\,\mathrm{m/s^2})t^2.$$

To solve any quadratic equation of the form $at^2 + bt + c = 0$, where $a$, $b$, and $c$ are constants ($a$ is *not* acceleration here), we use the **quadratic formula** (see Appendix A–4):

**PROBLEM SOLVING**
*Using the quadratic formula*

$$t = \frac{-b \pm \sqrt{b^2 - 4ac}}{2a}.$$

We rewrite our $y$ equation just above in standard form, $at^2 + bt + c = 0$:

$$(4.90\,\mathrm{m/s^2})t^2 - (15.0\,\mathrm{m/s})\,t + (8.00\,\mathrm{m}) = 0.$$

So the coefficient $a$ is $4.90\,\mathrm{m/s^2}$, $b$ is $-15.0\,\mathrm{m/s}$, and $c$ is 8.00 m. Putting these into the quadratic formula, we obtain

$$t = \frac{15.0\,\mathrm{m/s} \pm \sqrt{(15.0\,\mathrm{m/s})^2 - 4(4.90\,\mathrm{m/s^2})(8.00\,\mathrm{m})}}{2(4.90\,\mathrm{m/s^2})},$$

which gives us $t = 0.69\,\mathrm{s}$ and $t = 2.37\,\mathrm{s}$. Are both solutions valid? Yes, because the ball passes $y = 8.00\,\mathrm{m}$ when it goes up ($t = 0.69\,\mathrm{s}$) and again when it comes down ($t = 2.37\,\mathrm{s}$).

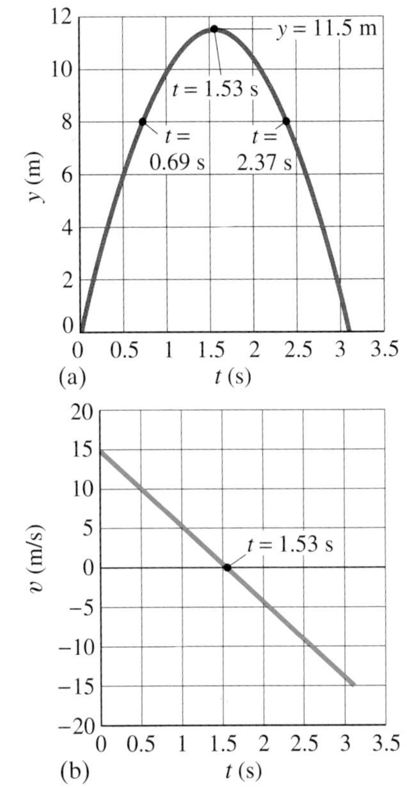

**FIGURE 2–23** Graphs of (a) $y$ vs. $t$, (b) $v$ vs. $t$ for a ball thrown upward, Examples 2–12, 2–14, and 2–15.

For some people, graphs can be a help in understanding. Figure 2–23 shows graphs of $y$ vs. $t$ and $v$ vs. $t$ for the ball thrown upward in Fig. 2–22, incorporating the results of Examples 2–12, 2–14, and 2–15. We shall discuss some useful properties of graphs in the next Section.

We will use the word "vertical" a lot in this book. What does it mean? (Try to respond before reading on.) Vertical is defined as the line along which an object falls. Or, if you put a small sphere on the end of a string and let it hang, the string represents a vertical line (sometimes called a *plumb line*).

**EXERCISE E** What does *horizontal* mean?

## * 2–8 Graphical Analysis of Linear Motion[†]

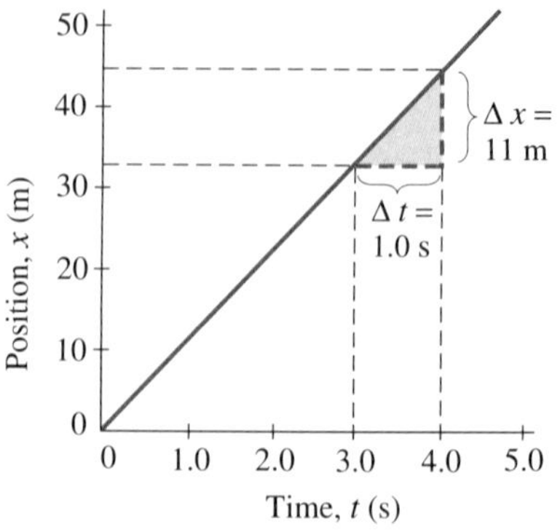


**FIGURE 2–24** Graph of position vs. time for an object moving at a uniform velocity of 11 m/s.

Figure 2–9 showed the graph of the velocity of a car versus time for two cases of linear motion: (a) constant velocity, and (b) a particular case in which the magnitude of the velocity varied. It is also useful to graph, or "plot," the position $x$ (or $y$) as a function of time, as we did in Fig. 2–23a. The time $t$ is considered the independent variable and is measured along the horizontal axis. The position, $x$, the dependent variable, is measured along the vertical axis.

Let us make a graph of $x$ vs. $t$, and make the choice that at $t = 0$, the position is $x_0 = 0$. First we consider a car moving at a constant velocity of 40 km/h, which is equivalent to 11 m/s. Equation 2–11b tells us $x = vt$, and we see that $x$ increases by 11 m every second. Thus, the position increases linearly in time, so the graph of $x$ vs. $t$ is a straight line, as shown in Fig. 2–24. Each point on this straight line tells us the car's position at a particular time. For example, at $t = 3.0\,\text{s}$, the position is 33 m, and at $t = 4.0\,\text{s}$, $x = 44\,\text{m}$, as indicated by the dashed lines. The small (shaded) triangle on the graph indicates the **slope** of the straight line, which is defined as the change in the dependent variable $(\Delta x)$ divided by the corresponding change in the independent variable $(\Delta t)$:

$$\text{slope} = \frac{\Delta x}{\Delta t}.$$

*Velocity = slope of x vs. t graph*

We see, using the definition of average velocity (Eq. 2–2), that the *slope of the x vs. t graph is equal to the velocity*. And, as can be seen from the small triangle on the graph, $\Delta x/\Delta t = (11\,\text{m})/(1.0\,\text{s}) = 11\,\text{m/s}$, which is the given velocity.

The slope of the $x$ vs. $t$ graph is everywhere the same if the velocity is constant, as in Fig. 2–24. But if the velocity changes, as in Fig. 2–25a, the slope of the $x$ vs. $t$ graph also varies. Consider, for example, a car that (1) accelerates uniformly from rest to 15 m/s in 15 s, after which (2) it remains at a constant velocity of 15 m/s for the next 5.0 s; (3) during the following 5.0 s, the car slows down uniformly to 5.0 m/s, and then (4) remains at this constant velocity. This velocity as a function of time is shown in the graph of Fig. 2–25a. To construct the $x$ vs. $t$ graph, we can use Eq. 2–11b $(x = x_0 + v_0 t + \frac{1}{2}at^2)$ with constant acceleration for the interval $t = 0$ to $t = 15\,\text{s}$ and for $t = 20\,\text{s}$ to $t = 25\,\text{s}$; for the constant velocity period $t = 15\,\text{s}$ to $t = 20\,\text{s}$, and after $t = 25\,\text{s}$, we set $a = 0$. The result is the $x$ vs. $t$ graph of Fig. 2–25b.

*Slope of a curve*

From the origin to point A, the $x$ vs. $t$ graph (Fig. 2–25b) is not a straight line, but is curved. The **slope** of a curve at any point is defined as the *slope of the tangent to the curve at that point*. (The *tangent* is a straight line drawn so it touches the curve only at that one point, but does not pass across or through the curve.) For example, the tangent to the $x$ vs. $t$ curve at the time $t = 10.0\,\text{s}$ is drawn on the graph of Fig. 2–25b. A triangle is drawn with $\Delta t$ chosen to be 4.0 s;

[†]Some Sections of this book, such as this one, may be considered *optional* at the discretion of the instructor. See the Preface for more details.

**FIGURE 2–25** (a) Velocity vs. time and (b) displacement vs. time for an object with variable velocity. (See text.)

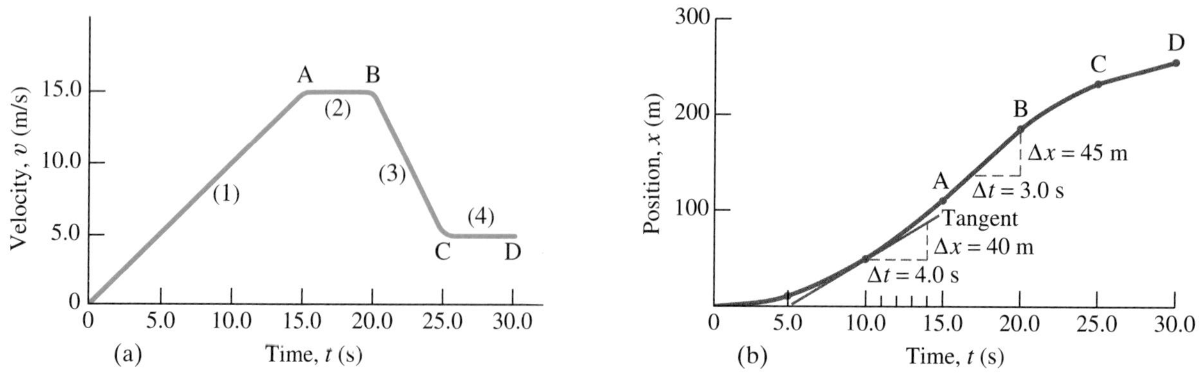

$\Delta x$ can be measured off the graph for this chosen $\Delta t$ and is found to be 40 m. Thus, the slope of the curve at $t = 10.0\,\text{s}$, which equals the instantaneous velocity at that instant, is $v = \Delta x/\Delta t = 40\,\text{m}/4.0\,\text{s} = 10\,\text{m/s}$.

In the region between A and B (Fig. 2–25b) the $x$ vs. $t$ graph is a straight line because the slope (equal to the velocity) is constant. The slope can be measured using the triangle shown for the time interval between $t = 17\,\text{s}$ and $t = 20\,\text{s}$, where the increase in $x$ is 45 m: $\Delta x/\Delta t = 45\,\text{m}/3.0\,\text{s} = 15\,\text{m/s}$.

The slope of an $x$ vs. $t$ graph at any point is $\Delta x/\Delta t$ and thus equals the velocity of the object being described at that moment. Similarly, the slope at any point of a $v$ vs. $t$ graph is $\Delta v/\Delta t$ and so (by Eq. 2–4) equals the acceleration at that moment.

Suppose we were given the $x$ vs. $t$ graph of Fig. 2–25b. We could measure the slopes at a number of points and plot these slopes as a function of time. Since the slope equals the velocity, we could thus reconstruct the $v$ vs. $t$ graph! In other words, given the graph of $x$ vs. $t$, we can determine the velocity as a function of time using graphical methods, instead of using equations. This technique is particularly useful when the acceleration is not constant, for then Eqs. 2–11 cannot be used.

If, instead, we are given the $v$ vs. $t$ graph, as in Fig. 2–25a, we can determine the position, $x$, as a function of time using a graphical procedure, which we illustrate by applying it to the $v$ vs. $t$ graph of Fig. 2–25a. We divide the total time interval into subintervals, as shown in Fig. 2–26a, where only six are shown (by dashed vertical lines). In each interval, a *horizontal* dashed line is drawn to indicate the average velocity during that time interval. For example, in the first interval, the velocity increases at a constant rate from zero to 5.0 m/s, so $\bar{v} = 2.5\,\text{m/s}$; and in the fourth interval the velocity is a constant 15 m/s, so $\bar{v} = 15\,\text{m/s}$ (no horizontal dashed line is shown in Fig. 2–26a since it coincides with the curve itself). The displacement (change in position) during any subinterval is $\Delta x = \bar{v}\,\Delta t$. Thus the displacement during each subinterval equals the product of $\bar{v}$ and $\Delta t$, which is just the *area of the rectangle* (height $\times$ base $= \bar{v} \times \Delta t$), shown shaded in rose, for that interval. The total displacement after 25 s, say, will be the sum of the areas of the first five rectangles.

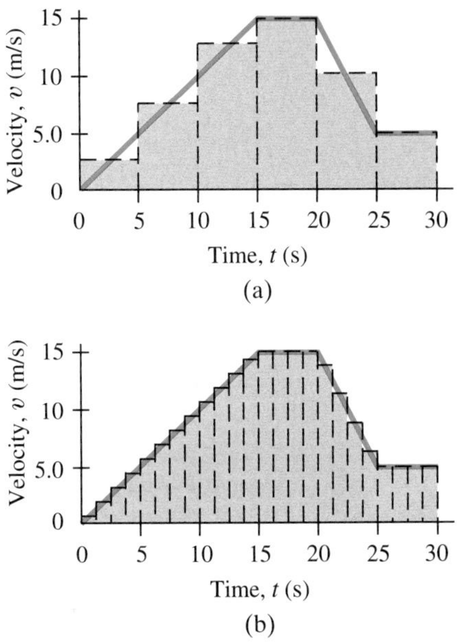


**FIGURE 2–26** Determining the displacement from the graph of $v$ vs. $t$ is done by calculating areas.

If the velocity varies a great deal, it may be difficult to estimate $\bar{v}$ from the graph. To reduce this difficulty, we can choose to divide the time interval into many more—but narrower—subintervals of time, making each $\Delta t$ smaller as shown in Fig. 2–26b. More intervals give a better approximation. Ideally, we could let $\Delta t$ approach zero; this leads to the techniques of integral calculus, which we don't discuss here. The result, in any case, is that *the total displacement between any two times is equal to the area under the v vs. t graph between these two times.*

*Displacement = area under v vs. t graph*

**EXAMPLE 2–16** **Displacement using $v$ vs. $t$ graph.** A space probe accelerates uniformly from 50 m/s at $t = 0$ to 150 m/s at $t = 10\,\text{s}$. How far did it move between $t = 2.0\,\text{s}$ and $t = 6.0\,\text{s}$?

**APPROACH** A graph of $v$ vs. $t$ can be drawn as shown in Fig. 2–27. We need to calculate the area of the shaded region, which is a trapezoid. The area will be the average of the heights (in units of velocity) times the width (which is 4.0 s).

**SOLUTION** The acceleration is $a = (150\,\text{m/s} - 50\,\text{m/s})/10\,\text{s} = 10\,\text{m/s}^2$. Using Eq. 2–11a, or Fig. 2–27, at $t = 2.0\,\text{s}$, $v = 70\,\text{m/s}$; and at $t = 6.0\,\text{s}$, $v = 110\,\text{m/s}$. Thus the area, $(\bar{v} \times \Delta t)$, which equals $\Delta x$, is

$$\Delta x = \left(\frac{70\,\text{m/s} + 110\,\text{m/s}}{2}\right)(4.0\,\text{s}) = 360\,\text{m}.$$

**NOTE** For this case of constant acceleration, we could use Eqs. 2–11 and we would get the same result.

**FIGURE 2–27** Example 2–16. The shaded area represents the displacement during the time interval $t = 2.0\,\text{s}$ to $t = 6.0\,\text{s}$.

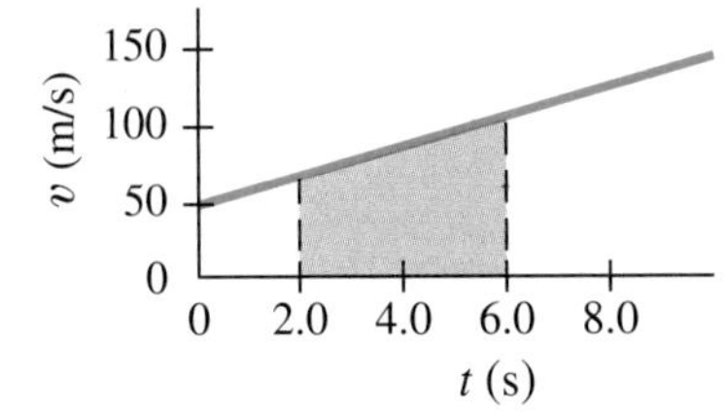


In cases where the acceleration is not constant, the area can be obtained by counting squares on graph paper.

## Summary

[The Summary that appears at the end of each Chapter in this book gives a brief overview of the main ideas of the Chapter. The Summary *cannot* serve to give an understanding of the material, which can be accomplished only by a detailed reading of the Chapter.]

**Kinematics** deals with the description of how objects move. The description of the motion of any object must always be given relative to some particular **reference frame**.

The **displacement** of an object is the change in position of the object.

**Average speed** is the distance traveled divided by the elapsed time or time interval, $\Delta t$, the time period over which we choose to make our observations. An object's **average velocity** over a particular time interval $\Delta t$ is its displacement $\Delta x$ during that time interval, divided by $\Delta t$:

$$\bar{v} = \frac{\Delta x}{\Delta t}. \tag{2–2}$$

The **instantaneous velocity**, whose magnitude is the same as the *instantaneous speed*, is defined as the average velocity taken over an infinitesimally short time interval.

Acceleration is the change of velocity per unit time. An object's **average acceleration** over a time interval $\Delta t$ is

$$\bar{a} = \frac{\Delta v}{\Delta t}, \tag{2–4}$$

where $\Delta v$ is the change of velocity during the time interval $\Delta t$. **Instantaneous acceleration** is the average acceleration taken over an infinitesimally short time interval.

If an object has position $x_0$ and velocity $v_0$ at time $t = 0$ and moves in a straight line with constant acceleration, the velocity $v$ and position $x$ at a later time $t$ are related to the acceleration $a$, the initial position $x_0$, and the initial velocity $v_0$ by Eqs. 2–11:

$$v = v_0 + at, \qquad x = x_0 + v_0 t + \tfrac{1}{2}at^2,$$
$$v^2 = v_0^2 + 2a(x - x_0), \qquad \bar{v} = \frac{v + v_0}{2}. \tag{2–11}$$

Objects that move vertically near the surface of the Earth, either falling or having been projected vertically up or down, move with the constant downward **acceleration due to gravity**, whose magnitude is $g = 9.80\,\text{m/s}^2$ if air resistance can be ignored. We can apply Eqs. 2–11 for constant acceleration to objects that move up or down freely near the Earth's surface.

[*The slope of a curve at any point on a graph is the slope of the tangent to the curve at that point. If the graph is $x$ vs. $t$, the slope is $\Delta x/\Delta t$ and equals the velocity at that point. The area under a $v$ vs. $t$ graph equals the displacement between any two chosen times.]

## Questions

1. Does a car speedometer measure speed, velocity, or both?
2. Can an object have a varying speed if its velocity is constant? If yes, give examples.
3. When an object moves with constant velocity, does its average velocity during any time interval differ from its instantaneous velocity at any instant?
4. In drag racing, is it possible for the car with the greatest speed crossing the finish line to lose the race? Explain.
5. If one object has a greater speed than a second object, does the first necessarily have a greater acceleration? Explain, using examples.
6. Compare the acceleration of a motorcycle that accelerates from 80 km/h to 90 km/h with the acceleration of a bicycle that accelerates from rest to 10 km/h in the same time.
7. Can an object have a northward velocity and a southward acceleration? Explain.
8. Can the velocity of an object be negative when its acceleration is positive? What about vice versa?
9. Give an example where both the velocity and acceleration are negative.
10. Two cars emerge side by side from a tunnel. Car A is traveling with a speed of 60 km/h and has an acceleration of 40 km/h/min. Car B has a speed of 40 km/h and has an acceleration of 60 km/h/min. Which car is passing the other as they come out of the tunnel? Explain your reasoning.
11. Can an object be increasing in speed as its acceleration decreases? If so, give an example. If not, explain.
12. A baseball player hits a foul ball straight up into the air. It leaves the bat with a speed of 120 km/h. In the absence of air resistance, how fast will the ball be traveling when the catcher catches it?
13. As a freely falling object speeds up, what is happening to its acceleration due to gravity—does it increase, decrease, or stay the same?
14. How would you estimate the maximum height you could throw a ball vertically upward? How would you estimate the maximum speed you could give it?
15. You travel from point A to point B in a car moving at a constant speed of 70 km/h. Then you travel the same distance from point B to another point C, moving at a constant speed of 90 km/h. Is your average speed for the entire trip from A to C 80 km/h? Explain why or why not.
16. In a lecture demonstration, a 3.0-m-long vertical string with ten bolts tied to it at equal intervals is dropped from the ceiling of the lecture hall. The string falls on a tin plate, and the class hears the clink of each bolt as it hits the plate. The sounds will not occur at equal time intervals. Why? Will the time between clinks increase or decrease near the end of the fall? How could the bolts be tied so that the clinks occur at equal intervals?
17. Which one of these motions is *not* at constant acceleration: a rock falling from a cliff, an elevator moving from the second floor to the fifth floor making stops along the way, a dish resting on a table?
18. An object that is thrown vertically upward will return to its original position with the same speed as it had initially if air resistance is negligible. If air resistance is appreciable, will this result be altered, and if so, how? [*Hint*: The acceleration due to air resistance is always in a direction opposite to the motion.]
19. Can an object have zero velocity and nonzero acceleration at the same time? Give examples.
20. Can an object have zero acceleration and nonzero velocity at the same time? Give examples.

* **21.** Describe in words the motion plotted in Fig. 2–28 in terms of $v$, $a$, etc. [*Hint*: First try to duplicate the motion plotted by walking or moving your hand.]

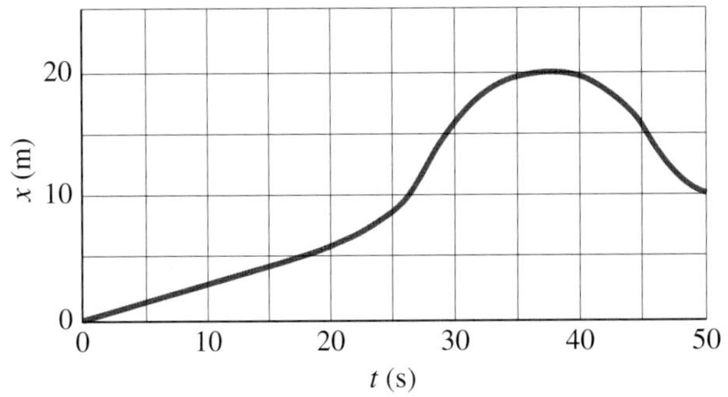


**FIGURE 2–28** Question 21, Problems 50, 51, and 55.

* **22.** Describe in words the motion of the object graphed in Fig. 2–29.

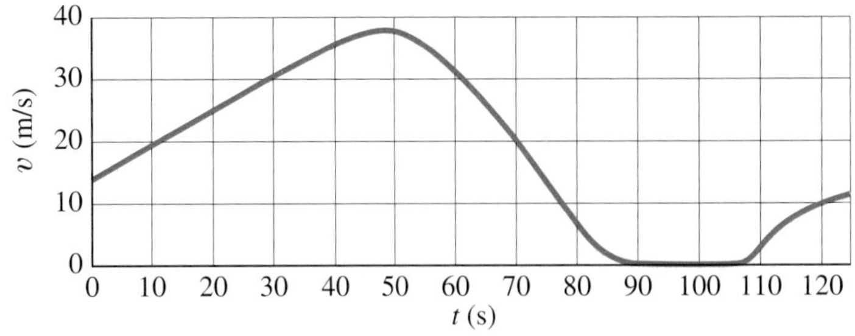


**FIGURE 2–29** Question 22, Problems 49 and 54.

## Problems

[The Problems at the end of each Chapter are ranked I, II, or III according to estimated difficulty, with (I) Problems being easiest. Level III are meant as challenges for the best students. The Problems are arranged by Section, meaning that the reader should have read up to and including that Section, but not only that Section—Problems often depend on earlier material. Finally, there is a set of unranked "General Problems" not arranged by Section number.]

### 2–1 to 2–3 Speed and Velocity

1. (I) What must be your car's average speed in order to travel 235 km in 3.25 h?
2. (I) A bird can fly 25 km/h. How long does it take to fly 15 km?
3. (I) If you are driving 110 km/h along a straight road and you look to the side for 2.0 s, how far do you travel during this inattentive period?
4. (I) Convert 35 mi/h to (*a*) km/h, (*b*) m/s, and (*c*) ft/s.
5. (I) A rolling ball moves from $x_1 = 3.4$ cm to $x_2 = -4.2$ cm during the time from $t_1 = 3.0$ s to $t_2 = 6.1$ s. What is its average velocity?
6. (II) A particle at $t_1 = -2.0$ s is at $x_1 = 3.4$ cm and at $t_2 = 4.5$ s is at $x_2 = 8.5$ cm. What is its average velocity? Can you calculate its average speed from these data?
7. (II) You are driving home from school steadily at 95 km/h for 130 km. It then begins to rain and you slow to 65 km/h. You arrive home after driving 3 hours and 20 minutes. (*a*) How far is your hometown from school? (*b*) What was your average speed?
8. (II) According to a rule-of-thumb, every five seconds between a lightning flash and the following thunder gives the distance to the flash in miles. Assuming that the flash of light arrives in essentially no time at all, estimate the speed of sound in m/s from this rule.
9. (II) A person jogs eight complete laps around a quarter-mile track in a total time of 12.5 min. Calculate (*a*) the average speed and (*b*) the average velocity, in m/s.
10. (II) A horse canters away from its trainer in a straight line, moving 116 m away in 14.0 s. It then turns abruptly and gallops halfway back in 4.8 s. Calculate (*a*) its average speed and (*b*) its average velocity for the entire trip, using "away from the trainer" as the positive direction.
11. (II) Two locomotives approach each other on parallel tracks. Each has a speed of 95 km/h with respect to the ground. If they are initially 8.5 km apart, how long will it be before they reach each other? (See Fig. 2–30).

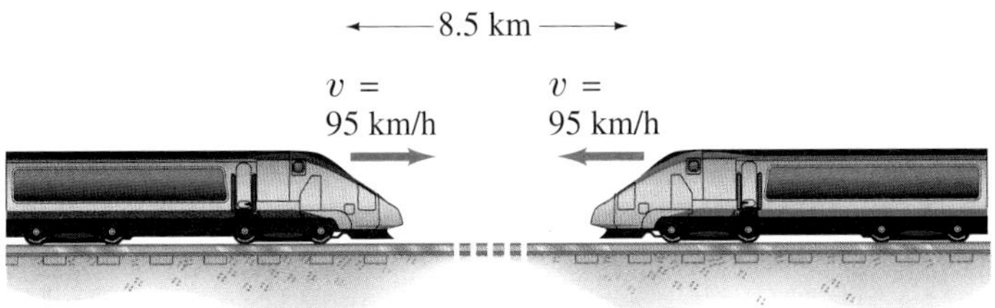


**FIGURE 2–30** Problem 11.

12. (II) A car traveling 88 km/h is 110 m behind a truck traveling 75 km/h. How long will it take the car to reach the truck?
13. (II) An airplane travels 3100 km at a speed of 790 km/h, and then encounters a tailwind that boosts its speed to 990 km/h for the next 2800 km. What was the total time for the trip? What was the average speed of the plane for this trip? [*Hint*: Think carefully before using Eq. 2–11d.]
14. (II) Calculate the average speed and average velocity of a complete round-trip in which the outgoing 250 km is covered at 95 km/h, followed by a 1.0-hour lunch break, and the return 250 km is covered at 55 km/h.
15. (III) A bowling ball traveling with constant speed hits the pins at the end of a bowling lane 16.5 m long. The bowler hears the sound of the ball hitting the pins 2.50 s after the ball is released from his hands. What is the speed of the ball? The speed of sound is 340 m/s.

### 2–4 Acceleration

16. (I) A sports car accelerates from rest to 95 km/h in 6.2 s. What is its average acceleration in $m/s^2$?
17. (I) A sprinter accelerates from rest to 10.0 m/s in 1.35 s. What is her acceleration (*a*) in $m/s^2$, and (*b*) in $km/h^2$?

18. (II) At highway speeds, a particular automobile is capable of an acceleration of about $1.6\ \mathrm{m/s^2}$. At this rate, how long does it take to accelerate from 80 km/h to 110 km/h?

19. (II) A sports car moving at constant speed travels 110 m in 5.0 s. If it then brakes and comes to a stop in 4.0 s, what is its acceleration in $\mathrm{m/s^2}$? Express the answer in terms of "g's," where $1.00\ g = 9.80\ \mathrm{m/s^2}$.

20. (III) The position of a racing car, which starts from rest at $t = 0$ and moves in a straight line, is given as a function of time in the following Table. Estimate (*a*) its velocity and (*b*) its acceleration as a function of time. Display each in a Table and on a graph.

| | | | | | | | | |
|---|---|---|---|---|---|---|---|---|
| $t$ (s) | 0 | 0.25 | 0.50 | 0.75 | 1.00 | 1.50 | 2.00 | 2.50 |
| $x$ (m) | 0 | 0.11 | 0.46 | 1.06 | 1.94 | 4.62 | 8.55 | 13.79 |
| $t$ (s) | 3.00 | 3.50 | 4.00 | 4.50 | 5.00 | 5.50 | 6.00 | |
| $x$ (m) | 20.36 | 28.31 | 37.65 | 48.37 | 60.30 | 73.26 | 87.16 | |

## 2–5 and 2–6 Motion at Constant Acceleration

21. (I) A car accelerates from 13 m/s to 25 m/s in 6.0 s. What was its acceleration? How far did it travel in this time? Assume constant acceleration.

22. (I) A car slows down from 23 m/s to rest in a distance of 85 m. What was its acceleration, assumed constant?

23. (I) A light plane must reach a speed of 33 m/s for takeoff. How long a runway is needed if the (constant) acceleration is $3.0\ \mathrm{m/s^2}$?

24. (II) A world-class sprinter can burst out of the blocks to essentially top speed (of about 11.5 m/s) in the first 15.0 m of the race. What is the average acceleration of this sprinter, and how long does it take her to reach that speed?

25. (II) A car slows down uniformly from a speed of 21.0 m/s to rest in 6.00 s. How far did it travel in that time?

26. (II) In coming to a stop, a car leaves skid marks 92 m long on the highway. Assuming a deceleration of $7.00\ \mathrm{m/s^2}$, estimate the speed of the car just before braking.

27. (II) A car traveling 85 km/h strikes a tree. The front end of the car compresses and the driver comes to rest after traveling 0.80 m. What was the average acceleration of the driver during the collision? Express the answer in terms of "g's," where $1.00\ g = 9.80\ \mathrm{m/s^2}$.

28. (II) Determine the stopping distances for a car with an initial speed of 95 km/h and human reaction time of 1.0 s, for an acceleration (*a*) $a = -4.0\ \mathrm{m/s^2}$; (*b*) $a = -8.0\ \mathrm{m/s^2}$.

29. (III) Show that the equation for the stopping distance of a car is $d_S = v_0 t_R - v_0^2/(2a)$, where $v_0$ is the initial speed of the car, $t_R$ is the driver's reaction time, and $a$ is the constant acceleration (and is negative).

30. (III) A car is behind a truck going 25 m/s on the highway. The car's driver looks for an opportunity to pass, guessing that his car can accelerate at $1.0\ \mathrm{m/s^2}$. He gauges that he has to cover the 20-m length of the truck, plus 10 m clear room at the rear of the truck and 10 m more at the front of it. In the oncoming lane, he sees a car approaching, probably also traveling at 25 m/s. He estimates that the car is about 400 m away. Should he attempt the pass? Give details.

31. (III) A runner hopes to complete the 10,000-m run in less than 30.0 min. After exactly 27.0 min, there are still 1100 m to go. The runner must then accelerate at $0.20\ \mathrm{m/s^2}$ for how many seconds in order to achieve the desired time?

32. (III) A person driving her car at 45 km/h approaches an intersection just as the traffic light turns yellow. She knows that the yellow light lasts only 2.0 s before turning red, and she is 28 m away from the near side of the intersection (Fig. 2–31). Should she try to stop, or should she speed up to cross the intersection before the light turns red? The intersection is 15 m wide. Her car's maximum deceleration is $-5.8\ \mathrm{m/s^2}$, whereas it can accelerate from 45 km/h to 65 km/h in 6.0 s. Ignore the length of her car and her reaction time.

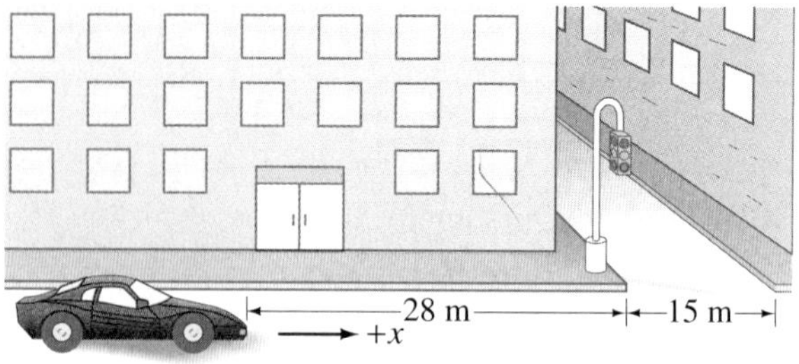


**FIGURE 2–31** Problem 32.

## 2–7 Falling Objects [neglect air resistance]

33. (I) A stone is dropped from the top of a cliff. It hits the ground below after 3.25 s. How high is the cliff?

34. (I) If a car rolls gently ($v_0 = 0$) off a vertical cliff, how long does it take it to reach 85 km/h?

35. (I) Estimate (*a*) how long it took King Kong to fall straight down from the top of the Empire State Building (380 m high), and (*b*) his velocity just before "landing"?

36. (II) A baseball is hit nearly straight up into the air with a speed of 22 m/s. (*a*) How high does it go? (*b*) How long is it in the air?

37. (II) A ballplayer catches a ball 3.0 s after throwing it vertically upward. With what speed did he throw it, and what height did it reach?

38. (II) An object starts from rest and falls under the influence of gravity. Draw graphs of (*a*) its speed and (*b*) the distance it has fallen, as a function of time from $t = 0$ to $t = 5.00$ s. Ignore air resistance.

39. (II) A helicopter is ascending vertically with a speed of 5.20 m/s. At a height of 125 m above the Earth, a package is dropped from a window. How much time does it take for the package to reach the ground? [*Hint*: The package's initial speed equals the helicopter's.]

40. (II) For an object falling freely from rest, show that the distance traveled during each successive second increases in the ratio of successive odd integers (1, 3, 5, etc.). This was first shown by Galileo. See Figs. 2–18 and 2–21.

41. (II) If air resistance is neglected, show (algebraically) that a ball thrown vertically upward with a speed $v_0$ will have the same speed, $v_0$, when it comes back down to the starting point.

42. (II) A stone is thrown vertically upward with a speed of 18.0 m/s. (*a*) How fast is it moving when it reaches a height of 11.0 m? (*b*) How long is required to reach this height? (*c*) Why are there two answers to (*b*)?

43. (III) Estimate the time between each photoflash of the apple in Fig. 2–18 (or number of photoflashes per second). Assume the apple is about 10 cm in diameter. [*Hint*: Use two apple positions, but not the unclear ones at the top.]

44. (III) A falling stone takes 0.28 s to travel past a window 2.2 m tall (Fig. 2–32). From what height above the top of the window did the stone fall?

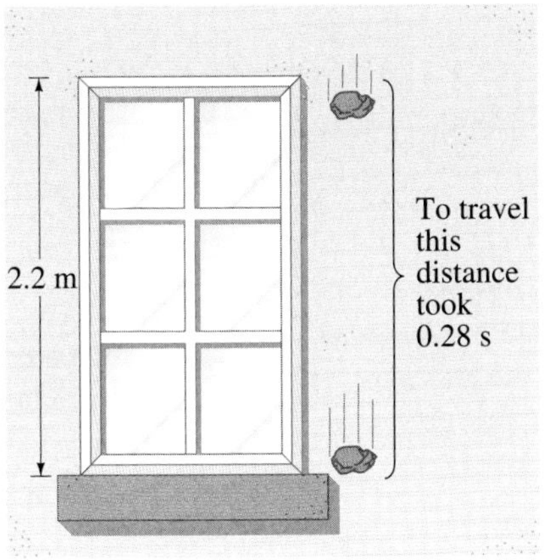


**FIGURE 2–32** Problem 44.

45. (III) A rock is dropped from a sea cliff, and the sound of it striking the ocean is heard 3.2 s later. If the speed of sound is 340 m/s, how high is the cliff?

46. (III) Suppose you adjust your garden hose nozzle for a hard stream of water. You point the nozzle vertically upward at a height of 1.5 m above the ground (Fig. 2–33). When you quickly move the nozzle away from the vertical, you hear the water striking the ground next to you for another 2.0 s. What is the water speed as it leaves the nozzle?

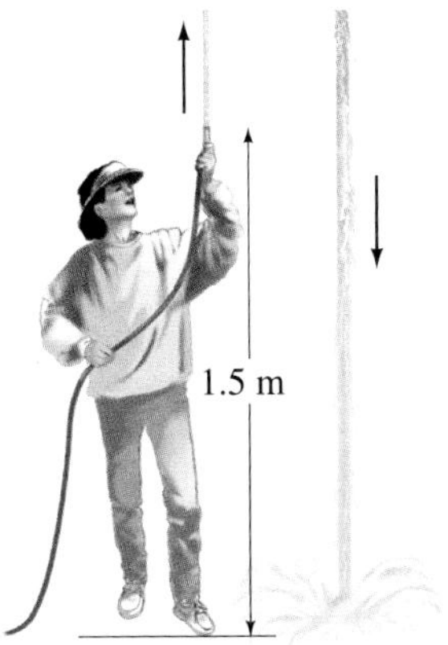


**FIGURE 2–33** Problem 46.

47. (III) A stone is thrown vertically upward with a speed of 12.0 m/s from the edge of a cliff 70.0 m high (Fig. 2–34). (*a*) How much later does it reach the bottom of the cliff? (*b*) What is its speed just before hitting? (*c*) What total distance did it travel?

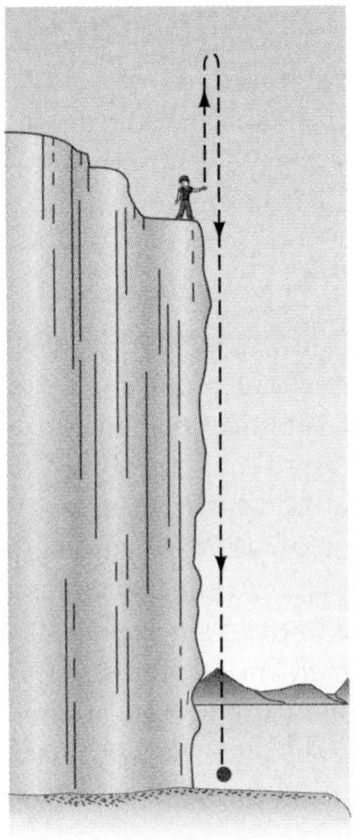

**FIGURE 2–34** Problem 47.

48. (III) A baseball is seen to pass upward by a window 28 m above the street with a vertical speed of 13 m/s. If the ball was thrown from the street, (*a*) what was its initial speed, (*b*) what altitude does it reach, (*c*) when was it thrown, and (*d*) when does it reach the street again?

## * 2–8 Graphical Analysis

* 49. (I) Figure 2–29 shows the velocity of a train as a function of time. (*a*) At what time was its velocity greatest? (*b*) During what periods, if any, was the velocity constant? (*c*) During what periods, if any, was the acceleration constant? (*d*) When was the magnitude of the acceleration greatest?

* 50. (II) The position of a rabbit along a straight tunnel as a function of time is plotted in Fig. 2–28. What is its instantaneous velocity (*a*) at $t = 10.0$ s and (*b*) at $t = 30.0$ s? What is its average velocity (*c*) between $t = 0$ and $t = 5.0$ s, (*d*) between $t = 25.0$ s and $t = 30.0$ s, and (*e*) between $t = 40.0$ s and $t = 50.0$ s?

* 51. (II) In Fig. 2–28, (*a*) during what time periods, if any, is the velocity constant? (*b*) At what time is the velocity greatest? (*c*) At what time, if any, is the velocity zero? (*d*) Does the object move in one direction or in both directions during the time shown?

* 52. (II) A certain type of automobile can accelerate approximately as shown in the velocity–time graph of Fig. 2–35. (The short flat spots in the curve represent shifting of the gears.) (*a*) Estimate the average acceleration of the car in second gear and in fourth gear. (*b*) Estimate how far the car traveled while in fourth gear.

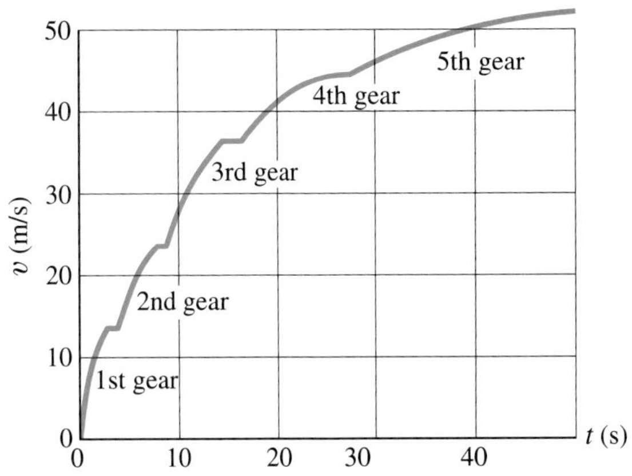


**FIGURE 2–35** Problems 52 and 53. The velocity of an automobile as a function of time, starting from a dead stop. The jumps in the curve represent gear shifts.

* 53. (II) Estimate the average acceleration of the car in the previous Problem (Fig. 2–35) when it is in (*a*) first, (*b*) third, and (*c*) fifth gear. (*d*) What is its average acceleration through the first four gears?

* 54. (II) In Fig. 2–29, estimate the distance the object traveled during (*a*) the first minute, and (*b*) the second minute.

* 55. (II) Construct the $v$ vs. $t$ graph for the object whose displacement as a function of time is given by Fig. 2–28.

* 56. (II) Figure 2–36 is a position versus time graph for the motion of an object along the $x$ axis. Consider the time interval from A to B. (*a*) Is the object moving in the positive or negative direction? (*b*) Is the object speeding up or slowing down? (*c*) Is the acceleration of the object positive or negative? Now consider the time interval from D to E. (*d*) Is the object moving in the positive or negative direction? (*e*) Is the object speeding up or slowing down? (*f*) Is the acceleration of the object positive or negative? (*g*) Finally, answer these same three questions for the time interval from C to D.

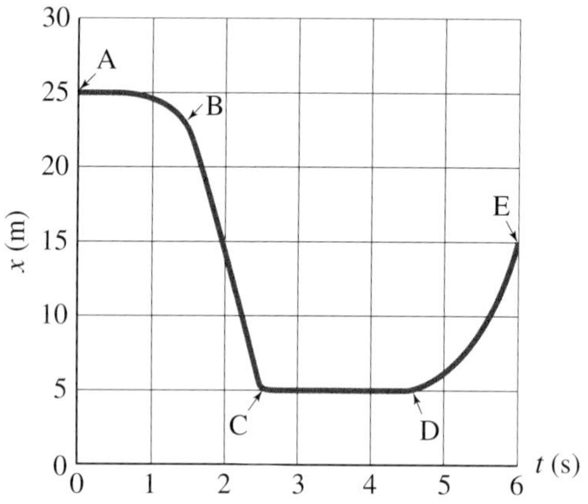


**FIGURE 2–36** Problem 56.

## General Problems

57. A person jumps from a fourth-story window 15.0 m above a firefighter's safety net. The survivor stretches the net 1.0 m before coming to rest, Fig. 2–37. (*a*) What was the average deceleration experienced by the survivor when she was slowed to rest by the net? (*b*) What would you do to make it "safer" (that is, to generate a smaller deceleration): would you stiffen or loosen the net? Explain.

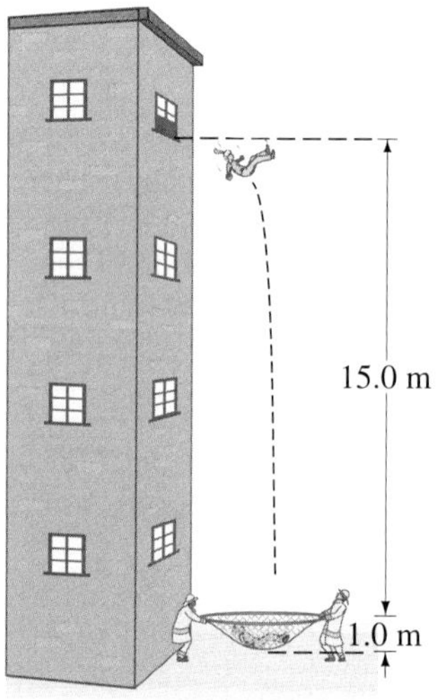


**FIGURE 2–37** Problem 57.

58. The acceleration due to gravity on the Moon is about one-sixth what it is on Earth. If an object is thrown vertically upward on the Moon, how many times higher will it go than it would on Earth, assuming the same initial velocity?

59. A person who is properly constrained by an over-the-shoulder seat belt has a good chance of surviving a car collision if the deceleration does not exceed about 30 "$g$'s" ($1.0\,g = 9.8\,\text{m/s}^2$). Assuming uniform deceleration of this value, calculate the distance over which the front end of the car must be designed to collapse if a crash brings the car to rest from 100 km/h.

60. Agent Bond is standing on a bridge, 12 m above the road below, and his pursuers are getting too close for comfort. He spots a flatbed truck approaching at 25 m/s, which he measures by knowing that the telephone poles the truck is passing are 25 m apart in this country. The bed of the truck is 1.5 m above the road, and Bond quickly calculates how many poles away the truck should be when he jumps down from the bridge onto the truck to make his getaway. How many poles is it?

61. Suppose a car manufacturer tested its cars for front-end collisions by hauling them up on a crane and dropping them from a certain height. (*a*) Show that the speed just before a car hits the ground, after falling from rest a vertical distance $H$, is given by $\sqrt{2gH}$. What height corresponds to a collision at (*b*) 60 km/h? (*c*) 100 km/h?

62. Every year the Earth travels about $10^9$ km as it orbits the Sun. What is Earth's average speed in km/h?

63. A 95-m-long train begins uniform acceleration from rest. The front of the train has a speed of 25 m/s when it passes a railway worker who is standing 180 m from where the front of the train started. What will be the speed of the last car as it passes the worker? (See Fig. 2–38.)

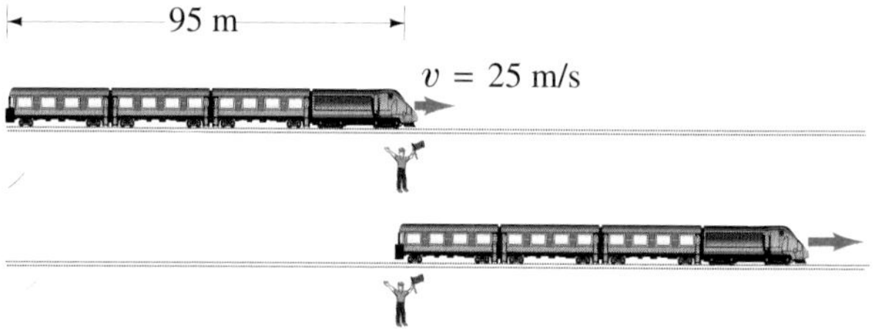


**FIGURE 2–38** Problem 63.

64. A person jumps off a diving board 4.0 m above the water's surface into a deep pool. The person's downward motion stops 2.0 m below the surface of the water. Estimate the average deceleration of the person while under the water.

65. In the design of a rapid transit system, it is necessary to balance the average speed of a train against the distance between stops. The more stops there are, the slower the train's average speed. To get an idea of this problem, calculate the time it takes a train to make a 9.0-km trip in two situations: (*a*) the stations at which the trains must stop are 1.8 km apart (a total of 6 stations, including those at the ends); and (*b*) the stations are 3.0 km apart (4 stations total). Assume that at each station the train accelerates at a rate of $1.1\,\text{m/s}^2$ until it reaches 90 km/h, then stays at this speed until its brakes are applied for arrival at the next station, at which time it decelerates at $-2.0\,\text{m/s}^2$. Assume it stops at each intermediate station for 20 s.

66. Pelicans tuck their wings and free fall straight down when diving for fish. Suppose a pelican starts its dive from a height of 16.0 m and cannot change its path once committed. If it takes a fish 0.20 s to perform evasive action, at what minimum height must it spot the pelican to escape? Assume the fish is at the surface of the water.

67. In putting, the force with which a golfer strikes a ball is planned so that the ball will stop within some small distance of the cup, say, 1.0 m long or short, in case the putt is missed. Accomplishing this from an uphill lie (that is, putting downhill, see Fig. 2–39) is more difficult than from a downhill lie. To see why, assume that on a particular green the ball decelerates constantly at $2.0\ m/s^2$ going downhill, and constantly at $3.0\ m/s^2$ going uphill. Suppose we have an uphill lie 7.0 m from the cup. Calculate the allowable range of initial velocities we may impart to the ball so that it stops in the range 1.0 m short to 1.0 m long of the cup. Do the same for a downhill lie 7.0 m from the cup. What in your results suggests that the downhill putt is more difficult?

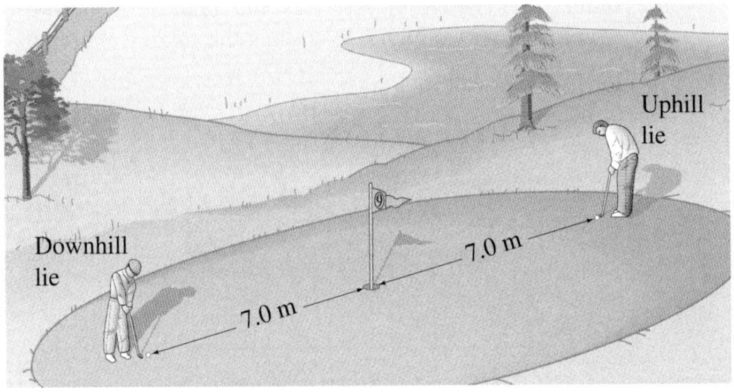


**FIGURE 2–39** Problem 67. Golf on Wednesday morning.

68. A fugitive tries to hop on a freight train traveling at a constant speed of 6.0 m/s. Just as an empty box car passes him, the fugitive starts from rest and accelerates at $a = 4.0\ m/s^2$ to his maximum speed of 8.0 m/s. (*a*) How long does it take him to catch up to the empty box car? (*b*) What is the distance traveled to reach the box car?

69. A stone is dropped from the roof of a high building. A second stone is dropped 1.50 s later. How far apart are the stones when the second one has reached a speed of 12.0 m/s?

70. A race car driver must average 200.0 km/h over the course of a time trial lasting ten laps. If the first nine laps were done at 198.0 km/h, what average speed must be maintained for the last lap?

71. A bicyclist in the Tour de France crests a mountain pass as he moves at 18 km/h. At the bottom, 4.0 km farther, his speed is 75 km/h. What was his average acceleration (in $m/s^2$) while riding down the mountain?

72. Two children are playing on two trampolines. The first child can bounce up one-and-a-half times higher than the second child. The initial speed up of the second child is 5.0 m/s. (*a*) Find the maximum height the second child reaches. (*b*) What is the initial speed of the first child? (*c*) How long was the first child in the air?

73. An automobile traveling 95 km/h overtakes a 1.10-km-long train traveling in the same direction on a track parallel to the road. If the train's speed is 75 km/h, how long does it take the car to pass it, and how far will the car have traveled in this time? See Fig. 2–40. What are the results if the car and train are traveling in opposite directions?

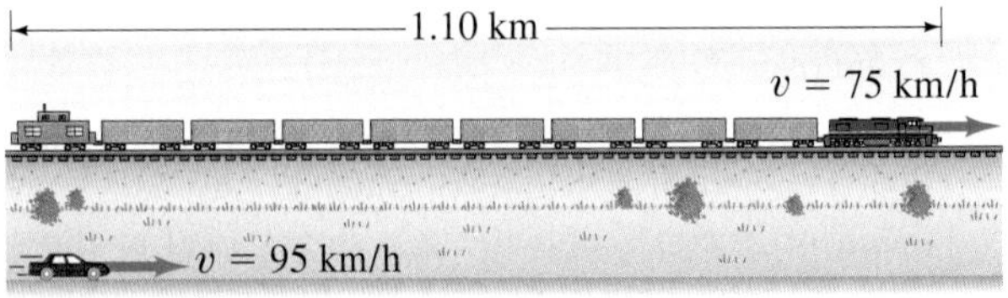


**FIGURE 2–40** Problem 73.

74. A baseball pitcher throws a baseball with a speed of 44 m/s. In throwing the baseball, the pitcher accelerates the ball through a displacement of about 3.5 m, from behind the body to the point where it is released (Fig. 2–41). Estimate the average acceleration of the ball during the throwing motion.

**FIGURE 2–41** Problem 74.

75. A rocket rises vertically, from rest, with an acceleration of $3.2\ m/s^2$ until it runs out of fuel at an altitude of 1200 m. After this point, its acceleration is that of gravity, downward. (*a*) What is the velocity of the rocket when it runs out of fuel? (*b*) How long does it take to reach this point? (*c*) What maximum altitude does the rocket reach? (*d*) How much time (total) does it take to reach maximum altitude? (*e*) With what velocity does the rocket strike the Earth? (*f*) How long (total) is it in the air?

76. Consider the street pattern shown in Fig. 2–42. Each intersection has a traffic signal, and the speed limit is 50 km/h. Suppose you are driving from the west at the speed limit. When you are 10 m from the first intersection, all the lights turn green. The lights are green for 13 s each. (*a*) Calculate the time needed to reach the third stoplight. Can you make it through all three lights without stopping? (*b*) Another car was stopped at the first light when all the lights turned green. It can accelerate at the rate of $2.0\ m/s^2$ to the speed limit. Can the second car make it through all three lights without stopping?

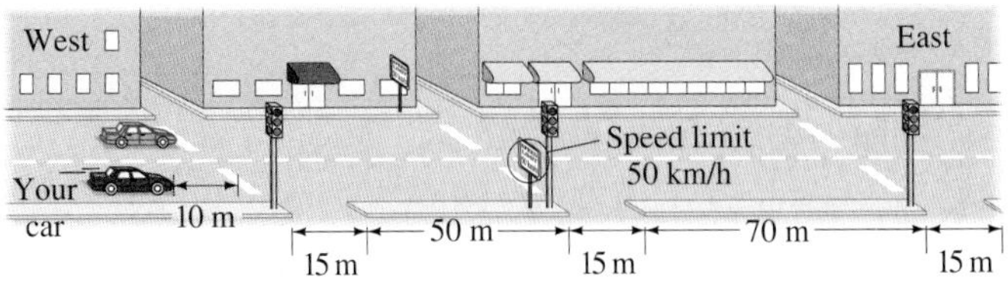


**FIGURE 2–42** Problem 76.

77. A police car at rest, passed by a speeder traveling at a constant 120 km/h, takes off in hot pursuit. The police officer catches up to the speeder in 750 m, maintaining a constant acceleration. (*a*) Qualitatively plot the position vs. time graph for both cars from the police car's start to the catch-up point. Calculate (*b*) how long it took the police officer to overtake the speeder, (*c*) the required police car acceleration, and (*d*) the speed of the police car at the overtaking point.

78. A stone is dropped from the roof of a building; 2.00 s after that, a second stone is thrown straight down with an initial speed of 25.0 m/s, and the two stones land at the same time. (*a*) How long did it take the first stone to reach the ground? (*b*) How high is the building? (*c*) What are the speeds of the two stones just before they hit the ground?

79. Two stones are thrown vertically up at the same time. The first stone is thrown with an initial velocity of 11.0 m/s from a 12th-floor balcony of a building and hits the ground after 4.5 s. With what initial velocity should the second stone be thrown from a $4^{th}$-floor balcony so that it hits the ground at the same time as the first stone? Make simple assumptions, like equal-height floors.

80. If there were no air resistance, how long would it take a free-falling parachutist to fall from a plane at 3200 m to an altitude of 350 m, where she will pull her ripcord? What would her speed be at 350 m? (In reality, the air resistance will restrict her speed to perhaps 150 km/h.)

81. A fast-food restaurant uses a conveyor belt to send the burgers through a grilling machine. If the grilling machine is 1.1 m long and the burgers require 2.5 min to cook, how fast must the conveyor belt travel? If the burgers are spaced 15 cm apart, what is the rate of burger production (in burgers/min)?

82. Bill can throw a ball vertically at a speed 1.5 times faster than Joe can. How many times higher will Bill's ball go than Joe's?

83. You stand at the top of a cliff while your friend stands on the ground below you. You drop a ball from rest and see that it takes 1.2 s for the ball to hit the ground below. Your friend then picks up the ball and throws it up to you, such that it just comes to rest in your hand. What is the speed with which your friend threw the ball?

84. Two students are asked to find the height of a particular building using a barometer. Instead of using the barometer as an altitude-measuring device, they take it to the roof of the building and drop it off, timing its fall. One student reports a fall time of 2.0 s, and the other, 2.3 s. How much difference does the 0.3 s make for the estimates of the building's height?

* 85. Figure 2–43 shows the position vs. time graph for two bicycles, A and B. (*a*) Is there any instant at which the two bicycles have the same velocity? (*b*) Which bicycle has the larger acceleration? (*c*) At which instant(s) are the bicycles passing each other? Which bicycle is passing the other? (*d*) Which bicycle has the highest instantaneous velocity? (*e*) Which bicycle has the higher average velocity?

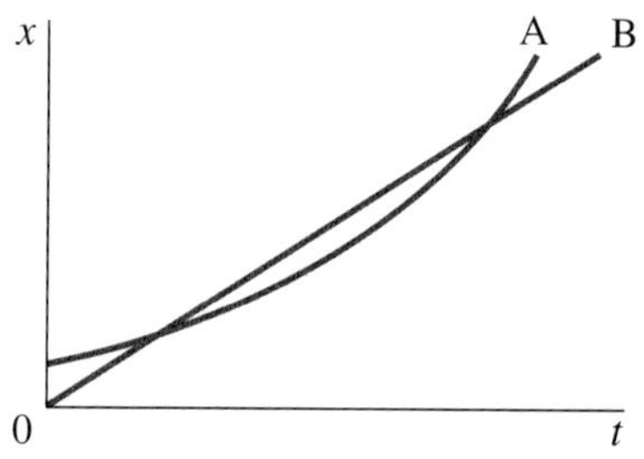


**FIGURE 2–43** Problem 85.

## Answers to Exercises

**A:** (*b*).
**B:** (*a*) +; (*b*) −; (*c*) −; (*d*) +.
**C:** (*c*).
**D:** 4.9 m/s$^2$.
**E:** That plane on which a smooth ball will not roll; or perpendicular to vertical.

This multiflash photograph of a ping pong ball shows examples of motion in two dimensions. The arcs of the ping pong ball are parabolas that represent "projectile motion." Galileo analyzed projectile motion into its horizontal and vertical components; the gold arrow represents the downward acceleration of gravity, $\vec{\mathbf{g}}$. We will discuss how to manipulate vectors and how to add them. Besides analyzing projectile motion, we will also see how to work with relative velocity.

CHAPTER 3

# Kinematics in Two Dimensions; Vectors

In Chapter 2 we dealt with motion along a straight line. We now consider the description of the motion of objects that move in paths in two (or three) dimensions. In particular, we discuss an important type of motion known as *projectile motion*: objects projected outward near the surface of the Earth, such as struck baseballs and golf balls, kicked footballs, and other projectiles. Before beginning our discussion of motion in two dimensions, we first need to present a new tool—vectors—and how to add them.

## 3–1 Vectors and Scalars

We mentioned in Chapter 2 that the term *velocity* refers not only to how fast something is moving but also to its direction. A quantity such as velocity, which has *direction* as well as *magnitude*, is a **vector** quantity. Other quantities that are also vectors are displacement, force, and momentum. However, many quantities have no direction associated with them, such as mass, time, and temperature. They are specified completely by a number and units. Such quantities are called **scalar** quantities.

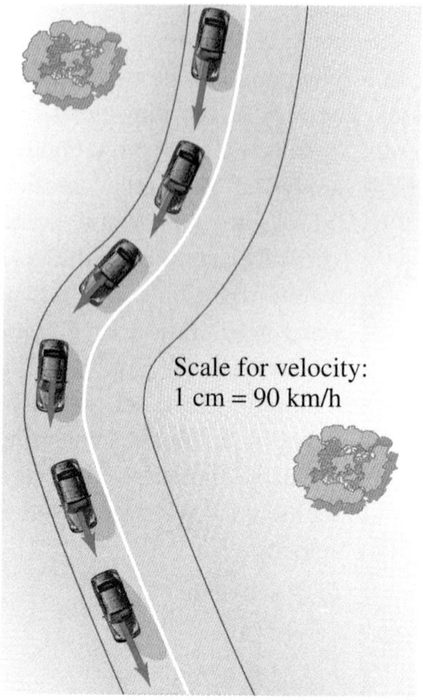


**FIGURE 3–1** Car traveling on a road. The green arrows represent the velocity vector at each position.

Drawing a diagram of a particular physical situation is always helpful in physics, and this is especially true when dealing with vectors. On a diagram, each vector is represented by an arrow. The arrow is always drawn so that it points in the direction of the vector quantity it represents. The length of the arrow is drawn proportional to the magnitude of the vector quantity. For example, in Fig. 3–1, green arrows have been drawn representing the velocity of a car at various places as it rounds a curve. The magnitude of the velocity at each point can be read off Fig. 3–1 by measuring the length of the corresponding arrow and using the scale shown ($1\text{ cm} = 90\text{ km/h}$).

When we write the symbol for a vector, we will always use boldface type, with a tiny arrow over the symbol. Thus for velocity we write $\vec{\mathbf{v}}$. If we are concerned only with the magnitude of the vector, we will write simply $v$, in italics, as we do for other symbols.

## 3–2 Addition of Vectors—Graphical Methods

Because vectors are quantities that have direction as well as magnitude, they must be added in a special way. In this Chapter, we will deal mainly with displacement vectors, for which we now use the symbol $\vec{\mathbf{D}}$, and velocity vectors, $\vec{\mathbf{v}}$. But the results will apply for other vectors we encounter later.

**FIGURE 3–2** Combining vectors in one dimension.

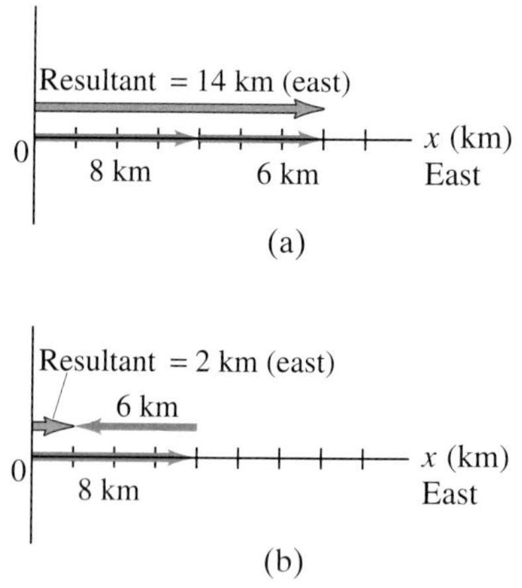


We use simple arithmetic for adding scalars. Simple arithmetic can also be used for adding vectors if they are in the same direction. For example, if a person walks 8 km east one day, and 6 km east the next day, the person will be $8\text{ km} + 6\text{ km} = 14\text{ km}$ east of the point of origin. We say that the *net* or *resultant* displacement is 14 km to the east (Fig. 3–2a). If, on the other hand, the person walks 8 km east on the first day, and 6 km west (in the reverse direction) on the second day, then the person will end up 2 km from the origin (Fig. 3–2b), so the resultant displacement is 2 km to the east. In this case, the resultant displacement is obtained by subtraction: $8\text{ km} - 6\text{ km} = 2\text{ km}$.

But simple arithmetic cannot be used if the two vectors are not along the same line. For example, suppose a person walks 10.0 km east and then walks 5.0 km north. These displacements can be represented on a graph in which the positive $y$ axis points north and the positive $x$ axis points east, Fig. 3–3. On this graph, we draw an arrow, labeled $\vec{\mathbf{D}}_1$, to represent the displacement vector of the 10.0-km displacement to the east. Then we draw a second arrow, $\vec{\mathbf{D}}_2$, to represent the 5.0-km displacement to the north. Both vectors are drawn to scale, as in Fig. 3–3.

After taking this walk, the person is now 10.0 km east and 5.0 km north of the point of origin. The **resultant displacement** is represented by the arrow labeled $\vec{\mathbf{D}}_R$ in Fig. 3–3. Using a ruler and a protractor, you can measure on this diagram that the person is 11.2 km from the origin at an angle $\theta = 27°$ north of east. In other words, the resultant displacement vector has a magnitude of 11.2 km and makes an angle $\theta = 27°$ with the positive $x$ axis. The magnitude (length) of $\vec{\mathbf{D}}_R$ can also be obtained using the theorem of Pythagoras in this case, since $D_1$, $D_2$, and $D_R$ form a right triangle with $D_R$ as the hypotenuse. Thus

$$D_R = \sqrt{D_1^2 + D_2^2} = \sqrt{(10.0\text{ km})^2 + (5.0\text{ km})^2} = \sqrt{125\text{ km}^2} = 11.2\text{ km}.$$

You can use the Pythagorean theorem, of course, only when the vectors are *perpendicular* to each other.

**FIGURE 3–3** A person walks 10.0 km east and then 5.0 km north. These two displacements are represented by the vectors $\vec{\mathbf{D}}_1$ and $\vec{\mathbf{D}}_2$, which are shown as arrows. The resultant displacement vector, $\vec{\mathbf{D}}_R$, which is the vector sum of $\vec{\mathbf{D}}_1$ and $\vec{\mathbf{D}}_2$, is also shown. Measurement on the graph with ruler and protractor shows that $\vec{\mathbf{D}}_R$ has a magnitude of 11.2 km and points at an angle $\theta = 27°$ north of east.

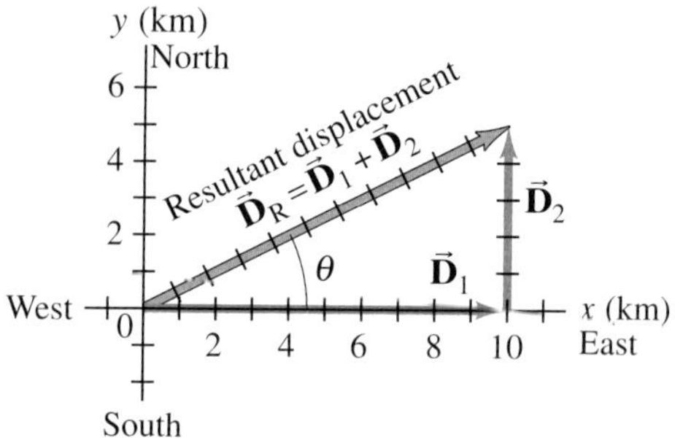

The resultant displacement vector, $\vec{\mathbf{D}}_R$, is the sum of the vectors $\vec{\mathbf{D}}_1$ and $\vec{\mathbf{D}}_2$. That is,

$$\vec{\mathbf{D}}_R = \vec{\mathbf{D}}_1 + \vec{\mathbf{D}}_2.$$

*Vector equation*

This is a *vector* equation. An important feature of adding two vectors that are not along the same line is that the magnitude of the resultant vector is not equal to the sum of the magnitudes of the two separate vectors, but is smaller than their sum:

$$D_R < D_1 + D_2. \qquad \text{[vectors not along the same line]}$$

In our example (Fig. 3–3), $D_R = 11.2\,\text{km}$, whereas $D_1 + D_2$ equals 15 km. Note also that we cannot set $\vec{\mathbf{D}}_R$ equal to 11.2 km, because we have a vector equation and 11.2 km is only a part of the resultant vector, its magnitude. We could write something like this, though: $\vec{\mathbf{D}}_R = \vec{\mathbf{D}}_1 + \vec{\mathbf{D}}_2 = (11.2\,\text{km}, 27^\circ \text{ N of E})$.

**EXERCISE A** Under what conditions can the magnitude of the resultant vector above be $D_R = D_1 + D_2$?

Figure 3–3 illustrates the general rules for graphically adding two vectors together, no matter what angles they make, to get their sum. The rules are as follows:

1. On a diagram, draw one of the vectors—call it $\vec{\mathbf{D}}_1$—to scale.
2. Next draw the second vector, $\vec{\mathbf{D}}_2$, to scale, placing its tail at the tip of the first vector and being sure its direction is correct.
3. The arrow drawn from the tail of the first vector to the tip of the second vector represents the *sum*, or **resultant**, of the two vectors.

*Tail-to-tip method of adding vectors*

The length of the resultant vector represents its magnitude. Note that vectors can be translated parallel to themselves (maintaining the same length and angle) to accomplish these manipulations. The length of the resultant can be measured with a ruler and compared to the scale. Angles can be measured with a protractor. This method is known as the **tail-to-tip method of adding vectors**.

It is not important in which order the vectors are added. For example, a displacement of 5.0 km north, to which is added a displacement of 10.0 km east, yields a resultant of 11.2 km and angle $\theta = 27^\circ$ (see Fig. 3–4), the same as when they were added in reverse order (Fig. 3–3). That is,

$$\vec{\mathbf{V}}_1 + \vec{\mathbf{V}}_2 = \vec{\mathbf{V}}_2 + \vec{\mathbf{V}}_1.$$

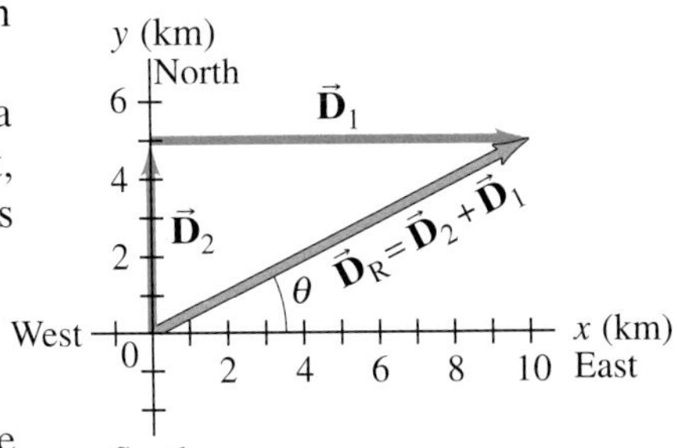


**FIGURE 3–4** If the vectors are added in reverse order, the resultant is the same. (Compare to Fig. 3–3.)

The tail-to-tip method of adding vectors can be extended to three or more vectors. The resultant is drawn from the tail of the first vector to the tip of the last one added. An example is shown in Fig. 3–5; the three vectors could represent displacements (northeast, south, west) or perhaps three forces. Check for yourself that you get the same resultant no matter in which order you add the three vectors.

**FIGURE 3–5** The resultant of three vectors: $\vec{\mathbf{V}}_R = \vec{\mathbf{V}}_1 + \vec{\mathbf{V}}_2 + \vec{\mathbf{V}}_3$.

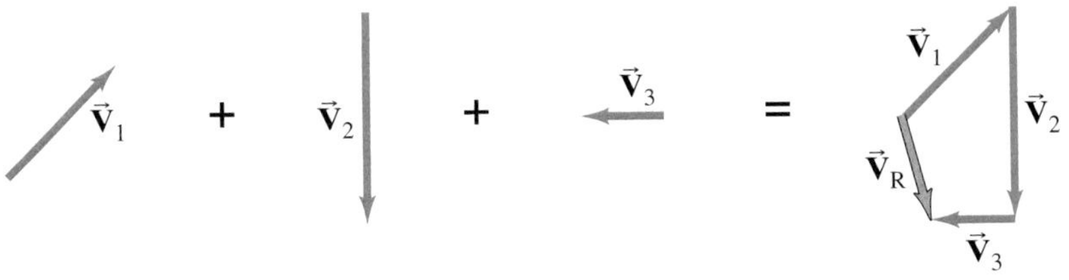

*Parallelogram method of adding vectors*

A second way to add two vectors is the **parallelogram method**. It is fully equivalent to the tail-to-tip method. In this method, the two vectors are drawn starting from a common origin, and a parallelogram is constructed using these two vectors as adjacent sides as shown in Fig. 3–6b. The resultant is the diagonal drawn from the common origin. In Fig. 3–6a, the tail-to-tip method is shown, and it is clear that both methods yield the same result.

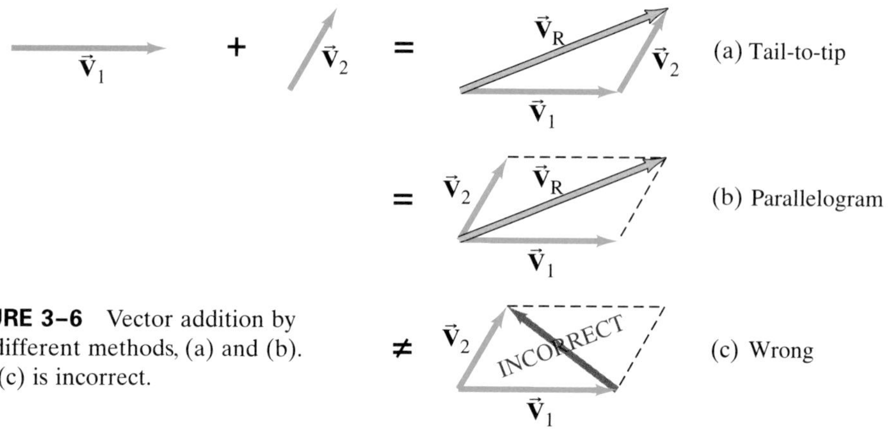


**FIGURE 3–6** Vector addition by two different methods, (a) and (b). Part (c) is incorrect.

**CAUTION**

*Be sure to use the correct diagonal on parallelogram to get the resultant*

It is a common error to draw the sum vector as the diagonal running between the tips of the two vectors, as in Fig. 3–6c. *This is incorrect*: it does not represent the sum of the two vectors. (In fact, it represents their difference, $\vec{\mathbf{V}}_2 - \vec{\mathbf{V}}_1$, as we will see in the next Section.)

**CONCEPTUAL EXAMPLE 3–1** **Range of vector lengths.** Suppose two vectors each have length 3.0 units. What is the range of possible lengths for the vector representing the sum of the two?

**RESPONSE** The sum can take on any value from 6.0 (= 3.0 + 3.0) where the vectors point in the same direction, to 0 (= 3.0 − 3.0) when the vectors are antiparallel.

**EXERCISE B** If the two vectors of Conceptual Example 3–1 are perpendicular to each other, what is the resultant vector length?

## 3–3 Subtraction of Vectors, and Multiplication of a Vector by a Scalar

Given a vector $\vec{\mathbf{V}}$, we define the *negative* of this vector $(-\vec{\mathbf{V}})$ to be a vector with the same magnitude as $\vec{\mathbf{V}}$ but opposite in direction, Fig. 3–7. Note, however, that no vector is ever negative in the sense of its magnitude: the magnitude of every vector is positive. Rather, a minus sign tells us about its direction.

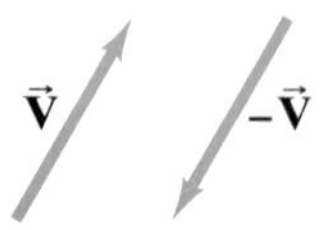


**FIGURE 3–7** The negative of a vector is a vector having the same length but opposite direction.

We can now define the subtraction of one vector from another: the difference between two vectors $\vec{\mathbf{V}}_2 - \vec{\mathbf{V}}_1$ is defined as

$$\vec{\mathbf{V}}_2 - \vec{\mathbf{V}}_1 = \vec{\mathbf{V}}_2 + \left(-\vec{\mathbf{V}}_1\right).$$

That is, the difference between two vectors is equal to the sum of the first plus the negative of the second. Thus our rules for addition of vectors can be applied as shown in Fig. 3–8 using the tail-to-tip method.

**FIGURE 3–8** Subtracting two vectors: $\vec{\mathbf{V}}_2 - \vec{\mathbf{V}}_1$.

A vector $\vec{\mathbf{V}}$ can be multiplied by a scalar $c$. We define their product so that $c\vec{\mathbf{V}}$ has the same direction as $\vec{\mathbf{V}}$ and has magnitude $cV$. That is, multiplication of a vector by a positive scalar $c$ changes the magnitude of the vector by a factor $c$ but doesn't alter the direction. If $c$ is a negative scalar, the magnitude of the product $c\vec{\mathbf{V}}$ is still $cV$ (without the minus sign), but the direction is precisely opposite to that of $\vec{\mathbf{V}}$. See Fig. 3–9.

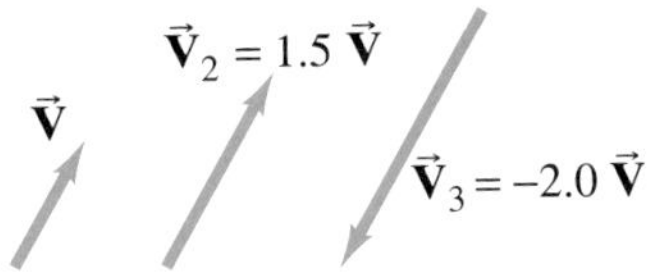


**FIGURE 3–9** Multiplying a vector $\vec{\mathbf{V}}$ by a scalar $c$ gives a vector whose magnitude is $c$ times greater and in the same direction as $\vec{\mathbf{V}}$ (or opposite direction if $c$ is negative).

## 3–4 Adding Vectors by Components

Adding vectors graphically using a ruler and protractor is often not sufficiently accurate and is not useful for vectors in three dimensions. We discuss now a more powerful and precise method for adding vectors. But do not forget graphical methods—they are always useful for visualizing, for checking your math, and thus for getting the correct result.

Consider first a vector $\vec{\mathbf{V}}$ that lies in a particular plane. It can be expressed as the sum of two other vectors, called the **components** of the original vector. The components are usually chosen to be along two perpendicular directions. The process of finding the components is known as **resolving the vector into its components**. An example is shown in Fig. 3–10; the vector $\vec{\mathbf{V}}$ could be a displacement vector that points at an angle $\theta = 30°$ north of east, where we have chosen the positive $x$ axis to be to the east and the positive $y$ axis north. This vector $\vec{\mathbf{V}}$ is resolved into its $x$ and $y$ components by drawing dashed lines out from the tip (A) of the vector (lines AB and AC) making them perpendicular to the $x$ and $y$ axes. Then the lines 0B and 0C represent the $x$ and $y$ components of $\vec{\mathbf{V}}$, respectively, as shown in Fig. 3–10b. These **vector components** are written $\vec{\mathbf{V}}_x$ and $\vec{\mathbf{V}}_y$. We generally show vector components as arrows, like vectors, but dashed. The *scalar components*, $V_x$ and $V_y$, are numbers, with units, that are given a positive or negative sign depending on whether they point along the positive or negative $x$ or $y$ axis. As can be seen in Fig. 3–10, $\vec{\mathbf{V}}_x + \vec{\mathbf{V}}_y = \vec{\mathbf{V}}$ by the parallelogram method of adding vectors.

*Resolving a vector into components*

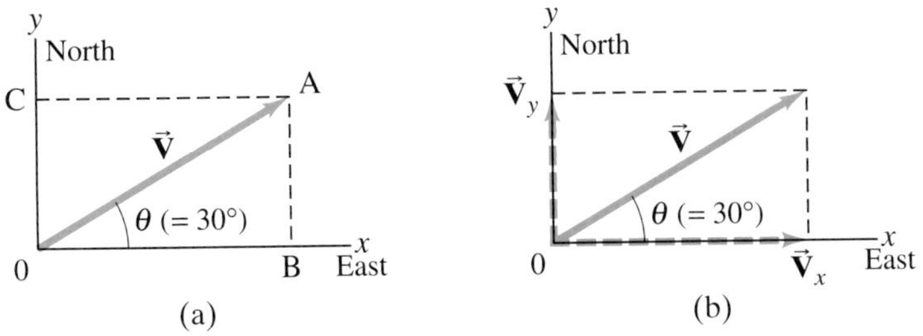


**FIGURE 3–10** Resolving a vector $\vec{\mathbf{V}}$ into its components along an arbitrarily chosen set of $x$ and $y$ axes. The components, once found, themselves represent the vector. That is, the components contain as much information as the vector itself.

Space is made up of three dimensions, and sometimes it is necessary to resolve a vector into components along three mutually perpendicular directions. In rectangular coordinates the components are $\vec{\mathbf{V}}_x$, $\vec{\mathbf{V}}_y$, and $\vec{\mathbf{V}}_z$. Resolution of a vector in three dimensions is merely an extension of the above technique. We will mainly be concerned with situations in which the vectors are in a plane and two components are all that are necessary.

To add vectors using the method of components, we need to use the trigonometric functions sine, cosine, and tangent, which we now review.

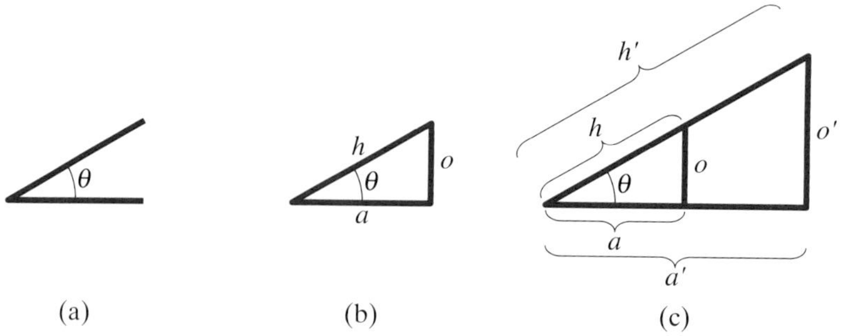


**FIGURE 3–11** Starting with an angle $\theta$ as in (a), we can construct right triangles of different sizes, (b) and (c), but the ratio of the lengths of the sides does not depend on the size of the triangle.

Given any angle $\theta$, as in Fig. 3–11a, a right triangle can be constructed by drawing a line perpendicular to either of its sides, as in Fig. 3–11b. The longest side of a right triangle, opposite the right angle, is called the hypotenuse, which we label $h$. The side opposite the angle $\theta$ is labeled $o$, and the side adjacent is labeled $a$. We let $h$, $o$, and $a$ represent the lengths of these sides, respectively. We now define the three trigonometric functions, sine, cosine, and tangent (abbreviated sin, cos, tan), in terms of the right triangle, as follows:

*Trigonometric functions defined*

$$\sin\theta = \frac{\text{side opposite}}{\text{hypotenuse}} = \frac{o}{h}$$
$$\cos\theta = \frac{\text{side adjacent}}{\text{hypotenuse}} = \frac{a}{h} \qquad \textbf{(3–1)}$$
$$\tan\theta = \frac{\text{side opposite}}{\text{side adjacent}} = \frac{o}{a}.$$

If we make the triangle bigger, but keep the same angles, then the ratio of the length of one side to the other, or of one side to the hypotenuse, remains the same. That is, in Fig. 3–11c we have: $a/h = a'/h'$; $o/h = o'/h'$; and $o/a = o'/a'$. Thus the values of sine, cosine, and tangent do not depend on how big the triangle is. They depend only on the size of the angle. The values of sine, cosine, and tangent for different angles can be found using a scientific calculator, or from the Table in Appendix A.

A useful trigonometric identity is

$$\sin^2\theta + \cos^2\theta = 1 \qquad \textbf{(3–2)}$$

which follows from the Pythagorean theorem ($o^2 + a^2 = h^2$ in Fig. 3–11). That is:

$$\sin^2\theta + \cos^2\theta = \frac{o^2}{h^2} + \frac{a^2}{h^2} = \frac{o^2 + a^2}{h^2} = \frac{h^2}{h^2} = 1.$$

(See also Appendix A for other details on trigonometric functions and identities.)

The use of trigonometric functions for finding the components of a vector is illustrated in Fig. 3–12, where a vector and its two components are thought of as making up a right triangle. We then see that the sine, cosine, and tangent are as given in the Figure. If we multiply the definition of $\sin\theta = V_y/V$ by $V$ on both sides, we get

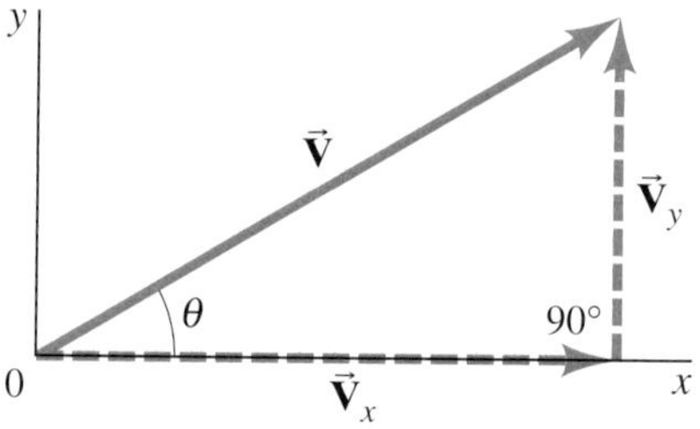


$$\sin\theta = \frac{V_y}{V}$$
$$\cos\theta = \frac{V_x}{V}$$
$$\tan\theta = \frac{V_y}{V_x}$$
$$V^2 = V_x^2 + V_y^2$$

**FIGURE 3–12** Finding the components of a vector using trigonometric functions.

*Components of a vector*

$$V_y = V\sin\theta. \qquad \textbf{(3–3a)}$$

Similarly, from the definition of $\cos\theta$, we obtain

$$V_x = V\cos\theta. \qquad \textbf{(3–3b)}$$

Note that $\theta$ is chosen (by convention) to be the angle that the vector makes with the positive $x$ axis.

Using Eqs. 3–3, we can calculate $V_x$ and $V_y$ for any vector, such as that illustrated in Fig. 3–10 or Fig. 3–12. Suppose $\vec{\mathbf{V}}$ represents a displacement of 500 m

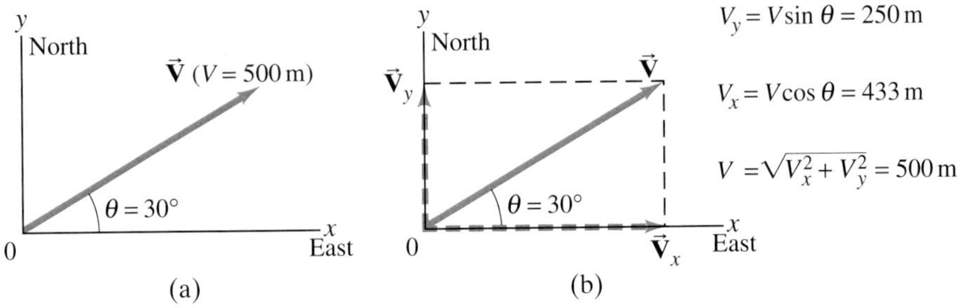


**FIGURE 3–13** (a) Vector $\vec{\mathbf{V}}$ represents a displacement of 500 m at a 30° angle north of east. (b) The components of $\vec{\mathbf{V}}$ are $\vec{\mathbf{V}}_x$ and $\vec{\mathbf{V}}_y$, whose magnitudes are given on the right.

in a direction 30° north of east, as shown in Fig. 3–13. Then $V = 500\,\text{m}$. From a calculator or Tables, $\sin 30° = 0.500$ and $\cos 30° = 0.866$. Then

$$V_x = V\cos\theta = (500\,\text{m})(0.866) = 433\,\text{m (east)},$$
$$V_y = V\sin\theta = (500\,\text{m})(0.500) = 250\,\text{m (north)}.$$

There are two ways to specify a vector in a given coordinate system:

*Two ways to specify a vector*

1. We can give its components, $V_x$ and $V_y$.
2. We can give its magnitude $V$ and the angle $\theta$ it makes with the positive $x$ axis.

We can shift from one description to the other using Eqs. 3–3, and, for the reverse, by using the theorem of Pythagoras† and the definition of tangent:

*Components related to magnitude and direction*

$$V = \sqrt{V_x^2 + V_y^2} \qquad \textbf{(3–4a)}$$

$$\tan\theta = \frac{V_y}{V_x} \qquad \textbf{(3–4b)}$$

as can be seen in Fig. 3–12.

We can now discuss how to add vectors using components. The first step is to resolve each vector into its components. Next we can see, using Fig. 3–14, that the addition of any two vectors $\vec{\mathbf{V}}_1$ and $\vec{\mathbf{V}}_2$ to give a resultant, $\vec{\mathbf{V}} = \vec{\mathbf{V}}_1 + \vec{\mathbf{V}}_2$, implies that

*Adding vectors analytically (by components)*

$$\begin{aligned} V_x &= V_{1x} + V_{2x} \\ V_y &= V_{1y} + V_{2y}. \end{aligned} \qquad \textbf{(3–5)}$$

That is, the sum of the $x$ components equals the $x$ component of the resultant, and similarly for $y$. That this is valid can be verified by a careful examination of Fig. 3–14. But note that we add all the $x$ components together to get the $x$ component of the resultant; and we add all the $y$ components together to get the $y$ component of the resultant. We do *not* add $x$ components to $y$ components.

If the magnitude and direction of the resultant vector are desired, they can be obtained using Eqs. 3–4.

† In three dimensions, the theorem of Pythagoras becomes $V = \sqrt{V_x^2 + V_y^2 + V_z^2}$, where $V_z$ is the component along the third, or $z$, axis.

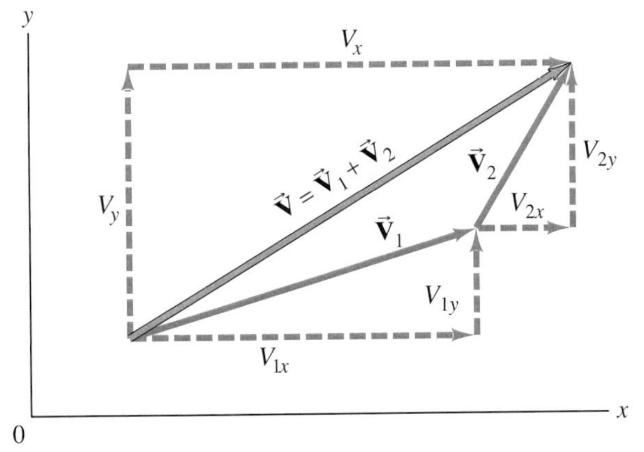


**FIGURE 3–14** The components of $\vec{\mathbf{V}} = \vec{\mathbf{V}}_1 + \vec{\mathbf{V}}_2$ are $V_x = V_{1x} + V_{2x}$ and $V_y = V_{1y} + V_{2y}$.

*Choice of axes can simplify effort needed*

The components of a given vector will be different for different choices of coordinate axes. The choice of coordinate axes is always arbitrary. You can often reduce the work involved in adding vectors by a good choice of axes—for example, by choosing one of the axes to be in the same direction as one of the vectors. Then that vector will have only one nonzero component.

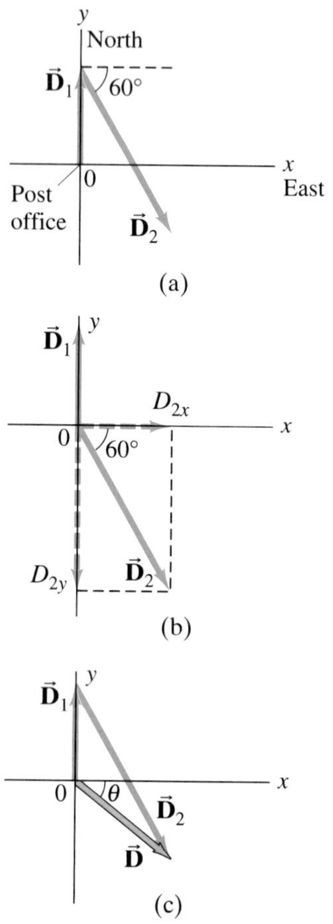


**FIGURE 3–15** Example 3–2. (a) The two displacement vectors, $\vec{\mathbf{D}}_1$ and $\vec{\mathbf{D}}_2$. (b) $\vec{\mathbf{D}}_2$ is resolved into its components. (c) $\vec{\mathbf{D}}_1$ and $\vec{\mathbf{D}}_2$ are added graphically to obtain the resultant $\vec{\mathbf{D}}$. The component method of adding the vectors is explained in the Example.

**EXAMPLE 3–2** **Mail carrier's displacement.** A rural mail carrier leaves the post office and drives 22.0 km in a northerly direction. She then drives in a direction 60.0° south of east for 47.0 km (Fig. 3–15a). What is her displacement from the post office?

**APPROACH** We resolve each vector into its $x$ and $y$ components. We add the $x$ components together, and then the $y$ components together, giving us the $x$ and $y$ components of the resultant. We choose the positive $x$ axis to be east and the positive $y$ axis to be north, since those are the compass directions used on most maps.

**SOLUTION** Resolve each displacement vector into its components, as shown in Fig. 3–15b. Since $\vec{\mathbf{D}}_1$ has magnitude 22.0 km and points north, it has only a $y$ component:

$$D_{1x} = 0, \qquad D_{1y} = 22.0\text{ km}.$$

$\vec{\mathbf{D}}_2$ has both $x$ and $y$ components:

$$D_{2x} = +(47.0\text{ km})(\cos 60°) = +(47.0\text{ km})(0.500) = +23.5\text{ km}$$
$$D_{2y} = -(47.0\text{ km})(\sin 60°) = -(47.0\text{ km})(0.866) = -40.7\text{ km}.$$

Notice that $D_{2y}$ is negative because this vector component points along the negative $y$ axis. The resultant vector, $\vec{\mathbf{D}}$, has components:

$$D_x = D_{1x} + D_{2x} = \quad 0\text{ km} + \quad 23.5\text{ km} = +23.5\text{ km}$$
$$D_y = D_{1y} + D_{2y} = 22.0\text{ km} + (-40.7\text{ km}) = -18.7\text{ km}.$$

This specifies the resultant vector completely:

$$D_x = 23.5\text{ km}, \qquad D_y = -18.7\text{ km}.$$

We can also specify the resultant vector by giving its magnitude and angle using Eqs. 3–4:

$$D = \sqrt{D_x^2 + D_y^2} = \sqrt{(23.5\text{ km})^2 + (-18.7\text{ km})^2} = 30.0\text{ km}$$
$$\tan\theta = \frac{D_y}{D_x} = \frac{-18.7\text{ km}}{23.5\text{ km}} = -0.796.$$

A calculator with an INV TAN, an ARC TAN, or a TAN$^{-1}$ key gives $\theta = \tan^{-1}(-0.796) = -38.5°$. The negative sign means $\theta = 38.5°$ below the $x$ axis, Fig. 3–15c. So, the resultant displacement is 30.0 km directed at 38.5° in a southeasterly direction.

**NOTE** Always be attentive about the quadrant in which the resultant vector lies. An electronic calculator does not fully give this information, but a good diagram does.

**PROBLEM SOLVING**

*Identify the correct quadrant by drawing a careful diagram*

The signs of trigonometric functions depend on which "quadrant" the angle falls in: for example, the tangent is positive in the first and third quadrants (from 0° to 90°, and 180° to 270°), but negative in the second and fourth quadrants; see Appendix A–7. The best way to keep track of angles, and to check any vector result, is always to draw a vector diagram. A vector diagram gives you something tangible to look at when analyzing a problem, and provides a check on the results.

The following Problem Solving Box should not be considered a prescription. Rather it is a summary of things to do to get you thinking and involved in the problem at hand.

## PROBLEM SOLVING Adding Vectors

Here is a brief summary of how to add two or more vectors using components:

1. **Draw a diagram**, adding the vectors graphically by either the parallelogram or tail-to-tip method.
2. **Choose** $x$ and $y$ **axes**. Choose them in a way, if possible, that will make your work easier. (For example, choose one axis along the direction of one of the vectors so that vector will have only one component.)
3. **Resolve each vector** into its $x$ and $y$ components, showing each component along its appropriate ($x$ or $y$) axis as a (dashed) arrow.
4. **Calculate each component** (when not given) using sines and cosines. If $\theta_1$ is the angle that vector $\vec{\mathbf{V}}_1$ makes with the positive $x$ axis, then:
$$V_{1x} = V_1 \cos\theta_1, \qquad V_{1y} = V_1 \sin\theta_1.$$
Pay careful attention to **signs**: any component that points along the negative $x$ or $y$ axis gets a $-$ sign.
5. **Add** the $x$ **components** together to get the $x$ component of the resultant. Ditto for $y$:
$$V_x = V_{1x} + V_{2x} + \text{any others}$$
$$V_y = V_{1y} + V_{2y} + \text{any others.}$$
This is the answer: the components of the resultant vector. Check signs to see if they fit the quadrant shown in your diagram (point 1 above).
6. If you want to know the **magnitude and direction** of the resultant vector, use Eqs. 3–4:
$$V = \sqrt{V_x^2 + V_y^2}, \qquad \tan\theta = \frac{V_y}{V_x}.$$
The vector diagram you already drew helps to obtain the correct position (quadrant) of the angle $\theta$.

**EXAMPLE 3–3 Three short trips.** An airplane trip involves three legs, with two stopovers, as shown in Fig. 3–16a. The first leg is due east for 620 km; the second leg is southeast (45°) for 440 km; and the third leg is at 53° south of west, for 550 km, as shown. What is the plane's total displacement?

**APPROACH** We follow the steps in the above Problem Solving Box.

**SOLUTION**

1. **Draw a diagram** such as Fig. 3–16a, where $\vec{\mathbf{D}}_1$, $\vec{\mathbf{D}}_2$, and $\vec{\mathbf{D}}_3$ represent the three legs of the trip, and $\vec{\mathbf{D}}_R$ is the plane's total displacement.
2. **Choose axes**: Axes are also shown in Fig. 3–16a.
3. **Resolve components**: It is imperative to draw a good figure. The components are drawn in Fig. 3–16b. Instead of drawing all the vectors starting from a common origin, as we did in Fig. 3–15b, here we draw them "tail-to-tip" style, which is just as valid and may make it easier to see.
4. **Calculate the components**:
$$\begin{aligned}
\vec{\mathbf{D}}_1:\ D_{1x} &= +D_1\cos 0^\circ = D_1 = 620\text{ km}\\
D_{1y} &= +D_1\sin 0^\circ = 0\text{ km}\\
\vec{\mathbf{D}}_2:\ D_{2x} &= +D_2\cos 45^\circ = +(440\text{ km})(0.707) = +311\text{ km}\\
D_{2y} &= -D_2\sin 45^\circ = -(440\text{ km})(0.707) = -311\text{ km}\\
\vec{\mathbf{D}}_3:\ D_{3x} &= -D_3\cos 53^\circ = -(550\text{ km})(0.602) = -331\text{ km}\\
D_{3y} &= -D_3\sin 53^\circ = -(550\text{ km})(0.799) = -439\text{ km}.
\end{aligned}$$
We have given a minus sign to each component that in Fig. 3–16b points in the $-x$ or $-y$ direction. The components are shown in the Table in the margin.
5. **Add the components**: We add the $x$ components together, and we add the $y$ components together to obtain the $x$ and $y$ components of the resultant:
$$D_x = D_{1x} + D_{2x} + D_{3x} = 620\text{ km} + 311\text{ km} - 331\text{ km} = 600\text{ km}$$
$$D_y = D_{1y} + D_{2y} + D_{3y} = 0\text{ km} - 311\text{ km} - 439\text{ km} = -750\text{ km}.$$
The $x$ and $y$ components are 600 km and $-750$ km, and point respectively to the east and south. This is one way to give the answer.
6. **Magnitude and direction**: We can also give the answer as
$$D_R = \sqrt{D_x^2 + D_y^2} = \sqrt{(600)^2 + (-750)^2}\text{ km} = 960\text{ km}$$
$$\tan\theta = \frac{D_y}{D_x} = \frac{-750\text{ km}}{600\text{ km}} = -1.25, \qquad \text{so } \theta = -51^\circ.$$
Thus, the total displacement has magnitude 960 km and points 51° below the $x$ axis (south of east), as was shown in our original sketch, Fig. 3–16a.

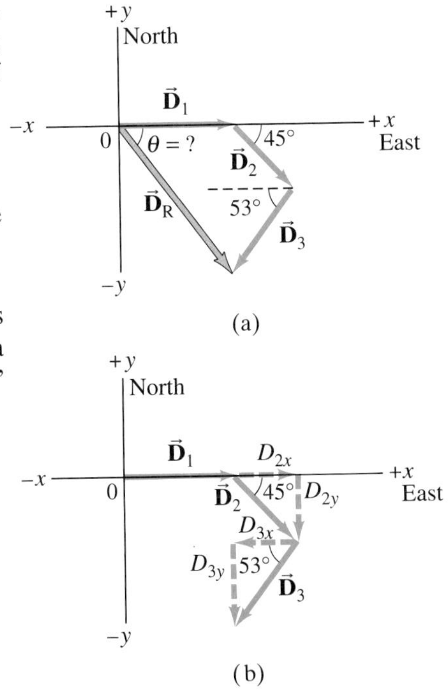


**FIGURE 3–16** Example 3–3.

| Vector | Components $x$ (km) | Components $y$ (km) |
|---|---|---|
| $\vec{\mathbf{D}}_1$ | 620 | 0 |
| $\vec{\mathbf{D}}_2$ | 311 | −311 |
| $\vec{\mathbf{D}}_3$ | −331 | −439 |
| $\vec{\mathbf{D}}_R$ | 600 | −750 |

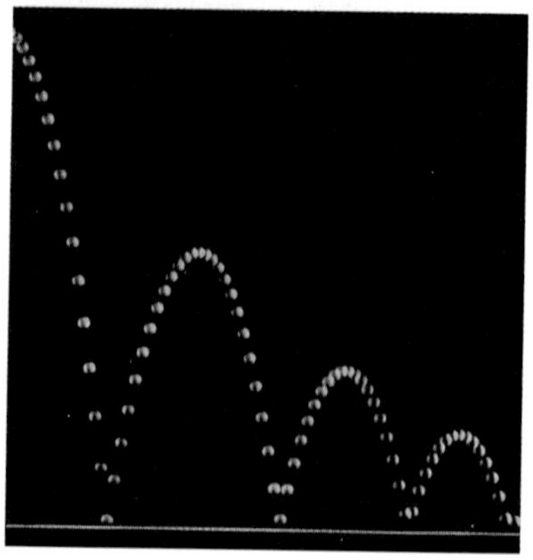

**FIGURE 3–17** This strobe photograph of a ball making a series of bounces shows the characteristic "parabolic" path of projectile motion.

## 3–5 Projectile Motion

In Chapter 2, we studied the motion of objects in one dimension in terms of displacement, velocity, and acceleration, including purely vertical motion of falling bodies undergoing acceleration due to gravity. Now we examine the more general motion of objects moving through the air in two dimensions near the Earth's surface, such as a golf ball, a thrown or batted baseball, kicked footballs, and speeding bullets. These are all examples of **projectile motion** (see Fig. 3–17), which we can describe as taking place in two dimensions. Although air resistance is often important, in many cases its effect can be ignored, and we will ignore it in the following analysis. We will not be concerned now with the process by which the object is thrown or projected. We consider only its motion *after* it has been projected, and *before* it lands or is caught—that is, we analyze our projected object only when it is moving freely through the air under the action of gravity alone. Then the acceleration of the object is that due to gravity, which acts downward with magnitude $g = 9.80\ \mathrm{m/s^2}$, and we assume it is constant.†

*Horizontal and vertical motion analyzed separately*

Galileo was the first to describe projectile motion accurately. He showed that it could be understood by analyzing the horizontal and vertical components of the motion separately. For convenience, we assume that the motion begins at time $t = 0$ at the origin of an $xy$ coordinate system (so $x_0 = y_0 = 0$).

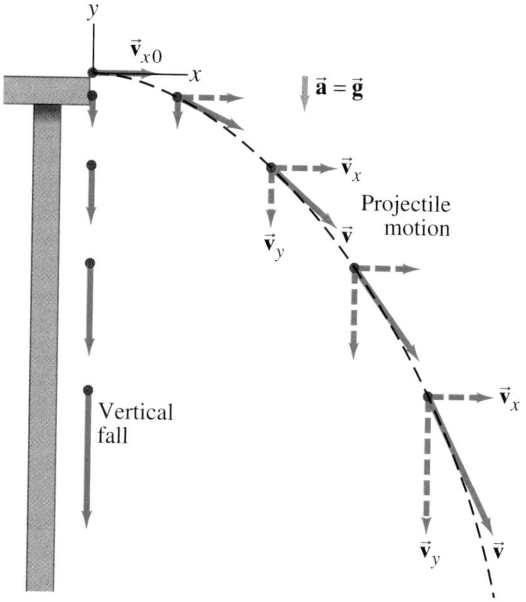


**FIGURE 3–18** Projectile motion of a small ball projected horizontally. The dashed black line represents the path of the object. The velocity vector $\vec{\mathbf{v}}$ at each point is in the direction of motion and thus is tangent to the path. The velocity vectors are green arrows, and velocity components are dashed. (A vertically falling object starting at the same point is shown at the left for comparison; $v_y$ is the same for the falling object and the projectile.)

*$\vec{\mathbf{v}}$ is tangent to the path*

Let us look at a (tiny) ball rolling off the end of a horizontal table with an initial velocity in the horizontal ($x$) direction, $v_{x0}$. See Fig. 3–18, where an object falling vertically is also shown for comparison. The velocity vector $\vec{\mathbf{v}}$ at each instant points in the direction of the ball's motion at that instant and is always tangent to the path. Following Galileo's ideas, we treat the horizontal and vertical components of the velocity, $v_x$ and $v_y$, separately, and we can apply the kinematic equations (Eqs. 2–11a through 2–11c) to the $x$ and $y$ components of the motion.

*Vertical motion ($a_y$ = constant = $-g$)*

First we examine the vertical ($y$) component of the motion. At the instant the ball leaves the table's top ($t = 0$), it has only an $x$ component of velocity. Once the ball leaves the table (at $t = 0$), it experiences a vertically downward acceleration $g$, the acceleration due to gravity. Thus $v_y$ is initially zero $(v_{y0} = 0)$ but increases continually in the downward direction (until the ball hits the ground). Let us take $y$ to be positive upward. Then $a_y = -g$, and from Eq. 2–11a we can write $v_y = -gt$ since we set $v_{y0} = 0$. The vertical displacement is given by $y = -\frac{1}{2}gt^2$.

†This restricts us to objects whose distance traveled and maximum height above the Earth are small compared to the Earth's radius (6400 km).

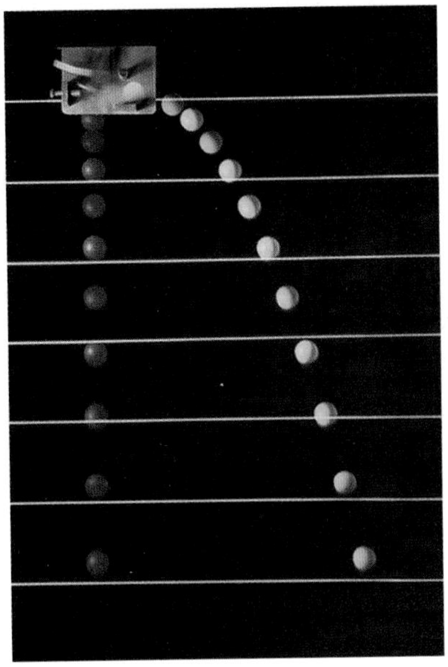

**FIGURE 3–19** Multiple-exposure photograph showing positions of two balls at equal time intervals. One ball was dropped from rest at the same time the other was projected horizontally outward. The vertical position of each ball is seen to be the same.

*Horizontal motion* *($a_x = 0$, $v_x$ = constant)*

In the horizontal direction, on the other hand, there is no acceleration (we are ignoring air resistance). So the horizontal component of velocity, $v_x$, remains constant, equal to its initial value, $v_{x0}$, and thus has the same magnitude at each point on the path. The horizontal displacement is then given by $x = v_{x0}t$. The two vector components, $\vec{\mathbf{v}}_x$ and $\vec{\mathbf{v}}_y$, can be added vectorially at any instant to obtain the velocity $\vec{\mathbf{v}}$ at that time (that is, for each point on the path), as shown in Fig. 3–18.

One result of this analysis, which Galileo himself predicted, is that *an object projected horizontally will reach the ground in the same time as an object dropped vertically*. This is because the vertical motions are the same in both cases, as shown in Fig. 3–18. Figure 3–19 is a multiple-exposure photograph of an experiment that confirms this.

**EXERCISE C** Two balls having different speeds roll off the edge of a horizontal table at the same time. Which hits the floor sooner, the faster ball or the slower one?

*Object projected upward*

If an object is projected at an upward angle, as in Fig. 3–20, the analysis is similar, except that now there is an initial vertical component of velocity, $v_{y0}$. Because of the downward acceleration of gravity, $v_y$ gradually decreases with time until the object reaches the highest point on its path, at which point $v_y = 0$. Subsequently the object moves downward (Fig. 3–20) and $v_y$ increases in the downward direction, as shown (that is, becoming more negative). As before, $v_x$ remains constant.

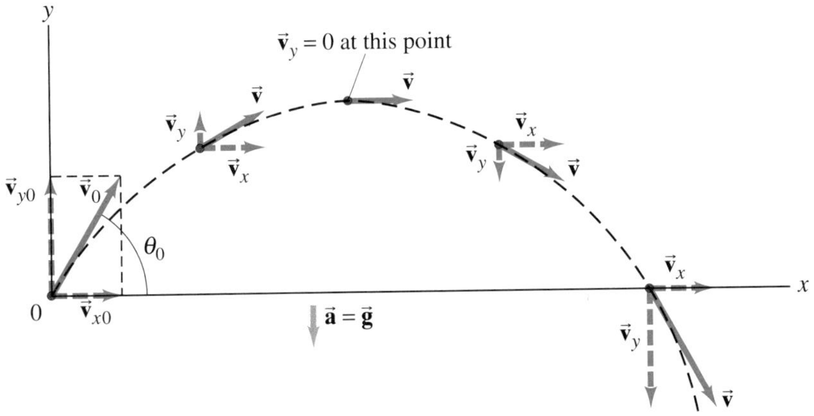


**FIGURE 3–20** Path of a projectile fired with initial velocity $\vec{\mathbf{v}}_0$ at angle $\theta$ to the horizontal. Path is shown in black, the velocity vectors are green arrows, and velocity components are dashed.

## 3–6 Solving Problems Involving Projectile Motion

We now work through several Examples of projectile motion quantitatively. We use the kinematic equations (2–11a through 2–11c) separately for the vertical and horizontal components of the motion. These equations are shown separately for the $x$ and $y$ components of the motion in Table 3–1, for the general case of two-dimensional motion at constant acceleration. Note that $x$ and $y$ are the respective displacements, that $v_x$ and $v_y$ are the components of the velocity, and that $a_x$ and $a_y$ are the components of the acceleration, each of which is constant. The subscript 0 means "at $t = 0$."

**TABLE 3–1 General Kinematic Equations for Constant Acceleration in Two Dimensions**

| $x$ component (horizontal) | | $y$ component (vertical) |
|---|---|---|
| $v_x = v_{x0} + a_x t$ | (Eq. 2–11a) | $v_y = v_{y0} + a_y t$ |
| $x = x_0 + v_{x0} t + \frac{1}{2} a_x t^2$ | (Eq. 2–11b) | $y = y_0 + v_{y0} t + \frac{1}{2} a_y t^2$ |
| $v_x^2 = v_{x0}^2 + 2a_x(x - x_0)$ | (Eq. 2–11c) | $v_y^2 = v_{y0}^2 + 2a_y(y - y_0)$ |

We can simplify these equations for the case of projectile motion because we can set $a_x = 0$. See Table 3–2, which assumes $y$ is positive upward, so $a_y = -g = -9.80\,\text{m/s}^2$. Note that if $\theta$ is chosen relative to the $+x$ axis, as in Fig. 3–20, then

$$v_{x0} = v_0 \cos\theta, \quad \text{and} \quad v_{y0} = v_0 \sin\theta.$$

**PROBLEM SOLVING**
*Choice of time interval*

In doing Problems involving projectile motion, we must consider a time interval for which our chosen object is in the air, influenced only by gravity. We do not consider the throwing (or projecting) process, nor the time after the object lands or is caught, because then other influences act on the object, and we can no longer set $\vec{\mathbf{a}} = \vec{\mathbf{g}}$.

**TABLE 3–2 Kinematic Equations for Projectile Motion**
**($y$ positive upward; $a_x = 0$, $a_y = -g = -9.80\,\text{m/s}^2$)**

| Horizontal Motion ($a_x = 0$, $v_x$ = constant) | | Vertical Motion† ($a_y = -g$ = constant) |
|---|---|---|
| $v_x = v_{x0}$ | (Eq. 2–11a) | $v_y = v_{y0} - gt$ |
| $x = x_0 + v_{x0} t$ | (Eq. 2–11b) | $y = y_0 + v_{y0} t - \frac{1}{2} g t^2$ |
| | (Eq. 2–11c) | $v_y^2 = v_{y0}^2 - 2g(y - y_0)$ |

† If $y$ is taken positive downward, the minus (−) signs in front of $g$ become + signs.

### PROBLEM SOLVING Projectile Motion

Our approach to solving problems in Section 2–6 also applies here. Solving problems involving projectile motion can require creativity, and cannot be done just by following some rules. Certainly you must avoid just plugging numbers into equations that seem to "work."

1. As always, **read** carefully; **choose** the object (or objects) you are going to analyze.
2. **Draw** a careful **diagram** showing what is happening to the object.
3. **Choose** an origin and an $xy$ **coordinate system**.
4. Decide on the **time interval**, which for projectile motion can only include motion under the effect of gravity alone, not throwing or landing. The time interval must be the same for the $x$ and $y$ analyses. The $x$ and $y$ motions are connected by the common time.
5. **Examine** the horizontal ($x$) and vertical ($y$) **motions** separately. If you are given the initial velocity, you may want to resolve it into its $x$ and $y$ components.
6. List the **known** and **unknown** quantities, choosing $a_x = 0$ and $a_y = -g$ or $+g$, where $g = 9.80\,\text{m/s}^2$, and using the + or − sign, depending on whether you choose $y$ positive down or up. Remember that $v_x$ never changes throughout the trajectory, and that $v_y = 0$ at the highest point of any trajectory that returns downward. The velocity just before landing is generally not zero.
7. Think for a minute before jumping into the equations. A little planning goes a long way. **Apply** the relevant **equations** (Table 3–2), combining equations if necessary. You may need to combine components of a vector to get magnitude and direction (Eqs. 3–4).

**EXAMPLE 3–4** **Driving off a cliff.** A movie stunt driver on a motorcycle speeds horizontally off a 50.0-m-high cliff. How fast must the motorcycle leave the cliff top to land on level ground below, 90.0 m from the base of the cliff where the cameras are? Ignore air resistance.

**APPROACH** We explicitly follow the steps of the Problem Solving Box.

**SOLUTION**

1. and 2. **Read, choose the object, and draw a diagram**. Our object is the motorcycle and driver, taken as a single unit. The diagram is shown in Fig. 3–21.
3. **Choose a coordinate system**. We choose the $y$ direction to be positive upward, with the top of the cliff as $y_0 = 0$. The $x$ direction is horizontal with $x_0 = 0$ at the point where the motorcycle leaves the cliff.
4. **Choose a time interval**. We choose our time interval to begin ($t = 0$) just as the motorcycle leaves the cliff top at position $x_0 = 0$, $y_0 = 0$; our time interval ends just before the motorcycle hits the ground below.
5. **Examine $x$ and $y$ motions**. In the horizontal ($x$) direction, the acceleration $a_x = 0$, so the velocity is constant. The value of $x$ when the motorcycle reaches the ground is $x = +90.0\,\text{m}$. In the vertical direction, the acceleration is the acceleration due to gravity, $a_y = -g = -9.80\,\text{m/s}^2$. The value of $y$ when the motorcycle reaches the ground is $y = -50.0\,\text{m}$. The initial velocity is horizontal and is our unknown, $v_{x0}$; the initial vertical velocity is zero, $v_{y0} = 0$.
6. **List knowns and unknowns**. See the Table in the margin. Note that in addition to not knowing the initial horizontal velocity $v_{x0}$ (which stays constant until landing), we also do not know the time $t$ when the motorcycle reaches the ground.
7. **Apply relevant equations**. The motorcycle maintains constant $v_x$ as long as it is in the air. The time it stays in the air is determined by the $y$ motion—when it hits the ground. So we first find the time using the $y$ motion, and then use this time value in the $x$ equations. To find out how long it takes the motorcycle to reach the ground below, we use Eq. 2–11b (Table 3–2) for the vertical ($y$) direction with $y_0 = 0$ and $v_{y0} = 0$:

$$\begin{aligned} y &= y_0 + v_{y0}t + \tfrac{1}{2}a_y t^2 \\ &= 0 + 0 + \tfrac{1}{2}(-g)t^2 \end{aligned}$$

or

$$y = -\tfrac{1}{2}gt^2.$$

We solve for $t$ and set $y = -50.0\,\text{m}$:

$$t = \sqrt{\frac{2y}{-g}} = \sqrt{\frac{2(-50.0\,\text{m})}{-9.80\,\text{m/s}^2}} = 3.19\,\text{s}.$$

To calculate the initial velocity, $v_{x0}$, we again use Eq. 2–11b, but this time for the horizontal ($x$) direction, with $a_x = 0$ and $x_0 = 0$:

$$\begin{aligned} x &= x_0 + v_{x0}t + \tfrac{1}{2}a_x t^2 \\ &= 0 + v_{x0}t + 0 \end{aligned}$$

or

$$x = v_{x0}t.$$

Then

$$v_{x0} = \frac{x}{t} = \frac{90.0\,\text{m}}{3.19\,\text{s}} = 28.2\,\text{m/s},$$

which is about 100 km/h (roughly 60 mi/h).

**NOTE** In the time interval of the projectile motion, the only acceleration is $g$ in the negative $y$ direction. The acceleration in the $x$ direction is zero.

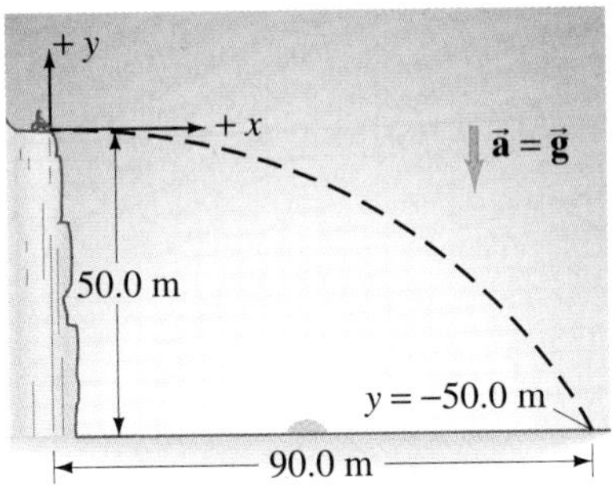


**FIGURE 3–21** Example 3–4.

| Known | Unknown |
|---|---|
| $x_0 = y_0 = 0$ | $v_{x0}$ |
| $x = 90.0\,\text{m}$ | $t$ |
| $y = -50.0\,\text{m}$ | |
| $a_x = 0$ | |
| $a_y = -g = -9.80\,\text{m/s}^2$ | |
| $v_{y0} = 0$ | |

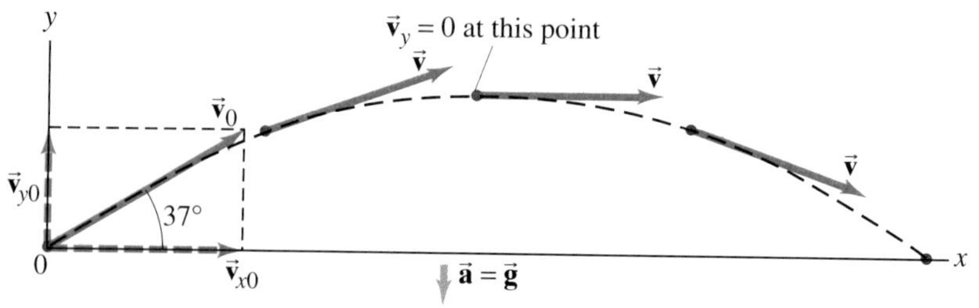


**FIGURE 3–22** Example 3–5.

PHYSICS APPLIED
*Sports*

**EXAMPLE 3–5** **A kicked football.** A football is kicked at an angle $\theta_0 = 37.0°$ with a velocity of 20.0 m/s, as shown in Fig. 3–22. Calculate (*a*) the maximum height, (*b*) the time of travel before the football hits the ground, (*c*) how far away it hits the ground, (*d*) the velocity vector at the maximum height, and (*e*) the acceleration vector at maximum height. Assume the ball leaves the foot at ground level, and ignore air resistance and rotation of the ball.

**APPROACH** This may seem difficult at first because there are so many questions. But we can deal with them one at a time. We take the *y* direction as positive upward, and treat the *x* and *y* motions separately. The total time in the air is again determined by the *y* motion. The *x* motion occurs at constant velocity. The *y* component of velocity varies, being positive (upward) initially, decreasing to zero at the highest point, and then becoming negative as the football falls.

**SOLUTION** We resolve the initial velocity into its components (Fig. 3–22):

$$v_{x0} = v_0 \cos 37.0° = (20.0\,\text{m/s})(0.799) = 16.0\,\text{m/s}$$
$$v_{y0} = v_0 \sin 37.0° = (20.0\,\text{m/s})(0.602) = 12.0\,\text{m/s}.$$

(*a*) We consider a time interval that begins just after the football loses contact with the foot until it reaches its maximum height. During this time interval, the acceleration is *g* downward. At the maximum height, the velocity is horizontal (Fig. 3–22), so $v_y = 0$; and this occurs at a time given by $v_y = v_{y0} - gt$ with $v_y = 0$ (see Eq. 2–11a in Table 3–2). Thus

$$t = \frac{v_{y0}}{g} = \frac{(12.0\,\text{m/s})}{(9.80\,\text{m/s}^2)} = 1.22\,\text{s}.$$

From Eq. 2–11b, with $y_0 = 0$, we have

$$y = v_{y0}t - \tfrac{1}{2}gt^2$$
$$= (12.0\,\text{m/s})(1.22\,\text{s}) - \tfrac{1}{2}(9.80\,\text{m/s}^2)(1.22\,\text{s})^2 = 7.35\,\text{m}.$$

Alternatively, we could have used Eq. 2–11c, solved for *y*, and found

$$y = \frac{v_{y0}^2 - v_y^2}{2g} = \frac{(12.0\,\text{m/s})^2 - (0\,\text{m/s})^2}{2(9.80\,\text{m/s}^2)} = 7.35\,\text{m}.$$

The maximum height is 7.35 m.

(*b*) To find the time it takes for the ball to return to the ground, we consider a different time interval, starting at the moment the ball leaves the foot $(t = 0, y_0 = 0)$ and ending just before the ball touches the ground ($y = 0$ again). We can use Eq. 2–11b with $y_0 = 0$ and also set $y = 0$ (ground level):

$$y = y_0 + v_{y0}t - \tfrac{1}{2}gt^2$$
$$0 = 0 + (12.0\,\text{m/s})t - \tfrac{1}{2}(9.80\,\text{m/s}^2)t^2.$$

This equation can be easily factored:

$$\left[\tfrac{1}{2}(9.80\,\text{m/s}^2)t - 12.0\,\text{m/s}\right]t = 0.$$

There are two solutions, $t = 0$ (which corresponds to the initial point, $y_0$), and

$$t = \frac{2(12.0\,\text{m/s})}{(9.80\,\text{m/s}^2)} = 2.45\,\text{s},$$

which is the total travel time of the football.

**NOTE** The time $t = 2.45\text{ s}$ for the whole trip is double the time to reach the highest point, calculated in (*a*). That is, the time to go up equals the time to come back down to the same level, but only in the absence of air resistance.

*Time up = time down*

(*c*) The total distance traveled in the $x$ direction is found by applying Eq. 2–11b with $x_0 = 0$, $a_x = 0$, $v_{x0} = 16.0\text{ m/s}$:

$$x = v_{x0}t = (16.0\text{ m/s})(2.45\text{ s}) = 39.2\text{ m}.$$

(*d*) At the highest point, there is no vertical component to the velocity. There is only the horizontal component (which remains constant throughout the flight), so $v = v_{x0} = v_0 \cos 37.0° = 16.0\text{ m/s}$.

(*e*) The acceleration vector is the same at the highest point as it is throughout the flight, which is $9.80\text{ m/s}^2$ downward.

**NOTE** We treated the football as if it were a particle, ignoring its rotation. We also ignored air resistance, which is considerable on a rotating football, so our results are not very accurate.

**EXERCISE D** Two balls are thrown in the air at different angles, but each reaches the same height. Which ball remains in the air longer: the one thrown at the steeper angle or the one thrown at a shallower angle?

CONCEPTUAL EXAMPLE 3–6 **Where does the apple land?** A child sits upright in a wagon which is moving to the right at constant speed as shown in Fig. 3–23. The child extends her hand and throws an apple straight upward (from her own point of view, Fig. 3–23a), while the wagon continues to travel forward at constant speed. If air resistance is neglected, will the apple land (*a*) behind the wagon, (*b*) in the wagon, or (*c*) in front of the wagon?

**RESPONSE** The child throws the apple straight up from her own reference frame with initial velocity $\vec{\mathbf{v}}_{y0}$ (Fig. 3–23a). But when viewed by someone on the ground, the apple also has an initial horizontal component of velocity equal to the speed of the wagon, $\vec{\mathbf{v}}_{x0}$. Thus, to a person on the ground, the apple will follow the path of a projectile as shown in Fig. 3–23b. The apple experiences no horizontal acceleration, so $\vec{\mathbf{v}}_{x0}$ will stay constant and equal to the speed of the wagon. As the apple follows its arc, the wagon will be directly under the apple at all times because they have the same horizontal velocity. When the apple comes down, it will drop right into the outstretched hand of the child. The answer is (*b*).

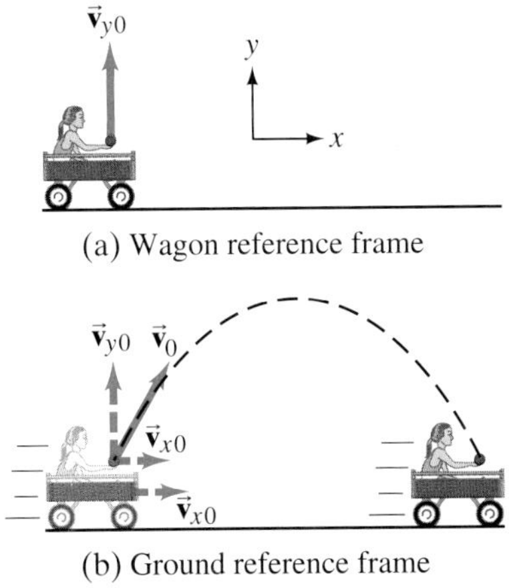


**FIGURE 3–23** Example 3–6.

CONCEPTUAL EXAMPLE 3–7 **The wrong strategy.** A boy on a small hill aims his water-balloon slingshot horizontally, straight at a second boy hanging from a tree branch a distance $d$ away, Fig. 3–24. At the instant the water balloon is released, the second boy lets go and falls from the tree, hoping to avoid being hit. Show that he made the wrong move. (He hadn't studied physics yet.) Ignore air resistance.

**RESPONSE** Both the water balloon and the boy in the tree start falling at the same instant, and in a time $t$ they each fall the same vertical distance $y = \frac{1}{2}gt^2$, much like Fig. 3–19. In the time it takes the water balloon to travel the horizontal distance $d$, the balloon will have the same $y$ position as the falling boy. Splat. If the boy had stayed in the tree, he would have avoided the humiliation.

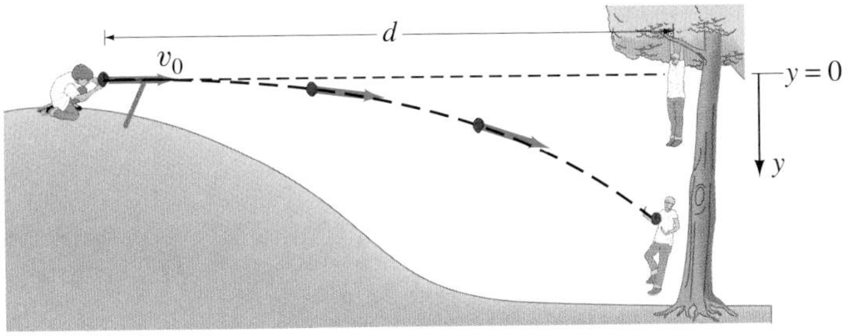


**FIGURE 3–24** Example 3–7.

**EXERCISE E** A package is dropped from a plane flying at constant velocity parallel to the ground. If air resistance is ignored, the package will (*a*) fall behind the plane, (*b*) remain directly below the plane until hitting the ground, (*c*) move ahead of the plane, or (*d*) it depends on the speed of the plane.

*Horizontal range of a projectile*

**EXAMPLE 3–8** **Level horizontal range.** (*a*) Derive a formula for the horizontal range $R$ of a projectile in terms of its initial velocity $v_0$ and angle $\theta_0$. The horizontal *range* is defined as the horizontal distance the projectile travels before returning to its original height (which is typically the ground); that is, $y$ (final) $= y_0$. See Fig. 3–25a. (*b*) Suppose one of Napoleon's cannons had a muzzle velocity, $v_0$, of 60.0 m/s. At what angle should it have been aimed (ignore air resistance) to strike a target 320 m away?

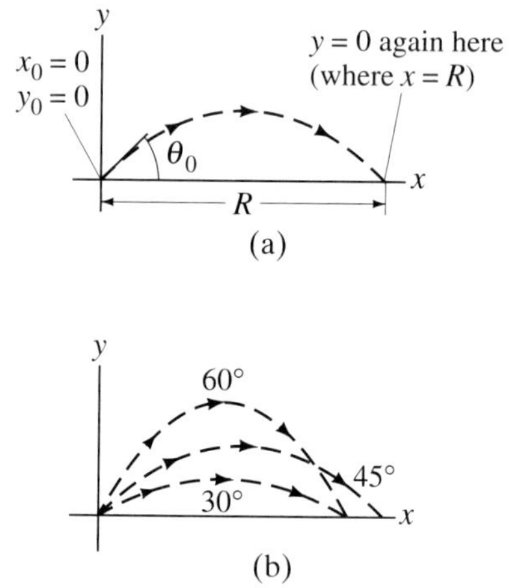


**FIGURE 3–25** Example 3–8. (a) The range $R$ of a projectile; (b) there are generally two angles $\theta_0$ that will give the same range. Can you show that if one angle is $\theta_{01}$, the other is $\theta_{02} = 90° - \theta_{01}$?

**APPROACH** The situation is the same as in Example 3–5, except we are not now given numbers in (*a*). We will algebraically manipulate equations to obtain our result.

**SOLUTION** (*a*) We set $x_0 = 0$ and $y_0 = 0$ at $t = 0$. After the projectile travels a horizontal distance $R$, it returns to the same level, $y = 0$, the final point. We choose our time interval to start ($t = 0$) just after the projectile is fired and to end when it returns to the same vertical height. To find a general expression for $R$, we set both $y = 0$ and $y_0 = 0$ in Eq. 2–11b for the vertical motion, and obtain

$$y = y_0 + v_{y0}t + \tfrac{1}{2}a_y t^2$$

so

$$0 = 0 + v_{y0}t - \tfrac{1}{2}gt^2.$$

We solve for $t$, which gives two solutions: $t = 0$ and $t = 2v_{y0}/g$. The first solution corresponds to the initial instant of projection and the second is the time when the projectile returns to $y = 0$. Then the range, $R$, will be equal to $x$ at the moment $t$ has this value, which we put into Eq. 2–11b for the *horizontal* motion ($x = v_{x0}t$, with $x_0 = 0$). Thus we have:

$$R = x = v_{x0}t = v_{x0}\left(\frac{2v_{y0}}{g}\right) = \frac{2v_{x0}v_{y0}}{g} = \frac{2v_0^2\sin\theta_0\cos\theta_0}{g} \qquad [y = y_0]$$

where we have written $v_{x0} = v_0\cos\theta_0$ and $v_{y0} = v_0\sin\theta_0$. This is the result we sought. It can be rewritten, using the trigonometric identity $2\sin\theta\cos\theta = \sin 2\theta$ (Appendix A or inside the rear cover):

*Level range formula* $[y \text{ (final)} = y_0]$

$$R = \frac{v_0^2\sin 2\theta_0}{g}. \qquad [y = y_0]$$

We see that the maximum range, for a given initial velocity $v_0$, is obtained when $\sin 2\theta$ takes on its maximum value of 1.0, which occurs for $2\theta_0 = 90°$; so

$$\theta_0 = 45° \text{ for maximum range, and } R_{max} = v_0^2/g.$$

[When air resistance is important, the range is less for a given $v_0$, and the maximum range is obtained at an angle smaller than 45°.]

**NOTE** The maximum range increases by the square of $v_0$, so doubling the muzzle velocity of a cannon increases its maximum range by a factor of 4.

(*b*) We put $R = 320$ m into the equation we just derived, and (assuming, unrealistically, no air resistance) we solve it to find

$$\sin 2\theta_0 = \frac{Rg}{v_0^2} = \frac{(320\text{ m})(9.80\text{ m/s}^2)}{(60.0\text{ m/s})^2} = 0.871.$$

We want to solve for an angle $\theta_0$ that is between 0° and 90°, which means $2\theta_0$ in this equation can be as large as 180°. Thus, $2\theta_0 = 60.6°$ is a solution, but

$2\theta_0 = 180° - 60.6° = 119.4°$ is also a solution (see Appendix A–7). In general we will have two solutions (see Fig. 3–25b), which in the present case are given by

$$\theta_0 = 30.3° \quad \text{or} \quad 59.7°.$$

Either angle gives the same range. Only when $\sin 2\theta_0 = 1$ (so $\theta_0 = 45°$) is there a single solution (that is, both solutions are the same).

## Additional Example: slightly more Complicated, but Fun

**EXAMPLE 3–9** **A punt.** Suppose the football in Example 3–5 was a punt and left the punter's foot at a height of 1.00 m above the ground. How far did the football travel before hitting the ground? Set $x_0 = 0$, $y_0 = 0$.

PHYSICS APPLIED
*Sports*

**APPROACH** The $x$ and $y$ motions are again treated separately. But we cannot use the range formula from Example 3–8 because it is valid only if $y$ (final) $= y_0$, which is not the case here. Now we have $y_0 = 0$, and the football hits the ground where $y = -1.00$ m (see Fig. 3–26). We choose our time interval to start when the ball leaves his foot $(t = 0, y_0 = 0, x_0 = 0)$ and end just before the ball hits the ground $(y = -1.00\text{ m})$. We can get $x$ from Eq. 2–11b, $x = v_{x0}t$, since we know that $v_{x0} = 16.0$ m/s from Example 3–5. But first we must find $t$, the time at which the ball hits the ground, which we obtain from the $y$ motion.

PROBLEM SOLVING
*Do not use any formula unless you are sure its range of validity fits the problem. The range formula does not apply here because $y \neq y_0$*

**SOLUTION** With $y = -1.00$ m and $v_{y0} = 12.0$ m/s (see Example 3–5), we use the equation

$$y = y_0 + v_{y0}t - \tfrac{1}{2}gt^2,$$

and obtain

$$-1.00\text{ m} = 0 + (12.0\text{ m/s})t - (4.90\text{ m/s}^2)t^2.$$

We rearrange this equation into standard form so we can use the quadratic formula (Appendix A–4; also Example 2–15):

$$(4.90\text{ m/s}^2)t^2 - (12.0\text{ m/s})t - (1.00\text{ m}) = 0.$$

Using the quadratic formula gives

$$t = \frac{12.0\text{ m/s} \pm \sqrt{(12.0\text{ m/s})^2 - 4(4.90\text{ m/s}^2)(-1.00\text{ m})}}{2(4.90\text{ m/s}^2)}$$

$$= 2.53\text{ s} \quad \text{or} \quad -0.081\text{ s}.$$

The second solution would correspond to a time prior to the kick, so it doesn't apply. With $t = 2.53$ s for the time at which the ball touches the ground, the horizontal distance the ball traveled is (using $v_{x0} = 16.0$ m/s from Example 3–5):

$$x = v_{x0}t = (16.0\text{ m/s})(2.53\text{ s}) = 40.5\text{ m}.$$

Our assumption in Example 3–5 that the ball leaves the foot at ground level results in an underestimate of about 1.3 m in the distance traveled.

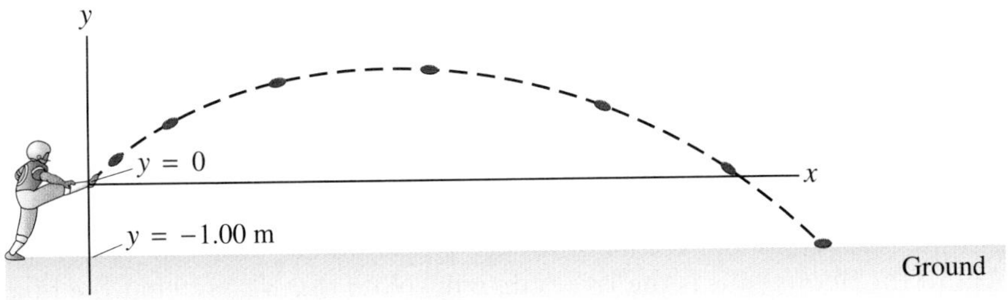


**FIGURE 3–26** Example 3–9: the football leaves the punter's foot at $y = 0$, and reaches the ground where $y = -1.00$ m.

# * 3–7 Projectile Motion Is Parabolic

We now show that the path followed by any projectile is a parabola, if we ignore air resistance and assume that $\vec{\mathbf{g}}$ is constant. To show this, we need to find $y$ as a function of $x$ by eliminating $t$ between the two equations for horizontal and vertical motion (Eq. 2–11b), and we set $x_0 = y_0 = 0$:

$$x = v_{x0}t$$
$$y = v_{y0}t - \tfrac{1}{2}gt^2.$$

From the first equation, we have $t = x/v_{x0}$, and we substitute this into the second one to obtain

$$y = \left(\frac{v_{y0}}{v_{x0}}\right)x - \left(\frac{g}{2v_{x0}^2}\right)x^2.$$

If we write $v_{x0} = v_0 \cos\theta_0$ and $v_{y0} = v_0 \sin\theta_0$, we can also write

$$y = (\tan\theta_0)x - \left(\frac{g}{2v_0^2\cos^2\theta_0}\right)x^2.$$

In either case, we see that $y$ as a function of $x$ has the form

$$y = Ax - Bx^2,$$

where $A$ and $B$ are constants for any specific projectile motion. This is the well-known equation for a parabola. See Figs. 3–17 and 3–27.

The idea that projectile motion is parabolic was, in Galileo's day, at the forefront of physics research. Today we discuss it in Chapter 3 of introductory physics!

(a)

(b)

(c)

**FIGURE 3–27** Examples of projectile motion—sparks (small hot glowing pieces of metal), water, and fireworks. All exhibit the parabolic path characteristic of projectile motion, although the effects of air resistance can be seen to alter the path of some trajectories.

# * 3–8 Relative Velocity

We now consider how observations made in different reference frames are related to each other. For example, consider two trains approaching one another, each with a constant speed of 80 km/h with respect to the Earth. Observers on the Earth beside the tracks will measure 80 km/h for the speed of each train. Observers on either of the trains (a different reference frame) will measure a speed of 160 km/h for the other train approaching them.

Similarly, when one car traveling 90 km/h passes a second car traveling in the same direction at 75 km/h, the first car has a speed relative to the second car of 90 km/h − 75 km/h = 15 km/h.

When the velocities are along the same line, simple addition or subtraction is sufficient to obtain the relative velocity. But if they are not along the same line, we must use vector addition. We emphasize, as mentioned in Section 2–1, that when specifying a velocity, it is important to specify what the reference frame is.

**PROBLEM SOLVING**

*Subscripts for adding velocities: first subscript for the object; second subscript for the reference frame*

When determining relative velocity, it is easy to make a mistake by adding or subtracting the wrong velocities. It is important, therefore, to draw a diagram and use a careful labeling process. Each velocity is labeled by *two subscripts: the first refers to the object, the second to the reference frame in which it has this velocity*. For example, suppose a boat is to cross a river to the opposite side, as shown in Fig. 3–28. We let $\vec{\mathbf{v}}_{BW}$ be the velocity of the **B**oat with respect to the **W**ater. (This is also what the boat's velocity would be relative to the shore if the water were still.) Similarly, $\vec{\mathbf{v}}_{BS}$ is the velocity of the **B**oat with respect to the **S**hore, and $\vec{\mathbf{v}}_{WS}$ is the velocity of the **W**ater with respect to the **S**hore (this is the river current). Note that $\vec{\mathbf{v}}_{BW}$ is what the boat's motor produces (against the water), whereas $\vec{\mathbf{v}}_{BS}$ is equal to $\vec{\mathbf{v}}_{BW}$ plus the effect of the current, $\vec{\mathbf{v}}_{WS}$. Therefore, the velocity of the boat relative to the shore is

(see vector diagram, Fig. 3–28)

$$\vec{\mathbf{v}}_{BS} = \vec{\mathbf{v}}_{BW} + \vec{\mathbf{v}}_{WS}. \quad \textbf{(3–6)}$$

*Follow the subscripts*

By writing the subscripts using this convention, we see that the inner subscripts (the two W's) on the right-hand side of Eq. 3–6 are the same, whereas the outer subscripts on the right of Eq. 3–6 (the B and the S) are the same as the two subscripts for the sum vector on the left, $\vec{\mathbf{v}}_{BS}$. By following this convention (first subscript for the object, second for the reference frame), one can write down the correct equation relating velocities in different reference frames.† Equation 3–6 is valid in general and can be extended to three or more velocities. For example, if a fisherman on the boat walks with a velocity $\vec{\mathbf{v}}_{FB}$ relative to the boat, his velocity relative to the shore is $\vec{\mathbf{v}}_{FS} = \vec{\mathbf{v}}_{FB} + \vec{\mathbf{v}}_{BW} + \vec{\mathbf{v}}_{WS}$. The equations involving relative velocity will be correct when adjacent inner subscripts are identical and when the outermost ones correspond exactly to the two on the velocity on the left of the equation. But this works only with plus signs (on the right), not minus signs.

It is often useful to remember that for any two objects or reference frames, A and B, the velocity of A relative to B has the same magnitude, but opposite direction, as the velocity of B relative to A:

$$\vec{\mathbf{v}}_{BA} = -\vec{\mathbf{v}}_{AB}. \quad \textbf{(3–7)}$$

For example, if a train is traveling 100 km/h relative to the Earth in a certain direction, objects on the Earth (such as trees) appear to an observer on the train to be traveling 100 km/h in the opposite direction.

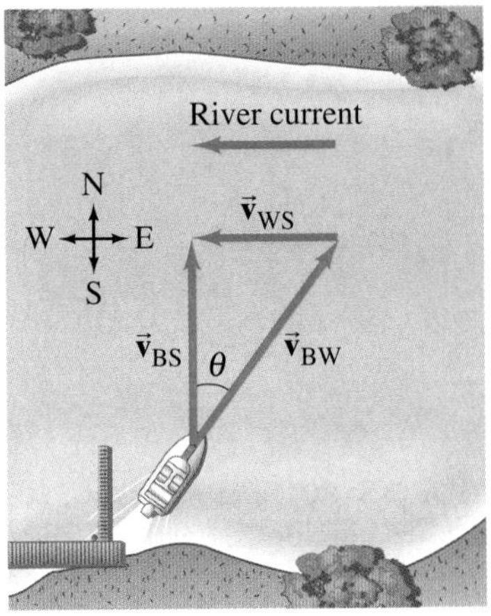


**FIGURE 3–28** To move directly across the river, the boat must head upstream at an angle $\theta$. Velocity vectors are shown as green arrows:

$\vec{\mathbf{v}}_{BS}$ = velocity of **B**oat with respect to the **S**hore,
$\vec{\mathbf{v}}_{BW}$ = velocity of **B**oat with respect to the **W**ater,
$\vec{\mathbf{v}}_{WS}$ = velocity of **W**ater with respect to the **S**hore (river current).

**CONCEPTUAL EXAMPLE 3–10** **Crossing a river.** A man in a small motor boat is trying to cross a river that flows due west with a strong current. The man starts on the south bank and is trying to reach the north bank directly north from his starting point. Should he (*a*) head due north, (*b*) head due west, (*c*) head in a northwesterly direction, (*d*) head in a northeasterly direction?

**RESPONSE** If the man heads straight across the river, the current will drag the boat downstream (westward). To overcome the river's westward current, the boat must acquire an eastward component of velocity as well as a northward component. Thus the boat must (*d*) head in a northeasterly direction (see Fig. 3–28). The actual angle depends on the strength of the current and how fast the boat moves relative to the water. If the current is weak and the motor is strong, then the boat can head almost, but not quite, due north.

**EXAMPLE 3–11** **Heading upstream.** A boat's speed in still water is $v_{BW} = 1.85\,\mathrm{m/s}$. If the boat is to travel directly across a river whose current has speed $v_{WS} = 1.20\,\mathrm{m/s}$, at what upstream angle must the boat head? (See Fig. 3–29.)

**APPROACH** We reason as in Example 3–10, and use subscripts as in Eq. 3–6. Figure 3–29 has been drawn with $\vec{\mathbf{v}}_{BS}$, the velocity of the **B**oat relative to the **S**hore, pointing directly across the river since this is how the boat is supposed to move. (Note that $\vec{\mathbf{v}}_{BS} = \vec{\mathbf{v}}_{BW} + \vec{\mathbf{v}}_{WS}$.) To accomplish this, the boat needs to head upstream to offset the current pulling it downstream.

**SOLUTION** Vector $\vec{\mathbf{v}}_{BW}$ points upstream at an angle $\theta$ as shown. From the diagram,

$$\sin\theta = \frac{v_{WS}}{v_{BW}} = \frac{1.20\,\mathrm{m/s}}{1.85\,\mathrm{m/s}} = 0.6486.$$

Thus $\theta = 40.4°$, so the boat must head upstream at a 40.4° angle.

**FIGURE 3–29** Example 3–11.

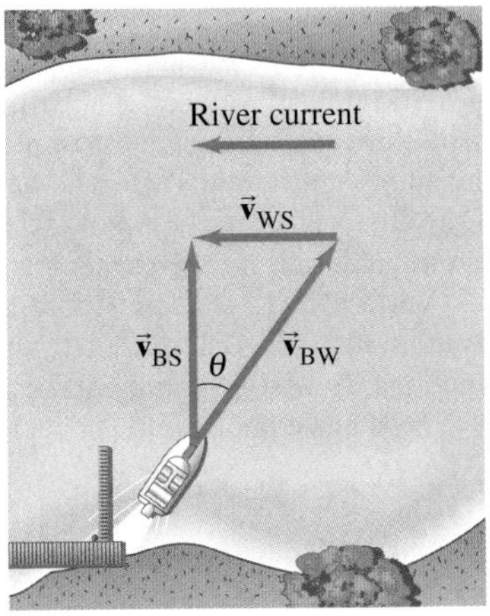


† We thus would know by inspection that (for example) the equation $\vec{\mathbf{v}}_{BW} = \vec{\mathbf{v}}_{BS} + \vec{\mathbf{v}}_{WS}$ is wrong: the inner subscripts are not the same, and the outer ones on the right are not the same as the subscripts on the left.

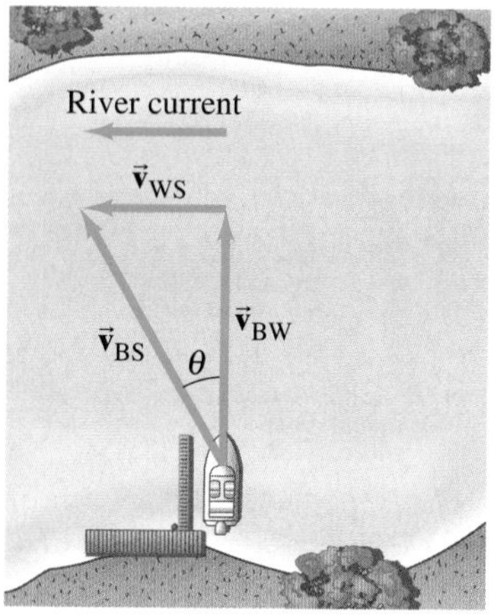


**FIGURE 3–30** Example 3–12. A boat heading directly across a river whose current moves at 1.20 m/s.

**EXAMPLE 3–12** **Heading across the river.** The same boat ($v_{BW}$ = 1.85 m/s) now heads directly across the river whose current is still 1.20 m/s. (*a*) What is the velocity (magnitude and direction) of the boat relative to the shore? (*b*) If the river is 110 m wide, how long will it take to cross and how far downstream will the boat be then?

**APPROACH** The boat now heads directly across the river and is pulled downstream by the current, as shown in Fig. 3–30. The boat's velocity with respect to the shore, $\vec{\mathbf{v}}_{BS}$, is the sum of its velocity with respect to the water, $\vec{\mathbf{v}}_{BW}$, plus the velocity of the water with respect to the shore, $\vec{\mathbf{v}}_{WS}$:

$$\vec{\mathbf{v}}_{BS} = \vec{\mathbf{v}}_{BW} + \vec{\mathbf{v}}_{WS},$$

just as before.

**SOLUTION** (*a*) Since $\vec{\mathbf{v}}_{BW}$ is perpendicular to $\vec{\mathbf{v}}_{WS}$, we can get $v_{BS}$ using the theorem of Pythagoras:

$$v_{BS} = \sqrt{v_{BW}^2 + v_{WS}^2} = \sqrt{(1.85\text{ m/s})^2 + (1.20\text{ m/s})^2} = 2.21\text{ m/s}.$$

We can obtain the angle (note how $\theta$ is defined in the diagram) from:

$$\tan\theta = v_{WS}/v_{BW} = (1.20\text{ m/s})/(1.85\text{ m/s}) = 0.6486.$$

A calculator with an INV TAN, an ARC TAN, or a $\text{TAN}^{-1}$ key gives $\theta = \tan^{-1}(0.6486) = 33.0°$. Note that this angle is not equal to the angle calculated in Example 3–11.
(*b*) The travel time for the boat is determined by the time it takes to cross the river. Given the river's width $D = 110$ m, we can use the velocity component in the direction of $D$, $v_{BW} = D/t$. Solving for $t$, we get $t = 110\text{ m}/1.85\text{ m/s} = 60$ s. The boat will have been carried downstream, in this time, a distance

$$d = v_{WS}t = (1.20\text{ m/s})(60\text{ s}) = 72\text{ m}.$$

**NOTE** There is no acceleration in this Example, so the motion involves only constant velocities (of the boat or of the river).

## Summary

A quantity such as velocity, that has both a magnitude and a direction, is called a **vector**. A quantity such as mass, that has only a magnitude, is called a **scalar**.

Addition of vectors can be done graphically by placing the tail of each successive arrow at the tip of the previous one. The sum, or **resultant vector**, is the arrow drawn from the tail of the first vector to the tip of the last vector. Two vectors can also be added using the parallelogram method.

Vectors can be added more accurately by adding their **components** along chosen axes with the aid of trigonometric functions. A vector of magnitude $V$ making an angle $\theta$ with the $x$ axis has components

$$V_x = V\cos\theta, \qquad V_y = V\sin\theta. \tag{3–3}$$

Given the components, we can find a vector's magnitude and direction from

$$V = \sqrt{V_x^2 + V_y^2}, \qquad \tan\theta = \frac{V_y}{V_x}. \tag{3–4}$$

**Projectile motion** is the motion of an object in an arc near the Earth's surface under the effect of gravity alone. It can be analyzed as two separate motions if air resistance can be ignored. The horizontal component of motion is at constant velocity, whereas the vertical component is at constant acceleration, $\vec{\mathbf{g}}$, just as for a body falling vertically under the action of gravity.

[*The velocity of an object relative to one frame of reference can be found by vector addition if its velocity relative to a second frame of reference, and the **relative velocity** of the two reference frames, are known.]

## Questions

1. One car travels due east at 40 km/h, and a second car travels north at 40 km/h. Are their velocities equal? Explain.
2. Can you give several examples of an object's motion in which a great distance is traveled but the displacement is zero?
3. Can the displacement vector for a particle moving in two dimensions ever be longer than the length of path traveled by the particle over the same time interval? Can it ever be less? Discuss.
4. During baseball practice, a batter hits a very high fly ball and then runs in a straight line and catches it. Which had the greater displacement, the batter or the ball?
5. If $\vec{\mathbf{V}} = \vec{\mathbf{V}}_1 + \vec{\mathbf{V}}_2$, is $V$ necessarily greater than $V_1$ and/or $V_2$? Discuss.
6. Two vectors have length $V_1 = 3.5$ km and $V_2 = 4.0$ km. What are the maximum and minimum magnitudes of their vector sum?
7. Can two vectors of unequal magnitude add up to give the zero vector? Can *three* unequal vectors? Under what conditions?
8. Can the magnitude of a vector ever (*a*) be equal to one of its components, or (*b*) be less than one of its components?
9. Can a particle with constant speed be accelerating? What if it has constant velocity?
10. A child wishes to determine the speed a slingshot imparts to a rock. How can this be done using only a meter stick, a rock, and the slingshot?
11. It was reported in World War I that a pilot flying at an altitude of 2 km caught in his bare hands a bullet fired at the plane! Using the fact that a bullet slows down considerably due to air resistance, explain how this incident occurred.
12. At some amusement parks, to get on a moving "car" the riders first hop onto a moving walkway and then onto the cars themselves. Why is this done?
13. If you are riding on a train that speeds past another train moving in the same direction on an adjacent track, it appears that the other train is moving backward. Why?
14. If you stand motionless under an umbrella in a rainstorm where the drops fall vertically, you remain relatively dry. However, if you start running, the rain begins to hit your legs even if they remain under the umbrella. Why?
15. A person sitting in an enclosed train car, moving at constant velocity, throws a ball straight up into the air in her reference frame. (*a*) Where does the ball land? What is your answer if the car (*b*) accelerates, (*c*) decelerates, (*d*) rounds a curve, (*e*) moves with constant velocity but is open to the air?
16. Two rowers, who can row at the same speed in still water, set off across a river at the same time. One heads straight across and is pulled downstream somewhat by the current. The other one heads upstream at an angle so as to arrive at a point opposite the starting point. Which rower reaches the opposite side first?
17. How do you think a baseball player "judges" the flight of a fly ball? Which equation in this Chapter becomes part of the player's intuition?
18. In archery, should the arrow be aimed directly at the target? How should your angle of aim depend on the distance to the target?
19. A projectile is launched at an angle of 30° to the horizontal with a speed of 30 m/s. How does the horizontal component of its velocity 1.0 s after launch compare with its horizontal component of velocity 2.0 s after launch?
20. Two cannonballs, A and B, are fired from the ground with identical initial speeds, but with $\theta_A$ larger than $\theta_B$. (*a*) Which cannonball reaches a higher elevation? (*b*) Which stays longer in the air? (*c*) Which travels farther?

## Problems

### 3–2 to 3–4 Vector Addition

1. (I) A car is driven 215 km west and then 85 km southwest. What is the displacement of the car from the point of origin (magnitude and direction)? Draw a diagram.
2. (I) A delivery truck travels 18 blocks north, 10 blocks east, and 16 blocks south. What is its final displacement from the origin? Assume the blocks are equal length.
3. (I) Show that the vector labeled "incorrect" in Fig. 3–6c is actually the difference of the two vectors. Is it $\vec{\mathbf{V}}_2 - \vec{\mathbf{V}}_1$, or $\vec{\mathbf{V}}_1 - \vec{\mathbf{V}}_2$?
4. (I) If $V_x = 6.80$ units and $V_y = -7.40$ units, determine the magnitude and direction of $\vec{\mathbf{V}}$.
5. (II) Graphically determine the resultant of the following three vector displacements: (1) 34 m, 25° north of east; (2) 48 m, 33° east of north; and (3) 22 m, 56° west of south.
6. (II) The components of a vector $\vec{\mathbf{V}}$ can be written $(V_x, V_y, V_z)$. What are the components and length of a vector which is the sum of the two vectors, $\vec{\mathbf{V}}_1$ and $\vec{\mathbf{V}}_2$, whose components are (8.0, −3.7, 0.0) and (3.9, −8.1, −4.4)?
7. (II) $\vec{\mathbf{V}}$ is a vector 14.3 units in magnitude and points at an angle of 34.8° above the negative $x$ axis. (*a*) Sketch this vector. (*b*) Find $V_x$ and $V_y$. (*c*) Use $V_x$ and $V_y$ to obtain (again) the magnitude and direction of $\vec{\mathbf{V}}$. [*Note*: Part (*c*) is a good way to check if you've resolved your vector correctly.]
8. (II) Vector $\vec{\mathbf{V}}_1$ is 6.6 units long and points along the negative $x$ axis. Vector $\vec{\mathbf{V}}_2$ is 8.5 units long and points at +45° to the positive $x$ axis. (*a*) What are the $x$ and $y$ components of each vector? (*b*) Determine the sum $\vec{\mathbf{V}}_1 + \vec{\mathbf{V}}_2$ (magnitude and angle).

9. (II) An airplane is traveling 735 km/h in a direction 41.5° west of north (Fig. 3–31). (*a*) Find the components of the velocity vector in the northerly and westerly directions. (*b*) How far north and how far west has the plane traveled after 3.00 h?

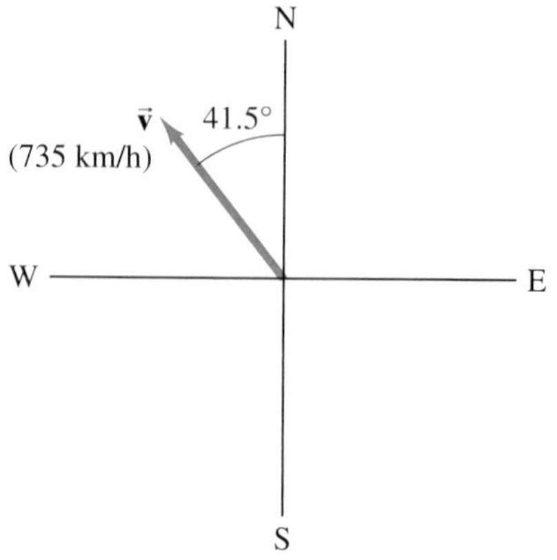


**FIGURE 3–31** Problem 9.

10. (II) Three vectors are shown in Fig. 3–32. Their magnitudes are given in arbitrary units. Determine the sum of the three vectors. Give the resultant in terms of (*a*) components, (*b*) magnitude and angle with the *x* axis.

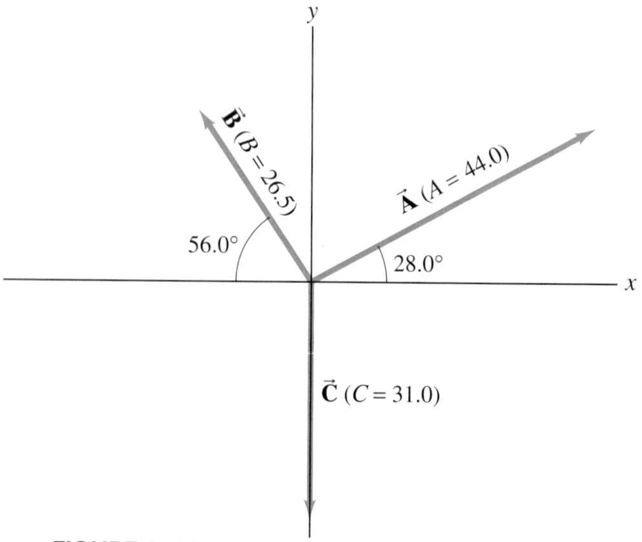


**FIGURE 3–32** Problems 10, 11, 12, 13, and 14. Vector magnitudes are given in arbitrary units.

11. (II) Determine the vector $\vec{\mathbf{A}} - \vec{\mathbf{C}}$, given the vectors $\vec{\mathbf{A}}$ and $\vec{\mathbf{C}}$ in Fig. 3–32.
12. (II) (*a*) Given the vectors $\vec{\mathbf{A}}$ and $\vec{\mathbf{B}}$ shown in Fig. 3–32, determine $\vec{\mathbf{B}} - \vec{\mathbf{A}}$. (*b*) Determine $\vec{\mathbf{A}} - \vec{\mathbf{B}}$ without using your answer in (*a*). Then compare your results and see if they are opposite.
13. (II) For the vectors given in Fig. 3–32, determine (*a*) $\vec{\mathbf{A}} - \vec{\mathbf{B}} + \vec{\mathbf{C}}$, (*b*) $\vec{\mathbf{A}} + \vec{\mathbf{B}} - \vec{\mathbf{C}}$, and (*c*) $\vec{\mathbf{C}} - \vec{\mathbf{A}} - \vec{\mathbf{B}}$.
14. (II) For the vectors shown in Fig. 3–32, determine (*a*) $\vec{\mathbf{B}} - 2\vec{\mathbf{A}}$, (*b*) $2\vec{\mathbf{A}} - 3\vec{\mathbf{B}} + 2\vec{\mathbf{C}}$.
15. (II) The summit of a mountain, 2450 m above base camp, is measured on a map to be 4580 m horizontally from the camp in a direction 32.4° west of north. What are the components of the displacement vector from camp to summit? What is its magnitude? Choose the *x* axis east, *y* axis north, and *z* axis up.
16. (II) You are given a vector in the *xy* plane that has a magnitude of 70.0 units and a *y* component of −55.0 units. What are the two possibilities for its *x* component?

### 3–5 and 3–6 Projectile Motion (neglect air resistance)

17. (I) A tiger leaps horizontally from a 6.5-m-high rock with a speed of 3.5 m/s. How far from the base of the rock will she land?
18. (I) A diver running 1.8 m/s dives out horizontally from the edge of a vertical cliff and 3.0 s later reaches the water below. How high was the cliff, and how far from its base did the diver hit the water?
19. (II) A fire hose held near the ground shoots water at a speed of 6.8 m/s. At what angle(s) should the nozzle point in order that the water land 2.0 m away (Fig. 3–33)? Why are there two different angles? Sketch the two trajectories.

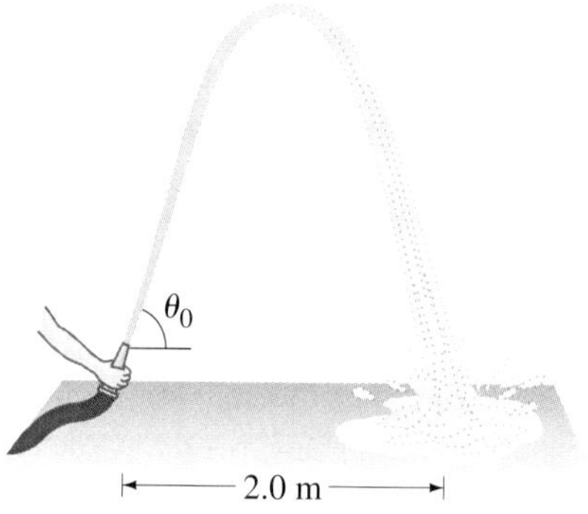


**FIGURE 3–33** Problem 19.

20. (II) Romeo is chucking pebbles gently up to Juliet's window, and he wants the pebbles to hit the window with only a horizontal component of velocity. He is standing at the edge of a rose garden 4.5 m below her window and 5.0 m from the base of the wall (Fig. 3–34). How fast are the pebbles going when they hit her window?

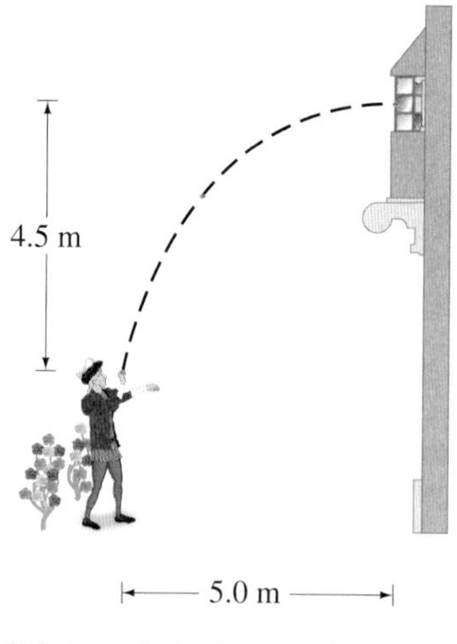


**FIGURE 3–34** Problem 20.

21. (II) A ball is thrown horizontally from the roof of a building 45.0 m tall and lands 24.0 m from the base. What was the ball's initial speed?
22. (II) A football is kicked at ground level with a speed of 18.0 m/s at an angle of 35.0° to the horizontal. How much later does it hit the ground?
23. (II) A ball thrown horizontally at 22.2 m/s from the roof of a building lands 36.0 m from the base of the building. How tall is the building?

24. (II) An athlete executing a long jump leaves the ground at a 28.0° angle and travels 7.80 m. (*a*) What was the takeoff speed? (*b*) If this speed were increased by just 5.0%, how much longer would the jump be?

25. (II) Determine how much farther a person can jump on the Moon as compared to the Earth if the takeoff speed and angle are the same. The acceleration due to gravity on the Moon is one-sixth what it is on Earth.

26. (II) A hunter aims directly at a target (on the same level) 75.0 m away. (*a*) If the bullet leaves the gun at a speed of 180 m/s, by how much will it miss the target? (*b*) At what angle should the gun be aimed so as to hit the target?

27. (II) The pilot of an airplane traveling 180 km/h wants to drop supplies to flood victims isolated on a patch of land 160 m below. The supplies should be dropped how many seconds before the plane is directly overhead?

28. (II) Show that the speed with which a projectile leaves the ground is equal to its speed just before it strikes the ground at the end of its journey, assuming the firing level equals the landing level.

29. (II) Suppose the kick in Example 3–5 is attempted 36.0 m from the goalposts, whose crossbar is 3.00 m above the ground. If the football is directed correctly between the goalposts, will it pass over the bar and be a field goal? Show why or why not.

30. (II) A projectile is fired with an initial speed of 65.2 m/s at an angle of 34.5° above the horizontal on a long flat firing range. Determine (*a*) the maximum height reached by the projectile, (*b*) the total time in the air, (*c*) the total horizontal distance covered (that is, the range), and (*d*) the velocity of the projectile 1.50 s after firing.

31. (II) A projectile is shot from the edge of a cliff 125 m above ground level with an initial speed of 65.0 m/s at an angle of 37.0° with the horizontal, as shown in Fig. 3–35. (*a*) Determine the time taken by the projectile to hit point P at ground level. (*b*) Determine the range $X$ of the projectile as measured from the base of the cliff. At the instant just before the projectile hits point P, find (*c*) the horizontal and the vertical components of its velocity, (*d*) the magnitude of the velocity, and (*e*) the angle made by the velocity vector with the horizontal. (*f*) Find the maximum height above the cliff top reached by the projectile.

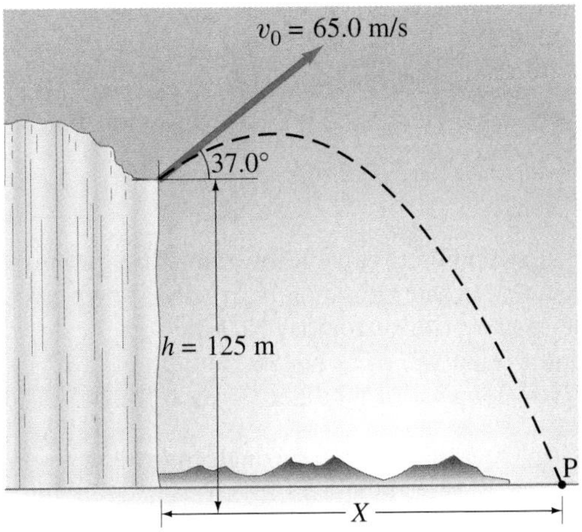


**FIGURE 3–35** Problem 31.

32. (II) A shotputter throws the shot with an initial speed of 15.5 m/s at a 34.0° angle to the horizontal. Calculate the horizontal distance traveled by the shot if it leaves the athlete's hand at a height of 2.20 m above the ground.

33. (II) At what projection angle will the range of a projectile equal its maximum height?

34. (III) Revisit Conceptual Example 3–7, and assume that the boy with the slingshot is *below* the boy in the tree (Fig. 3–36), and so aims *upward*, directly at the boy in the tree. Show that again the boy in the tree makes the wrong move by letting go at the moment the water balloon is shot.

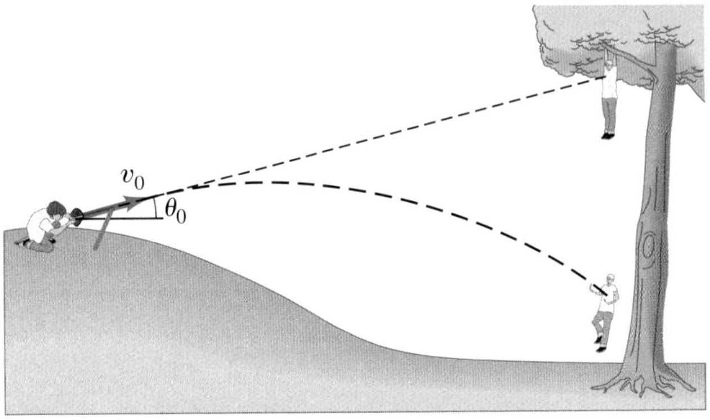


**FIGURE 3–36** Problem 34.

35. (III) A rescue plane wants to drop supplies to isolated mountain climbers on a rocky ridge 235 m below. If the plane is traveling horizontally with a speed of 250 km/h (69.4 m/s), (*a*) how far in advance of the recipients (horizontal distance) must the goods be dropped (Fig. 3–37a)? (*b*) Suppose, instead, that the plane releases the supplies a horizontal distance of 425 m in advance of the mountain climbers. What vertical velocity (up or down) should the supplies be given so that they arrive precisely at the climbers' position (Fig. 3–37b)? (*c*) With what speed do the supplies land in the latter case?

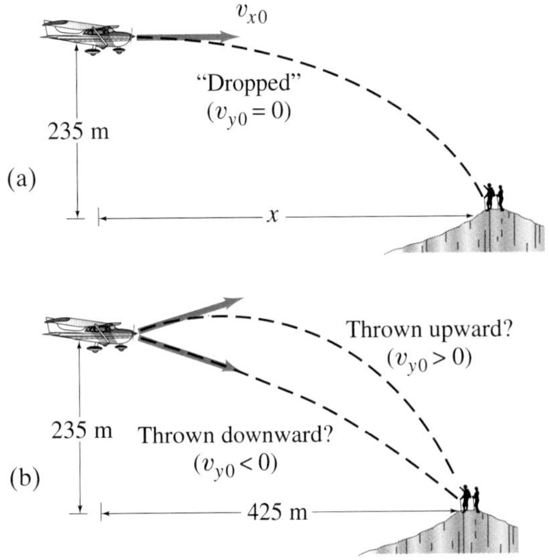


**FIGURE 3–37** Problem 35.

## * 3–8 Relative Velocity

* 36. (I) A person going for a morning jog on the deck of a cruise ship is running toward the bow (front) of the ship at 2.2 m/s while the ship is moving ahead at 7.5 m/s. What is the velocity of the jogger relative to the water? Later, the jogger is moving toward the stern (rear) of the ship. What is the jogger's velocity relative to the water now?

* 37. (II) Huck Finn walks at a speed of 0.60 m/s across his raft (that is, he walks perpendicular to the raft's motion relative to the shore). The raft is traveling down the Mississippi River at a speed of 1.70 m/s relative to the river bank (Fig. 3–38). What is Huck's velocity (speed and direction) relative to the river bank?

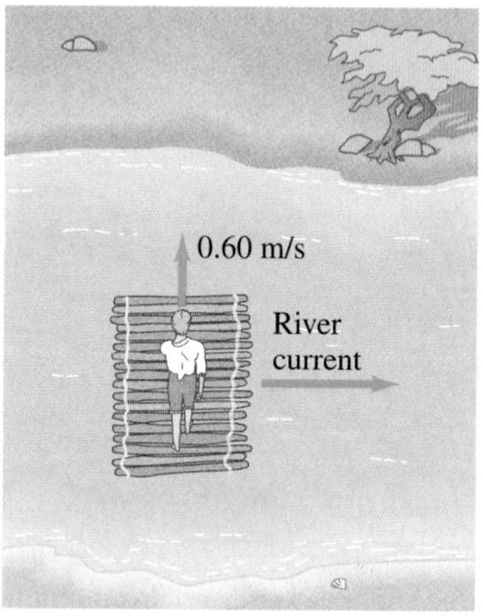


**FIGURE 3–38** Problem 37.

* 38. (II) You are driving south on a highway at 25 m/s (approximately 55 mi/h) in a snowstorm. When you last stopped, you noticed that the snow was coming down vertically, but it is passing the windows of the moving car at an angle of 30° to the horizontal. Estimate the speed of the snowflakes relative to the car and relative to the ground.

* 39. (II) A boat can travel 2.30 m/s in still water. (*a*) If the boat points its prow directly across a stream whose current is 1.20 m/s, what is the velocity (magnitude and direction) of the boat relative to the shore? (*b*) What will be the position of the boat, relative to its point of origin, after 3.00 s? (See Fig. 3–30.)

* 40. (II) Two planes approach each other head-on. Each has a speed of 785 km/h, and they spot each other when they are initially 11.0 km apart. How much time do the pilots have to take evasive action?

* 41. (II) An airplane is heading due south at a speed of 600 km/h. If a wind begins blowing from the southwest at a speed of 100 km/h (average), calculate: (*a*) the velocity (magnitude and direction) of the plane relative to the ground, and (*b*) how far from its intended position will it be after 10 min if the pilot takes no corrective action. [*Hint*: First draw a diagram.]

* 42. (II) In what direction should the pilot aim the plane in Problem 41 so that it will fly due south?

* 43. (II) Determine the speed of the boat with respect to the shore in Example 3–11.

* 44. (II) A passenger on a boat moving at 1.50 m/s on a still lake walks up a flight of stairs at a speed of 0.50 m/s (Fig. 3–39). The stairs are angled at 45° pointing in the direction of motion as shown. What is the velocity of the passenger relative to the water?

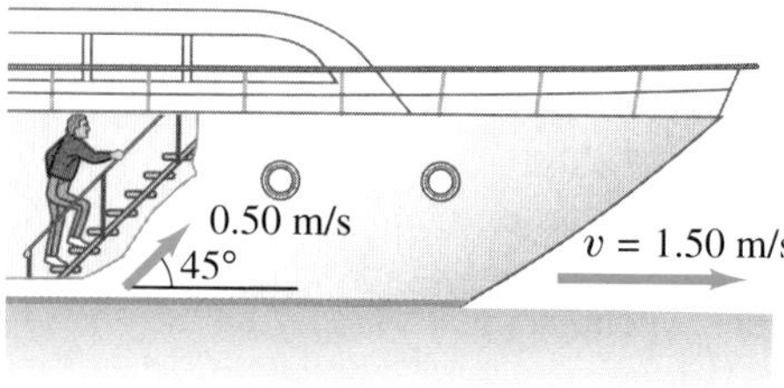


**FIGURE 3–39** Problem 44.

* 45. (II) A motorboat whose speed in still water is 2.60 m/s must aim upstream at an angle of 28.5° (with respect to a line perpendicular to the shore) in order to travel directly across the stream. (*a*) What is the speed of the current? (*b*) What is the resultant speed of the boat with respect to the shore? (See Fig. 3–28.)

* 46. (II) A boat, whose speed in still water is 1.70 m/s, must cross a 260-m-wide river and arrive at a point 110 m upstream from where it starts (Fig. 3–40). To do so, the pilot must head the boat at a 45° upstream angle. What is the speed of the river's current?

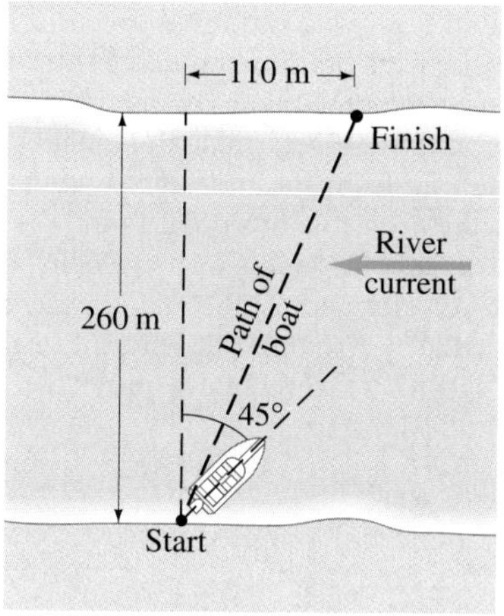


**FIGURE 3–40** Problem 46.

* 47. (II) A swimmer is capable of swimming 0.45 m/s in still water. (*a*) If she aims her body directly across a 75-m-wide river whose current is 0.40 m/s, how far downstream (from a point opposite her starting point) will she land? (*b*) How long will it take her to reach the other side?

* 48. (II) (*a*) At what upstream angle must the swimmer in Problem 47 aim, if she is to arrive at a point directly across the stream? (*b*) How long would it take her?

* 49. (III) An airplane whose air speed is 620 km/h is supposed to fly in a straight path 35.0° north of east. But a steady 95 km/h wind is blowing from the north. In what direction should the plane head?

* 50. (III) An unmarked police car, traveling a constant 95 km/h, is passed by a speeder traveling 145 km/h. Precisely 1.00 s after the speeder passes, the policeman steps on the accelerator. If the police car's acceleration is $2.00\ \text{m/s}^2$, how much time elapses after the police car is passed until it overtakes the speeder (assumed moving at constant speed)?

* 51. (III) Assume in Problem 50 that the speeder's speed is not known. If the police car accelerates uniformly as given above, and overtakes the speeder after 7.00 s, what was the speeder's speed?

* 52. (III) Two cars approach a street corner at right angles to each other (Fig. 3–41). Car 1 travels at a speed relative to Earth $v_{1E} = 35$ km/h, and car 2 at $v_{2E} = 55$ km/h. What is the relative velocity of car 1 as seen by car 2? What is the velocity of car 2 relative to car 1?

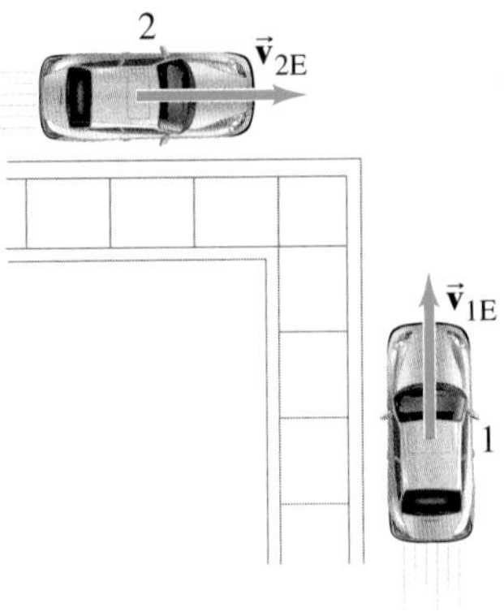


**FIGURE 3–41** Problem 52.

## General Problems

53. William Tell must split the apple atop his son's head from a distance of 27 m. When William aims directly at the apple, the arrow is horizontal. At what angle must he aim it to hit the apple if the arrow travels at a speed of 35 m/s?

54. A plumber steps out of his truck, walks 50 m east and 25 m south, and then takes an elevator 10 m down into the subbasement of a building where a bad leak is occurring. What is the displacement of the plumber relative to his truck? Give your answer in components, and also give the magnitude and angles with the $x$ axis in the vertical and horizontal planes. Assume $x$ is east, $y$ is north, and $z$ is up.

55. On mountainous downhill roads, escape routes are sometimes placed to the side of the road for trucks whose brakes might fail. Assuming a constant upward slope of 32°, calculate the horizontal and vertical components of the acceleration of a truck that slowed from 120 km/h to rest in 6.0 s. See Fig. 3–42.

**FIGURE 3–42** Problem 55.

56. What is the $y$ component of a vector (in the $xy$ plane) whose magnitude is 88.5 and whose $x$ component is 75.4? What is the direction of this vector (angle it makes with the $x$ axis)?

57. Raindrops make an angle $\theta$ with the vertical when viewed through a moving train window (Fig. 3–43). If the speed of the train is $v_T$, what is the speed of the raindrops in the reference frame of the Earth in which they are assumed to fall vertically?

**FIGURE 3–43** Problem 57.

58. A light plane is headed due south with a speed of 155 km/h relative to still air. After 1.00 hour, the pilot notices that they have covered only 125 km and their direction is not south but southeast (45.0°). What is the wind velocity?

59. A car moving at 95 km/h passes a 1.00-km-long train traveling in the same direction on a track that is parallel to the road. If the speed of the train is 75 km/h, how long does it take the car to pass the train, and how far will the car have traveled in this time? What are the results if the car and train are instead traveling in opposite directions?

60. An Olympic long jumper is capable of jumping 8.0 m. Assuming his horizontal speed is 9.1 m/s as he leaves the ground, how long is he in the air and how high does he go? Assume that he lands standing upright—that is, the same way he left the ground.

61. *Apollo* astronauts took a "nine iron" to the Moon and hit a golf ball about 180 m! Assuming that the swing, launch angle, and so on, were the same as on Earth where the same astronaut could hit it only 35 m, estimate the acceleration due to gravity on the surface of the Moon. (Neglect air resistance in both cases, but on the Moon there is none!)

62. When Babe Ruth hit a homer over the 7.5-m-high right-field fence 95 m from home plate, roughly what was the minimum speed of the ball when it left the bat? Assume the ball was hit 1.0 m above the ground and its path initially made a 38° angle with the ground.

63. The cliff divers of Acapulco push off horizontally from rock platforms about 35 m above the water, but they must clear rocky outcrops at water level that extend out into the water 5.0 m from the base of the cliff directly under their launch point. See Fig. 3–44. What minimum pushoff speed is necessary to clear the rocks? How long are they in the air?

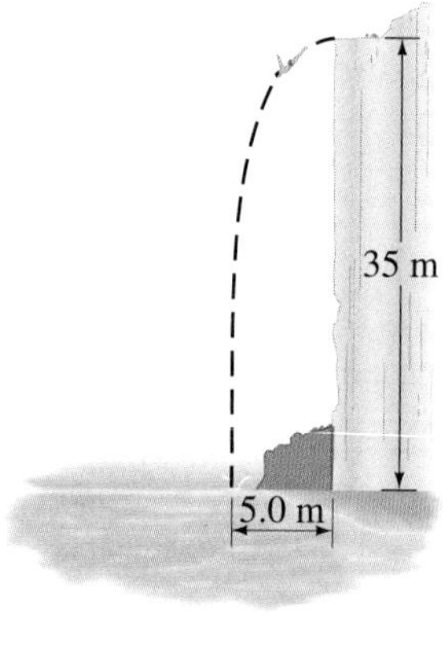


**FIGURE 3–44** Problem 63.

64. At serve, a tennis player aims to hit the ball horizontally. What minimum speed is required for the ball to clear the 0.90-m-high net about 15.0 m from the server if the ball is "launched" from a height of 2.50 m? Where will the ball land if it just clears the net (and will it be "good" in the sense that it lands within 7.0 m of the net)? How long will it be in the air? See Fig. 3–45.

**FIGURE 3–45** Problem 64.

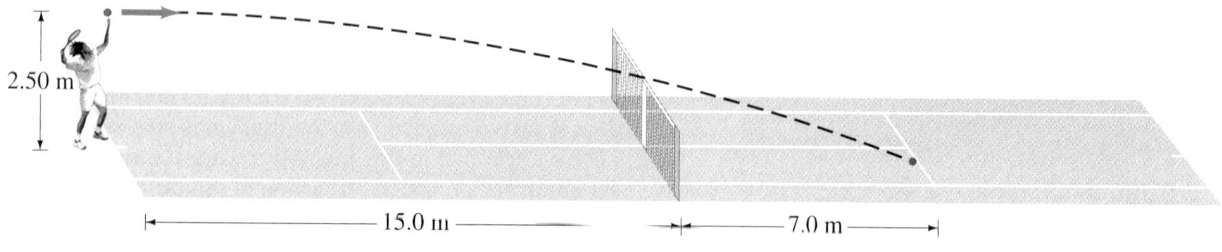


65. Spymaster Paul, flying a constant 215 km/h horizontally in a low-flying helicopter, wants to drop secret documents into his contact's open car which is traveling 155 km/h on a level highway 78.0 m below. At what angle (to the horizontal) should the car be in his sights when the packet is released (Fig. 3–46)?

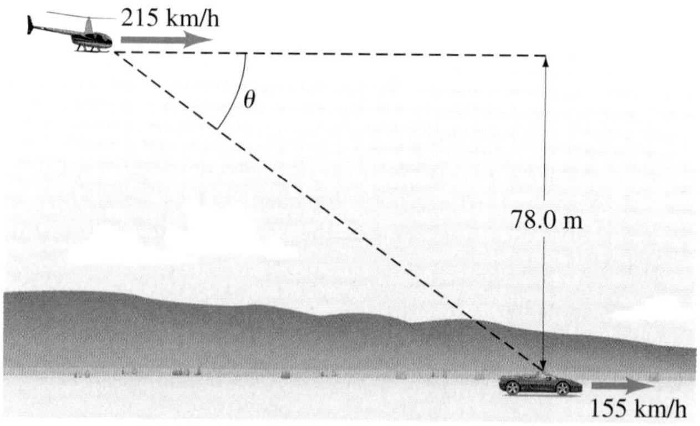


**FIGURE 3–46** Problem 65.

66. The speed of a boat in still water is $v$. The boat is to make a round trip in a river whose current travels at speed $u$. Derive a formula for the time needed to make a round trip of total distance $D$ if the boat makes the round trip by moving ($a$) upstream and back downstream, ($b$) directly across the river and back. We must assume $u < v$; why?

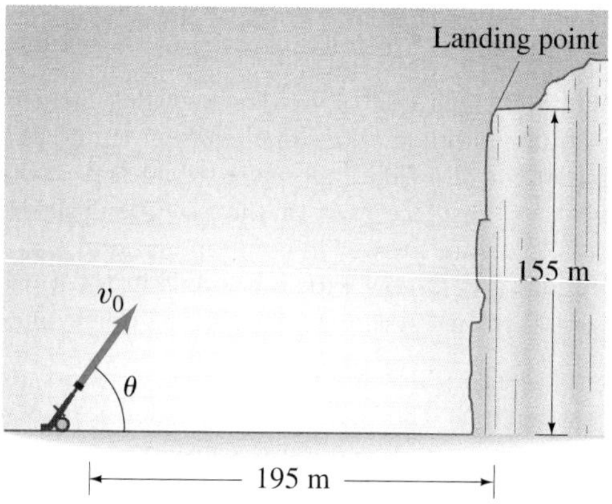


**FIGURE 3–47** Problem 67.

67. A projectile is launched from ground level to the top of a cliff which is 195 m away and 155 m high (see Fig. 3–47). If the projectile lands on top of the cliff 7.6 s after it is fired, find the initial velocity of the projectile (magnitude and direction). Neglect air resistance.

68. (*a*) A skier is accelerating down a 30.0° hill at $1.80\ \mathrm{m/s^2}$ (Fig. 3–48). What is the vertical component of her acceleration? (*b*) How long will it take her to reach the bottom of the hill, assuming she starts from rest and accelerates uniformly, if the elevation change is 335 m?

**FIGURE 3–48** Problem 68.

69. A basketball leaves a player's hands at a height of 2.10 m above the floor. The basket is 2.60 m above the floor. The player likes to shoot the ball at a 38.0° angle. If the shot is made from a horizontal distance of 11.00 m and must be accurate to ± 0.22 m (horizontally), what is the range of initial speeds allowed to make the basket?

70. A high diver leaves the end of a 5.0-m-high diving board and strikes the water 1.3 s later, 3.0 m beyond the end of the board. Considering the diver as a particle, determine (*a*) her initial velocity, $\vec{\mathbf{v}}_0$, (*b*) the maximum height reached, and (*c*) the velocity $\vec{\mathbf{v}}_f$ with which she enters the water.

71. A stunt driver wants to make his car jump over eight cars parked side by side below a horizontal ramp (Fig. 3–49). (*a*) With what minimum speed must he drive off the horizontal ramp? The vertical height of the ramp is 1.5 m above the cars, and the horizontal distance he must clear is 20 m. (*b*) If the ramp is now tilted upward, so that "takeoff angle" is 10° above the horizontal, what is the new minimum speed?

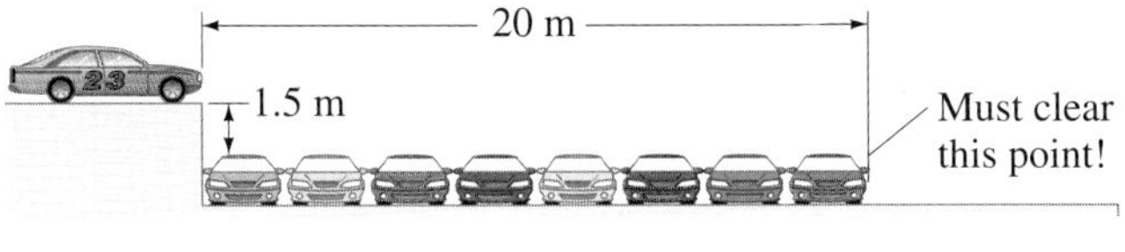


**FIGURE 3–49** Problem 71.

72. A batter hits a fly ball which leaves the bat 0.90 m above the ground at an angle of 61° with an initial speed of 28 m/s heading toward centerfield. Ignore air resistance. (*a*) How far from home plate would the ball land if not caught? (*b*) The ball is caught by the centerfielder who, starting at a distance of 105 m from home plate, runs straight toward home plate at a constant speed and makes the catch at ground level. Find his speed.

73. At $t = 0$ a batter hits a baseball with an initial speed of 32 m/s at a 55° angle to the horizontal. An outfielder is 85 m from the batter at $t = 0$, and, as seen from home plate, the line of sight to the outfielder makes a horizontal angle of 22° with the plane in which the ball moves (see Fig. 3–50). What speed and direction must the fielder take in order to catch the ball at the same height from which it was struck? Give angle with respect to the outfielder's line of sight to home plate.

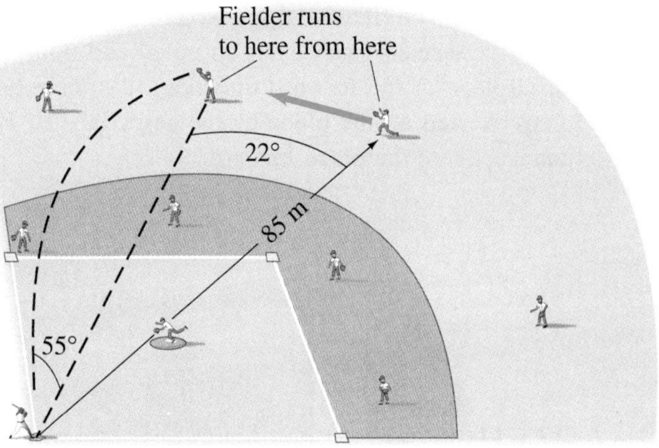


**FIGURE 3–50** Problem 73.

74. A ball is shot from the top of a building with an initial velocity of 18 m/s at an angle $\theta = 42°$ above the horizontal. (*a*) What are the *x* and *y* components of the initial velocity? (*b*) If a nearby building is the same height and 55 m away, how far below the top of the building will the ball strike the nearby building?

75. You buy a plastic dart gun, and being a clever physics student you decide to do a quick calculation to find its maximum horizontal range. You shoot the gun straight up, and it takes 4.0 s for the dart to land back at the barrel. What is the maximum horizontal range of your gun?

## Answers to Exercises

**A:** When the two vectors $D_1$ and $D_2$ point in the same direction.

**B:** $3\sqrt{2} = 4.24$.

**C:** They hit at the same time.

**D:** Both balls reach the same height; therefore they are in the air for the same length of time.

**E:** (*b*).

This airplane is taking off. It is accelerating, increasing in speed rapidly. To do so, a force must be exerted on it according to Newton's second law, $\Sigma\vec{\mathbf{F}} = m\vec{\mathbf{a}}$. What exerts this force? The two jet engines of this plane exert a strong force on the gases they push out toward the rear of the plane (labeled $\vec{\mathbf{F}}_{GP}$). According to Newton's third law, these ejected gases exert an equal and opposite force on the airplane in the forward direction. It is these "reaction" forces exerted on the **p**lane by the **g**ases, labeled $\vec{\mathbf{F}}_{PG}$, that accelerate the plane forward.

CHAPTER 4

# Dynamics: Newton's Laws of Motion

We have discussed how motion is described in terms of velocity and acceleration. Now we deal with the question of *why* objects move as they do: What makes an object at rest begin to move? What causes an object to accelerate or decelerate? What is involved when an object moves in a circle? We can answer in each case that a force is required. In this Chapter, we will investigate the connection between force and motion, which is the subject called **dynamics**.

We begin with intuitive ideas of what a force is, and then discuss Newton's three laws of motion. We next look at several types of force, including friction and the force of gravity. We then apply Newton's laws to real problems.

**FIGURE 4–1** A force exerted on a grocery cart—in this case exerted by a child.

## 4–1 Force

Intuitively, we experience **force** as any kind of a push or a pull on an object. When you push a stalled car or a grocery cart (Fig. 4–1), you are exerting a force on it. When a motor lifts an elevator, or a hammer hits a nail, or the wind blows the leaves of a tree, a force is being exerted. We say that an object falls because of the *force of gravity*.

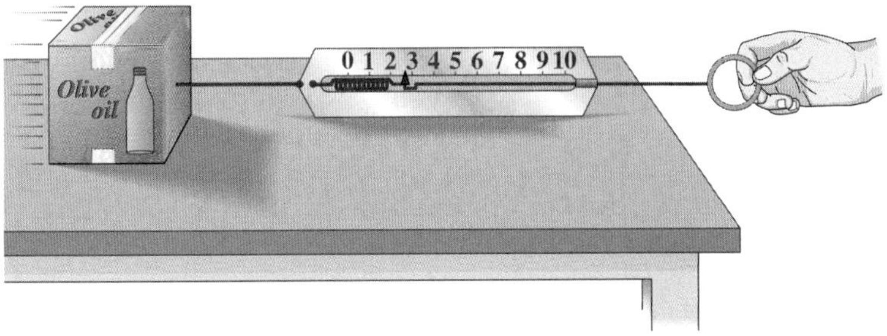


**FIGURE 4–2** A spring scale used to measure a force.

If an object is at rest, to start it moving requires force—that is, a force is needed to accelerate an object from zero velocity to a nonzero velocity. For an object already moving, if you want to change its velocity—either in direction or in magnitude—again a force is required. In other words, to accelerate an object, a force is required.

One way to measure the magnitude (or strength) of a force is to use a spring scale (Fig. 4–2). Normally, such a spring scale is used to find the weight of an object; by weight we mean the force of gravity acting on the object (Section 4–6). The spring scale, once calibrated, can be used to measure other kinds of forces as well, such as the pulling force shown in Fig. 4–2.

*Measuring force*

A force exerted in different directions has a different effect. Clearly, force has direction as well as magnitude, and is indeed a vector that follows the rules of vector addition discussed in Chapter 3. We can represent any force on a diagram by an arrow, just as we did with velocity. The direction of the arrow is the direction of the push or pull, and its length is drawn proportional to the magnitude of the force.

## 4–2 Newton's First Law of Motion

*Aristotle vs. Galileo*

What is the relationship between force and motion? Aristotle (384–322 B.C.) believed that a force was required to keep an object moving along a horizontal plane. To Aristotle, the natural state of an object was at rest, and a force was believed necessary to keep an object in motion. Furthermore, Aristotle argued, the greater the force on the object, the greater its speed.

Some 2000 years later, Galileo disagreed: He maintained that it is just as natural for an object to be in motion with a constant velocity as it is for it to be at rest.

To understand Galileo's idea, consider the following observations involving motion along a horizontal plane. To push an object with a rough surface along a tabletop at constant speed requires a certain amount of force. To push an equally heavy object with a very smooth surface across the table at the same speed will require less force. If a layer of oil or other lubricant is placed between the surface of the object and the table, then almost no force is required to move the object. Notice that in each successive step, less force is required. As the next step, we imagine that the object does not rub against the table at all—or there is a perfect lubricant between the object and the table—and theorize that once started, the object would move across the table at constant speed with *no* force applied. A steel ball bearing rolling on a hard horizontal surface approaches this situation. So does a puck on an air table, in which a thin layer of air reduces friction almost to zero.

It was Galileo's genius to imagine such an idealized world—in this case, one where there is no friction—and to see that it could lead to a more accurate and richer understanding of the real world. This idealization led him to his remarkable conclusion that if no force is applied to a moving object, it will continue to move with constant speed in a straight line. An object slows down only if a force is exerted on it. Galileo thus interpreted friction as a force akin to ordinary pushes and pulls.

*Friction as a force*

To push an object across a table at constant speed requires a force from your hand that can balance out the force of friction (Fig. 4–3). When the object moves at constant speed, your pushing force is equal in magnitude to the friction force, but these two forces are in opposite directions, so the *net* force on the object (the vector sum of the two forces) is zero. This is consistent with Galileo's viewpoint, for the object moves with constant speed when no net force is exerted on it.

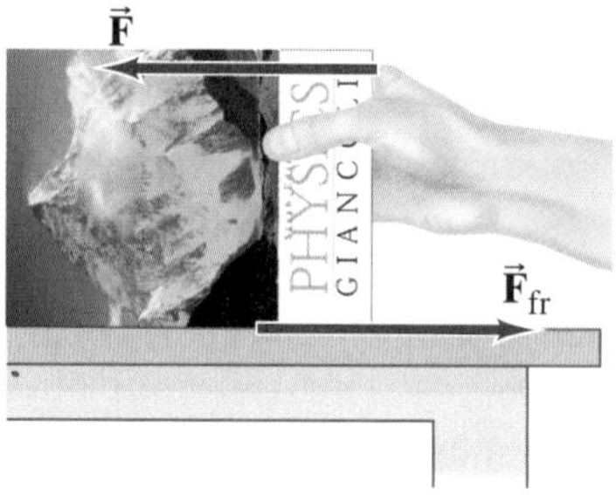


**FIGURE 4–3** $\vec{\mathbf{F}}$ represents the force applied by the person and $\vec{\mathbf{F}}_{fr}$ represents the force of friction.

Upon this foundation laid by Galileo, Isaac Newton (Fig. 4–4) built his great theory of motion. Newton's analysis of motion is summarized in his famous "three laws of motion." In his great work, the *Principia* (published in 1687), Newton readily acknowledged his debt to Galileo. In fact, **Newton's first law of motion** is close to Galileo's conclusions. It states that

*NEWTON'S FIRST LAW OF MOTION*

**Every object continues in its state of rest, or of uniform velocity in a straight line, as long as no net force acts on it.**

*Inertia*

The tendency of an object to maintain its state of rest or of uniform motion in a straight line is called **inertia**. As a result, Newton's first law is often called the **law of inertia**.

**FIGURE 4–4** Isaac Newton (1642–1727).

CONCEPTUAL EXAMPLE 4–1 **Newton's first law.** A school bus comes to a sudden stop, and all of the backpacks on the floor start to slide forward. What force causes them to do that?

**RESPONSE** It isn't "force" that does it. The backpacks continue their state of motion, maintaining their velocity (friction may slow them down), as the velocity of the bus decreases.

## Inertial Reference Frames

*Inertial reference frames*

Newton's first law does not hold in every reference frame. For example, if your reference frame is fixed in an accelerating car, an object such as a cup resting on the dashboard may begin to move toward you (it stayed at rest as long as the car's velocity remained constant). The cup accelerated toward you, but neither you nor anything else exerted a force on it in that direction. Similarly, in the reference frame of the bus in Example 4–1, there was no force pushing the backpacks forward. In accelerating reference frames, Newton's first law does not hold. Reference frames in which Newton's first law does hold are called **inertial reference frames** (the law of inertia is valid in them). For most purposes, we can usually assume that reference frames fixed on the Earth are inertial frames. (This is not precisely true, due to the Earth's rotation, but usually it is close enough.) Any reference frame that moves with constant velocity (say, a car or an airplane) relative to an inertial frame is also an inertial reference frame. Reference frames where the law of inertia does *not* hold, such as the accelerating reference frames discussed above, are called **noninertial** reference frames. How can we be sure a reference frame is inertial or not? By checking to see if Newton's first law holds. Thus Newton's first law serves as the definition of inertial reference frames.

## 4–3 Mass

Newton's second law, which we come to in the next Section, makes use of the concept of mass. Newton used the term *mass* as a synonym for *quantity of matter*. This intuitive notion of the mass of an object is not very precise because the concept "quantity of matter" is not very well defined. More precisely, we can say that **mass** is a *measure of the inertia* of an object. The more mass an object has, the greater the force needed to give it a particular acceleration. It is harder to start it moving from rest, or to stop it when it is moving, or to change its velocity sideways out of a straight-line path. A truck has much more inertia than a baseball moving at the same speed, and it requires a much greater force to change the truck's velocity at the same rate as the ball's. The truck therefore has much more mass.

*Mass as inertia*

To quantify the concept of mass, we must define a standard. In SI units, the unit of mass is the **kilogram** (kg) as we discussed in Chapter 1, Section 1–5.

CAUTION
*Distinguish mass from weight*

The terms *mass* and *weight* are often confused with one another, but it is important to distinguish between them. Mass is a property of an object itself (a measure of an object's inertia, or its "quantity of matter"). Weight, on the other hand, is a force, the pull of gravity acting on an object. To see the difference, suppose we take an object to the Moon. The object will weigh only about one-sixth as much as it did on Earth, since the force of gravity is weaker. But its mass will be the same. It will have the same amount of matter as on Earth, and will have just as much inertia—for in the absence of friction, it will be just as hard to start it moving on the Moon as on Earth, or to stop it once it is moving. (More on weight in Section 4–6.)

## 4–4 Newton's Second Law of Motion

Newton's first law states that if no net force is acting on an object at rest, the object remains at rest; or if the object is moving, it continues moving with constant speed in a straight line. But what happens if a net force *is* exerted on an object? Newton perceived that the object's velocity will change (Fig. 4–5). A net force exerted on an object may make its velocity increase. Or, if the net force is in a direction opposite to the motion, the force will reduce the object's velocity. If the net force acts sideways on a moving object, the *direction* of the object's velocity changes (and the magnitude may as well). Since a change in velocity is an acceleration (Section 2–4), we can say that *a net force causes acceleration.*

**FIGURE 4–5** The bobsled accelerates because the team exerts a force.

What precisely is the relationship between acceleration and force? Everyday experience can suggest an answer. Consider the force required to push a cart when friction is small enough to ignore. (If there is friction, consider the *net* force, which is the force you exert minus the force of friction.) Now if you push with a gentle but constant force for a certain period of time, you will make the cart accelerate from rest up to some speed, say 3 km/h. If you push with twice the force, the cart will reach 3 km/h in half the time. The acceleration will be twice as great. If you triple the force, the acceleration is tripled, and so on. Thus, the acceleration of an object is directly proportional[†] to the net applied force. But the acceleration depends on the mass of the object as well. If you push an empty grocery cart with the same force as you push one that is filled with groceries, you will find that the full cart accelerates more slowly. The greater the mass, the less the acceleration for the same net force. The mathematical relation, as Newton argued, is that the acceleration of an object is inversely proportional to its mass. These relationships are found to hold in general and can be summarized as follows:

> **The acceleration of an object is directly proportional to the net force acting on it, and is inversely proportional to its mass. The direction of the acceleration is in the direction of the net force acting on the object.**

*NEWTON'S SECOND LAW OF MOTION*

This is **Newton's second law of motion**.

[†] A review of proportionality is given in Appendix A, at the back of this book.

Newton's second law can be written as an equation:

$$\vec{\mathbf{a}} = \frac{\Sigma \vec{\mathbf{F}}}{m},$$

where $\vec{\mathbf{a}}$ stands for acceleration, $m$ for the mass, and $\Sigma \vec{\mathbf{F}}$ for the *net force* on the object. The symbol $\Sigma$ (Greek "sigma") stands for "sum of"; $\vec{\mathbf{F}}$ stands for force, so $\Sigma \vec{\mathbf{F}}$ means the *vector sum of all forces* acting on the object, which we define as the **net force**.

*Net force*

We rearrange this equation to obtain the familiar statement of Newton's second law:

*NEWTON'S SECOND LAW OF MOTION*

$$\Sigma \vec{\mathbf{F}} = m\vec{\mathbf{a}}. \qquad \textbf{(4–1)}$$

Newton's second law relates the description of motion to the cause of motion, force. It is one of the most fundamental relationships in physics. From Newton's second law we can make a more precise definition of **force** as *an action capable of accelerating an object*.

*Force defined*

Every force $\vec{\mathbf{F}}$ is a vector, with magnitude and direction. Equation 4–1 is a vector equation valid in any inertial reference frame. It can be written in component form in rectangular coordinates as

$$\Sigma F_x = ma_x, \qquad \Sigma F_y = ma_y, \qquad \Sigma F_z = ma_z.$$

If the motion is all along a line (one-dimensional), we can leave out the subscripts and simply write $\Sigma F = ma$.

*Unit of force: the newton*

In SI units, with the mass in kilograms, the unit of force is called the **newton** (N). One newton, then, is the force required to impart an acceleration of $1\,\mathrm{m/s^2}$ to a mass of 1 kg. Thus $1\,\mathrm{N} = 1\,\mathrm{kg \cdot m/s^2}$.

In cgs units, the unit of mass is the gram (g) as mentioned earlier.† The unit of force is the *dyne*, which is defined as the net force needed to impart an acceleration of $1\,\mathrm{cm/s^2}$ to a mass of 1 g. Thus $1\,\mathrm{dyne} = 1\,\mathrm{g \cdot cm/s^2}$. It is easy to show that $1\,\mathrm{dyne} = 10^{-5}\,\mathrm{N}$.

In the British system, the unit of force is the *pound* (abbreviated lb), where $1\,\mathrm{lb} = 4.44822\,\mathrm{N} \approx 4.45\,\mathrm{N}$. The unit of mass is the *slug*, which is defined as that mass which will undergo an acceleration of $1\,\mathrm{ft/s^2}$ when a force of 1 lb is applied to it. Thus $1\,\mathrm{lb} = 1\,\mathrm{slug \cdot ft/s^2}$. Table 4–1 summarizes the units in the different systems.

**PROBLEM SOLVING**
*Use a consistent set of units*

It is very important that only one set of units be used in a given calculation or problem, with the SI being preferred. If the force is given in, say, newtons, and the mass in grams, then before attempting to solve for the acceleration in SI units, we must change the mass to kilograms. For example, if the force is given as 2.0 N along the $x$ axis and the mass is 500 g, we change the latter to 0.50 kg, and the acceleration will then automatically come out in $\mathrm{m/s^2}$ when Newton's second law is used (we set $1\,\mathrm{N} = 1\,\mathrm{kg \cdot m/s^2}$):

$$a_x = \frac{\Sigma F_x}{m} = \frac{2.0\,\mathrm{N}}{0.50\,\mathrm{kg}} = \frac{2.0\,\mathrm{kg \cdot m/s^2}}{0.50\,\mathrm{kg}} = 4.0\,\mathrm{m/s^2}.$$

**TABLE 4–1**
**Units for Mass and Force**

| System | Mass | Force |
|---|---|---|
| SI | kilogram (kg) | newton (N) ($=\mathrm{kg \cdot m/s^2}$) |
| cgs | gram (g) | dyne ($=\mathrm{g \cdot cm/s^2}$) |
| British | slug | pound (lb) |

Conversion factors: $1\,\mathrm{dyne} = 10^{-5}\,\mathrm{N}$; $1\,\mathrm{lb} \approx 4.45\,\mathrm{N}$.

**EXAMPLE 4–2 ESTIMATE** **Force to accelerate a fast car.** Estimate the net force needed to accelerate (*a*) a 1000-kg car at $\frac{1}{2}g$; (*b*) a 200-g apple at the same rate.

**APPROACH** We can use Newton's second law to find the net force needed for each object, because we are given the mass and the acceleration. This is an estimate (the $\frac{1}{2}$ is not said to be precise) so we round off to one significant figure.

† Be careful not to confuse g for gram with $g$ for the acceleration due to gravity. The latter is always italicized (or boldface when a vector).

**SOLUTION** (*a*) The car's acceleration is $a = \frac{1}{2}g = \frac{1}{2}(9.8\,\mathrm{m/s^2}) \approx 5\,\mathrm{m/s^2}$. We use Newton's second law to get the net force needed to achieve this acceleration:

$$\Sigma F = ma \approx (1000\,\mathrm{kg})(5\,\mathrm{m/s^2}) = 5000\,\mathrm{N}.$$

(If you are used to British units, to get an idea of what a 5000-N force is, you can divide by 4.45 N/lb and get a force of about 1000 lb.)
(*b*) For the apple, $m = 200\,\mathrm{g} = 0.200\,\mathrm{kg}$, so

$$\Sigma F = ma \approx (0.200\,\mathrm{kg})(5\,\mathrm{m/s^2}) = 1\,\mathrm{N}.$$

**EXAMPLE 4–3** **Force to stop a car.** What average net force is required to bring a 1500-kg car to rest from a speed of 100 km/h within a distance of 55 m?

**APPROACH** We can use Newton's second law, $\Sigma F = ma$, to determine the force if we know the mass and acceleration of the car. We are given the mass, but we will have to calculate the acceleration $a$. We assume the acceleration is constant, so we can use the kinematic equations, Eqs. 2–11, to calculate it.

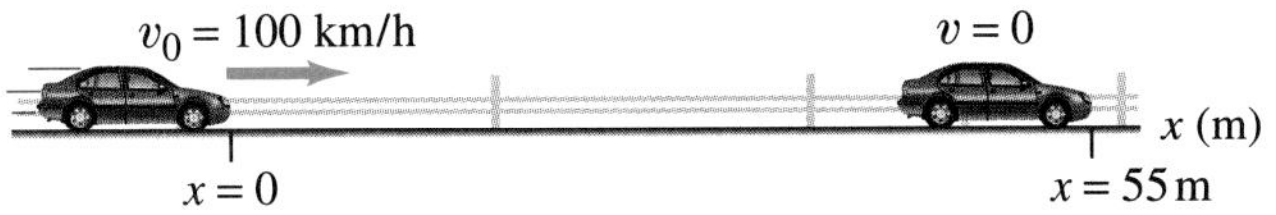


**FIGURE 4–6** Example 4–3.

**SOLUTION** We assume the motion is along the $+x$ axis (Fig. 4–6). We are given the initial velocity $v_0 = 100\,\mathrm{km/h} = 28\,\mathrm{m/s}$ (Section 1–6), the final velocity $v = 0$, and the distance traveled $x - x_0 = 55\,\mathrm{m}$. From Eq. 2–11c, we have

$$v^2 = v_0^2 + 2a(x - x_0),$$

so

$$a = \frac{v^2 - v_0^2}{2(x - x_0)} = \frac{0 - (28\,\mathrm{m/s})^2}{2(55\,\mathrm{m})} = -7.1\,\mathrm{m/s^2}.$$

The net force required is then

$$\Sigma F = ma = (1500\,\mathrm{kg})(-7.1\,\mathrm{m/s^2}) = -1.1 \times 10^4\,\mathrm{N}.$$

The force must be exerted in the direction *opposite* to the initial velocity, which is what the negative sign means.

**NOTE** When we assume the acceleration is constant, even though it may not be precisely true, we are determining an "average" acceleration and we obtain an "average" net force (or vice versa).

Newton's second law, like the first law, is valid only in inertial reference frames (Section 4–2). In the noninertial reference frame of an accelerating car, for example, a cup on the dashboard starts sliding—it accelerates—even though the net force on it is zero; thus $\Sigma\vec{\mathbf{F}} = m\vec{\mathbf{a}}$ doesn't work in such an accelerating reference frame.

## 4–5 Newton's Third Law of Motion

*A force is exerted* **on** *an object and is exerted* **by** *another object*

Newton's second law of motion describes quantitatively how forces affect motion. But where, we may ask, do forces come from? Observations suggest that a force applied to any object is always applied *by another object.* A horse pulls a wagon, a person pushes a grocery cart, a hammer pushes on a nail, a magnet attracts a paper clip. In each of these examples, a force is exerted *on* one object, and that force is exerted *by* another object. For example, the force exerted *on* the nail is exerted *by* the hammer.

But Newton realized that things are not so one-sided. True, the hammer exerts a force on the nail (Fig. 4–7). But the nail evidently exerts a force back on the hammer as well, for the hammer's speed is rapidly reduced to zero upon contact. Only a strong force could cause such a rapid deceleration of the hammer. Thus, said Newton, the two objects must be treated on an equal basis. The hammer exerts a force on the nail, and the nail exerts a force back on the hammer. This is the essence of **Newton's third law of motion**:

*NEWTON'S THIRD LAW OF MOTION*

**Whenever one object exerts a force on a second object, the second exerts an equal force in the opposite direction on the first.**

**CAUTION**
*Action and reaction forces act on different objects*

This law is sometimes paraphrased as "to every action there is an equal and opposite reaction." This is perfectly valid. But to avoid confusion, it is very important to remember that the "action" force and the "reaction" force are acting on *different* objects.

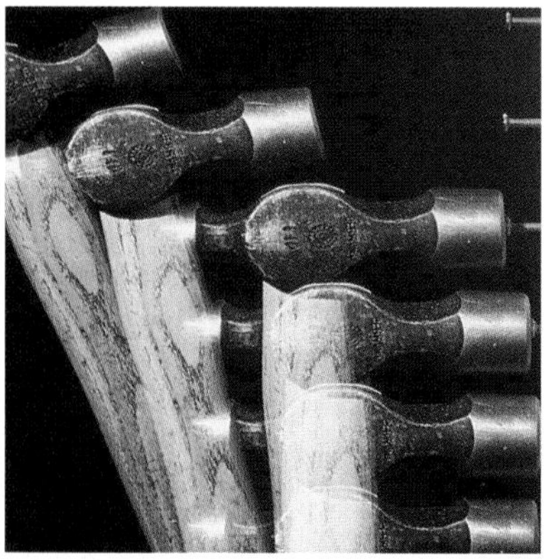

**FIGURE 4–7** A hammer striking a nail. The hammer exerts a force on the nail and the nail exerts a force back on the hammer. The latter force decelerates the hammer and brings it to rest.

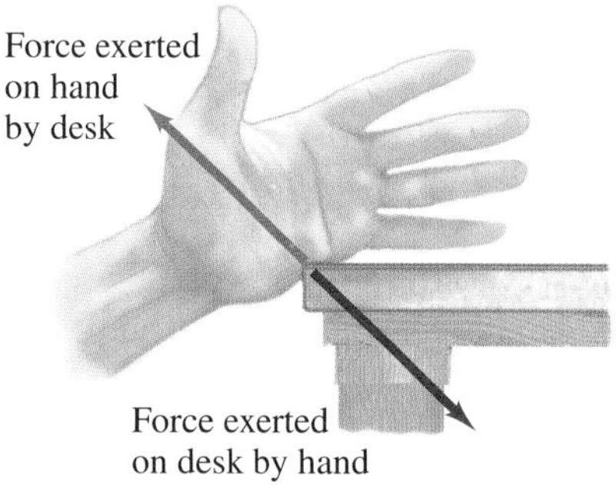


**FIGURE 4–8** If your hand pushes against the edge of a desk (the force vector is shown in red), the desk pushes back against your hand (this force vector is shown in a different color, violet, to remind us that this force acts on a different object).

As evidence for the validity of Newton's third law, look at your hand when you push against the edge of a desk, Fig. 4–8. Your hand's shape is distorted, clear evidence that a force is being exerted on it. You can *see* the edge of the desk pressing into your hand. You can even *feel* the desk exerting a force on your hand; it hurts! The harder you push against the desk, the harder the desk pushes back on your hand. (You only feel forces exerted *on* you; when you exert a force on another object, what you feel is that object pushing back on you.)

As another demonstration of Newton's third law, consider the ice skater in Fig. 4–9. There is very little friction between her skates and the ice, so she will move freely if a force is exerted on her. She pushes against the wall; and then *she* starts moving backward. The force she exerts on the wall cannot make *her* start moving, for that force acts on the wall. Something had to exert a force *on her* to start her moving, and that force could only have been exerted by the wall. The force with which the wall pushes on her is, by Newton's third law, equal and opposite to the force she exerts on the wall.

**FIGURE 4–9** An example of Newton's third law: when an ice skater pushes against the wall, the wall pushes back and this force causes her to accelerate away.

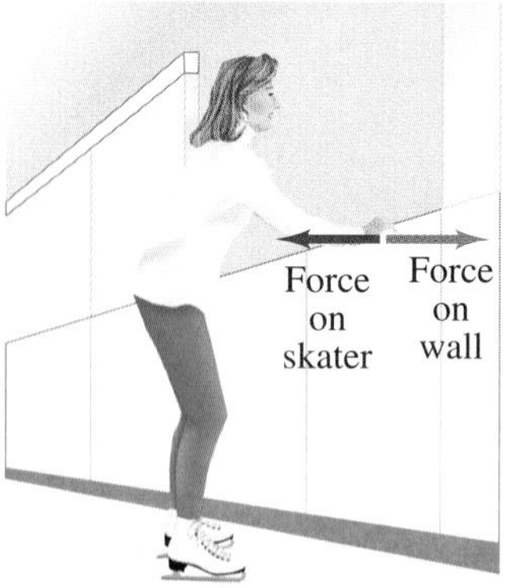


When a person throws a package out of a boat (initially at rest), the boat starts moving in the opposite direction. The person exerts a force on the package. The package exerts an equal and opposite force back on the person, and this force propels the person (and the boat) backward slightly.

*Rocket acceleration*

Rocket propulsion also is explained using Newton's third law (Fig. 4–10). A common misconception is that rockets accelerate because the gases rushing out the back of the engine push against the ground or the atmosphere. Not true. What happens, instead, is that a rocket exerts a strong force on the gases, expelling them; and the gases exert an equal and opposite force *on the rocket*. It is this latter force that propels the rocket forward—the force exerted *on* the rocket *by* the gases. Thus, a space vehicle is maneuvered in empty space by firing its rockets in the direction opposite to that in which it needs to accelerate. When the rocket pushes on the gases in one direction, the gases push back on the rocket in the opposite direction.

**FIGURE 4–10** Another example of Newton's third law: the launch of a rocket. The rocket engine pushes the gases downward, and the gases exert an equal and opposite force upward on the rocket, accelerating it upward. (A rocket does *not* accelerate as a result of its propelling gases pushing against the ground.)

*How we can walk*

Consider how we walk. A person begins walking by pushing with the foot backward against the ground. The ground then exerts an equal and opposite force forward on the person (Fig. 4–11), and it is this force, *on* the person, that moves the person forward. (If you doubt this, try walking normally where there is no friction, such as on very smooth slippery ice.) In a similar way, a bird flies forward by exerting a backward force on the air, but it is the air pushing forward on the bird's wings that propels the bird forward.

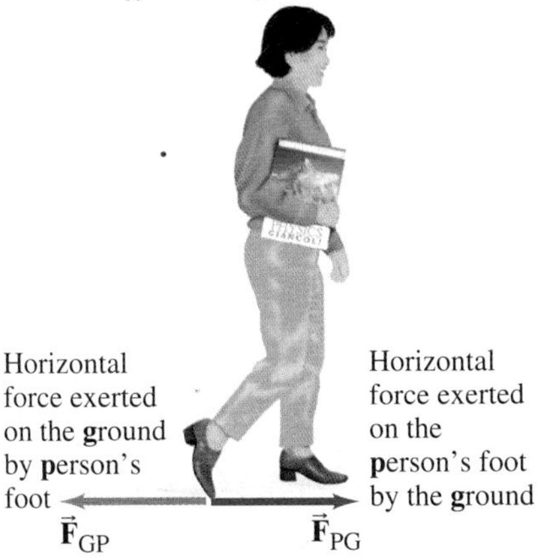


**FIGURE 4–11** We can walk forward because, when one foot pushes backward against the ground, the ground pushes forward on that foot. The two forces shown *act on different objects*.

**CONCEPTUAL EXAMPLE 4–4** **What exerts the force on a car?** What makes a car go forward?

**RESPONSE** A common answer is that the engine makes the car move forward. But it is not so simple. The engine makes the wheels go around. But if the tires are on slick ice or deep mud, they just spin. Friction is needed. On *solid* ground, the tires push backward against the ground because of friction. By Newton's third law, the ground pushes on the tires in the opposite direction, accelerating the car forward.

*Inanimate objects can exert a force (due to elasticity)*

We tend to associate forces with active objects such as humans, animals, engines, or a moving object like a hammer. It is often difficult to see how an inanimate object at rest, such as a wall or a desk, or the wall of an ice rink (Fig. 4–9), can exert a force. The explanation is that every material, no matter how hard, is elastic (springy), at least to some degree. A stretched rubber band can exert a force on a wad of paper and accelerate it to fly across the room. Other materials may not stretch as readily as rubber, but they do stretch or compress when a force is applied to them. And just as a stretched rubber band exerts a force, so does a stretched (or compressed) wall, desk, or car fender.

**PROBLEM SOLVING**

*For each force, be clear* **on** *which object it acts, and* **by** *which object it is exerted.* $\Sigma\vec{\mathbf{F}} = m\vec{\mathbf{a}}$ *applies only to forces acting* **on** *an object.*

From the examples discussed above, we can see how important it is to remember *on* what object a given force is exerted and *by* what object that force is exerted. A force influences the motion of an object only when it is applied *on* that object. A force exerted *by* an object does not influence that same object; it only influences the other object *on* which it is exerted. Thus, to avoid confusion, the two prepositions *on* and *by* must always be used—and used with care.

One way to keep clear which force acts on which object is to use double subscripts. For example, the force exerted on the **P**erson by the **G**round as the person walks in Fig. 4–11 can be labeled $\vec{\mathbf{F}}_{PG}$. And the force exerted on the ground by the person is $\vec{\mathbf{F}}_{GP}$. By Newton's third law

*NEWTON'S THIRD LAW OF MOTION*

$$\vec{\mathbf{F}}_{GP} = -\vec{\mathbf{F}}_{PG}. \tag{4–2}$$

$\vec{\mathbf{F}}_{GP}$ and $\vec{\mathbf{F}}_{PG}$ have the same magnitude (Newton's third law), and the minus sign reminds us that these two forces are in opposite directions.

Note carefully that the two forces shown in Fig. 4–11 act on different objects—hence we used slightly different colors for the vector arrows representing these forces. These two forces would never appear together in a sum of forces in Newton's second law, $\Sigma\vec{\mathbf{F}} = m\vec{\mathbf{a}}$. Why not? Because they act on different objects: $\vec{\mathbf{a}}$ is the acceleration of one particular object, and $\Sigma\vec{\mathbf{F}}$ must include *only* the forces on that *one* object.

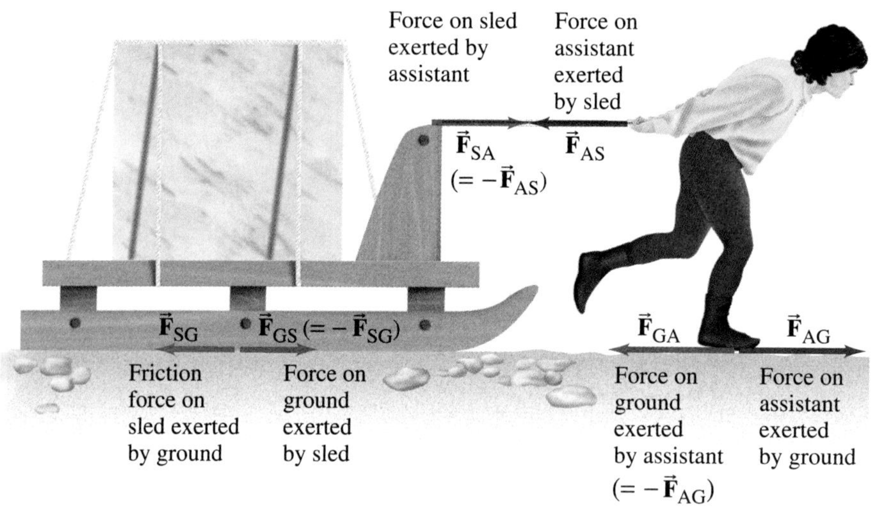


**FIGURE 4–12** Example 4–5, showing only horizontal forces. Seventy-year-old Michelangelo has selected a fine block of marble for his next sculpture. Shown here is his assistant pulling it on a sled away from the quarry. Forces on the assistant are shown as red (magenta) arrows. Forces on the sled are purple arrows. Forces acting on the ground are orange arrows. Action–reaction forces that are equal and opposite are labeled by the same subscripts but reversed (such as $\vec{F}_{GA}$ and $\vec{F}_{AG}$) and are of different colors because they act on different objects.

**CONCEPTUAL EXAMPLE 4–5** **Third law clarification.** Michelangelo's assistant has been assigned the task of moving a block of marble using a sled (Fig. 4–12). He says to his boss, "When I exert a forward force on the sled, the sled exerts an equal and opposite force backward. So how can I ever start it moving? No matter how hard I pull, the backward reaction force always equals my forward force, so the net force must be zero. I'll never be able to move this load." Is this a case of a little knowledge being dangerous? Explain.

**RESPONSE** Yes. Although it is true that the action and reaction forces are equal in magnitude, the assistant has forgotten that they are exerted on different objects. The forward ("action") force is exerted by the assistant on the sled (Fig. 4–12), whereas the backward "reaction" force is exerted by the sled on the assistant. To determine if the *assistant* moves or not, we must consider only the forces *on the assistant* and then apply $\Sigma\vec{F} = m\vec{a}$, where $\Sigma\vec{F}$ is the net force *on the assistant*, $\vec{a}$ is the acceleration of the assistant, and $m$ is the assistant's mass. There are two forces on the assistant that affect his forward motion; they are shown as bright red (magenta) arrows in Figs. 4–12 and 4–13: they are (1) the horizontal force $\vec{F}_{AG}$ exerted on the assistant by the ground (the harder he pushes backward against the ground, the harder the ground pushes forward on him—Newton's third law), and (2) the force $\vec{F}_{AS}$ exerted on the assistant by the sled, pulling backward on him; see Fig. 4–13. If he pushes hard enough on the ground, the force on him exerted by the ground, $\vec{F}_{AG}$, will be larger than the sled pulling back, $\vec{F}_{AS}$, and the assistant accelerates forward (Newton's second law). The sled, on the other hand, accelerates forward when the force on *it* exerted by the assistant is greater than the frictional force exerted backward on it by the ground (that is, when $\vec{F}_{SA}$ has greater magnitude than $\vec{F}_{SG}$ in Fig. 4–12).

**PROBLEM SOLVING**
*A study of Newton's second and third laws*

**FIGURE 4–13** Example 4–5. The horizontal forces on the assistant.

Using double subscripts to clarify Newton's third law can become cumbersome, and we won't usually use them in this way. Nevertheless, if there is any confusion in your mind about a given force, go ahead and use them to identify *on* what object and *by* what object the force is exerted. We will usually use a single subscript referring to what exerts the force on the object being discussed.

**EXERCISE A** A massive truck collides head-on with a small sports car. (*a*) Which vehicle experiences the greater force of impact? (*b*) Which experiences the greater acceleration? (*c*) Which of Newton's laws is useful to obtain the correct answer?

## 4–6 Weight—the Force of Gravity; and the Normal Force

As we saw in Chapter 2, Galileo claimed that all objects dropped near the surface of the Earth will fall with the same acceleration, $\vec{g}$, if air resistance can be neglected. The force that causes this acceleration is called the *force of gravity* or *gravitational force*. What exerts the gravitational force on an object? It is the Earth, as we will discuss in Chapter 5, and the force acts vertically† downward, toward the center of the Earth. Let us apply Newton's second law to an object of mass $m$ falling due to gravity; for the acceleration, $\vec{\mathbf{a}}$, we use the downward acceleration due to gravity, $\vec{\mathbf{g}}$. Thus, the **gravitational force** on an object, $\vec{\mathbf{F}}_G$, can be written as

$$\vec{\mathbf{F}}_G = m\vec{\mathbf{g}}. \tag{4–3}$$

*Weight = gravitational force*

The direction of this force is down toward the center of the Earth. The magnitude of the force of gravity on an object is commonly called the object's **weight**.

In SI units, $g = 9.80\,\text{m/s}^2 = 9.80\,\text{N/kg}$,‡ so the weight of a 1.00-kg mass on Earth is $1.00\,\text{kg} \times 9.80\,\text{m/s}^2 = 9.80\,\text{N}$. We will mainly be concerned with the weight of objects on Earth, but we note that on the Moon, on other planets, or in space, the weight of a given mass will be different than it is on Earth. For example, on the Moon the acceleration due to gravity is about one-sixth what it is on Earth, and a 1.0-kg mass weighs only 1.7 N. Although we will not use British units, we note that for practical purposes on the Earth, a mass of 1 kg weighs about 2.2 lb. (On the Moon, 1 kg weighs only about 0.4 lb.)

**CAUTION**
*Mass vs. weight*

The force of gravity acts on an object when it is falling. When an object is at rest on the Earth, the gravitational force on it does not disappear, as we know if we weigh it on a spring scale. The same force, given by Eq. 4–3, continues to act. Why, then, doesn't the object move? From Newton's second law, the net force on an object that remains at rest is zero. There must be another force on the object to balance the gravitational force. For an object resting on a table, the table exerts this upward force; see Fig. 4–14a. The table is compressed slightly beneath the object, and due to its elasticity, it pushes up on the object as shown. The force exerted by the table is often called a **contact force**, since it occurs when two objects are in contact. (The force of your hand pushing on a cart is also a contact force.) When a contact force acts *perpendicular* to the common surface of contact, it is referred to as the **normal force** ("normal" means perpendicular); hence it is labeled $\vec{\mathbf{F}}_N$ in Fig. 4–14a.

*Contact force*

*Normal force*

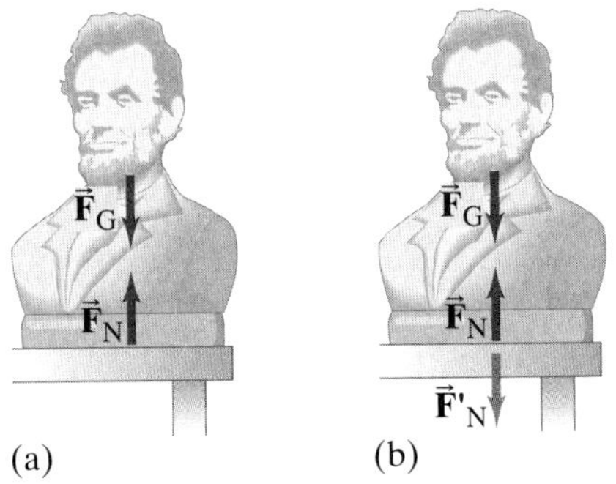


**FIGURE 4–14** (a) The net force on an object at rest is zero according to Newton's second law. Therefore the downward force of gravity ($\vec{\mathbf{F}}_G$) on an object must be balanced by an upward force (the normal force $\vec{\mathbf{F}}_N$) exerted by the table in this case. (b) $\vec{\mathbf{F}}'_N$ is the force exerted on the table by the statue and is the reaction force to $\vec{\mathbf{F}}_N$ per Newton's third law. ($\vec{\mathbf{F}}'_N$ is shown in a different color to remind us it acts on a different object.) The reaction to $\vec{\mathbf{F}}_G$ is not shown.

The two forces shown in Fig. 4–14a are both acting on the statue, which remains at rest, so the vector sum of these two forces must be zero (Newton's second law). Hence $\vec{\mathbf{F}}_G$ and $\vec{\mathbf{F}}_N$ must be of equal magnitude and in opposite directions. But they are *not* the equal and opposite forces spoken of in Newton's third law. The action and reaction forces of Newton's third law act on *different objects*, whereas the two forces shown in Fig. 4–14a act on the *same* object. For each of the forces shown in Fig. 4–14a, we can ask, "What is the reaction force?" The upward force, $\vec{\mathbf{F}}_N$, on the statue is exerted by the table. The reaction to this force is a force exerted by the statue downward on the table. It is shown in Fig. 4–14b, where it is labeled $\vec{\mathbf{F}}'_N$. This force, $\vec{\mathbf{F}}'_N$, exerted on the table by the statue, is the reaction force to $\vec{\mathbf{F}}_N$ in accord with Newton's third law. What about the other force on the statue, the force of gravity $\vec{\mathbf{F}}_G$ exerted by the Earth? Can you guess what the reaction is to this force? We will see in Chapter 5 that the reaction force is also a gravitational force, exerted on the Earth by the statue.

**CAUTION**
*Weight and normal force are* **not** *action–reaction pairs*

†The concept of "vertical" is tied to gravity. The best definition of *vertical* is that it is the direction in which objects fall. A surface that is "horizontal," on the other hand, is a surface on which a round object won't start rolling: gravity has no effect. Horizontal is perpendicular to vertical.

‡Since $1\,\text{N} = 1\,\text{kg}\cdot\text{m/s}^2$ (Section 4–4), $1\,\text{m/s}^2 = 1\,\text{N/kg}$.

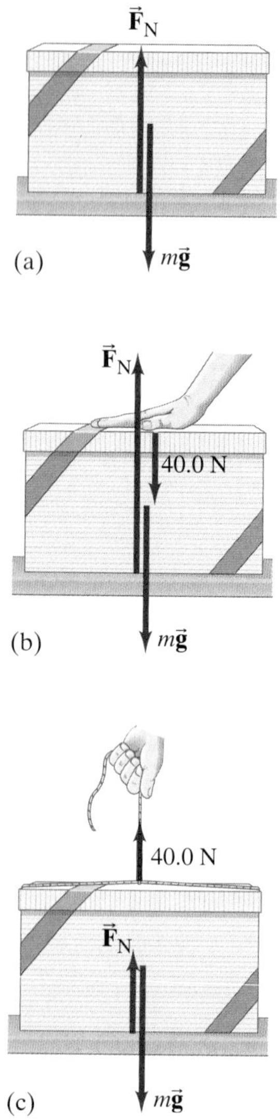


**FIGURE 4–15** Example 4–6. (a) A 10-kg gift box is at rest on a table. (b) A person pushes down on the box with a force of 40.0 N. (c) A person pulls upward on the box with a force of 40.0 N. The forces are all assumed to act along a line; they are shown slightly displaced in order to be distinguishable. Only forces acting on the box are shown.

**CAUTION**
*The normal force is not necessarily equal to the weight*

**EXAMPLE 4–6** **Weight, normal force, and a box.** A friend has given you a special gift, a box of mass 10.0 kg with a mystery surprise inside. The box is resting on the smooth (frictionless) horizontal surface of a table (Fig. 4–15a). (*a*) Determine the weight of the box and the normal force exerted on it by the table. (*b*) Now your friend pushes down on the box with a force of 40.0 N, as in Fig. 4–15b. Again determine the normal force exerted on the box by the table. (*c*) If your friend pulls upward on the box with a force of 40.0 N (Fig. 4–15c), what now is the normal force exerted on the box by the table?

**APPROACH** The box is at rest on the table, so the net force on the box in each case is zero (Newton's second law). The weight of the box equals $mg$ in all three cases.

**SOLUTION** (*a*) The weight of the box is $mg = (10.0\,\text{kg})(9.80\,\text{m/s}^2) = 98.0\,\text{N}$, and this force acts downward. The only other force on the box is the normal force exerted upward on it by the table, as shown in Fig. 4–15a. We chose the upward direction as the positive $y$ direction; then the net force $\Sigma F_y$ on the box is $\Sigma F_y = F_N - mg$. The box is at rest, so the net force on it must be zero (Newton's second law, $\Sigma F_y = ma_y$, and $a_y = 0$). Thus

$$\Sigma F_y = F_N - mg = 0,$$

and we have in this case

$$F_N = mg.$$

The normal force on the box, exerted by the table, is 98.0 N upward, and has magnitude equal to the box's weight.
(*b*) Your friend is pushing down on the box with a force of 40.0 N. So instead of only two forces acting on the box, now there are three forces acting on the box, as shown in Fig. 4–15b. The weight of the box is still $mg = 98.0\,\text{N}$. The net force is $\Sigma F_y = F_N - mg - 40.0\,\text{N}$, and is equal to zero because the box remains at rest. Thus, since $a = 0$, Newton's second law gives

$$\Sigma F_y = F_N - mg - 40.0\,\text{N} = 0.$$

We solve this equation for the normal force:

$$F_N = mg + 40.0\,\text{N} = 98.0\,\text{N} + 40.0\,\text{N} = 138.0\,\text{N},$$

which is greater than in (*a*). The table pushes back with more force when a person pushes down on the box. The normal force is not always equal to the weight!
(*c*) The box's weight is still 98.0 N and acts downward. The force exerted by your friend and the normal force both act upward (positive direction), as shown in Fig. 4–15c. The box doesn't move since your friend's upward force is less than the weight. The net force, again set to zero in Newton's second law because $a = 0$, is

$$\Sigma F_y = F_N - mg + 40.0\,\text{N} = 0,$$

so

$$F_N = mg - 40.0\,\text{N} = 98.0\,\text{N} - 40.0\,\text{N} = 58.0\,\text{N}.$$

The table does not push against the full weight of the box because of the upward pull exerted by your friend.

**NOTE** The weight of the box ($= mg$) does not change as a result of your friend's push or pull. Only the normal force is affected.

**CAUTION**
*The normal force, $\vec{F}_N$, is not necessarily vertical*

Recall that the normal force is elastic in origin (the table in Fig. 4–15 sags slightly under the weight of the box). The normal force in Example 4–6 is vertical, perpendicular to the horizontal table. The normal force is not always vertical, however. When you push against a vertical wall, for example, the normal force with which the wall pushes back on you is horizontal. For an object on a plane inclined at an angle to the horizontal, such as a skier or car on a hill, the normal force acts perpendicular to the plane and so is not vertical.

**EXAMPLE 4–7** **Accelerating the box.** What happens when a person pulls upward on the box in Example 4–6 (*c*) with a force equal to, or greater than, the box's weight, say $F_P = 100.0\,\text{N}$ rather than the 40.0 N shown in Fig. 4–15c?

**APPROACH** We can start just as in Example 4–6, but be ready for a surprise.

**SOLUTION** The net force on the box is

$$\begin{aligned}\Sigma F_y &= F_N - mg + F_P \\ &= F_N - 98.0\,\text{N} + 100.0\,\text{N},\end{aligned}$$

and if we set this equal to zero (thinking the acceleration might be zero), we would get $F_N = -2.0\,\text{N}$. This is nonsense, since the negative sign implies $F_N$ points downward, and the table surely cannot *pull* down on the box (unless there's glue on the table). The least $F_N$ can be is zero, which it will be in this case. What really happens here is that the box accelerates upward because the net force is not zero. The net force (setting the normal force $F_N = 0$) is

$$\begin{aligned}\Sigma F_y = F_P - mg &= 100.0\,\text{N} - 98.0\,\text{N} \\ &= 2.0\,\text{N}\end{aligned}$$

upward. See Fig. 4–16. We apply Newton's second law and see that the box moves upward with an acceleration

$$\begin{aligned}a_y = \frac{\Sigma F_y}{m} &= \frac{2.0\,\text{N}}{10.0\,\text{kg}} \\ &= 0.20\,\text{m/s}^2.\end{aligned}$$

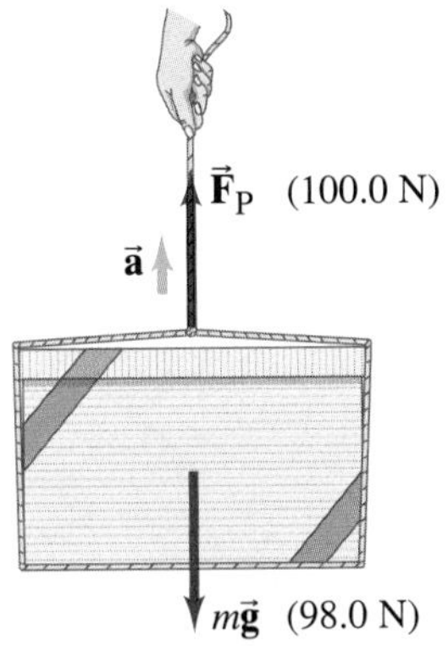

**FIGURE 4–16** Example 4–7. The box accelerates upward because $F_P > mg$.

## Additional Example

**EXAMPLE 4–8** **Apparent weight loss.** A 65-kg woman descends in an elevator that briefly accelerates at $0.20g$ downward when leaving a floor. She stands on a scale that reads in kg. (*a*) During this acceleration, what is her weight and what does the scale read? (*b*) What does the scale read when the elevator descends at a constant speed of 2.0 m/s?

**APPROACH** Figure 4–17 shows all the forces that act on the woman (and *only* those that act on her). The direction of the acceleration is downward, which we take as positive.

**SOLUTION** (*a*) From Newton's second law,

$$\begin{aligned}\Sigma F &= ma \\ mg - F_N &= m(0.20g).\end{aligned}$$

We solve for $F_N$:

$$F_N = mg - 0.20mg = 0.80mg,$$

and it acts upward. The normal force $\vec{\mathbf{F}}_N$ is the force the scale exerts on the person, and is equal and opposite to the force she exerts on the scale: $F'_N = 0.80mg$ downward. Her weight (force of gravity on her) is still $mg = (65\,\text{kg})(9.8\,\text{m/s}^2) = 640\,\text{N}$. But the scale, needing to exert a force of only $0.80mg$, will give a reading of $0.80m = 52\,\text{kg}$.
(*b*) Now there is no acceleration, $a = 0$, so by Newton's second law, $mg - F_N = 0$ and $F_N = mg$. The scale reads her true mass of 65 kg.

**NOTE** The scale in (*a*) may give a reading of 52 kg (as an "apparent mass"), but her mass doesn't change as a result of the acceleration: it stays at 65 kg.

**FIGURE 4–17** Example 4–8.

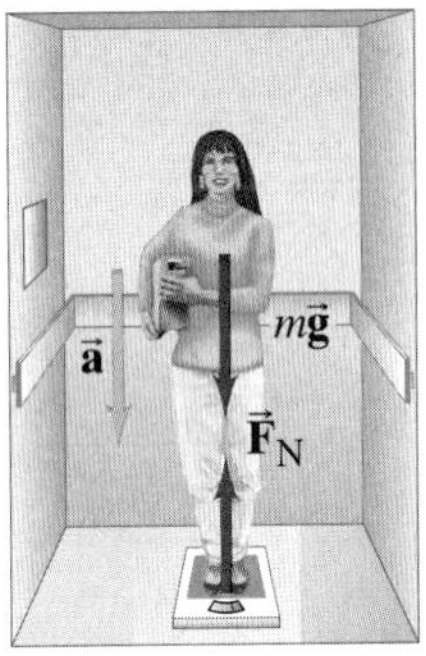

## 4–7 Solving Problems with Newton's Laws: Free-Body Diagrams

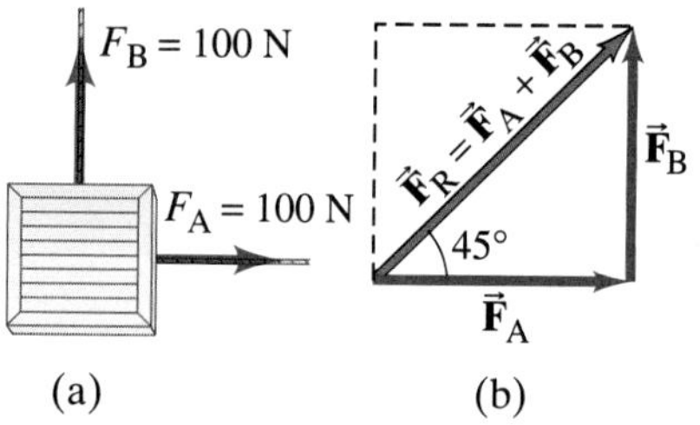


**FIGURE 4–18** (a) Two forces, $\vec{F}_A$ and $\vec{F}_B$, exerted by workers A and B, act on a crate. (b) The sum, or resultant, of $\vec{F}_A$ and $\vec{F}_B$ is $\vec{F}_R$.

Newton's second law tells us that the acceleration of an object is proportional to the *net force* acting on the object. The **net force**, as mentioned earlier, is the *vector sum* of all forces acting on the object. Indeed, extensive experiments have shown that forces do add together as vectors precisely according to the rules we developed in Chapter 3. For example, in Fig. 4–18, two forces of equal magnitude (100 N each) are shown acting on an object at right angles to each other. Intuitively, we can see that the object will start moving at a 45° angle and thus the net force acts at a 45° angle. This is just what the rules of vector addition give. From the theorem of Pythagoras, the magnitude of the resultant force is $F_R = \sqrt{(100\,\text{N})^2 + (100\,\text{N})^2} = 141\,\text{N}$.

**FIGURE 4–19** Example 4–9: Two force vectors act on a boat.

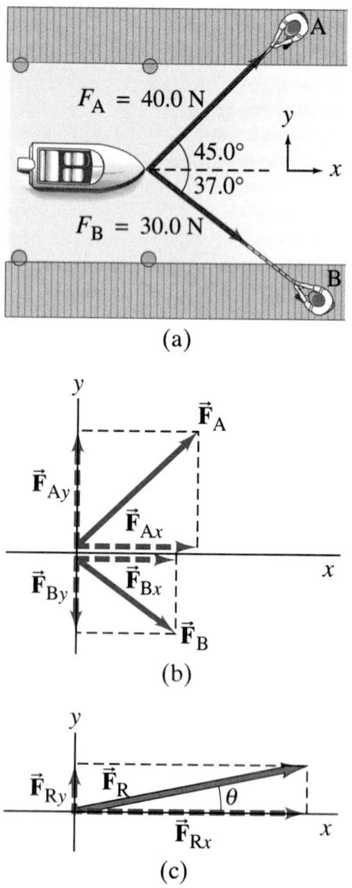


**EXAMPLE 4–9 Adding force vectors.** Calculate the sum of the two forces exerted on the boat by workers A and B in Fig. 4–19a.

**APPROACH** We add force vectors like any other vectors as described in Chapter 3. The first step is to choose an $xy$ coordinate system, as in Fig. 4–19a, and then resolve vectors into their components.

**SOLUTION** The two force vectors are shown resolved into components in Fig. 4–19b. We add the forces using the method of components. The components of $\vec{F}_A$ are

$$F_{Ax} = F_A \cos 45.0° = (40.0\,\text{N})(0.707) = 28.3\,\text{N},$$
$$F_{Ay} = F_A \sin 45.0° = (40.0\,\text{N})(0.707) = 28.3\,\text{N}.$$

The components of $\vec{F}_B$ are

$$F_{Bx} = +F_B \cos 37.0° = +(30.0\,\text{N})(0.799) = +24.0\,\text{N},$$
$$F_{By} = -F_B \sin 37.0° = -(30.0\,\text{N})(0.602) = -18.1\,\text{N}.$$

$F_{By}$ is negative because it points along the negative $y$ axis. The components of the resultant force are (see Fig. 4–19c)

$$F_{Rx} = F_{Ax} + F_{Bx} = 28.3\,\text{N} + 24.0\,\text{N} = 52.3\,\text{N},$$
$$F_{Ry} = F_{Ay} + F_{By} = 28.3\,\text{N} - 18.1\,\text{N} = 10.2\,\text{N}.$$

To find the magnitude of the resultant force, we use the Pythagorean theorem:

$$F_R = \sqrt{F_{Rx}^2 + F_{Ry}^2} = \sqrt{(52.3)^2 + (10.2)^2}\,\text{N} = 53.3\,\text{N}.$$

The only remaining question is the angle $\theta$ that the net force $\vec{F}_R$ makes with the $x$ axis. We use:

$$\tan\theta = \frac{F_{Ry}}{F_{Rx}} = \frac{10.2\,\text{N}}{52.3\,\text{N}} = 0.195,$$

and $\tan^{-1}(0.195) = 11.0°$. The net force on the boat has magnitude 53.3 N and acts at an 11.0° angle to the $x$ axis.

**PROBLEM SOLVING**

*Free-body diagram*

*Identifying every force*

When solving problems involving Newton's laws and force, it is very important to draw a diagram showing all the forces acting *on* each object involved. Such a diagram is called a **free-body diagram**, or **force diagram**: choose one object, and draw an arrow to represent each force acting on it. Include *every* force acting on that object. Do not show forces that the chosen object exerts on *other* objects. To help you identify each and every force that is exerted on your chosen object, ask yourself what other objects could exert a force on it. If your problem involves more than one object, a separate free-body diagram is needed for each object.

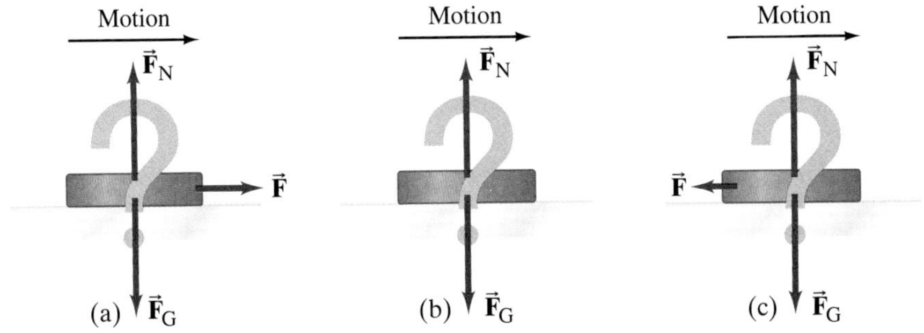


**FIGURE 4–20** Example 4–10. Which is the correct free-body diagram for a hockey puck sliding across frictionless ice?

**CONCEPTUAL EXAMPLE 4–10** **The hockey puck.** A hockey puck is sliding at constant velocity across a flat horizontal ice surface that is assumed to be frictionless. Which of the sketches in Fig. 4–20 is the correct free-body diagram for this puck? What would your answer be if the puck slowed down?

**RESPONSE** Did you choose (*a*)? If so, can you answer the question: what exerts the horizontal force labeled $\vec{\mathbf{F}}$ on the puck? If you say that it is the force needed to maintain the motion, ask yourself: what exerts this force? Remember that another object must exert any force—and there simply isn't any possibility here. Therefore, (*a*) is wrong. Besides, the force $\vec{\mathbf{F}}$ in Fig. 4–20a would give rise to an acceleration by Newton's second law. It is (*b*) that is correct, as long as there is no friction. No net force acts on the puck, and the puck slides at constant velocity across the ice.

In the real world, where even smooth ice exerts at least a tiny friction force, then (*c*) is the correct answer. The tiny friction force is in the direction opposite to the motion, and the puck's velocity decreases, even if very slowly.

Here now is a brief summary of how to approach solving problems involving Newton's laws.

## PROBLEM SOLVING Newton's Laws; Free-Body Diagrams

1. **Draw a sketch** of the situation.
2. Consider only one object (at a time), and draw a **free-body diagram** for that object, showing *all* the forces acting *on* that object. Include any unknown forces that you have to solve for. Do not show any forces that the chosen object exerts on other objects. Draw the arrow for each force vector reasonably accurately for direction and magnitude. Label each force, including forces you must solve for, as to its source (gravity, person, friction, and so on).

   If several objects are involved, draw a free-body diagram for each object *separately*, showing all the forces acting *on that object* (and *only* forces acting on that object). For each (and every) force, you must be clear about: *on* what object that force acts, and *by* what object that force is exerted. Only forces acting *on* a given object can be included in $\Sigma\vec{\mathbf{F}} = m\vec{\mathbf{a}}$ for that object.
3. Newton's second law involves vectors, and it is usually important to **resolve vectors** into components. **Choose** $x$ and $y$ **axes** in a way that simplifies the calculation. For example, it often saves work if you choose one coordinate axis to be in the direction of the acceleration.
4. For each object, **apply Newton's second law** to the $x$ and $y$ components separately. That is, the $x$ component of the net force on that object is related to the $x$ component of that object's acceleration: $\Sigma F_x = ma_x$, and similarly for the $y$ direction.
5. **Solve** the equation or equations for the unknown(s).

This Problem Solving Box should not be considered a prescription. Rather it is a summary of things to do that will start you thinking and getting involved in the problem at hand.

*Force arrow placement on diagrams*

When we are concerned only about translational motion, all the forces on a given object can be drawn as acting at the center of the object, thus treating the object as a point particle. However, for problems involving rotation or statics, the place *where* each force acts is also important, as we shall see in Chapters 8 and 9.

In the Examples that follow, we assume that all surfaces are very smooth so that friction can be ignored. (Friction, and Examples using it, are discussed in Section 4–8.)

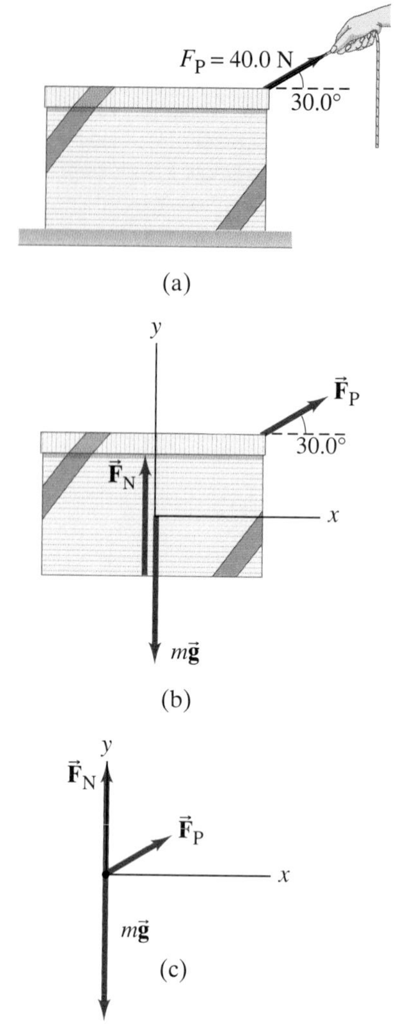


**FIGURE 4–21** (a) Pulling the box, Example 4–11; (b) is the free-body diagram for the box, and (c) is the free-body diagram considering all the forces to act at a point (translational motion only, which is what we have here).

**EXAMPLE 4–11** **Pulling the mystery box.** Suppose a friend asks to examine the 10.0-kg box you were given (Example 4–6, Fig. 4–15), hoping to guess what is inside; and you respond, "Sure, pull the box over to you." She then pulls the box by the attached cord, as shown in Fig. 4–21a, along the smooth surface of the table. The magnitude of the force exerted by the person is $F_P = 40.0\,\text{N}$, and it is exerted at a 30.0° angle as shown. Calculate (*a*) the acceleration of the box, and (*b*) the magnitude of the upward force $F_N$ exerted by the table on the box. Assume that friction can be neglected.

**APPROACH** We follow the Problem Solving Box on the previous page.

**SOLUTION**

1. **Draw a sketch**: The situation is shown in Fig. 4–21a; it shows the box and the force applied by the person, $F_P$.
2. **Free-body diagram**: Figure 4–21b shows the free-body diagram of the box. To draw it correctly, we show *all* the forces acting on the box and *only* the forces acting on the box. They are: the force of gravity $m\vec{g}$; the normal force exerted by the table $\vec{F}_N$; and the force exerted by the person $\vec{F}_P$. We are interested only in translational motion, so we can show the three forces acting at a point, Fig. 4–21c.
3. **Choose axes and resolve vectors**: We expect the motion to be horizontal, so we choose the $x$ axis horizontal and the $y$ axis vertical. The pull of 40.0 N has components

$$F_{Px} = (40.0\,\text{N})(\cos 30.0°) = (40.0\,\text{N})(0.866) = 34.6\,\text{N},$$
$$F_{Py} = (40.0\,\text{N})(\sin 30.0°) = (40.0\,\text{N})(0.500) = 20.0\,\text{N}.$$

In the horizontal ($x$) direction, $\vec{F}_N$ and $m\vec{g}$ have zero components. Thus the horizontal component of the net force is $F_{Px}$.

4. (*a*) **Apply Newton's second law** to determine the $x$ component of the acceleration:

$$F_{Px} = ma_x.$$

5. (*a*) **Solve**:

$$a_x = \frac{F_{Px}}{m} = \frac{(34.6\,\text{N})}{(10.0\,\text{kg})} = 3.46\,\text{m/s}^2.$$

The acceleration of the box is $3.46\,\text{m/s}^2$ to the right.

(*b*) Next we want to find $F_N$.

4. (*b*) **Apply Newton's second law** to the vertical ($y$) direction, with upward as positive:

$$\Sigma F_y = ma_y$$
$$F_N - mg + F_{Py} = ma_y.$$

5. (*b*) **Solve**: We have $mg = (10.0\,\text{kg})(9.80\,\text{m/s}^2) = 98.0\,\text{N}$ and, from point 3 above, $F_{Py} = 20.0\,\text{N}$. Furthermore, since $F_{Py} < mg$, the box does not move vertically, so $a_y = 0$. Thus

$$F_N - 98.0\,\text{N} + 20.0\,\text{N} = 0,$$

so

$$F_N = 78.0\,\text{N}.$$

**NOTE** $F_N$ is less than $mg$: the table does not push against the full weight of the box because part of the pull exerted by the person is in the upward direction.

## Tension in a Flexible Cord

**PROBLEM SOLVING**

*Cords can pull but can't push; tension exists throughout a cord*

When a flexible cord pulls on an object, the cord is said to be under **tension**, and the force it exerts on the object is the tension $F_T$. If the cord has negligible mass, the force exerted at one end is transmitted undiminished to each adjacent piece of cord along the entire length to the other end. Why? Because $\Sigma\vec{F} = m\vec{a} = 0$ for the cord if the cord's mass $m$ is zero (or negligible) no matter what $\vec{a}$ is. Hence the forces pulling on the cord at its two ends must add up to zero ($F_T$ and $-F_T$). Note that flexible cords and strings can only pull. They can't push because they bend.

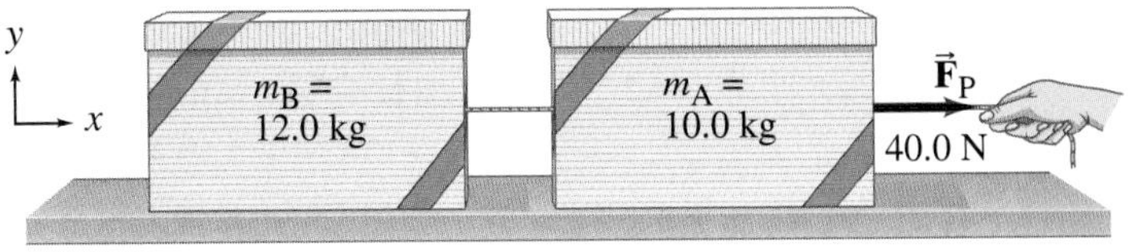


**FIGURE 4–22** Example 4–12. (a) Two boxes, A and B, are connected by a cord. A person pulls horizontally on box A with force $F_P = 40.0\text{ N}$. (b) Free-body diagram for box A. (c) Free-body diagram for box B.

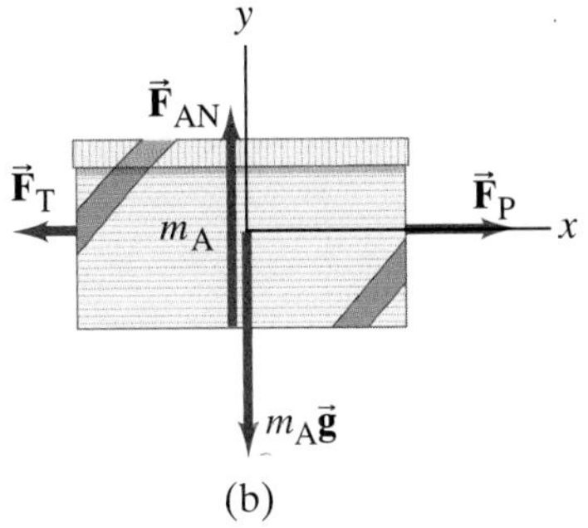


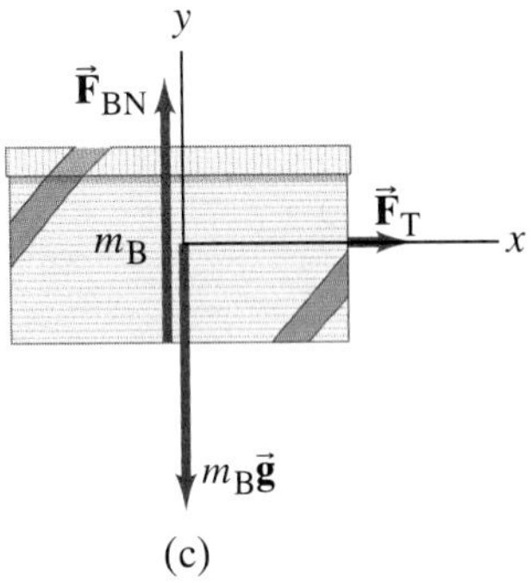


Our next Example involves two boxes connected by a cord. We can refer to this group of objects as a system. A *system* is any group of one or more objects we choose to consider and study.

**EXAMPLE 4–12** **Two boxes connected by a cord.** Two boxes, A and B, are connected by a lightweight cord and are resting on a smooth (frictionless) table. The boxes have masses of 12.0 kg and 10.0 kg. A horizontal force $F_P$ of 40.0 N is applied to the 10.0-kg box, as shown in Fig. 4–22a. Find (*a*) the acceleration of each box, and (*b*) the tension in the cord connecting the boxes.

**APPROACH** We streamline our approach by not listing each step. We have two boxes so we need to draw a free-body diagram for each box. To draw them correctly, we must consider the forces on *each* box by itself, so that Newton's second law can be applied to each. The person exerts a force $F_P$ on box A. Box A exerts a force $F_T$ on the connecting cord, and the cord exerts an opposite but equal magnitude force $F_T$ back on box A (Newton's third law). These two horizontal forces on box A are shown in Fig. 4–22b, along with the force of gravity $m_A\vec{g}$ downward and the normal force $\vec{F}_{AN}$ exerted upward by the table. The cord is light, so we neglect its mass. The tension at each end of the cord is thus the same. Hence the cord exerts a force $F_T$ on the second box. Figure 4–22c shows the forces on box B, which are $\vec{F}_T$, $m_B\vec{g}$, and the normal force $\vec{F}_{BN}$. There will be only horizontal motion. We take the positive $x$ axis to the right.

**SOLUTION** (*a*) We apply $\Sigma F_x = ma_x$ to box A:

$$\Sigma F_x = F_P - F_T = m_A a_A. \qquad \text{[box A]}$$

For box B, the only horizontal force is $F_T$, so

$$\Sigma F_x = F_T = m_B a_B. \qquad \text{[box B]}$$

The boxes are connected, and if the cord remains taut and doesn't stretch, then the two boxes will have the same acceleration $a$. Thus $a_A = a_B = a$. We are given $m_A = 10.0\text{ kg}$ and $m_B = 12.0\text{ kg}$. We can add the two equations above to eliminate an unknown $(F_T)$ and obtain

$$(m_A + m_B)a = F_P - F_T + F_T = F_P$$

or

$$a = \frac{F_P}{m_A + m_B} = \frac{40.0\text{ N}}{22.0\text{ kg}} = 1.82\text{ m/s}^2.$$

This is what we sought.

**➥ PROBLEM SOLVING**

*An alternate analysis*

***Alternate Solution*** We would have obtained the same result had we considered a single system, of mass $m_A + m_B$, acted on by a net horizontal force equal to $F_P$. (The tension forces $F_T$ would then be considered internal to the system as a whole, and summed together would make zero contribution to the net force on the *whole* system.)

(*b*) From the equation above for box B $(F_T = m_B a_B)$, the tension in the cord is

$$F_T = m_B a = (12.0\text{ kg})(1.82\text{ m/s}^2) = 21.8\text{ N}.$$

Thus, $F_T$ is less than $F_P (= 40.0\text{ N})$, as we expect, since $F_T$ acts to accelerate only $m_B$.

**NOTE** It might be tempting to say that the force the person exerts, $F_P$, acts not only on box A but also on box B. It doesn't. $F_P$ acts only on box A. It affects box B via the tension in the cord, $F_T$, which acts on box B and accelerates it.

**⚠ CAUTION**

*For any object, use only the forces on that object in calculating $\Sigma F = ma$*

## Additional Examples

Here are some more worked-out Examples to give you practice in solving a wide range of Problems.

**PHYSICS APPLIED**
*Elevator (as Atwood's machine)*

**EXAMPLE 4–13 Elevator and counterweight (Atwood's machine).** A system of two objects suspended over a pulley by a flexible cable, as shown in Fig. 4–23a, is sometimes referred to as an *Atwood's machine*. Consider the real-life application of an elevator $(m_E)$ and its counterweight $(m_C)$. To minimize the work done by the motor to raise and lower the elevator safely, $m_E$ and $m_C$ are similar in mass. We leave the motor out of the system for this calculation, and assume that the cable's mass is negligible and that the mass of the pulley, as well as any friction, is small and ignorable. These assumptions ensure that the tension $F_T$ in the cable has the same magnitude on both sides of the pulley. Let the mass of the counterweight be $m_C = 1000\text{ kg}$. Assume the mass of the empty elevator is 850 kg, and its mass when carrying four passengers is $m_E = 1150\text{ kg}$. For the latter case $(m_E = 1150\text{ kg})$, calculate (*a*) the acceleration of the elevator and (*b*) the tension in the cable.

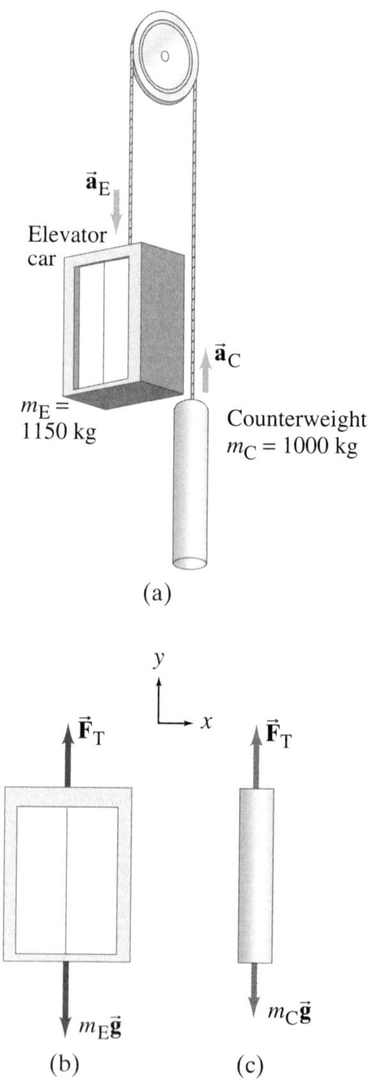


**FIGURE 4–23** Example 4–13. (a) Atwood's machine in the form of an elevator–counterweight system. (b) and (c) Free-body diagrams for the two objects.

**APPROACH** Again we have two objects, and we will need to apply Newton's second law to each of them separately. Each mass has two forces acting on it: gravity downward and the cable tension pulling upward, $\vec{\mathbf{F}}_T$. Figures 4–23b and c show the free-body diagrams for the elevator $(m_E)$ and for the counterweight $(m_C)$. The elevator, being the heavier, will accelerate downward, whereas the counterweight will accelerate upward. The magnitudes of their accelerations will be equal (we assume the cable doesn't stretch). For the counterweight, $m_C g = (1000\text{ kg})(9.80\text{ m/s}^2) = 9800\text{ N}$, so $F_T$ must be greater than 9800 N (in order that $m_C$ will accelerate upward). For the elevator, $m_E g = (1150\text{ kg})(9.80\text{ m/s}^2) = 11{,}300\text{ N}$, which must have greater magnitude than $F_T$ so that $m_E$ accelerates downward. Thus our calculation must give $F_T$ between 9800 N and 11,300 N.

**SOLUTION** (*a*) To find $F_T$ as well as the acceleration $a$, we apply Newton's second law, $\Sigma F = ma$, to each object. We take upward as the positive $y$ direction for both objects. With this choice of axes, $a_C = a$ because $m_C$ accelerates upward, and $a_E = -a$ because $m_E$ accelerates downward. Thus

$$F_T - m_E g = m_E a_E = -m_E a$$
$$F_T - m_C g = m_C a_C = +m_C a.$$

We can subtract the first equation from the second to get

$$(m_E - m_C)g = (m_E + m_C)a,$$

where $a$ is now the only unknown. We solve this for $a$:

$$a = \frac{m_E - m_C}{m_E + m_C}\,g = \frac{1150\text{ kg} - 1000\text{ kg}}{1150\text{ kg} + 1000\text{ kg}}\,g = 0.070\,g = 0.68\text{ m/s}^2.$$

The elevator $(m_E)$ accelerates downward (and the counterweight $m_C$ upward) at $a = 0.070g = 0.68\text{ m/s}^2$.

(*b*) The tension in the cable $F_T$ can be obtained from either of the two $\Sigma F = ma$ equations, setting $a = 0.070g = 0.68\text{ m/s}^2$:

$$F_T = m_E g - m_E a = m_E(g - a)$$
$$= 1150\text{ kg}\,(9.80\text{ m/s}^2 - 0.68\text{ m/s}^2) = 10{,}500\text{ N},$$
$$F_T = m_C g + m_C a = m_C(g + a)$$
$$= 1000\text{ kg}\,(9.80\text{ m/s}^2 + 0.68\text{ m/s}^2) = 10{,}500\text{ N},$$

which are consistent. As predicted, our result lies between 9800 N and 11,300 N.

**PROBLEM SOLVING**
*Check your result by seeing if it works in situations where the answer is easily guessed*

**NOTE** We can check our equation for the acceleration $a$ in this Example by noting that if the masses were equal $(m_E = m_C)$, then our equation above for $a$ would give $a = 0$, as we should expect. Also, if one of the masses is zero (say, $m_C = 0$), then the other mass $(m_E \neq 0)$ would be predicted by our equation to accelerate at $a = g$, again as expected.

**CONCEPTUAL EXAMPLE 4–14** **The advantage of a pulley.** A mover is trying to lift a piano (slowly) up to a second-story apartment (Fig. 4–24). He is using a rope looped over two pulleys as shown. What force must he exert on the rope to slowly lift the piano's 2000-N weight?

**RESPONSE** The magnitude of the tension force $F_T$ within the rope is the same at any point along the rope if we assume we can ignore its mass. First notice the forces acting on the lower pulley at the piano. The weight of the piano pulls down on the pulley via a short cable. The tension in the rope, looped through this pulley, pulls up *twice*, once on each side of the pulley. Let us apply Newton's second law to the pulley–piano combination (of mass $m$):

$$2F_T - mg = ma.$$

To move the piano with constant speed (set $a = 0$ in this equation) thus requires a tension in the rope, and hence a pull on the rope, of $F_T = mg/2$. The mover can exert a force equal to half the piano's weight. We say the pulley has given a **mechanical advantage** of 2, since without the pulley the mover would have to exert twice the force.

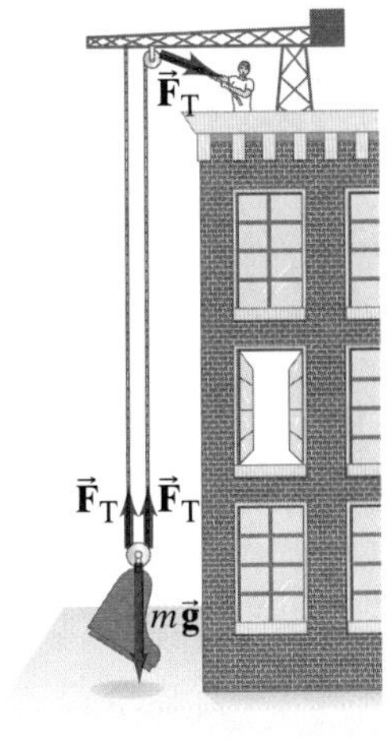


**FIGURE 4–24** Example 4–14.

**EXAMPLE 4–15** **Getting the car out of the mud.** Finding her car stuck in the mud, a bright graduate of a good physics course ties a strong rope to the back bumper of the car, and the other end to a boulder, as shown in Fig. 4–25a. She pushes at the midpoint of the rope with her maximum effort, which she estimates to be a force $F_P \approx 300$ N. The car just begins to budge with the rope at an angle $\theta$ (see the Figure), which she estimates to be 5°. With what force is the rope pulling on the car? Neglect the mass of the rope.

*How to get out of the mud*

**APPROACH** First, note that the tension in a rope is always along the rope. Any component perpendicular to the rope would cause the rope to bend or buckle (as it does here where $\vec{\mathbf{F}}_P$ acts)—in other words, a rope can support a tension force only along its length. Let $\vec{\mathbf{F}}_{BR}$ and $\vec{\mathbf{F}}_{CR}$ be the forces on the boulder and on the car, exerted via the tension in the rope, as shown in Fig. 4–25a. Let us choose to look at the forces on the tiny section of rope where she pushes. The free-body diagram is shown in Fig. 4–25b, which shows $\vec{\mathbf{F}}_P$ as well as the tensions in the rope (note that we have used Newton's third law: $\vec{\mathbf{F}}_{RB} = -\vec{\mathbf{F}}_{BR}$, $\vec{\mathbf{F}}_{RC} = -\vec{\mathbf{F}}_{CR}$). At the moment the car budges, the acceleration is still essentially zero, so $\vec{\mathbf{a}} = 0$.

**SOLUTION** For the $x$ component of $\Sigma\vec{\mathbf{F}} = m\vec{\mathbf{a}} = 0$ on that small section of rope (Fig. 4–25b), we have

$$\Sigma F_x = F_{RB}\cos\theta - F_{RC}\cos\theta = 0.$$

Hence $F_{RB} = F_{RC}$, and these forces represent the magnitude of the tension in the rope, call it $F_T$; then we can write $F_T = F_{RB} = F_{RC}$. In the $y$ direction, the forces acting are $F_P$, and the components of $F_{RB}$ and $F_{RC}$ that point in the negative $y$ direction (each equal to $F_T\sin\theta$). So for the $y$ component of $\Sigma\vec{\mathbf{F}} = m\vec{\mathbf{a}}$, we have

$$\Sigma F_y = F_P - 2F_T\sin\theta = 0.$$

We solve this for $F_T$, and insert $\theta = 5°$ and $F_P \approx 300$ N, which were given:

$$F_T = \frac{F_P}{2\sin\theta} \approx \frac{300\text{ N}}{2\sin 5°} \approx 1700\text{ N}.$$

When our physics graduate exerted a force of 300 N on the rope, the force produced on the car was 1700 N. She was able to magnify her effort almost six times using this technique!

**NOTE** Notice the symmetry of the problem, which ensures that $F_{RB} = F_{RC}$.

**NOTE** Compare Figs. 4–25a and b. Notice that we cannot write down Newton's second law using Fig. 4–25a because the force vectors are not acting on the same object. It is only by choosing a tiny section of rope as our object, and using Newton's third law (in this case, the boulder and the car pulling back on the rope with forces $F_{RB}$ and $F_{RC}$), that all forces apply to the same object.

**FIGURE 4–25** Example 4–15. (a) Getting a car out of the mud, showing the forces on the boulder, on the car, and exerted by the person. (b) The free-body diagram: forces on a small segment of rope.

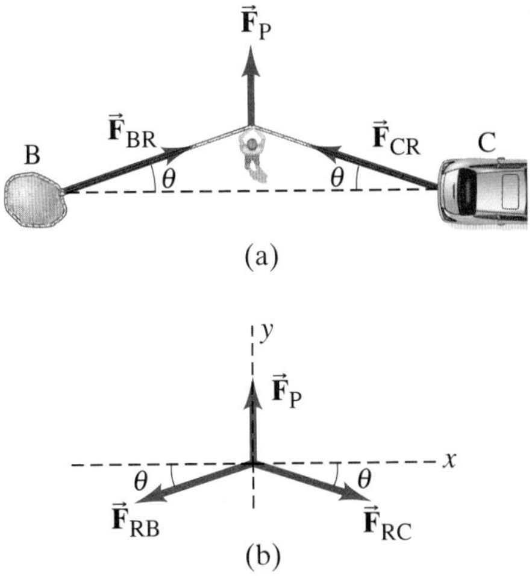


➡ **PROBLEM SOLVING**
*Use any symmetry present to simplify a problem*

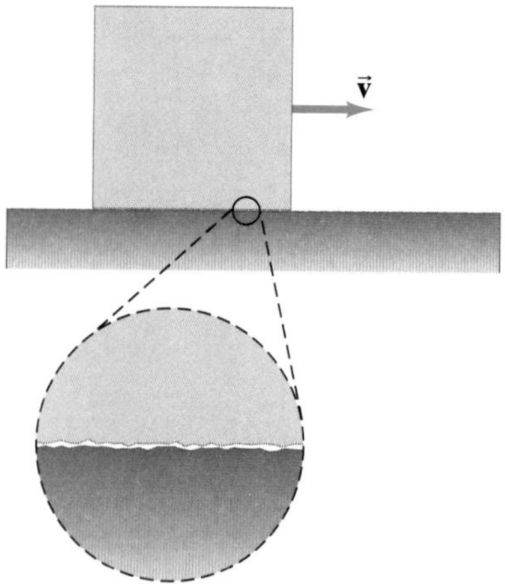


**FIGURE 4–26** An object moving to the right on a table or floor. The two surfaces in contact are rough, at least on a microscopic scale.

## 4–8 Problems Involving Friction, Inclines

### Friction

Until now we have ignored friction, but it must be taken into account in most practical situations. Friction exists between two solid surfaces because even the smoothest looking surface is quite rough on a microscopic scale, Fig. 4–26. When we try to slide an object across another surface, these microscopic bumps impede the motion. Exactly what is happening at the microscopic level is not yet fully understood. It is thought that the atoms on a bump of one surface may come so close to the atoms of the other surface that attractive electric forces between the atoms can "bond" as a tiny weld between the two surfaces. Sliding an object across a surface is often jerky, perhaps due to the making and breaking of these bonds. Even when a round object rolls across a surface, there is still some friction, called *rolling friction*, although it is generally much less than when an object slides across a surface. We focus now on sliding friction, which is usually called **kinetic friction** (*kinetic* is from the Greek for "moving").

When an object slides along a rough surface, the force of kinetic friction acts opposite to the direction of the object's velocity. The magnitude of the force of kinetic friction depends on the nature of the two sliding surfaces. For given surfaces, experiment shows that the friction force is approximately proportional to the *normal force* between the two surfaces, which is the force that either object exerts on the other, perpendicular to their common surface of contact (see Fig. 4–27). The force of friction between hard surfaces in many cases depends very little on the total surface area of contact; that is, the friction force on this book is roughly the same whether it is being slid on its wide face or on its spine, assuming the surfaces have the same smoothness. We consider a simple model of friction in which we make this assumption that the friction force is independent of area. Then we write the proportionality between the friction force $F_{fr}$ and the normal force $F_N$ as an equation by inserting a constant of proportionality, $\mu_k$:

*Kinetic friction*

$$F_{fr} = \mu_k F_N .$$

This relation is not a fundamental law; it is an experimental relation between the magnitude of the friction force $F_{fr}$, which acts parallel to the two surfaces, and the magnitude of the normal force $F_N$, which acts perpendicular to the surfaces. It is *not* a vector equation since the two forces have directions perpendicular to one another. The term $\mu_k$ is called the *coefficient of kinetic friction*, and its value depends on the nature of the two surfaces. Measured values for a variety of surfaces are given in Table 4–2. These are only approximate, however, since $\mu$ depends on whether the surfaces are wet or dry, on how much they have been sanded or rubbed, if any burrs remain, and other such factors. But $\mu_k$ is roughly independent of the sliding speed, as well as the area in contact.

$\vec{\mathbf{F}}_{fr} \perp \vec{\mathbf{F}}_N$

**FIGURE 4–27** When an object is pulled by an applied force ($\vec{\mathbf{F}}_A$) along a surface, the force of friction $\vec{\mathbf{F}}_{fr}$ opposes the motion. The magnitude of $\vec{\mathbf{F}}_{fr}$ is proportional to the magnitude of the normal force ($F_N$).

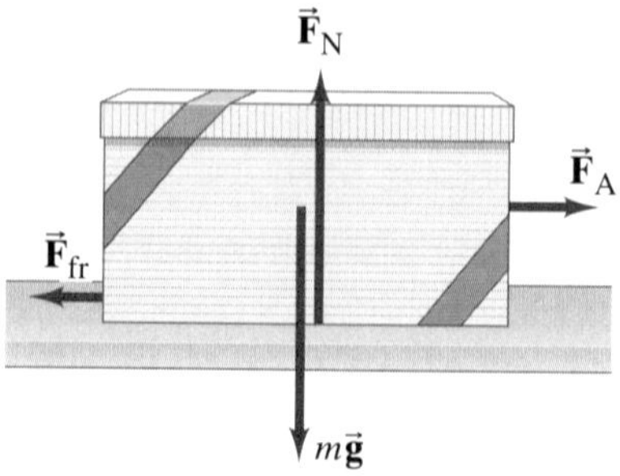


**TABLE 4–2 Coefficients of Friction†**

| Surfaces | Coefficient of Static Friction, $\mu_s$ | Coefficient of Kinetic Friction, $\mu_k$ |
|---|---|---|
| Wood on wood | 0.4 | 0.2 |
| Ice on ice | 0.1 | 0.03 |
| Metal on metal (lubricated) | 0.15 | 0.07 |
| Steel on steel (unlubricated) | 0.7 | 0.6 |
| Rubber on dry concrete | 1.0 | 0.8 |
| Rubber on wet concrete | 0.7 | 0.5 |
| Rubber on other solid surfaces | 1–4 | 1 |
| Teflon® on Teflon in air | 0.04 | 0.04 |
| Teflon on steel in air | 0.04 | 0.04 |
| Lubricated ball bearings | $<0.01$ | $<0.01$ |
| Synovial joints (in human limbs) | 0.01 | 0.01 |

† Values are approximate and intended only as a guide.

What we have been discussing up to now is *kinetic friction*, when one object slides over another. There is also **static friction**, which refers to a force parallel to the two surfaces that can arise even when they are not sliding. Suppose an object such as a desk is resting on a horizontal floor. If no horizontal force is exerted on the desk, there also is no friction force. But now suppose you try to push the desk, and it doesn't move. You are exerting a horizontal force, but the desk isn't moving, so there must be another force on the desk keeping it from moving (the net force is zero on an object that doesn't move). This is the force of *static friction* exerted by the floor on the desk. If you push with a greater force without moving the desk, the force of static friction also has increased. If you push hard enough, the desk will eventually start to move, and kinetic friction takes over. At this point, you have exceeded the maximum force of static friction, which is given by $F_{\mathrm{fr}}(\max) = \mu_{\mathrm{s}} F_{\mathrm{N}}$, where $\mu_{\mathrm{s}}$ is the *coefficient of static friction* (Table 4–2). Since the force of static friction can vary from zero to this maximum value, we write

$$F_{\mathrm{fr}} \leq \mu_{\mathrm{s}} F_{\mathrm{N}}.$$

*Static friction*

You may have noticed that it is often easier to keep a heavy object sliding than it is to start it sliding in the first place. This is consistent with $\mu_{\mathrm{s}}$ generally being greater than $\mu_{\mathrm{k}}$ (see Table 4–2).

**EXAMPLE 4–16** **Friction: static and kinetic.** Our 10.0-kg mystery box rests on a horizontal floor. The coefficient of static friction is $\mu_{\mathrm{s}} = 0.40$ and the coefficient of kinetic friction is $\mu_{\mathrm{k}} = 0.30$. Determine the force of friction, $F_{\mathrm{fr}}$, acting on the box if a horizontal external applied force $F_{\mathrm{A}}$ is exerted on it of magnitude: (*a*) 0, (*b*) 10 N, (*c*) 20 N, (*d*) 38 N, and (*e*) 40 N.

**APPROACH** We don't know, right off, if we are dealing with static friction or kinetic friction, nor if the box remains at rest or accelerates. We need to draw a free-body diagram, and then determine in each case whether or not the box will move, by using Newton's second law. The forces on the box are gravity $m\vec{\mathbf{g}}$, the normal force exerted by the floor $\vec{\mathbf{F}}_{\mathrm{N}}$, the horizontal applied force $\vec{\mathbf{F}}_{\mathrm{A}}$, and the friction force $\vec{\mathbf{F}}_{\mathrm{fr}}$, as shown in Fig. 4–27.

**SOLUTION** The free-body diagram of the box is shown in Fig. 4–27. In the vertical direction there is no motion, so Newton's second law in the vertical direction gives $\Sigma F_y = ma_y = 0$, which tells us $F_{\mathrm{N}} - mg = 0$. Hence the normal force is

$$F_{\mathrm{N}} = mg = (10.0\,\mathrm{kg})(9.8\,\mathrm{m/s^2}) = 98\,\mathrm{N}.$$

(*a*) Since no external force $F_{\mathrm{A}}$ is applied in this first case, the box doesn't move, and $F_{\mathrm{fr}} = 0$.
(*b*) The force of static friction will oppose any applied force up to a maximum of

$$\mu_{\mathrm{s}} F_{\mathrm{N}} = (0.40)(98\,\mathrm{N}) = 39\,\mathrm{N}.$$

When the applied force is $F_{\mathrm{A}} = 10\,\mathrm{N}$, the box will not move. Since $\Sigma F_x = F_{\mathrm{A}} - F_{\mathrm{fr}} = 0$, then $F_{\mathrm{fr}} = 10\,\mathrm{N}$.
(*c*) An applied force of 20 N is also not sufficient to move the box. Thus $F_{\mathrm{fr}} = 20\,\mathrm{N}$ to balance the applied force.
(*d*) The applied force of 38 N is still not quite large enough to move the box; so the friction force has now increased to 38 N to keep the box at rest.
(*e*) A force of 40 N will start the box moving since it exceeds the maximum force of static friction, $\mu_{\mathrm{s}} F_{\mathrm{N}} = (0.40)(98\,\mathrm{N}) = 39\,\mathrm{N}$. Instead of static friction, we now have kinetic friction, and its magnitude is

$$F_{\mathrm{fr}} = \mu_{\mathrm{k}} F_{\mathrm{N}} = (0.30)(98\,\mathrm{N}) = 29\,\mathrm{N}.$$

There is now a net (horizontal) force on the box of magnitude $F = 40\,\mathrm{N} - 29\,\mathrm{N} = 11\,\mathrm{N}$, so the box will accelerate at a rate

$$a_x = \frac{\Sigma F}{m} = \frac{11\,\mathrm{N}}{10\,\mathrm{kg}} = 1.1\,\mathrm{m/s^2}$$

as long as the applied force is 40 N. Figure 4–28 shows a graph that summarizes this Example.

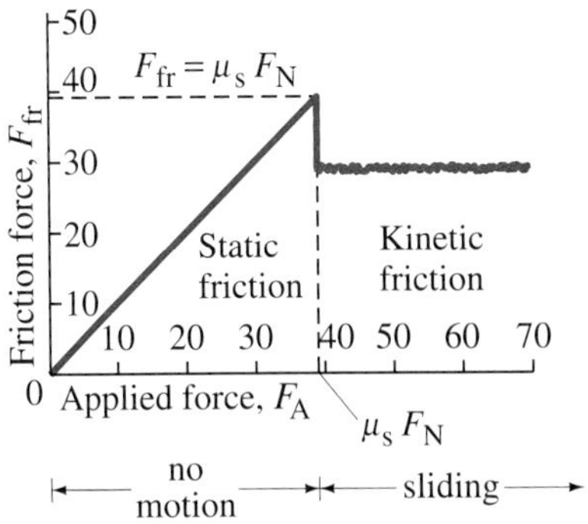


**FIGURE 4–28** Example 4–16. Magnitude of the force of friction as a function of the external force applied to an object initially at rest. As the applied force is increased in magnitude, the force of static friction increases linearly to just match it, until the applied force equals $\mu_{\mathrm{s}} F_{\mathrm{N}}$. If the applied force increases further, the object will begin to move, and the friction force drops to a roughly constant value characteristic of kinetic friction.

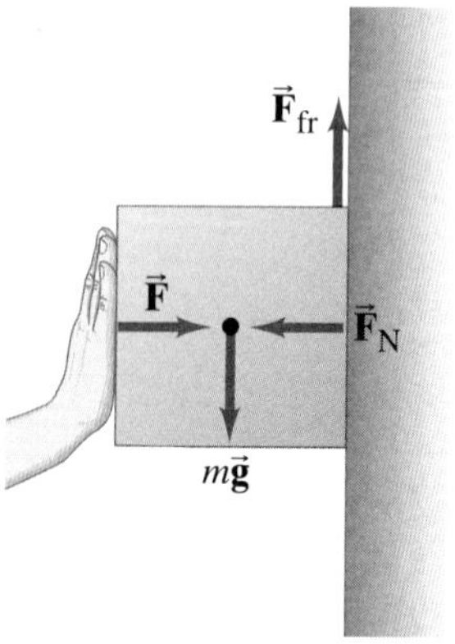


**FIGURE 4–29** Example 4–17.

CONCEPTUAL EXAMPLE 4–17 **A box against a wall.** You can hold a box against a rough wall (Fig. 4–29) and prevent it from slipping down by pressing hard horizontally. How does the application of a horizontal force keep an object from moving vertically?

**RESPONSE** This won't work well if the wall is slippery. You need friction. Even then, if you don't press hard enough, the box will slip. The horizontal force you apply produces a normal force on the box exerted by the wall. The force of gravity $mg$, acting downward on the box, can now be balanced by an upward friction force whose magnitude is proportional to the normal force. The harder you push, the greater $F_N$ is and the greater $F_{fr}$ can be. If you don't press hard enough, then $mg > \mu_s F_N$ and the box begins to slide down.

## Additional Examples

Here are some more worked-out Examples that can help you for solving Problems.

CONCEPTUAL EXAMPLE 4–18 **To push or to pull a sled?** Your little sister wants a ride on her sled. If you are on flat ground, will you exert less force if you push her or pull her? See Figs. 4–30a and b. Assume the same angle $\theta$ in each case.

**RESPONSE** Let us draw free-body diagrams for the sled–sister combination, as shown in Figs. 4–30c and d. They show, for the two cases, the forces exerted by you, $\vec{\mathbf{F}}$ (an unknown), by the snow, $\vec{\mathbf{F}}_N$ and $\vec{\mathbf{F}}_{fr}$, and gravity $m\vec{\mathbf{g}}$. (*a*) If you push her, and $\theta > 0$, there is a vertically downward component to your force. Hence the normal force upward exerted by the ground (Fig. 4–30c) will be larger than $mg$ (where $m$ is the mass of sister plus sled). (*b*) If you pull her, your force has a vertically upward component, so the normal force $F_N$ will be less than $mg$, Fig. 4–30d. Because the friction force is proportional to the normal force, $F_{fr}$ will be less if you pull her. So you exert less force if you pull her.

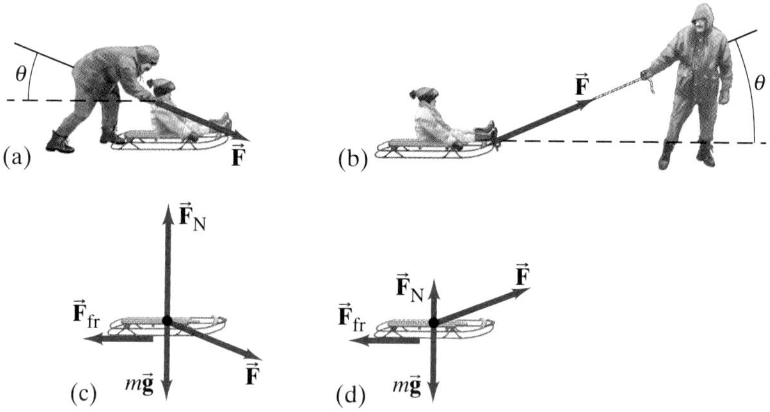


**FIGURE 4–30** Example 4–18.

EXAMPLE 4–19 **Pulling against friction.** A 10.0-kg box is pulled along a horizontal surface by a force $F_P$ of 40.0 N applied at a 30.0° angle. This is like Example 4–11 except now there is friction, and we assume a coefficient of kinetic friction of 0.30. Calculate the acceleration.

**FIGURE 4–31** Example 4–19.

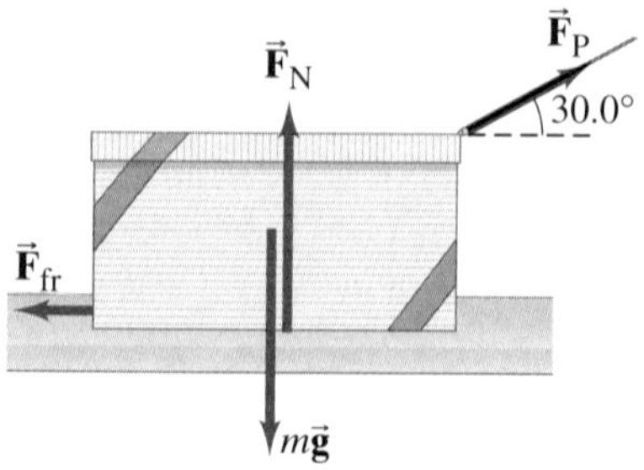


**APPROACH** The free-body diagram is like that in Fig. 4–21, but with one more force, that of friction; see Fig. 4–31.

**SOLUTION** The calculation for the vertical ($y$) direction is just the same as in Example 4–11, where we saw that $F_{Py} = 20.0\,\text{N}$, $F_{Px} = 34.6\,\text{N}$, and the normal force is $F_N = 78.0\,\text{N}$. Now we apply Newton's second law for the horizontal ($x$) direction (positive to the right), and include the friction force:

$$F_{Px} - F_{fr} = ma_x.$$

The friction force is kinetic as long as $F_{fr} = \mu_k F_N$ is less than $F_{Px}\,(= 34.6\,\text{N})$, which it is:

$$F_{fr} = \mu_k F_N = (0.30)(78.0\,\text{N}) = 23.4\,\text{N}.$$

Hence the box does accelerate:

$$a_x = \frac{F_{Px} - F_{fr}}{m} = \frac{34.6\,\text{N} - 23.4\,\text{N}}{10.0\,\text{kg}} = 1.1\,\text{m/s}^2.$$

In the absence of friction, as we saw in Example 4–11, the acceleration would be much greater than this.

**NOTE** Our final answer has only two significant figures because our least significant input value $(\mu_k = 0.30)$ has two.

**EXERCISE B** If $\mu_k F_N$ were greater than $F_{Px}$, what would you conclude?

**EXAMPLE 4–20** **Two boxes and a pulley.** In Fig. 4–32a, two boxes are connected by a cord running over a pulley. The coefficient of kinetic friction between box A and the table is 0.20. We ignore the mass of the cord and pulley and any friction in the pulley, which means we can assume that a force applied to one end of the cord will have the same magnitude at the other end. We wish to find the acceleration, $a$, of the system, which will have the same magnitude for both boxes assuming the cord doesn't stretch. As box B moves down, box A moves to the right.

**APPROACH** We need a free-body diagram for each box, Figs. 4–32b and c, so we can apply Newton's second law to each. The forces on box A are the pulling force of the cord $F_T$, gravity $m_A g$, the normal force exerted by the table $F_N$, and a friction force exerted by the table $F_{fr}$; the forces on box B are gravity $m_B g$, and the cord pulling up, $F_T$.

**SOLUTION** Box A does not move vertically, so Newton's second law tells us the normal force just balances the weight,

$$F_N = m_A g = (5.0\,\text{kg})(9.8\,\text{m/s}^2) = 49\,\text{N}.$$

In the horizontal direction, there are two forces on box A (Fig. 4–32b): $F_T$, the tension in the cord (whose value we don't know), and the force of friction

$$F_{fr} = \mu_k F_N = (0.20)(49\,\text{N}) = 9.8\,\text{N}.$$

The horizontal acceleration is what we wish to find; we use Newton's second law in the $x$ direction, $\Sigma F_{Ax} = m_A a_x$, which becomes (taking the positive direction to the right and setting $a_{Ax} = a$):

$$\Sigma F_{Ax} = F_T - F_{fr} = m_A a. \qquad \text{[box A]}$$

Next consider box B. The force of gravity $m_B g = (2.0\,\text{kg})(9.8\,\text{m/s}^2) = 19.6\,\text{N}$ pulls downward; and the cord pulls upward with a force $F_T$. So we can write Newton's second law for box B (taking the downward direction as positive):

$$\Sigma F_{By} = m_B g - F_T = m_B a. \qquad \text{[box B]}$$

[Notice that if $a \neq 0$, then $F_T$ is not equal to $m_B g$.]

We have two unknowns, $a$ and $F_T$, and we also have two equations. We solve the box A equation for $F_T$:

$$F_T = F_{fr} + m_A a,$$

and substitute this into the box B equation:

$$m_B g - F_{fr} - m_A a = m_B a.$$

Now we solve for $a$ and put in numerical values:

$$a = \frac{m_B g - F_{fr}}{m_A + m_B} = \frac{19.6\,\text{N} - 9.8\,\text{N}}{5.0\,\text{kg} + 2.0\,\text{kg}} = 1.4\,\text{m/s}^2,$$

which is the acceleration of box A to the right, and of box B down.

If we wish, we can calculate $F_T$ using the first equation:

$$F_T = F_{fr} + m_A a = 9.8\,\text{N} + (5.0\,\text{kg})(1.4\,\text{m/s}^2) = 17\,\text{N}.$$

**NOTE** Box B is not in free fall. It does not fall at $a = g$ because an additional force, $F_T$, is acting upward on it.

**FIGURE 4–32** Example 4–20.

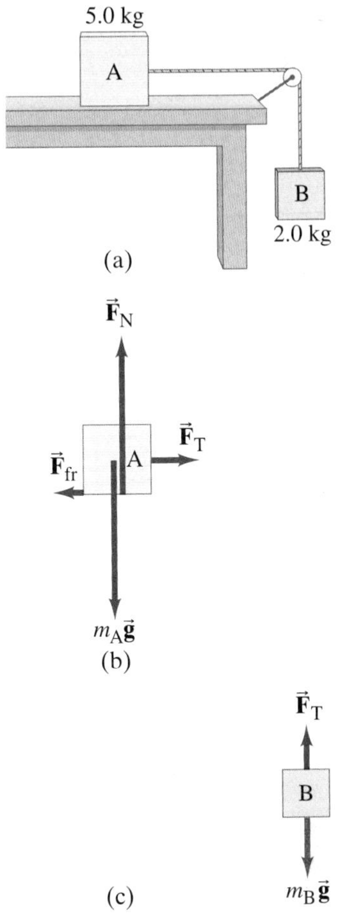


**CAUTION**

*Tension in a cord supporting a falling object may not equal object's weight*

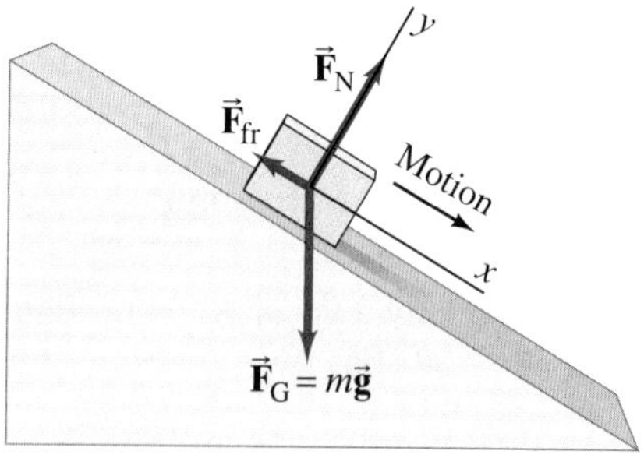


**FIGURE 4–33** Forces on an object sliding down an incline.

## Inclines

**PROBLEM SOLVING**
*Good choice of coordinate system simplifies the calculation*

Now we consider what happens when an object slides down an incline, such as a hill or ramp. Such problems are interesting because gravity is the accelerating force, yet the acceleration is not vertical. Solving problems is usually easier if we choose the *xy* coordinate system so the *x* axis points along the incline and the *y* axis is perpendicular to the incline, as shown in Fig. 4–33. Note also that the normal force is not vertical, but is perpendicular to the sloping surface of the plane in Fig. 4–33.

**EXERCISE C** Is the gravitational force always perpendicular to an inclined plane? Is it always vertical?

**EXERCISE D** Is the normal force always perpendicular to an inclined plane? Is it always vertical?

**PHYSICS APPLIED**
*Skiing*

**EXAMPLE 4–21** **The skier.** The skier in Fig. 4–34 has just begun descending the 30° slope. Assuming the coefficient of kinetic friction is 0.10, calculate (*a*) her acceleration and (*b*) the speed she will reach after 4.0 s.

**APPROACH** We choose the *x* axis along the slope, positive pointing downslope in the direction of the skier's motion. The *y* axis is perpendicular to the surface as shown. The forces acting on the skier are gravity, $\vec{F}_G = m\vec{g}$, which points vertically downward (*not* perpendicular to the slope), and the two forces exerted on her skis by the snow—the normal force perpendicular to the snowy slope (*not* vertical), and the friction force parallel to the surface. These three forces are shown acting at one point in Fig. 4–34b, for convenience, and is our free-body diagram for the skier.

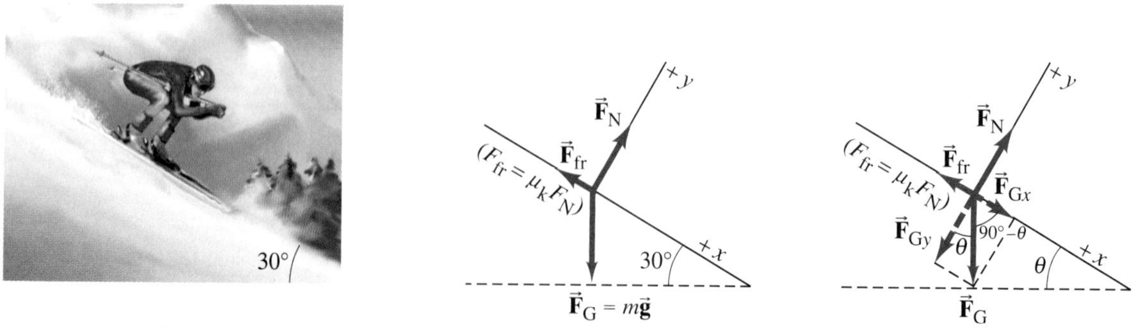


(a) (b) (c)

**FIGURE 4–34** Example 4–21. A skier descending a slope; $\vec{F}_G = m\vec{g}$ is the force of gravity (weight) on the skier.

**SOLUTION** We have to resolve only one vector into components, the weight $\vec{\mathbf{F}}_G$, and its components are shown as dashed lines in Fig. 4–34c. To be general, we use $\theta$ rather than 30° for now. We use the definitions of sine ("side opposite") and cosine ("side adjacent") to obtain the components:

$$F_{Gx} = mg \sin\theta,$$
$$F_{Gy} = -mg \cos\theta.$$

where $F_{Gy}$ is in the negative $y$ direction.
(*a*) To calculate the skier's acceleration down the hill, $a_x$, we apply Newton's second law to the $x$ direction:

$$\Sigma F_x = ma_x$$
$$mg\sin\theta - \mu_k F_N = ma_x$$

where the two forces are the $x$ component of the gravity force ($+x$ direction) and the friction force ($-x$ direction). We want to find the value of $a_x$, but we don't yet know $F_N$ in the last equation. Let's see if we can get $F_N$ from the $y$ component of Newton's second law:

$$\Sigma F_y = ma_y$$
$$F_N - mg\cos\theta = ma_y = 0$$

where we set $a_y = 0$ because there is no motion in the $y$ direction (perpendicular to the slope). Thus we can solve for $F_N$:

$$F_N = mg\cos\theta$$

and we can substitute this into our equation above for $ma_x$:

$$mg\sin\theta - \mu_k(mg\cos\theta) = ma_x.$$

There is an $m$ in each term which can be canceled out. Thus (setting $\theta = 30°$ and $\mu_k = 0.10$):

$$a_x = g\sin 30° - \mu_k g\cos 30°$$
$$= 0.50g - (0.10)(0.866)g = 0.41g.$$

The skier's acceleration is 0.41 times the acceleration of gravity, which in numbers is $a = (0.41)(9.8\,\mathrm{m/s^2}) = 4.0\,\mathrm{m/s^2}$. It is interesting that the mass canceled out here, and so we have the useful conclusion that *the acceleration doesn't depend on the mass*. That such a cancellation sometimes occurs, and thus may give a useful conclusion as well as saving calculation, is a big advantage of working with the algebraic equations and putting in the numbers only at the end.

**PROBLEM SOLVING**
*It is often helpful to put in numbers only at the end*

(*b*) The speed after 4.0 s is found, since the acceleration is constant, by using Eq. 2–11a:

$$v = v_0 + at$$
$$= 0 + (4.0\,\mathrm{m/s^2})(4.0\,\mathrm{s}) = 16\,\mathrm{m/s},$$

where we assumed a start from rest.

In problems involving a slope or "inclined plane," it is common to make an error in the direction of the normal force or in the direction of gravity. The normal force is *not* vertical in Example 4–21. It is perpendicular to the slope or plane. And gravity is *not* perpendicular to the slope or plane—gravity acts vertically downward toward the center of the Earth.

**CAUTION**
*Directions of gravity and the normal force*

## 4–9 Problem Solving—A General Approach

A basic part of a physics course is solving problems effectively. The approach discussed here, though emphasizing Newton's laws, can be applied generally for other topics discussed throughout this book.

### PROBLEM SOLVING In General

1. **Read** and reread written problems carefully. A common error is to skip a word or two when reading, which can completely change the meaning of a problem.
2. **Draw** an accurate picture or diagram of the situation. (This is probably the most overlooked, yet most crucial, part of solving a problem.) Use arrows to represent vectors such as velocity or force, and label the vectors with appropriate symbols. When dealing with forces and applying Newton's laws, make sure to include all forces on a given object, including unknown ones, and make clear what forces act on what object (otherwise you may make an error in determining the *net force* on a particular object). A separate **free-body diagram** needs to be drawn for each object involved, and it must show *all* the forces acting on a given object (and only on that object). Do not show forces that act on other objects.
3. Choose a convenient *xy* **coordinate system** (one that makes your calculations easier, such as one axis in the direction of the acceleration). Vectors are to be resolved into components along the coordinate axes. When using Newton's second law, apply $\Sigma\vec{\mathbf{F}} = m\vec{\mathbf{a}}$ separately to $x$ and $y$ components, remembering that $x$ direction forces are related to $a_x$, and similarly for $y$. If more than one object is involved, you can choose different (convenient) coordinate systems for each.
4. List the knowns and the unknowns (what you are trying to determine), and decide what you need in order to find the unknowns. For problems in the present Chapter, we use Newton's laws. More generally, it may help to see if one or more **relationships** (or **equations**) relate the unknowns to the knowns. But be sure each relationship is applicable in the given case. It is very important to know the limitations of each formula or relationship—when it is valid and when not. In this book, the more general equations have been given numbers, but even these can have a limited range of validity (often stated in brackets to the right of the equation).
5. Try to solve the problem approximately, to see if it is doable (to check if enough information has been given) and reasonable. Use your intuition, and make **rough calculations**—see "Order of Magnitude Estimating" in Section 1–7. A rough calculation, or a reasonable guess about what the range of final answers might be, is very useful. And a rough calculation can be checked against the final answer to catch errors in calculation, such as in a decimal point or the powers of 10.
6. **Solve** the problem, which may include algebraic manipulation of equations and/or numerical calculations. Recall the mathematical rule that you need as many independent equations as you have unknowns; if you have three unknowns, for example, then you need three independent equations. It is usually best to work out the algebra symbolically before putting in the numbers. Why? Because (*a*) you can then solve a whole class of similar problems with different numerical values; (*b*) you can check your result for cases already understood (say, $\theta = 0°$ or $90°$); (*c*) there may be cancellations or other simplifications; (*d*) there is usually less chance for numerical error; and (*e*) you may gain better insight into the problem.
7. Be sure to keep track of **units**, for they can serve as a check (they must balance on both sides of any equation).
8. Again consider if your answer is **reasonable.** The use of dimensional analysis, described in Section 1–8, can also serve as a check for many problems.

## Summary

**Newton's three laws of motion** are the basic classical laws describing motion.

**Newton's first law** (the **law of inertia**) states that if the net force on an object is zero, an object originally at rest remains at rest, and an object in motion remains in motion in a straight line with constant velocity.

**Newton's second law** states that the acceleration of an object is directly proportional to the net force acting on it, and inversely proportional to its mass:

$$\Sigma\vec{\mathbf{F}} = m\vec{\mathbf{a}}. \quad \textbf{(4–1)}$$

Newton's second law is one of the most important and fundamental laws in classical physics.

**Newton's third law** states that whenever one object exerts a force on a second object, the second object always exerts a force on the first object which is equal in magnitude but opposite in direction:

$$\vec{\mathbf{F}}_{AB} = -\vec{\mathbf{F}}_{BA} \qquad \textbf{(4–2)}$$

where $\vec{\mathbf{F}}_{BA}$ is the force on object B exerted by object A.

The tendency of an object to resist a change in its motion is called **inertia**. **Mass** is a measure of the inertia of an object.

**Weight** refers to the **gravitational force** on an object, and is equal to the product of the object's mass $m$ and the acceleration of gravity $\vec{\mathbf{g}}$:

$$\vec{\mathbf{F}}_G = m\vec{\mathbf{g}}. \qquad \textbf{(4–3)}$$

**Force**, which is a vector, can be considered as a push or pull; or, from Newton's second law, force can be defined as an action capable of giving rise to acceleration. The **net force** on an object is the vector sum of all forces acting on it.

When two objects slide over one another, the force of friction that each object exerts on the other can be written approximately as $F_{fr} = \mu_k F_N$, where $F_N$ is the **normal force** (the force each object exerts on the other perpendicular to their contact surfaces), and $\mu_k$ is the coefficient of **kinetic friction**. If the objects are at rest relative to each other, then $F_{fr}$ is just large enough to hold them at rest and satisfies the inequality $F_{fr} < \mu_s F_N$, where $\mu_s$ is the coefficient of **static friction**.

For solving problems involving the forces on one or more objects, it is essential to draw a **free-body diagram** for each object, showing all the forces acting on only that object. Newton's second law can be applied to the vector components for each object.

## Questions

1. Why does a child in a wagon seem to fall backward when you give the wagon a sharp pull forward?
2. A box rests on the (frictionless) bed of a truck. The truck driver starts the truck and accelerates forward. The box immediately starts to slide toward the rear of the truck bed. Discuss the motion of the box, in terms of Newton's laws, as seen (*a*) by Mary standing on the ground beside the truck, and (*b*) by Chris who is riding on the truck (Fig. 4–35).

**FIGURE 4–35** Question 2.

3. If the acceleration of an object is zero, are no forces acting on it? Explain.
4. Only one force acts on an object. Can the object have zero acceleration? Can it have zero velocity? Explain.
5. When a golf ball is dropped to the pavement, it bounces back up. (*a*) Is a force needed to make it bounce back up? (*b*) If so, what exerts the force?
6. If you walk along a log floating on a lake, why does the log move in the opposite direction?
7. Why might your foot hurt if you kick a heavy desk or a wall?
8. When you are running and want to stop quickly, you must decelerate quickly. (*a*) What is the origin of the force that causes you to stop? (*b*) Estimate (using your own experience) the maximum rate of deceleration of a person running at top speed to come to rest.
9. A stone hangs by a fine thread from the ceiling, and a section of the same thread dangles from the bottom of the stone (Fig. 4–36). If a person gives a sharp pull on the dangling thread, where is the thread likely to break: below the stone or above it? What if the person gives a slow and steady pull? Explain your answers.

**FIGURE 4–36** Question 9.

10. The force of gravity on a 2-kg rock is twice as great as that on a 1-kg rock. Why then doesn't the heavier rock fall faster?
11. Would a spring scale carried to the Moon give accurate results if the scale had been calibrated (*a*) in pounds, or (*b*) in kilograms?
12. You pull a box with a constant force across a frictionless table using an attached rope held horizontally. If you now pull the rope with the same force at an angle to the horizontal (with the box remaining flat on the table), does the acceleration of the box (*a*) remain the same, (*b*) increase, or (*c*) decrease? Explain.
13. When an object falls freely under the influence of gravity there is a net force $mg$ exerted on it by the Earth. Yet by Newton's third law the object exerts an equal and opposite force on the Earth. Why doesn't the Earth move?
14. Compare the effort (or force) needed to lift a 10-kg object when you are on the Moon with the force needed to lift it on Earth. Compare the force needed to throw a 2-kg object horizontally with a given speed on the Moon and on Earth.

**15.** According to Newton's third law, each team in a tug of war (Fig. 4–37) pulls with equal force on the other team. What, then, determines which team will win?

**FIGURE 4–37** Question 15. A tug of war. Describe the forces on each of the teams and on the rope.

**16.** A person exerts an upward force of 40 N to hold a bag of groceries. Describe the "reaction" force (Newton's third law) by stating (*a*) its magnitude, (*b*) its direction, (*c*) *on* what object it is exerted, and (*d*) *by* what object it is exerted.

**17.** When you stand still on the ground, how large a force does the ground exert on you? Why doesn't this force make you rise up into the air?

**18.** Whiplash sometimes results from an automobile accident when the victim's car is struck violently from the rear. Explain why the head of the victim seems to be thrown backward in this situation. Is it really?

**19.** A heavy crate rests on the bed of a flatbed truck. When the truck accelerates, the crate remains where it is on the truck, so it, too, accelerates. What force causes the crate to accelerate?

**20.** A block is given a push so that it slides up a ramp. After the block reaches its highest point, it slides back down but the magnitude of its acceleration is less on the descent than on the ascent. Why?

**21.** What would your bathroom scale read if you weighed yourself on an inclined plane? Assume the mechanism functions properly, even at an angle.

## Problems

### 4–4 to 4–6 Newton's Laws, Gravitational Force, Normal Force

1. (I) What force is needed to accelerate a child on a sled (total mass = 60.0 kg) at $1.25\ \mathrm{m/s^2}$?

2. (I) A net force of 265 N accelerates a bike and rider at $2.30\ \mathrm{m/s^2}$. What is the mass of the bike and rider together?

3. (I) How much tension must a rope withstand if it is used to accelerate a 960-kg car horizontally along a frictionless surface at $1.20\ \mathrm{m/s^2}$?

4. (I) What is the weight of a 76-kg astronaut (*a*) on Earth, (*b*) on the Moon $(g = 1.7\ \mathrm{m/s^2})$, (*c*) on Mars $(g = 3.7\ \mathrm{m/s^2})$, (*d*) in outer space traveling with constant velocity?

5. (II) A 20.0-kg box rests on a table. (*a*) What is the weight of the box and the normal force acting on it? (*b*) A 10.0-kg box is placed on top of the 20.0-kg box, as shown in Fig. 4–38. Determine the normal force that the table exerts on the 20.0-kg box and the normal force that the 20.0-kg box exerts on the 10.0-kg box.

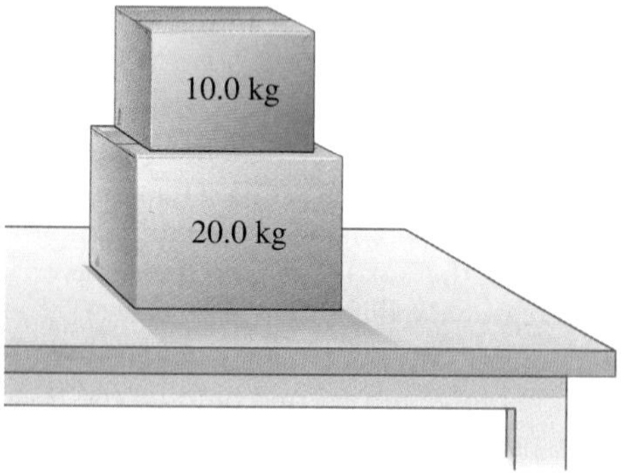


**FIGURE 4–38** Problem 5.

6. (II) What average force is required to stop an 1100-kg car in 8.0 s if the car is traveling at 95 km/h?

7. (II) What average force is needed to accelerate a 7.00-gram pellet from rest to 125 m/s over a distance of 0.800 m along the barrel of a rifle?

8. (II) A fisherman yanks a fish vertically out of the water with an acceleration of $2.5\ \mathrm{m/s^2}$ using very light fishing line that has a breaking strength of 22 N. The fisherman unfortunately loses the fish as the line snaps. What can you say about the mass of the fish?

9. (II) A 0.140-kg baseball traveling 35.0 m/s strikes the catcher's mitt, which, in bringing the ball to rest, recoils backward 11.0 cm. What was the average force applied by the ball on the glove?

10. (II) How much tension must a rope withstand if it is used to accelerate a 1200-kg car vertically upward at $0.80\ \mathrm{m/s^2}$?

11. (II) A particular race car can cover a quarter-mile track (402 m) in 6.40 s starting from a standstill. Assuming the acceleration is constant, how many "*g*'s" does the driver experience? If the combined mass of the driver and race car is 485 kg, what horizontal force must the road exert on the tires?

12. (II) A 12.0-kg bucket is lowered vertically by a rope in which there is 163 N of tension at a given instant. What is the acceleration of the bucket? Is it up or down?

13. (II) An elevator (mass 4850 kg) is to be designed so that the maximum acceleration is $0.0680g$. What are the maximum and minimum forces the motor should exert on the supporting cable?

14. (II) A 75-kg petty thief wants to escape from a third-story jail window. Unfortunately, a makeshift rope made of sheets tied together can support a mass of only 58 kg. How might the thief use this "rope" to escape? Give a quantitative answer.

15. (II) A person stands on a bathroom scale in a motionless elevator. When the elevator begins to move, the scale briefly reads only 0.75 of the person's regular weight. Calculate the acceleration of the elevator, and find the direction of acceleration.

16. (II) The cable supporting a 2125-kg elevator has a maximum strength of 21,750 N. What maximum upward acceleration can it give the elevator without breaking?

17. (II) (*a*) What is the acceleration of two falling sky divers (mass 132 kg including parachute) when the upward force of air resistance is equal to one-fourth of their weight? (*b*) After popping open the parachute, the divers descend leisurely to the ground at constant speed. What now is the force of air resistance on the sky divers and their parachute? See Fig. 4–39.

**FIGURE 4–39** Problem 17.

18. (III) A person jumps from the roof of a house 3.9-m high. When he strikes the ground below, he bends his knees so that his torso decelerates over an approximate distance of 0.70 m. If the mass of his torso (excluding legs) is 42 kg, find (*a*) his velocity just before his feet strike the ground, and (*b*) the average force exerted on his torso by his legs during deceleration.

## 4–7 Newton's Laws and Vectors

19. (I) A box weighing 77.0 N rests on a table. A rope tied to the box runs vertically upward over a pulley and a weight is hung from the other end (Fig. 4–40). Determine the force that the table exerts on the box if the weight hanging on the other side of the pulley weighs (*a*) 30.0 N, (*b*) 60.0 N, and (*c*) 90.0 N.

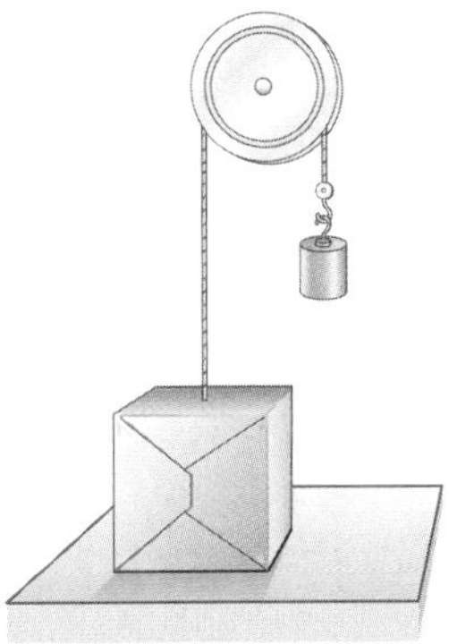

**FIGURE 4–40** Problem 19.

20. (I) Draw the free-body diagram for a basketball player (*a*) just before leaving the ground on a jump, and (*b*) while in the air. See Fig. 4–41.

**FIGURE 4–41** Problem 20.

21. (I) Sketch the free-body diagram of a baseball (*a*) at the moment it is hit by the bat, and again (*b*) after it has left the bat and is flying toward the outfield.

22. (I) A 650-N force acts in a northwesterly direction. A second 650-N force must be exerted in what direction so that the resultant of the two forces points westward? Illustrate your answer with a vector diagram.

23. (II) Arlene is to walk across a "high wire" strung horizontally between two buildings 10.0 m apart. The sag in the rope when she is at the midpoint is 10.0°, as shown in Fig. 4–42. If her mass is 50.0 kg, what is the tension in the rope at this point?

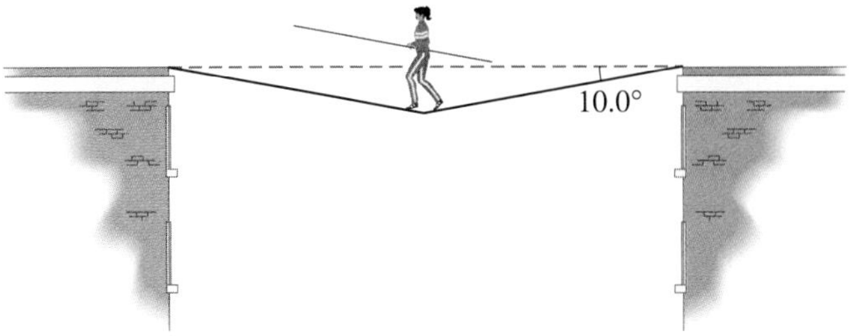


**FIGURE 4–42** Problem 23.

24. (II) The two forces $\vec{\mathbf{F}}_1$ and $\vec{\mathbf{F}}_2$ shown in Fig. 4–43a and b (looking down) act on a 27.0-kg object on a frictionless tabletop. If $F_1 = 10.2\text{ N}$ and $F_2 = 16.0\text{ N}$, find the net force on the object and its acceleration for (*a*) and (*b*).

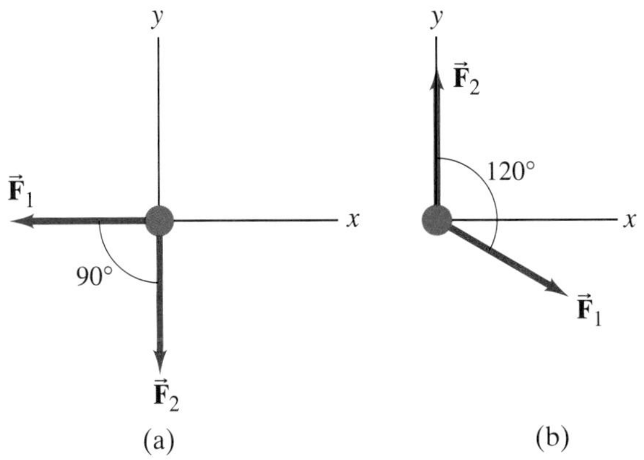


**FIGURE 4–43** Problem 24.

25. (II) One 3.2-kg paint bucket is hanging by a massless cord from another 3.2-kg paint bucket, also hanging by a massless cord, as shown in Fig. 4–44. (*a*) If the buckets are at rest, what is the tension in each cord? (*b*) If the two buckets are pulled upward with an acceleration of $1.60\text{ m/s}^2$ by the upper cord, calculate the tension in each cord.

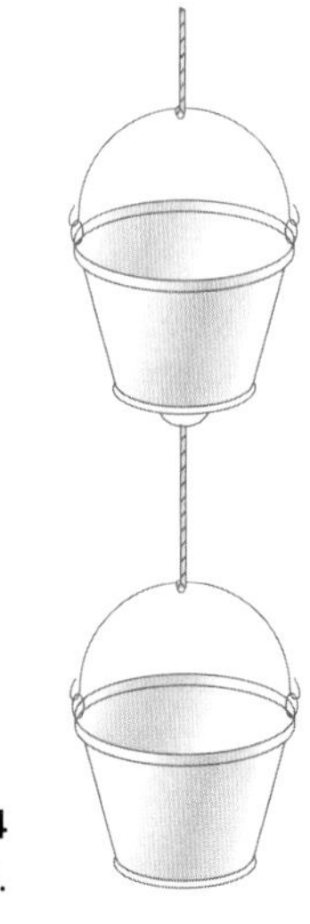

**FIGURE 4–44** Problem 25.

26. (II) A person pushes a 14.0-kg lawn mower at constant speed with a force of $F = 88.0\,\text{N}$ directed along the handle, which is at an angle of 45.0° to the horizontal (Fig. 4–45). (*a*) Draw the free-body diagram showing all forces acting on the mower. Calculate (*b*) the horizontal friction force on the mower, then (*c*) the normal force exerted vertically upward on the mower by the ground. (*d*) What force must the person exert on the lawn mower to accelerate it from rest to 1.5 m/s in 2.5 seconds, assuming the same friction force?

**FIGURE 4–45** Problem 26.

27. (II) Two snowcats tow a housing unit to a new location at McMurdo Base, Antarctica, as shown in Fig. 4–46. The sum of the forces $\vec{F}_A$ and $\vec{F}_B$ exerted on the unit by the horizontal cables is parallel to the line L, and $F_A = 4500\,\text{N}$. Determine $F_B$ and the magnitude of $\vec{F}_A + \vec{F}_B$.

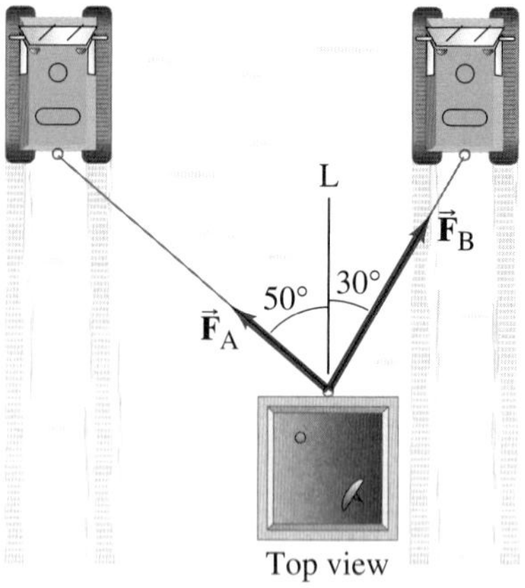


**FIGURE 4–46** Problem 27.

28. (II) A train locomotive is pulling two cars of the same mass behind it, Fig. 4–47. Determine the ratio of the tension in the coupling between the locomotive and the first car ($F_{T1}$), to that between the first car and the second car ($F_{T2}$), for any nonzero acceleration of the train.

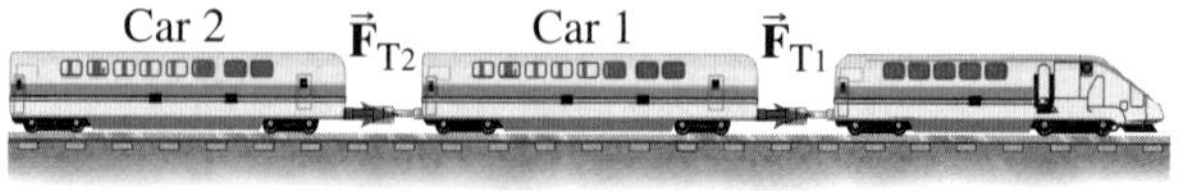


**FIGURE 4–47** Problem 28.

29. (II) A window washer pulls herself upward using the bucket–pulley apparatus shown in Fig. 4–48. (*a*) How hard must she pull downward to raise herself slowly at constant speed? (*b*) If she increases this force by 15%, what will her acceleration be? The mass of the person plus the bucket is 65 kg.

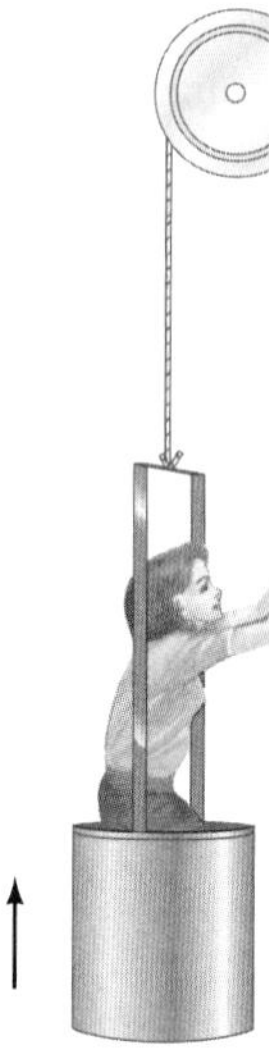

**FIGURE 4–48**
Problem 29.

30. (II) At the instant a race began, a 65-kg sprinter exerted a force of 720 N on the starting block at a 22° angle with respect to the ground. (*a*) What was the horizontal acceleration of the sprinter? (*b*) If the force was exerted for 0.32 s, with what speed did the sprinter leave the starting block?

31. (II) Figure 4–49 shows a block (mass $m_A$) on a smooth horizontal surface, connected by a thin cord that passes over a pulley to a second block ($m_B$), which hangs vertically. (*a*) Draw a free-body diagram for each block, showing the force of gravity on each, the force (tension) exerted by the cord, and any normal force. (*b*) Apply Newton's second law to find formulas for the acceleration of the system and for the tension in the cord. Ignore friction and the masses of the pulley and cord.

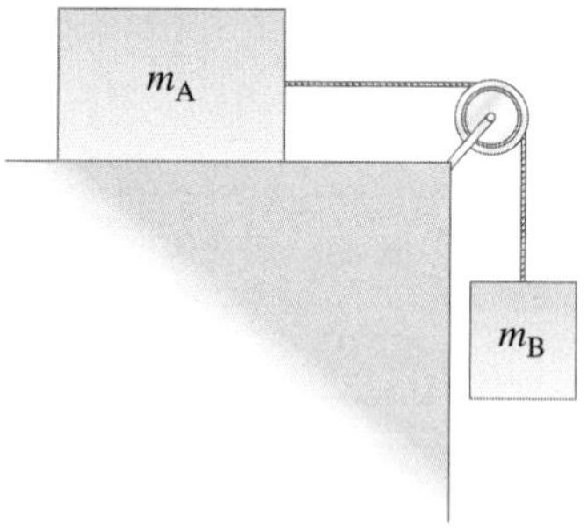


**FIGURE 4–49**
Problem 31. Mass $m_A$ rests on a smooth horizontal surface, $m_B$ hangs vertically.

32. (II) A pair of fuzzy dice is hanging by a string from your rearview mirror. While you are accelerating from a stoplight to 28 m/s in 6.0 s, what angle $\theta$ does the string make with the vertical? See Fig. 4–50.

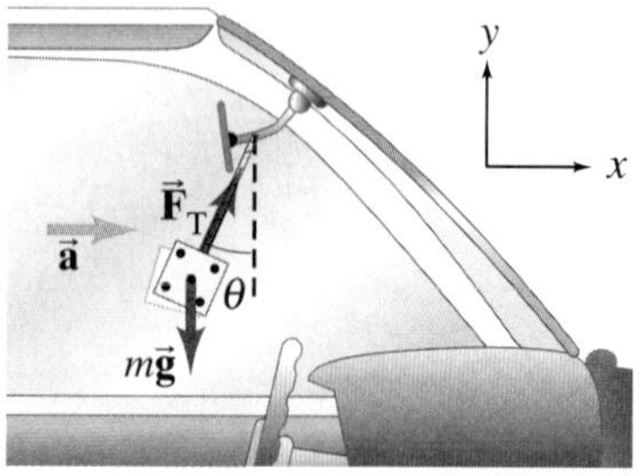


**FIGURE 4–50**
Problem 32.

33. (III) Three blocks on a frictionless horizontal surface are in contact with each other, as shown in Fig. 4–51. A force $\vec{\mathbf{F}}$ is applied to block A (mass $m_A$). (*a*) Draw a free-body diagram for each block. Determine (*b*) the acceleration of the system (in terms of $m_A$, $m_B$, and $m_C$), (*c*) the net force on each block, and (*d*) the force of contact that each block exerts on its neighbor. (*e*) If $m_A = m_B = m_C = 12.0$ kg and $F = 96.0$ N, give numerical answers to (*b*), (*c*), and (*d*). Do your answers make sense intuitively?

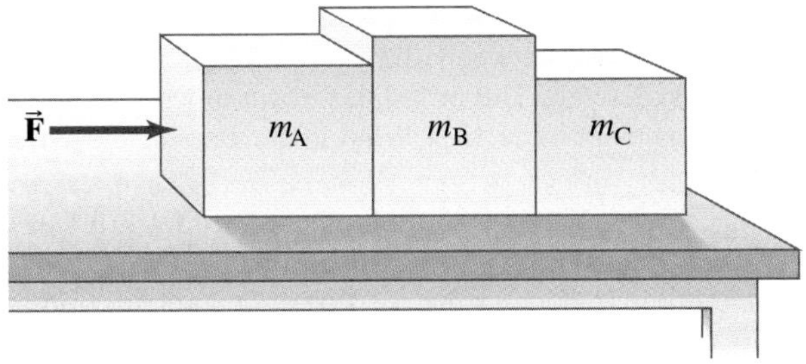


**FIGURE 4–51** Problem 33.

34. (III) The two masses shown in Fig. 4–52 are each initially 1.80 m above the ground, and the massless frictionless pulley is 4.8 m above the ground. What maximum height does the lighter object reach after the system is released? [*Hint*: First determine the acceleration of the lighter mass and then its velocity at the moment the heavier one hits the ground. This is its "launch" speed. Assume it doesn't hit the pulley.]

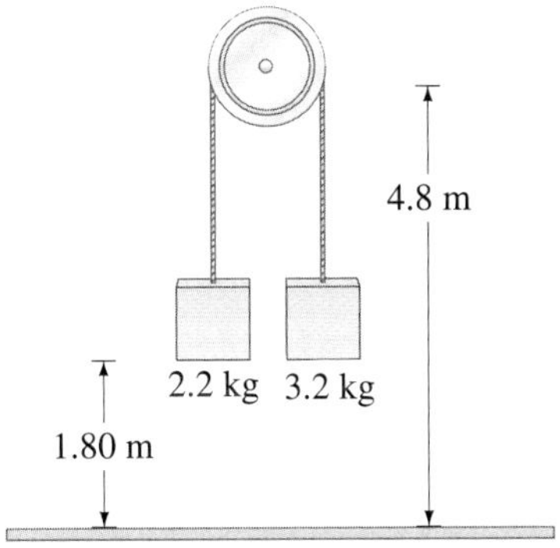


**FIGURE 4–52** Problem 34.

35. (III) Suppose two boxes on a frictionless table are connected by a heavy cord of mass 1.0 kg. Calculate the acceleration of each box and the tension at each end of the cord, using the free-body diagrams shown in Fig. 4–53. Assume $F_P = 40.0$ N, and ignore sagging of the cord. Compare your results to Example 4–12 and Fig. 4–22.

## 4–8 Newton's Laws with Friction; Inclines

36. (I) If the coefficient of kinetic friction between a 35-kg crate and the floor is 0.30, what horizontal force is required to move the crate at a steady speed across the floor? What horizontal force is required if $\mu_k$ is zero?

37. (I) A force of 48.0 N is required to start a 5.0-kg box moving across a horizontal concrete floor. (*a*) What is the coefficient of static friction between the box and the floor? (*b*) If the 48.0-N force continues, the box accelerates at $0.70\ \mathrm{m/s^2}$. What is the coefficient of kinetic friction?

38. (I) Suppose that you are standing on a train accelerating at 0.20*g*. What minimum coefficient of static friction must exist between your feet and the floor if you are not to slide?

39. (I) What is the maximum acceleration a car can undergo if the coefficient of static friction between the tires and the ground is 0.80?

40. (II) The coefficient of static friction between hard rubber and normal street pavement is about 0.8. On how steep a hill (maximum angle) can you leave a car parked?

41. (II) A 15.0-kg box is released on a 32° incline and accelerates down the incline at $0.30\ \mathrm{m/s^2}$. Find the friction force impeding its motion. What is the coefficient of kinetic friction?

42. (II) A car can decelerate at $-4.80\ \mathrm{m/s^2}$ without skidding when coming to rest on a level road. What would its deceleration be if the road were inclined at 13° uphill? Assume the same static friction coefficient.

43. (II) (*a*) A box sits at rest on a rough 30° inclined plane. Draw the free-body diagram, showing all the forces acting on the box. (*b*) How would the diagram change if the box were sliding down the plane? (*c*) How would it change if the box were sliding up the plane after an initial shove?

44. (II) Drag-race tires in contact with an asphalt surface have a very high coefficient of static friction. Assuming a constant acceleration and no slipping of tires, estimate the coefficient of static friction needed for a drag racer to cover 1.0 km in 12 s, starting from rest.

45. (II) The coefficient of kinetic friction for a 22-kg bobsled on a track is 0.10. What force is required to push it down a 6.0° incline and achieve a speed of 60 km/h at the end of 75 m?

46. (II) For the system of Fig. 4–32 (Example 4–20) how large a mass would box A have to have to prevent any motion from occurring? Assume $\mu_s = 0.30$.

47. (II) A box is given a push so that it slides across the floor. How far will it go, given that the coefficient of kinetic friction is 0.20 and the push imparts an initial speed of 4.0 m/s?

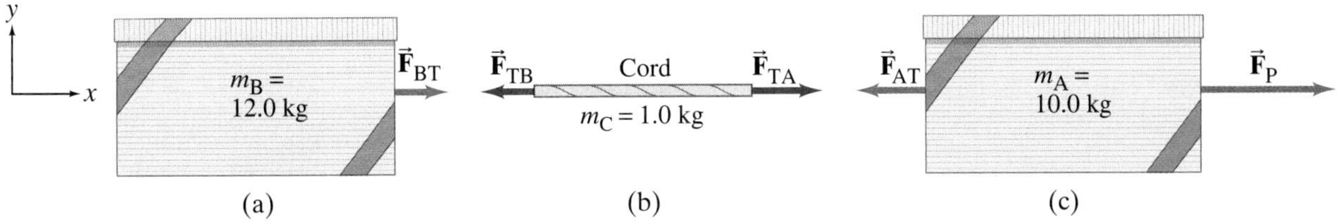


**FIGURE 4–53** Problem 35. Free-body diagrams for two boxes on a table connected by a heavy cord, and being pulled to the right as in Fig. 4–22a. Vertical forces, $\vec{\mathbf{F}}_N$ and $\vec{\mathbf{F}}_G$, are not shown.

48. (II) Two crates, of mass 75 kg and 110 kg, are in contact and at rest on a horizontal surface (Fig. 4–54). A 620-N force is exerted on the 75-kg crate. If the coefficient of kinetic friction is 0.15, calculate (*a*) the acceleration of the system, and (*b*) the force that each crate exerts on the other. (*c*) Repeat with the crates reversed.

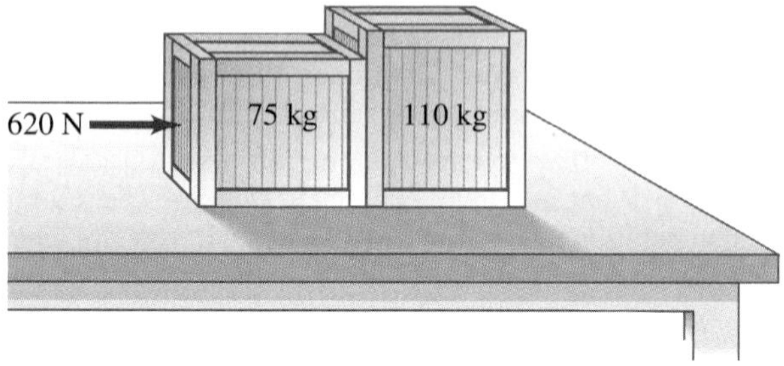


**FIGURE 4–54** Problem 48.

49. (II) A flatbed truck is carrying a heavy crate. The coefficient of static friction between the crate and the bed of the truck is 0.75. What is the maximum rate at which the driver can decelerate and still avoid having the crate slide against the cab of the truck?

50. (II) On an icy day, you worry about parking your car in your driveway, which has an incline of 12°. Your neighbor's driveway has an incline of 9.0°, and the driveway across the street is at 6.0°. The coefficient of static friction between tire rubber and ice is 0.15. Which driveway(s) will be safe to park in?

51. (II) A child slides down a slide with a 28° incline, and at the bottom her speed is precisely half what it would have been if the slide had been frictionless. Calculate the coefficient of kinetic friction between the slide and the child.

52. (II) The carton shown in Fig. 4–55 lies on a plane tilted at an angle $\theta = 22.0°$ to the horizontal, with $\mu_k = 0.12$. (*a*) Determine the acceleration of the carton as it slides down the plane. (*b*) If the carton starts from rest 9.30 m up the plane from its base, what will be the carton's speed when it reaches the bottom of the incline?

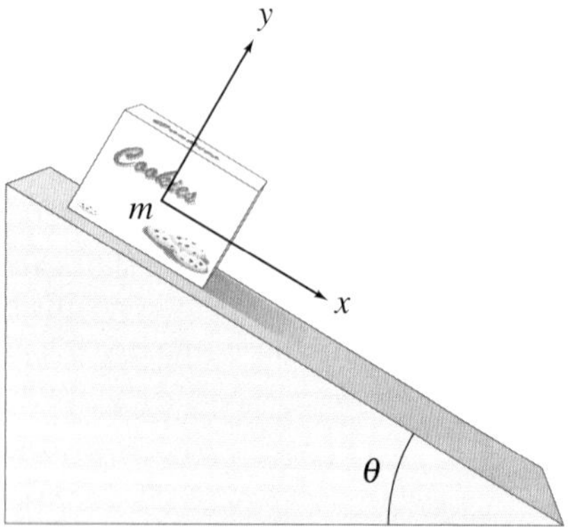


**FIGURE 4–55** Carton on inclined plane. Problems 52 and 53.

53. (II) A carton is given an initial speed of 3.0 m/s up the 22.0° plane shown in Fig. 4–55. (*a*) How far up the plane will it go? (*b*) How much time elapses before it returns to its starting point? Ignore friction.

54. (II) A roller coaster reaches the top of the steepest hill with a speed of 6.0 km/h. It then descends the hill, which is at an average angle of 45° and is 45.0 m long. Estimate its speed when it reaches the bottom. Assume $\mu_k = 0.18$.

55. (II) An 18.0-kg box is released on a 37.0° incline and accelerates down the incline at $0.270 \text{ m/s}^2$. Find the friction force impeding its motion. How large is the coefficient of kinetic friction?

56. (II) A small box is held in place against a rough wall by someone pushing on it with a force directed upward at 28° above the horizontal. The coefficients of static and kinetic friction between the box and wall are 0.40 and 0.30, respectively. The box slides down unless the applied force has magnitude 13 N. What is the mass of the box?

57. (II) Piles of snow on slippery roofs can become dangerous projectiles as they melt. Consider a chunk of snow at the ridge of a roof with a pitch of 30°. (*a*) What is the minimum value of the coefficient of static friction that will keep the snow from sliding down? (*b*) As the snow begins to melt, the coefficient of static friction decreases and the snow eventually slips. Assuming that the distance from the chunk to the edge of the roof is 5.0 m and the coefficient of kinetic friction is 0.20, calculate the speed of the snow chunk when it slides off the roof. (*c*) If the edge of the roof is 10.0 m above ground, what is the speed of the snow when it hits the ground?

58. (III) (*a*) Show that the minimum stopping distance for an automobile traveling at speed $v$ is equal to $v^2/2\mu_s g$, where $\mu_s$ is the coefficient of static friction between the tires and the road, and $g$ is the acceleration of gravity. (*b*) What is this distance for a 1200-kg car traveling 95 km/h if $\mu_s = 0.75$?

59. (III) A coffee cup on the dashboard of a car slides forward on the dash when the driver decelerates from 45 km/h to rest in 3.5 s or less, but not if he decelerates in a longer time. What is the coefficient of static friction between the cup and the dash?

60. (III) A small block of mass $m$ is given an initial speed $v_0$ up a ramp inclined at angle $\theta$ to the horizontal. It travels a distance $d$ up the ramp and comes to rest. Determine a formula for the coefficient of kinetic friction between block and ramp.

61. (III) The 75-kg climber in Fig. 4–56 is supported in the "chimney" by the friction forces exerted on his shoes and back. The static coefficients of friction between his shoes and the wall, and between his back and the wall, are 0.80 and 0.60, respectively. What is the minimum normal force he must exert? Assume the walls are vertical and that friction forces are both at a maximum. Ignore his grip on the rope.

**FIGURE 4–56** Problem 61.

62. (III) Boxes are moved on a conveyor belt from where they are filled to the packing station 11.0 m away. The belt is initially stationary and must finish with zero speed. The most rapid transit is accomplished if the belt accelerates for half the distance, then decelerates for the final half of the trip. If the coefficient of static friction between a box and the belt is 0.60, what is the minimum transit time for each box?

63. (III) A block (mass $m_1$) lying on a frictionless inclined plane is connected to a mass $m_2$ by a massless cord passing over a pulley, as shown in Fig. 4–57. (*a*) Determine a formula for the acceleration of the system of the two blocks in terms of $m_1$, $m_2$, $\theta$ and $g$. (*b*) What conditions apply to masses $m_1$ and $m_2$ for the acceleration to be in one direction (say, $m_1$ down the plane), or in the opposite direction?

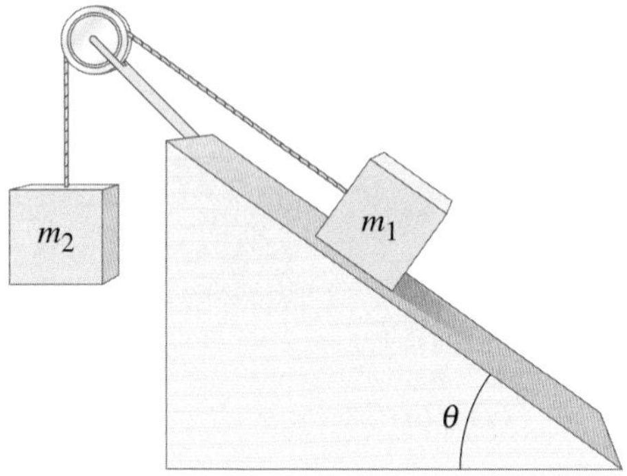


**FIGURE 4–57** Problems 63 and 64.

64. (III) (*a*) Suppose the coefficient of kinetic friction between $m_1$ and the plane in Fig. 4–57 is $\mu_k = 0.15$, and that $m_1 = m_2 = 2.7$ kg. As $m_2$ moves down, determine the magnitude of the acceleration of $m_1$ and $m_2$, given $\theta = 25°$. (*b*) What smallest value of $\mu_k$ will keep this system from accelerating?

65. (III) A bicyclist of mass 65 kg (including the bicycle) can coast down a 6.0° hill at a steady speed of 6.0 km/h because of air resistance. How much force must be applied to climb the hill at the same speed and same air resistance?

## General Problems

66. According to a simplified model of a mammalian heart, at each pulse approximately 20 g of blood is accelerated from 0.25 m/s to 0.35 m/s during a period of 0.10 s. What is the magnitude of the force exerted by the heart muscle?

67. A person has a reasonable chance of surviving an automobile crash if the deceleration is no more than 30 "*g*'s." Calculate the force on a 70-kg person undergoing this acceleration. What distance is traveled if the person is brought to rest at this rate from 100 km/h?

68. (*a*) If the horizontal acceleration produced by an earthquake is *a*, and if an object is going to "hold its place" on the ground, show that the coefficient of static friction with the ground must be at least $\mu_s = a/g$. (*b*) The famous Loma Prieta earthquake that stopped the 1989 World Series produced ground accelerations of up to 4.0 m/s$^2$ in the San Francisco Bay Area. Would a chair have started to slide on a linoleum floor with coefficient of static friction 0.25?

69. An 1150-kg car pulls a 450-kg trailer. The car exerts a horizontal force of $3.8 \times 10^3$ N against the ground in order to accelerate. What force does the car exert on the trailer? Assume an effective friction coefficient of 0.15 for the trailer.

70. Police investigators, examining the scene of an accident involving two cars, measure 72-m-long skid marks of one of the cars, which nearly came to a stop before colliding. The coefficient of kinetic friction between rubber and the pavement is about 0.80. Estimate the initial speed of that car assuming a level road.

71. A car starts rolling down a 1-in-4 hill (1-in-4 means that for each 4 m traveled along the road, the elevation change is 1 m). How fast is it going when it reaches the bottom after traveling 55 m? (*a*) Ignore friction. (*b*) Assume an effective coefficient of friction equal to 0.10.

72. A 2.0-kg purse is dropped from the top of the Leaning Tower of Pisa and falls 55 m before reaching the ground with a speed of 29 m/s. What was the average force of air resistance?

73. A cyclist is coasting at a steady speed of 12 m/s but enters a muddy stretch where the effective coefficient of friction is 0.60. Will the cyclist emerge from the muddy stretch without having to pedal if the mud lasts for 11 m? If so, what will be the speed upon emerging?

74. A city planner is working on the redesign of a hilly portion of a city. An important consideration is how steep the roads can be so that even low-powered cars can get up the hills without slowing down. A particular small car, with a mass of 1100 kg, can accelerate on a level road from rest to 21 m/s (75 km/h) in 14.0 s. Using these data, calculate the maximum steepness of a hill.

75. Francesca, who likes physics experiments, dangles her watch from a thin piece of string while the jetliner she is in takes off from JFK Airport (Fig. 4–58). She notices that the string makes an angle of 25° with respect to the vertical as the aircraft accelerates for takeoff, which takes about 18 s. Estimate the takeoff speed of the aircraft.

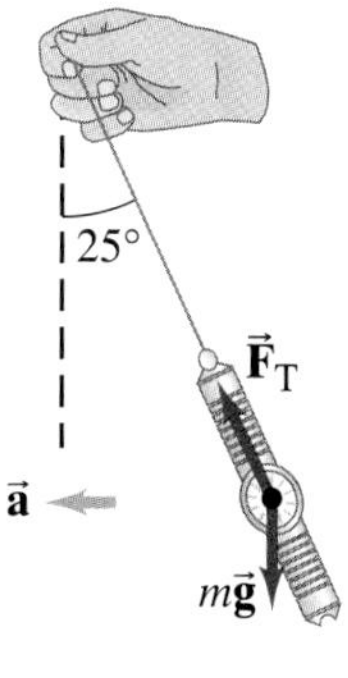


**FIGURE 4–58** Problem 75.

76. A 28.0-kg block is connected to an empty 1.35-kg bucket by a cord running over a frictionless pulley (Fig. 4–59). The coefficient of static friction between the table and the block is 0.450 and the coefficient of kinetic friction between the table and the block is 0.320. Sand is gradually added to the bucket until the system just begins to move. (*a*) Calculate the mass of sand added to the bucket. (*b*) Calculate the acceleration of the system.

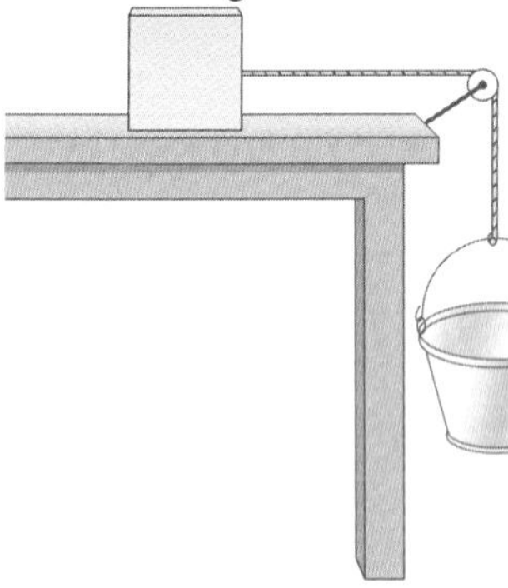


**FIGURE 4–59** Problem 76.

77. In the design of a supermarket, there are to be several ramps connecting different parts of the store. Customers will have to push grocery carts up the ramps and it is obviously desirable that this not be too difficult. The engineer has done a survey and found that almost no one complains if the force directed up the ramp is no more than 20 N. Ignoring friction, at what maximum angle $\theta$ should the ramps be built, assuming a full 30-kg grocery cart?

78. (*a*) What minimum force $F$ is needed to lift the piano (mass $M$) using the pulley apparatus shown in Fig. 4–60? (*b*) Determine the tension in each section of rope: $F_{T1}$, $F_{T2}$, $F_{T3}$, and $F_{T4}$.

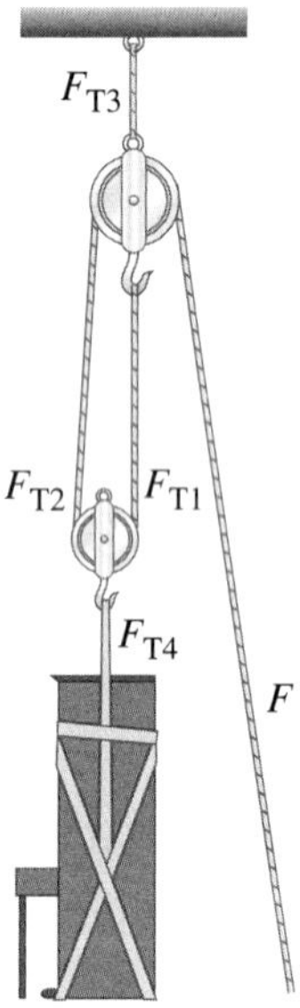


**FIGURE 4–60** Problem 78.

79. A jet aircraft is accelerating at 3.5 m/s$^2$ at an angle of 45° above the horizontal. What is the total force that the cockpit seat exerts on the 75-kg pilot?

80. In the design process for a child-restraint chair, an engineer considers the following set of conditions: A 12-kg child is riding in the chair, which is securely fastened to the seat of an automobile (Fig. 4–61). Assume the automobile is involved in a head-on collision with another vehicle. The initial speed $v_0$ of the car is 45 km/h, and this speed is reduced to zero during the collision time of 0.20 s. Assume a constant car deceleration during the collision and estimate the net horizontal force $F$ that the straps of the restraint chair must exert on the child in order to keep her fixed to the chair. Treat the child as a particle and state any additional assumptions made during your analysis.

**FIGURE 4–61** Problem 80.

81. A 7650-kg helicopter accelerates upward at 0.80 m/s$^2$ while lifting a 1250-kg frame at a construction site, Fig. 4–62. (*a*) What is the lift force exerted by the air on the helicopter rotors? (*b*) What is the tension in the cable (ignore its mass) that connects the frame to the helicopter? (*c*) What force does the cable exert on the helicopter?

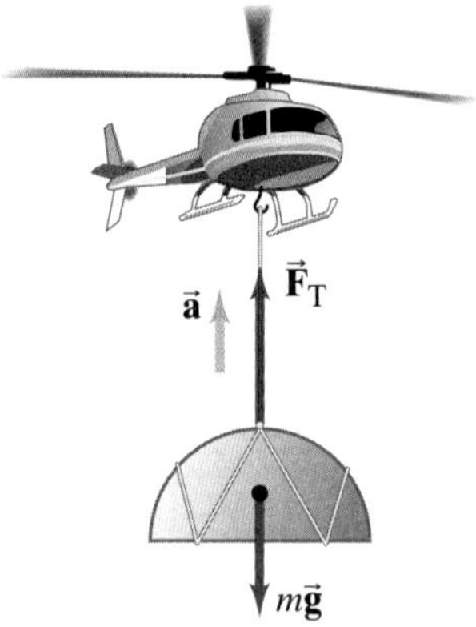


**FIGURE 4–62** Problem 81.

82. A super high-speed 12-car Italian train has a mass of 660 metric tons (660,000 kg). It can exert a maximum force of 400 kN horizontally against the tracks, whereas at maximum velocity (300 km/h), it exerts a force of about 150 kN. Calculate (*a*) its maximum acceleration, and (*b*) estimate the force of air resistance at top speed.

83. A 65-kg ice skater coasts with no effort for 75 m until she stops. If the coefficient of kinetic friction between her skates and the ice is $\mu_k = 0.10$, how fast was she moving at the start of her coast?

84. Two rock climbers, Bill and Karen, use safety ropes of similar length. Karen's rope is more elastic, called a *dynamic rope* by climbers. Bill has a *static rope*, not recommended for safety purposes in pro climbing. Karen falls freely about 2.0 m and then the rope stops her over a distance of 1.0 m (Fig. 4–63). (*a*) Estimate, assuming that the force is constant, how large a force she will feel from the rope. (Express the result in multiples of her weight.) (*b*) In a similar fall, Bill's rope stretches by 30 cm only. How many times his weight will the rope pull on him? Which climber is more likely to be hurt?

**FIGURE 4–63** Problem 84.

85. A fisherman in a boat is using a "10-lb test" fishing line. This means that the line can exert a force of 45 N without breaking (1 lb = 4.45 N). (*a*) How heavy a fish can the fisherman land if he pulls the fish up vertically at constant speed? (*b*) If he accelerates the fish upward at $2.0\,\mathrm{m/s^2}$, what maximum weight fish can he land? (*c*) Is it possible to land a 15-lb trout on 10-lb test line? Why or why not?

86. An elevator in a tall building is allowed to reach a maximum speed of 3.5 m/s going down. What must the tension be in the cable to stop this elevator over a distance of 2.6 m if the elevator has a mass of 1300 kg including occupants?

87. Two boxes, $m_1 = 1.0$ kg with a coefficient of kinetic friction of 0.10, and $m_2 = 2.0$ kg with a coefficient of 0.20, are placed on a plane inclined at $\theta = 30°$. (*a*) What acceleration does each box experience? (*b*) If a taut string is connected to the boxes (Fig. 4–64), with $m_2$ initially farther down the slope, what is the acceleration of each box? (*c*) If the initial configuration is reversed with $m_1$ starting lower with a taut string, what is the acceleration of each box?

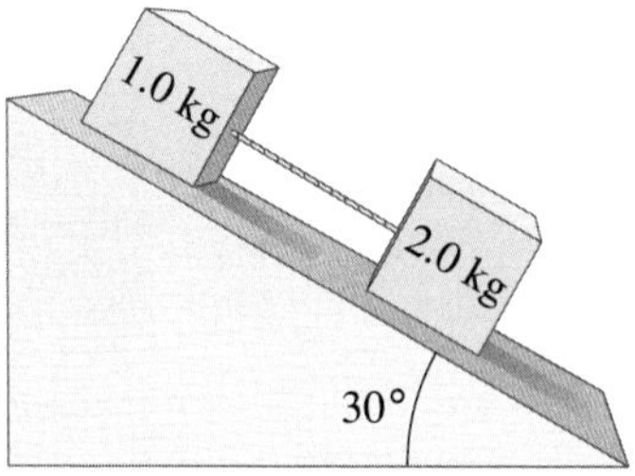


**FIGURE 4–64** Problem 87.

88. A 75.0-kg person stands on a scale in an elevator. What does the scale read (in N and in kg) when the elevator is (*a*) at rest, (*b*) ascending at a constant speed of 3.0 m/s, (*c*) falling at 3.0 m/s, (*d*) accelerating upward at $3.0\,\mathrm{m/s^2}$, (*e*) accelerating downward at $3.0\,\mathrm{m/s^2}$?

89. Three mountain climbers who are roped together are ascending an icefield inclined at 21.0° to the horizontal. The last climber slips, pulling the second climber off his feet. The first climber is able to hold them both. If each climber has a mass of 75 kg, calculate the tension in each of the two sections of rope between the three climbers. Ignore friction between the ice and the fallen climbers.

## Answers to Exercises

**A:** (*a*) The same; (*b*) the sports car; (*c*) third law for part (a), second law for part (b).

**B:** The force applied by the person is insufficient to keep the box moving.

**C:** No; yes.

**D:** Yes; no.

The astronauts in the upper left of this photo are working on the space shuttle. As they orbit the Earth—at a rather high speed—they experience apparent weightlessness. The Moon, in the background, also is orbiting the Earth at high speed. Both the Moon and the space shuttle move in nearly circular orbits, and each undergoes a centripetal acceleration. What keeps the Moon and the space shuttle (and its astronauts) from moving off in a straight line away from Earth? It is the force of gravity. Newton's law of universal gravitation states that all objects attract all other objects with a force proportional to their masses and inversely proportional to the square of the distance between them.

CHAPTER 5

# Circular Motion; Gravitation

An object moves in a straight line if the net force on it acts in the direction of motion, or the net force is zero. If the net force acts at an angle to the direction of motion at any moment, then the object moves in a curved path. An example of the latter is projectile motion, which we discussed in Chapter 3. Another important case is that of an object moving in a circle, such as a ball at the end of a string revolving around one's head, or the nearly circular motion of the Moon about the Earth.

In this Chapter, we study the circular motion of objects, and how Newton's laws of motion apply. We also discuss how Newton conceived of another great law by applying the concepts of circular motion to the motion of the Moon and the planets. This is the law of universal gravitation, which was the capstone of Newton's analysis of the physical world.

**FIGURE 5–1** A small object moving in a circle, showing how the velocity changes. At each point, the instantaneous velocity is in a direction tangent to the circular path.

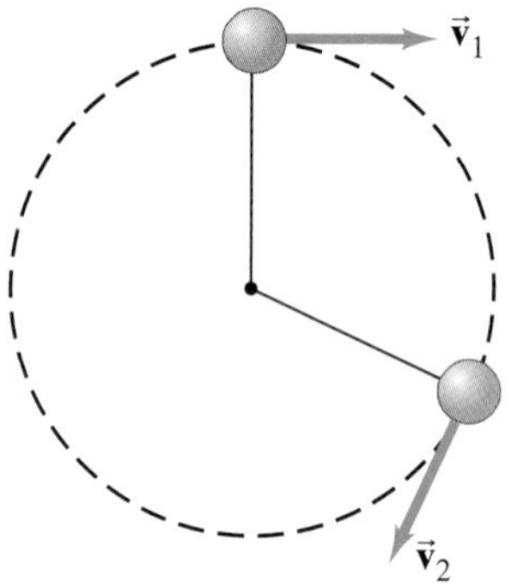


## 5–1 Kinematics of Uniform Circular Motion

An object that moves in a circle at constant speed $v$ is said to experience **uniform circular motion**. The *magnitude* of the velocity remains constant in this case, but the *direction* of the velocity continuously changes as the object moves around the circle (Fig. 5–1). Because acceleration is defined as the rate of change of velocity, a change in direction of velocity constitutes an acceleration, just as a change in magnitude of velocity does. Thus, an object revolving in a circle is continuously accelerating, even when the speed remains constant $(v_1 = v_2 = v)$. We now investigate this acceleration quantitatively.

Acceleration is defined as

$$\vec{\mathbf{a}} = \frac{\vec{\mathbf{v}}_2 - \vec{\mathbf{v}}_1}{\Delta t} = \frac{\Delta \vec{\mathbf{v}}}{\Delta t},$$

where $\Delta \vec{\mathbf{v}}$ is the change in velocity during the short time interval $\Delta t$. We will eventually consider the situation in which $\Delta t$ approaches zero and thus obtain the instantaneous acceleration. But for purposes of making a clear drawing, Fig. 5–2, we consider a nonzero time interval. During the time interval $\Delta t$, the particle in Fig. 5–2a moves from point A to point B, covering a distance $\Delta l$ *along the arc* which subtends an angle $\Delta\theta$. The change in the velocity vector is $\vec{\mathbf{v}}_2 - \vec{\mathbf{v}}_1 = \Delta\vec{\mathbf{v}}$, and is shown in Fig. 5–2b.

FIGURE 5–2 Determining the change in velocity, $\Delta\vec{\mathbf{v}}$, for a particle moving in a circle. The length $\Delta l$ is the distance along the arc, from A to B.

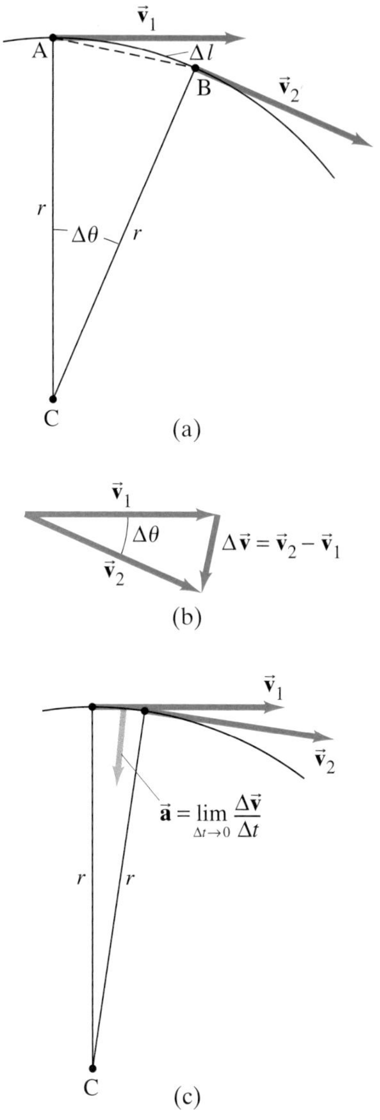


If we let $\Delta t$ be very small (approaching zero), then $\Delta l$ and $\Delta\theta$ are also very small, and $\vec{\mathbf{v}}_2$ will be almost parallel to $\vec{\mathbf{v}}_1$; $\Delta\vec{\mathbf{v}}$ will be essentially perpendicular to them (Fig. 5–2c). Thus $\Delta\vec{\mathbf{v}}$ points toward the center of the circle. Since $\vec{\mathbf{a}}$, by definition, is in the same direction as $\Delta\vec{\mathbf{v}}$, it too must point toward the center of the circle. Therefore, this acceleration is called **centripetal acceleration** ("center-pointing" acceleration) or **radial acceleration** (since it is directed along the radius, toward the center of the circle), and we denote it by $\vec{\mathbf{a}}_R$.

We next determine the magnitude of the centripetal (radial) acceleration, $a_R$. Because CA in Fig. 5–2a is perpendicular to $\vec{\mathbf{v}}_1$, and CB is perpendicular to $\vec{\mathbf{v}}_2$, it follows that the angle $\Delta\theta$, defined as the angle between CA and CB, is also the angle between $\vec{\mathbf{v}}_1$ and $\vec{\mathbf{v}}_2$. Hence the vectors $\vec{\mathbf{v}}_1$, $\vec{\mathbf{v}}_2$, and $\Delta\vec{\mathbf{v}}$ in Fig. 5–2b form a triangle that is geometrically similar† to triangle CAB in Fig. 5–2a. If we take $\Delta\theta$ to be very small (letting $\Delta t$ be very small) and setting $v = v_1 = v_2$ because the magnitude of the velocity is assumed not to change, we can write

$$\frac{\Delta v}{v} \approx \frac{\Delta l}{r}.$$

This is an exact equality when $\Delta t$ approaches zero, for then the arc length $\Delta l$ equals the cord length AB. We want to find the instantaneous acceleration, so we let $\Delta t$ approach zero, write the above expression as an equality, and then solve for $\Delta v$:

$$\Delta v = \frac{v}{r}\,\Delta l.$$

To get the centripetal acceleration, $a_R$, we divide $\Delta v$ by $\Delta t$:

$$a_R = \frac{\Delta v}{\Delta t} = \frac{v}{r}\frac{\Delta l}{\Delta t}.$$

But $\Delta l / \Delta t$ is just the linear speed, $v$, of the object, so

$$a_R = \frac{v^2}{r}. \qquad \textbf{(5–1)}$$

*Centripetal (radial) acceleration*

Equation 5–1 is valid even when $v$ is not constant.

To summarize, *an object moving in a circle of radius r at constant speed v has an acceleration whose direction is toward the center of the circle and whose magnitude is* $a_R = v^2/r$. It is not surprising that this acceleration depends on $v$ and $r$. The greater the speed $v$, the faster the velocity changes direction; and the larger the radius, the less rapidly the velocity changes direction.

**CAUTION**

*In uniform circular motion, the speed is constant, but the acceleration is not zero*

† Appendix A contains a review of geometry.

The acceleration vector points toward the center of the circle. But the velocity vector always points in the direction of motion, which is tangential to the circle. Thus the velocity and acceleration vectors are perpendicular to each other at every point in the path for uniform circular motion (Fig. 5–3). This is another example that illustrates the error in thinking that acceleration and velocity are always in the same direction. For an object falling vertically, $\vec{\mathbf{a}}$ and $\vec{\mathbf{v}}$ are indeed parallel. But in circular motion, $\vec{\mathbf{a}}$ and $\vec{\mathbf{v}}$ are perpendicular, not parallel (nor were they parallel in projectile motion, Section 3–5).

**CAUTION**

*The direction of motion ($\vec{\mathbf{v}}$) and the acceleration ($\vec{\mathbf{a}}$) are not in the same direction; instead, $\vec{\mathbf{a}} \perp \vec{\mathbf{v}}$*

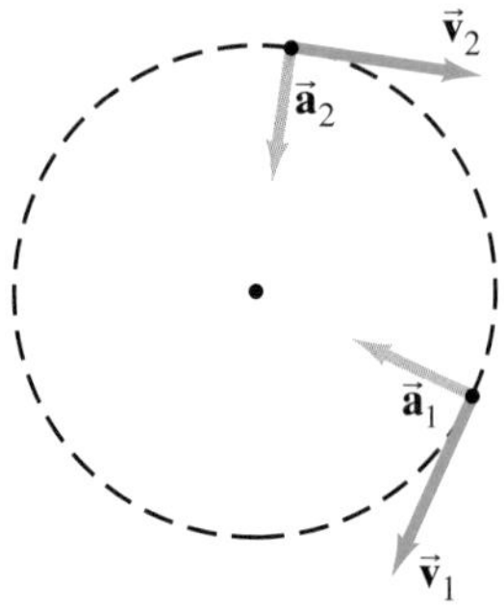


**FIGURE 5–3** For uniform circular motion, $\vec{\mathbf{a}}$ is always perpendicular to $\vec{\mathbf{v}}$.

*Period and frequency*

Circular motion is often described in terms of the **frequency** $f$, the number of revolutions per second. The **period** $T$ of an object revolving in a circle is the time required for one complete revolution. Period and frequency are related by

$$T = \frac{1}{f}. \tag{5–2}$$

For example, if an object revolves at a frequency of 3 rev/s, then each revolution takes $\frac{1}{3}$ s. For an object revolving in a circle (of circumference $2\pi r$) at constant speed $v$, we can write

$$v = \frac{2\pi r}{T},$$

since in one revolution the object travels one circumference.

**EXAMPLE 5–1** **Acceleration of a revolving ball.** A 150-g ball at the end of a string is revolving uniformly in a horizontal circle of radius 0.600 m, as in Fig. 5–1 or 5–3. The ball makes 2.00 revolutions in a second. What is its centripetal acceleration?

**APPROACH** The centripetal acceleration is $a_R = v^2/r$. We are given $r$, and we can find the speed of the ball, $v$, from the given radius and frequency.

**SOLUTION** If the ball makes two complete revolutions per second, then the ball travels in a complete circle in a time interval equal to 0.500 s, which is its period $T$. The distance traveled in this time is the circumference of the circle, $2\pi r$, where $r$ is the radius of the circle. Therefore, the ball has speed

$$v = \frac{2\pi r}{T} = \frac{2(3.14)(0.600\,\text{m})}{(0.500\,\text{s})} = 7.54\,\text{m/s}.$$

The centripetal acceleration† is

$$a_R = \frac{v^2}{r} = \frac{(7.54\,\text{m/s})^2}{(0.600\,\text{m})} = 94.7\,\text{m/s}^2.$$

**EXERCISE A** If the string is doubled in length to 1.20 m but all else stays the same, by what factor will the centripetal acceleration change?

†Differences in the final digit can depend on whether you keep all digits in your calculator for $v$ (which gives $a_R = 94.7\,\text{m/s}^2$), or if you use $v = 7.54\,\text{m/s}$ in which case you get $a_R = 94.8\,\text{m/s}^2$. Both results are valid since our assumed accuracy is about $\pm\,0.1\,\text{m/s}$ (see Section 1–4).

**EXAMPLE 5–2** **Moon's centripetal acceleration.** The Moon's nearly circular orbit about the Earth has a radius of about 384,000 km and a period $T$ of 27.3 days. Determine the acceleration of the Moon toward the Earth.

**APPROACH** Again we need to find the velocity $v$ in order to find $a_R$. We will need to convert to SI units to get $v$ in m/s.

**SOLUTION** In one orbit around the Earth, the Moon travels a distance $2\pi r$, where $r = 3.84 \times 10^8$ m is the radius of its circular path. The time required for one complete orbit is the Moon's period of 27.3 d. The speed of the Moon in its orbit about the Earth is $v = 2\pi r/T$. The period $T$ in seconds is $T = (27.3\text{ d})(24.0\text{ h/d})(3600\text{ s/h}) = 2.36 \times 10^6$ s. Therefore,

$$a_R = \frac{v^2}{r} = \frac{(2\pi r)^2}{T^2 r} = \frac{4\pi^2 r}{T^2} = \frac{4\pi^2(3.84 \times 10^8\text{ m})}{(2.36 \times 10^6\text{ s})^2}$$
$$= 0.00272\text{ m/s}^2 = 2.72 \times 10^{-3}\text{ m/s}^2.$$

We can write this acceleration in terms of $g = 9.80\text{ m/s}^2$ (the acceleration of gravity at the Earth's surface) as

$$a = 2.72 \times 10^{-3}\text{ m/s}^2\left(\frac{g}{9.80\text{ m/s}^2}\right) = 2.78 \times 10^{-4}\,g.$$

**NOTE** The centripetal acceleration of the Moon, $a = 2.78 \times 10^{-4}\,g$, is *not* the acceleration of gravity for objects at the Moon's surface due to the Moon's gravity. Rather, it is the acceleration due to the *Earth's* gravity for any object (such as the Moon) that is 384,000 km from the Earth. Notice how small this acceleration is compared to the acceleration of objects near the Earth's surface.

**CAUTION**
*Distinguish Moon's gravity on objects at its surface, from Earth's gravity acting on Moon (this Example)*

## 5–2 Dynamics of Uniform Circular Motion

*Force is needed to provide centripetal acceleration*

According to Newton's second law ($\Sigma\vec{\mathbf{F}} = m\vec{\mathbf{a}}$), an object that is accelerating must have a net force acting on it. An object moving in a circle, such as a ball on the end of a string, must therefore have a force applied to it to keep it moving in that circle. That is, a net force is necessary to give it centripetal acceleration. The magnitude of the required force can be calculated using Newton's second law for the radial component, $\Sigma F_R = ma_R$, where $a_R$ is the centripetal acceleration, $a_R = v^2/r$, and $\Sigma F_R$ is the total (or net) force in the radial direction:

$$\Sigma F_R = ma_R = m\frac{v^2}{r}. \qquad \text{[circular motion]} \quad \textbf{(5–3)}$$

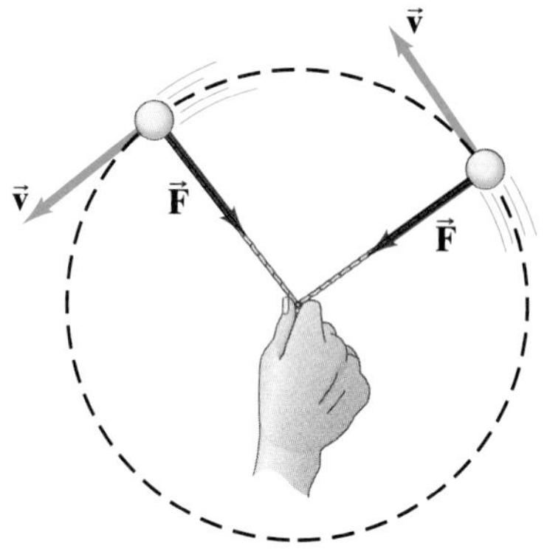

**FIGURE 5–4** A force is required to keep an object moving in a circle. If the speed is constant, the force is directed toward the circle's center.

For uniform circular motion ($v$ = constant), the acceleration is $a_R$, which is directed toward the center of the circle at any moment. Thus the *net force too must be directed toward the center of the circle* (Fig. 5–4). A net force is necessary because otherwise, if no net force were exerted on the object, it would not move in a circle but in a straight line, as Newton's first law tells us. The direction of the net force is continually changing so that it is always directed toward the center of the circle. This force is sometimes called a centripetal ("pointing toward the center") force. But be aware that "centripetal force" does not indicate some new kind of force. The term merely describes the *direction* of the net force needed to provide a circular path: the net force is directed toward the circle's center. The force *must be applied by other objects*. For example, to swing a ball in a circle on the end of a string, you pull on the string and the string exerts the force on the ball. (Try it.)

**CAUTION**
*Centripetal force is not a new kind of force*
*(Every force must be exerted by an object)*

**CAUTION**
*There is no real "centrifugal force"*

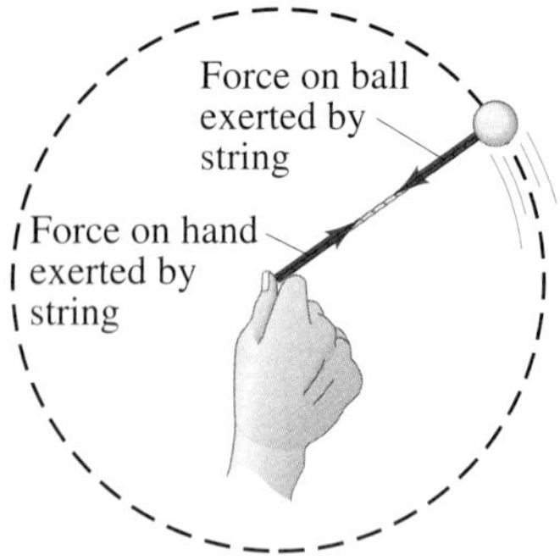


**FIGURE 5–5** Swinging a ball on the end of a string.

There is a common misconception that an object moving in a circle has an outward force acting on it, a so-called centrifugal ("center-fleeing") force. This is incorrect: *there is no outward force* on the revolving object. Consider, for example, a person swinging a ball on the end of a string around her head (Fig. 5–5). If you have ever done this yourself, you know that you feel a force pulling outward on your hand. The misconception arises when this pull is interpreted as an outward "centrifugal" force pulling on the ball that is transmitted along the string to your hand. This is not what is happening at all. To keep the ball moving in a circle, you pull *inwardly* on the string, and the string exerts this force on the ball. The ball exerts an equal and opposite force on the string (Newton's third law), and *this* is the outward force your hand feels (see Fig. 5–5).

The force *on the ball* is the one exerted *inwardly* on it by you, via the string. To see even more convincing evidence that a "centrifugal force" does not act on the ball, consider what happens when you let go of the string. If a centrifugal force were acting, the ball would fly outward, as shown in Fig. 5–6a. But it doesn't; the ball flies off tangentially (Fig. 5–6b), in the direction of the velocity it had at the moment it was released, because the inward force no longer acts. Try it and see!

**FIGURE 5–6** If centrifugal force existed, the revolving ball would fly outward as in (a) when released. In fact, it flies off tangentially as in (b). For example, in (c) sparks fly in straight lines tangentially from the edge of a rotating grinding wheel.

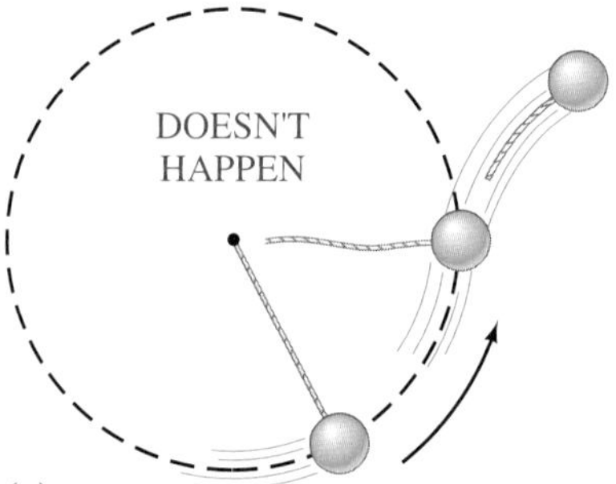


(a)

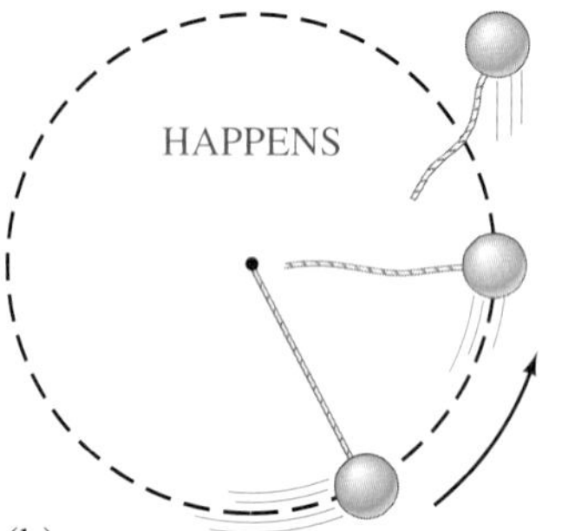


(b)

(c)

**EXAMPLE 5–3 ESTIMATE Force on revolving ball (horizontal).** Estimate the force a person must exert on a string attached to a 0.150-kg ball to make the ball revolve in a horizontal circle of radius 0.600 m. The ball makes 2.00 revolutions per second ($T = 0.500\,\mathrm{s}$), as in Example 5–1.

**APPROACH** First we need to draw the free-body diagram for the ball. The forces acting on the ball are the force of gravity, $m\vec{\mathbf{g}}$ downward, and the tension force $\vec{\mathbf{F}}_\mathrm{T}$ that the string exerts toward the hand at the center (which occurs because the person exerts that same force on the string). The free-body diagram for the ball is as shown in Fig. 5–7. The ball's weight complicates matters and makes it impossible to revolve a ball with the cord perfectly horizontal. We assume the weight is small, and put $\phi \approx 0$ in Fig. 5–7. Thus $\vec{\mathbf{F}}_\mathrm{T}$ will act nearly horizontally and, in any case, provides the force necessary to give the ball its centripetal acceleration.

**SOLUTION** We apply Newton's second law to the radial direction, which we assume is horizontal:

$$(\Sigma F)_\mathrm{R} = ma_\mathrm{R},$$

where $a_\mathrm{R} = v^2/r$ and $v = 2\pi r/T = 2\pi(0.600\,\mathrm{m})/(0.500\,\mathrm{s}) = 7.54\,\mathrm{m/s}$. Thus

$$F_\mathrm{T} = m\frac{v^2}{r} = (0.150\,\mathrm{kg})\frac{(7.54\,\mathrm{m/s})^2}{(0.600\,\mathrm{m})} \approx 14\,\mathrm{N}.$$

**NOTE** We keep only two significant figures in the answer because $mg = (0.150\,\mathrm{kg})(9.80\,\mathrm{m/s^2}) = 1.5\,\mathrm{N}$, being about $\frac{1}{10}$ of our result, is small but not so small as to justify stating a more precise answer since we ignored the effect of $mg$.

**NOTE** To include the effect of $m\vec{\mathbf{g}}$, resolve $\vec{\mathbf{F}}_\mathrm{T}$ in Fig. 5–7 into components, and set the horizontal component of $\vec{\mathbf{F}}_\mathrm{T}$ equal to $mv^2/r$ and its vertical component equal to $mg$.

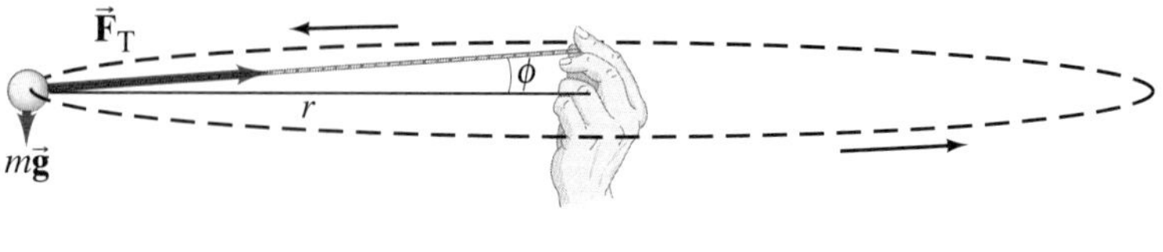


**FIGURE 5–7** Example 5–3.

**EXAMPLE 5–4** **Revolving ball (vertical circle).** A 0.150-kg ball on the end of a 1.10-m-long cord (negligible mass) is swung in a *vertical* circle. (*a*) Determine the minimum speed the ball must have at the top of its arc so that the ball continues moving in a circle. (*b*) Calculate the tension in the cord at the bottom of the arc, assuming the ball is moving at twice the speed of part (*a*).

**APPROACH** The ball moves in a vertical circle and is *not* undergoing uniform circular motion. The radius is assumed constant, but the speed $v$ changes because of gravity. Nonetheless, Eq. 5–1 is valid at each point along the circle, and we use it at points 1 and 2. The free-body diagram is shown in Fig. 5–8 for both positions 1 and 2.

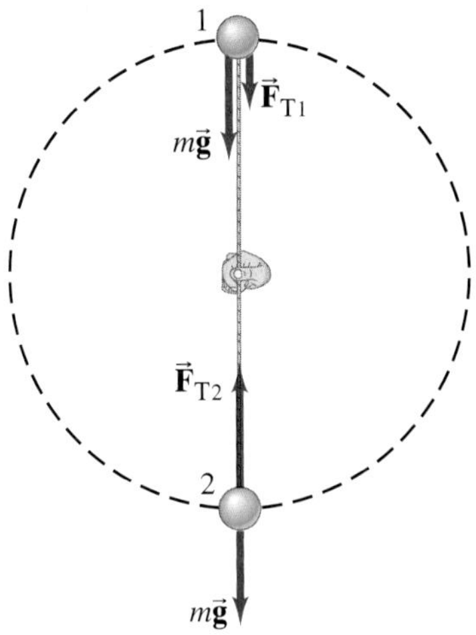


**FIGURE 5–8** Example 5–4. Free-body diagrams for positions 1 and 2.

**SOLUTION** (*a*) At the top (point 1), two forces act on the ball: $m\vec{\mathbf{g}}$, the force of gravity, and $\vec{\mathbf{F}}_{T1}$, the tension force the cord exerts at point 1. Both act downward, and their vector sum acts to give the ball its centripetal acceleration $a_R$. We apply Newton's second law, for the vertical direction, choosing downward as positive since the acceleration is downward (toward the center):

$$(\Sigma F)_R = ma_R$$

$$F_{T1} + mg = m\frac{v_1^2}{r}. \qquad \text{[at top]}$$

*Cord tension and gravity together provide centripetal acceleration*

From this equation we can see that the tension force $F_{T1}$ at point 1 will get larger if $v_1$ (ball's speed at top of circle) is made larger, as expected. But we are asked for the *minimum* speed to keep the ball moving in a circle. The cord will remain taut as long as there is tension in it. But if the tension disappears (because $v_1$ is too small) the cord can go limp, and the ball will fall out of its circular path. Thus, the minimum speed will occur if $F_{T1} = 0$, for which we have

$$mg = m\frac{v_1^2}{r}. \qquad \text{[minimum speed at top]}$$

*Gravity provides centripetal acceleration*

We solve for $v_1$:

$$v_1 = \sqrt{gr} = \sqrt{(9.80\,\text{m/s}^2)(1.10\,\text{m})} = 3.28\,\text{m/s}.$$

This is the minimum speed at the top of the circle if the ball is to continue moving in a circular path.

(*b*) When the ball is at the bottom of the circle (point 2 in Fig. 5–8), the cord exerts its tension force $F_{T2}$ upward, whereas the force of gravity, $m\vec{\mathbf{g}}$, still acts downward. So we apply Newton's second law, this time choosing *upward* as positive since the acceleration is upward (toward the center):

$$(\Sigma F)_R = ma_R$$

$$F_{T2} - mg = m\frac{v_2^2}{r}. \qquad \text{[at bottom]}$$

*String tension and gravity acting in opposite directions provide centripetal acceleration*

The speed $v_2$ is given as twice that in (*a*), namely 6.56 m/s. We solve for $F_{T2}$:

$$F_{T2} = m\frac{v_2^2}{r} + mg$$

$$= (0.150\,\text{kg})\frac{(6.56\,\text{m/s})^2}{(1.10\,\text{m})} + (0.150\,\text{kg})(9.80\,\text{m/s}^2) = 7.34\,\text{N}.$$

**EXERCISE B** In a tumble dryer, the speed of the drum should be just large enough so that the clothes are carried nearly to the top of the drum and then fall away, rather than being pressed against the drum for the whole revolution. Determine whether this speed will be different for heavier wet clothes than for lighter dry clothes.

**EXERCISE C** A rider on a Ferris wheel moves in a vertical circle of radius $r$ at constant speed $v$ (Fig. 5–9). Is the normal force that the seat exerts on the rider at the top of the wheel (*a*) less than, (*b*) more than, or (*c*) the same as, the force the seat exerts at the bottom of the wheel?

**FIGURE 5–9** Exercise C.

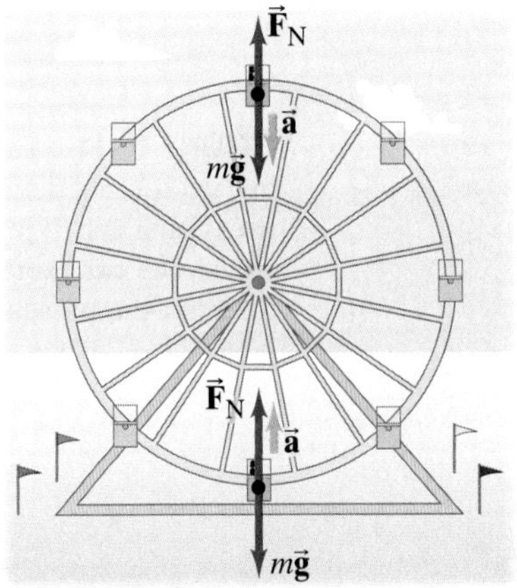

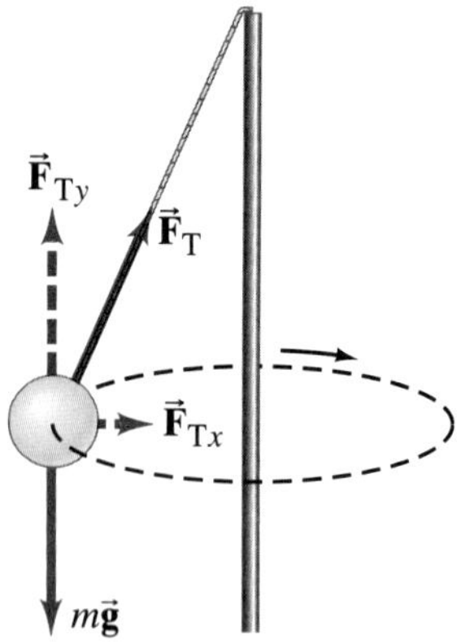


**FIGURE 5–10** Example 5–5.

**CONCEPTUAL EXAMPLE 5–5** **Tetherball.** The game of tetherball is played with a ball tied to a pole with a string. After the ball is struck, it revolves around the pole as shown in Fig. 5–10. In what direction is the acceleration of the ball, and what force causes the acceleration?

**RESPONSE** If the ball revolves in a horizontal plane as shown, then the acceleration points horizontally toward the center of the ball's circular path (not toward the top of the pole). The force responsible for the acceleration may not be obvious at first, since there seems to be no force pointing directly horizontally. But it is the *net* force (the sum of $m\vec{g}$ and $\vec{F}_T$ here) that must point in the direction of the acceleration. The vertical component of the string tension, $F_{Ty}$, balances the ball's weight, $m\vec{g}$. The horizontal component of the string tension, $F_{Tx}$, is the force that produces the centripetal acceleration toward the center.

**PROBLEM SOLVING** Uniform Circular Motion

1. **Draw a free-body diagram**, showing all the forces acting on each object under consideration. Be sure you can identify the source of each force (tension in a cord, Earth's gravity, friction, normal force, and so on). Don't put in something that doesn't belong (like a centrifugal force).
2. **Determine** which of the forces, or which of their components, act to provide the centripetal acceleration—that is, all the **forces or components that act radially**, toward or away from the center of the circular path. The sum of these forces (or components) provides the centripetal acceleration, $a_R = v^2/r$.
3. **Choose a convenient coordinate system**, preferably with one axis along the acceleration direction.
4. **Apply Newton's second law** to the radial component:

$$(\Sigma F)_R = ma_R = m\frac{v^2}{r}. \qquad \text{[radial direction]}$$

## 5–3 Highway Curves, Banked and Unbanked

PHYSICS APPLIED
*Driving around a curve*

An example of circular dynamics occurs when an automobile rounds a curve, say to the left. In such a situation, you may feel that you are thrust outward toward the right side door. But there is no mysterious centrifugal force pulling on you. What is happening is that you tend to move in a straight line, whereas the car has begun to follow a curved path. To make you go in the curved path, the seat (friction) or the door of the car (direct contact) exerts a force on you (Fig. 5–11). The car also must have a force exerted on it toward the center of the curve if it is to move in that curve. On a flat road, this force is supplied by friction between the tires and the pavement.

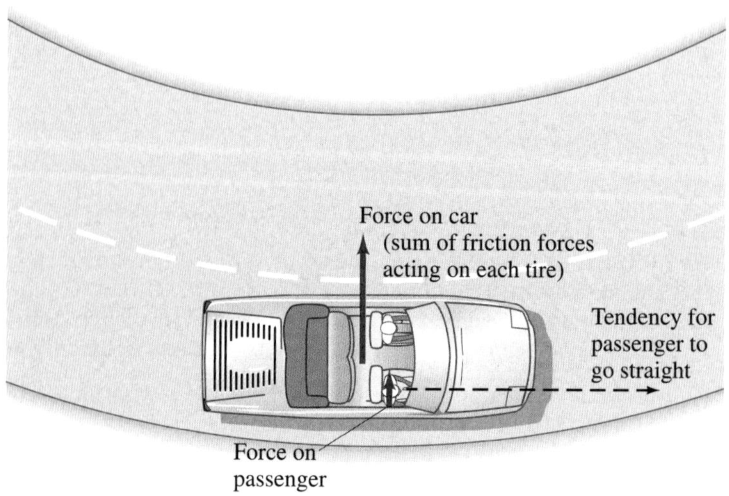


**FIGURE 5–11** The road exerts an inward force (friction against the tires) on a car to make it move in a circle. The car exerts an inward force on the passenger.

If the wheels and tires of the car are rolling normally without slipping or sliding, the bottom of the tire is at rest against the road at each instant; so the friction force the road exerts on the tires is static friction. But if the static friction force is not great enough, as under icy conditions, sufficient friction force cannot be applied and the car will skid out of a circular path into a more nearly straight path. See Fig. 5–12. Once a car skids or slides, the friction force becomes kinetic friction, which is less than static friction.

**FIGURE 5–12** Race car heading into a curve. From the tire marks we see that most cars experienced a sufficient friction force to give them the needed centripetal acceleration for rounding the curve safely. But, we also see tire tracks of cars on which there was not sufficient force—and which followed more nearly straight-line paths.

**EXAMPLE 5–6** **Skidding on a curve.** A 1000-kg car rounds a curve on a flat road of radius 50 m at a speed of 50 km/h (14 m/s). Will the car follow the curve, or will it skid? Assume: (*a*) the pavement is dry and the coefficient of static friction is $\mu_s = 0.60$; (*b*) the pavement is icy and $\mu_s = 0.25$.

**APPROACH** The forces on the car are gravity $mg$ downward, the normal force $F_N$ exerted upward by the road, and a horizontal friction force due to the road. They are shown in Fig. 5–13, which is the free-body diagram for the car. The car will follow the curve if the maximum static friction force is greater than the mass times the centripetal acceleration.

**SOLUTION** In the vertical direction there is no acceleration. Newton's second law tells us that the normal force $F_N$ on the car is equal to the weight $mg$ since the road is flat:

$$F_N = mg = (1000\,\text{kg})(9.8\,\text{m/s}^2) = 9800\,\text{N}.$$

In the horizontal direction the only force is friction, and we must compare it to the force needed to produce the centripetal acceleration to see if it is sufficient. The net horizontal force required to keep the car moving in a circle around the curve is

$$(\Sigma F)_R = ma_R = m\frac{v^2}{r} = (1000\,\text{kg})\frac{(14\,\text{m/s})^2}{(50\,\text{m})} = 3900\,\text{N}.$$

Now we compute the maximum total static friction force (the sum of the friction forces acting on each of the four tires) to see if it can be large enough to provide a safe centripetal acceleration. For (*a*), $\mu_s = 0.60$, and the maximum friction force attainable (recall from Section 4–8 that $F_{fr} \leq \mu_s F_N$) is

$$(F_{fr})_{max} = \mu_s F_N = (0.60)(9800\,\text{N}) = 5900\,\text{N}.$$

Since a force of only 3900 N is needed, and that is, in fact, how much will be exerted by the road as a static friction force, the car can follow the curve. But in (*b*) the maximum static friction force possible is

$$(F_{fr})_{max} = \mu_s F_N = (0.25)(9800\,\text{N}) = 2500\,\text{N}.$$

The car will skid because the ground cannot exert sufficient force (3900 N is needed) to keep it moving in a curve of radius 50 m at a speed of 50 km/h.

**FIGURE 5–13** Example 5–6. Forces on a car rounding a curve on a flat road. (a) Front view, (b) top view.

(a)

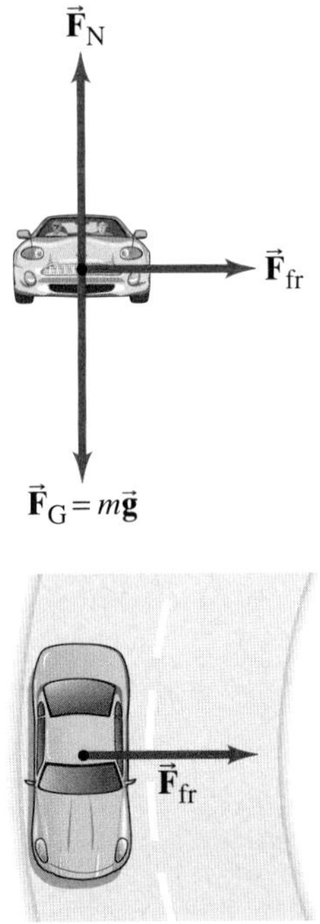


(b)

The possibility of skidding is worse if the wheels lock (stop rotating) when the brakes are applied too hard. When the tires are rolling, static friction exists. But if the wheels lock (stop rotating), the tires slide and the friction force, which is now kinetic friction, is less. More importantly, the *direction* of the friction force changes suddenly if the wheels lock. Static friction can point perpendicular to the velocity, as in Fig. 5–13b, but if the car slides, kinetic friction points *opposite* to the velocity. The force no longer points toward the center of the circle, and the car cannot continue in a curved path (see Fig. 5–12). Even worse, if the road is wet or icy, locking of the wheels occurs with less force on the brake pedal since there is less road friction to keep the wheels turning rather than sliding. Antilock brakes (ABS) are designed to limit brake pressure just before the point where sliding would occur, by means of delicate sensors and a fast computer.

PHYSICS APPLIED
*Antilock brakes*

PHYSICS APPLIED
*Banked curves*

The banking of curves can reduce the chance of skidding. The normal force exerted by a banked road, acting perpendicular to the road, will have a component toward the center of the circle (Fig. 5–14), thus reducing the reliance on friction. For a given banking angle $\theta$, there will be one speed for which no friction at all is required. This will be the case when the horizontal component of the normal force toward the center of the curve, $F_N \sin\theta$ (see Fig. 5–14), is just equal to the force required to give a vehicle its centripetal acceleration—that is, when

$$F_N \sin\theta = m\frac{v^2}{r}. \qquad \text{[no friction required]}$$

The banking angle of a road, $\theta$, is chosen so that this condition holds for a particular speed, called the "design speed."

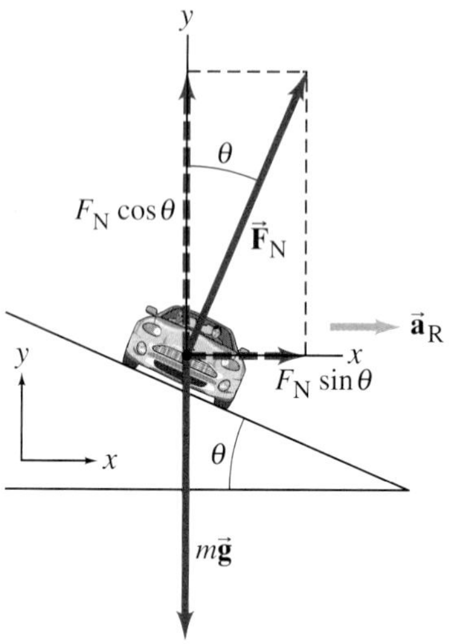


**FIGURE 5–14** Normal force on a car rounding a banked curve, resolved into its horizontal and vertical components. The centripetal acceleration is horizontal (*not* parallel to the sloping road). The friction force on the tires, not shown, could point up or down along the slope, depending on the car's speed. The friction force will be zero for one particular speed.

**EXAMPLE 5–7 Banking angle.** (*a*) For a car traveling with speed $v$ around a curve of radius $r$, determine a formula for the angle at which a road should be banked so that no friction is required. (*b*) What is this angle for an expressway off-ramp curve of radius 50 m at a design speed of 50 km/h?

**APPROACH** Even though the road is banked, the car is still moving along a horizontal circle, so the centripetal acceleration needs to be horizontal. We choose our $x$ and $y$ axes as horizontal and vertical so that $a_R$, which is horizontal, is along the $x$ axis. The forces on the car are the Earth's gravity $mg$ downward, and the normal force $F_N$ exerted by the road perpendicular to its surface. See Fig. 5–14, where the components of $F_N$ are also shown. We don't need to consider the friction of the road because we are designing a road to be banked so as to eliminate dependence on friction.

**SOLUTION** (*a*) For the horizontal direction, $\Sigma F_R = ma_R$ gives

$$F_N \sin\theta = \frac{mv^2}{r}.$$

Since there is no vertical motion, the $y$ component of the acceleration is zero, so $\Sigma F_y = ma_y$ gives us

$$F_N \cos\theta - mg = 0.$$

Thus,

$$F_N = \frac{mg}{\cos\theta}.$$

CAUTION
*$F_N$ is not always equal to $mg$*

[Note in this case that $F_N \geq mg$ since $\cos\theta \leq 1$.]
We substitute this relation for $F_N$ into the equation for the horizontal motion,

*Horizontal component of normal force acts to provide centripetal acceleration (friction is desired to be zero—otherwise it too would contribute)*

$$F_N \sin\theta = m\frac{v^2}{r},$$

and obtain

$$\frac{mg}{\cos\theta}\sin\theta = m\frac{v^2}{r}$$

or

$$mg\tan\theta = m\frac{v^2}{r},$$

so

*Banking angle (friction not needed)*

$$\tan\theta = \frac{v^2}{rg}.$$

This is the formula for the banking angle $\theta$: no friction needed at speed $v$.

(*b*) For $r = 50$ m and $v = 50$ km/h (or 14 m/s),

$$\tan\theta = \frac{(14\text{ m/s})^2}{(50\text{ m})(9.8\text{ m/s}^2)} = 0.40,$$

so $\theta = 22°$.

**EXERCISE D** To negotiate an unbanked curve at a *faster* speed, a driver puts a couple of sand bags in his van aiming to increase the force of friction between the tires and the road. Will the sand bags help?

**EXERCISE E** Can a heavy truck and a small car travel safely at the same speed around an icy, banked-curve road?

## *5–4 Nonuniform Circular Motion

Circular motion at constant speed occurs when the net force on an object is exerted toward the center of the circle. If the net force is not directed toward the center but is at an angle, as shown in Fig. 5–15a, the force has two components. The component directed toward the center of the circle, $F_R$, gives rise to the centripetal acceleration, $a_R$, and keeps the object moving in a circle. The component tangent to the circle, $F_{tan}$, acts to increase (or decrease) the speed, and thus gives rise to a component of the acceleration tangent to the circle, $a_{tan}$. When the speed of the object is changing, a tangential component of force is acting.

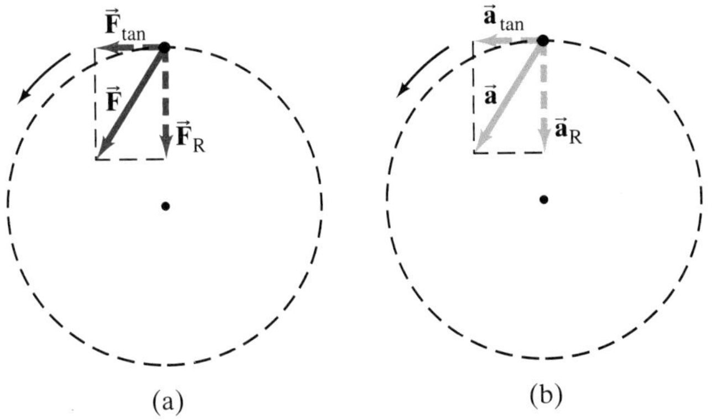


**FIGURE 5–15** The speed of an object moving in a circle changes if the force on it has a tangential component, $F_{tan}$. Part (a) shows the force $\vec{F}$ and its vector components; part (b) shows the acceleration vector and its vector components.

When you first start revolving a ball on the end of a string around your head, you must give it tangential acceleration. You do this by pulling on the string with your hand displaced from the center of the circle. In athletics, a hammer thrower accelerates the hammer tangentially in a similar way so that it reaches a high speed before release.

The tangential component of the acceleration, $a_{tan}$, is equal to the rate of change of the *magnitude* of the object's velocity:

$$a_{tan} = \frac{\Delta v}{\Delta t}.$$

The radial (centripetal) acceleration arises from the change in *direction* of the velocity and, as we have seen (Eq. 5–1), is given by

$$a_R = \frac{v^2}{r}.$$

The tangential acceleration always points in a direction tangent to the circle, and is in the direction of motion (parallel to $\vec{v}$, which is always tangent to the circle) if the speed is increasing, as shown in Fig. 5–15b. If the speed is decreasing, $\vec{a}_{tan}$ points antiparallel to $\vec{v}$. In either case, $\vec{a}_{tan}$ and $\vec{a}_R$ are always perpendicular to each other; and *their directions change* continually as the object moves along its circular path. The total vector acceleration $\vec{a}$ is the sum of these two:

$$\vec{a} = \vec{a}_{tan} + \vec{a}_R.$$

Since $\vec{a}_R$ and $\vec{a}_{tan}$ are always perpendicular to each other, the magnitude of $\vec{a}$ at any moment is

$$a = \sqrt{a_{tan}^2 + a_R^2}.$$

**EXAMPLE 5–8 Two components of acceleration.** A race car starts from rest in the pit area and accelerates at a uniform rate to a speed of 35 m/s in 11 s, moving on a circular track of radius 500 m. Assuming constant tangential acceleration, find (*a*) the tangential acceleration, and (*b*) the radial acceleration, at the instant when the speed is $v = 15\,\text{m/s}$.

**APPROACH** The tangential acceleration relates to the change in speed of the car, and can be calculated as $a_{\text{tan}} = \Delta v/\Delta t$. The centripetal acceleration relates to the change in the *direction* of the velocity vector and is calculated using $a_R = v^2/r$.

**SOLUTION** (*a*) During the 11-s time interval, we assume the tangential acceleration $a_{\text{tan}}$ is constant. Its magnitude is

$$a_{\text{tan}} = \frac{\Delta v}{\Delta t} = \frac{(35\,\text{m/s} - 0\,\text{m/s})}{11\,\text{s}} = 3.2\,\text{m/s}^2.$$

(*b*) When $v = 15\,\text{m/s}$, the centripetal acceleration is

$$a_R = \frac{v^2}{r} = \frac{(15\,\text{m/s})^2}{(500\,\text{m})} = 0.45\,\text{m/s}^2.$$

**EXERCISE F** When the speed of the race car in Example 5–8 is 30 m/s, how are (*a*) $a_{\text{tan}}$ and (*b*) $a_R$ changed?

These concepts can be used for an object moving along any curved path, such as that shown in Fig. 5–16. We can treat any portion of the curve as an arc of a circle with a radius of curvature *r*. The velocity at any point is always tangent to the path. The acceleration can be written, in general, as a vector sum of two components: the tangential component $a_{\text{tan}} = \Delta v/\Delta t$, and the radial (centripetal) component $a_R = v^2/r$.

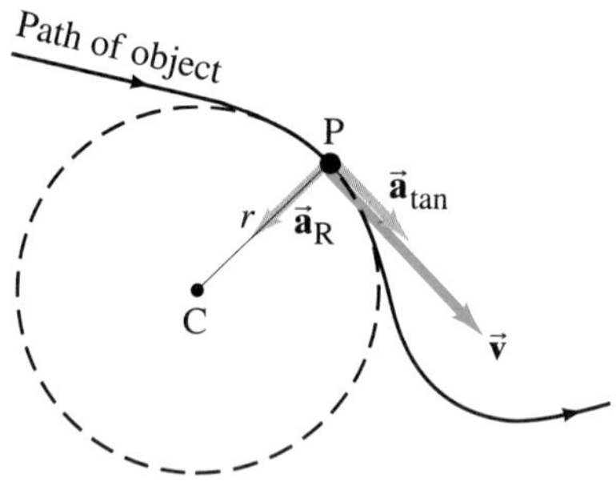


**FIGURE 5–16** Object following a curved path (solid line). At point P the path has a radius of curvature *r*. The object has velocity $\vec{\mathbf{v}}$, tangential acceleration $\vec{\mathbf{a}}_{\text{tan}}$ (the object is increasing in speed), and radial (centripetal) acceleration $\vec{\mathbf{a}}_R$ (magnitude $a_R = v^2/r$) which points toward the center of curvature C.

## *5–5 Centrifugation

PHYSICS APPLIED
*Centrifuge*

A useful device that nicely illustrates circular motion is the centrifuge, or the very high speed ultracentrifuge. These devices are used to sediment materials quickly or to separate materials. Test tubes are held in the centrifuge rotor, which is accelerated to very high rotational speeds: see Fig. 5–17, where one test tube is shown in two positions as the rotor turns. The small green dot represents a small particle, perhaps a macromolecule, in a fluid-filled test tube. When the tube is at position A and the rotor is turning, the particle has a tendency to move in a straight line in the direction of the dashed arrow. But the fluid, resisting the motion of the particles, exerts a centripetal force that keeps the particles moving nearly in a circle. Usually, the resistance of the fluid (a liquid, a gas, or a gel, depending on the application) does not quite equal $mv^2/r$, and the particles eventually reach the bottom of the tube. The purpose of a centrifuge is to provide an "effective gravity" much larger than normal gravity because of the high rotational speeds, thus causing more rapid sedimentation.

**EXAMPLE 5–9** **Ultracentrifuge.** The rotor of an ultracentrifuge rotates at 50,000 rpm (revolutions per minute). The top of a 4.00-cm-long test tube (Fig. 5–17) is 6.00 cm from the rotation axis and is perpendicular to it. The bottom of the tube is 10.00 cm from the axis of rotation. Calculate the centripetal acceleration, in "$g$'s," at the top and the bottom of the tube.

**APPROACH** We can calculate the centripetal acceleration from $a_R = v^2/r$. We divide by $g = 9.80\,\mathrm{m/s^2}$ to find $a_R$ in $g$'s.

**SOLUTION** At the top of the tube, a particle revolves in a circle of circumference $2\pi r$, which is a distance

$$2\pi r = (2\pi)(0.0600\,\mathrm{m}) = 0.377\,\mathrm{m}\text{ per revolution.}$$

It makes $5.00 \times 10^4$ such revolutions each minute, or, dividing by 60 s/min, 833 rev/s. The time to make one revolution, the period $T$, is

$$T = \frac{1}{(833\,\mathrm{rev/s})} = 1.20 \times 10^{-3}\,\mathrm{s/rev}.$$

The speed of the particle is then

$$v = \frac{2\pi r}{T} = \left(\frac{0.377\,\mathrm{m/rev}}{1.20 \times 10^{-3}\,\mathrm{s/rev}}\right) = 3.14 \times 10^2\,\mathrm{m/s}.$$

The centripetal acceleration is

$$a_R = \frac{v^2}{r} = \frac{(3.14 \times 10^2\,\mathrm{m/s})^2}{0.0600\,\mathrm{m}} = 1.64 \times 10^6\,\mathrm{m/s^2},$$

which, dividing by $g = 9.80\,\mathrm{m/s^2}$, is $1.67 \times 10^5$ $g$'s.

At the bottom of the tube ($r = 0.1000\,\mathrm{m}$), the speed is

$$v = \frac{2\pi r}{T} = \frac{(2\pi)(0.1000\,\mathrm{m})}{1.20 \times 10^{-3}\,\mathrm{s/rev}} = 523.6\,\mathrm{m/s}.$$

Then

$$a_R = \frac{v^2}{r} = \frac{(523.6\,\mathrm{m/s})^2}{(0.1000\,\mathrm{m})} = 2.74 \times 10^6\,\mathrm{m/s^2}$$
$$= 2.80 \times 10^5\ g\text{'s},$$

or 280,000 $g$'s.

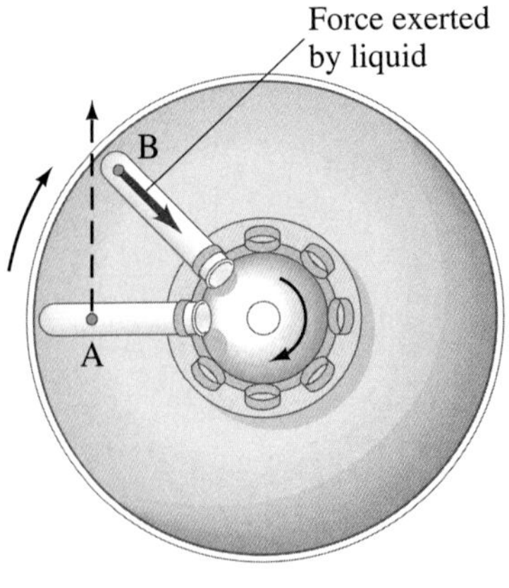


**FIGURE 5–17** Two positions of a rotating test tube in a centrifuge (top view). At A, the green dot represents a macromolecule or other particle being sedimented. It would tend to follow the dashed line, heading toward the bottom of the tube, but the fluid resists this motion by exerting a force on the particle as shown at point B.

## 5–6 Newton's Law of Universal Gravitation

Besides developing the three laws of motion, Sir Isaac Newton also examined the motion of the planets and the Moon. In particular, he wondered about the nature of the force that must act to keep the Moon in its nearly circular orbit around the Earth.

Newton was also thinking about the problem of gravity. Since falling objects accelerate, Newton had concluded that they must have a force exerted on them, a force we call the force of gravity. Whenever an object has a force exerted *on* it, that force is exerted *by* some other object. But what *exerts* the force of gravity? Every object on the surface of the Earth feels the force of gravity, and no matter where the object is, the force is directed toward the center of the Earth (Fig. 5–18). Newton concluded that it must be the Earth itself that exerts the gravitational force on objects at its surface.

According to legend, Newton noticed an apple drop from a tree. He is said to have been struck with a sudden inspiration: If gravity acts at the tops of trees, and even at the tops of mountains, then perhaps it acts all the way to the Moon!

**FIGURE 5–18** Anywhere on Earth, whether in Alaska, Peru, or Australia, the force of gravity acts downward toward the Earth's center.

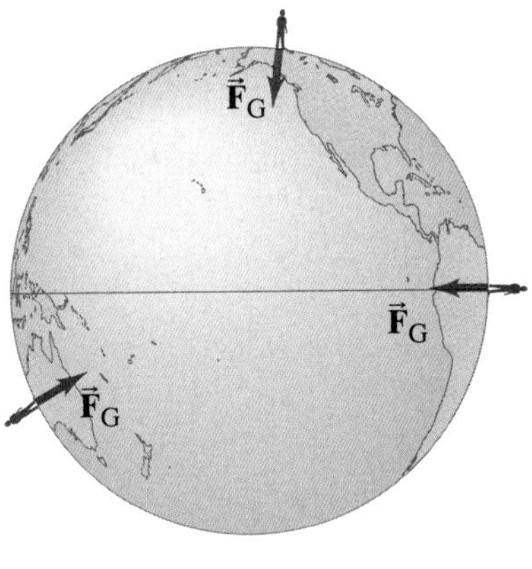

With this idea that it is the Earth's gravity that holds the Moon in its orbit, Newton developed his great theory of gravitation. But there was controversy at the time. Many thinkers had trouble accepting the idea of a force "acting at a distance." Typical forces act through contact—your hand pushes a cart and pulls a wagon, a bat hits a ball, and so on. But gravity acts without contact, said Newton: the Earth exerts a force on a falling apple and on the Moon, even though there is no contact, and the two objects may even be very far apart.

Newton set about determining the magnitude of the gravitational force that the Earth exerts on the Moon as compared to the gravitational force on objects at the Earth's surface. The centripetal acceleration of the Moon, as we calculated in Example 5–2, is $a_R = 0.00272\,\mathrm{m/s^2}$. In terms of the acceleration of gravity at the Earth's surface, $g = 9.80\,\mathrm{m/s^2}$,

*The Moon's acceleration toward Earth*

$$a_R = \frac{0.00272\,\mathrm{m/s^2}}{9.8\,\mathrm{m/s^2}} \approx \frac{1}{3600}\,g.$$

That is, the acceleration of the Moon toward the Earth is about $\frac{1}{3600}$ as great as the acceleration of objects at the Earth's surface. The Moon is 384,000 km from the Earth, which is about 60 times the Earth's radius of 6380 km. That is, the Moon is 60 times farther from the Earth's center than are objects at the Earth's surface. But $60 \times 60 = 60^2 = 3600$. Again that number 3600. Newton concluded that the gravitational force exerted by the Earth on any object decreases with the square of its distance $r$ from the Earth's center:

$$\text{force of gravity} \propto \frac{1}{r^2}.$$

The Moon is 60 Earth radii away, so it feels a gravitational force only $\frac{1}{60^2} = \frac{1}{3600}$ times as strong as an equal mass would at the Earth's surface.

Newton realized that the force of gravity on an object depends not only on distance but also on the object's mass. In fact, it is directly proportional to its mass, as we have seen. According to Newton's third law, when the Earth exerts its gravitational force on any object, such as the Moon, that object exerts an equal and opposite force on the Earth (Fig. 5–19). Because of this symmetry, Newton reasoned, the magnitude of the force of gravity must be proportional to *both* the masses. Thus

$$F \propto \frac{m_E m_{Obj}}{r^2},$$

where $m_E$ is the mass of the Earth, $m_{Obj}$ the mass of the other object, and $r$ the distance from the Earth's center to the center of the other object.

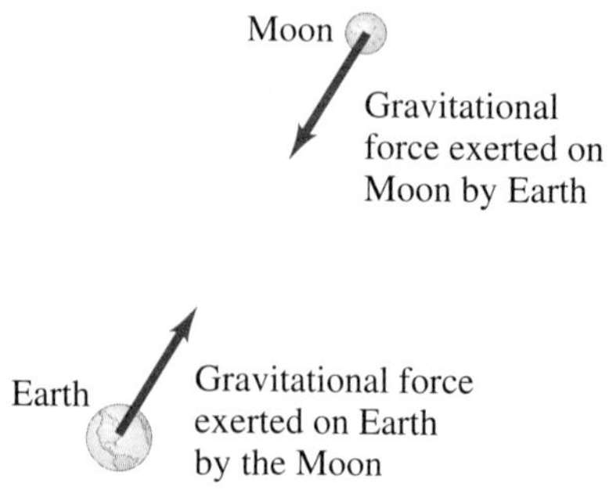


**FIGURE 5–19** The gravitational force one object exerts on a second object is directed toward the first object, and (by Newton's third law) is equal and opposite to the force exerted by the second object on the first.

Newton went a step further in his analysis of gravity. In his examination of the orbits of the planets, he concluded that the force required to hold the planets in their orbits around the Sun seems to diminish as the inverse square of their distance from the Sun. This led him to believe that it is also the gravitational force that acts between the Sun and each of the planets to keep them in their orbits. And if gravity acts between these objects, why not between all objects?

Thus he proposed his **law of universal gravitation**, which we can state as follows:

**Every particle in the universe attracts every other particle with a force that is proportional to the product of their masses and inversely proportional to the square of the distance between them. This force acts along the line joining the two particles.**

NEWTON'S LAW OF UNIVERSAL GRAVITATION

The magnitude of the gravitational force can be written as

$$F = G\frac{m_1 m_2}{r^2}, \tag{5–4}$$

where $m_1$ and $m_2$ are the masses of the two particles, $r$ is the distance between them, and $G$ is a universal constant which must be measured experimentally and has the same numerical value for all objects.

The value of $G$ must be very small, since we are not aware of any force of attraction between ordinary-sized objects, such as between two baseballs. The force between two ordinary objects was first measured by Henry Cavendish in 1798, over 100 years after Newton published his law. To detect and measure the incredibly small force between ordinary objects, he used an apparatus like that shown in Fig. 5–20. Cavendish confirmed Newton's hypothesis that two objects attract one another, and that Eq. 5–4 accurately describes this force. In addition, because Cavendish could measure $F$, $m_1$, $m_2$, and $r$ accurately, he was able to determine the value of the constant $G$ as well. The accepted value today is

$$G = 6.67 \times 10^{-11}\,\mathrm{N\cdot m^2/kg^2}.$$

[Strictly speaking, Eq. 5–4 gives the magnitude of the gravitational force that one particle exerts on a second particle that is a distance $r$ away. For an extended object (that is, not a point), we must consider how to measure the distance $r$. This is often best done using integral calculus, which Newton himself invented. Newton showed that for two uniform spheres, Eq. 5–4 gives the correct force where $r$ is the distance between their centers. When extended objects are small compared to the distance between them (as for the Earth–Sun system), little inaccuracy results from considering them as point particles.]

**EXAMPLE 5–10 ESTIMATE Can you attract another person gravitationally?** A 50-kg person and a 75-kg person are sitting on a bench. Estimate the magnitude of the gravitational force each exerts on the other.

**APPROACH** This is an estimate: we let the distance between the people be $\frac{1}{2}$ m, and round off $G$ to $10^{-10}\,\mathrm{N\cdot m^2/kg^2}$.

**SOLUTION** We use Eq. 5–4:

$$F = G\frac{m_1 m_2}{r^2} \approx \frac{(10^{-10}\,\mathrm{N\cdot m^2/kg^2})(50\,\mathrm{kg})(75\,\mathrm{kg})}{(0.5\,\mathrm{m})^2} \approx 10^{-6}\,\mathrm{N},$$

which is unnoticeably small unless very delicate instruments are used.

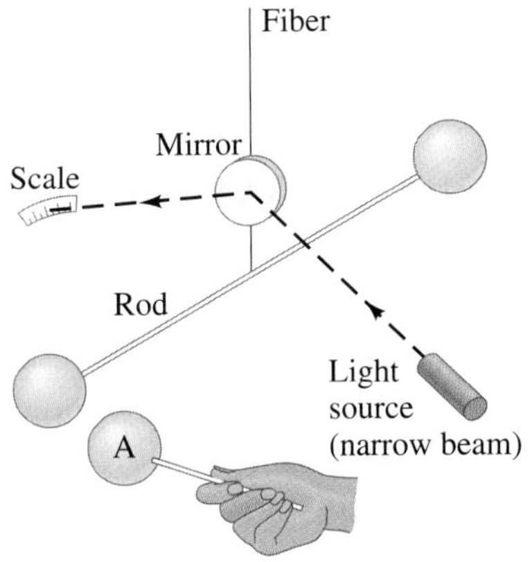


**FIGURE 5–20** Schematic diagram of Cavendish's apparatus. Two spheres are attached to a lightweight horizontal rod, which is suspended at its center by a thin fiber. When a third sphere labeled A is brought close to one of the suspended spheres, the gravitational force causes the latter to move, and this twists the fiber slightly. The tiny movement is magnified by the use of a narrow light beam directed at a mirror mounted on the fiber. The beam reflects onto a scale. Previous determination of how large a force will twist the fiber a given amount then allows one to determine the magnitude of the gravitational force between two objects.

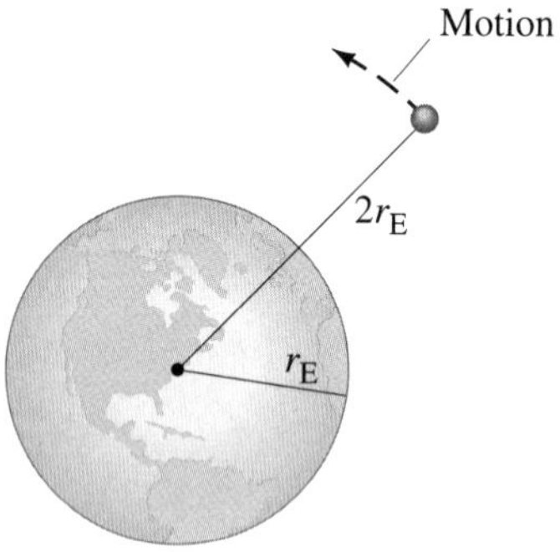


**FIGURE 5–21** Example 5–11.

**EXAMPLE 5–11** **Spacecraft at $2r_E$.** What is the force of gravity acting on a 2000-kg spacecraft when it orbits two Earth radii from the Earth's center (that is, a distance $r_E = 6380\,\text{km}$ above the Earth's surface, Fig. 5–21)? The mass of the Earth is $M_E = 5.98 \times 10^{24}\,\text{kg}$.

**APPROACH** We could plug all the numbers into Eq. 5–4, but there is a simpler approach. The spacecraft is twice as far from the Earth's center as when it is at the surface of the Earth. Therefore, since the force of gravity decreases as the square of the distance (and $\frac{1}{2^2} = \frac{1}{4}$), the force of gravity on the satellite will be only one-fourth its weight at the Earth's surface.

**SOLUTION** At the surface of the Earth, $F_G = mg$. At a distance from the Earth's center of $2r_E$, $F_G$ is $\frac{1}{4}$ as great:

$$F_G = \tfrac{1}{4}mg = \tfrac{1}{4}(2000\,\text{kg})(9.80\,\text{m/s}^2)$$
$$= 4900\,\text{N}.$$

**FIGURE 5–22** Example 5–12. Orientation of Sun (S), Earth (E), and Moon (M) at right angles to each other (not to scale).

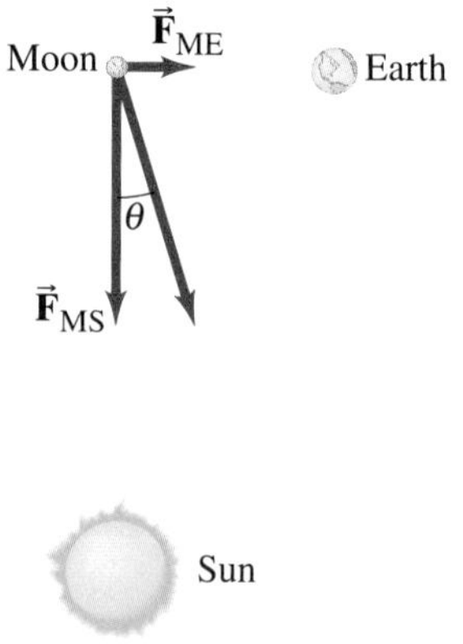


**EXAMPLE 5–12** **Force on the Moon.** Find the net force on the Moon $(m_M = 7.35 \times 10^{22}\,\text{kg})$ due to the gravitational attraction of both the Earth $(m_E = 5.98 \times 10^{24}\,\text{kg})$ and the Sun $(m_S = 1.99 \times 10^{30}\,\text{kg})$, assuming they are at right angles to each other as in Fig. 5–22.

**APPROACH** The forces on our object, the Moon, are the gravitational force exerted on the Moon by the Earth $F_{ME}$ and that exerted by the Sun $F_{MS}$, as shown in the free-body diagram of Fig. 5–22. We use the law of universal gravitation to find the magnitude of each force, and then add the two forces as vectors.

**SOLUTION** The Earth is $3.84 \times 10^5\,\text{km} = 3.84 \times 10^8\,\text{m}$ from the Moon, so $F_{ME}$ (the gravitational force on the Moon due to the Earth) is

$$F_{ME} = \frac{(6.67 \times 10^{-11}\,\text{N}\cdot\text{m}^2/\text{kg}^2)(7.35 \times 10^{22}\,\text{kg})(5.98 \times 10^{24}\,\text{kg})}{(3.84 \times 10^8\,\text{m})^2}$$
$$= 1.99 \times 10^{20}\,\text{N}.$$

The Sun is $1.50 \times 10^8\,\text{km}$ from the Earth and the Moon, so $F_{MS}$ (the gravitational force on the Moon due to the Sun) is

$$F_{MS} = \frac{(6.67 \times 10^{-11}\,\text{N}\cdot\text{m}^2/\text{kg}^2)(7.35 \times 10^{22}\,\text{kg})(1.99 \times 10^{30}\,\text{kg})}{(1.50 \times 10^{11}\,\text{m})^2}$$
$$= 4.34 \times 10^{20}\,\text{N}.$$

The two forces act at right angles in the case we are considering (Fig. 5–22), so we can apply the Pythagorean theorem to find the magnitude of the total force:

$$F = \sqrt{(1.99 \times 10^{20}\,\text{N})^2 + (4.34 \times 10^{20}\,\text{N})^2} = 4.77 \times 10^{20}\,\text{N}.$$

The force acts at an angle $\theta$ (Fig. 5–22) given by $\theta = \tan^{-1}(1.99/4.34) = 24.6°$.

**CAUTION**

*Distinguish between Newton's second law and the law of universal gravitation*

Don't confuse the law of universal gravitation with Newton's second law of motion, $\Sigma\vec{\mathbf{F}} = m\vec{\mathbf{a}}$. The former describes a particular force, gravity, and how its strength varies with the distance and masses involved. Newton's second law, on the other hand, relates the net force on an object (i.e., the vector sum of all the different forces acting on the object, whatever their sources) to the mass and acceleration of that object.

## 5–7 Gravity Near the Earth's Surface; Geophysical Applications

When Eq. 5–4 is applied to the gravitational force between the Earth and an object at its surface, $m_1$ becomes the mass of the Earth $m_E$, $m_2$ becomes the mass of the object $m$, and $r$ becomes the distance of the object from the Earth's center,† which is the radius of the Earth $r_E$. This force of gravity due to the Earth is the weight of the object, which we have been writing as $mg$. Thus,

$$mg = G\frac{mm_E}{r_E^2}.$$

We can solve this for $g$, the acceleration of gravity at the Earth's surface:

$$g = G\frac{m_E}{r_E^2}. \qquad (5\text{–}5)$$

*g in terms of G*

Thus, the acceleration of gravity at the surface of the Earth, $g$, is determined by $m_E$ and $r_E$. (Don't confuse $G$ with $g$; they are very different quantities, but are related by Eq. 5–5.)

**CAUTION**
*Distinguish G from g*

Until $G$ was measured, the mass of the Earth was not known. But once $G$ was measured, Eq. 5–5 could be used to calculate the Earth's mass, and Cavendish was the first to do so. Since $g = 9.80\,\text{m/s}^2$ and the radius of the Earth is $r_E = 6.38 \times 10^6\,\text{m}$, then, from Eq. 5–5, we obtain

$$m_E = \frac{gr_E^2}{G} = \frac{(9.80\,\text{m/s}^2)(6.38 \times 10^6\,\text{m})^2}{6.67 \times 10^{-11}\,\text{N}\cdot\text{m}^2/\text{kg}^2} = 5.98 \times 10^{24}\,\text{kg}$$

*Mass of the Earth*

for the mass of the Earth.

Equation 5–5 can be applied to other planets, where $g$, $m$, and $r$ would refer to that planet.

**EXAMPLE 5–13 ESTIMATE Gravity on Everest.** Estimate the effective value of $g$ on the top of Mt. Everest, 8850 m (29,035 ft) above sea level. That is, what is the acceleration due to gravity of objects allowed to fall freely at this altitude?

**APPROACH** The force of gravity (and the acceleration due to gravity $g$) depends on the distance from the center of the Earth, so there will be an effective value $g'$ on top of Mt. Everest which will be smaller than $g$ at sea level. We assume the Earth is a uniform sphere (a reasonable "estimate").

**SOLUTION** We use Eq. 5–5, with $r_E$ replaced by $r = 6380\,\text{km} + 8.9\,\text{km} = 6389\,\text{km} = 6.389 \times 10^6\,\text{m}$:

$$g = G\frac{m_E}{r^2} = \frac{(6.67 \times 10^{-11}\,\text{N}\cdot\text{m}^2/\text{kg}^2)(5.98 \times 10^{24}\,\text{kg})}{(6.389 \times 10^6\,\text{m})^2} = 9.77\,\text{m/s}^2,$$

which is a reduction of about 3 parts in a thousand (0.3%).

**NOTE** This is an estimate because, among other things, we ignored the mass accumulated under the mountaintop.

Note that Eq. 5–5 does not give precise values for $g$ at different locations because the Earth is not a perfect sphere. The Earth not only has mountains and valleys, and bulges at the equator, but also its mass is not distributed precisely uniformly (see Table 5–1). The Earth's rotation also affects the value of $g$. However, for most practical purposes, when an object is near the Earth's surface, we will simply use $g = 9.80\,\text{m/s}^2$ and write the weight of an object as $mg$.

**TABLE 5–1 Acceleration Due to Gravity at Various Locations on Earth**

| Location | Elevation (m) | $g$ (m/s²) |
|---|---|---|
| New York | 0 | 9.803 |
| San Francisco | 0 | 9.800 |
| Denver | 1650 | 9.796 |
| Pikes Peak | 4300 | 9.789 |
| Sydney, Australia | 0 | 9.798 |
| Equator | 0 | 9.780 |
| North Pole (calculated) | 0 | 9.832 |

†That the distance is measured from the Earth's center does not imply that the force of gravity somehow emanates from that one point. Rather, all parts of the Earth attract gravitationally, but the net effect is a force acting toward the Earth's center.

The value of $g$ can vary locally on the Earth's surface because of the presence of irregularities and rocks of different densities. Such variations in $g$, known as "gravity anomalies," are very small—on the order of 1 part per $10^6$ or $10^7$ in the value of $g$. But they can be measured by "gravimeters" which detect variations in $g$ to 1 part in $10^9$. Geophysicists use such measurements as part of their investigations into the structure of the Earth's crust, and in mineral and oil exploration. Mineral deposits, for example, often have a greater density than does surrounding material. Because of the greater mass in a given volume, $g$ can have a slightly greater value on top of such a deposit than at its flanks. "Salt domes," under which petroleum is often found, have a lower than average density; searches for a slight reduction in the value of $g$ in certain locales have led to the discovery of oil.

PHYSICS APPLIED
*Geology—mineral and oil exploration*

## 5–8 Satellites and "Weightlessness"

### Satellite Motion

PHYSICS APPLIED
*Artificial Earth satellites*

Artificial satellites circling the Earth are now commonplace (Fig. 5–23). A satellite is put into orbit by accelerating it to a sufficiently high tangential speed with the use of rockets, as shown in Fig. 5–24. If the speed is too high, the spacecraft will not be confined by the Earth's gravity and will escape, never to return. If the speed is too low, it will return to Earth. Satellites are usually put into circular (or nearly circular) orbits, because such orbits require the least takeoff speed.

**FIGURE 5–23** A satellite circling the Earth.

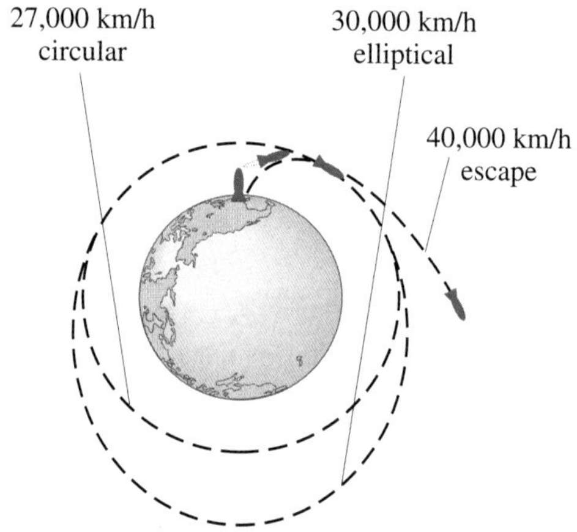


**FIGURE 5–24** Artificial satellites launched at different speeds.

It is sometimes asked: "What keeps a satellite up?" The answer is: its high speed. If a satellite stopped moving, it would fall directly to Earth. But at the very high speed a satellite has, it would quickly fly out into space (Fig. 5–25) if it weren't for the gravitational force of the Earth pulling it into orbit. In fact, a satellite *is* falling (accelerating toward Earth), but its high tangential speed keeps it from hitting Earth.

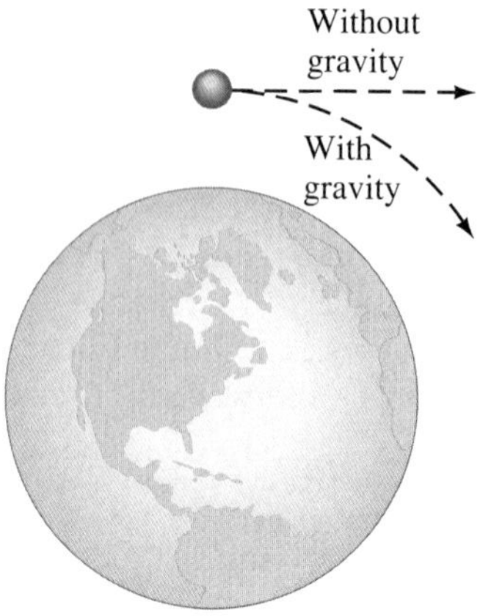


**FIGURE 5–25** A moving satellite "falls" out of a straight-line path toward the Earth.

**EXAMPLE 5–14** **Geosynchronous satellite.** A *geosynchronous* satellite is one that stays above the same point on the Earth, which is possible only if it is above a point on the equator. Such satellites are used for TV and radio transmission, for weather forecasting, and as communication relays. Determine (*a*) the height above the Earth's surface such a satellite must orbit, and (*b*) such a satellite's speed. (*c*) Compare to the speed of a satellite orbiting 200 km above Earth's surface.

PHYSICS APPLIED

*Geosynchronous satellites*

**APPROACH** To remain above the same point on Earth as the Earth rotates, the satellite must have a period of one day. We can apply Newton's second law, $F = ma$, where $a = v^2/r$ if we assume the orbit is circular.

**SOLUTION** (*a*) The only force on the satellite is the force of universal gravitation. So Eq. 5–4 gives us the force $F$, which we insert into Newton's second law:

$$F = ma$$

$$G\frac{m_{\text{Sat}}m_{\text{E}}}{r^2} = m_{\text{Sat}}\frac{v^2}{r}. \qquad \text{[satellite equation]}$$

This equation has two unknowns, $r$ and $v$. But the satellite revolves around the Earth with the same period that the Earth rotates on its axis, namely once in 24 hours. Thus the speed of the satellite must be

$$v = \frac{2\pi r}{T},$$

where $T = 1\text{ day} = (24\text{ h})(3600\text{ s/h}) = 86{,}400\text{ s}$. We substitute this into the "satellite equation" above and obtain (after canceling $m_{\text{Sat}}$ on both sides)

$$G\frac{m_{\text{E}}}{r^2} = \frac{(2\pi r)^2}{rT^2}.$$

After cancelling an $r$, we can solve for $r^3$:

$$r^3 = \frac{Gm_{\text{E}}T^2}{4\pi^2} = \frac{(6.67\times10^{-11}\,\text{N}\cdot\text{m}^2/\text{kg}^2)(5.98\times10^{24}\,\text{kg})(86{,}400\,\text{s})^2}{4\pi^2}$$

$$= 7.54\times10^{22}\,\text{m}^3.$$

Taking the cube root, we get $r = 4.23\times10^7\,\text{m}$, or 42,300 km from the Earth's center. We subtract the Earth's radius of 6380 km to find that a geosynchronous satellite must orbit about 36,000 km (about 6 $r_{\text{E}}$) above the Earth's surface.
(*b*) We solve for $v$ in the satellite equation given in part (*a*):

$$v = \sqrt{\frac{Gm_{\text{E}}}{r}} = \sqrt{\frac{(6.67\times10^{-11}\,\text{N}\cdot\text{m}^2/\text{kg}^2)(5.98\times10^{24}\,\text{kg})}{(4.23\times10^7\,\text{m})}} = 3070\,\text{m/s}.$$

We get the same result if we use $v = 2\pi r/T$.
(*c*) The equation in part (*b*) for $v$ shows $v \propto \sqrt{1/r}$. So for $r = r_{\text{E}} + h = 6380\text{ km} + 200\text{ km} = 6580\text{ km}$, we get

$$v' = v\sqrt{\frac{r}{r'}} = (3070\,\text{m/s})\sqrt{\frac{(42{,}300\,\text{km})}{(6580\,\text{km})}} = 7780\,\text{m/s}.$$

**NOTE** The center of a satellite orbit is always at the center of the Earth; so it is not possible to have a satellite orbiting above a fixed point on the Earth at any latitude other than 0°.

**EXERCISE G** Two satellites orbit the Earth in circular orbits of the same radius. One satellite is twice as massive as the other. Which of the following statements is true about the speeds of these satellites? (*a*) The heavier satellite moves twice as fast as the lighter one. (*b*) The two satellites have the same speed. (*c*) The lighter satellite moves twice as fast as the heavier one. (*d*) The heavier satellite moves four times as fast as the lighter one.

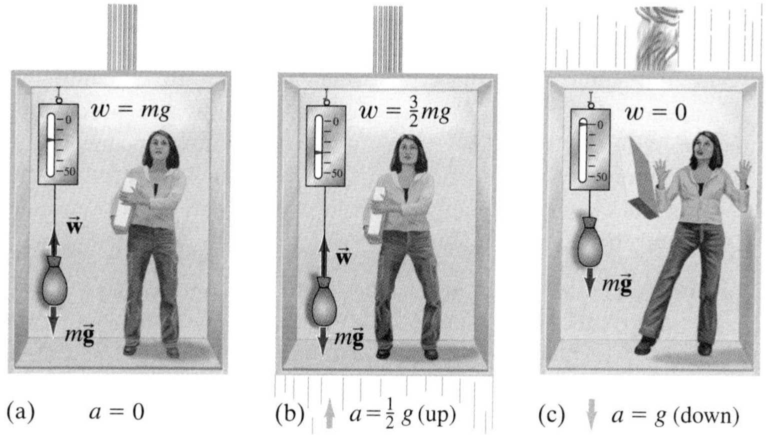


**FIGURE 5–26** (a) An object in an elevator at rest exerts a force on a spring scale equal to its weight. (b) In an elevator accelerating upward at $\frac{1}{2}g$, the object's apparent weight is $1\frac{1}{2}$ times larger than its true weight. (c) In a freely falling elevator, the object experiences "weightlessness": the scale reads zero.

## Weightlessness

*"Weightlessness" in a falling elevator*

People and other objects in a satellite circling the Earth are said to experience apparent weightlessness. Let us first look at a simpler case, that of a falling elevator. In Fig. 5–26a, an elevator is at rest with a bag hanging from a spring scale. The scale reading indicates the downward force exerted on it by the bag. This force, exerted *on* the scale, is equal and opposite to the force exerted *by* the scale upward on the bag, and we call its magnitude $w$. Two forces act on the bag: the downward gravitational force and the upward force exerted by the scale (Newton's third law) equal to $w$. Because the bag is not accelerating, when we apply $\Sigma F = ma$ to the bag in Fig. 5–26a we obtain

$$w - mg = 0,$$

where $mg$ is the weight of the bag. Thus, $w = mg$, and since the scale indicates the force $w$ exerted on it by the bag, it registers a force equal to the weight of the bag, as we expect.

If, now, the elevator has an acceleration, $a$, then applying $\Sigma F = ma$ to the bag, we have

$$w - mg = ma.$$

Solving for $w$, we have

$$w = mg + ma. \qquad [a \text{ is } + \text{ upward}]$$

We have chosen the positive direction up. Thus, if the acceleration $a$ is up, $a$ is positive; and the scale, which measures $w$, will read more than $mg$. We call $w$ the *apparent weight* of the bag, which in this case would be greater than its actual weight ($mg$). If the elevator accelerates downward, $a$ will be negative and $w$, the apparent weight, will be less than $mg$. The direction of the velocity $\vec{\mathbf{v}}$ doesn't matter. Only the direction of the acceleration $\vec{\mathbf{a}}$ influences the scale reading.

Suppose, for example, the elevator's acceleration is $\frac{1}{2}g$ upward; then we find

$$w = mg + m(\tfrac{1}{2}g) = \tfrac{3}{2}mg.$$

That is, the scale reads $1\frac{1}{2}$ times the actual weight of the bag (Fig. 5–26b). The apparent weight of the bag is $1\frac{1}{2}$ times its real weight. The same is true of the person: her apparent weight (equal to the normal force exerted on her by the elevator floor) is $1\frac{1}{2}$ times her real weight. We can say that she is experiencing $1\frac{1}{2}g$'s, just as astronauts experience so many $g$'s at a rocket's launch.

If, instead, the elevator's acceleration is $a = -\frac{1}{2}g$ (downward), then $w = mg - \frac{1}{2}mg = \frac{1}{2}mg$. That is, the scale reads half the actual weight. If the elevator is in *free fall* (for example, if the cables break), then $a = -g$ and $w = mg - mg = 0$. The scale reads zero. See Fig. 5–26c. The bag appears weightless. If the person in the elevator accelerating at $-g$ let go of a pencil, say, it would not fall to the floor. True, the pencil would be falling with acceleration $g$. But so would the floor of the elevator and the person. The pencil would hover right in front of the person. This phenomenon is called *apparent weightlessness* because in the reference frame of the person, objects don't fall or seem to have weight—yet gravity does not disappear. It is still acting on the object, whose

**FIGURE 5–27** Experiencing weightlessness on Earth.

weight is still $mg$. The objects seem weightless only because the elevator is in free fall, and there is no contact force to make us feel the weight.

The "weightlessness" experienced by people in a satellite orbit close to the Earth is the same apparent weightlessness experienced in a freely falling elevator. It may seem strange, at first, to think of a satellite as freely falling. But a satellite is indeed falling toward the Earth, as was shown in Fig. 5–25. The force of gravity causes it to "fall" out of its natural straight-line path. The acceleration of the satellite must be the acceleration due to gravity at that point, since the only force acting on it is gravity. Thus, although the force of gravity acts on objects within the satellite, the objects experience an apparent weightlessness because they, and the satellite, are all accelerating as in free fall.

*"Weightlessness" in a satellite*

Figure 5–27 shows some examples of "free fall," or apparent weightlessness, experienced by people on Earth for brief moments.

A different situation occurs when a spacecraft is out in space far from the Earth, the Moon, and other attracting objects. The force of gravity due to the Earth and other heavenly bodies will then be quite small because of the distances involved, and people in such a spacecraft will experience real weightlessness.

## * 5–9 Kepler's Laws and Newton's Synthesis

More than a half century before Newton proposed his three laws of motion and his law of universal gravitation, the German astronomer Johannes Kepler (1571–1630) had worked out a detailed description of the motion of the planets about the Sun: three empirical findings that we now refer to as **Kepler's laws of planetary motion**. They are summarized as follows, with additional explanation in Figs. 5–28 and 5–29.

*Kepler's first law*: The path of each planet about the Sun is an ellipse with the Sun at one focus (Fig. 5–28).

*Kepler's second law*: Each planet moves so that an imaginary line drawn from the Sun to the planet sweeps out equal areas in equal periods of time (Fig. 5–29).

*Kepler's third law*: The ratio of the squares of the periods $T$ of any two planets revolving about the Sun is equal to the ratio of the cubes of their mean distances $s$ from the Sun: $(T_1/T_2)^2 = (s_1/s_2)^3$. [Actually, $s$ is the semimajor axis, defined as half the long (major) axis of the orbit, as shown in Fig. 5–28. We can also call it the mean distance of the planet from the Sun.] Present-day data are given in Table 5–2: see the last column.

Kepler arrived at his laws through careful analysis of experimental data. Fifty years later, Newton was able to show that Kepler's laws could be derived mathematically from the law of universal gravitation and the laws of motion. Newton also showed that for any reasonable form for the gravitational force law, only one that depends on the inverse square of the distance is fully consistent with Kepler's laws. He thus used Kepler's laws as evidence in favor of his law of universal gravitation, Eq. 5–4.

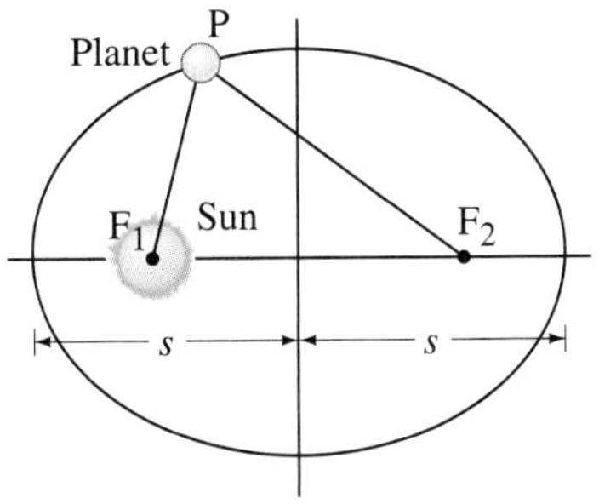


**FIGURE 5–28** (a) *Kepler's first law*. An ellipse is a closed curve such that the sum of the distances from any point P on the curve to two fixed points (called the foci, $F_1$ and $F_2$) remains constant. That is, the sum of the distances, $F_1P + F_2P$, is the same for all points on the curve. A circle is a special case of an ellipse in which the two foci coincide, at the center of the circle.

**FIGURE 5–29** *Kepler's second law*. The two shaded regions have equal areas. The planet moves from point 1 to point 2 in the same time as it takes to move from point 3 to point 4. Planets move fastest in that part of their orbit where they are closest to the Sun. Exaggerated scale.

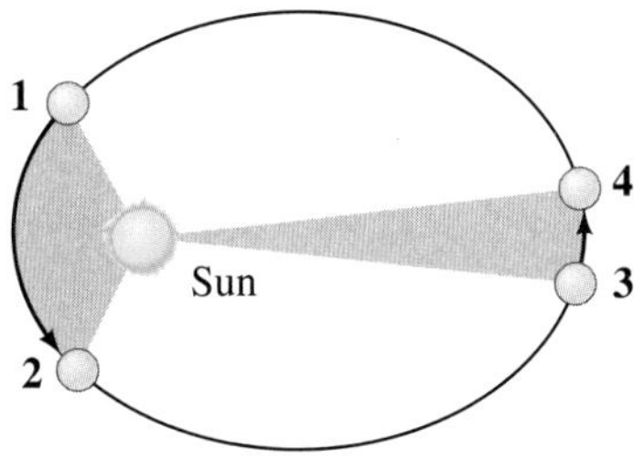


**TABLE 5–2 Planetary Data Applied to Kepler's Third Law**

| Planet | Mean Distance from Sun, $s$ ($10^6$ km) | Period, $T$ (Earth years) | $s^3/T^2$ ($10^{24}$ km$^3$/y$^2$) |
|---|---|---|---|
| Mercury | 57.9 | 0.241 | 3.34 |
| Venus | 108.2 | 0.615 | 3.35 |
| Earth | 149.6 | 1.0 | 3.35 |
| Mars | 227.9 | 1.88 | 3.35 |
| Jupiter | 778.3 | 11.86 | 3.35 |
| Saturn | 1427 | 29.5 | 3.34 |
| Uranus | 2870 | 84.0 | 3.35 |
| Neptune | 4497 | 165 | 3.34 |
| Pluto | 5900 | 248 | 3.34 |

*Derivation of Kepler's third law*

We will derive Kepler's third law for the special case of a circular orbit. (Most planetary orbits are close to a circle.) First, we write Newton's second law of motion, $\Sigma F = ma$. For $F$ we use the gravitational force (Eq. 5–4) between the Sun and a planet of mass $m_1$, and for $a$ the centripetal acceleration, $v^2/r$. We assume the mass of the Sun, $M_S$, is much greater than the mass of its planets. Then

$$\Sigma F = ma$$

$$G\frac{m_1 M_S}{r_1^2} = m_1 \frac{v_1^2}{r_1}.$$

Here $r_1$ is the distance of one planet from the Sun, and $v_1$ is its average speed in orbit; $M_S$ is the mass of the Sun, since it is the gravitational attraction of the Sun that keeps each planet in its orbit. The period $T_1$ of the planet is the time required for one complete orbit, a distance equal to the circumference of its orbit, $2\pi r_1$. Thus

$$v_1 = \frac{2\pi r_1}{T_1}.$$

We substitute this formula for $v_1$ into the equation above:

$$G\frac{m_1 M_S}{r_1^2} = m_1 \frac{4\pi^2 r_1}{T_1^2}.$$

We rearrange this to get

$$\frac{T_1^2}{r_1^3} = \frac{4\pi^2}{GM_S}. \qquad \textbf{(5–6a)}$$

We derived this for planet 1 (say, Mars). The same derivation would apply for a second planet (say, Saturn) orbiting the Sun,

$$\frac{T_2^2}{r_2^3} = \frac{4\pi^2}{GM_S},$$

where $T_2$ and $r_2$ are the period and orbit radius, respectively, for the second planet. Since the right sides of the two previous equations are equal, we have $T_1^2/r_1^3 = T_2^2/r_2^3$ or, rearranging,

*Kepler's third law*

$$\left(\frac{T_1}{T_2}\right)^2 = \left(\frac{r_1}{r_2}\right)^3, \qquad \textbf{(5–6b)}$$

which is Kepler's third law.

The derivations of Eqs. 5–6a and 5–6b (Kepler's third law) compared two planets revolving around the Sun; but they are general enough to be applied to other systems. For example, we could apply Eq. 5–6a to our Moon revolving around Earth (then $M_S$ would be $M_E$, the mass of the Earth). Or we could apply Eq. 5–6b to compare two moons revolving around Jupiter. But Kepler's third law applies only to objects orbiting the same attracting center. Do not use Eq. 5–6b to compare, say, the Moon's orbit around the Earth to the orbit of Mars around the Sun because they depend on different attracting centers.

**CAUTION**

*Compare orbits of objects only around the same center*

In the following Examples, we assume the orbits are circles, although it is not quite true in general.

**EXAMPLE 5–15** **Where is Mars?** Mars' period (its "year") was noted by Kepler to be about 687 days (Earth days), which is (687 d/365 d) = 1.88 yr. Determine the distance of Mars from the Sun using the Earth as a reference.

**APPROACH** We know the periods of Earth and Mars, and the distance from the Sun to Earth. We can use Kepler's third law to obtain the distance from the Sun to Mars.

**SOLUTION** The period of the Earth is $T_E = 1$ yr, and the distance of Earth from the Sun is $r_{ES} = 1.50 \times 10^{11}$ m. From Kepler's third law (Eq. 5–6b):

$$\frac{r_{MS}}{r_{ES}} = \left(\frac{T_M}{T_E}\right)^{\frac{2}{3}} = \left(\frac{1.88\text{ yr}}{1\text{ yr}}\right)^{\frac{2}{3}} = 1.52.$$

So Mars is 1.52 times the Earth's distance from the Sun, or $2.28 \times 10^{11}$ m.

**EXAMPLE 5–16** **The Sun's mass determined.** Determine the mass of the Sun given the Earth's distance from the Sun as $r_{ES} = 1.5 \times 10^{11}$ m.

PHYSICS APPLIED
*Determining the Sun's mass*

**APPROACH** Equation 5–6a relates the mass of the Sun $M_S$ to the period and distance of any planet. We use the Earth.

**SOLUTION** The Earth's period is $T_E = 1\text{ yr} = \left(365\frac{1}{4}\text{ d}\right)(24\text{ h/d})(3600\text{ s/h}) = 3.16 \times 10^7$ s. We solve Eq. 5–6a for $M_S$:

$$M_S = \frac{4\pi^2 r_{ES}^3}{G T_E^2} = \frac{4\pi^2\left(1.5 \times 10^{11}\text{ m}\right)^3}{\left(6.67 \times 10^{-11}\text{ N}\cdot\text{m}^2/\text{kg}^2\right)\left(3.16 \times 10^7\text{ s}\right)^2} = 2.0 \times 10^{30}\text{ kg}.$$

Accurate measurements on the orbits of the planets indicated that they did not precisely follow Kepler's laws. For example, slight deviations from perfectly elliptical orbits were observed. Newton was aware that this was to be expected because any planet would be attracted gravitationally not only by the Sun but also (to a much lesser extent) by the other planets. Such deviations, or **perturbations**, in the orbit of Saturn were a hint that helped Newton formulate the law of universal gravitation, that all objects attract gravitationally. Observation of other perturbations later led to the discovery of Neptune and Pluto. Deviations in the orbit of Uranus, for example, could not all be accounted for by perturbations due to the other known planets. Careful calculation in the nineteenth century indicated that these deviations could be accounted for if another planet existed farther out in the solar system. The position of this planet was predicted from the deviations in the orbit of Uranus, and telescopes focused on that region of the sky quickly found it; the new planet was called Neptune. Similar but much smaller perturbations of Neptune's orbit led to the discovery of Pluto in 1930.

*Perturbations and discovery of planets*

Starting in the mid–1990s, planets revolving about distant stars (Fig. 5–30) were inferred from the regular "wobble" of each star due to the gravitational attraction of the revolving planet(s).

*Planets around other stars*

The development by Newton of the law of universal gravitation and the three laws of motion was a major intellectual achievement: with these laws, he was able to describe the motion of objects on Earth and in the heavens. The motions of heavenly bodies and objects on Earth were seen to follow the same laws. For this reason, and also because Newton integrated the results of earlier scientists into his system, we sometimes speak of *Newton's synthesis*.

*Newton's synthesis*

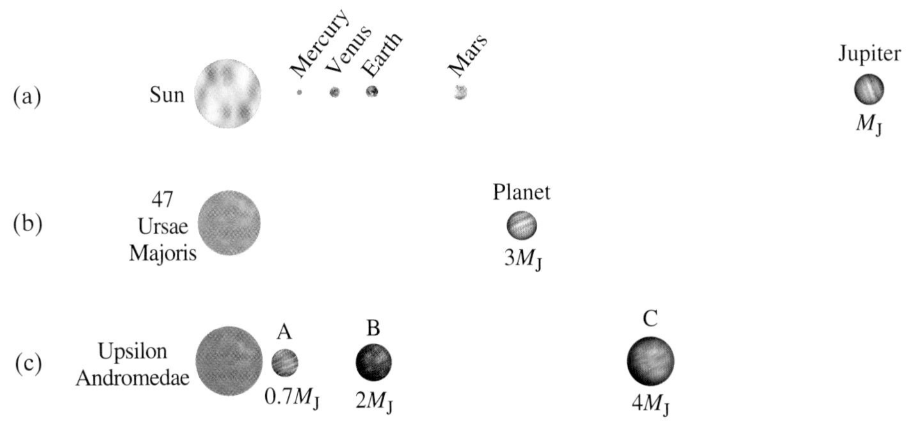


**FIGURE 5–30** Our solar system (a) is compared to recently discovered planets orbiting (b) the star 47 Ursae Majoris and (c) the star Upsilon Andromedae with at least three planets. $M_J$ is the mass of Jupiter. (Sizes not to scale.)

*Causality*

The laws formulated by Newton are referred to as **causal laws**. By **causality** we mean the idea that one occurrence can cause another. When a rock strikes a window, we infer that the rock *causes* the window to break. This idea of "cause and effect" relates to Newton's laws: the acceleration of an object was seen to be *caused* by the net force acting on it.

## 5–10 Types of Forces in Nature

We have already discussed that Newton's law of universal gravitation, Eq. 5–4, describes how a particular type of force—gravity—depends on the masses of the objects involved and the distance between them. Newton's second law, $\Sigma\vec{\mathbf{F}} = m\vec{\mathbf{a}}$, on the other hand, tells how an object will accelerate due to *any* type of force. But what are the types of forces that occur in nature besides gravity?

In the twentieth century, physicists came to recognize four fundamental forces in nature: (1) the gravitational force; (2) the electromagnetic force (we shall see later that electric and magnetic forces are intimately related); (3) the strong nuclear force; and (4) the weak nuclear force. In this Chapter, we discussed the gravitational force in detail. The nature of the electromagnetic force will be discussed in Chapters 16 to 22. The strong and weak nuclear forces, which are discussed in Chapters 30 to 32, operate at the level of the atomic nucleus; although they manifest themselves in such phenomena as radioactivity and nuclear energy, they are much less obvious in our daily lives.

Physicists have been working on theories that would unify these four forces—that is, to consider some or all of these forces as different manifestations of the same basic force. So far, the electromagnetic and weak nuclear forces have been theoretically united to form *electroweak* theory, in which the electromagnetic and weak forces are seen as two different manifestations of a single *electroweak force*. Attempts to further unify the forces, such as in *grand unified theories* (GUT), are hot research topics today.

*Electroweak and GUT*

But where do everyday forces fit into this scheme? Ordinary forces, other than gravity, such as pushes, pulls, and other contact forces like the normal force and friction, are today considered to be due to the electromagnetic force acting at the atomic level. For example, the force your fingers exert on a pencil is the result of electrical repulsion between the outer electrons of the atoms of your finger and those of the pencil.

*Everyday forces are gravity and electromagnetic*

## Summary

An object moving in a circle of radius $r$ with constant speed $v$ is said to be in **uniform circular motion**. It has a **centripetal acceleration** $a_R$ that is directed radially toward the center of the circle (also called **radial acceleration**), and has magnitude

$$a_R = \frac{v^2}{r}. \qquad \textbf{(5–1)}$$

The direction of the velocity vector and that of the acceleration $\vec{\mathbf{a}}_R$ are continually changing in direction, but are perpendicular to each other at each moment.

A force is needed to keep a particle revolving in a circle, and the direction of this force is toward the center of the circle. This force may be due to gravity, to tension in a cord, to a component of the normal force, to another type of force, or to a combination of forces.

[*When the speed of circular motion is not constant, the acceleration has two components, tangential as well as centripetal.]

Newton's **law of universal gravitation** states that every particle in the universe attracts every other particle with a force proportional to the product of their masses and inversely proportional to the square of the distance between them:

$$F = G\frac{m_1 m_2}{r^2}. \qquad \textbf{(5–4)}$$

The direction of this force is along the line joining the two particles. It is this gravitational force that keeps the Moon revolving around the Earth, and the planets revolving around the Sun.

Satellites revolving around the Earth are acted on by gravity, but "stay up" because of their high tangential speed.

[*Newton's three laws of motion, plus his law of universal gravitation, constituted a wide-ranging theory of the universe. With them, motion of objects on Earth and in the heavens could be accurately described. And they provided a theoretical base for **Kepler's laws** of planetary motion.]

The four fundamental forces in nature are (1) the gravitational force, (2) electromagnetic force, (3) strong nuclear force, and (4) weak nuclear force. The first two fundamental forces are responsible for nearly all "everyday" forces.

## Questions

1. Sometimes people say that water is removed from clothes in a spin dryer by centrifugal force throwing the water outward. What is wrong with this statement?

2. Will the acceleration of a car be the same when the car travels around a sharp curve at a constant 60 km/h as when it travels around a gentle curve at the same speed? Explain.

3. Suppose a car moves at constant speed along a hilly road. Where does the car exert the greatest and least forces on the road: (*a*) at the top of a hill, (*b*) at a dip between two hills, (*c*) on a level stretch near the bottom of a hill?

4. Describe all the forces acting on a child riding a horse on a merry-go-round. Which of these forces provides the centripetal acceleration of the child?

5. A bucket of water can be whirled in a vertical circle without the water spilling out, even at the top of the circle when the bucket is upside down. Explain.

6. How many "accelerators" do you have in your car? There are at least three controls in the car which can be used to cause the car to accelerate. What are they? What accelerations do they produce?

7. A child on a sled comes flying over the crest of a small hill, as shown in Fig. 5–31. His sled does not leave the ground (he does not achieve "air"), but he feels the normal force between his chest and the sled decrease as he goes over the hill. Explain this decrease using Newton's second law.

**FIGURE 5–31** Question 7.

8. Why do bicycle riders lean inward when rounding a curve at high speed?

9. Why do airplanes bank when they turn? How would you compute the banking angle given its speed and radius of the turn?

10. A girl is whirling a ball on a string around her head in a horizontal plane. She wants to let go at precisely the right time so that the ball will hit a target on the other side of the yard. When should she let go of the string?

11. Does an apple exert a gravitational force on the Earth? If so, how large a force? Consider an apple (*a*) attached to a tree, and (*b*) falling.

12. If the Earth's mass were double what it is, in what ways would the Moon's orbit be different?

13. Which pulls harder gravitationally, the Earth on the Moon, or the Moon on the Earth? Which accelerates more?

14. The Sun's gravitational pull on the Earth is much larger than the Moon's. Yet the Moon's is mainly responsible for the tides. Explain. [*Hint*: Consider the difference in gravitational pull from one side of the Earth to the other.]

15. Will an object weigh more at the equator or at the poles? What two effects are at work? Do they oppose each other?

16. The gravitational force on the Moon due to the Earth is only about half the force on the Moon due to the Sun. Why isn't the Moon pulled away from the Earth?

17. Is the centripetal acceleration of Mars in its orbit around the Sun larger or smaller than the centripetal acceleration of the Earth?

18. Would it require less speed to launch a satellite (*a*) toward the east or (*b*) toward the west? Consider the Earth's rotation direction.

19. When will your apparent weight be the greatest, as measured by a scale in a moving elevator: when the elevator (*a*) accelerates downward, (*b*) accelerates upward, (*c*) is in free fall, (*d*) moves upward at constant speed? In which case would your weight be the least? When would it be the same as when you are on the ground?

20. What keeps a satellite up in its orbit around the Earth?

21. Astronauts who spend long periods in outer space could be adversely affected by weightlessness. One way to simulate gravity is to shape the spaceship like a cylindrical shell that rotates, with the astronauts walking on the inside surface (Fig. 5–32). Explain how this simulates gravity. Consider (*a*) how objects fall, (*b*) the force we feel on our feet, and (*c*) any other aspects of gravity you can think of.

**FIGURE 5–32** Question 21 and Problem 45.

22. Explain how a runner experiences "free fall" or "apparent weightlessness" between steps.

* 23. The Earth moves faster in its orbit around the Sun in January than in July. Is the Earth closer to the Sun in January, or in July? Explain. [*Note*: This is not much of a factor in producing the seasons—the main factor is the tilt of the Earth's axis relative to the plane of its orbit.]

* 24. The mass of Pluto was not known until it was discovered to have a moon. Explain how this discovery enabled an estimate of Pluto's mass.

## Problems

### 5–1 to 5–3 Uniform Circular Motion; Highway Curves

1. (I) A child sitting 1.10 m from the center of a merry-go-round moves with a speed of 1.25 m/s. Calculate (*a*) the centripetal acceleration of the child, and (*b*) the net horizontal force exerted on the child (mass = 25.0 kg).

2. (I) A jet plane traveling 1890 km/h (525 m/s) pulls out of a dive by moving in an arc of radius 6.00 km. What is the plane's acceleration in *g*'s?

3. (I) Calculate the centripetal acceleration of the Earth in its orbit around the Sun, and the net force exerted on the Earth. What exerts this force on the Earth? Assume that the Earth's orbit is a circle of radius $1.50 \times 10^{11}$ m. [*Hint*: see the Tables inside the front cover of this book.]

4. (I) A horizontal force of 210 N is exerted on a 2.0-kg discus as it rotates uniformly in a horizontal circle (at arm's length) of radius 0.90 m. Calculate the speed of the discus.

5. (II) Suppose the space shuttle is in orbit 400 km from the Earth's surface, and circles the Earth about once every 90 minutes. Find the centripetal acceleration of the space shuttle in its orbit. Express your answer in terms of *g*, the gravitational acceleration at the Earth's surface.

6. (II) What is the magnitude of the acceleration of a speck of clay on the edge of a potter's wheel turning at 45 rpm (revolutions per minute) if the wheel's diameter is 32 cm?

7. (II) A ball on the end of a string is revolved at a uniform rate in a vertical circle of radius 72.0 cm, as shown in Fig. 5–33. If its speed is 4.00 m/s and its mass is 0.300 kg, calculate the tension in the string when the ball is (*a*) at the top of its path, and (*b*) at the bottom of its path.

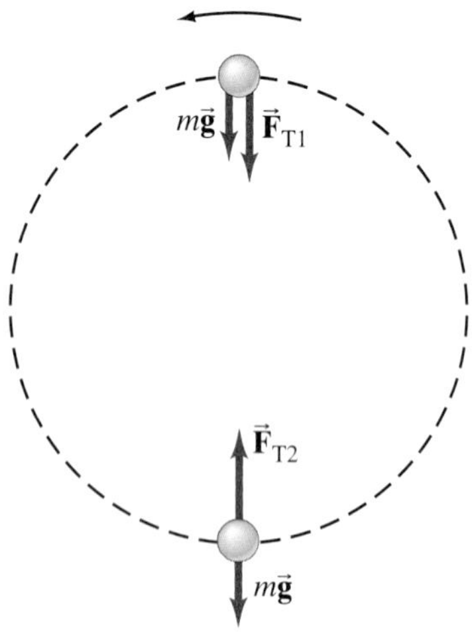


**FIGURE 5–33** Problem 7.

8. (II) A 0.45-kg ball, attached to the end of a horizontal cord, is rotated in a circle of radius 1.3 m on a frictionless horizontal surface. If the cord will break when the tension in it exceeds 75 N, what is the maximum speed the ball can have?

9. (II) What is the maximum speed with which a 1050-kg car can round a turn of radius 77 m on a flat road if the coefficient of static friction between tires and road is 0.80? Is this result independent of the mass of the car?

10. (II) How large must the coefficient of static friction be between the tires and the road if a car is to round a level curve of radius 85 m at a speed of 95 km/h?

11. (II) A device for training astronauts and jet fighter pilots is designed to rotate a trainee in a horizontal circle of radius 12.0 m. If the force felt by the trainee on her back is 7.85 times her own weight, how fast is she rotating? Express your answer in both m/s and rev/s.

12. (II) A coin is placed 11.0 cm from the axis of a rotating turntable of variable speed. When the speed of the turntable is slowly increased, the coin remains fixed on the turntable until a rate of 36 rpm is reached and the coin slides off. What is the coefficient of static friction between the coin and the turntable?

13. (II) At what minimum speed must a roller coaster be traveling when upside down at the top of a circle (Fig. 5–34) so that the passengers will not fall out? Assume a radius of curvature of 7.4 m.

**FIGURE 5–34** Problem 13.

14. (II) A sports car of mass 950 kg (including the driver) crosses the rounded top of a hill (radius = 95 m) at 22 m/s. Determine (*a*) the normal force exerted by the road on the car, (*b*) the normal force exerted by the car on the 72-kg driver, and (*c*) the car speed at which the normal force on the driver equals zero.

15. (II) How many revolutions per minute would a 15-m-diameter Ferris wheel need to make for the passengers to feel "weightless" at the topmost point?

16. (II) A bucket of mass 2.00 kg is whirled in a vertical circle of radius 1.10 m. At the lowest point of its motion the tension in the rope supporting the bucket is 25.0 N. (*a*) Find the speed of the bucket. (*b*) How fast must the bucket move at the top of the circle so that the rope does not go slack?

17. (II) How fast (in rpm) must a centrifuge rotate if a particle 9.00 cm from the axis of rotation is to experience an acceleration of 115,000 *g*'s?

18. (II) In a "Rotor-ride" at a carnival, people are rotated in a cylindrically walled "room." (See Fig. 5–35.) The room radius is 4.6 m, and the rotation frequency is 0.50 revolutions per second when the floor drops out. What is the minimum coefficient of static friction so that the people will not slip down? People on this ride say they were "pressed against the wall." Is there really an outward force pressing them against the wall? If so, what is its source? If not, what is the proper description of their situation (besides "scary")? [*Hint*: First draw the free-body diagram for a person.]

**FIGURE 5–35** Problem 18.

19. (II) A flat puck (mass $M$) is rotated in a circle on a frictionless air-hockey tabletop, and is held in this orbit by a light cord connected to a dangling block (mass $m$) through a central hole as shown in Fig. 5–36. Show that the speed of the puck is given by

$$v = \sqrt{\frac{mgR}{M}}.$$

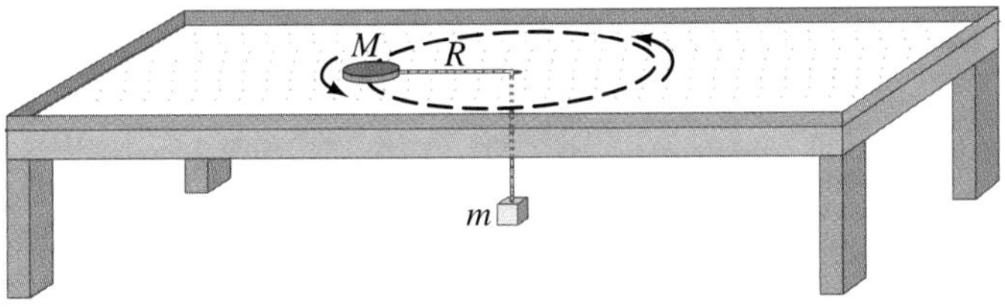


**FIGURE 5–36** Problem 19.

20. (II) Redo Example 5–3, precisely this time, by not ignoring the weight of the ball which revolves on a string 0.600 m long. In particular, find the magnitude of $\vec{\mathbf{F}}_T$, and the angle it makes with the horizontal. [*Hint*: Set the horizontal component of $\vec{\mathbf{F}}_T$ equal to $ma_R$; also, since there is no vertical motion, what can you say about the vertical component of $\vec{\mathbf{F}}_T$?]

21. (III) If a curve with a radius of 88 m is perfectly banked for a car traveling 75 km/h, what must be the coefficient of static friction for a car not to skid when traveling at 95 km/h?

22. (III) A 1200-kg car rounds a curve of radius 67 m banked at an angle of 12°. If the car is traveling at 95 km/h, will a friction force be required? If so, how much and in what direction?

23. (III) Two blocks, of masses $m_1$ and $m_2$, are connected to each other and to a central post by cords as shown in Fig. 5–37. They rotate about the post at a frequency $f$ (revolutions per second) on a frictionless horizontal surface at distances $r_1$ and $r_2$ from the post. Derive an algebraic expression for the tension in each segment of the cord.

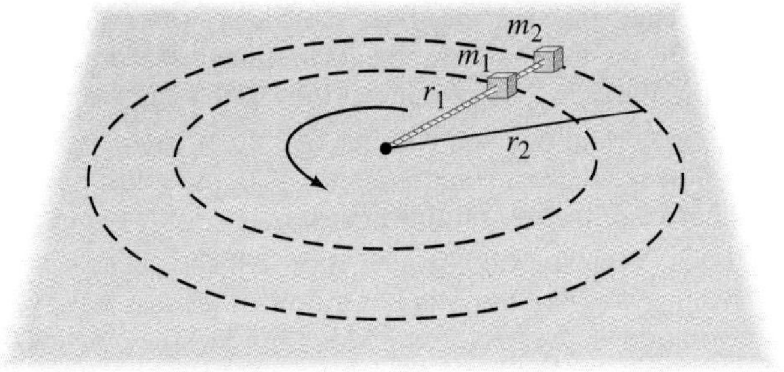


**FIGURE 5–37** Problem 23.

24. (III) A pilot performs an evasive maneuver by diving vertically at 310 m/s. If he can withstand an acceleration of 9.0 g's without blacking out, at what altitude must he begin to pull out of the dive to avoid crashing into the sea?

### * 5–4 Nonuniform Circular Motion

* 25. (I) Determine the tangential and centripetal components of the net force exerted on the car (by the ground) in Example 5–8 when its speed is 15 m/s. The car's mass is 1100 kg.

* 26. (II) A car at the Indianapolis 500 accelerates uniformly from the pit area, going from rest to 320 km/h in a semicircular arc with a radius of 220 m. Determine the tangential and radial acceleration of the car when it is halfway through the turn, assuming constant tangential acceleration. If the curve were flat, what would the coefficient of static friction have to be between the tires and the road to provide this acceleration with no slipping or skidding?

* 27. (III) A particle revolves in a horizontal circle of radius 2.90 m. At a particular instant, its acceleration is 1.05 m/s², in a direction that makes an angle of 32.0° to its direction of motion. Determine its speed (*a*) at this moment, and (*b*) 2.00 s later, assuming constant tangential acceleration.

### 5–6 and 5–7 Law of Universal Gravitation

28. (I) Calculate the force of Earth's gravity on a spacecraft 12,800 km (2 Earth radii) above the Earth's surface if its mass is 1350 kg.

29. (I) At the surface of a certain planet, the gravitational acceleration *g* has a magnitude of 12.0 m/s². A 21.0-kg brass ball is transported to this planet. What is (*a*) the mass of the brass ball on the Earth and on the planet, and (*b*) the weight of the brass ball on the Earth and on the planet?

30. (II) Calculate the acceleration due to gravity on the Moon. The Moon's radius is $1.74 \times 10^6$ m and its mass is $7.35 \times 10^{22}$ kg.

31. (II) A hypothetical planet has a radius 1.5 times that of Earth, but has the same mass. What is the acceleration due to gravity near its surface?

32. (II) A hypothetical planet has a mass 1.66 times that of Earth, but the same radius. What is $g$ near its surface?

33. (II) Two objects attract each other gravitationally with a force of $2.5 \times 10^{-10}$ N when they are 0.25 m apart. Their total mass is 4.0 kg. Find their individual masses.

34. (II) Calculate the effective value of $g$, the acceleration of gravity, at (*a*) 3200 m, and (*b*) 3200 km, above the Earth's surface.

35. (II) What is the distance from the Earth's center to a point outside the Earth where the gravitational acceleration due to the Earth is $\frac{1}{10}$ of its value at the Earth's surface?

36. (II) A certain neutron star has five times the mass of our Sun packed into a sphere about 10 km in radius. Estimate the surface gravity on this monster.

37. (II) A typical white-dwarf star, which once was an average star like our Sun but is now in the last stage of its evolution, is the size of our Moon but has the mass of our Sun. What is the surface gravity on this star?

38. (II) You are explaining why astronauts feel weightless while orbiting in the space shuttle. Your friends respond that they thought gravity was just a lot weaker up there. Convince them and yourself that it isn't so by calculating the acceleration of gravity 250 km above the Earth's surface in terms of $g$.

39. (II) Four 9.5-kg spheres are located at the corners of a square of side 0.60 m. Calculate the magnitude and direction of the total gravitational force exerted on one sphere by the other three.

40. (II) Every few hundred years most of the planets line up on the same side of the Sun. Calculate the total force on the Earth due to Venus, Jupiter, and Saturn, assuming all four planets are in a line (Fig. 5–38). The masses are $M_V = 0.815M_E$, $M_J = 318M_E$, $M_S = 95.1M_E$, and their mean distances from the Sun are 108, 150, 778, and 1430 million km, respectively. What fraction of the Sun's force on the Earth is this?

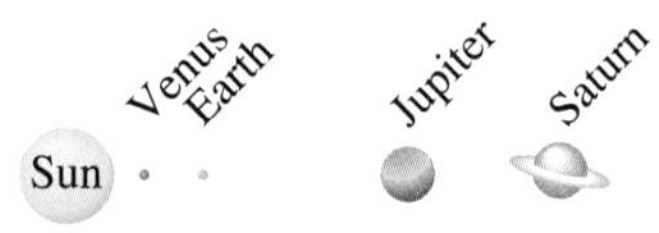


**FIGURE 5–38** Problem 40. (Not to scale.)

41. (II) Given that the acceleration of gravity at the surface of Mars is 0.38 of what it is on Earth, and that Mars' radius is 3400 km, determine the mass of Mars.

42. (III) Determine the mass of the Sun using the known value for the period of the Earth and its distance from the Sun. [*Note*: Compare your answer to that obtained using Kepler's laws, Example 5–16.]

### 5–8 Satellites; Weightlessness

43. (I) Calculate the speed of a satellite moving in a stable circular orbit about the Earth at a height of 3600 km.

44. (I) The space shuttle releases a satellite into a circular orbit 650 km above the Earth. How fast must the shuttle be moving (relative to Earth) when the release occurs?

45. (II) At what rate must a cylindrical spaceship rotate if occupants are to experience simulated gravity of 0.60 $g$? Assume the spaceship's diameter is 32 m, and give your answer as the time needed for one revolution. (See Question 21, Fig 5–32.)

46. (II) Determine the time it takes for a satellite to orbit the Earth in a circular "near-Earth" orbit. A "near-Earth" orbit is one at a height above the surface of the Earth which is very small compared to the radius of the Earth. Does your result depend on the mass of the satellite?

47. (II) At what horizontal velocity would a satellite have to be launched from the top of Mt. Everest to be placed in a circular orbit around the Earth?

48. (II) During an *Apollo* lunar landing mission, the command module continued to orbit the Moon at an altitude of about 100 km. How long did it take to go around the Moon once?

49. (II) The rings of Saturn are composed of chunks of ice that orbit the planet. The inner radius of the rings is 73,000 km, while the outer radius is 170,000 km. Find the period of an orbiting chunk of ice at the inner radius and the period of a chunk at the outer radius. Compare your numbers with Saturn's mean rotation period of 10 hours and 39 minutes. The mass of Saturn is $5.7 \times 10^{26}$ kg.

50. (II) A Ferris wheel 24.0 m in diameter rotates once every 15.5 s (see Fig. 5–9). What is the ratio of a person's apparent weight to her real weight (*a*) at the top, and (*b*) at the bottom?

51. (II) What is the apparent weight of a 75-kg astronaut 4200 km from the center of the Earth's Moon in a space vehicle (*a*) moving at constant velocity, and (*b*) accelerating toward the Moon at 2.9 m/s$^2$? State the "direction" in each case.

52. (II) Suppose that a binary-star system consists of two stars of equal mass. They are observed to be separated by 360 million km and take 5.7 Earth years to orbit about a point midway between them. What is the mass of each?

53. (II) What will a spring scale read for the weight of a 55-kg woman in an elevator that moves (*a*) upward with constant speed of 6.0 m/s, (*b*) downward with constant speed of 6.0 m/s, (*c*) upward with acceleration of 0.33 $g$, (*d*) downward with acceleration 0.33 $g$, and (*e*) in free fall?

54. (II) A 17.0-kg monkey hangs from a cord suspended from the ceiling of an elevator. The cord can withstand a tension of 220 N and breaks as the elevator accelerates. What was the elevator's minimum acceleration (magnitude and direction)?

55. (III) (*a*) Show that if a satellite orbits very near the surface of a planet with period $T$, the density (mass/volume) of the planet is $\rho = m/V = 3\pi/GT^2$. (*b*) Estimate the density of the Earth, given that a satellite near the surface orbits with a period of about 85 min.

### * 5–9 Kepler's Laws

* 56. (I) Use Kepler's laws and the period of the Moon (27.4 d) to determine the period of an artificial satellite orbiting very near the Earth's surface.

* 57. (I) The asteroid Icarus, though only a few hundred meters across, orbits the Sun like the planets. Its period is 410 d. What is its mean distance from the Sun?

* 58. (I) Neptune is an average distance of $4.5 \times 10^9$ km from the Sun. Estimate the length of the Neptunian year given that the Earth is $1.50 \times 10^8$ km from the Sun on the average.

* 59. (II) Halley's comet orbits the Sun roughly once every 76 years. It comes very close to the surface of the Sun on its closest approach (Fig. 5–39). Estimate the greatest distance of the comet from the Sun. Is it still "in" the Solar System? What planet's orbit is nearest when it is out there? [*Hint*: The mean distance $s$ in Kepler's third law is half the sum of the nearest and farthest distance from the Sun.]

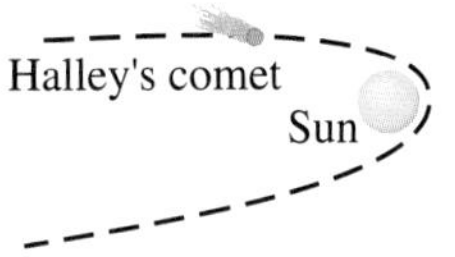


**FIGURE 5–39**
Problem 59.

* 60. (II) Our Sun rotates about the center of the Galaxy $\left(M_G \approx 4 \times 10^{41}\,\text{kg}\right)$ at a distance of about $3 \times 10^4$ light-years $\left(1\,\text{ly} = 3 \times 10^8\,\text{m/s} \times 3.16 \times 10^7\,\text{s/y} \times 1\,\text{y}\right)$. What is the period of our orbital motion about the center of the Galaxy?

* 61. (II) Table 5–3 gives the mass, period, and mean distance for the four largest moons of Jupiter (those discovered by Galileo in 1609). (*a*) Determine the mass of Jupiter using the data for Io. (*b*) Determine the mass of Jupiter using data for each of the other three moons. Are the results consistent?

**TABLE 5–3 Principal Moons of Jupiter**

| Moon | Mass (kg) | Period (Earth days) | Mean distance from Jupiter (km) |
|---|---|---|---|
| Io | $8.9 \times 10^{22}$ | 1.77 | $422 \times 10^3$ |
| Europa | $4.9 \times 10^{22}$ | 3.55 | $671 \times 10^3$ |
| Ganymede | $15 \times 10^{22}$ | 7.16 | $1070 \times 10^3$ |
| Callisto | $11 \times 10^{22}$ | 16.7 | $1883 \times 10^3$ |

* 62. (II) Determine the mass of the Earth from the known period and distance of the Moon.

* 63. (II) Determine the mean distance from Jupiter for each of Jupiter's moons, using Kepler's third law. Use the distance of Io and the periods given in Table 5–3. Compare to the values in the Table.

* 64. (II) The asteroid belt between Mars and Jupiter consists of many fragments (which some space scientists think came from a planet that once orbited the Sun but was destroyed). (*a*) If the center of mass of the asteroid belt (where the planet would have been) is about three times farther from the Sun than the Earth is, how long would it have taken this hypothetical planet to orbit the Sun? (*b*) Can we use these data to deduce the mass of this planet?

* 65. (III) A science-fiction tale describes an artificial "planet" in the form of a band completely encircling a sun (Fig. 5–40). The inhabitants live on the inside surface (where it is always noon). Imagine that this sun is exactly like our own, that the distance to the band is the same as the Earth–Sun distance (to make the climate temperate), and that the ring rotates quickly enough to produce an apparent gravity of $g$ as on Earth. What will be the period of revolution, this planet's year, in Earth days?

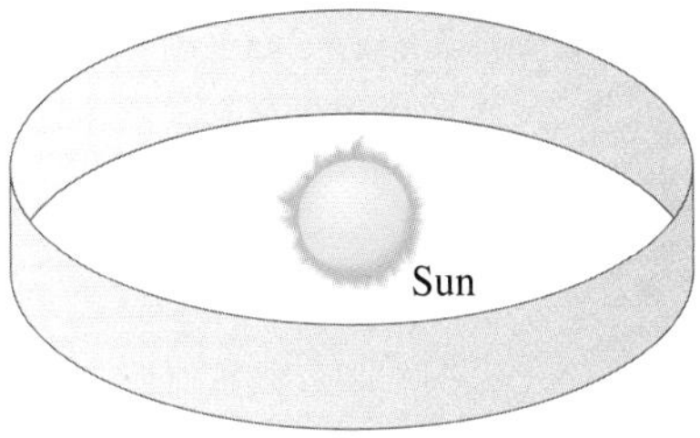


**FIGURE 5–40**
Problem 65.

## General Problems

66. Tarzan plans to cross a gorge by swinging in an arc from a hanging vine (Fig. 5–41). If his arms are capable of exerting a force of 1400 N on the vine, what is the maximum speed he can tolerate at the lowest point of his swing? His mass is 80 kg, and the vine is 5.5 m long.

**FIGURE 5–41**
Problem 66.

67. How far above the Earth's surface will the acceleration of gravity be half what it is on the surface?

68. On an ice rink, two skaters of equal mass grab hands and spin in a mutual circle once every 2.5 s. If we assume their arms are each 0.80 m long and their individual masses are 60.0 kg, how hard are they pulling on one another?

69. Because the Earth rotates once per day, the apparent acceleration of gravity at the equator is slightly less than it would be if the Earth didn't rotate. Estimate the magnitude of this effect. What fraction of $g$ is this?

70. At what distance from the Earth will a spacecraft traveling directly from the Earth to the Moon experience zero net force because the Earth and Moon pull with equal and opposite forces?

71. You know your mass is 65 kg, but when you stand on a bathroom scale in an elevator, it says your mass is 82 kg. What is the acceleration of the elevator, and in which direction?

72. A projected space station consists of a circular tube that will rotate about its center (like a tubular bicycle tire) (Fig. 5–42). The circle formed by the tube has a diameter of about 1.1 km. What must be the rotation speed (revolutions per day) if an effect equal to gravity at the surface of the Earth (1.0 $g$) is to be felt?

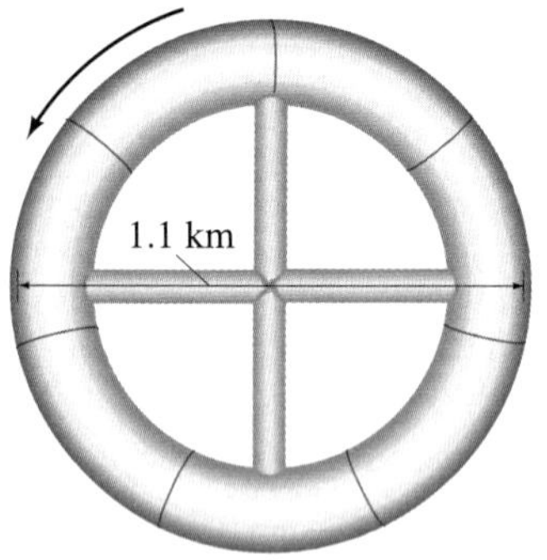


**FIGURE 5–42** Problem 72.

73. A jet pilot takes his aircraft in a vertical loop (Fig. 5–43). (*a*) If the jet is moving at a speed of 1300 km/h at the lowest point of the loop, determine the minimum radius of the circle so that the centripetal acceleration at the lowest point does not exceed 6.0 $g$'s. (*b*) Calculate the 78-kg pilot's effective weight (the force with which the seat pushes up on him) at the bottom of the circle, and (*c*) at the top of the circle (assume the same speed).

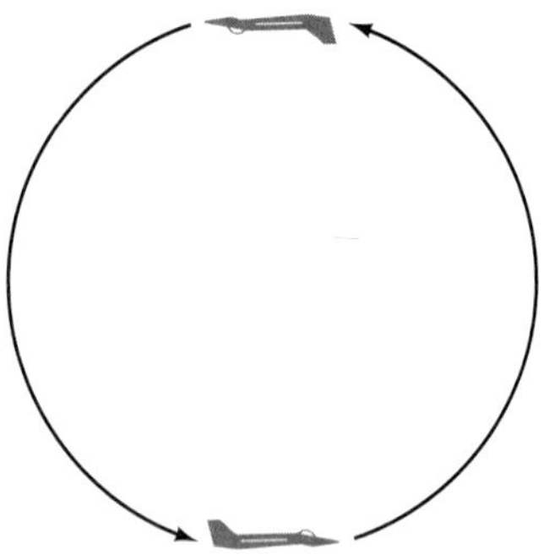

**FIGURE 5–43** Problem 73.

74. Derive a formula for the mass of a planet in terms of its radius $r$, the acceleration due to gravity at its surface $g_P$, and the gravitational constant $G$.

75. A plumb bob (a mass $m$ hanging on a string) is deflected from the vertical by an angle $\theta$ due to a massive mountain nearby (Fig. 5–44). (*a*) Find an approximate formula for $\theta$ in terms of the mass of the mountain, $m_M$, the distance to its center, $D_M$, and the radius and mass of the Earth. (*b*) Make a rough estimate of the mass of Mt. Everest, assuming it has the shape of a cone 4000 m high and base of diameter 4000 m. Assume its mass per unit volume is 3000 kg per m$^3$. (*c*) Estimate the angle $\theta$ of the plumb bob if it is 5 km from the center of Mt. Everest.

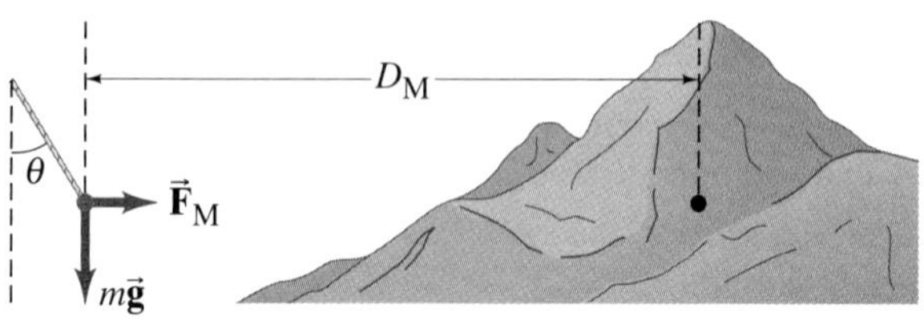


**FIGURE 5–44** Problem 75.

76. A curve of radius 67 m is banked for a design speed of 95 km/h. If the coefficient of static friction is 0.30 (wet pavement), at what range of speeds can a car safely handle the curve?

77. How long would a day be if the Earth were rotating so fast that objects at the equator were apparently weightless?

78. Two equal-mass stars maintain a constant distance apart of $8.0 \times 10^{10}$ m and rotate about a point midway between them at a rate of one revolution every 12.6 yr. (*a*) Why don't the two stars crash into one another due to the gravitational force between them? (*b*) What must be the mass of each star?

79. A train traveling at a constant speed rounds a curve of radius 235 m. A lamp suspended from the ceiling swings out to an angle of 17.5° throughout the curve. What is the speed of the train?

80. Jupiter is about 320 times as massive as the Earth. Thus, it has been claimed that a person would be crushed by the force of gravity on a planet the size of Jupiter since people can't survive more than a few $g$'s. Calculate the number of $g$'s a person would experience at the equator of such a planet. Use the following data for Jupiter: mass $= 1.9 \times 10^{27}$ kg, equatorial radius $= 7.1 \times 10^4$ km, rotation period $= 9$ hr 55 min. Take the centripetal acceleration into account.

81. Astronomers using the Hubble Space Telescope deduced the presence of an extremely massive core in the distant galaxy M87, so dense that it could be a black hole (from which no light escapes). They did this by measuring the speed of gas clouds orbiting the core to be 780 km/s at a distance of 60 light-years $(5.7 \times 10^{17}\ \text{m})$ from the core. Deduce the mass of the core, and compare it to the mass of our Sun.

82. A car maintains a constant speed $v$ as it traverses the hill and valley shown in Fig. 5–45. Both the hill and valley have a radius of curvature $R$. (*a*) How do the normal forces acting on the car at A, B, and C compare? (Which is largest? Smallest?) Explain. (*b*) Where would the driver feel heaviest? Lightest? Explain. (*c*) How fast can the car go without losing contact with the road at A?

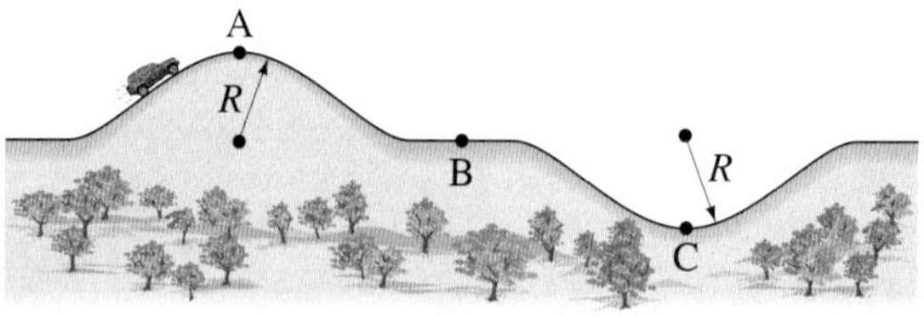


**FIGURE 5–45** Problem 82.

83. The Navstar **Global Positioning System (GPS)** utilizes a group of 24 satellites orbiting the Earth. Using "triangulation" and signals transmitted by these satellites, the position of a receiver on the Earth can be determined to within an accuracy of a few centimeters. The satellite orbits are distributed evenly around the Earth, with four satellites in each of six orbits, allowing continuous navigational "fixes." The satellites orbit at an altitude of approximately 11,000 nautical miles [1 nautical mile = 1.852 km = 6076 ft]. (*a*) Determine the speed of each satellite. (*b*) Determine the period of each satellite.

84. The *Near Earth Asteroid Rendezvous* (*NEAR*), after traveling 2.1 billion km, is meant to orbit the asteroid Eros at a height of about 15 km. Eros is roughly 40 km × 6 km × 6 km. Assume Eros has a density (mass/volume) of about $2.3 \times 10^3\ \text{kg/m}^3$. (*a*) What will be the period of *NEAR* as it orbits Eros? (*b*) If Eros were a sphere with the same mass and density, what would its radius be? (*c*) What would $g$ be at the surface of this spherical Eros?

85. You are an astronaut in the space shuttle pursuing a satellite in need of repair. You are in a circular orbit of the same radius as the satellite (400 km above the Earth), but 25 km behind it. (*a*) How long will it take to overtake the satellite if you reduce your orbital radius by 1.0 km? (*b*) By how much must you reduce your orbital radius to catch up in 7.0 hours?

* 86. The comet Hale-Bopp has a period of 3000 years. (*a*) What is its mean distance from the Sun? (*b*) At its closest approach, the comet is about 1 A.U. from the Sun (1 A.U. = distance from Earth to the Sun). What is the farthest distance? (*c*) What is the ratio of the speed at the closest point to the speed at the farthest point? [*Hint*: Use Kepler's second law and estimate areas by a triangle (as in Fig. 5–29, but smaller distance travelled; see also Hint for Problem 59.]

87. Estimate what the value of $G$ would need to be if you could actually "feel" yourself gravitationally attracted to someone near you. Make reasonable assumptions, like $F \approx 1\ \text{N}$.

* 88. The Sun rotates around the center of the Milky Way Galaxy (Fig. 5–46) at a distance of about 30,000 light-years from the center $(1\ \text{ly} = 9.5 \times 10^{15}\ \text{m})$. If it takes about 200 million years to make one rotation, estimate the mass of our Galaxy. Assume that the mass distribution of our Galaxy is concentrated mostly in a central uniform sphere. If all the stars had about the mass of our Sun $(2 \times 10^{30}\ \text{kg})$, how many stars would there be in our Galaxy?

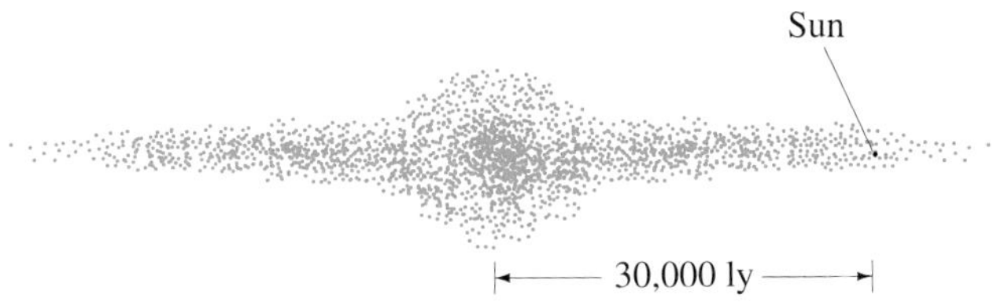


**FIGURE 5–46** Problem 88. Edge-on view of our Galaxy.

89. Four 1.0-kg masses are located at the corners of a square 0.50 m on each side. Find the magnitude and direction of the gravitational force on a fifth 1.0-kg mass placed at the midpoint of the bottom side of the square.

90. A satellite of mass 5500 kg orbits the Earth (mass $= 6.0 \times 10^{24}\ \text{kg}$) and has a period of 6200 s. Find (*a*) the magnitude of the Earth's gravitational force on the satellite, (*b*) the altitude of the satellite.

91. What is the acceleration experienced by the tip of the 1.5-cm-long sweep second hand on your wrist watch?

92. While fishing, you get bored and start to swing a sinker weight around in a circle below you on a 0.25-m piece of fishing line. The weight makes a complete circle every 0.50 s. What is the angle that the fishing line makes with the vertical? [*Hint*: See Fig. 5–10.]

93. A circular curve of radius $R$ in a new highway is designed so that a car traveling at speed $v_0$ can negotiate the turn safely on glare ice (zero friction). If a car travels too slowly, then it will slip toward the center of the circle. If it travels too fast, then it will slip away from the center of the circle. If the coefficient of static friction increases, a car can stay on the road while traveling at any speed within a range from $v_{min}$ to $v_{max}$. Derive formulas for $v_{min}$ and $v_{max}$ as functions of $\mu_s$, $v_0$, and $R$.

94. Amtrak's high speed train, the *Acela*, utilizes tilt of the cars when negotiating curves. The angle of tilt is adjusted so that the main force exerted on the passengers, to provide the centripetal acceleration, is the normal force. The passengers experience less friction force against the seat, thus feeling more comfortable. Consider an *Acela* train that rounds a curve with a radius of 620 m at a speed of 160 km/h (approximately 100 mi/h). (*a*) Calculate the friction force needed on a train passenger of mass 75 kg if the track is not banked and the train does not tilt. (*b*) Calculate the friction force on the passenger if the train tilts to its maximum tilt of 8.0° toward the center of the curve.

## Answers to Exercises

**A:** A factor of two (doubles).
**B:** Speed is independent of the mass of the clothes.
**C:** (*a*).
**D:** No.
**E:** Yes.
**F:** (*a*) No change; (*b*) four times larger.
**G:** (*b*).

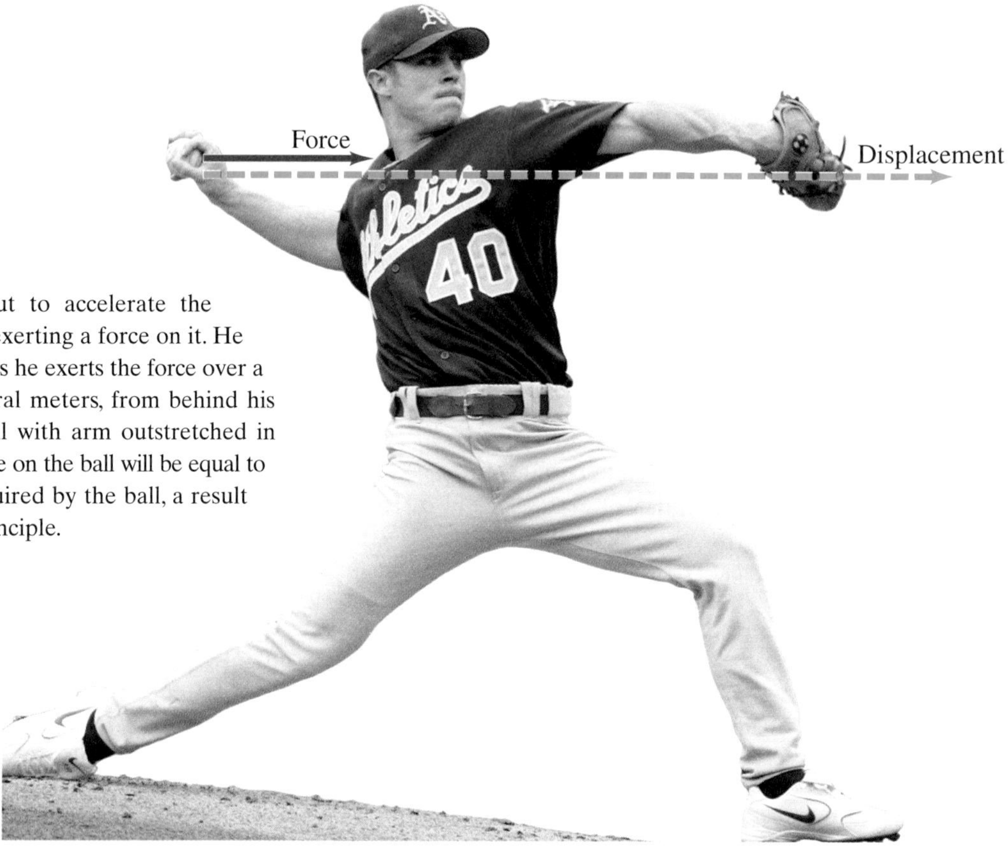


This baseball pitcher is about to accelerate the baseball to a high velocity by exerting a force on it. He will be doing work on the ball as he exerts the force over a displacement of perhaps several meters, from behind his head until he releases the ball with arm outstretched in front of him. The total work done on the ball will be equal to the kinetic energy $\left(\frac{1}{2}mv^2\right)$ acquired by the ball, a result known as the work-energy principle.

CHAPTER 6

# Work and Energy

Until now we have been studying the translational motion of an object in terms of Newton's three laws of motion. In this analysis, *force* has played a central role as the quantity determining the motion. In this Chapter and the next, we discuss an alternative analysis of the translational motion of objects in terms of the quantities *energy* and *momentum*. The significance of energy and momentum is that they are *conserved*. That is, in quite general circumstances they remain constant. That conserved quantities exist gives us not only a deeper insight into the nature of the world, but also gives us another way to approach solving practical problems.

The conservation laws of energy and momentum are especially valuable in dealing with systems of many objects, in which a detailed consideration of the forces involved would be difficult or impossible. These laws are applicable to a wide range of phenomena, including the atomic and subatomic worlds, where Newton's laws do not apply.

This Chapter is devoted to the very important concepts of *work* and *energy*. These two quantities are scalars and so have no direction associated with them, which often makes them easier to work with than vector quantities.

## 6–1 Work Done by a Constant Force

The word *work* has a variety of meanings in everyday language. But in physics, work is given a very specific meaning to describe what is accomplished when a force acts on an object, and the object moves through a distance. Specifically, the **work** done on an object by a constant force (constant in both magnitude and direction) is defined to be *the product of the magnitude of the displacement times the component of the force parallel to the displacement*. In equation form, we can write

*Work*

$$W = F_{\parallel} d,$$

where $F_{\parallel}$ is the component of the constant force $\vec{\mathbf{F}}$ parallel to the displacement $\vec{\mathbf{d}}$. We can also write

$$W = Fd\cos\theta, \qquad \textbf{(6–1)}$$

*Work defined (for constant force)*

where $F$ is the magnitude of the constant force, $d$ is the magnitude of the displacement of the object, and $\theta$ is the angle between the directions of the force and the displacement (Fig. 6–1). The $\cos\theta$ factor appears in Eq. 6–1 because $F\cos\theta\,(=F_{\parallel})$ is the component of $\vec{\mathbf{F}}$ that is parallel to $\vec{\mathbf{d}}$. Work is a scalar quantity—it has only magnitude, which can be positive or negative.

Let us first consider the case in which the motion and the force are in the same direction, so $\theta = 0$ and $\cos\theta = 1$; in this case, $W = Fd$. For example, if you push a loaded grocery cart a distance of 50 m by exerting a horizontal force of 30 N on the cart, you do $30\,\mathrm{N} \times 50\,\mathrm{m} = 1500\,\mathrm{N\cdot m}$ of work on the cart.

As this example shows, in SI units work is measured in newton-meters (N·m). A special name is given to this unit, the **joule** (J): $1\,\mathrm{J} = 1\,\mathrm{N\cdot m}$. In the cgs system, the unit of work is called the *erg* and is defined as $1\,\mathrm{erg} = 1\,\mathrm{dyne\cdot cm}$. In British units, work is measured in foot-pounds. It is easy to show that $1\,\mathrm{J} = 10^7\,\mathrm{erg} = 0.7376\,\mathrm{ft\cdot lb}$.

*Units for work: the joule*

**FIGURE 6–1** A person pulling a crate along the floor. The work done by the force $\vec{\mathbf{F}}$ is $W = Fd\cos\theta$, where $\vec{\mathbf{d}}$ is the displacement.

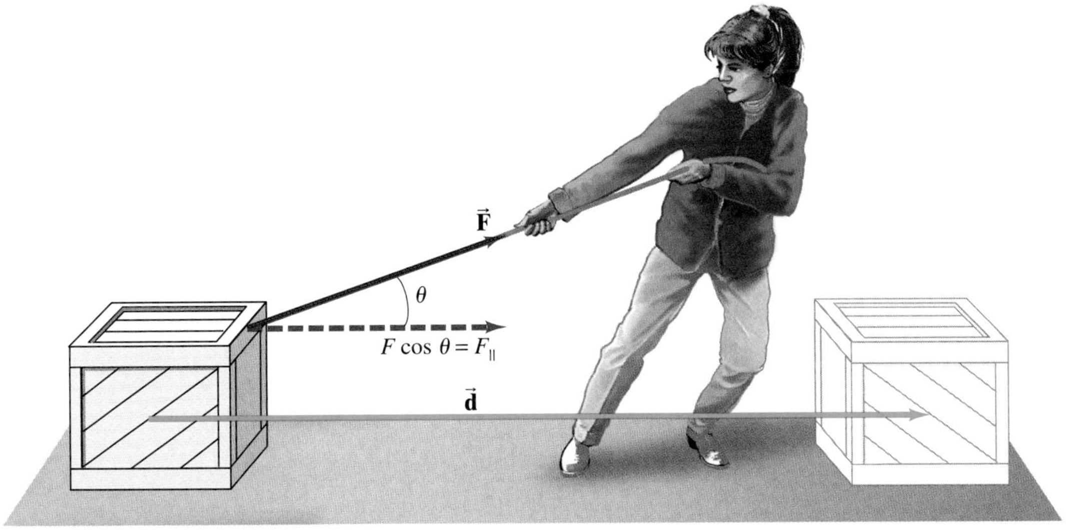

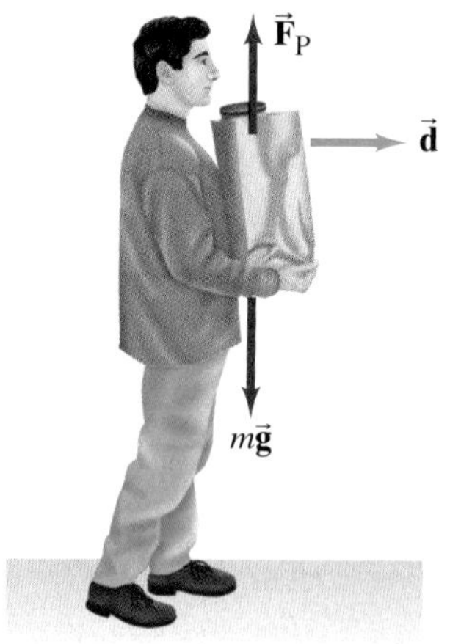


**FIGURE 6–2** The person does no work on the bag of groceries since $\vec{\mathbf{F}}_P$ is perpendicular to the displacement $\vec{\mathbf{d}}$.

**CAUTION**
*Force without work*

A force can be exerted on an object and yet do no work. For example, if you hold a heavy bag of groceries in your hands at rest, you do no work on it. You do exert a force on the bag, but the displacement of the bag is zero, so the work done by you on the bag is $W = 0$. You need both a force and a displacement to do work. You also do no work on the bag of groceries if you carry it as you walk horizontally across the floor at constant velocity, as shown in Fig. 6–2. No horizontal force is required to move the bag at a constant velocity. The person shown in Fig. 6–2 does exert an upward force $\vec{\mathbf{F}}_P$ on the bag equal to its weight. But this upward force is perpendicular to the horizontal displacement of the bag and thus has nothing to do with that motion. Hence, the upward force is doing no work. This conclusion comes from our definition of work, Eq. 6–1: $W = 0$, because $\theta = 90°$ and $\cos 90° = 0$. Thus, when a particular force is perpendicular to the displacement, no work is done by that force. (When you start or stop walking, there is a horizontal acceleration and you do briefly exert a horizontal force, and thus do work on the bag.)

**CAUTION**
*State that work is done on or by an object*

When we deal with work, as with force, it is necessary to specify whether you are talking about work done *by* a specific object or done *on* a specific object. It is also important to specify whether the work done is due to one particular force (and which one), or the total (net) work done by the *net force* on the object.

**EXAMPLE 6–1** **Work done on a crate.** A person pulls a 50-kg crate 40 m along a horizontal floor by a constant force $F_P = 100\,\text{N}$, which acts at a 37° angle as shown in Fig. 6–3. The floor is rough and exerts a friction force $F_{fr} = 50\,\text{N}$. Determine (*a*) the work done by each force acting on the crate, and (*b*) the net work done on the crate.

**APPROACH** We choose our coordinate system so that $\vec{\mathbf{x}}$ can be the vector that represents the 40-m displacement (that is, along the $x$ axis). Four forces act on the crate, as shown in Fig. 6–3: the force exerted by the person $\vec{\mathbf{F}}_P$; the friction force $\vec{\mathbf{F}}_{fr}$ due to the floor; the crate's weight $m\vec{\mathbf{g}}$; and the normal force $\vec{\mathbf{F}}_N$ exerted upward by the floor. The net force on the crate is the vector sum of these four forces.

**SOLUTION** (*a*) The work done by the gravitational and normal forces is zero, since they are perpendicular to the displacement $\vec{\mathbf{x}}$ ($\theta = 90°$ in Eq. 6–1):

$$W_G = mgx\cos 90° = 0$$
$$W_N = F_N x\cos 90° = 0.$$

The work done by $\vec{\mathbf{F}}_P$ is

$$W_P = F_P x\cos\theta = (100\,\text{N})(40\,\text{m})\cos 37° = 3200\,\text{J}.$$

The work done by the friction force is

$$W_{fr} = F_{fr} x\cos 180° = (50\,\text{N})(40\,\text{m})(-1) = -2000\,\text{J}.$$

The angle between the displacement $\vec{\mathbf{x}}$ and the force $\vec{\mathbf{F}}_{fr}$ is 180° because they point in opposite directions. Since the force of friction is opposing the motion (and $\cos 180° = -1$), the work done by friction on the crate is *negative*.

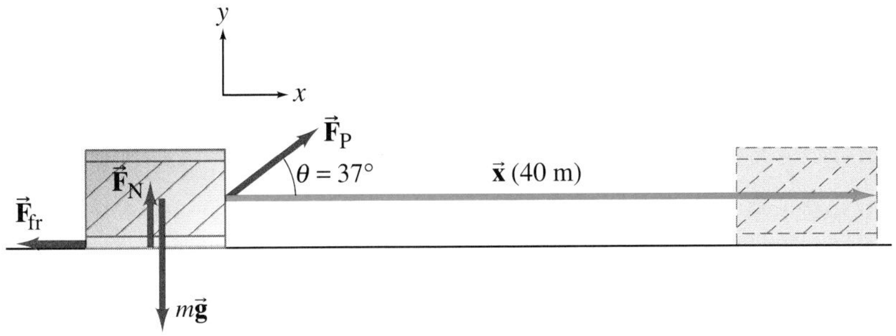


**FIGURE 6–3** Example 6–1. A 50-kg crate is pulled along a floor.

(*b*) The net work can be calculated in two equivalent ways:
(1) The net work done on an object is the algebraic sum of the work done by each force, since work is a scalar:

$$\begin{aligned} W_{net} &= W_G + W_N + W_P + W_{fr} \\ &= 0 + 0 + 3200\text{ J} - 2000\text{ J} \\ &= 1200\text{ J}. \end{aligned}$$

*$W_{net}$ is the work done by all the forces acting on the object*

(2) The net work can also be calculated by first determining the net force on the object and then taking its component along the displacement: $(F_{net})_x = F_P \cos\theta - F_{fr}$. Then the net work is

$$\begin{aligned} W_{net} = (F_{net})_x x &= (F_P \cos\theta - F_{fr})x \\ &= (100\text{ N} \cos 37° - 50\text{ N})(40\text{ m}) \\ &= 1200\text{ J}. \end{aligned}$$

In the vertical $(y)$ direction, there is no displacement and no work done.

In Example 6–1 we saw that friction did negative work. In general, the work done by a force is negative whenever the force (or the component of the force, $F_{\parallel}$) acts in the direction opposite to the direction of motion. Also, we can see that when the work done by a force on an object is negative, that force is trying to slow the object down (and would slow it down if that were the only force acting). When the work is positive, the force involved is trying to speed up the object.

**CAUTION**
*Negative work*

**EXERCISE A** A box is dragged across a floor by a force $\vec{F}_P$ which makes an angle $\theta$ with the horizontal as in Fig. 6–1 or 6–3. If the magnitude of $\vec{F}_P$ is held constant but the angle $\theta$ is increased, the work done by $\vec{F}_P$ (*a*) remains the same; (*b*) increases; (*c*) decreases; (*d*) first increases, then decreases.

## PROBLEM SOLVING Work

1. **Draw a free-body diagram** showing all the forces acting on the object you choose to study.
2. **Choose** an *xy* **coordinate system**. If the object is in motion, it may be convenient to choose one of the coordinate directions as the direction of one of the forces, or as the direction of motion. [Thus, for an object on an incline, you might choose one coordinate axis to be parallel to the incline.]
3. Apply **Newton's laws** to determine any unknown forces.
4. Find the **work done *by* a specific force** *on* the object by using $W = Fd\cos\theta$ for a constant force. Note that the work done is negative when a force tends to oppose the displacement.
5. To find the **net work** done on the object, either (*a*) find the work done by each force and add the results algebraically; or (*b*) find the net force on the object, $F_{net}$, and then use it to find the net work done, which for constant net force is:

$$W_{net} = F_{net}\, d\cos\theta.$$

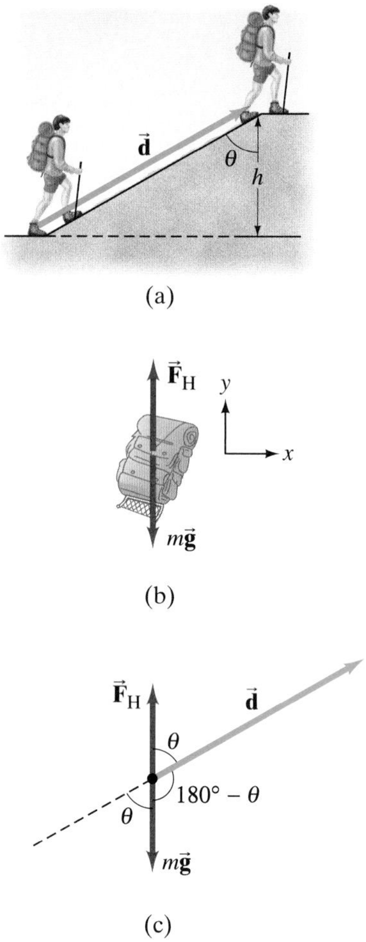


**FIGURE 6–4** Example 6–2.

**EXAMPLE 6–2** **Work on a backpack.** (*a*) Determine the work a hiker must do on a 15.0-kg backpack to carry it up a hill of height $h = 10.0\,\text{m}$, as shown in Fig. 6–4a. Determine also (*b*) the work done by gravity on the backpack, and (*c*) the net work done on the backpack. For simplicity, assume the motion is smooth and at constant velocity (i.e., acceleration is negligible).

**APPROACH** We explicitly follow the Problem Solving Box step by step.

**SOLUTION**

1. **Draw a free-body diagram.** The forces on the backpack are shown in Fig. 6–4b: the force of gravity, $m\vec{\mathbf{g}}$, acting downward; and $\vec{\mathbf{F}}_\text{H}$, the force the hiker must exert upward to support the backpack. Since we assume there is negligible acceleration, horizontal forces on the backpack are negligible.
2. **Choose a coordinate system.** We are interested in the vertical motion of the backpack, so we choose the $y$ coordinate as positive vertically upward.
3. **Apply Newton's laws.** Newton's second law applied in the vertical direction to the backpack gives

$$\Sigma F_y = ma_y$$

$$F_\text{H} - mg = 0.$$

Hence,

$$F_\text{H} = mg = (15.0\,\text{kg})(9.80\,\text{m/s}^2) = 147\,\text{N}.$$

4. **Find the work done by a specific force.** (*a*) To calculate the work done by the hiker on the backpack, we write Eq. 6–1 as

$$W_\text{H} = F_\text{H}(d\cos\theta),$$

and we note from Fig. 6–4a that $d\cos\theta = h$. So the work done by the hiker is

$$W_\text{H} = F_\text{H}(d\cos\theta) = F_\text{H}h = mgh$$
$$= (147\,\text{N})(10.0\,\text{m}) = 1470\,\text{J}.$$

Note that the work done depends only on the change in elevation and not on the angle of the hill, $\theta$. The hiker would do the same work to lift the pack vertically the same height $h$.

(*b*) The work done by gravity on the backpack is (from Eq. 6–1 and Fig. 6–4c)

$$W_\text{G} = F_\text{G}\,d\cos(180^\circ - \theta).$$

Since $\cos(180^\circ - \theta) = -\cos\theta$, we have

$$W_\text{G} = F_\text{G}\,d(-\cos\theta) = mg(-d\cos\theta)$$
$$= -mgh$$
$$= -(15.0\,\text{kg})(9.80\,\text{m/s}^2)(10.0\,\text{m}) = -1470\,\text{J}.$$

➡ **PROBLEM SOLVING**

*Work done by gravity depends on the height of the hill and not on the angle of incline*

**NOTE** The work done by gravity (which is negative here) doesn't depend on the angle of the incline, only on the vertical height $h$ of the hill. This is because gravity acts vertically, so only the vertical component of displacement contributes to work done.

5. **Find the net work done.** (*a*) The *net* work done on the backpack is $W_\text{net} = 0$, since the net force on the backpack is zero (it is assumed not to accelerate significantly). We can also determine the net work done by adding the work done by each force:

$$W_\text{net} = W_\text{G} + W_\text{H} = -1470\,\text{J} + 1470\,\text{J} = 0.$$

**NOTE** Even though the *net* work done by all the forces on the backpack is zero, the hiker does do work on the backpack equal to 1470 J.

**CONCEPTUAL EXAMPLE 6–3** **Does the Earth do work on the Moon?** The Moon revolves around the Earth in a nearly circular orbit, kept there by the gravitational force exerted by the Earth. Does gravity do (*a*) positive work, (*b*) negative work, or (*c*) no work on the Moon?

**RESPONSE** The gravitational force exerted by the Earth on the Moon (Fig. 6–5) acts toward the Earth and provides its centripetal acceleration, inward along the radius of the Moon's orbit. The Moon's displacement at any moment is tangent to the circle, in the direction of its velocity, perpendicular to the radius and perpendicular to the force of gravity. Hence the angle $\theta$ between the force $\vec{\mathbf{F}}_G$ and the instantaneous displacement of the Moon is 90°, and the work done by the Earth's gravity on the Moon as it orbits is therefore zero ($\cos 90° = 0$). This is why the Moon, as well as artificial satellites, can stay in orbit without expenditure of fuel: no net work needs to be done against the force of gravity.

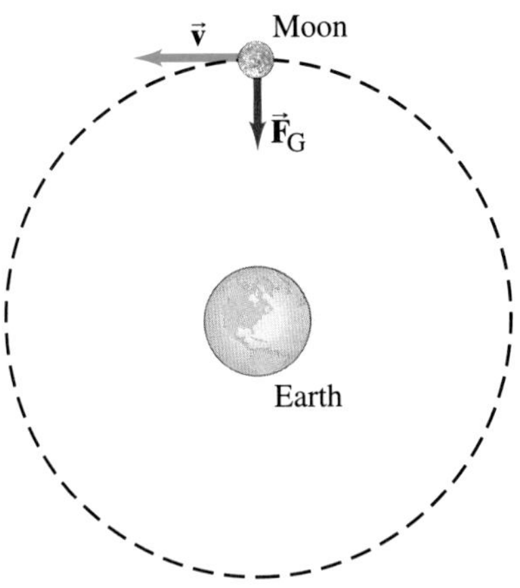


**FIGURE 6–5** Example 6–3.

## * 6–2 Work Done by a Varying Force

If the force acting on an object is constant, the work done by that force can be calculated using Eq. 6–1. But in many cases, the force varies in magnitude or direction during a process. For example, as a rocket moves away from Earth, work is done to overcome the force of gravity, which varies as the inverse square of the distance from the Earth's center. Other examples are the force exerted by a spring, which increases with the amount of stretch, or the work done by a varying force in pulling a box or cart up an uneven hill.

The work done by a varying force can be determined graphically. The procedure is like that for determining displacement when the velocity is known as a function of time (Section 2–8). To determine the work done by a variable force, we plot $F_{\parallel}$ ($= F\cos\theta$, the component of $\vec{\mathbf{F}}$ parallel to the direction of motion at any point) as a function of distance $d$, as in Fig. 6–6a. We divide the distance into small segments $\Delta d$. For each segment, we indicate the average of $F_{\parallel}$ by a horizontal dashed line. Then the work done for each segment is $\Delta W = F_{\parallel}\,\Delta d$, which is the area of a rectangle $\Delta d$ wide and $F_{\parallel}$ high. The total work done to move the object a total distance $d = d_B - d_A$ is the sum of the areas of the rectangles (five in the case shown in Fig. 6–6a). Usually, the average value of $F_{\parallel}$ for each segment must be estimated, and a reasonable approximation of the work done can then be made. If we subdivide the distance into many more segments, $\Delta d$ can be made smaller and our estimate of the work done would be more accurate. In the limit as $\Delta d$ approaches zero, the total area of the many narrow rectangles approaches the area under the curve, Fig. 6–6b. That is, *the work done by a variable force in moving an object between two points is equal to the area under the $F_{\parallel}$ vs. d curve between those two points.*

**FIGURE 6–6** The work done by a force $F$ can be calculated by taking: (a) the sum of the areas of the rectangles; (b) the area under the curve of $F_{\parallel}$ vs. $d$.

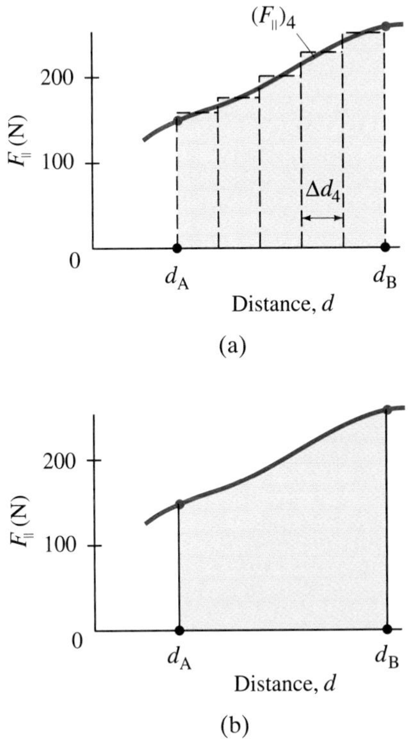


## 6–3 Kinetic Energy, and the Work-Energy Principle

*Energy* is one of the most important concepts in science. Yet we cannot give a simple general definition of energy in only a few words. Nonetheless, each specific type of energy can be defined fairly simply. In this Chapter, we define translational kinetic energy and some types of potential energy. In later Chapters, we will examine other types of energy, such as that related to heat (Chapters 14 and 15). The crucial aspect of all the types of energy is that the sum of all types, the *total energy*, is the same after any process as it was before: that is, the quantity "energy" is a conserved quantity.

For the purposes of this Chapter, we can define energy in the traditional way as "the ability to do work." This simple definition is not very precise, nor is it really valid for all types of energy.† It is valid, however, for mechanical energy which we discuss in this Chapter, and it serves to underscore the fundamental

†Energy associated with heat is often not available to do work, as we will discuss in Chapter 15.

FIGURE 6–7 A constant net force $F_{net}$ accelerates a bus from speed $v_1$ to speed $v_2$ over a displacement $d$. The net work done is $W_{net} = F_{net}d$.

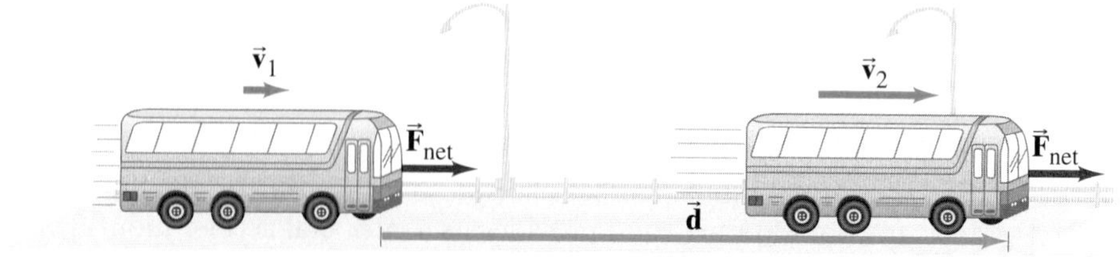


connection between work and energy. We now define and discuss one of the basic types of energy, kinetic energy.

A moving object can do work on another object it strikes. A flying cannonball does work on a brick wall it knocks down; a moving hammer does work on a nail it drives into wood. In either case, a moving object exerts a force on a second object which undergoes a displacement. An object in motion has the ability to do work and thus can be said to have energy. The energy of motion is called **kinetic energy**, from the Greek word *kinetikos*, meaning "motion."

To obtain a quantitative definition for kinetic energy, let us consider a rigid object of mass $m$ that is moving in a straight line with an initial speed $v_1$. To accelerate it uniformly to a speed $v_2$, a constant net force $F_{net}$ is exerted on it parallel to its motion over a displacement $d$, Fig. 6–7. Then the net work done on the object is $W_{net} = F_{net}d$. We apply Newton's second law, $F_{net} = ma$, and use Eq. 2–11c, which we now write as $v_2^2 = v_1^2 + 2ad$, with $v_1$ as the initial speed and $v_2$ the final speed. We solve for $a$ in Eq. 2–11c,

$$a = \frac{v_2^2 - v_1^2}{2d},$$

then substitute this into $F_{net} = ma$, and determine the work done:

$$W_{net} = F_{net}d = mad = m\left(\frac{v_2^2 - v_1^2}{2d}\right)d = m\left(\frac{v_2^2 - v_1^2}{2}\right)$$

or

$$W_{net} = \tfrac{1}{2}mv_2^2 - \tfrac{1}{2}mv_1^2. \qquad \textbf{(6–2)}$$

We *define* the quantity $\frac{1}{2}mv^2$ to be the **translational kinetic energy (KE)** of the object:

*Kinetic energy defined*

$$\text{KE} = \tfrac{1}{2}mv^2. \qquad \textbf{(6–3)}$$

(We call this "translational" kinetic energy to distinguish it from rotational kinetic energy, which we will discuss in Chapter 8.) Equation 6–2, derived here for one-dimensional motion with a constant force, is valid in general for translational motion of an object in three dimensions and even if the force varies. We can rewrite Eq. 6–2 as:

$$W_{net} = \text{KE}_2 - \text{KE}_1$$

or

WORK-ENERGY PRINCIPLE

$$W_{net} = \Delta\text{KE}. \qquad \textbf{(6–4)}$$

Equation 6–4 (or Eq. 6–2) is an important result known as the **work-energy principle**. It can be stated in words:

WORK-ENERGY PRINCIPLE

**The net work done on an object is equal to the change in the object's kinetic energy.**

CAUTION
*Work-energy valid only for net work*

Notice that we made use of Newton's second law, $F_{net} = ma$, where $F_{net}$ is the *net* force—the sum of all forces acting on the object. Thus, the work-energy principle is valid only if $W$ is the *net work* done on the object—that is, the work done by all forces acting on the object.

The work-energy principle is a very useful reformulation of Newton's laws. It tells us that if (positive) net work $W$ is done on an object, the object's kinetic energy increases by an amount $W$. The principle also holds true for the reverse situation: if the net work $W$ done on an object is negative, the object's kinetic energy decreases by an amount $W$. That is, a net force exerted on an object opposite to the object's direction of motion decreases its speed and its kinetic energy. An example is a moving hammer (Fig. 6–8) striking a nail. The net force on the hammer ($-\vec{\mathbf{F}}$ in Fig. 6–8, where $\vec{\mathbf{F}}$ is assumed constant for simplicity) acts toward the left, whereas the displacement $\vec{\mathbf{d}}$ of the hammer is toward the right. So the net work done on the hammer, $W_h = (F)(d)(\cos 180°) = -Fd$, is negative and the hammer's kinetic energy decreases (usually to zero).

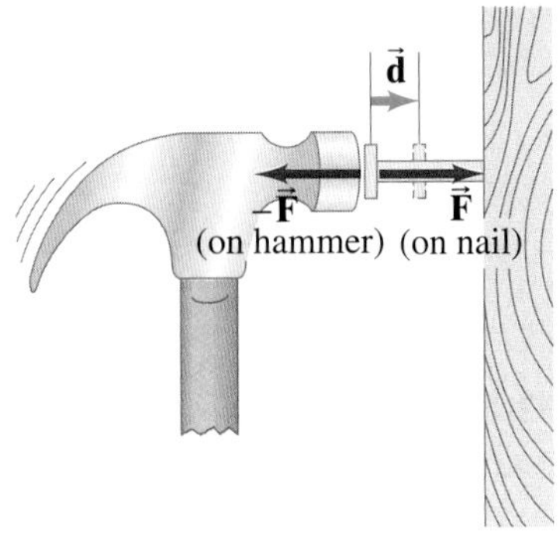


**FIGURE 6–8** A moving hammer strikes a nail and comes to rest. The hammer exerts a force $F$ on the nail; the nail exerts a force $-F$ on the hammer (Newton's third law). The work done on the nail by the hammer is positive $(W_n = Fd > 0)$. The work done on the hammer by the nail is negative $(W_h = -Fd)$.

Figure 6–8 also illustrates how energy can be considered the ability to do work. The hammer, as it slows down, does positive work on the nail: if the nail exerts a force $-\vec{\mathbf{F}}$ on the hammer to slow it down, the hammer exerts a force $+\vec{\mathbf{F}}$ on the nail (Newton's third law) through the distance $d$. Hence the work done on the nail by the hammer is $W_n = (+F)(+d) = Fd$ and is positive. We also see that $W_n = Fd = -W_h$: the work done on the nail $W_n$ equals the negative of the work done on the hammer. That is, the decrease in kinetic energy of the hammer is equal to the work the hammer can do on another object—which is consistent with energy being the ability to do work.

Whereas the translational kinetic energy $\left(= \frac{1}{2}mv^2\right)$ is directly proportional to the mass of the object, it is proportional to the *square* of the speed. Thus, if the mass is doubled, the kinetic energy is doubled. But if the speed is doubled, the object has four times as much kinetic energy and is therefore capable of doing four times as much work.

*If $W_{net} > 0$, KE increases*
*If $W_{net} < 0$, KE decreases*

Let us summarize the relationship between work and kinetic energy (Eq. 6–4): if the net work $W$ done on an object is positive, then the object's kinetic energy increases. If the net work $W$ done on an object is negative, its kinetic energy decreases. If the net work done on the object is zero, its kinetic energy remains constant (which also means its speed is constant).

*Energy units: the joule*

Because of the direct connection between work and kinetic energy (Eq. 6–4), energy is measured in the same units as work: joules in SI units, ergs in the cgs, and foot-pounds in the British system. Like work, kinetic energy is a scalar quantity. The kinetic energy of a group of objects is the sum of the kinetic energies of the individual objects.

**EXAMPLE 6–4** **KE and work done on a baseball.** A 145-g baseball is thrown so that it acquires a speed of 25 m/s. (*a*) What is its kinetic energy? (*b*) What was the net work done on the ball to make it reach this speed, if it started from rest?

**APPROACH** We use the definition of kinetic energy, Eq. 6–3, and then the work-energy principle, Eq. 6–4.

**SOLUTION** (*a*) The kinetic energy of the ball after the throw is

$$\text{KE} = \tfrac{1}{2}mv^2 = \tfrac{1}{2}(0.145\text{ kg})(25\text{ m/s})^2 = 45\text{ J}.$$

(*b*) Since the initial kinetic energy was zero, the net work done is just equal to the final kinetic energy, 45 J.

**EXAMPLE 6–5** **Work on a car, to increase its KE.** How much net work is required to accelerate a 1000-kg car from 20 m/s to 30 m/s (Fig. 6–9)?

**APPROACH** To simplify a complex situation, let us treat the car as a particle or simple rigid object. We can then use the work-energy principle.

**SOLUTION** The net work needed is equal to the increase in kinetic energy:

$$\begin{aligned} W &= \text{KE}_2 - \text{KE}_1 = \tfrac{1}{2}mv_2^2 - \tfrac{1}{2}mv_1^2 \\ &= \tfrac{1}{2}(1000\text{ kg})(30\text{ m/s})^2 - \tfrac{1}{2}(1000\text{ kg})(20\text{ m/s})^2 = 2.5\times10^5\text{ J}. \end{aligned}$$

**FIGURE 6–9** Example 6–5.

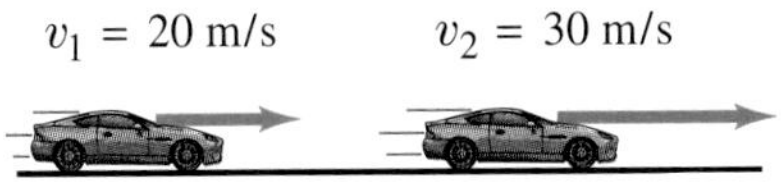


**NOTE** You might be tempted to work this Example by finding the force and using Eq. 6–1. That won't work, however, because we don't know how far or for how long the car was accelerated. In fact, a large force could be acting for a small distance, or a small force could be acting over a long distance; both could give the same net work.

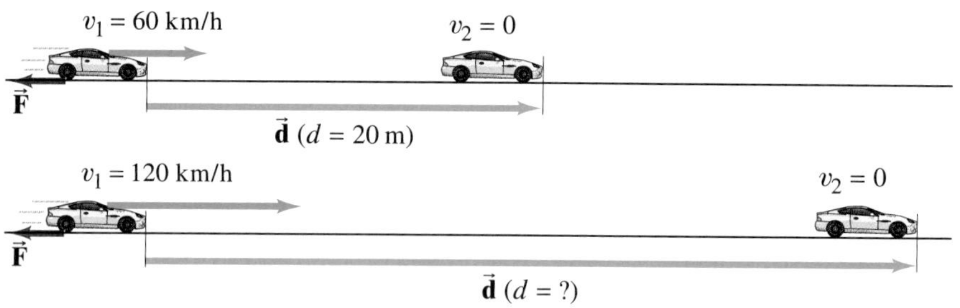


**FIGURE 6–10** Example 6–6.

**CONCEPTUAL EXAMPLE 6–6** **Work to stop a car.** A car traveling 60 km/h can brake to a stop within a distance $d$ of 20 m (Fig. 6–10a). If the car is going twice as fast, 120 km/h, what is its stopping distance (Fig. 6–10b)? Assume the maximum braking force is approximately independent of speed.

**RESPONSE** Since the stopping force $F$ is approximately constant, the work needed to stop the car, $Fd$, is proportional to the distance traveled. We apply the work-energy principle, noting that $\vec{\mathbf{F}}$ and $\vec{\mathbf{d}}$ are in opposite directions and that the final speed of the car is zero:

$$W_{\text{net}} = Fd\cos 180^\circ = -Fd.$$

Then

$$-Fd = \Delta\text{KE} = \tfrac{1}{2}mv_2^2 - \tfrac{1}{2}mv_1^2$$
$$= 0 - \tfrac{1}{2}mv_1^2.$$

Thus, since the force and mass are constant, we see that the stopping distance, $d$, increases with the square of the speed:

PHYSICS APPLIED
*Car's stopping distance ∝ initial speed squared*

$$d \propto v^2.$$

If the car's initial speed is doubled, the stopping distance is $(2)^2 = 4$ times as great, or 80 m.

**EXERCISE B** Can kinetic energy ever be negative?

## 6–4 Potential Energy

*Potential energy*

We have just discussed how an object is said to have energy by virtue of its motion, which we call kinetic energy. But it is also possible to have **potential energy**, which is the energy associated with forces that depend on the position or configuration of an object (or objects) relative to the surroundings. Various types of potential energy (PE) can be defined, and each type is associated with a particular force.

The spring of a wind-up toy is an example of an object with potential energy. The spring acquired its potential energy because work was done *on* it by the person winding the toy. As the spring unwinds, it exerts a force and does work to make the toy move.

*Gravitational PE*

Perhaps the most common example of potential energy is *gravitational potential energy*. A heavy brick held high in the air has potential energy because of its position relative to the Earth. The raised brick has the ability to do work, for if it is released, it will fall to the ground due to the gravitational force, and can do work on, say, a stake, driving it into the ground. Let us seek the form for the gravitational potential energy of an object near the surface of the Earth. For an object of mass $m$ to be lifted vertically, an upward force at least equal to its weight, $mg$, must be exerted on it, say by a person's hand.

To lift it without acceleration a vertical displacement of height $h$, from position $y_1$ to $y_2$ in Fig. 6–11 (upward direction chosen positive), a person must do work equal to the product of the needed external force, $F_{ext} = mg$ upward, and the vertical displacement $h$. That is,

$$W_{ext} = F_{ext}\, d\cos 0° = mgh$$
$$= mg(y_2 - y_1). \qquad \textbf{(6–5a)}$$

Gravity is also acting on the object as it moves from $y_1$ to $y_2$, and does work on it equal to

$$W_G = F_G\, d\cos\theta = mgh\cos 180°,$$

where $\theta = 180°$ because $\vec{\mathbf{F}}_G$ and $\vec{\mathbf{d}}$ point in opposite directions. So

$$W_G = -mgh$$
$$= -mg(y_2 - y_1). \qquad \textbf{(6–5b)}$$

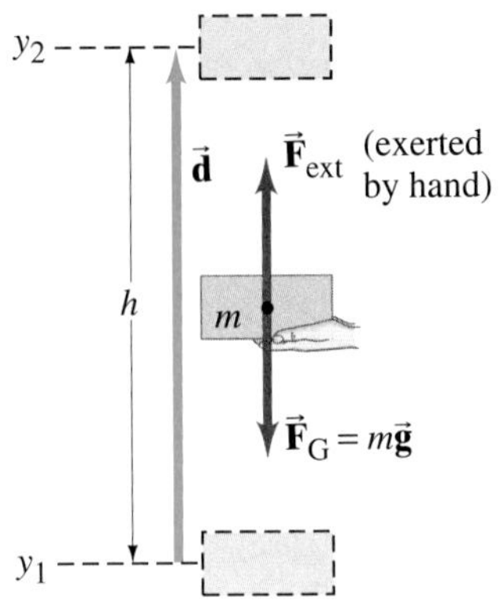


**FIGURE 6–11** A person exerts an upward force $F_{ext} = mg$ to lift a brick from $y_1$ to $y_2$.

If we now allow the object to start from rest and fall freely under the action of gravity, it acquires a velocity given by $v^2 = 2gh$ (Eq. 2–11c) after falling a height $h$. It then has kinetic energy $\frac{1}{2}mv^2 = \frac{1}{2}m(2gh) = mgh$, and if it strikes a stake it can do work on the stake equal to $mgh$ (work-energy principle). Thus, to raise an object of mass $m$ to a height $h$ *requires* an amount of work equal to $mgh$ (Eq. 6–5a). And once at height $h$, the object has the *ability* to do an amount of work equal to $mgh$.

We therefore define the **gravitational potential energy** of an object, due to Earth's gravity, as the product of the object's weight $mg$ and its height $y$ above some reference level (such as the ground):

*Gravitational PE*

$$\text{PE}_{grav} = mgy. \qquad \textbf{(6–6)}$$

The higher an object is above the ground, the more gravitational potential energy it has. We combine Eq. 6–5a with Eq. 6–6:

$$W_{ext} = mg(y_2 - y_1)$$
$$W_{ext} = \text{PE}_2 - \text{PE}_1 = \Delta\text{PE}. \qquad \textbf{(6–7a)}$$

That is, the work done by an external force to move the object of mass $m$ from point 1 to point 2 (without acceleration) is equal to the change in potential energy between positions 1 and 2.

Alternatively, we can write the change in potential energy, $\Delta$PE, in terms of the work done by gravity itself: starting from Eq. 6–5b, we obtain

$$W_G = -mg(y_2 - y_1)$$
$$W_G = -(\text{PE}_2 - \text{PE}_1) = -\Delta\text{PE}. \qquad \textbf{(6–7b)}$$

That is, the work done by gravity as the object of mass $m$ moves from point 1 to point 2 is equal to the negative of the difference in potential energy between positions 1 and 2.

**CAUTION**

*Potential energy belongs to a system, not to a single object*

Potential energy belongs to a system, and not to a single object alone. Potential energy is associated with a force, and a force on one object is always exerted by some other object. Thus potential energy is a property of the system as a whole. For an object raised to a height $y$ above the Earth's surface, the change in gravitational potential energy is $mgy$. The system here is the object plus the Earth, and properties of both are involved: object ($m$) and Earth ($g$).

Gravitational potential energy depends on the *vertical height* of the object *above some reference level* (Eq. 6–6). In some situations, you may wonder from what point to measure the height $y$. The gravitational potential energy of a book held high above a table, for example, depends on whether we measure $y$ from the top of the table, from the floor, or from some other reference point.

CAUTION

*Change in* PE *is what is physically meaningful*

What is physically important in any situation is the *change* in potential energy, $\Delta$PE, because that is what is related to the work done, Eqs. 6–7; and it is $\Delta$PE that can be measured. We can thus choose to measure $y$ from any reference point that is convenient, but we must choose the reference point at the start and be consistent throughout a calculation. The *change* in potential energy between any two points does not depend on this choice.

*Grav.* PE *depends on* vertical *height*

An important result we discussed earlier (see Example 6–2 and Fig. 6–4) concerns the gravity force, which does work only in the vertical direction: the work done by gravity depends only on the vertical height $h$, and not on the path taken, whether it be purely vertical motion or, say, motion along an incline. Thus, from Eqs. 6–7 we see that changes in gravitational potential energy depend only on the change in vertical height and not on the path taken.

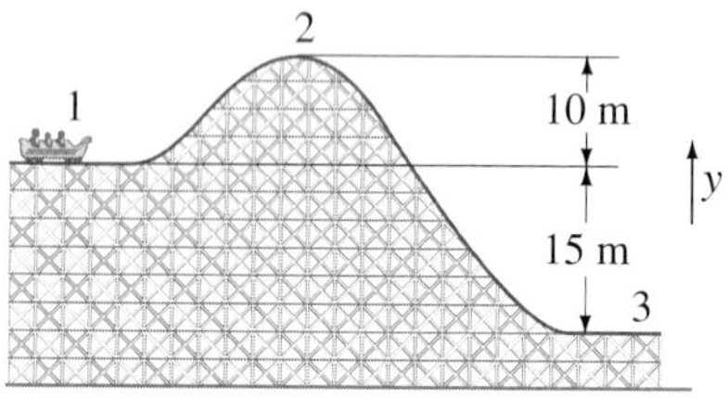


**FIGURE 6–12** Example 6–7.

**EXAMPLE 6–7 Potential energy changes for a roller coaster.** A 1000-kg roller-coaster car moves from point 1, Fig. 6–12, to point 2 and then to point 3. (*a*) What is the gravitational potential energy at 2 and 3 relative to point 1? That is, take $y = 0$ at point 1. (*b*) What is the change in potential energy when the car goes from point 2 to point 3? (*c*) Repeat parts (*a*) and (*b*), but take the reference point ($y = 0$) to be at point 3.

**APPROACH** We are interested in the potential energy of the car–Earth system. We take upward as the positive $y$ direction, and use the definition of gravitational potential energy to calculate PE.

**SOLUTION** (*a*) We measure heights from point 1, which means initially that the gravitational potential energy is zero. At point 2, where $y_2 = 10\,\mathrm{m}$,

$$\mathrm{PE}_2 = mgy_2 = (1000\,\mathrm{kg})(9.8\,\mathrm{m/s^2})(10\,\mathrm{m}) = 9.8 \times 10^4\,\mathrm{J}.$$

At point 3, $y_3 = -15\,\mathrm{m}$, since point 3 is below point 1. Therefore,

$$\mathrm{PE}_3 = mgy_3 = (1000\,\mathrm{kg})(9.8\,\mathrm{m/s^2})(-15\,\mathrm{m}) = -1.5 \times 10^5\,\mathrm{J}.$$

(*b*) In going from point 2 to point 3, the potential energy change $(\mathrm{PE_{final}} - \mathrm{PE_{initial}})$ is

$$\mathrm{PE}_3 - \mathrm{PE}_2 = (-1.5 \times 10^5\,\mathrm{J}) - (9.8 \times 10^4\,\mathrm{J}) = -2.5 \times 10^5\,\mathrm{J}.$$

The gravitational potential energy decreases by $2.5 \times 10^5$ J.

(*c*) In this instance, $y_1 = +15\,\mathrm{m}$ at point 1, so the potential energy initially (at point 1) is

$$\mathrm{PE}_1 = (1000\,\mathrm{kg})(9.8\,\mathrm{m/s^2})(15\,\mathrm{m}) = 1.5 \times 10^5\,\mathrm{J}.$$

At point 2, $y_2 = 25\,\mathrm{m}$, so the potential energy is

$$\mathrm{PE}_2 = 2.5 \times 10^5\,\mathrm{J}.$$

At point 3, $y_3 = 0$, so the potential energy is zero. The change in potential energy going from point 2 to point 3 is

$$\mathrm{PE}_3 - \mathrm{PE}_2 = 0 - 2.5 \times 10^5\,\mathrm{J} = -2.5 \times 10^5\,\mathrm{J},$$

which is the same as in part (*b*).

PE *defined in general*

There are other kinds of potential energy besides gravitational. Each form of potential energy is associated with a particular force, and can be defined analogously to gravitational potential energy. In general, the *change in potential energy associated with a particular force is equal to the negative of the work done by that force if the object is moved from one point to a second point* (as in Eq. 6–7b for gravity). Alternatively, because of Newton's third law, we can define the *change in potential energy as the work required of an external force to move the object without acceleration between the two points*, as in Eq. 6–7a.

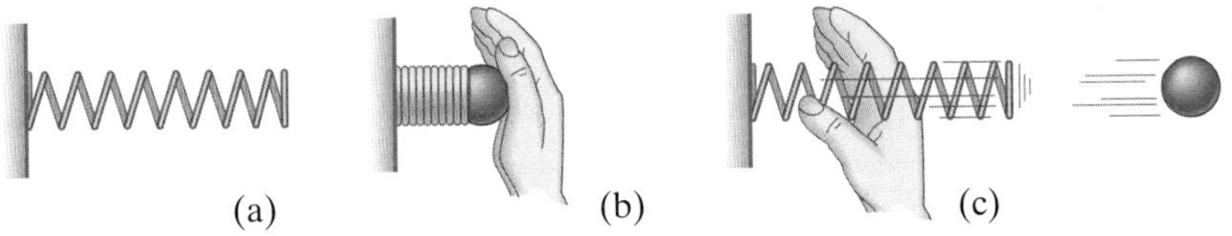


**FIGURE 6–13** (a) A spring can store energy (elastic PE) when compressed as in (b) and can do work when released (c).

*PE of elastic spring*

We now consider another type of potential energy, that associated with elastic materials. This includes a great variety of practical applications. Consider the simple coil spring shown in Fig. 6–13. The spring has potential energy when compressed (or stretched), for when it is released, it can do work on a ball as shown. To hold a spring either stretched or compressed an amount $x$ from its natural (unstretched) length requires the hand to exert a force on the spring, $F_P$, that is directly proportional to $x$. That is,

$$F_P = kx,$$

where $k$ is a constant, called the *spring stiffness constant*, and is a measure of the stiffness of the particular spring. The stretched or compressed spring exerts a force $F_S$ in the opposite direction on the hand, as shown in Fig. 6–14:

$$F_S = -kx. \quad \textbf{(6–8)}$$

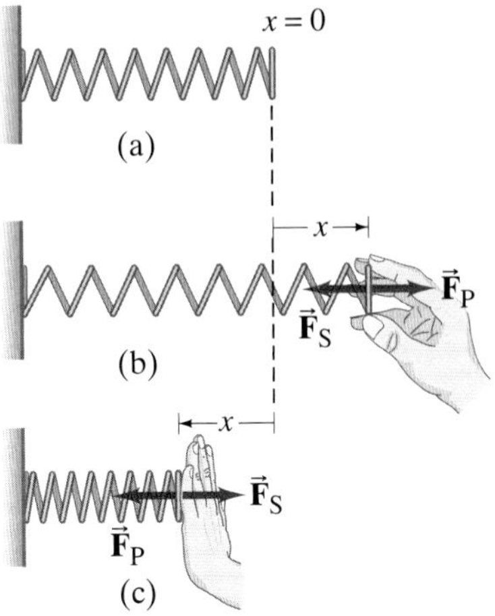


**FIGURE 6–14** (a) Spring in natural (unstretched) position. (b) Spring is stretched by a person exerting a force $\vec{\mathbf{F}}_P$ to the right (positive direction). The spring pulls back with a force $\vec{\mathbf{F}}_S$, where $F_S = -kx$. (c) Person compresses the spring ($x < 0$) by exerting a force $\vec{\mathbf{F}}_P$ to the left; the spring pushes back with a force $F_S = -kx$, where $F_S > 0$ because $x < 0$.

This force is sometimes called a "restoring force" because the spring exerts its force in the direction opposite the displacement (hence the minus sign), acting to return it to its natural length. Equation 6–8 is known as the **spring equation** and also as **Hooke's law**, and is accurate for springs as long as $x$ is not too great.

To calculate the potential energy of a stretched spring, let us calculate the work required to stretch it (Fig. 6–14b). We might expect to use Eq. 6–1 for the work done on it, $W = Fx$, where $x$ is the amount it is stretched from its natural length. But this would be incorrect since the force $F_P (= kx)$ is not constant but varies over this distance, becoming greater the more the spring is stretched, as shown graphically in Fig. 6–15. So let us use the average force, $\bar{F}$. Since $F_P$ varies linearly—from zero at the unstretched position to $kx$ when stretched to $x$—the average force is $\bar{F} = \frac{1}{2}[0 + kx] = \frac{1}{2}kx$, where $x$ here is the final amount stretched (shown as $x_f$ in Fig. 6–15 for clarity). The work done is then

$$W = \bar{F}x = \left(\tfrac{1}{2}kx\right)(x) = \tfrac{1}{2}kx^2.$$

Hence the **elastic potential energy** is proportional to the square of the amount stretched:

*Elastic PE*

$$\text{elastic PE} = \tfrac{1}{2}kx^2. \quad \textbf{(6–9)}$$

If a spring is *compressed* a distance $x$ from its natural length, the average force is again $\bar{F} = \frac{1}{2}kx$, and again the potential energy is given by Eq. 6–9. Thus $x$ can be either the amount compressed or amount stretched from the spring's natural length.† Note that for a spring, we choose the reference point for zero PE at the spring's natural position.

†We can also obtain Eq. 6–9 using Section 6–2. The work done, and hence $\Delta$PE, equals the area under the $F$ vs. $x$ graph of Fig. 6–15. This area is a triangle (colored in Fig. 6–15) of altitude $kx$ and base $x$, and hence of area (for a triangle) equal to $\frac{1}{2}(kx)(x) = \frac{1}{2}kx^2$.

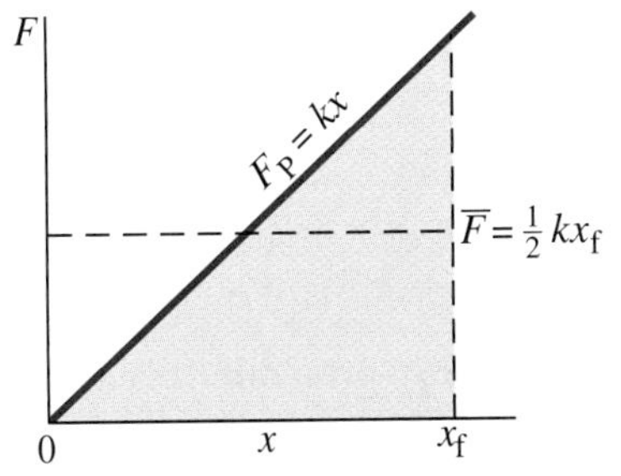


**FIGURE 6–15** As a spring is stretched (or compressed), the force needed increases linearly as $x$ increases: graph of $F = kx$ vs. $x$ from $x = 0$ to $x = x_f$.

In each of the above examples of potential energy—from a brick held at a height $y$, to a stretched or compressed spring—an object has the capacity or *potential* to do work even though it is not yet actually doing it. These examples show that energy can be *stored*, for later use, in the form of potential energy (Fig. 6–13, for instance, for a spring).

Note that there is a single universal formula for the translational kinetic energy of an object, $\frac{1}{2}mv^2$, but there is no single formula for potential energy. Instead, the mathematical form of the potential energy depends on the force involved.

## 6–5 Conservative and Nonconservative Forces

The work done against gravity in moving an object from one point to another does not depend on the path taken. For example, it takes the same work $(= mgy)$ to lift an object of mass $m$ vertically a certain height as to carry it up an incline of the same vertical height, as in Fig. 6–4 (see Example 6–2). Forces such as gravity, for which the work done does not depend on the path taken but only on the initial and final positions, are called **conservative forces**. The elastic force of a spring (or other elastic material) in which $F = -kx$, is also a conservative force. An object that starts at a given point and returns to that same point under the action of a conservative force has no net work done on it because the potential energy is the same at the start and the finish of such a round trip.

**TABLE 6–1 Conservative and Nonconservative Forces**

| Conservative Forces | Nonconservative Forces |
|---|---|
| Gravitational | Friction |
| Elastic | Air resistance |
| Electric | Tension in cord |
| | Motor or rocket propulsion |
| | Push or pull by a person |

Friction, on the other hand, is a **nonconservative force** since the work it does depends on the path. For example, when a crate is moved across a floor from one point to another, the work done depends on whether the path taken is straight, or is curved or zigzag. As shown in Fig. 6–16, if a crate is pushed from point 1 to point 2 along the longer semicircular path rather than along the straight path, more work is done against friction. That is because the distance is greater and, unlike the gravitational force, the friction force is always directed opposite to the direction of motion. (The $\cos\theta$ term in Eq. 6–1 is always $\cos 180° = -1$ at all points on the path for the friction force.) Thus the work done by friction in Fig. 6–16 does not depend *only* on points 1 and 2. Other forces that are nonconservative include the force exerted by a person and tension in a rope (see Table 6–1).

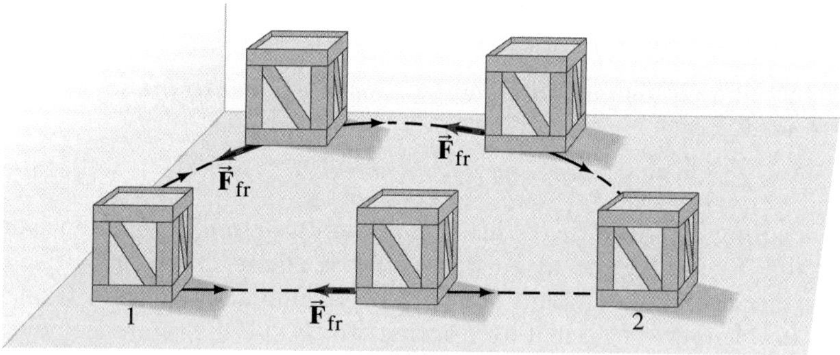


**FIGURE 6–16** A crate is pushed across the floor from position 1 to position 2 via two paths, one straight and one curved. The friction force is always in the direction exactly opposed to the direction of motion. Hence, for a constant magnitude friction force, $W_{fr} = -F_{fr}d$, so if $d$ is greater (as for the curved path), then $W$ is greater. The work done does not depend only on points 1 and 2.

*PE is defined only for a conservative force*

*There is no PE for friction*

Because potential energy is energy associated with the position or configuration of objects, potential energy can only make sense if it can be stated uniquely for a given point. This cannot be done with nonconservative forces since the work done depends on the path taken (as in Fig. 6–16). Hence, *potential energy can be defined only for a conservative force*. Thus, although potential energy is always associated with a force, not all forces have a potential energy. For example, there is no potential energy for friction.

**EXERCISE C** An object acted on by a constant force $F$ moves from point 1 to point 2 and back again. The work done by the force $F$ in this round trip is 60 J. Can you determine from this information if $F$ is a conservative or nonconservative force?

We can now extend the **work-energy principle** (discussed in Section 6–3) to include potential energy. Suppose several forces act on an object which can undergo translational motion. And suppose only some of these forces are conservative. We write the total (net) work $W_{net}$ as a sum of the work done by conservative forces, $W_C$, and the work done by nonconservative forces, $W_{NC}$:

$$W_{net} = W_C + W_{NC}.$$

Then, from the work-energy principle, Eq. 6–4, we have

$$W_{net} = \Delta KE$$
$$W_C + W_{NC} = \Delta KE$$

where $\Delta KE = KE_2 - KE_1$. Then

$$W_{NC} = \Delta KE - W_C.$$

Work done by a conservative force can be written in terms of potential energy, as we saw in Eq. 6–7b for gravitational potential energy:

$$W_C = -\Delta PE.$$

We combine these last two equations:

$$W_{NC} = \Delta KE + \Delta PE. \quad \textbf{(6–10)}$$

WORK-ENERGY PRINCIPLE *(general form)*

Thus, *the work $W_{NC}$ done by the nonconservative forces acting on an object is equal to the total change in kinetic and potential energies.*

It must be emphasized that *all* the forces acting on an object must be included in Eq. 6–10, either in the potential energy term on the right (if it is a conservative force), or in the work term on the left (but not in both!).

## 6–6 Mechanical Energy and Its Conservation

If only conservative forces are acting in a system, we arrive at a particularly simple and beautiful relation involving energy.

When no nonconservative forces are present, then $W_{NC} = 0$ in Eq. 6–10, the general form of the work-energy principle. Then we have

$$\Delta KE + \Delta PE = 0 \quad \begin{bmatrix}\text{conservative}\\ \text{forces only}\end{bmatrix} \quad \textbf{(6–11a)}$$

or

$$(KE_2 - KE_1) + (PE_2 - PE_1) = 0. \quad \begin{bmatrix}\text{conservative}\\ \text{forces only}\end{bmatrix} \quad \textbf{(6–11b)}$$

We now define a quantity $E$, called the **total mechanical energy** of our system, as the sum of the kinetic and potential energies at any moment:

$$E = KE + PE.$$

*Total mechanical energy defined*

Now we can rewrite Eq. 6–11b as

$$KE_2 + PE_2 = KE_1 + PE_1 \quad \begin{bmatrix}\text{conservative}\\ \text{forces only}\end{bmatrix} \quad \textbf{(6–12a)}$$

CONSERVATION OF MECHANICAL ENERGY

or

$$E_2 = E_1 = \text{constant.} \quad \begin{bmatrix}\text{conservative}\\ \text{forces only}\end{bmatrix} \quad \textbf{(6–12b)}$$

Equations 6–12 express a useful and profound principle regarding the total mechanical energy of a system—namely, that it is a **conserved quantity**. The total mechanical energy $E$ remains constant as long as no nonconservative forces act: $(KE + PE)$ at some initial time 1 is equal to the $(KE + PE)$ at any later time 2.

To say it another way, consider Eq. 6–11a which tells us $\Delta PE = -\Delta KE$; that is, if the kinetic energy KE of a system increases, then the potential energy PE must decrease by an equivalent amount to compensate. Thus, the total, KE + PE, remains constant:

**If only conservative forces are acting, the total mechanical energy of a system neither increases nor decreases in any process. It stays constant—it is conserved.**

CONSERVATION OF MECHANICAL ENERGY

This is the **principle of conservation of mechanical energy** for conservative forces.

In the next Section we shall see the great usefulness of the conservation of mechanical energy principle in a variety of situations, and how it is often easier to use than the kinematic equations or Newton's laws. After that we will discuss how other forms of energy can be included in the general conservation of energy law that includes energy associated with nonconservative forces.

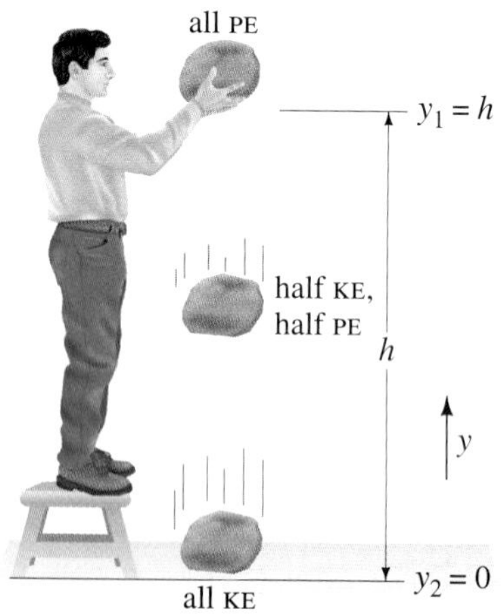


**FIGURE 6–17** As it falls, the rock's potential energy changes to kinetic energy.

## 6–7 Problem Solving Using Conservation of Mechanical Energy

A simple example of the conservation of mechanical energy (neglecting air resistance) is a rock allowed to fall under gravity from a height $h$ above the ground, as shown in Fig. 6–17. If the rock starts from rest, all of the initial energy is potential energy. As the rock falls, the potential energy decreases (because $y$ decreases), but the rock's kinetic energy increases to compensate, so that the sum of the two remains constant. At any point along the path, the total mechanical energy is given by

$$E = \text{KE} + \text{PE} = \tfrac{1}{2}mv^2 + mgy$$

where $y$ is the rock's height above the ground at a given instant and $v$ is its speed at that point. If we let the subscript 1 represent the rock at one point along its path (for example, the initial point), and the subscript 2 represent it at some other point, then we can write

total mechanical energy at point 1 = total mechanical energy at point 2

or (see also Eq. 6–12a)

*Conservation of mechanical energy when only gravity acts*

$$\tfrac{1}{2}mv_1^2 + mgy_1 = \tfrac{1}{2}mv_2^2 + mgy_2. \qquad \text{[grav. PE only]} \quad \textbf{(6–13)}$$

Just before the rock hits the ground, where we chose $y = 0$, all of the initial potential energy will have been transformed into kinetic energy.

**EXAMPLE 6–8** **Falling rock.** If the original height of the rock in Fig. 6–17 is $y_1 = h = 3.0\,\text{m}$, calculate the rock's speed when it has fallen to 1.0 m above the ground.

**APPROACH** One approach is to use the kinematic equations of Chapter 2. Let us instead apply the principle of conservation of mechanical energy, Eq. 6–13, assuming that only gravity acts on the rock. We choose the ground as our reference level ($y = 0$).

**SOLUTION** At the moment of release (point 1) the rock's position is $y_1 = 3.0\,\text{m}$ and it is at rest: $v_1 = 0$. We want to find $v_2$ when the rock is at position $y_2 = 1.0\,\text{m}$. Equation 6–13 gives

$$\tfrac{1}{2}mv_1^2 + mgy_1 = \tfrac{1}{2}mv_2^2 + mgy_2.$$

The $m$'s cancel out; setting $v_1 = 0$ and solving for $v_2^2$ we find

$$v_2^2 = 2g(y_1 - y_2)$$
$$= 2(9.8\,\text{m/s}^2)[(3.0\,\text{m}) - (1.0\,\text{m})] = 39.2\,\text{m}^2/\text{s}^2,$$

and

$$v_2 = \sqrt{39.2}\,\text{m/s} = 6.3\,\text{m/s}.$$

The rock's speed 1.0 m above the ground is 6.3 m/s downward.

**NOTE** The velocity at point 2 is independent of the rock's mass.

**FIGURE 6–18** Energy buckets (for Example 6–8). Kinetic energy is red and potential energy is blue. The total (KE + PE) is the same for the three points shown. The speed at $y = 0$, just before the rock hits the ground, is $\sqrt{2(9.8\,\text{m/s}^2)(3.0\,\text{m})} = 7.7\,\text{m/s}$.

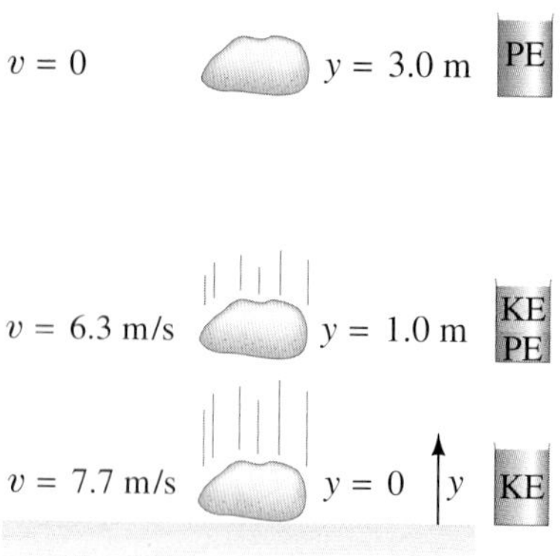


**EXERCISE D** Solve Example 6–8 by using the work-energy principle applied to the rock, without the concept of potential energy. Show all equations you use, starting with Eq. 6–4.

A simple way to visualize energy conservation is with an "energy bucket" as shown in Fig. 6–18. At each point in the fall of the rock, for example, the amount of kinetic energy and potential energy are shown as if they were two differently colored materials in the bucket. The total amount of material in the bucket (= total mechanical energy) remains constant.

Equation 6–13 can be applied to any object moving without friction under the action of gravity. For example, Fig. 6–19 shows a roller-coaster car starting from rest at the top of a hill, and coasting without friction to the bottom and up the hill on the other side.† Initially, the car has only potential energy. As it coasts down the hill, it loses potential energy and gains in kinetic energy, but the sum of the two remains constant. At the bottom of the hill it has its maximum kinetic energy; as it climbs up the other side, the kinetic energy changes back to potential energy. When the car comes to rest again, all of its energy will be potential energy. Given that the potential energy is proportional to the vertical height, energy conservation tells us that (in the absence of friction) the car comes to rest at a height equal to its original height. If the two hills are the same height, the car will just barely reach the top of the second hill when it stops. If the second hill is lower than the first, not all of the car's kinetic energy will be transformed to potential energy and the car can continue over the top and down the other side. If instead the second hill is higher, the car will only reach a height on it equal to its original height on the first hill. This is true (in the absence of friction) no matter how steep the hill is, since potential energy depends only on the vertical height (Eq. 6–6).

**FIGURE 6–19** A roller-coaster car moving without friction illustrates the conservation of mechanical energy.

*Grav. PE depends on vertical height, not path length (Eq. 6–6)*

**EXAMPLE 6–9 Roller-coaster speed using energy conservation.** Assuming the height of the hill in Fig. 6–19 is 40 m, and the roller-coaster car starts from rest at the top, calculate (*a*) the speed of the roller-coaster car at the bottom of the hill, and (*b*) at what height it will have half this speed. Take $y = 0$ at the bottom of the hill.

**APPROACH** We choose point 1 to be where the car starts from rest $(v_1 = 0)$ at the top of the hill $(y_1 = 40\text{ m})$. Point 2 is the bottom of the hill, which we choose as our reference level, so $y_2 = 0$. We use conservation of mechanical energy.

**SOLUTION** (*a*) We use Eq. 6–13 with $v_1 = 0$ and $y_2 = 0$. Then

$$\tfrac{1}{2}mv_1^2 + mgy_1 = \tfrac{1}{2}mv_2^2 + mgy_2$$
$$mgy_1 = \tfrac{1}{2}mv_2^2.$$

The *m*'s cancel out and, setting $y_1 = 40\text{ m}$, we find

$$v_2 = \sqrt{2gy_1} = \sqrt{2(9.8\text{ m/s}^2)(40\text{ m})} = 28\text{ m/s}.$$

(*b*) We again use conservation of energy,

$$\tfrac{1}{2}mv_1^2 + mgy_1 = \tfrac{1}{2}mv_2^2 + mgy_2,$$

but now $v_2 = 14\text{ m/s}$ (half of 28 m/s) and $y_2$ is unknown. We cancel the *m*'s, set $v_1 = 0$, and solve for $y_2$:

$$y_2 = y_1 - \frac{v_2^2}{2g} = 30\text{ m}.$$

That is, the car has a speed of 14 m/s when it is 30 *vertical* meters above the lowest point, both when descending the left-hand hill and when ascending the right-hand hill.

**NOTE** The mathematics of this Example is almost the same as that in Example 6–8. But there is an important difference between them. Example 6–8 could have been solved using force, acceleration, and the kinematic equations (Eqs. 2–11). But here, where the motion is not vertical, that approach would have been too complicated, whereas energy conservation readily gives us the answer.

†The forces on the car are gravity, the normal force exerted by the track, and friction (here, assumed zero). The normal force acts perpendicular to the track, and so is always perpendicular to the motion and does no work. Thus $W_{NC} = 0$ in Eq. 6–10 (so mechanical energy is conserved) and we can use Eq. 6–13 with the potential energy being only gravitational potential energy. We will see how to deal with friction, for which $W_{NC} \neq 0$, in Section 6–9.

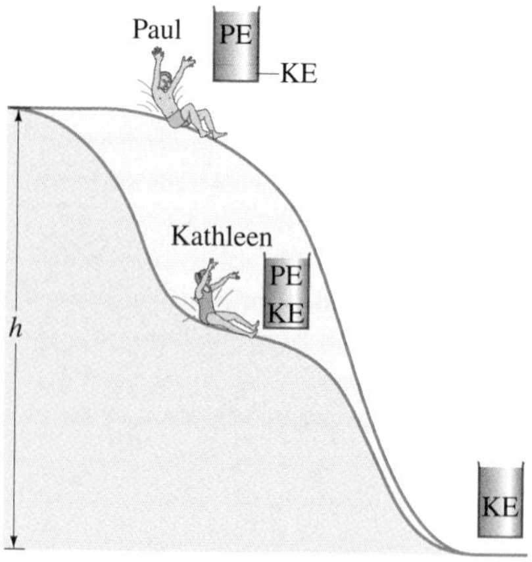


**FIGURE 6–20** Example 6–10.

**CONCEPTUAL EXAMPLE 6–10** **Speeds on two water slides.** Two water slides at a pool are shaped differently, but have the same length and start at the same height $h$ (Fig. 6–20). Two riders, Paul and Kathleen, start from rest at the same time on different slides. (*a*) Which rider, Paul or Kathleen, is traveling faster at the bottom? (*b*) Which rider makes it to the bottom first? Ignore friction.

**RESPONSE** (*a*) Each rider's initial potential energy $mgh$ gets transformed to kinetic energy, so the speed $v$ at the bottom is obtained from $\frac{1}{2}mv^2 = mgh$. The mass cancels and so the speed will be the same, regardless of the mass of the rider. Since they descend the same vertical height, they will finish with the same speed.

(*b*) Note that Kathleen is consistently at a lower elevation than Paul at any instant, until the end. This means she has converted her potential energy to kinetic energy earlier. Consequently, she is traveling faster than Paul for the whole trip, except toward the end where Paul finally gets up to the same speed. Since she was going faster for the whole trip, and the distance is the same, Kathleen gets to the bottom first.

**EXERCISE E** Two balls are released from the same height above the floor. Ball A falls freely through the air, whereas ball B slides on a curved frictionless track to the floor. How do the speeds of the balls compare when they reach the floor?

**PROBLEM SOLVING**
*Whether to use energy, or Newton's laws?*

You may wonder sometimes whether to approach a problem using work and energy, or instead to use Newton's laws. As a rough guideline, if the force(s) involved are constant, either approach may succeed. If the forces are not constant, and/or the path is not simple, energy may be the surest approach.

**PHYSICS APPLIED**
*Sports*

There are many interesting examples of the conservation of energy in sports, such as the pole vault illustrated in Fig. 6–21. We often have to make approximations, but the sequence of events in broad outline for the pole vault is as follows. The initial kinetic energy of the running athlete is transformed into elastic potential energy of the bending pole and, as the athlete leaves the ground, into gravitational potential energy. When the vaulter reaches the top and the pole has straightened out again, the energy has all been transformed into gravitational potential energy (if we ignore the vaulter's low horizontal speed over the bar). The pole does not supply any energy, but it acts as a device to *store* energy and thus aid in the transformation of kinetic energy into gravitational potential energy, which is the net result. The energy required to pass over the bar depends on how high the center of mass (CM) of the vaulter must be raised. By bending their bodies, pole vaulters keep their CM so low that it can actually pass slightly beneath the bar (Fig. 6–22), thus enabling them to cross over a higher bar than would otherwise be possible. (Center of mass is covered in Chapter 7.)

**FIGURE 6–21** Transformation of energy during a pole vault.

**FIGURE 6–22** By bending their bodies, pole vaulters can keep their center of mass so low that it may even pass below the bar. By changing their kinetic energy (of running) into gravitational potential energy ($= mgy$) in this way, vaulters can cross over a higher bar than if the change in potential energy were accomplished without carefully bending the body.

As another example of the conservation of mechanical energy, let us consider an object of mass $m$ connected to a horizontal spring whose own mass can be neglected and whose spring stiffness constant is $k$. The mass $m$ has speed $v$ at any moment. The potential energy of the system (object plus spring) is given by Eq. 6–9, $\text{PE} = \frac{1}{2}kx^2$, where $x$ is the displacement of the spring from its unstretched length. If neither friction nor any other force is acting, conservation of mechanical energy tells us that

$$\tfrac{1}{2}mv_1^2 + \tfrac{1}{2}kx_1^2 = \tfrac{1}{2}mv_2^2 + \tfrac{1}{2}kx_2^2, \qquad \text{[elastic PE only]} \quad \textbf{(6–14)}$$

*Conservation of mechanical energy when PE is elastic*

where the subscripts 1 and 2 refer to the velocity and displacement at two different moments.

**EXAMPLE 6–11** **Toy dart gun.** A dart of mass 0.100 kg is pressed against the spring of a toy dart gun as shown in Fig. 6–23a. The spring (with spring stiffness constant $k = 250\,\text{N/m}$) is compressed 6.0 cm and released. If the dart detaches from the spring when the spring reaches its natural length $(x = 0)$, what speed does the dart acquire?

**APPROACH** The dart is initially at rest (point 1), so $\text{KE}_1 = 0$. We ignore friction and use conservation of mechanical energy; the only potential energy is elastic.

**SOLUTION** We use Eq. 6–14 with point 1 being at the maximum compression of the spring, so $v_1 = 0$ (dart not yet released) and $x_1 = -0.060\,\text{m}$. Point 2 we choose to be the instant the dart flies off the end of the spring (Fig. 6–23b), so $x_2 = 0$ and we want to find $v_2$. Thus Eq. 6–14 can be written

$$0 + \tfrac{1}{2}kx_1^2 = \tfrac{1}{2}mv_2^2 + 0.$$

Then

$$v_2^2 = \frac{kx_1^2}{m}$$

$$= \frac{(250\,\text{N/m})(-0.060\,\text{m})^2}{(0.100\,\text{kg})} = 9.0\,\text{m}^2/\text{s}^2$$

so $v_2 = \sqrt{v_2^2} = 3.0\,\text{m/s}$.

**NOTE** In the horizontal direction, the only force on the dart (neglecting friction) was the force exerted by the spring. Vertically, gravity was counterbalanced by the normal force exerted on the dart by the gun barrel. After it leaves the barrel, the dart will follow a projectile's path under gravity.

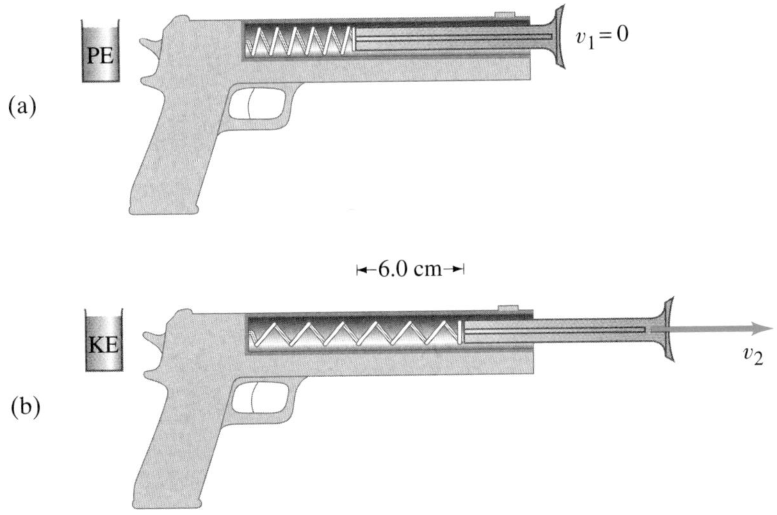


**FIGURE 6–23** Example 6–11. (a) A dart is pushed against a spring, compressing it 6.0 cm. The dart is then released, and in (b) it leaves the spring at velocity $v_2$.

## Additional Example

The next Example shows how to solve a problem involving two types of potential energy.

**EXAMPLE 6–12** **Two kinds of PE.** A ball of mass $m = 2.60\text{ kg}$, starting from rest, falls a vertical distance $h = 55.0\text{ cm}$ before striking a vertical coiled spring, which it compresses an amount $Y = 15.0\text{ cm}$ (Fig. 6–24). Determine the spring stiffness constant of the spring. Assume the spring has negligible mass, and ignore air resistance. Measure all distances from the point where the ball first touches the uncompressed spring ($y = 0$ at this point).

**APPROACH** The forces acting on the ball are the gravitational pull of the Earth and the elastic force exerted by the spring. Both forces are conservative, so we can use conservation of mechanical energy, including both types of potential energy. We must be careful, however: gravity acts throughout the fall (Fig. 6–24), whereas the elastic force does not act until the ball touches the spring (Fig. 6–24b). We choose $y$ positive upward, and $y = 0$ at the end of the spring in its natural (uncompressed) state.

**SOLUTION** We divide this solution into two parts. (An alternate solution follows.) *Part 1*: Let us first consider the energy changes as the ball falls from a height $y_1 = h = 0.55\text{ m}$, Fig. 6–24a, to $y_2 = 0$, just as it touches the spring, Fig. 6–24b. Our system is the ball acted on by gravity plus the spring, which up to this point doesn't do anything. Thus

$$\tfrac{1}{2}mv_1^2 + mgy_1 = \tfrac{1}{2}mv_2^2 + mgy_2$$

$$0 + mgh = \tfrac{1}{2}mv_2^2 + 0.$$

We solve for $v_2 = \sqrt{2gh} = \sqrt{2(9.80\text{ m/s}^2)(0.550\text{ m})} = 3.283\text{ m/s} \approx 3.28\text{ m/s}$. This is the speed of the ball just as it touches the top of the spring, Fig. 6–24b. *Part 2*: Let's see what happens as the ball compresses the spring, Figs. 6–24b to c. Now there are two conservative forces on the ball—gravity and the spring force. So our conservation of energy equation becomes

*Conservation of energy: gravity and elastic PE*

$$E(\text{ball touches spring}) = E(\text{spring compresses})$$

$$\tfrac{1}{2}mv_2^2 + mgy_2 + \tfrac{1}{2}ky_2^2 = \tfrac{1}{2}mv_3^2 + mgy_3 + \tfrac{1}{2}ky_3^2.$$

We take point 2 to be the instant when the ball just touches the spring, so $y_2 = 0$ and $v_2 = 3.283\text{ m/s}$ (keeping an extra digit for now). We take point 3 to be when the ball comes to rest (for an instant) and the spring is fully compressed, so $v_3 = 0$ and $y_3 = -Y = -0.150\text{ m}$ (given). Substituting into the above energy equation, we get

$$\tfrac{1}{2}mv_2^2 + 0 + 0 = 0 - mgY + \tfrac{1}{2}kY^2.$$

We know $m$, $v_2$, and $Y$, so we can solve for $k$:

$$k = \frac{2}{Y^2}\left[\tfrac{1}{2}mv_2^2 + mgY\right] = \frac{m}{Y^2}\left[v_2^2 + 2gY\right]$$

$$= \frac{(2.60\text{ kg})}{(0.150\text{ m})^2}\left[(3.283\text{ m/s})^2 + 2(9.80\text{ m/s}^2)(0.150\text{ m})\right] = 1590\text{ N/m},$$

which is the result we sought.

**FIGURE 6–24** Example 6–12.

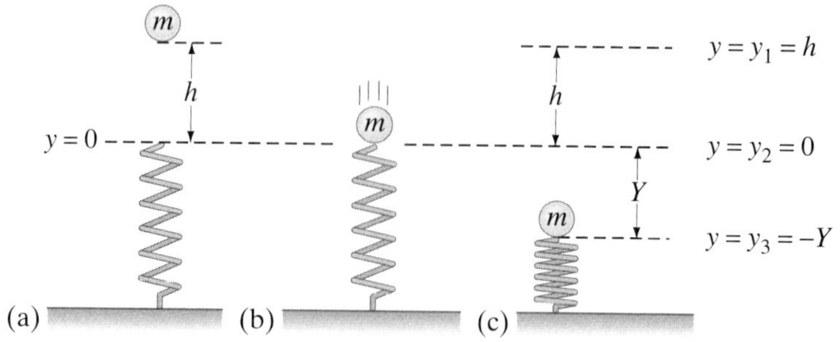

**PROBLEM SOLVING**
*Alternate Solution*

***Alternate Solution*** Instead of dividing the solution into two parts, we can do it all at once. After all, we get to choose what two points are used on the left and right of the energy equation. Let us write the energy equation for points 1 and 3 (Fig. 6–24). Point 1 is the initial point just before the ball starts to fall (Fig. 6–24a), so $v_1 = 0, y_1 = h = 0.550\text{ m}$; and point 3 is when the spring is fully compressed (Fig. 6–24c), so $v_3 = 0, y_3 = -Y = -0.150\text{ m}$. The forces on the ball in this process are gravity and (at least part of the time) the spring. So conservation of energy tells us

$$\tfrac{1}{2}mv_1^2 + mgy_1 + \tfrac{1}{2}k(0)^2 = \tfrac{1}{2}mv_3^2 + mgy_3 + \tfrac{1}{2}ky_3^2$$
$$0 + mgh + 0 = 0 - mgY + \tfrac{1}{2}kY^2$$

where we have set $y = 0$ for the spring at point 1 because it is not acting and is not compressed or stretched at point 1. We solve for $k$:

$$k = \frac{2\,mg(h+Y)}{Y^2} = \frac{2(2.60\text{ kg})(9.80\text{ m/s}^2)(0.550\text{ m} + 0.150\text{ m})}{(0.150\text{ m})^2} = 1590\text{ N/m}$$

just as in our first method of solution.

## 6–8 Other Forms of Energy; Energy Transformations and the Law of Conservation of Energy

Besides the kinetic energy and potential energy of ordinary objects, other forms of energy can be defined as well. These include electric energy, nuclear energy, thermal energy, and the chemical energy stored in food and fuels. With the advent of the atomic theory, these other forms of energy have come to be considered as kinetic or potential energy at the atomic or molecular level. For example, according to the atomic theory, thermal energy is the kinetic energy of rapidly moving molecules—when an object is heated, the molecules that make up the object move faster. On the other hand, the energy stored in food and fuel such as gasoline is potential energy stored by virtue of the relative positions of the atoms within a molecule due to electric forces between the atoms (referred to as chemical bonds). For the energy in chemical bonds to be used to do work, it must be released, usually through chemical reactions. This is analogous to a compressed spring which, when released, can do work. Electric, magnetic, and nuclear energies also can be considered examples of kinetic and potential (or stored) energies. We will deal with these other forms of energy in detail in later Chapters.

Energy can be transformed from one form to another, and we have already encountered several examples of this. A rock held high in the air has potential energy; as it falls, it loses potential energy, since its height above the ground decreases. At the same time, it gains in kinetic energy, since its velocity is increasing. Potential energy is being transformed into kinetic energy.

Often the transformation of energy involves a transfer of energy from one object to another. The potential energy stored in the spring of Fig. 6–13b is transformed into the kinetic energy of the ball, Fig. 6–13c. Water at the top of a dam has potential energy, which is transformed into kinetic energy as the water falls. At the base of the dam, the kinetic energy of the water can be transferred to turbine blades and further transformed into electric energy, as we shall see in a later Chapter. The potential energy stored in a bent bow can be transformed into kinetic energy of the arrow (Fig. 6–25).

**FIGURE 6–25** Potential energy of a bent bow about to be transformed into kinetic energy of an arrow.

In each of these examples, the transfer of energy is accompanied by the performance of work. The spring of Fig. 6–13 does work on the ball. Water does work on turbine blades. A bow does work on an arrow. This observation gives us a further insight into the relation between work and energy: *work is done when energy is transferred from one object to another.*† A person throwing a ball or pushing a grocery cart provides another example. The work done is a manifestation of energy being transferred from the person (ultimately derived from the chemical energy of food) to the ball or cart.

*Work is done when energy is transferred from one object to another*

† If the objects are at different temperatures, heat can flow between them instead, or in addition. See Chapters 14 and 15.

One of the great results of physics is that whenever energy is transferred or transformed, it is found that no energy is gained or lost in the process.

This is the **law of conservation of energy**, one of the most important principles in physics; it can be stated as:

*LAW OF CONSERVATION OF ENERGY*

**The total energy is neither increased nor decreased in any process. Energy can be transformed from one form to another, and transferred from one object to another, but the total amount remains constant.**

We have already discussed the conservation of energy for mechanical systems involving conservative forces, and we saw how it could be derived from Newton's laws and thus is equivalent to them. But in its full generality, the validity of the law of conservation of energy, encompassing all forms of energy including those associated with nonconservative forces like friction, rests on experimental observation. Even though Newton's laws are found to fail in the submicroscopic world of the atom, the law of conservation of energy has been found to hold in every experimental situation so far tested.

## 6–9 Energy Conservation with Dissipative Forces: Solving Problems

In our applications of energy conservation in Section 6–7, we neglected friction, a nonconservative force. But in many situations it cannot be ignored. In a real situation, the roller-coaster car in Fig. 6–19, for example, will not in fact reach the same height on the second hill as it had on the first hill because of friction. In this, and in other natural processes, the mechanical energy (sum of the kinetic and potential energies) does not remain constant but decreases. Because frictional forces reduce the mechanical energy (but *not* the total energy), they are called **dissipative forces**. Historically, the presence of dissipative forces hindered the formulation of a comprehensive conservation of energy law until well into the nineteenth century. It was only then that heat, which is always produced when there is friction (try rubbing your hands together), was interpreted in terms of energy. Quantitative studies by nineteenth-century scientists (discussed in Chapters 14 and 15) demonstrated that if heat is considered as a transfer of energy (thermal energy), then the total energy is conserved in any process. For example, if the roller-coaster car in Fig. 6–19 is subject to frictional forces, then the initial total energy of the car will be equal to the kinetic plus potential energy of the car at any subsequent point along its path plus the amount of thermal energy produced in the process. The thermal energy produced by a constant friction force $F_{fr}$ is equal to the work done by friction. We now apply the general form of the work-energy principle, Eq. 6–10:

*Dissipative forces*

$$W_{NC} = \Delta \text{KE} + \Delta \text{PE}.$$

We can write $W_{NC} = -F_{fr}d$, where $d$ is the distance over which the friction force acts. ($\vec{\mathbf{F}}$ and $\vec{\mathbf{d}}$ are in opposite directions, hence the minus sign.) Thus, with $\text{KE} = \frac{1}{2}mv^2$ and $\text{PE} = mgy$, we have

$$-F_{fr}d = \tfrac{1}{2}mv_2^2 - \tfrac{1}{2}mv_1^2 + mgy_2 - mgy_1$$

or

*Conservation of energy with gravity and friction*

$$\tfrac{1}{2}mv_1^2 + mgy_1 = \tfrac{1}{2}mv_2^2 + mgy_2 + F_{fr}d, \quad \begin{bmatrix}\text{gravity and}\\ \text{friction acting}\end{bmatrix} \quad \textbf{(6–15)}$$

where $d$ is the distance along the path traveled by the object in going from point 1 to point 2. Equation 6–15 can be seen to be Eq. 6–13 modified to include friction. It can be interpreted in a simple way: the initial mechanical energy of the car (point 1) equals the (reduced) final mechanical energy of the car plus the energy transformed by friction into thermal energy.

When other forms of energy are involved, such as chemical or electrical energy, the total amount of energy is always found to be conserved. Hence the law of conservation of energy is believed to be universally valid.

## Work-Energy versus Energy Conservation

The work-energy principle and the law of conservation of energy are basically equivalent. The difference between them is in how you use them, and in particular on your *choice of the system* under study. If you choose as your system one or more objects on which external forces do work, then you must use the work-energy principle: the work done by the external forces on your system equals the total change in energy of your chosen system.

On the other hand, if you choose a system on which no external forces do work, then you can apply conservation of energy to that system.

Consider, for example, a spring connected to a block on a frictionless table (Fig. 6–26). If you choose the block as your system, then the work done on the block by the spring equals the change in kinetic energy of the block: the work-energy principle. (Energy conservation does not apply to this system—the block's energy changes.) If instead you choose the block plus the spring as your system, no external forces do work (since the spring is part of the chosen system). To this system you can apply conservation of energy: if you compress the spring and then release it, the spring still exerts a force on the block, but the subsequent motion can be discussed in terms of kinetic energy $\left(\frac{1}{2}mv^2\right)$ plus potential energy $\left(\frac{1}{2}kx^2\right)$, whose total remains constant.

Conservation of energy applies to any system on which no work is done by external forces.

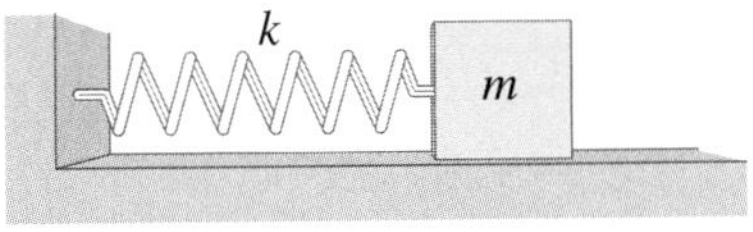


**FIGURE 6–26** A spring connected to a block on a frictionless table. If you choose your system to be the block plus spring, then

$$E = \tfrac{1}{2}mv^2 + \tfrac{1}{2}kx^2$$

is conserved.

### PROBLEM SOLVING Conservation of Energy

1. **Draw a picture** of the physical situation.
2. Determine **the system** for which energy will be conserved: the object or objects and the forces acting.
3. Ask yourself what quantity you are looking for, and decide what are **the initial** (point 1) **and final** (point 2) **positions.**
4. If the object under investigation changes its height during the problem, then **choose a reference frame** with a convenient $y = 0$ level for gravitational potential energy; the lowest point in the problem is often a good choice.

   If springs are involved, choose the unstretched spring position to be $x$ (or $y$) $= 0$.
5. **Apply conservation of energy.** If no friction or other nonconservative forces act, then conservation of mechanical energy holds:
   $$\text{KE}_1 + \text{PE}_1 = \text{KE}_2 + \text{PE}_2 .$$
   If friction or other nonconservative forces are present, then an additional term $(W_{\text{NC}})$ will be needed:
   $$W_{\text{NC}} = \Delta\text{KE} + \Delta\text{PE}.$$
   To be sure which sign to give $W_{\text{NC}}$, you can use your intuition: is the total mechanical energy increased or decreased in the process?
6. Use the equation(s) you develop to **solve** for the unknown quantity.

**EXAMPLE 6–13** **Friction on the roller coaster.** The roller-coaster car in Example 6–9 reaches a vertical height of only 25 m on the second hill before coming to a momentary stop (Fig. 6–27). It traveled a total distance of 400 m. Estimate the average friction force (assume constant) on the car, whose mass is 1000 kg.

**APPROACH** We explicitly follow the Problem Solving Box step by step.

**SOLUTION** 1. **Draw a Picture.** See Fig. 6–27.

2. **The system.** The system is the roller-coaster car (and the Earth since it exerts the gravitational force). The forces acting on the car are gravity and friction. (The normal force also acts on the car, but does no work, so it does not affect the energy.)
3. **Choose initial and final positions.** We take point 1 to be the instant when the car started coasting (at the top of the first hill), and point 2 to be the instant it stopped 25 m up the second hill.
4. **Choose a reference frame.** We choose the lowest point in the motion to be $y = 0$ for the gravitational potential energy.
5. **Apply conservation of energy.** There is friction acting on the car, so we use conservation of energy in the form of Eq. 6–15, with $v_1 = 0$, $y_1 = 40\text{ m}$, $v_2 = 0$, $y_2 = 25\text{ m}$, and $d = 400\text{ m}$. Thus
   $$0 + (1000\text{ kg})(9.8\text{ m/s}^2)(40\text{ m}) = 0 + (1000\text{ kg})(9.8\text{ m/s}^2)(25\text{ m}) + F_{\text{fr}}(400\text{ m}).$$
6. **Solve.** We can solve this equation for $F_{\text{fr}}$: $F_{\text{fr}} = 370\text{ N}$.

**FIGURE 6–27** Example 6–13. Because of friction, a roller coaster car does not reach the original height on the second hill.

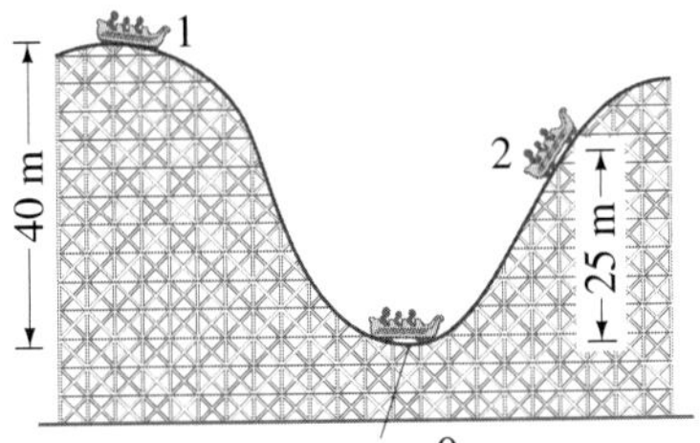

Problem solving is not a process that can be done by following a set of rules. The Problem Solving Box on page 157 is thus not a prescription, but is a *summary* of steps to help you get started in solving problems involving energy.

## 6–10 Power

*Power defined*

**Power** is defined as the *rate at which work is done*. Average power equals the work done divided by the time to do it. Power can also be defined as the *rate at which energy is transformed*. Thus

*Average power*

$$\overline{P} = \text{average power} = \frac{\text{work}}{\text{time}} = \frac{\text{energy transformed}}{\text{time}}. \qquad (6\text{–}16)$$

*Power units: the watt*

*The horsepower*

The power of a horse refers to how much work it can do per unit time. The power rating of an engine refers to how much chemical or electrical energy can be transformed into mechanical energy per unit time. In SI units, power is measured in joules per second, and this unit is given a special name, the **watt** (W): $1\text{ W} = 1\text{ J/s}$. We are most familiar with the watt for electrical devices: the rate at which an electric lightbulb or heater changes electric energy into light or thermal energy; but the watt is used for other types of energy transformations as well. In the British system, the unit of power is the foot-pound per second ($\text{ft}\cdot\text{lb/s}$). For practical purposes, a larger unit is often used, the **horsepower**. One horsepower† (hp) is defined as $550\text{ ft}\cdot\text{lb/s}$, which equals 746 W.

**CAUTION**

*Distinguish between power and energy*

To see the distinction between energy and power, consider the following example. A person is limited in the work he or she can do, not only by the total energy required, but also by how fast this energy is transformed: that is, by power. For example, a person may be able to walk a long distance or climb many flights of stairs before having to stop because so much energy has been expended. On the other hand, a person who runs very quickly upstairs may fall exhausted after only a flight or two. He or she is limited in this case by power, the rate at which his or her body can transform chemical energy into mechanical energy.

**FIGURE 6–28** Example 6–14.

**EXAMPLE 6–14** **Stair-climbing power.** A 60-kg jogger runs up a long flight of stairs in 4.0 s (Fig. 6–28). The vertical height of the stairs is 4.5 m. (*a*) Estimate the jogger's power output in watts and horsepower. (*b*) How much energy did this require?

**APPROACH** The work done by the jogger is against gravity, and equals $W = mgy$. To get her power output we divide $W$ by the time it took.

**SOLUTION** (*a*) The average power output was

$$\overline{P} = \frac{W}{t} = \frac{mgy}{t} = \frac{(60\text{ kg})(9.8\text{ m/s}^2)(4.5\text{ m})}{4.0\text{ s}} = 660\text{ W}.$$

Since there are 746 W in 1 hp, the jogger is doing work at a rate of just under 1 hp. A human cannot do work at this rate for very long.
(*b*) The energy required is $E = \overline{P}t$ (Eq. 6–16). Since $\overline{P} = 660\text{ W} = 660\text{ J/s}$, then $E = (660\text{ J/s})(4.0\text{ s}) = 2600\text{ J}$. This result equals $W = mgy$.

**NOTE** The person had to transform more energy than this 2600 J. The total energy transformed by a person or an engine always includes some thermal energy (recall how hot you get running up stairs).

†The unit was chosen by James Watt (1736–1819), who needed a way to specify the power of his newly developed steam engines. He found by experiment that a good horse can work all day at an average rate of about $360\text{ ft}\cdot\text{lb/s}$. So as not to be accused of exaggeration in the sale of his steam engines, he multiplied this by $1\frac{1}{2}$ when he defined the hp.

Automobile engines do work to overcome the force of friction (including air resistance), to climb hills, and to accelerate. A car is limited by the rate at which it can do work, which is why automobile engines are rated in horsepower. A car needs power most when climbing hills and when accelerating. In the next Example, we will calculate how much power is needed in these situations for a car of reasonable size. Even when a car travels on a level road at constant speed, it needs some power just to do work to overcome the retarding forces of internal friction and air resistance. These forces depend on the conditions and speed of the car, but are typically in the range 400 N to 1000 N.

It is often convenient to write power in terms of the net force $F$ applied to an object and its speed $v$. This is readily done since $\overline{P} = W/t$ and $W = Fd$, where $d$ is the distance traveled. Then

$$\overline{P} = \frac{W}{t} = \frac{Fd}{t} = F\overline{v}, \tag{6–17}$$

where $\overline{v} = d/t$ is the average speed of the object.

**EXAMPLE 6–15** **Power needs of a car.** Calculate the power required of a 1400-kg car under the following circumstances: (*a*) the car climbs a 10° hill (a fairly steep hill) at a steady 80 km/h; and (*b*) the car accelerates along a level road from 90 to 110 km/h in 6.0 s to pass another car. Assume the retarding force on the car is $F_R = 700\text{ N}$ throughout. See Fig. 6–29.

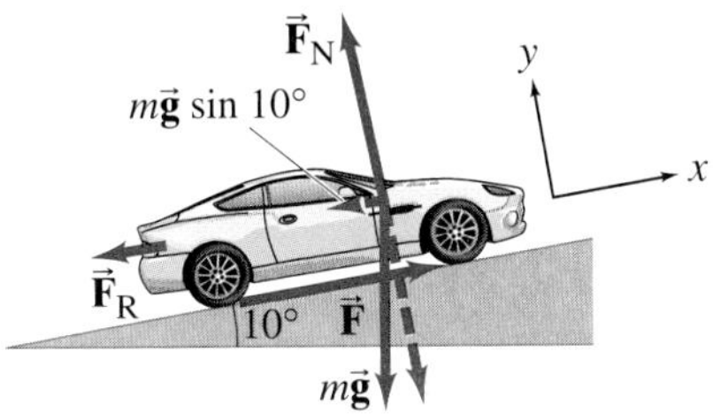


**FIGURE 6–29** Example 6–15a. Calculation of power needed for a car to climb a hill.

**APPROACH** First we must be careful not to confuse $\vec{F}_R$, which is due to air resistance and friction that retards the motion, with the force $\vec{F}$ needed to accelerate the car, which is the frictional force exerted by the road on the tires—the reaction to the motor-driven tires pushing against the road. We must determine the latter force $F$ before calculating the power.

**SOLUTION** (*a*) To move at a steady speed up the hill, the car must, by Newton's second law, exert a force $F$ equal to the sum of the retarding force, 700 N, and the component of gravity parallel to the hill, $mg \sin 10°$. Thus

$$\begin{aligned} F &= 700\text{ N} + mg\sin 10° \\ &= 700\text{ N} + (1400\text{ kg})(9.80\text{ m/s}^2)(0.174) = 3100\text{ N}. \end{aligned}$$

Since $\overline{v} = 80\text{ km/h} = 22\text{ m/s}$ and is parallel to $\vec{F}$, then (Eq. 6–17) the power is

$$\overline{P} = F\overline{v} = (3100\text{ N})(22\text{ m/s}) = 6.80 \times 10^4\text{ W} = 91\text{ hp}.$$

(*b*) The car accelerates from 25.0 m/s to 30.6 m/s (90 to 110 km/h). Thus the car must exert a force that overcomes the 700-N retarding force plus that required to give it the acceleration

$$\overline{a}_x = \frac{(30.6\text{ m/s} - 25.0\text{ m/s})}{6.0\text{ s}} = 0.93\text{ m/s}^2.$$

We apply Newton's second law with $x$ being the direction of motion:

$$ma_x = \Sigma F_x = F - F_R.$$

Then the force required, $F$, is

$$\begin{aligned} F &= ma_x + F_R \\ &= (1400\text{ kg})(0.93\text{ m/s}^2) + 700\text{ N} \\ &= 1300\text{ N} + 700\text{ N} = 2000\text{ N}. \end{aligned}$$

Since $\overline{P} = F\overline{v}$, the required power increases with speed and the motor must be able to provide a maximum power output of

$$\overline{P} = (2000\text{ N})(30.6\text{ m/s}) = 6.12 \times 10^4\text{ W} = 82\text{ hp}.$$

**NOTE** Even taking into account the fact that only 60 to 80% of the engine's power output reaches the wheels, it is clear from these calculations that an engine of 100 to 150 hp is quite adequate from a practical point of view.

We mentioned in Example 6–15 that only part of the energy output of a car engine reaches the wheels. Not only is some energy wasted in getting from the engine to the wheels, in the engine itself much of the input energy (from the gasoline) does not do useful work. An important characteristic of all engines is their overall *efficiency e*, defined as the ratio of the useful power output of the engine, $P_{out}$, to the power input, $P_{in}$:

*Efficiency*

$$e = \frac{P_{out}}{P_{in}}.$$

The efficiency is always less than 1.0 because no engine can create energy, and no engine can even transform energy from one form to another without some energy going to friction, thermal energy, and other nonuseful forms of energy. For example, an automobile engine converts chemical energy released in the burning of gasoline into mechanical energy that moves the pistons and eventually the wheels. But nearly 85% of the input energy is "wasted" as thermal energy that goes into the cooling system or out the exhaust pipe, plus friction in the moving parts. Thus car engines are roughly only about 15% efficient. We will discuss efficiency in detail in Chapter 15.

## Summary


**Work** is done on an object by a force when the object moves through a distance $d$. If the direction of a constant force $F$ makes an angle $\theta$ with the direction of motion, the work done by this force is

$$W = Fd\cos\theta. \qquad \textbf{(6–1)}$$

**Energy** can be defined as the ability to do work. In SI units, work and energy are measured in **joules** (1 J = 1 N·m).

**Kinetic energy** (KE) is energy of motion. An object of mass $m$ and speed $v$ has translational kinetic energy

$$\text{KE} = \tfrac{1}{2}mv^2. \qquad \textbf{(6–3)}$$

**Potential energy** (PE) is energy associated with forces that depend on the position or configuration of objects. Gravitational potential energy is

$$\text{PE}_{grav} = mgy, \qquad \textbf{(6–6)}$$

where $y$ is the height of the object of mass $m$ above an arbitrary reference point. Elastic potential energy is given by

$$\text{elastic PE} = \tfrac{1}{2}kx^2 \qquad \textbf{(6–9)}$$

for a stretched or compressed spring, where $x$ is the displacement from the unstretched position and $k$ is the spring stiffness constant. Other potential energies include chemical, electrical, and nuclear energy. The change in potential energy when an object changes position is equal to the external work needed to take the object from one position to the other.

The **work-energy principle** states that the *net* work done on an object (by the *net* force) equals the change in kinetic energy of that object:

$$W_{net} = \Delta\text{KE} = \tfrac{1}{2}mv_2^2 - \tfrac{1}{2}mv_1^2. \qquad \textbf{(6–2, 6–4)}$$

The **law of conservation of energy** states that energy can be transformed from one type to another, but the total energy remains constant. It is valid even when friction is present, since the heat generated can be considered a form of energy transfer. When only *conservative forces* act, the total mechanical energy is conserved:

$$\text{KE} + \text{PE} = \text{constant}.$$

When nonconservative forces such as friction act, then

$$W_{NC} = \Delta\text{KE} + \Delta\text{PE}, \qquad \textbf{(6–10)}$$

where $W_{NC}$ is the work done by nonconservative forces.

**Power** is defined as the rate at which work is done, or the rate at which energy is transformed. The SI unit of power is the **watt** (1 W = 1 J/s).


## Questions

1. In what ways is the word "work" as used in everyday language the same as that defined in physics? In what ways is it different? Give examples of both.
2. Can a centripetal force ever do work on an object? Explain.
3. Can the normal force on an object ever do work? Explain.
4. A woman swimming upstream is not moving with respect to the shore. Is she doing any work? If she stops swimming and merely floats, is work done on her?
5. Is the work done by kinetic friction forces always negative? [*Hint*: Consider what happens to the dishes when you pull a tablecloth out from under them.]
6. Why is it tiring to push hard against a solid wall even though you are doing no work?
7. You have two springs that are identical except that spring 1 is stiffer than spring 2 ($k_1 > k_2$). On which spring is more work done (*a*) if they are stretched using the same force, (*b*) if they are stretched the same distance?

8. A hand exerts a constant horizontal force on a block that is free to slide on a frictionless surface (Fig. 6–30). The block starts from rest at point A, and by the time it has traveled a distance $d$ to point B it is traveling with speed $v_B$. When the block has traveled another distance $d$ to point C, will its speed be greater than, less than, or equal to $2v_B$? Explain your reasoning.

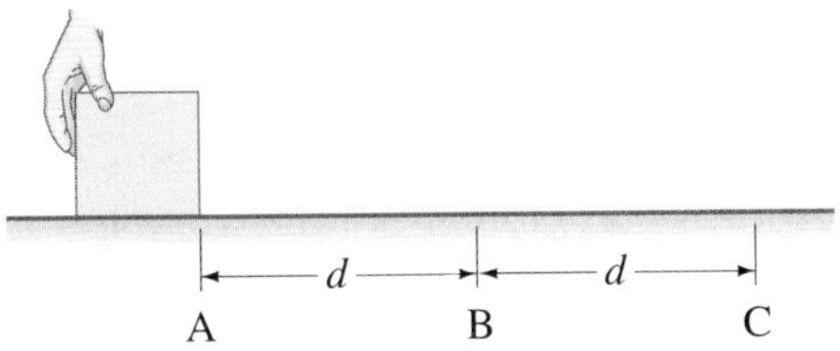


**FIGURE 6–30** Question 8.

9. By approximately how much does your gravitational potential energy change when you jump as high as you can?

10. In Fig. 6–31, water balloons are tossed from the roof of a building, all with the same speed but with different launch angles. Which one has the highest speed on impact? Ignore air resistance.

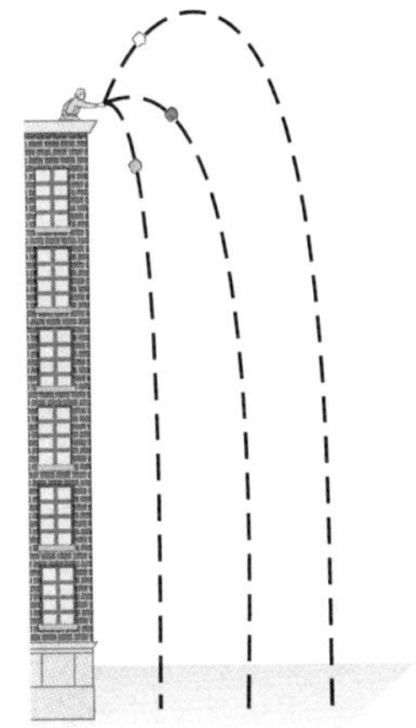

**FIGURE 6–31** Question 10.

11. A pendulum is launched from a point that is a height $h$ above its lowest point in two different ways (Fig. 6–32). During both launches, the pendulum is given an initial speed of 3.0 m/s. On the first launch, the initial velocity of the pendulum is directed upward along the trajectory, and on the second launch it is directed downward along the trajectory. Which launch will cause it to swing the largest angle from the equilibrium position? Explain.

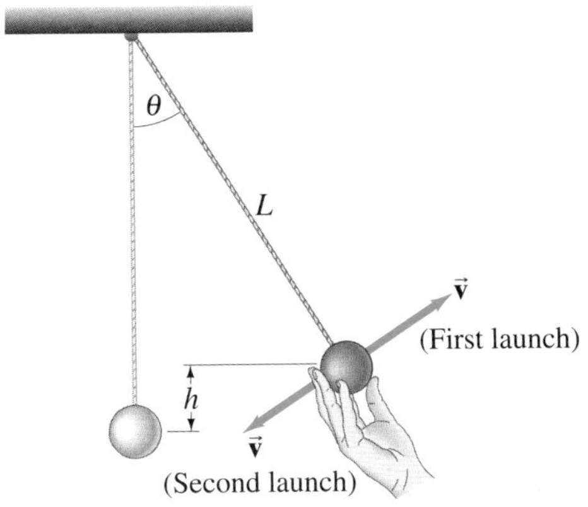


**FIGURE 6–32** Question 11.

12. A coil spring of mass $m$ rests upright on a table. If you compress the spring by pressing down with your hand and then release it, can the spring leave the table? Explain, using the law of conservation of energy.

13. A bowling ball is hung from the ceiling by a steel wire (Fig. 6–33). The instructor pulls the ball back and stands against the wall with the ball against his nose. To avoid injury the instructor is supposed to release the ball without pushing it. Why?

**FIGURE 6–33** Question 13.

14. What happens to the gravitational potential energy when water at the top of a waterfall falls to the pool below?

15. Describe the energy transformations when a child hops around on a pogo stick.

16. Describe the energy transformations that take place when a skier starts skiing down a hill, but after a time is brought to rest by striking a snowdrift.

17. A child on a sled (total mass $m$) starts from rest at the top of a hill of height $h$ and slides down. Does the velocity at the bottom depend on the angle of the hill if ($a$) it is icy and there is no friction, and ($b$) there is friction (deep snow)?

18. Seasoned hikers prefer to step over a fallen log in their path rather than stepping on top and jumping down on the other side. Explain.

19. Two identical arrows, one with twice the speed of the other, are fired into a bale of hay. Assuming the hay exerts a constant frictional force on the arrows, the faster arrow will penetrate how much farther than the slower arrow? Explain.

20. Analyze the motion of a simple swinging pendulum in terms of energy, ($a$) ignoring friction, and ($b$) taking friction into account. Explain why a grandfather clock has to be wound up.

21. When a "superball" is dropped, can it rebound to a height greater than its original height? Explain.

22. Suppose you lift a suitcase from the floor to a table. The work you do on the suitcase depends on which of the following: ($a$) whether you lift it straight up or along a more complicated path, ($b$) the time it takes, ($c$) the height of the table, and ($d$) the weight of the suitcase?

23. Repeat Question 22 for the *power* needed rather than the work.

24. Why is it easier to climb a mountain via a zigzag trail than to climb straight up?

25. Recall from Chapter 4, Example 4–14, that you can use a pulley and ropes to decrease the force needed to raise a heavy load (see Fig. 6–34). But for every meter the load is raised, how much rope must be pulled up? Account for this, using energy concepts.

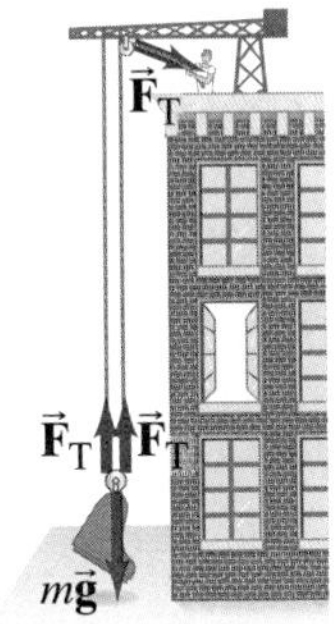


**FIGURE 6–34** Question 25.

# Problems

### 6–1 Work, Constant Force

1. (I) How much work is done by the gravitational force when a 265-kg pile driver falls 2.80 m?
2. (I) A 65.0-kg firefighter climbs a flight of stairs 20.0 m high. How much work is required?
3. (I) A 1300-N crate rests on the floor. How much work is required to move it at constant speed (*a*) 4.0 m along the floor against a friction force of 230 N, and (*b*) 4.0 m vertically?
4. (I) How much work did the movers do (horizontally) pushing a 160-kg crate 10.3 m across a rough floor without acceleration, if the effective coefficient of friction was 0.50?
5. (II) A box of mass 5.0 kg is accelerated from rest across a floor at a rate of $2.0\ \mathrm{m/s^2}$ for 7.0 s. Find the net work done on the box.
6. (II) Eight books, each 4.3 cm thick with mass 1.7 kg, lie flat on a table. How much work is required to stack them one on top of another?
7. (II) A lever such as that shown in Fig. 6–35 can be used to lift objects we might not otherwise be able to lift. Show that the ratio of output force, $F_{\mathrm{O}}$, to input force, $F_{\mathrm{I}}$, is related to the lengths $l_{\mathrm{I}}$ and $l_{\mathrm{O}}$ from the pivot point by $F_{\mathrm{O}}/F_{\mathrm{I}} = l_{\mathrm{I}}/l_{\mathrm{O}}$ (ignoring friction and the mass of the lever), given that the work output equals work input.

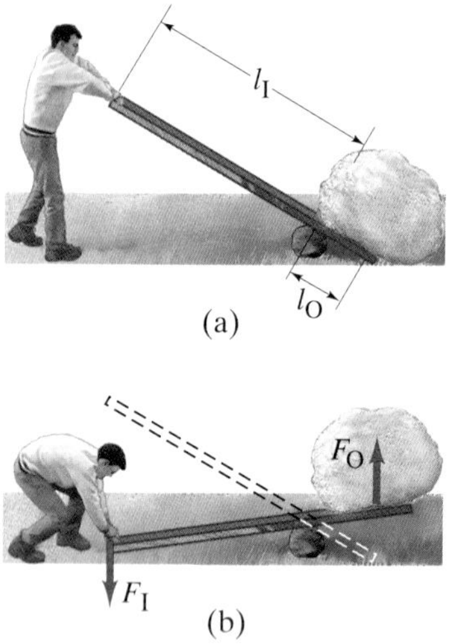


**FIGURE 6–35** Problem 7. A simple lever.

8. (II) A 330-kg piano slides 3.6 m down a 28° incline and is kept from accelerating by a man who is pushing back on it *parallel to the incline* (Fig. 6–36). The effective coefficient of kinetic friction is 0.40. Calculate: (*a*) the force exerted by the man, (*b*) the work done by the man on the piano, (*c*) the work done by the friction force, (*d*) the work done by the force of gravity, and (*e*) the net work done on the piano.

**FIGURE 6–36** Problem 8.

9. (II) (*a*) Find the force required to give a helicopter of mass $M$ an acceleration of $0.10\,g$ upward. (*b*) Find the work done by this force as the helicopter moves a distance $h$ upward.
10. (II) What is the minimum work needed to push a 950-kg car 810 m up along a 9.0° incline? (*a*) Ignore friction. (*b*) Assume the effective coefficient of friction retarding the car is 0.25.

### * 6–2 Work, Varying Force

* 11. (II) In Fig. 6–6a, assume the distance axis is linear and that $d_{\mathrm{A}} = 10.0\ \mathrm{m}$ and $d_{\mathrm{B}} = 35.0\ \mathrm{m}$. Estimate the work done by force $F$ in moving a 2.80-kg object from $d_{\mathrm{A}}$ to $d_{\mathrm{B}}$.

* 12. (II) The force on an object, acting along the $x$ axis, varies as shown in Fig. 6–37. Determine the work done by this force to move the object (*a*) from $x = 0.0$ to $x = 10.0\ \mathrm{m}$, and (*b*) from $x = 0.0$ to $x = 15.0\ \mathrm{m}$.

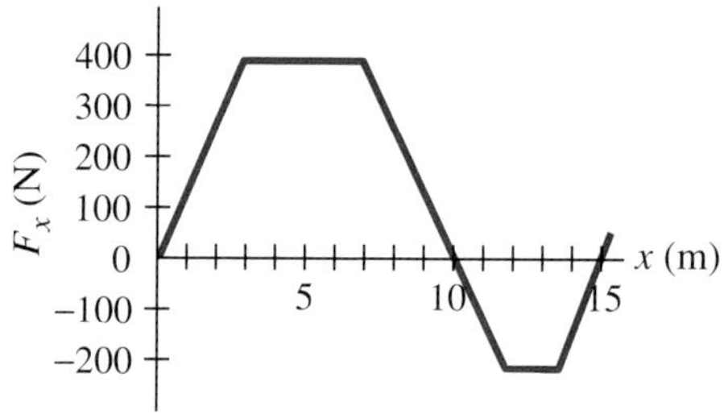


**FIGURE 6–37** Problem 12.

* 13. (II) A spring has $k = 88\ \mathrm{N/m}$. Use a graph to determine the work needed to stretch it from $x = 3.8\ \mathrm{cm}$ to $x = 5.8\ \mathrm{cm}$, where $x$ is the displacement from its unstretched length.

* 14. (II) The net force exerted on a particle acts in the $+x$ direction. Its magnitude increases linearly from zero at $x = 0$, to 24.0 N at $x = 3.0\ \mathrm{m}$. It remains constant at 24.0 N from $x = 3.0\ \mathrm{m}$ to $x = 8.0\ \mathrm{m}$, and then decreases linearly to zero at $x = 13.0\ \mathrm{m}$. Determine the work done to move the particle from $x = 0$ to $x = 13.0\ \mathrm{m}$ graphically by determining the area under the $F_x$ vs. $x$ graph.

### 6–3 Kinetic Energy; Work-Energy Principle

15. (I) At room temperature, an oxygen molecule, with mass of $5.31 \times 10^{-26}\ \mathrm{kg}$, typically has a KE of about $6.21 \times 10^{-21}\ \mathrm{J}$. How fast is the molecule moving?
16. (I) (*a*) If the KE of an arrow is doubled, by what factor has its speed increased? (*b*) If its speed is doubled, by what factor does its KE increase?
17. (I) How much work is required to stop an electron $(m = 9.11 \times 10^{-31}\ \mathrm{kg})$ which is moving with a speed of $1.90 \times 10^{6}\ \mathrm{m/s}$?
18. (I) How much work must be done to stop a 1250-kg car traveling at 105 km/h?
19. (II) An 88-g arrow is fired from a bow whose string exerts an average force of 110 N on the arrow over a distance of 78 cm. What is the speed of the arrow as it leaves the bow?
20. (II) A baseball $(m = 140\ \mathrm{g})$ traveling 32 m/s moves a fielder's glove backward 25 cm when the ball is caught. What was the average force exerted by the ball on the glove?
21. (II) If the speed of a car is increased by 50%, by what factor will its minimum braking distance be increased, assuming all else is the same? Ignore the driver's reaction time.

22. (II) At an accident scene on a level road, investigators measure a car's skid mark to be 88 m long. The accident occurred on a rainy day, and the coefficient of kinetic friction was estimated to be 0.42. Use these data to determine the speed of the car when the driver slammed on (and locked) the brakes. (Why does the car's mass not matter?)

23. (II) A softball having a mass of 0.25 kg is pitched at 95 km/h. By the time it reaches the plate, it may have slowed by 10%. Neglecting gravity, estimate the average force of air resistance during a pitch, if the distance between the plate and the pitcher is about 15 m.

24. (II) How high will a 1.85-kg rock go if thrown straight up by someone who does 80.0 J of work on it? Neglect air resistance.

25. (III) A 285-kg load is lifted 22.0 m vertically with an acceleration $a = 0.160\,g$ by a single cable. Determine (*a*) the tension in the cable, (*b*) the net work done on the load, (*c*) the work done by the cable on the load, (*d*) the work done by gravity on the load, and (*e*) the final speed of the load assuming it started from rest.

### 6–4 and 6–5 Potential Energy

26. (I) A spring has a spring stiffness constant, $k$, of 440 N/m. How much must this spring be stretched to store 25 J of potential energy?

27. (I) A 7.0-kg monkey swings from one branch to another 1.2 m higher. What is the change in potential energy?

28. (I) By how much does the gravitational potential energy of a 64-kg pole vaulter change if his center of mass rises about 4.0 m during the jump?

29. (II) A 1200-kg car rolling on a horizontal surface has speed $v = 65$ km/h when it strikes a horizontal coiled spring and is brought to rest in a distance of 2.2 m. What is the spring stiffness constant of the spring?

30. (II) A 1.60-m tall person lifts a 2.10-kg book from the ground so it is 2.20 m above the ground. What is the potential energy of the book relative to (*a*) the ground, and (*b*) the top of the person's head? (*c*) How is the work done by the person related to the answers in parts (*a*) and (*b*)?

31. (II) A 55-kg hiker starts at an elevation of 1600 m and climbs to the top of a 3300-m peak. (*a*) What is the hiker's change in potential energy? (*b*) What is the minimum work required of the hiker? (*c*) Can the actual work done be more than this? Explain why.

32. (II) A spring with $k = 53$ N/m hangs vertically next to a ruler. The end of the spring is next to the 15-cm mark on the ruler. If a 2.5-kg mass is now attached to the end of the spring, where will the end of the spring line up with the ruler marks?

### 6–6 and 6–7 Conservation of Mechanical Energy

33. (I) Jane, looking for Tarzan, is running at top speed (5.3 m/s) and grabs a vine hanging vertically from a tall tree in the jungle. How high can she swing upward? Does the length of the vine affect your answer?

34. (I) A novice skier, starting from rest, slides down a frictionless 35.0° incline whose vertical height is 185 m. How fast is she going when she reaches the bottom?

35. (I) A sled is initially given a shove up a frictionless 28.0° incline. It reaches a maximum vertical height 1.35 m higher than where it started. What was its initial speed?

36. (II) In the high jump, Fran's kinetic energy is transformed into gravitational potential energy without the aid of a pole. With what minimum speed must Fran leave the ground in order to lift her center of mass 2.10 m and cross the bar with a speed of 0.70 m/s?

37. (II) A 65-kg trampoline artist jumps vertically upward from the top of a platform with a speed of 5.0 m/s. (*a*) How fast is he going as he lands on the trampoline, 3.0 m below (Fig. 6–38)? (*b*) If the trampoline behaves like a spring with spring stiffness constant $6.2 \times 10^4$ N/m, how far does he depress it?

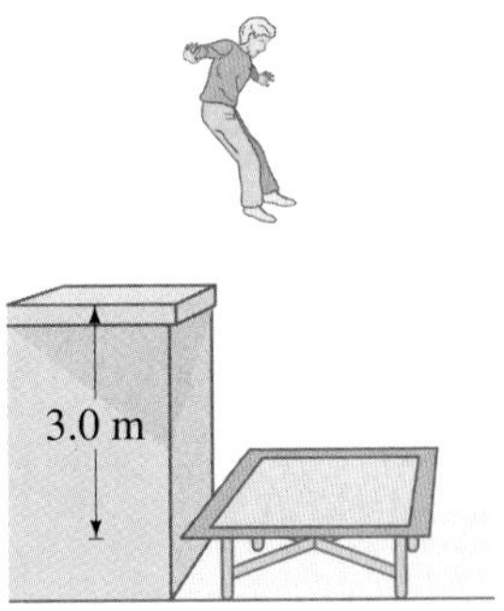


**FIGURE 6–38** Problem 37.

38. (II) A projectile is fired at an upward angle of 45.0° from the top of a 265-m cliff with a speed of 185 m/s. What will be its speed when it strikes the ground below? (Use conservation of energy.)

39. (II) A vertical spring (ignore its mass), whose spring stiffness constant is 950 N/m, is attached to a table and is compressed down 0.150 m. (*a*) What upward speed can it give to a 0.30-kg ball when released? (*b*) How high above its original position (spring compressed) will the ball fly?

40. (II) A block of mass $m$ slides without friction along the looped track shown in Fig. 6–39. If the block is to remain on the track, even at the top of the circle (whose radius is $r$), from what minimum height $h$ must it be released?

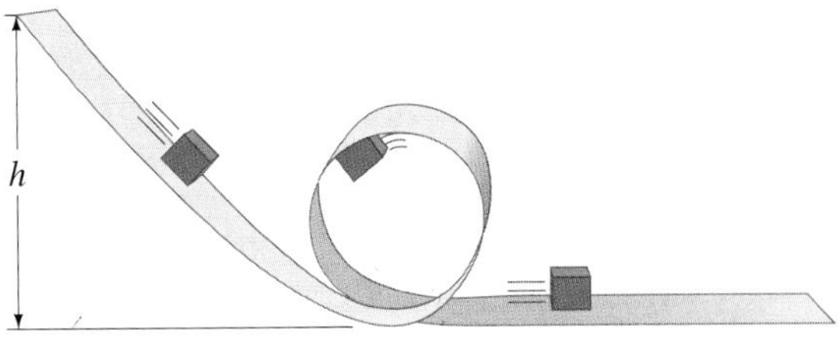


**FIGURE 6–39** Problems 40 and 75.

41. (II) A block of mass $m$ is attached to the end of a spring (spring stiffness constant $k$), Fig. 6–40. The block is given an initial displacement $x_0$, after which it oscillates back and forth. Write a formula for the total mechanical energy (ignore friction and the mass of the spring) in terms of $x_0$, position $x$, and speed $v$.

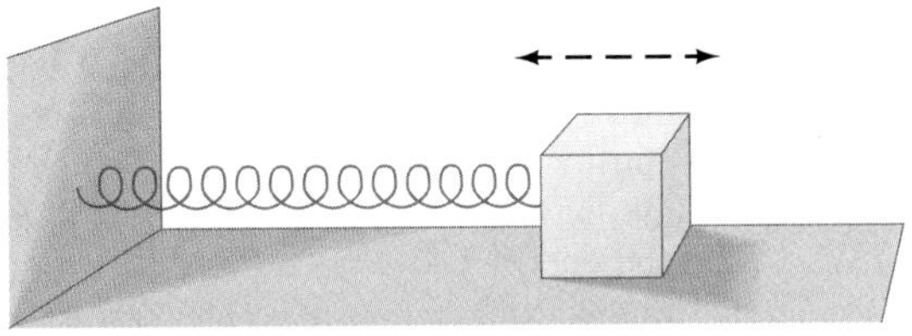

**FIGURE 6–40** Problems 41, 55, and 56.

42. (II) A 62-kg bungee jumper jumps from a bridge. She is tied to a bungee cord whose unstretched length is 12 m, and falls a total of 31 m. (*a*) Calculate the spring stiffness constant $k$ of the bungee cord, assuming Hooke's law applies. (*b*) Calculate the maximum acceleration she experiences.

43. (II) The roller-coaster car shown in Fig. 6–41 is dragged up to point 1 where it is released from rest. Assuming no friction, calculate the speed at points 2, 3, and 4.

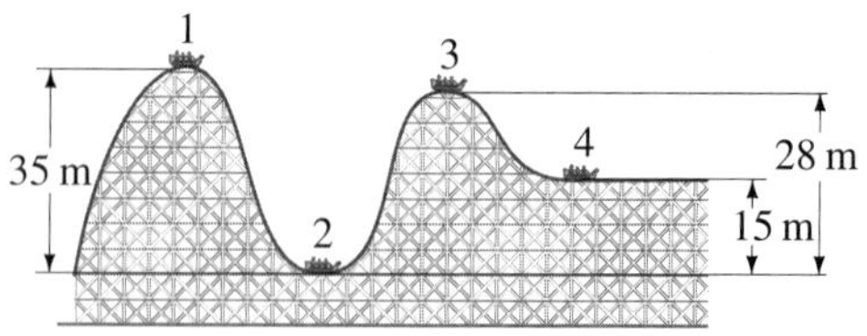


**FIGURE 6–41** Problems 43 and 53.

44. (II) A 0.40-kg ball is thrown with a speed of 12 m/s at an angle of 33°. (*a*) What is its speed at its highest point, and (*b*) how high does it go? (Use conservation of energy, and ignore air resistance.)

45. (III) An engineer is designing a spring to be placed at the bottom of an elevator shaft. If the elevator cable should break when the elevator is at a height $h$ above the top of the spring, calculate the value that the spring stiffness constant $k$ should have so that passengers undergo an acceleration of no more than 5.0 $g$ when brought to rest. Let $M$ be the total mass of the elevator and passengers.

46. (III) A cyclist intends to cycle up a 7.8° hill whose vertical height is 150 m. Assuming the mass of bicycle plus cyclist is 75 kg, (*a*) calculate how much work must be done against gravity. (*b*) If each complete revolution of the pedals moves the bike 5.1 m along its path, calculate the average force that must be exerted on the pedals tangent to their circular path. Neglect work done by friction and other losses. The pedals turn in a circle of diameter 36 cm.

### 6–8 and 6–9 Law of Conservation of Energy

47. (I) Two railroad cars, each of mass 7650 kg and traveling 95 km/h in opposite directions, collide head-on and come to rest. How much thermal energy is produced in this collision?

48. (II) A 21.7-kg child descends a slide 3.5 m high and reaches the bottom with a speed of 2.2 m/s. How much thermal energy due to friction was generated in this process?

49. (II) A ski starts from rest and slides down a 22° incline 75 m long. (*a*) If the coefficient of friction is 0.090, what is the ski's speed at the base of the incline? (*b*) If the snow is level at the foot of the incline and has the same coefficient of friction, how far will the ski travel along the level? Use energy methods.

50. (II) A 145-g baseball is dropped from a tree 13.0 m above the ground. (*a*) With what speed would it hit the ground if air resistance could be ignored? (*b*) If it actually hits the ground with a speed of 8.00 m/s, what is the average force of air resistance exerted on it?

51. (II) You drop a ball from a height of 2.0 m, and it bounces back to a height of 1.5 m. (*a*) What fraction of its initial energy is lost during the bounce? (*b*) What is the ball's speed just as it leaves the ground after the bounce? (*c*) Where did the energy go?

52. (II) A 110-kg crate, starting from rest, is pulled across a floor with a constant horizontal force of 350 N. For the first 15 m the floor is frictionless, and for the next 15 m the coefficient of friction is 0.30. What is the final speed of the crate?

53. (II) Suppose the roller coaster in Fig. 6–41 passes point 1 with a speed of 1.70 m/s. If the average force of friction is equal to one-fifth of its weight, with what speed will it reach point 2? The distance traveled is 45.0 m.

54. (II) A skier traveling 12.0 m/s reaches the foot of a steady upward 18.0° incline and glides 12.2 m up along this slope before coming to rest. What was the average coefficient of friction?

55. (III) A 0.620-kg wood block is firmly attached to a very light horizontal spring ($k = 180\,\text{N/m}$) as shown in Fig. 6–40. It is noted that the block–spring system, when compressed 5.0 cm and released, stretches out 2.3 cm beyond the equilibrium position before stopping and turning back. What is the coefficient of kinetic friction between the block and the table?

56. (III) A 280-g wood block is firmly attached to a very light horizontal spring, Fig. 6–40. The block can slide along a table where the coefficient of friction is 0.30. A force of 22 N compresses the spring 18 cm. If the spring is released from this position, how far beyond its equilibrium position will it stretch at its first maximum extension?

57. (III) Early test flights for the space shuttle used a "glider" (mass of 980 kg including pilot) that was launched horizontally at 500 km/h from a height of 3500 m. The glider eventually landed at a speed of 200 km/h. (*a*) What would its landing speed have been in the absence of air resistance? (*b*) What was the average force of air resistance exerted on it if it came in at a constant glide of 10° to the Earth?

### 6–10 Power

58. (I) How long will it take a 1750-W motor to lift a 315-kg piano to a sixth-story window 16.0 m above?

59. (I) If a car generates 18 hp when traveling at a steady 88 km/h, what must be the average force exerted on the car due to friction and air resistance?

60. (I) A 1400-kg sports car accelerates from rest to 95 km/h in 7.4 s. What is the average power delivered by the engine?

61. (I) (*a*) Show that one British horsepower (550 ft·lb/s) is equal to 746 W. (*b*) What is the horsepower rating of a 75-W lightbulb?

62. (II) Electric energy units are often expressed in the form of "kilowatt-hours." (*a*) Show that one kilowatt-hour (kWh) is equal to $3.6 \times 10^6$ J. (*b*) If a typical family of four uses electric energy at an average rate of 520 W, how many kWh would their electric bill be for one month, and (*c*) how many joules would this be? (*d*) At a cost of $0.12 per kWh, what would their monthly bill be in dollars? Does the monthly bill depend on the *rate* at which they use the electric energy?

63. (II) A driver notices that her 1150-kg car slows down from 85 km/h to 65 km/h in about 6.0 s on the level when it is in neutral. Approximately what power (watts and hp) is needed to keep the car traveling at a constant 75 km/h?

64. (II) How much work can a 3.0-hp motor do in 1.0 h?

65. (II) A shot-putter accelerates a 7.3-kg shot from rest to 14 m/s. If this motion takes 1.5 s, what average power was developed?

66. (II) A pump is to lift 18.0 kg of water per minute through a height of 3.60 m. What output rating (watts) should the pump motor have?

67. (II) During a workout, the football players at State U. ran up the stadium stairs in 66 s. The stairs are 140 m long and inclined at an angle of 32°. If a typical player has a mass of 95 kg, estimate the average power output on the way up. Ignore friction and air resistance.

68. (II) How fast must a cyclist climb a 6.0° hill to maintain a power output of 0.25 hp? Neglect work done by friction, and assume the mass of cyclist plus bicycle is 68 kg.

69. (II) A 1200-kg car has a maximum power output of 120 hp. How steep a hill can it climb at a constant speed of 75 km/h if the frictional forces add up to 650 N?

70. (II) What minimum horsepower must a motor have to be able to drag a 310-kg box along a level floor at a speed of 1.20 m/s if the coefficient of friction is 0.45?

71. (III) A bicyclist coasts down a 7.0° hill at a steady speed of 5.0 m/s. Assuming a total mass of 75 kg (bicycle plus rider), what must be the cyclist's power output to climb the same hill at the same speed?

## General Problems

72. Designers of today's cars have built "5 mi/h (8 km/h) bumpers" that are designed to compress and rebound elastically without any physical damage at speeds below 8 km/h. If the material of the bumpers permanently deforms after a compression of 1.5 cm, but remains like an elastic spring up to that point, what must the effective spring stiffness constant of the bumper be, assuming the car has a mass of 1300 kg and is tested by ramming into a solid wall?

73. In a certain library the first shelf is 10.0 cm off the ground, and the remaining four shelves are each spaced 30.0 cm above the previous one. If the average book has a mass of 1.5 kg with a height of 21 cm, and an average shelf holds 25 books, how much work is required to fill all the shelves, assuming the books are all laying flat on the floor to start?

74. A film of Jesse Owens's famous long jump (Fig. 6–42) in the 1936 Olympics shows that his center of mass rose 1.1 m from launch point to the top of the arc. What minimum speed did he need at launch if he was traveling at 6.5 m/s at the top of the arc?

**FIGURE 6–42**
Problem 74.

75. The block of mass $m$ sliding without friction along the looped track shown in Fig. 6–39 is to remain on the track at all times, even at the very top of the loop of radius $r$. ($a$) In terms of the given quantities, determine the minimum release height $h$ (as in Problem 40). Next, if the actual release height is $2h$, calculate ($b$) the normal force exerted by the track at the bottom of the loop, ($c$) the normal force exerted by the track at the top of the loop, and ($d$) the normal force exerted by the track after the block exits the loop onto the flat section.

76. An airplane pilot fell 370 m after jumping from an aircraft without his parachute opening. He landed in a snowbank, creating a crater 1.1 m deep, but survived with only minor injuries. Assuming the pilot's mass was 78 kg and his terminal velocity was 35 m/s, estimate ($a$) the work done by the snow in bringing him to rest; ($b$) the average force exerted on him by the snow to stop him; and ($c$) the work done on him by air resistance as he fell.

77. A ball is attached to a horizontal cord of length $L$ whose other end is fixed (Fig. 6–43). ($a$) If the ball is released, what will be its speed at the lowest point of its path? ($b$) A peg is located a distance $h$ directly below the point of attachment of the cord. If $h = 0.80L$, what will be the speed of the ball when it reaches the top of its circular path about the peg?

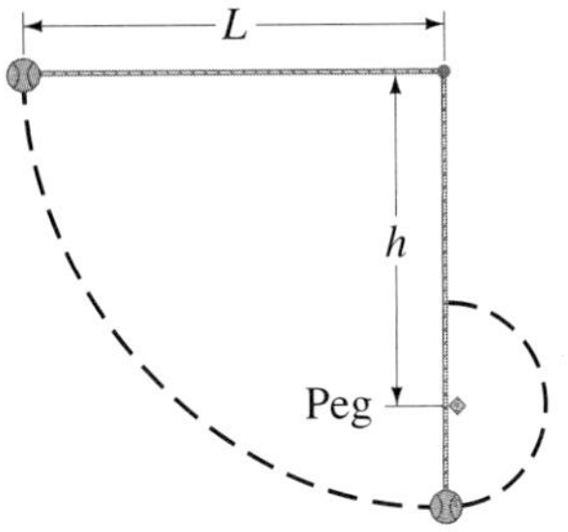


**FIGURE 6–43**
Problem 77.

78. A 65-kg hiker climbs to the top of a 3700-m-high mountain. The climb is made in 5.0 h starting at an elevation of 2300 m. Calculate ($a$) the work done by the hiker against gravity, ($b$) the average power output in watts and in horsepower, and ($c$) assuming the body is 15% efficient, what rate of energy input was required.

79. An elevator cable breaks when a 920-kg elevator is 28 m above a huge spring ($k = 2.2 \times 10^5$ N/m) at the bottom of the shaft. Calculate ($a$) the work done by gravity on the elevator before it hits the spring, ($b$) the speed of the elevator just before striking the spring, and ($c$) the amount the spring compresses (note that work is done by both the spring and gravity in this part).

80. Squaw Valley ski area in California claims that its lifts can move 47,000 people per hour. If the average lift carries people about 200 m (vertically) higher, estimate the power needed.

81. Water flows ($v \approx 0$) over a dam at the rate of 650 kg/s and falls vertically 81 m before striking the turbine blades. Calculate ($a$) the speed of the water just before striking the turbine blades (neglect air resistance), and ($b$) the rate at which mechanical energy is transferred to the turbine blades, assuming 58% efficiency.

82. Show that on a roller coaster with a circular vertical loop (Fig. 6–44), the difference in your apparent weight at the top of the circular loop and the bottom of the circular loop is 6 $g$'s—that is, six times your weight. Ignore friction. Show also that as long as your speed is above the minimum needed, this answer doesn't depend on the size of the loop or how fast you go through it.

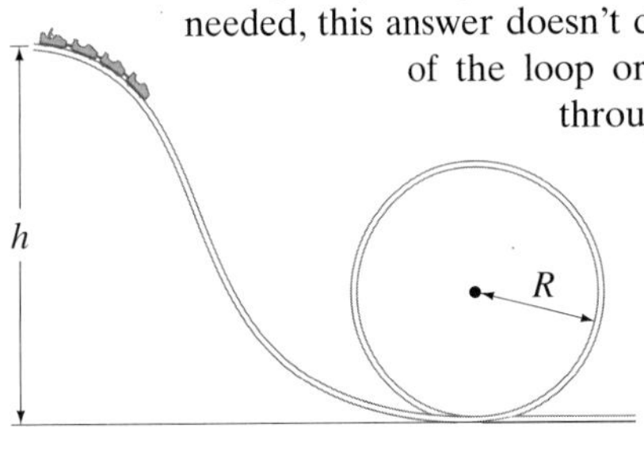


**FIGURE 6–44**
Problem 82.

83. (*a*) If the human body could convert a candy bar directly into work, how high could an 82-kg man climb a ladder if he were fueled by one bar (= 1100 kJ)? (*b*) If the man then jumped off the ladder, what will be his speed when he reaches the bottom?

84. A projectile is fired at an upward angle of 45.0° from the top of a 165-m cliff with a speed of 175 m/s. What will be its speed when it strikes the ground below? (Use conservation of energy and neglect air resistance.)

85. If you stand on a bathroom scale, the spring inside the scale compresses 0.60 mm, and it tells you your weight is 710 N. Now if you jump on the scale from a height of 1.0 m, what does the scale read at its peak?

86. A 65-kg student runs at 5.0 m/s, grabs a rope, and swings out over a lake (Fig. 6–45). He releases the rope when his velocity is zero. (*a*) What is the angle $\theta$ when he releases the rope? (*b*) What is the tension in the rope just before he releases it? (*c*) What is the maximum tension in the rope?

**FIGURE 6–45** Problem 86.

87. In the rope climb, a 72-kg athlete climbs a vertical distance of 5.0 m in 9.0 s. What minimum power output was used to accomplish this feat?

88. Some electric-power companies use water to store energy. Water is pumped by reversible turbine pumps from a low to a high reservoir. To store the energy produced in 1.0 hour by a 120-MW $(120 \times 10^6\,\text{W})$ electric-power plant, how many cubic meters of water will have to be pumped from the lower to the upper reservoir? Assume the upper reservoir is 520 m above the lower and we can neglect the small change in depths within each. Water has a mass of 1000 kg for every 1.0 m$^3$.

89. A spring with spring stiffness constant $k$ is cut in half. What is the spring stiffness constant for each of the two resulting springs?

90. A 6.0-kg block is pushed 8.0 m up a rough 37° inclined plane by a horizontal force of 75 N. If the initial speed of the block is 2.2 m/s up the plane and a constant kinetic friction force of 25 N opposes the motion, calculate (*a*) the initial kinetic energy of the block; (*b*) the work done by the 75-N force; (*c*) the work done by the friction force; (*d*) the work done by gravity; (*e*) the work done by the normal force; (*f*) the final kinetic energy of the block.

91. If a 1500-kg car can accelerate from 35 km/h to 55 km/h in 3.2 s, how long will it take to accelerate from 55 km/h to 75 km/h? Assume the power stays the same, and neglect frictional losses.

92. In a common test for cardiac function (the "stress test"), the patient walks on an inclined treadmill (Fig. 6–46). Estimate the power required from a 75-kg patient when the treadmill is sloping at an angle of 15° and the velocity is 3.3 km/h. (How does this power compare to the power rating of a lightbulb?)

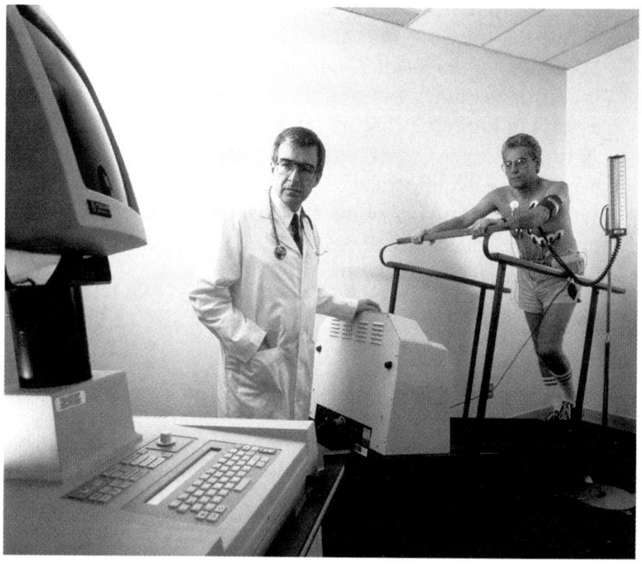

**FIGURE 6–46** Problem 92.

93. (*a*) If a volcano spews a 500-kg rock vertically upward a distance of 500 m, what was its velocity when it left the volcano? (*b*) If the volcano spews the equivalent of 1000 rocks of this size every minute, what is its power output?

94. Water falls onto a water wheel from a height of 2.0 m at a rate of 95 kg/s. (*a*) If this water wheel is set up to provide electricity output, what is its maximum power output? (*b*) What is the speed of the water as it hits the wheel?

## Answers to Exercises

**A:** (*c*).

**B:** No, because the speed $v$ would be the square root of a negative number, which is not real.

**C:** It is nonconservative, because for a conservative force $W = 0$ in a round trip.

**D:** $W_{\text{net}} = \Delta\text{KE}$, where $W_{\text{net}} = mg(y_1 - y_2)$ and $\Delta\text{KE} = \frac{1}{2}mv_2^2 - \frac{1}{2}mv_1^2 = \frac{1}{2}mv_2^2$. Then $v_2^2 = 2g(y_1 - y_2)$.

**E:** Equal speeds.

Conservation of linear momentum is another of the great conservation laws of physics. Collisions, as between billiard or pool balls, illustrate this vector law very nicely: the total vector momentum before the collision equals the total vector momentum just after the collision. In this photo, the moving cue ball strikes the 11 ball at rest. Both balls move after the collision, at angles, but the sum of their vector momenta equals the initial momentum of the incoming cue ball.

We will consider both elastic collisions (where kinetic energy is also conserved) and inelastic collisions. We also examine the concept of center of mass, and how it can make the study of complex motion more readily analyzed and understood.

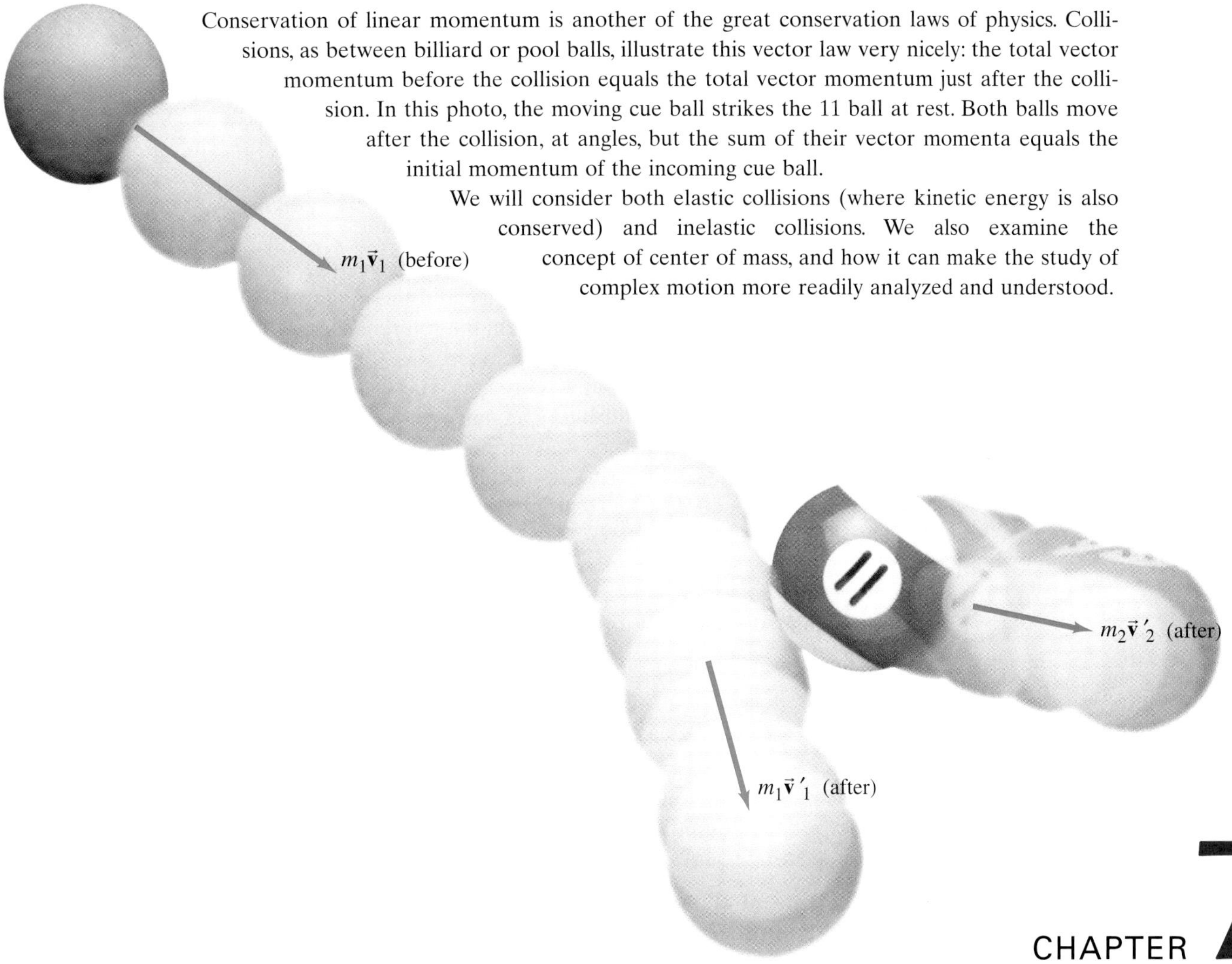


CHAPTER 7

# Linear Momentum

The law of conservation of energy, which we discussed in the previous Chapter, is one of several great conservation laws in physics. Among the other quantities found to be conserved are linear momentum, angular momentum, and electric charge. We will eventually discuss all of these because the conservation laws are among the most important ideas in science. In this Chapter, we discuss linear momentum, and its conservation. The law of conservation of momentum is essentially a reworking of Newton's laws that gives us tremendous physical insight and problem-solving power.

We make use of the laws of conservation of linear momentum and of energy to analyze collisions. Indeed, the law of conservation of momentum is particularly useful when dealing with a system of two or more objects that interact with each other, such as in collisions.

Our focus up to now has been mainly on the motion of a single object, often thought of as a "particle" in the sense that we have ignored any rotation or internal motion. In this Chapter we will deal with systems of two or more objects, and toward the end of the Chapter, the concept of center of mass.

## 7–1 Momentum and Its Relation to Force

The **linear momentum** (or "momentum" for short) of an object is defined as the product of its mass and its velocity. Momentum (plural is *momenta*) is represented by the symbol $\vec{\mathbf{p}}$. If we let $m$ represent the mass of an object and $\vec{\mathbf{v}}$ represent its velocity, then its momentum $\vec{\mathbf{p}}$ is defined as

*Linear momentum defined*

$$\vec{\mathbf{p}} = m\vec{\mathbf{v}}. \tag{7–1}$$

Velocity is a vector, so momentum too is a vector. The direction of the momentum is the direction of the velocity, and the magnitude of the momentum is $p = mv$. Because velocity depends on the reference frame, so does momentum; thus the reference frame must be specified. The unit of momentum is that of mass × velocity, which in SI units is kg·m/s. There is no special name for this unit.

*Units of momentum*

Everyday usage of the term *momentum* is in accord with the definition above. According to Eq. 7–1, a fast-moving car has more momentum than a slow-moving car of the same mass; a heavy truck has more momentum than a small car moving with the same speed. The more momentum an object has, the harder it is to stop it, and the greater effect it will have if it is brought to rest by striking another object. A football player is more likely to be stunned if tackled by a heavy opponent running at top speed than by a lighter or slower-moving tackler. A heavy, fast-moving truck can do more damage than a slow-moving motorcycle.

**EXERCISE A** Can a small sports car ever have the same momentum as a large sport-utility vehicle with three times the sports car's mass? Explain.

A force is required to change the momentum of an object, whether it is to increase the momentum, to decrease it, or to change its direction. Newton originally stated his second law in terms of momentum (although he called the product $mv$ the "quantity of motion"). Newton's statement of the **second law of motion**, translated into modern language, is as follows:

*NEWTON'S SECOND LAW*

**The rate of change of momentum of an object is equal to the net force applied to it.**

We can write this as an equation,

*NEWTON'S SECOND LAW*

$$\Sigma\vec{\mathbf{F}} = \frac{\Delta\vec{\mathbf{p}}}{\Delta t}, \tag{7–2}$$

**CAUTION**
*The change in the momentum vector is in the direction of the net force*

where $\Sigma\vec{\mathbf{F}}$ is the net force applied to the object (the vector sum of all forces acting on it) and $\Delta\vec{\mathbf{p}}$ is the resulting momentum change that occurs during the time interval† $\Delta t$.

We can readily derive the familiar form of the second law, $\Sigma\vec{\mathbf{F}} = m\vec{\mathbf{a}}$, from Eq. 7–2 for the case of constant mass. If $\vec{\mathbf{v}}_1$ is the initial velocity of an object and $\vec{\mathbf{v}}_2$ is its velocity after a time interval $\Delta t$ has elapsed, then

$$\Sigma\vec{\mathbf{F}} = \frac{\Delta\vec{\mathbf{p}}}{\Delta t} = \frac{m\vec{\mathbf{v}}_2 - m\vec{\mathbf{v}}_1}{\Delta t} = \frac{m(\vec{\mathbf{v}}_2 - \vec{\mathbf{v}}_1)}{\Delta t}$$
$$= m\frac{\Delta\vec{\mathbf{v}}}{\Delta t}.$$

By definition, $\vec{\mathbf{a}} = \Delta\vec{\mathbf{v}}/\Delta t$, so

*Newton's second law for constant mass*

$$\Sigma\vec{\mathbf{F}} = m\vec{\mathbf{a}}. \qquad \text{[constant mass]}$$

Newton's statement, Eq. 7–2, is more general than the more familiar version because it includes the situation in which the mass may change. A change in mass occurs in certain circumstances, such as for rockets which lose mass as they burn fuel, and also in the theory of relativity (Chapter 26).

†Normally we think of $\Delta t$ as being a small time interval. If it is not small, then Eq. 7–2 is valid if $\Sigma\vec{\mathbf{F}}$ is constant during that time interval, or if $\Sigma\vec{\mathbf{F}}$ is the average net force during that time interval.

**EXAMPLE 7–1 ESTIMATE Force of a tennis serve.** For a top player, a tennis ball may leave the racket on the serve with a speed of 55 m/s (about 120 mi/h), Fig. 7–1. If the ball has a mass of 0.060 kg and is in contact with the racket for about 4 ms $(4 \times 10^{-3}\ \text{s})$, estimate the average force on the ball. Would this force be large enough to lift a 60-kg person?

**APPROACH** The tennis ball is hit when its initial velocity is very nearly zero at the top of the throw, so we take $v_1 = 0$. We use Newton's second law, Eq. 7–2, to calculate the force, ignoring all other forces such as gravity in comparison to that exerted by the tennis racket.

**SOLUTION** The force exerted on the ball by the racket is

$$F = \frac{\Delta p}{\Delta t} = \frac{mv_2 - mv_1}{\Delta t}$$

where $v_2 = 55\ \text{m/s}$, $v_1 = 0$, and $\Delta t = 0.004\ \text{s}$. Thus

$$F = \frac{\Delta p}{\Delta t} = \frac{(0.060\ \text{kg})(55\ \text{m/s}) - 0}{0.004\ \text{s}} \approx 800\ \text{N}.$$

This is a large force, larger than the weight of a 60-kg person, which would require a force $mg = (60\ \text{kg})(9.8\ \text{m/s}^2) \approx 600\ \text{N}$ to lift.

**NOTE** The force of gravity acting on the tennis ball is $mg = (0.060\ \text{kg})(9.8\ \text{m/s}^2) = 0.59\ \text{N}$, which justifies our ignoring it compared to the enormous force the racket exerts.

**NOTE** High-speed photography and radar can give us an estimate of the contact time and the velocity of the ball leaving the racket. But a direct measurement of the force is not practical. Our calculation shows a handy technique for determining an unknown force in the real world.

**FIGURE 7–1** Example 7–1.

*Measuring force*

**EXAMPLE 7–2 Washing a car: momentum change and force.** Water leaves a hose at a rate of 1.5 kg/s with a speed of 20 m/s and is aimed at the side of a car, which stops it, Fig. 7–2. (That is, we ignore any splashing back.) What is the force exerted by the water on the car?

**APPROACH** The water leaving the hose has mass and velocity, so it has a momentum $p_{\text{initial}}$. When the water hits the car, the water loses this momentum $(p_{\text{final}} = 0)$. We use Newton's second law in the momentum form, Eq. 7–2, to find the force that the car exerts on the water to stop it. By Newton's third law, the force exerted by the water on the car is equal and opposite. We have a continuing process: 1.5 kg of water leaves the hose in each 1.0-s time interval. So let us choose $\Delta t = 1.0\ \text{s}$, and $m = 1.5\ \text{kg}$ in Eq. 7–2.

**SOLUTION** We take the $x$ direction positive to the right. In each 1.0-s time interval, water with a momentum of $p_x = mv_x = (1.5\ \text{kg})(20\ \text{m/s}) = 30\ \text{kg}\cdot\text{m/s}$ is brought to rest when it hits the car. The magnitude of the force (assumed constant) that the car must exert to change the momentum of the water by this amount is

$$F = \frac{\Delta p}{\Delta t} = \frac{p_{\text{final}} - p_{\text{initial}}}{\Delta t} = \frac{0 - 30\ \text{kg}\cdot\text{m/s}}{1.0\ \text{s}} = -30\ \text{N}.$$

The minus sign indicates that the force on the water is opposite to the water's original velocity. The car exerts a force of 30 N to the left to stop the water, so by Newton's third law, the water exerts a force of 30 N to the right on the car.

**NOTE** Keep track of signs, although common sense helps too. The water is moving to the right, so common sense tells us the force on the car must be to the right.

**FIGURE 7–2** Example 7–2.

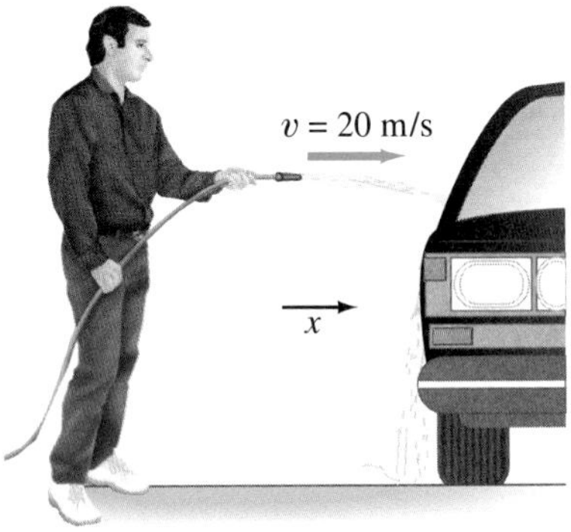


**EXERCISE B** If the water splashes back from the car in Example 7–2, would the force on the car be larger or smaller?

## 7–2 Conservation of Momentum

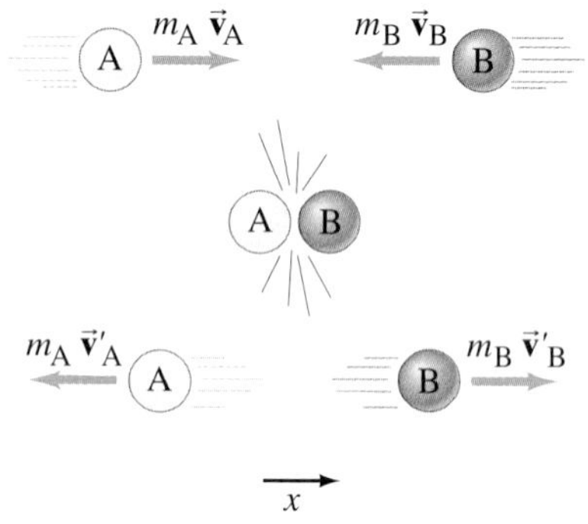


**FIGURE 7–3** Momentum is conserved in a collision of two balls, labelled A and B.

The concept of momentum is particularly important because, under certain circumstances, momentum is a conserved quantity. Consider, for example, the head-on collision of two billiard balls, as shown in Fig. 7–3. We assume the net external force on this system of two balls is zero—that is, the only significant forces during the collision are the forces that each ball exerts on the other. Although the momentum of each of the two balls changes as a result of the collision, the *sum* of their momenta is found to be the same before as after the collision. If $m_A \vec{v}_A$ is the momentum of ball A and $m_B \vec{v}_B$ the momentum of ball B, both measured just before the collision, then the total momentum of the two balls before the collision is the vector sum $m_A \vec{v}_A + m_B \vec{v}_B$. Immediately after the collision, the balls each have a different velocity and momentum, which we designate by a "prime" on the velocity: $m_A \vec{v}'_A$ and $m_B \vec{v}'_B$. The total momentum after the collision is the vector sum $m_A \vec{v}'_A + m_B \vec{v}'_B$. No matter what the velocities and masses are, experiments show that the total momentum before the collision is the same as afterward, whether the collision is head-on or not, as long as no net external force acts:

*CONSERVATION OF MOMENTUM (for two objects colliding)*

$$\text{momentum before} = \text{momentum after}$$

$$m_A \vec{v}_A + m_B \vec{v}_B = m_A \vec{v}'_A + m_B \vec{v}'_B. \tag{7–3}$$

That is, the total vector momentum of the system of two colliding balls is conserved: it stays constant.

*Momentum conservation related to Newton's laws*

Although the law of conservation of momentum was discovered experimentally, it is closely connected to Newton's laws of motion and they can be shown to be equivalent. We will do a derivation for the head–on collision illustrated in Fig. 7–3. We assume the force $F$ that one ball exerts on the other during the collision is constant over the brief time interval of the collision $\Delta t$. We use Newton's second law as expressed in Eq. 7–2, and rewrite it by multiplying both sides by $\Delta t$:

$$\Delta \vec{p} = \vec{F}\, \Delta t. \tag{7–4}$$

We apply this to ball B alone, noting that the force $\vec{F}_{BA}$ on ball B exerted by ball A during the collision is to the right ($+x$ direction—see Fig. 7–4):

**FIGURE 7–4** Forces on the balls during the collision of Fig. 7–3.

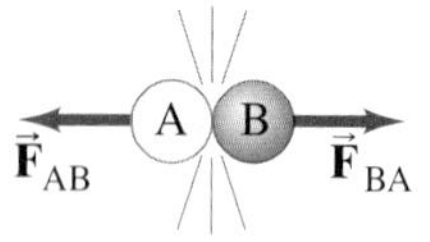


$$\Delta \vec{p}_B = \vec{F}_{BA}\, \Delta t$$
$$m_B \vec{v}'_B - m_B \vec{v}_B = \vec{F}_{BA}\, \Delta t.$$

By Newton's third law, the force $\vec{F}_{AB}$ on ball A due to ball B is $\vec{F}_{AB} = -\vec{F}_{BA}$ and acts to the left. Then applying Newton's second law in the same way to ball A yields

$$\Delta \vec{p}_A = \vec{F}_{AB}\, \Delta t$$

or

$$m_A \vec{v}'_A - m_A \vec{v}_A = \vec{F}_{AB}\, \Delta t$$
$$= -\vec{F}_{BA}\, \Delta t.$$

We combine these two $\Delta \vec{p}$ equations (their right sides differ only by a minus sign):

$$m_A \vec{v}'_A - m_A \vec{v}_A = -(m_B \vec{v}'_B - m_B \vec{v}_B)$$

or

$$m_A \vec{v}_A + m_B \vec{v}_B = m_A \vec{v}'_A + m_B \vec{v}'_B$$

which is Eq. 7–3, the conservation of momentum.

The above derivation can be extended to include any number of interacting objects. To show this, we let $\vec{p}$ in Eq. 7–2 represent the total momentum of a system—that is, the vector sum of the momenta of all objects in the system. (For our two-object system above, $\vec{p} = m_A \vec{v}_A + m_B \vec{v}_B$.) If the net force $\Sigma \vec{F}$ on the system is zero [as it was above for our two-object system, $\vec{F} + (-\vec{F}) = 0$,] then from Eq. 7–2, $\Delta \vec{\mathbf{p}} = \vec{\mathbf{F}}\,\Delta t = 0$, so the total momentum doesn't change. Thus the general statement of the **law of conservation of momentum** is

*LAW OF CONSERVATION OF MOMENTUM*

**The total momentum of an isolated system of objects remains constant.**

*Systems*

*Isolated system*

By a **system**, we simply mean a set of objects that we choose, and which may interact with each other. An **isolated system** is one in which the only (significant) forces are those between the objects in the system. The sum of all these "internal" forces within the system will be zero because of Newton's third law. If there are *external forces*—by which we mean forces exerted by objects outside the system—and they don't add up to zero (vectorially), then the total momentum of the system won't be conserved. However, if the system can be redefined so as to include the other objects exerting these forces, then the conservation of momentum principle can apply. For example, if we take as our system a rock falling under gravity, the momentum of this system (the rock) is not conserved: an external force, the force of gravity exerted by the Earth, is acting on it and changes its momentum. However, if we include the Earth in the system, the total momentum of rock plus Earth is conserved. (This means that the Earth comes up to meet the rock. But the Earth's mass is so great, its upward velocity is very tiny.)

**EXAMPLE 7–3** **Railroad cars collide: momentum conserved.** A 10,000-kg railroad car, A, traveling at a speed of 24.0 m/s strikes an identical car, B, at rest. If the cars lock together as a result of the collision, what is their common speed just afterward? See Fig. 7–5.

**APPROACH** We choose our system to be the two railroad cars. We consider a very brief time interval, from just before the collision until just after, so that external forces such as friction can be ignored. Then we apply conservation of momentum.

**SOLUTION** The initial total momentum is

$$p_{\text{initial}} = m_A v_A + m_B v_B = m_A v_A$$

because car B is at rest initially $(v_B = 0)$. The direction is to the right in the $+x$ direction. After the collision, the two cars become attached, so they will have the same speed, call it $v'$. Then the total momentum after the collision is

$$p_{\text{final}} = (m_A + m_B)v'.$$

We have assumed there are no external forces, so momentum is conserved:

$$p_{\text{initial}} = p_{\text{final}}$$
$$m_A v_A = (m_A + m_B)v'.$$

Solving for $v'$, we obtain

$$v' = \frac{m_A}{m_A + m_B} v_A = \left(\frac{10{,}000\text{ kg}}{10{,}000\text{ kg} + 10{,}000\text{ kg}}\right)(24.0\text{ m/s}) = 12.0\text{ m/s},$$

to the right. Their mutual speed after collision is half the initial speed of car A.

**NOTE** We kept symbols until the very end, so we have an equation we can use in other (related) situations.

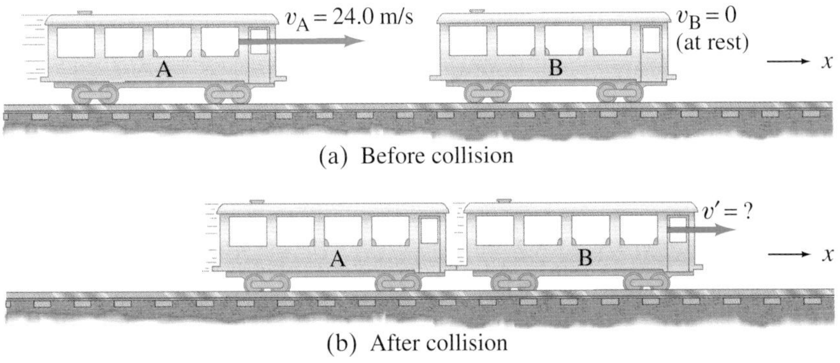


**FIGURE 7–5** Example 7–3.

**EXERCISE C** In Example 7–3, $m_A = m_B$, so in the last equation, $m_A/(m_A + m_B) = \frac{1}{2}$. Hence $v' = \frac{1}{2}v_A$. What result do you get if (*a*) $m_B = 3m_A$, (*b*) $m_B$ is much larger than $m_A$ ($m_B \gg m_A$), and (*c*) $m_B \ll m_A$?

As long as no external forces act on our chosen system, conservation of momentum is valid. In the real world, external forces do act: friction on billiard balls, gravity acting on a baseball, and so on. So it may seem that conservation of momentum cannot be applied. Or can it? In a collision, the force each object exerts on the other acts only over a very brief time interval, and is very strong. When a racket hits a tennis ball (or a bat hits a baseball), both before and after the "collision" the ball moves as a projectile under the action of gravity and air resistance. During the brief time of the collision, however, when the racket hits the ball, external forces (gravity, air resistance) are insignificant compared to the collision forces that the racket and ball exert on each other. So if we measure the momenta just before and just after the collision, we can apply momentum conservation with high accuracy.

PHYSICS APPLIED

*Rocket propulsion*

CAUTION

*A rocket pushes on the gases released by the fuel, not on the Earth or other objects*

The law of conservation of momentum is particularly useful when we are dealing with fairly simple systems such as colliding objects and certain types of "explosions". For example, *rocket propulsion*, which we saw in Chapter 4 can be understood on the basis of action and reaction, can also be explained on the basis of the conservation of momentum. We can consider the rocket and fuel as an isolated system if it is far out in space (no external forces). In the reference frame of the rocket, the total momentum of rocket plus fuel is zero. When the fuel burns, the total momentum remains unchanged: the backward momentum of the expelled gases is just balanced by the forward momentum gained by the rocket itself (see Fig. 7–6). Thus, a rocket can accelerate in empty space. There is no need for the expelled gases to push against the Earth or the air (as is sometimes erroneously thought). Similar examples of (nearly) isolated systems where momentum is conserved are the recoil of a gun when a bullet is fired, and the movement of a rowboat just after a package is thrown from it.

(a)

(b)

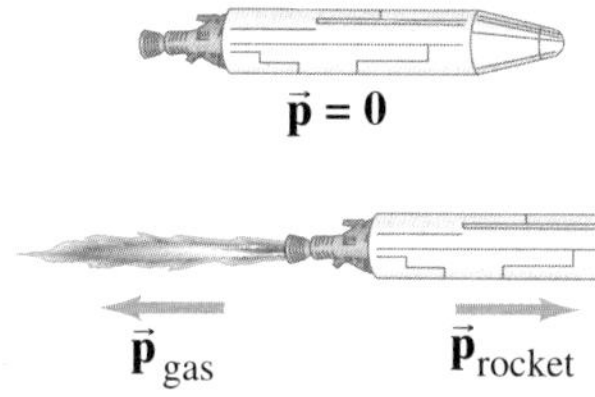


**FIGURE 7–6** (a) A rocket, containing fuel, at rest in some reference frame. (b) In the same reference frame, the rocket fires and gases are expelled at high speed out the rear. The total vector momentum, $\vec{\mathbf{p}}_{gas} + \vec{\mathbf{p}}_{rocket}$, remains zero.

**EXAMPLE 7–4** **Rifle recoil.** Calculate the recoil velocity of a 5.0-kg rifle that shoots a 0.020-kg bullet at a speed of 620 m/s, Fig. 7–7.

**FIGURE 7–7** Example 7–4.

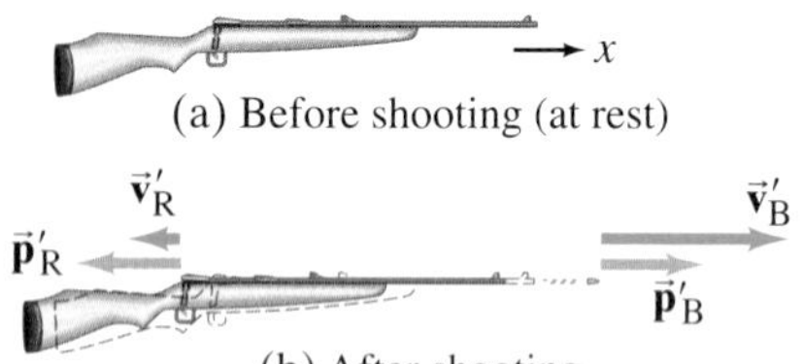


**APPROACH** Our system is the rifle and the bullet, both at rest initially, just before the trigger is pulled. The trigger is pulled, an explosion occurs, and we look at the rifle and bullet just as the bullet leaves the barrel. The bullet moves to the right ($+x$), and the gun recoils to the left. During the very short time interval of the explosion, we can assume the external forces are small compared to the forces exerted by the exploding gunpowder. Thus we can apply conservation of momentum, at least approximately.

**SOLUTION** Let subscript B represent the bullet and R the rifle; the final velocities are indicated by primes. Then momentum conservation in the $x$ direction gives

$$\begin{aligned} \text{momentum before} &= \text{momentum after} \\ m_B v_B + m_R v_R &= m_B v'_B + m_R v'_R \\ 0 + 0 &= m_B v'_B + m_R v'_R \end{aligned}$$

so

$$v'_R = -\frac{m_B v'_B}{m_R} = -\frac{(0.020\text{ kg})(620\text{ m/s})}{(5.0\text{ kg})} = -2.5\text{ m/s}.$$

Since the rifle has a much larger mass, its (recoil) velocity is much less than that of the bullet. The minus sign indicates that the velocity (and momentum) of the rifle is in the negative $x$ direction, opposite to that of the bullet.

**CONCEPTUAL EXAMPLE 7–5** **Falling on or off a sled.** (*a*) An empty sled is sliding on frictionless ice when Susan drops vertically from a tree above onto the sled. When she lands, does the sled speed up, slow down, or keep the same speed? (*b*) Later. Susan falls sideways off the sled. When she drops off, does the sled speed up, slow down, or keep the same speed?

**RESPONSE** (*a*) Because Susan falls vertically onto the sled, she has no initial horizontal momentum. Thus the total horizontal momentum afterward equals the momentum of the sled initially. Since the mass of the system (sled + person) has increased, the speed must decrease.
(*b*) At the instant Susan falls off, she is moving with the same horizontal speed as she was while on the sled. At the moment she leaves the sled, she has the same momentum she had an instant before. Because momentum is conserved, the sled keeps the same speed.

## 7–3 Collisions and Impulse

Collisions are a common occurrence in everyday life: a tennis racket or a baseball bat striking a ball, billiard balls colliding, a hammer hitting a nail. When a collision occurs, the interaction between the objects involved is usually far stronger than any interaction between our system of objects and their environment. We can then ignore the effects of any other forces during the brief time interval of the collision.

During a collision of two ordinary objects, both objects are deformed, often considerably, because of the large forces involved (Fig. 7–8). When the collision occurs, the force usually jumps from zero at the moment of contact to a very large force within a very short time, and then rapidly returns to zero again. A graph of the magnitude of the force that one object exerts on the other during a collision, as a function of time, is something like the red curve in Fig. 7–9. The time interval $\Delta t$ is usually very distinct and very small.

**FIGURE 7–8** Tennis racket striking a ball. Both the ball and the racket strings are deformed due to the large force each exerts on the other.

From Newton's second law, Eq. 7–2, the *net* force on one object is equal to the rate of change of its momentum:

$$\vec{\mathbf{F}} = \frac{\Delta \vec{\mathbf{p}}}{\Delta t}.$$

(We have written $\vec{\mathbf{F}}$ instead of $\Sigma\vec{\mathbf{F}}$ for the net force, which we assume is entirely due to the brief but large average force that acts during the collision.) This equation applies to *each* of the two objects in a collision. We multiply both sides of this equation by the time interval $\Delta t$, and obtain

$$\vec{\mathbf{F}}\,\Delta t = \Delta \vec{\mathbf{p}}. \qquad (7\text{–}5)$$

**FIGURE 7–9** Force as a function of time during a typical collision.

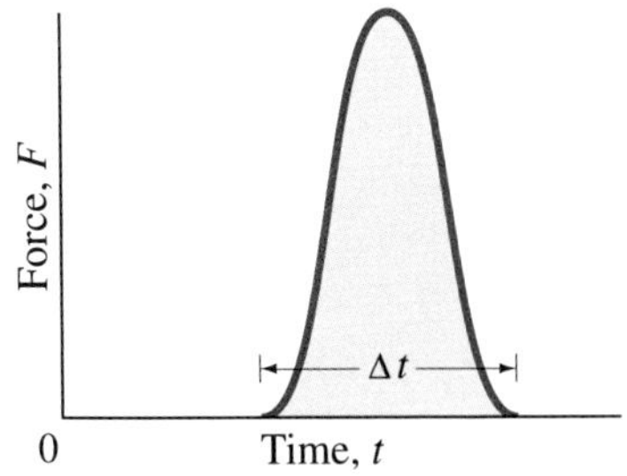


The quantity on the left, the product of the force $\vec{\mathbf{F}}$ times the time $\Delta t$ over which the force acts, is called the **impulse**:

$$\text{Impulse} = \vec{\mathbf{F}}\,\Delta t.$$

We see that the total change in momentum is equal to the impulse. The concept of impulse is useful mainly when dealing with forces that act during a short time interval, as when a bat hits a baseball. The force is generally not constant, and often its variation in time is like that graphed in Figs. 7–9 and 7–10. We can often approximate such a varying force as an average force $\bar{F}$ acting during a time interval $\Delta t$, as indicated by the dashed line in Fig. 7–10. $\bar{F}$ is chosen so that the area shown shaded in Fig. 7–10 (equal to $\bar{F} \times \Delta t$) is equal to the area under the actual curve of $F$ vs. $t$, Fig. 7–9 (which represents the actual impulse).

**FIGURE 7–10** The average force $\bar{F}$ acting over an interval of time $\Delta t$ gives the same impulse ($\bar{F}\,\Delta t$) as the actual force.

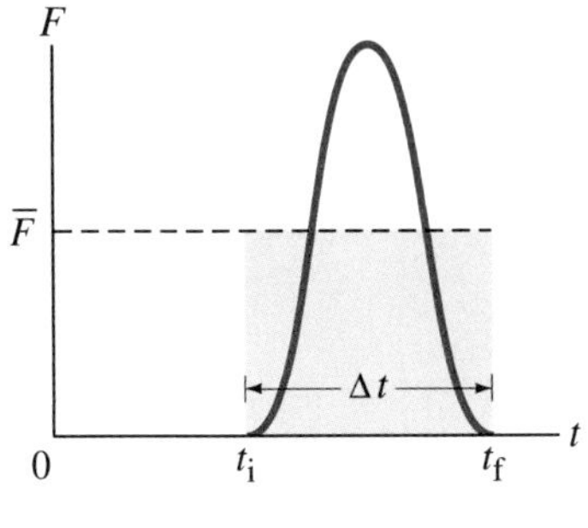


**EXERCISE D** Suppose Fig. 7–9 illustrates the force on a golf ball vs. the time when the ball hits a wall. How would the shape of this curve change if a softer rubber ball with the same mass and speed hit the same wall?

**EXAMPLE 7–6** **Bend your knees when landing.** (*a*) Calculate the impulse experienced when a 70-kg person lands on firm ground after jumping from a height of 3.0 m. (*b*) Estimate the average force exerted on the person's feet by the ground if the landing is stiff-legged, and again (*c*) with bent legs. With stiff legs, assume the body moves 1.0 cm during impact, and when the legs are bent, about 50 cm.

PHYSICS APPLIED
*How not to break a leg*

**APPROACH** We consider the short time interval that starts just before the person hits the ground and ends when he is brought to rest. During this time interval, the ground exerts a force on him and gives him an impulse which equals his change in momentum (Eq. 7–5). For part (*a*) we know his final speed (zero, when he comes to rest), but we need to calculate his "initial" speed just before impact with the ground. The latter is found using kinematics and his drop from a height of 3.0 m. Then Eq. 7–5 gives us $F\Delta t$. In parts (*b*) and (*c*) we calculate how long, $\Delta t$, it takes him to slow down as he hits the ground, using kinematics, and then obtain $F$ because we know $F\Delta t$.

**SOLUTION** (*a*) First we need to determine the velocity of the person just before striking the ground, which we do by considering the earlier time period between the initial jump from a height of 3.0 m until just before he touches the ground. The person falls under gravity, so we can use the kinematic Eq. 2–11c, $v^2 = v_0^2 + 2a(y - y_0)$ with $a = -g$ and $v_0 = 0$, so

$$v^2 = 2g(y_0 - y)$$

or

$$v = \sqrt{2g(y_0 - y)} = \sqrt{2(9.8\,\text{m/s}^2)(3.0\,\text{m})} = 7.7\,\text{m/s}.$$

**FIGURE 7–11** Example 7–6. Time interval $\Delta t$ during which the impulse acts.

This $v = 7.7\,\text{m/s}$ is his speed just before hitting the ground, and so it is the initial speed for the short time interval of the impact with the ground, $\Delta t$. Now we can determine the impulse by examining this brief time interval as the person hits the ground and is brought to rest (Fig. 7–11). We don't know $F$ and thus can't calculate the impulse $F\Delta t$ directly; but we can use Eq. 7–5: the impulse equals the change in momentum of the object

$$\bar{F}\,\Delta t = \Delta p = m\,\Delta v$$
$$= (70\,\text{kg})(0 - 7.7\,\text{m/s}) = -540\,\text{N}\cdot\text{s}.$$

The negative sign tells us that the force is opposed to the original (downward) momentum; that is, the force acts upward.

(*b*) In coming to rest, the person decelerates from 7.7 m/s to zero in a distance $d = 1.0\,\text{cm} = 1.0 \times 10^{-2}\,\text{m}$. If we assume the upward force exerted on him by the ground is constant, then the average speed during this brief period is

$$\bar{v} = \frac{(7.7\,\text{m/s} + 0\,\text{m/s})}{2} = 3.9\,\text{m/s}.$$

Thus the collision with the ground lasts for a time interval (recall the definition of speed, $\bar{v} = d/\Delta t$):

$$\Delta t = \frac{d}{\bar{v}} = \frac{(1.0 \times 10^{-2}\,\text{m})}{(3.9\,\text{m/s})} = 2.6 \times 10^{-3}\,\text{s}.$$

Since the magnitude of the impulse is $\bar{F}\,\Delta t = 540\,\text{N}\cdot\text{s}$, and $\Delta t = 2.6 \times 10^{-3}\,\text{s}$, the average net force $\bar{F}$ on the person has magnitude

$$\bar{F} = \frac{540\,\text{N}\cdot\text{s}}{2.6 \times 10^{-3}\,\text{s}} = 2.1 \times 10^5\,\text{N}.$$

PROBLEM SOLVING
*Free-body diagrams are always useful!*

We are almost there. $\bar{F}$ equals the vector sum of the average force upward on the legs exerted by the ground, $F_{\text{grd}}$, which we take as positive, plus the downward force of gravity, $-mg$ (see Fig. 7–12):

$$\bar{F} = F_{\text{grd}} - mg.$$

Since $mg = (70\,\text{kg})(9.8\,\text{m/s}^2) = 690\,\text{N}$, then

$$F_{\text{grd}} = \bar{F} + mg = (2.1 \times 10^5\,\text{N}) + (0.690 \times 10^3\,\text{N}) \approx 2.1 \times 10^5\,\text{N}.$$

($c$) This is just like part ($b$), except $d = 0.50\,\text{m}$, so

$$\Delta t = \frac{d}{\bar{v}} = \frac{0.50\,\text{m}}{3.9\,\text{m/s}} = 0.13\,\text{s}$$

and

$$\bar{F} = \frac{540\,\text{N}\cdot\text{s}}{0.13\,\text{s}} = 4.2 \times 10^3\,\text{N}.$$

The upward force exerted on the person's feet by the ground is, as in part ($b$):

$$F_{\text{grd}} = \bar{F} + mg = \left(4.2 \times 10^3\,\text{N}\right) + \left(0.69 \times 10^3\,\text{N}\right) = 4.9 \times 10^3\,\text{N}.$$

Clearly, the force on the feet and legs is much less now with the knees bent, and the impulse occurs over a longer time interval. In fact, the ultimate strength of the leg bone (see Chapter 9, Table 9–2) is not great enough to support the force calculated in part ($b$), so the leg would likely break in such a stiff landing, whereas it probably wouldn't in part ($c$) with bent legs.

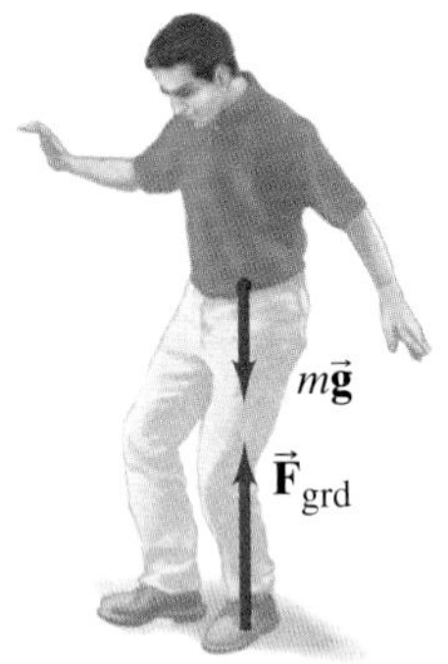


**FIGURE 7–12** Example 7–6. When the person lands on the ground, the average net force during impact is $\bar{F} = F_{\text{grd}} - mg$, where $F_{\text{grd}}$ is the force the ground exerts upward on the person.

**EXERCISE E** In part ($b$) of Example 7–6, we calculated the force exerted by the ground on the person during the collision, $F_{\text{grd}}$. Was $F_{\text{grd}}$ much greater than the "external" force of gravity on the person? By what factor?

## 7–4 Conservation of Energy and Momentum in Collisions

During most collisions, we usually don't know how the collision force varies over time, and so analysis using Newton's second law becomes difficult or impossible. But by making use of the conservation laws for momentum and energy, we can still determine a lot about the motion after a collision, given the motion before the collision. We saw in Section 7–2 that in the collision of two objects such as billiard balls, the total momentum is conserved. If the two objects are very hard and no heat or other form of energy is produced in the collision, then kinetic energy is conserved as well. By this we mean that the sum of the kinetic energies of the two objects is the same after the collision as before. For the brief moment during which the two objects are in contact, some (or all) of the energy is stored momentarily in the form of elastic potential energy. But if we compare the total kinetic energy just before the collision with the total kinetic energy just after the collision, they are found to be the same. Such a collision, in which the total kinetic energy is conserved, is called an **elastic collision**. If we use the subscripts A and B to represent the two objects, we can write the equation for conservation of total kinetic energy as

$$\text{total KE before} = \text{total KE after}$$

$$\tfrac{1}{2}m_{\text{A}}v_{\text{A}}^2 + \tfrac{1}{2}m_{\text{B}}v_{\text{B}}^2 = \tfrac{1}{2}m_{\text{A}}v_{\text{A}}'^2 + \tfrac{1}{2}m_{\text{B}}v_{\text{B}}'^2. \quad \text{[elastic collision]} \quad \textbf{(7–6)}$$

Here, primed quantities ($'$) mean after the collision and unprimed mean before the collision, just as in Eq. 7–3 for conservation of momentum.

At the atomic level the collisions of atoms and molecules are often elastic. But in the "macroscopic" world of ordinary objects, an elastic collision is an ideal that is never quite reached, since at least a little thermal energy (and perhaps sound and other forms of energy) is always produced during a collision. The collision of two hard elastic balls, such as billiard balls, however, is very close to being perfectly elastic, and we often treat it as such.

We do need to remember that even when the kinetic energy is not conserved, the *total* energy is always conserved.

Collisions in which kinetic energy is not conserved are said to be **inelastic collisions**. The kinetic energy that is lost is changed into other forms of energy, often thermal energy, so that the total energy (as always) is conserved. In this case,

$$\text{KE}_{\text{A}} + \text{KE}_{\text{B}} = \text{KE}_{\text{A}}' + \text{KE}_{\text{B}}' + \text{thermal and other forms of energy.}$$

See Fig. 7–13, and the details in its caption.

**FIGURE 7–13** Two equal-mass objects (a) approach each other with equal speeds, (b) collide, and then (c) bounce off with equal speeds in the opposite directions if the collision is elastic, or (d) bounce back much less or not at all if the collision is inelastic.

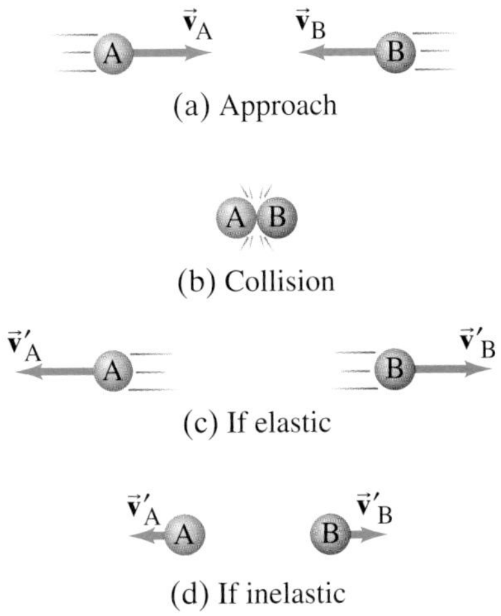

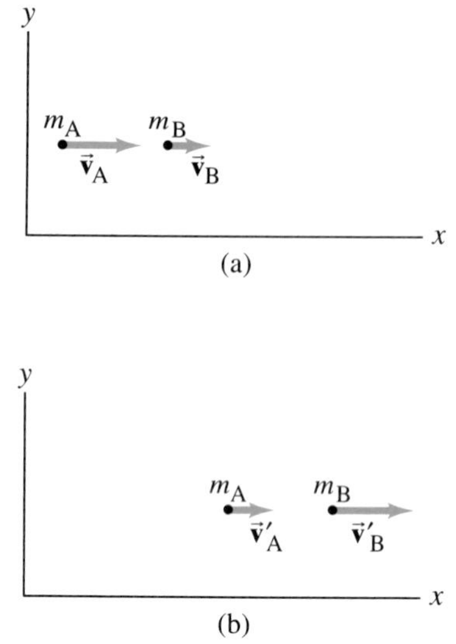


**FIGURE 7–14** Two small objects of masses $m_A$ and $m_B$, (a) before the collision and (b) after the collision.

## 7–5 Elastic Collisions in One Dimension

We now apply the conservation laws for momentum and kinetic energy to an elastic collision between two small objects that collide head-on, so all the motion is along a line. Let us assume that the two objects are moving with velocities $v_A$ and $v_B$ along the $x$ axis before the collision, Fig. 7–14a. After the collision, their velocities are $v'_A$ and $v'_B$, Fig. 7–14b. For any $v > 0$, the object is moving to the right (increasing $x$), whereas for $v < 0$, the object is moving to the left (toward decreasing values of $x$).

From conservation of momentum, we have

$$m_A v_A + m_B v_B = m_A v'_A + m_B v'_B.$$

Because the collision is assumed to be elastic, kinetic energy is also conserved:

$$\tfrac{1}{2}m_A v_A^2 + \tfrac{1}{2}m_B v_B^2 = \tfrac{1}{2}m_A v_A'^2 + \tfrac{1}{2}m_B v_B'^2.$$

We have two equations, so we can solve for two unknowns. If we know the masses and velocities before the collision, then we can solve these two equations for the velocities after the collision, $v'_A$ and $v'_B$. We derive a helpful result by rewriting the momentum equation as

$$m_A(v_A - v'_A) = m_B(v'_B - v_B), \qquad \textbf{(i)}$$

and we rewrite the kinetic energy equation as

$$m_A(v_A^2 - v_A'^2) = m_B(v_B'^2 - v_B^2).$$

Noting that algebraically $(a - b)(a + b) = a^2 - b^2$, we write this last equation as

$$m_A(v_A - v'_A)(v_A + v'_A) = m_B(v'_B - v_B)(v'_B + v_B). \qquad \textbf{(ii)}$$

We divide Eq. (ii) by Eq. (i), and (assuming $v_A \neq v'_A$ and $v_B \neq v'_B$) obtain

$$v_A + v'_A = v'_B + v_B.$$

We can rewrite this equation as

$$v_A - v_B = v'_B - v'_A$$

or

*Relative speeds (one dimension only)*

$$v_A - v_B = -(v'_A - v'_B). \qquad \text{[head-on elastic collision]} \quad \textbf{(7–7)}$$

This is an interesting result: it tells us that for any elastic head-on collision, the relative speed of the two objects after the collision has the same magnitude (but opposite direction) as before the collision, no matter what the masses are.

Equation 7–7 was derived from conservation of kinetic energy for elastic collisions, and can be used in place of it. Because the $v$'s are not squared in Eq. 7–7, it is simpler to use in calculations than the conservation of kinetic energy equation (Eq. 7–6) directly.

**EXAMPLE 7–7** **Pool or billiards.** Billiard ball A of mass $m$ moving with speed $v$ collides head-on with ball B of equal mass at rest $(v_B = 0)$. What are the speeds of the two balls after the collision, assuming it is elastic?

**APPROACH** There are two unknowns, $v'_A$ and $v'_B$, so we need two independent equations. We focus on the time interval from just before the collision until just after. No net external force acts on our system of two balls ($mg$ and the normal force cancel), so momentum is conserved. Conservation of kinetic energy applies as well because the collision is elastic.

**SOLUTION** Given $v_A = v$ and $v_B = 0$, and $m_A = m_B = m$, then conservation of momentum gives

$$mv = mv'_A + mv'_B$$

or, since the $m$'s cancel out,

$$v = v'_A + v'_B.$$

We have two unknowns ($v'_A$ and $v'_B$) and need a second equation, which could be the conservation of kinetic energy or the simpler Eq. 7–7 we derived from it:

$$v_A - v_B = v'_B - v'_A, \qquad \text{or} \qquad v = v'_B - v'_A$$

since $v_A = v$ and $v_B = 0$. We subtract $v = v'_B - v'_A$ from our momentum equation $(v = v'_A + v'_B)$ and obtain

$$0 = 2v'_A.$$

Hence $v'_A = 0$. We can now solve for the other unknown $(v'_B)$ since $v = v'_B - v'_A$:

$$v'_B = v + v'_A = v + 0 = v.$$

To summarize, before the collision we have

$$v_A = v, \qquad v_B = 0$$

and after the collision

$$v'_A = 0, \qquad v'_B = v.$$

That is, ball A is brought to rest by the collision, whereas ball B acquires the original velocity of ball A. See Fig. 7–15.

**NOTE** Our result is often observed by billiard and pool players, and is valid only if the two balls have equal masses (and no spin is given to the balls).

**FIGURE 7–15** In this multiflash photo of a head-on collision between two balls of equal mass, the white cue ball is accelerated from rest by the cue stick and then strikes the red ball, initially at rest. The white ball stops in its tracks, and the (equal mass) red ball moves off with the same speed as the white ball had before the collision. See Example 7–7.

**EXAMPLE 7–8** **A nuclear collision.** A proton (p) of mass 1.01 u (unified atomic mass units) traveling with a speed of $3.60 \times 10^4$ m/s has an elastic head-on collision with a helium (He) nucleus $(m_{He} = 4.00\text{ u})$ initially at rest. What are the velocities of the proton and helium nucleus after the collision? (As mentioned in Chapter 1, $1\text{ u} = 1.66 \times 10^{-27}$ kg, but we won't need this fact.) Assume the collision takes place in nearly empty space.

**APPROACH** Like Example 7–7, this is an elastic head-on collision, but now the masses of our two-particle system are not equal. The only external force is Earth's gravity, but it is insignificant compared to the strong force during the collision. So again we use the conservation laws of momentum and of kinetic energy, and apply them to our system of two particles.

**SOLUTION** Let the proton (p) be particle A and the helium nucleus (He) be particle B. We have $v_B = v_{He} = 0$ and $v_A = v_p = 3.60 \times 10^4$ m/s. We want to find the velocities $v'_p$ and $v'_{He}$ after the collision. From conservation of momentum,

$$m_p v_p + 0 = m_p v'_p + m_{He} v'_{He}.$$

Because the collision is elastic, the kinetic energy of our system of two particles is conserved and we can use Eq. 7–7, which becomes

$$v_p - 0 = v'_{He} - v'_p.$$

Thus

$$v'_p = v'_{He} - v_p,$$

and substituting this into our momentum equation displayed above, we get

$$m_p v_p = m_p v'_{He} - m_p v_p + m_{He} v'_{He}.$$

Solving for $v'_{He}$, we obtain

$$v'_{He} = \frac{2m_p v_p}{m_p + m_{He}} = \frac{2(1.01\text{ u})(3.60 \times 10^4\text{ m/s})}{5.01\text{ u}} = 1.45 \times 10^4\text{ m/s}.$$

The other unknown is $v'_p$, which we can now obtain from

$$v'_p = v'_{He} - v_p = (1.45 \times 10^4\text{ m/s}) - (3.60 \times 10^4\text{ m/s}) = -2.15 \times 10^4\text{ m/s}.$$

The minus sign for $v'_p$ tells us that the proton reverses direction upon collision, and we see that its speed is less than its initial speed (see Fig. 7–16).

**NOTE** This result makes sense: the lighter proton would be expected to "bounce back" from the more massive helium nucleus, but not with its full original velocity as from a rigid wall (which corresponds to extremely large, or infinite, mass).

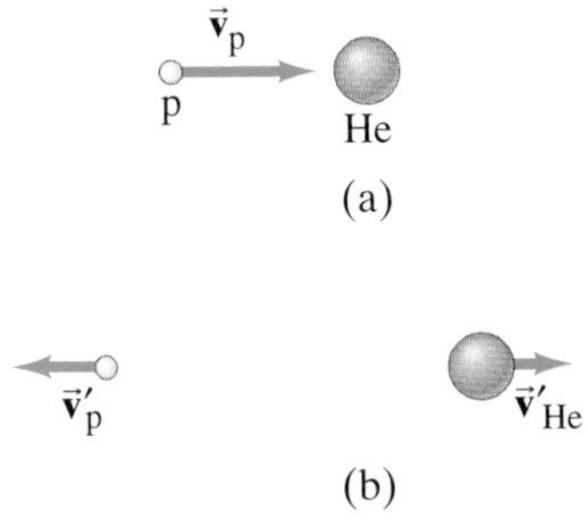


**FIGURE 7–16** Example 7–8: (a) before collision, (b) after collision.

## 7–6 Inelastic Collisions

Collisions in which kinetic energy is not conserved are called *inelastic collisions*. Some of the initial kinetic energy is transformed into other types of energy, such as thermal or potential energy, so the total kinetic energy after the collision is less than the total kinetic energy before the collision. The inverse can also happen when potential energy (such as chemical or nuclear) is released, in which case the total kinetic energy after the interaction can be greater than the initial kinetic energy. Explosions are examples of this type.

*Completely inelastic collision*

Typical macroscopic collisions are inelastic, at least to some extent, and often to a large extent. If two objects stick together as a result of a collision, the collision is said to be **completely inelastic**. Two colliding balls of putty that stick together or two railroad cars that couple together when they collide are examples of completely inelastic collisions. The kinetic energy in some cases is all transformed to other forms of energy in an inelastic collision, but in other cases only part of it is. In Example 7–3, for instance, we saw that when a traveling railroad car collided with a stationary one, the coupled cars traveled off with some kinetic energy. In a completely inelastic collision, the maximum amount of kinetic energy is transformed to other forms consistent with conservation of momentum. Even though kinetic energy is not conserved in inelastic collisions, the total energy is always conserved, and the total vector momentum is also conserved.

**EXAMPLE 7–9** **Railroad cars again.** For the completely inelastic collision of two railroad cars that we considered in Example 7–3, calculate how much of the initial kinetic energy is transformed to thermal or other forms of energy.

**APPROACH** The railroad cars stick together after the collision, so this is a completely inelastic collision. By subtracting the total kinetic energy after the collision from the total initial kinetic energy, we can find how much energy is transformed to other types of energy.

**SOLUTION** Before the collision, only car A is moving, so the total initial kinetic energy is

$$\tfrac{1}{2} m_A v_A^2 = \tfrac{1}{2}(10{,}000\,\text{kg})(24.0\,\text{m/s})^2 = 2.88 \times 10^6\,\text{J}.$$

After the collision, both cars are moving with a speed of 12.0 m/s, by conservation of momentum (Example 7–3). So the total kinetic energy afterward is

$$\tfrac{1}{2}(20{,}000\,\text{kg})(12.0\,\text{m/s})^2 = 1.44 \times 10^6\,\text{J}.$$

Hence the energy transformed to other forms is

$$\left(2.88 \times 10^6\,\text{J}\right) - \left(1.44 \times 10^6\,\text{J}\right) = 1.44 \times 10^6\,\text{J},$$

which is just half the original kinetic energy.

*Ballistic pendulum*

**EXAMPLE 7–10** **Ballistic pendulum.** The *ballistic pendulum* is a device used to measure the speed of a projectile, such as a bullet. The projectile, of mass $m$, is fired into a large block (of wood or other material) of mass $M$, which is suspended like a pendulum. (Usually, $M$ is somewhat greater than $m$.) As a result of the collision, the pendulum and projectile together swing up to a maximum height $h$, Fig. 7–17. Determine the relationship between the initial horizontal speed of the projectile, $v$, and the maximum height $h$.

**APPROACH** We can analyze the process by dividing it into two parts or two time intervals: (1) the time interval from just before to just after the collision itself, and (2) the subsequent time interval in which the pendulum moves from the vertical hanging position to the maximum height $h$.

In part (1), Fig. 7–17a, we assume the collision time is very short, so the projectile comes to rest in the block before the block has moved significantly from its position directly below its support. Thus there is effectively no net external force, and we can apply conservation of momentum to this completely inelastic collision. In part (2), Fig. 7–17b, the pendulum begins to move, subject to a net external force (gravity, tending to pull it back to the vertical position); so for part (2), we cannot use conservation of momentum. But we can use conservation of mechanical energy because gravity is a conservative force (Chapter 6). The kinetic energy immediately after the collision is changed entirely to gravitational potential energy when the pendulum reaches its maximum height, $h$.

**SOLUTION** In part (1) momentum is conserved:

$$\text{total } p \text{ before} = \text{total } p \text{ after}$$

$$mv = (m + M)v', \qquad \textbf{(i)}$$

where $v'$ is the speed of the block and embedded projectile just after the collision, before they have moved significantly.

In part (2), mechanical energy is conserved. We choose $y = 0$ when the pendulum hangs vertically, and then $y = h$ when the pendulum–projectile system reaches its maximum height. Thus we write

$$(\text{KE} + \text{PE}) \text{ just after collision} = (\text{KE} + \text{PE}) \text{ at pendulum's maximum height}$$

or

$$\tfrac{1}{2}(m + M)v'^2 + 0 = 0 + (m + M)gh. \qquad \textbf{(ii)}$$

We solve for $v'$:

$$v' = \sqrt{2gh}.$$

Inserting this result for $v'$ into Eq. (i) above, and solving for $v$, gives

$$v = \frac{m + M}{m}v' = \frac{m + M}{m}\sqrt{2gh},$$

which is our final result.

**NOTE** The separation of the process into two parts was crucial. Such an analysis is a powerful problem-solving tool. But how do you decide how to make such a division? Think about the conservation laws. They are your *tools*. Start a problem by asking yourself whether the conservation laws apply in the given situation. Here, we determined that momentum is conserved only during the brief collision, which we called part (1). But in part (1), because the collision is inelastic, the conservation of mechanical energy is not valid. Then in part (2), conservation of mechanical energy is valid, but not conservation of momentum.

Note, however, that if there had been significant motion of the pendulum during the deceleration of the projectile in the block, then there *would* have been an external force (gravity) during the collision, so conservation of momentum would not have been valid in part (1).

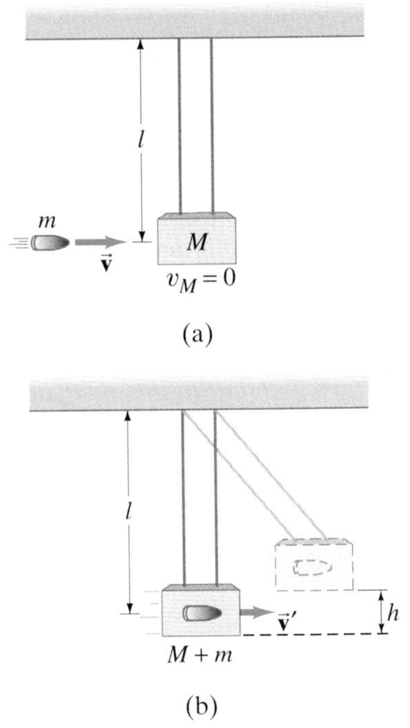


**FIGURE 7–17** Ballistic pendulum. Example 7–10.

**PROBLEM SOLVING**

*Use the conservation laws to analyze a problem*

## * 7–7 Collisions in Two or Three Dimensions

Conservation of momentum and energy can also be applied to collisions in two or three dimensions, where the vector nature of momentum is especially important. One common type of non-head-on collision is that in which a moving object (called the "projectile") strikes a second object initially at rest (the "target"). This is the common situation in games such as billiards and pool, and for experiments in atomic and nuclear physics (the projectiles, from radioactive decay or a high-energy accelerator, strike a stationary target nucleus; Fig. 7–18).

**FIGURE 7–18** A recent color-enhanced version of a cloud-chamber photograph made in the early days (1920s) of nuclear physics. Green lines are paths of helium nuclei (He) coming from the left. One He, highlighted in yellow, strikes a proton of the hydrogen gas in the chamber, and both scatter at an angle; the scattered proton's path is shown in red.

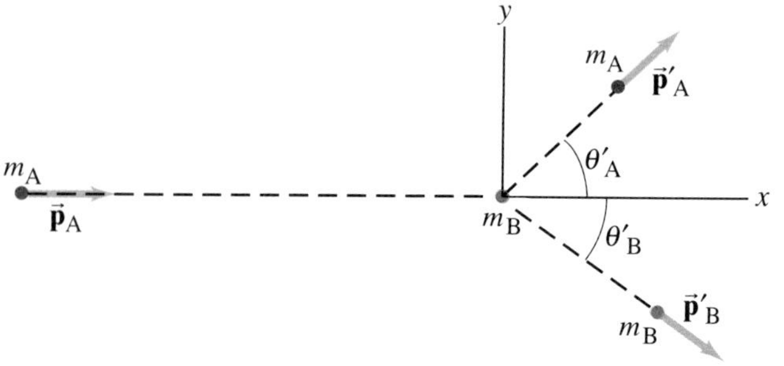


**FIGURE 7–19** Object A, the projectile, collides with object B, the target. After the collision, they move off with momenta $\vec{\mathbf{p}}'_A$ and $\vec{\mathbf{p}}'_B$ at angles $\theta'_A$ and $\theta'_B$.

Figure 7–19 shows the incoming projectile, $m_A$, heading along the $x$ axis toward the target object, $m_B$, which is initially at rest. If these are billiard balls, $m_A$ strikes $m_B$ and they go off at the angles $\theta'_A$ and $\theta'_B$, respectively, which are measured relative to $m_A$'s initial direction (the $x$ axis).†

Let us apply the law of conservation of momentum to a collision like that of Fig. 7–19. We choose the $xy$ plane to be the plane in which the initial and final momenta lie. Momentum is a vector, and because the total momentum is conserved, its components in the $x$ and $y$ directions also are conserved. The $x$ component of momentum conservation gives

$$p_{Ax} + p_{Bx} = p'_{Ax} + p'_{Bx}$$

or, with $p_{Bx} = m_B v_{Bx} = 0,$

*$p_x$ conserved*

$$m_A v_A = m_A v'_A \cos\theta'_A + m_B v'_B \cos\theta'_B, \qquad \textbf{(7–8a)}$$

where the primes (′) refer to quantities *after* the collision. Because there is no motion in the $y$ direction initially, the $y$ component of the total momentum is zero before the collision. The $y$ component equation of momentum conservation is then

$$p_{Ay} + p_{By} = p'_{Ay} + p'_{By}$$

or

*$p_y$ conserved*

$$0 = m_A v'_A \sin\theta'_A + m_B v'_B \sin\theta'_B. \qquad \textbf{(7–8b)}$$

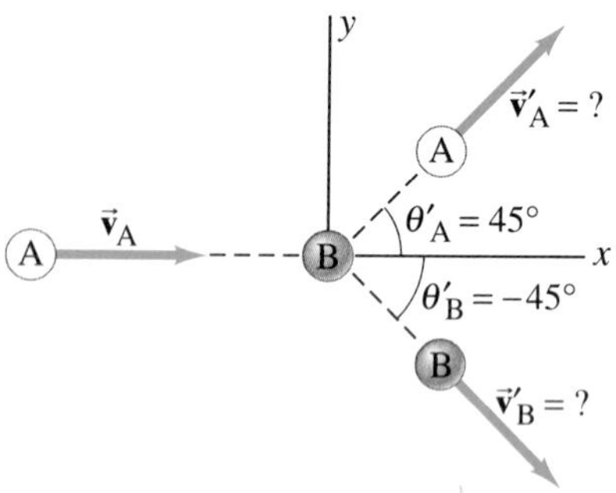


**FIGURE 7–20** Example 7–11.

**EXAMPLE 7–11 Billiard ball collision in 2-D.** Billiard ball A moving with speed $v_A = 3.0\,\text{m/s}$ in the $+x$ direction (Fig. 7–20) strikes an equal-mass ball B initially at rest. The two balls are observed to move off at 45° to the $x$ axis, ball A above the $x$ axis and ball B below. That is, $\theta'_A = 45°$ and $\theta'_B = -45°$ in Fig. 7–20. What are the speeds of the two balls after the collision?

**APPROACH** There is no net external force on our system of two balls, assuming the table is level (the normal force balances gravity). Thus momentum conservation applies, and we apply it to both the $x$ and $y$ components using the $xy$ coordinate system shown in Fig. 7–20. We get two equations, and we have two unknowns, $v'_A$ and $v'_B$. From symmetry we might guess that the two balls have the same speed. But let us not assume that now. Even though we aren't told whether the collision is elastic or inelastic, we can still use conservation of momentum.

**SOLUTION** We apply conservation of momentum, Eqs. 7–8a and b, and we solve for $v'_A$ and $v'_B$. We are given $m_A = m_B(=m)$, so

$$(\text{for } x) \qquad mv_A = mv'_A\cos(45°) + mv'_B\cos(-45°)$$

and

$$(\text{for } y) \qquad 0 = mv'_A\sin(45°) + mv'_B\sin(-45°).$$

The $m$'s cancel out in both equations (the masses are equal).

†The objects may begin to deflect even before they touch if electric, magnetic, or nuclear forces act between them. You might think, for example, of two magnets oriented so that they repel each other: when one moves toward the other, the second moves away before the first one touches it.

The second equation yields [recall that $\sin(-\theta) = -\sin\theta$]:

$$v'_B = -v'_A \frac{\sin(45°)}{\sin(-45°)} = -v'_A\left(\frac{\sin 45°}{-\sin 45°}\right) = v'_A.$$

So they do have equal speeds as we guessed at first. The $x$ component equation gives [recall that $\cos(-\theta) = \cos\theta$]:

$$v_A = v'_A\cos(45°) + v'_B\cos(45°) = 2v'_A\cos(45°),$$

so

$$v'_A = v'_B = \frac{v_A}{2\cos(45°)} = \frac{3.0\text{ m/s}}{2(0.707)} = 2.1\text{ m/s}.$$

**NOTE** When we have two independent equations, we can solve for, at most, two unknowns.

**EXERCISE F** Make a calculation to see if kinetic energy was conserved in the collision of Example 7–11.

If we know that a collision is elastic, we can also apply conservation of kinetic energy and obtain a third equation in addition to Eqs. 7–8a and b:

$$\text{KE}_A + \text{KE}_B = \text{KE}'_A + \text{KE}'_B$$

or, for the collision shown in Fig. 7–20,

$$\tfrac{1}{2}m_A v_A^2 = \tfrac{1}{2}m_A v_A'^2 + \tfrac{1}{2}m_B v_B'^2. \qquad \text{[elastic collision]} \quad \textbf{(7–8c)}$$

*KE conserved*

If the collision is elastic, we have three independent equations and can solve for three unknowns. If we are given $m_A$, $m_B$, $v_A$ (and $v_B$, if it is not zero), we cannot, for example, predict the final variables, $v'_A$, $v'_B$, $\theta'_A$, and $\theta'_B$, because there are four of them. However, if we measure one of these variables, say $\theta'_A$, then the other three variables ($v'_A$, $v'_B$, and $\theta'_B$) are uniquely determined, and we can determine them using Eqs. 7–8a, b, c.

A note of caution: Eq. 7–7 does *not* apply for two-dimensional collisions. It works only when a collision occurs along a line.

**CAUTION**
*Equation 7–7 applies only in 1-D*

## PROBLEM SOLVING Momentum Conservation and Collisions

1. Choose your **system**. If the situation is complex, think about how you might break it up into separate parts when one or more conservation laws apply.
2. Consider whether a significant **net external force** acts on your chosen system; if it does, be sure the time interval $\Delta t$ is so short that the effect on momentum is neglible. That is, the forces that act between the interacting objects must be the significant ones if momentum conservation is to be used. [Note: If this is valid for a portion of the problem, you can use momentum conservation only for that portion.]
3. Draw a **diagram** of the initial situation, just before the interaction (collision, explosion) takes place, and represent the momentum of each object with an arrow and a label. Do the same for the final situation, just after the interaction.
4. Choose a **coordinate system** and "+" and "–" directions. (For a head-on collision, you will need only an $x$ axis.) It is often convenient to choose the $+x$ axis in the direction of one object's initial velocity.
5. Apply the **momentum conservation** equation(s):

   total initial momentum = total final momentum.

   You have one equation for each component ($x$, $y$, $z$): only one equation for a head-on collision. [Don't forget that it is the *total* momentum of the system that is conserved, not the momenta of individual objects.]
6. If the collision is elastic, you can also write down a **conservation of kinetic energy** equation:

   total initial KE = total final KE.

   [Alternately, you could use Eq. 7–7: $v_A - v_B = v'_B - v'_A$, if the collision is one dimensional (head-on).]
7. Solve for the **unknown(s)**.
8. **Check** your work, check the units, and ask yourself whether the results are reasonable.

## 7–8 Center of Mass (CM)

Momentum is a powerful concept not only for analyzing collisions but also for analyzing the translational motion of real extended objects. Until now, whenever we have dealt with the motion of an extended object (that is, an object that has size), we have assumed that it could be approximated as a point particle or that it undergoes only translational motion. Real extended objects, however, can undergo rotational and other types of motion as well. For example, the diver in Fig. 7–21a undergoes only translational motion (all parts of the object follow the same path), whereas the diver in Fig. 7–21b undergoes both translational and rotational motion. We will refer to motion that is not pure translation as *general motion*.

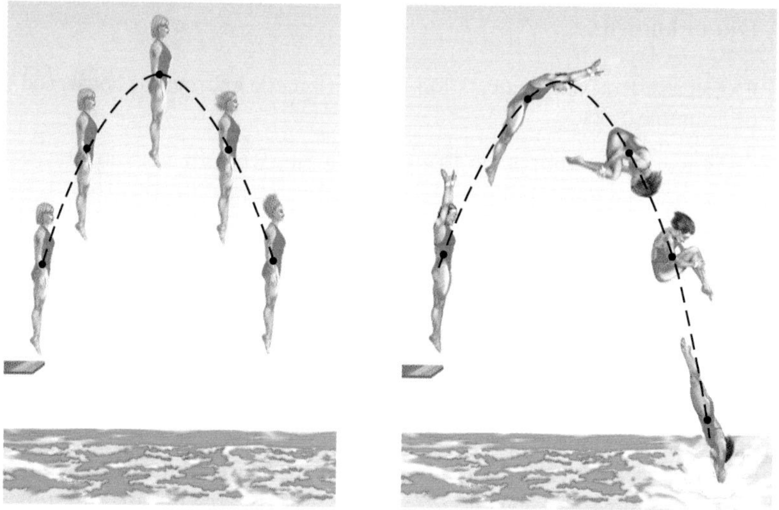

(a) (b)

**FIGURE 7–21** The motion of the diver is pure translation in (a), but is translation plus rotation in (b). The black dot represents the diver's CM at each moment.

*Center of mass*
*General motion*

Observations indicate that even if an object rotates, or several parts of a system of objects move relative to one another, there is one point that moves in the same path that a particle would move if subjected to the same net force. This point is called the **center of mass** (abbreviated CM). The general motion of an extended object (or system of objects) can be considered as *the sum of the translational motion of the CM, plus rotational, vibrational, or other types of motion about the CM.*

As an example, consider the motion of the center of mass of the diver in Fig. 7–21; the CM follows a parabolic path even when the diver rotates, as shown in Fig. 7–21b. This is the same parabolic path that a projected particle follows when acted on only by the force of gravity (that is, projectile motion). Other points in the rotating diver's body, such as her feet or head, follow more complicated paths.

Figure 7–22 shows a wrench acted on by zero net force, translating and rotating along a horizontal surface. Note that its CM, marked by a red cross, moves in a straight line, as shown by the dashed white line.

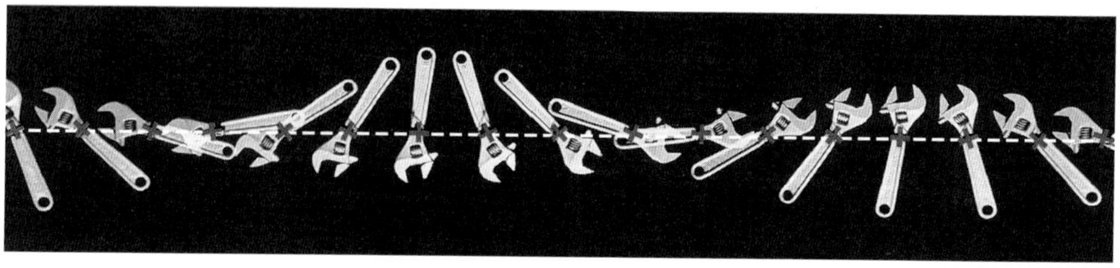

**FIGURE 7–22** Translation plus rotation: a wrench moving over a horizontal surface. The CM, marked with a red cross, moves in a straight line.

We will show in Section 7–10 that the important properties of the CM follow from Newton's laws if the CM is defined in the following way. We can consider any extended object as being made up of many tiny particles. But first we consider a system made up of only two particles (or small objects), of masses $m_A$ and $m_B$. We choose a coordinate system so that both particles lie on the $x$ axis at positions $x_A$ and $x_B$, Fig. 7–23. The center of mass of this system is defined to be at the position $x_{CM}$, given by

$$x_{CM} = \frac{m_A x_A + m_B x_B}{m_A + m_B} = \frac{m_A x_A + m_B x_B}{M},$$

*x coordinate of CM (2 particles)*

where $M = m_A + m_B$ is the total mass of the system. The center of mass lies on the line joining $m_A$ and $m_B$. If the two masses are equal $(m_A = m_B = m)$, then $x_{CM}$ is midway between them, since in this case

$$x_{CM} = \frac{m(x_A + x_B)}{2m} = \frac{(x_A + x_B)}{2}.$$

If one mass is greater than the other, say, $m_A > m_B$, then the CM is closer to the larger mass. If all the mass is concentrated at $x_B$, say, so $m_A = 0$, then $x_{CM} = (0x_A + m_B x_B)/(0 + m_B) = x_B$, as we would expect.

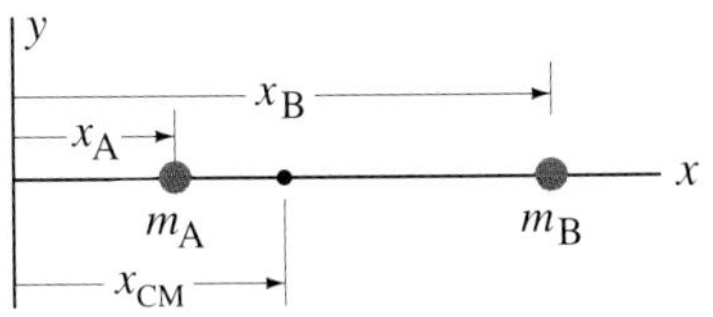


**FIGURE 7–23** The center of mass of a two-particle system lies on the line joining the two masses. Here $m_A > m_B$, so the CM is closer to $m_A$ than to $m_B$.

If there are more than two particles along a line, there will be additional terms:

$$x_{CM} = \frac{m_A x_A + m_B x_B + m_C x_C + \cdots}{m_A + m_B + m_C + \cdots} = \frac{m_A x_A + m_B x_B + m_C x_C + \cdots}{M}, \quad \textbf{(7–9a)}$$

*x coordinate of CM (many particles)*

where $M$ is the total mass of all the particles.

**EXAMPLE 7–12** **CM of three guys on a raft.** Three people of roughly equal masses $m$ on a lightweight (air-filled) banana boat sit along the $x$ axis at positions $x_A = 1.0$ m, $x_B = 5.0$ m, and $x_C = 6.0$ m, measured from the left-hand end as shown in Fig. 7–24. Find the position of the CM. Ignore mass of boat.

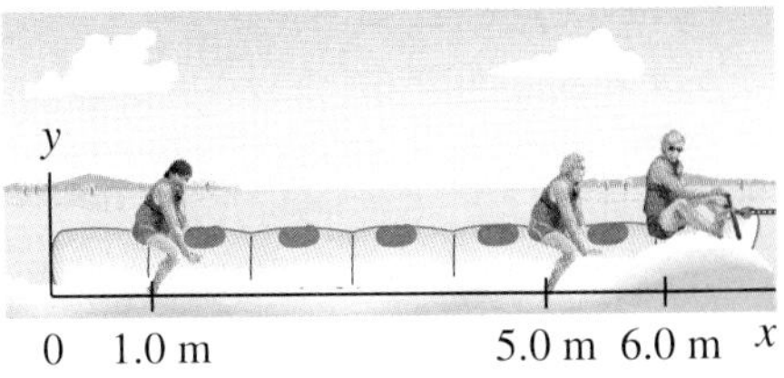


**FIGURE 7–24** Example 7–12.

**APPROACH** We are given the mass and location of the three people, so we use three terms in Eq. 7–9a. We approximate each person as a point particle. Equivalently, the location of each person is the position of that person's own CM.

**SOLUTION** We use Eq. 7–9a with three terms:

$$x_{CM} = \frac{m x_A + m x_B + m x_C}{m + m + m} = \frac{m(x_A + x_B + x_C)}{3m}$$
$$= \frac{(1.0\text{ m} + 5.0\text{ m} + 6.0\text{ m})}{3} = \frac{12.0\text{ m}}{3} = 4.0\text{ m}.$$

The CM is 4.0 m from the left-hand end of the boat.

**NOTE** The coordinates of the CM depend on the reference frame or coordinate system chosen. But the physical location of the CM is independent of that choice.

**EXERCISE G** Calculate the CM of the three people in Example 7–12 taking the origin at the driver $(x_C = 0)$ on the right. Is the physical location of the CM the same?

If the particles are spread out in two or three dimensions, then we must specify not only the $x$ coordinate of the CM $(x_{CM})$, but also the $y$ and $z$ coordinates, which will be given by formulas like Eq. 7–9a. For example, the $y$ coordinate of the CM will be:

$$y_{CM} = \frac{m_A y_A + m_B y_B + \cdots}{m_A + m_B + \cdots} = \frac{m_A y_A + m_B y_B + \cdots}{M}. \quad \textbf{(7–9b)}$$

*y coordinate of CM*

*Center of gravity*

A concept similar to *center of mass* is **center of gravity** (CG). The CG of an object is that point at which the force of gravity can be considered to act. The force of gravity actually acts on *all* the different parts or particles of an object, but for purposes of determining the translational motion of an object as a whole, we can assume that the entire weight of the object (which is the sum of the weights of all its parts) acts at the CG. There is a conceptual difference between the center of gravity and the center of mass, but for nearly all practical purposes, they are at the same point.[†]

It is often easier to determine the CM or CG of an extended object experimentally rather than analytically. If an object is suspended from any point, it will swing (Fig. 7–25) unless it is placed so its CG lies on a vertical line directly below the point from which it is suspended. If the object is two dimensional, or has a plane of symmetry, it need only be hung from two different pivot points and the respective vertical (plumb) lines drawn. Then the center of gravity will be at the intersection

**FIGURE 7–25** The force of gravity, considered to act at the CG, causes this object to rotate about the pivot point; if the CG were on a vertical line directly below the pivot, the object would remain at rest.

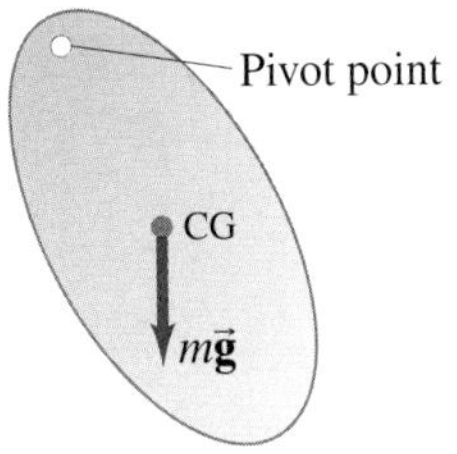


[†]There would be a difference between the CM and CG only in the unusual case of an object so large that the acceleration due to gravity, $g$, was different at different parts of the object.

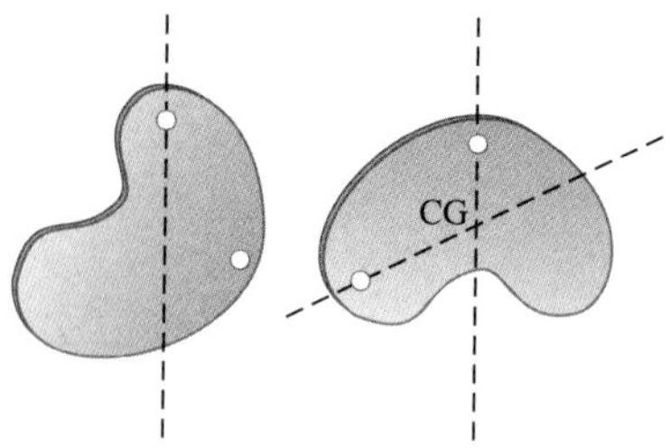


**FIGURE 7–26** Finding the CG.

of the two lines, as in Fig. 7–26. If the object doesn't have a plane of symmetry, the CG with respect to the third dimension is found by suspending the object from at least three points whose plumb lines do not lie in the same plane. For symmetrically shaped objects such as uniform cylinders (wheels), spheres, and rectangular solids, the CM is located at the geometric center of the object.

For some objects, the CM may actually lie outside the object. The CM of a donut, for example, lies at the center of the hole.

## * 7–9 CM for the Human Body

If we have a group of extended objects, each of whose CM is known, we can find the CM of the group using Eqs. 7–9a and b. As an example, we consider the human body. Table 7–1 indicates the CM and hinge points (joints) for the different components of a "representative" person. Of course, there are wide variations among people, so these data represent only a very rough average. The numbers represent a percentage of the total height, which is regarded as 100 units; similarly, the total mass is 100 units. For example, if a person is 1.70 m tall, his or her shoulder joint would be $(1.70\text{ m})(81.2/100) = 1.38\text{ m}$ above the floor.

**TABLE 7–1 Center of Mass of Parts of Typical Human Body**
**(full height and mass = 100 units)**

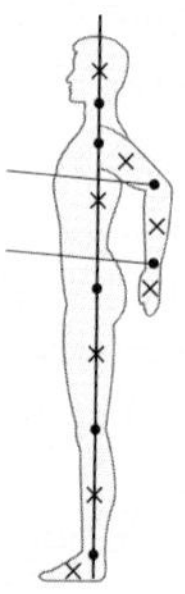

| Distance Above Floor of Hinge Points (%) | Hinge Points (•) (Joints) | Center of Mass (×) (% Height Above Floor) | | Percent Mass |
|---|---|---|---|---|
| 91.2 | Base of skull | Head | 93.5 | 6.9 |
| 81.2 | Shoulder joint | Trunk and neck | 71.1 | 46.1 |
| | elbow 62.2 | Upper arms | 71.7 | 6.6 |
| | wrist 46.2 | Lower arms | 55.3 | 4.2 |
| 52.1 | Hip joint | Hands | 43.1 | 1.7 |
| | | Upper legs (thighs) | 42.5 | 21.5 |
| 28.5 | Knee joint | | | |
| | | Lower legs | 18.2 | 9.6 |
| 4.0 | Ankle joint | Feet | 1.8 | 3.4 |
| | | Body CM = | 58.0 | 100.0 |

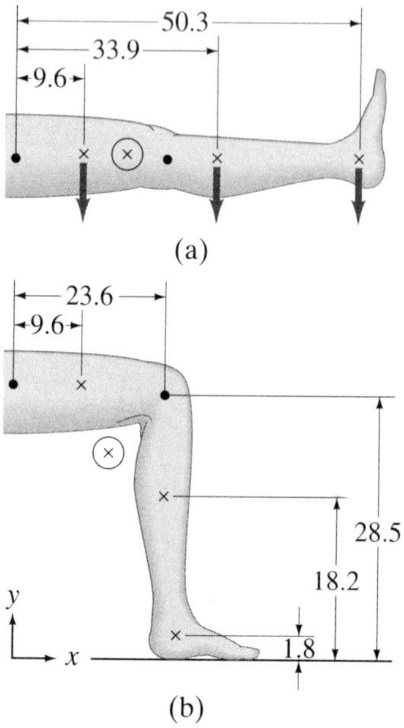


**FIGURE 7–27** Example 7–13: finding the CM of a leg in two different positions using percentages from Table 7–1. (⊗ represents the calculated CM).

**EXAMPLE 7–13** **A leg's CM.** Determine the position of the CM of a whole leg (*a*) when stretched out, and (*b*) when bent at 90°. See Fig. 7–27. Assume the person is 1.70 m tall.

**APPROACH** Our system consists of three objects: upper leg, lower leg, and foot. The location of the CM of each object, as well as the mass of each, is given in Table 7–1, where they are expressed in percentage units. To express the results in meters, these percentage values need to be multiplied by (1.70 m/100). When the leg is stretched out, the problem is one dimensional and we can solve for the $x$ coordinate of the CM. When the leg is bent, the problem is two dimensional and we need to find both the $x$ and $y$ coordinates.

**SOLUTION** (*a*) We determine the distances from the hip joint using Table 7–1 and obtain the numbers (%) shown in Fig. 7–27a. Using Eq. 7–9a, we obtain

$$x_{\text{CM}} = \frac{(21.5)(9.6) + (9.6)(33.9) + (3.4)(50.3)}{21.5 + 9.6 + 3.4} = 20.4\text{ units}.$$

Thus, the center of mass of the leg and foot is 20.4 units from the hip joint, or $52.1 - 20.4 = 31.7\text{ units}$ from the base of the foot. Since the person is 1.70 m tall, this is $(1.70\text{ m})(31.7/100) = 0.54\text{ m}$ above the bottom of the foot.

(*b*) We use an $xy$ coordinate system, as shown in Fig. 7–27b. First, we calculate how far to the right of the hip joint the CM lies, accounting for all three parts:

$$x_{\text{CM}} = \frac{(21.5)(9.6) + (9.6)(23.6) + (3.4)(23.6)}{21.5 + 9.6 + 3.4} = 14.9\text{ units}.$$

For our 1.70-m-tall person, this is $(1.70\,\text{m})(14.9/100) = 0.25\,\text{m}$ from the hip joint. Next, we calculate the distance, $y_{\text{CM}}$, of the CM above the floor:

$$y_{\text{CM}} = \frac{(3.4)(1.8) + (9.6)(18.2) + (21.5)(28.5)}{21.5 + 9.6 + 3.4} = 23.0\ \text{units},$$

or $(1.70\,\text{m})(23.0/100) = 0.39\,\text{m}$. Thus, the CM is located 39 cm above the floor and 25 cm to the right of the hip joint.

**NOTE** The CM actually lies *outside* the body in (*b*).

**FIGURE 7–28** A high jumper's CM may actually pass beneath the bar.

PHYSICS APPLIED
*High jumping*

Knowing the CM of the body when it is in various positions is of great use in studying body mechanics. One simple example from athletics is shown in Fig. 7–28. If high jumpers can get into the position shown, their CM can pass below the bar which their bodies go over, meaning that for a particular takeoff speed, they can clear a higher bar. This is indeed what they try to do.

## * 7–10 Center of Mass and Translational Motion

As mentioned in Section 7–8, a major reason for the importance of the concept of center of mass is that the motion of the CM for a system of particles (or an extended object) is directly related to the net force acting on the system as a whole. We now show this, taking the simple case of one-dimensional motion ($x$ direction) and only three particles, but the extension to more objects and to three dimensions follows the same lines.

Suppose the three particles lie on the $x$ axis and have masses $m_{\text{A}}, m_{\text{B}}, m_{\text{C}}$, and positions $x_{\text{A}}, x_{\text{B}}, x_{\text{C}}$. From Eq. 7–9a for the center of mass, we can write

$$Mx_{\text{CM}} = m_{\text{A}}x_{\text{A}} + m_{\text{B}}x_{\text{B}} + m_{\text{C}}x_{\text{C}}, \qquad \text{(i)}$$

where $M = m_{\text{A}} + m_{\text{B}} + m_{\text{C}}$ is the total mass of the system. If these particles are in motion (say, along the $x$ axis with velocities $v_{\text{A}}, v_{\text{B}}$, and $v_{\text{C}}$, respectively), then in a short time interval $\Delta t$ they each will have traveled a distance

$$\begin{aligned}\Delta x_{\text{A}} &= x'_{\text{A}} - x_{\text{A}} = v_{\text{A}}\,\Delta t\\ \Delta x_{\text{B}} &= x'_{\text{B}} - x_{\text{B}} = v_{\text{B}}\,\Delta t\\ \Delta x_{\text{C}} &= x'_{\text{C}} - x_{\text{C}} = v_{\text{C}}\,\Delta t,\end{aligned}$$

where $x'_{\text{A}}, x'_{\text{B}}$, and $x'_{\text{C}}$ represent their new positions after time interval $\Delta t$. The position of the new CM is given by

$$Mx'_{\text{CM}} = m_{\text{A}}x'_{\text{A}} + m_{\text{B}}x'_{\text{B}} + m_{\text{C}}x'_{\text{C}}. \qquad \text{(ii)}$$

If we subtract from this equation (ii) the previous CM equation (i), we get

$$M\,\Delta x_{\text{CM}} = m_{\text{A}}\,\Delta x_{\text{A}} + m_{\text{B}}\,\Delta x_{\text{B}} + m_{\text{C}}\,\Delta x_{\text{C}}.$$

During time interval $\Delta t$, the center of mass will have moved a distance

$$\Delta x_{\text{CM}} = x'_{\text{CM}} - x_{\text{CM}} = v_{\text{CM}}\,\Delta t,$$

where $v_{\text{CM}}$ is the velocity of the center of mass. We now substitute the relations for all the $\Delta x$'s into the equation just before the last one:

$$Mv_{\text{CM}}\,\Delta t = m_{\text{A}}v_{\text{A}}\,\Delta t + m_{\text{B}}v_{\text{B}}\,\Delta t + m_{\text{C}}v_{\text{C}}\,\Delta t.$$

We cancel $\Delta t$ and get

$$Mv_{\text{CM}} = m_{\text{A}}v_{\text{A}} + m_{\text{B}}v_{\text{B}} + m_{\text{C}}v_{\text{C}}. \qquad \text{(7–10)}$$

Since $m_{\text{A}}v_{\text{A}} + m_{\text{B}}v_{\text{B}} + m_{\text{C}}v_{\text{C}}$ is the sum of the momenta of the particles of the system, it represents the *total momentum* of the system. Thus we see from Eq. 7–10 that *the total (linear) momentum of a system of particles is equal to the product of the total mass M and the velocity of the center of mass of the system.* Or, *the linear momentum of an extended object is the product of the object's mass and the velocity of its CM.*

*Total momentum, and velocity of CM*

If forces are acting on the particles, then the particles may be accelerating. In a short time interval $\Delta t$, each particle's velocity will change by an amount

$$\Delta v_A = a_A\,\Delta t, \qquad \Delta v_B = a_B\,\Delta t, \qquad \Delta v_C = a_C\,\Delta t.$$

If we now use the same reasoning as we did to derive Eq. 7–10, we obtain

$$Ma_{CM} = m_A a_A + m_B a_B + m_C a_C.$$

According to Newton's second law, $m_A a_A = F_A$, $m_B a_B = F_B$, and $m_C a_C = F_C$, where $F_A$, $F_B$, and $F_C$ are the net forces on the three particles, respectively. Thus we get for the system as a whole $Ma_{CM} = F_A + F_B + F_C$, or

*Newton's second law for a system of particles or an extended object*

$$Ma_{CM} = F_{net}. \tag{7–11}$$

That is, *the sum of all the forces acting on the system is equal to the total mass of the system times the acceleration of its center of mass.* This is **Newton's second law** for a system of particles, and it also applies to an extended object (which can be thought of as a collection of particles). Thus we conclude that the *center of mass of a system of particles (or of an extended object) with total mass M moves like a single particle of mass M acted on by the same net external force.* That is, the system moves as if all its mass were concentrated at the center of mass and all the external forces acted at that point. We can thus treat the translational motion of any object or system of objects as the motion of a particle (see Figs. 7–21 and 7–22). This result simplifies our analysis of the motion of complex systems and extended objects. Although the motion of various parts of the system may be complicated, we may often be satisfied with knowing the motion of the center of mass. This result also allows us to solve certain types of problems very easily, as illustrated by the following Example.

**CONCEPTUAL EXAMPLE 7–14** **A two-stage rocket.** A rocket is shot into the air as shown in Fig. 7–29. At the moment the rocket reaches its highest point, a horizontal distance $d$ from its starting point, a prearranged explosion separates it into two parts of equal mass. Part I is stopped in midair by the explosion, and it falls vertically to Earth. Where does part II land? Assume $\vec{\mathbf{g}}$ = constant.

**RESPONSE** After the rocket is fired, the path of the CM of the system continues to follow the parabolic trajectory of a projectile acted on by only a constant gravitational force. The CM will thus land at a point $2d$ from the starting point. Since the masses of I and II are equal, the CM must be midway between them at any time. Therefore, part II lands a distance $3d$ from the starting point.

**NOTE** If part I had been given a kick up or down, instead of merely falling, the solution would have been more complicated.

**EXERCISE H** A woman stands up in a rowboat and walks from one end of the boat to the other. How does the boat move, as seen from the shore?

**FIGURE 7–29** Example 7–14.

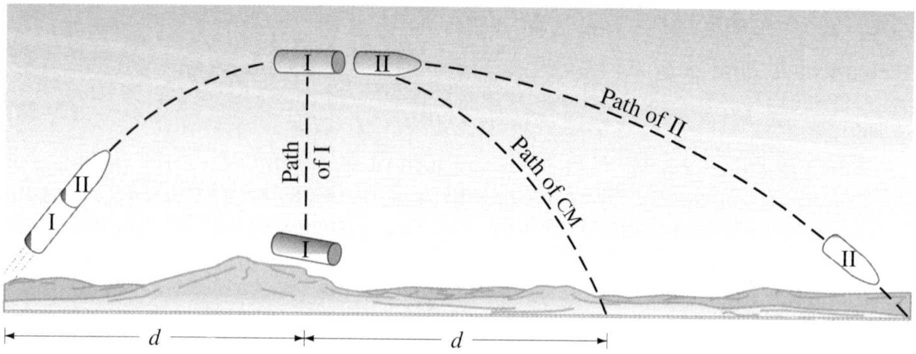

## Summary

The **momentum**, $\vec{\mathbf{p}}$, of an object is defined as the product of its mass times its velocity,

$$\vec{\mathbf{p}} = m\vec{\mathbf{v}}. \tag{7–1}$$

In terms of momentum, **Newton's second law** can be written as

$$\Sigma\vec{\mathbf{F}} = \frac{\Delta\vec{\mathbf{p}}}{\Delta t}. \tag{7–2}$$

That is, the rate of change of momentum equals the net applied force.

The **law of conservation of momentum** states that the total momentum of an isolated system of objects remains constant. An **isolated system** is one on which the net external force is zero.

The law of conservation of momentum is very useful in dealing with **collisions**. In a collision, two (or more) objects interact with each other over a very short time interval, and the forces between them during this time interval are very large.

The **impulse** of a force on an object is defined as $\vec{\mathbf{F}}\,\Delta t$, where $\vec{\mathbf{F}}$ is the average force acting during the (usually short) time interval $\Delta t$. The impulse is equal to the change in momentum of the object:

$$\text{Impulse} = \vec{\mathbf{F}}\,\Delta t = \Delta\vec{\mathbf{p}}. \tag{7–5}$$

Total momentum is conserved in *any* collision as long as any net external force is zero or negligible. If $m_{\mathrm{A}}\vec{\mathbf{v}}_{\mathrm{A}}$ and $m_{\mathrm{B}}\vec{\mathbf{v}}_{\mathrm{B}}$ are the momenta of two objects before the collision and $m_{\mathrm{A}}\vec{\mathbf{v}}_{\mathrm{A}}'$ and $m_{\mathrm{B}}\vec{\mathbf{v}}_{\mathrm{B}}'$ are their momenta after, then momentum conservation tell us that

$$m_{\mathrm{A}}\vec{\mathbf{v}}_{\mathrm{A}} + m_{\mathrm{B}}\vec{\mathbf{v}}_{\mathrm{B}} = m_{\mathrm{A}}\vec{\mathbf{v}}_{\mathrm{A}}' + m_{\mathrm{B}}\vec{\mathbf{v}}_{\mathrm{B}}' \tag{7–3}$$

for this two-object system.

Total energy is also conserved, but this may not be helpful in problem solving unless the only type of energy transformation involves kinetic energy. In that case kinetic energy is conserved and the collision is called an **elastic collision**, and we can write

$$\tfrac{1}{2}m_{\mathrm{A}}v_{\mathrm{A}}^2 + \tfrac{1}{2}m_{\mathrm{B}}v_{\mathrm{B}}^2 = \tfrac{1}{2}m_{\mathrm{A}}v_{\mathrm{A}}'^2 + \tfrac{1}{2}m_{\mathrm{B}}v_{\mathrm{B}}'^2. \tag{7–6}$$

If kinetic energy is not conserved, the collision is called **inelastic**. A **completely inelastic** collision is one in which the colliding objects stick together after the collision.

The **center of mass** (CM) of an extended object (or group of objects) is that point at which the net force can be considered to act, for purposes of determining the translational motion of the object as a whole. The $x$ component of the CM for objects with mass $m_{\mathrm{A}}, m_{\mathrm{B}}, \ldots$, is given by

$$x_{\mathrm{CM}} = \frac{m_{\mathrm{A}}x_{\mathrm{A}} + m_{\mathrm{B}}x_{\mathrm{B}} + \cdots}{m_{\mathrm{A}} + m_{\mathrm{B}} + \cdots}. \tag{7–9a}$$

[*The complete motion of an object can be described as the translational motion of its center of mass plus rotation (or other internal motion) about its center of mass.]

## Questions

1. We claim that momentum is conserved, yet most moving objects eventually slow down and stop. Explain.
2. When a person jumps from a tree to the ground, what happens to the momentum of the person upon striking the ground?
3. When you release an inflated but untied balloon, why does it fly across the room?
4. It is said that in ancient times a rich man with a bag of gold coins froze to death while stranded on a frozen lake. Because the ice was frictionless, he could not push himself to shore. What could he have done to save himself had he not been so miserly?
5. How can a rocket change direction when it is far out in space and is essentially in a vacuum?
6. According to Eq. 7–5, the longer the impact time of an impulse, the smaller the force can be for the same momentum change, and hence the smaller the deformation of the object on which the force acts. On this basis, explain the value of air bags, which are intended to inflate during an automobile collision and reduce the possibility of fracture or death.
7. Cars used to be built as rigid as possible to withstand collisions. Today, though, cars are designed to have "crumple zones" that collapse upon impact. What is the advantage of this new design?
8. Why can a batter hit a pitched baseball further than a ball tossed in the air by the batter?
9. Is it possible for an object to receive a larger impulse from a small force than from a large force? Explain.
10. A light object and a heavy object have the same kinetic energy. Which has the greater momentum? Explain.
11. Describe a collision in which all kinetic energy is lost.
12. At a hydroelectric power plant, water is directed at high speed against turbine blades on an axle that turns an electric generator. For maximum power generation, should the turbine blades be designed so that the water is brought to a dead stop, or so that the water rebounds?
13. A squash ball hits a wall at a 45° angle as shown in Fig. 7–30. What is the direction (*a*) of the change in momentum of the ball, (*b*) of the force on the wall?

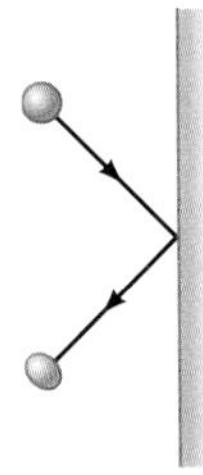

**FIGURE 7–30** Question 13.

14. A Superball is dropped from a height $h$ onto a hard steel plate (fixed to the Earth), from which it rebounds at very nearly its original speed. (*a*) Is the momentum of the ball conserved during any part of this process? (*b*) If we consider the ball and Earth as our system, during what parts of the process is momentum conserved? (*c*) Answer part (*b*) for a piece of putty that falls and sticks to the steel plate.
15. Why do you tend to lean backward when carrying a heavy load in your arms?
16. Why is the CM of a 1-m length of pipe at its mid-point, whereas this is not true for your arm or leg?

* 17. Show on a diagram how your CM shifts when you change from a lying position to a sitting position.

* 18. If only an external force can change the momentum of the center of mass of an object, how can the internal force of an engine accelerate a car?

* 19. A rocket following a parabolic path through the air suddenly explodes into many pieces. What can you say about the motion of this system of pieces?

## Problems

### 7–1 and 7–2 Momentum and Its Conservation

1. (I) What is the magnitude of the momentum of a 28-g sparrow flying with a speed of 8.4 m/s?
2. (I) A constant friction force of 25 N acts on a 65-kg skier for 20 s. What is the skier's change in velocity?
3. (II) A 0.145-kg baseball pitched at 39.0 m/s is hit on a horizontal line drive straight back toward the pitcher at 52.0 m/s. If the contact time between bat and ball is $3.00 \times 10^{-3}$ s, calculate the average force between the ball and bat during contact.
4. (II) A child in a boat throws a 6.40-kg package out horizontally with a speed of 10.0 m/s, Fig. 7–31. Calculate the velocity of the boat immediately after, assuming it was initially at rest. The mass of the child is 26.0 kg, and that of the boat is 45.0 kg. Ignore water resistance.

**FIGURE 7–31** Problem 4.

5. (II) Calculate the force exerted on a rocket, given that the propelling gases are expelled at a rate of 1500 kg/s with a speed of $4.0 \times 10^4$ m/s (at the moment of takeoff).
6. (II) A 95-kg halfback moving at 4.1 m/s on an apparent breakaway for a touchdown is tackled from behind. When he was tackled by an 85-kg cornerback running at 5.5 m/s in the same direction, what was their mutual speed immediately after the tackle?
7. (II) A 12,600-kg railroad car travels alone on a level frictionless track with a constant speed of 18.0 m/s. A 5350-kg load, initially at rest, is dropped onto the car. What will be the car's new speed?
8. (II) A 9300-kg boxcar traveling at 15.0 m/s strikes a second boxcar at rest. The two stick together and move off with a speed of 6.0 m/s. What is the mass of the second car?
9. (II) During a Chicago storm, winds can whip horizontally at speeds of 100 km/h. If the air strikes a person at the rate of 40 kg/s per square meter and is brought to rest, estimate the force of the wind on a person. Assume the person is 1.50 m high and 0.50 m wide. Compare to the typical maximum force of friction ($\mu \approx 1.0$) between the person and the ground, if the person has a mass of 70 kg.
10. (II) A 3800-kg open railroad car coasts along with a constant speed of 8.60 m/s on a level track. Snow begins to fall vertically and fills the car at a rate of 3.50 kg/min. Ignoring friction with the tracks, what is the speed of the car after 90.0 min?
11. (II) An atomic nucleus initially moving at 420 m/s emits an alpha particle in the direction of its velocity, and the remaining nucleus slows to 350 m/s. If the alpha particle has a mass of 4.0 u and the original nucleus has a mass of 222 u, what speed does the alpha particle have when it is emitted?
12. (II) A 23-g bullet traveling 230 m/s penetrates a 2.0-kg block of wood and emerges cleanly at 170 m/s. If the block is stationary on a frictionless surface when hit, how fast does it move after the bullet emerges?
13. (III) A 975-kg two-stage rocket is traveling at a speed of $5.80 \times 10^3$ m/s with respect to Earth when a pre-designed explosion separates the rocket into two sections of equal mass that then move at a speed of $2.20 \times 10^3$ m/s relative to each other along the original line of motion. (*a*) What are the speed and direction of each section (relative to Earth) after the explosion? (*b*) How much energy was supplied by the explosion? [*Hint*: What is the change in KE as a result of the explosion?]
14. (III) A rocket of total mass 3180 kg is traveling in outer space with a velocity of 115 m/s. To alter its course by 35.0°, its rockets can be fired briefly in a direction perpendicular to its original motion. If the rocket gases are expelled at a speed of 1750 m/s, how much mass must be expelled?

### 7–3 Collisions and Impulse

15. (II) A golf ball of mass 0.045 kg is hit off the tee at a speed of 45 m/s. The golf club was in contact with the ball for $3.5 \times 10^{-3}$ s. Find (*a*) the impulse imparted to the golf ball, and (*b*) the average force exerted on the ball by the golf club.
16. (II) A 12-kg hammer strikes a nail at a velocity of 8.5 m/s and comes to rest in a time interval of 8.0 ms. (*a*) What is the impulse given to the nail? (*b*) What is the average force acting on the nail?
17. (II) A tennis ball of mass $m = 0.060$ kg and speed $v = 25$ m/s strikes a wall at a 45° angle and rebounds with the same speed at 45° (Fig. 7–32). What is the impulse (magnitude and direction) given to the ball?

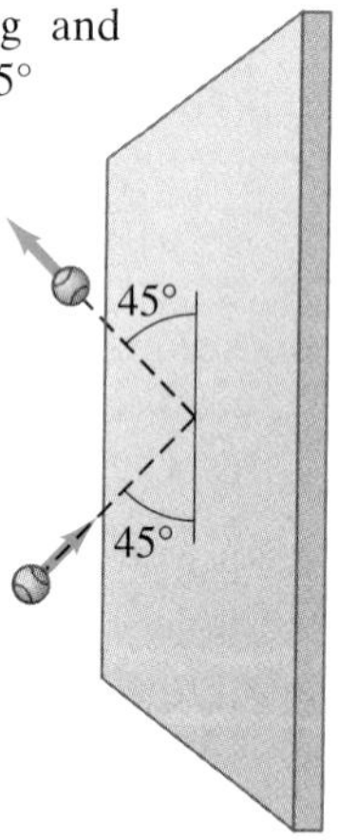


**FIGURE 7–32** Problem 17.

18. (II) You are the design engineer in charge of the crashworthiness of new automobile models. Cars are tested by smashing them into fixed, massive barriers at 50 km/h (30 mph). A new model of mass 1500 kg takes 0.15 s from the time of impact until it is brought to rest. (*a*) Calculate the average force exerted on the car by the barrier. (*b*) Calculate the average deceleration of the car.

19. (II) A 95-kg fullback is running at 4.0 m/s to the east and is stopped in 0.75 s by a head-on tackle by a tackler running due west. Calculate (*a*) the original momentum of the fullback, (*b*) the impulse exerted on the fullback, (*c*) the impulse exerted on the tackler, and (*d*) the average force exerted on the tackler.

20. (II) Suppose the force acting on a tennis ball (mass 0.060 kg) points in the $+x$ direction and is given by the graph of Fig. 7–33 as a function of time. Use graphical methods to estimate (*a*) the total impulse given the ball, and (*b*) the velocity of the ball after being struck, assuming the ball is being served so it is nearly at rest initially.

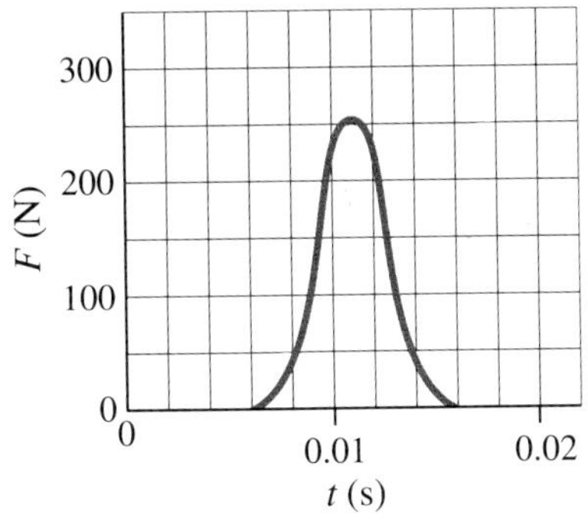


**FIGURE 7–33** Problem 20.

21. (III) From what maximum height can a 75-kg person jump without breaking the lower leg bone of either leg? Ignore air resistance and assume the CM of the person moves a distance of 0.60 m from the standing to the seated position (that is, in breaking the fall). Assume the breaking strength (force per unit area) of bone is $170 \times 10^6\ \mathrm{N/m^2}$, and its smallest cross-sectional area is $2.5 \times 10^{-4}\ \mathrm{m^2}$. [*Hint*: Do not try this experimentally.]

## 7–4 and 7–5 Elastic Collisions

22. (II) A ball of mass 0.440 kg moving east ($+x$ direction) with a speed of 3.30 m/s collides head-on with a 0.220-kg ball at rest. If the collision is perfectly elastic, what will be the speed and direction of each ball after the collision?

23. (II) A 0.450-kg ice puck, moving east with a speed of 3.00 m/s, has a head-on collision with a 0.900-kg puck initially at rest. Assuming a perfectly elastic collision, what will be the speed and direction of each object after the collision?

24. (II) Two billiard balls of equal mass undergo a perfectly elastic head-on collision. If one ball's initial speed was 2.00 m/s, and the other's was 3.00 m/s in the opposite direction, what will be their speeds after the collision?

25. (II) A 0.060-kg tennis ball, moving with a speed of 2.50 m/s, collides head-on with a 0.090-kg ball initially moving away from it at a speed of 1.15 m/s. Assuming a perfectly elastic collision, what are the speed and direction of each ball after the collision?

26. (II) A softball of mass 0.220 kg that is moving with a speed of 8.5 m/s collides head-on and elastically with another ball initially at rest. Afterward the incoming softball bounces backward with a speed of 3.7 m/s. Calculate (*a*) the velocity of the target ball after the collision, and (*b*) the mass of the target ball.

27. (II) Two bumper cars in an amusement park ride collide elastically as one approaches the other directly from the rear (Fig. 7–34). Car A has a mass of 450 kg and car B 550 kg, owing to differences in passenger mass. If car A approaches at 4.50 m/s and car B is moving at 3.70 m/s, calculate (*a*) their velocities after the collision, and (*b*) the change in momentum of each.

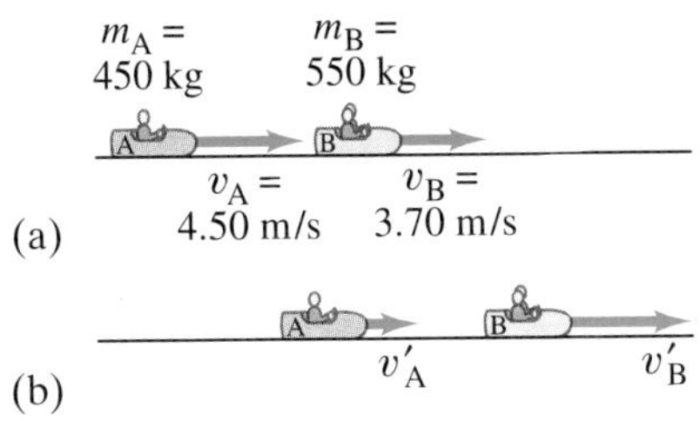


**FIGURE 7–34** Problem 27: (a) before collision, (b) after collision.

28. (II) A 0.280-kg croquet ball makes an elastic head-on collision with a second ball initially at rest. The second ball moves off with half the original speed of the first ball. (*a*) What is the mass of the second ball? (*b*) What fraction of the original kinetic energy ($\Delta\mathrm{KE}/\mathrm{KE}$) gets transferred to the second ball?

29. (III) In a physics lab, a cube slides down a frictionless incline as shown in Fig. 7–35, and elastically strikes another cube at the bottom that is only one-half its mass. If the incline is 30 cm high and the table is 90 cm off the floor, where does each cube land? [*Hint*: Both leave the incline moving horizontally.]

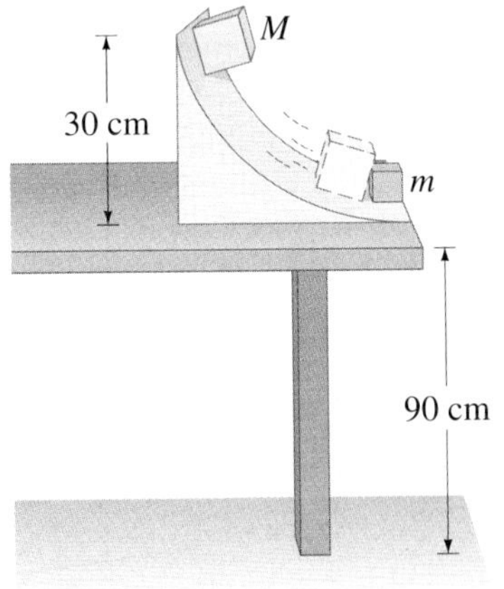


**FIGURE 7–35** Problem 29.

30. (III) Take the general case of an object of mass $m_A$ and velocity $v_A$ elastically striking a stationary ($v_B = 0$) object of mass $m_B$ head-on. (*a*) Show that the final velocities $v'_A$ and $v'_B$ are given by

$$v'_A = \left(\frac{m_A - m_B}{m_A + m_B}\right) v_A,$$

$$v'_B = \left(\frac{2m_A}{m_A + m_B}\right) v_A.$$

(*b*) What happens in the extreme case when $m_A$ is much smaller than $m_B$? Cite a common example of this. (*c*) What happens in the extreme case when $m_A$ is much larger than $m_B$? Cite a common example of this. (*d*) What happens in the case when $m_A = m_B$? Cite a common example.

## 7–6 Inelastic Collisions

31. (I) In a ballistic pendulum experiment, projectile 1 results in a maximum height $h$ of the pendulum equal to 2.6 cm. A second projectile causes the the pendulum to swing twice as high, $h_2 = 5.2$ cm. The second projectile was how many times faster than the first?

32. (II) A 28-g rifle bullet traveling 230 m/s buries itself in a 3.6-kg pendulum hanging on a 2.8-m-long string, which makes the pendulum swing upward in an arc. Determine the vertical and horizontal components of the pendulum's displacement.

33. (II) (*a*) Derive a formula for the fraction of kinetic energy lost, $\Delta\text{KE}/\text{KE}$, for the ballistic pendulum collision of Example 7–10. (*b*) Evaluate for $m = 14.0\text{ g}$ and $M = 380\text{ g}$.

34. (II) An internal explosion breaks an object, initially at rest, into two pieces, one of which has 1.5 times the mass of the other. If 7500 J were released in the explosion, how much kinetic energy did each piece acquire?

35. (II) A 920-kg sports car collides into the rear end of a 2300-kg SUV stopped at a red light. The bumpers lock, the brakes are locked, and the two cars skid forward 2.8 m before stopping. The police officer, knowing that the coefficient of kinetic friction between tires and road is 0.80, calculates the speed of the sports car at impact. What was that speed?

36. (II) A ball is dropped from a height of 1.50 m and rebounds to a height of 1.20 m. Approximately how many rebounds will the ball make before losing 90% of its energy?

37. (II) A measure of inelasticity in a head-on collision of two objects is the *coefficient of restitution*, *e*, defined as

$$e = \frac{v'_A - v'_B}{v_B - v_A},$$

where $v'_A - v'_B$ is the relative velocity of the two objects after the collision and $v_B - v_A$ is their relative velocity before it. (*a*) Show that $e = 1$ for a perfectly elastic collision, and $e = 0$ for a completely inelastic collision. (*b*) A simple method for measuring the coefficient of restitution for an object colliding with a very hard surface like steel is to drop the object onto a heavy steel plate, as shown in Fig. 7–36. Determine a formula for *e* in terms of the original height *h* and the maximum height *h'* reached after one collision.

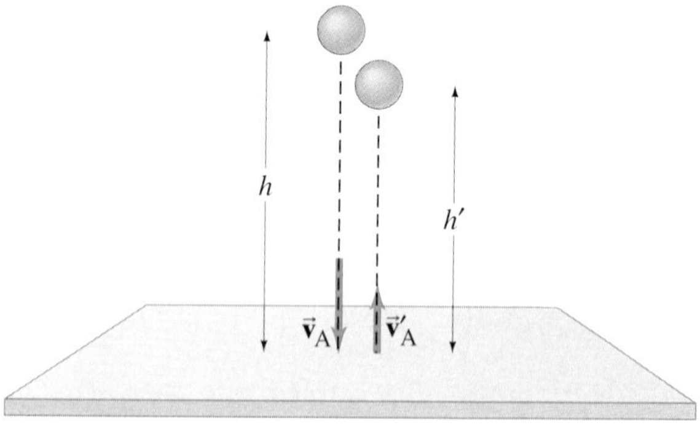


**FIGURE 7–36** Problem 37. Measurement of the coefficient of restitution.

38. (II) A wooden block is cut into two pieces, one with three times the mass of the other. A depression is made in both faces of the cut, so that a firecracker can be placed in it with the block reassembled. The reassembled block is set on a rough-surfaced table, and the fuse is lit. When the firecracker explodes, the two blocks separate and slide apart. What is the ratio of distances each block travels?

39. (III) A 15.0-kg object moving in the $+x$ direction at 5.5 m/s collides head-on with a 10.0-kg object moving in the $-x$ direction at 4.0 m/s. Find the final velocity of each mass if: (*a*) the objects stick together; (*b*) the collision is elastic; (*c*) the 15.0-kg object is at rest after the collision; (*d*) the 10.0-kg object is at rest after the collision; (*e*) the 15.0-kg object has a velocity of 4.0 m/s in the $-x$ direction after the collision. Are the results in (*c*), (*d*), and (*e*) "reasonable"? Explain.

## * 7–7 Collisions in Two Dimensions

* 40. (II) A radioactive nucleus at rest decays into a second nucleus, an electron, and a neutrino. The electron and neutrino are emitted at right angles and have momenta of $9.30 \times 10^{-23}\text{ kg}\cdot\text{m/s}$ and $5.40 \times 10^{-23}\text{ kg}\cdot\text{m/s}$, respectively. What are the magnitude and direction of the momentum of the second (recoiling) nucleus?

* 41. (II) An eagle $(m_A = 4.3\text{ kg})$ moving with speed $v_A = 7.8\text{ m/s}$ is on a collision course with a second eagle $(m_B = 5.6\text{ kg})$ moving at $v_B = 10.2\text{ m/s}$ in a direction perpendicular to the first. After they collide, they hold onto one another. In what direction, and with what speed, are they moving after the collision?

* 42. (II) Billiard ball A of mass $m_A = 0.400\text{ kg}$ moving with speed $v_A = 1.80\text{ m/s}$ strikes ball B, initially at rest, of mass $m_B = 0.500\text{ kg}$. As a result of the collision, ball A is deflected off at an angle of 30.0° with a speed $v'_A = 1.10\text{ m/s}$. (*a*) Taking the *x* axis to be the original direction of motion of ball A, write down the equations expressing the conservation of momentum for the components in the *x* and *y* directions separately. (*b*) Solve these equations for the speed $v'_B$ and angle $\theta'_B$ of ball B. Do not assume the collision is elastic.

* 43. (III) After a completely inelastic collision between two objects of equal mass, each having initial speed *v*, the two move off together with speed $v/3$. What was the angle between their initial directions?

* 44. (III) Two billiard balls of equal mass move at right angles and meet at the origin of an *xy* coordinate system. Ball A is moving upward along the *y* axis at 2.0 m/s, and ball B is moving to the right along the *x* axis with speed 3.7 m/s. After the collision, assumed elastic, ball B is moving along the positive *y* axis (Fig. 7–37). What is the final direction of ball A and what are their two speeds?

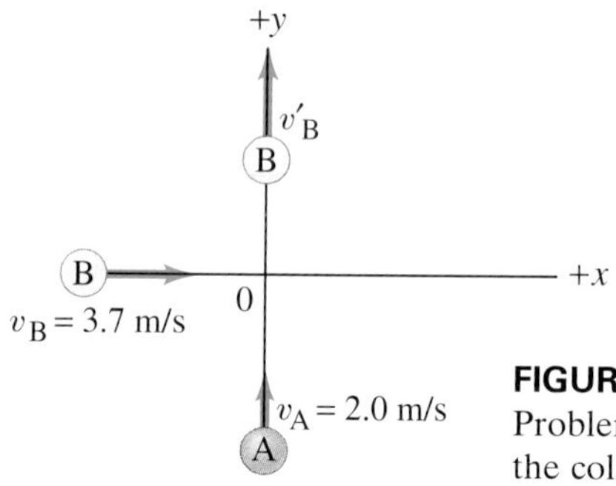


**FIGURE 7–37** Problem 44. (Ball A after the collision is not shown.)

* 45. (III) A neon atom $(m = 20.0\text{ u})$ makes a perfectly elastic collision with another atom at rest. After the impact, the neon atom travels away at a 55.6° angle from its original direction and the unknown atom travels away at a $-50.0°$ angle. What is the mass (in u) of the unknown atom? [*Hint*: You can use the law of sines.]

## 7–8 Center of Mass

46. (I) Find the center of mass of the three-mass system shown in Fig. 7–38. Specify relative to the left-hand 1.00-kg mass.

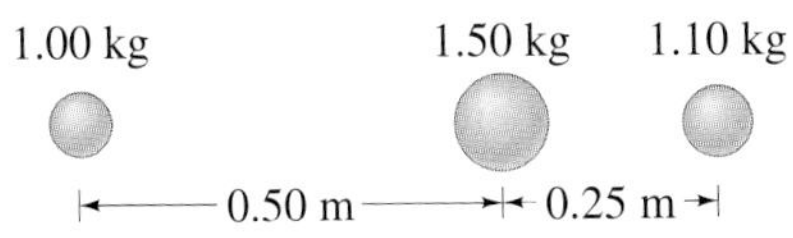


**FIGURE 7–38** Problem 46.

47. (I) The distance between a carbon atom $(m_C = 12\,u)$ and an oxygen atom $(m_O = 16\,u)$ in the CO molecule is $1.13 \times 10^{-10}$ m. How far from the carbon atom is the center of mass of the molecule?

48. (I) The CM of an empty 1050-kg car is 2.50 m behind the front of the car. How far from the front of the car will the CM be when two people sit in the front seat 2.80 m from the front of the car, and three people sit in the back seat 3.90 m from the front? Assume that each person has a mass of 70.0 kg.

49. (II) A square uniform raft, 18 m by 18 m, of mass 6800 kg, is used as a ferryboat. If three cars, each of mass 1200 kg, occupy its NE, SE, and SW corners, determine the CM of the loaded ferryboat.

50. (II) Three cubes, of sides $l_0$, $2l_0$, and $3l_0$, are placed next to one another (in contact) with their centers along a straight line and the $l = 2l_0$ cube in the center (Fig. 7–39). What is the position, along this line, of the CM of this system? Assume the cubes are made of the same uniform material.

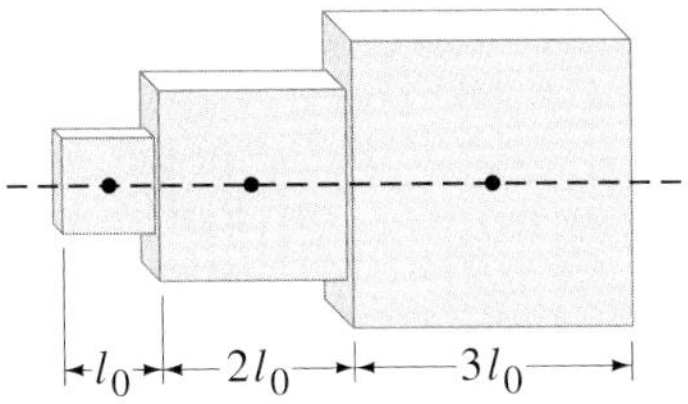


**FIGURE 7–39** Problem 50.

51. (II) A (lightweight) pallet has a load of identical cases of tomato paste (see Fig. 7–40), each of which is a cube of length $l$. Find the center of gravity in the horizontal plane, so that the crane operator can pick up the load without tipping it.

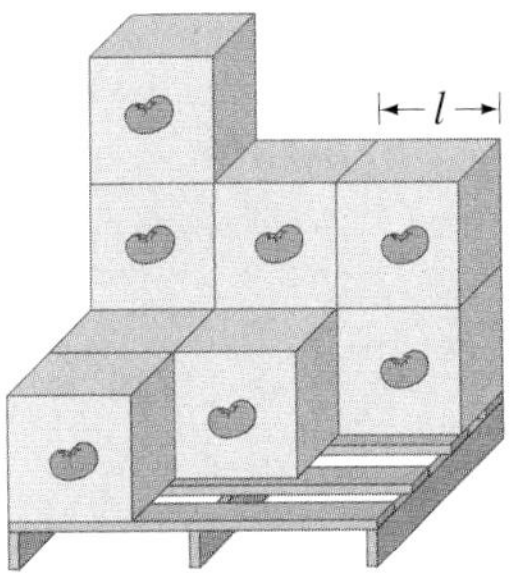


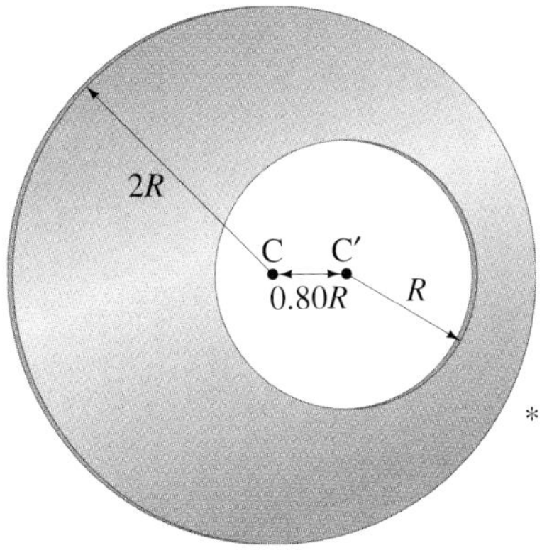


**FIGURE 7–40** Problem 51. **FIGURE 7–41** Problem 52.

52. (III) A uniform circular plate of radius $2R$ has a circular hole of radius $R$ cut out of it. The center C′ of the smaller circle is a distance $0.80R$ from the center C of the larger circle, Fig. 7–41. What is the position of the center of mass of the plate? [*Hint*: Try subtraction.]

## * 7–9 CM for the Human Body

* 53. (I) Assume that your proportions are the same as those in Table 7–1, and calculate the mass of one of your legs.

* 54. (I) Determine the CM of an outstretched arm using Table 7–1.

* 55. (II) Use Table 7–1 to calculate the position of the CM of an arm bent at a right angle. Assume that the person is 155 cm tall.

* 56. (II) When a high jumper is in a position such that his arms and legs are hanging vertically, and his trunk and head are horizontal, calculate how far below the torso's median line the CM will be. Will this CM be outside the body? Use Table 7–1.

## * 7–10 CM and Translational Motion

* 57. (II) The masses of the Earth and Moon are $5.98 \times 10^{24}$ kg and $7.35 \times 10^{22}$ kg, respectively, and their centers are separated by $3.84 \times 10^{8}$ m. (*a*) Where is the CM of this system located? (*b*) What can you say about the motion of the Earth–Moon system about the Sun, and of the Earth and Moon separately about the Sun?

* 58. (II) A 55-kg woman and an 80-kg man stand 10.0 m apart on frictionless ice. (*a*) How far from the woman is their CM? (*b*) If each holds one end of a rope, and the man pulls on the rope so that he moves 2.5 m, how far from the woman will he be now? (*c*) How far will the man have moved when he collides with the woman?

* 59. (II) A mallet consists of a uniform cylindrical head of mass 2.00 kg and a diameter 0.0800 m mounted on a uniform cylindrical handle of mass 0.500 kg and length 0.240 m, as shown in Fig. 7–42. If this mallet is tossed, spinning, into the air, how far above the bottom of the handle is the point that will follow a parabolic trajectory?

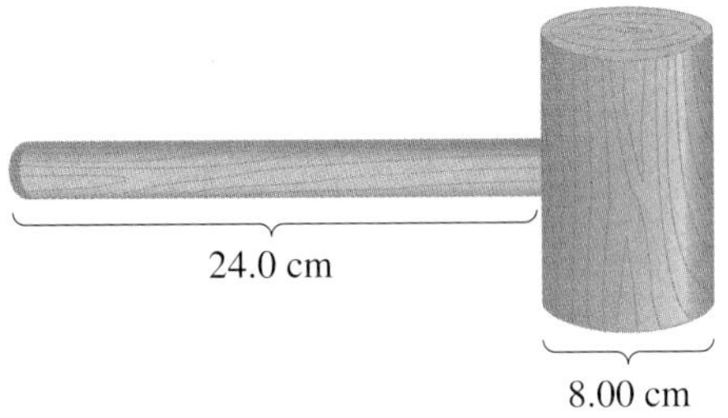


**FIGURE 7–42** Problem 59.

* 60. (II) (*a*) Suppose that in Example 7–14 (Fig. 7–29), $m_{II} = 3m_I$. Where then would $m_{II}$ land? (*b*) What if $m_I = 3m_{II}$?

* 61. (III) A helium balloon and its gondola, of mass $M$, are in the air and stationary with respect to the ground. A passenger, of mass $m$, then climbs out and slides down a rope with speed $v$, measured with respect to the balloon. With what speed and direction (relative to Earth) does the balloon then move? What happens if the passenger stops?

## General Problems

62\. A 0.145-kg baseball pitched horizontally at 35.0 m/s strikes a bat and is popped straight up to a height of 55.6 m. If the contact time is 1.4 ms, calculate the average force on the ball during the contact.

63\. A rocket of mass $m$ traveling with speed $v_0$ along the $x$ axis suddenly shoots out fuel, equal to one-third of its mass, parallel to the $y$ axis (perpendicular to the rocket as seen from the ground) with speed $2v_0$. Give the components of the final velocity of the rocket.

* 64. A novice pool player is faced with the corner pocket shot shown in Fig. 7–43. Relative dimensions are also shown. Should the player be worried about this being a "scratch shot," in which the cue ball will also fall into a pocket? Give details.

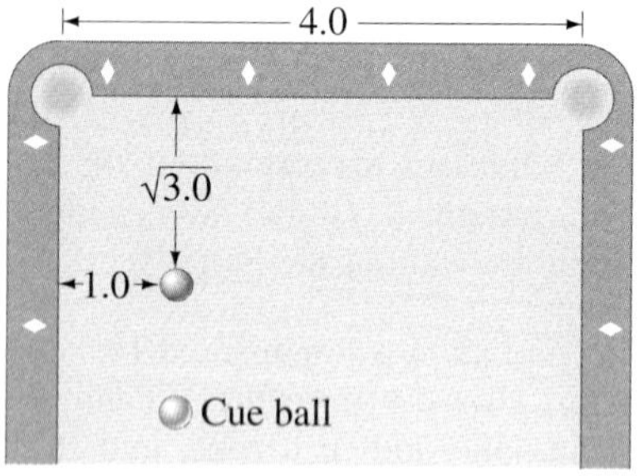


**FIGURE 7–43** Problem 64.

65\. A 140-kg astronaut (including space suit) acquires a speed of 2.50 m/s by pushing off with his legs from an 1800-kg space capsule. (*a*) What is the change in speed of the space capsule? (*b*) If the push lasts 0.40 s, what is the average force exerted on the astronaut by the space capsule? As the reference frame, use the position of the space capsule before the push.

66\. Two astronauts, one of mass 60 kg and the other 80 kg, are initially at rest in outer space. They then push each other apart. How far apart are they when the lighter astronaut has moved 12 m?

67\. A ball of mass $m$ makes a head-on elastic collision with a second ball (at rest) and rebounds in the opposite direction with a speed equal to one-fourth its original speed. What is the mass of the second ball?

68\. You have been hired as an expert witness in a court case involving an automobile accident. The accident involved car A of mass 1900 kg which crashed into stationary car B of mass 1100 kg. The driver of car A applied his brakes 15 m before he crashed into car B. After the collision, car A slid 18 m while car B slid 30 m. The coefficient of kinetic friction between the locked wheels and the road was measured to be 0.60. Show that the driver of car A was exceeding the 55-mph (90 km/h) speed limit before applying the brakes.

69\. A golf ball rolls off the top of a flight of concrete steps of total vertical height 4.00 m. The ball hits four times on the way down, each time striking the horizontal part of a different step 1.0 m lower. If all collisions are perfectly elastic, what is the bounce height on the fourth bounce when the ball reaches the bottom of the stairs?

70\. A bullet is fired vertically into a 1.40-kg block of wood at rest directly above it. If the bullet has a mass of 29.0 g and a speed of 510 m/s, how high will the block rise after the bullet becomes embedded in it?

71\. A 25-g bullet strikes and becomes embedded in a 1.35-kg block of wood placed on a horizontal surface just in front of the gun. If the coefficient of kinetic friction between the block and the surface is 0.25, and the impact drives the block a distance of 9.5 m before it comes to rest, what was the muzzle speed of the bullet?

72\. Two people, one of mass 75 kg and the other of mass 60 kg, sit in a rowboat of mass 80 kg. With the boat initially at rest, the two people, who have been sitting at opposite ends of the boat 3.2 m apart from each other, now exchange seats. How far and in what direction will the boat move?

73\. A meteor whose mass was about $1.0 \times 10^8$ kg struck the Earth $\left(m_E = 6.0 \times 10^{24}\,\text{kg}\right)$ with a speed of about 15 km/s and came to rest in the Earth. (*a*) What was the Earth's recoil speed? (*b*) What fraction of the meteor's kinetic energy was transformed to kinetic energy of the Earth? (*c*) By how much did the Earth's kinetic energy change as a result of this collision?

74\. An object at rest is suddenly broken apart into two fragments by an explosion. One fragment acquires twice the kinetic energy of the other. What is the ratio of their masses?

75\. The force on a bullet is given by the formula $F = 580 - \left(1.8 \times 10^5\right)t$ over the time interval $t = 0$ to $t = 3.0 \times 10^{-3}$ s. In this formula, $t$ is in seconds and $F$ is in newtons. (*a*) Plot a graph of $F$ vs. $t$ for $t = 0$ to $t = 3.0$ ms. (*b*) Estimate, using graphical methods, the impulse given the bullet. (*c*) If the bullet achieves a speed of 220 m/s as a result of this impulse, given to it in the barrel of a gun, what must its mass be?

76\. Two balls, of masses $m_A = 40$ g and $m_B = 60$ g, are suspended as shown in Fig. 7–44. The lighter ball is pulled away to a 60° angle with the vertical and released. (*a*) What is the velocity of the lighter ball before impact? (*b*) What is the velocity of each ball after the elastic collision? (*c*) What will be the maximum height of each ball after the elastic collision?

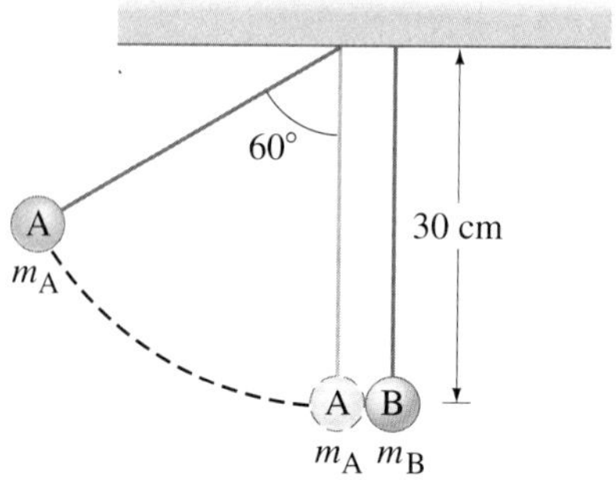


**FIGURE 7–44** Problem 76.

77\. An atomic nucleus at rest decays radioactively into an alpha particle and a smaller nucleus. What will be the speed of this recoiling nucleus if the speed of the alpha particle is $3.8 \times 10^5$ m/s? Assume the recoiling nucleus has a mass 57 times greater than that of the alpha particle.

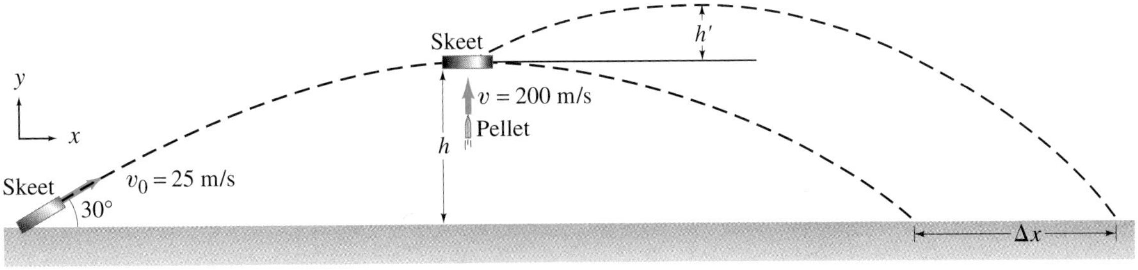


**FIGURE 7–45** Problem 78.

78. A 0.25-kg skeet (clay target) is fired at an angle of 30° to the horizon with a speed of 25 m/s (Fig. 7–45). When it reaches the maximum height, it is hit from below by a 15-g pellet traveling vertically upward at a speed of 200 m/s. The pellet is embedded in the skeet. (*a*) How much higher did the skeet go up? (*b*) How much extra distance, $\Delta x$, does the skeet travel because of the collision?

79. A block of mass $m = 2.20$ kg slides down a 30.0° incline which is 3.60 m high. At the bottom, it strikes a block of mass $M = 7.00$ kg which is at rest on a horizontal surface, Fig. 7–46. (Assume a smooth transition at the bottom of the incline.) If the collision is elastic, and friction can be ignored, determine (*a*) the speeds of the two blocks after the collision, and (*b*) how far back up the incline the smaller mass will go.

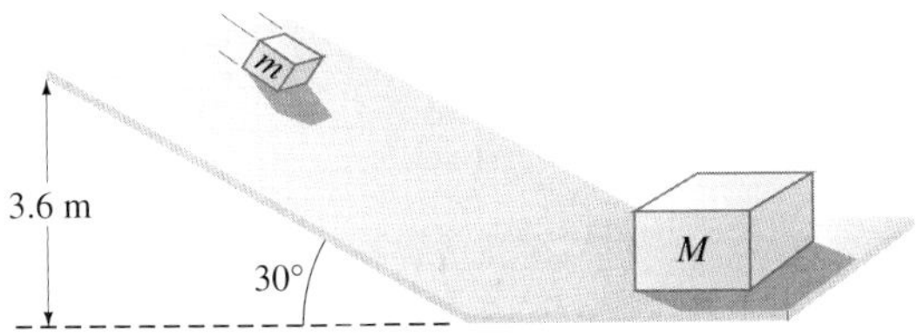


**FIGURE 7–46** Problems 79 and 80.

80. In Problem 79 (Fig. 7–46), what is the upper limit on mass $m$ if it is to rebound from $M$, slide up the incline, stop, slide down the incline, and collide with $M$ again?

81. *The gravitational slingshot effect.* Figure 7–47 shows the planet Saturn moving in the negative $x$ direction at its orbital speed (with respect to the Sun) of 9.6 km/s. The mass of Saturn is $5.69 \times 10^{26}$ kg. A spacecraft with mass 825 kg approaches Saturn. When far from Saturn, it moves in the $+x$ direction at 10.4 km/s. The gravitational attraction of Saturn (a conservative force) acting on the spacecraft causes it to swing around the planet (orbit shown as dashed line) and head off in the opposite direction. Estimate the final speed of the spacecraft after it is far enough away to be considered free of Saturn's gravitational pull.

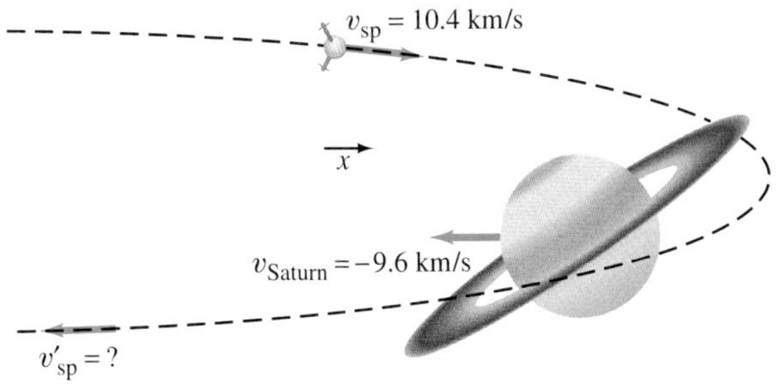


**FIGURE 7–47** Problem 81.

## Answers to Exercises

**A:** Yes, if the sports car's speed is three times greater.
**B:** Larger.
**C:** (*a*) 6.0 m/s; (*b*) almost zero; (*c*) almost 24.0 m/s.
**D:** The curve would be wider and less high.
**E:** Yes, by 300 times.
**F:** Yes, KE was conserved.
**G:** $x_{CM} = -2.0$ m; yes.
**H:** The boat moves in the opposite direction.

You too can experience rapid rotation—if your stomach can take the high angular velocity and centripetal acceleration of some of the faster amusement park rides. If not, try the slower merry-go-round or Ferris wheel. Rotating carnival rides have rotational KE as well as angular momentum.

CHAPTER 8

# Rotational Motion

Until now, we have been concerned mainly with translational motion. We discussed the kinematics and dynamics of translational motion (the role of force), and the energy and momentum associated with it. In this Chapter we will deal with rotational motion. We will discuss the kinematics of rotational motion and then its dynamics (involving torque), as well as rotational kinetic energy and angular momentum (the rotational analog of linear momentum). We will find many analogies with translational motion, which will make our study easier. Our understanding of the world around us will be increased significantly—from rotating bicycle wheels and compact disks to amusement park rides, a spinning skater, the rotating Earth, and a centrifuge—and there may be a few surprises.

We will consider mainly the rotation of rigid objects. A **rigid object** is an object with a definite shape that doesn't change, so that the particles composing it stay in fixed positions relative to one another. Any real object is capable of vibrating or deforming when a force is exerted on it. But these effects are often very small, so the concept of an ideal rigid object is very useful as a good approximation.

## 8–1 Angular Quantities

We saw in Chapter 7 (Section 7–8) that the motion of a rigid object can be analyzed as the translational motion of the object's center of mass, plus rotational motion *about* its center of mass. We have already discussed translational motion in detail, so now we focus on purely rotational motion. By *purely rotational motion*, we mean that all points in the object move in circles, such as the point P in the rotating wheel of Fig. 8–1, and that the centers of these circles all lie on a line called the **axis of rotation**. In Fig. 8–1 the axis of rotation is perpendicular to the page and passes through point O.

Every point in an object rotating about a fixed axis moves in a circle (shown dashed in Fig. 8–1 for point P) whose center is on the axis and whose radius is $r$, the distance of that point from the axis of rotation. A straight line drawn from the axis to any point sweeps out the same angle $\theta$ in the same time.

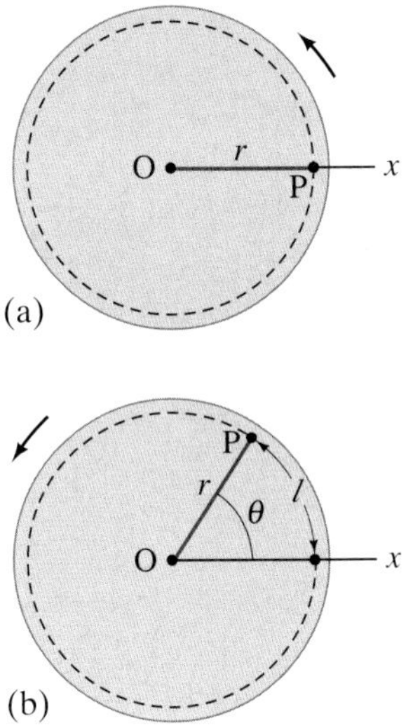


**FIGURE 8–1** Looking at a wheel that is rotating counterclockwise about an axis through the wheel's center at O (axis perpendicular to the page). Each point, such as point P, moves in a circular path; $l$ is the distance P travels as the wheel rotates through the angle $\theta$.

To indicate the angular position of a rotating object, or how far it has rotated, we specify the angle $\theta$ of some particular line in the object (red in Fig. 8–1) with respect to a reference line, such as the $x$ axis in Fig. 8–1. A point in the object, such as P in Fig. 8–1, moves through an angle $\theta$ when it travels the distance $l$ measured along the circumference of its circular path. Angles are commonly measured in degrees, but the mathematics of circular motion is much simpler if we use the *radian* for angular measure. One **radian** (abbreviated rad) is defined as the angle subtended by an arc whose length is equal to the radius. For example, in Fig. 8–1b, point P is a distance $r$ from the axis of rotation, and it has moved a distance $l$ along the arc of a circle. The arc length $l$ is said to "subtend" the angle $\theta$. If $l = r$, then $\theta$ is exactly equal to 1 rad. In radians, any angle $\theta$ is given by

$$\theta = \frac{l}{r}, \qquad \textbf{(8–1a)}$$

*$\theta$ in radians*

where $r$ is the radius of the circle, and $l$ is the arc length subtended by the angle specified in radians. If $l = r$, then $\theta = 1$ rad.

*1 rad: arc length = radius*

The radian is dimensionless since it is the ratio of two lengths. Nonetheless when giving an angle in radians, we always mention rad to remind us it is not degrees. It is often useful to rewrite Eq. 8–1a in terms of arc length $l$:

$$l = r\theta. \qquad \textbf{(8–1b)}$$

Radians can be related to degrees in the following way. In a complete circle there are 360°, which must correspond to an arc length equal to the circumference of the circle, $l = 2\pi r$. Thus $\theta = l/r = 2\pi r/r = 2\pi$ rad in a complete circle, so

$$360° = 2\pi \text{ rad}.$$

*Conversion, degrees to rad*

One radian is therefore $360°/2\pi \approx 360°/6.28 \approx 57.3°$. An object that makes one complete revolution (rev) has rotated through 360°, or $2\pi$ radians:

*1 rad ≈ 57.3°*

$$1 \text{ rev} = 360° = 2\pi \text{ rad}.$$

**EXAMPLE 8–1** **Bike wheel.** A bike wheel rotates 4.50 revolutions. How many radians has it rotated?

**APPROACH** All we need is a straightforward conversion of units using

$$1 \text{ revolution} = 360° = 2\pi \text{ rad} = 6.28 \text{ rad}.$$

**SOLUTION**

$$4.50 \text{ revolutions} = (4.50 \text{ rev})\left(2\pi \frac{\text{rad}}{\text{rev}}\right) = 9.00\pi \text{ rad} = 28.3 \text{ rad}.$$

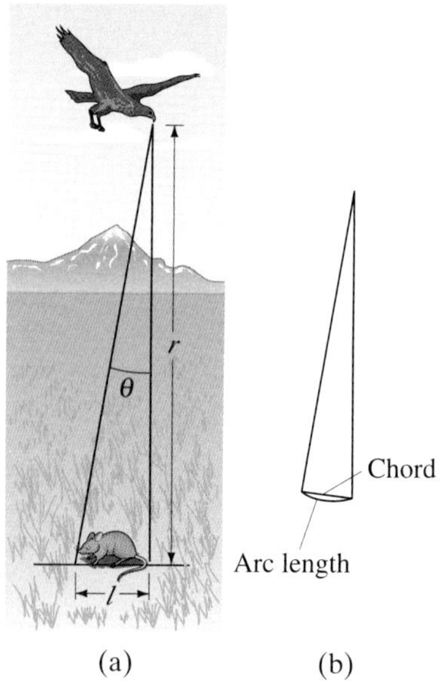


**FIGURE 8–2** (a) Example 8–2. (b) For small angles, arc length and the chord length (straight line) are nearly equal.

**EXAMPLE 8–2** **Birds of prey—in radians.** A particular bird's eye can just distinguish objects that subtend an angle no smaller than about $3 \times 10^{-4}$ rad. (*a*) How many degrees is this? (*b*) How small an object can the bird just distinguish when flying at a height of 100 m (Fig. 8–2a)?

**APPROACH** For (*a*) we use the relation $360° = 2\pi$ rad. For (*b*) we use Eq. 8–1b, $l = r\theta$, to find the arc length.

**SOLUTION** (*a*) We convert $3 \times 10^{-4}$ rad to degrees:

$$\left(3 \times 10^{-4}\,\text{rad}\right)\left(\frac{360°}{2\pi\,\text{rad}}\right) = 0.017°.$$

(*b*) We use Eq. 8–1b, $l = r\theta$. For small angles, the arc length $l$ and the chord length are approximately[†] the same (Fig. 8–2b). Since $r = 100$ m and $\theta = 3 \times 10^{-4}$ rad, we find

$$l = (100\,\text{m})\left(3 \times 10^{-4}\,\text{rad}\right) = 3 \times 10^{-2}\,\text{m} = 3\,\text{cm}.$$

A bird can distinguish a small mouse (about 3 cm long) from a height of 100 m. That is good eyesight.

**NOTE** Had the angle been given in degrees, we would first have had to convert it to radians to make this calculation. Equation 8–1 is valid *only* if the angle is specified in radians. Degrees (or revolutions) won't work.

To describe rotational motion, we make use of angular quantities, such as angular velocity and angular acceleration. These are defined in analogy to the corresponding quantities in linear motion, and are chosen to describe the rotating object as a whole, so they are the same for each point in the rotating object. Each point in a rotating object may also have translational velocity and acceleration, but they have different values for different points in the object.

*Angular displacement (rad)*

When an object, such as the bicycle wheel in Fig. 8–3, rotates from some initial position, specified by $\theta_1$, to some final position, $\theta_2$, its *angular displacement* is

$$\Delta\theta = \theta_2 - \theta_1 .$$

**FIGURE 8–3** A wheel rotates from (a) initial position $\theta_1$ to (b) final position $\theta_2$. The angular displacement is $\Delta\theta = \theta_2 - \theta_1$.

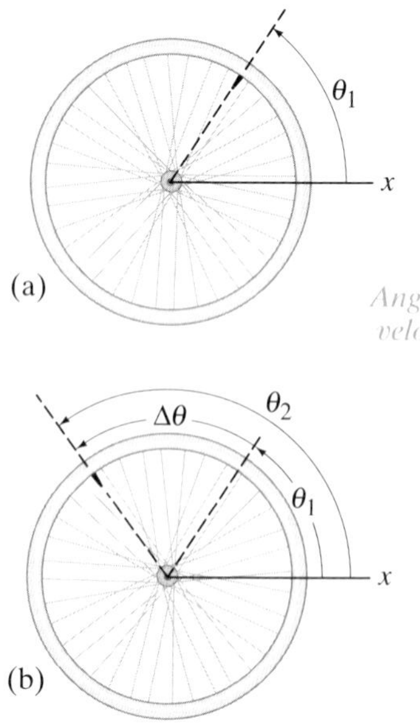


The *angular velocity* (denoted by $\omega$, the Greek lowercase letter omega) is defined in analogy with linear (translational) velocity that was discussed in Chapter 2. Instead of linear displacement, we use the angular displacement. Thus the **average angular velocity** is defined as

$$\bar{\omega} = \frac{\Delta\theta}{\Delta t}, \qquad \textbf{(8–2a)}$$

where $\Delta\theta$ is the angle through which the object has rotated in the time interval $\Delta t$. We define the **instantaneous angular velocity** as the very small angle $\Delta\theta$, through which the object turns in the very short time interval $\Delta t$:

*Angular velocity*

$$\omega = \lim_{\Delta t \to 0} \frac{\Delta\theta}{\Delta t}. \qquad \textbf{(8–2b)}$$

Angular velocity is generally specified in radians per second (rad/s). Note that *all points in a rigid object rotate with the same angular velocity*, since every position in the object moves through the same angle in the same time interval.

An object such as the wheel in Fig. 8–3 can rotate about a fixed axis either clockwise or counterclockwise. The direction can be specified with a + or − sign, just as we did in Chapter 2 for linear motion along the $+x$ or $-x$ axis. The usual convention is to choose the angular displacement $\Delta\theta$ and angular velocity $\omega$ as positive when the wheel rotates counterclockwise. If the rotation is clockwise, then $\theta$ would decrease, so $\Delta\theta$ and $\omega$ would be negative.[‡]

[†] Even for an angle as large as 15°, the error in making this estimate is only 1%, but for larger angles the error increases rapidly.

[‡] The vector nature of angular velocity and other angular quantities is discussed in Section 8–9 (optional).

*Angular acceleration* (denoted by $\alpha$, the Greek lowercase letter alpha), in analogy to linear acceleration, is defined as the change in angular velocity divided by the time required to make this change. The **average angular acceleration** is defined as

$$\bar{\alpha} = \frac{\omega_2 - \omega_1}{\Delta t} = \frac{\Delta\omega}{\Delta t}, \qquad \textbf{(8–3a)}$$

where $\omega_1$ is the angular velocity initially, and $\omega_2$ is the angular velocity after a time interval $\Delta t$. **Instantaneous angular acceleration** is defined in the usual way as the limit of this ratio as $\Delta t$ approaches zero:

$$\alpha = \lim_{\Delta t \to 0} \frac{\Delta\omega}{\Delta t}. \qquad \textbf{(8–3b)}$$

*Angular acceleration*

Since $\omega$ is the same for all points of a rotating object, Eq. 8–3 tells us that $\alpha$ also will be the same for all points. Thus, $\omega$ and $\alpha$ are properties of the rotating object as a whole. With $\omega$ measured in radians per second and $t$ in seconds, $\alpha$ will be expressed as radians per second squared $(\text{rad/s}^2)$.

Each point or particle of a rotating rigid object has, at any moment, a linear velocity $v$ and a linear acceleration $a$. We can relate the linear quantities at each point, $v$ and $a$, to the angular quantities of the rotating object, $\omega$ and $\alpha$. Consider a point P located a distance $r$ from the axis of rotation, as in Fig. 8–4. If the object rotates with angular velocity $\omega$, any point will have a linear velocity whose direction is tangent to its circular path. The magnitude of that point's linear velocity is $v = \Delta l/\Delta t$. From Eq. 8–1b, a change in rotation angle $\Delta\theta$ (in radians) is related to the linear distance traveled by $\Delta l = r\,\Delta\theta$. Hence

$$v = \frac{\Delta l}{\Delta t} = r\frac{\Delta\theta}{\Delta t}$$

or

$$v = r\omega. \qquad \textbf{(8–4)}$$

*Linear and angular velocity related*

Thus, although $\omega$ is the same for every point in the rotating object at any instant, the linear velocity $v$ is greater for points farther from the axis (Fig. 8–5). Note that Eq. 8–4 is valid both instantaneously and on the average.

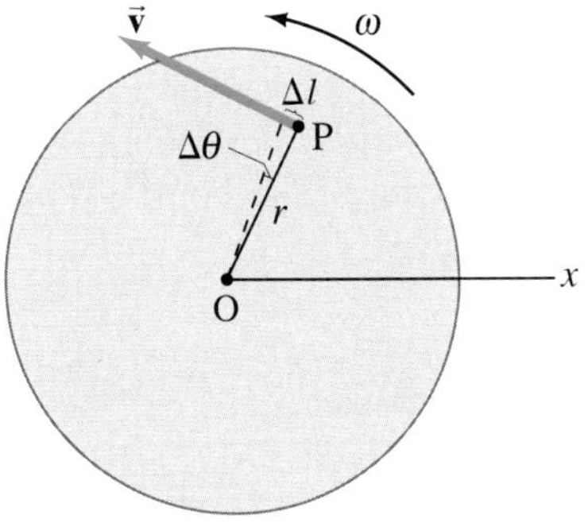


**FIGURE 8–4** A point P on a rotating wheel has a linear velocity $\vec{\mathbf{v}}$ at any moment.

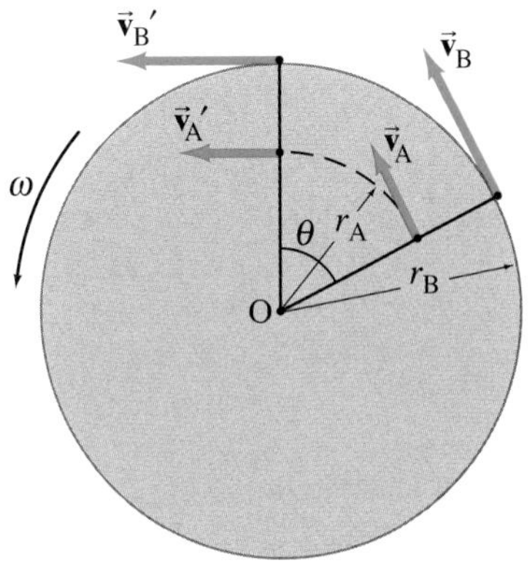


**FIGURE 8–5** A wheel rotating uniformly counterclockwise. Two points on the wheel, at distances $r_A$ and $r_B$ from the center, have the same angular velocity $\omega$ because they travel through the same angle $\theta$ in the same time interval. But the two points have different linear velocities because they travel different distances in the same time interval. Since $r_B > r_A$, then $v_B > v_A$ $(v = r\omega)$.

**CONCEPTUAL EXAMPLE 8–3** **Is the lion faster than the horse?** On a rotating carousel or merry-go-round, one child sits on a horse near the outer edge and another child sits on a lion halfway out from the center. (*a*) Which child has the greater linear velocity? (*b*) Which child has the greater angular velocity?

**RESPONSE** (*a*) The *linear* velocity is the distance traveled divided by the time interval. In one rotation the child on the outer edge travels a longer distance than the child near the center, but the time interval is the same for both. Thus the child at the outer edge, on the horse, has the greater linear velocity.
(*b*) The *angular* velocity is the angle of rotation divided by the time interval. In one rotation both children rotate through the same angle ($360° = 2\pi$ radians). The two children have the same angular velocity.

If the angular velocity of a rotating object changes, the object as a whole—and each point in it—has an angular acceleration. Each point also has a linear acceleration whose direction is tangent to that point's circular path. We use Eq. 8–4 ($v = r\omega$) to show that the angular acceleration $\alpha$ is related to the tangential linear acceleration $a_{tan}$ of a point in the rotating object by

$$a_{tan} = \frac{\Delta v}{\Delta t} = r\frac{\Delta \omega}{\Delta t}$$

or

*Tangential acceleration*

$$a_{tan} = r\alpha. \tag{8–5}$$

In this equation, $r$ is the radius of the circle in which the particle is moving, and the subscript "tan" in $a_{tan}$ stands for "tangential."

The total linear acceleration of a point is the vector sum of two components:

$$\vec{\mathbf{a}} = \vec{\mathbf{a}}_{tan} + \vec{\mathbf{a}}_R,$$

where the radial† component, $\vec{\mathbf{a}}_R$, is the radial or "centripetal" acceleration and its direction is toward the center of the point's circular path; see Fig. 8–6. We saw in Chapter 5 (Eq. 5–1) that $a_R = v^2/r$, and we can rewrite this in terms of $\omega$ using Eq. 8–4:

*Centripetal (or radial) acceleration*

$$a_R = \frac{v^2}{r} = \frac{(r\omega)^2}{r} = \omega^2 r. \tag{8–6}$$

Thus the centripetal acceleration is greater the farther you are from the axis of rotation: the children farthest out on a carousel feel the greatest acceleration. Equations 8–4, 8–5, and 8–6 relate the angular quantities describing the rotation of an object to the linear quantities for each point of the object. Table 8–1 summarizes these relationships.

**FIGURE 8–6** On a rotating wheel whose angular speed is increasing, a point P has both tangential and radial (centripetal) components of linear acceleration. (See also Chapter 5.)

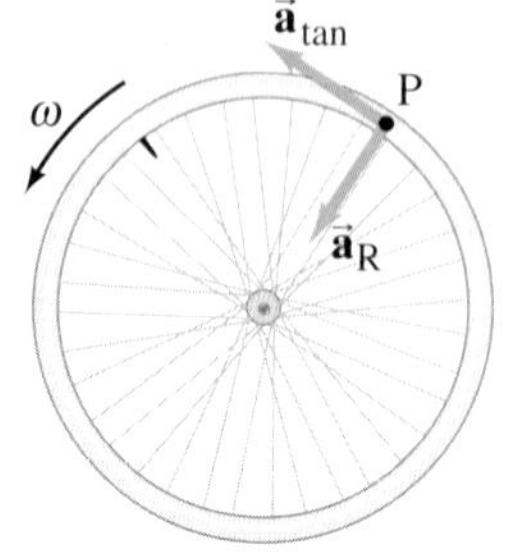


**TABLE 8–1 Linear and Rotational Quantities**

| Linear | Type | Rotational | Relation |
|---|---|---|---|
| $x$ | displacement | $\theta$ | $x = r\theta$ |
| $v$ | velocity | $\omega$ | $v = r\omega$ |
| $a_{tan}$ | acceleration | $\alpha$ | $a_{tan} = r\alpha$ |

† "Radial" means along the radius—that is, toward or away from the center or axis.

**EXAMPLE 8–4** **Angular and linear velocities and accelerations.** A carousel is initially at rest. At $t = 0$ it is given a constant angular acceleration $\alpha = 0.060\ \text{rad/s}^2$, which increases its angular velocity for 8.0 s. At $t = 8.0\ \text{s}$, determine the following quantities: (*a*) the angular velocity of the carousel; (*b*) the linear velocity of a child (Fig. 8–7a) located 2.5 m from the center, point P in Fig. 8–7b; (*c*) the tangential (linear) acceleration of that child; (*d*) the centripetal acceleration of the child; and (*e*) the total linear acceleration of the child.

**APPROACH** The angular acceleration $\alpha$ is constant, so we can use Eq. 8–3a to solve for $\omega$ after a time $t = 8.0\ \text{s}$. With this $\omega$ and the given $\alpha$, we determine the other quantities using the relations we just developed, Eqs. 8–4, 8–5, and 8–6.

**SOLUTION** (*a*) Equation 8–3a tells us

$$\bar{\alpha} = \frac{\omega_2 - \omega_1}{\Delta t}.$$

We are given $\Delta t = 8.0\ \text{s}$, $\bar{\alpha} = 0.060\ \text{rad/s}^2$, and $\omega_1 = 0$. Solving for $\omega_2$, we get

$$\begin{aligned} \omega_2 &= \omega_1 + \bar{\alpha}\,\Delta t \\ &= 0 + \left(0.060\ \text{rad/s}^2\right)(8.0\ \text{s}) = 0.48\ \text{rad/s}. \end{aligned}$$

During the 8.0-s interval, the carousel has accelerated from $\omega_1 = 0$ (rest) to $\omega_2 = 0.48\ \text{rad/s}$.
(*b*) The linear velocity of the child with $r = 2.5\ \text{m}$ at time $t = 8.0\ \text{s}$ is found using Eq. 8–4:

$$v = r\omega = (2.5\ \text{m})(0.48\ \text{rad/s}) = 1.2\ \text{m/s}.$$

Note that the "rad" has been dropped here because it is dimensionless (and only a reminder)—it is a ratio of two distances, Eq. 8–1b.
(*c*) The child's tangential acceleration is given by Eq. 8–5:

$$a_{\text{tan}} = r\alpha = (2.5\ \text{m})\left(0.060\ \text{rad/s}^2\right) = 0.15\ \text{m/s}^2,$$

and it is the same throughout the 8.0-s acceleration interval.
(*d*) The child's centripetal acceleration at $t = 8.0\ \text{s}$ is given by Eq. 8–6:

$$a_{\text{R}} = \frac{v^2}{r} = \frac{(1.2\ \text{m/s})^2}{(2.5\ \text{m})} = 0.58\ \text{m/s}^2.$$

(*e*) The two components of linear acceleration calculated in parts (*c*) and (*d*) are perpendicular to each other. Thus the total linear acceleration at $t = 8.0\ \text{s}$ has magnitude

$$\begin{aligned} a &= \sqrt{a_{\text{tan}}^2 + a_{\text{R}}^2} \\ &= \sqrt{\left(0.15\ \text{m/s}^2\right)^2 + \left(0.58\ \text{m/s}^2\right)^2} = 0.60\ \text{m/s}^2. \end{aligned}$$

Its direction (Fig. 8–7b) is

$$\theta = \tan^{-1}\left(\frac{a_{\text{tan}}}{a_{\text{R}}}\right) = \tan^{-1}\left(\frac{0.15\ \text{m/s}^2}{0.58\ \text{m/s}^2}\right) = 0.25\ \text{rad},$$

so $\theta \approx 15°$.

**NOTE** The linear acceleration is mostly centripetal, keeping the child moving in a circle with the carousel. The tangential component that speeds up the motion is smaller.

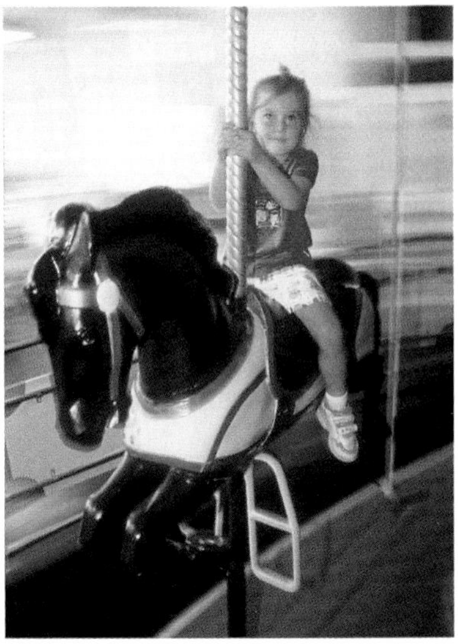

(a)

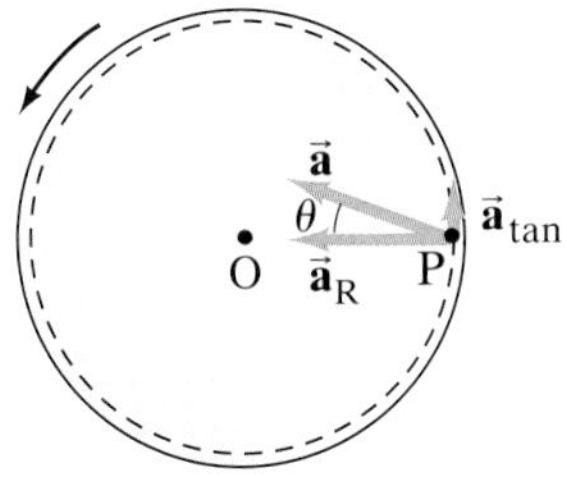


(b)

**FIGURE 8–7** Example 8–4. The total acceleration vector $\vec{\mathbf{a}} = \vec{\mathbf{a}}_{\text{tan}} + \vec{\mathbf{a}}_{\text{R}}$, at $t = 8.0\ \text{s}$.

We can relate the angular velocity $\omega$ to the frequency of rotation, $f$. The **frequency** is the number of complete revolutions (rev) per second, as we saw in Chapter 5. One revolution (of a wheel, say) corresponds to an angle of $2\pi$ radians, and thus $1\text{ rev/s} = 2\pi\text{ rad/s}$. Hence, in general, the frequency $f$ is related to the angular velocity $\omega$ by

*Frequency*

$$f = \frac{\omega}{2\pi}$$

or

$$\omega = 2\pi f. \quad \textbf{(8–7)}$$

The unit for frequency, revolutions per second (rev/s), is given the special name the hertz (Hz). That is

$$1\text{ Hz} = 1\text{ rev/s}.$$

Note that "revolution" is not really a unit, so we can also write $1\text{ Hz} = 1\text{ s}^{-1}$.

The time required for one complete revolution is called the **period** $T$, and it is related to the frequency by

*Period*

$$T = \frac{1}{f}. \quad \textbf{(8–8)}$$

If a particle rotates at a frequency of three revolutions per second, then the period of each revolution is $\frac{1}{3}$ s.

**EXERCISE A** In Example 8–4, we found that the carousel, after 8.0 s, rotates at an angular velocity $\omega = 0.48\text{ rad/s}$, and continues to do so after $t = 8.0\text{ s}$ because the acceleration ceased. What are the frequency and period of the carousel?

PHYSICS APPLIED

*Hard drive and bit speed*

**EXAMPLE 8–5 Hard drive.** The platter of the hard drive of a computer rotates at 7200 rpm (revolutions per minute = rev/min). (*a*) What is the angular velocity of the platter? (*b*) If the reading head of the drive is located 3.00 cm from the rotation axis, what is the linear speed of the point on the platter just below it? (*c*) If a single bit requires 0.50 $\mu$m of length along the direction of motion, how many bits per second can the writing head write when it is 3.00 cm from the axis?

**APPROACH** We use the given frequency $f$ to find the angular velocity $\omega$ of the platter and then the linear speed of a point on the platter ($v = r\omega$). The bit rate is found by dividing the linear speed by the length of one bit ($v$ = distance/time).

**SOLUTION** (*a*) First we find the frequency in rev/s, given $f = 7200\text{ rev/min}$:

$$f = \frac{(7200\text{ rev/min})}{(60\text{ s/min})} = 120\text{ rev/s} = 120\text{ Hz}.$$

Then the angular velocity is

$$\omega = 2\pi f = 754\text{ rad/s}.$$

(*b*) The linear speed of a point 3.00 cm out from the axis is given by Eq. 8–4:

$$v = r\omega = \left(3.00 \times 10^{-2}\text{ m}\right)(754\text{ rad/s}) = 22.6\text{ m/s}.$$

(*c*) Each bit requires $0.50 \times 10^{-6}$ m, so at a speed of 22.6 m/s, the number of bits passing the head per second is

$$\frac{22.6\text{ m/s}}{0.50 \times 10^{-6}\text{ m/bit}} = 45 \times 10^{6}\text{ bits per second,}$$

or 45 megabits/s (Mbps).

## 8–2 Constant Angular Acceleration

In Chapter 2, we derived the useful kinematic equations (Eqs. 2–11) that relate acceleration, velocity, distance, and time for the special case of uniform linear acceleration. Those equations were derived from the definitions of linear velocity and acceleration, assuming constant acceleration. The definitions of angular velocity and angular acceleration are the same as those for their linear counterparts, except that $\theta$ has replaced the linear displacement $x$, $\omega$ has replaced $v$, and $\alpha$ has replaced $a$. Therefore, the angular equations for **constant angular acceleration** will be analogous to Eqs. 2–11 with $x$ replaced by $\theta$, $v$ by $\omega$, and $a$ by $\alpha$, and they can be derived in exactly the same way. We summarize them here, opposite their linear equivalents (we've chosen $x_0 = 0$, and $\theta_0 = 0$ at the initial time $t = 0$):

| Angular | Linear | | | |
|---|---|---|---|---|
| $\omega = \omega_0 + \alpha t$ | $v = v_0 + at$ | [constant $\alpha$, $a$] | **(8–9a)** | *Kinematic equations* |
| $\theta = \omega_0 t + \frac{1}{2}\alpha t^2$ | $x = v_0 t + \frac{1}{2}at^2$ | [constant $\alpha$, $a$] | **(8–9b)** | *for constant* |
| $\omega^2 = \omega_0^2 + 2\alpha\theta$ | $v^2 = v_0^2 + 2ax$ | [constant $\alpha$, $a$] | **(8–9c)** | *angular acceleration* |
| $\overline{\omega} = \dfrac{\omega + \omega_0}{2}$ | $\overline{v} = \dfrac{v + v_0}{2}$ | [constant $\alpha$, $a$] | **(8–9d)** | $(x_0 = 0, \theta_0 = 0)$ |

Note that $\omega_0$ represents the angular velocity at $t = 0$, whereas $\theta$ and $\omega$ represent the angular position and velocity, respectively, at time $t$. Since the angular acceleration is constant, $\alpha = \overline{\alpha}$.

**EXAMPLE 8–6 Centrifuge acceleration.** A centrifuge rotor is accelerated from rest to 20,000 rpm in 30 s. (*a*) What is its average angular acceleration? (*b*) Through how many revolutions has the centrifuge rotor turned during its acceleration period, assuming constant angular acceleration?

**APPROACH** To determine $\overline{\alpha} = \Delta\omega/\Delta t$, we need the initial and final angular velocities. For (*b*), we use Eqs. 8–9 (recall that one revolution corresponds to $\theta = 2\pi$ rad).

**SOLUTION** (*a*) The initial angular velocity is $\omega = 0$. The final angular velocity is

$$\omega = 2\pi f = (2\pi\ \text{rad/rev})\frac{(20{,}000\ \text{rev/min})}{(60\ \text{s/min})} = 2100\ \text{rad/s}.$$

Then, since $\overline{\alpha} = \Delta\omega/\Delta t$ and $\Delta t = 30\ \text{s}$, we have

$$\overline{\alpha} = \frac{\omega - \omega_0}{\Delta t} = \frac{2100\ \text{rad/s} - 0}{30\ \text{s}} = 70\ \text{rad/s}^2.$$

That is, every second the rotor's angular velocity increases by 70 rad/s, or by $(70/2\pi) = 11$ revolutions per second.

(*b*) To find $\theta$ we could use either Eq. 8–9b or 8–9c, or both to check our answer. The former gives

$$\theta = 0 + \tfrac{1}{2}(70\ \text{rad/s}^2)(30\ \text{s})^2 = 3.15 \times 10^4\ \text{rad},$$

where we have kept an extra digit because this is an intermediate result. To find the total number of revolutions, we divide by $2\pi$ rad/rev and obtain

$$\frac{3.15 \times 10^4\ \text{rad}}{2\pi\ \text{rad/rev}} = 5.0 \times 10^3\ \text{rev}.$$

**NOTE** Let us calculate $\theta$ using Eq. 8–9c:

$$\theta = \frac{\omega^2 - \omega_0^2}{2\alpha} = \frac{(2100\ \text{rad/s})^2 - 0}{2(70\ \text{rad/s}^2)} = 3.15 \times 10^4\ \text{rad}$$

which checks our answer perfectly.

## 8–3 Rolling Motion (Without Slipping)

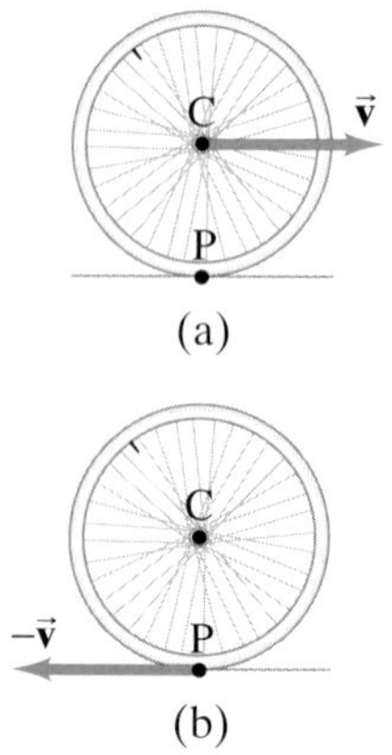


**FIGURE 8–8** (a) A wheel rolling to the right. Its center C moves with velocity $\vec{\mathbf{v}}$. Point P is at rest at this instant. (b) The same wheel as seen from a reference frame in which the axle of the wheel C is at rest—that is, we are moving to the right with velocity $\vec{\mathbf{v}}$ relative to the ground. Point P, which was at rest in (a), here in (b) is moving to the left with velocity $-\vec{\mathbf{v}}$ as shown. (See also Section 3–8 on relative velocity.)

The rolling motion of a ball or wheel is familiar in everyday life: a ball rolling across the floor, or the wheels and tires of a car or bicycle rolling along the pavement. Rolling *without slipping* is readily analyzed and depends on static friction between the rolling object and the ground. The friction is static because the rolling object's point of contact with the ground is at rest at each moment.

Rolling without slipping involves both rotation and translation. There is then a simple relation between the linear speed $v$ of the axle and the angular velocity $\omega$ of the rotating wheel or sphere: namely, $v = r\omega$ (where $r$ is the radius) as we now show. Figure 8–8a shows a wheel rolling to the right without slipping. At the moment shown, point P on the wheel is in contact with the ground and is momentarily at rest. The velocity of the axle at the wheel's center C is $\vec{\mathbf{v}}$. In Fig. 8–8b we have put ourselves in the reference frame of the wheel—that is, we are moving to the right with velocity $\vec{\mathbf{v}}$ relative to the ground. In this reference frame the axle C is at rest, whereas the ground and point P are moving to the left with velocity $-\vec{\mathbf{v}}$ as shown. Here we are seeing pure rotation. So we can use Eq. 8–4 to obtain $v = r\omega$, where $r$ is the radius of the wheel. This is the same $v$ as in Fig. 8–8a, so we see that the linear speed $v$ of the axle relative to the ground is related to the angular velocity $\omega$ by

$$v = r\omega. \qquad \text{[rolling without slipping]}$$

This relationship is valid only if there is no slipping.

**EXAMPLE 8–7** **Bicycle.** A bicycle slows down uniformly from $v_0 = 8.40\,\text{m/s}$ to rest over a distance of 115 m, Fig. 8–9. Each wheel and tire has an overall diameter of 68.0 cm. Determine (*a*) the angular velocity of the wheels at the initial instant ($t = 0$); (*b*) the total number of revolutions each wheel rotates before coming to rest; (*c*) the angular acceleration of the wheel; and (*d*) the time it took to come to a stop.

**APPROACH** We assume the bicycle wheels roll without slipping and the tire is in firm contact with the ground. The speed of the bike $v$ and the angular velocity of the wheels $\omega$ are related by $v = r\omega$. The bike slows down uniformly, so the angular acceleration is constant and we can use Eqs. 8–9.

**SOLUTION** (*a*) The initial angular velocity of the wheel, whose radius is 34.0 cm, is

$$\omega_0 = \frac{v_0}{r} = \frac{8.40\,\text{m/s}}{0.340\,\text{m}} = 24.7\,\text{rad/s}.$$

(*b*) In coming to a stop, the bike passes over 115 m of ground. The circumference of the wheel is $2\pi r$, so each revolution of the wheel corresponds to a distance traveled of $2\pi r = (2\pi)(0.340\,\text{m})$. Thus the number of revolutions the wheel makes in coming to a stop is

$$\frac{115\,\text{m}}{2\pi r} = \frac{115\,\text{m}}{(2\pi)(0.340\,\text{m})} = 53.8\,\text{rev}.$$

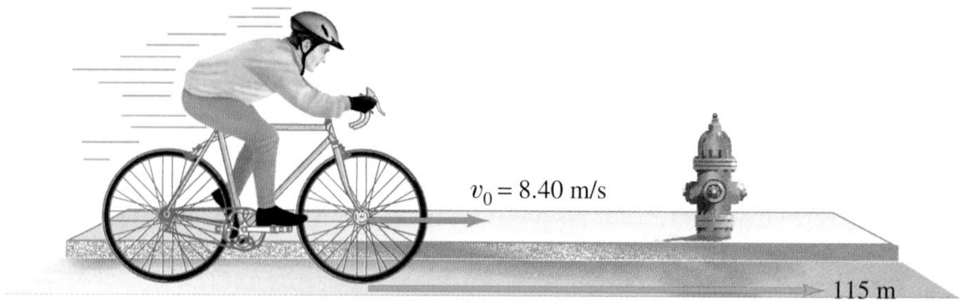


**FIGURE 8–9** Example 8–7.

(c) The angular acceleration of the wheel can be obtained from Eq. 8–9c, for which we set $\omega = 0$ and $\omega_0 = 24.7\,\text{rad/s}$. Because each revolution corresponds to $2\pi$ radians of angle, then $\theta = 2\pi\,\text{rad/rev} \times 53.8\,\text{rev}\ (= 338\,\text{rad})$ and

$$\alpha = \frac{\omega^2 - \omega_0^2}{2\theta} = \frac{0 - (24.7\,\text{rad/s})^2}{2(2\pi\,\text{rad/rev})(53.8\,\text{rev})} = -0.902\,\text{rad/s}^2.$$

(d) Equation 8–9a or b allows us to solve for the time. The first is easier:

$$t = \frac{\omega - \omega_0}{\alpha} = \frac{0 - 24.7\,\text{rad/s}}{-0.902\,\text{rad/s}^2} = 27.4\,\text{s}.$$

**NOTE** When the bike tire completes one revolution, the bike advances linearly a distance equal to the outer circumference $(2\pi r)$ of the tire, as long as there is no slipping or sliding.

## 8–4 Torque

We have so far discussed rotational kinematics—the description of rotational motion in terms of angle, angular velocity, and angular acceleration. Now we discuss the dynamics, or causes, of rotational motion. Just as we found analogies between linear and rotational motion for the description of motion, so rotational equivalents for dynamics exist as well.

To make an object start rotating about an axis clearly requires a force. But the direction of this force, and where it is applied, are also important. Take, for example, an ordinary situation such as the overhead view of the door in Fig. 8–10. If you apply a force $\vec{\mathbf{F}}_A$ to the door as shown, you will find that the greater the magnitude, $F_A$, the more quickly the door opens. But now if you apply the same magnitude force at a point closer to the hinge—say, $\vec{\mathbf{F}}_B$ in Fig. 8–10—the door will not open so quickly. The effect of the force is less: where the force acts, as well as its magnitude and direction, affects how quickly the door opens. Indeed, if only this one force acts, the angular acceleration of the door is proportional not only to the magnitude of the force, but is also directly proportional to *the perpendicular distance from the axis of rotation to the line along which the force acts.* This distance is called the **lever arm**, or **moment arm**, of the force, and is labeled $r_A$ and $r_B$ for the two forces in Fig. 8–10. Thus, if $r_A$ in Fig. 8–10 is three times larger than $r_B$, then the angular acceleration of the door will be three times as great, assuming that the magnitudes of the forces are the same. To say it another way, if $r_A = 3r_B$, then $F_B$ must be three times as large as $F_A$ to give the same angular acceleration. (Figure 8–11 shows two examples of tools whose long lever arms are very effective.)

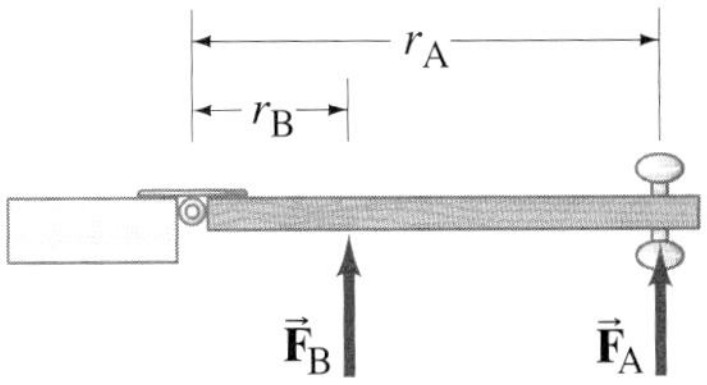


**FIGURE 8–10** Applying the same force with different lever arms, $r_A$ and $r_B$. If $r_A = 3r_B$, then to create the same effect (angular acceleration), $F_B$ needs to be three times $F_A$, or $F_A = \frac{1}{3}F_B$.

*Lever arm*

**FIGURE 8–11** (a) A plumber can exert greater torque using a wrench with a long lever arm. (b) A tire iron too can have a long lever arm.

*Torque defined*

The angular acceleration, then, is proportional to the product of the *force times the lever arm*. This product is called the *moment of the force* about the axis, or, more commonly, it is called the **torque**, and is represented by $\tau$ (Greek lowercase letter tau). Thus, the angular acceleration $\alpha$ of an object is directly proportional to the net applied torque $\tau$:

$$\alpha \propto \tau,$$

and we see that it is torque that gives rise to angular acceleration. This is the rotational analog of Newton's second law for linear motion, $a \propto F$.

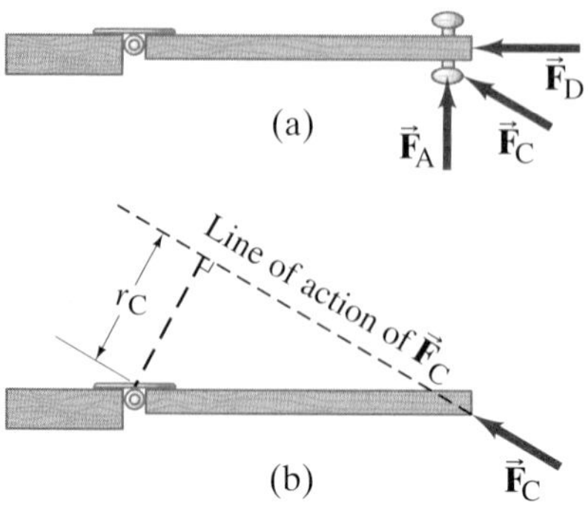


**FIGURE 8–12** (a) Forces acting at different angles at the doorknob. (b) The lever arm is defined as the perpendicular distance from the axis of rotation (the hinge) to the line of action of the force.

We defined the lever arm as the *perpendicular* distance from the axis of rotation to the line of action of the force—that is, the distance which is perpendicular both to the axis of rotation and to an imaginary line drawn along the direction of the force. We do this to take into account the effect of forces acting at an angle. It is clear that a force applied at an angle, such as $\vec{\mathbf{F}}_C$ in Fig. 8–12, will be less effective than the same magnitude force applied perpendicular to the door, such as $\vec{\mathbf{F}}_A$ (Fig. 8–12a). And if you push on the end of the door so that the force is directed at the hinge (the axis of rotation), as indicated by $\vec{\mathbf{F}}_D$, the door will not rotate at all.

The lever arm for a force such as $\vec{\mathbf{F}}_C$ is found by drawing a line along the direction of $\vec{\mathbf{F}}_C$ (this is the "line of action" of $\vec{\mathbf{F}}_C$). Then we draw another line, perpendicular to this line of action, that goes to the axis of rotation and is perpendicular also to it. The length of this second line is the lever arm for $\vec{\mathbf{F}}_C$ and is labeled $r_C$ in Fig. 8–12b. The lever arm is perpendicular both to the line of action of the force and, at its other end, perpendicular to the rotation axis.

The magnitude of the torque associated with $\vec{\mathbf{F}}_C$ is then $r_C F_C$. This short lever arm $r_C$ and the corresponding smaller torque associated with $\vec{\mathbf{F}}_C$ is consistent with the observation that $\vec{\mathbf{F}}_C$ is less effective in accelerating the door than is $\vec{\mathbf{F}}_A$. When the lever arm is defined in this way, experiment shows that the relation $\alpha \propto \tau$ is valid in general. Notice in Fig. 8–12 that the line of action of the force $\vec{\mathbf{F}}_D$ passes through the hinge, and hence its lever arm is zero. Consequently, zero torque is associated with $\vec{\mathbf{F}}_D$ and it gives rise to no angular acceleration, in accord with everyday experience.

**FIGURE 8–13**
Torque $= r_{\perp} F = r F_{\perp}$.

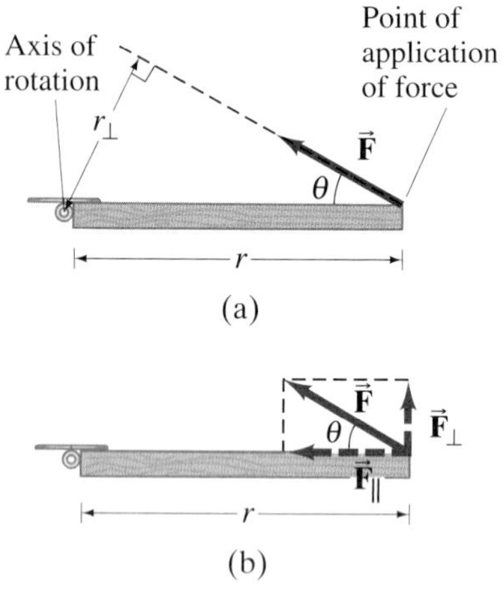


In general, then, we can write the magnitude of the torque about a given axis as

$$\tau = r_{\perp} F, \tag{8–10a}$$

where $r_{\perp}$ is the lever arm, and the perpendicular symbol ($\perp$) reminds us that we must use the distance from the axis of rotation that is perpendicular to the line of action of the force (Fig. 8–13a).

An equivalent way of determining the torque associated with a force is to resolve the force into components parallel and perpendicular to the line that connects the axis to the point of application of the force, as shown in Fig. 8–13b. The component $F_{\parallel}$ exerts no torque since it is directed at the rotation axis (its moment arm is zero). Hence the torque will be equal to $F_{\perp}$ times the distance $r$ from the axis to the point of application of the force:

$$\tau = r F_{\perp}. \tag{8–10b}$$

That this gives the same result as Eq. 8–10a can be seen from the relations $F_{\perp} = F \sin\theta$ and $r_{\perp} = r \sin\theta$. [Note that $\theta$ is the angle between the directions of $\vec{\mathbf{F}}$ and $r$ (radial line from the axis to the point where $\vec{\mathbf{F}}$ acts)]. So

*Magnitude of a torque*

$$\tau = rF \sin\theta \tag{8–10c}$$

in either case. We can use any of Eqs. 8–10 to calculate the torque, whichever is easiest.

Since torque is a distance times a force, it is measured in units of m·N in SI units,[†] cm·dyne in the cgs system, and ft·lb in the English system.

[†]Note that the units for torque are the same as those for energy. We write the unit for torque here as m·N (in SI) to distinguish it from energy (N·m) because the two quantities are very different. An obvious difference is that energy is a scalar, whereas torque has a direction and is a vector. The special name *joule* (1 J = 1 N·m) is used only for energy (and for work), *never* for torque.

**EXAMPLE 8–8** **Biceps torque.** The biceps muscle exerts a vertical force on the lower arm, bent as shown in Figs. 8–14a and b. For each case, calculate the torque about the axis of rotation through the elbow joint, assuming the muscle is attached 5.0 cm from the elbow as shown.

**APPROACH** The force is given, and the lever arm in (*a*) is given. In (*b*) we have to take into account the angle to get the lever arm.

**SOLUTION** (*a*) $F = 700\,\text{N}$ and $r_\perp = 0.050\,\text{m}$, so

$$\tau = r_\perp F = (0.050\,\text{m})(700\,\text{N}) = 35\,\text{m}\cdot\text{N}.$$

(*b*) Because the arm is at an angle below the horizontal, the lever arm is shorter (Fig. 8–14c) than in part (*a*): $r_\perp = (0.050\,\text{m})(\sin 60^\circ)$, where $\theta = 60^\circ$ is the angle between $\vec{\mathbf{F}}$ and $r$. $F$ is still 700 N, so

$$\tau = (0.050\,\text{m})(0.866)(700\,\text{N}) = 30\,\text{m}\cdot\text{N}.$$

The arm can exert less torque at this angle than when it is at 90°. Weight machines at gyms are often designed to take this variation with angle into account.

**NOTE** In (*b*), we could instead have used $\tau = rF_\perp$. As shown in Fig. 8–14d, $F_\perp = F\sin 60^\circ$. Then $\tau = rF_\perp = rF\sin\theta = (0.050\,\text{m})(700\,\text{N})(0.866)$ gives the same result.

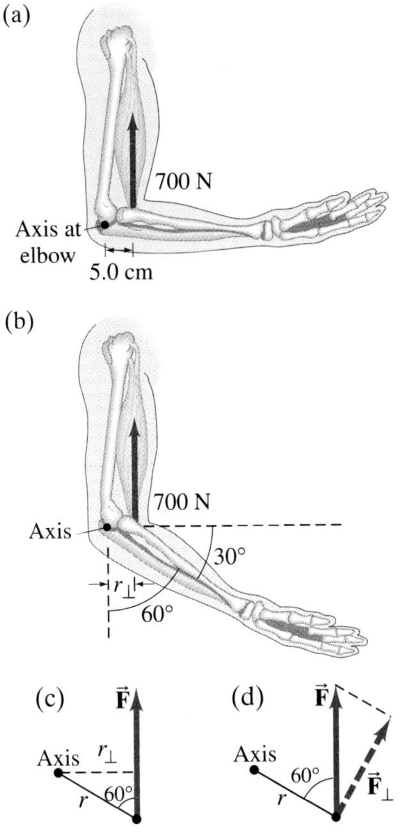


**FIGURE 8–14** Example 8–8.

**EXERCISE B** Two forces ($F_B = 20\,\text{N}$ and $F_A = 30\,\text{N}$) are applied to a meter stick which can rotate about its left end, Fig. 8–15. Force $\vec{\mathbf{F}}_B$ is applied perpendicularly at the midpoint. Which force exerts the greater torque?

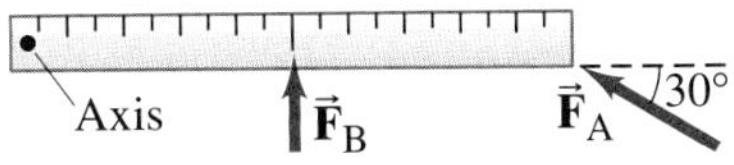


**FIGURE 8–15** Exercise B.

When more than one torque acts on an object, the angular acceleration $\alpha$ is found to be proportional to the *net* torque. If all the torques acting on an object tend to rotate it in the same direction about a fixed axis of rotation, the net torque is the sum of the torques. But if, say, one torque acts to rotate an object in one direction, and a second torque acts to rotate the object in the opposite direction (as in Fig. 8–16), the net torque is the difference of the two torques. We normally assign a positive sign to torques that act to rotate the object counterclockwise, and a negative sign to torques that act to rotate the object clockwise.

**EXAMPLE 8–9** **Torque on a compound wheel.** Two thin disk-shaped wheels, of radii $r_A = 30\,\text{cm}$ and $r_B = 50\,\text{cm}$, are attached to each other on an axle that passes through the center of each, as shown in Fig. 8–16. Calculate the net torque on this compound wheel due to the two forces shown, each of magnitude 50 N.

**APPROACH** The force $\vec{\mathbf{F}}_A$ acts to rotate the system counterclockwise, whereas $\vec{\mathbf{F}}_B$ acts to rotate it clockwise. So the two forces act in opposition to each other. We must choose one direction of rotation to be positive—say, counterclockwise. Then $\vec{\mathbf{F}}_A$ exerts a positive torque, $\tau_A = r_A F_A$, since the lever arm is $r_A$. $\vec{\mathbf{F}}_B$, on the other hand, produces a negative (clockwise) torque and does not act perpendicular to $r_B$, so we must use its perpendicular component to calculate the torque it produces: $\tau_B = -r_B F_{B\perp} = -r_B F_B \sin\theta$, where $\theta = 60^\circ$. (Note that $\theta$ must be the angle between $\vec{\mathbf{F}}_B$ and a radial line from the axis.)

**SOLUTION** The net torque is

$$\begin{aligned}\tau &= r_A F_A - r_B F_B \sin 60^\circ \\ &= (0.30\,\text{m})(50\,\text{N}) - (0.50\,\text{m})(50\,\text{N})(0.866) = -6.7\,\text{m}\cdot\text{N}.\end{aligned}$$

This net torque acts to accelerate the rotation of the wheel in the clockwise direction.

**NOTE** The two forces have the same magnitude, yet they produce a net torque because their lever arms are different.

**FIGURE 8–16** Example 8–9. The torque due to $\vec{\mathbf{F}}_A$ tends to accelerate the wheel counterclockwise, whereas the torque due to $\vec{\mathbf{F}}_B$ tends to accelerate the wheel clockwise.

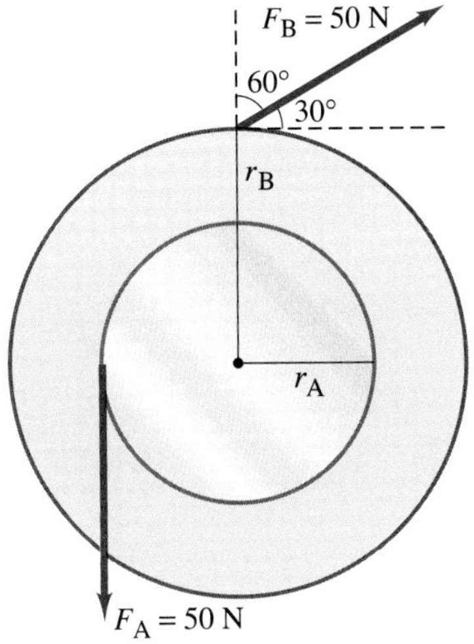

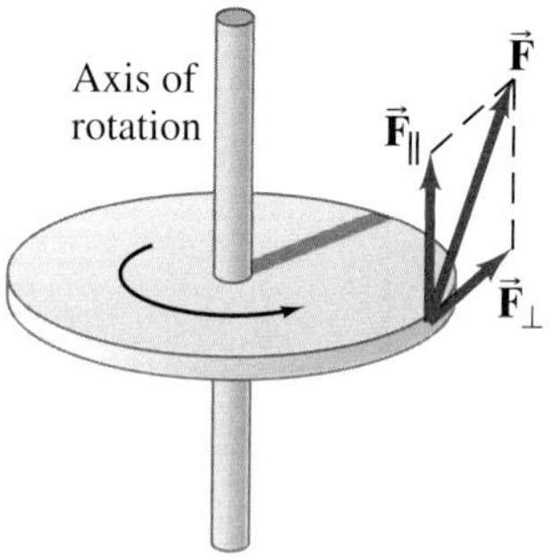


**FIGURE 8–17** Only the component of $\vec{F}$ that acts in the plane perpendicular to the rotation axis, $\vec{F}_{\perp}$, acts to turn the wheel about the axis. The component parallel to the axis, $\vec{F}_{\parallel}$, would tend to move the axis itself, which we assume is held fixed.

### * Forces that Act to Tilt the Axis

We are considering only rotation about a fixed axis, and so we consider only forces that act in a plane perpendicular to the axis of rotation. If there is a force (or component of a force) acting parallel to the axis of rotation, it will tend to tilt the axis of rotation—the component $\vec{F}_{\parallel}$ in Fig. 8–17 is an example. Since we are assuming the axis remains fixed in direction, either there can be no such forces or else the axis must be mounted in bearings or hinges that hold the axis fixed. Thus, only a force, or component of a force ($\mathbf{F}_{\perp}$ in Fig. 8–17), in a plane perpendicular to the axis will give rise to rotation about the axis, and it is only these that we consider.

## 8–5 Rotational Dynamics; Torque and Rotational Inertia

We have discussed that the angular acceleration $\alpha$ of a rotating object is proportional to the net torque $\tau$ applied to it:

$$\alpha \propto \Sigma\tau,$$

where we write $\Sigma\tau$ to remind us† that it is the *net* torque (sum of all torques acting on the object) that is proportional to $\alpha$. This corresponds to Newton's second law for translational motion, $a \propto \Sigma F$, but here torque has taken the place of force, and, correspondingly, the angular acceleration $\alpha$ takes the place of the linear acceleration $a$. In the linear case, the acceleration is not only proportional to the net force, but it is also inversely proportional to the inertia of the object, which we call its mass, $m$. Thus we could write $a = \Sigma F/m$. But what plays the role of mass for the rotational case? That is what we now set out to determine. At the same time, we will see that the relation $\alpha \propto \Sigma\tau$ follows directly from Newton's second law, $\Sigma F = ma$.

We first consider a very simple case: a particle of mass $m$ rotating in a circle of radius $r$ at the end of a string or rod whose mass we can ignore compared to $m$ (Fig. 8–18), and we assume a single force $F$ acts on $m$ as shown. The torque that gives rise to the angular acceleration is $\tau = rF$. If we use Newton's second law for linear quantities, $\Sigma F = ma$, and Eq. 8–5 relating the angular acceleration to the tangential linear acceleration, $a_{\tan} = r\alpha$, then we have

**FIGURE 8–18** A mass $m$ rotating in a circle of radius $r$ about a fixed point.

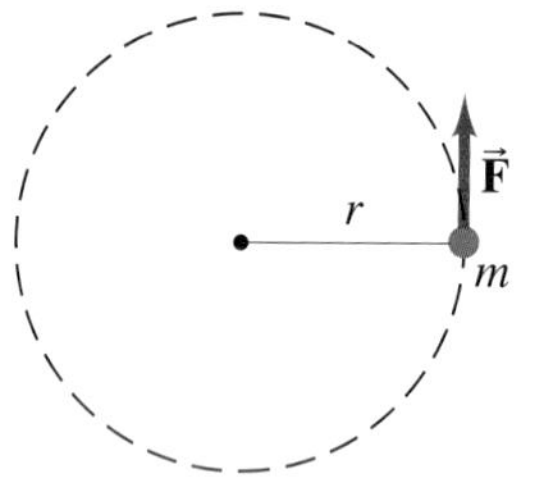


$$F = ma$$
$$= mr\alpha.$$

When we multiply both sides of this equation by $r$, we find that the torque $\tau = rF$ is given by

$$\tau = mr^2\alpha. \qquad \text{[single particle]} \quad \textbf{(8–11)}$$

Here at last we have a direct relation between the angular acceleration and the applied torque $\tau$. The quantity $mr^2$ represents the *rotational inertia* of the particle and is called its *moment of inertia*.

Now let us consider a rotating rigid object, such as a wheel rotating about an axis through its center, which could be an axle. We can think of the wheel as consisting of many particles located at various distances from the axis of rotation. We can apply Eq. 8–11 to each particle of the object, and then sum over all the particles. The sum of the various torques is just the total torque, $\Sigma\tau$, so we obtain:

$$\Sigma\tau = \left(\Sigma mr^2\right)\alpha \qquad \textbf{(8–12)}$$

where we factored out $\alpha$ because it is the same for all the particles of the object. The sum $\Sigma mr^2$ represents the sum of the masses of each particle in the object multiplied by the square of the distance of that particle from the axis of

†Recall from Chapter 4 that $\Sigma$ (Greek letter sigma) means "sum of."

rotation. If we assign each particle a number (1, 2, 3, ...), then $\Sigma mr^2 = m_1 r_1^2 + m_2 r_2^2 + m_3 r_3^2 + \cdots$. This quantity is called the **moment of inertia** (or *rotational inertia*) $I$ of the object:

$$I = \Sigma mr^2 = m_1 r_1^2 + m_2 r_2^2 + \cdots. \qquad \textbf{(8–13)}$$

*Moment of inertia*

Combining Eqs. 8–12 and 8–13, we can write

$$\Sigma\tau = I\alpha. \qquad \textbf{(8–14)}$$

*NEWTON'S SECOND LAW FOR ROTATION*

This is the rotational equivalent of Newton's second law. It is valid for the rotation of a rigid object about a fixed axis.†

We see that the moment of inertia, $I$, which is a measure of the rotational inertia of an object, plays the same role for rotational motion that mass does for translational motion. As can be seen from Eq. 8–13, the rotational inertia of an object depends not only on its mass, but also on how that mass is distributed with respect to the axis. For example, a large-diameter cylinder will have greater rotational inertia than one of equal mass but smaller diameter (and therefore greater length), Fig. 8–19. The former will be harder to start rotating, and harder to stop. When the mass is concentrated farther from the axis of rotation, the rotational inertia is greater. For rotational motion, the mass of an object *cannot* be considered as concentrated at its center of mass.

**CAUTION**
*Mass can* not *be considered concentrated at* CM *for rotational motion*

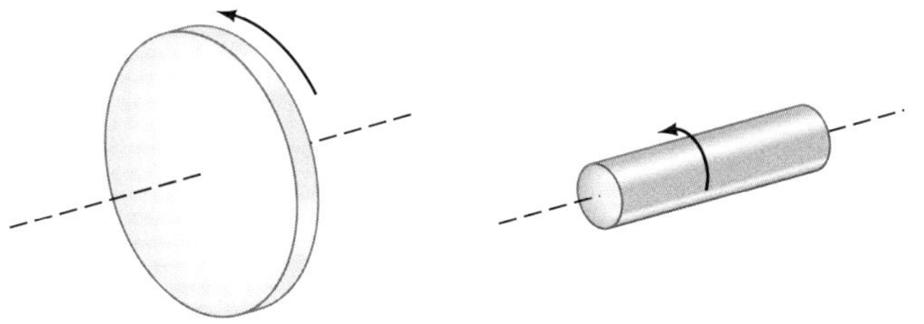

**FIGURE 8–19** A large-diameter cylinder has greater rotational inertia than one of smaller diameter but equal mass.

**EXAMPLE 8–10** **Two weights on a bar: different axis, different *I*.** Two small "weights," of mass 5.0 kg and 7.0 kg, are mounted 4.0 m apart on a light rod (whose mass can be ignored), as shown in Fig. 8–20. Calculate the moment of inertia of the system (*a*) when rotated about an axis halfway between the weights, Fig. 8–20a, and (*b*) when rotated about an axis 0.50 m to the left of the 5.0-kg mass (Fig. 8–20b).

**APPROACH** In each case, the moment of inertia of the system is found by summing over the two parts using Eq. 8–13.

**SOLUTION** (*a*) Both weights are the same distance, 2.0 m, from the axis of rotation. Thus

$$\begin{aligned} I = \Sigma mr^2 &= (5.0\,\text{kg})(2.0\,\text{m})^2 + (7.0\,\text{kg})(2.0\,\text{m})^2 \\ &= 20\,\text{kg}\cdot\text{m}^2 + 28\,\text{kg}\cdot\text{m}^2 = 48\,\text{kg}\cdot\text{m}^2. \end{aligned}$$

(*b*) The 5.0-kg mass is now 0.50 m from the axis, and the 7.0-kg mass is 4.50 m from the axis. Then

$$\begin{aligned} I = \Sigma mr^2 &= (5.0\,\text{kg})(0.50\,\text{m})^2 + (7.0\,\text{kg})(4.5\,\text{m})^2 \\ &= 1.3\,\text{kg}\cdot\text{m}^2 + 142\,\text{kg}\cdot\text{m}^2 = 143\,\text{kg}\cdot\text{m}^2. \end{aligned}$$

**NOTE** This Example illustrates two important points. First, the moment of inertia of a given system is different for different axes of rotation. Second, we see in part (*b*) that mass close to the axis of rotation contributes little to the total moment of inertia; here, the 5.0-kg object contributed less than 1% to the total.

**FIGURE 8–20** Example 8–10: calculating the moment of inertia.

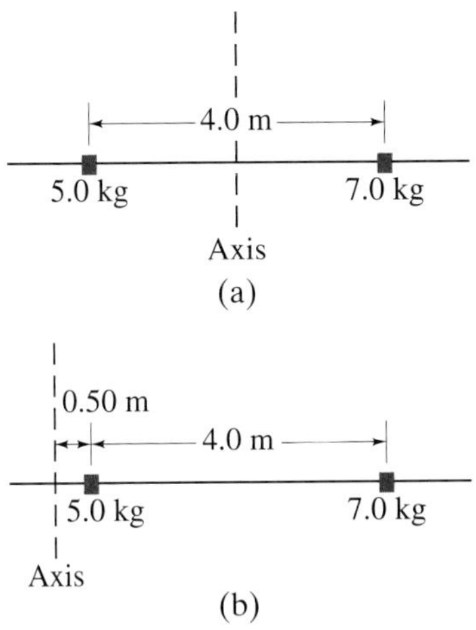


**CAUTION**
*I depends on axis of rotation and on distribution of mass*

†Equation 8–14 is also valid when the object is translating with acceleration, as long as $I$ and $\alpha$ are calculated about the center of mass of the object, and the rotation axis through the CM doesn't change direction.

**FIGURE 8–21** Moments of inertia for various objects of uniform composition.

| | Object | Location of axis | | Moment of inertia |
|---|---|---|---|---|
| (a) | **Thin hoop,** radius $R$ | Through center | 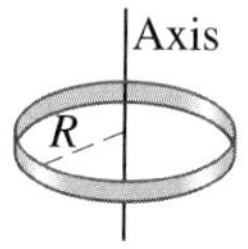 | $MR^2$ |
| (b) | **Thin hoop,** radius $R$ width $W$ | Through central diameter | 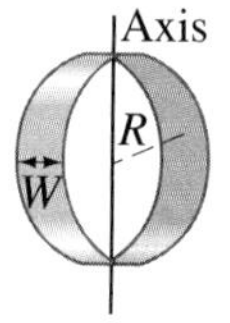 | $\frac{1}{2}MR^2 + \frac{1}{12}MW^2$ |
| (c) | **Solid cylinder,** radius $R$ | Through center | 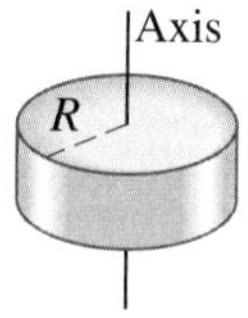 | $\frac{1}{2}MR^2$ |
| (d) | **Hollow cylinder,** inner radius $R_1$ outer radius $R_2$ | Through center | 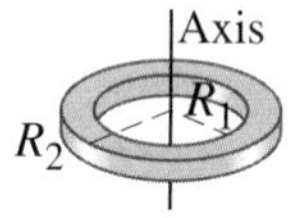 | $\frac{1}{2}M(R_1^2 + R_2^2)$ |
| (e) | **Uniform sphere,** radius $R$ | Through center | 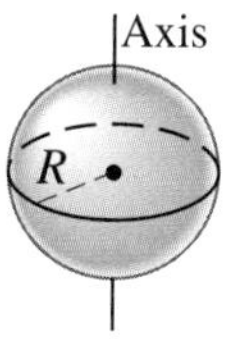 | $\frac{2}{5}MR^2$ |
| (f) | **Long uniform rod,** length $L$ | Through center | 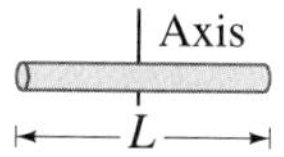 | $\frac{1}{12}ML^2$ |
| (g) | **Long uniform rod,** length $L$ | Through end | 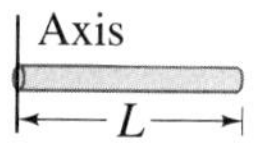 | $\frac{1}{3}ML^2$ |
| (h) | **Rectangular thin plate,** length $L$, width $W$ | Through center | 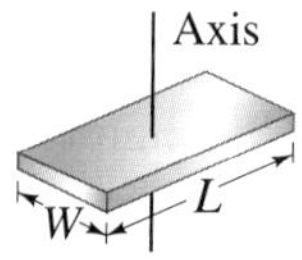 | $\frac{1}{12}M(L^2 + W^2)$ |

For most ordinary objects, the mass is distributed continuously, and the calculation of the moment of inertia, $\Sigma mr^2$, can be difficult. Expressions can, however, be worked out (using calculus) for the moments of inertia of regularly shaped objects in terms of the dimensions of the objects. Figure 8–21 gives these expressions for a number of solids rotated about the axes specified. The only one for which the result is obvious is that for the thin hoop or ring rotated about an axis passing through its center perpendicular to the plane of the hoop (Fig. 8–21a). For this object, all the mass is concentrated at the same distance from the axis, $R$. Thus $\Sigma mr^2 = (\Sigma m)R^2 = MR^2$, where $M$ is the total mass of the hoop.

When calculation is difficult, $I$ can be determined experimentally by measuring the angular acceleration $\alpha$ about a fixed axis due to a known net torque, $\Sigma\tau$, and applying Newton's second law, $I = \Sigma\tau/\alpha$, Eq. 8–14.

## 8–6 Solving Problems in Rotational Dynamics

When working with torque and angular acceleration (Eq. 8–14), it is important to use a consistent set of units, which in SI is: $\alpha$ in rad/s$^2$; $\tau$ in m·N; and the moment of inertia, $I$, in kg·m$^2$.

## PROBLEM SOLVING Rotational Motion

1. As always, draw a clear and complete **diagram**.
2. Choose the object or objects that will be the **system** to be studied.
3. Draw a **free-body diagram** for the object under consideration (or for each object, if more than one), showing only (and all) the forces acting on that object and exactly where they act, so you can determine the torque due to each. Gravity acts at the CG of the object (Section 7–8).
4. Identify the axis of rotation and determine the **torques** about it. Choose positive and negative directions of rotation (counterclockwise and clockwise), and assign the correct sign to each torque.
5. Apply **Newton's second law for rotation**, $\Sigma\tau = I\alpha$. If the moment of inertia is not given, and it is not the unknown sought, you need to determine it first. Use consistent units, which in SI are: $\alpha$ in rad/s$^2$; $\tau$ in m·N; and $I$ in kg·m$^2$.
6. Also apply **Newton's second law for translation**, $\Sigma\vec{\mathbf{F}} = m\vec{\mathbf{a}}$, and **other** laws or principles as needed.
7. **Solve** the resulting equation(s) for the unknown(s).
8. Do a rough **estimate** to determine if your answer is reasonable.

**EXAMPLE 8–11** **A heavy pulley.** A 15.0-N force (represented by $\vec{\mathbf{F}}_T$) is applied to a cord wrapped around a pulley of mass $M = 4.00$ kg and radius $R = 33.0$ cm, Fig. 8–22. The pulley accelerates uniformly from rest to an angular speed of 30.0 rad/s in 3.00 s. If there is a frictional torque $\tau_{fr} = 1.10$ m·N at the axle, determine the moment of inertia of the pulley. The pulley rotates about its center.

**APPROACH** We follow the steps of the Problem Solving Box explicitly.

**SOLUTION**

1. **Draw a diagram.** The pulley and the attached cord are shown in Fig. 8–22.
2. **Choose the system**: the pulley.
3. **Draw a free-body diagram.** The force that the cord exerts on the pulley is shown as $\vec{\mathbf{F}}_T$ in Fig. 8–22. The friction force is also shown, but we are given only its torque. Two other forces could be included in the diagram: the force of gravity $mg$ down and whatever force keeps the axle in place. They do not contribute to the torque (their lever arms are zero) and so are not shown.
4. **Determine the torques.** The cord exerts a force $\vec{\mathbf{F}}_T$ that acts at the edge of the pulley, so its lever arm is $R$. The torque exerted by the cord equals $RF_T$ and is counterclockwise, which we choose to be positive. The frictional torque is given as $\tau_{fr} = 1.10$ m·N; it opposes the motion and is negative.
5. **Apply Newton's second law for rotation.** The net torque is

$$\Sigma\tau = RF_T - \tau_{fr}$$
$$= (0.330\,\text{m})(15.0\,\text{N}) - 1.10\,\text{m}\cdot\text{N} = 3.85\,\text{m}\cdot\text{N}.$$

The angular acceleration $\alpha$ is found from the given data that it takes 3.0 s to accelerate the pulley from rest to $\omega = 30.0$ rad/s:

$$\alpha = \frac{\Delta\omega}{\Delta t} = \frac{30.0\,\text{rad/s} - 0}{3.00\,\text{s}} = 10.0\,\text{rad/s}^2.$$

We can now solve for $I$ in Newton's second law (see step 7).

6. **Other calculations**: None needed.
7. **Solve for unknowns.** We solve for $I$ in Newton's second law for rotation, $\Sigma\tau = I\alpha$, and insert our values for $\Sigma\tau$ and $\alpha$:

$$I = \frac{\Sigma\tau}{\alpha} = \frac{3.85\,\text{m}\cdot\text{N}}{10.0\,\text{rad/s}^2} = 0.385\,\text{kg}\cdot\text{m}^2.$$

8. **Do a rough estimate.** We can do a rough estimate of the moment of inertia by assuming the pulley is a uniform cylinder and using Fig. 8–21c:

$$I = \tfrac{1}{2}MR^2 = \tfrac{1}{2}(4.00\,\text{kg})(0.330\,\text{m})^2 = 0.218\,\text{kg}\cdot\text{m}^2.$$

This is the same order of magnitude as our result, but numerically somewhat less. This makes sense, though, because a pulley is not usually a uniform cylinder but instead has more of its mass concentrated toward the outside edge. Such a pulley would be expected to have a greater moment of inertia than a solid cylinder of equal mass; a thin hoop, Fig. 8–21a, ought to have a greater $I$ than our pulley, and indeed it does: $I = MR^2 = 0.436\,\text{kg}\cdot\text{m}^2$.

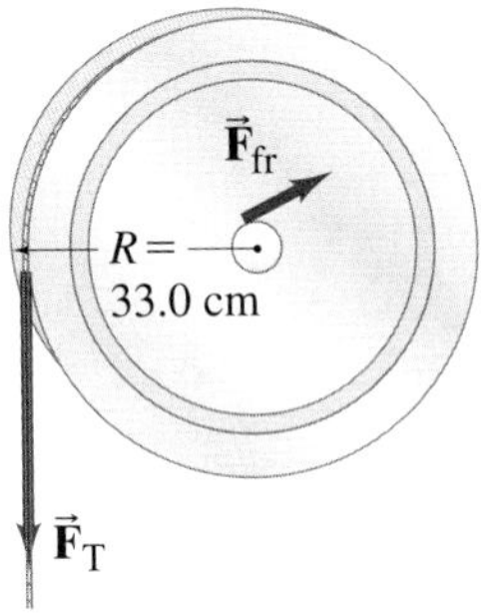

**FIGURE 8–22** Example 8–11.

*Usefulness and power of rough estimates*

## Additional Example—a bit more challenging

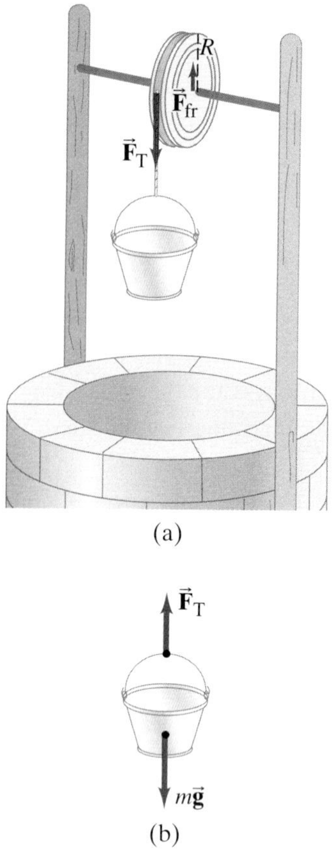


**FIGURE 8–23** Example 8–12. (a) Pulley and falling bucket of mass $m$. (b) Free-body diagram for the bucket.

**EXAMPLE 8–12** **Pulley and bucket.** Consider again the pulley in Fig. 8–22 and Example 8–11. But this time, instead of a constant 15.0-N force being exerted on the cord, we now have a bucket of weight $w = 15.0\text{ N}$ (mass $m = w/g = 1.53\text{ kg}$) hanging from the cord. See Fig. 8–23a. We assume the cord has negligible mass and does not stretch or slip on the pulley. Calculate the angular acceleration $\alpha$ of the pulley and the linear acceleration $a$ of the bucket.

**APPROACH** This situation looks a lot like Example 8–11, Fig. 8–22. But there is a big difference: the tension in the cord is now an unknown, and it is no longer equal to the weight of the bucket if the bucket accelerates. Our system has two parts: the bucket, which can undergo translational motion (Fig. 8–23b is its free-body diagram); and the pulley. The pulley does not translate, but it can rotate. We apply the rotational version of Newton's second law to the pulley, $\Sigma\tau = I\alpha$, and the linear version to the bucket, $\Sigma F = ma$.

**SOLUTION** Let $F_T$ be the tension in the cord. Then a force $F_T$ acts at the edge of the pulley, and we apply Newton's second law, Eq. 8–14, for the rotation of the pulley:

$$I\alpha = \Sigma\tau = RF_T - \tau_{fr}. \qquad \text{[pulley]}$$

Next we look at the (linear) motion of the bucket of mass $m$. Figure 8–23b, the free-body diagram for the bucket, shows that two forces act on the bucket: the force of gravity $mg$ acts downward, and the tension of the cord $F_T$ pulls upward. Applying Newton's second law, $\Sigma F = ma$, for the bucket, we have (taking downward as positive):

$$mg - F_T = ma. \qquad \text{[bucket]}$$

Note that the tension $F_T$, which is the force exerted on the edge of the pulley, is *not* equal to the weight of the bucket ($= mg = 15.0\text{ N}$). There must be a net force on the bucket if it is accelerating, so $F_T < mg$. We can also see this from the last equation above, $F_T = mg - ma$.

To obtain $\alpha$, we note that the tangential acceleration of a point on the edge of the pulley is the same as the acceleration of the bucket if the cord doesn't stretch or slip. Hence we can use Eq. 8–5, $a_{tan} = a = R\alpha$. Substituting $F_T = mg - ma = mg - mR\alpha$ into the first equation above (Newton's second law for rotation of the pulley), we obtain

$$I\alpha = \Sigma\tau = RF_T - \tau_{fr} = R(mg - mR\alpha) - \tau_{fr} = mgR - mR^2\alpha - \tau_{fr}.$$

$\alpha$ appears in the second term on the right, so we bring that term to the left side and solve for $\alpha$:

$$\alpha = \frac{mgR - \tau_{fr}}{I + mR^2}.$$

The numerator ($mgR - \tau_{fr}$) is the net torque, and the denominator ($I + mR^2$) is the total rotational inertia of the system. Then, since $I = 0.385\text{ kg}\cdot\text{m}^2$, $m = 1.53\text{ kg}$, and $\tau_{fr} = 1.10\text{ m}\cdot\text{N}$ (from Example 8–11),

$$\alpha = \frac{(15.0\text{ N})(0.330\text{ m}) - 1.10\text{ m}\cdot\text{N}}{0.385\text{ kg}\cdot\text{m}^2 + (1.53\text{ kg})(0.330\text{ m})^2} = 6.98\text{ rad/s}^2.$$

The angular acceleration is somewhat less in this case than the $10.0\text{ rad/s}^2$ of Example 8–11. Why? Because $F_T$ ($= mg - ma$) is less than the 15.0-N weight of the bucket, $mg$. The linear acceleration of the bucket is

$$a = R\alpha = (0.330\text{ m})(6.98\text{ rad/s}^2) = 2.30\text{ m/s}^2.$$

**NOTE** The tension in the cord $F_T$ is less than $mg$ because the bucket accelerates.

## 8–7 Rotational Kinetic Energy

The quantity $\frac{1}{2}mv^2$ is the kinetic energy of an object undergoing translational motion. An object rotating about an axis is said to have **rotational kinetic energy**. By analogy with translational kinetic energy, we would expect this to be given by the expression $\frac{1}{2}I\omega^2$, where $I$ is the moment of inertia of the object and $\omega$ is its angular velocity. We can indeed show that this is true.

Consider any rigid rotating object as made up of many tiny particles, each of mass $m$. If we let $r$ represent the distance of any one particle from the axis of rotation, then its linear velocity is $v = r\omega$. The total kinetic energy of the whole object will be the sum of the kinetic energies of all its particles:

$$\text{KE} = \Sigma\left(\tfrac{1}{2}mv^2\right) = \Sigma\left(\tfrac{1}{2}mr^2\omega^2\right)$$
$$= \tfrac{1}{2}\Sigma\left(mr^2\right)\omega^2.$$

We have factored out the $\frac{1}{2}$ and the $\omega^2$ since they are the same for every particle of a rigid object. Since $\Sigma mr^2 = I$, the moment of inertia, we see that the kinetic energy of a rigid rotating object is, as expected,

$$\text{rotational KE} = \tfrac{1}{2}I\omega^2. \qquad \textbf{(8–15)}$$

*Rotational KE*

The units are joules, as with all other forms of energy.

An object that rotates while its center of mass (CM) undergoes translational motion will have both translational and rotational kinetic energies. Equation 8–15 gives the rotational kinetic energy if the rotation axis is fixed. If the object is moving (such as a wheel rolling down a hill), this equation is still valid as long as the rotation axis is fixed in direction. Then the total kinetic energy is

$$\text{KE} = \tfrac{1}{2}Mv_{\text{CM}}^2 + \tfrac{1}{2}I_{\text{CM}}\,\omega^2, \qquad \textbf{(8–16)}$$

*Total KE (translation + rotation)*

where $v_{\text{CM}}$ is the linear velocity of the center of mass, $I_{\text{CM}}$ is the moment of inertia about an axis through the center of mass, $\omega$ is the angular velocity about this axis, and $M$ is the total mass of the object.

**EXAMPLE 8–13** **Sphere rolling down an incline.** What will be the speed of a solid sphere of mass $M$ and radius $R$ when it reaches the bottom of an incline if it starts from rest at a vertical height $H$ and rolls without slipping? See Fig. 8–24. (Assume plenty of static friction, which does no work, so no slipping takes place.) Compare your result to that for an object *sliding* down a frictionless incline.

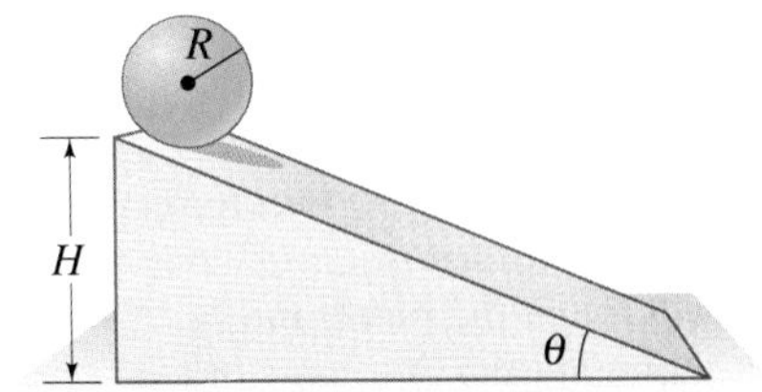


**FIGURE 8–24** A sphere rolling down a hill has both translational and rotational kinetic energy. Example 8–13.

**APPROACH** We use the law of conservation of energy with gravitational potential energy, now including rotational kinetic energy as well as translational KE.

**SOLUTION** The total energy at any point a vertical distance $y$ above the base of the incline is

$$\tfrac{1}{2}Mv^2 + \tfrac{1}{2}I_{\text{CM}}\,\omega^2 + Mgy,$$

where $v$ is the speed of the center of mass, and $Mgy$ is the gravitational PE. Applying conservation of energy, we equate the total energy at the top ($y = H, v = 0, \omega = 0$) to the total energy at the bottom ($y = 0$):

**➡ PROBLEM SOLVING**

*Rotational energy adds to other forms of energy to get the total energy which is conserved*

$$0 + 0 + MgH = \tfrac{1}{2}Mv^2 + \tfrac{1}{2}I_{\text{CM}}\omega^2 + 0.$$

The moment of inertia of a solid sphere about an axis through its center of mass is $I_{\text{CM}} = \frac{2}{5}MR^2$, Fig. 8–21e. Since the sphere rolls without slipping, we have $\omega = v/R$ (recall Fig. 8–8). Hence

$$MgH = \tfrac{1}{2}Mv^2 + \tfrac{1}{2}\left(\tfrac{2}{5}MR^2\right)\left(\frac{v^2}{R^2}\right).$$

Canceling the $M$'s and $R$'s, we obtain

$$\left(\tfrac{1}{2} + \tfrac{1}{5}\right)v^2 = gH$$

or

$$v = \sqrt{\tfrac{10}{7}gH}.$$

We can compare this result for the speed of a rolling sphere to that for an object sliding down a plane without rotating and without friction, $\frac{1}{2}mv^2 = mgH$ (see our energy equation above, removing the rotational term). Then $v = \sqrt{2gH}$, which is greater than our result. An object sliding without friction or rotation transforms its initial potential energy entirely into translational KE (none into rotational KE), so the speed of its center of mass is greater.

**NOTE** Our result for the rolling sphere shows (perhaps surprisingly) that $v$ is independent of both the mass $M$ and the radius $R$ of the sphere.

**CONCEPTUAL EXAMPLE 8–14** **Who's fastest?** Several objects roll without slipping down an incline of vertical height $H$, all starting from rest at the same moment. The objects are a thin hoop (or a plain wedding band), a spherical marble, a solid cylinder (a D-cell battery), and an empty soup can. In addition, a greased box slides down without friction. In what order do they reach the bottom of the incline?

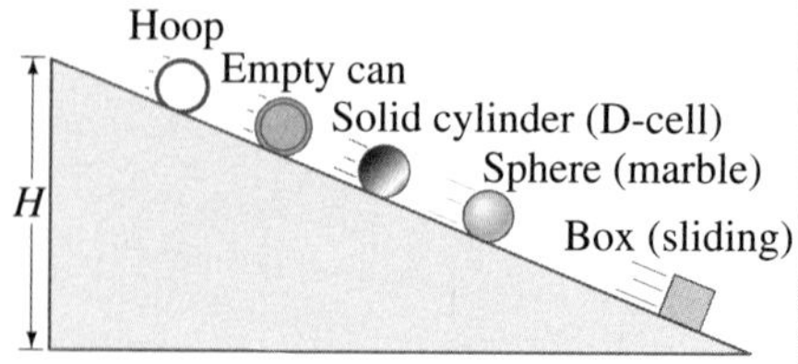


**FIGURE 8–25** Example 8–14.

**RESPONSE** The sliding box wins because the potential energy loss ($MgH$) is transformed completely into translational KE for the box, whereas for rolling objects the initial PE is shared between translational and rotational kinetic energies, and so their linear speed is less. For each of the rolling objects we can state that the loss in potential energy equals the increase in kinetic energy:

$$MgH = \tfrac{1}{2}Mv^2 + \tfrac{1}{2}I_{CM}\,\omega^2.$$

For all our rolling objects, the moment of inertia $I_{CM}$ is a numerical factor times the mass $M$ and the radius $R^2$ (Fig. 8–21). The mass $M$ is in each term, so the translational speed $v$ doesn't depend on $M$; nor does it depend on the radius $R$ since $\omega = v/R$, so $R^2$ cancels out for all the rolling objects, just as in Example 8–13. Thus the speed $v$ at the bottom depends only on that numerical factor in $I_{CM}$ which expresses how the mass is distributed. The hoop, with all its mass concentrated at radius $R$ $\left(I_{CM} = MR^2\right)$, has the largest moment of inertia; hence it will have the lowest speed and will arrive at the bottom behind the D-cell $\left(I_{CM} = \tfrac{1}{2}MR^2\right)$, which in turn will be behind the marble $\left(I_{CM} = \tfrac{2}{5}MR^2\right)$. The empty can, which is mainly a hoop plus a small disk, has most of its mass concentrated at $R$; so it will be a bit faster than the pure hoop but slower than the D-cell. See Fig. 8–25.

**NOTE** As in Example 8–13, the speed at the bottom does not depend on the object's mass $M$ or radius $R$, but only on its shape (and the height of the hill $H$).

**FIGURE 8–26** A sphere rolling to the right on a plane surface. The point in contact with the ground at any moment, point P, is momentarily at rest. Point A to the left of P is moving nearly vertically upward at the instant shown, and point B to the right is moving nearly vertically downward. An instant later, point B will touch the plane and be at rest momentarily. Thus no work is done by the force of static friction.

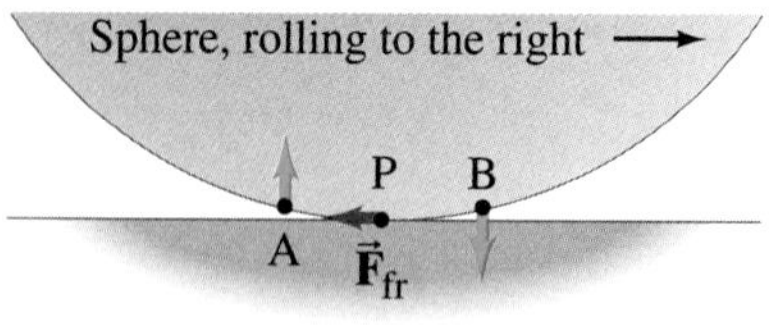


**CAUTION**

*Rolling objects go slower than sliding objects because of rotational KE, not because of friction*

If there had been little or no static friction between the rolling objects and the plane in these Examples, the round objects would have slid rather than rolled, or a combination of both. Static friction must be present to make a round object roll. We did not need to take friction into account in the energy equation because it is *static* friction and does no work—the point of contact of the sphere at each instant does not slide, but moves perpendicular to the plane (first down and then up as shown in Fig. 8–26) as the sphere rolls. Thus, no work is done by the static friction force because the force and the motion (displacement) are perpendicular. The reason the rolling objects in Examples 8–13 and 8–14 move down the slope more slowly than if they were sliding is *not* because friction is doing work. Rather, it is because some of the gravitional PE is converted to rotational KE, leaving less for the translational KE.

## Work Done by Torque

The work done on an object rotating about a fixed axis, such as the pulleys in Figs. 8–22 and 8–23, can be written using angular quantities. As shown in Fig. 8–27, a force $F$ exerting a torque $\tau = rF$ on a wheel does work $W = F\Delta l$ in rotating the wheel a small distance $\Delta l$ at the point of application of $\vec{\mathbf{F}}$.

**FIGURE 8–27** Torque $\tau = rF$ does work when rotating a wheel equal to $W = F\Delta l = Fr\Delta\theta = \tau\Delta\theta$.

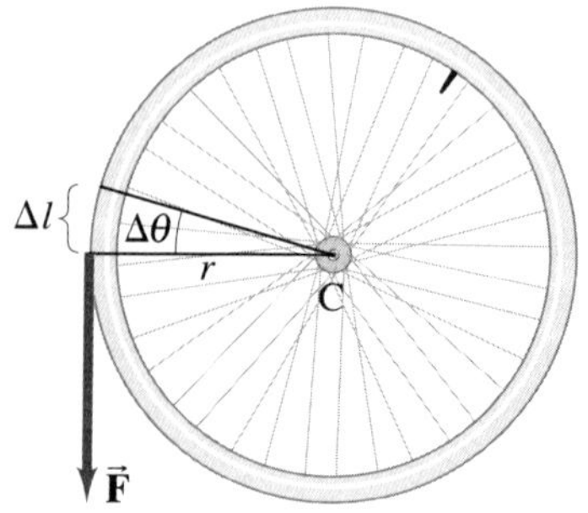

The wheel has rotated through a small angle $\Delta\theta = \Delta l/r$ (Eq. 8–1). Hence

$$W = F\Delta l = Fr\Delta\theta.$$

Since $\tau = rF$, then

$$W = \tau\Delta\theta \qquad \textbf{(8–17)}$$

*Work done by torque*

is the work done by the torque $\tau$ when rotating the wheel through an angle $\Delta\theta$. Finally, power $P$ is the rate work is done: $P = W/\Delta t = \tau\Delta\theta/\Delta t = \tau\omega$.

## 8–8 Angular Momentum and Its Conservation

Throughout this Chapter we have seen that if we use the appropriate angular variables, the kinematic and dynamic equations for rotational motion are analogous to those for ordinary linear motion. We saw in the previous Section, for example, that rotational kinetic energy can be written as $\frac{1}{2}I\omega^2$, which is analogous to the translational kinetic energy, $\frac{1}{2}mv^2$. In like manner, the linear momentum, $p = mv$, has a rotational analog. It is called **angular momentum**, $L$. For an object rotating about a fixed axis, it is defined as

$$L = I\omega, \qquad \textbf{(8–18)}$$

*Angular momentum*

where $I$ is the moment of inertia and $\omega$ is the angular velocity about the axis of rotation. The SI units for $L$ are $\mathrm{kg\cdot m^2/s}$, which has no special name.

We saw in Chapter 7 (Section 7–1) that Newton's second law can be written not only as $\Sigma F = ma$ but also more generally in terms of momentum (Eq. 7–2), $\Sigma F = \Delta p/\Delta t$. In a similar way, the rotational equivalent of Newton's second law, which we saw in Eq. 8–14 can be written as $\Sigma\tau = I\alpha$, can also be written in terms of angular momentum:

$$\Sigma\tau = \frac{\Delta L}{\Delta t}, \qquad \textbf{(8–19)}$$

*NEWTON'S SECOND LAW FOR ROTATION*

where $\Sigma\tau$ is the net torque acting to rotate the object, and $\Delta L$ is the change in angular momentum in a time interval $\Delta t$. Equation 8–14, $\Sigma\tau = I\alpha$, is a special case of Eq. 8–19 when the moment of inertia is constant. This can be seen as follows. If an object has angular velocity $\omega_0$ at time $t = 0$, and angular velocity $\omega$ after a time interval $\Delta t$, then its angular acceleration (Eq. 8–3) is

$$\alpha = \frac{\Delta\omega}{\Delta t} = \frac{\omega - \omega_0}{\Delta t}.$$

Then from Eq. 8–19, we have

$$\Sigma\tau = \frac{\Delta L}{\Delta t} = \frac{I\omega - I\omega_0}{\Delta t} = \frac{I(\omega - \omega_0)}{\Delta t} = I\frac{\Delta\omega}{\Delta t} = I\alpha,$$

which is Eq. 8–14.

Angular momentum is an important concept in physics because, under certain conditions, it is a conserved quantity. We can see from Eq. 8–19 that if the net torque $\Sigma\tau$ on an object is zero, then $\Delta L/\Delta t$ equals zero. That is, $L$ does not change. This is the **law of conservation of angular momentum** for a rotating object:

**The total angular momentum of a rotating object remains constant if the net torque acting on it is zero.**

*CONSERVATION OF ANGULAR MOMENTUM*

The law of conservation of angular momentum is one of the great conservation laws of physics, along with energy and linear momentum.

When there is zero net torque acting on an object, and the object is rotating about a fixed axis or about an axis through its center of mass whose direction doesn't change, we can write

$$I\omega = I_0\omega_0 = \text{constant}.$$

$I_0$ and $\omega_0$ are the moment of inertia and angular velocity, respectively, about that axis at some initial time ($t = 0$), and $I$ and $\omega$ are their values at some other time.

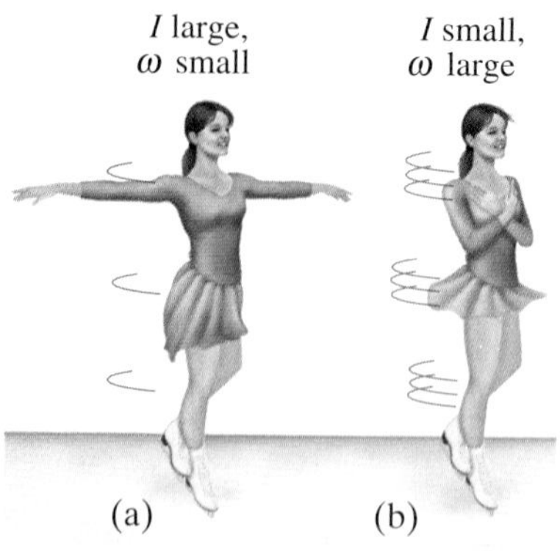


**FIGURE 8–28** A skater doing a spin on ice, illustrating conservation of angular momentum. In (a), $I$ is large and $\omega$ is small; in (b), $I$ is smaller so $\omega$ is larger.

**PHYSICS APPLIED**
*Spins in figure skating and diving*

**FIGURE 8–29** A diver rotates faster when arms and legs are tucked in than when they are outstretched. Angular momentum is conserved.

**FIGURE 8–30** Example 8–15.

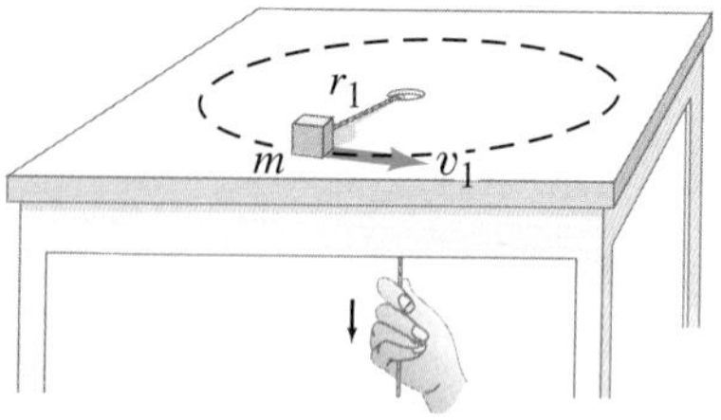


The parts of the object may alter their positions relative to one another, so $I$ changes. But then $\omega$ changes as well to ensure that the product $I\omega$ remains constant.

Many interesting phenomena can be understood on the basis of conservation of angular momentum. Consider a skater doing a spin on the tips of her skates, Fig. 8–28. She rotates at a relatively low speed when her arms are outstretched; when she brings her arms in close to her body, she suddenly spins much faster. From the definition of moment of inertia, $I = \Sigma mr^2$, it is clear that when she pulls her arms in closer to the axis of rotation, $r$ is reduced for the arms, so her moment of inertia is reduced. Since the angular momentum $I\omega$ remains constant (we ignore the small torque due to friction), if $I$ decreases, then the angular velocity $\omega$ must increase. If the skater reduces her moment of inertia by a factor of 2, she will then rotate with twice the angular velocity.

**EXERCISE C** When a spinning figure skater pulls in her arms, her moment of inertia decreases; to conserve angular momentum, her angular velocity increases. Does her rotational kinetic energy also increase? If so, where does the energy come from?

A similar example is the diver shown in Fig. 8–29. The push as she leaves the board gives her an initial angular momentum about her center of mass. When she curls herself into the tuck position, she rotates quickly one or more times. She then stretches out again, increasing her moment of inertia which reduces the angular velocity to a small value, and then she enters the water. The change in moment of inertia from the straight position to the tuck position can be a factor of as much as $3\frac{1}{2}$.

Note that for angular momentum to be conserved, the net torque must be zero, but the net force does not necessarily have to be zero. The net force on the diver in Fig. 8–29, for example, is not zero (gravity is acting), but the net torque on her is zero because the force of gravity acts at her center of mass.

**EXAMPLE 8–15** **Object rotating on a string of changing length.** A small mass $m$ attached to the end of a string revolves in a circle on a frictionless tabletop. The other end of the string passes through a hole in the table (Fig. 8–30). Initially, the mass revolves with a speed $v_1 = 2.4\,\mathrm{m/s}$ in a circle of radius $r_1 = 0.80\,\mathrm{m}$. The string is then pulled slowly through the hole so that the radius is reduced to $r_2 = 0.48\,\mathrm{m}$. What is the speed, $v_2$, of the mass now?

**APPROACH** There is no net torque on the mass $m$ because the force exerted by the string to keep it moving in a circle is exerted toward the axis; hence the lever arm is zero. We can thus apply conservation of angular momentum.

**SOLUTION** Conservation of angular momentum gives

$$I_1\omega_1 = I_2\omega_2.$$

Our small mass is essentially a particle whose moment of inertia about the hole is $I = mr^2$ (Section 8–5, Eq. 8–11), so we have

$$mr_1^2\omega_1 = mr_2^2\omega_2,$$

or

$$\omega_2 = \omega_1\left(\frac{r_1^2}{r_2^2}\right).$$

Then, since $v = r\omega$, we can write

$$v_2 = r_2\omega_2 = r_2\omega_1\left(\frac{r_1^2}{r_2^2}\right) = r_2\frac{v_1}{r_1}\left(\frac{r_1^2}{r_2^2}\right) = v_1\frac{r_1}{r_2}$$

$$= (2.4\,\mathrm{m/s})\left(\frac{0.80\,\mathrm{m}}{0.48\,\mathrm{m}}\right) = 4.0\,\mathrm{m/s}.$$

The speed increases as the radius decreases.

**EXERCISE D** The speed of mass $m$ in Example 8–15 increased, so its kinetic energy increased. Where did the energy come from?

**EXAMPLE 8–16** **ESTIMATE** **Star collapse.** Astronomers often detect stars that are rotating extremely rapidly, known as neutron stars. These stars are believed to have formed from the inner core of a larger star that collapsed, due to its own gravitation, to a star of very small radius and very high density. Before collapse, suppose the core of such a star is the size of our Sun $(R \approx 7 \times 10^5\,\text{km})$ with mass 2.0 times as great as the Sun, and is rotating at a speed of 1.0 revolution every 10 days. If it were to undergo gravitational collapse to a neutron star of radius 10 km, what would its rotation speed be? Assume the star is a uniform sphere at all times.

PHYSICS APPLIED
*Neutron star*

**APPROACH** The star is isolated (no external forces), so we can use conservation of angular momentum for this process.

**SOLUTION** From conservation of angular momentum,

$$I_1\omega_1 = I_2\omega_2$$

where the subscripts 1 and 2 refer to initial (normal star) and final (neutron star), respectively. Then, assuming no mass is lost in the process,

$$\omega_2 = \left(\frac{I_1}{I_2}\right)\omega_1 = \left(\frac{\frac{2}{5}M_1R_1^2}{\frac{2}{5}M_2R_2^2}\right)\omega_1 = \frac{R_1^2}{R_2^2}\,\omega_1.$$

The frequency $f = \omega/2\pi$, so

$$f_2 = \frac{\omega_2}{2\pi} = \frac{R_1^2}{R_2^2}f_1$$

$$= \left(\frac{7\times10^5\,\text{km}}{10\,\text{km}}\right)^2\left(\frac{1.0\,\text{rev}}{10\,\text{d}(24\,\text{h/d})(3600\,\text{s/h})}\right) \approx 6\times10^3\,\text{rev/s}.$$

## * 8–9 Vector Nature of Angular Quantities

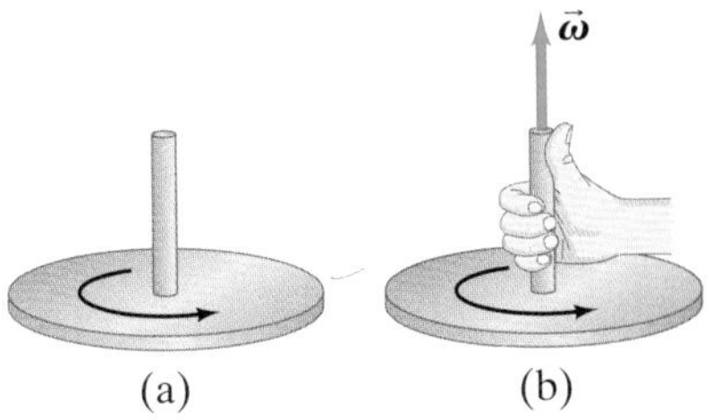

**FIGURE 8–31** (a) Rotating wheel. (b) Right-hand rule for obtaining the direction of $\vec{\omega}$.

Up to now we have considered only the magnitudes of angular quantities such as $\omega$, $\alpha$, and $L$. But they have a vector aspect too, and now we consider the directions. In fact, we have to *define* the directions for rotational quantities, and we take first the angular velocity, $\vec{\omega}$.

Consider the rotating wheel shown in Fig. 8–31a. The linear velocities of different particles of the wheel point in all different directions. The only unique direction in space associated with the rotation is along the axis of rotation, perpendicular to the actual motion. We therefore choose the axis of rotation to be the direction of the angular velocity vector, $\vec{\omega}$. Actually, there is still an ambiguity since $\vec{\omega}$ could point in either direction along the axis of rotation (up or down in Fig. 8–31a). The convention we use, called **the right-hand rule**, is the following: When the fingers of the right hand are curled around the rotation axis and point in the direction of the rotation, then the thumb points in the direction of $\vec{\omega}$. This is shown in Fig. 8–31b. Note that $\vec{\omega}$ points in the direction a right-handed screw would move when turned in the direction of rotation. Thus, if the rotation of the wheel in Fig. 8–31b is counterclockwise, the direction of $\vec{\omega}$ is upward. If the wheel rotates clockwise, then $\vec{\omega}$ points in the opposite direction, downward. Note that no part of the rotating object moves in the direction of $\vec{\omega}$.

*Right-hand rule*

If the axis of rotation is fixed, then $\vec{\omega}$ can change only in magnitude. Thus $\vec{\alpha} = \Delta\vec{\omega}/\Delta t$ must also point along the axis of rotation. If the rotation is counterclockwise as in Fig. 8–31a, and if the magnitude $\omega$ is increasing, then $\vec{\alpha}$ points upward; but if $\omega$ is decreasing (the wheel is slowing down), $\vec{\alpha}$ points downward. If the rotation is clockwise, $\vec{\alpha}$ will point downward if $\omega$ is increasing, and point upward if $\omega$ is decreasing.

Angular momentum, like linear momentum, is a vector quantity. For a symmetrical object rotating about a symmetry axis (such as a wheel, cylinder, hoop, or sphere), we can write the vector angular momentum as

$$\vec{\mathbf{L}} = I\vec{\boldsymbol{\omega}}. \qquad \textbf{(8–20)}$$

The angular velocity vector $\vec{\boldsymbol{\omega}}$ (and therefore also $\vec{\mathbf{L}}$) points along the axis of rotation in the direction given by the right-hand rule (Fig. 8–31b).

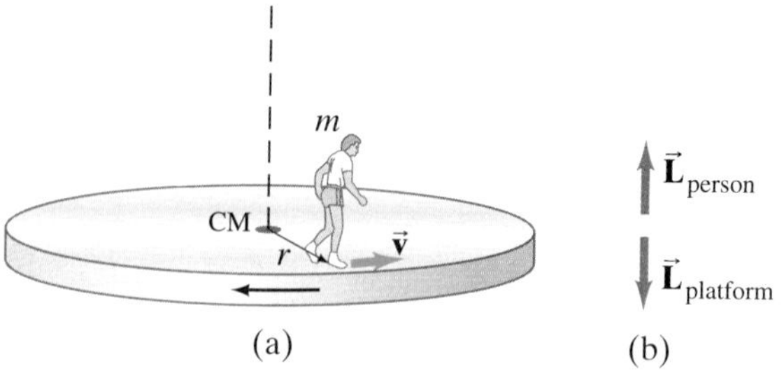


**FIGURE 8–32** (a) A person standing on a circular platform, initially at rest, begins walking along the edge at speed $v$. The platform, assumed to be mounted on friction-free bearings, begins rotating in the opposite direction, so that the total angular momentum remains zero, as shown in (b).

The vector nature of angular momentum can be used to explain a number of interesting (and sometimes surprising) phenomena. For example, consider a person standing at rest on a circular platform capable of rotating without friction about an axis through its center (that is, a simplified merry-go-round). If the person now starts to walk along the edge of the platform, Fig. 8–32a, the platform starts rotating in the opposite direction. Why? One way to look at it is that the person's foot exerts a force on the platform. Another way to look at it (and this is the most useful analysis here) is that this is an example of the conservation of angular momentum. If the person starts walking counterclockwise, the person's angular momentum will point upward along the axis of rotation (remember how we defined the direction of $\vec{\boldsymbol{\omega}}$ using the right-hand rule). The magnitude of the person's angular momentum will be $L = I\omega = (mr^2)(v/r)$, where $v$ is the person's speed (relative to Earth, not to the platform), $r$ is his distance from the rotation axis, $m$ is his mass, and $mr^2$ is his moment of inertia if we consider him a particle (mass concentrated at one point). The platform rotates in the opposite direction, so its angular momentum points downward. If the initial total angular momentum of the system (person and platform) was zero (person and platform at rest), it will remain zero after the person starts walking. That is, the upward angular momentum of the person just balances the oppositely directed downward angular momentum of the platform (Fig. 8–32b), so the total vector angular momentum remains zero. Even though the person exerts a force (and torque) on the platform, the platform exerts an equal and opposite torque on the person. So the net torque on the *system* of person plus platform is zero (ignoring friction), and the total angular momentum remains constant.

**FIGURE 8–33** Example 8–17.

CONCEPTUAL EXAMPLE 8–17 **Spinning bicycle wheel.** Your physics teacher is holding a spinning bicycle wheel while he stands on a stationary frictionless turntable (Fig. 8–33). What will happen if the teacher suddenly flips the bicycle wheel over so that it is spinning in the opposite direction?

**RESPONSE** We consider the system of turntable, teacher, and bicycle wheel. The total angular momentum initially is $\vec{\mathbf{L}}$ vertically upward. That is also what the system's angular momentum must be afterward, since $\vec{\mathbf{L}}$ is conserved when there is no net torque. Thus, if the wheel's angular momentum after being flipped over is $-\vec{\mathbf{L}}$ downward, then the angular momentum of teacher plus turntable will have to be $+2\vec{\mathbf{L}}$ upward. We can safely predict that the teacher will begin spinning around in the same direction the wheel was spinning originally.

# Summary


When a rigid object rotates about a fixed axis, each point of the object moves in a circular path. Lines drawn perpendicularly from the rotation axis to various points in the object all sweep out the same angle $\theta$ in any given time interval.

Angles are conveniently measured in **radians**, where one radian is the angle subtended by an arc whose length is equal to the radius, or

$$2\pi\ \text{rad} = 360^\circ$$
$$1\ \text{rad} \approx 57.3^\circ.$$

**Angular velocity**, $\omega$, is defined as the rate of change of angular position:

$$\omega = \frac{\Delta\theta}{\Delta t}. \qquad \textbf{(8–2)}$$

All parts of a rigid object rotating about a fixed axis have the same angular velocity at any instant.

**Angular acceleration**, $\alpha$, is defined as the rate of change of angular velocity:

$$\alpha = \frac{\Delta\omega}{\Delta t}. \qquad \textbf{(8–3)}$$

The linear velocity $v$ and acceleration $a$ of a point fixed at a distance $r$ from the axis of rotation are related to $\omega$ and $\alpha$ by

$$v = r\omega, \qquad \textbf{(8–4)}$$
$$a_{\text{tan}} = r\alpha, \qquad \textbf{(8–5)}$$
$$a_{\text{R}} = \omega^2 r, \qquad \textbf{(8–6)}$$

where $a_{\text{tan}}$ and $a_{\text{R}}$ are the tangential and radial (centripetal) components of the linear acceleration, respectively.

The frequency $f$ is related to $\omega$ by

$$\omega = 2\pi f, \qquad \textbf{(8–7)}$$

and to the period $T$ by

$$T = 1/f. \qquad \textbf{(8–8)}$$

The equations describing uniformly accelerated rotational motion ($\alpha$ = constant) have the same form as for uniformly accelerated linear motion:

$$\omega = \omega_0 + \alpha t, \qquad \theta = \omega_0 t + \tfrac{1}{2}\alpha t^2,$$
$$\omega^2 = \omega_0^2 + 2\alpha\theta, \qquad \overline{\omega} = \frac{\omega + \omega_0}{2}. \qquad \textbf{(8–9)}$$

The dynamics of rotation is analogous to the dynamics of linear motion. Force is replaced by **torque** $\tau$, which is defined as the product of force times lever arm (perpendicular distance from the line of action of the force to the axis of rotation):

$$\tau = rF\sin\theta = r_\perp F = rF_\perp. \qquad \textbf{(8–10)}$$

Mass is replaced by **moment of inertia** $I$, which depends not only on the mass of the object, but also on how the mass is distributed about the axis of rotation. Linear acceleration is replaced by angular acceleration. The rotational equivalent of Newton's second law is then

$$\Sigma\tau = I\alpha. \qquad \textbf{(8–14)}$$

The **rotational kinetic energy** of an object rotating about a fixed axis with angular velocity $\omega$ is

$$\text{KE} = \tfrac{1}{2}I\omega^2. \qquad \textbf{(8–15)}$$

For an object both translating and rotating, the total kinetic energy is the sum of the translational kinetic energy of the object's center of mass plus the rotational kinetic energy of the object about its center of mass:

$$\text{KE} = \tfrac{1}{2}Mv_{\text{CM}}^2 + \tfrac{1}{2}I_{\text{CM}}\omega^2 \qquad \textbf{(8–16)}$$

as long as the rotation axis is fixed in direction.

The **angular momentum** $L$ of an object about a fixed rotation axis is given by

$$L = I\omega. \qquad \textbf{(8–18)}$$

Newton's second law, in terms of angular momentum, is

$$\Sigma\tau = \frac{\Delta L}{\Delta t}. \qquad \textbf{(8–19)}$$

If the net torque on the object is zero, $\Delta L/\Delta t = 0$, so $L$ = constant. This is the **law of conservation of angular momentum** for a rotating object.

The following Table summarizes angular (or rotational) quantities, comparing them to their translational analogs.


| Translation | Rotation | Connection |
|---|---|---|
| $x$ | $\theta$ | $x = r\theta$ |
| $v$ | $\omega$ | $v = r\omega$ |
| $a$ | $\alpha$ | $a = r\alpha$ |
| $m$ | $I$ | $I = \Sigma mr^2$ |
| $F$ | $\tau$ | $\tau = rF\sin\theta$ |
| $\text{KE} = \frac{1}{2}mv^2$ | $\frac{1}{2}I\omega^2$ | |
| $p = mv$ | $L = I\omega$ | |
| $W = Fd$ | $W = \tau\theta$ | |
| $\Sigma F = ma$ | $\Sigma\tau = I\alpha$ | |
| $\Sigma F = \frac{\Delta p}{\Delta t}$ | $\Sigma\tau = \frac{\Delta L}{\Delta t}$ | |

# Questions

1. A bicycle odometer (which measures distance traveled) is attached near the wheel hub and is designed for 27-inch wheels. What happens if you use it on a bicycle with 24-inch wheels?
2. Suppose a disk rotates at constant angular velocity. Does a point on the rim have radial and/or tangential acceleration? If the disk's angular velocity increases uniformly, does the point have radial and/or tangential acceleration? For which cases would the magnitude of either component of linear acceleration change?
3. Could a nonrigid body be described by a single value of the angular velocity $\omega$? Explain.
4. Can a small force ever exert a greater torque than a larger force? Explain.

5. If a force $\vec{\mathbf{F}}$ acts on an object such that its lever arm is zero, does it have any effect on the object's motion? Explain.
6. Why is it more difficult to do a sit-up with your hands behind your head than when your arms are stretched out in front of you? A diagram may help you to answer this.
7. A 21-speed bicycle has seven sprockets at the rear wheel and three at the pedal cranks. In which gear is it harder to pedal, a small rear sprocket or a large rear sprocket? Why? In which gear is it harder to pedal, a small front sprocket or a large front sprocket? Why?
8. Mammals that depend on being able to run fast have slender lower legs with flesh and muscle concentrated high, close to the body (Fig. 8–34). On the basis of rotational dynamics, explain why this distribution of mass is advantageous.

**FIGURE 8–34** Question 8. A gazelle.

**FIGURE 8–35** Question 9.

9. Why do tightrope walkers (Fig. 8–35) carry a long, narrow beam?
10. If the net force on a system is zero, is the net torque also zero? If the net torque on a system is zero, is the net force zero?
11. Two inclines have the same height but make different angles with the horizontal. The same steel ball is rolled down each incline. On which incline will the speed of the ball at the bottom be greater? Explain.
12. Two solid spheres simultaneously start rolling (from rest) down an incline. One sphere has twice the radius and twice the mass of the other. Which reaches the bottom of the incline first? Which has the greater speed there? Which has the greater total kinetic energy at the bottom?
13. A sphere and a cylinder have the same radius and the same mass. They start from rest at the top of an incline. Which reaches the bottom first? Which has the greater speed at the bottom? Which has the greater total kinetic energy at the bottom? Which has the greater rotational KE?
14. We claim that momentum and angular momentum are conserved. Yet most moving or rotating objects eventually slow down and stop. Explain.
15. If there were a great migration of people toward the Earth's equator, how would this affect the length of the day?
16. Can the diver of Fig. 8–29 do a somersault without having any initial rotation when she leaves the board?
17. The moment of inertia of a rotating solid disk about an axis through its center of mass is $\frac{1}{2}MR^2$ (Fig. 8–21c). Suppose instead that the axis of rotation passes through a point on the edge of the disk. Will the moment of inertia be the same, larger, or smaller?
18. Suppose you are sitting on a rotating stool holding a 2-kg mass in each outstretched hand. If you suddenly drop the masses, will your angular velocity increase, decrease, or stay the same? Explain.
19. Two spheres look identical and have the same mass. However, one is hollow and the other is solid. Describe an experiment to determine which is which.

* 20. In what direction is the Earth's angular velocity vector as it rotates daily about its axis?

* 21. The angular velocity of a wheel rotating on a horizontal axle points west. In what direction is the linear velocity of a point on the top of the wheel? If the angular acceleration points east, describe the tangential linear acceleration of this point at the top of the wheel. Is the angular speed increasing or decreasing?

* 22. Suppose you are standing on the edge of a large freely rotating turntable. What happens if you walk toward the center?

* 23. A shortstop may leap into the air to catch a ball and throw it quickly. As he throws the ball, the upper part of his body rotates. If you look quickly you will notice that his hips and legs rotate in the opposite direction (Fig. 8–36). Explain.

**FIGURE 8–36** Question 23. A shortstop in the air, throwing the ball.

* 24. On the basis of the law of conservation of angular momentum, discuss why a helicopter must have more than one rotor (or propeller). Discuss one or more ways the second propeller can operate to keep the helicopter stable.

# Problems

## 8–1 Angular Quantities

1. (I) Express the following angles in radians: (*a*) 30°, (*b*) 57°, (*c*) 90°, (*d*) 360°, and (*e*) 420°. Give as numerical values and as fractions of $\pi$.
2. (I) Eclipses happen on Earth because of an amazing coincidence. Calculate, using the information inside the Front Cover, the angular diameters (in radians) of the Sun and the Moon, as seen on Earth.
3. (I) A laser beam is directed at the Moon, 380,000 km from Earth. The beam diverges at an angle $\theta$ (Fig. 8–37) of $1.4 \times 10^{-5}$ rad. What diameter spot will it make on the Moon?

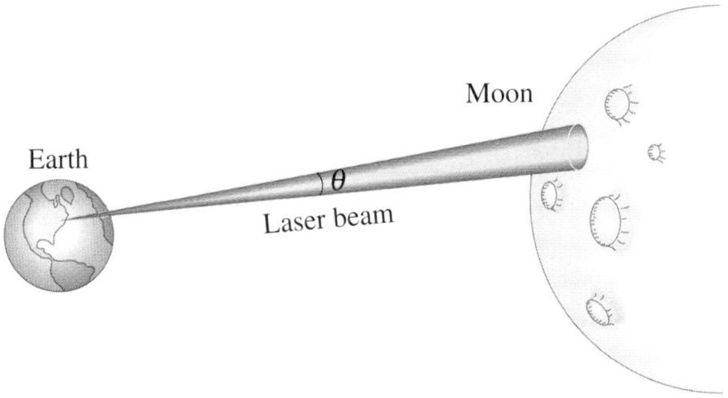


**FIGURE 8–37** Problem 3.

4. (I) The blades in a blender rotate at a rate of 6500 rpm. When the motor is turned off during operation, the blades slow to rest in 3.0 s. What is the angular acceleration as the blades slow down?
5. (II) A child rolls a ball on a level floor 3.5 m to another child. If the ball makes 15.0 revolutions, what is its diameter?
6. (II) A bicycle with tires 68 cm in diameter travels 8.0 km. How many revolutions do the wheels make?
7. (II) (*a*) A grinding wheel 0.35 m in diameter rotates at 2500 rpm. Calculate its angular velocity in rad/s. (*b*) What are the linear speed and acceleration of a point on the edge of the grinding wheel?
8. (II) A rotating merry-go-round makes one complete revolution in 4.0 s (Fig. 8–38). (*a*) What is the linear speed of a child seated 1.2 m from the center? (*b*) What is her acceleration (give components)?

**FIGURE 8–38** Problem 8.

9. (II) Calculate the angular velocity of the Earth (*a*) in its orbit around the Sun, and (*b*) about its axis.
10. (II) What is the linear speed of a point (*a*) on the equator, (*b*) on the Arctic Circle (latitude 66.5° N), and (*c*) at a latitude of 45.0° N, due to the Earth's rotation?
11. (II) How fast (in rpm) must a centrifuge rotate if a particle 7.0 cm from the axis of rotation is to experience an acceleration of 100,000 *g*'s?
12. (II) A 70-cm-diameter wheel accelerates uniformly about its center from 130 rpm to 280 rpm in 4.0 s. Determine (*a*) its angular acceleration, and (*b*) the radial and tangential components of the linear acceleration of a point on the edge of the wheel 2.0 s after it has started accelerating.
13. (II) A turntable of radius $R_1$ is turned by a circular rubber roller of radius $R_2$ in contact with it at their outer edges. What is the ratio of their angular velocities, $\omega_1/\omega_2$?
14. (III) In traveling to the Moon, astronauts aboard the *Apollo* spacecraft put themselves into a slow rotation to distribute the Sun's energy evenly. At the start of their trip, they accelerated from no rotation to 1.0 revolution every minute during a 12-min time interval. The spacecraft can be thought of as a cylinder with a diameter of 8.5 m. Determine (*a*) the angular acceleration, and (*b*) the radial and tangential components of the linear acceleration of a point on the skin of the ship 5.0 min after it started this acceleration.

## 8–2 and 8–3 Constant Angular Acceleration; Rolling

15. (I) A centrifuge accelerates uniformly from rest to 15,000 rpm in 220 s. Through how many revolutions did it turn in this time?
16. (I) An automobile engine slows down from 4500 rpm to 1200 rpm in 2.5 s. Calculate (*a*) its angular acceleration, assumed constant, and (*b*) the total number of revolutions the engine makes in this time.
17. (I) Pilots can be tested for the stresses of flying high-speed jets in a whirling "human centrifuge," which takes 1.0 min to turn through 20 complete revolutions before reaching its final speed. (*a*) What was its angular acceleration (assumed constant), and (*b*) what was its final angular speed in rpm?
18. (II) A wheel 33 cm in diameter accelerates uniformly from 240 rpm to 360 rpm in 6.5 s. How far will a point on the edge of the wheel have traveled in this time?
19. (II) A cooling fan is turned off when it is running at 850 rev/min. It turns 1500 revolutions before it comes to a stop. (*a*) What was the fan's angular acceleration, assumed constant? (*b*) How long did it take the fan to come to a complete stop?
20. (II) A small rubber wheel is used to drive a large pottery wheel, and they are mounted so that their circular edges touch. The small wheel has a radius of 2.0 cm and accelerates at the rate of $7.2\ \text{rad/s}^2$, and it is in contact with the pottery wheel (radius 25.0 cm) without slipping. Calculate (*a*) the angular acceleration of the pottery wheel, and (*b*) the time it takes the pottery wheel to reach its required speed of 65 rpm.

21. (II) The tires of a car make 65 revolutions as the car reduces its speed uniformly from 95 km/h to 45 km/h. The tires have a diameter of 0.80 m. (*a*) What was the angular acceleration of the tires? (*b*) If the car continues to decelerate at this rate, how much more time is required for it to stop?

## 8–4 Torque

22. (I) A 55-kg person riding a bike puts all her weight on each pedal when climbing a hill. The pedals rotate in a circle of radius 17 cm. (*a*) What is the maximum torque she exerts? (*b*) How could she exert more torque?

23. (I) A person exerts a force of 55 N on the end of a door 74 cm wide. What is the magnitude of the torque if the force is exerted (*a*) perpendicular to the door, and (*b*) at a 45° angle to the face of the door?

24. (II) Calculate the net torque about the axle of the wheel shown in Fig. 8–39. Assume that a friction torque of 0.40 m·N opposes the motion.

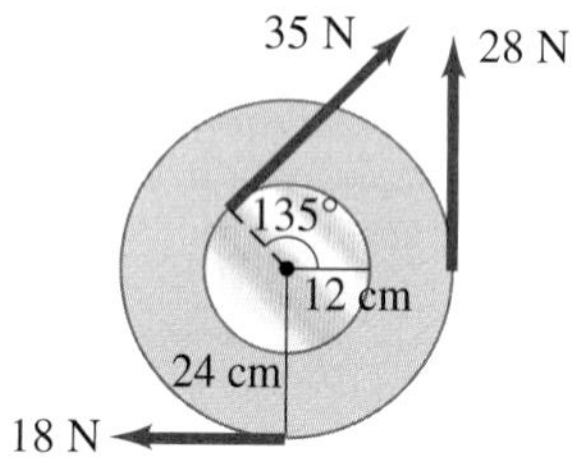


**FIGURE 8–39** Problem 24.

25. (II) Two blocks, each of mass *m*, are attached to the ends of a massless rod which pivots as shown in Fig. 8–40. Initially the rod is held in the horizontal position and then released. Calculate the magnitude and direction of the net torque on this system.

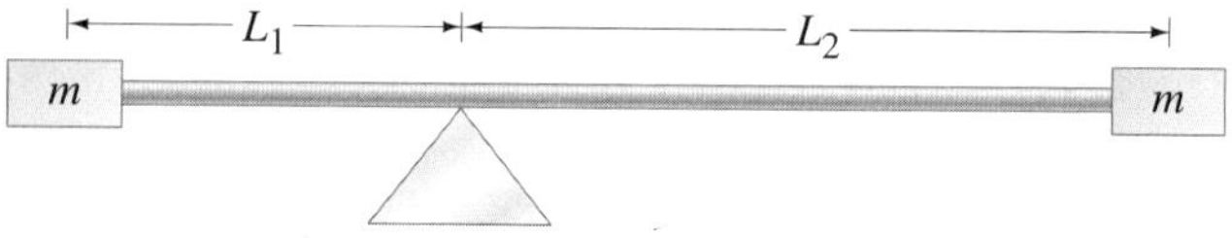


**FIGURE 8–40** Problem 25.

26. (II) The bolts on the cylinder head of an engine require tightening to a torque of 88 m·N. If a wrench is 28 cm long, what force perpendicular to the wrench must the mechanic exert at its end? If the six-sided bolt head is 15 mm in diameter, estimate the force applied near each of the six points by a socket wrench (Fig. 8–41).

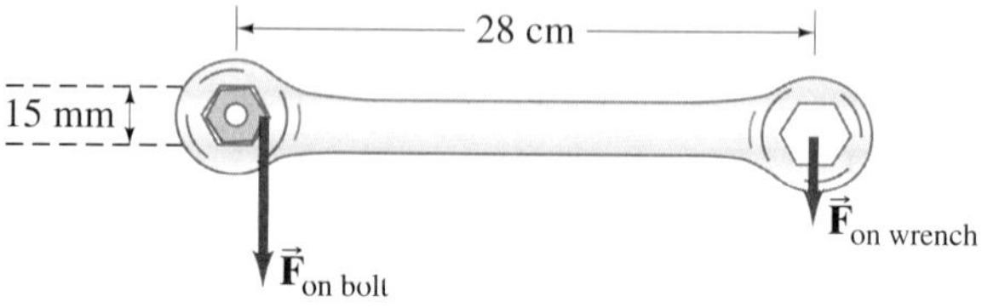


**FIGURE 8–41** Problem 26.

## 8–5 and 8–6 Rotational Dynamics

27. (I) Determine the moment of inertia of a 10.8-kg sphere of radius 0.648 m when the axis of rotation is through its center.

28. (I) Calculate the moment of inertia of a bicycle wheel 66.7 cm in diameter. The rim and tire have a combined mass of 1.25 kg. The mass of the hub can be ignored (why?).

29. (II) A small 650-gram ball on the end of a thin, light rod is rotated in a horizontal circle of radius 1.2 m. Calculate (*a*) the moment of inertia of the ball about the center of the circle, and (*b*) the torque needed to keep the ball rotating at constant angular velocity if air resistance exerts a force of 0.020 N on the ball. Ignore the rod's moment of inertia and air resistance.

30. (II) A potter is shaping a bowl on a potter's wheel rotating at constant angular speed (Fig. 8–42). The friction force between her hands and the clay is 1.5 N total. (*a*) How large is her torque on the wheel, if the diameter of the bowl is 12 cm? (*b*) How long would it take for the potter's wheel to stop if the only torque acting on it is due to the potter's hand? The initial angular velocity of the wheel is 1.6 rev/s, and the moment of inertia of the wheel and the bowl is 0.11 kg·m$^2$.

**FIGURE 8–42** Problem 30.

31. (II) Calculate the moment of inertia of the array of point objects shown in Fig. 8–43 about (*a*) the vertical axis, and (*b*) the horizontal axis. Assume $m = 1.8$ kg, $M = 3.1$ kg, and the objects are wired together by very light, rigid pieces of wire. The array is rectangular and is split through the middle by the horizontal axis. (*c*) About which axis would it be harder to accelerate this array?

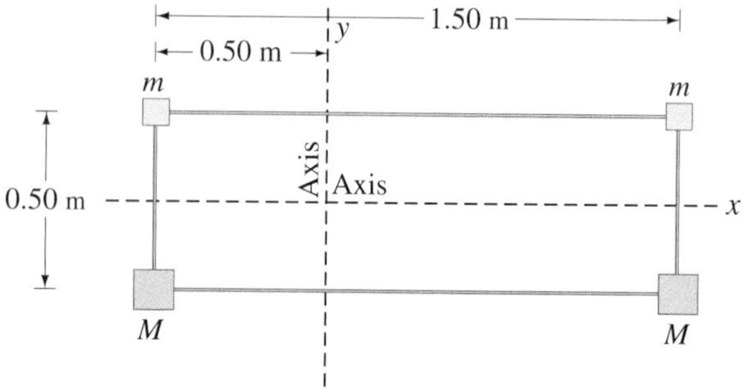


**FIGURE 8–43** Problem 31.

32. (II) An oxygen molecule consists of two oxygen atoms whose total mass is $5.3 \times 10^{-26}$ kg and whose moment of inertia about an axis perpendicular to the line joining the two atoms, midway between them, is $1.9 \times 10^{-46}\ \text{kg}\cdot\text{m}^2$. From these data, estimate the effective distance between the atoms.

33. (II) To get a flat, uniform cylindrical satellite spinning at the correct rate, engineers fire four tangential rockets as shown in Fig. 8–44. If the satellite has a mass of 3600 kg and a radius of 4.0 m, what is the required steady force of each rocket if the satellite is to reach 32 rpm in 5.0 min?

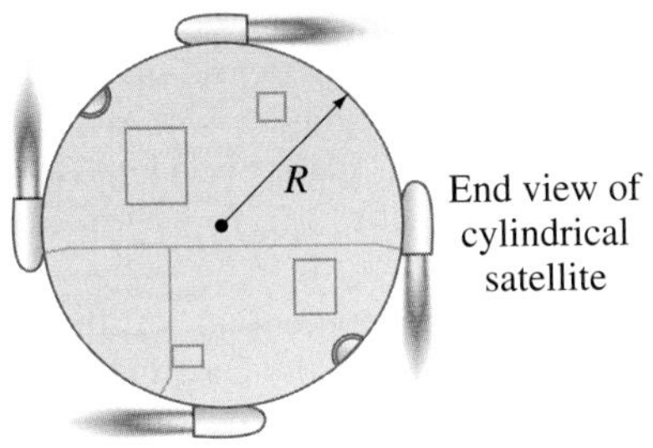


**FIGURE 8–44**
Problem 33.

34. (II) A grinding wheel is a uniform cylinder with a radius of 8.50 cm and a mass of 0.580 kg. Calculate (*a*) its moment of inertia about its center, and (*b*) the applied torque needed to accelerate it from rest to 1500 rpm in 5.00 s if it is known to slow down from 1500 rpm to rest in 55.0 s.

35. (II) A softball player swings a bat, accelerating it from rest to 3.0 rev/s in a time of 0.20 s. Approximate the bat as a 2.2-kg uniform rod of length 0.95 m, and compute the torque the player applies to one end of it.

36. (II) A teenager pushes tangentially on a small hand-driven merry-go-round and is able to accelerate it from rest to a frequency of 15 rpm in 10.0 s. Assume the merry-go-round is a uniform disk of radius 2.5 m and has a mass of 760 kg, and two children (each with a mass of 25 kg) sit opposite each other on the edge. Calculate the torque required to produce the acceleration, neglecting frictional torque. What force is required at the edge?

37. (II) A centrifuge rotor rotating at 10,300 rpm is shut off and is eventually brought uniformly to rest by a frictional torque of $1.20\ \text{m}\cdot\text{N}$. If the mass of the rotor is 4.80 kg and it can be approximated as a solid cylinder of radius 0.0710 m, through how many revolutions will the rotor turn before coming to rest, and how long will it take?

38. (II) The forearm in Fig. 8–45 accelerates a 3.6-kg ball at $7.0\ \text{m/s}^2$ by means of the triceps muscle, as shown. Calculate (*a*) the torque needed, and (*b*) the force that must be exerted by the triceps muscle. Ignore the mass of the arm.

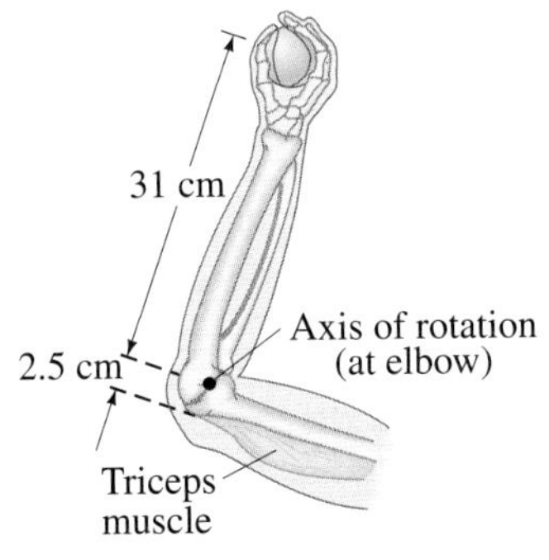


**FIGURE 8–45**
Problems 38 and 39.

39. (II) Assume that a 1.00-kg ball is thrown solely by the action of the forearm, which rotates about the elbow joint under the action of the triceps muscle, Fig. 8–45. The ball is accelerated uniformly from rest to 10.0 m/s in 0.350 s, at which point it is released. Calculate (*a*) the angular acceleration of the arm, and (*b*) the force required of the triceps muscle. Assume that the forearm has a mass of 3.70 kg and rotates like a uniform rod about an axis at its end.

40. (II) A helicopter rotor blade can be considered a long thin rod, as shown in Fig. 8–46. (*a*) If each of the three rotor helicopter blades is 3.75 m long and has a mass of 160 kg, calculate the moment of inertia of the three rotor blades about the axis of rotation. (*b*) How much torque must the motor apply to bring the blades up to a speed of 5.0 rev/s in 8.0 s?

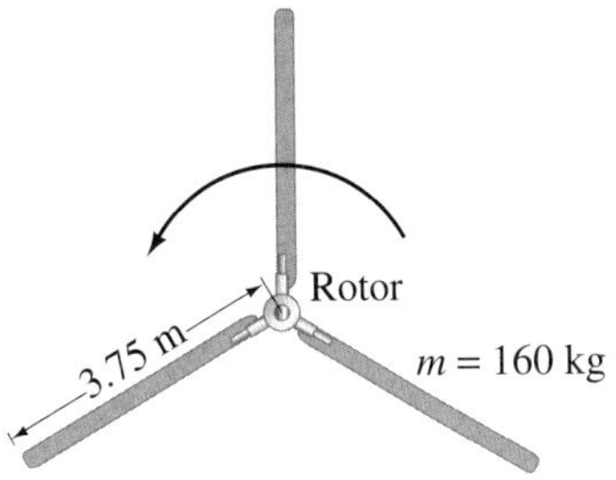


**FIGURE 8–46**
Problem 40.

41. (III) An *Atwood's machine* consists of two masses, $m_1$ and $m_2$, which are connected by a massless inelastic cord that passes over a pulley, Fig. 8–47. If the pulley has radius $R$ and moment of inertia $I$ about its axle, determine the acceleration of the masses $m_1$ and $m_2$, and compare to the situation in which the moment of inertia of the pulley is ignored. [*Hint*: The tensions $F_{T1}$ and $F_{T2}$ are not equal. We discussed this situation in Example 4–13, assuming $I = 0$ for the pulley.]

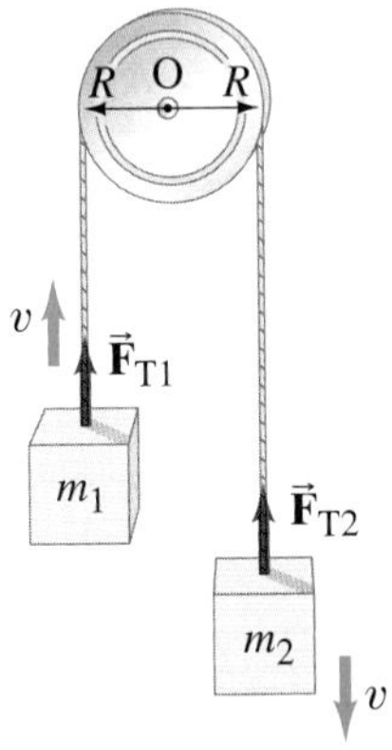


**FIGURE 8–47**
Problems 41 and 49.
Atwood's machine.

42. (III) A hammer thrower accelerates the hammer (mass = 7.30 kg) from rest within four full turns (revolutions) and releases it at a speed of 28.0 m/s. Assuming a uniform rate of increase in angular velocity and a horizontal circular path of radius 1.20 m, calculate (*a*) the angular acceleration, (*b*) the (linear) tangential acceleration, (*c*) the centripetal acceleration just before release, (*d*) the net force being exerted on the hammer by the athlete just before release, and (*e*) the angle of this force with respect to the radius of the circular motion.

## 8–7 Rotational Kinetic Energy

43. (I) A centrifuge rotor has a moment of inertia of $3.75 \times 10^{-2}\ \text{kg}\cdot\text{m}^2$. How much energy is required to bring it from rest to 8250 rpm?

44. (II) An automobile engine develops a torque of $280\ \text{m}\cdot\text{N}$ at 3800 rpm. What is the power in watts and in horsepower?

45. (II) A bowling ball of mass 7.3 kg and radius 9.0 cm rolls without slipping down a lane at 3.3 m/s. Calculate its total kinetic energy.

46. (II) Estimate the kinetic energy of the Earth with respect to the Sun as the sum of two terms, (*a*) that due to its daily rotation about its axis, and (*b*) that due to its yearly revolution about the Sun. [Assume the Earth is a uniform sphere with mass $= 6.0 \times 10^{24}$ kg and radius $= 6.4 \times 10^{6}$ m, and is $1.5 \times 10^{8}$ km from the Sun.]

47. (II) A merry-go-round has a mass of 1640 kg and a radius of 7.50 m. How much net work is required to accelerate it from rest to a rotation rate of 1.00 revolution per 8.00 s? Assume it is a solid cylinder.

48. (II) A sphere of radius 20.0 cm and mass 1.80 kg starts from rest and rolls without slipping down a 30.0° incline that is 10.0 m long. (*a*) Calculate its translational and rotational speeds when it reaches the bottom. (*b*) What is the ratio of translational to rotational KE at the bottom? Avoid putting in numbers until the end so you can answer: (*c*) do your answers in (*a*) and (*b*) depend on the radius of the sphere or its mass?

49. (III) Two masses, $m_1 = 18.0$ kg and $m_2 = 26.5$ kg, are connected by a rope that hangs over a pulley (as in Fig. 8–47). The pulley is a uniform cylinder of radius 0.260 m and mass 7.50 kg. Initially, $m_1$ is on the ground and $m_2$ rests 3.00 m above the ground. If the system is now released, use conservation of energy to determine the speed of $m_2$ just before it strikes the ground. Assume the pulley is frictionless.

50. (III) A 2.30-m-long pole is balanced vertically on its tip. It starts to fall and its lower end does not slip. What will be the speed of the upper end of the pole just before it hits the ground? [*Hint*: Use conservation of energy.]

## 8–8 Angular Momentum

51. (I) What is the angular momentum of a 0.210-kg ball rotating on the end of a thin string in a circle of radius 1.10 m at an angular speed of 10.4 rad/s?

52. (I) (*a*) What is the angular momentum of a 2.8-kg uniform cylindrical grinding wheel of radius 18 cm when rotating at 1500 rpm? (*b*) How much torque is required to stop it in 6.0 s?

53. (II) A person stands, hands at his side, on a platform that is rotating at a rate of 1.30 rev/s. If he raises his arms to a horizontal position, Fig. 8–48, the speed of rotation decreases to 0.80 rev/s. (*a*) Why? (*b*) By what factor has his moment of inertia changed?

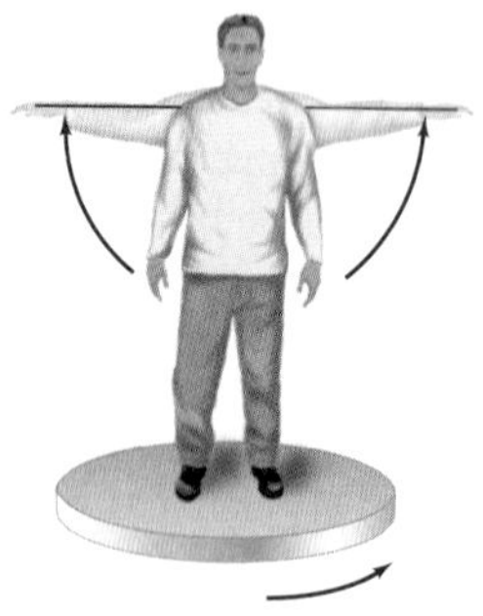

**FIGURE 8–48**
Problem 53.

54. (II) A diver (such as the one shown in Fig. 8–29) can reduce her moment of inertia by a factor of about 3.5 when changing from the straight position to the tuck position. If she makes 2.0 rotations in 1.5 s when in the tuck position, what is her angular speed (rev/s) when in the straight position?

55. (II) A figure skater can increase her spin rotation rate from an initial rate of 1.0 rev every 2.0 s to a final rate of 3.0 rev/s. If her initial moment of inertia was 4.6 kg·m$^2$, what is her final moment of inertia? How does she physically accomplish this change?

56. (II) A potter's wheel is rotating around a vertical axis through its center at a frequency of 1.5 rev/s. The wheel can be considered a uniform disk of mass 5.0 kg and diameter 0.40 m. The potter then throws a 3.1-kg chunk of clay, approximately shaped as a flat disk of radius 8.0 cm, onto the center of the rotating wheel. What is the frequency of the wheel after the clay sticks to it?

57. (II) (*a*) What is the angular momentum of a figure skater spinning at 3.5 rev/s with arms in close to her body, assuming her to be a uniform cylinder with a height of 1.5 m, a radius of 15 cm, and a mass of 55 kg? (*b*) How much torque is required to slow her to a stop in 5.0 s, assuming she does *not* move her arms?

58. (II) Determine the angular momentum of the Earth (*a*) about its rotation axis (assume the Earth is a uniform sphere), and (*b*) in its orbit around the Sun (treat the Earth as a particle orbiting the Sun). The Earth has mass $= 6.0 \times 10^{24}$ kg and radius $= 6.4 \times 10^{6}$ m, and is $1.5 \times 10^{8}$ km from the Sun.

59. (II) A nonrotating cylindrical disk of moment of inertia $I$ is dropped onto an identical disk rotating at angular speed $\omega$. Assuming no external torques, what is the final common angular speed of the two disks?

60. (II) A uniform disk turns at 2.4 rev/s around a frictionless spindle. A nonrotating rod, of the same mass as the disk and length equal to the disk's diameter, is dropped onto the freely spinning disk, Fig. 8–49. They then both turn around the spindle with their centers superposed. What is the angular frequency in rev/s of the combination?

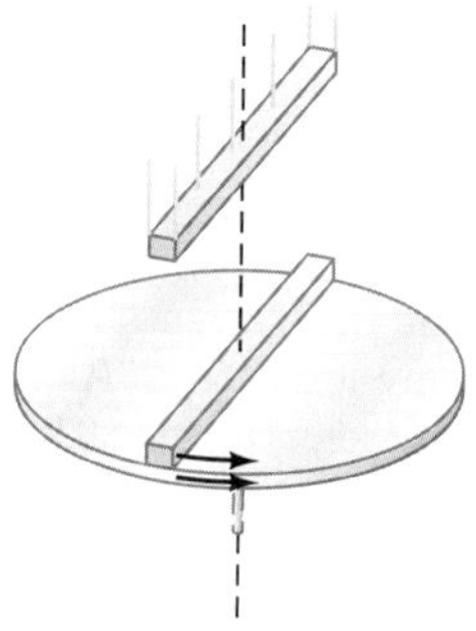

**FIGURE 8–49**
Problem 60.

61. (II) A person of mass 75 kg stands at the center of a rotating merry-go-round platform of radius 3.0 m and moment of inertia 920 kg·m$^2$. The platform rotates without friction with angular velocity 2.0 rad/s. The person walks radially to the edge of the platform. (*a*) Calculate the angular velocity when the person reaches the edge. (*b*) Calculate the rotational kinetic energy of the system of platform plus person before and after the person's walk.

62. (II) A 4.2-m-diameter merry-go-round is rotating freely with an angular velocity of 0.80 rad/s. Its total moment of inertia is 1760 kg·m$^2$. Four people standing on the ground, each of mass 65 kg, suddenly step onto the edge of the merry-go-round. What is the angular velocity of the merry-go-round now? What if the people were on it initially and then jumped off in a radial direction (relative to the merry-go-round)?

63. (II) Suppose our Sun eventually collapses into a white dwarf, losing about half its mass in the process, and winding up with a radius 1.0% of its existing radius. Assuming the lost mass carries away no angular momentum, what would the Sun's new rotation rate be? (Take the Sun's current period to be about 30 days.) What would be its final KE in terms of its initial KE of today?

64. (III) Hurricanes can involve winds in excess of 120 km/h at the outer edge. Make a crude estimate of (*a*) the energy, and (*b*) the angular momentum, of such a hurricane, approximating it as a rigidly rotating uniform cylinder of air (density $1.3\ \mathrm{kg/m^3}$) of radius 100 km and height 4.0 km.

65. (III) An asteroid of mass $1.0 \times 10^5$ kg, traveling at a speed of 30 km/s relative to the Earth, hits the Earth at the equator tangentially, and in the direction of Earth's rotation. Use angular momentum to estimate the percent change in the angular speed of the Earth as a result of the collision.

### * 8–9 Angular Quantities as Vectors

* 66. (II) A person stands on a platform, initially at rest, that can rotate freely without friction. The moment of inertia of the person plus the platform is $I_P$. The person holds a spinning bicycle wheel with its axis horizontal. The wheel has moment of inertia $I_W$ and angular velocity $\omega_W$. What will be the angular velocity $\omega_P$ of the platform if the person moves the axis of the wheel so that it points (*a*) vertically upward, (*b*) at a 60° angle to the vertical, (*c*) vertically downward? (*d*) What will $\omega_P$ be if the person reaches up and stops the wheel in part (*a*)?

* 67. (III) Suppose a 55-kg person stands at the edge of a 6.5-m diameter merry-go-round turntable that is mounted on frictionless bearings and has a moment of inertia of $1700\ \mathrm{kg \cdot m^2}$. The turntable is at rest initially, but when the person begins running at a speed of 3.8 m/s (with respect to the turntable) around its edge, the turntable begins to rotate in the opposite direction. Calculate the angular velocity of the turntable.

## General Problems

68. A large spool of rope rolls on the ground with the end of the rope lying on the top edge of the spool. A person grabs the end of the rope and walks a distance $L$, holding onto it, Fig. 8–50. The spool rolls behind the person without slipping. What length of rope unwinds from the spool? How far does the spool's center of mass move?

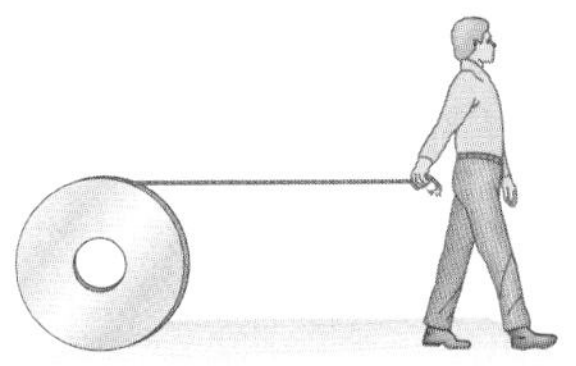

**FIGURE 8–50** Problem 68.

69. The Moon orbits the Earth such that the same side always faces the Earth. Determine the ratio of the Moon's spin angular momentum (about its own axis) to its orbital angular momentum. (In the latter case, treat the Moon as a particle orbiting the Earth.)

70. A cyclist accelerates from rest at a rate of $1.00\ \mathrm{m/s^2}$. How fast will a point on the rim of the tire (diameter = 68 cm) at the top be moving after 3.0 s? [*Hint*: At any moment, the lowest point on the tire is in contact with the ground and is at rest—see Fig. 8–51.]

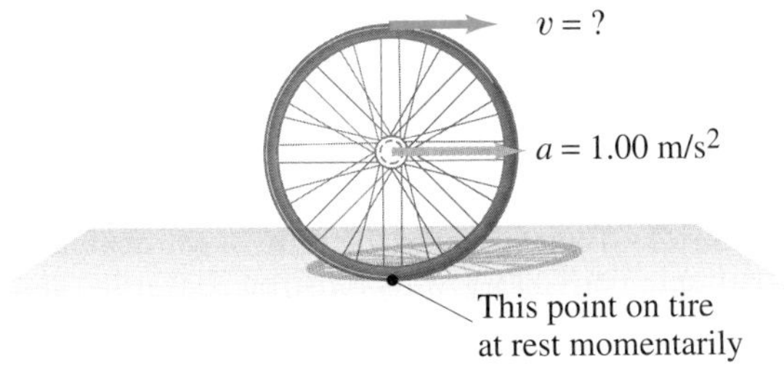


**FIGURE 8–51** Problem 70.

71. A 1.4-kg grindstone in the shape of a uniform cylinder of radius 0.20 m acquires a rotational rate of 1800 rev/s from rest over a 6.0-s interval at constant angular acceleration. Calculate the torque delivered by the motor.

72. (*a*) A yo-yo is made of two solid cylindrical disks, each of mass 0.050 kg and diameter 0.075 m, joined by a (concentric) thin solid cylindrical hub of mass 0.0050 kg and diameter 0.010 m. Use conservation of energy to calculate the linear speed of the yo-yo when it reaches the end of its 1.0-m-long string, if it is released from rest. (*b*) What fraction of its kinetic energy is rotational?

73. (*a*) For a bicycle, how is the angular speed of the rear wheel ($\omega_R$) related to that of the pedals and front sprocket ($\omega_F$), Fig. 8–52? That is, derive a formula for $\omega_R/\omega_F$. Let $N_F$ and $N_R$ be the number of teeth on the front and rear sprockets, respectively. The teeth are spaced equally on all sprockets so that the chain meshes properly. (*b*) Evaluate the ratio $\omega_R/\omega_F$ when the front and rear sprockets have 52 and 13 teeth, respectively, and (*c*) when they have 42 and 28 teeth.

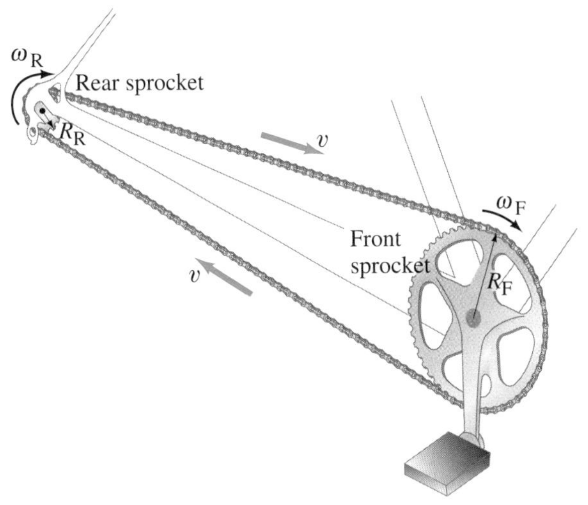


**FIGURE 8–52** Problem 73.

74. Suppose a star the size of our Sun, but with mass 8.0 times as great, were rotating at a speed of 1.0 revolution every 12 days. If it were to undergo gravitational collapse to a neutron star of radius 11 km, losing three-quarters of its mass in the process, what would its rotation speed be? Assume that the star is a uniform sphere at all times, and that the lost mass carries off no angular momentum.

75. One possibility for a low-pollution automobile is for it to use energy stored in a heavy rotating flywheel. Suppose such a car has a total mass of 1400 kg, uses a uniform cylindrical flywheel of diameter 1.50 m and mass 240 kg, and should be able to travel 350 km without needing a flywheel "spinup." (*a*) Make reasonable assumptions (average frictional retarding force = 450 N, twenty acceleration periods from rest to 95 km/h, equal uphill and downhill, and that energy can be put back into the flywheel as the car goes downhill), and show that the total energy needed to be stored in the flywheel is about $1.7 \times 10^8$ J. (*b*) What is the angular velocity of the flywheel when it has a full "energy charge"? (*c*) About how long would it take a 150-hp motor to give the flywheel a full energy charge before a trip?

76. Figure 8–53 illustrates an $H_2O$ molecule. The O–H bond length is 0.96 nm and the H–O–H bonds make an angle of 104°. Calculate the moment of inertia for the $H_2O$ molecule about an axis passing through the center of the oxygen atom (*a*) perpendicular to the plane of the molecule, and (*b*) in the plane of the molecule, bisecting the H–O–H bonds.

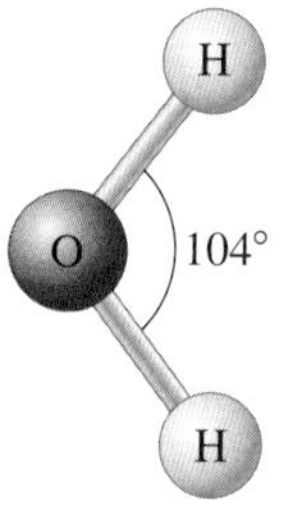

**FIGURE 8–53** Problem 76.

77. A hollow cylinder (hoop) is rolling on a horizontal surface at speed $v = 3.3$ m/s when it reaches a 15° incline. (*a*) How far up the incline will it go? (*b*) How long will it be on the incline before it arrives back at the bottom?

78. A uniform rod of mass $M$ and length $L$ can pivot freely (i.e., we ignore friction) about a hinge attached to a wall, as in Fig. 8–54. The rod is held horizontally and then released. At the moment of release, determine (*a*) the angular acceleration of the rod, and (*b*) the linear acceleration of the tip of the rod. Assume that the force of gravity acts at the center of mass of the rod, as shown. [*Hint*: See Fig. 8–21g.]

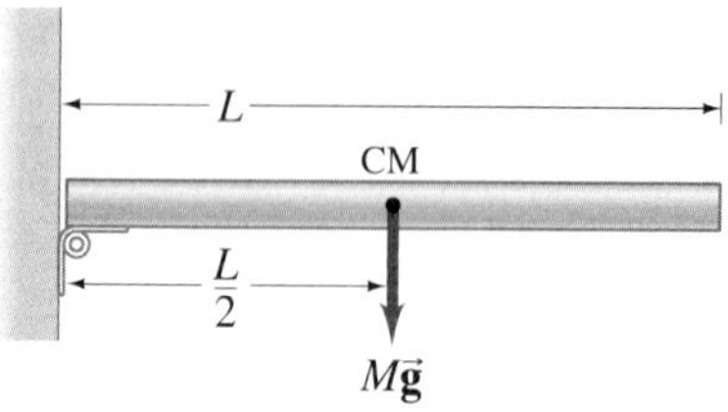

**FIGURE 8–54** Problem 78.

79. A wheel of mass $M$ has radius $R$. It is standing vertically on the floor, and we want to exert a horizontal force $F$ at its axle so that it will climb a step against which it rests (Fig. 8–55). The step has height $h$, where $h < R$. What minimum force $F$ is needed?

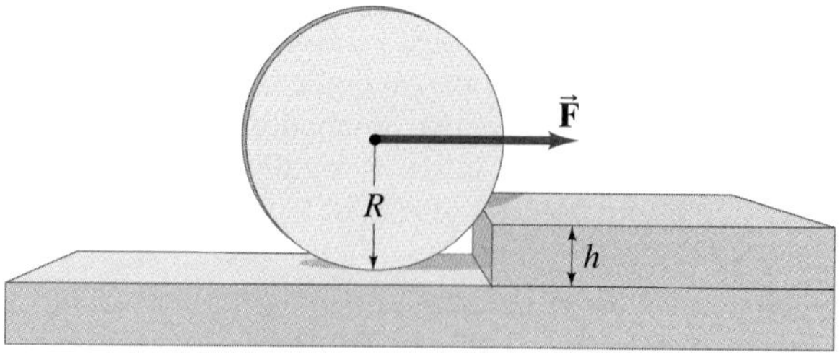

**FIGURE 8–55** Problem 79.

80. A bicyclist traveling with speed $v = 4.2$ m/s on a flat road is making a turn with a radius $r = 6.4$ m. The forces acting on the cyclist and cycle are the normal force $(\vec{\mathbf{F}}_N)$ and friction force $(\vec{\mathbf{F}}_{fr})$ exerted by the road on the tires, and $m\vec{\mathbf{g}}$, the total weight of the cyclist and cycle (see Fig. 8–56). (*a*) Explain carefully why the angle $\theta$ the bicycle makes with the vertical (Fig. 8–56) must be given by $\tan\theta = F_{fr}/F_N$ if the cyclist is to maintain balance. (*b*) Calculate $\theta$ for the values given. (*c*) If the coefficient of static friction between tires and road is $\mu_s = 0.70$, what is the minimum turning radius?

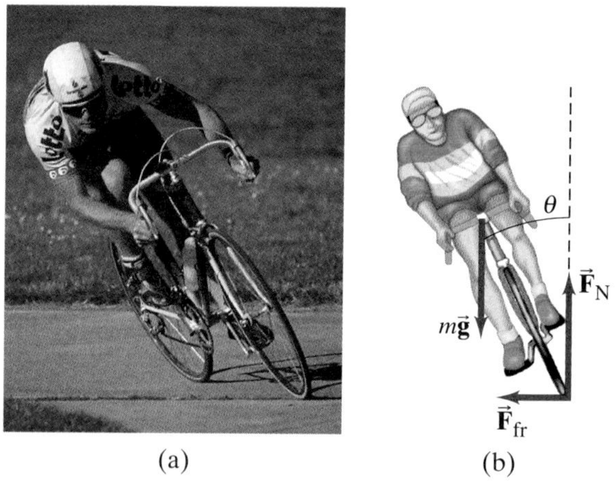

**FIGURE 8–56** Problem 80.

81. Suppose David puts a 0.50-kg rock into a sling of length 1.5 m and begins whirling the rock in a nearly horizontal circle above his head, accelerating it from rest to a rate of 120 rpm after 5.0 s. What is the torque required to achieve this feat, and where does the torque come from?

82. Model a figure skater's body as a solid cylinder and her arms as thin rods, making reasonable estimates for the dimensions. Then calculate the ratio of the angular speeds for a spinning skater with outstretched arms, and with arms held tightly against her body.

83. You are designing a clutch assembly which consists of two cylindrical plates, of mass $M_A = 6.0\,\text{kg}$ and $M_B = 9.0\,\text{kg}$, with equal radii $R = 0.60\,\text{m}$. They are initially separated (Fig. 8–57). Plate $M_A$ is accelerated from rest to an angular velocity $\omega_1 = 7.2\,\text{rad/s}$ in time $\Delta t = 2.0\,\text{s}$. Calculate (*a*) the angular momentum of $M_A$, and (*b*) the torque required to have accelerated $M_A$ from rest to $\omega_1$. (*c*) Plate $M_B$, initially at rest but free to rotate without friction, is allowed to fall vertically (or pushed by a spring), so it is in firm contact with plate $M_A$ (their contact surfaces are high-friction). Before contact, $M_A$ was rotating at constant $\omega_1$. After contact, at what constant angular velocity $\omega_2$ do the two plates rotate?

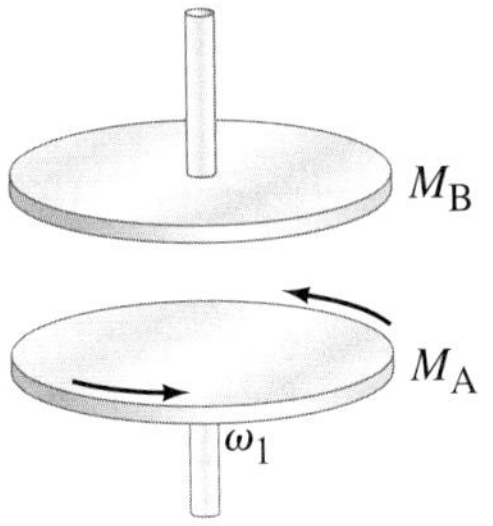


**FIGURE 8–57** Problem 83.

84. A marble of mass $m$ and radius $r$ rolls along the looped rough track of Fig. 8–58. What is the minimum value of the vertical height $h$ that the marble must drop if it is to reach the highest point of the loop without leaving the track? Assume $r \ll R$, and ignore frictional losses.

85. Repeat Problem 84, but do not assume $r \ll R$.

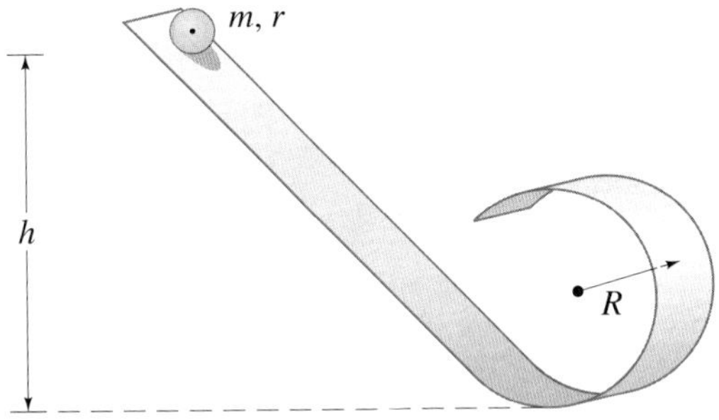


**FIGURE 8–58** Problems 84 and 85.

86. The tires of a car make 85 revolutions as the car reduces its speed uniformly from 90.0 km/h to 60.0 km/h. The tires have a diameter of 0.90 m. (*a*) What was the angular acceleration of each tire? (*b*) If the car continues to decelerate at this rate, how much more time is required for it to stop?

## Answers to Exercises

**A:** $f = 0.076\,\text{Hz}$; $T = 13\,\text{s}$.

**B:** $\vec{\mathbf{F}}_A$.

**C:** Yes; she does work to pull in her arms.

**D:** Work was done in pulling the string and decreasing the circle's radius.

Our whole built environment, from modern bridges to skyscrapers, has required architects and engineers to determine the forces and stresses within these structures. The object is to keep these structures static—that is, not in motion, especially not falling down.

The study of statics applies equally well to the human body, including balance, the forces in muscles, joints, and bones, and ultimately the possibility of fracture.

# CHAPTER 9

# Static Equilibrium; Elasticity and Fracture

*This Chapter deals with forces within objects at rest*

In this Chapter, we will study a special case in mechanics—when the net force and the net torque on an object, or system of objects, are both zero. In this case both the linear acceleration and the angular acceleration of the object or system are zero. The object is either at rest, or its center of mass is moving at constant velocity. We will be concerned mainly with the first situation, in which the object or objects are all at rest. Now, you may think that the study of objects at rest is not very interesting since the objects will have neither velocity nor acceleration, and the net force and the net torque will be zero. But this does not imply that no forces at all act on the objects. In fact it is virtually impossible to find an object on which no forces act. Just how and where these forces act can be very important, both for buildings and other structures, and in the human body.

Sometimes, as we shall see in this Chapter, the forces may be so great that the object is seriously *deformed*, or it may even *fracture* (break)—and avoiding such problems gives this field of *statics* even greater importance.

**Statics** is concerned with the calculation of the forces acting on and within structures that are in *equilibrium*. Determination of these forces, which occupies us in the first part of this Chapter, then allows a determination of whether the structures can sustain the forces without significant deformation or fracture, subjects we discuss later in this Chapter. These techniques can be applied in a wide range of fields. Architects and engineers must be able to calculate the forces on the structural components of buildings, bridges, machines, vehicles, and other structures, since any material will buckle or break if too much force is applied (Fig. 9–1). In the human body a knowledge of the forces in muscles and joints is of great value for doctors, physical therapists, and athletes.

FIGURE 9–1 Elevated walkway collapse in a Kansas City hotel in 1981. How a simple physics calculation could have prevented the tragic loss of over 100 lives is considered in Example 9–12.

## 9–1 The Conditions for Equilibrium

Objects in daily life have at least one force acting on them (gravity). If they are at rest, then there must be other forces acting on them as well so that the net force is zero. A book at rest on a table, for example, has two forces acting on it, the downward force of gravity and the normal force the table exerts upward on it (Fig. 9–2). Since the net force on the book is zero, the upward force exerted by the table on the book must be equal in magnitude to the force of gravity acting downward on the book. Such an object is said to be in **equilibrium** (Latin for "equal forces" or "balance") under the action of these two forces.

Do not confuse the two forces in Fig. 9–2 with the equal and opposite forces of Newton's third law, which act on different objects. Here, both forces act on the same object.

PHYSICS APPLIED
*Orthodontia*

**EXAMPLE 9–1 Straightening teeth.** The wire band shown in Fig. 9–3a has a tension $F_T$ of 2.0 N along it. It therefore exerts forces of 2.0 N on the highlighted tooth (to which it is attached) in the two directions shown. Calculate the resultant force on the tooth due to the wire, $F_R$.

**APPROACH** Since the two forces $F_T$ are equal, their sum will be directed along the line that bisects the angle between them, which we have chosen to be the $y$ axis. The $x$ components of the two forces add up to zero.

**SOLUTION** The $y$ component of each force is $(2.0\,\text{N})(\cos 70°) = 0.684\,\text{N}$: adding the two together, we get a resultant force $F_R = 1.37\,\text{N}$ as shown in Fig. 9–3b. We assume that the tooth is in equilibrium because the gums exert an equal and opposite force. Actually that is not quite so since the objective is to move the tooth ever so slowly.

**NOTE** If the wire is firmly attached to the tooth, the tension to the right, say, can be made larger than that to the left, and the resultant force would correspondingly be directed more toward the right.

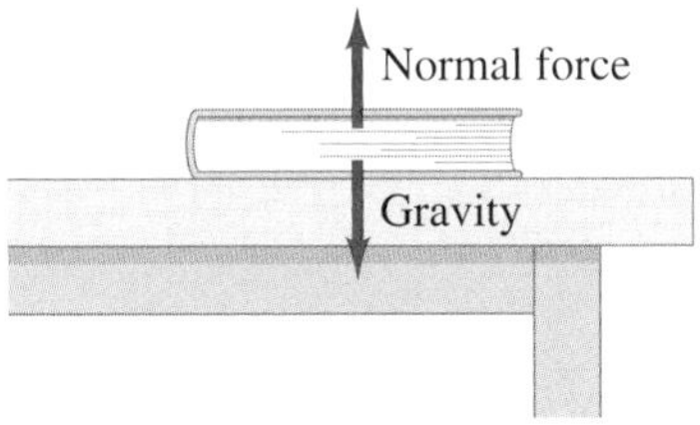


FIGURE 9–2 The book is in equilibrium; the net force on it is zero.

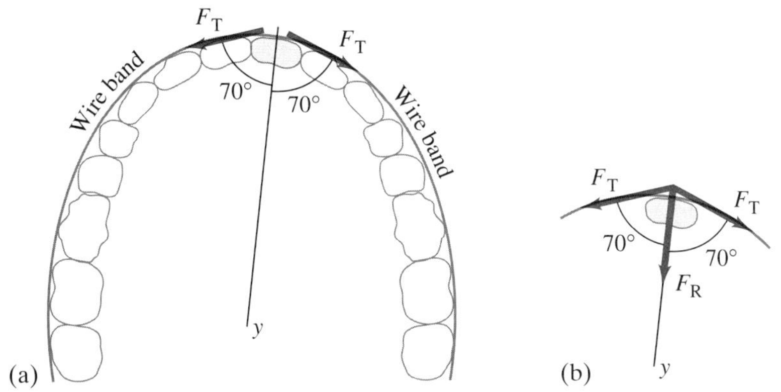


FIGURE 9–3 Forces on a tooth. Example 9–1.

### The First Condition for Equilibrium

For an object to be at rest, Newton's second law tells us that the sum of the forces acting on it must add up to zero. Since force is a vector, the components of the net force must each be zero. Hence, a condition for equilibrium is that

*First condition for equilibrium: the sum of all forces is zero*

$$\Sigma F_x = 0, \qquad \Sigma F_y = 0, \qquad \Sigma F_z = 0. \tag{9–1}$$

We will mainly be dealing with forces that act in a plane, so we usually need only the $x$ and $y$ components. We must remember that if a particular force component points along the negative $x$ or $y$ axis, it must have a negative sign. Equations 9–1 are called the **first condition for equilibrium**.

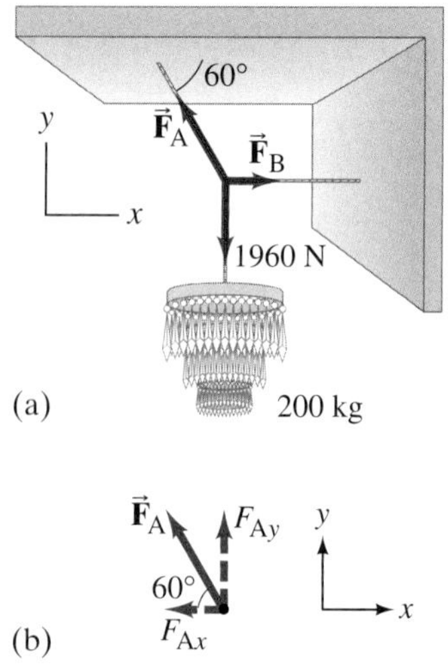


**FIGURE 9–4** Example 9–2.

**EXAMPLE 9–2** **Chandelier cord tension.** Calculate the tensions $\vec{\mathbf{F}}_A$ and $\vec{\mathbf{F}}_B$ in the two cords that are connected to the vertical cord supporting the 200-kg chandelier in Fig. 9–4.

**APPROACH** We need a free-body diagram, but for which object? If we choose the chandelier, the cord supporting it must exert a force equal to the chandelier's weight $mg = (200\,\text{kg})(9.8\,\text{m/s}^2) = 1960\,\text{N}$. But the forces $\vec{\mathbf{F}}_A$ and $\vec{\mathbf{F}}_B$ don't get involved. Instead, let us choose as our object the point where the three cords join (it could be a knot). The free-body diagram is then as shown in Fig. 9–4a. The three forces—$\vec{\mathbf{F}}_A$, $\vec{\mathbf{F}}_B$, and the tension in the vertical cord equal to the weight of the 200-kg chandelier—act at this point where the three cords join. For this junction point we write $\Sigma F_x = 0$ and $\Sigma F_y = 0$, since the problem is laid out in two dimensions. The directions of $\vec{\mathbf{F}}_A$ and $\vec{\mathbf{F}}_B$ are known, since tension in a rope can only be along the rope—any other direction would cause the rope to bend, as already pointed out in Chapter 4. Thus, our unknowns are the magnitudes $F_A$ and $F_B$.

**SOLUTION** We first resolve $\vec{\mathbf{F}}_A$ into its horizontal ($x$) and vertical ($y$) components. Although we don't know the value of $F_A$, we can write (see Fig. 9–4b) $F_{Ax} = -F_A \cos 60°$ and $F_{Ay} = F_A \sin 60°$. $\vec{\mathbf{F}}_B$ has only an $x$ component. In the vertical direction, we have the downward force exerted by the vertical cord equal to the weight of the chandelier $= (200\,\text{kg})(g)$, and the vertical component of $\vec{\mathbf{F}}_A$ upward. Since $\Sigma F_y = 0$, we have

$$\Sigma F_y = F_A \sin 60° - (200\,\text{kg})(g) = 0$$

so

$$F_A = \frac{(200\,\text{kg})g}{\sin 60°} = \frac{(200\,\text{kg})g}{0.866} = (231\,\text{kg})g = 2260\,\text{N}.$$

In the horizontal direction,

$$\Sigma F_x = F_B - F_A \cos 60° = 0.$$

Thus

$$F_B = F_A \cos 60° = (231\,\text{kg})(g)(0.500) = (115\,\text{kg})g = 1130\,\text{N}.$$

The magnitudes of $\vec{\mathbf{F}}_A$ and $\vec{\mathbf{F}}_B$ determine the strength of cord or wire that must be used. In this case, the wire must be able to hold more than 230 kg.

**NOTE** We didn't insert the value of $g$, the acceleration due to gravity, until the end. In this way we found the magnitude of the force in terms of $g$ times the number of kilograms (which may be a more familiar quantity than newtons).

**EXERCISE A** In Example 9–2, $F_A$ has to be greater than the chandelier's weight, $mg$. Why?

**FIGURE 9–5** Although the net force on it is zero, the ruler will move (rotate). A pair of equal forces acting in opposite directions but at different points on an object (as shown here) is referred to as a *couple.*

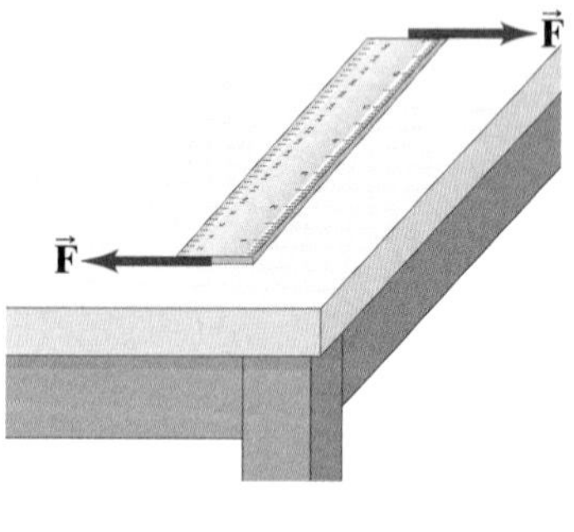


## The Second Condition for Equilibrium

Although Eqs. 9–1 are a necessary condition for an object to be in equilibrium, they are not always a sufficient condition. Figure 9–5 shows an object on which the net force is zero. Although the two forces labeled $\vec{\mathbf{F}}$ add up to give zero net force on the object, they do give rise to a net torque that will rotate the object. Referring to Eq. 8–14, $\Sigma\tau = I\alpha$, we see that if an object is to remain at rest, the net torque applied to it (calculated about *any* axis) must be zero. Thus we have the **second condition for equilibrium**: that the sum of the torques acting on an object, as calculated about any axis, must be zero:

*Second condition for equilibrium: the sum of all torques is zero*

$$\Sigma\tau = 0. \qquad \textbf{(9–2)}$$

This condition will ensure that the angular acceleration, $\alpha$, about any axis will be zero. If the object is not rotating initially ($\omega = 0$), it will not start rotating. Equations 9–1 and 9–2 are the only requirements for an object to be in equilibrium.

We will mainly consider cases in which the forces all act in a plane (we call it the $xy$ plane). In such cases the torque is calculated about an axis that is perpendicular to the $xy$ plane. *The choice of this axis is arbitrary*. If the object is at rest, then $\Sigma\tau = 0$ about any axis whatever. Therefore we can choose any axis that makes our calculation easier. Once the axis is chosen, all torques must be calculated about that axis.

**CAUTION**

*Axis choice for $\Sigma\tau = 0$ is arbitrary. All torques must be calculated about the same axis.*

**CONCEPTUAL EXAMPLE 9–3** **A lever.** The bar in Fig. 9–6 is being used as a lever to pry up a large rock. The small rock acts as a fulcrum (pivot point). The force $F_P$ required at the long end of the bar can be quite a bit smaller than the rock's weight $mg$, since it is the *torques* that balance in the rotation about the fulcrum. If, however, the leverage isn't sufficient, and the large rock isn't budged, what are two ways to increase the leverage?

**PHYSICS APPLIED**

*The lever*

**RESPONSE** One way is to increase the lever arm of the force $F_P$ by slipping a pipe over the end of the bar and thereby pushing with a longer lever arm. A second way is to move the fulcrum closer to the large rock. This may change the long lever arm $R$ only a little, but it changes the short lever arm $r$ by a substantial fraction and therefore changes the ratio of $R/r$ dramatically. In order to pry the rock, the torque due to $F_P$ must at least balance the torque due to $mg$, so $mgr = F_P R$ and

$$\frac{r}{R} = \frac{F_P}{mg}.$$

With $r$ smaller, the weight $mg$ can be balanced with less force $F_P$. The ratio $R/r$ is the **mechanical advantage** of the system. A lever is a "simple machine." We discussed another simple machine, the pulley, in Chapter 4, Example 4–14.

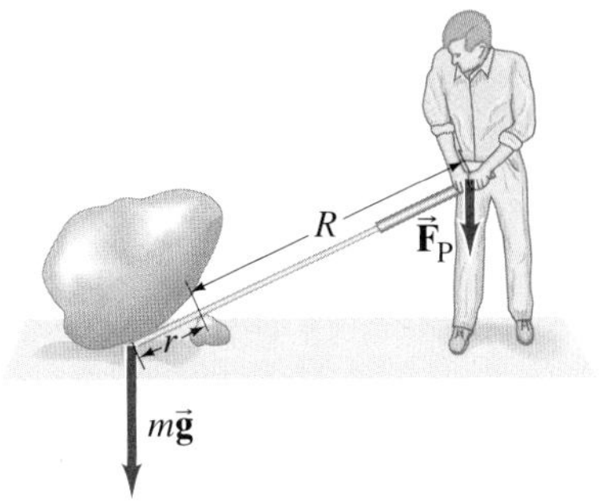


**FIGURE 9–6** Example 9–3. A lever can "multiply" your force.

**EXERCISE B** For simplicity, we wrote the equation in Example 9–3 as if the lever were perpendicular to the forces. Would the equation be valid even for a lever at an angle as shown in Fig. 9–6?

## 9–2 Solving Statics Problems

This subject of statics is important because it allows us to calculate certain forces on (or within) a structure when some of the forces on it are already known. We will mainly consider situations in which all the forces act in a plane, so we can have two force equations ($x$ and $y$ components) and one torque equation, for a total of three equations. Of course, you do not have to use all three equations if they are not needed. When using a torque equation, a torque that tends to rotate the object counterclockwise is usually considered positive, whereas a torque that tends to rotate it clockwise is considered negative. (But the opposite convention would not be wrong.)

**PROBLEM SOLVING**

*$\tau > 0$ counterclockwise*
*$\tau < 0$ clockwise*

One of the forces that acts on objects is the force of gravity. Our analysis in this Chapter is greatly simplified if we use the concept of center of gravity (CG) or center of mass (CM), which for practical purposes are the same point. As we discussed in Section 7–8, we can consider the force of gravity on the object as acting at its CG. For uniform symmetrically shaped objects, the CG is at the geometric center. For more complicated objects, the CG can be determined as discussed in Section 7–8.

There is no single technique for attacking statics problems, but the following procedure may be helpful.

## PROBLEM SOLVING Statics

1. Choose one object at a time for consideration. Make a careful **free-body diagram** by showing all the forces acting on that object and the points at which these forces act. If you aren't sure of the direction of a force, choose a direction; if the actual direction is opposite, your eventual calculation will give a result with a minus sign.
2. Choose a convenient **coordinate system**, and resolve the forces into their components.
3. Using letters to represent unknowns, write down the **equilibrium equations** for the **forces**:
$$\Sigma F_x = 0 \quad \text{and} \quad \Sigma F_y = 0,$$
assuming all the forces act in a plane.
4. For the **torque equation**,
$$\Sigma \tau = 0,$$
choose any axis perpendicular to the $xy$ plane that might make the calculation easier. (For example, you can reduce the number of unknowns in the resulting equation by choosing the axis so that one of the unknown forces acts through that axis; then this force will have zero lever arm and produce zero torque, and so won't appear in the equation.) Pay careful attention to determining the lever arm for each force correctly. Give each torque a + or − sign to indicate torque direction. For example, if torques tending to rotate the object counterclockwise are positive, then those tending to rotate it clockwise are negative.
5. **Solve** these equations for the unknowns. Three equations allow a maximum of three unknowns to be solved for. They can be forces, distances, or even angles.

PHYSICS APPLIED
*Balancing a seesaw*

**EXAMPLE 9–4 Balancing a seesaw.** A board of mass $M = 2.0\,\text{kg}$ serves as a seesaw for two children, as shown in Fig. 9–7a. Child A has a mass of 30 kg and sits 2.5 m from the pivot point, P (his center of gravity is 2.5 m from the pivot). At what distance $x$ from the pivot must child B, of mass 25 kg, place herself to balance the seesaw? Assume the board is uniform and centered over the pivot.

**APPROACH** We follow the steps of the Problem Solving Box explicitly.

**SOLUTION**

1. **Free-body diagram**. We choose the board as our object, and assume it is horizontal. Its free-body diagram is shown in Fig. 9–7b. The forces acting on the board are the forces exerted downward on it by each child, $\vec{\mathbf{F}}_A$ and $\vec{\mathbf{F}}_B$, the upward force exerted by the pivot $\vec{\mathbf{F}}_N$, and the force of gravity on the board ($= Mg$) which acts at the center of the uniform board.
2. **Coordinate system**. We choose $y$ to be vertical, with positive upward, and $x$ horizontal to the right, with origin at the pivot.
3. **Force equation**. All the forces are in the $y$ (vertical) direction, so
$$\Sigma F_y = 0$$
$$F_N - m_A g - m_B g - Mg = 0,$$
where $F_A = m_A g$ and $F_B = m_B g$ because each child is in equilibrium when the seesaw is balanced.

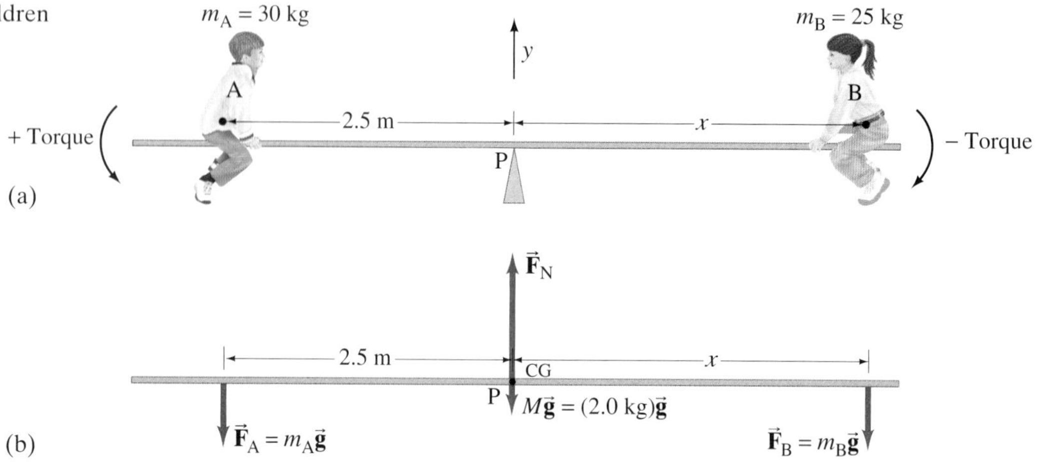


**FIGURE 9–7** (a) Two children on a seesaw, Example 9–4. (b) Free-body diagram of the board.

4. **Torque equation**. Let us calculate the torque about an axis through the board at the pivot point, P. Then the lever arms for $F_N$ and for the weight of the board are zero, and they will contribute zero torque (about point P) in our torque equation. Thus the torque equation will involve only the forces $\vec{\mathbf{F}}_A$ and $\vec{\mathbf{F}}_B$, which are equal to the weights of the children. The torque exerted by each child will be $mg$ times the appropriate lever arm, which here is the distance of each child from the pivot point. Hence the torque equation is

$$\Sigma\tau = 0$$

$$m_A g(2.5\,\text{m}) - m_B gx + Mg(0\,\text{m}) + F_N(0\,\text{m}) = 0$$

or

$$m_A g(2.5\,\text{m}) - m_B gx = 0,$$

where two terms were dropped because their lever arms were zero.

5. **Solve**. We solve the torque equation for $x$ and find

$$x = \frac{m_A}{m_B}(2.5\,\text{m}) = \frac{30\,\text{kg}}{25\,\text{kg}}(2.5\,\text{m}) = 3.0\,\text{m}.$$

To balance the seesaw, child B must sit so that her CM is 3.0 m from the pivot point. This makes sense: since she is lighter, she must sit farther from the pivot than the heavier child.

**EXERCISE C** We did not need to use the force equation to solve Example 9–4 because of our choice of the axis. Use the force equation to find the force exerted by the pivot.

**EXAMPLE 9–5** **Forces on a beam and supports.** A uniform 1500-kg beam, 20.0 m long, supports a 15,000-kg printing press 5.0 m from the right support column (Fig. 9–8). Calculate the force on each of the vertical support columns.

**APPROACH** We analyze the forces on the beam (the force the beam exerts on each column is equal and opposite to the force exerted by the column on the beam). We label these forces $\vec{\mathbf{F}}_A$ and $\vec{\mathbf{F}}_B$ in Fig. 9–8. The weight of the beam itself acts at its center of gravity, 10.0 m from either end. We choose a convenient axis for writing the torque equation: the point of application of $\vec{\mathbf{F}}_A$ (labeled P), so $\vec{\mathbf{F}}_A$ will not enter the equation (its lever arm will be zero) and we will have an equation in only one unknown, $F_B$.

**SOLUTION** The torque equation, $\Sigma\tau = 0$, with the counterclockwise direction as positive gives

$$\Sigma\tau = -(10.0\,\text{m})(1500\,\text{kg})g - (15.0\,\text{m})(15{,}000\,\text{kg})g + (20.0\,\text{m})F_B = 0.$$

Solving for $F_B$, we find $F_B = (12{,}000\,\text{kg})g = 118{,}000\,\text{N}$. To find $F_A$, we use $\Sigma F_y = 0$, with $+y$ upward:

$$\Sigma F_y = F_A - (1500\,\text{kg})g - (15{,}000\,\text{kg})g + F_B = 0.$$

Putting in $F_B = (12{,}000\,\text{kg})g$, we find that $F_A = (4500\,\text{kg})g = 44{,}100\,\text{N}$.

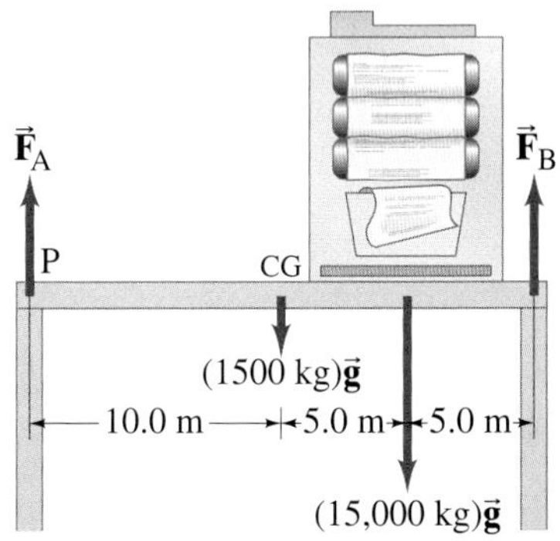


**FIGURE 9–8** A 1500-kg beam supports a 15,000-kg machine. Example 9–5.

Figure 9–9 shows a uniform beam that extends beyond its support like a diving board. Such a beam is called a **cantilever**. The forces acting on the beam in Fig. 9–9 are those due to the supports, $\vec{\mathbf{F}}_A$ and $\vec{\mathbf{F}}_B$, and the force of gravity which acts at the CG, 5.0 m to the right of the right-hand support. If you follow the procedure of the last Example and calculate $F_A$ and $F_B$, assuming they point upward as shown in Fig. 9–9, you will find that $F_A$ comes out negative. If the beam has a mass of 1200 kg and a weight $mg = 12{,}000\,\text{N}$, then $F_B = 15{,}000\,\text{N}$ and $F_A = -3000\,\text{N}$ (see Problem 10). Whenever an unknown force comes out negative, it merely means that the force actually points in the opposite direction from what you assumed. Thus in Fig. 9–9, $\vec{\mathbf{F}}_A$ actually points downward. With a little reflection it should become clear that the left-hand support must indeed pull downward on the beam (by means of bolts, screws, fasteners and/or glue) if the beam is to be in equilibrium; otherwise the sum of the torques about the CG (or about the point where $\vec{\mathbf{F}}_B$ acts) could not be zero.

PHYSICS APPLIED
*Cantilever*

PROBLEM SOLVING
*If a force comes out negative*

**FIGURE 9–9** A cantilever.

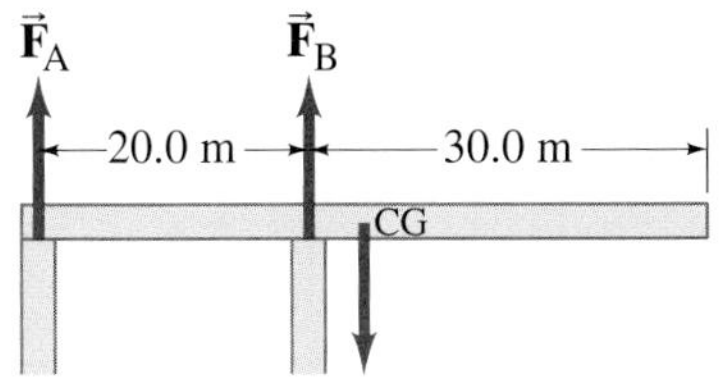

*Hinges and cords*

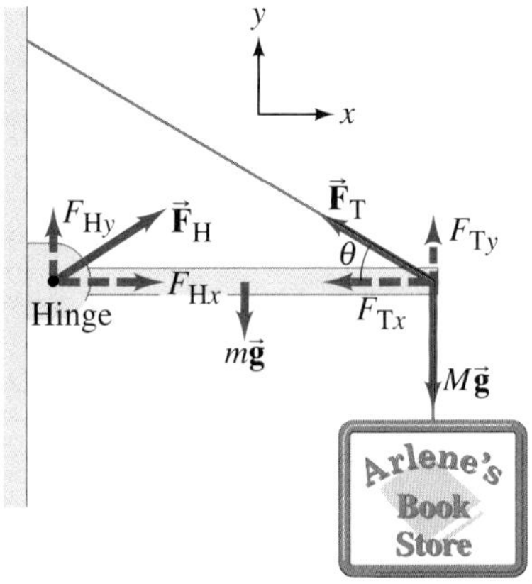


**FIGURE 9–10** Example 9–6.

Our next Example involves a beam that is attached to a wall by a hinge and is supported by a cable or cord (Fig. 9–10). It is important to remember that a flexible cable can support a force only along its length. (If there were a component of force perpendicular to the cable, it would bend because it is flexible.) But for a rigid device, such as the hinge in Fig. 9–10, the force can be in any direction and we can know the direction only after solving the problem. The hinge is assumed small and smooth, so it can exert no internal torque (about its center) on the beam.

**EXAMPLE 9–6 Hinged beam and cable.** A uniform beam, 2.20 m long with mass $m = 25.0\text{ kg}$, is mounted by a hinge on a wall as shown in Fig. 9–10. The beam is held in a horizontal position by a cable that makes an angle $\theta = 30.0°$ as shown. The beam supports a sign of mass $M = 28.0\text{ kg}$ suspended from its end. Determine the components of the force $\vec{\mathbf{F}}_H$ that the hinge exerts on the beam, and the tension $F_T$ in the supporting cable.

**APPROACH** Figure 9–10 is the free-body diagram for the beam, showing all the forces acting on the beam. It also shows the components of $\vec{\mathbf{F}}_H$ and $\vec{\mathbf{F}}_T$. We have three unknowns, $F_{Hx}$, $F_{Hy}$, and $F_T$ (we are given $\theta$), so we will need all three equations, $\Sigma F_x = 0$, $\Sigma F_y = 0$, $\Sigma\tau = 0$.

**SOLUTION** The sum of the forces in the vertical $(y)$ direction is

$$\Sigma F_y = 0$$

$$F_{Hy} + F_{Ty} - mg - Mg = 0. \qquad \textbf{(i)}$$

In the horizontal $(x)$ direction, the sum of the forces is

$$\Sigma F_x = 0$$

$$F_{Hx} - F_{Tx} = 0. \qquad \textbf{(ii)}$$

For the torque equation, we choose the axis at the point where $\vec{\mathbf{F}}_T$ and $M\vec{\mathbf{g}}$ act (so our equation then contains only one unknown, $F_{Hy}$). We choose torques that tend to rotate the beam counterclockwise as positive. The weight $mg$ of the (uniform) beam acts at its center, so we have

$$\Sigma\tau = 0$$

$$-(F_{Hy})(2.20\text{ m}) + mg(1.10\text{ m}) = 0.$$

We solve for $F_{Hy}$:

$$F_{Hy} = \left(\frac{1.10\text{ m}}{2.20\text{ m}}\right)mg = (0.500)(25.0\text{ kg})(9.80\text{ m/s}^2) = 123\text{ N}. \qquad \textbf{(iii)}$$

Next, since the tension $\vec{\mathbf{F}}_T$ in the cable acts along the cable $(\theta = 30.0°)$, we see from Fig. 9–10 that $\tan\theta = F_{Ty}/F_{Tx}$, or

$$F_{Ty} = F_{Tx}\tan\theta = F_{Tx}(\tan 30.0°) = 0.577\,F_{Tx}. \qquad \textbf{(iv)}$$

Equation (i) above gives

$$F_{Ty} = (m + M)g - F_{Hy} = (53.0\text{ kg})(9.80\text{ m/s}^2) - 123\text{ N} = 396\text{ N};$$

Equations (iv) and (ii) give

$$F_{Tx} = F_{Ty}/0.577 = 687\text{ N};$$

$$F_{Hx} = F_{Tx} = 687\text{ N}.$$

The components of $\vec{\mathbf{F}}_H$ are $F_{Hy} = 123\text{ N}$ and $F_{Hx} = 687\text{ N}$. The tension in the wire is $F_T = \sqrt{F_{Tx}^2 + F_{Ty}^2} = 793\text{ N}$.

***Alternate Solution*** Let us see the effect of choosing a different axis for calculating torques, such as an axis through the hinge. Then the lever arm for $F_H$ is zero, and the torque equation $(\Sigma\tau = 0)$ becomes

$$-mg(1.10\,\text{m}) - Mg(2.20\,\text{m}) + F_{Ty}(2.20\,\text{m}) = 0.$$

We solve this for $F_{Ty}$ and find

$$F_{Ty} = \frac{m}{2}g + Mg = (12.5\,\text{kg} + 28.0\,\text{kg})(9.80\,\text{m/s}^2) = 397\,\text{N}.$$

We get the same result, within the precision of our significant figures.

**NOTE** It doesn't matter which axis we choose for $\Sigma\tau = 0$. Using a second axis can serve as a check.

## Additional Example—The Ladder

**EXAMPLE 9–7** **Ladder.** A 5.0-m-long ladder leans against a wall at a point 4.0 m above a cement floor as shown in Fig. 9–11. The ladder is uniform and has mass $m = 12.0\,\text{kg}$. Assuming the wall is frictionless (but the floor is not), determine the forces exerted on the ladder by the floor and by the wall.

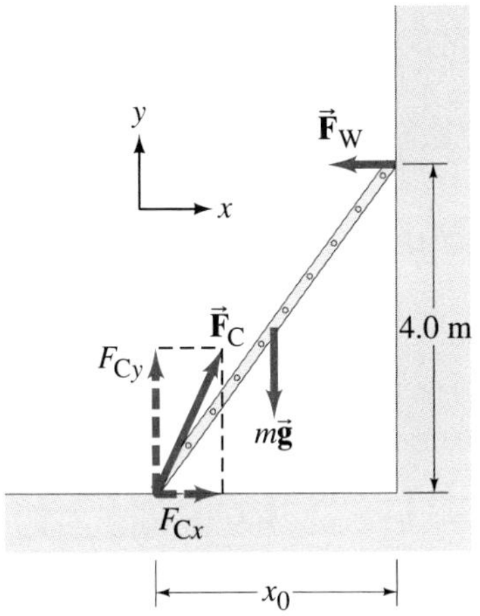


**FIGURE 9–11** A ladder leaning against a wall. Example 9–7.

**APPROACH** Figure 9–11 is the free-body diagram for the ladder, showing all the forces acting on the ladder. The wall, since it is frictionless, can exert a force only perpendicular to the wall, and we label that force $\vec{\mathbf{F}}_W$. The cement floor exerts a force $\vec{\mathbf{F}}_C$ which has both horizontal and vertical force components: $F_{Cx}$ is frictional and $F_{Cy}$ is the normal force. Finally, gravity exerts a force $mg = (12.0\,\text{kg})(9.80\,\text{m/s}^2) = 118\,\text{N}$ on the ladder at its midpoint, since the ladder is uniform.

**SOLUTION** Again we use the equilibrium conditions, $\Sigma F_x = 0$, $\Sigma F_y = 0$, $\Sigma\tau = 0$. We will need all three since there are three unknowns: $F_W$, $F_{Cx}$, and $F_{Cy}$. The $y$ component of the force equation is

$$\Sigma F_y = F_{Cy} - mg = 0,$$

so immediately we have

$$F_{Cy} = mg = 118\,\text{N}.$$

The $x$ component of the force equation is

$$\Sigma F_x = F_{Cx} - F_W = 0.$$

To determine both $F_{Cx}$ and $F_W$, we need a torque equation. If we choose to calculate torques about an axis through the point where the ladder touches the cement floor, then $\vec{\mathbf{F}}_C$, which acts at this point, will have a lever arm of zero and so won't enter the equation. The ladder touches the floor a distance $x_0 = \sqrt{(5.0\,\text{m})^2 - (4.0\,\text{m})^2} = 3.0\,\text{m}$ from the wall. The lever arm for $mg$ is half this, or 1.5 m, and the lever arm for $F_W$ is 4.0 m, Fig. 9–11. We get

$$\Sigma\tau = (4.0\,\text{m})F_W - (1.5\,\text{m})mg = 0.$$

Thus

$$F_W = \frac{(1.5\,\text{m})(12.0\,\text{kg})(9.8\,\text{m/s}^2)}{4.0\,\text{m}} = 44\,\text{N}.$$

Then, from the $x$ component of the force equation,

$$F_{Cx} = F_W = 44\,\text{N}.$$

Since the components of $\vec{\mathbf{F}}_C$ are $F_{Cx} = 44\,\text{N}$ and $F_{Cy} = 118\,\text{N}$, then

$$F_C = \sqrt{(44\,\text{N})^2 + (118\,\text{N})^2} = 126\,\text{N} \approx 130\,\text{N}$$

(rounded off to two significant figures), and it acts at an angle to the floor of

$$\theta = \tan^{-1}(118\,\text{N}/44\,\text{N}) = 70°.$$

**NOTE** The force $\vec{\mathbf{F}}_C$ does *not* have to act along the ladder's direction because the ladder is rigid and not flexible like a cord or cable.

**EXERCISE D** Why is it reasonable to ignore friction along the wall, but not reasonable to ignore it along the floor?

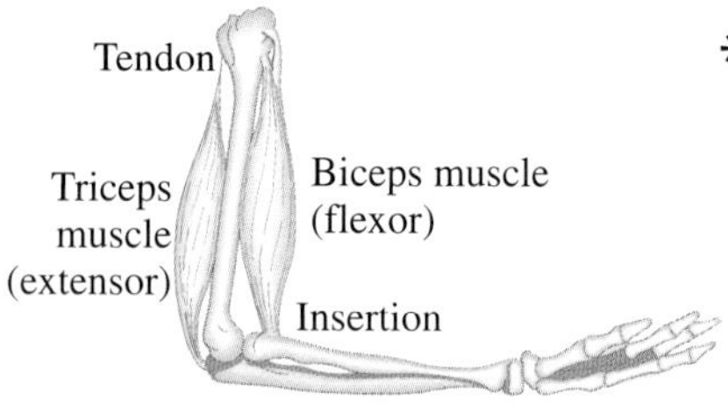


**FIGURE 9–12** The biceps (flexor) and triceps (extensor) muscles in the human arm.

## * 9–3 Applications to Muscles and Joints

The techniques we have been discussing for calculating forces on objects in equilibrium can readily be applied to the human (or animal) body, and can be of great use in studying the forces on muscles, bones, and joints for organisms in motion or at rest. Generally a muscle is attached, via tendons, to two different bones, as in Fig. 9–12. The points of attachment are called *insertions*. Two bones are flexibly connected at a *joint*, such as those at the elbow, knee, and hip. A muscle exerts a pull when its fibers contract under stimulation by a nerve, but a muscle cannot exert a push. Muscles that tend to bring two limbs closer together, such as the biceps muscle in the upper arm (Fig. 9–12) are called *flexors*; those that act to extend a limb outward, such as the triceps muscle in Fig. 9–12, are called *extensors*. You use the flexor muscle in the upper arm when lifting an object in your hand; you use the extensor muscle when throwing a ball.

PHYSICS APPLIED
*Forces in muscles and joints*

**EXAMPLE 9–8** **Force exerted by biceps muscle.** How much force must the biceps muscle exert when a 5.0-kg mass is held in the hand (*a*) with the arm horizontal as in Fig. 9–13a, and (*b*) when the arm is at a 45° angle as in Fig. 9–13b? Assume that the mass of forearm and hand together is 2.0 kg and their CG is as shown.

**FIGURE 9–13** Example 9–8.

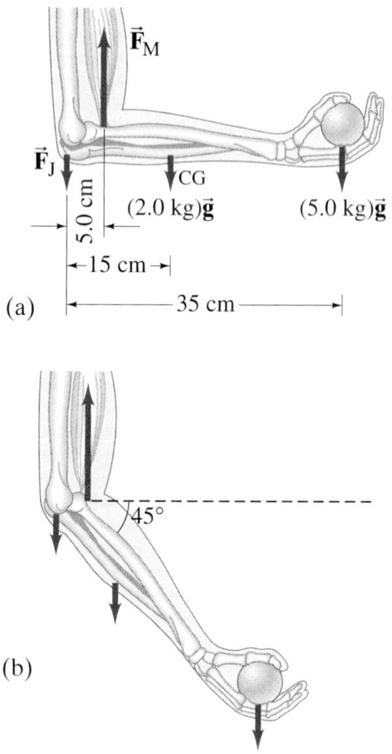


**APPROACH** The forces acting on the forearm are shown in Fig. 9–13 and include the weights of the arm and ball, the upward force $\vec{F}_M$ exerted by the muscle, and a force $\vec{F}_J$ exerted at the joint by the bone in the upper arm (all assumed to act vertically). We wish to find the magnitude of $\vec{F}_M$, which is done most easily by using the torque equation and by choosing our axis through the joint so that $\vec{F}_J$ contributes zero torque.

**SOLUTION** (*a*) We calculate torques about the point where $\vec{F}_J$ acts in Fig. 9–13a. The $\Sigma\tau = 0$ equation gives

$$(0.050\,\text{m})F_M - (0.15\,\text{m})(2.0\,\text{kg})g - (0.35\,\text{m})(5.0\,\text{kg})g = 0.$$

We solve for $F_M$:

$$F_M = \frac{(0.15\,\text{m})(2.0\,\text{kg})g + (0.35\,\text{m})(5.0\,\text{kg})g}{0.050\,\text{m}} = (41\,\text{kg})g = 400\,\text{N}.$$

(*b*) The lever arm, as calculated about the joint, is reduced by the factor sin 45° for all three forces. Our torque equation will look like the one just above, except that each term will have its lever arm reduced by the same factor, which will cancel out. The same result is obtained, $F_M = 400\,\text{N}$.

**NOTE** The force required of the muscle (400 N) is quite large compared to the weight of the object lifted (49 N). Indeed, the muscles and joints of the body are generally subjected to quite large forces.

PHYSICS APPLIED
*Muscle insertion and lever arm*

The point of insertion of a muscle varies from person to person. A slight increase in the distance of the joint to the point of insertion of the biceps muscle from 5.0 cm to 5.5 cm can be a considerable advantage for lifting and throwing. Champion athletes are often found to have muscle insertions farther from the joint than the average person, and if this applies to one muscle, it usually applies to all.

PHYSICS APPLIED
*Forces on the spine, and back pain*

As another example of the large forces acting within the human body, we consider the muscles used to support the trunk when a person bends forward (Fig. 9–14a). The lowest vertebra on the spinal column (fifth lumbar vertebra) acts as a fulcrum for this bending position. The "erector spinae" muscles in the back that support the trunk act at an effective angle of about 12° to the axis of the spine. Figure 9–14b is a simplified schematic drawing showing the forces on the upper body. We assume the trunk makes an angle of 30° with the horizontal.

The force exerted by the back muscles is represented by $\vec{\mathbf{F}}_\mathrm{M}$, the force exerted on the base of the spine at the lowest vertebra is $\vec{\mathbf{F}}_\mathrm{V}$, and $\vec{\mathbf{w}}_\mathrm{H}$, $\vec{\mathbf{w}}_\mathrm{A}$, and $\vec{\mathbf{w}}_\mathrm{T}$ represent the weights of the **h**ead, freely hanging **a**rms, and **t**runk, respectively. The values shown are approximations taken from Table 7–1. The distances (in cm) refer to a person 180 cm tall, but are approximately in the same ratio of 1:2:3 for an average person of any height, and the result in the following Example is then independent of the height of the person.

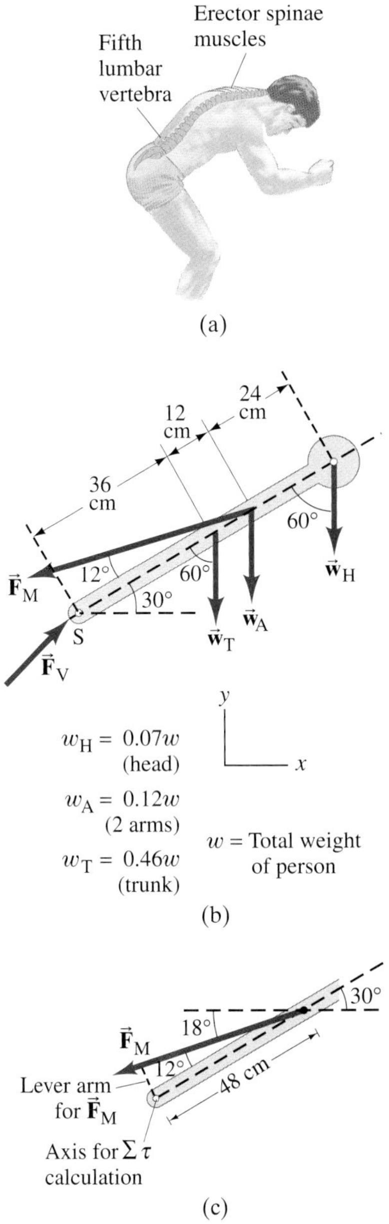


**FIGURE 9–14** (a) A person bending over. (b) Forces on the back exerted by the back muscles ($\vec{\mathbf{F}}_\mathrm{M}$) and by the vertebrae ($\vec{\mathbf{F}}_\mathrm{V}$) when a person bends over. (c) Finding the lever arm for $\vec{\mathbf{F}}_\mathrm{M}$.

**EXAMPLE 9–9** **Forces on your back.** Calculate the magnitude and direction of the force $\vec{\mathbf{F}}_\mathrm{V}$ acting on the fifth lumbar vertebra for the example shown in Fig. 9–14b.

**APPROACH** We use the model of the upper body described above and shown in Fig. 9–14b. We can calculate $F_\mathrm{M}$ using the torque equation if we take the axis at the base of the spine (point S); with this choice, the other unknown, $F_\mathrm{V}$, doesn't appear in the equation because its lever arm is zero. To figure the lever arms, we need to use trigonometric functions.

**SOLUTION** For $\vec{\mathbf{F}}_\mathrm{M}$, the lever arm (perpendicular distance from axis to line of action of the force) will be the real distance to where the force acts (48 cm) multiplied by sin 12°, as shown in Fig. 9–14c. The lever arms for $\vec{\mathbf{w}}_\mathrm{H}$, $\vec{\mathbf{w}}_\mathrm{A}$, and $\vec{\mathbf{w}}_\mathrm{T}$ can be seen from Fig. 9–14b to be their respective distances from S times sin 60°. $F_\mathrm{M}$ tends to rotate the trunk counterclockwise, which we take to be positive. Then $\vec{\mathbf{w}}_\mathrm{H}$, $\vec{\mathbf{w}}_\mathrm{A}$, $\vec{\mathbf{w}}_\mathrm{T}$ will contribute negative torques. Thus $\Sigma\tau = 0$ gives

$$(0.48\,\mathrm{m})(\sin 12^\circ)(F_\mathrm{M}) - (0.72\,\mathrm{m})(\sin 60^\circ)(w_\mathrm{H}) \\ - (0.48\,\mathrm{m})(\sin 60^\circ)(w_\mathrm{A}) - (0.36\,\mathrm{m})(\sin 60^\circ)(w_\mathrm{T}) = 0.$$

Solving for $F_\mathrm{M}$ and putting in the values for $w_\mathrm{H}, w_\mathrm{A}, w_\mathrm{T}$ given in Fig. 9–14b, we find

$$F_\mathrm{M} = \frac{(0.72\,\mathrm{m})(0.07w) + (0.48\,\mathrm{m})(0.12w) + (0.36\,\mathrm{m})(0.46w)}{(0.48\,\mathrm{m})(\sin 12^\circ)}(\sin 60^\circ)$$
$$= 2.37w \approx 2.4w,$$

where $w$ is the total weight of the body. To get the components of $\vec{\mathbf{F}}_\mathrm{V}$ we use the $x$ and $y$ components of the force equation (noting that $30^\circ - 12^\circ = 18^\circ$):

$$\Sigma F_y = F_{\mathrm{V}y} - F_\mathrm{M}\sin 18^\circ - w_\mathrm{H} - w_\mathrm{A} - w_\mathrm{T} = 0$$

so

$$F_{\mathrm{V}y} = 1.38w \approx 1.4w,$$

and

$$\Sigma F_x = F_{\mathrm{V}x} - F_\mathrm{M}\cos 18^\circ = 0$$

so

$$F_{\mathrm{V}x} = 2.25w \approx 2.3w,$$

where we keep 3 significant figures for calculating, but round off to 2 for giving the answer. Then

$$F_\mathrm{V} = \sqrt{F_{\mathrm{V}x}^2 + F_{\mathrm{V}y}^2} = 2.6w.$$

The angle $\theta$ that $F_\mathrm{V}$ makes with the horizontal is given by $\tan\theta = F_{\mathrm{V}y}/F_{\mathrm{V}x} = 0.61$, so $\theta = 32^\circ$.

**NOTE** The force on the lowest vertebra is over $2\frac{1}{2}$ times the total body weight! This force is exerted by the "sacral" bone at the base of the spine, through the fluid-filled and somewhat flexible *intervertebral disc*. The discs at the base of the spine are clearly being compressed under very large forces. [If the body was less bent over (say, the 30° angle in Fig. 9–14b becomes 40° or 50°), then the stress on the lower back will be less (see Problem 35).]

If the person in Fig. 9–14 has a mass of 90 kg and is holding 20 kg in his hands (this increases $w_\mathrm{A}$ to $0.34w$), then $F_\mathrm{V}$ is increased to almost four times the person's weight ($3.7w$). For this 200-lb person, the force on the disc would be over 700 lb! With such strong forces acting, it is little wonder that so many people suffer from low back pain at one time or another.

## 9–4 Stability and Balance

An object in static equilibrium, if left undisturbed, will undergo no translational or rotational acceleration since the sum of all the forces and the sum of all the torques acting on it are zero. However, if the object is displaced slightly, three outcomes are possible: (1) the object returns to its original position, in which case it is said to be in **stable equilibrium**; (2) the object moves even farther from its original position, and it is said to be in **unstable equilibrium**; or (3) the object remains in its new position, and it is said to be in **neutral equilibrium**.

*Stable and unstable equilibria*

Consider the following examples. A ball suspended freely from a string is in stable equilibrium, for if it is displaced to one side, it will return to its original position (Fig. 9–15a) due to the net force and torque exerted on it. On the other hand, a pencil standing on its point is in unstable equilibrium. If its center of gravity is directly over its tip (Fig. 9–15b), the net force and net torque on it will be zero. But if it is displaced ever so slightly as shown—say, by a slight vibration or tiny air current—there will be a torque on it, and this torque acts to make the pencil continue to fall in the direction of the original displacement. Finally, an example of an object in neutral equilibrium is a sphere resting on a horizontal tabletop. If it is placed slightly to one side, it will remain in its new position—no net torque acts on it.

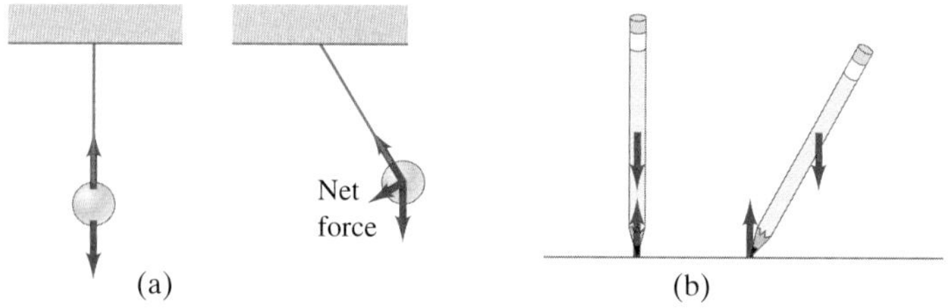


**FIGURE 9–15** (a) Stable equilibrium, and (b) unstable equilibrium.

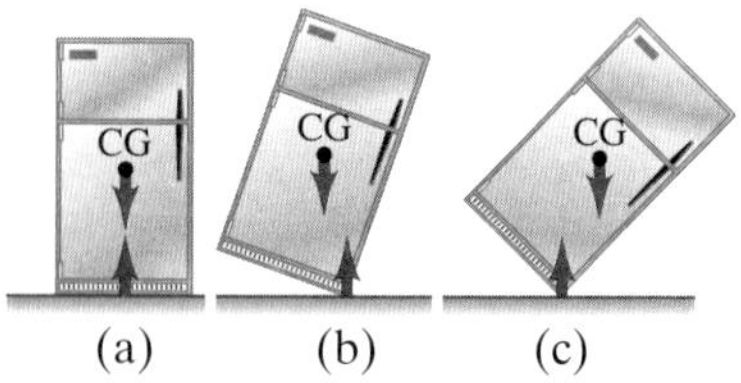


**FIGURE 9–16** Equilibrium of a refrigerator resting on a flat floor.

In most situations, such as in the design of structures and in working with the human body, we are interested in maintaining stable equilibrium, or *balance*, as we sometimes say. In general, an object whose center of gravity (CG) is below its point of support, such as a ball on a string, will be in stable equilibrium. If the CG is above the base of support, we have a more complicated situation. Consider a standing refrigerator (Fig. 9–16a). If it is tipped slightly, it will return to its original position due to the torque on it as shown in Fig. 9–16b. But if it is tipped too far, Fig. 9–16c, it will fall over. The critical point is reached when the CG shifts from one side of the pivot point to the other. When the CG is on one side, the torque pulls the object back onto its original base of support, Fig. 9–16b. If the object is tipped further, the CG goes past the pivot point and the torque causes the object to topple, Fig. 9–16c. In general, *an object whose center of gravity is above its base of support will be stable if a vertical line projected downward from the CG falls within the base of support.* This is because the normal force upward on the object (which balances out gravity) can be exerted only within the area of contact, so if the force of gravity acts beyond this area, a net torque will act to topple the object.

**FIGURE 9–17** Humans adjust their posture to achieve stability when carrying loads.

Stability, then, can be relative. A brick lying on its widest face is more stable than a brick standing on its end, for it will take more of an effort to tip it over. In the extreme case of the pencil in Fig. 9–15b, the base is practically a point and the slightest disturbance will topple it. In general, the larger the base and the lower the CG, the more stable the object.

**PHYSICS APPLIED**
*Humans and balance*

In this sense, humans are much less stable than four-legged mammals, which not only have a larger base of support because of their four legs, but also have a lower center of gravity. When walking and performing other kinds of movement, a person continually shifts the body so that its CG is over the feet, although in the normal adult this requires no conscious thought. Even as simple a movement as bending over requires moving the hips backward so that the CG remains over the feet, and you do this repositioning without thinking about it. To see this, position yourself with your heels and back to a wall and try to touch your toes. You won't be able to do it without falling. Persons carrying heavy loads automatically adjust their posture so that the CG of the total mass is over their feet, Fig. 9–17.

## * 9–5 Elasticity; Stress and Strain

In the first part of this Chapter we studied how to calculate the forces on objects in equilibrium. In this Section we study the effects of these forces: any object changes shape under the action of applied forces. If the forces are great enough, the object will break, or *fracture*, as we will discuss in Section 9–6.

### * Elasticity and Hooke's Law

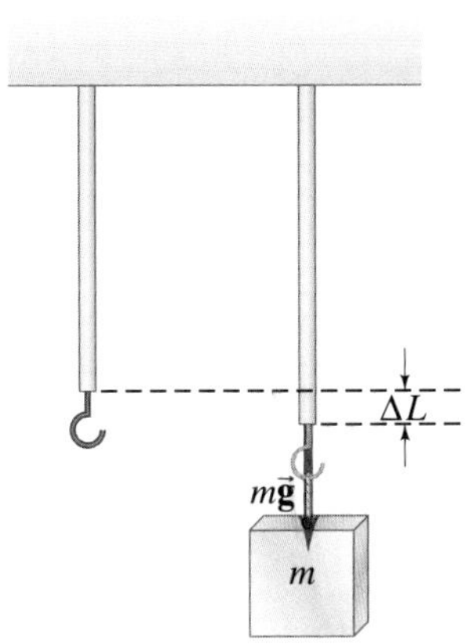


**FIGURE 9–18** Hooke's law: $\Delta L \propto$ applied force.

If a force is exerted on an object, such as the vertically suspended metal rod shown in Fig. 9–18, the length of the object changes. If the amount of elongation, $\Delta L$, is small compared to the length of the object, experiment shows that $\Delta L$ is proportional to the force exerted on the object. This proportionality, as we saw in Section 6–4, can be written as an equation:

$$F = k\,\Delta L. \tag{9–3}$$

*Hooke's law (again)*

Here $F$ represents the force pulling on the object, $\Delta L$ is the change in length, and $k$ is a proportionality constant. Equation 9–3, which is sometimes called **Hooke's law**† after Robert Hooke (1635–1703), who first noted it, is found to be valid for almost any solid material from iron to bone—but it is valid only up to a point. For if the force is too great, the object stretches excessively and eventually breaks.

Figure 9–19 shows a typical graph of applied force versus elongation. Up to a point called the **proportional limit**, Eq. 9–3 is a good approximation for many common materials, and the curve is a straight line. Beyond this point, the graph deviates from a straight line, and no simple relationship exists between $F$ and $\Delta L$. Nonetheless, up to a point farther along the curve called the **elastic limit**, the object will return to its original length if the applied force is removed. The region from the origin to the elastic limit is called the *elastic region*. If the object is stretched beyond the elastic limit, it enters the *plastic region*: it does not return to the original length upon removal of the external force, but remains permanently deformed (such as a bent paper clip). The maximum elongation is reached at the *breaking point*. The maximum force that can be applied without breaking is called the **ultimate strength** of the material (actually, force per unit area as we discuss in Section 9–6).

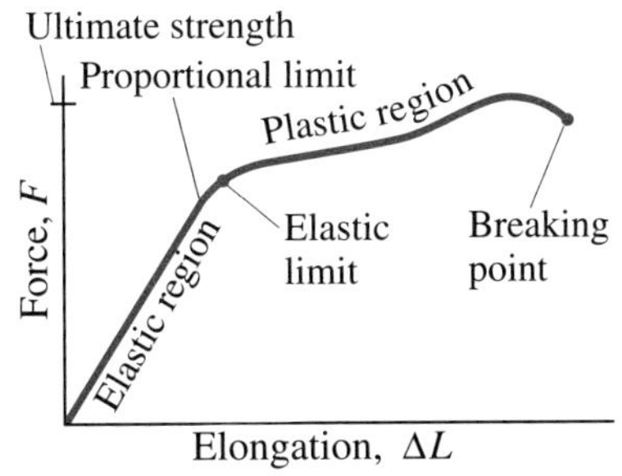


**FIGURE 9–19** Applied force vs. elongation for a typical metal under tension.

### * Young's Modulus

The amount of elongation of an object, such as the rod shown in Fig. 9–18, depends not only on the force applied to it, but also on the material of which it is made and on its dimensions. That is, the constant $k$ in Eq. 9–3 can be written in terms of these factors.

†The term "law" applied to this relation is not really appropriate, since first of all, it is only an approximation, and secondly, it refers only to a limited set of phenomena. Most physicists prefer to reserve the word "law" for those relations that are deeper and more encompassing and precise, such as Newton's laws of motion or the law of conservation of energy.

**TABLE 9–1 Elastic Moduli**

| Material | Young's Modulus, $E$ (N/m$^2$) | Shear Modulus, $G$ (N/m$^2$) | Bulk Modulus, $B$ (N/m$^2$) |
|---|---|---|---|
| *Solids* | | | |
| Iron, cast | $100 \times 10^9$ | $40 \times 10^9$ | $90 \times 10^9$ |
| Steel | $200 \times 10^9$ | $80 \times 10^9$ | $140 \times 10^9$ |
| Brass | $100 \times 10^9$ | $35 \times 10^9$ | $80 \times 10^9$ |
| Aluminum | $70 \times 10^9$ | $25 \times 10^9$ | $70 \times 10^9$ |
| Concrete | $20 \times 10^9$ | | |
| Brick | $14 \times 10^9$ | | |
| Marble | $50 \times 10^9$ | | $70 \times 10^9$ |
| Granite | $45 \times 10^9$ | | $45 \times 10^9$ |
| Wood (pine) (parallel to grain) | $10 \times 10^9$ | | |
| (perpendicular to grain) | $1 \times 10^9$ | | |
| Nylon | $5 \times 10^9$ | | |
| Bone (limb) | $15 \times 10^9$ | $80 \times 10^9$ | |
| *Liquids* | | | |
| Water | | | $2.0 \times 10^9$ |
| Alcohol (ethyl) | | | $1.0 \times 10^9$ |
| Mercury | | | $2.5 \times 10^9$ |
| *Gases*† | | | |
| Air, $H_2$, He, $CO_2$ | | | $1.01 \times 10^5$ |

† At normal atmospheric pressure; no variation in temperature during process.

If we compare rods made of the same material but of different lengths and cross-sectional areas, it is found that for the same applied force, the amount of stretch (again assumed small compared to the total length) is proportional to the original length and inversely proportional to the cross-sectional area. That is, the longer the object, the more it elongates for a given force; and the thicker it is, the less it elongates. These findings can be combined with Eq. 9–3 to yield

$$\Delta L = \frac{1}{E}\frac{F}{A} L_0, \qquad \textbf{(9–4)}$$

where $L_0$ is the original length of the object, $A$ is the cross-sectional area, and $\Delta L$ is the change in length due to the applied force $F$. $E$ is a constant of proportionality‡ known as the **elastic modulus**, or **Young's modulus**; its value depends only on the material. The value of Young's modulus for various materials is given in Table 9–1 (the shear modulus and bulk modulus in this Table are discussed later in this Section). Because $E$ is a property only of the material and is independent of the object's size or shape, Eq. 9–4 is far more useful for practical calculation than Eq. 9–3.

*Young's modulus*

**EXAMPLE 9–10 Tension in piano wire.** A 1.60-m-long steel piano wire has a diameter of 0.20 cm. How great is the tension in the wire if it stretches 0.25 cm when tightened?

**APPROACH** We assume Hooke's law holds, and use it in the form of Eq. 9–4, finding $E$ for steel in Table 9–1.

**SOLUTION** We solve for $F$ in Eq. 9–4 and note that the area of the wire is $A = \pi r^2 = (3.14)(0.0010\,\mathrm{m})^2 = 3.14 \times 10^{-6}\,\mathrm{m}^2$. Then

$$F = E\frac{\Delta L}{L_0}A = \left(2.0 \times 10^{11}\,\mathrm{N/m^2}\right)\left(\frac{0.0025\,\mathrm{m}}{1.60\,\mathrm{m}}\right)\left(3.14 \times 10^{-6}\,\mathrm{m}^2\right) = 980\,\mathrm{N}.$$

The large tension in all the wires in a piano must be supported by a strong frame.

‡The fact that $E$ is in the denominator, so $1/E$ is the actual proportionality constant, is merely a convention. When we rewrite Eq. 9–4 to get Eq. 9–5, $E$ is found in the numerator.

## * Stress and Strain

Let us return to solid objects. From Eq. 9–4, we see that the change in length of an object is directly proportional to the product of the object's length $L_0$ and the force per unit area $F/A$ applied to it. It is general practice to define the force per unit area as the **stress**:

*Stress defined*

$$\text{stress} = \frac{\text{force}}{\text{area}} = \frac{F}{A},$$

which has SI units of $N/m^2$. Also, the **strain** is defined to be the ratio of the change in length to the original length:

*Strain defined*

$$\text{strain} = \frac{\text{change in length}}{\text{original length}} = \frac{\Delta L}{L_0},$$

and is dimensionless (no units). Strain is thus the fractional change in length of the object, and is a measure of how much the rod has been deformed. Stress is applied to the material by external agents, whereas strain is the material's response to the stress. Equation 9–4 can be rewritten as

$$\frac{F}{A} = E\frac{\Delta L}{L_0} \qquad \textbf{(9–5)}$$

or

*Young's modulus*

$$E = \frac{F/A}{\Delta L/L_0} = \frac{\text{stress}}{\text{strain}}.$$

Thus we see that the strain is directly proportional to the stress, in the linear (elastic) region of Fig. 9–19.

## * Tension, Compression, and Shear Stress

*Tension and compression*

The rod shown in Fig. 9–20a is said to be under *tension* or **tensile stress**. Not only is there a force pulling down on the rod at its lower end, but since the rod is in equilibrium we know that the support at the top is exerting an equal[†] upward force on the rod at its upper end, Fig. 9–20a. In fact, this tensile stress exists throughout the material. Consider, for example, the lower half of a suspended rod as shown in Fig. 9–20b. This lower half is in equilibrium, so there must be an upward force on it to balance the downward force at its lower end. What exerts this upward force? It must be the upper part of the rod. Thus we see that external forces applied to an object give rise to internal forces, or stress, within the material itself. (Recall also the discussion of tension in a cord, page 86.)

Strain or deformation due to tensile stress is but one type of stress to which materials can be subjected. There are two other common types of stress: compressive and shear. **Compressive stress** is the exact opposite of tensile stress. Instead of being stretched, the material is compressed: the forces act inwardly on the object. Columns that support a weight, such as the columns of a Greek temple (Fig. 9–21), are subjected to compressive stress. Equations 9–4 and 9–5 apply equally well to compression and tension, and the values for the modulus $E$ are usually the same.

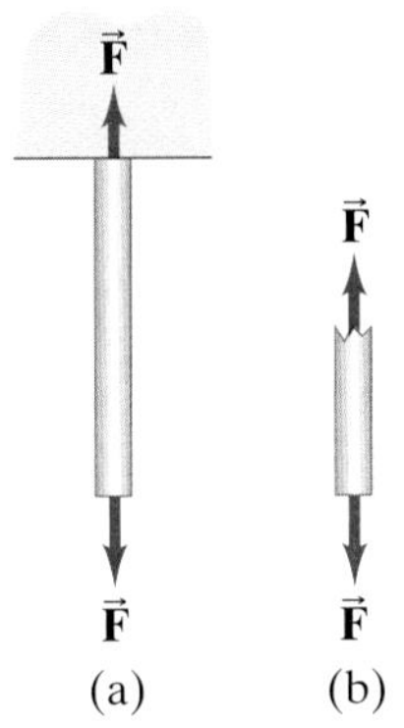


**FIGURE 9–20** Stress exists *within* the material.

[†]If the weight of the rod can be ignored compared to $F$.

**FIGURE 9–21** This Greek temple, in Agrigento, Sicily, built 2500 years ago, shows the post-and-beam construction. The columns are under compression.

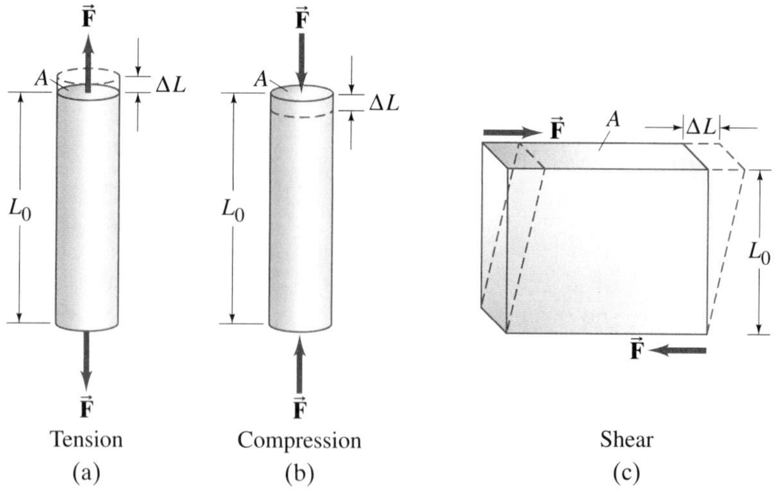


**FIGURE 9–22** The three types of stress for rigid objects.

Figure 9–22 compares tensile and compressive stresses as well as the third type, shear stress. An object under **shear stress** has equal and opposite forces applied *across* its opposite faces. A simple example is a book or brick firmly attached to a tabletop, on which a force is exerted parallel to the top surface. The table exerts an equal and opposite force along the bottom surface. Although the dimensions of the object do not change significantly, the shape of the object does change, Fig. 9–22c. An equation similar to Eq. 9–4 can be applied to calculate shear strain:

*Shear*

$$\Delta L = \frac{1}{G}\frac{F}{A}L_0, \tag{9–6}$$

but $\Delta L$, $L_0$, and $A$ must be reinterpreted as indicated in Fig. 9–22c. Note that $A$ is the area of the surface *parallel* to the applied force (and not perpendicular as for tension and compression), and $\Delta L$ is *perpendicular* to $L_0$. The constant of proportionality $G$ is called the **shear modulus** and is generally one-half to one-third the value of Young's modulus $E$ (see Table 9–1). Figure 9–23 illustrates why $\Delta L \propto L_0$: the fatter book shifts more for the same shearing force.

*Shear modulus*

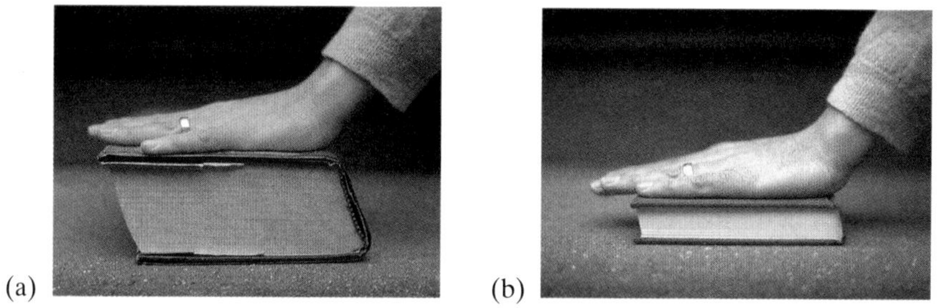


**FIGURE 9–23**
The fatter book (a) shifts more than the thinner book (b) with the same applied shear force.

## * Volume Change—Bulk Modulus

If an object is subjected to inward forces from all sides, its volume will decrease. A common situation is an object submerged in a fluid; in this case, the fluid exerts a pressure on the object in all directions, as we shall see in Chapter 10. *Pressure* is defined as force per unit area, and thus is the equivalent of stress. For this situation the change in volume, $\Delta V$, is proportional to the original volume, $V_0$, and to the change in the pressure, $\Delta P$. We thus obtain a relation of the same form as Eq. 9–4 but with a proportionality constant called the **bulk modulus** $B$:

$$\frac{\Delta V}{V_0} = -\frac{1}{B}\Delta P \tag{9–7}$$

or

*Bulk modulus defined*

$$B = -\frac{\Delta P}{\Delta V/V_0}.$$

The minus sign means the volume *decreases* with an increase in pressure.

Values for the bulk modulus are given in Table 9–1. Since liquids and gases do not have a fixed shape, only the bulk modulus (not the Young's or shear moduli) applies to them.

## * 9–6 Fracture

If the stress on a solid object is too great, the object fractures, or breaks (Fig. 9–24). Table 9–2 lists the ultimate strengths for tension, compression, and shear for a variety of materials. These values give the maximum force per unit area, or stress, that an object can withstand under each of these three types of stress for various types of material. They are, however, representative values only, and the actual value for a given specimen can differ considerably. It is therefore necessary to maintain a *safety factor* of from 3 to perhaps 10 or more—that is, the actual stresses on a structure should not exceed one-tenth to one-third of the values given in the Table. You may encounter tables of "allowable stresses" in which appropriate safety factors have already been included.

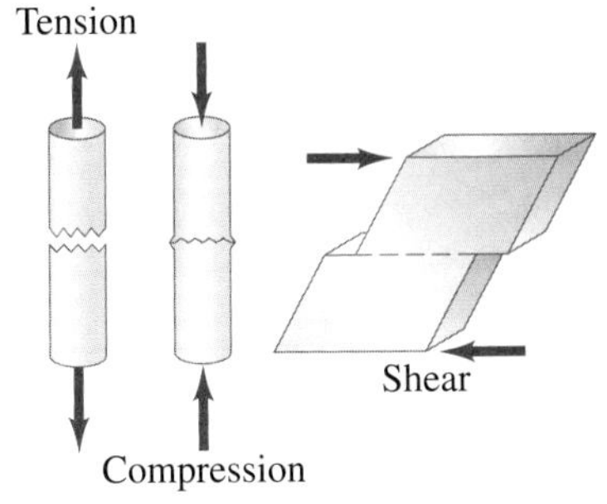

**FIGURE 9–24** Fracture as a result of the three types of stress.

**TABLE 9–2 Ultimate Strengths of Materials (force/area)**

| Material | Tensile Strength ($N/m^2$) | Compressive Strength ($N/m^2$) | Shear Strength ($N/m^2$) |
|---|---|---|---|
| Iron, cast | $170 \times 10^6$ | $550 \times 10^6$ | $170 \times 10^6$ |
| Steel | $500 \times 10^6$ | $500 \times 10^6$ | $250 \times 10^6$ |
| Brass | $250 \times 10^6$ | $250 \times 10^6$ | $200 \times 10^6$ |
| Aluminum | $200 \times 10^6$ | $200 \times 10^6$ | $200 \times 10^6$ |
| Concrete | $2 \times 10^6$ | $20 \times 10^6$ | $2 \times 10^6$ |
| Brick | | $35 \times 10^6$ | |
| Marble | | $80 \times 10^6$ | |
| Granite | | $170 \times 10^6$ | |
| Wood (pine) (parallel to grain) | $40 \times 10^6$ | $35 \times 10^6$ | $5 \times 10^6$ |
| (perpendicular to grain) | | $10 \times 10^6$ | |
| Nylon | $500 \times 10^6$ | | |
| Bone (limb) | $130 \times 10^6$ | $170 \times 10^6$ | |

**EXAMPLE 9–11** **Breaking the piano wire.** The steel piano wire we discussed in Example 9–10 was 1.60 m long with a diameter of 0.20 cm. Approximately what tension force would break it?

**APPROACH** We set the tensile stress $F/A$ equal to the tensile strength of steel given in Table 9–2.

**SOLUTION** The area of the wire is $A = \pi r^2$, where $r = 0.10\,\text{cm} = 1.0 \times 10^{-3}\,\text{m}$. Then

$$\frac{F}{A} = 500 \times 10^6\,\text{N/m}^2$$

so the wire would likely break if the force exceeded

$$F = \left(500 \times 10^6\,\text{N/m}^2\right)(\pi)\left(1.0 \times 10^{-3}\,\text{m}\right)^2 = 1600\,\text{N}.$$

As can be seen in Table 9–2, concrete (like stone and brick) is reasonably strong under compression but extremely weak under tension. Thus concrete can be used as vertical columns placed under compression, but is of little value as a beam because it cannot withstand the tensile forces that result from the inevitable sagging of the lower edge of a beam (see Fig. 9–25).

**FIGURE 9–25** A beam sags, at least a little (but is exaggerated here), even under its own weight. The beam thus changes shape: the upper edge is compressed, and the lower edge is under tension (elongated). Shearing stress also occurs within the beam.

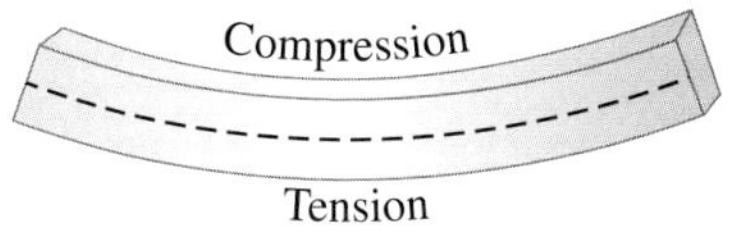

FIGURE 9–26 Steel rods around which concrete will be poured to form a new highway.

PHYSICS APPLIED
*Reinforced concrete and prestressed concrete*

*Reinforced concrete*, in which iron rods are embedded in the concrete (Fig. 9–26), is much stronger. But the concrete on the lower edge of a loaded beam still tends to crack because it is weak under tension. This problem is solved with *prestressed concrete*, which also contains iron rods or a wire mesh, but during the pouring of the concrete, the rods or wire are held under tension. After the concrete dries, the tension on the iron is released, putting the concrete under compression. The amount of compressive stress is carefully predetermined so that when loads are applied to the beam, they reduce the compression on the lower edge, but never put the concrete into tension.

PHYSICS APPLIED
*A tragic collapse*

CONCEPTUAL EXAMPLE 9–12 **A tragic substitution.** Two walkways, one above the other, are suspended from vertical rods attached to the ceiling of a high hotel lobby, Fig. 9–27a. The original design called for single rods 14 m long, but when such long rods proved to be unwieldy to install, it was decided to replace each long rod with two shorter ones as shown schematically in Fig. 9–27b. Determine the net force exerted by the rods on the supporting pin A (assumed to be the same size) for each design. Assume each vertical rod supports a mass $m$ of each bridge.

FIGURE 9–27 Example 9–12.

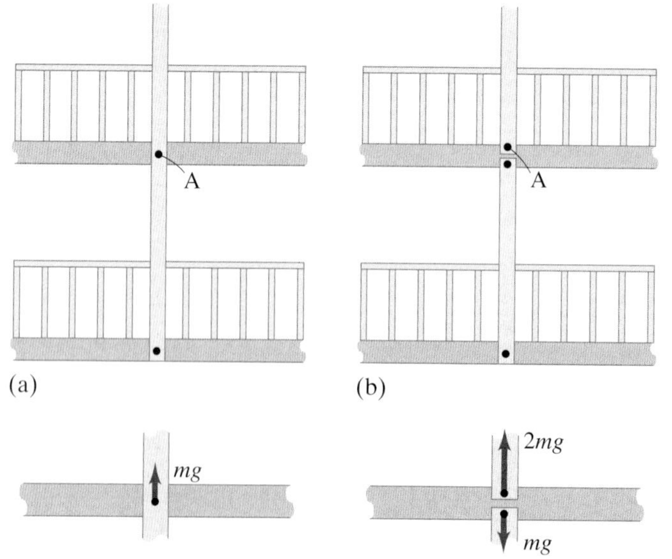


(c) Force on pin A exerted by vertical rod

(d) Forces on pins at A exerted by vertical rods

**RESPONSE** The single long vertical rod in Fig. 9–27a exerts an upward force equal to $mg$ on pin A to support the mass $m$ of the upper bridge. Why? Because the pin is in equilibrium, and the other force that balances this is the downward force $mg$ exerted on it by the upper bridge (Fig. 9–27c). There is thus a shear stress on the pin because the rod pulls up on one end of the pin, and the bridge pulls down on the other end. The situation when two shorter rods support the bridges (Fig. 9–27b) is shown in Fig. 9–27d, in which only the connections at the upper bridge are shown. The lower rod exerts a force of $mg$ downward on the lower of the two pins because it supports the lower bridge. The upper rod exerts a force of $2mg$ on the upper pin (pin A) because the upper rod supports both bridges. Thus we see that when the builders substituted two shorter rods for each single long one, the stress in the supporting pin A was *doubled*. What perhaps seemed like a simple substitution did, in fact, lead to a tragic collapse in 1981 with a loss of life of over 100 people (see Fig. 9–1). Having a feel for physics, and being able to make simple calculations based on physics, can have a great effect, literally, on people's lives.

## * 9–7 Spanning a Space: Arches and Domes

There are a great many areas where the arts and humanities overlap the sciences, and this is especially clear in architecture, where the forces in the materials that make up a structure need to be understood to avoid excessive deformation and collapse. Many of the features we admire in the architecture of the past were introduced not simply for their decorative effect, but for technical reasons. One example is the development of methods to span a space, from the simple beam to arches and domes.

PHYSICS APPLIED
*Architecture: beams, arches and domes*

The first important architectural invention was the post-and-beam (or post-and-lintel) construction, in which two upright posts support a horizontal beam. Before steel was introduced in the nineteenth century, the length of a beam was quite limited because the strongest building materials were then stone and brick. Hence the width of a span was limited by the size of available stones. Equally important, stone and brick, though strong under compression—are very weak under tension and shear; all three types of stress occur in a beam (see Fig. 9–25). The minimal space that could be spanned using stone is shown by the closely spaced columns of the great Greek temples (Fig. 9–21).

The introduction of the semicircular **arch** by the Romans (Fig. 9–28), aside from its aesthetic appeal, was a tremendous technological innovation.

(a)

(b)

**FIGURE 9–28** (a) 2000-year-old round arches in Rome. The one in the background is the Arch of Titus. (b) A modern arch used to span a chasm on the California coast.

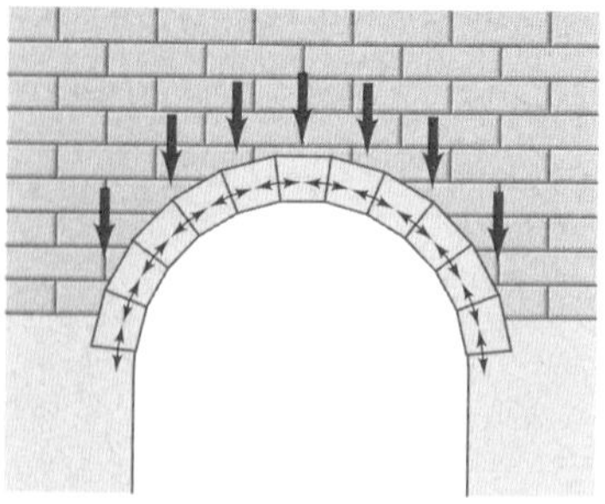

**FIGURE 9–29** Stones in a round (or "true") arch are mainly under compression.

**FIGURE 9–30** Flying buttresses (on the cathedral of Notre Dame, in Paris).

The advantage of the "true" or round (semicircular) arch is that, if well designed, its wedge-shaped stones experience stress which is mainly compressive (Fig. 9–29) even when supporting a large load such as the wall and roof of a cathedral. A round arch consisting of many well-shaped stones could span a very wide space. However, considerable buttressing on the sides was needed to support the horizontal components of the forces, which we discuss shortly.

The pointed arch came into use about A.D. 1100 and became the hallmark of the great Gothic cathedrals. It too was an important technical innovation, and was first used to support heavy loads such as the tower of a cathedral, and as the central arch. Because of the steepness of the pointed arch, the forces due to the weight above could be brought down more nearly vertically, so less horizontal buttressing would be needed. The pointed arch reduced the load on the walls, so there could be more openness and light. The smaller buttressing needed was provided on the outside by graceful flying buttresses (Fig. 9–30).

The technical innovation of the pointed arch was achieved not through calculation but through experience and intuition; it was not until much later that detailed calculations, such as those presented earlier in this Chapter, came into use. To make an accurate analysis of a stone arch is quite difficult in practice. But if we make some simplifying assumptions, we can show why the horizontal component of the force at the base is less for a pointed arch than for a round one. Figure 9–31 shows a round arch and a pointed arch, each with an 8.0-m span. The height of the round arch is thus 4.0 m, whereas that of the pointed arch is larger and has been chosen to be 8.0 m. Each arch supports a weight of $12.0 \times 10^4\,\mathrm{N}$ ($\approx 12{,}000\,\mathrm{kg} \times g$), which, for simplicity, we have divided into two parts (each $6.0 \times 10^4\,\mathrm{N}$) acting on the two halves of each arch as shown. For the arch to be in equilibrium, each of the supports must exert an upward force of $6.0 \times 10^4\,\mathrm{N}$. Each support also exerts a horizontal force, $F_{\mathrm{H}}$, at the base of the arch, and it is this we want to calculate. We focus only on the right half of each arch. We set equal to zero the total torque calculated about the apex of the arch due to the forces exerted on that half arch, as if there were a hinge at the apex. For the round arch, the torque equation ($\Sigma\tau = 0$) is

$$(4.0\,\mathrm{m})(6.0 \times 10^4\,\mathrm{N}) - (2.0\,\mathrm{m})(6.0 \times 10^4\,\mathrm{N}) - (4.0\,\mathrm{m})(F_{\mathrm{H}}) = 0.$$

Thus $F_{\mathrm{H}} = 3.0 \times 10^4\,\mathrm{N}$ for the round arch. For the pointed arch, the torque equation is

$$(4.0\,\mathrm{m})(6.0 \times 10^4\,\mathrm{N}) - (2.0\,\mathrm{m})(6.0 \times 10^4\,\mathrm{N}) - (8.0\,\mathrm{m})(F_{\mathrm{H}}) = 0.$$

Solving, we find that $F_{\mathrm{H}} = 1.5 \times 10^4\,\mathrm{N}$—only half as much as for the round arch! From this calculation we can see that the horizontal buttressing force required for a pointed arch is less because the arch is higher, and there is therefore a longer lever arm for this force. Indeed, the steeper the arch, the less the horizontal component of the force needs to be, and hence the more nearly vertical is the force exerted at the base of the arch.

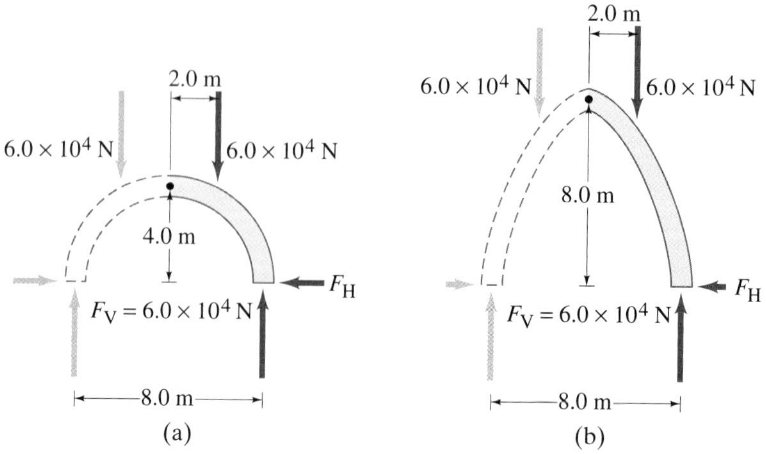


**FIGURE 9–31** Forces in (a) a round arch, compared with those in (b) a pointed arch.

Whereas an arch spans a two-dimensional space, a **dome**—which is basically an arch rotated about a vertical axis—spans a three-dimensional space. The Romans built the first large domes. Their shape was hemispherical and some still stand, such as that of the Pantheon in Rome (Fig. 9–32), built 2000 years ago.

Fourteen centuries later, a new cathedral was being built in Florence. It was to have a dome 43 m in diameter to rival that of the Pantheon, whose construction has remained a mystery. The new dome was to rest on a "drum" with no external abutments. Filippo Brunelleschi (1377–1446) designed a pointed dome (Fig. 9–33), since a pointed dome, like a pointed arch, exerts a smaller side thrust against its base. A dome, like an arch, is not stable until all the stones are in place. To support smaller domes during construction, wooden frameworks were used. But no trees big enough or strong enough could be found to span the 43-m space required. Brunelleschi decided to try to build the dome in horizontal layers, each bonded to the previous one, holding it in place until the last stone of the circle was placed. Each closed ring was then strong enough to support the next layer. It was an amazing feat. Only in the twentieth century were larger domes built, the largest being that of the Superdome in New Orleans, completed in 1975.

**FIGURE 9–32** Interior of the Pantheon in Rome, built in the first century. This view, showing the great dome and its central opening for light, was painted about 1740 by Panini. Photographs do not capture its grandeur as well as this painting does.

**FIGURE 9–33** The skyline of Florence, showing Brunelleschi's dome on the cathedral.

**EXAMPLE 9–13** **A modern dome.** The $1.2 \times 10^6$ kg dome of the Small Sports Palace in Rome (Fig. 9–34a) is supported by 36 buttresses positioned at a 38° angle so that they connect smoothly with the dome. Calculate the components of the force, $F_H$ and $F_V$, that each buttress exerts on the dome so that the force acts purely in compression—that is, at a 38° angle (Fig. 9–34b).

**APPROACH** We can find the vertical component $F_V$ exerted upward by each buttress because each supports $\frac{1}{36}$ of the dome's weight. We find $F_H$ knowing that the buttress needs to be under compression so $\vec{\mathbf{F}} = \vec{\mathbf{F}}_V + \vec{\mathbf{F}}_H$ acts at a 38° angle.

**SOLUTION** The vertical load on *each* buttress is $\frac{1}{36}$ of the total weight. Thus

$$F_V = \frac{mg}{36} = \frac{(1.2 \times 10^6\,\text{kg})(9.8\,\text{m/s}^2)}{36} = 330{,}000\,\text{N}.$$

The force must act at a 38° angle at the base of the dome in order to be purely compressive. Thus

$$\tan 38^\circ = \frac{F_V}{F_H};$$

$$F_H = \frac{F_V}{\tan 38^\circ} = \frac{330{,}000\,\text{N}}{\tan 38^\circ} = 420{,}000\,\text{N}.$$

**NOTE** For each buttress to exert this 420,000-N horizontal force, a prestressed-concrete tension ring surrounds the base of the buttresses beneath the ground (see Problem 56 and Fig. 9–70).

(a)

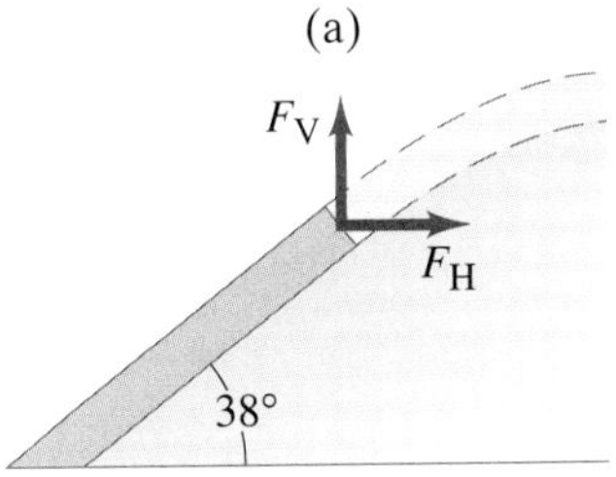


(b)

**FIGURE 9–34** Example 9–13. (a) The dome of the Small Sports Palace in Rome, built for the 1960 Olympics. (b) The force components each buttress exerts on the dome.

# Summary

An object at rest is said to be in **equilibrium**. The subject concerned with the determination of the forces within a structure at rest is called **statics**.

The two necessary conditions for an object to be in equilibrium are that (1) the vector sum of all the forces on it must be zero, and (2) the sum of all the torques (calculated about any arbitrary axis) must also be zero:

$$\Sigma F_x = 0, \qquad \Sigma F_y = 0, \qquad \Sigma \tau = 0. \qquad \textbf{(9–1, 9–2)}$$

It is important when doing statics problems to apply the equilibrium conditions to only one object at a time.

[*An object in static equilibrium is said to be in (*a*) **stable**, (*b*) **unstable**, or (*c*) **neutral equilibrium**, depending on whether a slight displacement leads to (*a*) a return to the original position, (*b*) further movement away from the original position, or (*c*) rest in the new position. An object in stable equilibrium is also said to be in **balance**.]

[***Hooke's law** applies to many elastic solids, and states that the change in length of an object is proportional to the applied force:

$$F = k\,\Delta L. \qquad \textbf{(9–3)}$$

If the force is too great, the object will exceed its **elastic limit**, which means it will no longer return to its original shape when the distorting force is removed. If the force is even greater, the **ultimate strength** of the material can be exceeded, and the object will **fracture**. The force per unit area acting on an object is called the **stress**, and the resulting fractional change in length is called the **strain**. The stress on an object is present within the object and can be of three types: **compression**, **tension**, or **shear**. The ratio of stress to strain is called the **elastic modulus** of the material. **Young's modulus** applies for compression and tension, and the **shear modulus** for shear; **bulk modulus** applies to an object whose volume changes as a result of pressure on all sides. All three moduli are constants for a given material when distorted within the elastic region.]

# Questions

**1.** Describe several situations in which an object is not in equilibrium, even though the net force on it is zero.

**2.** A bungee jumper momentarily comes to rest at the bottom of the dive before he springs back upward. At that moment, is the bungee jumper in equilibrium? Explain.

**3.** You can find the center of gravity of a meter stick by resting it horizontally on your two index fingers, and then slowly drawing your fingers together. First the meter stick will slip on one finger, and then on the other, but eventually the fingers meet at the CG. Why does this work?

**4.** Your doctor's scale has arms on which weights slide to counter your weight, Fig. 9–35. These weights are much lighter than you are. How does this work?

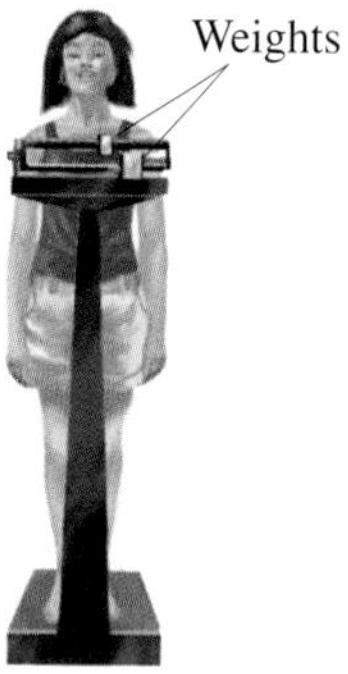


**FIGURE 9–35** Question 4.

**5.** A ground retaining wall is shown in Fig. 9–36a. The ground, particularly when wet, can exert a significant force $F$ on the wall. (*a*) What force produces the torque to keep the wall upright? (*b*) Explain why the retaining wall in Fig. 9–36b would be much less likely to overturn than that in Fig. 9–36a.

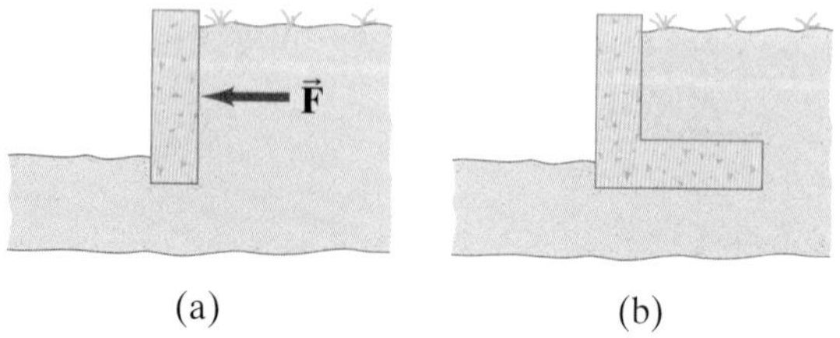


**FIGURE 9–36** Question 5.

**6.** Explain why touching your toes while you are seated on the floor with outstretched legs produces less stress on the lower spinal column than when touching your toes from a standing position. Use a diagram.

**7.** A ladder, leaning against a wall, makes a 60° angle with the ground. When is it more likely to slip: when a person stands on the ladder near the top or near the bottom? Explain.

**8.** A uniform meter stick supported at the 25-cm mark is in equilibrium when a 1-kg rock is suspended at the 0-cm end (as shown in Fig. 9–37). Is the mass of the meter stick greater than, equal to, or less than the mass of the rock? Explain your reasoning.

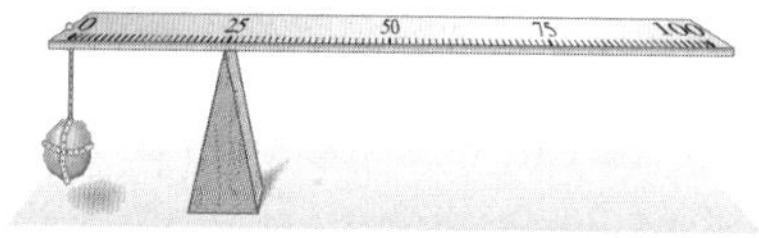

**FIGURE 9–37** Question 8.

**9.** Can the sum of the torques on an object be zero while the net force on the object is nonzero? Explain.

**10.** Figure 9–38 shows a cone. Explain how to lay it on a flat table so that it is in (*a*) stable equilibrium, (*b*) unstable equilibrium, (*c*) neutral equilibrium.

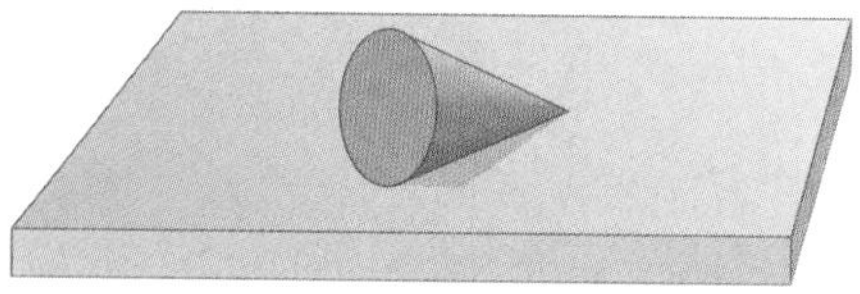

**FIGURE 9–38** Question 10.

**11.** Which of the configurations of brick, (*a*) or (*b*) of Fig. 9–39, is the more likely to be stable? Why?

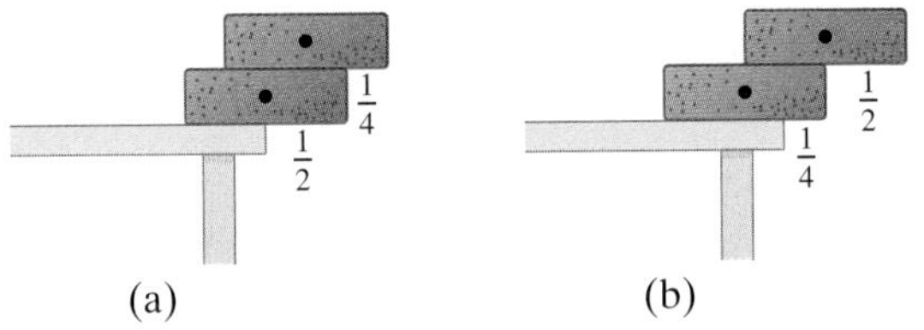


**FIGURE 9–39** Question 11. The dots indicate the CG of each brick. The fractions $\frac{1}{4}$ and $\frac{1}{2}$ indicate what portion of each brick is hanging beyond its support.

**12.** Why do you tend to lean backward when carrying a heavy load in your arms?

**13.** Place yourself facing the edge of an open door. Position your feet astride the door with your nose and abdomen touching the door's edge. Try to rise on your tiptoes. Why can't this be done?

**14.** Why is it not possible to sit upright in a chair and rise to your feet without first leaning forward?

**15.** Why is it more difficult to do sit-ups when your knees are bent than when your legs are stretched out?

**16.** Name the type of equilibrium for each position of the ball in Fig. 9–40.

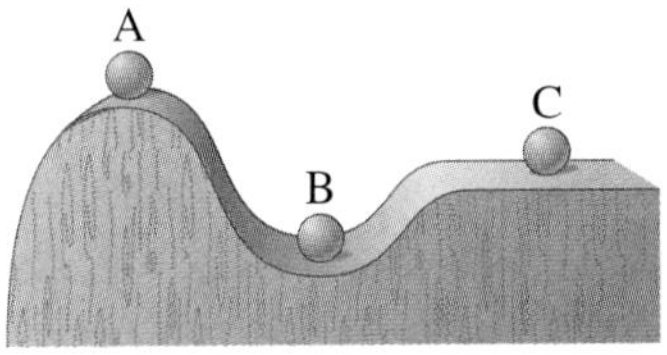


**FIGURE 9–40** Question 16.

* **17.** Is the Young's modulus for a bungee cord smaller or larger than that for an ordinary rope?

* **18.** Examine how a pair of scissors or shears cuts through a piece of cardboard. Is the name "shears" justified? Explain.

* **19.** Materials such as ordinary concrete and stone are very weak under tension or shear. Would it be wise to use such a material for either of the supports of the cantilever shown in Fig. 9–9? If so, which one(s)? Explain.

## Problems

### 9–1 and 9–2 Equilibrium

1. (I) Three forces are applied to a tree sapling, as shown in Fig. 9–41, to stabilize it. If $\vec{\mathbf{F}}_A = 310\,\text{N}$ and $\vec{\mathbf{F}}_B = 425\,\text{N}$, find $\vec{\mathbf{F}}_C$ in magnitude and direction.

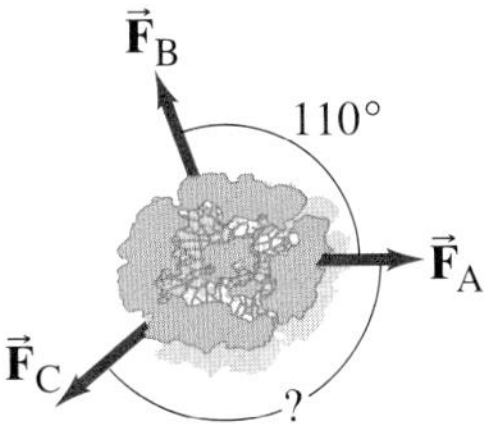


**FIGURE 9–41** Problem 1.

2. (I) Calculate the torque about the front support post (B) of a diving board, Fig. 9–42, exerted by a 58-kg person 3.0 m from that post.

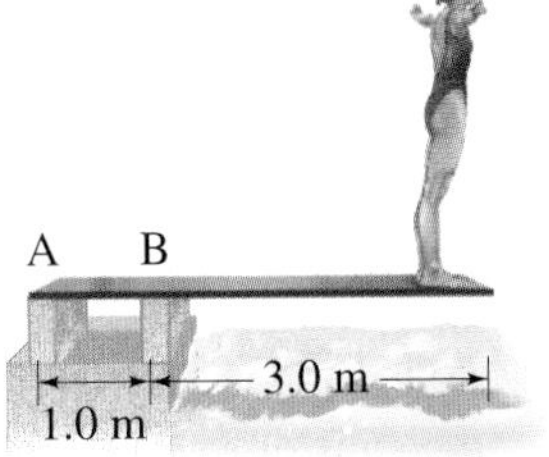


**FIGURE 9–42** Problems 2, 4, and 6.

3. (I) Calculate the mass $m$ needed in order to suspend the leg shown in Fig. 9–43. Assume the leg (with cast) has a mass of 15.0 kg, and its CG is 35.0 cm from the hip joint; the sling is 80.5 cm from the hip joint.

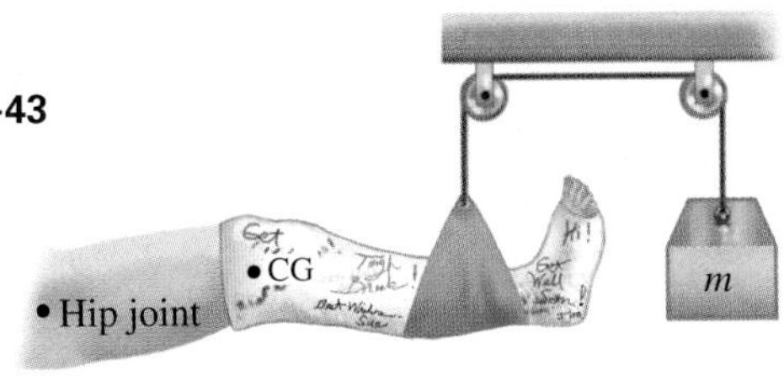


**FIGURE 9–43** Problem 3.

4. (I) How far out on the diving board (Fig. 9–42) would a 58-kg diver have to be to exert a torque of $1100\,\text{m}\cdot\text{N}$ on the board, relative to the left (A) support post?

5. (II) Two cords support a chandelier in the manner shown in Fig. 9–4 except that the upper wire makes an angle of 45° with the ceiling. If the cords can sustain a force of 1550 N without breaking, what is the maximum chandelier weight that can be supported?

6. (II) Calculate the forces $F_A$ and $F_B$ that the supports exert on the diving board of Fig. 9–42 when a 58-kg person stands at its tip. (*a*) Ignore the weight of the board. (*b*) Take into account the board's mass of 35 kg. Assume the board's CG is at its center.

7. (II) A uniform steel beam has a mass of 940 kg. On it is resting half of an identical beam, as shown in Fig. 9–44. What is the vertical support force at each end?

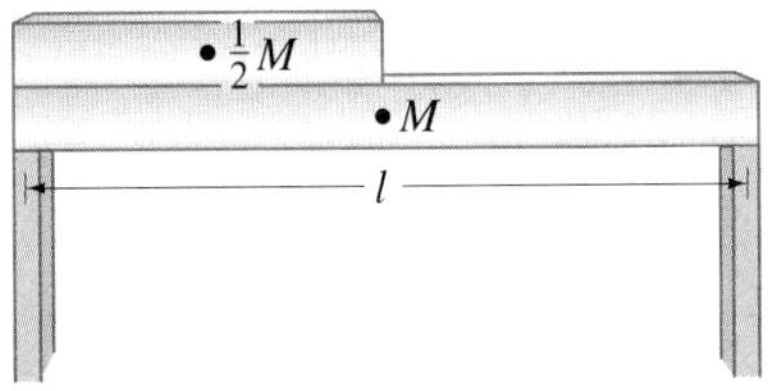


**FIGURE 9–44** Problem 7.

8. (II) A 140-kg horizontal beam is supported at each end. A 320-kg piano rests a quarter of the way from one end. What is the vertical force on each of the supports?

9. (II) A 75-kg adult sits at one end of a 9.0-m-long board. His 25-kg child sits on the other end. (*a*) Where should the pivot be placed so that the board is balanced, ignoring the board's mass? (*b*) Find the pivot point if the board is uniform and has a mass of 15 kg.

10. (II) Calculate $F_A$ and $F_B$ for the uniform cantilever shown in Fig. 9–9 whose mass is 1200 kg.

11. (II) Find the tension in the two cords shown in Fig. 9–45. Neglect the mass of the cords, and assume that the angle $\theta$ is 33° and the mass $m$ is 170 kg.

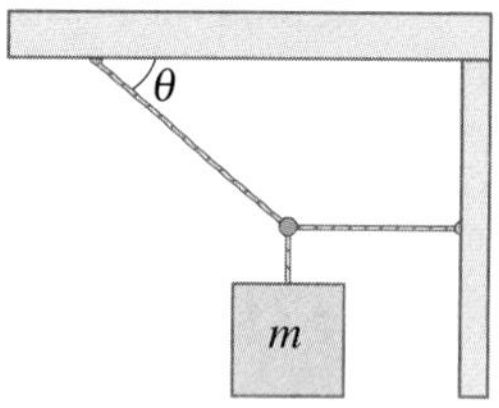


FIGURE 9–45 Problem 11.

12. (II) Find the tension in the two wires supporting the traffic light shown in Fig. 9–46.

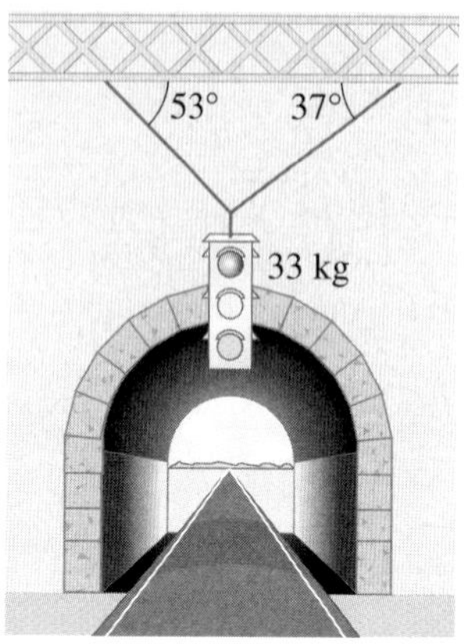


FIGURE 9–46 Problem 12.

13. (II) How close to the edge of the 20.0-kg table shown in Fig. 9–47 can a 66.0-kg person sit without tipping it over?

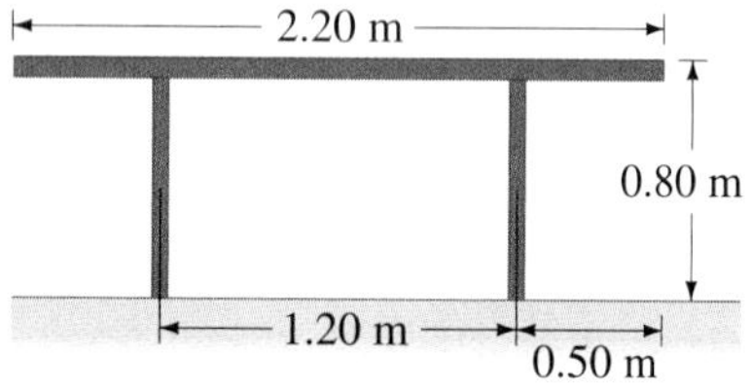


FIGURE 9–47 Problem 13.

14. (II) A 0.60-kg sheet hangs from a massless clothesline as shown in Fig. 9–48. The clothesline on either side of the sheet makes an angle of 3.5° with the horizontal. Calculate the tension in the clothesline on either side of the sheet. Why is the tension so much greater than the weight of the sheet?

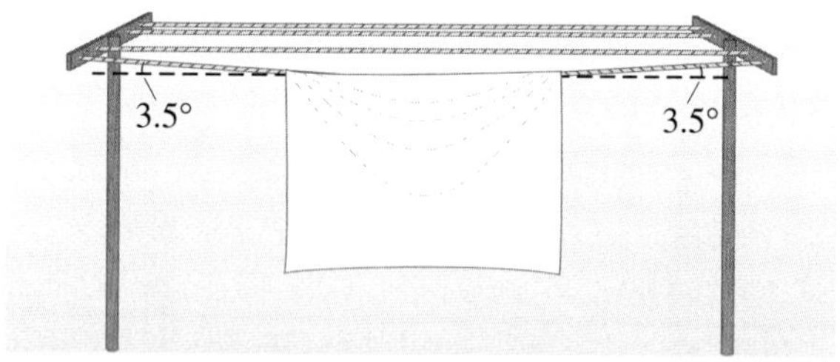


FIGURE 9–48 Problem 14.

15. (II) Calculate $F_A$ and $F_B$ for the beam shown in Fig. 9–49. The downward forces represent the weights of machinery on the beam. Assume the beam is uniform and has a mass of 250 kg.

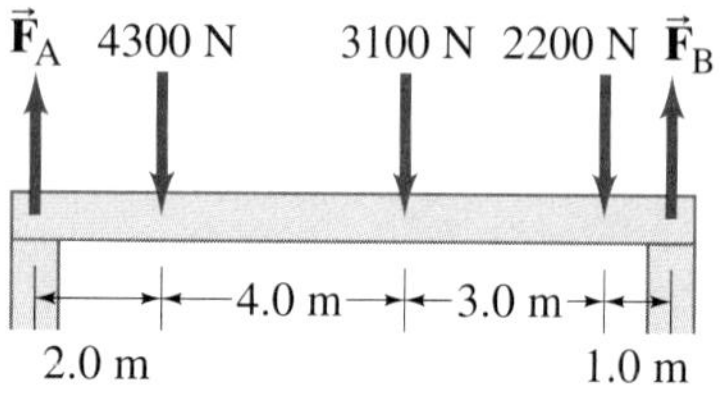


FIGURE 9–49 Problem 15.

16. (II) Three children are trying to balance on a seesaw, which consists of a fulcrum rock, acting as a pivot at the center, and a very light board 3.6 m long (Fig. 9–50). Two playmates are already on either end. Boy A has a mass of 50 kg, and girl B a mass of 35 kg. Where should girl C, whose mass is 25 kg, place herself so as to balance the seesaw?

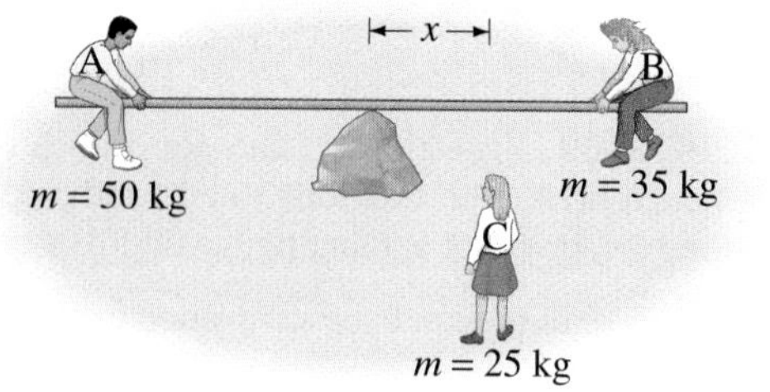


FIGURE 9–50 Problem 16.

17. (II) Figure 9–51 shows a pair of forceps used to hold a thin plastic rod firmly. If each finger squeezes with a force $F_T = F_B = 11.0\,\text{N}$, what force do the forceps jaws exert on the plastic rod?

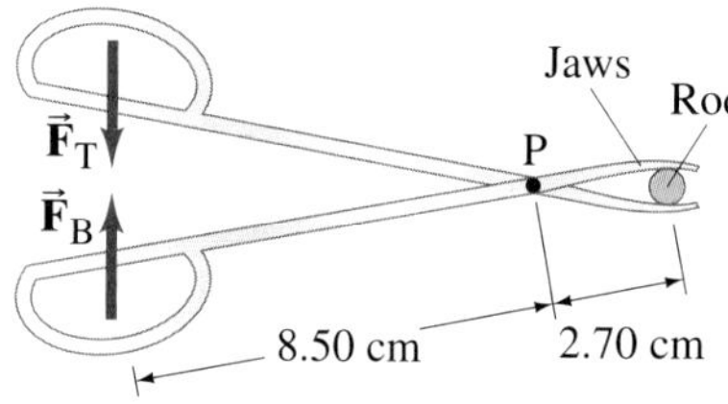


FIGURE 9–51 Problem 17.

18. (II) Calculate (*a*) the tension $F_T$ in the wire that supports the 27-kg beam shown in Fig. 9–52, and (*b*) the force $\vec{F}_W$ exerted by the wall on the beam (give magnitude and direction).

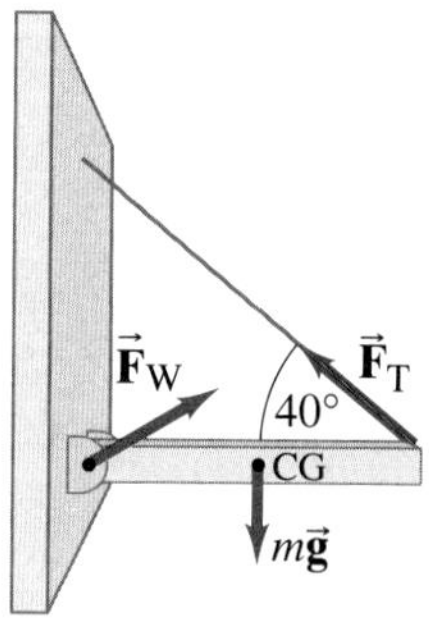


FIGURE 9–52 Problem 18.

19. (II) A 172-cm-tall person lies on a light (massless) board which is supported by two scales, one under the top of her head and one beneath the bottom of her feet (Fig. 9–53). The two scales read, respectively, 35.1 and 31.6 kg. What distance is the center of gravity of this person from the bottom of her feet?

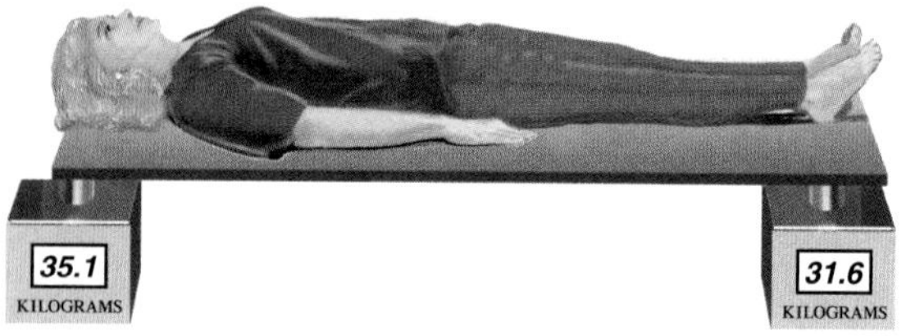


FIGURE 9–53 Problem 19.

20. (II) A shop sign weighing 245 N is supported by a uniform 155-N beam as shown in Fig. 9–54. Find the tension in the guy wire and the horizontal and vertical forces exerted by the hinge on the beam.

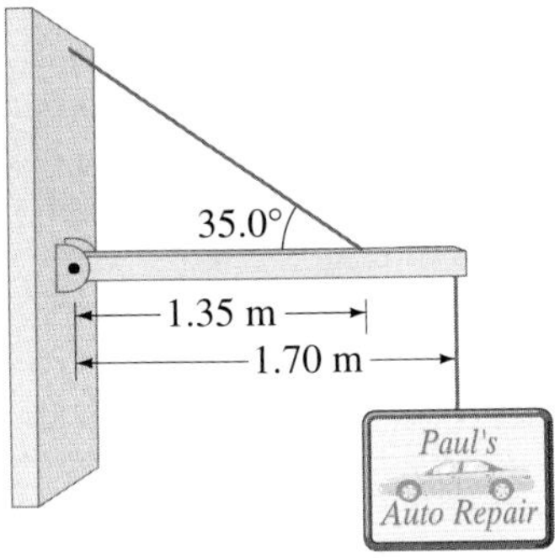


**FIGURE 9–54** Problem 20.

21. (II) A traffic light hangs from a pole as shown in Fig. 9–55. The uniform aluminum pole AB is 7.50 m long and has a mass of 12.0 kg. The mass of the traffic light is 21.5 kg. Determine (*a*) the tension in the horizontal massless cable CD, and (*b*) the vertical and horizontal components of the force exerted by the pivot A on the aluminum pole.

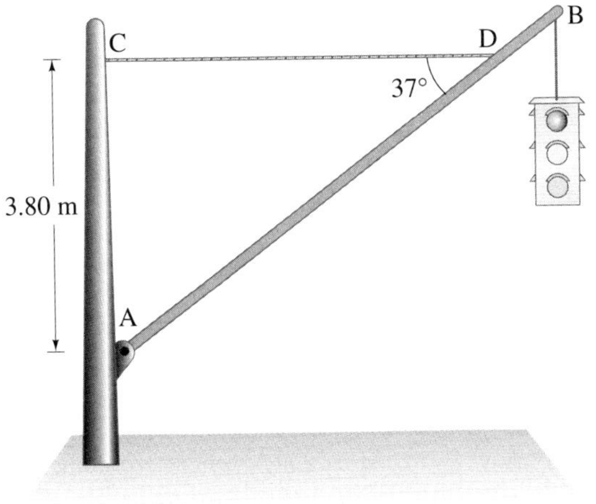


**FIGURE 9–55** Problem 21.

22. (II) The 72-kg-man's hands in Fig. 9–56 are 36 cm apart. His CG is located 75% of the distance from his right hand toward his left. Find the force on each hand due to the ground.

**FIGURE 9–56** Problem 22.

23. (II) A uniform meter stick with a mass of 180 g is supported horizontally by two vertical strings, one at the 0-cm mark and the other at the 90-cm mark (Fig. 9–57). What is the tension in the string (*a*) at 0 cm? (*b*) at 90 cm?

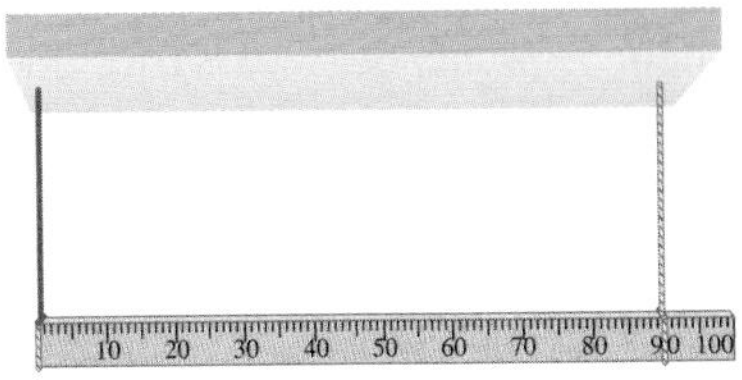


**FIGURE 9–57** Problem 23.

24. (II) The two trees in Fig. 9–58 are 7.6 m apart. A backpacker is trying to lift his pack out of the reach of bears. Calculate the magnitude of the force $\vec{\mathbf{F}}$ that he must exert downward to hold a 19-kg backpack so that the rope sags at its midpoint by (*a*) 1.5 m, (*b*) 0.15 m.

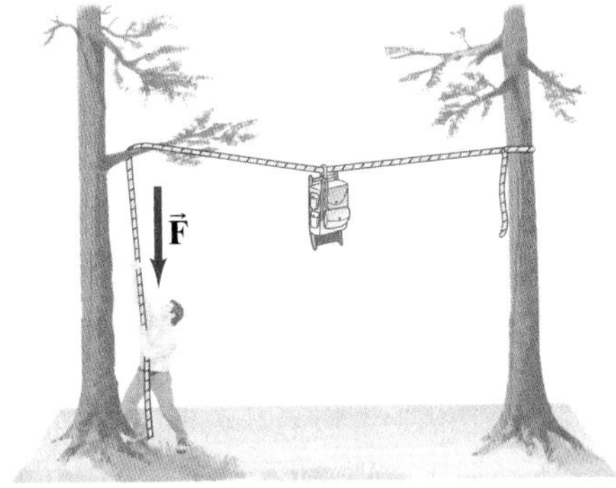


**FIGURE 9–58** Problem 24.

25. (III) A door 2.30 m high and 1.30 m wide has a mass of 13.0 kg. A hinge 0.40 m from the top and another hinge 0.40 m from the bottom each support half the door's weight (Fig. 9–59). Assume that the center of gravity is at the geometrical center of the door, and determine the horizontal and vertical force components exerted by each hinge on the door.

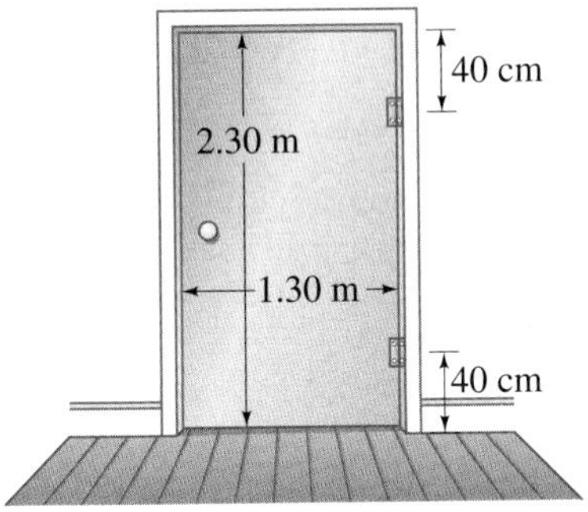


**FIGURE 9–59** Problem 25.

26. (III) A uniform ladder of mass $m$ and length $l$ leans at an angle $\theta$ against a frictionless wall, Fig. 9–60. If the coefficient of static friction between the ladder and the ground is $\mu$, determine a formula for the minimum angle at which the ladder will not slip.

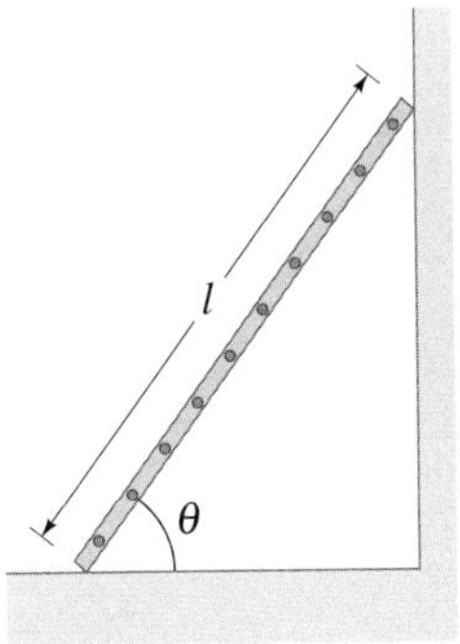


**FIGURE 9–60** Problem 26.

27. (III) Consider a ladder with a painter climbing up it (Fig. 9–61). If the mass of the ladder is 12.0 kg, the mass of the painter is 55.0 kg, and the ladder begins to slip at its base when her feet are 70% of the way up the length of the ladder, what is the coefficient of static friction between the ladder and the floor? Assume the wall is frictionless.

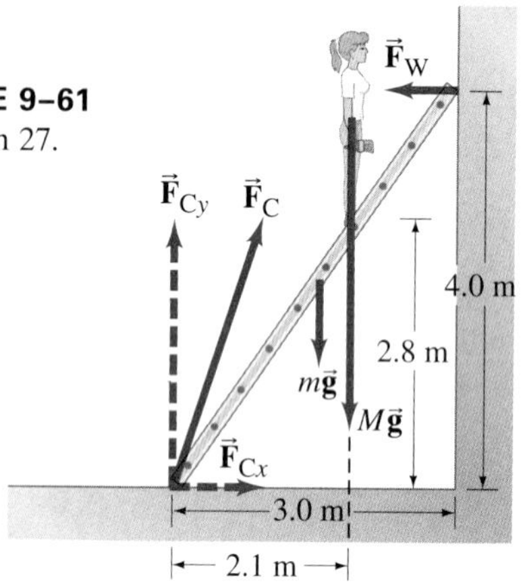


**FIGURE 9–61** Problem 27.

28. (III) A person wants to push a lamp (mass 7.2 kg) across the floor, for which the coefficient of friction is 0.20. Calculate the maximum height $x$ above the floor at which the person can push the lamp so that it slides rather than tips (Fig. 9–62).

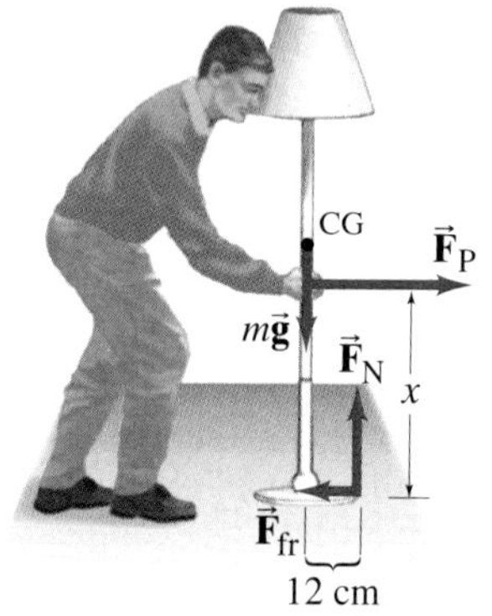


**FIGURE 9–62** Problem 28.

29. (III) Two wires run from the top of a pole 2.6 m tall that supports a volleyball net. The two wires are anchored to the ground 2.0 m apart, and each is 2.0 m from the pole (Fig. 9–63). The tension in each wire is 95 N. What is the tension in the net, assumed horizontal and attached at the top of the pole?

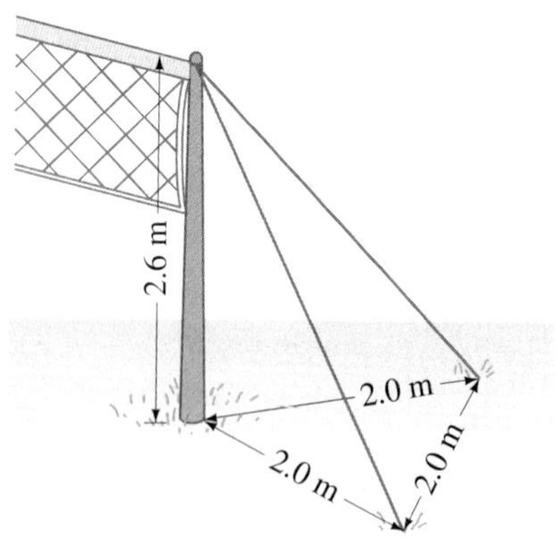


**FIGURE 9–63** Problem 29.

## * 9–3 Muscles and Joints

* 30. (I) Suppose the point of insertion of the biceps muscle into the lower arm shown in Fig. 9–13a (Example 9–8) is 6.0 cm instead of 5.0 cm; how much mass could the person hold with a muscle exertion of 450 N?

* 31. (I) Approximately what magnitude force, $F_M$, must the extensor muscle in the upper arm exert on the lower arm to hold a 7.3-kg shot put (Fig. 9–64)? Assume the lower arm has a mass of 2.8 kg and its CG is 12 cm from the elbow-joint pivot.

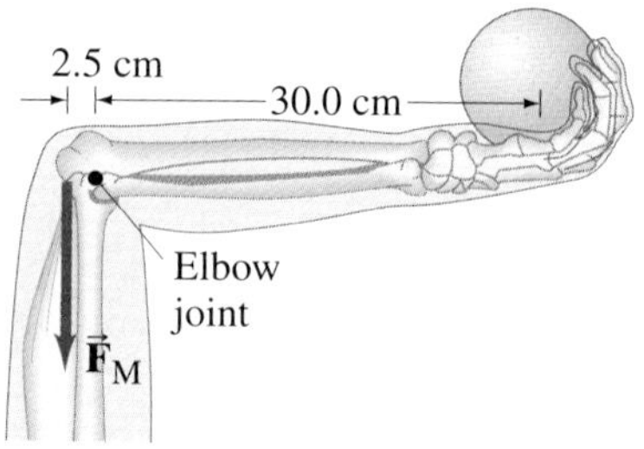


**FIGURE 9–64** Problem 31.

* 32. (II) (*a*) Calculate the force, $F_M$, required of the "deltoid" muscle to hold up the outstretched arm shown in Fig. 9–65. The total mass of the arm is 3.3 kg. (*b*) Calculate the magnitude of the force $F_J$ exerted by the shoulder joint on the upper arm.

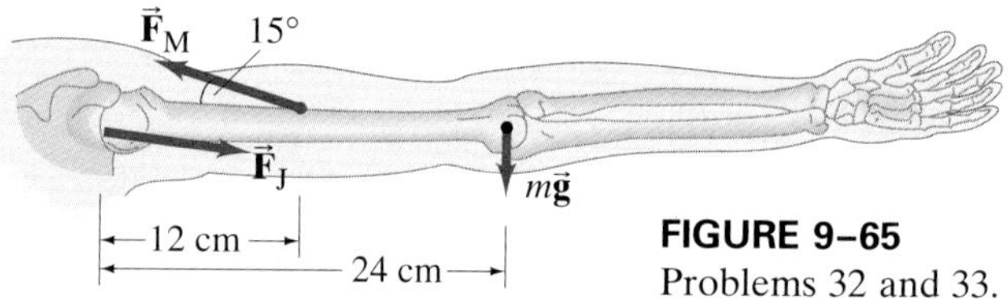


**FIGURE 9–65** Problems 32 and 33.

* 33. (II) Suppose the hand in Problem 32 holds a 15-kg mass. What force, $F_M$, is required of the deltoid muscle, assuming the mass is 52 cm from the shoulder joint?

* 34. (II) The Achilles tendon is attached to the rear of the foot as shown in Fig. 9–66. When a person elevates himself just barely off the floor on the "ball of one foot," estimate the tension $F_T$ in the Achilles tendon (pulling upward), and the (downward) force $F_B$ exerted by the lower leg bone on the foot. Assume the person has a mass of 72 kg and $D$ is twice as long as $d$.

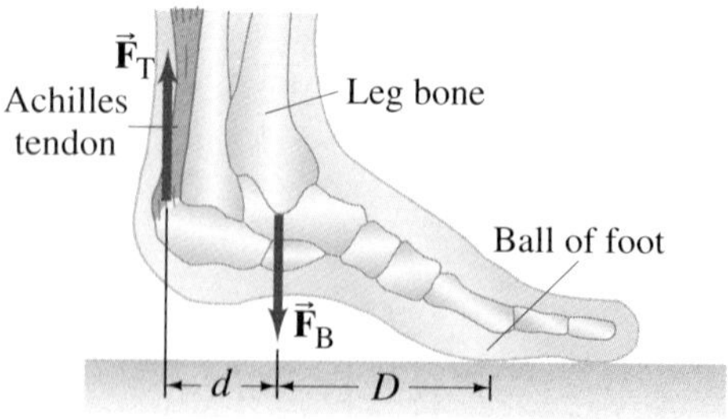


**FIGURE 9–66** Problem 34.

* 35. (II) Redo Example 9–9, assuming now that the person is less bent over so that the 30° in Fig. 9–14b is instead 45°. What will be the magnitude of $F_V$ on the vertebra?

## 9–4 Stability and Balance

36. (II) The Leaning Tower of Pisa is 55 m tall and about 7.0 m in diameter. The top is 4.5 m off center. Is the tower in stable equilibrium? If so, how much farther can it lean before it becomes unstable? Assume the tower is of uniform composition.

37. (III) Four bricks are to be stacked at the edge of a table, each brick overhanging the one below it, so that the top brick extends as far as possible beyond the edge of the table. (*a*) To achieve this, show that successive bricks must extend no more than (starting at the top) $\frac{1}{2}, \frac{1}{4}, \frac{1}{6}$, and $\frac{1}{8}$ of their length beyond the one below (Fig. 9–67a). (*b*) Is the top brick completely beyond the base? (*c*) Determine a general formula for the maximum total distance spanned by $n$ bricks if they are to remain stable. (*d*) A builder wants to construct a corbeled arch (Fig. 9–67b) based on the principle of stability discussed in (*a*) and (*c*) above. What minimum number of bricks, each 0.30 m long, is needed if the arch is to span 1.0 m?

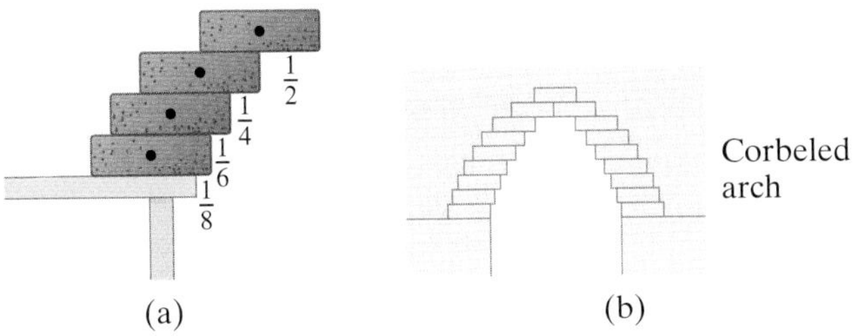


**FIGURE 9–67** Problem 37.

## * 9–5 Elasticity; Stress and Strain

* 38. (I) A nylon string on a tennis racket is under a tension of 275 N. If its diameter is 1.00 mm, by how much is it lengthened from its untensioned length of 30.0 cm?

* 39. (I) A marble column of cross-sectional area $1.2\ m^2$ supports a mass of 25,000 kg. (*a*) What is the stress within the column? (*b*) What is the strain?

* 40. (I) By how much is the column in Problem 39 shortened if it is 9.6 m high?

* 41. (I) A sign (mass 2100 kg) hangs from the end of a vertical steel girder with a cross-sectional area of $0.15\ m^2$. (*a*) What is the stress within the girder? (*b*) What is the strain on the girder? (*c*) If the girder is 9.50 m long, how much is it lengthened? (Ignore the mass of the girder itself.)

* 42. (II) One liter of alcohol $(1000\ cm^3)$ in a flexible container is carried to the bottom of the sea, where the pressure is $2.6 \times 10^6\ N/m^2$. What will be its volume there?

* 43. (II) A 15-cm-long tendon was found to stretch 3.7 mm by a force of 13.4 N. The tendon was approximately round with an average diameter of 8.5 mm. Calculate the Young's modulus of this tendon.

* 44. (II) How much pressure is needed to compress the volume of an iron block by 0.10%? Express your answer in $N/m^2$, and compare it to atmospheric pressure $(1.0 \times 10^5\ N/m^2)$.

* 45. (II) At depths of 2000 m in the sea, the pressure is about 200 times atmospheric pressure $(1\ atm = 1.0 \times 10^5\ N/m^2)$. By what percentage does the interior space of an iron bathysphere's volume change at this depth?

* 46. (III) A scallop forces open its shell with an elastic material called abductin, whose Young's modulus is about $2.0 \times 10^6\ N/m^2$. If this piece of abductin is 3.0 mm thick and has a cross-sectional area of $0.50\ cm^2$, how much potential energy does it store when compressed 1.0 mm?

* 47. (III) A pole projects horizontally from the front wall of a shop. A 5.1-kg sign hangs from the pole at a point 2.2 m from the wall (Fig. 9–68). (*a*) What is the torque due to this sign calculated about the point where the pole meets the wall? (*b*) If the pole is not to fall off, there must be another torque exerted to balance it. What exerts this torque? Use a diagram to show how this torque must act. (*c*) Discuss whether compression, tension, and/or shear play a role in part (*b*).

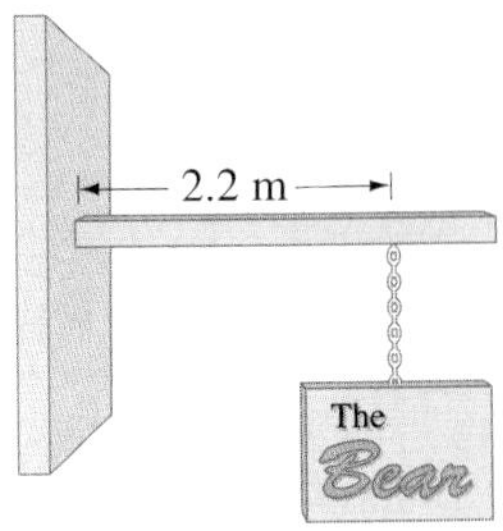


**FIGURE 9–68** Problem 47.

## * 9–6 Fracture

* 48. (I) The femur bone in the human leg has a minimum effective cross section of about $3.0\ cm^2\ (= 3.0 \times 10^{-4}\ m^2)$. How much compressive force can it withstand before breaking?

* 49. (II) (*a*) What is the maximum tension possible in a 1.00-mm-diameter nylon tennis racket string? (*b*) If you want tighter strings, what do you do to prevent breakage: use thinner or thicker strings? Why? What causes strings to break when they are hit by the ball?

* 50. (II) If a compressive force of $3.6 \times 10^4$ N is exerted on the end of a 22-cm-long bone of cross-sectional area $3.6\ cm^2$, (*a*) will the bone break, and (*b*) if not, by how much does it shorten?

* 51. (II) (*a*) What is the minimum cross-sectional area required of a vertical steel cable from which is suspended a 320-kg chandelier? Assume a safety factor of 7.0 (*b*) If the cable is 7.5 m long, how much does it elongate?

* 52. (II) Assume the supports of the uniform cantilever shown in Fig. 9–69 (mass = 2600 kg) are made of wood. Calculate the minimum cross-sectional area required of each, assuming a safety factor of 8.5.

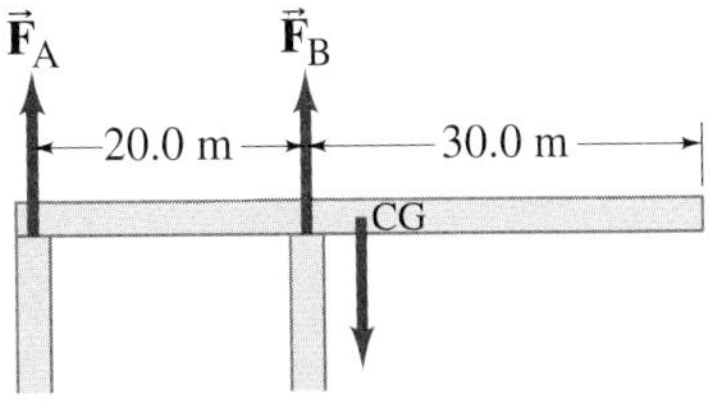


**FIGURE 9–69** Problem 52.

* 53. (II) An iron bolt is used to connect two iron plates together. The bolt must withstand shear forces up to about 3200 N. Calculate the minimum diameter for the bolt, based on a safety factor of 6.0.

* 54. (III) A steel cable is to support an elevator whose total (loaded) mass is not to exceed 3100 kg. If the maximum acceleration of the elevator is $1.2\ m/s^2$, calculate the diameter of cable required. Assume a safety factor of 7.0.

## * 9–7 Arches and Domes

* 55. (II) How high must a pointed arch be if it is to span a space 8.0 m wide and exert one-third the horizontal force at its base that a round arch would?

* 56. (II) The subterranean tension ring that exerts the balancing horizontal force on the abutments for the dome in Fig. 9–34 is 36-sided, so each segment makes a 10° angle with the adjacent one (Fig. 9–70). Calculate the tension $F$ that must exist in each segment so that the required force of $4.2 \times 10^5$ N can be exerted at each corner (Example 9–13).

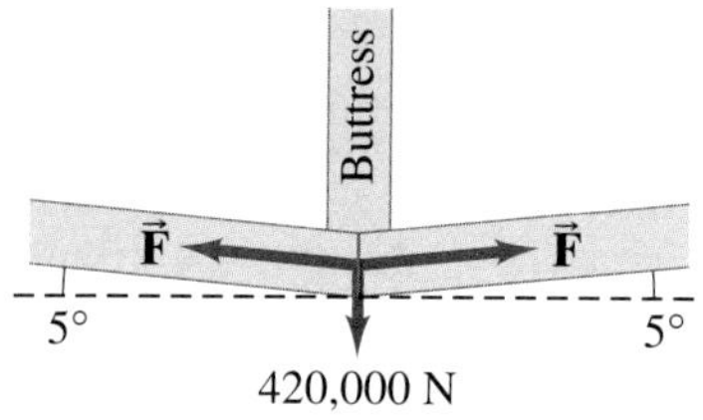


**FIGURE 9–70** Problem 56.

## General Problems

57. The mobile in Fig. 9–71 is in equilibrium. Object B has mass of 0.885 kg. Determine the masses of objects A, C, and D. (Neglect the weights of the crossbars.)

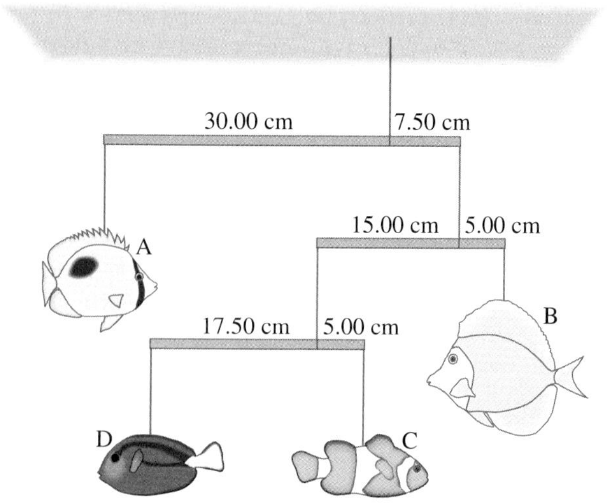


**FIGURE 9–71** Problem 57.

58. A tightly stretched "high wire" is 46 m long. It sags 2.2 m when a 60.0-kg tightrope walker stands at its center. What is the tension in the wire? Is it possible to increase the tension in the wire so that there is no sag?

59. What minimum horizontal force $F$ is needed to pull a wheel of radius $R$ and mass $M$ over a step of height $h$ as shown in Fig. 9–72 ($R > h$)? (*a*) Assume the force is applied at the top edge as shown. (*b*) Assume the force is applied instead at the wheel's center.

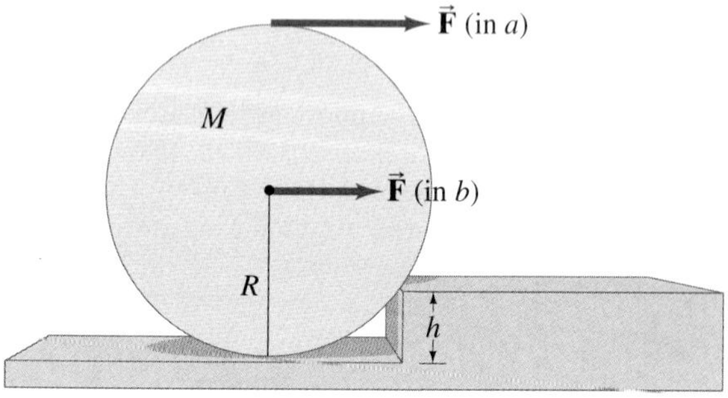


**FIGURE 9–72** Problem 59.

60. A 25-kg round table is supported by three legs equal distances apart on the edge. What minimum mass, placed on the table's edge, will cause the table to overturn?

61. When a wood shelf of mass 5.0 kg is fastened inside a slot in a vertical support as shown in Fig. 9–73, the support exerts a torque on the shelf. (*a*) Draw a free-body diagram for the shelf, assuming three vertical forces (two exerted by the support slot—explain why). Then calculate (*b*) the magnitudes of the three forces and (*c*) the torque exerted by the support (about the left end of the shelf).

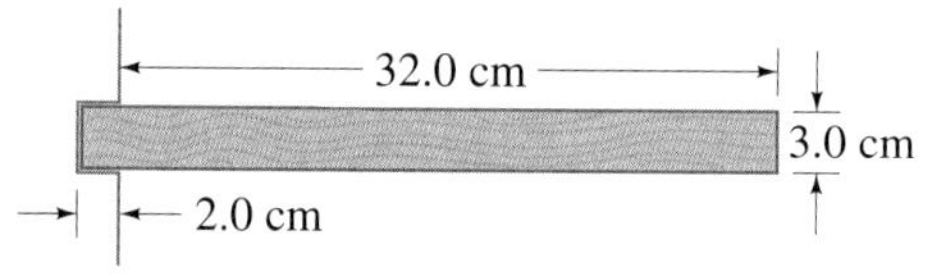


**FIGURE 9–73** Problem 61.

62. A 50-story building is being planned. It is to be 200.0 m high with a base 40.0 m by 70.0 m. Its total mass will be about $1.8 \times 10^7$ kg, and its weight therefore about $1.8 \times 10^8$ N. Suppose a 200-km/h wind exerts a force of 950 N/m$^2$ over the 70.0-m-wide face (Fig. 9–74). Calculate the torque about the potential pivot point, the rear edge of the building (where $\vec{\mathbf{F}}_E$ acts in Fig. 9–74), and determine whether the building will topple. Assume the total force of the wind acts at the midpoint of the building's face, and that the building is not anchored in bedrock. [*Hint*: $\vec{\mathbf{F}}_E$ in Fig. 9–74 represents the force that the Earth would exert on the building in the case where the building would just begin to tip.]

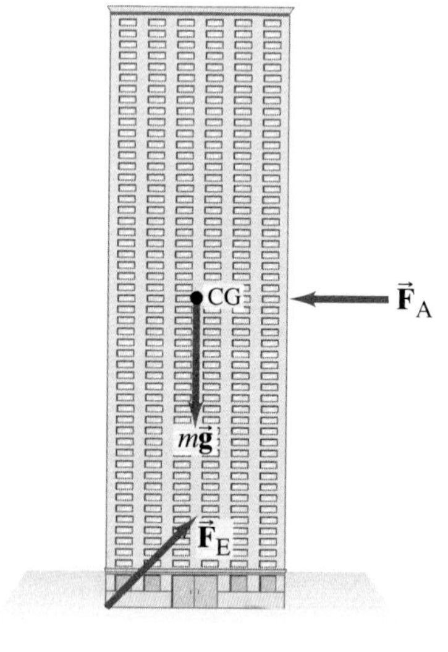


**FIGURE 9–74** Forces on a building subjected to wind ($\vec{\mathbf{F}}_A$), gravity ($m\vec{\mathbf{g}}$), and the force $\vec{\mathbf{F}}_E$ on the building due to the Earth if the building were just about to tip. Problem 62.

63. The center of gravity of a loaded truck depends on how the truck is packed. If it is 4.0 m high and 2.4 m wide, and its CG is 2.2 m above the ground, how steep a slope can the truck be parked on without tipping over (Fig. 9–75)?

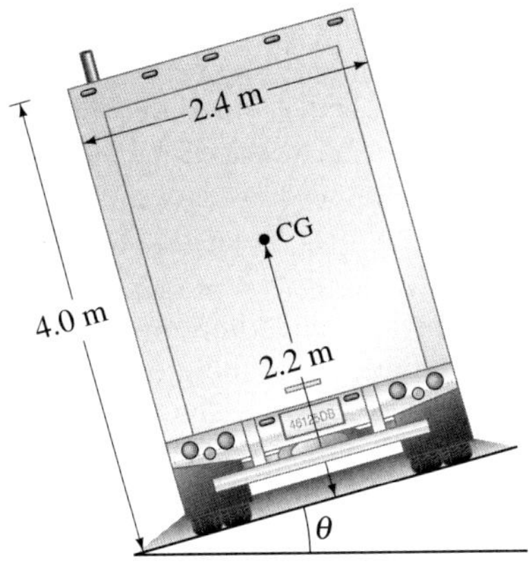


FIGURE 9–75 Problem 63.

64. In Fig. 9–76, consider the right-hand (northernmost) section of the Golden Gate Bridge, which has a length $d_1 = 343$ m. Assume the CG of this span is halfway between the tower and anchor. Determine $F_{T1}$ and $F_{T2}$ (which act on the northernmost cable) in terms of $mg$, the weight of the northernmost span, and calculate the tower height $h$ needed for equilibrium. Assume the roadway is supported only by the suspension cables, and neglect the mass of the cables and vertical wires. [*Hint*: $F_{T3}$ does not act on this section.]

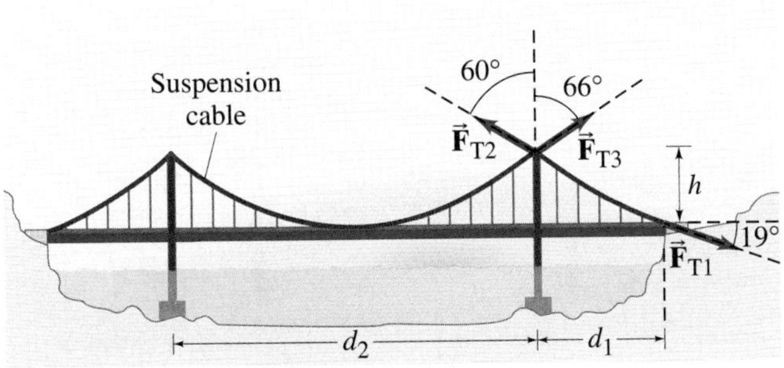


FIGURE 9–76 Problem 64.

65. When a mass of 25 kg is hung from the middle of a fixed straight aluminum wire, the wire sags to make an angle of 12° with the horizontal as shown in Fig. 9–77. Determine the radius of the wire.

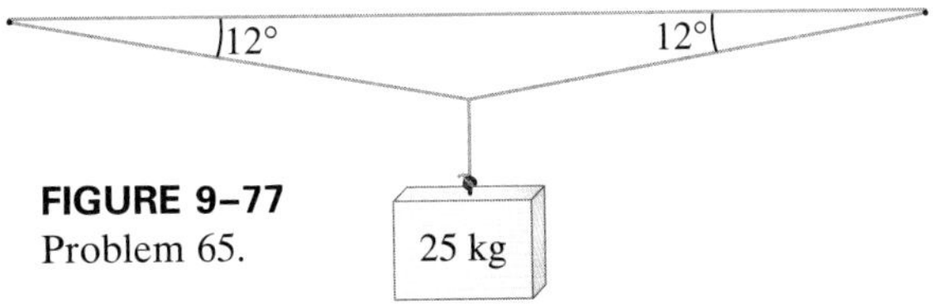


FIGURE 9–77 Problem 65.

66. The forces acting on a 67,000-kg aircraft flying at constant velocity are shown in Fig. 9–78. The engine thrust, $F_T = 5.0 \times 10^5$ N, acts on a line 1.6 m below the CM. Determine the drag force $F_D$ and the distance above the CM that it acts. Assume $\vec{F}_D$ and $\vec{F}_T$ are horizontal.

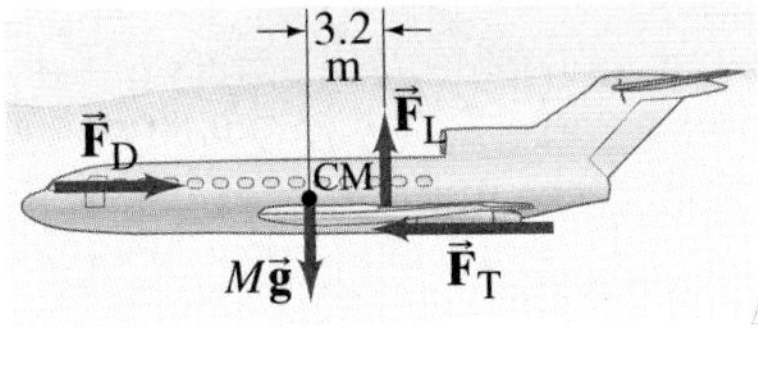


FIGURE 9–78 Problem 66.

67. A uniform flexible steel cable of weight $mg$ is suspended between two points at the same elevation as shown in Fig. 9–79, where $\theta = 60°$. Determine the tension in the cable (*a*) at its lowest point, and (*b*) at the points of attachment. (*c*) What is the direction of the tension force in each case?

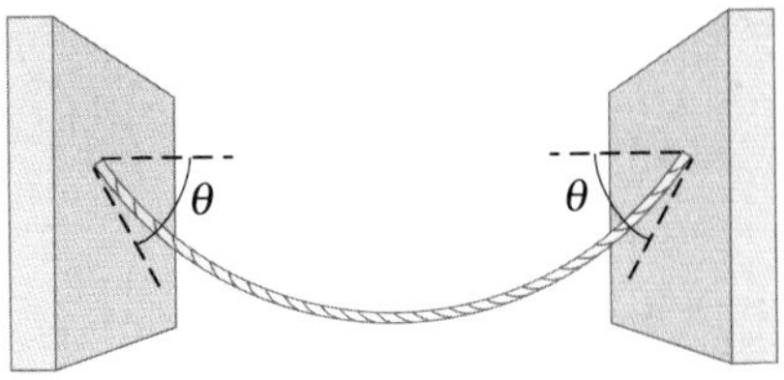


FIGURE 9–79 Problem 67.

68. A 20.0-m-long uniform beam weighing 550 N rests on walls A and B, as shown in Fig. 9–80. (*a*) Find the maximum weight of a person who can walk to the extreme end D without tipping the beam. Find the forces that the walls A and B exert on the beam when the person is standing: (*b*) at D; (*c*) at a point 2.0 m to the right of B; (*d*) 2.0 m to the right of A.

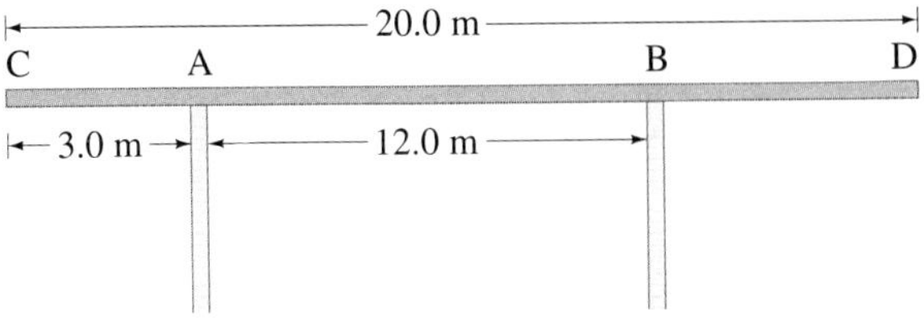


FIGURE 9–80 Problem 68.

69. A cube of side $l$ rests on a rough floor. It is subjected to a steady horizontal pull $F$, exerted a distance $h$ above the floor as shown in Fig. 9–81. As $F$ is increased, the block will either begin to slide, or begin to tip over. Determine the coefficient of static friction $\mu_s$ so that (*a*) the block begins to slide rather than tip; (*b*) the block begins to tip. [*Hint*: Where will the normal force on the block act if it tips?]

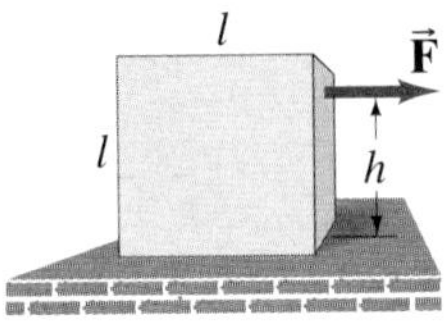


FIGURE 9–81 Problem 69.

70. A 60.0-kg painter is on a uniform 25-kg scaffold supported from above by ropes (Fig. 9–82). There is a 4.0-kg pail of paint to one side, as shown. Can the painter walk safely to both ends of the scaffold? If not, which end(s) is dangerous, and how close to the end can he approach safely?

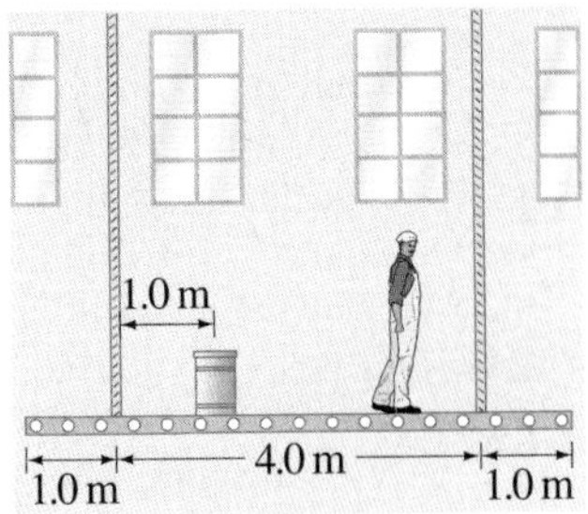


FIGURE 9–82 Problem 70.

71. A woman holds a 2.0-m-long uniform 10.0-kg pole as shown in Fig. 9–83. (*a*) Determine the forces she must exert with each hand (magnitude and direction). To what position should she move her left hand so that neither hand has to exert a force greater than (*b*) 150 N? (*c*) 85 N?

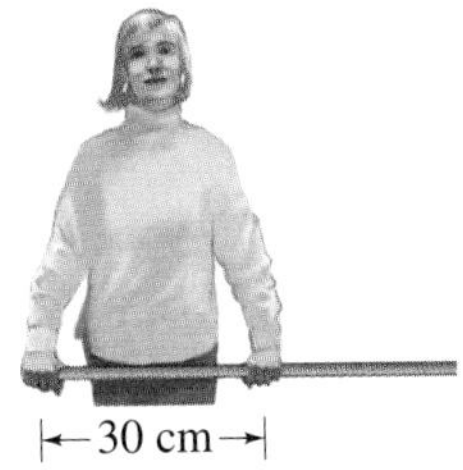


FIGURE 9–83 Problem 71.

72. A man doing push-ups pauses in the position shown in Fig. 9–84. His mass $m = 75$ kg. Determine the normal force exerted by the floor (*a*) on each hand; (*b*) on each foot.

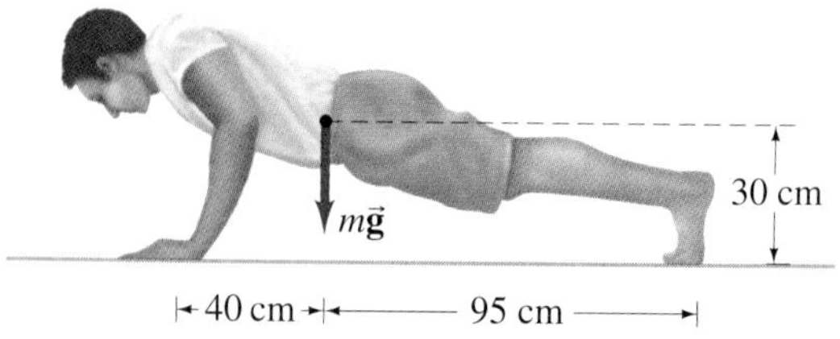


**FIGURE 9–84** Problem 72.

73. A 20-kg sphere rests between two smooth planes as shown in Fig. 9–85. Determine the magnitude of the force acting on the sphere exerted by each plane.

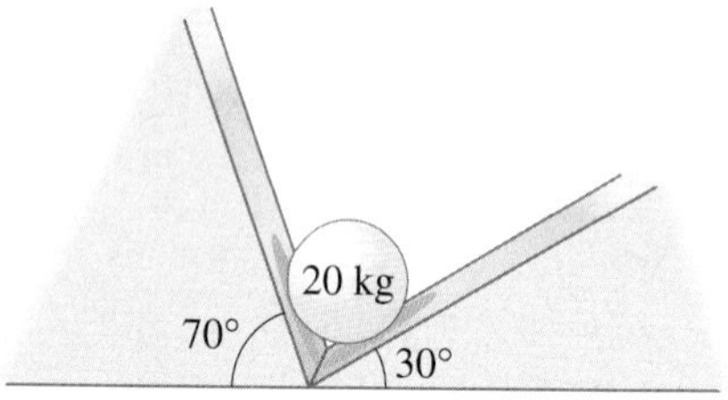


**FIGURE 9–85** Problem 73.

74. A 2200-kg trailer is attached to a stationary truck at point B, Fig. 9–86. Determine the normal force exerted by the road on the rear tires at A, and the vertical force exerted on the trailer by the support B.

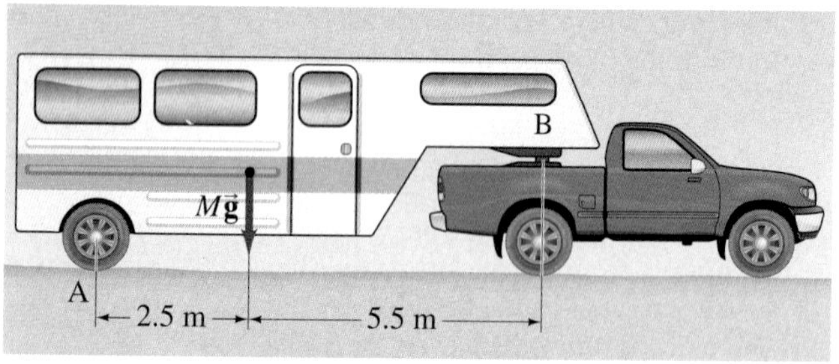


**FIGURE 9–86** Problem 74.

* 75. Parachutists whose chutes have failed to open have been known to survive if they land in deep snow. Assume that a 75-kg parachutist hits the ground with an area of impact of $0.30\ m^2$ at a velocity of 60 m/s, and that the ultimate strength of body tissue is $5 \times 10^5\ N/m^2$. Assume that the person is brought to rest in 1.0 m of snow. Show that the person may escape serious injury.

* 76. A steel wire 2.0 mm in diameter stretches by 0.030% when a mass is suspended from it. How large is the mass?

* 77. In Example 7–6 in Chapter 7, we calculated the impulse and average force on the leg of a person who jumps 3.0 m down to the ground. If the legs are not bent upon landing, so that the body moves a distance $d$ of only 1.0 cm during collision, determine (*a*) the stress in the tibia (a lower leg bone of area $= 3.0 \times 10^{-4}\ m^2$), and (*b*) whether or not the bone will break. (*c*) Repeat for a bent-knees landing ($d = 50.0$ cm).

* 78. The roof over a 7.0-m × 10.0-m room in a school has a total mass of 12,600 kg. The roof is to be supported by vertical "2 × 4s" (actually about 4.0 cm × 9.0 cm) along the 10.0-m sides. How many supports are required on each side, and how far apart must they be? Consider only compression, and assume a safety factor of 12.

* 79. A 25-kg object is being lifted by pulling on the ends of a 1.00-mm-diameter nylon string that goes over two 3.00-m-high poles that are 4.0 m apart, as shown in Fig. 9–87. How high above the floor will the object be when the string breaks?

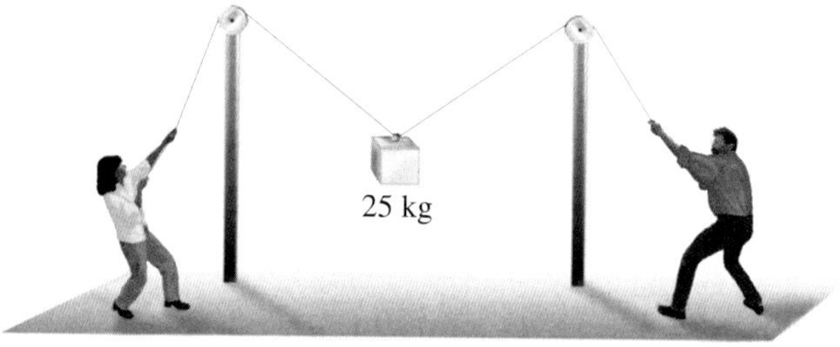


**FIGURE 9–87** Problem 79.

* 80. There is a maximum height of a uniform vertical column made of any material that can support itself without buckling, and it is independent of the cross-sectional area (why?). Calculate this height for (*a*) steel (density = mass/volume = $7.8 \times 10^3\ kg/m^3$), and (*b*) granite (density = $2.7 \times 10^3\ kg/m^3$).

## Answers to Exercises

**A:** $F_A$ also has a component to balance the sideways force $F_B$.

**B:** Yes: sin $\theta$ appears on both sides and cancels out.

**C:** $F_N = m_A g + m_B g + Mg = 560$ N.

**D:** Static friction at the cement floor $(= F_{Cx})$ is crucial, or else the ladder would slip. At the top, the ladder can move and adjust, so we wouldn't expect a strong static friction force there.

Scuba divers and sea creatures under water experience a buoyant force $(\vec{\mathbf{F}}_B)$ that almost exactly balances their weight $m\vec{\mathbf{g}}$. The buoyant force is equal to the weight of the volume of fluid displaced (Archimedes' principle) and arises because the pressure increases with depth in the fluid. Sea creatures have a density very close to that of water, so their weight very nearly equals the buoyant force. Humans have a density slightly less than water, so they can float.

When fluids flow, interesting effects occur because the pressure in the fluid is lower where the fluid velocity is higher (Bernoulli's principle).

CHAPTER 10

# Fluids

In previous Chapters we considered objects that were solid and assumed to maintain their shape except for a small amount of elastic deformation. We sometimes treated objects as point particles. Now we are going to shift our attention to materials that are very deformable and can flow. Such "fluids" include liquids and gases. We will examine fluids both at rest (fluid statics) and in motion (fluid dynamics).

## 10–1 Phases of Matter

*Phases of matter*

The three common **phases**, or **states**, of matter are solid, liquid, and gas. We can distinguish these three phases as follows. A **solid** maintains a fixed shape and a fixed size; even if a large force is applied to a solid, it does not readily change in shape or volume. A **liquid** does not maintain a fixed shape—it takes on the shape of its container—but like a solid it is not readily compressible, and its volume can be changed significantly only by a very large force. A **gas** has neither a fixed shape nor a fixed volume—it will expand to fill its container. For example, when air is pumped into an automobile tire, the air does not all run to the bottom of the tire as a liquid would; it spreads out to fill the whole volume of the tire. Since liquids and gases do not maintain a fixed shape, they both have the ability to flow; they are thus often referred to collectively as **fluids**.

The division of matter into three phases is not always simple. How, for example, should butter be classified? Furthermore, a fourth phase of matter can be distinguished, the **plasma** phase, which occurs only at very high temperatures and consists of ionized atoms (electrons separated from the nuclei). Some scientists believe that so-called colloids (suspensions of tiny particles in a liquid) should also be considered a separate phase of matter. **Liquid crystals**, which are used in laptop computer screens, calculators, digital watches, and so on can be considered a phase of matter intermediate between solids and liquids. However, for our present purposes we will mainly be interested in the three ordinary phases of matter.

## 10–2 Density and Specific Gravity

It is sometimes said that iron is "heavier" than wood. This cannot really be true since a large log clearly weighs more than an iron nail. What we should say is that iron is more *dense* than wood.

The **density**, $\rho$, of a substance ($\rho$ is the lowercase Greek letter rho) is defined as its mass per unit volume:

*Density defined*

$$\rho = \frac{m}{V}, \tag{10–1}$$

where $m$ is the mass of a sample of the substance and $V$ its volume. Density is a characteristic property of any pure substance. Objects made of a particular pure substance, such as pure gold, can have any size or mass, but the density will be the same for each. (We will sometimes use the concept of density, Eq. 10–1, to write the mass of an object as $m = \rho V$, and the weight of an object, $mg$, as $\rho V g$.)

The SI unit for density is $kg/m^3$. Sometimes densities are given in $g/cm^3$. Note that since $1\,kg/m^3 = 1000\,g/(100\,cm)^3 = 10^3\,g/10^6\,cm^3 = 10^{-3}\,g/cm^3$, then a density given in $g/cm^3$ must be multiplied by 1000 to give the result in $kg/m^3$. Thus the density of aluminum is $\rho = 2.70\,g/cm^3$, which is equal to $2700\,kg/m^3$. The densities of a variety of substances are given in Table 10–1. The Table specifies temperature and atmospheric pressure because they affect the density of substances (although the effect is slight for liquids and solids).

**TABLE 10–1 Densities of Substances**[†]

| Substance | Density, $\rho$ ($kg/m^3$) |
|---|---|
| *Solids* | |
| Aluminum | $2.70 \times 10^3$ |
| Iron and steel | $7.8 \times 10^3$ |
| Copper | $8.9 \times 10^3$ |
| Lead | $11.3 \times 10^3$ |
| Gold | $19.3 \times 10^3$ |
| Concrete | $2.3 \times 10^3$ |
| Granite | $2.7 \times 10^3$ |
| Wood (typical) | $0.3–0.9 \times 10^3$ |
| Glass, common | $2.4–2.8 \times 10^3$ |
| Ice ($H_2O$) | $0.917 \times 10^3$ |
| Bone | $1.7–2.0 \times 10^3$ |
| *Liquids* | |
| Water (4°C) | $1.00 \times 10^3$ |
| Blood, plasma | $1.03 \times 10^3$ |
| Blood, whole | $1.05 \times 10^3$ |
| Sea water | $1.025 \times 10^3$ |
| Mercury | $13.6 \times 10^3$ |
| Alcohol, ethyl | $0.79 \times 10^3$ |
| Gasoline | $0.68 \times 10^3$ |
| *Gases* | |
| Air | 1.29 |
| Helium | 0.179 |
| Carbon dioxide | 1.98 |
| Water (steam) (100°C) | 0.598 |

[†] Densities are given at 0°C and 1 atm pressure unless otherwise specified.

**EXAMPLE 10–1 Mass, given volume and density.** What is the mass of a solid iron wrecking ball of radius 18 cm?

**APPROACH** First we use the standard formula $V = \frac{4}{3}\pi r^3$ (see inside rear cover) to obtain the volume of the sphere. Then Eq. 10–1 and Table 10–1 give us the mass $m$.

**SOLUTION** The volume of the sphere is

$$V = \tfrac{4}{3}\pi r^3 = \tfrac{4}{3}(3.14)(0.18\,m)^3 = 0.024\,m^3.$$

From Table 10–1, the density of iron is $\rho = 7800\,kg/m^3$, so Eq. 10–1 gives

$$m = \rho V = \left(7800\,kg/m^3\right)\left(0.024\,m^3\right) = 190\,kg.$$

The **specific gravity** of a substance is defined as the ratio of the density of that substance to the density of water at 4.0°C. Because specific gravity (abbreviated SG) is a ratio, it is a simple number without dimensions or units. The density of water is $1.00\,g/cm^3 = 1.00 \times 10^3\,kg/m^3$, so the specific gravity of any substance will be equal numerically to its density specified in $g/cm^3$, or $10^{-3}$ times its density specified in $kg/m^3$. For example (see Table 10–1), the specific gravity of lead is 11.3, and that of alcohol is 0.79.

The concepts of density and specific gravity are especially helpful in the study of fluids because we are not always dealing with a fixed volume or mass.

## 10–3 Pressure in Fluids

**Pressure** is defined as force per unit area, where the force $F$ is understood to be the magnitude of the force acting perpendicular to the surface area $A$:

$$\text{pressure} = P = \frac{F}{A}. \qquad \text{(10–2)}$$

*Pressure defined*

**CAUTION**

*Pressure is a scalar, not a vector*

*The pascal (unit)*

Although force is a vector, pressure is a scalar. Pressure has magnitude only. The SI unit of pressure is $N/m^2$. This unit has the official name **pascal** (Pa), in honor of Blaise Pascal (see Section 10–5); that is, $1\ Pa = 1\ N/m^2$. However, for simplicity, we will often use $N/m^2$. Other units sometimes used are $dynes/cm^2$, and $lb/in.^2$ (abbreviated "psi"). Several other units for pressure are discussed, along with conversions between them, in Section 10–6 (see also the Table inside the front cover).

**EXAMPLE 10–2** **Calculating pressure.** The two feet of a 60-kg person cover an area of $500\ cm^2$. (*a*) Determine the pressure exerted by the two feet on the ground. (*b*) If the person stands on one foot, what will the pressure be under that foot?

**APPROACH** Assume the person is at rest. Then the ground pushes up on her with a force equal to her weight $mg$, and she exerts a force $mg$ on the ground where her feet (or foot) contact it. Because $1\ cm^2 = (10^{-2}\ m)^2 = 10^{-4}\ m^2$, then $500\ cm^2 = 0.050\ m^2$.

**SOLUTION** (*a*) The pressure on the ground exerted by the two feet is

$$P = \frac{F}{A} = \frac{mg}{A} = \frac{(60\ kg)(9.8\ m/s^2)}{(0.050\ m^2)} = 12 \times 10^3\ N/m^2.$$

(*b*) If the person stands on one foot, the force is still equal to the person's weight, but the area will be half as much, so the pressure will be twice as much: $24 \times 10^3\ N/m^2$.

*Fluids exert pressure in all directions*

Pressure is particularly useful for dealing with fluids. It is an experimental observation that *a fluid can exert a pressure in any direction*. This is well known to swimmers and divers who feel the water pressure on all parts of their bodies. At any point in a fluid at rest, the pressure is the same in all directions at a given depth. This is illustrated in Fig. 10–1. Consider a tiny cube of the fluid which is so small that we can ignore the force of gravity on it. The pressure on one side of it must equal the pressure on the opposite side. If this weren't true, there would be a net force on the cube and it would start moving. If the fluid is not flowing, then the pressures must be equal.

Another important property of a fluid at rest is that the force due to fluid pressure always acts *perpendicular* to any solid surface it is in contact with. If there were a component of the force parallel to the surface, as shown in Fig. 10–2, then according to Newton's third law the solid surface would exert a force back on the fluid that also would have a component parallel to the surface. Such a component would cause the fluid to flow, in contradiction to our assumption that the fluid is at rest. Thus the force due to the pressure in a fluid at rest is always perpendicular to the surface.

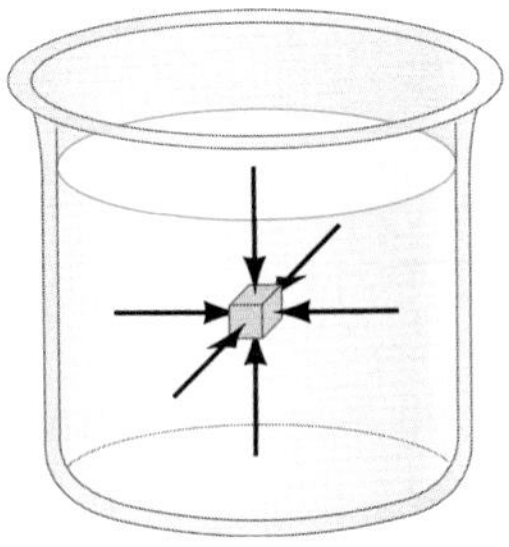

**FIGURE 10–1** Pressure is the same in every direction in a fluid at a given depth; if it weren't, the fluid would be in motion.

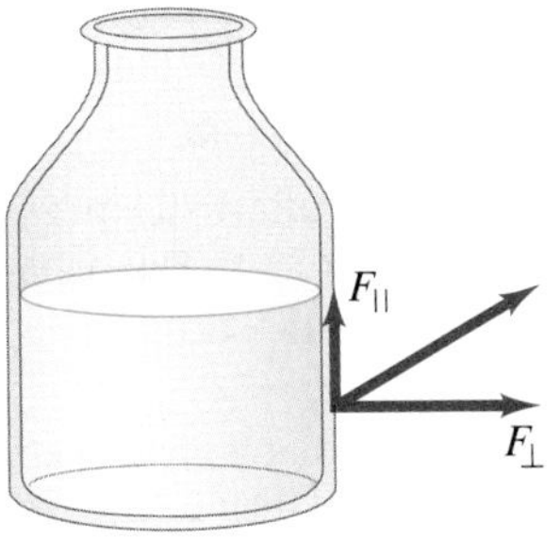


**FIGURE 10–2** If there were a component of force parallel to the solid surface of the container, the liquid would move in response to it. For a liquid at rest, $F_{\|} = 0$.

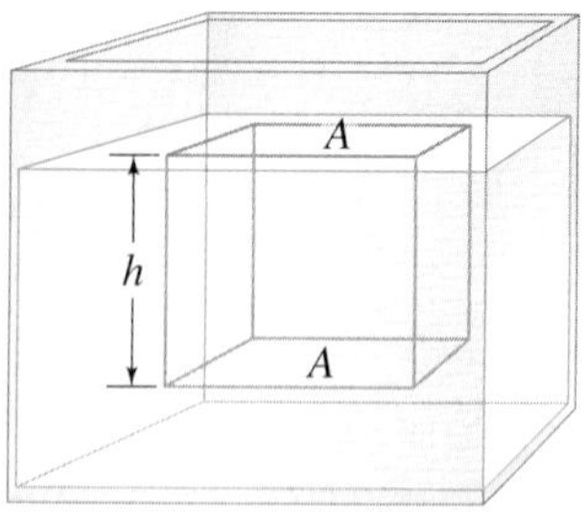


**FIGURE 10–3** Calculating the pressure at a depth $h$ in a liquid.

Let us now calculate quantitatively how the pressure in a liquid of uniform density varies with depth. Consider a point at a depth $h$ below the surface of the liquid (that is, the surface is a height $h$ above this point), as shown in Fig. 10–3. The pressure due to the liquid at this depth $h$ is due to the weight of the column of liquid above it. Thus the force due to the weight of liquid acting on the area $A$ is $F = mg = (\rho V)g = \rho Ahg$, where $Ah$ is the volume of the column of liquid, $\rho$ is the density of the liquid (assumed to be constant), and $g$ is the acceleration of gravity. The pressure $P$ due to the weight of liquid is then

*Pressure variation with depth*

$$P = \frac{F}{A} = \frac{\rho Ahg}{A}$$

$$P = \rho gh. \qquad \text{[liquid]} \quad \textbf{(10–3a)}$$

Note that the area $A$ doesn't affect the pressure at a given depth. The fluid pressure is directly proportional to the density of the liquid and to the depth within the liquid. In general, the pressure at equal depths within a uniform liquid is the same.

Equation 10–3a is extremely useful. It is valid for fluids whose density is constant and does not change with depth—that is, if the fluid is *incompressible*. This is usually a good approximation for liquids (although at great depths in the ocean, the density of water is increased substantially by compression due to the great weight of water above).

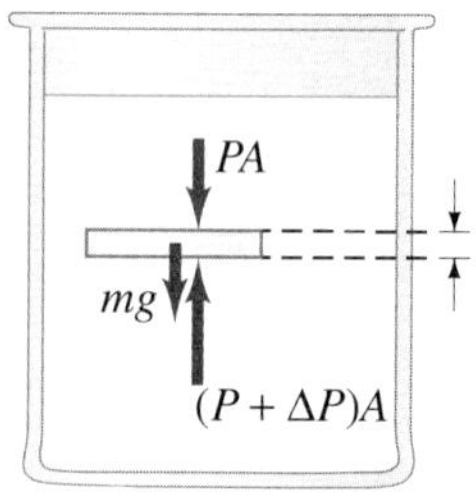


**FIGURE 10–4** Forces on a thin slab of fluid (shown as a liquid, but it could instead be a gas).

Gases, on the other hand, are very compressible, and density can vary significantly with depth. For this more general case, in which $\rho$ may vary, Eq. 10–3a may not be useful. So let us consider a thin slab of liquid of volume $V = A\,\Delta h$ as shown in Fig. 10–4. We choose $\Delta h$ thin enough so that $\rho$ doesn't vary significantly over the small thickness $\Delta h$. Let $P$ be the pressure exerted downward on the top surface, and let $P + \Delta P$ be the pressure upward on the bottom surface. The forces acting on our thin slab of fluid, as shown in Fig. 10–4, are $(P + \Delta P)A$ upward and $PA$ downward, and the downward weight of the slab, $mg = (\rho V)g = \rho A\,\Delta h\,g$. We assume the fluid is at rest, so the net force on the slab is zero. Then

$$(P + \Delta P)A - PA - \rho A\,\Delta h\,g = 0.$$

The area $A$ cancels from each term, and when we solve for $\Delta P$ we obtain

*Change in pressure with change in depth in a fluid*

$$\Delta P = \rho g\,\Delta h. \qquad [\rho \approx \text{constant over } \Delta h] \quad \textbf{(10–3b)}$$

Equation 10–3b tells us how the pressure changes over a small change in depth ($\Delta h$) within a fluid, even if compressible.

**PHYSICS APPLIED**

*Water supply*

**EXAMPLE 10–3** **Pressure at a faucet.** The surface of the water in a storage tank is 30 m above a water faucet in the kitchen of a house, Fig. 10–5. Calculate the difference in water pressure between the faucet and the surface of the water in the tank.

**FIGURE 10–5** Example 10–3.

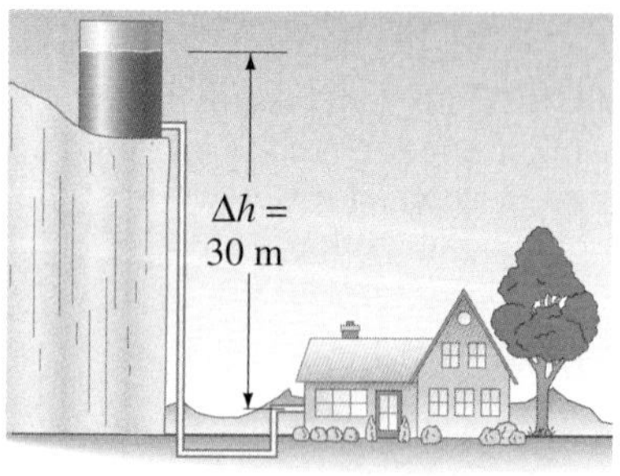


**APPROACH** Water is practically incompressible, so $\rho$ is constant even for a $\Delta h = 30\,\text{m}$ when used in Eq. 10–3b. Only $\Delta h$ matters; we can ignore the "route" of the pipe and its bends.

**SOLUTION** The same atmospheric pressure acts both at the surface of the water in the storage tank and on the water leaving the faucet. So, the water pressure difference between the faucet and the surface of the water in the tank is

$$\Delta P = \rho g\,\Delta h = (1.0 \times 10^3\,\text{kg/m}^3)(9.8\,\text{m/s}^2)(30\,\text{m})$$
$$= 2.9 \times 10^5\,\text{N/m}^2.$$

**NOTE** The height $h$ is sometimes called the **pressure head**. In this Example, the head of water is 30 m at the faucet. The very different diameters of the tank and faucet don't affect the result—only pressure does.

**EXERCISE A** A dam holds back a lake that is 85 m deep at the dam. If the lake is 20 km long, how much thicker should the dam be than if the lake were smaller, only 1.0 km long?

## 10–4 Atmospheric Pressure and Gauge Pressure

### Atmospheric Pressure

The pressure of the Earth's atmosphere, as in any fluid, changes with depth. But the Earth's atmosphere is somewhat complicated: not only does the density of air vary greatly with altitude but there is no distinct top surface to the atmosphere from which $h$ (in Eq. 10–3a) could be measured. We can, however, calculate the approximate difference in pressure between two altitudes using Eq. 10–3b.

The pressure of the air at a given place varies slightly according to the weather. At sea level, the pressure of the atmosphere on average is $1.013 \times 10^5\,\mathrm{N/m^2}$ (or $14.7\,\mathrm{lb/in.^2}$). This value lets us define a commonly used unit of pressure, the **atmosphere** (abbreviated atm):

$$1\,\mathrm{atm} = 1.013 \times 10^5\,\mathrm{N/m^2} = 101.3\,\mathrm{kPa}.$$

*One atmosphere (unit of pressure)*

Another unit of pressure sometimes used (in meteorology and on weather maps) is the **bar**, which is defined as

$$1\,\mathrm{bar} = 1.00 \times 10^5\,\mathrm{N/m^2}.$$

*The bar (unit of pressure)*

Thus standard atmospheric pressure is slightly more than 1 bar.

The pressure due to the weight of the atmosphere is exerted on all objects immersed in this great sea of air, including our bodies. How does a human body withstand the enormous pressure on its surface? The answer is that living cells maintain an internal pressure that closely equals the external pressure, just as the pressure inside a balloon closely matches the outside pressure of the atmosphere. An automobile tire, because of its rigidity, can maintain internal pressures much greater than the external pressure.

PHYSICS APPLIED
*Pressure on living cells*

CONCEPTUAL EXAMPLE 10–4 **Finger holds water in a straw.** You insert a straw of length $L$ into a tall glass of water. You place your finger over the top of the straw, capturing some air above the water but preventing any additional air from getting in or out, and then you lift the straw from the water. You find that the straw retains most of the water. (See Fig. 10–6a.) Does the air in the space between your finger and the top of the water have a pressure $P$ that is greater than, equal to, or less than, the atmospheric pressure $P_A$ outside the straw?

**RESPONSE** Consider the forces on the column of water (Fig. 10–6b). Atmospheric pressure outside the straw pushes upward on the water at the bottom of the straw, gravity pulls the water downward, and the air pressure inside the top of the straw pushes downward on the water. Since the water is in equilibrium, the upward force due to atmospheric pressure must balance the two downward forces. The only way this is possible is for the air pressure inside the straw to be less than the atmosphere pressure outside the straw. (When you initially remove the straw, a little water may leave the bottom of the straw, thus increasing the volume of trapped air and reducing its density and pressure.)

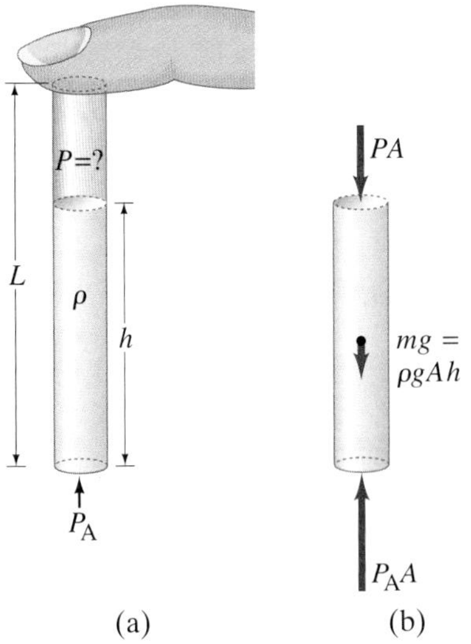


**FIGURE 10–6** Example 10–4.

### Gauge Pressure

It is important to note that tire gauges, and most other pressure gauges, register the pressure above and beyond atmospheric pressure. This is called **gauge pressure**. Thus, to get the **absolute pressure**, $P$, we must add the atmospheric pressure, $P_A$, to the gauge pressure, $P_G$:

*Gauge pressure*

$$P = P_A + P_G.$$

*Absolute pressure = atmospheric pressure + gauge pressure*

If a tire gauge registers 220 kPa, the absolute pressure within the tire is 220 kPa + 101 kPa = 321 kPa, equivalent to about 3.2 atm (2.2 atm gauge pressure).

## 10–5 Pascal's Principle

The Earth's atmosphere exerts a pressure on all objects with which it is in contact, including other fluids. External pressure acting on a fluid is transmitted throughout that fluid. For instance, according to Eq. 10–3a, the pressure due to the water at a depth of 100 m below the surface of a lake is $P = \rho g \Delta h = (1000\ \text{kg/m}^3)(9.8\ \text{m/s}^2)(100\ \text{m}) = 9.8 \times 10^5\ \text{N/m}^2$, or 9.7 atm. However, the total pressure at this point is due to the pressure of water plus the pressure of the air above it. Hence the total pressure (if the lake is near sea level) is 9.7 atm + 1.0 atm = 10.7 atm. This is just one example of a general principle attributed to the French philosopher and scientist Blaise Pascal (1623–1662).

*Pascal's principles*

**Pascal's principle** states that *if an external pressure is applied to a confined fluid, the pressure at every point within the fluid increases by that amount.*

PHYSICS APPLIED

*Hydraulic lift*

A number of practical devices make use of Pascal's principle. One example is the hydraulic lift, illustrated in Fig. 10–7a, in which a small input force is used to exert a large output force by making the area of the output piston larger than the area of the input piston. To see how this works, we assume the input and output pistons are at the same height (at least approximately). Then the external input force $F_{\text{in}}$, by Pascal's principle, increases the pressure equally throughout. Therefore, at the same level (see Fig. 10–7a),

$$P_{\text{out}} = P_{\text{in}}$$

where the input quantities are represented by the subscript "in" and the output by "out." Since $P = F/A$, we write the above equality as

$$\frac{F_{\text{out}}}{A_{\text{out}}} = \frac{F_{\text{in}}}{A_{\text{in}}},$$

or

$$\frac{F_{\text{out}}}{F_{\text{in}}} = \frac{A_{\text{out}}}{A_{\text{in}}}.$$

*Mechanical advantage*

The quantity $F_{\text{out}}/F_{\text{in}}$ is called the *mechanical advantage* of the hydraulic lift, and it is equal to the ratio of the areas. For example, if the area of the output piston is 20 times that of the input cylinder, the force is multiplied by a factor of 20: thus a force of 200 lb could lift a 4000-lb car.

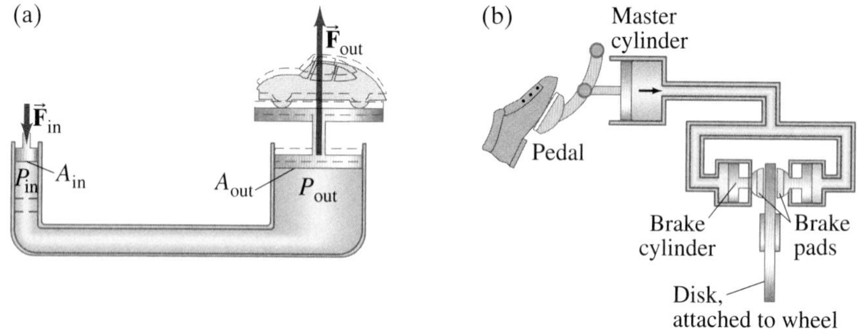


**FIGURE 10–7** Applications of Pascal's principle: (a) hydraulic lift; (b) hydraulic brakes in a car.

PHYSICS APPLIED

*Brakes*

Figure 10–7b illustrates the brake system of a car. When the driver presses the brake pedal, the pressure in the master cylinder increases. This pressure increase occurs throughout the brake fluid, thus pushing the brake pads against the disk attached to the car's wheel.

## 10–6 Measurement of Pressure; Gauges and the Barometer

*Manometer*

Many devices have been invented to measure pressure, some of which are shown in Fig. 10–8. The simplest is the open-tube *manometer* (Fig. 10–8a), which is a U-shaped tube partially filled with a liquid, usually mercury or water. The pressure $P$ being measured is related (by Eq. 10–3b) to the difference in

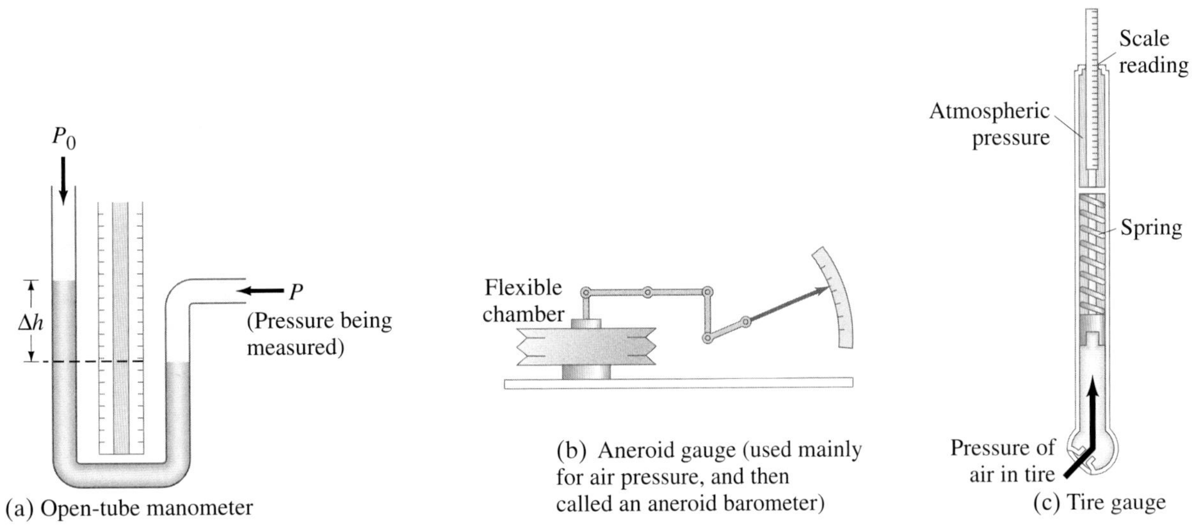


**FIGURE 10–8** Pressure gauges: (a) open-tube manometer, (b) aneroid gauge, and (c) common tire pressure gauge.

height $\Delta h$ of the two levels of the liquid by the relation

$$P = P_0 + \rho g \, \Delta h, \qquad \textbf{(10–3c)}$$

*Pressure beneath surface of liquid open to the atmosphere*

where $P_0$ is atmospheric pressure (acting on the top of the liquid in the left-hand tube), and $\rho$ is the density of the liquid. Note that the quantity $\rho g \, \Delta h$ is the gauge pressure—the amount by which $P$ exceeds atmospheric pressure $P_0$. If the liquid in the left-hand column were lower than that in the right-hand column, $P$ would have to be less than atmospheric pressure (and $\Delta h$ would be negative).

Instead of calculating the product $\rho g \, \Delta h$, sometimes only the change in height $\Delta h$ is specified. In fact, pressures are sometimes specified as so many "millimeters of mercury" (mm-Hg) or "mm of water" (mm-$H_2O$). The unit mm-Hg is equivalent to a pressure of 133 $N/m^2$, since $\rho g \, \Delta h$ for $1 \text{ mm} = 1.0 \times 10^{-3} \text{ m}$ of mercury gives

$$\rho g \, \Delta h = (13.6 \times 10^3 \text{ kg/m}^3)(9.80 \text{ m/s}^2)(1.00 \times 10^{-3} \text{ m}) = 1.33 \times 10^2 \text{ N/m}^2.$$

*The torr (unit of pressure)*

The unit mm-Hg is also called the **torr** in honor of Evangelista Torricelli (1608–1647), a student of Galileo's who invented the barometer (see below). Conversion factors among the various units of pressure (an incredible nuisance!) are given in Table 10–2. It is important that only $\text{N/m}^2 = \text{Pa}$, the proper SI unit, be used in calculations involving other quantities specified in SI units.

**➥ PROBLEM SOLVING**

*Use SI unit in calculations:* $1 \text{ Pa} = 1 \text{ N/m}^2$

Another type of pressure gauge is the aneroid gauge (Fig. 10–8b) in which the pointer is linked to the flexible ends of an evacuated thin metal chamber. In an electronic gauge, the pressure may be applied to a thin metal diaphragm whose resulting distortion is translated into an electrical signal by a transducer. How a common tire gauge is constructed is shown in Fig. 10–8c.

**TABLE 10–2 Conversion Factors Between Different Units of Pressure**

| In Terms of $1 \text{ Pa} = 1 \text{ N/m}^2$ | 1 atm in Different Units |
|---|---|
| $1 \text{ atm} = 1.013 \times 10^5 \text{ N/m}^2$ | $1 \text{ atm} = 1.013 \times 10^5 \text{ N/m}^2$ |
| $= 1.013 \times 10^5 \text{ Pa} = 101.3 \text{ kPa}$ | |
| $1 \text{ bar} = 1.000 \times 10^5 \text{ N/m}^2$ | $1 \text{ atm} = 1.013 \text{ bar}$ |
| $1 \text{ dyne/cm}^2 = 0.1 \text{ N/m}^2$ | $1 \text{ atm} = 1.013 \times 10^6 \text{ dyne/cm}^2$ |
| $1 \text{ lb/in.}^2 = 6.90 \times 10^3 \text{ N/m}^2$ | $1 \text{ atm} = 14.7 \text{ lb/in.}^2$ |
| $1 \text{ lb/ft}^2 = 47.9 \text{ N/m}^2$ | $1 \text{ atm} = 2.12 \times 10^3 \text{ lb/ft}^2$ |
| $1 \text{ cm-Hg} = 1.33 \times 10^3 \text{ N/m}^2$ | $1 \text{ atm} = 76 \text{ cm-Hg}$ |
| $1 \text{ mm-Hg} = 133 \text{ N/m}^2$ | $1 \text{ atm} = 760 \text{ mm-Hg}$ |
| $1 \text{ torr} = 133 \text{ N/m}^2$ | $1 \text{ atm} = 760 \text{ torr}$ |
| $1 \text{ mm-H}_2\text{O (4°C)} = 9.81 \text{ N/m}^2$ | $1 \text{ atm} = 1.03 \times 10^4 \text{ mm-H}_2\text{O (4°C)}$ |

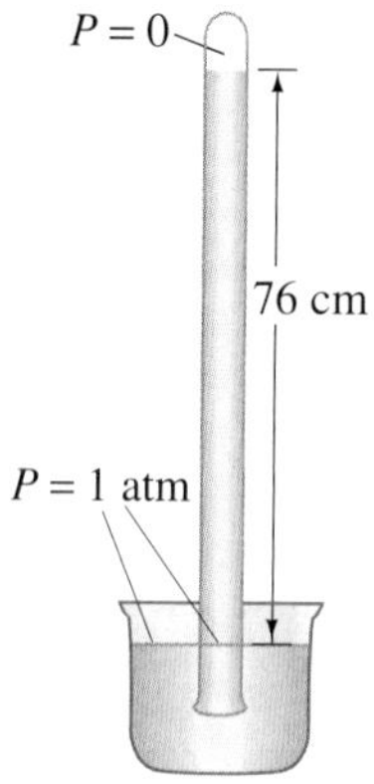


**FIGURE 10–9** A mercury barometer, invented by Torricelli, is shown here when the air pressure is standard atmospheric, 76 cm-Hg.

*Barometer*

Atmospheric pressure can be measured by a modified kind of mercury manometer with one end closed, called a mercury **barometer** (Fig. 10–9). The glass tube is completely filled with mercury and then inverted into the bowl of mercury. If the tube is long enough, the level of the mercury will drop, leaving a vacuum at the top of the tube, since atmospheric pressure can support a column of mercury only about 76 cm high (exactly 76.0 cm at standard atmospheric pressure). That is, a column of mercury 76 cm high exerts the same pressure as the atmosphere†:

$$P = \rho g \, \Delta h$$
$$= (13.6 \times 10^3\,\text{kg/m}^3)(9.80\,\text{m/s}^2)(0.760\,\text{m}) = 1.013 \times 10^5\,\text{N/m}^2 = 1.00\,\text{atm}.$$

Household barometers are usually of the aneroid type, either mechanical (Fig. 10–8b) or electronic.

A calculation similar to that above will show that atmospheric pressure can maintain a column of water 10.3 m high in a tube whose top is under vacuum (Fig. 10–10). No matter how good a vacuum pump is, it cannot lift water more than about 10 m. To pump water out of deep mine shafts with a vacuum pump requires multiple stages for depths greater than 10 m. Galileo studied this problem, and his student Torricelli was the first to explain it. The point is that a pump does not really suck water up a tube—it merely reduces the pressure at the top of the tube. Atmospheric air pressure *pushes* the water up the tube if the top end is at low pressure (under a vacuum), just as it is air pressure that pushes (or maintains) the mercury 76 cm high in a barometer.

**FIGURE 10–10** A water barometer: a full tube of water is inserted into a tub of water, keeping the spigot at the top closed. When the bottom end of the tube is uncovered, some water flows out of the tube into the tub, leaving a vacuum between the water's upper surface and the spigot. Why? Because air pressure can not support a column of water more than 10 m high.

**CONCEPTUAL EXAMPLE 10–5** **Suction.** You sit in a meeting where a novice NASA engineer proposes suction cup shoes for Space Shuttle astronauts working on the exterior of the spacecraft. Having just studied this Chapter, you gently remind him of the fallacy of this plan. What is it?

**RESPONSE** Suction cups work by pushing out the air underneath the cup. What holds the cup in place is the air pressure outside the cup. (This can be a substantial force when on Earth. For example, a 10-cm-diameter cup has an area of $7.9 \times 10^{-3}\,\text{m}^2$. The force of the atmosphere on it is $(7.9 \times 10^{-3}\,\text{m}^2)(1.0 \times 10^5\,\text{N/m}^2) \approx 800\,\text{N}$, about 180 lbs!). But in outer space, there is no air pressure to hold the suction cup onto the spacecraft.

We sometimes mistakenly think of suction as something we actively do. For example, we intuitively think that we pull the soda up through a straw. Instead, what we do is lower the pressure at the top of the straw, and the atmosphere *pushes* the soda up the straw.

† This calculation confirms the entry in Table 10–2, 1 atm = 76 cm-Hg.

## 10–7 Buoyancy and Archimedes' Principle

Objects submerged in a fluid appear to weigh less than they do when outside the fluid. For example, a large rock that you would have difficulty lifting off the ground can often be easily lifted from the bottom of a stream. When the rock breaks through the surface of the water, it suddenly seems to be much heavier. Many objects, such as wood, float on the surface of water. These are two examples of *buoyancy*. In each example, the force of gravity is acting downward. But in addition, an upward *buoyant force* is exerted by the liquid. The buoyant force on fish and underwater divers (as in the chapter-opening photo) almost exactly balances the force of gravity downward, and allows them to "hover" in equilibrium.

*Rocks seem to weigh less under water*

*Wood floats*

The buoyant force occurs because the pressure in a fluid increases with depth. Thus the upward pressure on the bottom surface of a submerged object is greater than the downward pressure on its top surface. To see this effect, consider a cylinder of height $\Delta h$ whose top and bottom ends have an area $A$ and which is completely submerged in a fluid of density $\rho_F$, as shown in Fig. 10–11. The fluid exerts a pressure $P_1 = \rho_F g h_1$ at the top surface of the

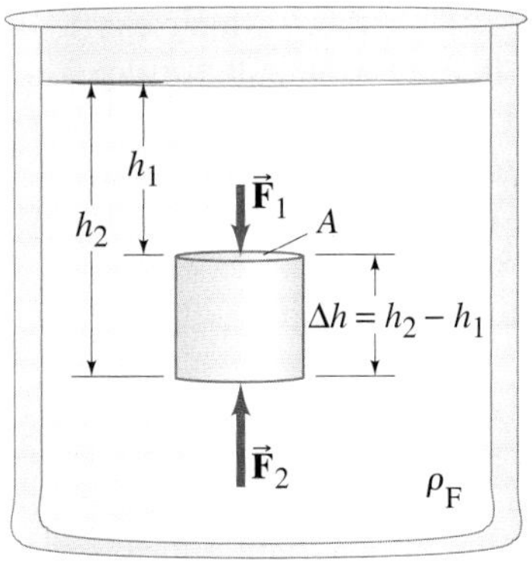


**FIGURE 10–11** Determination of the buoyant force.

cylinder (Eq. 10–3a). The force due to this pressure on top of the cylinder is $F_1 = P_1 A = \rho_F g h_1 A$, and it is directed downward. Similarly, the fluid exerts an upward force on the bottom of the cylinder equal to $F_2 = P_2 A = \rho_F g h_2 A$. The net force on the cylinder exerted by the fluid pressure, which is the **buoyant force**, $\vec{\mathbf{F}}_B$, acts upward and has the magnitude

$$\begin{aligned} F_B = F_2 - F_1 &= \rho_F g A(h_2 - h_1) \\ &= \rho_F g A \,\Delta h \\ &= \rho_F V g \\ &= m_F g, \end{aligned}$$

where $V = A\,\Delta h$ is the volume of the cylinder, the product $\rho_F V$ is its mass, and $\rho_F V g = m_F g$ is the weight of fluid which takes up a volume equal to the volume of the cylinder. Thus the buoyant force on the cylinder is equal to the weight of fluid displaced by the cylinder. This result is valid no matter what the shape of the object. Its discovery is credited to Archimedes (287?–212 B.C.), and it is called **Archimedes' principle**: *the buoyant force on an object immersed in a fluid is equal to the weight of the fluid displaced by that object.*

*Archimedes' principle*

By "fluid displaced," we mean a volume of fluid equal to the volume of the submerged object, or that part of the object submerged if it floats or is only partly submerged (the fluid that used to be where the object is). If the object is placed in a glass or tub initially filled to the brim with water, the water that flows over the top represents the water displaced by the object.

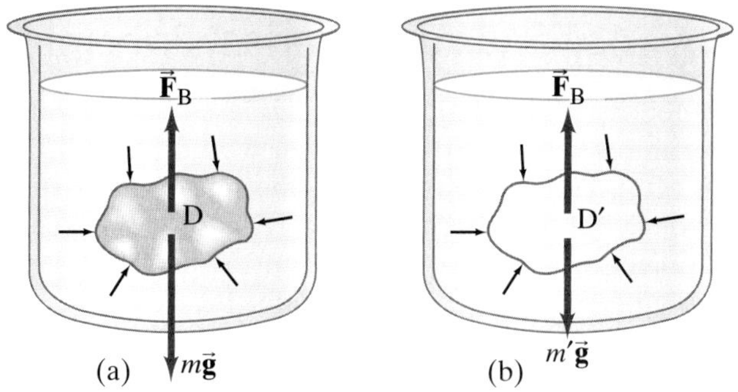


**FIGURE 10–12** Archimedes' principle.

We can derive Archimedes' principle in general by the following simple but elegant argument. The irregularly shaped object D shown in Fig. 10–12a is acted on by the force of gravity (its weight, $m\vec{g}$, downward) and the buoyant force, $\vec{F}_B$, upward. We wish to determine $F_B$. To do so, we next consider a body (D′ in Fig. 10–12b), this time made of the fluid itself, with the same shape and size as the original object, and located at the same depth. You might think of this body of fluid as being separated from the rest of the fluid by an imaginary membrane. The buoyant force $F_B$ on this body of fluid will be exactly the same as that on the original object since the surrounding fluid, which exerts $F_B$, is in exactly the same configuration. This body of fluid D′ is in equilibrium (the fluid as a whole is at rest). Therefore, $F_B = m'g$, where $m'g$ is the weight of the body of fluid. Hence the buoyant force $F_B$ is equal to the weight of the body of fluid whose volume equals the volume of the original submerged object, which is Archimedes' principle.

Archimedes' discovery was made by experiment. What we have done in the last two paragraphs is show that Archimedes' principle can be derived from Newtons' laws.

**CONCEPTUAL EXAMPLE 10–6** **Two pails of water.** Consider two identical pails of water filled to the brim. One pail contains only water, the other has a piece of wood floating in it. Which pail has the greater weight?

**RESPONSE** Both pails weigh the same. Recall Archimedes' principle: the wood displaces a volume of water with weight equal to the weight of the wood. Some water will overflow the pail, but Archimedes' principle tells us the spilled water has weight equal to that of the wood; so the pails have the same weight.

**EXAMPLE 10–7** **Recovering a submerged statue.** A 70-kg ancient statue lies at the bottom of the sea. Its volume is $3.0 \times 10^4\,\text{cm}^3$. How much force is needed to lift it?

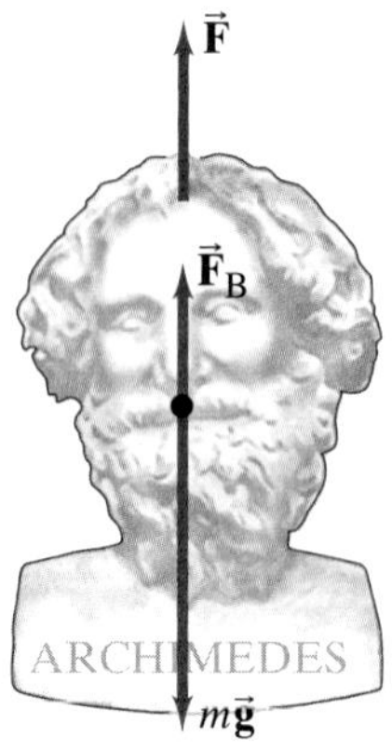


**FIGURE 10–13** Example 10–7. The force needed to lift the statue is $\vec{F}$.

**APPROACH** The force $F$ needed to lift the statue is equal to the statue's weight $mg$ minus the buoyant force $F_B$. Figure 10–13 is the free-body diagram.

**SOLUTION** The buoyant force on the statue due to the water is equal to the weight of $3.0 \times 10^4\,\text{cm}^3 = 3.0 \times 10^{-2}\,\text{m}^3$ of water (for seawater, $\rho = 1.025 \times 10^3\,\text{kg/m}^3$):

$$\begin{aligned} F_B = m_{H_2O}\,g &= \rho_{H_2O} V g \\ &= \left(1.025 \times 10^3\,\text{kg/m}^3\right)\left(3.0 \times 10^{-2}\,\text{m}^3\right)\left(9.8\,\text{m/s}^2\right) \\ &= 3.0 \times 10^2\,\text{N}. \end{aligned}$$

The weight of the statue is $mg = (70\,\text{kg})\left(9.8\,\text{m/s}^2\right) = 6.9 \times 10^2\,\text{N}$. Hence the force $F$ needed to lift it is $690\,\text{N} - 300\,\text{N} = 390\,\text{N}$. It is as if the statue had a mass of only $(390\,\text{N})/\left(9.8\,\text{m/s}^2\right) = 40\,\text{kg}$.

**NOTE** Here $F = 390\,\text{N}$ is the force needed to lift the statue without acceleration when it is under water. As the statue comes *out* of the water, the force $F$ increases, reaching 690 N when the statue is fully out of the water.

Archimedes is said to have discovered his principle in his bath while thinking how he might determine whether the king's new crown was pure gold or a fake. Gold has a specific gravity of 19.3, somewhat higher than that of most metals, but a determination of specific gravity or density is not readily done directly because, even if the mass is known, the volume of an irregularly shaped object is not easily calculated. However, if the object is weighed in air $(= w)$ and also "weighed" while it is under water $(= w')$, the density can be determined using Archimedes' principle, as the following Example shows. The quantity $w'$ is called the *apparent weight* in water, and is what a scale reads when the object is submerged in water (see Fig. 10–14); $w'$ equals the true weight $(w = mg)$ minus the buoyant force.

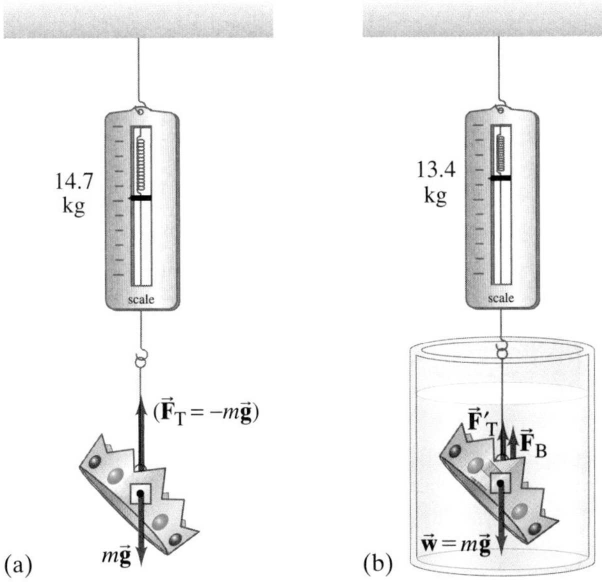


**FIGURE 10–14** (a) A scale reads the mass of an object in air—in this case the crown of Example 10–8. All objects are at rest, so the tension $F_T$ in the connecting cord equals the weight $w$ of the object: $F_T = mg$. We show the free-body diagram of the crown, and $F_T$ is what causes the scale reading (it's equal to the net downward force on the scale, by Newton's third law). (b) Submerged, the object has an additional force on it, the buoyant force $F_B$. The net force is zero, so $F'_T + F_B = mg\ (= w)$. The scale now reads $m' = 13.4$ kg, where $m'$ is related to the effective weight by $w' = m'g$. Thus $F'_T = w' = w - F_B$.

**EXAMPLE 10–8 Archimedes: Is the crown gold?** When a crown of mass 14.7 kg is submerged in water, an accurate scale reads only 13.4 kg. Is the crown made of gold?

**APPROACH** If the crown is gold, its density and specific gravity must be very high, SG = 19.3 (see Section 10–2 and Table 10–1). We determine the specific gravity using Archimedes' principle and the two free-body diagrams shown in Fig. 10–14.

**SOLUTION** The apparent weight of the submerged object (the crown) is $w'$, and it equals $F'_T$ in Fig. 10–14b. The sum of the forces on the object is zero, so $w'$ equals the actual weight $w\ (= mg)$ minus the buoyant force $F_B$:

$$w' = F'_T = w - F_B$$

so

$$w - w' = F_B.$$

Let $V$ be the volume of the completely submerged object and $\rho_O$ its density (so $\rho_O V$ is its mass), and let $\rho_F$ be the density of the fluid (water). Then $(\rho_F V)g$ is the weight of fluid displaced $(= F_B)$. Now we can write

*Recall $m = \rho V$ (Eq. 10–1)*

$$w = mg = \rho_O V g$$
$$w - w' = F_B = \rho_F V g.$$

We divide these two equations and obtain

$$\frac{w}{w - w'} = \frac{\rho_O V g}{\rho_F V g} = \frac{\rho_O}{\rho_F}.$$

We see that $w/(w - w')$ is equal to the specific gravity of the object if the fluid in which it is submerged is water $(\rho_F = 1.00 \times 10^3\ \mathrm{kg/m^3})$. Thus

$$\frac{\rho_O}{\rho_{H_2O}} = \frac{w}{w - w'} = \frac{(14.7\ \mathrm{kg})g}{(14.7\ \mathrm{kg} - 13.4\ \mathrm{kg})g} = \frac{14.7\ \mathrm{kg}}{1.3\ \mathrm{kg}} = 11.3.$$

This corresponds to a density of 11,300 kg/m$^3$. The crown seems to be made of lead (see Table 10–1)!

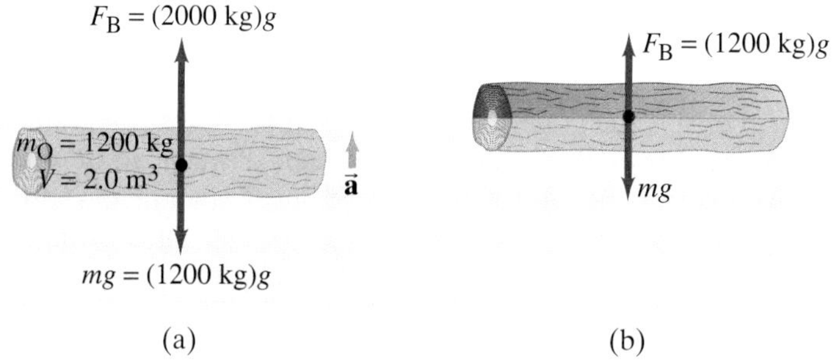


**FIGURE 10–15** (a) The fully submerged log accelerates upward because $F_B > mg$. It comes to equilibrium (b) when $\Sigma F = 0$, so $F_B = mg = (1200\text{ kg})g$. Thus 1200 kg, or $1.2\text{ m}^3$, of water is displaced.

*Floating*

Archimedes' principle applies equally well to objects that float, such as wood. In general, *an object floats on a fluid if its density is less than that of the fluid.* This is readily seen from Fig. 10–15a, where a submerged object will experience a net upward force and float to the surface if $F_B > mg$; that is, if $\rho_F Vg > \rho_O Vg$ or $\rho_F > \rho_O$. At equilibrium—that is, when floating—the buoyant force on an object has magnitude equal to the weight of the object. For example, a log whose specific gravity is 0.60 and whose volume is $2.0\text{ m}^3$ has a mass $m = \rho_O V = (0.60 \times 10^3\text{ kg/m}^3)(2.0\text{ m}^3) = 1200\text{ kg}$. If the log is fully submerged, it will displace a mass of water $m_F = \rho_F V = (1000\text{ kg/m}^3)(2.0\text{ m}^3) = 2000\text{ kg}$. Hence the buoyant force on the log will be greater than its weight, and it will float upward to the surface (Fig. 10–15). The log will come to equilibrium when it displaces 1200 kg of water, which means that $1.2\text{ m}^3$ of its volume will be submerged. This $1.2\text{ m}^3$ corresponds to 60% of the volume of the log $(1.2/2.0 = 0.60)$, so 60% of the log is submerged. In general when an object floats, we have $F_B = mg$, which we can write as (see Fig. 10–16)

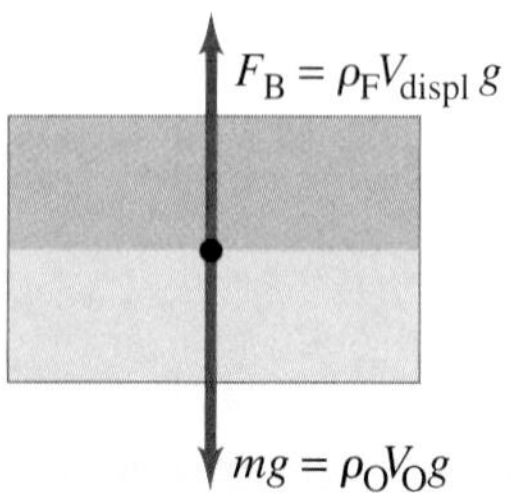


**FIGURE 10–16** An object floating in equilibrium: $F_B = mg$.

$$\rho_F V_{displ}\, g = \rho_O V_O\, g,$$

where $V_O$ is the full volume of the object and $V_{displ}$ is the volume of fluid it displaces (= volume submerged). Thus

$$\frac{V_{displ}}{V_O} = \frac{\rho_O}{\rho_F}.$$

*Fraction of floating object submerged in water = its SG*

That is, the fraction of the object submerged is given by the ratio of the object's density to that of the fluid. If the fluid is water, this fraction equals the specific gravity of the object.

**EXAMPLE 10–9** **Hydrometer calibration.** A **hydrometer** is a simple instrument used to measure the specific gravity of a liquid by indicating how deeply the instrument sinks in the liquid. A particular hydrometer (Fig. 10–17) consists of a glass tube, weighted at the bottom, which is 25.0 cm long and $2.00\text{ cm}^2$ in cross-sectional area, and has a mass of 45.0 g. How far from the end should the 1.000 mark be placed?

**APPROACH** The hydrometer will float in water if its density $\rho$ is less than $\rho_w = 1.000\text{ g/cm}^3$, the density of water. The fraction of the hydrometer submerged $(V_{displaced}/V_{total})$ is equal to the density ratio $\rho/\rho_w$.

**SOLUTION** The hydrometer has an overall density

$$\rho = \frac{m}{V} = \frac{45.0\text{ g}}{(2.00\text{ cm}^2)(25.0\text{ cm})} = 0.900\text{ g/cm}^3.$$

Thus, when placed in water, it will come to equilibrium when 0.900 of its volume is submerged. Since it is of uniform cross section, $(0.900)(25.0\text{ cm}) = 22.5\text{ cm}$ of its length will be submerged. The specific gravity of water is defined to be 1.000, so the mark should be placed 22.5 cm from the end.

**FIGURE 10–17** A hydrometer. Example 10–9.

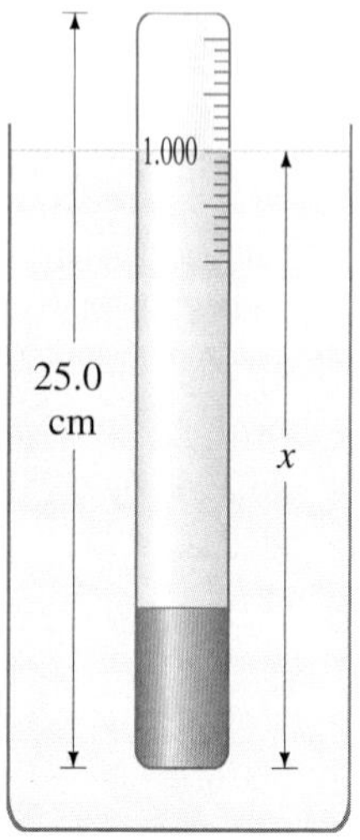

**EXERCISE B** On the hydrometer of Example 10–9, will the marks above the 1.000 mark represent higher or lower values of density of the liquid in which it is submerged?

PHYSICS APPLIED

*Continental drift—plate tectonics*

Archimedes principle is also useful in geology. According to the theories of plate tectonics and continental drift, the continents float on a fluid "sea" of slightly deformable rock (mantle rock). Some interesting calculations can be done using very simple models, which we consider in the Problems at the end of the Chapter.

*Weight affected by buoyancy of air*

Air is a fluid, and it too exerts a buoyant force. Ordinary objects weigh less in air than they do if weighed in a vacuum. Because the density of air is so small, the effect for ordinary solids is slight. There are objects, however, that *float* in air—helium-filled balloons, for example, because the density of helium is less than the density of air.

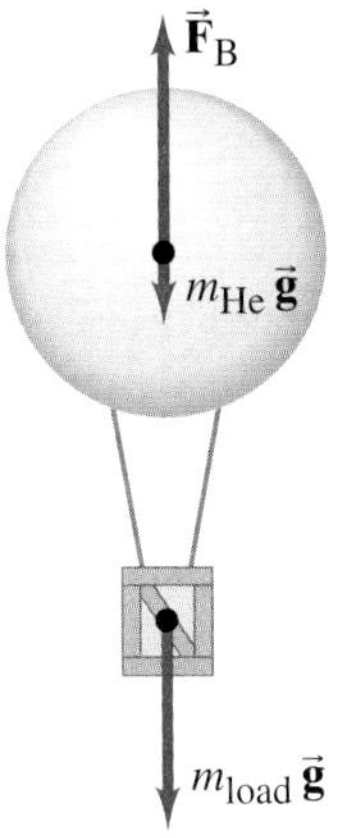


**FIGURE 10–18** Example 10–10.

**EXAMPLE 10–10** **Helium balloon.** What volume $V$ of helium is needed if a balloon is to lift a load of 180 kg (including the weight of the empty balloon)?

**APPROACH** The buoyant force on the helium balloon, $F_B$, which is equal to the weight of displaced air, must be at least equal to the weight of the helium plus the weight of the balloon and load (Fig. 10–18). Table 10–1 gives the density of helium as $0.179\ \mathrm{kg/m^3}$.

**SOLUTION** The buoyant force must have a minimum value of

$$F_B = (m_{He} + 180\ \mathrm{kg})g.$$

This equation can be written in terms of density using Archimedes' principle:

$$\rho_{air} V g = (\rho_{He} V + 180\ \mathrm{kg})g.$$

Solving now for $V$, we find

$$V = \frac{180\ \mathrm{kg}}{\rho_{air} - \rho_{He}} = \frac{180\ \mathrm{kg}}{(1.29\ \mathrm{kg/m^3} - 0.179\ \mathrm{kg/m^3})} = 160\ \mathrm{m^3}.$$

**NOTE** This is the minimum volume needed near the Earth's surface, where $\rho_{air} = 1.29\ \mathrm{kg/m^3}$. To reach a high altitude, a greater volume would be needed since the density of air decreases with altitude.

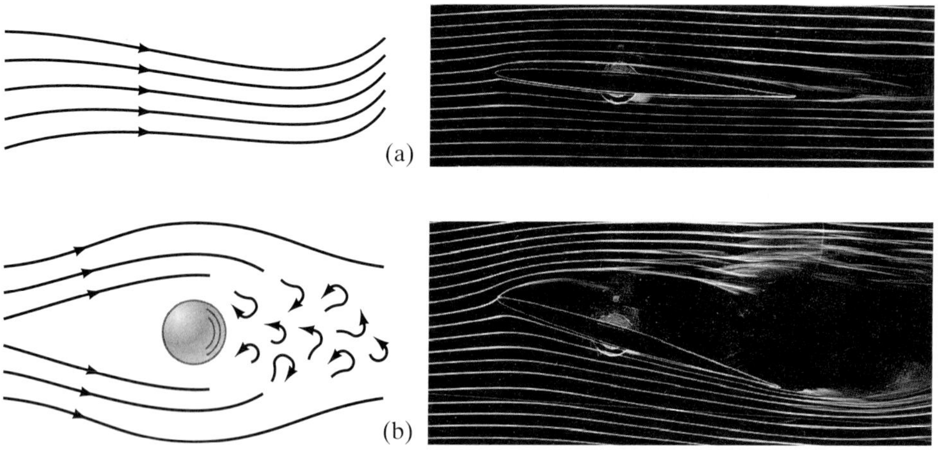


**FIGURE 10–19**
(a) Streamline, or laminar, flow;
(b) turbulent flow.

## 10–8 Fluids in Motion; Flow Rate and the Equation of Continuity

We now turn to the subject of fluids in motion, which is called **fluid dynamics**, or (especially if the fluid is water) **hydrodynamics**. Many aspects of fluid motion are still being studied (for example, turbulence as a manifestation of chaos is a "hot" topic today). Nonetheless, with certain simplifying assumptions, we can understand a lot about this subject.

We can distinguish two main types of fluid flow. If the flow is smooth, such that neighboring layers of the fluid slide by each other smoothly, the flow is said to be **streamline** or **laminar flow**.† In streamline flow, each particle of the fluid follows a smooth path, called a **streamline**, and these paths do not cross one another (Fig. 10–19a). Above a certain speed, the flow becomes turbulent. **Turbulent flow** is characterized by erratic, small, whirlpool-like circles called *eddy currents* or *eddies* (Fig. 10–19b). Eddies absorb a great deal of energy, and although a certain amount of internal friction called **viscosity** is present even during streamline flow, it is much greater when the flow is turbulent. A few tiny drops of ink or food coloring dropped into a moving liquid can quickly reveal whether the flow is streamline or turbulent.

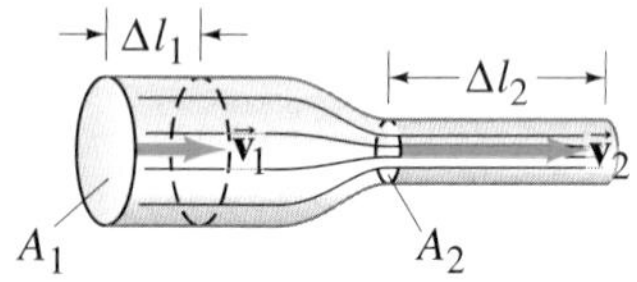


**FIGURE 10–20** Fluid flow through a pipe of varying diameter.

Let us consider the steady laminar flow of a fluid through an enclosed tube or pipe as shown in Fig. 10–20. First we determine how the speed of the fluid changes when the size of the tube changes. The mass **flow rate** is defined as the mass $\Delta m$ of fluid that passes a given point per unit time $\Delta t$:

$$\text{mass flow rate} = \frac{\Delta m}{\Delta t}.$$

In Fig. 10–20, the volume of fluid passing point 1 (that is, through area $A_1$) in a time $\Delta t$ is $A_1 \Delta l_1$, where $\Delta l_1$ is the distance the fluid moves in time $\Delta t$. Since the velocity‡ of fluid passing point 1 is $v_1 = \Delta l_1/\Delta t$, the mass flow rate $\Delta m_1/\Delta t$ through area $A_1$ is

$$\frac{\Delta m_1}{\Delta t} = \frac{\rho_1 \Delta V_1}{\Delta t} = \frac{\rho_1 A_1 \Delta l_1}{\Delta t} = \rho_1 A_1 v_1,$$

where $\Delta V_1 = A_1 \Delta l_1$ is the volume of mass $\Delta m_1$, and $\rho_1$ is the fluid density. Similarly, at point 2 (through area $A_2$), the flow rate is $\rho_2 A_2 v_2$. Since no fluid flows in or out the sides, the flow rates through $A_1$ and $A_2$ must be equal. Thus, since

$$\frac{\Delta m_1}{\Delta t} = \frac{\Delta m_2}{\Delta t},$$

then

*Equation of continuity (general)*

$$\rho_1 A_1 v_1 = \rho_2 A_2 v_2. \qquad \textbf{(10–4a)}$$

This is called the **equation of continuity**.

†The word laminar means "in layers."

‡If there were no viscosity, the velocity would be the same across a cross section of the tube. Real fluids have viscosity, and this internal friction causes different layers of the fluid to flow at different speeds. In this case $v_1$ and $v_2$ represent the average speeds at each cross section.

If the fluid is incompressible ($\rho$ doesn't change with pressure), which is an excellent approximation for liquids under most circumstances (and sometimes for gases as well), then $\rho_1 = \rho_2$, and the equation of continuity becomes

*Equation of continuity ($\rho$ = constant)*

$$A_1 v_1 = A_2 v_2. \qquad [\rho = \text{constant}] \quad \textbf{(10–4b)}$$

The product $Av$ represents the *volume rate of flow* (volume of fluid passing a given point per second), since $\Delta V/\Delta t = A\,\Delta l/\Delta t = Av$, which in SI units is $m^3/s$. Equation 10–4b tells us that where the cross-sectional area is large, the velocity is small, and where the area is small, the velocity is large. That this is reasonable can be seen by looking at a river. A river flows slowly through a meadow where it is broad, but speeds up to torrential speed when passing through a narrow gorge.

**EXAMPLE 10–11 ESTIMATE Blood flow.** In humans, blood flows from the heart into the aorta, from which it passes into the major arteries. These branch into the small arteries (arterioles), which in turn branch into myriads of tiny capillaries, Fig. 10–21. The blood returns to the heart via the veins. The radius of the aorta is about 1.2 cm, and the blood passing through it has a speed of about 40 cm/s. A typical capillary has a radius of about $4 \times 10^{-4}$ cm, and blood flows through it at a speed of about $5 \times 10^{-4}$ m/s. Estimate the number of capillaries that are in the body.

PHYSICS APPLIED
*Blood flow*

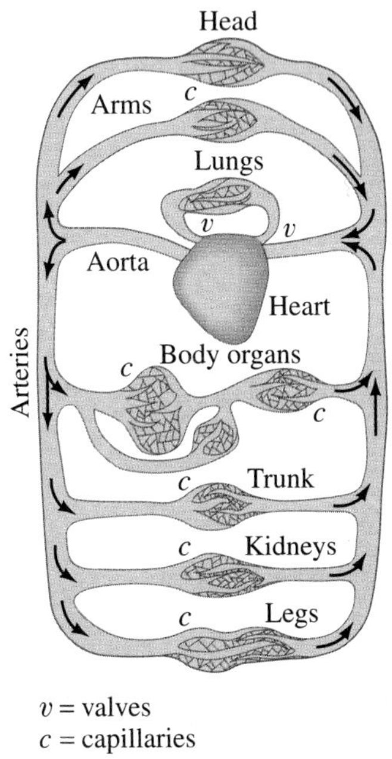


**FIGURE 10–21** Human circulatory system.

**APPROACH** We assume the density of blood doesn't vary significantly from the aorta to the capillaries. By the equation of continuity, the volume flow rate in the aorta must equal the volume flow rate through *all* the capillaries. The total area of all the capillaries is given by the area of one capillary multiplied by the total number $N$ of capillaries.

**SOLUTION** Let $A_1$ be the area of the aorta and $A_2$ be the area of *all* the capillaries through which blood flows. Then $A_2 = N\pi r_{cap}^2$, where $r_{cap} \approx 4 \times 10^{-4}$ cm is the estimated average radius of one capillary. From the equation of continuity (Eq. 10–4), we have

$$v_2 A_2 = v_1 A_1$$
$$v_2 N\pi r_{cap}^2 = v_1 \pi r_{aorta}^2$$

so

$$N = \frac{v_1}{v_2}\frac{r_{aorta}^2}{r_{cap}^2} = \left(\frac{0.40\text{ m/s}}{5 \times 10^{-4}\text{ m/s}}\right)\left(\frac{1.2 \times 10^{-2}\text{ m}}{4 \times 10^{-6}\text{ m}}\right)^2 \approx 7 \times 10^9,$$

or on the order of 10 billion capillaries.

**EXAMPLE 10–12 Heating duct to a room.** What area must a heating duct have if air moving 3.0 m/s along it can replenish the air every 15 minutes in a room of volume 300 $m^3$? Assume the air's density remains constant.

PHYSICS APPLIED
*Heating duct*

**APPROACH** We apply the equation of continuity at constant density, Eq. 10–4, to the air that flows through the duct (point 1 in Fig. 10–22) and then into the room (point 2). The volume flow rate in the room equals the volume of the room divided by the 15-minute replenishing time.

**FIGURE 10–22** Example 10–12.

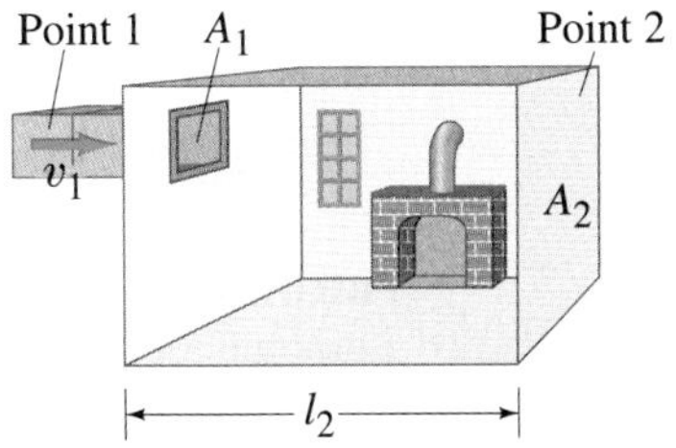


**SOLUTION** Consider the room as a large section of the duct, Fig. 10–22, and think of air equal to the volume of the room as passing by point 2 in $t$ = 15 minutes = 900 s. Reasoning in the same way we did to obtain Eq. 10–4a (changing $\Delta t$ to $t$), we write $v_2 = l_2/t$ so $A_2 v_2 = A_2 l_2/t = V_2/t$, where $V_2$ is the volume of the room. Then the equation of continuity becomes $A_1 v_1 = A_2 v_2 = V_2/t$ and

$$A_1 = \frac{V_2}{v_1 t} = \frac{300\text{ m}^3}{(3.0\text{ m/s})(900\text{ s})} = 0.11\text{ m}^2.$$

If the duct is square, then each side has length $l = \sqrt{A} = 0.33$ m, or 33 cm. A rectangular duct 20 cm × 55 cm will also do.

## 10–9 Bernoulli's Equation

Have you ever wondered why an airplane can fly, or how a sailboat can move against the wind? These are examples of a principle worked out by Daniel Bernoulli (1700–1782) concerning fluids in motion. In essence, **Bernoulli's principle** states that *where the velocity of a fluid is high, the pressure is low, and where the velocity is low, the pressure is high.* For example, if the pressures at points 1 and 2 in Fig. 10–20 are measured, it will be found that the pressure is lower at point 2, where the velocity is greater, than it is at point 1, where the velocity is smaller. At first glance, this might seem strange; you might expect that the greater speed at point 2 would imply a higher pressure. But this cannot be the case. For if the pressure at point 2 were higher than at 1, this higher pressure would slow the fluid down, whereas in fact it has sped up in going from point 1 to point 2. Thus the pressure at point 2 must be less than at point 1, to be consistent with the fact that the fluid accelerates. [To help clarify any misconceptions, a faster fluid *would* exert a greater force on an obstacle placed in its path if the fluid were stopped or bounced off the obstacle. But that is not what we mean by the pressure in a fluid, and besides we are not considering obstacles that interrupt the flow. We are examining smooth streamline flow. The fluid pressure is exerted in all directions, including on the walls of a pipe or surface of any material the fluid passes over.]

*Bernoulli's principle*

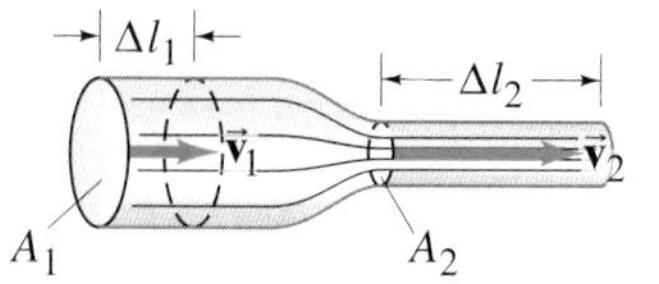


**FIGURE 10–20** (repeated) Fluid flow through a pipe of varying diameter.

Bernoulli developed an equation that expresses this principle quantitatively. To derive Bernoulli's equation, we assume the flow is steady and laminar, the fluid is incompressible, and the viscosity is small enough to be ignored. To be general, we assume the fluid is flowing in a tube of nonuniform cross section that varies in height above some reference level, Fig. 10–23. We will consider the volume of fluid shown in color and calculate the work done to move it from the position shown in Fig. 10–23a to that shown in Fig. 10–23b. In this process, fluid at point 1 flows a distance $\Delta l_1$ and forces the fluid at point 2 to move a distance $\Delta l_2$. The fluid to the left of point 1 exerts a pressure $P_1$ on our section of fluid and does an amount of work

$$W_1 = F_1 \Delta l_1 = P_1 A_1 \Delta l_1 .$$

At point 2, the work done on our cross section of fluid is

$$W_2 = -P_2 A_2 \Delta l_2 .$$

The negative sign is present because the force exerted on the fluid is opposite to the motion (thus the fluid shown in color does work on the fluid to the right of point 2). Work is also done on the fluid by the force of gravity. The net effect of the process shown in Fig. 10–23 is to move a mass $m$ of volume $A_1 \Delta l_1$ ($= A_2 \Delta l_2$, since the fluid is incompressible) from point 1 to point 2, so the work done by gravity is

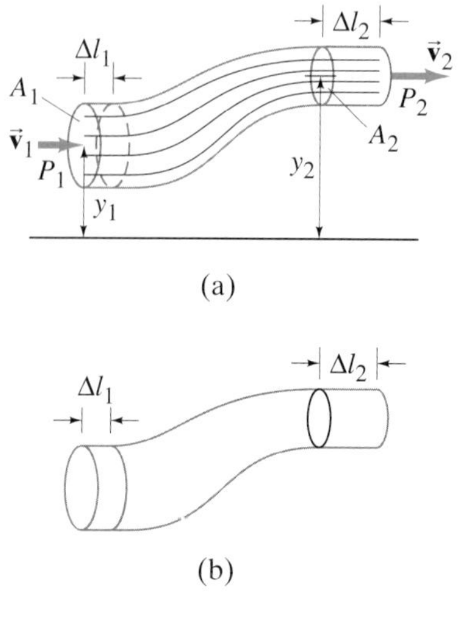


**FIGURE 10–23** Fluid flow: for derivation of Bernoulli's equation.

$$W_3 = -mg(y_2 - y_1),$$

where $y_1$ and $y_2$ are heights of the center of the tube above some (arbitrary) reference level. In the case shown in Fig. 10–23, this term is negative since the motion is uphill against the force of gravity. The net work $W$ done on the fluid is thus

$$W = W_1 + W_2 + W_3$$
$$W = P_1 A_1 \Delta l_1 - P_2 A_2 \Delta l_2 - mgy_2 + mgy_1.$$

According to the work-energy principle (Section 6–3), the net work done on a system is equal to its change in kinetic energy. Hence

$$\tfrac{1}{2}mv_2^2 - \tfrac{1}{2}mv_1^2 = P_1 A_1 \Delta l_1 - P_2 A_2 \Delta l_2 - mgy_2 + mgy_1.$$

The mass $m$ has volume $A_1 \Delta l_1 = A_2 \Delta l_2$. Thus we can substitute $m = \rho A_1 \Delta l_1 = \rho A_2 \Delta l_2$, and then divide through by $A_1 \Delta l_1 = A_2 \Delta l_2$, to obtain

$$\tfrac{1}{2}\rho v_2^2 - \tfrac{1}{2}\rho v_1^2 = P_1 - P_2 - \rho g y_2 + \rho g y_1,$$

which we rearrange to get

$$P_1 + \tfrac{1}{2}\rho v_1^2 + \rho g y_1 = P_2 + \tfrac{1}{2}\rho v_2^2 + \rho g y_2. \qquad \textbf{(10–5)}$$

*Bernoulli's equation*

This is **Bernoulli's equation**. Since points 1 and 2 can be any two points along a tube of flow, Bernoulli's equation can be written as

$$P + \tfrac{1}{2}\rho v^2 + \rho g y = \text{constant}$$

at every point in the fluid, where $y$ is the height of the center of the tube above a fixed reference level. [Note that if there is no flow $(v_1 = v_2 = 0)$, then Eq. 10–5 reduces to the hydrostatic equation, Eq. 10–3b or c.]

Bernoulli's equation is an expression of the law of energy conservation, since we derived it from the work-energy principle.

**EXERCISE C** As water in a level pipe passes from a narrow cross section of pipe to a wider cross section, how does the pressure change?

**EXAMPLE 10–13** **Flow and pressure in a hot-water heating system.** Water circulates throughout a house in a hot-water heating system. If the water is pumped at a speed of 0.50 m/s through a 4.0-cm-diameter pipe in the basement under a pressure of 3.0 atm, what will be the flow speed and pressure in a 2.6-cm-diameter pipe on the second floor 5.0 m above? Assume the pipes do not divide into branches.

PHYSICS APPLIED
*Hot-water heating system*

**APPROACH** We use the equation of continuity at constant density to determine the flow speed on the second floor, and then Bernoulli's equation to find the pressure.

**SOLUTION** We take $v_2$ in the equation of continuity, Eq. 10–4, as the flow speed on the second floor, and $v_1$ as the flow speed in the basement. Noting that the areas are proportional to the radii squared $(A = \pi r^2)$, we obtain

$$v_2 = \frac{v_1 A_1}{A_2} = \frac{v_1 \pi r_1^2}{\pi r_2^2} = (0.50\,\text{m/s})\frac{(0.020\,\text{m})^2}{(0.013\,\text{m})^2} = 1.2\,\text{m/s}.$$

To find the pressure on the second floor, we use Bernoulli's equation:

$$\begin{aligned} P_2 &= P_1 + \rho g(y_1 - y_2) + \tfrac{1}{2}\rho(v_1^2 - v_2^2) \\ &= (3.0 \times 10^5\,\text{N/m}^2) + (1.0 \times 10^3\,\text{kg/m}^3)(9.8\,\text{m/s}^2)(-5.0\,\text{m}) \\ &\quad + \tfrac{1}{2}(1.0 \times 10^3\,\text{kg/m}^3)[(0.50\,\text{m/s})^2 - (1.2\,\text{m/s})^2] \\ &= (3.0 \times 10^5\,\text{N/m}^2) - (4.9 \times 10^4\,\text{N/m}^2) - (6.0 \times 10^2\,\text{N/m}^2) \\ &= 2.5 \times 10^5\,\text{N/m}^2 = 2.5\,\text{atm}. \end{aligned}$$

**NOTE** The velocity term contributes very little in this case.

## 10–10 Applications of Bernoulli's Principle: from Torricelli to Airplanes, Baseballs, and TIA

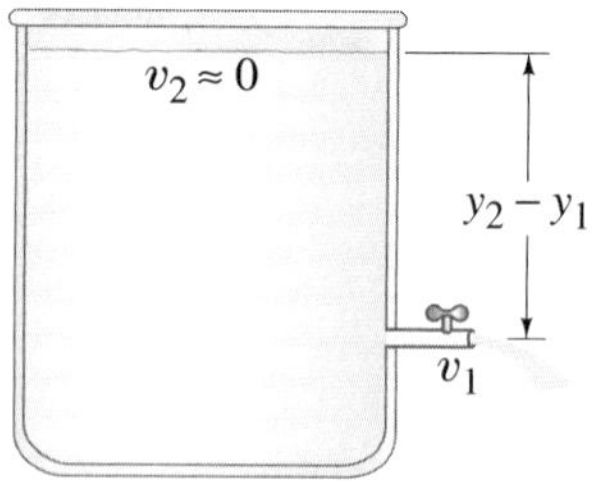


**FIGURE 10–24** Torricelli's theorem: $v_1 = \sqrt{2g(y_2 - y_1)}$.

Bernoulli's equation can be applied to many situations. One example is to calculate the velocity, $v_1$, of a liquid flowing out of a spigot at the bottom of a reservoir, Fig. 10–24. We choose point 2 in Eq. 10–5 to be the top surface of the liquid. Assuming the diameter of the reservoir is large compared to that of the spigot, $v_2$ will be almost zero. Points 1 (the spigot) and 2 (top surface) are open to the atmosphere, so the pressure at both points is equal to atmospheric pressure: $P_1 = P_2$. Then Bernoulli's equation becomes

$$\tfrac{1}{2}\rho v_1^2 + \rho g y_1 = \rho g y_2$$

or

*Torricelli's theorem*

$$v_1 = \sqrt{2g(y_2 - y_1)}. \qquad \textbf{(10–6)}$$

This result is called **Torricelli's theorem**. Although it is seen to be a special case of Bernoulli's equation, it was discovered a century earlier by Evangelista Torricelli. Equation 10–6 tells us that the liquid leaves the spigot with the same speed that a freely falling object would attain if falling from the same height. This should not be too surprising since the derivation of Bernoulli's equation relies on the conservation of energy.

Another special case of Bernoulli's equation arises when a fluid is flowing horizontally with no appreciable change in height; that is, $y_1 = y_2$. Then Eq. 10–5 becomes

$$P_1 + \tfrac{1}{2}\rho v_1^2 = P_2 + \tfrac{1}{2}\rho v_2^2, \qquad \textbf{(10–7)}$$

which tells us quantitatively that the speed is high where the pressure is low, and vice versa. It explains many common phenomena, some of which are illustrated in Figs. 10–25 to 10–31. The pressure in the air blown at high speed across the top of the vertical tube of a perfume atomizer (Fig. 10–25a) is less than the normal air pressure acting on the surface of the liquid in the bowl. Thus atmospheric pressure in the bowl pushes the perfume up the tube because of the lower pressure at the top. A Ping-Pong ball can be made to float above a blowing jet of air (some vacuum cleaners can blow air), Fig. 10–25b; if the ball begins to leave the jet of air, the higher pressure in the still air outside the jet pushes the ball back in.

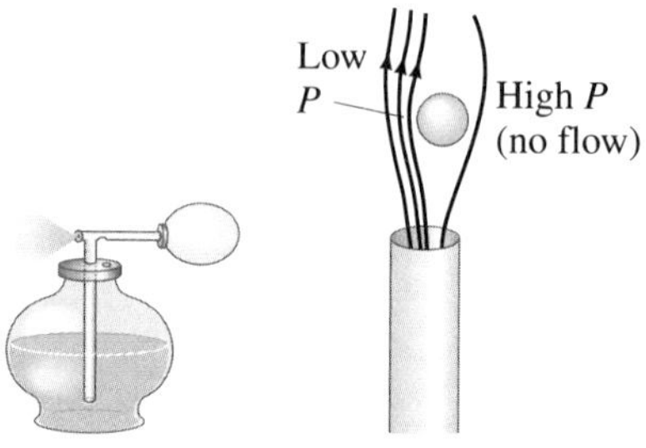


**FIGURE 10–25** Examples of Bernoulli's principle: (a) atomizer, (b) Ping-Pong ball in jet of air.

### Airplane Wings and Dynamic Lift

**FIGURE 10–26** Lift on an airplane wing. We are in the reference frame of the wing, seeing the air flow by.

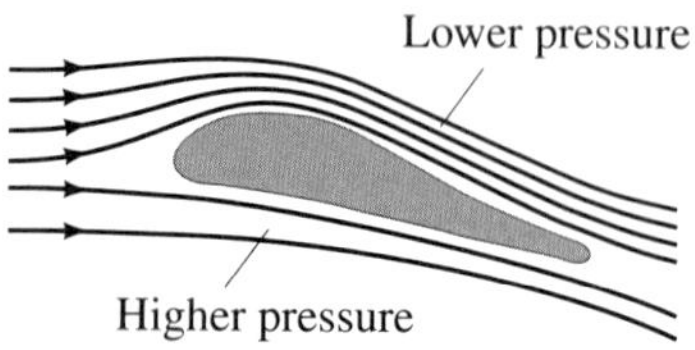


PHYSICS APPLIED

*Airplanes and dynamic lift*

Airplanes experience a "lift" force on their wings, keeping them up in the air, if they are moving at a sufficiently high speed relative to the air and the wing is tilted upward at a small angle (the "attack angle"), as in Fig. 10–26, where streamlines of air are shown rushing by the wing. (We are in the reference frame of the wing, as if sitting on the wing.) The upward tilt, as well as the rounded upper surface of the wing, causes the streamlines to be forced upward and to be crowded together above the wing. The area for air flow between any two streamlines is reduced as the streamlines get closer together, so from the equation of continuity $(A_1 v_1 = A_2 v_2)$, the air speed increases above the wing where the streamlines are squished together. (Recall also how the crowded streamlines in a pipe constriction, Fig. 10–20, indicate the velocity is higher in the constriction.) Because the air speed is greater above the wing than below it, the pressure above the wing is less than the pressure below the wing (Bernoulli's principle). Hence there is a net upward force on the wing called **dynamic lift**. Experiments show that the speed of air above the wing can even be double the speed of the air below it. (Friction between the air and wing exerts a *drag force*, toward the rear, which must be overcome by the plane's engines.)

A flat wing, or one with symmetric cross section, will experience lift as long as the front of the wing is tilted upward (attack angle). The wing shown in Fig. 10–26 can experience lift even if the attack angle is zero, because the rounded upper surface deflects air up, squeezing the streamlines together. Airplanes can fly upside down, experiencing lift, if the attack angle is sufficient to deflect streamlines up and closer together.

Our picture considers streamlines; but if the attack angle is larger than about 15°, turbulence sets in (Fig. 10–19b) leading to greater drag and less lift, causing the wing to "stall" and the plane to drop.

From another point of view, the upward tilt of a wing means the air moving horizontally in front of the wing is deflected downward; the change in momentum of the rebounding air molecules results in an upward force on the wing (Newtons' third law).

## Sailboats

A sailboat can move *against* the wind, with the aid of the Bernoulli effect, by setting the sails at an angle, as shown in Fig. 10–27. The air travels rapidly over the bulging front surface of the sail, and the relatively still air behind the sail exerts a greater pressure, resulting in a net force on the sail, $\vec{\mathbf{F}}_{\text{wind}}$. This force would tend to make the boat move sideways if it weren't for the keel that extends vertically downward beneath the water: the water exerts a force $(\vec{\mathbf{F}}_{\text{water}})$ on the keel nearly perpendicular to the keel. The resultant of these two forces $(\vec{\mathbf{F}}_{\text{R}})$ is almost directly forward as shown.

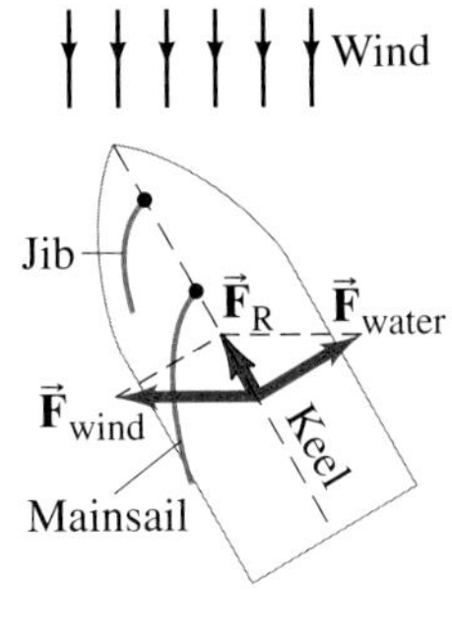


**FIGURE 10–27** Sailboat sailing against the wind.

## Baseball Curve

Why a spinning pitched baseball (or tennis ball) curves can also be explained using Bernoulli's principle. It is simplest if we put ourselves in the reference frame of the ball, with the air rushing by, just as we did for the airplane wing. Suppose the ball is rotating counterclockwise as seen from above, Fig. 10–28. A thin layer of air ("boundary layer") is being dragged around by the ball. We are looking down on the ball, and at point A in Fig. 10–28, this boundary layer tends to slow down the oncoming air. At point B, the air rotating with the ball adds its speed to that of the oncoming air, so the air speed is higher at B than at A. The higher speed at B means the pressure is lower at B than at A, resulting in a net force toward B. The ball's path curves toward the left (as seen by the pitcher).

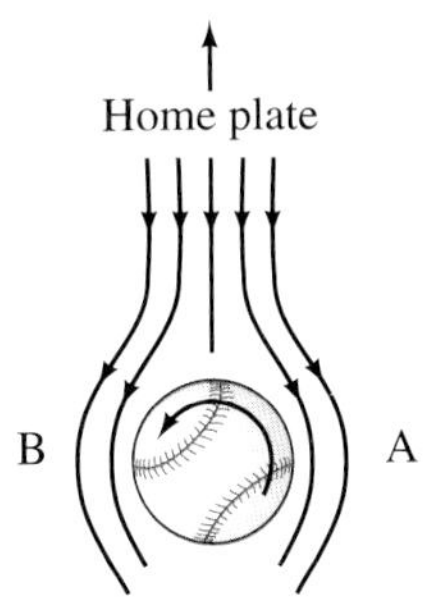


**FIGURE 10–28** Looking down on a pitched baseball heading toward home plate. We are in the reference frame of the baseball, with the air flowing by.

## Lack of Blood to the Brain—TIA

In medicine, one of many applications of Bernoulli's principle is to explain a TIA, a transient ischemic attack (meaning a temporary lack of blood supply to the brain). A person suffering a TIA may experience symptoms such as dizziness, double vision, headache, and weakness of the limbs. A TIA can occur as follows. Blood normally flows up to the brain at the back of the head via the two vertebral arteries—one going up each side of the neck—which meet to form the basilar artery just below the brain, as shown in Fig. 10–29. The vertebral arteries issue from the subclavian arteries, as shown, before the latter pass to the arms. When an arm is exercised vigorously, blood flow increases to meet the needs of the arm's muscles. If the subclavian artery on one side of the body is partially blocked, however, as in arteriosclerosis (hardening of the arteries), the blood velocity will have to be higher on that side to supply the needed blood. (Recall the equation of continuity: smaller area means larger velocity for the same flow rate, Eq. 10–4.) The increased blood velocity past the opening to the vertebral artery results in lower pressure (Bernoulli's principle). Thus, blood rising in the vertebral artery on the "good" side at normal pressure can be *diverted down* into the other vertebral artery because of the low pressure on that side, instead of passing upward to the brain. Hence the blood supply to the brain is reduced.

**FIGURE 10–29** Rear of the head and shoulders showing arteries leading to the brain and to the arms. High blood velocity past the constriction in the left subclavian artery causes low pressure in the left vertebral artery, in which a reverse (downward) blood flow can then occur, resulting in a TIA.

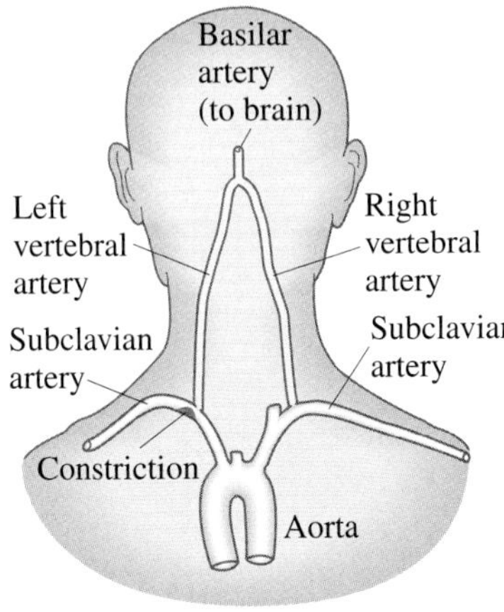

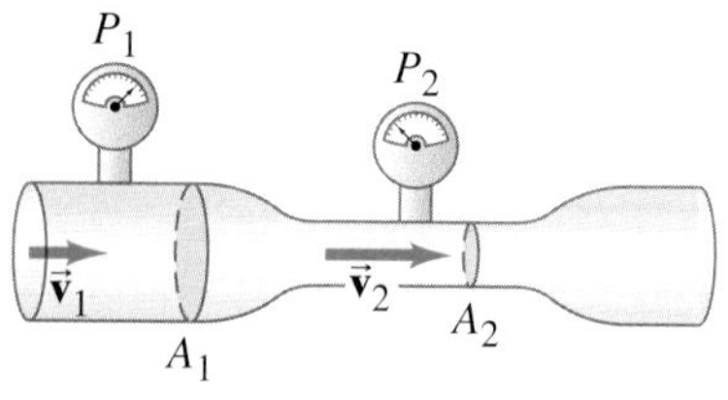


**FIGURE 10–30** Venturi meter.

## Other Applications

A **venturi tube** is essentially a pipe with a narrow constriction (the throat). The flowing air speeds up as it passes through this constriction, so the pressure is lower in the throat. A *venturi meter*, Fig. 10–30, is used to measure the flow speed of gases and liquids, including blood velocity in arteries.

PHYSICS APPLIED
*Smoke up a chimney*

Why does smoke go up a chimney? It's partly because hot air rises (it's less dense and therefore buoyant). But Bernoulli's principle also plays a role. When wind blows across the top of a chimney, the pressure is less there than inside the house. Hence, air and smoke are pushed up the chimney by the higher indoor pressure. Even on an apparently still night there is usually enough ambient air flow at the top of a chimney to assist upward flow of smoke.

PHYSICS APPLIED
*Underground air circulation for burrowing animals*

If gophers, prairie dogs, rabbits, and other animals that live underground are to avoid suffocation, the air must circulate in their burrows. The burrows always have at least two entrances (Fig. 10–31). The speed of air flow across different holes will usually be slightly different. This results in a slight pressure difference, which forces a flow of air through the burrow a la Bernoulli's principle. The flow of air is enhanced if one hole is higher than the other (animals often build mounds) since wind speed tends to increase with height.

**FIGURE 10–31** Bernoulli's principle explains air flow in underground burrows.

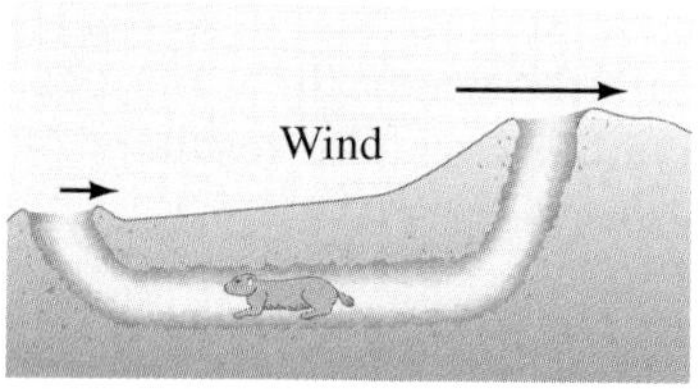


*Limitations on Bernoulli's equation*

Bernoulli's equation ignores the effects of friction (viscosity) and the compressibility of the fluid. The energy that is transformed to internal (or potential) energy due to compression and to thermal energy by friction can be taken into account by adding terms to Eq. 10–5. These terms are difficult to calculate theoretically and are normally determined empirically. They do not significantly alter the explanations for the phenomena described above.

## * 10–11 Viscosity

Real fluids have a certain amount of internal friction called **viscosity**, as mentioned in Section 10–8. Viscosity exists in both liquids and gases, and is essentially a frictional force between adjacent layers of fluid as the layers move past one another. In liquids, viscosity is due to the electrical cohesive forces between the molecules. In gases, it arises from collisions between the molecules.

The viscosity of different fluids can be expressed quantitatively by a *coefficient of viscosity*, $\eta$ (the Greek lowercase letter eta), which is defined in the following way. A thin layer of fluid is placed between two flat plates. One plate is stationary and the other is made to move, Fig. 10–32. The fluid directly in contact with each plate is held to the surface by the adhesive force between the molecules of the liquid and those of the plate. Thus the upper surface of the fluid moves with the same speed $v$ as the upper plate, whereas the fluid in contact with the stationary plate remains stationary. The stationary layer of fluid retards the flow of the layer just above it, which in turn retards the flow of the next layer, and so on. Thus the velocity varies continuously from 0 to $v$, as shown. The increase in velocity divided by the distance over which this change is made—equal to $v/l$—is called the *velocity gradient*. To move the upper plate requires a force, which you can verify by moving a flat plate across a puddle of syrup on a table. For a given fluid, it is found that the force required, $F$, is proportional to the area of fluid in contact with each plate, $A$, and to the speed, $v$, and is inversely proportional to the separation, $l$, of the plates: $F \propto vA/l$. For different fluids, the more viscous the fluid, the greater is the required force.

**FIGURE 10–32** Determination of viscosity.

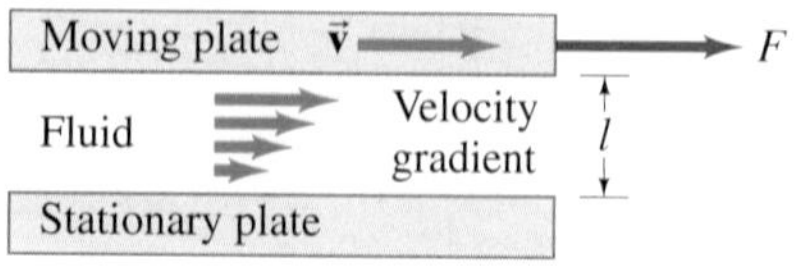

Hence the proportionality constant for this equation is defined as the coefficient of viscosity, $\eta$:

$$F = \eta A \frac{v}{l}. \tag{10-8}$$

Solving for $\eta$, we find $\eta = Fl/vA$. The SI unit for $\eta$ is $\text{N}\cdot\text{s/m}^2 = \text{Pa}\cdot\text{s}$ (pascal·second). In the cgs system, the unit is $\text{dyne}\cdot\text{s/cm}^2$, which is called a *poise* (P). Viscosities are often given in centipoise ($1\text{ cP} = 10^{-2}\text{ P}$). Table 10–3 lists the coefficient of viscosity for various fluids. The temperature is also specified, since it has a strong effect; the viscosity of liquids such as motor oil, for example, decreases rapidly as temperature increases.‡

**TABLE 10–3 Coefficients of Viscosity**

| Fluid (temperature in C°) | Coefficient of Viscosity, $\eta$ (Pa · s)† |
|---|---|
| Water (0°) | $1.8 \times 10^{-3}$ |
| (20°) | $1.0 \times 10^{-3}$ |
| (100°) | $0.3 \times 10^{-3}$ |
| Whole blood (37°) | $\approx 4 \times 10^{-3}$ |
| Blood plasma (37°) | $\approx 1.5 \times 10^{-3}$ |
| Ethyl alcohol (20°) | $1.2 \times 10^{-3}$ |
| Engine oil (30°) (SAE 10) | $200 \times 10^{-3}$ |
| Glycerine (20°) | $1500 \times 10^{-3}$ |
| Air (20°) | $0.018 \times 10^{-3}$ |
| Hydrogen (0°) | $0.009 \times 10^{-3}$ |
| Water vapor (100°) | $0.013 \times 10^{-3}$ |

† $1\text{ Pa}\cdot\text{s} = 10\text{ P} = 1000\text{ cP}$.

## * 10–12 Flow in Tubes: Poiseuille's Equation, Blood Flow

If a fluid had no viscosity, it could flow through a level tube or pipe without a force being applied. Viscosity acts like a sort of friction, so a pressure difference between the ends of a level tube is necessary for the steady flow of any real fluid, be it water or oil in a pipe, or blood in the circulatory system of a human.

The rate of flow of a fluid in a round tube depends on the viscosity of the fluid, the pressure difference, and the dimensions of the tube. The French scientist J. L. Poiseuille (1799–1869), who was interested in the physics of blood circulation (and after whom the "poise" is named), determined how the variables affect the flow rate of an incompressible fluid undergoing laminar flow in a cylindrical tube. His result, known as *Poiseuille's equation*, is:

*Poiseuille's equation for flow rate in a tube*

$$Q = \frac{\pi R^4 (P_1 - P_2)}{8\eta L}, \tag{10-9}$$

where $R$ is the inside radius of the tube, $L$ is its length, $P_1 - P_2$ is the pressure difference between the ends, $\eta$ is the coefficient of viscosity, and $Q$ is the volume rate of flow (volume of fluid flowing past a given point per unit time which in SI has units of $\text{m}^3/\text{s}$). Equation 10–9 applies only to laminar flow.

Poiseuille's equation tells us that the flow rate $Q$ is directly proportional to the "pressure gradient," $(P_1 - P_2)/L$, and it is inversely proportional to the viscosity of the fluid. This is just what we might expect. It may be surprising, however, that $Q$ also depends on the *fourth* power of the tube's radius. This means that for the same pressure gradient, if the tube radius is halved, the flow rate is decreased by a factor of 16! Thus the rate of flow, or alternately the pressure required to maintain a given flow rate, is greatly affected by only a small change in tube radius.

**PHYSICS APPLIED**
*Medicine—blood flow and heart disease*

An interesting example of this $R^4$ dependence is *blood flow* in the human body. Poiseuille's equation is valid only for the streamline flow of an incompressible fluid with constant viscosity $\eta$. So it cannot be precisely accurate for blood whose flow is not without turbulence and that contains blood cells (whose diameter is almost equal to that of a capillary). Hence $\eta$ depends to a certain extent on the blood flow speed $v$. Nonetheless, Poiseuille's equation does give a reasonable first approximation. The body controls the flow of blood by means of tiny bands of muscle surrounding the arteries. Contraction of these muscles reduces the diameter of an artery and, because of the $R^4$ term in Eq. 10–9, the flow rate is greatly reduced for only a small change in radius. Very small actions by these muscles can thus control precisely the flow of blood to

‡The Society of Automotive Engineers assigns numbers to represent the viscosity of oils: 30 weight (SAE 30) is more viscous than 10 weight. Multigrade oils, such as 20–50, are designed to maintain viscosity as temperature increases; 20–50 means the oil is 20 wt when cool but is like a 50-wt pure oil when it is hot (engine running temperature).

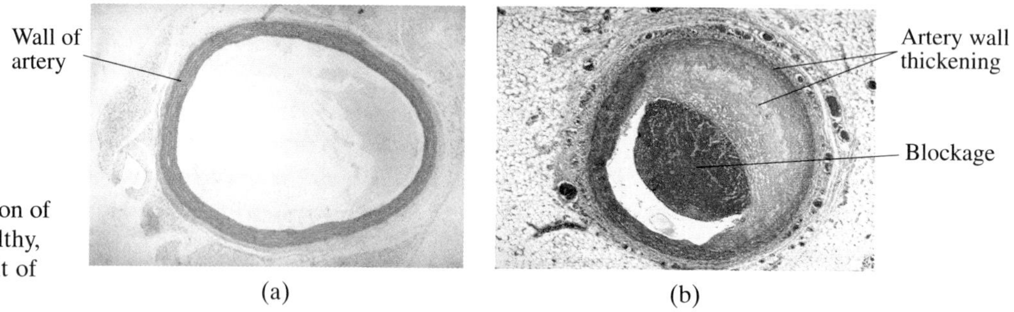


**FIGURE 10–33** A cross section of a human artery that (a) is healthy, (b) is partly blocked as a result of arteriosclerosis.

different parts of the body. Another aspect is that the radius of arteries is reduced as a result of arteriosclerosis (thickening and hardening of artery walls, Fig. 10–33) and by cholesterol buildup. When this happens, the pressure gradient must be increased to maintain the same flow rate. If the radius is reduced by half, the heart would have to increase the pressure by a factor of about $2^4 = 16$ in order to maintain the same blood-flow rate. The heart must work much harder under these conditions, but usually cannot maintain the original flow rate. Thus, high blood pressure is an indication both that the heart is working harder and that the blood-flow rate is reduced.

## * 10–13 Surface Tension and Capillarity

**FIGURE 10–34** Spherical water droplets, dew on a blade of grass.

The *surface* of a liquid at rest behaves in an interesting way, almost as if it were a stretched membrane under tension. For example, a drop of water on the end of a dripping faucet, or hanging from a thin branch in the early morning dew (Fig. 10–34), forms into a nearly spherical shape as if it were a tiny balloon filled with water. A steel needle can be made to float on the surface of water even though it is denser than the water. The surface of a liquid acts like it is under tension, and this tension, acting along the surface, arises from the attractive forces between the molecules. This effect is called **surface tension**. More specifically, a quantity called the *surface tension*, $\gamma$ (the Greek letter gamma), is defined as the force $F$ per unit length $L$ that acts perpendicular to any line or cut in a liquid surface, tending to pull the surface closed:

*Surface tension*

$$\gamma = \frac{F}{L}. \tag{10–10}$$

**FIGURE 10–35** U-shaped wire apparatus holding a film of liquid to measure surface tension ($\gamma = F/2L$).

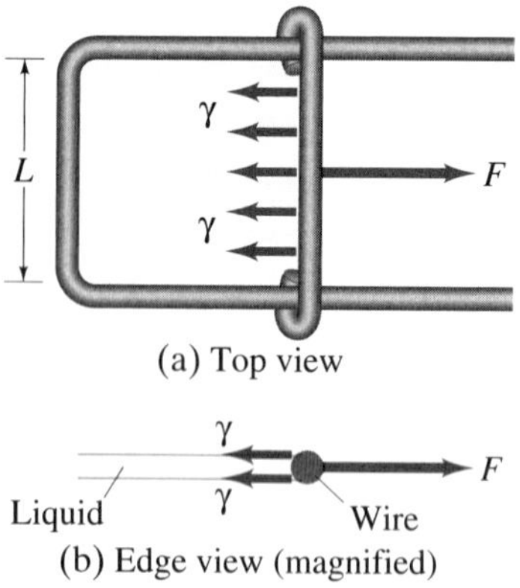


To understand this, consider the U-shaped apparatus shown in Fig. 10–35 which encloses a thin film of liquid. Because of surface tension, a force $F$ is required to pull the movable wire and thus increase the surface area of the liquid. The liquid contained by the wire apparatus is a thin film having both a top and a bottom surface. Hence the length of the surface being increased is $2L$, and the surface tension is $\gamma = F/2L$. A delicate apparatus of this type can be used to measure the surface tension of various liquids. The surface tension of water is 0.072 N/m at 20°C. Table 10–4 gives the values for several substances. Note that temperature has a considerable effect on the surface tension.

Because of surface tension, some insects (Fig. 10–36) can walk on water, and objects more dense than water, such as a steel needle, can float on the

**FIGURE 10–36** A water strider.

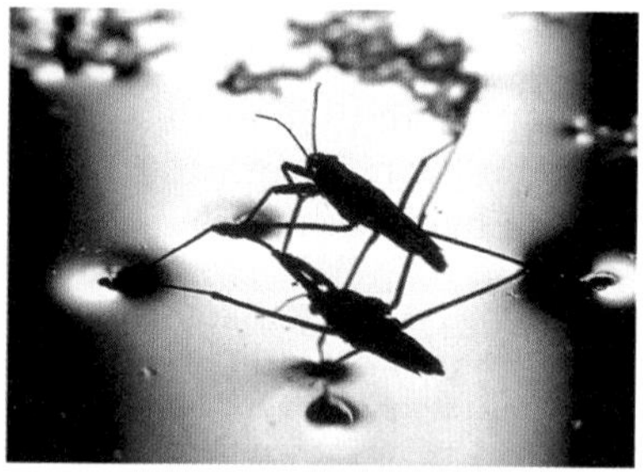

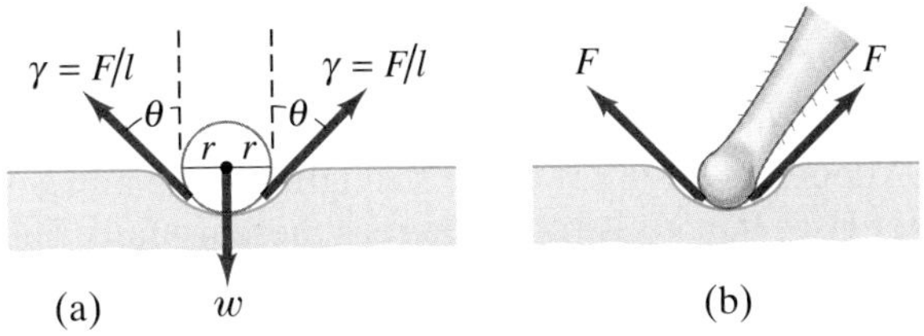


**FIGURE 10–37** Surface tension acting on (a) a sphere, and (b) an insect leg. Example 10–14.

**TABLE 10–4 Surface Tension of Some Substances**

| Substance | Surface Tension (N/m) |
| --- | --- |
| Mercury (20°C) | 0.44 |
| Blood, whole (37°C) | 0.058 |
| Blood, plasma (37°C) | 0.073 |
| Alcohol, ethyl (20°C) | 0.023 |
| Water (0°C) | 0.076 |
| (20°C) | 0.072 |
| (100°C) | 0.059 |
| Benzene (20°C) | 0.029 |
| Soap solution (20°C) | ≈0.025 |
| Oxygen (−193°C) | 0.016 |

surface. Figure 10–37a shows how the surface tension can support the weight $w$ of an object. Actually, the object sinks slightly into the fluid, so $w$ is the "effective weight" of that object—its true weight less the buoyant force.

**EXAMPLE 10–14 ESTIMATE Insect walks on water.** The base of an insect's leg is approximately spherical in shape, with a radius of about $2.0 \times 10^{-5}$ m. The 0.0030-g mass of the insect is supported equally by its six legs. Estimate the angle $\theta$ (see Fig. 10–37) for an insect on the surface of water. Assume the water temperature is 20°C.

**APPROACH** Since the insect is in equilibrium, the upward surface tension force is equal to the effective pull of gravity downward on each leg.

**SOLUTION** For each leg, we assume the surface tension force acts all around a circle of radius $r$, at an angle $\theta$, as shown in Fig. 10–37. Only the vertical component, $\gamma \cos\theta$, acts to balance the weight $mg$. So we set the length $L$ in Eq. 10–10 equal to the circumference of the circle, $L \approx 2\pi r$. Then the net upward force due to surface tension is $F_y \approx (\gamma\cos\theta)L \approx 2\pi r\gamma\cos\theta$. We set this surface tension force equal to one-sixth the weight of the insect since it has six legs:

$$2\pi r\gamma\cos\theta \approx \tfrac{1}{6}mg$$

$$(6.28)(2.0 \times 10^{-5}\,\text{m})(0.072\,\text{N/m})\cos\theta \approx \tfrac{1}{6}(3.0 \times 10^{-6}\,\text{kg})(9.8\,\text{m/s}^2)$$

$$\cos\theta \approx \frac{0.49}{0.90} = 0.54.$$

So $\theta \approx 57°$. If $\cos\theta$ had come out greater than 1, the surface tension would not be great enough to support the insect's weight.

**NOTE** Our estimate ignored the buoyant force and ignored any difference between the radius of the insect's "foot" and the radius of the surface depression.

PHYSICS APPLIED

*Soaps and detergents*

Soaps and detergents lower the surface tension of water. This is desirable for washing and cleaning since the high surface tension of pure water prevents it from penetrating easily between the fibers of material and into tiny crevices. Substances that reduce the surface tension of a liquid are called *surfactants*.

*Capillarity*

Surface tension plays a role in another interesting phenomenon, capillarity. It is a common observation that water in a glass container rises up slightly where it touches the glass, Fig. 10–38a. The water is said to "wet" the glass. Mercury, on the other hand, is depressed when it touches the glass, Fig. 10–38b; the mercury does not wet the glass. Whether a liquid wets a solid surface is determined by the relative strength of the cohesive forces between the molecules of the liquid compared to the adhesive forces between the molecules of the liquid and those of the container. *Cohesion* refers to the force between molecules of the same type, whereas *adhesion* refers to the force between molecules of different types. Water wets glass because the water molecules are more strongly attracted to the glass molecules than they are to other water molecules. The opposite is true for mercury: the cohesive forces are stronger than the adhesive forces.

**FIGURE 10–38** Water (a) "wets" the surface of glass, whereas (b) mercury does not "wet" the glass.

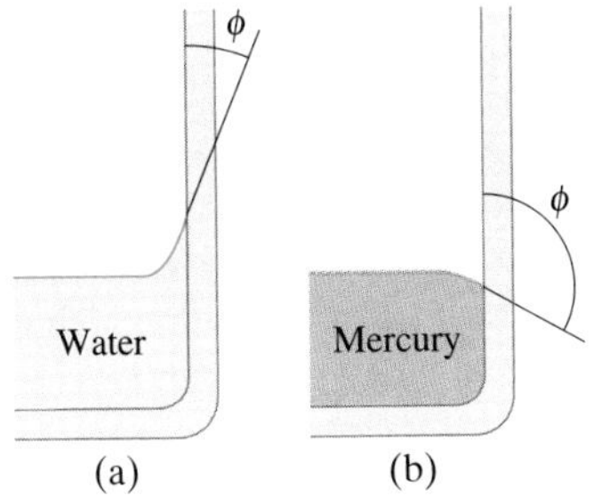

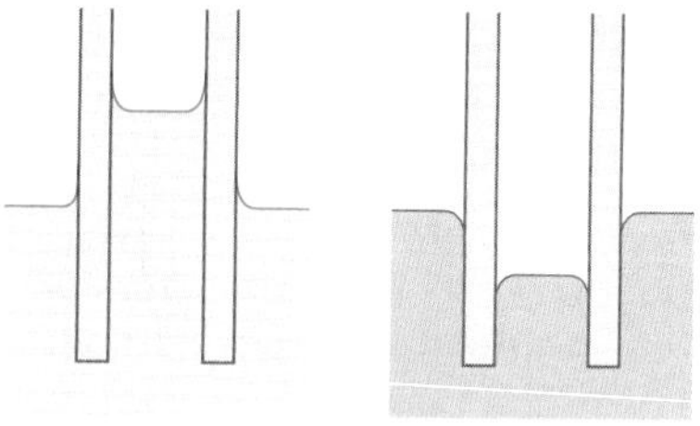


**FIGURE 10–39** Capillarity.

In tubes having very small diameters, liquids are observed to rise or fall relative to the level of the surrounding liquid. This phenomenon is called **capillarity**, and such thin tubes are called **capillaries**. Whether the liquid rises or falls (Fig. 10–39) depends on the relative strengths of the adhesive and cohesive forces. Thus water rises in a glass tube, whereas mercury falls. The actual amount of rise (or fall) depends on the surface tension—which is what keeps the liquid surface from breaking apart.

## * 10–14 Pumps, and the Heart

We conclude this Chapter with a brief discussion of pumps of various types, including the heart. Pumps can be classified into categories according to their function. A *vacuum pump* is designed to reduce the pressure (usually of air) in a given vessel. A *force pump*, on the other hand, is a pump that is intended to increase the pressure—for example, to lift a liquid (such as water from a well) or to push a fluid through a pipe. Figure 10–40 illustrates the principle behind a simple reciprocating pump. It could be a vacuum pump, in which case the intake is connected to the vessel to be evacuated. A similar mechanism is used in some force pumps, and in this case the fluid is forced under increased pressure through the outlet.

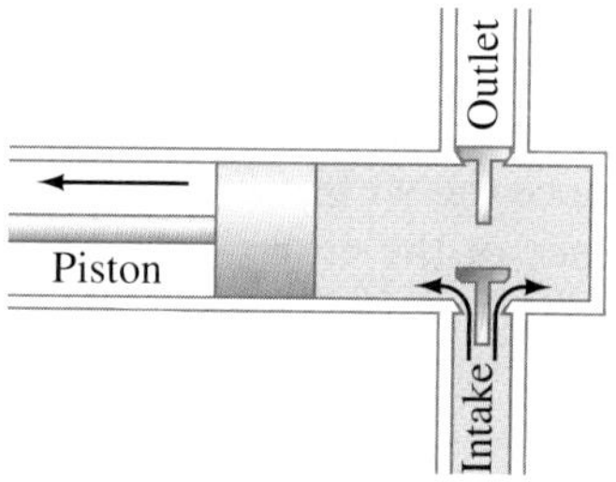


**FIGURE 10–40** One kind of pump: the intake valve opens and air (or fluid that is being pumped) fills the empty space when the piston moves to the left. When the piston moves to the right (not shown), the outlet valve opens and fluid is forced out.

Other kinds of pumps are illustrated in Fig. 10–41. The centrifugal pump, or any force pump, can be used as a *circulating pump*—that is, to circulate a fluid around a closed path, such as the cooling water or lubricating oil in an automobile.

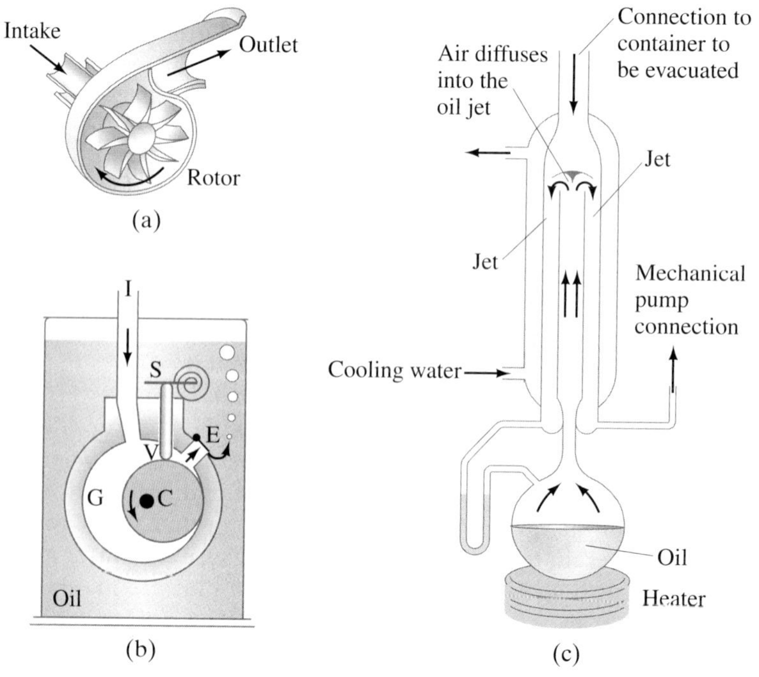


**FIGURE 10–41** (a) Centrifugal pump: the rotating blades force fluid through the outlet pipe; this kind of pump is used in vacuum cleaners and as a water pump in automobiles. (b) Rotary oil-seal pump, used to obtain vacuums as low as $10^{-4}$ mm-Hg: gas (usually air) from the vessel to be evacuated diffuses into the space G via the intake pipe I; the rotating off-center cylinder C traps the gas in G and carries it around to push it out the exhaust valve E, in the meantime allowing more gas to diffuse into G for the next cycle. The sliding valve V is kept in contact with C by a spring S, and this prevents the exhaust gas from returning to G. (c) Diffusion pump, used to obtain vacuums as low as $10^{-8}$ mm-Hg: air molecules from the vessel to be evacuated diffuse into the jet, where a rapidly moving jet of oil sweeps the molecules away. A "forepump" is needed, which is a mechanical pump, such as the rotary type (b), and acts as a first stage in reducing the pressure.

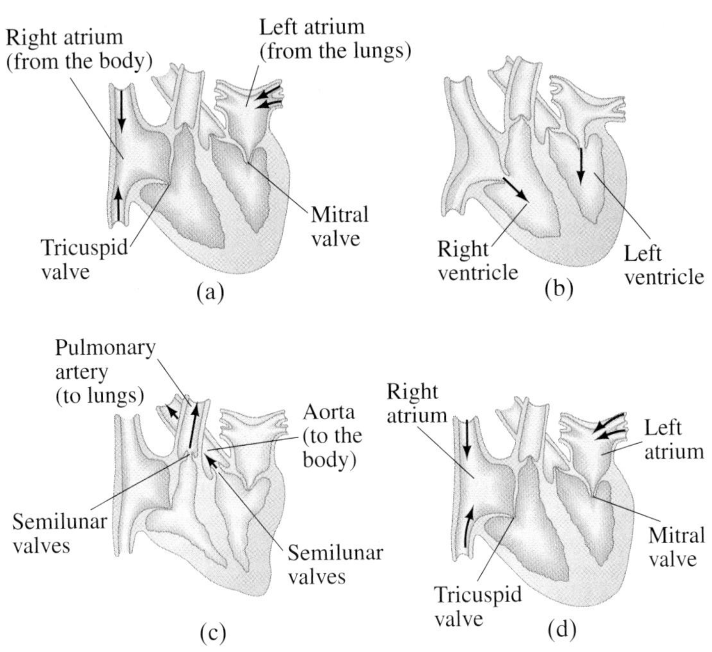


**FIGURE 10–42** (a) In the diastole phase, the heart relaxes between beats. Blood moves into the heart; both atria fill rapidly. (b) When the atria contract, the systole or pumping phase begins. The contraction pushes the blood through the mitral and tricuspid valves into the ventricles. (c) The contraction of the ventricles forces the blood through the semilunar valves into the pulmonary artery, which leads to the lungs, and to the aorta (the body's largest artery), which leads to the arteries serving all the body. (d) When the heart relaxes, the semilunar valves close; blood fills the atria, beginning the cycle again.

PHYSICS APPLIED
*Heart as a pump*

The heart of a human (and of other animals as well) is essentially a circulating pump. The action of a human heart is shown in Fig. 10–42. There are actually two separate paths for blood flow. The longer path takes blood to the parts of the body, via the arteries, bringing oxygen to body tissues and picking up carbon dioxide, which it carries back to the heart via veins. This blood is then pumped to the lungs (the second path), where the carbon dioxide is released and oxygen is taken up. The oxygen-laden blood is returned to the heart, where it is again pumped to the tissues of the body.

PHYSICS APPLIED
*Blood pressure*

Blood pressure is measured using either a mercury-filled manometer or one of the other types of gauge mentioned earlier (Section 10–6), and it is usually calibrated in mm-Hg. The gauge is attached to a closed, air-filled jacket that is wrapped around the upper arm at the level of the heart, Fig. 10–43. Two values of blood pressure are measured: the maximum pressure when the heart is pumping, called *systolic pressure*; and the pressure when the heart is in the resting part of the cycle, called *diastolic pressure*. Initially, the air pressure in the jacket is increased high above the systolic pressure by means of a hand pump, and this compresses the main (brachial) artery in the arm and briefly cuts off the flow of blood. The air pressure is then reduced slowly until blood again begins to flow into the arm; it is detected by listening with a stethoscope to the characteristic tapping sound† of the blood returning to the forearm. At this point, systolic pressure is just equal to the air pressure in the jacket which can be read off the gauge. The air pressure is subsequently reduced further, and the tapping sound disappears when blood at low pressure can enter the artery. At this point, the gauge indicates the diastolic pressure. Normal systolic pressure is around 120 mm-Hg, whereas normal diastolic pressure is around 80 mm-Hg.

**FIGURE 10–43** Device for measuring blood pressure.

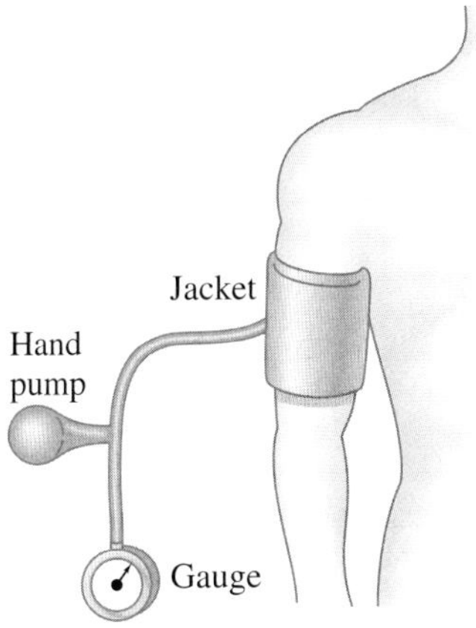


†When the blood starts flowing through the constriction caused by the tight jacket, its velocity is high and the flow is turbulent. It is the turbulence that causes the tapping sound.

## Summary

The three common phases of matter are **solid**, **liquid**, and **gas**. Liquids and gases are collectively called **fluids**, meaning they have the ability to flow. The **density** of a material is defined as its mass per unit volume:

$$\rho = \frac{m}{V}. \qquad \textbf{(10–1)}$$

**Specific gravity** is the ratio of the density of the material to the density of water (at 4°C).

**Pressure** is defined as force per unit area:

$$P = \frac{F}{A}. \qquad \textbf{(10–2)}$$

The pressure at a depth $h$ in a liquid of constant density $\rho$ is given by

$$P = \rho g h, \qquad \textbf{(10–3a)}$$

where $g$ is the acceleration due to gravity.

**Pascal's principle** says that an external pressure applied to a confined fluid is transmitted throughout the fluid.

Pressure is measured using a manometer or other type of gauge. A **barometer** is used to measure atmospheric pressure. Standard **atmospheric pressure** (average at sea level) is $1.013 \times 10^5\,\mathrm{N/m^2}$. **Gauge pressure** is the total (absolute) pressure less atmospheric pressure.

**Archimedes' principle** states that an object submerged wholly or partially in a fluid is buoyed up by a force equal to the weight of fluid it displaces $(F_B = m_F g = \rho_F V_{\text{displ}}\, g)$.

Fluid flow can be characterized either as **streamline** (sometimes called **laminar**), in which the layers of fluid move smoothly and regularly along paths called **streamlines**, or as **turbulent**, in which case the flow is not smooth and regular but is characterized by irregularly shaped whirlpools.

Fluid flow rate is the mass or volume of fluid that passes a given point per unit time. The **equation of continuity** states that for an incompressible fluid flowing in an enclosed tube, the product of the velocity of flow and the cross-sectional area of the tube remains constant:

$$Av = \text{constant}. \qquad \textbf{(10–4)}$$

**Bernoulli's principle** tells us that where the velocity of a fluid is high, the pressure in it is low, and where the velocity is low, the pressure is high. For steady laminar flow of an incompressible and nonviscous fluid, **Bernoulli's equation**, which is based on the law of conservation of energy, is

$$P_1 + \tfrac{1}{2}\rho v_1^2 + \rho g y_1 = P_2 + \tfrac{1}{2}\rho v_2^2 + \rho g y_2, \qquad \textbf{(10–5)}$$

for two points along the flow.

[***Viscosity** refers to friction within a fluid and is essentially a frictional force between adjacent layers of fluid as they move past one another.]

[*Liquid surfaces hold together as if under tension (**surface tension**), allowing drops to form and objects like needles and insects to stay on the surface.]

## Questions

1. If one material has a higher density than another, must the molecules of the first be heavier than those of the second? Explain.
2. Airplane travelers sometimes note that their cosmetics bottles and other containers have leaked during a flight. What might cause this?
3. The three containers in Fig. 10–44 are filled with water to the same height and have the same surface area at the base; hence the water pressure, and the total force on the base of each, is the same. Yet the total weight of water is different for each. Explain this "hydrostatic paradox."

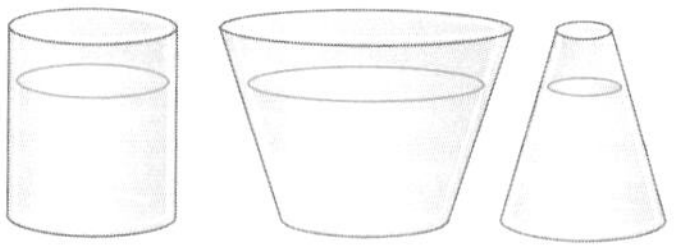

**FIGURE 10–44** Question 3.

4. Consider what happens when you push both a pin and the blunt end of a pen against your skin with the same force. Decide what determines whether your skin is cut—the net force applied to it or the pressure.
5. A small amount of water is boiled in a 1-gallon metal can. The can is removed from the heat and the lid put on. Shortly thereafter the can collapses. Explain.
6. When blood pressure is measured, why must the jacket be held at the level of the heart?
7. An ice cube floats in a glass of water filled to the brim. What can you say about the density of ice? As the ice melts, will the water overflow? Explain.
8. Will an ice cube float in a glass of alcohol? Why or why not?
9. A submerged can of Coke® will sink, but a can of Diet Coke® will float. (Try it!) Explain.
10. Why don't ships made of iron sink?
11. Explain how the tube in Fig. 10–45, known as a **siphon**, can transfer liquid from one container to a lower one even though the liquid must flow uphill for part of its journey. (Note that the tube must be filled with liquid to start with.)

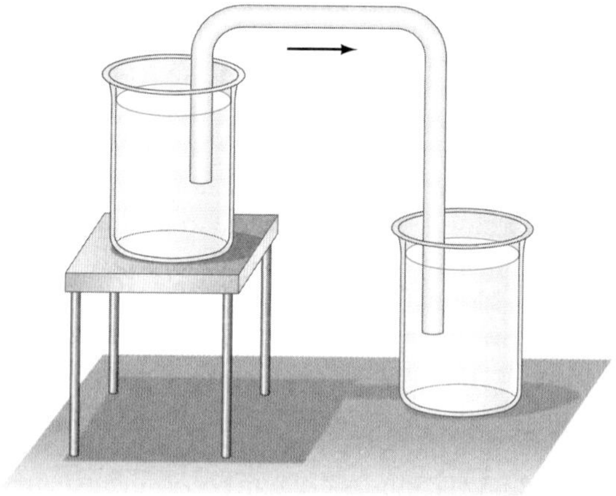

**FIGURE 10–45** Question 11. A siphon.

12. A barge filled high with sand approaches a low bridge over the river and cannot quite pass under it. Should sand be added to, or removed from, the barge? [*Hint*: Consider Archimedes' principle.]
13. Will an empty balloon have precisely the same apparent weight on a scale as a balloon filled with air? Explain.
14. Explain why helium weather balloons, which are used to measure atmospheric conditions at high altitudes, are normally released while filled to only 10%–20% of their maximum volume.

15. A small wooden boat floats in a swimming pool, and the level of the water at the edge of the pool is marked. Consider the following situations and explain whether the level of the water will rise, fall, or stay the same. (*a*) The boat is removed from the water. (*b*) The boat in the water holds an iron anchor which is removed from the boat and placed on the shore. (*c*) The iron anchor is removed from the boat and dropped in the pool.

16. Why do you float higher in salt water than in fresh?

17. If you dangle two pieces of paper vertically, a few inches apart (Fig. 10–46), and blow between them, how do you think the papers will move? Try it and see. Explain.

**FIGURE 10–46** Question 17.

18. Why does the canvas top of a convertible bulge out when the car is traveling at high speed? [*Hint*: the windshield deflects air upward, pushing streamlines closer together.]

19. Roofs of houses are sometimes "blown" off (or are they pushed off?) during a tornado or hurricane. Explain, using Bernoulli's principle.

20. Children are told to avoid standing too close to a rapidly moving train because they might get sucked under it. Is this possible? Explain.

21. A tall Styrofoam cup is filled with water. Two holes are punched in the cup near the bottom, and water begins rushing out. If the cup is dropped so it falls freely, will the water continue to flow from the holes? Explain.

22. Why do airplanes normally take off into the wind?

23. Why does the stream of water from a faucet become narrower as it falls (Fig. 10–47)?

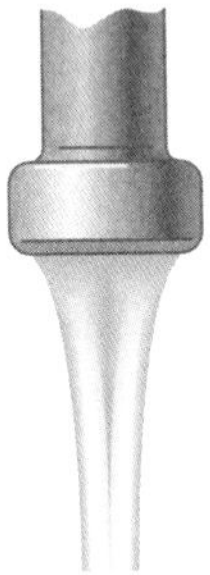

**FIGURE 10–47** Question 23 and Problem 82. Water coming from a faucet.

24. Two ships moving in parallel paths close to one another risk colliding. Why?

## Problems

### 10–2 Density and Specific Gravity

1. (I) The approximate volume of the granite monolith known as El Capitan in Yosemite National Park (Fig. 10–48) is about $10^8\,m^3$. What is its approximate mass?

**FIGURE 10–48** Problem 1.

2. (I) What is the approximate mass of air in a living room $4.8\,m \times 3.8\,m \times 2.8\,m$?

3. (I) If you tried to smuggle gold bricks by filling your backpack, whose dimensions are $60\,cm \times 28\,cm \times 18\,cm$, what would its mass be?

4. (I) State your mass and then estimate your volume. [*Hint*: Because you can swim on or just under the surface of the water in a swimming pool, you have a pretty good idea of your density.]

5. (II) A bottle has a mass of 35.00 g when empty and 98.44 g when filled with water. When filled with another fluid, the mass is 88.78 g. What is the specific gravity of this other fluid?

6. (II) If 5.0 L of antifreeze solution (specific gravity = 0.80) is added to 4.0 L of water to make a 9.0-L mixture, what is the specific gravity of the mixture?

### 10–3 to 10–6 Pressure; Pascal's Principle

7. (I) Estimate the pressure exerted on a floor by (*a*) one pointed chair leg (60 kg on all four legs) of area = $0.020\,cm^2$, and (*b*) a 1500-kg elephant standing on one foot (area = $800\,cm^2$).

8. (I) What is the difference in blood pressure (mm-Hg) between the top of the head and bottom of the feet of a 1.60-m-tall person standing vertically?

9. (I) (*a*) Calculate the total force of the atmosphere acting on the top of a table that measures $1.6\,m \times 2.9\,m$. (*b*) What is the total force acting upward on the underside of the table?

10. (II) In a movie, Tarzan evades his captors by hiding underwater for many minutes while breathing through a long, thin reed. Assuming the maximum pressure difference his lungs can manage and still breathe is −85 mm-Hg, calculate the deepest he could have been.

11. (II) The gauge pressure in each of the four tires of an automobile is 240 kPa. If each tire has a "footprint" of $220\,cm^2$, estimate the mass of the car.

12. (II) The maximum gauge pressure in a hydraulic lift is 17.0 atm. What is the largest size vehicle (kg) it can lift if the diameter of the output line is 28.0 cm?

13. (II) How high would the level be in an alcohol barometer at normal atmospheric pressure?

14. (II) (*a*) What are the total force and the absolute pressure on the bottom of a swimming pool 22.0 m by 8.5 m whose uniform depth is 2.0 m? (*b*) What will be the pressure against the *side* of the pool near the bottom?

15. (II) How high would the atmosphere extend if it were of uniform density throughout, equal to half the present density at sea level?

16. (II) Water and then oil (which don't mix) are poured into a U-shaped tube, open at both ends. They come to equilibrium as shown in Fig. 10–49. What is the density of the oil? [*Hint*: Pressures at points a and b are equal. Why?]

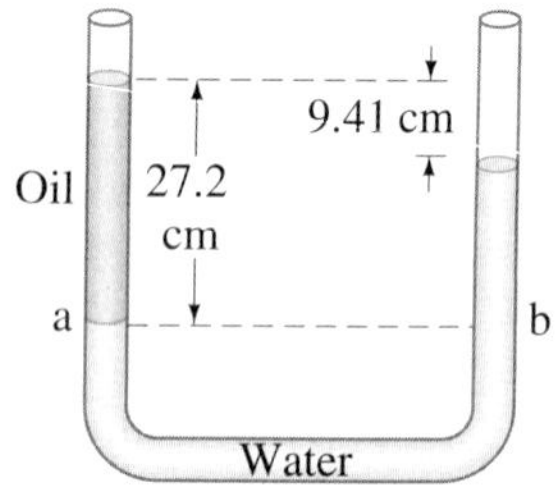


**FIGURE 10–49** Problem 16.

17. (II) A house at the bottom of a hill is fed by a full tank of water 5.0 m deep and connected to the house by a pipe that is 110 m long at an angle of 58° from the horizontal (Fig. 10–50). (*a*) Determine the water gauge pressure at the house. (*b*) How high could the water shoot if it came vertically out of a broken pipe in front of the house?

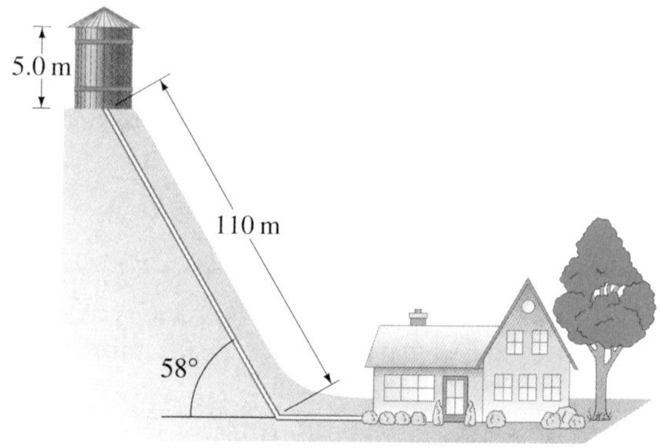


**FIGURE 10–50** Problem 17.

18. (II) Determine the minimum gauge pressure needed in the water pipe leading into a building if water is to come out of a faucet on the twelfth floor, 38 m above that pipe.

19. (II) An open-tube mercury manometer is used to measure the pressure in an oxygen tank. When the atmospheric pressure is 1040 mbar, what is the absolute pressure (in Pa) in the tank if the height of the mercury in the open tube is (*a*) 28.0 cm higher, (*b*) 4.2 cm lower, than the mercury in the tube connected to the tank?

20. (II) In working out his principle, Pascal showed dramatically how force can be multiplied with fluid pressure. He placed a long, thin tube of radius $r = 0.30$ cm vertically into a wine barrel of radius $R = 21$ cm, Fig. 10–51. He found that when the barrel was filled with water and the tube filled to a height of 12 m, the barrel burst. Calculate (*a*) the mass of water in the tube, and (*b*) the net force exerted by the water in the barrel on the lid just before rupture.

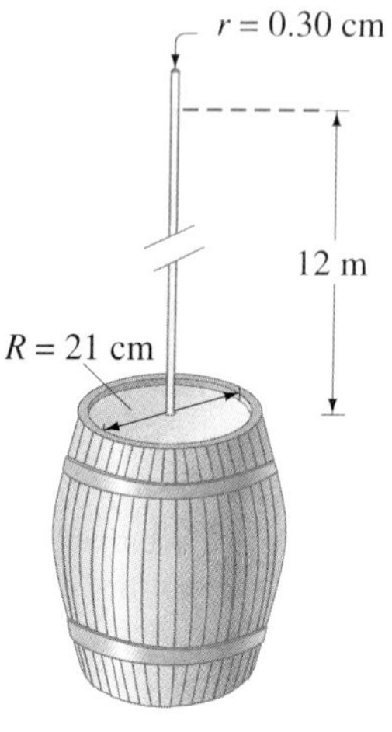


**FIGURE 10–51** Problem 20 (not to scale).

* 21. (III) Estimate the density of the water 6.0 km deep in the sea. (See Table 9–1 and Section 9–5 regarding bulk modulus.) By what fraction does it differ from the density at the surface?

## 10–7 Buoyancy and Archimedes' Principle

22. (I) A geologist finds that a Moon rock whose mass is 9.28 kg has an apparent mass of 6.18 kg when submerged in water. What is the density of the rock?

23. (I) What fraction of a piece of aluminum will be submerged when it floats in mercury?

24. (II) A crane lifts the 18,000-kg steel hull of a ship out of the water. Determine (*a*) the tension in the crane's cable when the hull is submerged in the water, and (*b*) the tension when the hull is completely out of the water.

25. (II) A spherical balloon has a radius of 7.35 m and is filled with helium. How large a cargo can it lift, assuming that the skin and structure of the balloon have a mass of 930 kg? Neglect the buoyant force on the cargo volume itself.

26. (II) A 78-kg person has an apparent mass of 54 kg (because of buoyancy) when standing in water that comes up to the hips. Estimate the mass of each leg. Assume the body has SG = 1.00.

27. (II) What is the likely identity of a metal (see Table 10–1) if a sample has a mass of 63.5 g when measured in air and an apparent mass of 55.4 g when submerged in water?

28. (II) Calculate the true mass (in vacuum) of a piece of aluminum whose apparent mass is 2.0000 kg when weighed in air.

29. (II) An undersea research chamber is spherical with an external diameter of 5.20 m. The mass of the chamber, when occupied, is 74,400 kg. It is anchored to the sea bottom by a cable. What is (*a*) the buoyant force on the chamber, and (*b*) the tension in the cable?

30. (II) A scuba diver and her gear displace a volume of 65.0 L and have a total mass of 68.0 kg. (*a*) What is the buoyant force on the diver in sea water? (*b*) Will the diver sink or float?

31. (II) Archimedes' principle can be used not only to determine the specific gravity of a solid using a known liquid (Example 10–8); the reverse can be done as well. (*a*) As an example, a 3.40-kg aluminum ball has an apparent mass of 2.10 kg when submerged in a particular liquid: calculate the density of the liquid. (*b*) Derive a formula for determining the density of a liquid using this procedure.

32. (II) A 0.48-kg piece of wood floats in water but is found to sink in alcohol (SG = 0.79), in which it has an apparent mass of 0.047 kg. What is the SG of the wood?

33. (II) The specific gravity of ice is 0.917, whereas that of seawater is 1.025. What fraction of an iceberg is above the surface of the water?

34. (III) A 5.25-kg piece of wood (SG = 0.50) floats on water. What minimum mass of lead, hung from the wood by a string, will cause it to sink?

## 10–8 to 10–10 Fluid Flow; Bernoulli's Equation

35. (I) Using the data of Example 10–11, calculate the average speed of blood flow in the major arteries of the body, which have a total cross-sectional area of about 2.0 $\text{cm}^2$.

36. (I) A 15-cm-radius air duct is used to replenish the air of a room 9.2 m × 5.0 m × 4.5 m every 16 min. How fast does air flow in the duct?

37. (I) Show that Bernoulli's equation reduces to the hydrostatic variation of pressure with depth (Eq. 10–3b) when there is no flow $(v_1 = v_2 = 0)$.

38. (I) How fast does water flow from a hole at the bottom of a very wide, 4.6-m-deep storage tank filled with water? Ignore viscosity.

39. (II) A $\frac{5}{8}$-inch (inside) diameter garden hose is used to fill a round swimming pool 6.1 m in diameter. How long will it take to fill the pool to a depth of 1.2 m if water issues from the hose at a speed of 0.40 m/s?

40. (II) What gauge pressure in the water mains is necessary if a firehose is to spray water to a height of 15 m?

41. (II) A 6.0-cm-diameter horizontal pipe gradually narrows to 4.0 cm. When water flows through this pipe at a certain rate, the gauge pressure in these two sections is 32.0 kPa and 24.0 kPa, respectively. What is the volume rate of flow?

42. (II) What is the volume rate of flow of water from a 1.85-cm-diameter faucet if the pressure head is 15.0 m?

43. (II) If wind blows at 35 m/s over a house, what is the net force on the roof if its area is 240 m$^2$ and is flat?

44. (II) What is the lift (in newtons) due to Bernoulli's principle on a wing of area 78 m$^2$ if the air passes over the top and bottom surfaces at speeds of 260 m/s and 150 m/s, respectively?

45. (II) Estimate the air pressure inside a category 5 hurricane, where the wind speed is 300 km/h (Fig. 10–52).

**FIGURE 10–52** Problem 45.

46. (II) Water at a gauge pressure of 3.8 atm at street level flows into an office building at a speed of 0.60 m/s through a pipe 5.0 cm in diameter. The pipe tapers down to 2.6 cm in diameter by the top floor, 18 m above (Fig. 10–53), where the faucet has been left open. Calculate the flow velocity and the gauge pressure in such a pipe on the top floor. Assume no branch pipes and ignore viscosity.

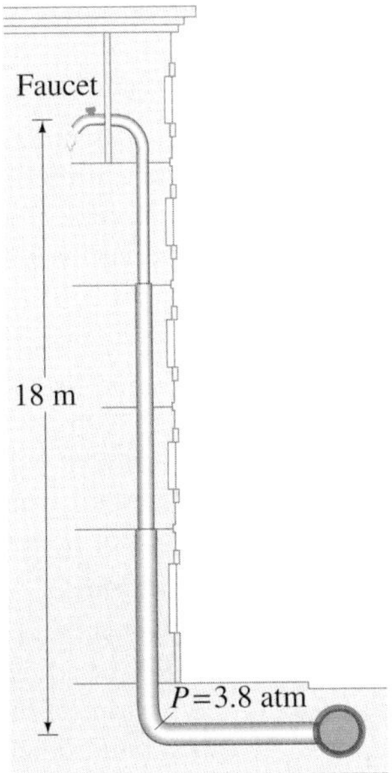


**FIGURE 10–53** Problem 46.

47. (III) (*a*) Show that the flow velocity measured by a venturi meter (see Fig. 10–30) is given by the relation

$$v_1 = A_2\sqrt{\frac{2(P_1 - P_2)}{\rho(A_1^2 - A_2^2)}}.$$

(*b*) A venturi tube is measuring the flow of water; it has a main diameter of 3.0 cm tapering down to a throat diameter of 1.0 cm. If the pressure difference is measured to be 18 mm-Hg, what is the velocity of the water?

48. (III) In Fig. 10–54, take into account the speed of the top surface of the tank and show that the speed of fluid leaving the opening at the bottom is

$$v_1 = \sqrt{\frac{2gh}{(1 - A_1^2/A_2^2)}},$$

where $h = y_2 - y_1$, and $A_1$ and $A_2$ are the areas of the opening and of the top surface, respectively. Assume $A_1 \ll A_2$ so that the flow remains nearly steady and laminar.

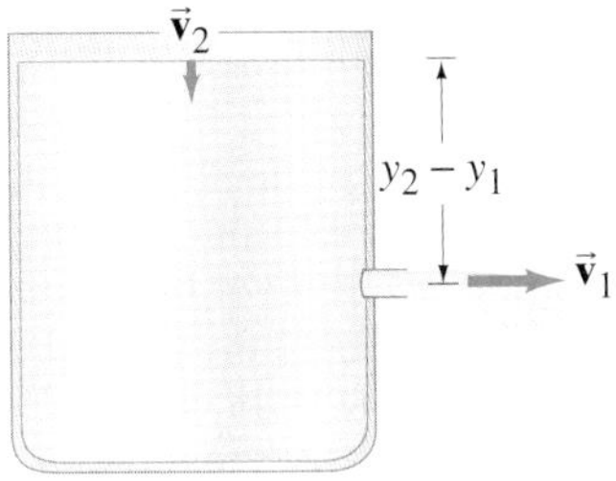


**FIGURE 10–54** Problems 48 and 49.

49. (III) Suppose the opening in the tank of Fig. 10–54 is a height $h_1$ above the base and the liquid surface is a height $h_2$ above the base. The tank rests on level ground. (*a*) At what horizontal distance from the base of the tank will the fluid strike the ground? (*b*) At what other height, $h_1'$, can a hole be placed so that the emerging liquid will have the same "range"? Assume $v_2 \approx 0$.

## * 10–11 Viscosity

* 50. (II) A *viscometer* consists of two concentric cylinders, 10.20 cm and 10.60 cm in diameter. A particular liquid fills the space between them to a depth of 12.0 cm. The outer cylinder is fixed, and a torque of 0.024 m·N keeps the inner cylinder turning at a steady rotational speed of 62 rev/min. What is the viscosity of the liquid?

## * 10–12 Flow in Tubes; Poiseuille's Equation

* 51. (I) A gardener feels it is taking him too long to water a garden with a $\frac{3}{8}$-in.-diameter hose. By what factor will his time be cut if he uses a $\frac{5}{8}$-in.-diameter hose? Assume nothing else is changed.

* 52. (II) Engine oil (assume SAE 10, Table 10–3) passes through a 1.80-mm-diameter tube in a prototype engine. The tube is 5.5 cm long. What pressure difference is needed to maintain a flow rate of 5.6 mL/min?

* 53. (II) What must be the pressure difference between the two ends of a 1.9-km section of pipe, 29 cm in diameter, if it is to transport oil ($\rho = 950\ \text{kg/m}^3$, $\eta = 0.20\ \text{Pa}\cdot\text{s}$) at a rate of 450 cm$^3$/s?

* 54. (II) What diameter must a 21.0-m-long air duct have if the ventilation and heating system is to replenish the air in a room 9.0 m × 12.0 m × 4.0 m every 10 min? Assume the pump can exert a gauge pressure of $0.71 \times 10^{-3}$ atm.

* 55. (II) Calculate the pressure drop per cm along the aorta using the data of Example 10–11 and Table 10–3.

* 56. (II) Assuming a constant pressure gradient, if blood flow is reduced by 75%, by what factor is a blood vessel decreased in radius?

* 57. (II) Poiseuille's equation does not hold if the flow velocity is high enough that turbulence sets in. The onset of turbulence occurs when the **Reynolds number**, *Re*, exceeds approximately 2000. *Re* is defined as

$$Re = \frac{2\bar{v}r\rho}{\eta},$$

where $\bar{v}$ is the average speed of the fluid, $\rho$ is its density, $\eta$ is its viscosity, and $r$ is the radius of the tube in which the fluid is flowing. (*a*) Determine if blood flow through the aorta is laminar or turbulent when the average speed of blood in the aorta ($r = 1.2$ cm) during the resting part of the heart's cycle is about 40 cm/s. (*b*) During exercise, the blood-flow speed approximately doubles. Calculate the Reynolds number in this case, and determine if the flow is laminar or turbulent.

* 58. (III) A patient is to be given a blood transfusion. The blood is to flow through a tube from a raised bottle to a needle inserted in the vein (Fig. 10–55). The inside diameter of the 4.0-cm-long needle is 0.40 mm, and the required flow rate is 4.0 cm$^3$ of blood per minute. How high $h$ should the bottle be placed above the needle? Obtain $\rho$ and $\eta$ from the Tables. Assume the blood pressure is 18 torr above atmospheric pressure.

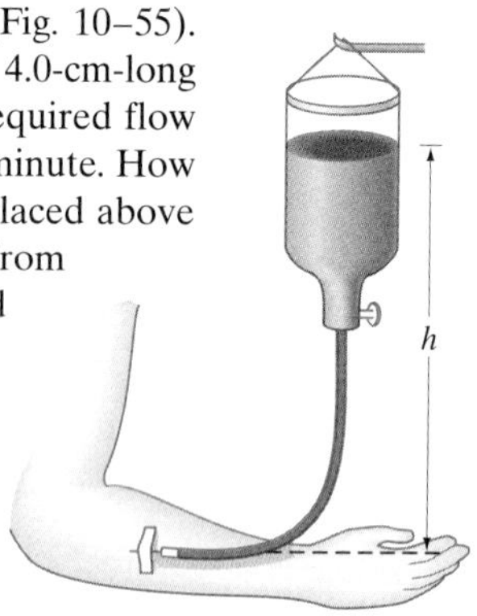


**FIGURE 10–55**
Problems 58 and 63.

### * 10–13 Surface Tension and Capillarity

* 59. (I) If the force $F$ needed to move the wire in Fig. 10–35 is $5.1 \times 10^{-3}$ N, calculate the surface tension $\gamma$ of the enclosed fluid. Assume $L = 0.070$ m.

* 60. (I) Calculate the force needed to move the wire in Fig. 10–35 if it is immersed in a soapy solution and the wire is 18.2 cm long.

* 61. (II) If the base of an insect's leg has a radius of about $3.0 \times 10^{-5}$ m and the insect's mass is 0.016 g, would you expect the six-legged insect to remain on top of the water? Why or why not?

* 62. (II) The surface tension of a liquid can be determined by measuring the force $F$ needed to just lift a circular platinum ring of radius $r$ from the surface of the liquid. (*a*) Find a formula for $\gamma$ in terms of $F$ and $r$. (*b*) At 30°C, if $F = 8.40 \times 10^{-3}$ N and $r = 2.8$ cm, calculate $\gamma$ for the tested liquid.

## General Problems

63. Intravenous infusions are often made under gravity, as shown in Fig. 10–55. Assuming the fluid has a density of 1.00 g/cm$^3$, at what height $h$ should the bottle be placed so the liquid pressure is (*a*) 55 mm-Hg, and (*b*) 650 mm-$H_2O$? (*c*) If the blood pressure is 18 mm-Hg above atmospheric pressure, how high should the bottle be placed so that the fluid just barely enters the vein?

64. A 2.4-N force is applied to the plunger of a hypodermic needle. If the diameter of the plunger is 1.3 cm and that of the needle 0.20 mm, (*a*) with what force does the fluid leave the needle? (*b*) What force on the plunger would be needed to push fluid into a vein where the gauge pressure is 18 mm-Hg? Answer for the instant just before the fluid starts to move.

65. A bicycle pump is used to inflate a tire. The initial tire (gauge) pressure is 210 kPa (30 psi). At the end of the pumping process, the final pressure is 310 kPa (45 psi). If the diameter of the plunger in the cylinder of the pump is 3.0 cm, what is the range of the force that needs to be applied to the pump handle from beginning to end?

66. Estimate the pressure on the mountains underneath the Antarctic ice sheet, which is typically 3 km thick.

67. What is the approximate difference in air pressure between the top and the bottom of the Empire State building in New York City? It is 380 m tall and is located at sea level. Express as a fraction of atmospheric pressure at sea level.

68. A hydraulic lift is used to jack a 970-kg car 12 cm off the floor. The diameter of the output piston is 18 cm, and the input force is 250 N. (*a*) What is the area of the input piston? (*b*) What is the work done in lifting the car 12 cm? (*c*) If the input piston moves 13 cm in each stroke, how high does the car move up for each stroke? (*d*) How many strokes are required to jack the car up 12 cm? (*e*) Show that energy is conserved.

69. Giraffes are a wonder of cardiovascular engineering. Calculate the difference in pressure (in atmospheres) that the blood vessels in a giraffe's head have to accommodate as the head is lowered from a full upright position to ground level for a drink. The height of an average giraffe is about 6 m.

70. When you ascend or descend a great deal when driving in a car, your ears "pop," which means that the pressure behind the eardrum is being equalized to that outside. If this did not happen, what would be the approximate force on an eardrum of area 0.50 cm$^2$ if a change in altitude of 950 m takes place?

71. One arm of a U-shaped tube (open at both ends) contains water, and the other alcohol. If the two fluids meet at exactly the bottom of the U, and the alcohol is at a height of 18.0 cm, at what height will the water be?

72. A simple model (Fig. 10–56) considers a continent as a block (density $\approx$ 2800 kg/m$^3$) floating in the mantle rock around it (density $\approx$ 3300 kg/m$^3$). Assuming the continent is 35 km thick (the average thickness of the Earth's continental crust), estimate the height of the continent above the surrounding rock.

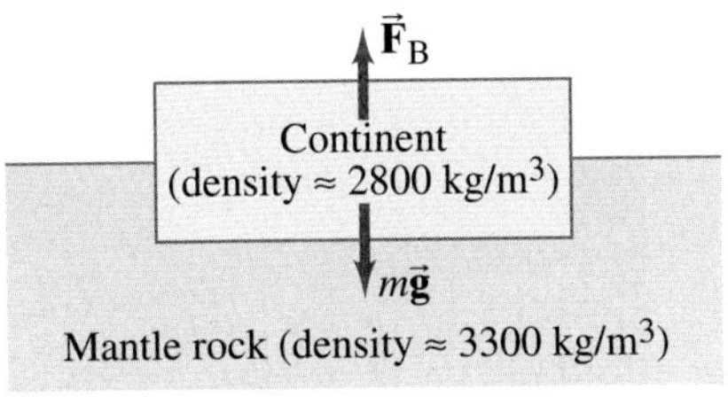


**FIGURE 10–56** Problem 72.

73. The contraction of the left ventricle (chamber) of the heart pumps blood to the body. Assuming that the inner surface of the left ventricle has an area of 82 cm$^2$ and the maximum pressure in the blood is 120 mm-Hg, estimate the force exerted by that ventricle at maximum pressure.

74. Estimate the total mass of the Earth's atmosphere, using the known value of atmospheric pressure at sea level.

75. Suppose a person can reduce the pressure in his lungs to −80 mm-Hg gauge pressure. How high can water then be sucked up a straw?

76. A ship, carrying fresh water to a desert island in the Caribbean, has a horizontal cross-sectional area of 2650 m$^2$ at the waterline. When unloaded, the ship rises 8.50 m higher in the sea. How much water was delivered?

77. A copper (Cu) weight is placed on top of a 0.50-kg block of wood (density = $0.60 \times 10^3$ kg/m$^3$) floating in water, as shown in Fig. 10–57. What is the mass of the copper if the top of the wood block is exactly at the water's surface?

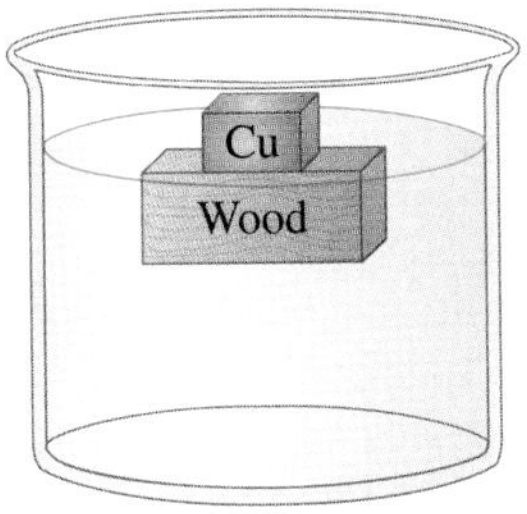


**FIGURE 10–57** Problem 77.

78. A raft is made of 10 logs lashed together. Each is 56 cm in diameter and has a length of 6.1 m. How many people can the raft hold before they start getting their feet wet, assuming the average person has a mass of 68 kg? Do *not* neglect the weight of the logs. Assume the specific gravity of wood is 0.60.

79. During each heartbeat, approximately 70 cm$^3$ of blood is pushed from the heart at an average pressure of 105 mm-Hg. Calculate the power output of the heart, in watts, assuming 70 beats per minute.

80. A bucket of water is accelerated upward at 2.4*g*. What is the buoyant force on a 3.0-kg granite rock (SG = 2.7) submerged in the water? Will the rock float? Why or why not?

81. How high should the pressure head be if water is to come from a faucet at a speed of 9.5 m/s? Ignore viscosity.

82. The stream of water from a faucet decreases in diameter as it falls (Fig. 10–47). Derive an equation for the diameter of the stream as a function of the distance $y$ below the faucet, given that the water has speed $v_0$ when it leaves the faucet, whose diameter is $d$.

83. Four lawn sprinkler heads are fed by a 1.9-cm-diameter pipe. The water comes out of the heads at an angle of 35° to the horizontal and covers a radius of 8.0 m. (*a*) What is the velocity of the water coming out of each sprinkler head? (Assume zero air resistance.) (*b*) If the output diameter of each head is 3.0 mm, how many liters of water do the four heads deliver per second? (*c*) How fast is the water flowing inside the 1.9-cm-diameter pipe?

84. You need to siphon water from a clogged sink. The sink has an area of 0.48 m$^2$ and is filled to a height of 4.0 cm. Your siphon tube rises 50 cm above the bottom of the sink and then descends 100 cm to a pail as shown in Fig. 10–58. The siphon tube has a diameter of 2.0 cm. (*a*) Assuming that the water enters the siphon tube with almost zero velocity, calculate its velocity when it enters the pail. (*b*) Estimate how long it will take to empty the sink.

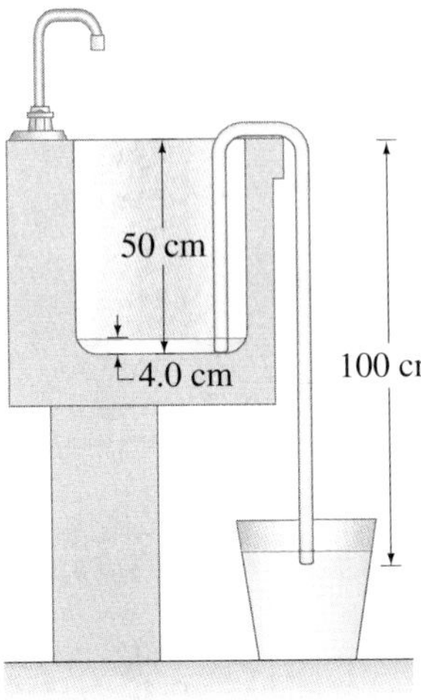


**FIGURE 10–58** Problems 84 and 85.

85. Consider a siphon which transfers water from one vessel to a second (lower) one, as in Fig. 10–58. Determine the rate of flow if the tube has a diameter of 1.2 cm and the difference in water levels of the two containers is 64 cm.

86. An airplane has a mass of $2.0 \times 10^6$ kg, and the air flows past the lower surface of the wings at 95 m/s. If the wings have a surface area of 1200 m$^2$, how fast must the air flow over the upper surface of the wing if the plane is to stay in the air? Consider only the Bernoulli effect.

* 87. Blood from an animal is placed in a bottle 1.70 m above a 3.8-cm-long needle, of inside diameter 0.40 mm, from which it flows at a rate of 4.1 cm$^3$/min. What is the viscosity of this blood?

* 88. If cholesterol build-up reduces the diameter of an artery by 15%, what will be the effect on blood flow?

## Answers to Exercises

**A:** The same. Pressure depends on depth, not on length.

**B:** Lower.

**C:** Increases.

The pendulum of a clock is an example of oscillatory motion. Many kinds of oscillatory motion are sinusoidal in time, or nearly so, and are referred to as being simple harmonic motion. Real systems generally have at least some friction, causing the motion to be "damped." When an external sinusoidal force is exerted on a system able to oscillate, resonance occurs if the driving force is at or near the natural frequency of vibration.

Vibrations can give rise to waves—such as water waves or waves traveling along a cord—which travel outward from their source.

# CHAPTER 11

# Vibrations and Waves

Many objects vibrate or oscillate—an object on the end of a spring, a tuning fork, the balance wheel of an old watch, a pendulum, a plastic ruler held firmly over the edge of a table and gently struck, the strings of a guitar or piano. Spiders detect prey by the vibrations of their webs; cars oscillate up and down when they hit a bump; buildings and bridges vibrate when heavy trucks pass or the wind is fierce. Indeed, because most solids are elastic (see Section 9–5), they vibrate (at least briefly) when given an impulse. Electrical oscillations occur in radio and television sets. At the atomic level, atoms vibrate within a molecule, and the atoms of a solid vibrate about their relatively fixed positions. Because it is so common in everyday life and occurs in so many areas of physics, oscillatory (or vibrational) motion is of great importance. Mechanical vibrations are fully described on the basis of Newtonian mechanics.

Vibrations and wave motion are intimately related subjects. Waves—whether ocean waves, waves on a string, earthquake waves, or sound waves in air—have as their source a vibration. In the case of sound, not only is the source a vibrating object, but so is the detector—the eardrum or the membrane of a microphone. Indeed, when a wave travels through a medium, the medium vibrates (such as air for sound waves). In the second half of this Chapter, after we discuss vibrations, we will discuss simple waves such as those on water or on a string. In Chapter 12 we will study sound waves, and in later Chapters we will encounter other forms of wave motion, including electromagnetic waves and light.

## 11–1 Simple Harmonic Motion

When an object **vibrates** or **oscillates** back and forth, over the same path, each vibration taking the same amount of time, the motion is **periodic**. The simplest form of periodic motion is represented by an object oscillating on the end of a uniform coil spring. Because many other types of vibrational motion closely resemble this system, we will look at it in detail. We assume that the mass of the spring can be ignored, and that the spring is mounted horizontally, as shown in Fig. 11–1a, so that the object of mass $m$ slides without friction on the horizontal surface. Any spring has a natural length at which it exerts no force on the mass $m$. The position of the mass at this point is called the **equilibrium position**. If the mass is moved either to the left, which compresses the spring, or to the right, which stretches it, the spring exerts a force on the mass that acts in the direction of returning the mass to the equilibrium position; hence it is called a *restoring force*. We consider the common situation where we can assume the magnitude of the restoring force $F$ is directly proportional to the displacement $x$ the spring has been stretched (Fig. 11–1b) or compressed (Fig. 11–1c) from the equilibrium position:

*Equilibrium position*

$$F = -kx. \qquad \text{[force exerted by spring]} \quad \textbf{(11–1)}$$

Note that the equilibrium position has been chosen at $x = 0$. Equation 11–1, which is often referred to as Hooke's law (see Sections 6–4 and 9–5), is accurate as long as the spring is not compressed to the point where the coils are close to touching, or stretched beyond the elastic region (see Fig. 9–19).

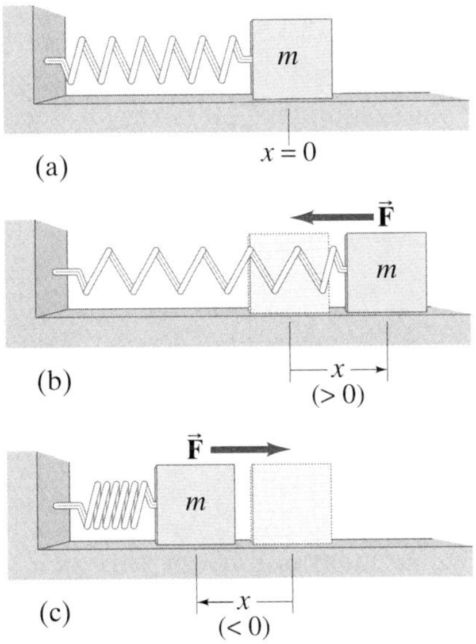


**FIGURE 11–1** A mass vibrating at the end of a uniform spring.

The minus sign in Eq. 11–1 indicates that the restoring force is always in the direction opposite to the displacement $x$. For example, if we choose the positive direction to the right in Fig. 11–1, $x$ is positive when the spring is stretched, but the direction of the restoring force is to the left (negative direction). If the spring is compressed, $x$ is negative (to the left) but the force $F$ acts toward the right (Fig. 11–1c).

The proportionality constant $k$ in Eq. 11–1 is called the *spring constant* or *spring stiffness constant*. To stretch the spring a distance $x$, one has to exert an (external) force on the free end of the spring at least equal to

$$F = +kx. \qquad \text{[external force on spring]}$$

The greater the value of $k$, the greater the force needed to stretch a spring a given distance. That is, the stiffer the spring, the greater the spring constant $k$.

Note that the force $F$ in Eq. 11–1 is *not* a constant, but varies with position. Therefore the acceleration of the mass $m$ is not constant, so we *cannot* use the equations for constant acceleration developed in Chapter 2.

**CAUTION**

*Force and acceleration are* not *constant; Eqs. 2–11 are not useful here*

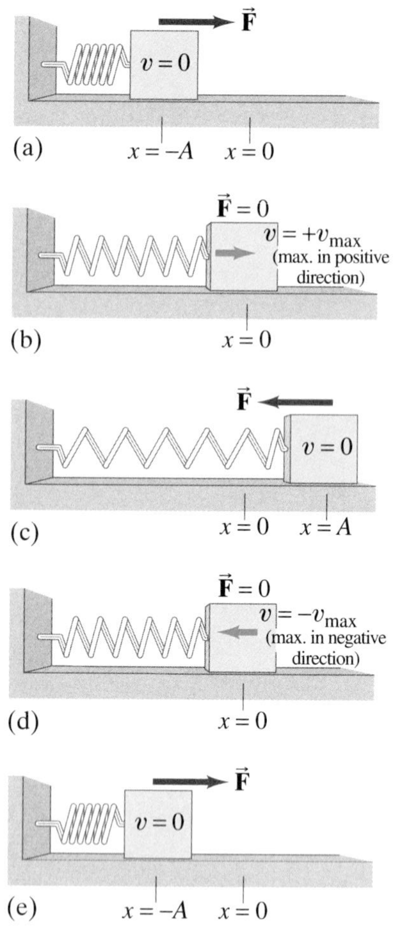


**FIGURE 11–2** Force on, and velocity of, a mass at different positions of its oscillation cycle on a frictionless surface.

Let us examine what happens when our uniform spring is initially compressed a distance $x = -A$, as shown in Fig. 11–2a, and then released. The spring exerts a force on the mass that pushes it toward the equilibrium position. But because the mass has been accelerated by the force, it passes the equilibrium position with considerable speed. Indeed, as the mass reaches the equilibrium position, the force on it decreases to zero, but its speed at this point is a maximum, $v_{max}$, Fig. 11–2b. As the mass moves farther to the right, the force on it acts to slow it down, and it stops momentarily at $x = A$, Fig. 11–2c. It then begins moving back in the opposite direction, accelerating until it passes the equilibrium point, Fig. 11–2d, and then slows down until it reaches zero speed at the original starting point, $x = -A$, Fig. 11–2e. It then repeats the motion, moving back and forth symmetrically between $x = A$ and $x = -A$.

**EXERCISE A** An object is oscillating back and forth. Which of the following statements are true at some time during the course of the motion? (*a*) The object can have zero velocity and, simultaneously, nonzero acceleration. (*b*) The object can have zero velocity and, simultaneously, zero acceleration. (*c*) The object can have zero acceleration and, simultaneously, nonzero velocity. (*d*) The object can have nonzero velocity and nonzero acceleration simultaneously.

To discuss vibrational motion, we need to define a few terms. The distance $x$ of the mass from the equilibrium point at any moment is called the **displacement**. The maximum displacement—the greatest distance from the equilibrium point—is called the **amplitude**, $A$. One **cycle** refers to the complete to-and-fro motion from some initial point back to that same point—say, from $x = -A$ to $x = A$ and back to $x = -A$. The **period**, $T$, is defined as the time required to complete one cycle. Finally, the **frequency**, $f$, is the number of complete cycles per second. Frequency is generally specified in hertz (Hz), where $1\text{ Hz} = 1$ cycle per second $(\text{s}^{-1})$. It is easy to see, from their definitions, that frequency and period are inversely related, as we saw earlier (Eqs. 5–2 and 8–8):

$$f = \frac{1}{T} \quad \text{and} \quad T = \frac{1}{f}; \qquad \textbf{(11–2)}$$

for example, if the frequency is 5 cycles per second, then each cycle takes $\frac{1}{5}$ s.

The oscillation of a spring hung vertically is essentially the same as that of a horizontal spring. Because of gravity, the length of a vertical spring with a mass $m$ on the end will be longer at equilibrium than when that same spring is horizontal, as shown in Fig. 11–3. The spring is in equilibrium when $\Sigma F = 0 = mg - kx_0$, so the spring stretches an extra amount $x_0 = mg/k$ to be in equilibrium. If $x$ is measured from this new equilibrium position, Eq. 11–1 can be used directly with the same value of $k$.

**CAUTION**

*For vertical spring, measure displacement (x or y) from the vertical equilibrium position*

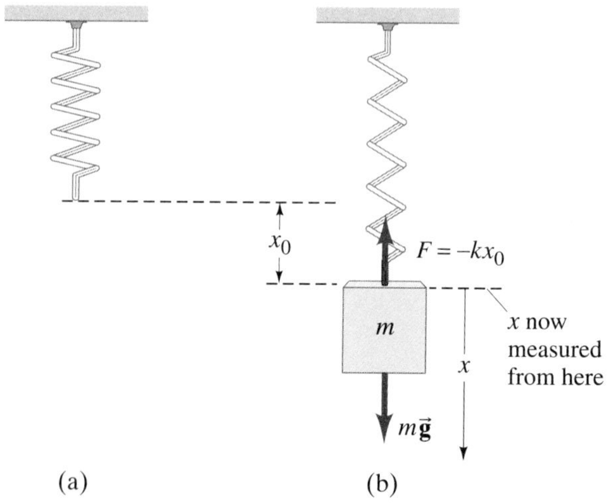


**FIGURE 11–3**
(a) Free spring, hung vertically.
(b) Mass $m$ attached to spring in new equilibrium position, which occurs when $\Sigma F = 0 = mg - kx_0$.

**EXAMPLE 11–1** **Car springs.** When a family of four with a total mass of 200 kg step into their 1200-kg car, the car's springs compress 3.0 cm. (*a*) What is the spring constant of the car's springs (Fig. 11–4), assuming they act as a single spring? (*b*) How far will the car lower if loaded with 300 kg rather than 200 kg?

**APPROACH** We use Hooke's law. The extra force equal to the weight of the people, $mg$, causes a 3.0-cm displacement.

**SOLUTION** (*a*) The added force of $(200\,\text{kg})(9.8\,\text{m/s}^2) = 1960\,\text{N}$ causes the springs to compress $3.0 \times 10^{-2}$ m. Therefore (Eq. 11–1), the spring constant is

$$k = \frac{F}{x} = \frac{1960\,\text{N}}{3.0 \times 10^{-2}\,\text{m}} = 6.5 \times 10^4\,\text{N/m}.$$

(*b*) If the car is loaded with 300 kg, Hooke's law gives

$$x = \frac{F}{k} = \frac{(300\,\text{kg})(9.8\,\text{m/s}^2)}{(6.5 \times 10^4\,\text{N/m})} = 4.5 \times 10^{-2}\,\text{m},$$

or 4.5 cm.

**NOTE** We could have obtained $x$ without solving for $k$: since $x$ is proportional to $F$, if 200 kg compresses the spring 3.0 cm, then 1.5 times the force will compress the spring 1.5 times as much, or 4.5 cm.

**FIGURE 11–4** Photo of a car's spring. (Also visible is the shock absorber, in red—see Section 11–5.)

Any vibrating system for which the restoring force is directly proportional to the negative of the displacement (as in Eq. 11–1, $F = -kx$) is said to exhibit **simple harmonic motion** (SHM).† Such a system is often called a **simple harmonic oscillator** (SHO). We saw in Section 9–5 that most solid materials stretch or compress according to Eq. 11–1 as long as the displacement is not too great. Because of this, many natural vibrations are simple harmonic, or sufficiently close to it that they can be treated using this SHM model.

*SHM*
*SHO*

**CONCEPTUAL EXAMPLE 11–2** **Is the motion simple harmonic?** Which of the following represent a simple harmonic oscillator: (*a*) $F = -0.5x^2$, (*b*) $F = -2.3y$, (*c*) $F = 8.6x$, (*d*) $F = -4\theta$?

**RESPONSE** Both (*b*) and (*d*) represent simple harmonic oscillators because they give the force as minus a constant times a displacement. The displacement need not be $x$, but the minus sign is required to restore the system to equilibrium, which is why (*c*) is not a SHO.

## 11–2 Energy in the Simple Harmonic Oscillator

With forces that are not constant, such as here with simple harmonic motion, it is often convenient and useful to use the energy approach, as we saw in Chapter 6.

To stretch or compress a spring, work has to be done. Hence potential energy is stored in a stretched or compressed spring. Indeed, we have already seen in Section 6–4 that elastic potential energy is given by

$$\text{PE} = \tfrac{1}{2}kx^2.$$

The total mechanical energy $E$ of a mass–spring system is the sum of the kinetic and potential energies,

$$E = \tfrac{1}{2}mv^2 + \tfrac{1}{2}kx^2, \qquad \textbf{(11–3)}$$

*Total energy of SHO*

where $v$ is the velocity of the mass $m$ when it is a distance $x$ from the equilibrium position. As long as there is no friction, the total mechanical energy $E$

†The word "harmonic" refers to the motion being *sinusoidal*, which we discuss in Section 11–3. It is "simple" when there is sinusoidal motion of a single frequency.

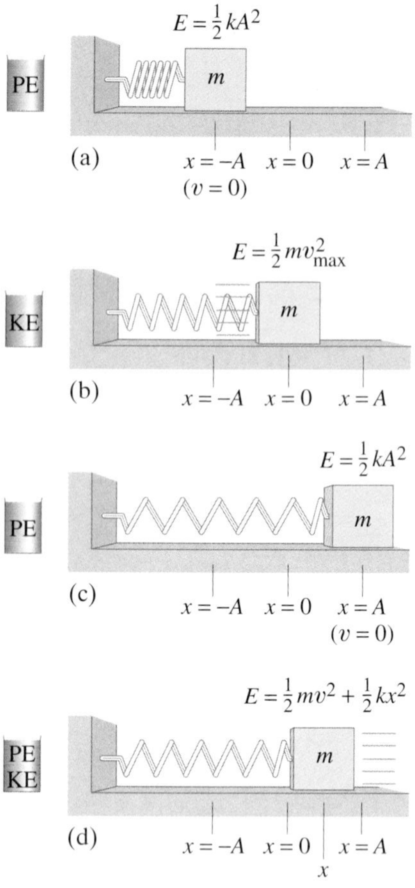


**FIGURE 11–5** Energy changes from potential energy to kinetic energy and back again as the spring oscillates. Energy "buckets" (on the left) are described in Section 6–7.

remains constant. As the mass oscillates back and forth, the energy continuously changes from potential energy to kinetic energy, and back again (Fig. 11–5). At the extreme points, $x = -A$ and $x = A$ (Fig. 11–5a, c), all the energy is stored in the spring as potential energy (and is the same whether the spring is compressed or stretched to the full amplitude). At these extreme points, the mass stops momentarily as it changes direction, so $v = 0$ and

$$E = \tfrac{1}{2}m(0)^2 + \tfrac{1}{2}kA^2 = \tfrac{1}{2}kA^2. \qquad \textbf{(11–4a)}$$

Thus, the **total mechanical energy of a simple harmonic oscillator is proportional to the square of the amplitude**. At the equilibrium point, $x = 0$ (Fig. 11–5b), all the energy is kinetic:

$$E = \tfrac{1}{2}mv_{max}^2 + \tfrac{1}{2}k(0)^2 = \tfrac{1}{2}mv_{max}^2, \qquad \textbf{(11–4b)}$$

where $v_{max}$ represents the *maximum* velocity during the motion (which occurs at $x = 0$). At intermediate points (Fig. 11–5d), the energy is part kinetic and part potential; because energy is conserved (we use Eqs. 11–3 and 11–4a),

$$\tfrac{1}{2}mv^2 + \tfrac{1}{2}kx^2 = \tfrac{1}{2}kA^2. \qquad \textbf{(11–4c)}$$

From this conservation of energy equation, we can obtain the velocity as a function of position. Solving for $v^2$, we have

$$v^2 = \frac{k}{m}\left(A^2 - x^2\right) = \frac{k}{m}A^2\left(1 - \frac{x^2}{A^2}\right).$$

From Eqs. 11–4a and 11–4b, we have $\frac{1}{2}mv_{max}^2 = \frac{1}{2}kA^2$, so $v_{max}^2 = (k/m)A^2$. Inserting this into the equation above and taking the square root, we have

$$v = \pm\, v_{max}\sqrt{1 - \frac{x^2}{A^2}}. \qquad \textbf{(11–5)}$$

This gives the velocity of the object at any position $x$. The object moves back and forth, so its velocity can be either in the + or − direction, but its magnitude depends only on the magnitude of $x$.

**CONCEPTUAL EXAMPLE 11–3** **Doubling the amplitude.** Suppose the spring in Fig. 11–5 is stretched twice as far (to $x = 2A$). What happens to (*a*) the energy of the system, (*b*) the maximum velocity of the oscillating mass, (*c*) the maximum acceleration of the mass?

**RESPONSE** (*a*) From Eq. 11–4a, the total energy is proportional to the square of the amplitude $A$, so stretching it twice as far quadruples the energy $(2^2 = 4)$. You may protest, "I did work stretching the spring from $x = 0$ to $x = A$. Don't I do the same work stretching it from $A$ to $2A$?" No. The force you exert is proportional to the displacement $x$, so for the second displacement, from $x = A$ to $2A$, you do more work than for the first displacement ($x = 0$ to $A$).
(*b*) From Eq. 11–4b, we can see that since the energy is quadrupled, the maximum velocity must be doubled. $[v_{max} \propto \sqrt{E} \propto A.]$
(*c*) Since the force is twice as great when we stretch the spring twice as far, the acceleration is also twice as great: $a \propto F \propto x$.

**EXERCISE B** Suppose the spring in Fig. 11–5 is compressed to $x = -A$, but is given a push to the right so that the initial speed of the mass $m$ is $v_0$. What effect does this push have on (*a*) the energy of the system, (*b*) the maximum velocity, (*c*) the maximum acceleration?

**EXAMPLE 11–4** **Spring calculations.** A spring stretches 0.150 m when a 0.300-kg mass is gently lowered on it as in Fig. 11–3b. The spring is then set up horizontally with the 0.300-kg mass resting on a frictionless table as in Fig. 11–5. The mass is pulled so that the spring is stretched 0.100 m from the equilibrium point, and released from rest. Determine (*a*) the spring stiffness constant $k$, (*b*) the amplitude of the horizontal oscillation $A$, (*c*) the magnitude of the maximum velocity $v_{max}$, (*d*) the magnitude of the velocity $v$ when the mass is 0.050 m from equilibrium, and (*e*) the magnitude of the maximum acceleration $a_{max}$ of the mass.

**APPROACH** When the 0.300-kg mass hangs at rest from the spring as in Fig. 11–3b, we apply Newton's second law for the vertical forces: $\Sigma F = 0 = mg - kx_0$, so $k = mg/x_0$. For the horizontal oscillations, the amplitude is given, the velocities are found using conservation of energy, and the acceleration from $F = ma$.

**SOLUTION** (*a*) The spring stretches 0.150 m due to the 0.300-kg load, so

$$k = \frac{F}{x_0} = \frac{mg}{x_0} = \frac{(0.300\,\text{kg})(9.80\,\text{m/s}^2)}{0.150\,\text{m}} = 19.6\,\text{N/m}.$$

(*b*) The spring is now horizontal (on a table). It is stretched 0.100 m from equilibrium and is given no initial speed, so $A = 0.100\,\text{m}$.

(*c*) The maximum velocity $v_{max}$ is attained as the mass passes through the equilibrium point where all the energy is kinetic. By comparing the total energy (see Eq. 11–3) at equilibrium with that at full extension, conservation of energy tells us that

$$\tfrac{1}{2}mv_{max}^2 + 0 = 0 + \tfrac{1}{2}kA^2,$$

where $A = 0.100\,\text{m}$. (Or, compare Eqs. 11–4a and b.) Solving for $v_{max}$, we have

$$v_{max} = A\sqrt{\frac{k}{m}} = (0.100\,\text{m})\sqrt{\frac{19.6\,\text{N/m}}{0.300\,\text{kg}}} = 0.808\,\text{m/s}.$$

(*d*) We use conservation of energy, or Eq. 11–5 derived from it, and find that

$$v = v_{max}\sqrt{1 - \frac{x^2}{A^2}} = (0.808\,\text{m/s})\sqrt{1 - \frac{(0.050\,\text{m})^2}{(0.100\,\text{m})^2}} = 0.70\,\text{m/s}.$$

(*e*) By Newton's second law, $F = ma$. So the maximum acceleration occurs where the force is greatest—that is, when $x = A = 0.100\,\text{m}$. Thus

$$a_{max} = \frac{F_{max}}{m} = \frac{kA}{m} = \frac{(19.6\,\text{N/m})(0.100\,\text{m})}{0.300\,\text{kg}} = 6.53\,\text{m/s}^2.$$

**NOTE** We cannot use the kinematic equations, Eqs. 2–11, because the acceleration is not constant in SHM.

**EXAMPLE 11–5** **More spring calculations—energy.** For the simple harmonic oscillator of Example 11–4, determine (*a*) the total energy, and (*b*) the kinetic and potential energies at half amplitude ($x = \pm A/2$).

**APPROACH** We use conservation of energy for a mass–spring system, Eqs. 11–3 and 11–4.

**SOLUTION** (*a*) With $k = 19.6\,\text{N/m}$ and $A = 0.100\,\text{m}$, the total energy $E$ from Eq. 11–4a is

$$E = \tfrac{1}{2}kA^2 = \tfrac{1}{2}(19.6\,\text{N/m})(0.100\,\text{m})^2 = 9.80 \times 10^{-2}\,\text{J}.$$

(*b*) At $x = A/2 = 0.050\,\text{m}$, we have

$$\text{PE} = \tfrac{1}{2}kx^2 = \tfrac{1}{2}(19.6\,\text{N/m})(0.050\,\text{m})^2 = 2.5 \times 10^{-2}\,\text{J}.$$

By conservation of energy, the kinetic energy must be

$$\text{KE} = E - \text{PE} = 7.3 \times 10^{-2}\,\text{J}.$$

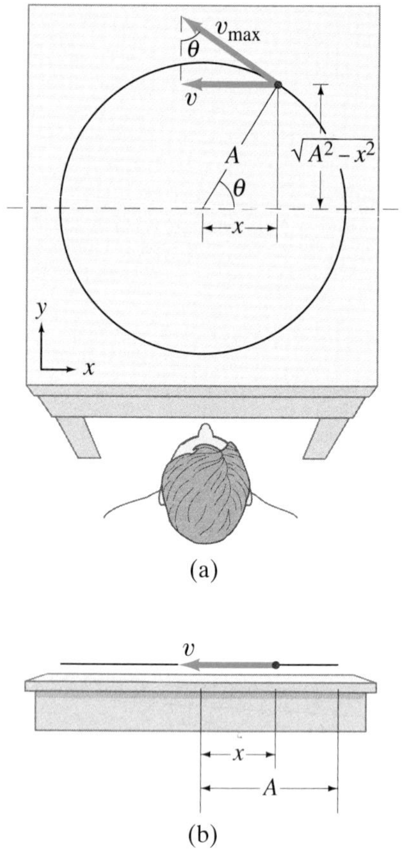


**FIGURE 11–6** (a) Circular motion of a small (red) object. (b) Side view of circular motion (x component) is simple harmonic motion.

## 11–3 The Period and Sinusoidal Nature of SHM

The period of a simple harmonic oscillator is found to depend on the stiffness of the spring and also on the mass $m$ that is oscillating. But—strange as it may seem—the *period does not depend on the amplitude*. You can find this out for yourself by using a watch and timing 10 or 20 cycles of an oscillating spring for a small amplitude and then for a large amplitude.

We can derive a formula for the period of simple harmonic motion (SHM) by comparing SHM to an object rotating in a circle. From this same "reference circle" we can obtain a second useful result—a formula for the position of an oscillating mass as a function of time. There is nothing actually rotating in a circle when a spring oscillates linearly, but it is the mathematical similarity that we find useful.

### Period and Frequency

Consider a small object of mass $m$ revolving counterclockwise in a circle of radius $A$, with constant speed $v_{max}$, on top of a table as shown in Fig. 11–6. As viewed from above, the motion is a circle in the $xy$ plane. But a person who looks at the motion from the edge of the table sees an oscillatory motion back and forth, and this one-dimensional motion corresponds precisely to simple harmonic motion, as we shall now see.

What the person sees, and what we are interested in, is the projection of the circular motion onto the $x$ axis (Fig. 11–6b). To see that this $x$-motion is analogous to SHM, let us calculate the magnitude of the $x$ component of the velocity $v_{max}$, which is labeled $v$ in Fig. 11–6. The two triangles involving $\theta$ in Fig. 11–6a are similar, so

$$\frac{v}{v_{max}} = \frac{\sqrt{A^2 - x^2}}{A}$$

or

$$v = v_{max}\sqrt{1 - \frac{x^2}{A^2}}.$$

This is exactly the equation for the speed of a mass oscillating with SHM, as we saw in Eq. 11–5. Thus the projection on the $x$ axis of an object revolving in a circle has the same motion as a mass at the end of a spring.

We can now determine the period of SHM because it is equal to that of the revolving object making one complete revolution. First we note that the velocity $v_{max}$ is equal to the circumference of the circle (distance) divided by the period $T$:

$$v_{max} = \frac{2\pi A}{T} = 2\pi A f. \qquad \textbf{(11–6)}$$

We solve for the period $T$:

$$T = \frac{2\pi A}{v_{max}}.$$

From energy conservation, Eqs. 11–4a and b, we have $\frac{1}{2}kA^2 = \frac{1}{2}mv_{max}^2$, so $A/v_{max} = \sqrt{m/k}$. Thus

*Period T of SHM*

$$T = 2\pi\sqrt{\frac{m}{k}}. \qquad \textbf{(11–7a)}$$

*Period and frequency of SHM don't depend on amplitude*

This is the formula we were looking for. The period depends on the mass $m$ and the spring stiffness constant $k$, but not on the amplitude $A$. We see from Eq. 11–7a that the larger the mass, the longer the period; and the stiffer the spring (larger $k$), the shorter the period. This makes sense since a larger mass means more inertia and therefore slower response (smaller acceleration). And larger $k$ means greater force and therefore quicker response (larger acceleration). Notice that Eq. 11–7a is not a direct proportion: the period varies as the *square root* of $m/k$. For example, the mass must be quadrupled to double the period.

Equation 11–7a is fully in accord with experiment and is valid not only for a spring, but for all kinds of simple harmonic motion—that is, for motion subject to a restoring force proportional to displacement, Eq. 11–1.

We can write the frequency using $f = 1/T$ (Eq. 11–2):

$$f = \frac{1}{T} = \frac{1}{2\pi}\sqrt{\frac{k}{m}}. \qquad \textbf{(11–7b)}$$

*Frequency f of SHM*

**EXERCISE C** Does a car bounce faster on its springs when empty or fully loaded?

**EXAMPLE 11–6 ESTIMATE Spider web.** A spider of mass 0.30 g waits in its web of negligible mass (Fig. 11–7). A slight movement causes the web to vibrate with a frequency of about 15 Hz. (*a*) Estimate the value of the spring stiffness constant $k$ for the web. (*b*) At what frequency would you expect the web to vibrate if an insect of mass 0.10 g were trapped in addition to the spider?

**APPROACH** We can only make a rough estimate because a spider's web is fairly complicated and may vibrate with a mixture of frequencies. We use SHM as an approximate model.

**SOLUTION** (*a*) The frequency of SHM is given by Eq. 11–7b,

$$f = \frac{1}{2\pi}\sqrt{\frac{k}{m}}.$$

We solve for $k$:

$$\begin{aligned} k &= (2\pi f)^2 m \\ &= (6.28 \times 15\,\mathrm{s}^{-1})^2(3.0 \times 10^{-4}\,\mathrm{kg}) = 2.7\,\mathrm{N/m}. \end{aligned}$$

(*b*) The total mass is now $0.10\,\mathrm{g} + 0.30\,\mathrm{g} = 4.0 \times 10^{-4}\,\mathrm{kg}$. We could substitute $m = 4.0 \times 10^{-4}\,\mathrm{kg}$ into Eq. 11–7b. Instead, we notice that the frequency decreases with the square root of the mass. Since the new mass is 4/3 times the first mass, the frequency changes by a factor of $1/\sqrt{4/3} = \sqrt{3/4}$. Thus $f = (15\,\mathrm{Hz})(\sqrt{3/4}) = 13\,\mathrm{Hz}$.

**NOTE** Check this result by direct substitution of $k$, found in part (*a*), and the new mass $m$ into Eq. 11–7b.

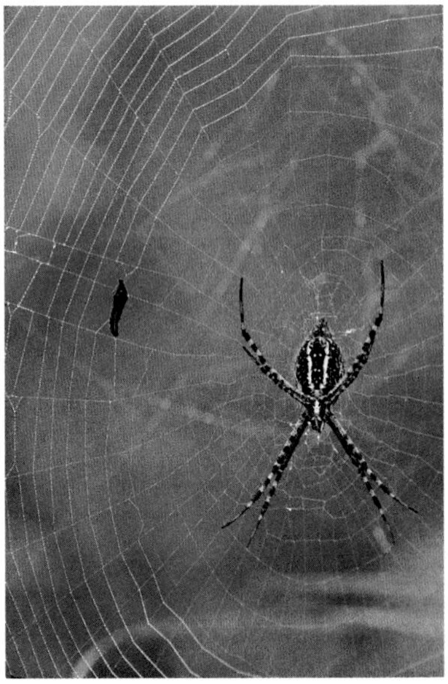

**FIGURE 11–7** A spider waits for its prey (Example 11–6).

## Position as a Function of Time

We now use the reference circle to find the position of a mass undergoing simple harmonic motion as a function of time. From Fig. 11–6, we see that $\cos\theta = x/A$, so the projection of the object's position on the $x$ axis is

$$x = A\cos\theta.$$

Because the mass is rotating with angular velocity $\omega$, we can write $\theta = \omega t$, where $\theta$ is in radians (Section 8–1). Thus

$$x = A\cos\omega t. \qquad \textbf{(11–8a)}$$

Furthermore, since the angular velocity $\omega$ (specified in radians per second) can be written as $\omega = 2\pi f$, where $f$ is the frequency (Eq. 8–7), we then write

$$x = A\cos(2\pi f t), \qquad \textbf{(11–8b)}$$

or in terms of the period $T$,

$$x = A\cos(2\pi t/T). \qquad \textbf{(11–8c)}$$

*Position as a function of time (SHM)*

Notice in Eq. 11–8c that when $t = T$ (that is, after a time equal to one period), we have the cosine of $2\pi$, which is the same as the cosine of zero. This makes sense since the motion repeats itself after a time $t = T$.

**CAUTION**

*$t$ is a variable (time); $T$ is a constant for a given situation*

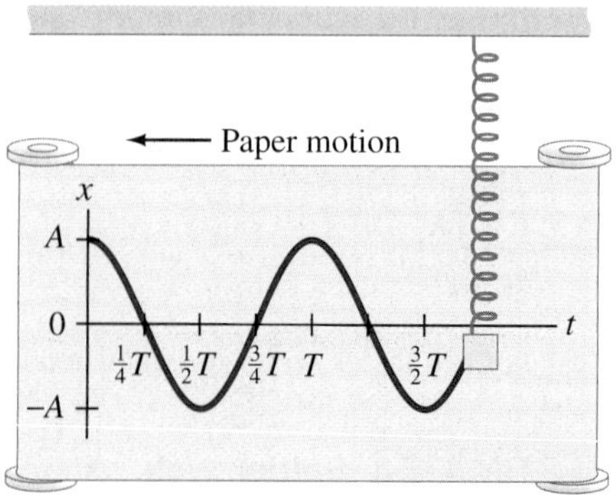


**FIGURE 11–8** Position as a function of time $x = A\cos(2\pi t/T)$.

As we have seen, the $x$ component of a uniformly rotating object's motion corresponds precisely to the motion of a simple harmonic oscillator. Thus Eqs. 11–8 give the position of an object undergoing simple harmonic motion. Since the cosine function varies between 1 and $-1$, $x$ varies between $A$ and $-A$, as it must. If a pen is attached to a vibrating mass as a sheet of paper is moved at a steady rate beneath it (Fig. 11–8), a curve will be drawn that accurately follows Eqs. 11–8.

**EXAMPLE 11–7** **Starting with $x = A\cos\omega t$.** The displacement of an object is described by the following equation, where $x$ is in meters and $t$ is in seconds:

$$x = (0.30\text{ m})\cos(8.0\,t).$$

Determine the oscillating object's (*a*) amplitude, (*b*) frequency, (*c*) period, (*d*) maximum speed, and (*e*) maximum acceleration.

**APPROACH** We start by comparing the given equation for $x$ with Eq. 11–8b, $x = A\cos(2\pi f t)$.

**SOLUTION** From $x = A\cos(2\pi f t)$, we see by inspection that (*a*) the amplitude $A = 0.30\text{ m}$, and (*b*) $2\pi f = 8.0\text{ s}^{-1}$; so $f = (8.0\text{ s}^{-1}/2\pi) = 1.27\text{ Hz}$. (*c*) Then $T = 1/f = 0.79\text{ s}$. (*d*) The maximum speed (see Eq. 11–6) is

$$v_{\text{max}} = 2\pi A f = (2\pi)(0.30\text{ m})(1.27\text{ s}^{-1}) = 2.4\text{ m/s}.$$

(*e*) The maximum acceleration, by Newton's second law, is $a_{\text{max}} = F_{\text{max}}/m = kA/m$, because $F\,(= kx)$ is greatest when $x$ is greatest. From Eq. 11–7b we see that $k/m = (2\pi f)^2$. Hence

$$a_{\text{max}} = \frac{k}{m}A = (2\pi f)^2 A = (2\pi)^2(1.27\text{ s}^{-1})^2(0.30\text{ m}) = 19\text{ m/s}^2.$$

## Sinusoidal Motion

Equation 11–8, $x = A\cos\omega t$, assumes that the oscillating object starts from rest ($v = 0$) at its maximum displacement ($x = A$) at $t = 0$. Other equations for simple harmonic motion are also possible, depending on the initial conditions (when you choose $t$ to be zero). For example, if at $t = 0$ the object is at the equilibrium position and the oscillations are begun by giving the object a push to the right ($+x$), the equation would be

$$x = A\sin\omega t = A\sin(2\pi t/T).$$

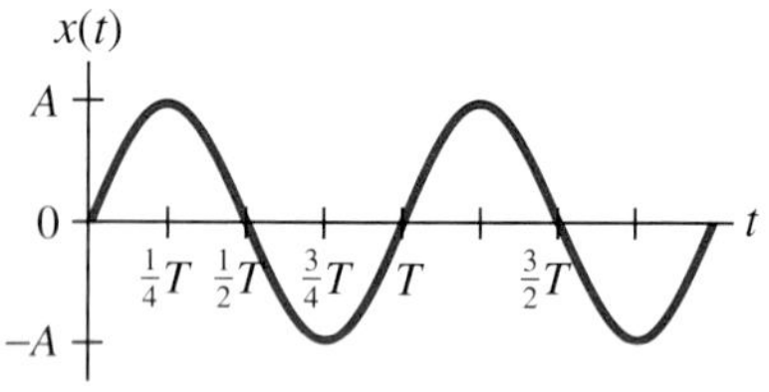


**FIGURE 11–9** Sinusoidal nature of SHM as a function of time; in this case, $x = A\sin(2\pi t/T)$ because at $t = 0$ the mass is at the equilibrium position $x = 0$, but it also has (or is given) an initial speed at $t = 0$ that carries it to $x = A$ at $t = \frac{1}{4}T$.

This curve (Fig. 11–9) has the same shape as the cosine curve shown in Fig. 11–8, except it is shifted to the right by a quarter cycle. Hence at $t = 0$ it starts out at $x = 0$ instead of at $x = A$.

*SHM is sinusoidal*

Both sine and cosine curves are referred to as being **sinusoidal** (having the shape of a sine function). Thus simple harmonic motion† is said to be sinusoidal because the position varies as a sinusoidal function of time.

†Simple harmonic motion can be *defined* as motion that is sinusoidal. This definition is fully consistent with our earlier definition in Section 11–1.

## * Velocity and Acceleration as Functions of Time

Figure 11–10a, like Fig. 11–8, shows a graph of displacement $x$ vs. time $t$, as given by Eqs. 11–8. We can also find the velocity $v$ as a function of time from Fig. 11–6a. For the position shown (red dot in Fig. 11–6a), we see that the magnitude of $v$ is $v_{max} \sin\theta$, but $\vec{\mathbf{v}}$ points to the left, so $v = -v_{max}\sin\theta$. Again setting $\theta = \omega t = 2\pi f t = 2\pi t/T$, we have

$$v = -v_{max}\sin\omega t = -v_{max}\sin(2\pi f t) = -v_{max}\sin(2\pi t/T). \qquad \textbf{(11–9)}$$

Just after $t = 0$, the velocity is negative (points to the left) and remains so until $t = \frac{1}{2}T$ (corresponding to $\theta = 180° = \pi$ radians). After $t = \frac{1}{2}T$ until $t = T$ the velocity is positive. The velocity as a function of time (Eq. 11–9) is plotted in Fig. 11–10b. From Eqs. 11–6 and 11–7b,

$$v_{max} = 2\pi A f = A\sqrt{\frac{k}{m}}.$$

For a given spring–mass system, the maximum speed $v_{max}$ is higher if the amplitude is larger, and always occurs as the mass passes the equilibrium point.

The acceleration as a function of time is found from Newton's second law:

$$a = \frac{F}{m} = \frac{-kx}{m} = -\left(\frac{kA}{m}\right)\cos\omega t = -a_{max}\cos(2\pi t/T) \qquad \textbf{(11–10)}$$

where the maximum acceleration is

$$a_{max} = kA/m.$$

Equation 11–10 is plotted in Fig. 11–10c. Because the acceleration of a SHO is *not* constant, the equations for uniformly accelerated motion do *not* apply to SHM.

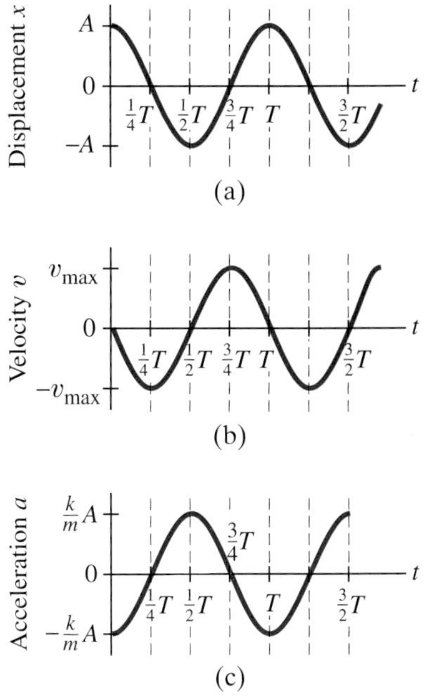


**FIGURE 11–10** Graphs showing (a) displacement $x$ as a function of time $t$: $x = A\cos(2\pi t/T)$; (b) velocity as a function of time: $v = -v_{max}\sin(2\pi t/T)$; (c) acceleration as a function of time: $a = -(kA/m)\cos(2\pi t/T)$.

**EXAMPLE 11–8** **Loudspeaker.** The cone of a loudspeaker vibrates in SHM at a frequency of 262 Hz ("middle C"). The amplitude at the center of the cone is $A = 1.5 \times 10^{-4}$ m, and at $t = 0$, $x = A$. (*a*) What equation describes the motion of the center of the cone? (*b*) What are the velocity and acceleration as a funcion of time? (*c*) What is the position of the cone at $t = 1.00$ ms ($= 1.00 \times 10^{-3}$ s)?

**APPROACH** The motion begins ($t = 0$) with the cone at its maximum displacement ($x = A$ at $t = 0$). So we use the cosine function, $x = A\cos\omega t$, to describe this SHM.

**SOLUTION** (*a*) Here

$$\omega = 2\pi f = (6.28\text{ rad})(262\text{ s}^{-1}) = 1650\text{ rad/s}.$$

The motion is described as

$$x = A\cos(2\pi f t) = (1.5 \times 10^{-4}\text{ m})\cos(1650t).$$

(*b*) The maximum velocity, from Eq. 11–6, is $v_{max} = 2\pi A f = 2\pi(1.5 \times 10^{-4}\text{ m})(262\text{ s}^{-1}) = 0.25$ m/s. Then by Eq. 11–9,

$$v = -(0.25\text{ m/s})\sin(1650t).$$

From Eqs. 11–10 and 11–7b, the maximum acceleration is $a_{max} = (k/m)A = (2\pi f)^2 A = 4\pi^2(262\text{ s}^{-1})^2(1.5 \times 10^{-4}\text{ m}) = 410\text{ m/s}^2$, which is more than 40 $g$'s. So

$$a = -(410\text{ m/s}^2)\cos(1650t).$$

(*c*) At $t = 1.00 \times 10^{-3}$ s, Eq. 11–8a gives us

$$x = A\cos\omega t = (1.5 \times 10^{-4}\text{ m})\cos[(1650\text{ rad/s})(1.00 \times 10^{-3}\text{ s})]$$
$$= (1.5 \times 10^{-4}\text{ m})\cos(1.65\text{ rad}) = -1.2 \times 10^{-5}\text{ m}.$$

**NOTE** Be sure your calculator is set in RAD mode, not DEG mode, for these $\cos\omega t$ calculations.

**CAUTION**

*Always be sure your calculator is in the correct mode for angles*

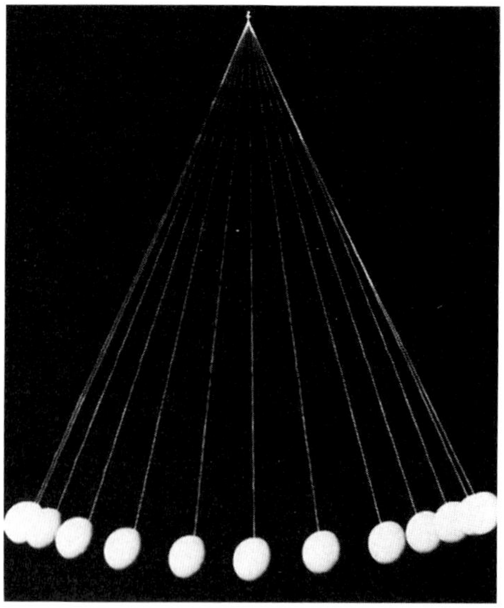

FIGURE 11–11 Strobe-light photo of an oscillating simple pendulum.

## 11–4 The Simple Pendulum

A **simple pendulum** consists of a small object (the pendulum bob) suspended from the end of a lightweight cord, Fig. 11–11. We assume that the cord doesn't stretch and that its mass can be ignored relative to that of the bob. The motion of a simple pendulum swinging back and forth with negligible friction resembles simple harmonic motion: the pendulum bob oscillates along the arc of a circle with equal amplitude on either side of its equilibrium point, and as it passes through the equilibrium point (where it would hang vertically) it has its maximum speed. But is it really undergoing SHM? That is, is the restoring force proportional to its displacement? Let us find out.

The displacement of the pendulum along the arc is given by $x = L\theta$, where $\theta$ is the angle the cord makes with the vertical and $L$ is the length of the cord (Fig. 11–12). If the restoring force is proportional to $x$ or to $\theta$, the motion will be simple harmonic. The restoring force is the net force on the bob, equal to the component of the weight, $mg$, tangent to the arc:

$$F = -mg\sin\theta,$$

where $g$ is the acceleration of gravity. The minus sign here, as in Eq. 11–1, means the force is in the direction opposite to the angular displacement $\theta$. Since $F$ is proportional to the sine of $\theta$ and not to $\theta$ itself, the motion is *not* SHM. However, if $\theta$ is small, then $\sin\theta$ is very nearly equal to $\theta$ when the latter is specified in radians. This can be seen by noting in Fig. 11–12 that the arc length $x\ (= L\theta)$ is nearly the same length as the chord $(= L\sin\theta)$ indicated by the horizontal straight dashed line, *if $\theta$ is small*. For angles less than 15°, the difference between $\theta$ (in radians) and $\sin\theta$ is less than 1%—see Table 11–1. Thus, to a very good approximation for small angles,

$$F = -mg\sin\theta \approx -mg\theta.$$

Substituting $x = L\theta$, or $\theta = x/L$, we have

$$F \approx -\frac{mg}{L}x.$$

Thus, for small displacements, the motion is essentially simple harmonic, since this equation fits Hooke's law, $F = -kx$. The effective force constant is $k = mg/L$.

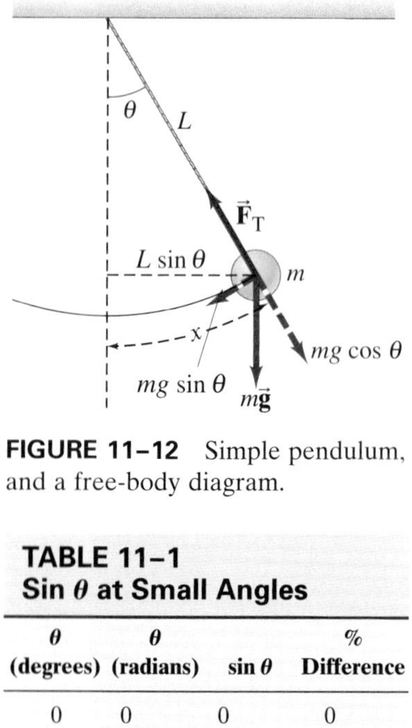


FIGURE 11–12 Simple pendulum, and a free-body diagram.

**TABLE 11–1**
**Sin θ at Small Angles**

| θ (degrees) | θ (radians) | sin θ | % Difference |
|---|---|---|---|
| 0 | 0 | 0 | 0 |
| 1° | 0.01745 | 0.01745 | 0.005% |
| 5° | 0.08727 | 0.08716 | 0.1% |
| 10° | 0.17453 | 0.17365 | 0.5% |
| 15° | 0.26180 | 0.25882 | 1.1% |
| 20° | 0.34907 | 0.34202 | 2.0% |
| 30° | 0.52360 | 0.50000 | 4.7% |

If we substitute $k = mg/L$ into Eq. 11–7a, we obtain the period of a simple pendulum:

$$T = 2\pi\sqrt{\frac{m}{k}} = 2\pi\sqrt{\frac{m}{mg/L}}$$

or

$$T = 2\pi\sqrt{\frac{L}{g}}. \qquad [\theta \text{ small}] \quad \textbf{(11–11a)}$$

*Period, simple pendulum*

The frequency is $f = 1/T$, so

$$f = \frac{1}{2\pi}\sqrt{\frac{g}{L}}. \qquad [\theta \text{ small}] \quad \textbf{(11–11b)}$$

*Frequency, simple pendulum*

The mass $m$ of the pendulum bob does not appear in these formulas for $T$ and $f$. Thus we have the surprising result that the period and frequency of a simple pendulum do not depend on the mass of the pendulum bob. You may have noticed this if you pushed a small child and a large one on the same swing.

We also see from Eq. 11–11a that the period of a pendulum does not depend on the amplitude (like any SHM, Section 11–3), as long as the amplitude $\theta$ is small. Galileo is said to have first noted this fact while watching a swinging lamp in the cathedral at Pisa (Fig. 11–13). This discovery led to the invention of the pendulum clock, the first really precise timepiece, which became the standard for centuries.

**PHYSICS APPLIED**
*Pendulum clock*

Because a pendulum does not undergo *precisely* SHM, the period does depend slightly on the amplitude—the more so for large amplitudes. The accuracy of a pendulum clock would be affected, after many swings, by the decrease in amplitude due to friction. But the mainspring in a pendulum clock (or the falling weight in a grandfather clock) supplies energy to compensate for the friction and to maintain the amplitude constant, so that the timing remains precise.

**EXAMPLE 11–9 Measuring *g*.** A geologist uses a simple pendulum that has a length of 37.10 cm and a frequency of 0.8190 Hz at a particular location on the Earth. What is the acceleration of gravity at this location?

**APPROACH** We can use the length $L$ and frequency $f$ of the pendulum in Eq. 11–11b, which contains our unknown, $g$.

**SOLUTION** We solve Eq. 11–11b for $g$ and obtain

$$g = (2\pi f)^2 L = (6.283 \times 0.8190\,\text{s}^{-1})^2(0.3710\,\text{m}) = 9.824\,\text{m/s}^2.$$

**EXERCISE D** (*a*) Estimate the length of the pendulum in a grandfather clock that ticks once per second. (*b*) What would be the period of a clock with a 1.0-m-long pendulum?

Equations 11–11 apply to a simple pendulum—a concentrated mass at the end of a string of negligible mass—but not to the oscillation of, say, a baseball bat suspended from one end.

**FIGURE 11–13** The swinging motion of this lamp, hanging by a very long cord from the ceiling of the cathedral at Pisa, is said to have been observed by Galileo and to have inspired him to the conclusion that the period of a pendulum does not depend on amplitude.

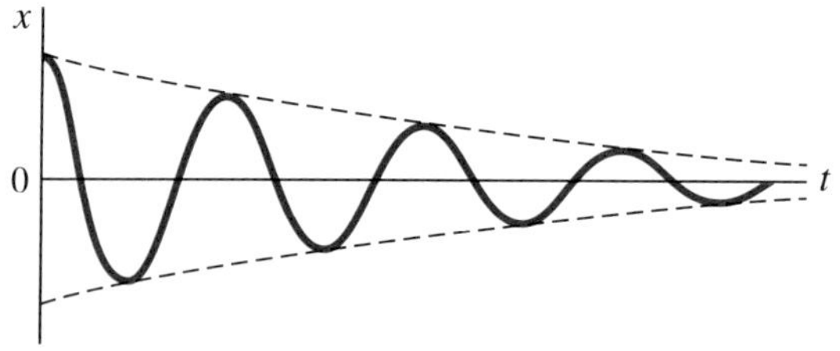


**FIGURE 11–14** Damped harmonic motion.

## 11–5 Damped Harmonic Motion

The amplitude of any real oscillating spring or swinging pendulum will slowly decrease in time until the oscillations stop altogether. Figure 11–14 shows a typical graph of the displacement as a function of time. This is called **damped harmonic motion**. The damping[†] is generally due to the resistance of air and to internal friction within the oscillating system. The energy that is dissipated to thermal energy results in a decreased amplitude of oscillation.

Since natural oscillating systems are damped in general, why do we even talk about (undamped) simple harmonic motion? The answer is that SHM is much easier to deal with mathematically. And if the damping is not large, the oscillations can be thought of as simple harmonic motion on which the damping is superposed. The decrease in amplitude shown by the dashed curves in Fig. 11–14 represents the damping. Although frictional damping does alter the frequency of vibration, the effect is usually small unless the damping is large; thus Eqs. 11–7 can still be used in most cases.

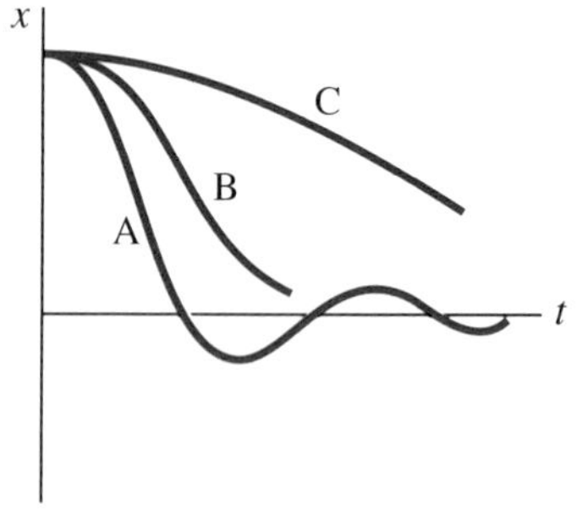


**FIGURE 11–15** Graphs that represent (A) underdamped, (B) critically damped, and (C) overdamped oscillatory motion.

Sometimes the damping is so large, however, that the motion no longer resembles simple harmonic motion. Three common cases of heavily damped systems are shown in Fig. 11–15. Curve A represents an **underdamped** situation, in which the system makes several swings before coming to rest, and corresponds to a more heavily damped version of Fig. 11–14. Curve C represents the **overdamped** situation, for which the damping is so large that it takes a long time to reach equilibrium. Curve B represents **critical damping**: in this case equilibrium is reached in the shortest time. These terms all derive from the use of practical damped systems such as door-closing mechanisms and shock absorbers in a car (Fig. 11–16). Such devices are usually designed to give critical damping. But as they wear out, underdamping occurs: a door slams or a car bounces up and down several times each time it hits a bump.

**PHYSICS APPLIED**
*Shock absorbers and building dampers*

In many systems, the oscillatory motion is what counts, as in clocks and watches, and damping needs to be minimized. In other systems, oscillations are the problem, such as a car's springs, so a proper amount of damping (i.e., critical) is desired. Well-designed damping is needed for all kinds of applications. Large buildings, especially in California, are now built (or retrofitted) with huge dampers to reduce earthquake damage (Fig. 11–17).

[†]To "damp" means to diminish, restrain, or extinguish, as to "dampen one's spirits."

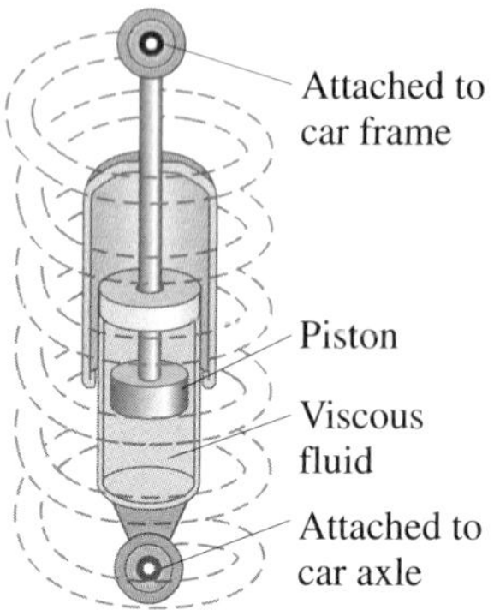


**FIGURE 11–16** Automobile spring and shock absorber to provide damping so that a car won't bounce up and down so much.

**FIGURE 11–17** These huge dampers placed in a building look a lot like huge automobile shock absorbers, and they serve a similar purpose—to reduce the amplitude and the acceleration of movement when the shock of an earthquake hits.

## 11–6 Forced Vibrations; Resonance

When a vibrating system is set into motion, it vibrates at its natural frequency (Eqs. 11–7b and 11–11b). However, a system may have an external force applied to it that has its own particular frequency. Then we have a **forced vibration**. For example, we might pull the mass on the spring of Fig. 11–1 back and forth at an externally applied frequency $f$. The mass then vibrates at the external frequency $f$ of the external force, even if this frequency is different from the **natural frequency** of the spring, which we will now denote by $f_0$, where (see Eq. 11–7b)

$$f_0 = \frac{1}{2\pi}\sqrt{\frac{k}{m}}.$$

For a forced vibration, the amplitude of vibration is found to depend on the difference between $f$ and $f_0$, and is a maximum when the frequency of the external force equals the natural frequency of the system—that is, when $f = f_0$. The amplitude is plotted in Fig. 11–18 as a function of the external frequency $f$. Curve A represents light damping and curve B heavy damping. The amplitude can become large when the external driving frequency $f$ is near the natural frequency, $f \approx f_0$, as long as the damping is not too large. When the damping is small, the increase in amplitude near $f = f_0$ is very large (and often dramatic). This effect is known as **resonance**. The natural vibrating frequency $f_0$ of a system is also called its **resonant frequency**.

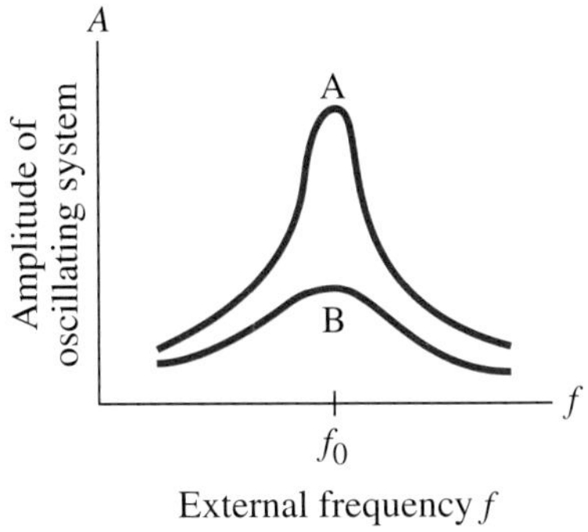


**FIGURE 11–18** Resonance for lightly damped (A) and heavily damped (B) systems.

**PHYSICS APPLIED**
*Swinging*

A simple illustration of resonance is pushing a child on a swing. A swing, like any pendulum, has a natural frequency of oscillation. If you push on the swing at a random frequency, the swing bounces around and reaches no great amplitude. But if you push with a frequency equal to the natural frequency of the swing, the amplitude increases greatly. At resonance, relatively little effort is required to obtain a large amplitude.

**PHYSICS APPLIED**
*Shattering glass via resonance*

The great tenor Enrico Caruso was said to be able to shatter a crystal goblet by singing a note of just the right frequency at full voice. This is an example of resonance, for the sound waves emitted by the voice act as a forced vibration on the glass. At resonance, the resulting vibration of the goblet may be large enough in amplitude that the glass exceeds its elastic limit and breaks.

**PHYSICS APPLIED**
*Resonant collapse*

Since material objects are, in general, elastic, resonance is an important phenomenon in a variety of situations. It is particularly important in building, although the effects are not always foreseen. For example, it has been reported that a railway bridge collapsed because a nick in one of the wheels of a crossing train set up a resonant vibration in the bridge. Marching soldiers break step when crossing a bridge to avoid the possibility that their rhythmic march might match a resonant frequency of the bridge. The collapse of the Tacoma Narrows Bridge (Fig. 11–19a) in 1940 occurred as a result of gusting winds whose approximate frequency matched that of a natural frequency of the bridge, thus driving the span into large-amplitude oscillatory motion. Bridges and tall buildings are now designed with more inherent damping. The Oakland freeway collapse in the 1989 California earthquake (Fig. 11–19b) involved resonant oscillation of a section built on mudfill.

Resonance can be very useful, too, and we will meet important examples later, such as in musical instruments and tuning a radio. We will also see that vibrating objects often have not one, but many resonant frequencies.

(a)

(b)

**FIGURE 11–19** (a) Large-amplitude oscillations of the Tacoma Narrows Bridge, due to gusty winds, led to its collapse (November 7, 1940). (b) Collapse of a freeway in California, due to the 1989 earthquake, in which resonance played a part.

**FIGURE 11–20** Water waves spreading outward from a source.

## 11–7 Wave Motion

When you throw a stone into a lake or pool of water, circular waves form and move outward, Fig. 11–20. Waves will also travel along a cord that is stretched out straight on a table if you vibrate one end back and forth as shown in Fig. 11–21. Water waves and waves on a cord are two common examples of wave motion. We will discuss other kinds of waves later, but for now we will concentrate on these **mechanical waves**.

If you have ever watched ocean waves moving toward shore before they break†, you may have wondered if the waves were carrying water from far out at sea into the beach. They don't. Water waves move with a recognizable velocity. But each particle (or molecule) of the water itself merely oscillates about an equilibrium point. This is clearly demonstrated by observing leaves on a pond as waves move by. The leaves (or a cork) are not carried forward by the waves, but simply oscillate about an equilibrium point because this is the motion of the water itself.

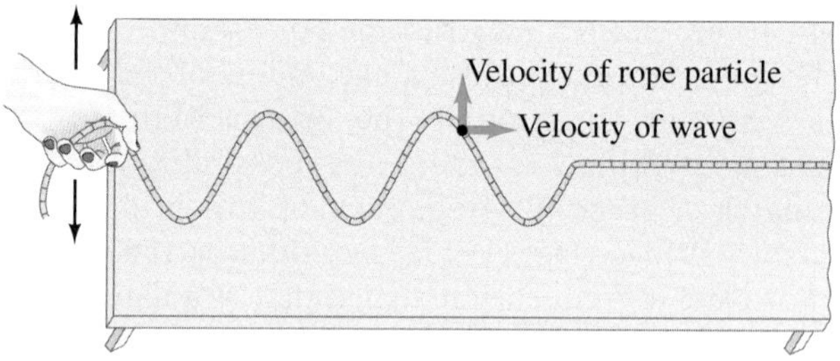


**FIGURE 11–21** Wave traveling on a cord. The wave travels to the right along the cord. Particles of the cord oscillate back and forth on the tabletop.

CONCEPTUAL EXAMPLE 11–10 **Wave vs. particle velocity.** Is the velocity of a wave moving along a cord the same as the velocity of a particle of the cord? See Fig. 11–21.

**RESPONSE** No. The two velocities are different, both in magnitude and direction. The wave on the rope of Fig. 11–21 moves to the right along the tabletop, but each piece of the rope only vibrates to and fro. (The rope clearly does not travel in the direction that the wave on it does.)

Waves can move over large distances, but the medium (the water or the rope) itself has only a limited movement, oscillating about an equilibrium point

†Do not be confused by the "breaking" of ocean waves, which occurs when a wave interacts with the ground in shallow water and hence is no longer a simple wave.

as in simple harmonic motion. Thus, although a wave is not matter, the wave pattern can travel in matter. A wave consists of oscillations that move without carrying matter with them.

*Waves are moving oscillations, not carrying matter along*

Waves carry energy from one place to another. Energy is given to a water wave, for example, by a rock thrown into the water, or by wind far out at sea. The energy is transported by waves to the shore. The oscillating hand in Fig. 11–21 transfers energy to the rope, and that energy is transported down the rope and can be transferred to an object at the other end. All forms of traveling waves transport energy.

*Wave pulse*

Let us look a little more closely at how a wave is formed and how it comes to "travel." We first look at a single wave bump, or **pulse**. A single pulse can be formed on a rope by a quick up-and-down motion of the hand, Fig. 11–22. The hand pulls up on one end of the rope. Because the end section is attached to adjacent sections, these also feel an upward force and they too begin to move upward. As each succeeding section of rope moves upward, the wave crest moves outward along the rope. Meanwhile, the end section of rope has been returned to its original position by the hand. As each succeeding section of rope reaches its peak position, it too is pulled back down again by the adjacent section of rope. Thus the source of a traveling wave pulse is a disturbance, and cohesive forces between adjacent sections of rope cause the pulse to travel outward. Waves in other media are created and propagate outward in a similar fashion.

*Periodic wave*

A **continuous** or **periodic wave**, such as that shown in Fig. 11–21, has as its source a disturbance that is continuous and oscillating; that is, the source is a *vibration* or *oscillation*. In Fig. 11–21, a hand oscillates one end of the rope. Water waves may be produced by any vibrating object at the surface, such as your hand; or the water itself is made to vibrate when wind blows across it or a rock is thrown into it. A vibrating tuning fork or drum membrane gives rise to sound waves in air. And we will see later that oscillating electric charges give rise to light waves. Indeed, almost any vibrating object sends out waves.

The source of any wave, then, is a vibration. And it is a *vibration* that propagates outward and thus constitutes the wave. If the source vibrates sinusoidally in SHM, then the wave itself—if the medium is perfectly elastic—will have a sinusoidal shape both in space and in time. (1) In space: if you take a picture of the wave in space at a given instant of time, the wave will have the shape of a sine or cosine as a function of position. (2) In time: if you look at the motion of the medium at one place over a long period of time—for example, if you look between two closely spaced posts of a pier or out of a ship's porthole as water waves pass by—the up-and-down motion of that small segment of water will be simple harmonic motion. The water moves up and down sinusoidally in time.

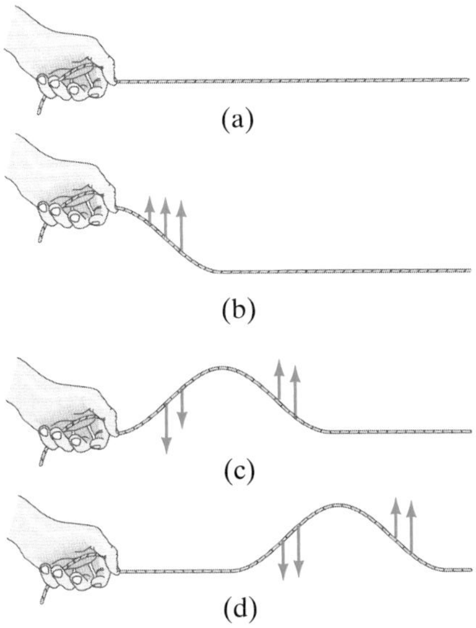


**FIGURE 11–22** Motion of a wave pulse to the right. Arrows indicate velocity of cord particles.

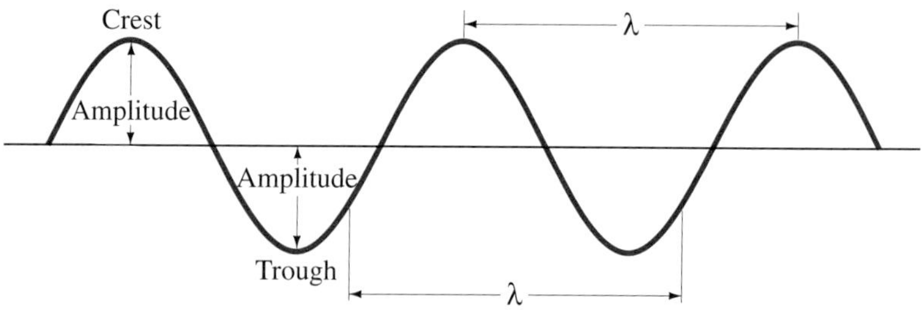


**FIGURE 11–23** Characteristics of a single-frequency continuous wave.

*Amplitude, A*

*Wavelength, λ*

*Frequency, f*
*Period, T*

*Wave velocity*

Some of the important quantities used to describe a periodic sinusoidal wave are shown in Fig. 11–23. The high points on a wave are called *crests*; the low points, *troughs*. The **amplitude**, $A$, is the maximum height of a crest, or depth of a trough, relative to the normal (or equilibrium) level. The total swing from a crest to a trough is twice the amplitude. The distance between two successive crests is called the **wavelength**, $\lambda$ (the Greek letter lambda). The wavelength is also equal to the distance between *any* two successive identical points on the wave. The **frequency**, $f$, is the number of crests—or complete cycles—that pass a given point per unit time. The **period**, $T$, equals $1/f$ and is the time elapsed between two successive crests passing by the same point in space.

The **wave velocity**, $v$, is the velocity at which wave crests (or any other part of the waveform) move. The wave velocity must be distinguished from the velocity of a particle of the medium itself as we saw in Example 11–10.

A wave crest travels a distance of one wavelength, $\lambda$, in a time equal to one period, $T$. Thus the wave velocity is $v = \lambda/T$. Then, since $1/T = f$,

*$v = \lambda f$ (sinusoidal waves)*

$$v = \lambda f. \tag{11–12}$$

For example, suppose a wave has a wavelength of 5 m and a frequency of 3 Hz. Since three crests pass a given point per second, and the crests are 5 m apart, the first crest (or any other part of the wave) must travel a distance of 15 m during the 1 s. So its speed is 15 m/s.

The magnitude of the velocity of a wave, or its speed, depends on the properties of the medium in which it travels. The speed of a wave on a stretched string or cord, for example, depends on the tension in the cord, $F_T$, and on the cord's mass per unit length, $m/L$. For waves of small amplitude, the relationship is

*Speed of wave on a cord*

$$v = \sqrt{\frac{F_T}{m/L}}. \tag{11–13}$$

This formula makes sense qualitatively on the basis of Newtonian mechanics. That is, we expect the tension to be in the numerator and the mass per unit length in the denominator. Why? Because when the tension is greater, we expect the velocity to be greater since each segment of cord is in tighter contact with its neighbor; and the greater the mass per unit length, the more inertia the cord has and the more slowly the wave would be expected to propagate.

**EXAMPLE 11–11** **Wave on a wire.** A wave whose wavelength is 0.30 m is traveling down a 300-m-long wire whose total mass is 15 kg. If the wire is under a tension of 1000 N, what are the speed and frequency of this wave?

**APPROACH** We assume the velocity of this wave on a wire is given by Eq. 11–13. We get the frequency from Eq. 11–12, $f = v/\lambda$.

**SOLUTION** From Eq. 11–13, the velocity is

$$v = \sqrt{\frac{1000\ \text{N}}{(15\ \text{kg})/(300\ \text{m})}} = \sqrt{\frac{1000\ \text{N}}{(0.050\ \text{kg/m})}} = 140\ \text{m/s}.$$

The frequency is

$$f = \frac{v}{\lambda} = \frac{140\ \text{m/s}}{0.30\ \text{m}} = 470\ \text{Hz}.$$

**NOTE** A higher tension would increase both $v$ and $f$, whereas a thicker, denser wire would reduce $v$ and $f$.

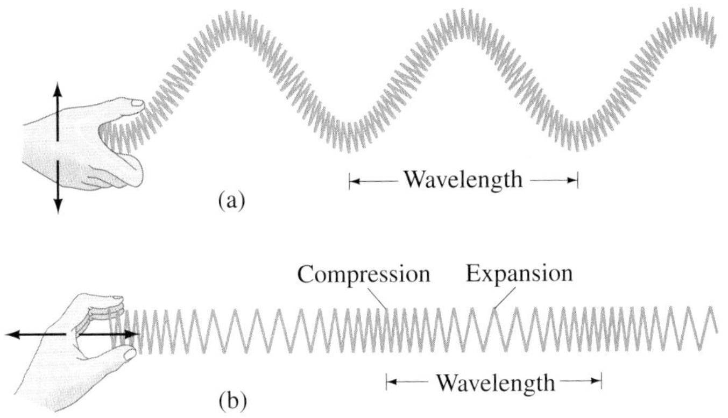


**FIGURE 11–24**
(a) Transverse wave;
(b) longitudinal wave.

## 11–8 Types of Waves: Transverse and Longitudinal

*Transverse and longitudinal waves*

When a wave travels down a rope—say, from left to right as in Fig. 11–21—the particles of the rope vibrate up and down in a direction transverse (that is, perpendicular) to the motion of the wave itself. Such a wave is called a **transverse wave** (Fig. 11–24a). There exists another type of wave known as a **longitudinal wave**. In a longitudinal wave, the vibration of the particles of the medium is *along* the direction of the wave's motion. Longitudinal waves are readily formed on a stretched spring or Slinky by alternately compressing and expanding one end. This is shown in Fig. 11–24b, and can be compared to the transverse wave in Fig. 11–24a. A series of compressions and expansions propagate along the spring. The *compressions* are those areas where the coils are momentarily close together. *Expansions* (sometimes called *rarefactions*) are regions where the coils are momentarily far apart. Compressions and expansions correspond to the crests and troughs of a transverse wave.

An important example of a longitudinal wave is a sound wave in air. A vibrating drumhead, for instance, alternately compresses and rarefies the air in contact with it, producing a longitudinal wave that travels outward in the air, as shown in Fig. 11–25.

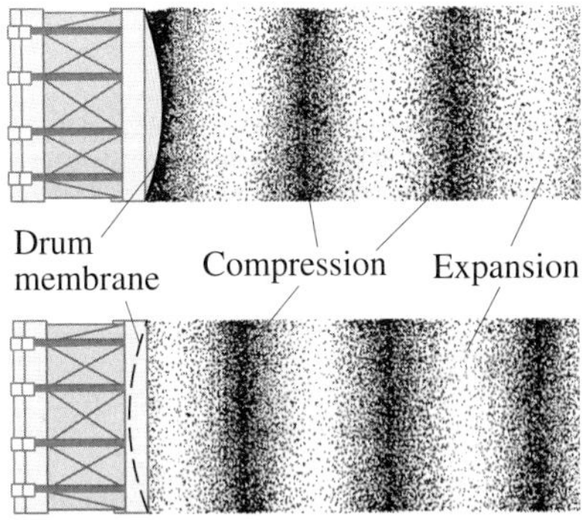


**FIGURE 11–25** Production of a sound wave, which is longitudinal, shown at two moments in time about a half period $\left(\frac{1}{2}T\right)$ apart.

As in the case of transverse waves, each section of the medium in which a longitudinal wave passes oscillates over a very small distance, whereas the wave itself can travel large distances. Wavelength, frequency, and wave velocity all have meaning for a longitudinal wave. The wavelength is the distance between successive compressions (or between successive expansions), and frequency is the number of compressions that pass a given point per second. The wave velocity is the velocity with which each compression appears to move; it is equal to the product of wavelength and frequency, $v = \lambda f$ (Eq. 11–12).

A longitudinal wave can be represented graphically by plotting the density of air molecules (or coils of a Slinky) versus position at a given instant, as shown in Fig. 11–26. Such a graphical representation makes it easy to illustrate what is happening. Note that the graph looks much like a transverse wave.

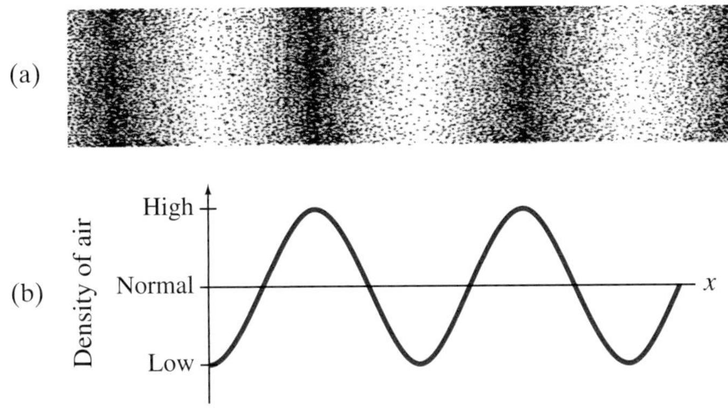


**FIGURE 11–26**
(a) A longitudinal wave with
(b) its graphical representation at a particular instant in time.

## * Speed of Longitudinal Waves

The speed of a longitudinal wave has a form similar to that for a transverse wave on a cord (Eq. 11–13):

$$v = \sqrt{\frac{\text{elastic force factor}}{\text{inertia factor}}}.$$

In particular, for a longitudinal wave traveling down a long solid rod,

*Longitudinal wave speed in a long solid rod*

$$v = \sqrt{\frac{E}{\rho}}, \qquad \textbf{(11–14a)}$$

where $E$ is the elastic modulus (Section 9–5) of the material and $\rho$ is its density. For a longitudinal wave traveling in a liquid or gas,

*Longitudinal wave speed in a fluid*

$$v = \sqrt{\frac{B}{\rho}}, \qquad \textbf{(11–14b)}$$

where $B$ is the bulk modulus (Section 9–5) and $\rho$ is the density.

PHYSICS APPLIED
*Space perception by animals using sound waves*

**EXAMPLE 11–12** **Echolocation.** Echolocation is a form of sensory perception used by animals such as bats, toothed whales, and porpoises. The animal emits a pulse of sound (a longitudinal wave) which, after reflection from objects, is detected by the animal. Echolocation waves emitted by whales (Fig. 11–27) have frequencies of about 200,000 Hz. (*a*) What is the wavelength of the whale's echolocation wave? (*b*) If an obstacle is 100 m from the whale, how long after the whale emits a wave is its reflection detected?

**APPROACH** We first compute the speed of longitudinal (sound) waves in sea water, using Eq. 11–14b and Tables 9–1 and 10–1. The wavelength is $\lambda = v/f$.

**SOLUTION** (*a*) The speed of longitudinal waves in sea water, which is slightly more dense than pure water, is

$$v = \sqrt{\frac{B}{\rho}} = \sqrt{\frac{2.0 \times 10^9\,\text{N/m}^2}{1.025 \times 10^3\,\text{kg/m}^3}} = 1.40 \times 10^3\,\text{m/s}.$$

Then, using Eq. 11–12, we find

$$\lambda = \frac{v}{f} = \frac{(1.40 \times 10^3\,\text{m/s})}{(2.0 \times 10^5\,\text{Hz})} = 7.0\,\text{mm}.$$

(*b*) The time required for the round-trip between the whale and the object is

$$t = \frac{\text{distance}}{\text{speed}} = \frac{2(100\,\text{m})}{1.40 \times 10^3\,\text{m/s}} = 0.14\,\text{s}.$$

**NOTE** We shall see later that waves can "resolve" (or detect) objects only if the wavelength is comparable to or smaller than the object. Thus, a whale can resolve objects on the order of a centimeter or larger in size.

**FIGURE 11–27** A toothed whale (Example 11–12).

## Other Waves

PHYSICS APPLIED
*Earthquake waves*

Both transverse and longitudinal waves are produced when an **earthquake** occurs. The transverse waves that travel through the body of the Earth are called S waves (S for shear), and the longitudinal waves are called P waves (P for pressure) or *compression* waves. Both longitudinal and transverse waves can travel through a solid since the atoms or molecules can vibrate about their relatively fixed positions in any direction. But in a fluid, only longitudinal waves can propagate, because any transverse motion would experience no restoring force since a fluid is readily deformable. This fact was used by geophysicists to infer that a portion of the Earth's core must be liquid: after an earthquake, longitudinal waves are detected diametrically across the Earth, but not transverse waves.

Besides these two types of waves, *surface waves* can travel along the boundary between two materials. A wave on water is actually a surface wave that moves on the boundary between water and air. The motion of each particle of water at the surface is circular or elliptical (Fig. 11–28), so it is a combination of transverse and longitudinal motions. Below the surface, there is also transverse plus longitudinal wave motion, as shown. At the bottom, the motion is only longitudinal. When a wave approaches shore, the water drags at the bottom and is slowed down, while the crests move ahead at higher speed (Fig. 11–29) and "spill" over the top.

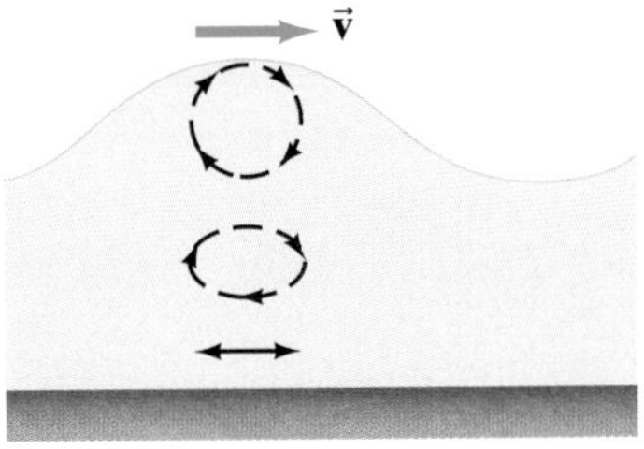


**FIGURE 11–28** A water wave is an example of a *surface wave*, which is a combination of transverse and longitudinal wave motions.

Surface waves are also set up on the Earth when an earthquake occurs. The waves that travel along the surface are mainly responsible for the damage caused by earthquakes.

Waves traveling along a line, as on a stretched string, are *one-dimensional waves*. Surface waves, such as the water waves of Fig. 11–20, are *two-dimensional waves*. Waves that move out from a source in all directions in a medium, such as sound from a speaker or earthquake waves through the Earth, are *three-dimensional waves*.

**FIGURE 11–29** How a wave breaks. The green arrows represent the local velocity of water molecules.

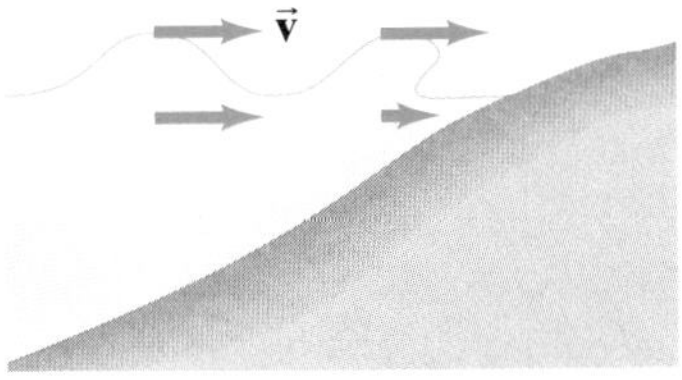


## 11–9 Energy Transported by Waves

Waves transport energy from one place to another. As waves travel through a medium, the energy is transferred as vibrational energy from particle to particle of the medium. For a sinusoidal wave of frequency $f$, the particles move in SHM as a wave passes, so each particle has an energy $E = \frac{1}{2}kA^2$, where $A$ is the amplitude of its motion, either transversely or longitudinally. (See Eq. 11–4a.)

Thus, we have the important result that the **energy transported by a wave is proportional to the square of the amplitude**. The **intensity** $I$ of a wave is defined as the power (energy per unit time) transported across unit area perpendicular to the direction of energy flow:

*Wave energy $\propto$ (amplitude)$^2$*

$$I = \frac{\text{energy/time}}{\text{area}} = \frac{\text{power}}{\text{area}}.$$

*Intensity (defined)*

The SI unit of intensity is watts per square meter $(\mathrm{W/m^2})$. Since the energy is proportional to the wave amplitude squared, so too is the intensity:

$$I \propto A^2. \qquad \textbf{(11–15)}$$

*Intensity $\propto$ (amplitude)$^2$*

If a wave flows out from the source in all directions, it is a three-dimensional wave. Examples are sound traveling in open air, earthquake waves, and light waves. If the medium is isotropic (same in all directions), the wave is a *spherical wave* (Fig. 11–30). As the wave moves outward, the energy it carries is spread over a larger and larger area since the surface area of a sphere of radius $r$ is $4\pi r^2$. Thus the intensity of a spherical wave is

$$I = \frac{\text{power}}{\text{area}} = \frac{P}{4\pi r^2}. \qquad \text{[spherical wave]} \quad \textbf{(11–16a)}$$

**FIGURE 11–30** A wave traveling outward in three dimensions from a source is spherical. Two crests (or compressions) are shown, of radii $r_1$ and $r_2$.

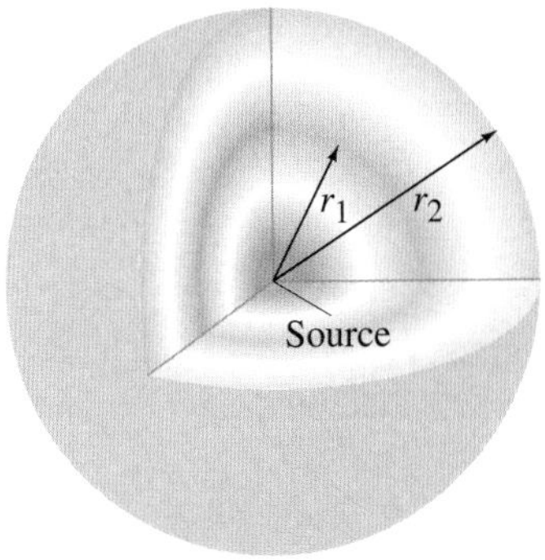


If the power output $P$ of the source is constant, then the intensity decreases as the inverse square of the distance from the source:

$$I \propto \frac{1}{r^2}. \qquad \textbf{(11–16b)}$$

If we consider two points at distances $r_1$ and $r_2$ from the source, as in Fig. 11–30, then $I_1 = P/4\pi r_1^2$ and $I_2 = P/4\pi r_2^2$, so

$$\frac{I_2}{I_1} = \frac{r_1^2}{r_2^2}. \qquad \textbf{(11–16c)}$$

*$I \propto \frac{1}{r^2}$*

Thus, for example, when the distance doubles $(r_2/r_1 = 2)$, the intensity is reduced to $\frac{1}{4}$ its earlier value: $I_2/I_1 = \left(\frac{1}{2}\right)^2 = \frac{1}{4}$.

*Sounds are quieter farther from the source*

The amplitude of a wave also decreases with distance. Since the intensity is proportional to the square of the amplitude (Eq. 11–15), the amplitude $A$ must decrease as $1/r$ so that $I \propto A^2$ will be proportional to $1/r^2$ (as in Eq. 11–16b). Hence

$$A \propto \frac{1}{r}.$$

If we consider again two distances from the source, $r_1$ and $r_2$, then

$$\frac{A_2}{A_1} = \frac{r_1}{r_2}.$$

When the wave is twice as far from the source, the amplitude is half as large, and so on (ignoring damping due to friction).

**EXAMPLE 11–13 Earthquake intensity.** The intensity of an earthquake P wave traveling through the Earth and detected 100 km from the source is $1.0 \times 10^6\ \mathrm{W/m^2}$. What is the intensity of that wave if detected 400 km from the source?

**APPROACH** We assume the wave is spherical, so the intensity decreases as the square of the distance from the source.

**SOLUTION** At 400 km the distance is 4 times greater than at 100 km, so the intensity will be $\left(\frac{1}{4}\right)^2 = \frac{1}{16}$ of its value at 100 km, or $(1.0 \times 10^6\ \mathrm{W/m^2})/16 = 6.3 \times 10^4\ \mathrm{W/m^2}$.

**NOTE** Using Eq. 11–16c directly gives:

$$I_2 = I_1 r_1^2/r_2^2 = (1.0 \times 10^6\ \mathrm{W/m^2})(100\ \mathrm{km})^2/(400\ \mathrm{km})^2 = 6.3 \times 10^4\ \mathrm{W/m^2}.$$

The situation is different for a one-dimensional wave, such as a transverse wave on a string or a longitudinal wave pulse traveling down a thin uniform metal rod. The area remains constant, so the amplitude $A$ also remains constant (ignoring friction). Thus the amplitude and the intensity do not decrease with distance.

In practice, frictional damping is generally present, and some of the energy is transformed into thermal energy. Thus the amplitude and intensity of a one-dimensional wave will decrease with distance from the source. For a three-dimensional wave, the decrease will be greater than that discussed above, although the effect may often be small.

## * 11–10 Intensity Related to Amplitude and Frequency

We can obtain an explicit relation between the energy carried by a wave, or the wave's intensity $I$, and the amplitude and frequency of the wave. For a sinusoidal wave of frequency $f$, the particles move in SHM as a wave passes, so each particle has an energy $E = \frac{1}{2}kA^2$, where $A$ is the amplitude of its motion, either transversely or longitudinally. Using Eq. 11–7b, we can write $k$ in terms of the frequency: $k = 4\pi^2 mf^2$, where $m$ is the mass of a particle (or small volume) of the medium. Then

$$E = \tfrac{1}{2}kA^2 = 2\pi^2 mf^2 A^2.$$

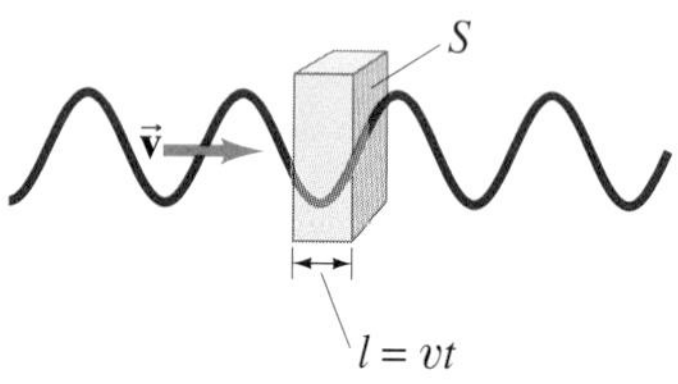

**FIGURE 11–31** Calculating the energy carried by a wave moving with velocity $v$.

The mass $m = \rho V$, where $\rho$ is the density of the medium and $V$ the volume of a small slice of the medium as shown in Fig. 11–31. The volume $V = Sl$, where $S$ is the cross-sectional surface area through which the wave travels. (We use $S$ instead of $A$ for area because we are using $A$ for amplitude.) We can write $l$ as the distance the wave travels in a time $t$ as $l = vt$, where $v$ is the speed of the wave. Thus $m = \rho V = \rho Sl = \rho Svt$, and

$$E = 2\pi^2 \rho Svtf^2 A^2. \qquad \textbf{(11–17a)}$$

From this equation, we see again the important result that the energy transported by a wave is proportional to the square of the amplitude. The power transported, $P = E/t$, is

$$P = \frac{E}{t} = 2\pi^2 \rho S v f^2 A^2. \qquad \textbf{(11–17b)}$$

Finally, the **intensity** $I$ of a wave is the power transported across unit area perpendicular to the direction of energy flow:

$$I = \frac{P}{S} = 2\pi^2 v \rho f^2 A^2. \qquad \textbf{(11–18)}$$

This relation shows explicitly that the intensity of a wave is proportional both to the square of the wave amplitude $A$ at any point and to the square of the frequency $f$.

## 11–11 Reflection and Transmission of Waves

When a wave strikes an obstacle, or comes to the end of the medium it is traveling in, at least a part of the wave is reflected. You have probably seen water waves reflect off a rock or the side of a swimming pool. And you may have heard a shout reflected from a distant cliff—which we call an "echo."

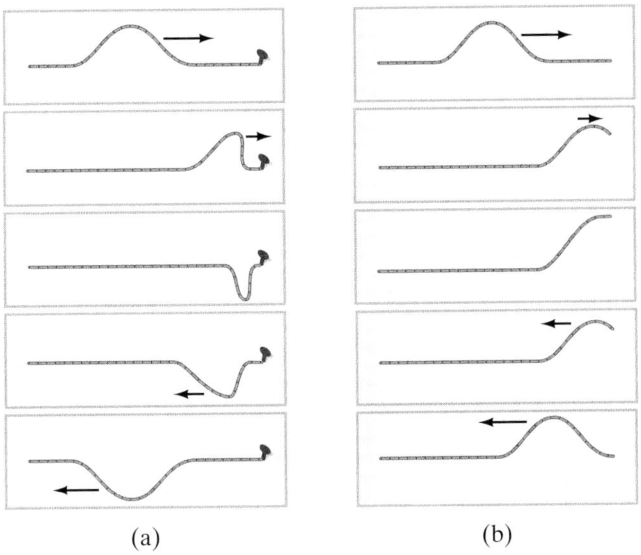


**FIGURE 11–32** Reflection of a wave pulse on a rope lying on a table top. (a) The end of the rope is fixed to a peg. (b) The end of the rope is free to move.

A wave pulse traveling down a rope is reflected as shown in Fig. 11–32. The reflected pulse returns inverted as in Fig. 11–32a if the end of the rope is fixed; it returns right side up if the end is free as in Fig. 11–32b. When the end is fixed to a support, as in Fig. 11–32a, the pulse reaching that fixed end exerts a force (upward) on the support. The support exerts an equal but opposite force downward on the rope (Newton's third law). This downward force on the rope is what "generates" the inverted reflected pulse.

Consider next a pulse that travels down a rope which consists of a light section and a heavy section, as shown in Fig. 11–33. When the wave pulse reaches the boundary between the two sections, part of the pulse is reflected and part is transmitted, as shown. The heavier the second section of rope, the less the energy that is transmitted. (When the second section is a wall or rigid support, very little is transmitted and most is reflected, as in Fig. 11–32a.) For a periodic wave, the frequency of the transmitted wave does not change across the boundary because the boundary point oscillates at that frequency. Thus if the transmitted wave has a lower speed, its wavelength is also shorter ($\lambda = v/f$).

**FIGURE 11–33** When a wave pulse traveling to the right along a thin cord (a) reaches a discontinuity where the rope becomes thicker and heavier, then part is reflected and part is transmitted (b).

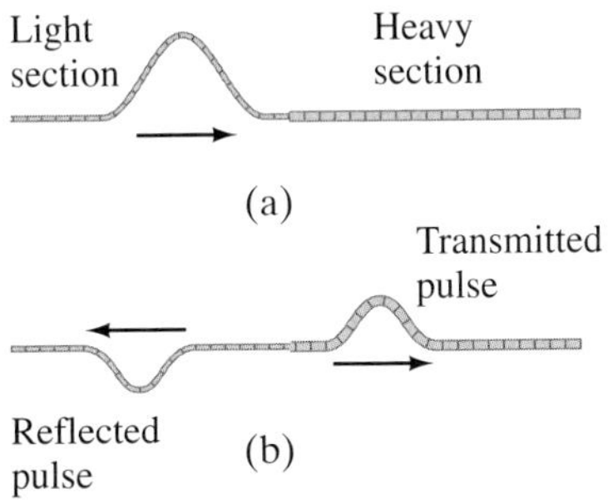

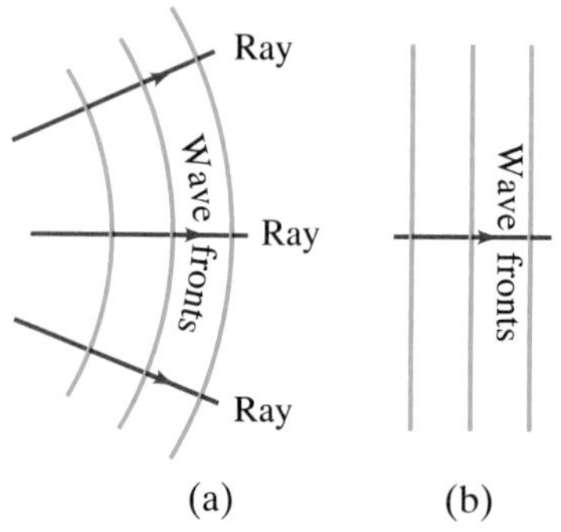


**FIGURE 11–34** Rays, signifying the direction of wave motion, are always perpendicular to the wave fronts (wave crests). (a) Circular or spherical waves near the source. (b) Far from the source, the wave fronts are nearly straight or flat, and are called plane waves.

For a two- or three-dimensional wave, such as a water wave, we are concerned with **wave fronts**, by which we mean all the points along the wave forming the wave crest (what we usually refer to simply as a "wave" at the seashore). A line drawn in the direction of wave motion, perpendicular to the wave front, is called a **ray**, as shown in Fig. 11–34. Wave fronts far from the source have lost almost all their curvature (Fig. 11–34b) and are nearly straight, as ocean waves often are; they are then called **plane waves**.

For reflection of a two- or three-dimensional plane wave, as shown in Fig. 11–35, the angle that the incoming or *incident wave* makes with the reflecting surface is equal to the angle made by the reflected wave. This is the **law of reflection: the angle of reflection equals the angle of incidence**. The "angle of incidence" is defined as the angle the incident ray makes with the perpendicular to the reflecting surface (or the wave front makes with a tangent to the surface). The "angle of reflection" is the corresponding angle for the reflected wave.

**FIGURE 11–35** Law of reflection.

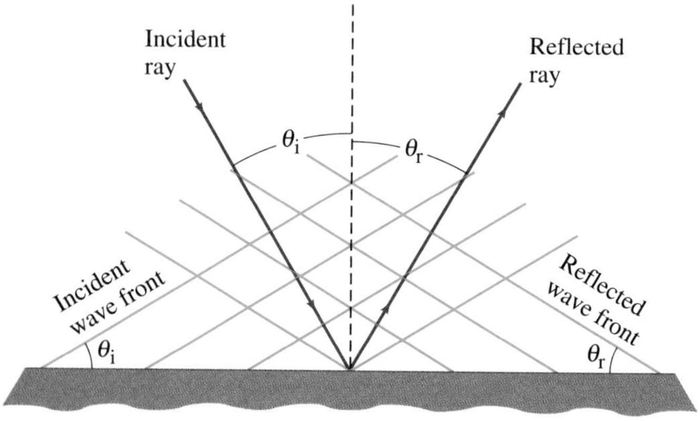


## 11–12 Interference; Principle of Superposition

**Interference** refers to what happens when two waves pass through the same region of space at the same time. Consider, for example, the two wave pulses on a string traveling toward each other as shown in Fig. 11–36. In Fig. 11–36a the two pulses have the same amplitude, but one is a crest and the other a trough; in Fig. 11–36b they are both crests. In both cases, the waves meet and pass right by each other. However, in the region where they overlap, the resultant displacement is the *algebraic sum of their separate displacements* (a crest is considered positive and a trough negative). This is called the **principle of superposition**. In Fig. 11–36a, the two waves have opposite displacements at the instant they pass one another, and they add to zero. The result is called **destructive interference**. In Fig. 11–36b, at the instant the two pulses overlap, they produce a resultant displacement that is greater than the displacement of either separate pulse, and the result is **constructive interference**.

*Superposition principle*

*Destructive interference*

*Constructive interference*

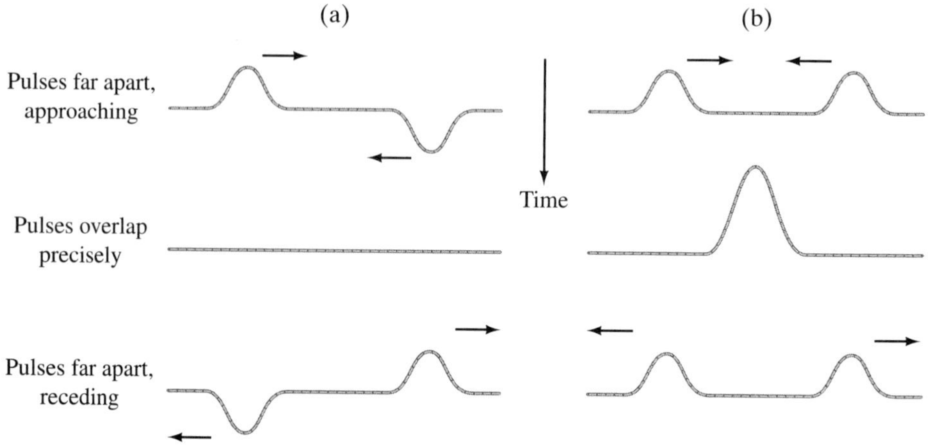


**FIGURE 11–36** Two wave pulses pass each other. Where they overlap, interference occurs: (a) destructive, and (b) constructive.

(a)

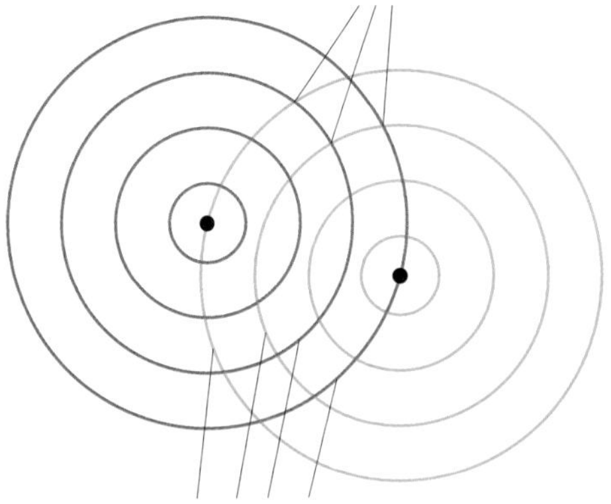


(b)

**FIGURE 11–37** Interference of water waves.

When two rocks are thrown into a pond simultaneously, the two sets of circular waves interfere with one another as shown in Fig. 11–37a. In some areas of overlap, crests of one wave repeatedly meet crests of the other (and troughs meet troughs); see Fig. 11–37b. Constructive interference is occurring at these points, and the water continuously oscillates up and down with greater amplitude than either wave separately. In other areas, destructive interference occurs where the water does not move up and down at all over time. This is where crests of one wave meet troughs of the other, and vice versa. Figure 11–38a shows the displacement of two waves graphically as a function of time, as well as their sum, for the case of constructive interference. For any two such waves, we use the term **phase** to describe the relative positions of their crests. When the crests and troughs are aligned as in Fig. 11–38a, for constructive interference, the two waves are **in phase**. At points where destructive interference occurs—see Fig. 11–38b—crests of one wave repeatedly meet troughs of the other wave and the two waves are said to be completely **out of phase** or, more precisely, out of phase by one-half wavelength. That is, the crests of one wave occur a half wavelength behind the crests of the other wave. The relative phase of the two water waves in Fig. 11–37 in most areas is intermediate between these two extremes, resulting in *partially* destructive interference, as illustrated in Fig. 11–38c. If the amplitudes of two interfering waves are not equal, fully destructive interference (as in Fig. 11–38b) does not occur.

*Phase*

**FIGURE 11–38** Graphs showing two waves, and their sum, as a function of time at three locations. In (a) the two waves interfere constructively, in (b) destructively, and in (c) partially destructively.

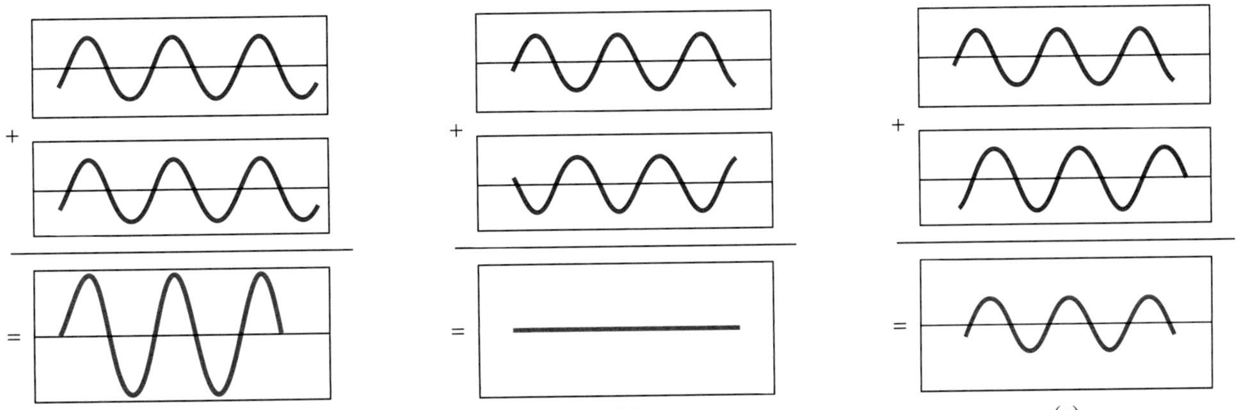


(a) (b) (c)

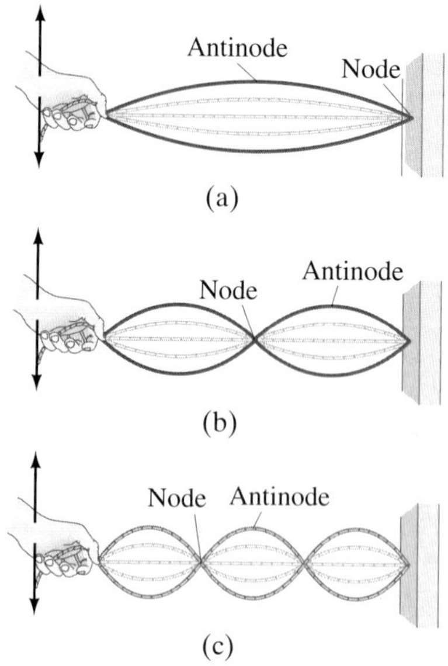


**FIGURE 11–39** Standing waves corresponding to three resonant frequencies.

## 11–13 Standing Waves; Resonance

If you shake one end of a cord and the other end is kept fixed, a continuous wave will travel down to the fixed end and be reflected back, inverted, as we saw in Fig. 11–32a. As you continue to vibrate the cord, waves will travel in both directions, and the wave traveling along the cord, away from your hand, will interfere with the reflected wave coming back. Usually there will be quite a jumble. But if you vibrate the cord at just the right frequency, the two traveling waves will interfere in such a way that a large-amplitude **standing wave** will be produced, Fig. 11–39. It is called a "standing wave" because it doesn't appear to be traveling. The cord simply appears to have segments that oscillate up and down in a fixed pattern. The points of destructive interference, where the cord remains still at all times, are called **nodes**. Points of constructive interference, where the cord oscillates with maximum amplitude, are called **antinodes**. The nodes and antinodes remain in fixed positions for a particular frequency.

Standing waves can occur at more than one frequency. The lowest frequency of vibration that produces a standing wave gives rise to the pattern shown in Fig. 11–39a. The standing waves shown in Figs. 11–39b and 11–39c are produced at precisely twice and three times the lowest frequency, respectively, assuming the tension in the cord is the same. The cord can also vibrate with four loops (four antinodes) at four times the lowest frequency, and so on.

*Resonant frequencies*

The frequencies at which standing waves are produced are the **natural frequencies** or **resonant frequencies** of the cord, and the different standing wave patterns shown in Fig. 11–39 are different "resonant modes of vibration." A standing wave on a cord is the result of the interference of two waves traveling in opposite directions. A standing wave is also a vibrating object at resonance. Standing waves represent the same phenomenon as the resonance of a vibrating spring or pendulum, which we discussed in Section 11–6. The only difference is that a spring or pendulum has only one resonant frequency, whereas the cord has an infinite number of resonant frequencies, each of which is a whole-number multiple of the lowest resonant frequency.

Consider a string stretched between two supports that is plucked like a guitar or violin string, Fig. 11–40a. Waves of a great variety of frequencies will

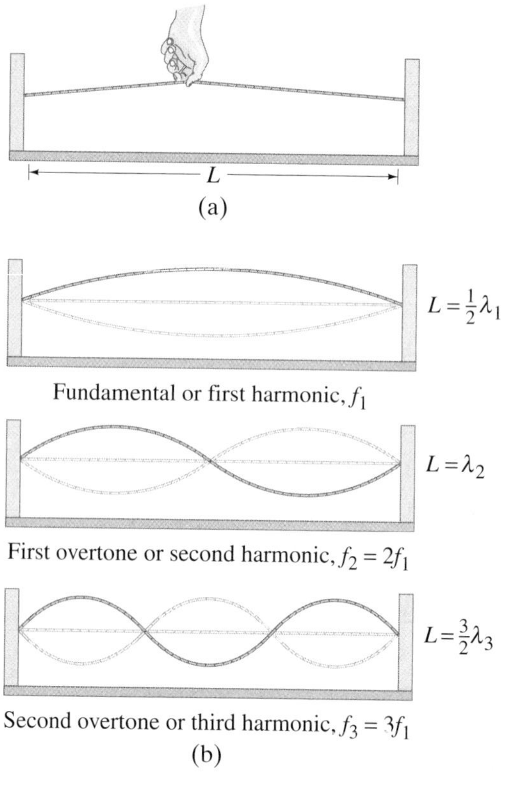


**FIGURE 11–40** (a) A string is plucked. (b) Only standing waves corresponding to resonant frequencies persist for long.

travel in both directions along the string, will be reflected at the ends, and will travel back in the opposite direction. Most of these waves interfere with each other and quickly die out. However, those waves that correspond to the resonant frequencies of the string will persist. The ends of the string, since they are fixed, will be nodes. There may be other nodes as well. Some of the possible resonant modes of vibration (standing waves) are shown in Fig. 11–40b. Generally, the motion will be a combination of these different resonant modes, but only those frequencies that correspond to a resonant frequency will be present.

To determine the resonant frequencies, we first note that the wavelengths of the standing waves bear a simple relationship to the length $L$ of the string. The lowest frequency, called the **fundamental frequency**, corresponds to one antinode (or loop). And as can be seen in Fig. 11–40b, the whole length corresponds to one-half wavelength. Thus $L = \frac{1}{2}\lambda_1$, where $\lambda_1$ stands for the wavelength of the fundamental frequency. The other natural frequencies are called **overtones**; for a vibrating string they are whole-number (integral) multiples of the fundamental, and then are also called **harmonics**, with the fundamental being referred to as the **first harmonic**.[†] The next mode of vibration after the fundamental has two loops and is called the **second harmonic** (or first overtone), Fig. 11–40b. The length of the string $L$ at the second harmonic corresponds to one complete wavelength: $L = \lambda_2$. For the third and fourth harmonics, $L = \frac{3}{2}\lambda_3$, and $L = 2\lambda_4$, respectively, and so on. In general, we can write

*Fundamental frequency*

*Overtones and harmonics*

$$L = \frac{n\lambda_n}{2}, \qquad \text{where } n = 1, 2, 3, \cdots.$$

The integer $n$ labels the number of the harmonic: $n = 1$ for the fundamental, $n = 2$ for the second harmonic, and so on. We solve for $\lambda_n$ and find

$$\lambda_n = \frac{2L}{n}, \qquad n = 1, 2, 3, \cdots. \tag{11–19a}$$

To find the frequency $f$ of each vibration we use Eq. 11–12, $f = v/\lambda$, and we see that

$$f_n = \frac{v}{\lambda_n} = n\frac{v}{2L} = nf_1, \qquad n = 1, 2, 3, \cdots, \tag{11–19b}$$

where $f_1 = v/\lambda_1 = v/2L$ is the fundamental frequency. We see that each resonant frequency is an integer multiple of the fundamental frequency.

Because a standing wave is equivalent to two traveling waves moving in opposite directions, the concept of wave velocity still makes sense and is given by Eq. 11–13 in terms of the tension $F_T$ in the string and its mass per unit length $(m/L)$. That is, $v = \sqrt{F_T/(m/L)}$ for waves traveling in both directions.

**EXAMPLE 11–14** **Piano string.** A piano string is 1.10 m long and has a mass of 9.00 g. (*a*) How much tension must the string be under if it is to vibrate at a fundamental frequency of 131 Hz? (*b*) What are the frequencies of the first four harmonics?

**APPROACH** To determine the tension, we need to find the wave speed using Eq. 11–12 $(v = \lambda f)$, and then use Eq. 11–13, solving it for $F_T$.

**SOLUTION** (*a*) The wavelength of the fundamental is $\lambda = 2L = 2.20\,\text{m}$ (Eq. 11–19a with $n = 1$). The speed of the wave on the string is $v = \lambda f = (2.20\,\text{m})(131\,\text{s}^{-1}) = 288\,\text{m/s}$. Then we have (Eq. 11–13)

$$F_T = \frac{m}{L}v^2 = \left(\frac{9.00 \times 10^{-3}\,\text{kg}}{1.10\,\text{m}}\right)(288\,\text{m/s})^2 = 679\,\text{N}.$$

(*b*) The frequencies of the second, third, and fourth harmonics are two, three, and four times the fundamental frequency: 262, 393, and 524 Hz.

**NOTE** The speed of the wave on the string is *not* the same as the speed of the sound that is produced in the air (as we shall see in Chapter 12).

[†] The term "harmonic" comes from music, because such integral multiples of frequencies "harmonize."

Standing waves are produced not only on strings, but on any object that is struck, such as a drum membrane or an object made of metal or wood. The resonant frequencies depend on the dimensions of the object, just as for a string they depend on its length. Large objects have lower resonant frequencies than small objects. All musical instruments, from stringed instruments to wind instruments (in which a column of air vibrates as a standing wave) to drums and other percussion instruments, depend on standing waves to produce their musical sounds, as we shall see in Chapter 12.

## * 11–14 Refraction†

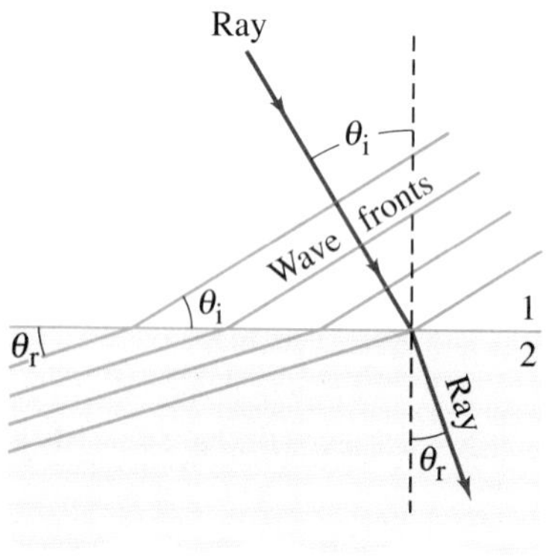


**FIGURE 11–41** Refraction of waves passing a boundary.

When any wave strikes a boundary, some of the energy is reflected and some is transmitted or absorbed. When a two- or three-dimensional wave traveling in one medium crosses a boundary into a medium where its speed is different, the transmitted wave may move in a different direction than the incident wave, as shown in Fig. 11–41. This phenomenon is known as **refraction**. One example is a water wave; the velocity decreases in shallow water and the waves refract, as shown in Fig. 11–42 below. [When the wave velocity changes gradually, as in Fig. 11–42, without a sharp boundary, the waves change direction (refract) gradually.]

In Fig. 11–41, the velocity of the wave in medium 2 is less than in medium 1. In this case, the wave front bends so it travels more nearly parallel to the boundary. That is, the *angle of refraction*, $\theta_r$, is less than the *angle of incidence*, $\theta_i$. To see why this is so, and to help us get a quantitative relation between $\theta_r$ and $\theta_i$, let us think of each wave front as a row of soldiers. The soldiers are marching from firm ground (medium 1) into mud (medium 2) and hence are slowed down after the boundary. The soldiers that reach the mud first are slowed down first, and the row bends as shown in Fig. 11–43a. Let us consider the wave front (or row of soldiers) labeled A in Fig. 11–43b. In the same time $t$ that $A_1$ moves a distance $l_1 = v_1 t$, we see that $A_2$ moves a distance $l_2 = v_2 t$. The two right triangles in Fig. 11–43b, shaded yellow and green, have the side labeled $a$ in common. Thus

$$\sin\theta_1 = \frac{l_1}{a} = \frac{v_1 t}{a}$$

since $a$ is the hypotenuse, and

$$\sin\theta_2 = \frac{l_2}{a} = \frac{v_2 t}{a}.$$

Dividing these two equations, we obtain the *law of refraction*:

*Law of refraction*

$$\frac{\sin\theta_2}{\sin\theta_1} = \frac{v_2}{v_1}. \qquad (11\text{–}20)$$

Since $\theta_1$ is the angle of incidence $(\theta_i)$, and $\theta_2$ is the angle of refraction $(\theta_r)$, Eq. 11–20 gives the quantitative relation between the two. If the wave were

†This Section and the next are covered in more detail in Chapters 23 to 25, on optics.

**FIGURE 11–42** Water waves refract gradually as they approach the shore, as their velocity decreases. There is no distinct boundary, as in Fig. 11–41, because the wave velocity changes gradually.

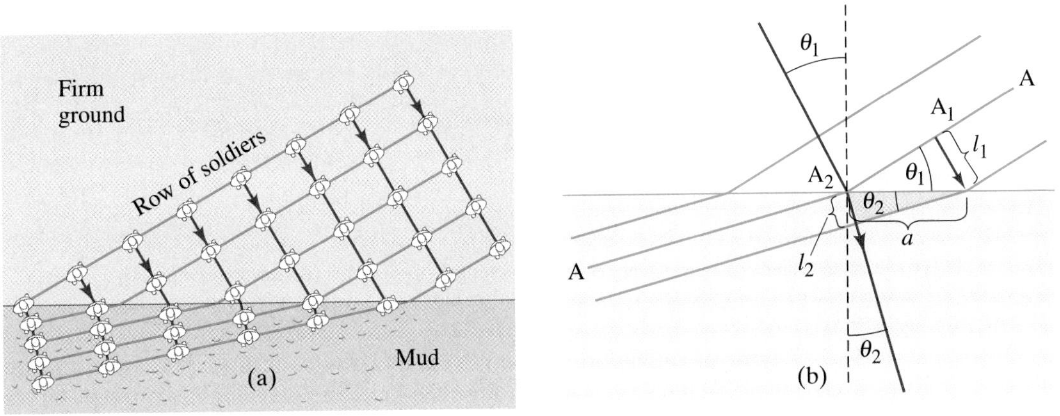


**FIGURE 11–43** (a) Soldier analogy to derive (b) law of refraction for waves.

going in the opposite direction, the geometry would not change; only $\theta_1$ and $\theta_2$ would change roles: $\theta_1$ would be the angle of refraction and $\theta_2$ the angle of incidence. Clearly then, if the wave travels into a medium where it can move faster, it will bend the opposite way, $\theta_r > \theta_i$. We see from Eq. 11–20 that if the velocity increases, the angle increases, and vice versa.

Earthquake waves refract within the Earth as they travel through rock layers of different densities (and therefore the velocity is different) just as water waves do. Light waves refract as well, and when we discuss light, we shall find Eq. 11–20 very useful.

**PHYSICS APPLIED**
*Earthquake wave refraction*

**EXAMPLE 11–15** **Refraction of an earthquake wave.** An earthquake P wave passes across a boundary in rock where its velocity increases from 6.5 km/s to 8.0 km/s. If it strikes this boundary at 30°, what is the angle of refraction?

**APPROACH** We apply the law of refraction, Eq. 11–20.

**SOLUTION** Since $\sin 30° = 0.50$, Eq. 11–20 yields

$$\sin\theta_2 = \frac{(8.0\ \mathrm{m/s})}{(6.5\ \mathrm{m/s})}(0.50) = 0.62.$$

So $\theta_2 = \sin^{-1}(0.62) = 38°$.

**NOTE** Be careful with angles of incidence and refraction. As we discussed in Section 11–11 (Fig. 11–35), these angles are between the wave front and the boundary line, or—equivalently—between the ray (direction of wave motion) and the line perpendicular to the boundary. Inspect Fig. 11–43b carefully.

## * 11–15 Diffraction

Waves spread as they travel. When they encounter an obstacle, they bend around it somewhat and pass into the region behind as shown in Fig. 11–44 for water waves. This phenomenon is called **diffraction**.

**FIGURE 11–44** Wave diffraction. The waves are coming from the upper left. Note how the waves, as they pass the obstacle, bend around it, into the "shadow region" behind it.

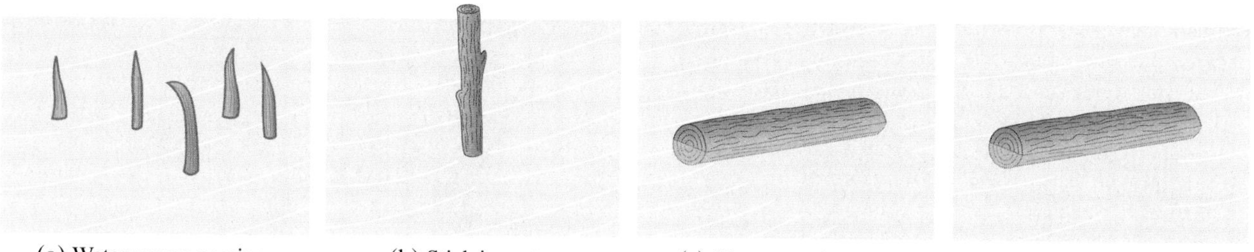

(a) Water waves passing blades of grass (b) Stick in water (c) Short-wavelength waves passing log (d) Long-wavelength waves passing log

**FIGURE 11–45** Water waves passing objects of various sizes. Note that the longer the wavelength compared to the size of the object, the more diffraction there is into the "shadow region."

The amount of diffraction depends on the wavelength of the wave and on the size of the obstacle, as shown in Fig. 11–45. If the wavelength is much larger than the object, as with the grass blades of Fig. 11–45a, the wave bends around them almost as if they are not there. For larger objects, parts (b) and (c), there is more of a "shadow" region behind the obstacle where we might not expect the waves to penetrate—but they do, at least a little. Then notice in part (d), where the obstacle is the same as in part (c) but the wavelength is longer, that there is more diffraction into the shadow region. As a rule of thumb, *only if the wavelength is smaller than the size of the object will there be a significant shadow region*. This rule applies to *reflection* from an obstacle as well. Very little of a wave is reflected unless the wavelength is smaller than the size of the obstacle.

A rough guide to the amount of diffraction is

$$\theta(\text{radians}) \approx \frac{\lambda}{L},$$

where $\theta$ is roughly the angular spread of waves after they have passed through an opening of width $L$ or around an obstacle of width $L$.

That waves can bend around obstacles, and thus can carry energy to areas behind obstacles, is very different from energy carried by material particles. A clear example is the following: if you are standing around a corner on one side of a building, you can't be hit by a baseball thrown from the other side, but you can hear a shout or other sound because the sound waves diffract around the edges.

CONCEPTUAL EXAMPLE 11–16 **Cell phones.** Cellular phones operate by radio waves with frequencies of about 1 or 2 GHz $(1 \text{ gigahertz} = 10^9\,\text{Hz})$. These waves cannot penetrate objects that conduct electricity, such as a tree trunk or a sheet of metal. The connection is best if the transmitting antenna is within clear view of the handset. Yet it is possible to carry on a phone conversation even if the tower is blocked by trees, or if the handset is inside a car. Why?

**RESPONSE** If the radio waves have a frequency of about 2 GHz, and the speed of propagation is equal to the speed of light, $3 \times 10^8$ m/s (Section 1–5), then the wavelength is $\lambda = v/f = (3 \times 10^8\,\text{m/s})/(2 \times 10^9\,\text{Hz}) = 0.15\,\text{m}$. The waves can diffract readily around objects 15 cm in diameter or smaller.

## * 11–16 Mathematical Representation of a Traveling Wave

**FIGURE 11–46** The characteristics of a single-frequency wave at $t = 0$ (just as in Fig. 11–23).

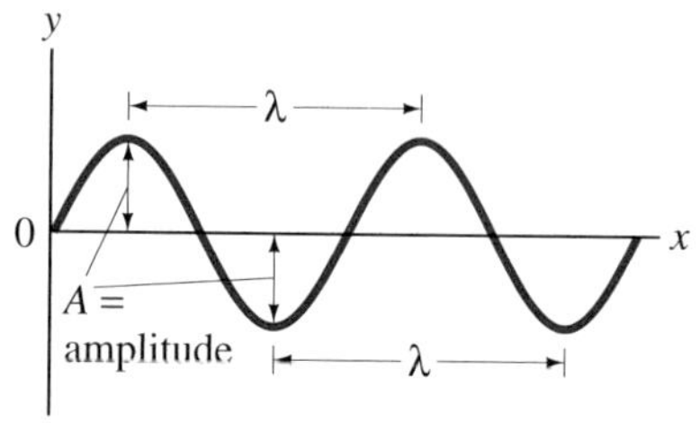


A simple wave with a single frequency, as in Fig. 11–46, is sinusoidal. To express such a wave mathematically, we assume it has a particular wavelength $\lambda$ and frequency $f$. At $t = 0$, the wave shape shown is

$$y = A \sin \frac{2\pi}{\lambda} x, \qquad \textbf{(11–21)}$$

where $y$ is the **displacement** of the wave (be it a longitudinal or transverse wave) at position $x$; $A$ is the **amplitude** of the wave, and $\lambda$ is the wavelength. [Equation 11–21 works because it repeats itself every wavelength: when $x = \lambda$, $y = \sin 2\pi = \sin 0$.]

Suppose the wave is moving to the right with velocity $v$. After a time $t$, each part of the wave (indeed, the whole wave "shape") has moved to the right a distance $vt$. Figure 11–47 shows the wave at $t = 0$ as a solid curve, and at a later time $t$ as a dashed curve. Consider any point on the wave at $t = 0$: say, a crest at some position $x$. After a time $t$, that crest will have traveled a distance $vt$, so its new position is a distance $vt$ greater than its old position. To describe this same point on the wave shape, the argument of the sine function must have the same numerical value, so we replace $x$ in Eq. 11–21 by $(x - vt)$:

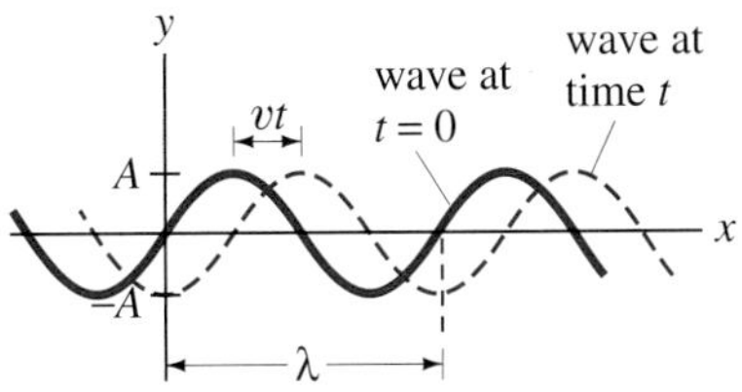


**FIGURE 11–47** A traveling wave. In time $t$, the wave moves a distance $vt$.

$$y = A\sin\left[\frac{2\pi}{\lambda}(x - vt)\right]. \qquad \textbf{(11–22)}$$

*1-D wave, moving in positive x direction*

Said another way, if you are on a crest, as $t$ increases, $x$ must increase at the same rate so that $(x - vt)$ remains constant.

For a wave traveling along the $x$ axis to the left, toward decreasing values of $x$, $v$ becomes $-v$, so

$$y = A\sin\left[\frac{2\pi}{\lambda}(x + vt)\right].$$

*1-D wave, traveling in negative x direction (to the left)*

## Summary

A vibrating object undergoes **simple harmonic motion** (SHM) if the restoring force is proportional to the displacement,

$$F = -kx. \qquad \textbf{(11–1)}$$

The maximum displacement is called the **amplitude**.

The **period**, $T$, is the time required for one complete cycle (back and forth), and the **frequency**, $f$, is the number of cycles per second; they are related by

$$f = \frac{1}{T}. \qquad \textbf{(11–2)}$$

The period of vibration for a mass $m$ on the end of a spring is given by

$$T = 2\pi\sqrt{\frac{m}{k}}. \qquad \textbf{(11–7a)}$$

SHM is **sinusoidal**, which means that the displacement as a function of time follows a sine or cosine curve.

During SHM, the total energy

$$E = \tfrac{1}{2}mv^2 + \tfrac{1}{2}kx^2 \qquad \textbf{(11–3)}$$

is continually changing from potential to kinetic and back again.

A **simple pendulum** of length $L$ approximates SHM if its amplitude is small and friction can be ignored. For small amplitudes, its period is then given by

$$T = 2\pi\sqrt{\frac{L}{g}}, \qquad \textbf{(11–11a)}$$

where $g$ is the acceleration of gravity.

When friction is present (for all real springs and pendulums), the motion is said to be **damped**. The maximum displacement decreases in time, and the energy is eventually all transformed to thermal energy.

If an oscillating force is applied to a system capable of vibrating, the system's amplitude of vibration can be very large if the frequency of the applied force matches the **natural** (or **resonant**) **frequency** of the oscillator. This effect is called **resonance**.

Vibrating objects act as sources of **waves** that travel outward from the source. Waves on water and on a string are examples. The wave may be a **pulse** (a single crest), or it may be continuous (many crests and troughs).

The **wavelength** of a continuous sinusoidal wave is the distance between two successive crests.

The **frequency** is the number of wavelengths (or crests) that pass a given point per unit time.

The **amplitude** of a wave is the maximum height of a crest, or depth of a trough, relative to the normal (or equilibrium) level.

The **wave velocity** (how fast a crest moves) is equal to the product of wavelength and frequency,

$$v = \lambda f. \qquad \textbf{(11–12)}$$

In a **transverse wave**, the oscillations are perpendicular to the direction in which the wave travels. An example is a wave on a string.

In a **longitudinal wave**, the oscillations are along (parallel to) the line of travel; sound is an example.

The **intensity** of a wave is the energy per unit time carried across unit area (in watts/$m^2$). For three-dimensional waves traveling in open space, the intensity decreases inversely as the distance from the source squared:

$$I \propto \frac{1}{r^2}. \qquad \textbf{(11–16b)}$$

[*Wave intensity is proportional to the amplitude squared and to the frequency squared.]

Waves reflect off objects in their path. When the **wave front** (of a two- or three-dimensional wave) strikes an object, the *angle of reflection* is equal to the *angle of incidence*. When a wave strikes a boundary between two materials in which it can travel, part of the wave is reflected and part is transmitted.

When two waves pass through the same region of space at the same time, they **interfere**. The resultant displacement at any point and time is the sum of their separate displacements; this can result in **constructive interference, destructive interference**, or something in between, depending on the amplitudes and relative phases of the waves.

Waves traveling on a string of fixed length interfere with waves that have reflected off the end and are traveling back in the opposite direction. At certain frequencies, **standing waves** can be produced in which the waves seem to be standing still rather than traveling. The string (or other medium) is vibrating as a whole. This is a resonance phenomenon, and the frequencies at which standing waves occur are called **resonant frequencies**. Points of destructive interference (no vibration) are called **nodes**. Points of constructive interference (maximum amplitude of vibration) are called **antinodes**.

[*Waves change direction, or **refract**, when traveling from one medium into a second medium where their speed is different. Waves spread, or **diffract**, as they travel and encounter obstacles. A rough guide to the amount of diffraction is $\theta \approx \lambda/L$, where $\lambda$ is the wavelength and $L$ the width of an opening or obstacle. There is a significant "shadow region" only if the wavelength $\lambda$ is smaller than the size of the obstacle.]

[*A traveling wave can be represented mathematically as $y = A \sin\{(2\pi/\lambda)(x - vt)\}$.]

# Questions

1. Give some examples of everyday vibrating objects. Which exhibit SHM, at least approximately?

2. Is the acceleration of a simple harmonic oscillator ever zero? If so, where?

3. Explain why the motion of a piston in an automobile engine is approximately simple harmonic.

4. Real springs have mass. Will the true period and frequency be larger or smaller than given by the equations for a mass oscillating on the end of an idealized massless spring? Explain.

5. How could you double the maximum speed of a simple harmonic oscillator (SHO)?

6. A 5.0-kg trout is attached to the hook of a vertical spring scale, and then is released. Describe the scale reading as a function of time.

7. If a pendulum clock is accurate at sea level, will it gain or lose time when taken to high altitude? Why?

8. A tire swing hanging from a branch reaches nearly to the ground (Fig. 11–48). How could you estimate the height of the branch using only a stopwatch?

**FIGURE 11–48** Question 8.

9. Why can you make water slosh back and forth in a pan only if you shake the pan at a certain frequency?

10. Give several everyday examples of resonance.

11. Is a rattle in a car ever a resonance phenomenon? Explain.

12. Is the frequency of a simple periodic wave equal to the frequency of its source? Why or why not?

13. Explain the difference between the speed of a transverse wave traveling down a cord and the speed of a tiny piece of the cord.

14. Why do the strings used for the lowest-frequency notes on a piano normally have wire wrapped around them?

15. What kind of waves do you think will travel down a horizontal metal rod if you strike its end (*a*) vertically from above and (*b*) horizontally parallel to its length?

* 16. Since the density of air decreases with an increase in temperature, but the bulk modulus $B$ is nearly independent of temperature, how would you expect the speed of sound waves in air to vary with temperature?

17. Give two reasons why circular water waves decrease in amplitude as they travel away from the source.

* 18. Two linear waves have the same amplitude and speed, and otherwise are identical, except one has half the wavelength of the other. Which transmits more energy? By what factor?

19. When a sinusoidal wave crosses the boundary between two sections of cord as in Fig. 11–33, the frequency does not change (although the wavelength and velocity do change). Explain why.

20. If a string is vibrating in three segments, are there any places you could touch it with a knife blade without disturbing the motion?

21. When a standing wave exists on a string, the vibrations of incident and reflected waves cancel at the nodes. Does this mean that energy was destroyed? Explain.

* 22. If we knew that energy was being transmitted from one place to another, how might we determine whether the energy was being carried by particles (material bodies) or by waves?

# Problems

## 11–1 to 11–3 Simple Harmonic Motion

1. (I) If a particle undergoes SHM with amplitude 0.18 m, what is the total distance it travels in one period?

2. (I) An elastic cord is 65 cm long when a weight of 75 N hangs from it but is 85 cm long when a weight of 180 N hangs from it. What is the "spring" constant $k$ of this elastic cord?

3. (I) The springs of a 1500-kg car compress 5.0 mm when its 68-kg driver gets into the driver's seat. If the car goes over a bump, what will be the frequency of vibrations?

4. (II) A fisherman's scale stretches 3.6 cm when a 2.7-kg fish hangs from it. (*a*) What is the spring stiffness constant and (*b*) what will be the amplitude and frequency of vibration if the fish is pulled down 2.5 cm more and released so that it vibrates up and down?

5. (II) An elastic cord vibrates with a frequency of 3.0 Hz when a mass of 0.60 kg is hung from it. What is its frequency if only 0.38 kg hangs from it?

6. (II) Construct a Table indicating the position $x$ of the mass in Fig. 11–2 at times $t = 0, \frac{1}{4}T, \frac{1}{2}T, \frac{3}{4}T, T,$ and $\frac{5}{4}T$, where $T$ is the period of oscillation. On a graph of $x$ vs. $t$, plot these six points. Now connect these points with a smooth curve. Based on these simple considerations, does your curve resemble that of a cosine or sine wave (Fig. 11–8a or 11–9)?

7. (II) A small fly of mass 0.25 g is caught in a spider's web. The web vibrates predominately with a frequency of 4.0 Hz. (*a*) What is the value of the effective spring stiffness constant $k$ for the web? (*b*) At what frequency would you expect the web to vibrate if an insect of mass 0.50 g were trapped?

8. (II) A mass $m$ at the end of a spring vibrates with a frequency of 0.88 Hz. When an additional 680-g mass is added to $m$, the frequency is 0.60 Hz. What is the value of $m$?

9. (II) A 0.60-kg mass at the end of a spring vibrates 3.0 times per second with an amplitude of 0.13 m. Determine (*a*) the velocity when it passes the equilibrium point, (*b*) the velocity when it is 0.10 m from equilibrium, (*c*) the total energy of the system, and (*d*) the equation describing the motion of the mass, assuming that $x$ was a maximum at $t = 0$.

10. (II) At what displacement from equilibrium is the speed of a SHO half the maximum value?

11. (II) A mass attached to the end of a spring is stretched a distance $x_0$ from equilibrium and released. At what distance from equilibrium will it have acceleration equal to half its maximum acceleration?

12. (II) A mass of 2.62 kg stretches a vertical spring 0.315 m. If the spring is stretched an additional 0.130 m and released, how long does it take to reach the (new) equilibrium position again?

13. (II) An object with mass 3.0 kg is attached to a spring with spring stiffness constant $k = 280\ \text{N/m}$ and is executing simple harmonic motion. When the object is 0.020 m from its equilibrium position, it is moving with a speed of 0.55 m/s. (*a*) Calculate the amplitude of the motion. (*b*) Calculate the maximum velocity attained by the object. [*Hint*: Use conservation of energy.]

14. (II) It takes a force of 80.0 N to compress the spring of a toy popgun 0.200 m to "load" a 0.180-kg ball. With what speed will the ball leave the gun?

15. (II) A mass sitting on a horizontal, frictionless surface is attached to one end of a spring; the other end is fixed to a wall. 3.0 J of work is required to compress the spring by 0.12 m. If the mass is released from rest with the spring compressed, the mass experiences a maximum acceleration of $15\ \text{m/s}^2$. Find the value of (*a*) the spring stiffness constant and (*b*) the mass.

16. (II) A 0.60-kg mass vibrates according to the equation $x = 0.45 \cos 6.40t$, where $x$ is in meters and $t$ is in seconds. Determine (*a*) the amplitude, (*b*) the frequency, (*c*) the total energy, and (*d*) the kinetic energy and potential energies when $x = 0.30$ m.

17. (II) At what displacement from equilibrium is the energy of a SHO half KE and half PE?

18. (II) If one vibration has 7.0 times the energy of a second, but their frequencies and masses are the same, what is the ratio of their amplitudes?

19. (II) A 2.00-kg pumpkin oscillates from a vertically hanging light spring once every 0.65 s. (*a*) Write down the equation giving the pumpkin's position $y$ (+ upward) as a function of time $t$, assuming it started by being compressed 18 cm from the equilibrium position (where $y = 0$), and released. (*b*) How long will it take to get to the equilibrium position for the first time? (*c*) What will be the pumpkin's maximum speed? (*d*) What will be its maximum acceleration, and where will that first be attained?

20. (II) A block of mass $m$ is supported by two identical parallel vertical springs, each with spring stiffness constant $k$ (Fig. 11–49). What will be the frequency of vibration?

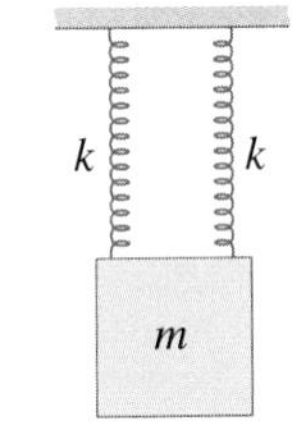


**FIGURE 11–49** Problem 20.

21. (II) A 300-g mass vibrates according to the equation $x = 0.38 \sin 6.50t$, where $x$ is in meters and $t$ is in seconds. Determine (*a*) the amplitude, (*b*) the frequency, (*c*) the period, (*d*) the total energy, and (*e*) the KE and PE when $x$ is 9.0 cm. (*f*) Draw a careful graph of $x$ vs. $t$ showing the correct amplitude and period.

22. (II) Figure 11–50 shows two examples of SHM, labeled A and B. For each, what is (*a*) the amplitude, (*b*) the frequency, and (*c*) the period? (*d*) Write the equations for both A and B in the form of a sine or cosine.

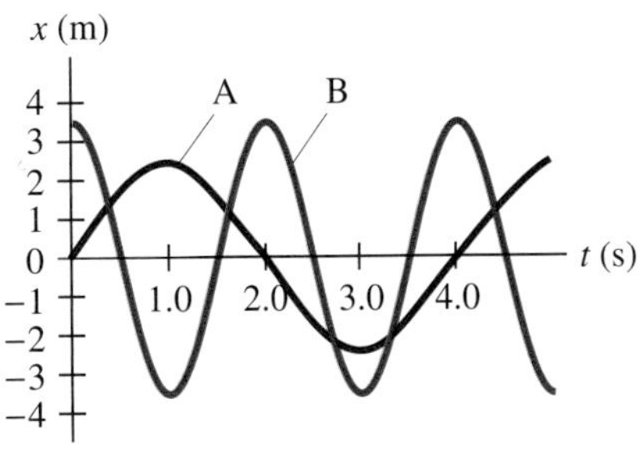


**FIGURE 11–50** Problem 22.

23. (II) At $t = 0$, a 755-g mass at rest on the end of a horizontal spring ($k = 124$ N/m) is struck by a hammer, which gives the mass an initial speed of 2.96 m/s. Determine (*a*) the period and frequency of the motion, (*b*) the amplitude, (*c*) the maximum acceleration, (*d*) the position as a function of time, and (*e*) the total energy.

24. (II) A vertical spring with spring stiffness constant 305 N/m vibrates with an amplitude of 28.0 cm when 0.260 kg hangs from it. The mass passes through the equilibrium point ($y = 0$) with positive velocity at $t = 0$. (*a*) What equation describes this motion as a function of time? (*b*) At what times will the spring have its maximum and minimum extensions?

25. (II) A mass $m$ is connected to two springs, with spring stiffness constants $k_1$ and $k_2$, as shown in Fig. 11–51. Ignore friction. Show that the period is given by

$$T = 2\pi\sqrt{\frac{m}{k_1 + k_2}}.$$

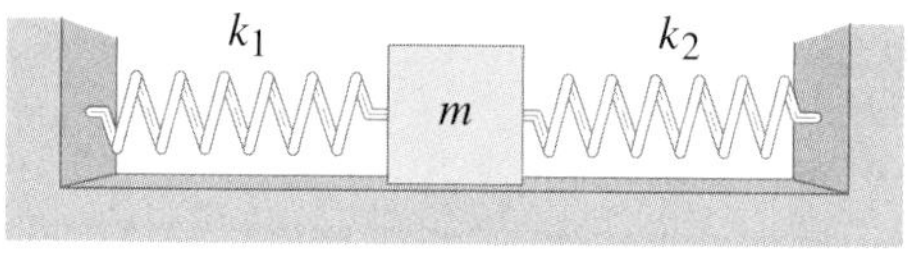


**FIGURE 11–51** Problem 25.

26. (III) A 25.0-g bullet strikes a 0.600-kg block attached to a fixed horizontal spring whose spring stiffness constant is $7.70 \times 10^3$ N/m. The block is set into vibration with an amplitude of 21.5 cm. What was the speed of the bullet before impact if the bullet and block move together after impact?

27. (III) A bungee jumper with mass 65.0 kg jumps from a high bridge. After reaching his lowest point, he oscillates up and down, hitting a low point eight more times in 38.0 s. He finally comes to rest 25.0 m below the level of the bridge. Calculate the spring stiffness constant and the unstretched length of the bungee cord.

## 11–4 Simple Pendulum

28. (I) A pendulum makes 36 vibrations in exactly 60 s. What is its (*a*) period, and (*b*) frequency?

29. (I) How long must a simple pendulum be if it is to make exactly one swing per second? (That is, one complete vibration takes exactly 2.0 s.)

30. (I) A pendulum has a period of 0.80 s on Earth. What is its period on Mars, where the acceleration of gravity is about 0.37 that on Earth?

31. (II) What is the period of a simple pendulum 80 cm long (*a*) on the Earth, and (*b*) when it is in a freely falling elevator?

32. (II) The length of a simple pendulum is 0.760 m, the pendulum bob has a mass of 365 grams, and it is released at an angle of 12.0° to the vertical. (*a*) With what frequency does it vibrate? Assume SHM. (*b*) What is the pendulum bob's speed when it passes through the lowest point of the swing? (*c*) What is the total energy stored in this oscillation, assuming no losses?

33. (II) Your grandfather clock's pendulum has a length of 0.9930 m. If the clock loses half a minute per day, how should you adjust the length of the pendulum?

34. (II) Derive a formula for the maximum speed $v_{max}$ of a simple pendulum bob in terms of $g$, the length $L$, and the angle of swing $\theta_0$.

35. (III) A clock pendulum oscillates at a frequency of 2.5 Hz. At $t = 0$, it is released from rest starting at an angle of 15° to the vertical. Ignoring friction, what will be the position (angle) of the pendulum at (*a*) $t = 0.25$ s, (*b*) $t = 1.60$ s, and (*c*) $t = 500$ s? [*Hint*: Do not confuse the angle of swing $\theta$ of the pendulum with the angle that appears as the argument of the cosine.]

## 11–7 and 11–8 Waves

36. (I) A fisherman notices that wave crests pass the bow of his anchored boat every 3.0 s. He measures the distance between two crests to be 6.5 m. How fast are the waves traveling?

37. (I) A sound wave in air has a frequency of 262 Hz and travels with a speed of 343 m/s. How far apart are the wave crests (compressions)?

38. (I) (*a*) AM radio signals have frequencies between 550 kHz and 1600 kHz (kilohertz) and travel with a speed of $3.00 \times 10^8$ m/s. What are the wavelengths of these signals? (*b*) On FM, the frequencies range from 88.0 MHz to 108 MHz (megahertz) and travel at the same speed; what are their wavelengths?

* 39. (I) Calculate the speed of longitudinal waves in (*a*) water, (*b*) granite, and (*c*) steel.

* 40. (II) Two solid rods have the same elastic modulus, but one is twice as dense as the other. In which rod will the speed of longitudinal waves be greater, and by what factor?

41. (II) A cord of mass 0.65 kg is stretched between two supports 28 m apart. If the tension in the cord is 150 N, how long will it take a pulse to travel from one support to the other?

42. (II) A ski gondola is connected to the top of a hill by a steel cable of length 620 m and diameter 1.5 cm. As the gondola comes to the end of its run, it bumps into the terminal and sends a wave pulse along the cable. It is observed that it took 16 s for the pulse to return. (*a*) What is the speed of the pulse? (*b*) What is the tension in the cable?

* 43. (II) A sailor strikes the side of his ship just below the surface of the sea. He hears the echo of the wave reflected from the ocean floor directly below 3.0 s later. How deep is the ocean at this point?

44. (II) P and S waves from an earthquake travel at different speeds, and this difference helps in locating the earthquake "epicenter" (where the disturbance took place). (*a*) Assuming typical speeds of 8.5 km/s and 5.5 km/s for P and S waves, respectively, how far away did the earthquake occur if a particular seismic station detects the arrival of these two types of waves 2.0 min apart? (*b*) Is one seismic station sufficient to determine the position of the epicenter? Explain.

45. (III) An earthquake-produced surface wave can be approximated by a sinusoidal transverse wave. Assuming a frequency of 0.50 Hz (typical of earthquakes, which actually include a mixture of frequencies), what amplitude is needed so that objects begin to leave contact with the ground? [*Hint*: Set the acceleration $a > g$.]

## 11–9 Wave Energy

46. (II) What is the ratio of (*a*) the intensities, and (*b*) the amplitudes, of an earthquake P wave passing through the Earth and detected at two points 10 km and 20 km from the source.

47. (II) The intensity of an earthquake wave passing through the Earth is measured to be $2.0 \times 10^6\ \mathrm{J/m^2 \cdot s}$ at a distance of 48 km from the source. (*a*) What was its intensity when it passed a point only 1.0 km from the source? (*b*) At what rate did energy pass through an area of $5.0\ \mathrm{m^2}$ at 1.0 km?

## * 11–10 Intensity Related to $A$ and $f$

* 48. (I) Two earthquake waves of the same frequency travel through the same portion of the Earth, but one is carrying twice the energy. What is the ratio of the amplitudes of the two waves?

* 49. (I) Two waves traveling along a stretched string have the same frequency, but one transports three times the power of the other. What is the ratio of the amplitudes of the two waves?

* 50. (II) A bug on the surface of a pond is observed to move up and down a total vertical distance of 6.0 cm, from the lowest to the highest point, as a wave passes. If the ripples decrease to 4.5 cm, by what factor does the bug's maximum KE change?

## 11–12 Interference

51. (I) The two pulses shown in Fig. 11–52 are moving toward each other. (*a*) Sketch the shape of the string at the moment they directly overlap. (*b*) Sketch the shape of the string a few moments later. (*c*) In Fig. 11–36a, at the moment the pulses pass each other, the string is straight. What has happened to the energy at this moment?

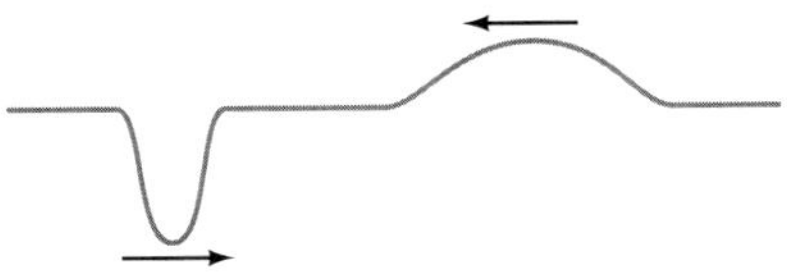

**FIGURE 11–52** Problem 51.

## 11–13 Standing Waves; Resonance

52. (I) If a violin string vibrates at 440 Hz as its fundamental frequency, what are the frequencies of the first four harmonics?

53. (I) A violin string vibrates at 294 Hz when unfingered. At what frequency will it vibrate if it is fingered one-third of the way down from the end? (That is, only two-thirds of the string vibrates as a standing wave.)

54. (I) A particular string resonates in four loops at a frequency of 280 Hz. Name at least three other frequencies at which it will resonate.

55. (II) The velocity of waves on a string is 92 m/s. If the frequency of standing waves is 475 Hz, how far apart are two adjacent nodes?

56. (II) If two successive overtones of a vibrating string are 280 Hz and 350 Hz, what is the frequency of the fundamental?

57. (II) A guitar string is 90 cm long and has a mass of 3.6 g. The distance from the bridge to the support post is $L = 62$ cm, and the string is under a tension of 520 N. What are the frequencies of the fundamental and first two overtones?

58. (II) A particular guitar string is supposed to vibrate at 200 Hz, but it is measured to vibrate at 205 Hz. By what percent should the tension in the string be changed to correct the frequency?

59. (II) One end of a horizontal string is attached to a small-amplitude mechanical 60-Hz vibrator. The string's mass per unit length is $3.9 \times 10^{-4}$ kg/m. The string passes over a pulley, a distance $L = 1.50$ m away, and weights are hung from this end, Fig. 11–53. What mass $m$ must be hung from this end of the string to produce (*a*) one loop, (*b*) two loops, and (*c*) five loops of a standing wave? Assume the string at the vibrator is a node, which is nearly true.

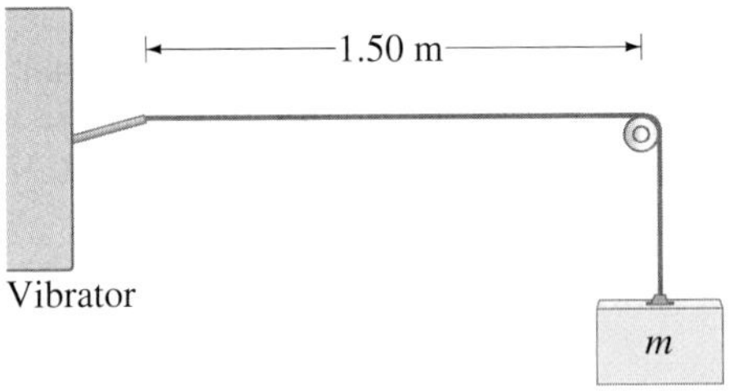


**FIGURE 11–53** Problems 59 and 60.

60. (II) In Problem 59, the length of the string may be adjusted by moving the pulley. If the hanging mass $m$ is fixed at 0.080 kg, how many different standing wave patterns may be achieved by varying $L$ between 10 cm and 1.5 m?

61. (II) When you slosh the water back and forth in a tub at just the right frequency, the water alternately rises and falls at each end, remaining relatively calm at the center. Suppose the frequency to produce such a standing wave in a 65-cm-wide tub is 0.85 Hz. What is the speed of the water wave?

## * 11–14 Refraction

* 62. (I) An earthquake P wave traveling at 8.0 km/s strikes a boundary within the Earth between two kinds of material. If it approaches the boundary at an incident angle of 47° and the angle of refraction is 35°, what is the speed in the second medium?

* 63. (I) Water waves approach an underwater "shelf" where the velocity changes from 2.8 m/s to 2.1 m/s. If the incident wave crests make a 34° angle with the shelf, what will be the angle of refraction?

* 64. (II) A sound wave is traveling in warm air when it hits a layer of cold, dense air. If the sound wave hits the cold air interface at an angle of 25°, what is the angle of refraction? Assume that the cold air temperature is −10°C and the warm air temperature is +10°C. The speed of sound as a function of temperature can be approximated by $v = (331 + 0.60\,T)$ m/s, where $T$ is in °C.

* 65. (III) A longitudinal earthquake wave strikes a boundary between two types of rock at a 38° angle. As the wave crosses the boundary, the specific gravity of the rock changes from 3.6 to 2.8. Assuming that the elastic modulus is the same for both types of rock, determine the angle of refraction.

## * 11–15 Diffraction

* 66. (II) A satellite dish is about 0.5 m in diameter. According to the user's manual, the dish has to be pointed in the direction of the satellite, but an error of about 2° is allowed without loss of reception. Estimate the wavelength of the electromagnetic waves received by the dish.

## General Problems

67. A tsunami of wavelength 250 km and velocity 750 km/h travels across the Pacific Ocean. As it approaches Hawaii, people observe an unusual decrease of sea level in the harbors. Approximately how much time do they have to run to safety? (In the absence of knowledge and warning, people have died during tsunamis, some of them attracted to the shore to see stranded fishes and boats.)

68. An energy-absorbing car bumper has a spring stiffness constant of 550 kN/m. Find the maximum compression of the bumper if the car, with mass 1500 kg, collides with a wall at a speed of 2.2 m/s (approximately 5 mi/h). [*Hint*: Use conservation of energy.]

69. A 65-kg person jumps from a window to a fire net 18 m below, which stretches the net 1.1 m. Assume that the net behaves like a simple spring, and (*a*) calculate how much it would stretch if the same person were lying in it. (*b*) How much would it stretch if the person jumped from 35 m?

70. A mass $m$ is gently placed on the end of a freely hanging spring. The mass then falls 33 cm before it stops and begins to rise. What is the frequency of the oscillation?

71. A 950-kg car strikes a huge spring at a speed of 22 m/s (Fig. 11–54), compressing the spring 5.0 m. (*a*) What is the spring stiffness constant of the spring? (*b*) How long is the car in contact with the spring before it bounces off in the opposite direction?

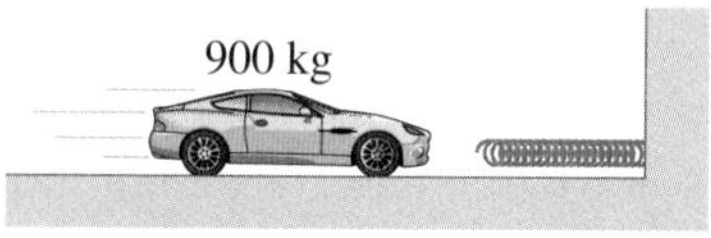


**FIGURE 11–54** Problem 71.

72. When you walk with a cup of coffee (diameter 8 cm) at just the right pace of about 1 step per second, the coffee sloshes more and more until eventually it starts to spill over the top (Fig. 11–55). Estimate the speed of waves in the coffee.

**FIGURE 11–55** Problem 72.

73. The ripples in a certain groove 10.8 cm from the center of a 33-rpm phonograph record have a wavelength of 1.70 mm. What will be the frequency of the sound emitted?

74. A 2.00-kg mass vibrates according to the equation $x = 0.650 \cos 7.40t$, where $x$ is in meters and $t$ in seconds. Determine (*a*) the amplitude, (*b*) the frequency, (*c*) the total energy, and (*d*) the kinetic energy and potential energy when $x = 0.260$ m.

75. A simple pendulum oscillates with frequency $f$. What is its frequency if it accelerates at $0.50g$ (*a*) upward, and (*b*) downward?

76. A 220-kg wooden raft floats on a lake. When a 75-kg man stands on the raft, it sinks 4.0 cm deeper into the water. When he steps off, the raft vibrates for a while. (*a*) What is the frequency of vibration? (*b*) What is the total energy of vibration (ignoring damping)?

77. Two strings on a musical instrument are tuned to play at 392 Hz (G) and 440 Hz (A). (*a*) What are the frequencies of the first two overtones for each string? (*b*) If the two strings have the same length and are under the same tension, what is the ratio of their masses $(m_G/m_A)$? (*c*) If the strings instead have the same mass per unit length and are under the same tension, what is the ratio of their lengths $(L_G/L_A)$? (*d*) If their masses and lengths are the same, what must be the ratio of the tensions in the two strings?

78. Consider a sine wave traveling down the stretched two-part cord of Fig. 11–33. Determine a formula (*a*) for the ratio of the speeds of the wave in the heavy section versus that in the lighter section, $v_H/v_L$, and (*b*) for the ratio of the wavelengths in the two sections. (The frequency is the same in both sections. Why?) (*c*) Is the wavelength greater in the heavier section of cord or the lighter?

79. A tuning fork vibrates at a frequency of 264 Hz, and the tip of each prong moves 1.8 mm to either side of center. Calculate (*a*) the maximum speed and (*b*) the maximum acceleration of the tip of a prong.

80. A diving board oscillates with simple harmonic motion of frequency 1.5 cycles per second. What is the maximum amplitude with which the end of the board can vibrate in order that a pebble placed there (Fig. 11–56) will not lose contact with the board during the oscillation?

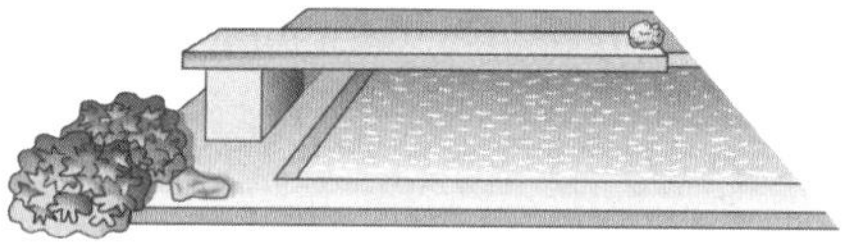

**FIGURE 11–56** Problem 80.

81. A string can have a "free" end if that end is attached to a ring that can slide without friction on a vertical pole (Fig. 11–57). Determine the wavelengths of the resonant vibrations of such a string with one end fixed and the other free.

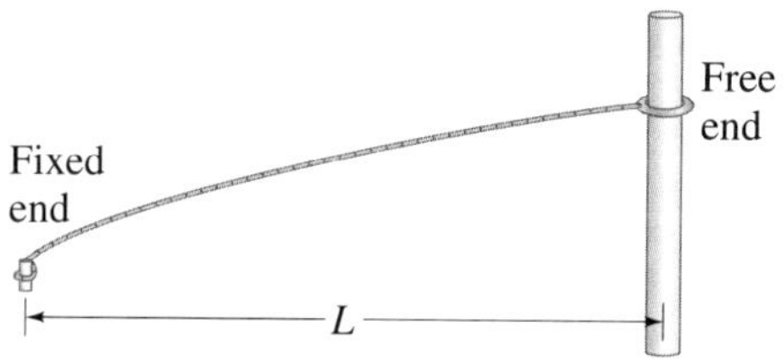


**FIGURE 11–57** Problem 81.

82. A "seconds" pendulum has a period of exactly 2.000 s—each one-way swing takes 1.000 s. (*a*) What is the length of a seconds pendulum in Austin, Texas, where $g = 9.793\ \mathrm{m/s^2}$? (*b*) If the pendulum is moved to Paris, where $g = 9.809\ \mathrm{m/s^2}$, by how many millimeters must we lengthen the pendulum? (*c*) What would be the length of a seconds pendulum on the Moon, where $g = 1.62\ \mathrm{m/s^2}$?

83. A mass hanging from a spring can oscillate in the vertical direction or can swing as a pendulum of small amplitude, but not both at the same time. Which one is longer, the period of the vertical oscillations or the period of the horizontal swings, and by what amount? [*Hint*: Let $l_0$ be the length of the unstretched spring, and $L$ be its length with the mass attached at rest.]

84. A block with mass $M = 5.0$ kg rests on a frictionless table and is attached by a horizontal spring ($k = 130\ \mathrm{N/m}$) to a wall. A second block, of mass $m = 1.25$ kg, rests on top of $M$. The coefficient of static friction between the two blocks is 0.30. What is the maximum possible amplitude of oscillation such that $m$ will not slip off $M$?

85. A 10.0-m-long wire of mass 123 g is stretched under a tension of 255 N. A pulse is generated at one end, and 20.0 ms later a second pulse is generated at the opposite end. Where will the two pulses first meet?

86. A block of mass $M$ is suspended from a ceiling by a spring with spring stiffness constant $k$. A penny of mass $m$ is placed on top of the block. What is the maximum amplitude of oscillations that will allow the penny to just stay on top of the block? (Assume $m \ll M$.)

* 87. A crane has hoisted a 1200-kg car at the junkyard. The steel crane cable is 22 m long and has a diameter of 6.4 mm. A breeze starts the car bouncing at the end of the cable. What is the period of the bouncing? [*Hint*: Refer to Table 9–1.]

* 88. A block of jello rests on a plate as shown in Fig. 11–58 (which also gives the dimensions of the block). You push it sideways as shown, and then you let go. The jello springs back and begins to vibrate. In analogy to a mass vibrating on a spring, estimate the frequency of this vibration, given that the shear modulus (Section 9–5) of jello is $520\ \mathrm{N/m^2}$ and its density is $1300\ \mathrm{kg/m^3}$.

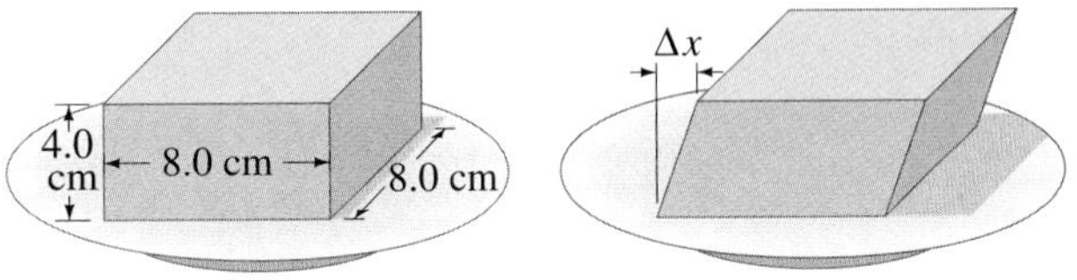


**FIGURE 11–58** Problem 88.

## Answers to Exercises

**A:** (*a*), (*c*), (*d*).

**B:** (*a*) Increases; (*b*) increases; (*c*) increases.

**C:** Empty.

**D:** (*a*) 25 cm; (*b*) 2.0 s.

If music be the food of physics, play on. [See Shakespeare, *Twelfth Night*, line 1.]

An orchestra contains stringed instruments, whose sound depends on transverse standing waves on strings, and wind instruments whose sound originates in longitudinal standing waves of an air column. Percussion instruments create more complicated standing waves.

Besides examining sources of sound, we also study the decibel scale of sound level, the ear's response, sound wave interference and beats, the Doppler effect, shock waves and sonic booms, and ultrasound imaging.

CHAPTER 12

# Sound

Sound is associated with our sense of hearing and, therefore, with the physiology of our ears and the psychology of our brain, which interprets the sensations that reach our ears. The term *sound* also refers to the physical sensation that stimulates our ears: namely, longitudinal waves.

We can distinguish three aspects of any sound. First, there must be a *source* for a sound; as with any wave, the source of a sound wave is a vibrating object. Second, the energy is transferred from the source in the form of longitudinal sound *waves*. And third, the sound is *detected* by an ear or by a microphone. We start this Chapter by looking at some aspects of sound waves themselves.

## 12–1 Characteristics of Sound

We saw in Chapter 11, Fig. 11–25, how a vibrating drumhead produces a sound wave in air. Indeed, we usually think of sound waves traveling in the air, for normally it is the vibrations of the air that force our eardrums to vibrate. But sound waves can also travel in other materials.

Two stones struck together under water can be heard by a swimmer beneath the surface, for the vibrations are carried to the ear by the water. When you put your ear flat against the ground, you can hear an approaching train or truck. In this case the ground does not actually touch your eardrum, but the longitudinal wave transmitted by the ground is called a sound wave just the same, for its vibrations cause the outer ear and the air within it to vibrate. Clearly, sound cannot travel in the absence of matter. For example, a bell ringing inside an evacuated jar cannot be heard, and sound cannot travel through the empty reaches of outer space.

The **speed of sound** is different in different materials. In air at 0°C and 1 atm, sound travels at a speed of 331 m/s. The speed of sound in various materials is given in Table 12–1. The values depend somewhat on temperature, especially for gases. For example, in air near room temperature, the speed increases approximately 0.60 m/s for each Celsius degree increase in temperature:

**TABLE 12–1 Speed of Sound in Various Materials (20°C and 1 atm)**

| Material | Speed (m/s) |
|---|---|
| Air | 343 |
| Air (0°C) | 331 |
| Helium | 1005 |
| Hydrogen | 1300 |
| Water | 1440 |
| Sea water | 1560 |
| Iron and steel | ≈5000 |
| Glass | ≈4500 |
| Aluminum | ≈5100 |
| Hardwood | ≈4000 |
| Concrete | ≈3000 |

*Speed of sound in air*

$$v \approx (331 + 0.60T)\,\mathrm{m/s},$$

where $T$ is the temperature in °C. Unless stated otherwise, we will assume in this Chapter that $T = 20°\mathrm{C}$, so $v = [331 + (0.60)(20)]\,\mathrm{m/s} = 343\,\mathrm{m/s}$.

**CONCEPTUAL EXAMPLE 12–1 Distance from a lightning strike.** A rule of thumb that tells how close lightning has hit is, "one mile for every five seconds before the thunder is heard." Justify, noting that the speed of light is so high ($3 \times 10^8$ m/s, almost a million times faster than sound) that the time for light to travel is negligible compared to the time for sound.

**RESPONSE** The speed of sound in air is about 340 m/s, so to travel 1 km = 1000 m takes about 3 seconds. One mile is about 1.6 kilometers, so the time for the thunder to travel a mile is about $(1.6)(3) \approx 5$ seconds.

PHYSICS APPLIED

*How far away is the lightning?*

**EXERCISE A** What would be the rule of thumb of Example 12–1 in terms of kilometers?

Two aspects of any sound are immediately evident to a human listener: "loudness" and "pitch." Each refers to a sensation in the consciousness of the listener. But to each of these subjective sensations there corresponds a physically measurable quantity. **Loudness** is related to the intensity (energy per unit time crossing unit area) in the sound wave, and we shall discuss it in the next Section.

*Loudness*

The **pitch** of a sound refers to whether it is high, like the sound of a piccolo or violin, or low, like the sound of a bass drum or string bass. The physical quantity that determines pitch is the frequency, as was first noted by Galileo. The lower the frequency, the lower the pitch; the higher the frequency, the higher the pitch.† The best human ears can respond to frequencies from about 20 Hz to almost 20,000 Hz. (Recall that 1 Hz is 1 cycle per second.) This frequency range is called the **audible range**. These limits vary somewhat from one individual to another. One general trend is that as people age, they are less able to hear high frequencies, so the high-frequency limit may be 10,000 Hz or less.

*Pitch*

*Audible frequency range*

Sound waves whose frequencies are outside the audible range may reach the ear, but we are not generally aware of them. Frequencies above 20,000 Hz are called **ultrasonic** (do not confuse with *supersonic*, which is used for an object moving with a speed faster than the speed of sound). Many animals can hear ultrasonic frequencies; dogs, for example, can hear sounds as high as 50,000 Hz, and bats can detect frequencies as high as 100,000 Hz. Ultrasonic waves have a number of applications in medicine and other fields, which we will discuss later in this Chapter.

CAUTION

*Do not confuse ultrasonic (high frequency) with supersonic (high speed)*

†Although pitch is determined mainly by frequency, it also depends to a slight extent on loudness. For example, a very loud sound may seem slightly lower in pitch than a quiet sound of the same frequency.

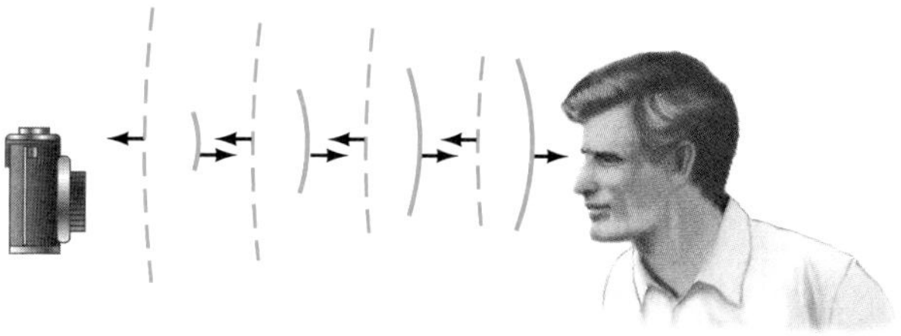

**FIGURE 12–1** Example 12–2. Autofocusing camera emits an ultrasonic pulse. Solid lines represent the wave front of the outgoing wave pulse moving to the right; dashed lines represent the wave front of the pulse reflected off the person's face, returning to the camera. The time information allows the camera mechanism to adjust the lens to focus at the proper distance.

PHYSICS APPLIED
*Autofocusing camera*

**EXAMPLE 12–2** **Autofocusing with sound waves.** Autofocusing cameras emit a pulse of very high frequency (ultrasonic) sound that travels to the object being photographed, and include a sensor that detects the returning reflected sound, as shown in Fig. 12–1. To get an idea of the time sensitivity of the detector, calculate the travel time of the pulse for an object (*a*) 1.0 m away, and (*b*) 20 m away.

**APPROACH** If we assume the temperature is about 20°C, then the speed of sound is 343 m/s. Using this speed $v$ and the total distance $d$ back and forth in each case, we can obtain the time $(v = d/t)$.

**SOLUTION** (*a*) The pulse travels 1.0 m to the object and 1.0 m back, for a total of 2.0 m. We solve for $t$ in $v = d/t$:

$$t = \frac{d}{v} = \frac{2.0\text{ m}}{343\text{ m/s}} = 0.0058\text{ s} = 5.8\text{ ms}.$$

(*b*) The total distance now is $2 \times 20\text{ m} = 40\text{ m}$, so

$$t = \frac{40\text{ m}}{343\text{ m/s}} = 0.12\text{ s} = 120\text{ ms}.$$

**NOTE** These times are very short, so the wait for the camera to focus is not noticeable.

Sound waves whose frequencies are below the audible range (that is, less than 20 Hz) are called **infrasonic**. Sources of infrasonic waves include earthquakes, thunder, volcanoes, and waves produced by vibrating heavy machinery. This last source can be particularly troublesome to workers, for infrasonic waves—even though inaudible—can cause damage to the human body. These low-frequency waves act in a resonant fashion, causing motion and irritation of the body's organs.

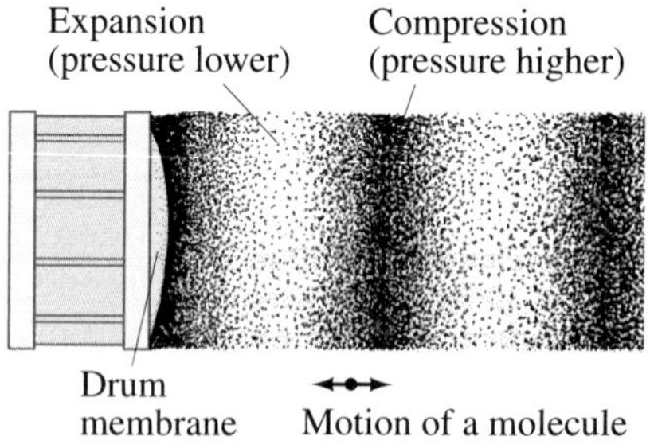


**FIGURE 12–2** The membrane of a drum, as it vibrates, alternately compresses the air and, as it recedes (moves to the left), leaves a rarefaction or expansion of air. See also Fig. 11–25.

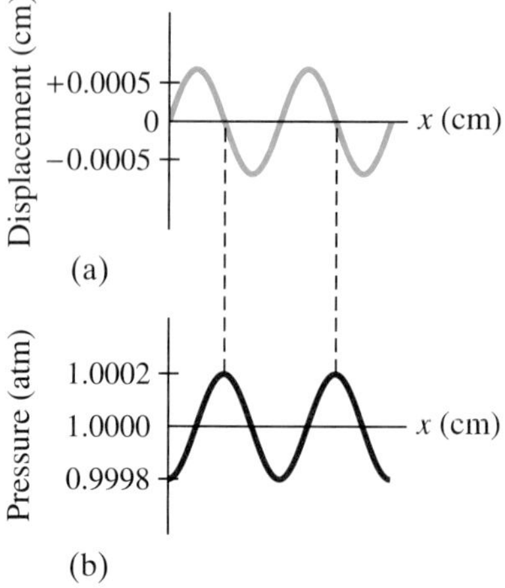


**FIGURE 12–3** Representation of a sound wave in space at a given instant in terms of (a) displacement, and (b) pressure.

We often describe a sound wave in terms of the vibration of the molecules of the medium in which it travels—that is, in terms of the motion or displacement of the molecules. But sound waves can also be analyzed from the point of view of pressure. Indeed, longitudinal waves are often called **pressure waves**. The pressure variation is usually easier to measure than the displacement. As Figure 12–2 shows, in a wave "compression" (where molecules are closest together), the pressure is higher than normal, whereas in an expansion (or *rarefaction*) the pressure is less than normal. Figure 12–3 shows a graphical representation of a sound wave in air in terms of (a) displacement and (b) pressure. Note that the displacement wave is a quarter wavelength out of phase with the pressure wave: where the pressure is a maximum or minimum, the displacement from equilibrium is zero; and where the pressure variation is zero, the displacement is a maximum or minimum.

## 12–2 Intensity of Sound: Decibels

*Loudness*

Like pitch, **loudness** is a sensation in the consciousness of a human being. It too is related to a physically measurable quantity, the **intensity** of the wave. Intensity is defined as the energy transported by a wave per unit time across a unit area perpendicular to the energy flow. As we saw in Chapter 11, intensity is proportional to the square of the wave amplitude. Intensity has units of power per unit area, or watts/meter$^2$ ($\mathrm{W/m^2}$).

PHYSICS APPLIED

*Wide range of human hearing*

The human ear can detect sounds with an intensity as low as $10^{-12}\,\mathrm{W/m^2}$ and as high as $1\,\mathrm{W/m^2}$ (and even higher, although above this it is painful). This is an incredibly wide range of intensity, spanning a factor of $10^{12}$ from lowest to highest. Presumably because of this wide range, what we perceive as loudness is not directly proportional to the intensity. To produce a sound that sounds about twice as loud requires a sound wave that has about 10 times the intensity. This is roughly valid at any sound level for frequencies near the middle of the audible range. For example, a sound wave of intensity $10^{-2}\,\mathrm{W/m^2}$ sounds to an average human being like it is about twice as loud as one whose intensity is $10^{-3}\,\mathrm{W/m^2}$, and four times as loud as $10^{-4}\,\mathrm{W/m^2}$.

### Sound Level

Because of this relationship between the subjective sensation of loudness and the physically measurable quantity "intensity," sound intensity levels are usually specified on a logarithmic scale. The unit on this scale is a **bel**, after the inventor Alexander Graham Bell, or much more commonly, the **decibel** (dB), which is $\frac{1}{10}$ bel (10 dB = 1 bel). The **sound level**, $\beta$, of any sound is defined in terms of its intensity, $I$, as

*The dB unit*

*Sound level (decibels)*

$$\beta\ (\text{in dB}) = 10\log\frac{I}{I_0}, \qquad \textbf{(12–1)}$$

where $I_0$ is the intensity of a chosen reference level, and the logarithm is to the base 10. $I_0$ is usually taken as the minimum intensity audible to a good ear—the "threshold of hearing," which is $I_0 = 1.0 \times 10^{-12}\,\mathrm{W/m^2}$. Thus, for example, the sound level of a sound whose intensity $I = 1.0 \times 10^{-10}\,\mathrm{W/m^2}$ will be

$$\beta = 10\log\left(\frac{1.0\times10^{-10}\,\mathrm{W/m^2}}{1.0\times10^{-12}\,\mathrm{W/m^2}}\right) = 10\log 100 = 20\ \mathrm{dB},$$

CAUTION

*0 dB does not mean zero intensity*

since log 100 is equal to 2.0. Notice that the sound level at the threshold of hearing is 0 dB. That is, $\beta = 10\log 10^{-12}/10^{-12} = 10\log 1 = 0$ since $\log 1 = 0$. Notice too that an increase in intensity by a factor of 10 corresponds to a sound level increase of 10 dB. An increase in intensity by a factor of 100 corresponds to a sound level increase of 20 dB. Thus a 50-dB sound is 100 times more intense than a 30-dB sound, and so on.

*Each 10 dB corresponds to a 10-fold change in intensity*

Intensities and sound levels for a number of common sounds are listed in Table 12–2.

**TABLE 12–2 Intensity of Various Sounds**

| Source of the Sound | Sound Level (dB) | Intensity ($\mathrm{W/m^2}$) |
|---|---|---|
| Jet plane at 30 m | 140 | 100 |
| Threshold of pain | 120 | 1 |
| Loud rock concert | 120 | 1 |
| Siren at 30 m | 100 | $1 \times 10^{-2}$ |
| Auto interior, at 90 km/h | 75 | $3 \times 10^{-5}$ |
| Busy street traffic | 70 | $1 \times 10^{-5}$ |
| Talk, at 50 cm | 65 | $3 \times 10^{-6}$ |
| Quiet radio | 40 | $1 \times 10^{-8}$ |
| Whisper | 20 | $1 \times 10^{-10}$ |
| Rustle of leaves | 10 | $1 \times 10^{-11}$ |
| Threshold of hearing | 0 | $1 \times 10^{-12}$ |

**EXAMPLE 12–3 Sound intensity on the street.** At a busy street corner, the sound level is 70 dB. What is the intensity of sound there?

**APPROACH** We have to solve Eq. 12–1 for intensity $I$, remembering that $I_0 = 1.0 \times 10^{-12}\,\mathrm{W/m^2}$.

**SOLUTION** From Eq. 12–1

$$\log\frac{I}{I_0} = \frac{\beta}{10},$$

so

$$\frac{I}{I_0} = 10^{\beta/10}.$$

With $\beta = 70$, then

$$I = I_0 10^{\beta/10} = \left(1.0\times10^{-12}\,\mathrm{W/m^2}\right)\left(10^7\right) = 1.0\times10^{-5}\,\mathrm{W/m^2}.$$

**NOTE** Recall (Appendix A) that $x = \log y$ is the same as $y = 10^x$.

PHYSICS APPLIED

*Loudspeaker response (± 3 dB)*

**EXAMPLE 12–4** **Loudspeaker response.** A high-quality loudspeaker is advertised to reproduce, at full volume, frequencies from 30 Hz to 18,000 Hz with uniform sound level ± 3 dB. That is, over this frequency range, the sound level output does not vary by more than 3 dB for a given input level. By what factor does the intensity change for the maximum output sound level change of 3 dB?

**APPROACH** Let us call the average intensity $I_1$ and the average sound level $\beta_1$. Then the maximum intensity, $I_2$, corresponds to a level $\beta_2 = \beta_1 + 3\text{ dB}$. We then use the relation between intensity and sound level, Eq. 12–1.

**SOLUTION** Equation 12–1 gives

$$\beta_2 - \beta_1 = 10\log\frac{I_2}{I_0} - 10\log\frac{I_1}{I_0}$$

$$3\text{ dB} = 10\left(\log\frac{I_2}{I_0} - \log\frac{I_1}{I_0}\right)$$

$$= 10\log\frac{I_2}{I_1}$$

because $(\log a - \log b) = \log a/b$ (see Appendix A). This last equation gives

$$\log\frac{I_2}{I_1} = 0.30,$$

or

*$x = \log y$ means $y = 10^x$*

$$\frac{I_2}{I_1} = 10^{0.30} = 2.0.$$

So ± 3 dB corresponds to a doubling or halving of the intensity.

**EXERCISE B** If an increase of 3 dB means "twice as intense," what does an increase of 6 dB mean?

It is worth noting that a sound-level difference of 3 dB (which corresponds to a doubled intensity, as we just saw) corresponds to only a very small change in the subjective sensation of apparent loudness. Indeed, the average human can distinguish a difference in sound level of only about 1 or 2 dB.

Normally, the loudness or intensity of a sound decreases as you get farther from the source of the sound. In interior rooms, this effect is reduced because of reflections from the walls. However, if a source is in the open so that sound can radiate out freely in all directions, the intensity decreases as the inverse square of the distance,

$$I \propto \frac{1}{r^2},$$

as we saw in Section 11–9. Over large distances, the intensity decreases faster than $1/r^2$ because some of the energy is transferred into irregular motion of air molecules. This loss happens more for higher frequencies, so any sound of mixed frequencies will be less "bright" at a distance.

PHYSICS APPLIED

*Jet plane noise*

**EXAMPLE 12–5** **Airplane roar.** The sound level measured 30 m from a jet plane is 140 dB. What is the sound level at 300 m? (Ignore reflections from the ground.)

**APPROACH** Given the sound level, we can determine the intensity at 30 m using Eq. 12–1. Because intensity decreases as the square of the distance, ignoring reflections, we can find $I$ at 300 m and again apply Eq. 12–1 to obtain the sound level.

**SOLUTION** The intensity $I$ at 30 m is

$$140\text{ dB} = 10\log\left(\frac{I}{10^{-12}\text{ W/m}^2}\right).$$

Reversing the log equation to solve for $I$, we have

$$10^{14} = \frac{I}{10^{-12}\text{ W/m}^2},$$

so $I = (10^{14})(10^{-12}\text{ W/m}^2) = 10^2\text{ W/m}^2$. At 300 m, 10 times as far, the intensity will be $(\frac{1}{10})^2 = 1/100$ as much, or $1\text{ W/m}^2$. Hence, the sound level is

$$\beta = 10\log\left(\frac{1\text{ W/m}^2}{10^{-12}\text{ W/m}^2}\right) = 120\text{ dB}.$$

Even at 300 m, the sound is at the threshold of pain. This is why workers at airports wear ear covers to protect their ears from damage (Fig. 12–4).

**NOTE** Here is a simpler approach that avoids Eq. 12–1: because the intensity decreases as the square of the distance, at 10 times the distance the intensity decreases by $(\frac{1}{10})^2 = \frac{1}{100}$. We can use the result that 10 dB corresponds to an intensity change by a factor of 10 (see just before Example 12–3). Then an intensity change by a factor of 100 corresponds to a sound-level change of (2)(10 dB) = 20 dB. This confirms our result above: 140 dB − 20 dB = 120 dB.

**FIGURE 12–4** Example 12–5. Airport worker with sound-intensity-reducing ear covers (headphones).

**EXERCISE C** If you double your distance from a source of sound that is radiating freely in all directions, how does the intensity that you hear change? By how many dB does the sound level change?

## * Intensity Related to Amplitude

The intensity $I$ of a wave is proportional to the square of the wave amplitude, $A$, as discussed in Sections 11–9 and 11–10. We can then relate the amplitude quantitatively to the intensity $I$ or level $\beta$, as the following Example shows.

**EXAMPLE 12–6** **How tiny the displacement is.** Calculate the displacement of air molecules for a sound having a frequency of 1000 Hz at the threshold of hearing.

PHYSICS APPLIED
*Incredible sensitivity of the ear*

**APPROACH** In Section 11–10 we found a relation between intensity $I$ and displacement amplitude $A$ of a wave, Eq. 11–18. The amplitude of oscillation of air molecules is what we want to solve for, given the intensity.

**SOLUTION** At the threshold of hearing, $I = 1 \times 10^{-12}\text{ W/m}^2$ (Table 12–2). We solve for the amplitude $A$ in Eq. 11–18:

$$\begin{aligned} A &= \frac{1}{\pi f}\sqrt{\frac{I}{2\rho v}} \\ &= \frac{1}{(3.14)(1.0 \times 10^3\text{ s}^{-1})}\sqrt{\frac{1.0 \times 10^{-12}\text{ W/m}^2}{(2)(1.29\text{ kg/m}^3)(343\text{ m/s})}} \\ &= 1.1 \times 10^{-11}\text{ m}, \end{aligned}$$

where we have taken the density of air to be $1.29\text{ kg/m}^3$ and the speed of sound in air (assumed 20°C) as 343 m/s.

**NOTE** We see how incredibly sensitive the human ear is: it can detect displacements of air molecules which are actually less than the diameter of atoms (about $10^{-10}$ m).

*Ear detects displacements smaller than size of atoms*

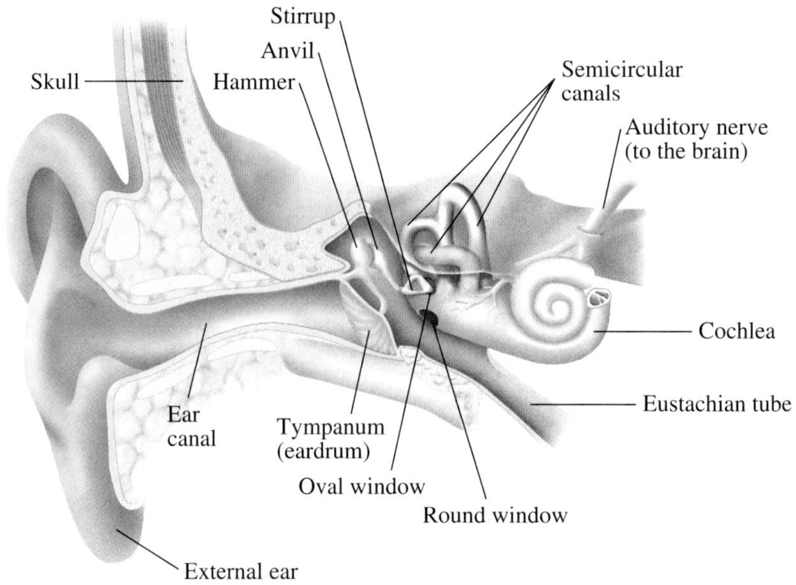


**FIGURE 12–5** Diagram of the human ear.

## * 12–3 The Ear and Its Response; Loudness

The human ear is a remarkably sensitive detector of sound. Mechanical detectors of sound (microphones) can barely match the ear in detecting low-intensity sounds.

The function of the ear is to transform the vibrational energy of waves into electrical signals which are carried to the brain by way of nerves. A microphone performs a similar task. Sound waves striking the diaphragm of a microphone set it into vibration, and these vibrations are transformed into an electrical signal with the same frequencies, which can then be amplified and sent to a loudspeaker or tape recorder. We shall discuss the operation of microphones when we study electricity and magnetism in later Chapters. Here we shall discuss the structure and response of the ear.

PHYSICS APPLIED
*Human ear*

Figure 12–5 is a diagram of the human ear. The ear consists of three main divisions: the outer ear, middle ear, and inner ear. In the outer ear, sound waves from the outside travel down the ear canal to the eardrum (the tympanum), which vibrates in response to the impinging waves. The middle ear consists of three small bones known as the hammer, anvil, and stirrup, which transfer the vibrations of the eardrum to the inner ear at the oval window. This delicate system of levers, coupled with the relatively large area of the eardrum compared to the area of the oval window, results in the pressure being amplified by a factor of about 40. The inner ear consists of the semicircular canals, which are important for controlling balance, and the liquid-filled cochlea where the vibrational energy of sound waves is transformed into electrical energy and sent to the brain.

### * The Ear's Response

*Sensitivity of the ear*

*Loudness (in "phons")*

The ear is not equally sensitive to all frequencies. To hear the same loudness for sounds of different frequencies requires different intensities. Studies averaged over large numbers of people have produced the curves shown in Fig. 12–6. On this graph, each curve represents sounds that seemed to be equally loud. The number labeling each curve represents the **loudness level** (the units are called *phons*), which is numerically equal to the sound level in dB at 1000 Hz. For example, the curve labeled 40 represents sounds that are heard by an average person to have the same loudness as a 1000-Hz sound with a sound level of 40 dB. From this 40-phon curve, we see that a 100-Hz tone must be at a level of about 62 dB to be perceived as loud as a 1000-Hz tone of only 40 dB.

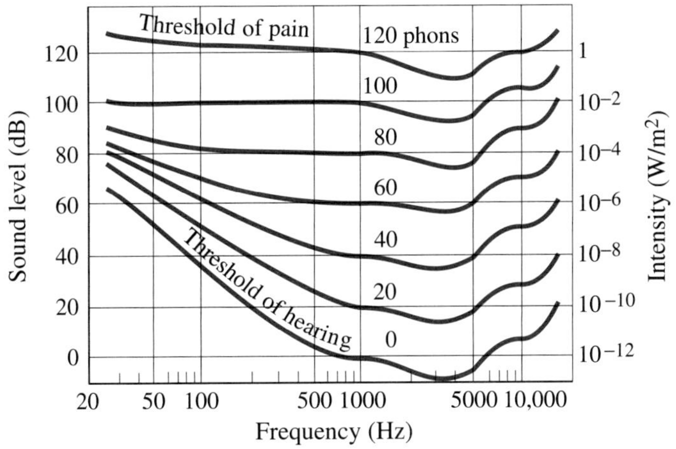


**FIGURE 12–6** Sensitivity of the human ear as a function of frequency (see text). Note that the frequency scale is "logarithmic" in order to cover a wide range of frequencies.

The lowest curve in Fig. 12–6 (labeled 0) represents the sound level, as a function of frequency, for the *threshold of hearing*, the softest sound that is just audible by a very good ear. Note that the ear is most sensitive to sounds of frequency between 2000 and 4000 Hz, which are common in speech and music. Note too that whereas a 1000-Hz sound is audible at a level of 0 dB, a 100-Hz sound must be nearly 40 dB to be heard. The top curve in Fig. 12–6, labeled 120 phons, represents the *threshold of pain*. Sounds above this level can actually be felt and cause pain.

Figure 12–6 shows that at lower sound levels, our ears are less sensitive to the high and low frequencies relative to middle frequencies. The "loudness" control on stereo systems is intended to compensate for this low-volume insensitivity. As the volume is turned down, the loudness control boosts the high and low frequencies relative to the middle frequencies so that the sound will have a more "normal-sounding" frequency balance. Many listeners, however, find the sound more pleasing or natural without the loudness control.

## 12–4 Sources of Sound: Vibrating Strings and Air Columns

The source of any sound is a vibrating object. Almost any object can vibrate and hence be a source of sound. We now discuss some simple sources of sound, particularly musical instruments. In musical instruments, the source is set into vibration by striking, plucking, bowing, or blowing. Standing waves are produced and the source vibrates at its natural resonant frequencies. The vibrating source is in contact with the air (or other medium) and pushes on it to produce sound waves that travel outward. The frequencies of the waves are the same as those of the source, but the speed and wavelengths can be different. A drum has a stretched membrane that vibrates. Xylophones and marimbas have metal or wood bars that can be set into vibration. Bells, cymbals, and gongs also make use of a vibrating metal. The most widely used instruments make use of vibrating strings, such as the violin, guitar, and piano, or make use of vibrating columns of air, such as the flute, trumpet, and pipe organ. We have already seen that the pitch of a pure sound is determined by the frequency. Typical frequencies for musical notes on the "equally tempered chromatic scale" are given in Table 12–3 for the octave beginning with middle C. Note that one octave corresponds to a doubling of frequency. For example, middle C has frequency of 262 Hz whereas C′ (C above middle C) has twice that frequency, 524 Hz. [Middle C is the C or "do" note at the middle of a piano keyboard.]

**TABLE 12–3 Equally Tempered Chromatic Scale**†

| Note | Frequency (Hz) |
|---|---|
| C | 262 |
| C# or D♭ | 277 |
| D | 294 |
| D# or E♭ | 311 |
| E | 330 |
| F | 349 |
| F# or G♭ | 370 |
| G | 392 |
| G# or A♭ | 415 |
| A | 440 |
| A# or B♭ | 466 |
| B | 494 |
| C′ | 524 |

† Only one octave is included.

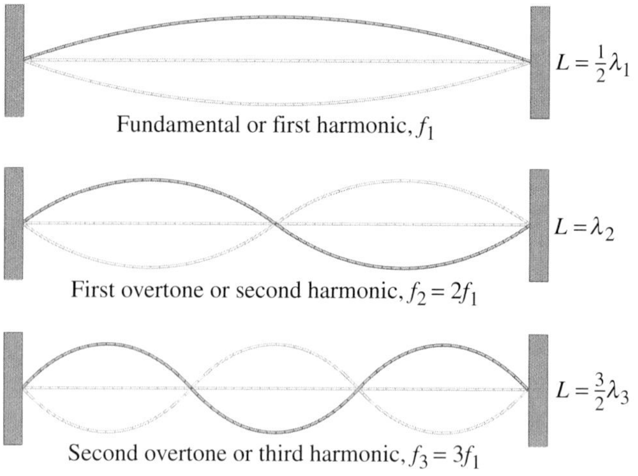


**FIGURE 12–7** Standing waves on a string—only the lowest three frequencies are shown.

## Stringed Instruments

PHYSICS APPLIED
*Stringed instruments*

We saw in Chapter 11, Fig. 11–40, how standing waves are established on a string, and we show this again here in Fig. 12–7. Such standing waves are the basis for all stringed instruments. The pitch is normally determined by the lowest resonant frequency, the **fundamental**, which corresponds to nodes occurring only at the ends. The string vibrating up and down as a whole corresponds to a half wavelength as shown at the top of Fig. 12–7; so the wavelength of the fundamental on the string is equal to twice the length of the string. Therefore, the fundamental frequency is $f_1 = v/\lambda = v/2L$, where $v$ is the velocity of the wave on the string. The possible frequencies for standing waves on a stretched string are whole-number multiples of the fundamental frequency:

$$f_n = nf_1 = n\frac{v}{2L}, \qquad n = 1, 2, 3, \cdots$$

(just as in Eq. 11–19b), where $n = 1$ refers to the fundamental and $n = 2, 3, \cdots$ are the overtones. All of the standing waves, $n = 1, 2, 3, \cdots$, are called harmonics[†], as we saw in Section 11–13.

When a finger is placed on the string of a guitar or violin, the effective length of the string is shortened. So its fundamental frequency, and pitch, is higher since the wavelength of the fundamental is shorter (Fig. 12–8). The strings on a guitar or violin are all the same length. They sound at a different pitch because the strings have different mass per unit length, $m/L$, which affects the velocity as seen in Eq. 11–13,

$$v = \sqrt{F_T/(m/L)}. \qquad \text{[stretched string]}$$

Thus the velocity on a heavier string is less and the frequency will be less for the same wavelength. The tension $F_T$ may also be different. Adjusting the tension is the means for tuning the pitch of each string. In pianos and harps, on the other hand, the strings are of different lengths. For the lower notes the strings are not only longer, but heavier as well, and the reason is illustrated in the following Example.

**FIGURE 12–8** The wavelength of (a) an unfingered string is longer than that of (b) a fingered string. Hence, the frequency of the fingered string is higher. Only one string is shown on this guitar, and only the simplest standing wave, the fundamental, is shown.

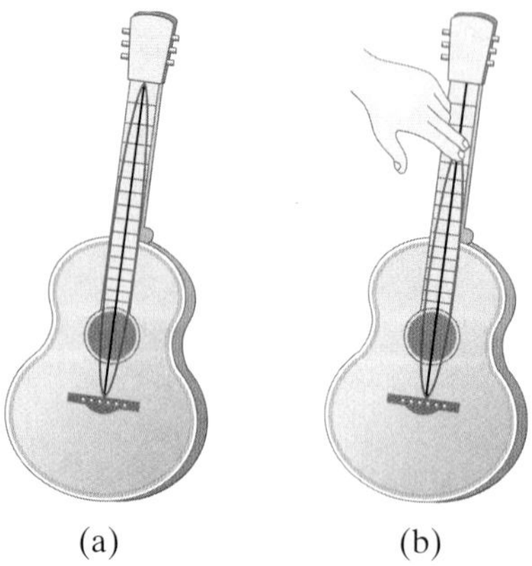


**EXAMPLE 12–7** **Piano strings.** The highest key on a piano corresponds to a frequency about 150 times that of the lowest key. If the string for the highest note is 5.0 cm long, how long would the string for the lowest note have to be if it had the same mass per unit length and was under the same tension?

**APPROACH** Since $v = \sqrt{F_T/(m/L)}$, the velocity would be the same on each string. So the frequency is inversely proportional to the length $L$ of the string ($f = v/\lambda = v/2L$).

[†]When the resonant frequencies above the fundamental (that is, the overtones) are integral multiples of the fundamental, as here, they are called harmonics. But if the overtones are not integral multiples of the fundamental, as is the case for a vibrating drumhead, for example, they are not harmonics.

**SOLUTION** We can write, for the fundamental frequencies of each string, the ratio

$$\frac{L_{\mathrm{L}}}{L_{\mathrm{H}}} = \frac{f_{\mathrm{H}}}{f_{\mathrm{L}}},$$

where the subscripts L and H refer to the lowest and highest notes, respectively. Thus $L_{\mathrm{L}} = L_{\mathrm{H}}(f_{\mathrm{H}}/f_{\mathrm{L}}) = (5.0\,\mathrm{cm})(150) = 750\,\mathrm{cm}$, or 7.5 m. This would be ridiculously long ($\approx 25$ ft) for a piano.

**NOTE** The longer strings of lower frequency are made heavier, so even on grand pianos the strings are less than 3 m long.

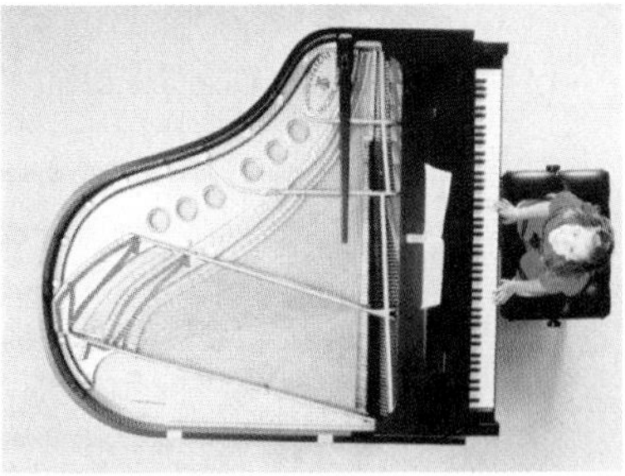

(a)

(b)

**FIGURE 12–9** (a) Piano, showing sounding board to which the strings are attached; (b) sounding box (guitar).

**EXAMPLE 12–8** **Frequencies and wavelengths in the violin.** A 0.32-m-long violin string is tuned to play A above middle C at 440 Hz. (*a*) What is the wavelength of the fundamental string vibration, and (*b*) what are the frequency and wavelength of the sound wave produced? (*c*) Why is there a difference?

**APPROACH** The wavelength of the fundamental string vibration equals twice the length of the string (Fig. 12–7). As the string vibrates, it pushes on the air, which is thus forced to oscillate at the same frequency as the string.

**SOLUTION** (*a*) From Fig. 12–7 the wavelength of the fundamental is

$$\lambda = 2L = 2(0.32\,\mathrm{m}) = 0.64\,\mathrm{m} = 64\,\mathrm{cm}.$$

This is the wavelength of the standing wave on the string.

(*b*) The sound wave that travels outward in the air (to reach our ears) has the same frequency, 440 Hz. Its wavelength is

$$\lambda = \frac{v}{f} = \frac{343\,\mathrm{m/s}}{440\,\mathrm{Hz}} = 0.78\,\mathrm{m} = 78\,\mathrm{cm},$$

where $v$ is the speed of sound in air (assumed at 20°C), Section 12–1.

(*c*) The wavelength of the sound wave is different from that of the standing wave on the string because the speed of sound in air (343 m/s at 20°C) is different from the speed of the wave on the string ($= f\lambda = 440\,\mathrm{Hz} \times 0.64\,\mathrm{m} = 280\,\mathrm{m/s}$) which depends on the tension in the string and its mass per unit length.

**NOTE** The frequencies on the string and in the air are the same: the string and air are in contact, and the string "forces" the air to vibrate at the same frequency. But the wavelengths are different because the wave speed on the string is different than that in air.

**CAUTION**

*Speed of standing wave on string ≠ speed of sound wave in air*

Stringed instruments would not be very loud if they relied on their vibrating strings to produce the sound waves since the strings are too thin to compress and expand much air. Stringed instruments therefore make use of a kind of mechanical amplifier known as a *sounding board* (piano) or *sounding box* (guitar, violin), which acts to amplify the sound by putting a greater surface area in contact with the air (Fig. 12–9). When the strings are set into vibration, the sounding board or box is set into vibration as well. Since it has much greater area in contact with the air, it can produce a more intense sound wave. On an electric guitar, the sounding box is not so important since the vibrations of the strings are amplified electronically.

## Wind Instruments

Instruments such as woodwinds, the brasses, and the pipe organ produce sound from the vibrations of standing waves in a column of air within a tube or pipe (Fig. 12–10). Standing waves can occur in the air of any cavity, but the frequencies present are complicated for any but very simple shapes such as the uniform, narrow tube of a flute or an organ pipe. In some instruments, a vibrating reed or the vibrating lip of the player helps to set up vibrations of the air column. In others, a stream of air is directed against one edge of the opening or mouthpiece, leading to turbulence which sets up the vibrations. Because of the disturbance, whatever its source, the air within the tube vibrates with a variety of frequencies, but only frequencies that correspond to standing waves will persist.

**FIGURE 12–10** Wind instruments: clarinet (left) and flute.

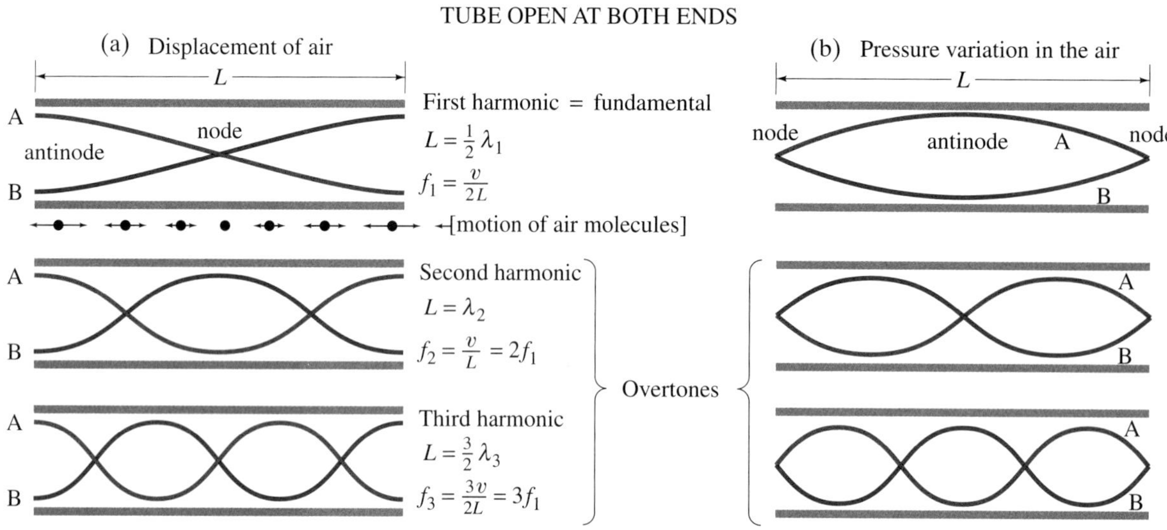


**FIGURE 12–11** Graphs of the three simplest modes of vibration (standing waves) for a uniform tube open at both ends ("open tube"). These simplest modes of vibration are shown in (a), on the left, in terms of the motion of the air (displacement), and in (b), on the right, in terms of air pressure. Each graph shows the wave format at two times, A and B, a half period apart. The actual motion of molecules for one case, the fundamental, is shown just below the tube at top left.

For a string fixed at both ends, Fig. 12–7, the standing waves have nodes (no movement) at the two ends, and one or more antinodes (large amplitude of vibration) in between. A node separates successive antinodes. The lowest-frequency standing wave, the *fundamental*, corresponds to a single antinode. The higher-frequency standing waves are called **overtones** or **harmonics**, as we saw in Section 11–13. Specifically, the first harmonic is the fundamental, the second harmonic (= first overtone) has twice the frequency of the fundamental, and so on.

PHYSICS APPLIED

*Wind instruments*

The situation is similar for a column of air in a tube of uniform diameter, but we must remember that it is now air itself that is vibrating. We can describe the waves either in terms of the flow of the air—that is, in terms of the *displacement* of air—or in terms of the *pressure* in the air (see Figs. 12–2 and 12–3). In terms of displacement, the air at the closed end of a tube is a displacement node since the air is not free to move there, whereas near the open end of a tube there will be an antinode since the air can move freely in and out. The air within the tube vibrates in the form of longitudinal standing waves. The possible modes of vibration for a tube open at both ends (called an **open tube**) are shown graphically in Fig. 12–11. They are shown for a tube that is open at one end but closed at the other (called a **closed tube**) in Fig. 12–12. [A tube closed at *both* ends, having no connection to the outside air, would be useless as an instrument.] The graphs in part (a) of each Figure (left-hand sides) represent the displacement amplitude of the vibrating air in the tube. Note that these are graphs, and that the air molecules themselves oscillate *horizontally*, parallel to the tube length, as shown by the small arrows in the top diagram of Fig. 12–11a (on the left). The exact position of the antinode near the open end of a tube depends on the diameter of the tube, but if the diameter is small compared to the length, which is the usual case, the antinode occurs very close to the end as shown. We assume this is the case in what follows. (The position of the antinode may also depend slightly on the wavelength and other factors.)

*Open tube*

Let us look in detail at the open tube, in Fig. 12–11a, which might be an organ pipe or a flute. An open tube has displacement antinodes at both ends since the air is free to move at open ends. There must be at least one node within an open tube if there is to be a standing wave at all. A single node corresponds to the *fundamental frequency* of the tube. Since the distance between two successive nodes, or between two successive antinodes, is $\frac{1}{2}\lambda$, there is one-half of a wavelength within the length of the tube for the simplest case of the fundamental (top diagram in Fig. 12–11a): $L = \frac{1}{2}\lambda$, or $\lambda = 2L$. So the fundamental frequency is $f_1 = v/\lambda = v/2L$, where $v$ is the velocity of sound in air (the air in the tube). The standing wave with two nodes is the *first overtone* or *second harmonic* and has half the wavelength ($L = \lambda$) and twice the frequency of the fundamental. Indeed, in a uniform tube open at both ends, the frequency of each overtone is an integral multiple of the fundamental frequency, as shown in Fig. 12–11a. This is just what is found for a string.

*Open tubes produce all harmonics*

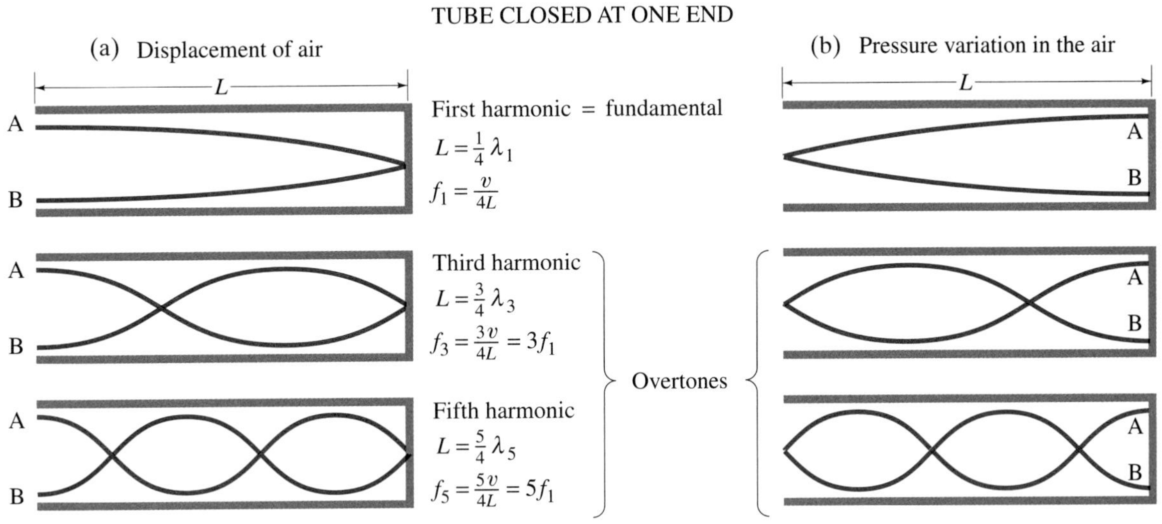


**FIGURE 12–12** Modes of vibration (standing waves) for a tube closed at one end ("closed tube"). See caption for Fig. 12–11.

*Closed tube*

For a closed tube, shown in Fig. 12–12a, which could be an organ pipe, there is always a displacement node at the closed end (because the air is not free to move) and an antinode at the open end (where the air can move freely). Since the distance between a node and the nearest antinode is $\frac{1}{4}\lambda$, we see that the fundamental in a closed tube corresponds to only one-fourth of a wavelength within the length of the tube: $L = \lambda/4$, and $\lambda = 4L$. The fundamental frequency is thus $f_1 = v/4L$, or half that for an open pipe of the same length. There is another difference, for as we can see from Fig. 12–12a, only the odd harmonics are present in a closed tube: the overtones have frequencies equal to $3, 5, 7, \cdots$ times the fundamental frequency. There is no way for waves with $2, 4, 6, \cdots$ times the fundamental frequency to have a node at one end and an antinode at the other, and thus they cannot exist as standing waves in a closed tube.

*Closed tubes produce only odd harmonics*

Another way to analyze the vibrations in a uniform tube is to consider a description in terms of the *pressure* in the air, shown in part (b) of Figs. 12–11 and 12–12 (right-hand sides). Where the air in a wave is compressed, the pressure is higher, whereas in a wave expansion (or rarefaction), the pressure is less than normal. The open end of a tube is open to the atmosphere. Hence the pressure variation at an open end must be a *node*: the pressure doesn't alternate, but remains at the outside atmospheric pressure. If a tube has a closed end, the pressure at that closed end can readily alternate to be above or below atmospheric pressure. Hence there is a pressure *antinode* at a closed end of a tube. There can be pressure nodes and antinodes within the tube. Some of the possible vibrational modes in terms of pressure for an open tube are shown in Fig. 12–11b, and for a closed tube are shown in Fig. 12–12b.

**EXAMPLE 12–9** **Organ pipes.** What will be the fundamental frequency and first three overtones for a 26-cm-long organ pipe at 20°C if it is (*a*) open and (*b*) closed?

**APPROACH** All our calculations can be based on Figs. 12–11a and 12–12a.

**SOLUTION** (*a*) For the open pipe, Fig. 12–11a, the fundamental frequency is

$$f_1 = \frac{v}{2L} = \frac{343\ \text{m/s}}{2(0.26\ \text{m})} = 660\ \text{Hz}.$$

The speed $v$ is the speed of sound in air (the air vibrating in the pipe). The overtones include all harmonics: 1320 Hz, 1980 Hz, 2640 Hz, and so on.
(*b*) For a closed pipe, Fig. 12–12a, the fundamental frequency is

$$f_1 = \frac{v}{4L} = \frac{343\ \text{m/s}}{4(0.26\ \text{m})} = 330\ \text{Hz}.$$

Only odd harmonics are present: the first three overtones are 990 Hz, 1650 Hz, and 2310 Hz.

**NOTE** The closed pipe plays 330 Hz, which, from Table 12–3, is E above middle C, whereas the open pipe of the same length plays 660 Hz, an octave higher.

Pipe organs use both open and closed pipes, with lengths from a few centimeters to 5 m or more. A flute acts as an open tube, for it is open not only where you blow into it, but also at the opposite end. The different notes on a flute are obtained by shortening the length of the vibrating air column, by uncovering holes along the tube (so a displacement antinode can occur at the hole). The shorter the length of the vibrating air column, the higher the fundamental frequency.

**EXAMPLE 12–10** **Flute.** A flute is designed to play middle C (262 Hz) as the fundamental frequency when all the holes are covered. Approximately how long should the distance be from the mouthpiece to the far end of the flute? (This is only approximate since the antinode does not occur precisely at the mouthpiece.) Assume the temperature is 20°C.

**APPROACH** When all holes are covered, the length of the vibrating air column is the full length. The speed of sound in air at 20°C is 343 m/s. Because a flute is open at both ends, we use Fig. 12–11: the fundamental frequency $f_1$ is related to the length $L$ of the vibrating air column by $f = v/2L$.

**SOLUTION** Solving for $L$, we find

$$L = \frac{v}{2f} = \frac{343\ \text{m/s}}{2(262\ \text{s}^{-1})} = 0.655\ \text{m}.$$

**EXERCISE D** To see why players of wind instruments "warm up" their instruments (so they will be in tune), determine the fundamental frequency of the flute of Example 12–10 when all holes are covered and the temperature is 10°C instead of 20°C.

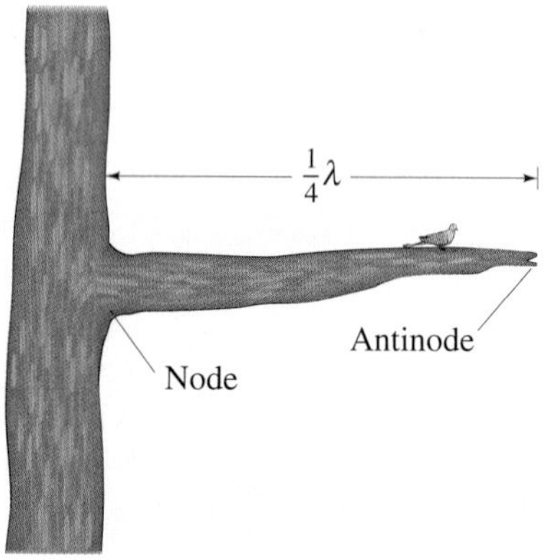


**FIGURE 12–13** Example 12–11.

**EXAMPLE 12–11** **ESTIMATE** **Wind noise frequencies.** Wind can be noisy—it can "howl" in trees; it can "moan" in chimneys. What is causing the noise, and about what range of frequencies would you expect to hear?

**APPROACH** Gusts of air in the wind cause vibrations or oscillations of the tree limb (or air column in the chimney), which produce sound waves of the same frequency. The end of a tree limb fixed to the tree trunk is a node, whereas the other end is free to move and therefore is an antinode; the tree limb is thus about $\frac{1}{4}\lambda$ (Fig. 12–13).

**SOLUTION** We estimate $v \approx 4000\ \text{m/s}$ for the speed of sound in wood (Table 12–1). Suppose that a tree limb has length $L \approx 2\ \text{m}$; then $\lambda = 4L = 8\ \text{m}$ and $f = v/\lambda = (4000\ \text{m/s})/(8\ \text{m}) \approx 500\ \text{Hz}$.

**NOTE** Wind can excite air oscillations in a chimney, much like in an organ pipe or flute. A chimney is a fairly long tube, perhaps 3 m in length, acting like a tube open at either one end or even both ends. If open at both ends ($\lambda = 2L$), with $v \approx 340\ \text{m/s}$, we find $f_1 \approx v/2L \approx 56\ \text{Hz}$, which is a fairly low note—no wonder chimneys "moan"!

## * 12–5 Quality of Sound, and Noise; Superposition

**FIGURE 12–14** The amplitudes of the fundamental and first two overtones are added at each point to get the "sum," or composite waveform.

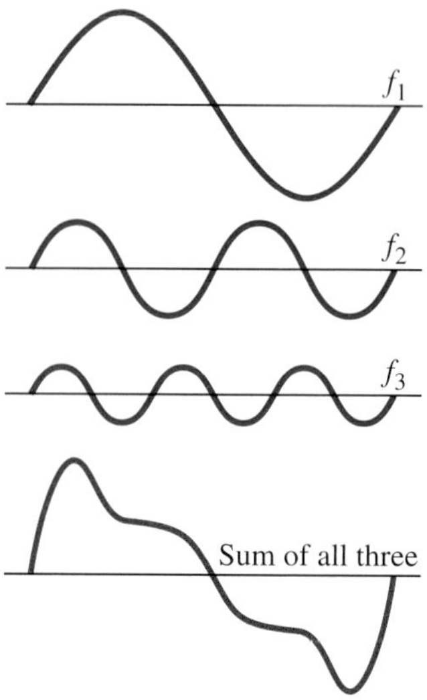


Whenever we hear a sound, particularly a musical sound, we are aware of its loudness, its pitch, and also of a third aspect called "quality." For example, when a piano and then a flute play a note of the same loudness and pitch (say, middle C), there is a clear difference in the overall sound. We would never mistake a piano for a flute. This is what is meant by the **quality** of a sound. For musical instruments, the terms *timbre* and *tone color* are also used.

Just as loudness and pitch can be related to physically measurable quantities, so too can quality. The quality of a sound depends on the presence of overtones—their number and their relative amplitudes. Generally, when a note is played on a musical instrument, the fundamental as well as overtones are present simultaneously. Figure 12–14 illustrates how the *principle of superposition* (Section 11–12) applies to three wave forms, in this case the fundamental and first two overtones (with particular amplitudes): they add together at each point to give a composite *waveform*. Of course, more than two overtones are

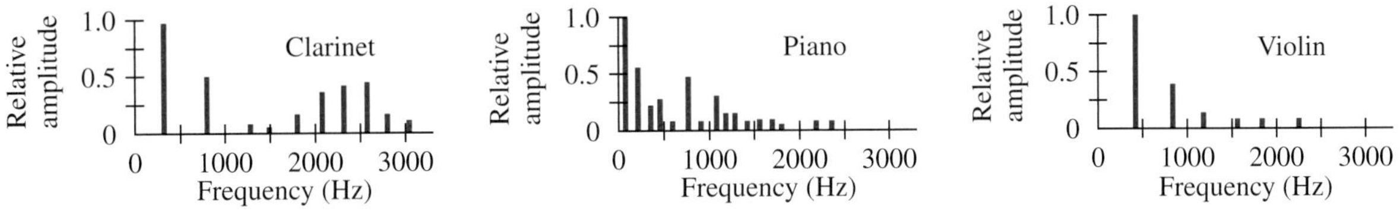


**FIGURE 12–15** Sound spectra for different instruments. The spectra change when the instruments play different notes. The clarinet is a bit complicated: it acts like a closed tube at lower frequencies, having only odd harmonics, but at higher frequencies all harmonics occur as for an open tube.

usually present. [Any complex wave can be analyzed into a superposition of sinusoidal waves of appropriate amplitudes, wavelengths, and frequencies. Such an analysis is called a *Fourier analysis*.]

The relative amplitudes of the overtones for a given note are different for different musical instruments, which is what gives each instrument its characteristic quality or timbre. A bar graph showing the relative amplitudes of the harmonics for a given note produced by an instrument is called a *sound spectrum*. Several typical examples for different musical instruments are shown in Fig. 12–15. The fundamental usually has the greatest amplitude, and its frequency is what is heard as the pitch.

The manner in which an instrument is played strongly influences the sound quality. Plucking a violin string, for example, makes a very different sound than pulling a bow across it. The sound spectrum at the very start (or end) of a note (as when a hammer strikes a piano string) can be very different from the subsequent sustained tone. This too affects the subjective tone quality of an instrument.

An ordinary sound, like that made by striking two stones together, is a noise that has a certain quality, but a clear pitch is not discernible. Such a noise is a mixture of many frequencies which bear little relation to one another. A sound spectrum made of that noise would not show discrete lines like those of Fig. 12–15. Instead it would show a continuous, or nearly continuous, spectrum of frequencies. Such a sound we call "noise" in comparison with the more harmonious sounds which contain frequencies that are simple multiples of the fundamental.

## 12–6 Interference of Sound Waves; Beats

### Interference in Space

We saw in Section 11–12 that when two waves simultaneously pass through the same region of space, they interfere with one another. Interference also occurs with sound waves.

Consider two large loudspeakers, A and B, a distance $d$ apart on the stage of an auditorium as shown in Fig. 12–16. Let us assume the two speakers are emitting sound waves of the same single frequency and that they are in phase: that is, when one speaker is forming a compression, so is the other. (We ignore reflections from walls, floor, etc.) The curved lines in the diagram represent the crests of sound waves from each speaker at one instant in time. We must remember that for a sound wave, a crest is a compression in the air whereas a trough—which falls between two crests—is a rarefaction. A person or detector at a point such as C, which is the same distance from each speaker, will experience a loud sound because the interference will be constructive—two crests reach it at one moment, two troughs reach it a moment later. On the other hand, at a point such as D in the diagram, little if any sound will be heard because destructive interference occurs—compressions of one wave meet rarefactions of the other and vice versa (see Fig. 11–37 and the related discussion on water waves in Section 11–12).

**FIGURE 12–16** Sound waves from two loudspeakers interfere.

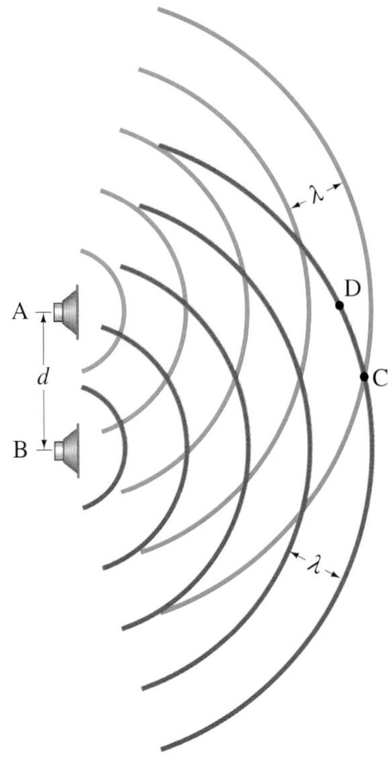

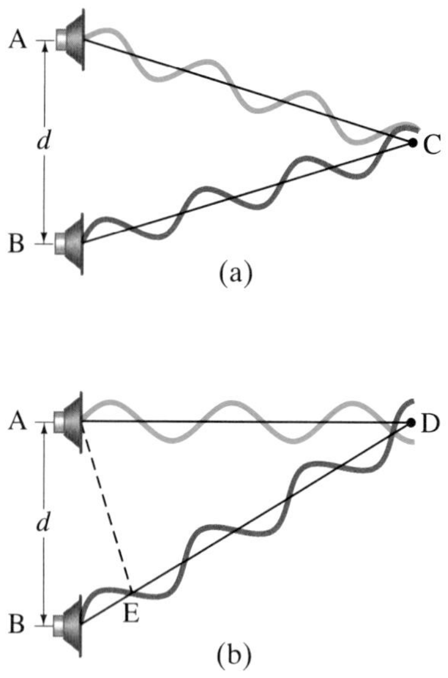


**FIGURE 12–17** Sound waves of a single frequency from loudspeakers A and B (see Fig. 12–16) constructively interfere at C and destructively interfere at D. [Shown here are graphical representations, not the actual longitudinal sound waves.]

An analysis of this situation is perhaps clearer if we graphically represent the waveforms as in Fig. 12–17. In Fig. 12–17a it can be seen that at point C, constructive interference occurs since both waves simultaneously have crests or simultaneously have troughs when they arrive at C. In Fig. 12–17b we see that, to reach point D, the wave from speaker B must travel a greater distance than the wave from A. Thus the wave from B lags behind that from A. In this diagram, point E is chosen so that the distance ED is equal to AD. Thus we see that if the distance BE is equal to precisely one-half the wavelength of the sound, the two waves will be exactly out of phase when they reach D, and destructive interference occurs. This then is the criterion for determining at what points destructive interference occurs: destructive interference occurs at any point whose distance from one speaker is greater than its distance from the other speaker by one-half wavelength. Notice that if this extra distance (BE in Fig. 12–17b) is equal to a whole wavelength (or 2, 3, ⋯ wavelengths), then the two waves will be in phase and *constructive interference* occurs. If the distance BE equals $\frac{1}{2}, 1\frac{1}{2}, 2\frac{1}{2}, \cdots$ wavelengths, *destructive interference* occurs.

It is important to realize that a person sitting at point D in Fig. 12–16 or 12–17 hears nothing at all (or nearly so), yet sound is coming from both speakers. Indeed, if one of the speakers is turned off, the sound from the other speaker will be clearly heard.

If a loudspeaker emits a whole range of frequencies, only specific wavelengths will destructively interfere completely at a given point.

**EXAMPLE 12–12** **Loudspeakers' interference.** Two loudspeakers are 1.00 m apart. A person stands 4.00 m from one speaker. How far must this person be from the second speaker to detect destructive interference when the speakers emit an 1150-Hz sound? Assume the temperature is 20°C.

**APPROACH** To sense destructive interference, the person must be one-half wavelength closer to or farther from one speaker than from the other—that is, at a distance = 4.00 m ± $\lambda/2$. We can determine $\lambda$ since we know $f$ and $v$.

**SOLUTION** The speed of sound at 20°C is 343 m/s, so the wavelength of this sound is (Eq. 11–12)

$$\lambda = \frac{v}{f} = \frac{343\ \text{m/s}}{1150\ \text{Hz}} = 0.30\ \text{m}.$$

For destructive interference to occur, the person must be one-half wavelength farther from one loudspeaker than from the other, or 0.15 m. Thus the person must be 3.85 m or 4.15 m from the second speaker.

**NOTE** If the speakers are less than 0.15 m apart, there will be no point that is 0.15 m farther from one speaker than the other, and there will be no point where destructive interference could occur.

## Beats—Interference in Time

We have been discussing interference of sound waves that takes place in space. An interesting and important example of interference that occurs in time is the phenomenon known as **beats**: If two sources of sound—say, two tuning forks—are close in frequency but not exactly the same, sound waves from the two sources interfere with each other. The sound level at a given position alternately rises and falls in time, because the two waves are sometimes in phase and sometimes out of phase due to their different wavelengths. The regularly spaced intensity changes are called beats.

*Beats*

To see how beats arise, consider two equal-amplitude sound waves of frequency $f_A = 50\ \text{Hz}$ and $f_B = 60\ \text{Hz}$, respectively. In 1.00 s, the first source makes 50 vibrations whereas the second makes 60. We now examine the waves at one point in space equidistant from the two sources. The waveforms for each wave as a function of time, at a fixed position, are shown on the top graph of Fig. 12–18; the magenta line represents the 50-Hz wave, and the blue line represents the 60-Hz wave.

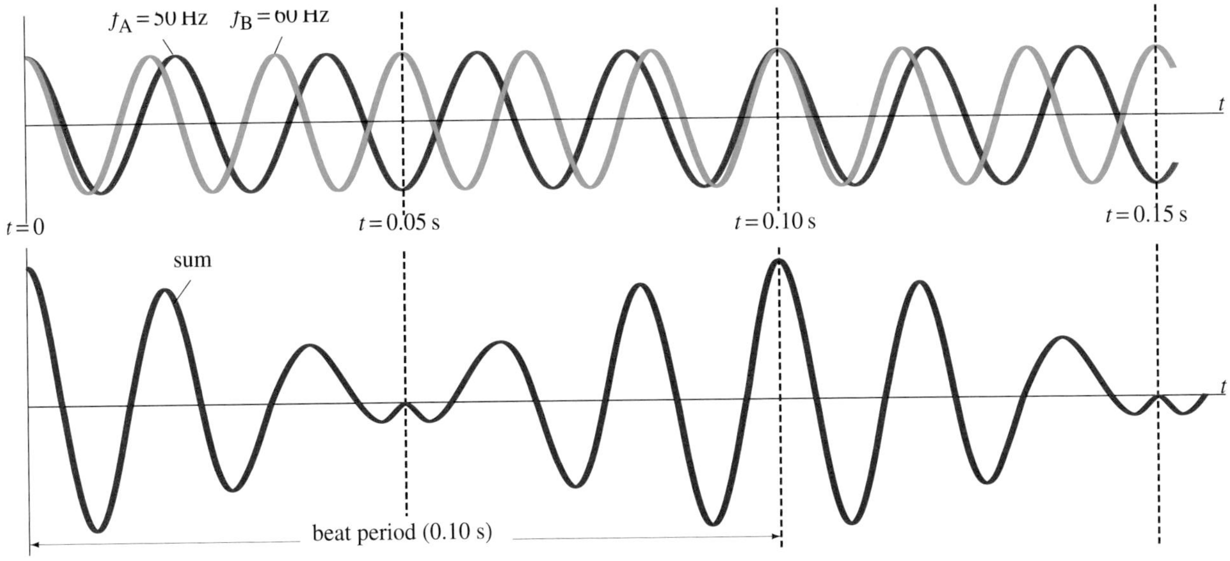


**FIGURE 12–18** Beats occur as a result of the superposition of two sound waves of slightly different frequency.

The lower graph in Fig. 12–18 shows the sum of the two waves as a function of time. At time $t = 0$ the two waves are shown to be in phase and interfere constructively. Because the two waves vibrate at different rates, at time $t = 0.05$ s they are completely out of phase and interfere destructively. At $t = 0.10$ s, they are again in phase and the resultant amplitude again is large. Thus the resultant amplitude is large every 0.10 s and drops drastically in between. This rising and falling of the intensity is what is heard as beats.[†] In this case the beats are 0.10 s apart. That is, the **beat frequency** is ten per second, or 10 Hz. This result, that the beat frequency equals the difference in frequency of the two waves is valid in general.

*Beat frequency = difference in the two wave frequencies*

The phenomenon of beats can occur with any kind of wave and is a very sensitive method for comparing frequencies. For example, to tune a piano, a piano tuner listens for beats produced between his standard tuning fork and that of a particular string on the piano, and knows it is in tune when the beats disappear. The members of an orchestra tune up by listening for beats between their instruments and that of a standard tone (usually A above middle C at 440 Hz) produced by a piano or an oboe.

PHYSICS APPLIED

*Tuning a piano*

**EXAMPLE 12–13** **Beats.** A tuning fork produces a steady 400-Hz tone. When this tuning fork is struck and held near a vibrating guitar string, twenty beats are counted in five seconds. What are the possible frequencies produced by the guitar string?

**APPROACH** For beats to occur, the string must vibrate at a frequency different from 400 Hz by whatever the beat frequency is.

**SOLUTION** The beat frequency is

$$f_{\text{beat}} = 20 \text{ vibrations}/5 \text{ s} = 4 \text{ Hz}.$$

This is the difference of the frequencies of the two waves. Because one wave is known to be 400 Hz, the other must be either 404 Hz or 396 Hz.

**EXERCISE E** What is the beat frequency for the tuning fork and guitar of Example 12–13 when 500-Hz and 506-Hz sounds are heard together?

[†]Beats will be heard even if the amplitudes are not equal, as long as the difference in amplitude is not great.

## 12–7 Doppler Effect

You may have noticed that you hear the pitch of the siren on a speeding firetruck drop abruptly as it passes you. Or you may have noticed the change in pitch of a blaring horn on a fast-moving car as it passes by you. The pitch of the engine noise of a race car changes as the car passes an observer. When a source of sound is moving toward an observer, the pitch the observer hears is higher than when the source is at rest; and when the source is traveling away from the observer, the pitch is lower. This phenomenon is known as the **Doppler effect**† and occurs for all types of waves. Let us now see why it occurs, and calculate the difference between the perceived and source frequencies when there is relative motion between source and observer.

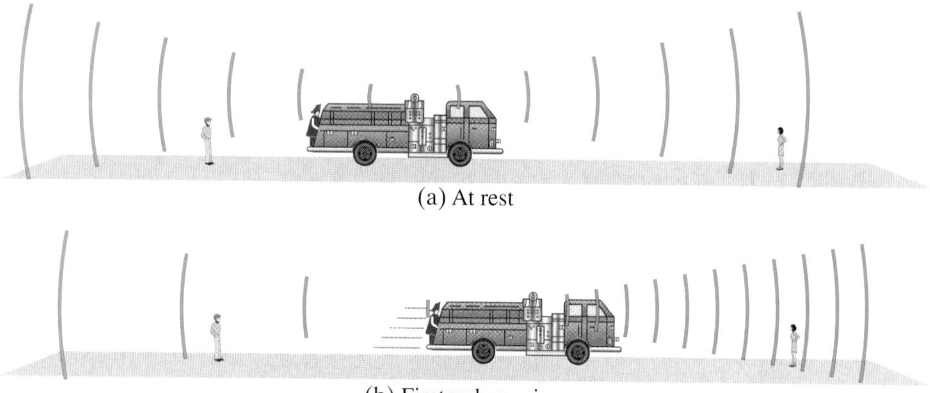


**FIGURE 12–19** (a) Both observers on the sidewalk hear the same frequency from the firetruck at rest. (b) Doppler effect: observer toward whom the firetruck moves hears a higher-frequency sound, and observer behind the firetruck hears a lower-frequency sound.

**FIGURE 12–20** Determination of the frequency shift in the Doppler effect (see text). The red dot is the source.

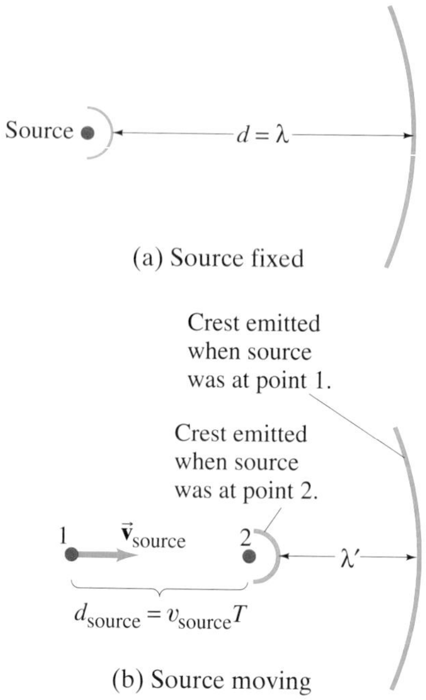


Consider the siren of a firetruck at rest, which is emitting sound of a particular frequency in all directions as shown in Fig. 12–19a. The sound waves are moving at the speed of sound in air, $v_{snd}$, which is independent of the velocity of the source or observer. If our source, the firetruck, is moving, the siren emits sound at the same frequency as it does at rest. But the sound wavefronts it emits forward, in front of it, are closer together than when the firetruck is at rest, as shown in Fig. 12–19b. This is because the firetruck, as it moves, is "chasing" the previously emitted wavefronts, and emits each crest closer to the previous one. Thus an observer on the sidewalk in front of the truck will detect more wave crests passing per second, so the frequency heard is higher. The wavefronts emitted behind the truck, on the other hand, are farther apart than when the truck is at rest because the truck is speeding away from them. Hence, fewer wave crests per second pass by an observer behind the moving truck (Fig. 12–19b) and the perceived pitch is lower.

We can calculate the frequency shift perceived by making use of Fig. 12–20, and we assume the air (or other medium) is at rest in our reference frame. (The stationary observer is off to the right.) In Fig. 12–20a, the source of the sound is shown as a red dot, and is at rest. Two successive wave crests are shown, the second of which has just been emitted and so is still near the source. The distance between these crests is $\lambda$, the wavelength. If the frequency of the source is $f$, then the time between emissions of wave crests is

$$T = \frac{1}{f} = \frac{\lambda}{v_{snd}}.$$

In Fig. 12–20b, the source is moving with a velocity $v_{source}$ toward the observer.

†After J. C. Doppler (1803–1853).

In a time $T$ (as just defined), the first wave crest has moved a distance $d = v_{snd} T = \lambda$, where $v_{snd}$ is the velocity of the sound wave in air (which is the same whether the source is moving or not). In this same time, the source has moved a distance $d_{source} = v_{source} T$. Then the distance between successive wave crests, which is the wavelength $\lambda'$ the observer will perceive, is

*Frequency change, moving source, fixed observer*

$$\begin{aligned}\lambda' &= d - d_{source} \\ &= \lambda - v_{source} T \\ &= \lambda - v_{source} \frac{\lambda}{v_{snd}} \\ &= \lambda\left(1 - \frac{v_{source}}{v_{snd}}\right).\end{aligned}$$

We subtract $\lambda$ from both sides of this equation and find that the shift in wavelength, $\Delta\lambda$, is

$$\Delta\lambda = \lambda' - \lambda = -\lambda \frac{v_{source}}{v_{snd}}.$$

So the shift in wavelength is directly proportional to the source speed $v_{source}$. The frequency $f'$ that will be perceived by our stationary observer on the ground is given by (Eq. 11–12)

$$f' = \frac{v_{snd}}{\lambda'} = \frac{v_{snd}}{\lambda\left(1 - \frac{v_{source}}{v_{snd}}\right)}.$$

Since $v_{snd}/\lambda = f$, then

$$f' = \frac{f}{\left(1 - \frac{v_{source}}{v_{snd}}\right)}. \qquad \left[\begin{array}{l}\text{source moving toward} \\ \text{stationary observer}\end{array}\right] \qquad \textbf{(12–2a)}$$

Because the denominator is less than 1, the observed frequency $f'$ is greater than the source frequency $f$. That is, $f' > f$. For example, if a source emits a sound of frequency 400 Hz when at rest, then when the source moves toward a fixed observer with a speed of 30 m/s, the observer hears a frequency (at 20°C) of

$$f' = \frac{400\text{ Hz}}{1 - \frac{30\text{ m/s}}{343\text{ m/s}}} = 438\text{ Hz}.$$

Now consider a source moving *away* from the stationary observer at a speed $v_{source}$. Using the same arguments as above, the wavelength $\lambda'$ perceived by our observer will have the minus sign on $d_{source}$ (at top of this page) changed to plus:

$$\begin{aligned}\lambda' &= d + d_{source} \\ &= \lambda\left(1 + \frac{v_{source}}{v_{snd}}\right).\end{aligned}$$

The difference between the observed and emitted wavelengths will be $\Delta\lambda = \lambda' - \lambda = +\lambda(v_{source}/v_{snd})$. The observed frequency of the wave, $f' = v_{snd}/\lambda'$, will be

$$f' = \frac{f}{\left(1 + \frac{v_{source}}{v_{snd}}\right)}. \qquad \left[\begin{array}{l}\text{source moving away from} \\ \text{stationary observer}\end{array}\right] \qquad \textbf{(12–2b)}$$

If a source emitting at 400 Hz is moving away from a fixed observer at 30 m/s, the observer hears a frequency $f' = (400\text{ Hz})/[1 + (30\text{ m/s})/(343\text{ m/s})] = 368\text{ Hz}$.

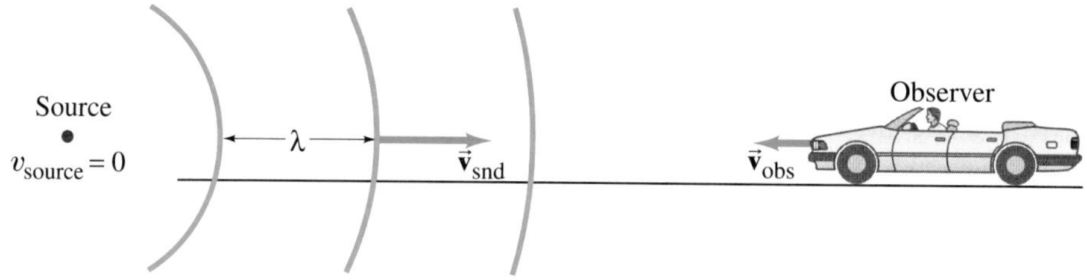


**FIGURE 12–21** Observer moving with speed $v_{obs}$ toward a stationary source detects wave crests passing at speed $v' = v_{snd} + v_{obs}$ where $v_{snd}$ is the speed of the sound waves in air.

*Frequency change, fixed source, moving observer*

The Doppler effect also occurs when the source is at rest and the observer is in motion. If the observer is traveling *toward* the source, the pitch heard is higher than that of the emitted source frequency. If the observer is traveling *away* from the source, the pitch heard is lower. Quantitatively the change in frequency is different than for the case of a moving source. With a fixed source and a moving observer, the distance between wave crests, the wavelength $\lambda$, is not changed. But the velocity of the crests with respect to the observer *is* changed. If the observer is moving toward the source, Fig. 12–21, the speed $v'$ of the waves relative to the observer is a simple addition of velocities: $v' = v_{snd} + v_{obs}$, where $v_{snd}$ is the velocity of sound in air (we assume the air is still) and $v_{obs}$ is the velocity of the observer. Hence, the frequency heard is

$$f' = \frac{v'}{\lambda} = \frac{v_{snd} + v_{obs}}{\lambda}.$$

Because $\lambda = v_{snd}/f$, then

$$f' = \frac{(v_{snd} + v_{obs})f}{v_{snd}},$$

or

$$f' = \left(1 + \frac{v_{obs}}{v_{snd}}\right)f. \qquad \begin{bmatrix}\text{observer moving toward}\\ \text{stationary source}\end{bmatrix} \qquad \textbf{(12–3a)}$$

If the observer is moving away from the source, the relative velocity is $v' = v_{snd} - v_{obs}$, so

$$f' = \left(1 - \frac{v_{obs}}{v_{snd}}\right)f. \qquad \begin{bmatrix}\text{observer moving away}\\ \text{from stationary source}\end{bmatrix} \qquad \textbf{(12–3b)}$$

**EXAMPLE 12–14** **A moving siren.** The siren of a police car at rest emits at a predominant frequency of 1600 Hz. What frequency will you hear if you are at rest and the police car moves at 25.0 m/s (*a*) toward you, and (*b*) away from you?

**APPROACH** The observer is fixed, and the source moves, so we use Eqs. 12–2. The frequency you (the observer) hear is the emitted frequency $f$ divided by the factor $(1 \pm v_{source}/v_{snd})$ where $v_{source}$ is the speed of the police car. Use the minus sign when the car moves toward you (giving a higher frequency); use the plus sign when the car moves away from you (lower frequency).

**SOLUTION** (*a*) The car is moving toward you, so (Eq. 12–2a)

$$f' = \frac{f}{\left(1 - \dfrac{v_{source}}{v_{snd}}\right)} = \frac{1600\text{ Hz}}{\left(1 - \dfrac{25.0\text{ m/s}}{343\text{ m/s}}\right)} = 1726\text{ Hz}.$$

(*b*) The car is moving away from you, so

$$f' = \frac{f}{\left(1 + \dfrac{v_{source}}{v_{snd}}\right)} = \frac{1600\text{ Hz}}{\left(1 + \dfrac{25.0\text{ m/s}}{343\text{ m/s}}\right)} = 1491\text{ Hz}.$$

**EXERCISE F** Suppose the police car of Example 12–14 is at rest and emits still at 1600 Hz. What frequency would you hear if you were moving at 25.0 m/s (*a*) toward it, and (*b*) away from it?

When a sound wave is reflected from a moving obstacle, the frequency of the reflected wave will, because of the Doppler effect, be different from that of the incident wave. This is illustrated in the following Example.

**EXAMPLE 12–15** **Two Doppler shifts.** A 5000-Hz sound wave is emitted by a stationary source. This sound wave reflects from an object moving 3.50 m/s toward the source (Fig. 12–22). What is the frequency of the wave reflected by the moving object as detected by a detector at rest near the source?

**APPROACH** There are actually two Doppler shifts in this situation. First, the moving object acts like an observer moving toward the source with speed $v_{obs} = 3.50\,\mathrm{m/s}$ (Fig. 12–22a) and so "detects" a sound wave of frequency (Eq. 12–3a) $f' = f[1 + (v_{obs}/v_{snd})]$. Second, reflection of the wave from the moving object is equivalent to the object reemitting the wave, acting effectively as a moving source with speed $v_{source} = 3.50\,\mathrm{m/s}$ (Fig. 12–22b). The final frequency detected, $f''$, is given by $f'' = f'/[1 - v_{source}/v_{snd}]$, Eq. 12–2a.

**SOLUTION** The frequency $f'$ that is "detected" by the moving object is (Eq. 12–3a):

$$f' = \left(1 + \frac{v_{obs}}{v_{snd}}\right)f = \left(1 + \frac{3.50\,\mathrm{m/s}}{343\,\mathrm{m/s}}\right)(5000\,\mathrm{Hz}) = 5051\,\mathrm{Hz}.$$

The moving object now "emits" (reflects) a sound of frequency (Eq. 12–2a)

$$f'' = \frac{f'}{\left(1 - \dfrac{v_{source}}{v_{snd}}\right)} = \frac{5051\,\mathrm{Hz}}{\left(1 - \dfrac{3.50\,\mathrm{m/s}}{343\,\mathrm{m/s}}\right)} = 5103\,\mathrm{Hz}.$$

Thus the frequency shifts by 103 Hz.

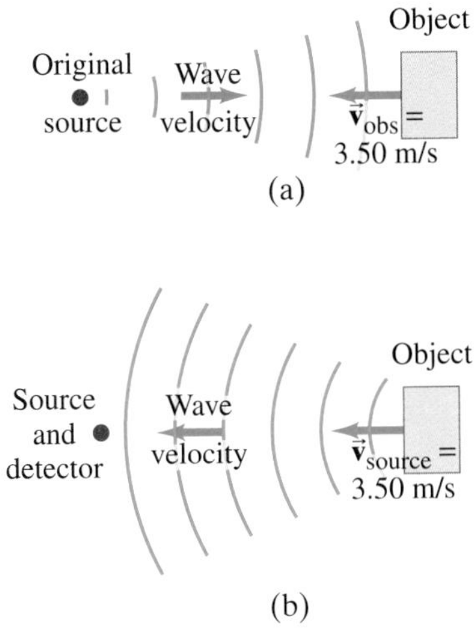


**FIGURE 12–22** Example 12–15.

The incident wave and the reflected wave in Example 12–15, when mixed together (say, electronically), interfere with one another and beats are produced. The beat frequency is equal to the difference in the two frequencies, 103 Hz. This Doppler technique is used in a variety of medical applications, usually with ultrasonic waves in the megahertz frequency range. For example, ultrasonic waves reflected from red blood cells can be used to determine the velocity of blood flow. Similarly, the technique can be used to detect the movement of the chest of a young fetus and to monitor its heartbeat.

PHYSICS APPLIED
*Doppler blood-flow meter and other medical uses*

For convenience, we can write Eqs. 12–2 and 12–3 as a single equation that covers all cases of both source and observer in motion:

$$f' = f\left(\frac{v_{snd} \pm v_{obs}}{v_{snd} \mp v_{source}}\right). \qquad \textbf{(12–4)}$$

*Source and observer moving*

To get the signs right, recall from your own experience that the frequency is higher when observer and source approach each other, and lower when they move apart. Thus the upper signs in numerator and denominator apply if source and/or observer move toward each other; the lower signs apply if they are moving apart.

PROBLEM SOLVING
*Getting the signs right*

## * Doppler Effect for Light

The Doppler effect occurs for other types of waves as well. Light and other types of electromagnetic waves (such as radar) exhibit the Doppler effect: although the formulas for the frequency shift are not identical to Eqs. 12–2 and 12–3, as we shall see in Chapter 33, the effect is similar. One important application is for weather forecasting using radar. The time delay between the emission of radar pulses and their reception after being reflected off raindrops gives the position of precipitation. Measuring the Doppler shift in frequency (as in Example 12–15) tells how fast the storm is moving and in which direction.

PHYSICS APPLIED
*Doppler effect for EM waves and weather forecasting*

PHYSICS APPLIED
*Redshift in cosmology*

Another important application is to astronomy, where the velocities of distant galaxies can be determined from the Doppler shift. Light from distant galaxies is shifted toward lower frequencies, indicating that the galaxies are moving away from us. This is called the **redshift** since red has the lowest frequency of visible light. The greater the frequency shift, the greater the velocity of recession. It is found that the farther the galaxies are from us, the faster they move away. This observation is the basis for the idea that the universe is expanding, and is one basis for the idea that the universe began as a great explosion, affectionately called the "Big Bang" (see Chapter 33).

## * 12–8 Shock Waves and the Sonic Boom

An object such as an airplane traveling faster than the speed of sound is said to have a **supersonic speed**. Such a speed is often given as a **Mach**[†] **number**, which is defined as the ratio of the speed of the object to the speed of sound in the surrounding medium. For example, a plane traveling 600 m/s high in the atmosphere, where the speed of sound is only 300 m/s, has a speed of Mach 2.

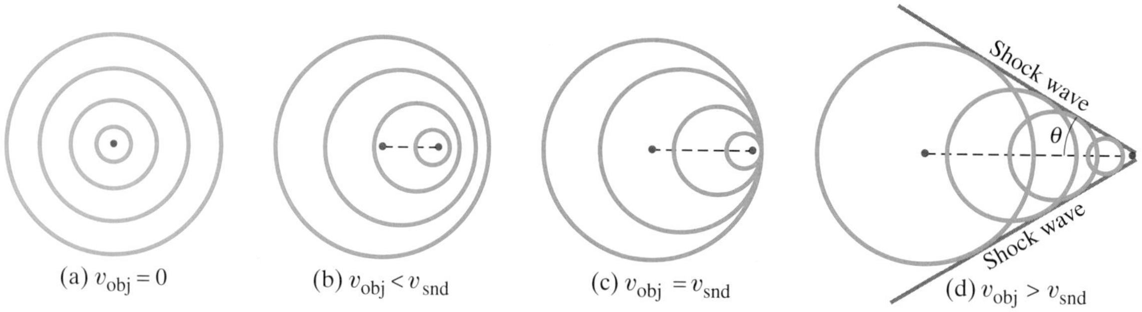


**FIGURE 12–23** Sound waves emitted by an object (a) at rest or (b, c, and d) moving. (b) If the object's velocity is less than the velocity of sound, the Doppler effect occurs; (d) if its velocity is greater than the velocity of sound, a shock wave is produced.

*Shock wave*

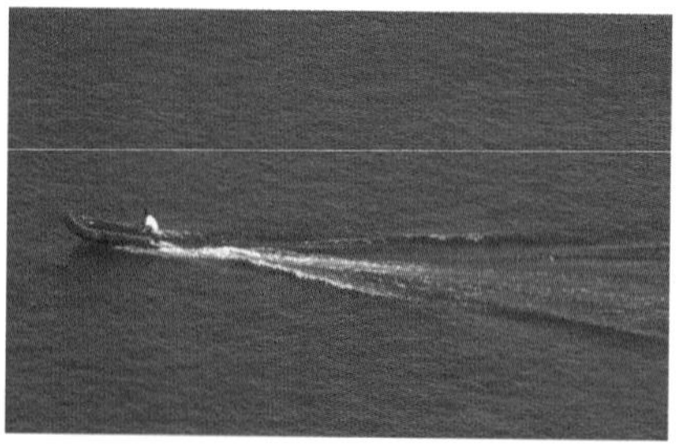

**FIGURE 12–24** Bow waves produced by a boat.

When a source of sound moves at subsonic speeds (less than the speed of sound), the pitch of the sound is altered as we have seen (the Doppler effect); see also Fig. 12–23a and b. But if a source of sound moves faster than the speed of sound, a more dramatic effect known as a **shock wave** occurs. In this case the source is actually "outrunning" the waves it produces. As shown in Fig. 12–23c, when the source is traveling *at* the speed of sound, the wave fronts it emits in the forward direction "pile up" directly in front of it. When the object moves faster, at a supersonic speed, the wave fronts pile up on one another along the sides, as shown in Fig. 12–23d. The different wave crests overlap one another and form a single very large crest which is the shock wave. Behind this very large crest there is usually a very large trough. A shock wave is essentially the result of constructive interference of a large number of wave fronts. A shock wave in air is analogous to the bow wave of a boat traveling faster than the speed of the water waves it produces, Fig. 12–24.

PHYSICS APPLIED
*Sonic boom*

When an airplane travels at supersonic speeds, the noise it makes and its disturbance of the air form into a shock wave containing a tremendous amount of sound energy. When the shock wave passes a listener, it is heard as a loud *sonic boom*. A sonic boom lasts only a fraction of a second, but the energy it contains is often sufficient to break windows and cause other damage. Actually, a sonic boom is made up of two or more booms since major shock waves can form at the front and the rear of the aircraft, as well as at the wings, etc. (Fig. 12–25). Bow waves of a boat are also multiple, as can be seen in Fig. 12–24.

[†] After the Austrian physicist Ernst Mach (1838–1916).

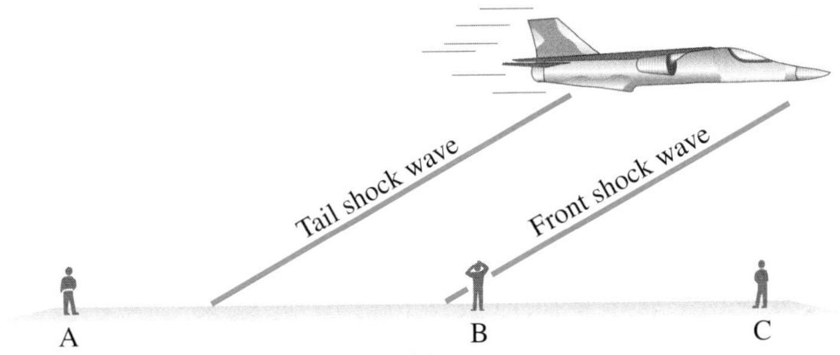


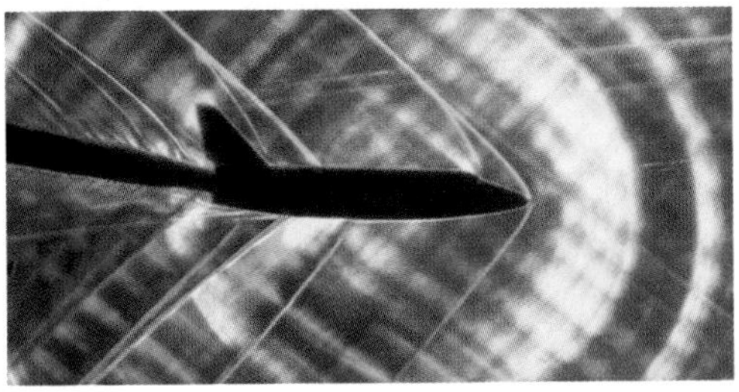


**FIGURE 12–25** (a) The (double) sonic boom has already been heard by person A on the left. It is just being heard by person B in the center. And it will shortly be heard by person C on the right. (b) Special photo of supersonic aircraft showing shock waves produced in the air. (Several closely spaced shock waves are produced by different parts of the aircraft.)

When an aircraft approaches the speed of sound, it encounters a barrier of sound waves in front of it (see Fig. 12–23c). To exceed the speed of sound, the aircraft needs extra thrust to pass through this "sound barrier." This is called "breaking the sound barrier." Once a supersonic speed is attained, this barrier no longer impedes the motion. It is sometimes erroneously thought that a sonic boom is produced only at the moment an aircraft is breaking through the sound barrier. Actually, a shock wave follows the aircraft at all times it is traveling at supersonic speeds. A series of observers on the ground will each hear a loud "boom" as the shock wave passes, Fig. 12–25. The shock wave consists of a cone whose apex is at the aircraft. The angle of this cone, $\theta$ (see Fig. 12–23d), is given by

$$\sin\theta = \frac{v_{\text{snd}}}{v_{\text{obj}}}, \tag{12–5}$$

where $v_{\text{obj}}$ is the velocity of the object (the aircraft) and $v_{\text{snd}}$ is the velocity of sound in the medium. (The proof is left as Problem 63.)

## * 12–9 Applications: Sonar, Ultrasound, and Medical Imaging

### * Sonar

PHYSICS APPLIED
*Sonar: depth finding, Earth soundings*

The reflection of sound is used in many applications to determine distance. The **sonar**† or pulse-echo technique is used to locate underwater objects. A transmitter sends out a sound pulse through the water, and a detector receives its reflection, or echo, a short time later. This time interval is carefully measured, and from it the distance to the reflecting object can be determined since the speed of sound in water is known. The depth of the sea and the location of reefs, sunken ships, submarines, or schools of fish can be determined in this way. The interior structure of the Earth is studied in a similar way by detecting reflections of waves traveling through the Earth whose source was a deliberate explosion (called "soundings"). An analysis of waves reflected from various structures and boundaries within the Earth reveals characteristic patterns that are also useful in the exploration for oil and minerals.

Sonar generally makes use of **ultrasonic** frequencies: that is, waves whose frequencies are above 20 kHz, beyond the range of human detection. For sonar, the frequencies are typically in the range 20 kHz to 100 kHz. One reason for using ultrasound waves, other than the fact that they are inaudible, is that for shorter wavelengths there is less diffraction (Section 11–15) so the beam spreads less and smaller objects can be detected.

† Sonar stands for "*so*und *na*vigation *r*anging."

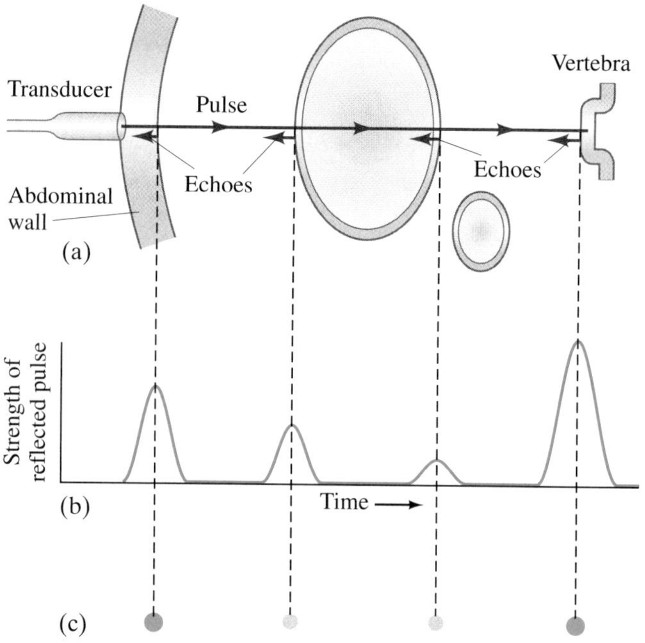


**FIGURE 12–26** (a) Ultrasound pulse passes through the abdomen, reflecting from surfaces in its path. (b) Reflected pulses plotted as a function of time when received by transducer. The vertical dashed lines point out which reflected pulse goes with which surface. (c) Dot display for the same echoes: brightness of each dot is related to signal strength.

## * Ultrasound Medical Imaging

The diagnostic use of ultrasound in medicine, in the form of images (sometimes called *sonograms*) is an important and interesting application of physical principles. A **pulse-echo technique** is used, much like sonar, except that the frequencies used are in the range of 1 to 10 MHz $(1\text{ MHz} = 10^6\text{ Hz})$. A high-frequency sound pulse is directed into the body, and its reflections from boundaries or interfaces between organs and other structures and lesions in the body are then detected. Tumors and other abnormal growths, or pockets of fluid, can be distinguished; the action of heart valves and the development of a fetus can be examined; and information about various organs of the body, such as the brain, heart, liver, and kidneys, can be obtained. Although ultrasound does not replace X-rays, for certain kinds of diagnosis it is more helpful. Some kinds of tissue or fluid are not detected in X-ray photographs, but ultrasound waves are reflected from their boundaries. "Real-time" ultrasound images are like a movie of a section of the interior of the body.

PHYSICS APPLIED
*Ultrasound medical imaging*

The pulse-echo technique for medical imaging works as follows. A brief pulse of ultrasound is emitted by a transducer that transforms an electrical pulse into a sound-wave pulse. Part of the pulse is reflected as echoes at each interface in the body, and most of the pulse (usually) continues on, Fig. 12–26a. The detection of reflected pulses by the same transducer can then be displayed on the screen of a display terminal or monitor. The time elapsed from when the pulse is emitted to when each reflection (echo) is received is proportional to the distance to the reflecting surface. For example, if the distance from transducer to the vertebra is 25 cm, the pulse travels a round-trip distance of $2 \times 25\text{ cm} = 0.50\text{ m}$. The speed of sound in human tissue is about 1540 m/s (close to that of sea water), so the time taken is

$$t = \frac{d}{v} = \frac{(0.50\text{ m})}{(1540\text{ m/s})} = 320\ \mu\text{s}.$$

The *strength* of a reflected pulse depends mainly on the difference in density of the two materials on either side of the interface and can be displayed as a pulse or as a dot (Figs. 12–26b and c). Each echo dot (Fig. 12–26c) can be represented as a point whose position is given by the time delay and whose brightness depends on the strength of the echo. A two-dimensional image can then be formed out of these dots from a series of scans. The transducer is

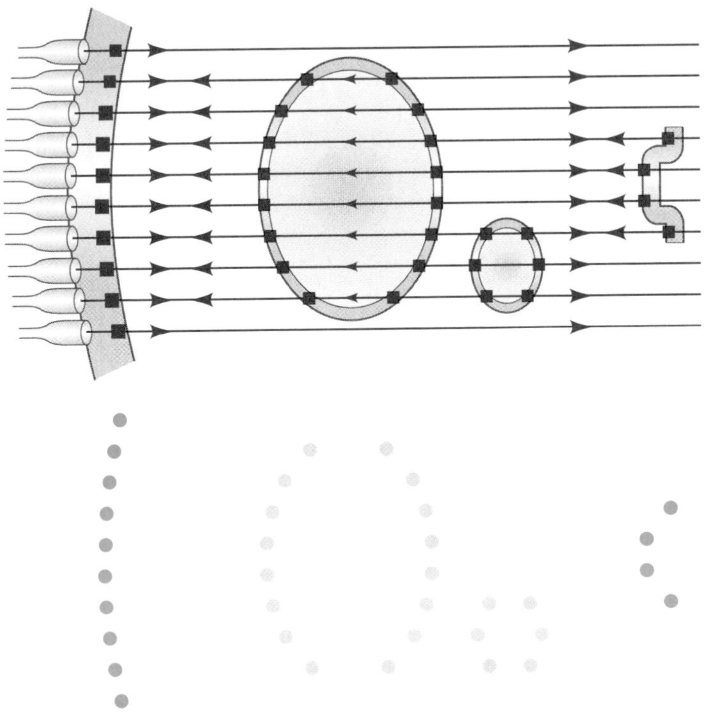

(a)

(b)

**FIGURE 12–27** (a) Ten traces are made across the abdomen by moving the transducer, or by using an array of transducers. (b) The echoes are plotted as dots to produce the image. More closely spaced traces would give a more detailed image.

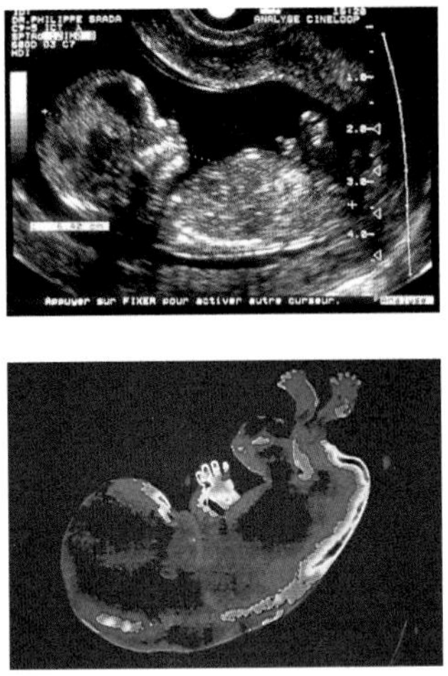

(a)

(b)

**FIGURE 12–28** (a) Ultrasound image of a human fetus (with head at the left) within the uterus. (b) False-color high-resolution ultrasound image of a fetus. (Different colors represent different intensities of reflected pulses.)

moved, or an array of transducers is used, each of which sends out a pulse at each position and receives echoes as shown in Fig. 12–27. Each trace can be plotted, spaced appropriately one below the other, to form an image on a display terminal as shown in Fig. 12–27b. Only 10 lines are shown in Fig. 12–27, so the image is crude. More lines give a more precise image.† Photographs of ultrasound images are shown in Fig. 12–28.

†*Radar* used for aircraft involves a similar pulse-echo technique except that it uses electromagnetic (EM) waves, which, like light, travel with a speed of $3 \times 10^8$ m/s.

## Summary

Sound travels as a longitudinal wave in air and other materials. In air, the speed of sound increases with temperature; at 20°C, it is about 343 m/s.

The **pitch** of a sound is determined by the frequency; the higher the frequency, the higher the pitch.

The **audible range** of frequencies for humans is roughly 20 Hz to 20,000 Hz (1 Hz = 1 cycle per second).

The **loudness** or **intensity** of a sound is related to the amplitude squared of the wave. Because the human ear can detect sound intensities from $10^{-12}\,\mathrm{W/m^2}$ to over $1\,\mathrm{W/m^2}$, sound levels are specified on a logarithmic scale. The **sound level** $\beta$, specified in decibels, is defined in terms of intensity $I$ as

$$\beta = 10 \log\left(\frac{I}{I_0}\right), \qquad \textbf{(12–1)}$$

where the reference intensity $I_0$ is usually taken to be $10^{-12}\,\mathrm{W/m^2}$.

Musical instruments are simple sources of sound in which *standing waves* are produced.

The strings of a stringed instrument may vibrate as a whole with nodes only at the ends; the frequency at which this standing wave occurs is called the **fundamental**. The fundamental frequency corresponds to a wavelength equal to twice the length of the string, $\lambda_1 = 2L$. The string can also vibrate at higher frequencies, called **overtones** or **harmonics**, in which there are one or more additional nodes. The frequency of each harmonic is a whole-number multiple of the fundamental.

In wind instruments, standing waves are set up in the column of air within the tube.

The vibrating air in an **open tube** (open at both ends) has displacement antinodes at both ends. The fundamental frequency corresponds to a wavelength equal to twice the tube length: $\lambda_1 = 2L$. The harmonics have frequencies that are $1, 2, 3, 4, \cdots$ times the fundamental frequency, just as for strings.

For a **closed tube** (closed at one end), the fundamental corresponds to a wavelength four times the length of the tube: $\lambda_1 = 4L$. Only the odd harmonics are present, equal to $1, 3, 5, 7, \cdots$ times the fundamental frequency.

Sound waves from different sources can interfere with each other. If two sounds are at slightly different frequencies, **beats** can be heard at a frequency equal to the difference in frequency of the two sources.

The **Doppler effect** refers to the change in pitch of a sound due to the motion either of the source or of the listener. If source and listener are approaching each other, the perceived pitch is higher; if they are moving apart, the perceived pitch is lower.

[*Shock waves and a sonic boom occur when an object moves at a supersonic speed—faster than the speed of sound. Ultrasonic-frequency (higher than 20 kHz) sound waves are used in many applications, including sonar and medical imaging.]

## Questions

1. What is the evidence that sound travels as a wave?
2. What is the evidence that sound is a form of energy?
3. Children sometimes play with a homemade "telephone" by attaching a string to the bottoms of two paper cups. When the string is stretched and a child speaks into one cup, the sound can be heard at the other cup (Fig. 12–29). Explain clearly how the sound wave travels from one cup to the other.

**FIGURE 12–29** Question 3.

4. When a sound wave passes from air into water, do you expect the frequency or wavelength to change?
5. What evidence can you give that the speed of sound in air does not depend significantly on frequency?
6. The voice of a person who has inhaled helium sounds very high-pitched. Why?
7. How will the air temperature in a room affect the pitch of organ pipes?
8. Explain how a tube might be used as a filter to reduce the amplitude of sounds in various frequency ranges. (An example is a car muffler.)
9. Why are the frets on a guitar (Fig. 12–30) spaced closer together as you move up the fingerboard toward the bridge?

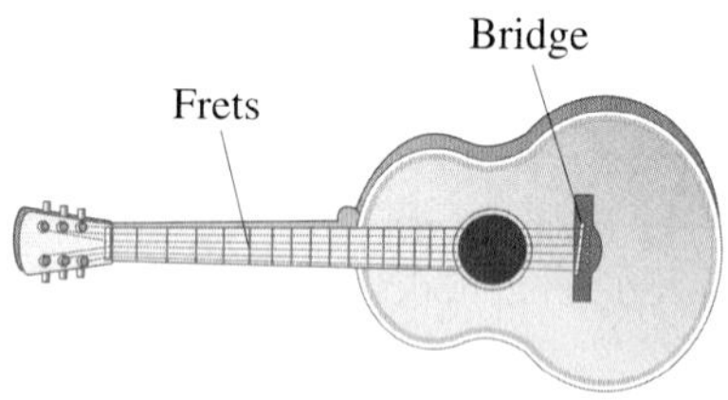


**FIGURE 12–30** Question 9.

10. A noisy truck approaches you from behind a building. Initially you hear it but cannot see it. When it emerges and you do see it, its sound is suddenly "brighter"—you hear more of the high-frequency noise. Explain. [*Hint*: See Section 11–15 on diffraction.]
11. Standing waves can be said to be due to "interference in space," whereas beats can be said to be due to "interference in time." Explain.
12. In Fig. 12–16, if the frequency of the speakers were lowered, would the points D and C (where destructive and constructive interference occur) move farther apart or closer together?
13. Traditional methods of protecting the hearing of people who work in areas with very high noise levels have consisted mainly of efforts to block or reduce noise levels. With a relatively new technology, headphones are worn that do not block the ambient noise. Instead, a device is used which detects the noise, inverts it electronically, then feeds it to the headphones *in addition to* the ambient noise. How could adding *more* noise reduce the sound levels reaching the ears?
14. Consider the two waves shown in Fig. 12–31. Each wave can be thought of as a superposition of two sound waves with slightly different frequencies, as in Fig. 12–18. In which of the waves, (a) or (b), are the two component frequencies farther apart? Explain.

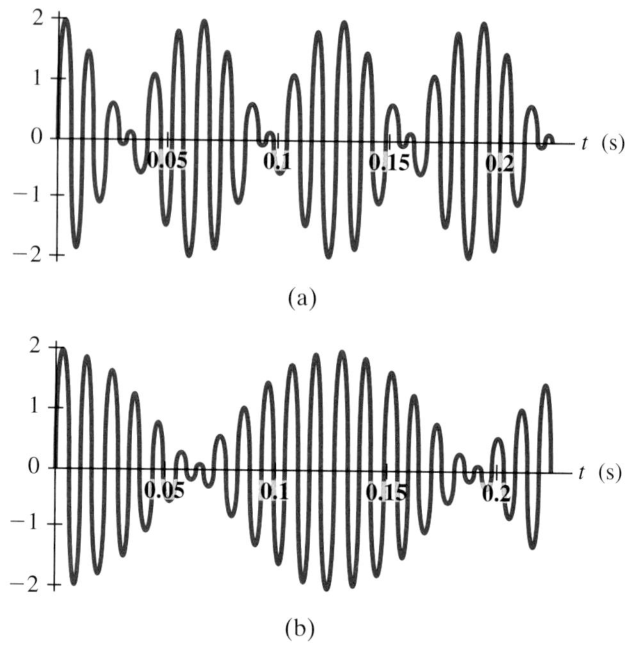


**FIGURE 12–31** Question 14.

15. Is there a Doppler shift if the source and observer move in the same direction, with the same velocity? Explain.
16. If a wind is blowing, will this alter the frequency of the sound heard by a person at rest with respect to the source? Is the wavelength or velocity changed?
17. Figure 12–32 shows various positions of a child in motion on a swing. A monitor is blowing a whistle in front of the child on the ground. At which position, A through E, will the child hear the highest frequency for the sound of the whistle? Explain your reasoning.

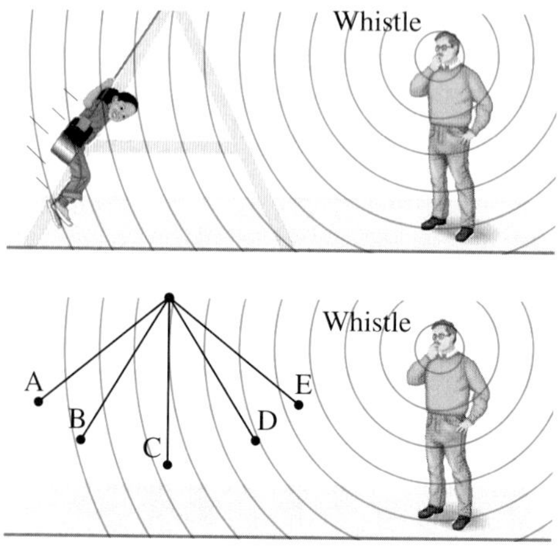


**FIGURE 12–32** Question 17.

## Problems

[Unless stated otherwise, assume $T = 20°C$ and $v_{sound} = 343\ m/s$ in air.]

### 12–1 Characteristics of Sound

1. (I) A hiker determines the length of a lake by listening for the echo of her shout reflected by a cliff at the far end of the lake. She hears the echo 2.0 s after shouting. Estimate the length of the lake.

2. (I) A sailor strikes the side of his ship just below the waterline. He hears the echo of the sound reflected from the ocean floor directly below 2.5 s later. How deep is the ocean at this point? Assume the speed of sound in seawater is 1560 m/s (Table 12–1) and does not vary significantly with depth.

3. (I) (*a*) Calculate the wavelengths in air at 20°C for sounds in the maximum range of human hearing, 20 Hz to 20,000 Hz. (*b*) What is the wavelength of a 10-MHz ultrasonic wave?

4. (II) An ocean fishing boat is drifting just above a school of tuna on a foggy day. Without warning, an engine backfire occurs on another boat 1.0 km away (Fig. 12–33). How much time elapses before the backfire is heard (*a*) by the fish, and (*b*) by the fishermen?

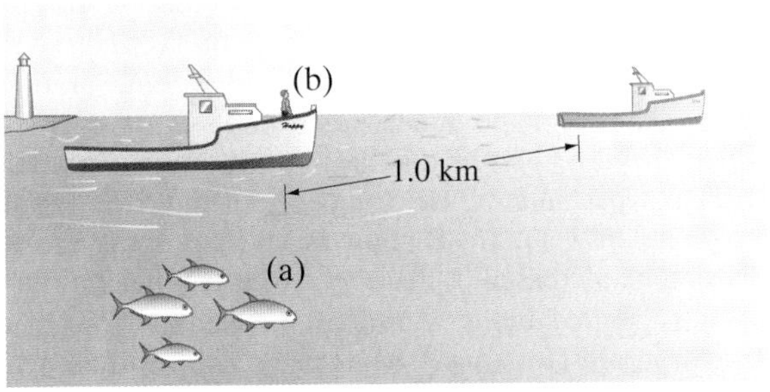


**FIGURE 12–33** Problem 4.

5. (II) A stone is dropped from the top of a cliff. The splash it makes when striking the water below is heard 3.5 s later. How high is the cliff?

6. (II) A person, with his ear to the ground, sees a huge stone strike the concrete pavement. A moment later two sounds are heard from the impact: one travels in the air and the other in the concrete, and they are 1.1 s apart. How far away did the impact occur? See Table 12–1.

7. (II) Calculate the percent error made over one mile of distance by the "5-second rule" for estimating the distance from a lightning strike if the temperature is (*a*) 30°C, and (*b*) 10°C.

### 12–2 Intensity of Sound; Decibels

8. (I) What is the intensity of a sound at the pain level of 120 dB? Compare it to that of a whisper at 20 dB.

9. (I) What is the sound level of a sound whose intensity is $2.0 \times 10^{-6}\ W/m^2$?

10. (II) If two firecrackers produce a sound level of 95 dB when fired simultaneously at a certain place, what will be the sound level if only one is exploded? [*Hint*: Add intensities, not dB's.]

11. (II) A person standing a certain distance from an airplane with four equally noisy jet engines is experiencing a sound level bordering on pain, 120 dB. What sound level would this person experience if the captain shut down all but one engine? [*Hint*: Add intensities, not dB's.]

12. (II) A cassette player is said to have a signal-to-noise ratio of 58 dB, whereas for a CD player it is 95 dB. What is the ratio of intensities of the signal and the background noise for each device?

13. (II) (*a*) Estimate the power output of sound from a person speaking in normal conversation. Use Table 12–2. Assume the sound spreads roughly uniformly over a sphere centered on the mouth. (*b*) How many people would it take to produce a total sound output of 100 W of ordinary conversation? [*Hint*: Add intensities, not dB's.]

14. (II) A 50-dB sound wave strikes an eardrum whose area is $5.0 \times 10^{-5}\ m^2$. (*a*) How much energy is absorbed by the eardrum per second? (*b*) At this rate, how long would it take your eardrum to receive a total energy of 1.0 J?

15. (II) Expensive amplifier A is rated at 250 W, while the more modest amplifier B is rated at 40 W. (*a*) Estimate the sound level in decibels you would expect at a point 3.5 m from a loudspeaker connected in turn to each amp. (*b*) Will the expensive amp sound twice as loud as the cheaper one?

16. (II) At a rock concert, a dB meter registered 130 dB when placed 2.8 m in front of a loudspeaker on the stage. (*a*) What was the power output of the speaker, assuming uniform spherical spreading of the sound and neglecting absorption in the air? (*b*) How far away would the sound level be a somewhat reasonable 90 dB?

17. (II) Human beings can typically detect a difference in sound level of 2.0 dB. What is the ratio of the amplitudes of two sounds whose levels differ by this amount? [*Hint*: See Section 11–9.]

18. (II) If the amplitude of a sound wave is tripled, (*a*) by what factor will the intensity increase? (*b*) By how many dB will the sound level increase?

* 19. (II) Two sound waves have equal displacement amplitudes, but one has twice the frequency of the other. What is the ratio of their intensities?

* 20. (II) What would be the sound level (in dB) of a sound wave in air that corresponds to a displacement amplitude of vibrating air molecules of 0.13 mm at 300 Hz?

### * 12–3 Loudness

* 21. (I) A 6000-Hz tone must have what sound level to seem as loud as a 100-Hz tone that has a 50-dB sound level? (See Fig. 12–6.)

* 22. (I) What are the lowest and highest frequencies that an ear can detect when the sound level is 30 dB? (See Fig. 12–6.)

* 23. (II) Your auditory system can accommodate a huge range of sound levels. What is the ratio of highest to lowest intensity at (*a*) 100 Hz, (*b*) 5000 Hz? (See Fig. 12–6.)

### 12–4 Sources of Sound: Strings and Air Columns

24. (I) The A string on a violin has a fundamental frequency of 440 Hz. The length of the vibrating portion is 32 cm, and it has a mass of 0.35 g. Under what tension must the string be placed?

25. (I) An organ pipe is 112 cm long. What are the fundamental and first three audible overtones if the pipe is (*a*) closed at one end, and (*b*) open at both ends?

26. (I) (*a*) What resonant frequency would you expect from blowing across the top of an empty soda bottle that is 18 cm deep, if you assumed it was a closed tube? (*b*) How would that change if it was one-third full of soda?

27. (I) If you were to build a pipe organ with open-tube pipes spanning the range of human hearing (20 Hz to 20 kHz), what would be the range of the lengths of pipes required?

28. (II) A tight guitar string has a frequency of 540 Hz as its third harmonic. What will be its fundamental frequency if it is fingered at a length of only 60% of its original length?

29. (II) An unfingered guitar string is 0.73 m long and is tuned to play E above middle C (330 Hz). (*a*) How far from the end of this string must a fret (and your finger) be placed to play A above middle C (440 Hz)? (*b*) What is the wavelength on the string of this 440-Hz wave? (*c*) What are the frequency and wavelength of the sound wave produced in air at 20°C by this fingered string?

30. (II) (*a*) Determine the length of an open organ pipe that emits middle C (262 Hz) when the temperature is 21°C. (*b*) What are the wavelength and frequency of the fundamental standing wave in the tube? (*c*) What are $\lambda$ and $f$ in the traveling sound wave produced in the outside air?

31. (II) An organ is in tune at 20°C. By what percent will the frequency be off at 5.0°C?

32. (II) How far from the mouthpiece of the flute in Example 12–10 should the hole be that must be uncovered to play D above middle C at 294 Hz?

33. (II) (*a*) At $T = 20°\text{C}$, how long must an open organ pipe be to have a fundamental frequency of 294 Hz? (*b*) If this pipe is filled with helium, what is its fundamental frequency?

34. (II) A particular organ pipe can resonate at 264 Hz, 440 Hz, and 616 Hz, but not at any other frequencies in between. (*a*) Show why this is an open or a closed pipe. (*b*) What is the fundamental frequency of this pipe?

35. (II) A uniform narrow tube 1.80 m long is open at both ends. It resonates at two successive harmonics of frequencies 275 Hz and 330 Hz. What is (*a*) the fundamental frequency, and (*b*) the speed of sound in the gas in the tube?

36. (II) A pipe in air at 20°C is to be designed to produce two successive harmonics at 240 Hz and 280 Hz. How long must the pipe be, and is it open or closed?

37. (II) How many overtones are present within the audible range for a 2.14-m-long organ pipe at 20°C (*a*) if it is open, and (*b*) if it is closed?

38. (III) The human ear canal is approximately 2.5 cm long. It is open to the outside and is closed at the other end by the eardrum. Estimate the frequencies (in the audible range) of the standing waves in the ear canal. What is the relationship of your answer to the information in the graph of Fig. 12–6?

### 12–6 Interference; Beats

39. (I) A piano tuner hears one beat every 2.0 s when trying to adjust two strings, one of which is sounding 440 Hz. How far off in frequency is the other string?

40. (I) What is the beat frequency if middle C (262 Hz) and C# (277 Hz) are played together? What if each is played two octaves lower (each frequency reduced by a factor of 4)?

41. (I) A certain dog whistle operates at 23.5 kHz, while another (brand X) operates at an unknown frequency. If neither whistle can be heard by humans when played separately, but a shrill whine of frequency 5000 Hz occurs when they are played simultaneously, estimate the operating frequency of brand X.

42. (II) A guitar string produces 4 beats/s when sounded with a 350-Hz tuning fork and 9 beats/s when sounded with a 355-Hz tuning fork. What is the vibrational frequency of the string? Explain your reasoning.

43. (II) Two violin strings are tuned to the same frequency, 294 Hz. The tension in one string is then decreased by 2.0%. What will be the beat frequency heard when the two strings are played together? [*Hint*: Recall Eq. 11–13.]

44. (II) How many beats will be heard if two identical flutes each try to play middle C (262 Hz), but one is at 5.0°C and the other at 25.0°C?

45. (II) You have three tuning forks, A, B, and C. Fork B has a frequency of 441 Hz; when A and B are sounded together, a beat frequency of 3 Hz is heard. When B and C are sounded together, the beat frequency is 4 Hz. What are the possible frequencies of A and C? What beat frequencies are possible when A and C are sounded together?

46. (II) Two loudspeakers are 1.80 m apart. A person stands 3.00 m from one speaker and 3.50 m from the other. (*a*) What is the lowest frequency at which destructive interference will occur at this point? (*b*) Calculate two other frequencies that also result in destructive interference at this point (give the next two highest). Let $T = 20°\text{C}$.

47. (III) Two piano strings are supposed to be vibrating at 132 Hz, but a piano tuner hears three beats every 2.0 s when they are played together. (*a*) If one is vibrating at 132 Hz, what must be the frequency of the other (is there only one answer)? (*b*) By how much (in percent) must the tension be increased or decreased to bring them in tune?

48. (III) A source emits sound of wavelengths 2.64 m and 2.76 m in air. How many beats per second will be heard? (Assume $T = 20°\text{C}$.)

### 12–7 Doppler Effect

49. (I) The predominant frequency of a certain fire engine's siren is 1550 Hz when at rest. What frequency do you detect if you move with a speed of 30.0 m/s (*a*) toward the fire engine, and (*b*) away from it?

50. (I) You are standing still. What frequency do you detect if a fire engine whose siren emits at 1550 Hz moves at a speed of 32 m/s (*a*) toward you, or (*b*) away from you?

51. (II) (*a*) Compare the shift in frequency if a 2000-Hz source is moving toward you at 15 m/s, versus you moving toward it at 15 m/s. Are the two frequencies exactly the same? Are they close? (*b*) Repeat the calculation for 150 m/s and then again (*c*) for 300 m/s. What can you conclude about the asymmetry of the Doppler formulas?

52. (II) Two automobiles are equipped with the same single-frequency horn. When one is at rest and the other is moving toward the first at 15 m/s, the driver at rest hears a beat frequency of 5.5 Hz. What is the frequency the horns emit? Assume $T = 20°\text{C}$.

53. (II) A bat at rest sends out ultrasonic sound waves at 50.0 kHz and receives them returned from an object moving directly away from it at 25.0 m/s. What is the received sound frequency?

54. (II) A bat flies toward a wall at a speed of 5.0 m/s. As it flies, the bat emits an ultrasonic sound wave with frequency 30.0 kHz. What frequency does the bat hear in the reflected wave?

55. (II) In one of the original Doppler experiments, a tuba was played on a moving flat train car at a frequency of 75 Hz, and a second identical tuba played the same tone while at rest in the railway station. What beat frequency was heard if the train car approached the station at a speed of 10.0 m/s?

56. (II) A *Doppler flow meter* uses ultrasound waves to measure blood-flow speeds. Suppose the device emits sound at 3.5 MHz, and the speed of sound in human tissue is taken to be 1540 m/s. What is the expected beat frequency if blood is flowing in large leg arteries at 2.0 cm/s directly away from the sound source?

57. (III) The Doppler effect using ultrasonic waves of frequency $2.25 \times 10^6$ Hz is used to monitor the heartbeat of a fetus. A (maximum) beat frequency of 500 Hz is observed. Assuming that the speed of sound in tissue is $1.54 \times 10^3$ m/s, calculate the maximum velocity of the surface of the beating heart.

58. (III) A factory whistle emits sound of frequency 570 Hz. When the wind velocity is 12.0 m/s from the north, what frequency will observers hear who are located, at rest, (*a*) due north, (*b*) due south, (*c*) due east, and (*d*) due west, of the whistle? What frequency is heard by a cyclist heading (*e*) north or (*f*) west, toward the whistle at 15.0 m/s? Assume $T = 20°$C.

### * 12–8 Shock Waves; Sonic Boom

* 59. (I) (*a*) How fast is an object moving on land if its speed at 20°C is Mach 0.33? (*b*) A high-flying jet cruising at 3000 km/h displays a Mach number of 3.2 on a screen. What is the speed of sound at that altitude?

* 60. (II) An airplane travels at Mach 2.3 where the speed of sound is 310 m/s. (*a*) What is the angle the shock wave makes with the direction of the airplane's motion? (*b*) If the plane is flying at a height of 7100 m, how long after it is directly overhead will a person on the ground hear the shock wave?

* 61. (II) A space probe enters the thin atmosphere of a planet where the speed of sound is only about 35 m/s. (*a*) What is the probe's Mach number if its initial speed is 15,000 km/h? (*b*) What is the angle of the shock wave relative to the direction of motion?

* 62. (II) A meteorite traveling 8500 m/s strikes the ocean. Determine the shock wave angle it produces (*a*) in the air just before entering the ocean, and (*b*) in the water just after entering. Assume $T = 20°$C.

* 63. (II) Show that the angle $\theta$ a sonic boom makes with the path of a supersonic object is given by Eq. 12–5.

* 64. (II) You look directly overhead and see a plane exactly 1.5 km above the ground flying faster than the speed of sound. By the time you hear the sonic boom, the plane has traveled a horizontal distance of 2.0 km. See Fig. 12–34. Determine (*a*) the angle of the shock cone, $\theta$, and (*b*) the speed of the plane (the Mach number). Assume the speed of sound is 330 m/s.

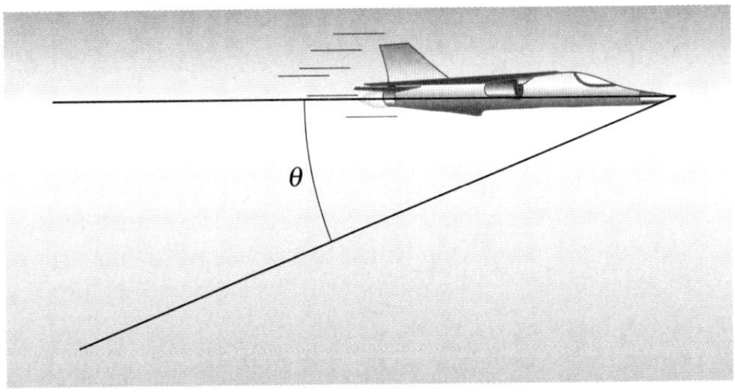


**FIGURE 12–34** Problem 64.

## General Problems

65. A fish finder uses a sonar device that sends 20,000-Hz sound pulses downward from the bottom of the boat, and then detects echoes. If the maximum depth for which it is designed to work is 200 m, what is the minimum time between pulses (in fresh water)?

66. Approximately how many octaves are there in the human audible range?

67. A science museum has a display called a sewer pipe symphony. It consists of many plastic pipes of various lengths, which are open on both ends. (*a*) If the pipes have lengths of 3.0 m, 2.5 m, 2.0 m, 1.5 m and 1.0 m, what frequencies will be heard by a visitor's ear placed near the ends of the pipes? (*b*) Why does this display work better on a noisy day than on a quiet day?

68. A single mosquito 5.0 m from a person makes a sound close to the threshold of human hearing (0 dB). What will be the sound level of 1000 such mosquitoes?

69. What is the resultant sound level when an 82-dB sound and an 87-dB sound are heard simultaneously?

70. The sound level 12.0 m from a loudspeaker, placed in the open, is 105 dB. What is the acoustic power output (W) of the speaker, assuming it radiates equally in all directions?

71. A stereo amplifier is rated at 150 W output at 1000 Hz. The power output drops by 10 dB at 15 kHz. What is the power output in watts at 15 kHz?

72. Workers around jet aircraft typically wear protective devices over their ears. Assume that the sound level of a jet airplane engine, at a distance of 30 m, is 140 dB, and that the average human ear has an effective radius of 2.0 cm. What would be the power intercepted by an unprotected ear at a distance of 30 m from a jet airplane engine?

73. In audio and communications systems, the *gain*, $\beta$, in decibels is defined as

$$\beta = 10 \log\left(\frac{P_{out}}{P_{in}}\right),$$

where $P_{in}$ is the power input to the system and $P_{out}$ is the power output. A particular stereo amplifier puts out 100 W of power for an input of 1 mW. What is its gain in dB?

74. Each string on a violin is tuned to a frequency $1\frac{1}{2}$ times that of its neighbor. The four equal-length strings are to be placed under the same tension; what must be the mass per unit length of each string relative to that of the lowest string?

75. The A string of a violin is 32 cm long between fixed points with a fundamental frequency of 440 Hz and a mass per unit length of $6.1 \times 10^{-4}$ kg/m. (*a*) What are the wave speed and tension in the string? (*b*) What is the length of the tube of a simple wind instrument (say, an organ pipe) closed at one end whose fundamental is also 440 Hz if the speed of sound is 343 m/s in air? (*c*) What is the frequency of the first overtone of each instrument?

76. A tuning fork is set into vibration above a vertical open tube filled with water (Fig. 12–35). The water level is allowed to drop slowly. As it does so, the air in the tube above the water level is heard to resonate with the tuning fork when the distance from the tube opening to the water level is 0.125 m and again at 0.395 m. What is the frequency of the tuning fork?

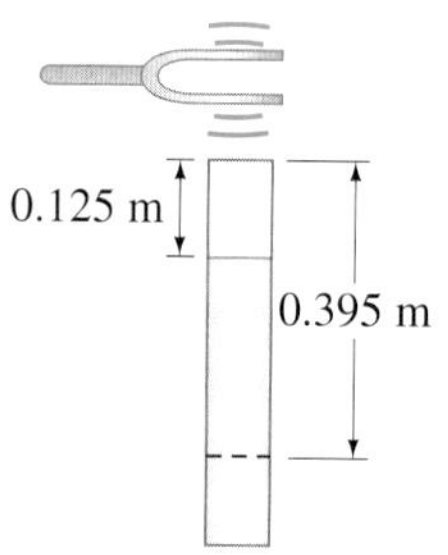


**FIGURE 12–35** Problem 76.

77. A 75-cm-long guitar string of mass 2.10 g is near a tube that is open at one end and also 75 cm long. How much tension should be in the string if it is to produce resonance (in its fundamental mode) with the third harmonic in the tube?

78. (II) A highway overpass was observed to resonate as one full loop $(\frac{1}{2}\lambda)$ when a small earthquake shook the ground vertically at 4.0 Hz. The highway department put a support at the center of the overpass, anchoring it to the ground as shown in Fig. 12–36. What resonant frequency would you now expect for the overpass? Earthquakes rarely do significant shaking above 5 or 6 Hz. Did the modifications do any good?

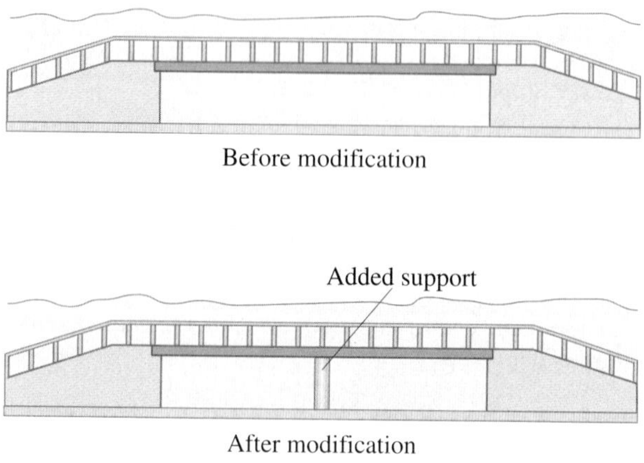


**FIGURE 12–36** Problem 78.

79. A person hears a pure tone in the 500–1000-Hz range coming from two sources. The sound is loudest at points equidistant from the two sources. To determine exactly what the frequency is, the person moves about and finds that the sound level is minimal at a point 0.34 m farther from one source than the other. What is the frequency of the sound?

80. Two trains emit 424-Hz whistles. One train is stationary. The conductor on the stationary train hears a 3.0-Hz beat frequency when the other train approaches. What is the speed of the moving train?

81. The frequency of a steam train whistle as it approaches you is 538 Hz. After it passes you, its frequency is measured as 486 Hz. How fast was the train moving (assume constant velocity)?

82. At a race track, you can estimate the speed of cars just by listening to the difference in pitch of the engine noise between approaching and receding cars. Suppose the sound of a certain car drops by a full octave (frequency halved) as it goes by on the straightaway. How fast is it going?

83. Two open organ pipes, sounding together, produce a beat frequency of 11 Hz. The shorter one is 2.40 m long. How long is the other?

84. Two loudspeakers are at opposite ends of a railroad car as it moves past a stationary observer at 10.0 m/s, as shown in Fig. 12–37. If the speakers have identical sound frequencies of 212 Hz, what is the beat frequency heard by the observer when (*a*) he listens from the position A, in front of the car, (*b*) he is between the speakers, at B, and (*c*) he hears the speakers after they have passed him, at C?

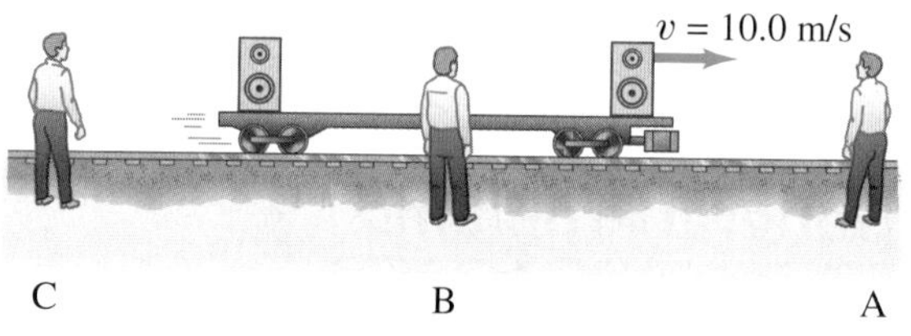


**FIGURE 12–37** Problem 84.

85. If the velocity of blood flow in the aorta is normally about 0.32 m/s, what beat frequency would you expect if 5.50-MHz ultrasound waves were directed along the flow and reflected from the red blood cells? Assume that the waves travel with a speed of $1.54 \times 10^3$ m/s.

86. A bat flies toward a moth at speed 6.5 m/s while the moth is flying toward the bat at speed 5.0 m/s. The bat emits a sound wave of 51.35 kHz. What is the frequency of the wave detected by the bat after that wave reflects off the moth?

87. A bat emits a series of high frequency sound pulses as it approaches a moth. The pulses are approximately 70.0 ms apart, and each is about 3.0 ms long. How far away can the moth be detected by the bat so that the echo from one chirp returns before the next chirp is emitted?

88. The "alpenhorn" (Fig. 12–38) was once used to send signals from one Alpine village to another. Since lower frequency sounds are less susceptible to intensity loss, long horns were used to create deep sounds. When played as a musical instrument, the alpenhorn must be blown in such a way that only one of the overtones is resonating. The most popular alpenhorn is about 3.4 m long, and it is called the F sharp (or G flat) horn. What is the fundamental frequency of this horn, and which overtone is close to F sharp? (See Table 12–3.) Model as an open tube.

**FIGURE 12–38** Problem 88.

89. Room acoustics for stereo listening can be compromised by the presence of standing waves, which can cause acoustic "dead spots" at the locations of the pressure nodes. Consider a living room 5.0 m long, 4.0 m wide, and 2.8 m high. Calculate the fundamental frequencies for the standing waves in this room.

90. A dramatic demonstration, called "singing rods," involves a long, slender aluminum rod held in the hand near the rod's midpoint. The rod is stroked with the other hand. With a little practice, the rod can be made to "sing," or emit a clear, loud, ringing sound. For a 90-cm-long rod, (*a*) what is the fundamental frequency of the sound? (*b*) What is its wavelength in the rod, and (*c*) what is the traveling wavelength in air at 20°C?

* 91. The intensity at the threshold of hearing for the human ear at a frequency of about 1000 Hz is $I_0 = 1.0 \times 10^{-12}\ \mathrm{W/m^2}$, for which $\beta$, the sound level, is 0 dB. The threshold of pain at the same frequency is about 120 dB, or $I = 1.0\ \mathrm{W/m^2}$, corresponding to an increase of intensity by a factor of $10^{12}$. By what factor does the displacement amplitude, $A$, vary?

* 92. A plane is traveling at Mach 2.0. An observer on the ground hears the sonic boom 1.5 min after the plane passes directly overhead. What is the plane's altitude?

* 93. The wake of a speedboat is 15° in a lake where the speed of the water wave is 2.2 km/h. What is the speed of the boat?

## Answers to Exercises

**A:** 1 km for every 3 s before the thunder is heard.
**B:** 4 times as intense.
**C:** One-quarter its original value; 6 dB.
**D:** 257 Hz.
**E:** 6 Hz.
**F:** (*a*) 1717 Hz, (*b*) 1483 Hz.

Heating the air inside a "hot-air" balloon raises the air's temperature, causing it to expand and forcing air out the opening at the bottom. The reduced amount of gas inside means its density is lower, so there is a net buoyant force upward on the balloon. In this Chapter we study temperature and its effects on matter: thermal expansion and the gas laws. Most important is the ideal gas law and its expression in terms of molecules.

CHAPTER 13

# Temperature and Kinetic Theory

This Chapter is the first of three (Chapters 13, 14, and 15) that are devoted to the subjects of temperature, heat, and thermodynamics. Much of this Chapter will be devoted to an investigation of the theory that matter is made up of atoms and that these atoms are in continuous random motion. This theory is called the *kinetic theory*. ("Kinetic," you may recall, is Greek for "moving.")

We also discuss the concept of temperature and how it is measured, as well as the experimentally measured properties of gases which serve as a foundation for the kinetic theory.

## 13–1 Atomic Theory of Matter

The idea that matter is made up of atoms dates back to the ancient Greeks. According to the Greek philosopher Democritus, if a pure substance—say, a piece of iron—were cut into smaller and smaller bits, eventually a smallest piece of that substance would be obtained which could not be divided further. This smallest piece was called an **atom**, which in Greek means "indivisible."†

*Atomic theory—the evidence*

Today the atomic theory is generally accepted. The experimental evidence in its favor, however, came mainly in the eighteenth, nineteenth, and twentieth centuries, and much of it was obtained from the analysis of chemical reactions.

†Today we don't consider the atom as indivisible, but rather as consisting of a nucleus (containing protons and neutrons) and electrons.

We will often speak of the relative masses of atoms and molecules—what we call the **atomic mass** or **molecular mass**, respectively.† These are based on arbitrarily assigning the abundant carbon atom, $^{12}C$, the value of exactly 12.0000 **unified atomic mass units** (u). In terms of kilograms,

*Atomic and molecular masses*

$$1\,u = 1.6605 \times 10^{-27}\,kg.$$

The atomic mass of hydrogen is then 1.0078 u, and the values for other atoms are as listed in the periodic table inside the back cover of this book, and also in Appendix B. The molecular mass of a compound is the sum of atomic masses of the atoms making up the molecules of that compound.‡

An important piece of evidence for the atomic theory is called **Brownian motion**, named after the biologist Robert Brown, who is credited with its discovery in 1827. While he was observing tiny pollen grains suspended in water under his microscope, Brown noticed that the tiny grains moved about in tortuous paths (Fig. 13–1), even though the water appeared to be perfectly still. The atomic theory easily explains Brownian motion if the further reasonable assumption is made that the atoms of any substance are continually in motion. Then Brown's tiny pollen grains are jostled about by the vigorous barrage of rapidly moving molecules of water.

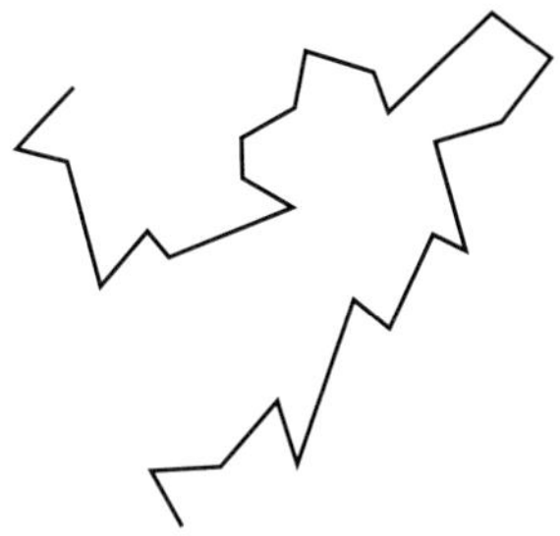

**FIGURE 13–1** Path of a tiny particle (pollen grain, for example) suspended in water. The straight lines connect observed positions of the particle at equal time intervals.

In 1905, Albert Einstein examined Brownian motion from a theoretical point of view and was able to calculate from the experimental data the approximate size and mass of atoms and molecules. His calculations showed that the diameter of a typical atom is about $10^{-10}$ m.

*Phases of matter*

*Macroscopic vs. microscopic properties*

At the start of Chapter 10, we distinguished the three common states, or phases, of matter—solid, liquid, gas—based on **macroscopic**, or "large-scale," properties. Now let us see how these three phases of matter differ, from the atomic or **microscopic** point of view. Clearly, atoms and molecules must exert attractive forces on each other. For how else could a brick or a piece of aluminum hold together in one piece? The attractive forces between molecules are of an electrical nature (more on this in later Chapters). When molecules come too close together, the force between them must become repulsive (electric repulsion between their outer electrons), for how else could matter take up space? Thus molecules maintain a minimum distance from each other. In a solid material, the attractive forces are strong enough that the atoms or molecules move only slightly (oscillate) about relatively fixed positions, often in an array known as a crystal lattice, as shown in Fig. 13–2a. In a liquid, the atoms or molecules are moving more rapidly, or the forces between them are weaker, so that they are sufficiently free to pass over one another, as in Fig. 13–2b. In a gas, the forces are so weak, or the speeds so high, that the molecules do not even stay close together. They move rapidly every which way, Fig. 13–2c, filling any container and occasionally

†The terms *atomic weight* and *molecular weight* are sometimes used for these quantities, but properly speaking we are comparing masses.

‡An *element* is a substance, such as gold, iron, or copper, that cannot be broken down into simpler substances by chemical means. *Compounds* are substances made up of elements, and can be broken down into them; examples are carbon dioxide and water. The smallest piece of an element is an atom; the smallest piece of a compound is a molecule. Molecules are made up of atoms; a molecule of water, for example, is made up of two atoms of hydrogen and one of oxygen; its chemical formula is $H_2O$.

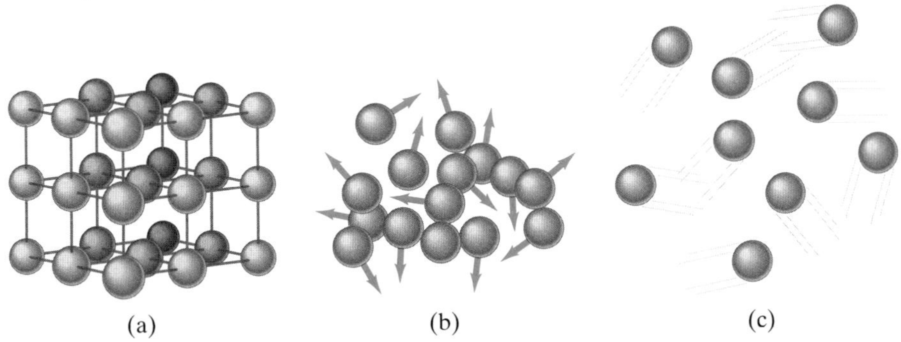


**FIGURE 13–2** Atomic arrangements in (a) a crystalline solid, (b) a liquid, and (c) a gas.

colliding with one another. On the average, the speeds are sufficiently high in a gas that when two molecules collide, the force of attraction is not strong enough to keep them close together and they fly off in new directions.

**EXAMPLE 13–1 ESTIMATE Distance between atoms.** The density of copper is $8.9 \times 10^3\ \mathrm{kg/m^3}$, and each copper atom has a mass of 63 u. Estimate the average distance between neighboring copper atoms.

**APPROACH** We consider a cube of copper 1 m on a side. From the given density we can calculate the mass of a $1\text{-m}^3$ cube. We divide this by the mass of one atom (63 u) to obtain the number of atoms in $1\ \mathrm{m}^3$. Let $N$ be the number of atoms in a 1-m length; then $(N)(N)(N) = N^3$ equals this total number of atoms in $1\ \mathrm{m}^3$.

**SOLUTION** The mass of 1 copper atom is $63\ \mathrm{u} = 63 \times 1.66 \times 10^{-27}\ \mathrm{kg} = 1.05 \times 10^{-25}\ \mathrm{kg}$. This means that in a cube of copper 1 m on a side $(\text{volume} = 1\ \mathrm{m}^3)$, there are

$$\frac{8.9 \times 10^3\ \mathrm{kg/m^3}}{1.05 \times 10^{-25}\ \mathrm{kg/atom}} = 8.5 \times 10^{28}\ \mathrm{atoms/m^3}.$$

The volume of a cube of side $l$ is $V = l^3$, so on one edge of the 1-m-long cube there are $(8.5 \times 10^{28})^{\frac{1}{3}}$ atoms $= 4.4 \times 10^9$ atoms. Hence the distance between neighboring atoms is

$$\frac{1\ \mathrm{m}}{4.4 \times 10^9\ \mathrm{atoms}} = 2.3 \times 10^{-10}\ \mathrm{m}.$$

**NOTE** Watch out for units. Even though "atoms" is not a unit, it is helpful to include it to make sure you calculate correctly.

## 13–2 Temperature and Thermometers

In everyday life, **temperature** is a measure of how hot or cold something is. A hot oven is said to have a high temperature, whereas the ice of a frozen lake is said to have a low temperature.

**FIGURE 13–3** Expansion joint on a bridge.

Many properties of matter change with temperature. For example, most materials expand when heated.[†] An iron beam is longer when hot than when cold. Concrete roads and sidewalks expand and contract slightly according to temperature, which is why compressible spacers or expansion joints (Fig. 13–3) are placed at regular intervals. The electrical resistance of matter changes with temperature (see Chapter 18). So too does the color radiated by objects, at least at high temperatures: you may have noticed that the heating element of an electric stove glows with a red color when hot. At higher temperatures, solids such as iron glow orange or even white. The white light from an ordinary incandescent lightbulb comes from an extremely hot tungsten wire. The surface temperatures of the Sun and other stars can be measured by the predominant color (more precisely, wavelengths) of light they emit.

Instruments designed to measure temperature are called **thermometers**. There are many kinds of thermometers, but their operation always depends on some property of matter that changes with temperature. Most common thermometers rely on the expansion of a material with an increase in temperature. The first idea for a thermometer (Fig. 13–4a), by Galileo, made use of the expansion of a gas. Common thermometers today consist of a hollow glass tube filled with mercury or with alcohol colored with a red dye, as were the earliest usable thermometers (Fig. 13–4b). Figure 13–4c shows an early clinical thermometer of a different type, also based on a change in density with temperature.

[†] Most materials expand when their temperature is raised, but not all. Water, for example, in the range 0°C to 4°C contracts with an increase in temperature (see Section 13–4).

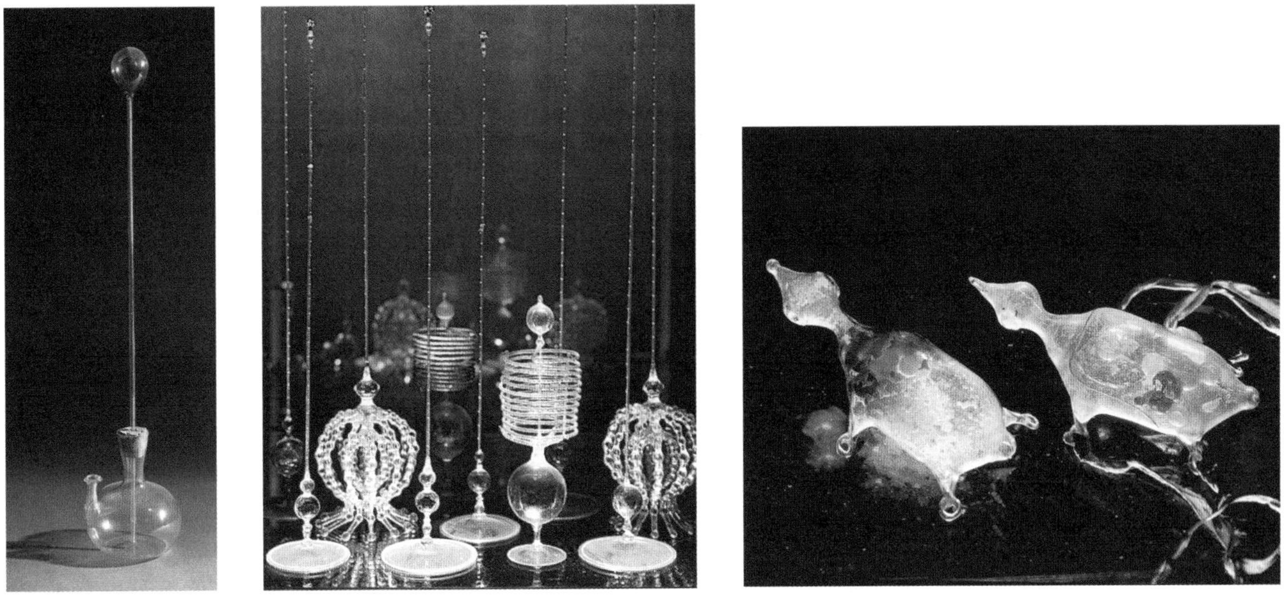

(a) (b) (c)

**FIGURE 13–4** (a) Model of Galileo's original idea for a thermometer. (b) Actual thermometers built by the Accademia del Cimento (1657–1667) in Florence are among the earliest known. These sensitive and exquisite instruments contained alcohol, sometimes colored, like many thermometers today. (c) Clinical thermometers in the shape of a frog, also built by the Accademia del Cimento, could be tied to a patient's wrist. The small spheres suspended in the liquid each have a slightly different density. The number of spheres that would sink was a measure of the patient's fever.

In the common liquid-in-glass thermometer, the liquid expands more than the glass when the temperature is increased, so the liquid level rises in the tube (Fig. 13–5a). Although metals also expand with temperature, the change in length of a metal rod, say, is generally too small to measure accurately for ordinary changes in temperature. However, a useful thermometer can be made by bonding together two dissimilar metals whose rates of expansion are different (Fig. 13–5b). When the temperature is increased, the different amounts of expansion cause the bimetallic strip to bend. Often the bimetallic strip is in the form of a coil, one end of which is fixed while the other is attached to a pointer, Fig. 13–6. This kind of thermometer is used as ordinary air thermometers, oven thermometers, automatic off switches in electric coffeepots, and in room thermostats for determining when the heater or air conditioner should go on or off. Very precise thermometers make use of electrical properties (Chapter 18), such as resistance thermometers, thermocouples, and thermistors, often with a digital readout.

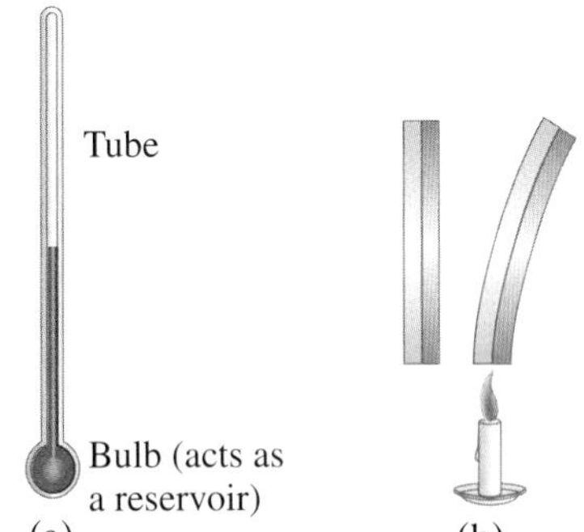


(a) (b)

**FIGURE 13–5** (a) Mercury- or alcohol-in-glass thermometer; (b) bimetallic strip.

**FIGURE 13–6** Photograph of a thermometer using a coiled bimetallic strip.

## Temperature Scales

In order to measure temperature quantitatively, some sort of numerical scale must be defined. The most common scale today is the **Celsius** scale, sometimes called the **centigrade** scale. In the United States, the **Fahrenheit** scale is also common. The most important scale in scientific work is the absolute, or Kelvin, scale, and it will be discussed later in this Chapter.

One way to define a temperature scale is to assign arbitrary values to two readily reproducible temperatures. For both the Celsius and Fahrenheit scales these two fixed points are chosen to be the freezing point and the boiling point† of water, both taken at atmospheric pressure. On the Celsius scale, the freezing

†The freezing point of a substance is defined as that temperature at which the solid and liquid phases coexist in equilibrium—that is, without any net liquid changing into the solid or vice versa. Experimentally, this is found to occur at only one definite temperature, for a given pressure. Similarly, the boiling point is defined as that temperature at which the liquid and gas coexist in equilibrium. Since these points vary with pressure, the pressure must be specified (usually it is 1 atm).

point of water is chosen to be 0°C ("zero degrees Celsius") and the boiling point 100°C. On the Fahrenheit scale, the freezing point is defined as 32°F and the boiling point 212°F. A practical thermometer is calibrated by placing it in carefully prepared environments at each of the two temperatures and marking the position of the liquid or pointer. For a Celsius scale, the distance between the two marks is divided into one hundred equal intervals representing each degree between 0°C and 100°C (hence the name "centigrade scale" meaning "hundred steps"). For a Fahrenheit scale, the two points are labeled 32°F and 212°F and the distance between them is divided into 180 equal intervals. For temperatures below the freezing point of water and above the boiling point of water, the scales may be extended using the same equally spaced intervals. However, thermometers can be used only over a limited temperature range because of their own limitations—for example, the liquid mercury in a mercury-in-glass thermometer solidifies at some point, below which the thermometer will be useless. It is also rendered useless above temperatures where the fluid vaporizes. For very low or very high temperatures, specialized thermometers are required, some of which we will mention later.

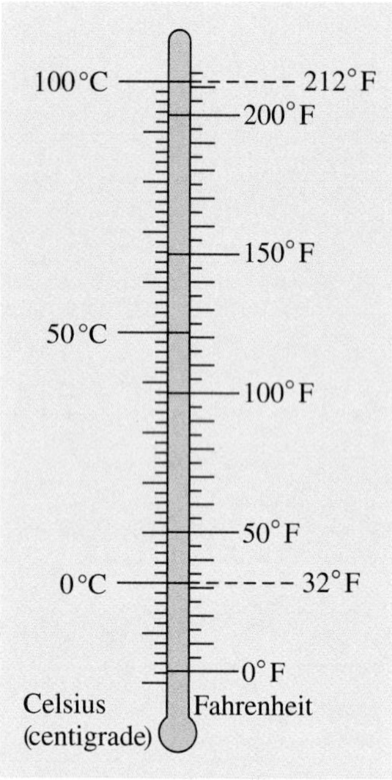

**FIGURE 13–7** Celsius and Fahrenheit scales compared.

Every temperature on the Celsius scale corresponds to a particular temperature on the Fahrenheit scale, Fig. 13–7. It is easy to convert from one to the other if you remember that 0°C corresponds to 32°F and that a range of 100°on the Celsius scale corresponds to a range of 180°on the Fahrenheit scale. Thus, one Fahrenheit degree (1 F°) corresponds to $100/180 = \frac{5}{9}$ of a Celsius degree (1 C°). That is, $1\,\mathrm{F}^\circ = \frac{5}{9}\,\mathrm{C}^\circ$. (Notice that when we refer to a specific temperature, we say "degrees Celsius," as in 20°C; but when we refer to a *change* in temperature or a temperature interval, we say "Celsius degrees," as in "2 C°.") The conversion between the two temperature scales can be written

$$T(^\circ\mathrm{C}) = \tfrac{5}{9}\left[T(^\circ\mathrm{F}) - 32\right] \quad \text{or} \quad T(^\circ\mathrm{F}) = \tfrac{9}{5}T(^\circ\mathrm{C}) + 32.$$

**CAUTION**
*Convert temperature by remembering 0°C = 32°F and a change of 5 C° = 9 F°*

Rather than memorizing these relations (it would be easy to confuse them), it is usually easier simply to remember that 0°C = 32°F and that a change of 5 C° = a change of 9 F°.

**EXAMPLE 13–2** **Taking your temperature.** Normal body temperature is 98.6°F. What is this on the Celsius scale?

**APPROACH** We recall that 0°C = 32°F and 5 C° = 9 F°.

**SOLUTION** First we relate the given temperature to the freezing point of water (0°C). That is, 98.6°F is $98.6 - 32.0 = 66.6\,\mathrm{F}^\circ$ above the freezing point of water. Since each F° is equal to $\frac{5}{9}\,\mathrm{C}^\circ$, this corresponds to $66.6 \times \frac{5}{9} = 37.0$ Celsius degrees above the freezing point. The freezing point is 0°C, so the temperature is 37.0°C.

**EXERCISE A** Determine the temperature at which both scales agree $(T_\mathrm{C} = T_\mathrm{F})$.

Different materials do not expand in quite the same way over a wide temperature range. Consequently, if we calibrate different kinds of thermometers exactly as described above, they will not usually agree precisely. Because of how we calibrated them, they will agree at 0°C and at 100°C. But because of different expansion properties, they may not agree precisely at intermediate temperatures (remember we arbitrarily divided the thermometer scale into 100 equal divisions between 0°C and 100°C). Thus a carefully calibrated mercury-in-glass thermometer might register 52.0°C, whereas a carefully calibrated thermometer of another type might read 52.6°C.

**FIGURE 13–8** Constant-volume gas thermometer.

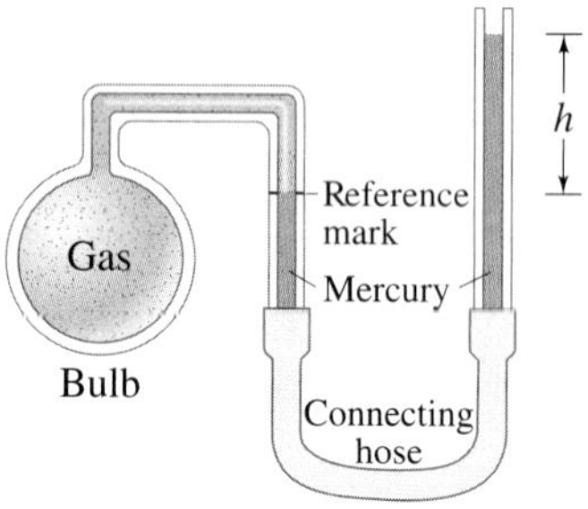


Because of this discrepancy, some standard kind of thermometer must be chosen so that these intermediate temperatures can be precisely defined. The chosen standard for this purpose is the **constant-volume gas thermometer**. As shown in the simplified diagram of Fig. 13–8, this thermometer consists of a bulb filled with a dilute gas connected by a thin tube to a mercury manometer. The volume of the gas is kept constant by raising or lowering the right-hand tube of the manometer so that the mercury in the left-hand tube coincides with the reference mark. An increase in temperature causes a proportional increase in pressure in the bulb. Thus the tube must be lifted higher to keep the gas volume constant. The height of the mercury in the right-hand column is then a measure of the temperature. This thermometer gives the same results for all gases in the limit of reducing the gas pressure in the bulb toward zero. The resulting scale serves as a basis for the standard temperature scale.

## * 13–3 Thermal Equilibrium and the Zeroth Law of Thermodynamics

We are all familiar with the fact that if two objects at different temperatures are placed in thermal contact (meaning thermal energy can transfer from one to the other), the two objects will eventually reach the same temperature. They are then said to be in **thermal equilibrium**. For example, you leave a fever thermometer in your mouth until it comes into thermal equilibrium with that environment, and then you read it. Two objects are defined to be in thermal equilibrium if, when placed in thermal contact, no energy flows from one to the other, and their temperatures don't change. Experiments indicate that *if two systems are in thermal equilibrium with a third system, then they are in thermal equilibrium with each other*. This postulate is called the **zeroth law of thermodynamics**. It has this unusual name since it was not until after the great first and second laws of thermodynamics (Chapter 15) were worked out that scientists realized that this apparently obvious postulate needed to be stated first.

Temperature is a property of a system that determines whether the system will be in thermal equilibrium with other systems. When two systems are in thermal equilibrium, their temperatures are, by definition, equal, and no net thermal energy will be exchanged between them. This is consistent with our everyday notion of temperature, since when a hot object and a cold one are put into contact, they eventually come to the same temperature. Thus the importance of the zeroth law is that it allows a useful definition of temperature.

## 13–4 Thermal Expansion

Most substances expand when heated and contract when cooled. However, the amount of expansion or contraction varies, depending on the material.

**FIGURE 13–9** A thin rod of length $L_0$ at temperature $T_0$ is heated to a new uniform temperature $T$ and acquires length $L$, where $L = L_0 + \Delta L$.

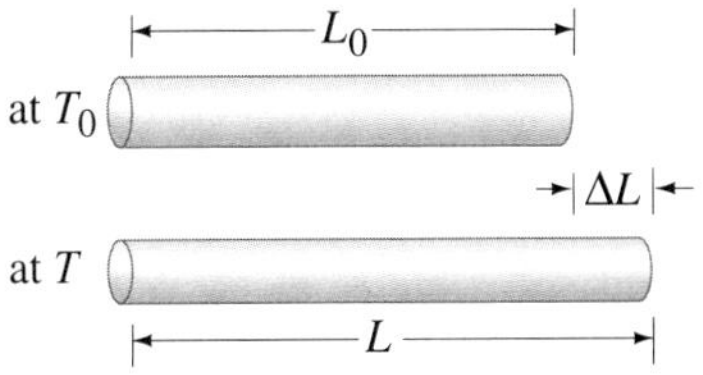


*Linear expansion*

### Linear Expansion

Experiments indicate that the change in length $\Delta L$ of almost all solids is, to a good approximation, directly proportional to the change in temperature $\Delta T$, as long as $\Delta T$ is not too large. As might be expected, the change in length is also proportional to the original length of the object, $L_0$, Fig. 13–9. That is, for the same temperature change, a 4-m-long iron rod will increase in length twice as much as a 2-m-long iron rod. We can write this proportionality as an equation:

$$\Delta L = \alpha L_0 \, \Delta T, \tag{13–1a}$$

where $\alpha$, the proportionality constant, is called the *coefficient of linear expansion* for the particular material and has units of $(\mathrm{C}^\circ)^{-1}$. We set $L = L_0 + \Delta L$, and rewrite this equation as

$$L = L_0(1 + \alpha \, \Delta T), \tag{13–1b}$$

where $L_0$ is the length initially, at temperature $T_0$, and $L$ is the length after heating or cooling to a temperature $T$. If the temperature change $\Delta T = T - T_0$ is negative, then $\Delta L = L - L_0$ is also negative; thus the length shortens as the temperature decreases.

**TABLE 13–1 Coefficients of Expansion, near 20°C**

| Material | Coefficient of Linear Expansion, $\alpha$ $(C°)^{-1}$ | Coefficient of Volume Expansion, $\beta$ $(C°)^{-1}$ |
|---|---|---|
| *Solids* | | |
| Aluminum | $25 \times 10^{-6}$ | $75 \times 10^{-6}$ |
| Brass | $19 \times 10^{-6}$ | $56 \times 10^{-6}$ |
| Copper | $17 \times 10^{-6}$ | $50 \times 10^{-6}$ |
| Gold | $14 \times 10^{-6}$ | $42 \times 10^{-6}$ |
| Iron or steel | $12 \times 10^{-6}$ | $35 \times 10^{-6}$ |
| Lead | $29 \times 10^{-6}$ | $87 \times 10^{-6}$ |
| Glass (Pyrex®) | $3 \times 10^{-6}$ | $9 \times 10^{-6}$ |
| Glass (ordinary) | $9 \times 10^{-6}$ | $27 \times 10^{-6}$ |
| Quartz | $0.4 \times 10^{-6}$ | $1 \times 10^{-6}$ |
| Concrete and brick | $\approx 12 \times 10^{-6}$ | $\approx 36 \times 10^{-6}$ |
| Marble | $1.4\text{–}3.5 \times 10^{-6}$ | $4\text{–}10 \times 10^{-6}$ |
| *Liquids* | | |
| Gasoline | | $950 \times 10^{-6}$ |
| Mercury | | $180 \times 10^{-6}$ |
| Ethyl alcohol | | $1100 \times 10^{-6}$ |
| Glycerin | | $500 \times 10^{-6}$ |
| Water | | $210 \times 10^{-6}$ |
| *Gases* | | |
| Air (and most other gases at atmospheric pressure) | | $3400 \times 10^{-6}$ |

The values of $\alpha$ for various materials at 20°C are listed in Table 13–1. Actually, $\alpha$ does vary slightly with temperature (which is why thermometers made of different materials do not agree precisely). However, if the temperature range is not too great, the variation can usually be ignored.

PHYSICS APPLIED
*Expansion in structures*

**EXAMPLE 13–3 Bridge expansion.** The steel bed of a suspension bridge is 200 m long at 20°C. If the extremes of temperature to which it might be exposed are −30°C to +40°C, how much will it contract and expand?

**APPROACH** We assume the bridge bed will expand and contract linearly with temperature, as given by Eq. 13–1a.

**SOLUTION** From Table 13–1, we find that $\alpha = 12 \times 10^{-6}(C°)^{-1}$ for steel. The increase in length when it is at 40°C will be

$$\Delta L = \alpha L_0 \, \Delta T = (12 \times 10^{-6}/C°)(200\,\text{m})(40°C - 20°C) = 4.8 \times 10^{-2}\,\text{m},$$

or 4.8 cm. When the temperature decreases to −30°C, $\Delta T = -50\,C°$. Then

$$\Delta L = (12 \times 10^{-6}/C°)(200\,\text{m})(-50\,C°) = -12.0 \times 10^{-2}\,\text{m},$$

or a decrease in length of 12 cm. The total range the expansion joints must accommodate is 12 cm + 4.8 cm ≈ 17 cm.

**CONCEPTUAL EXAMPLE 13–4 Do holes expand or contract?** If you heat a thin, circular ring (Fig. 13–10a) in the oven, does the ring's hole get larger or smaller?

**RESPONSE** You might guess that the metal expands into the hole, making the hole smaller. But it is not so. Imagine the ring is solid, like a coin (Fig. 13–10b). Draw a circle on it with a pen as shown. When the metal expands, the material inside the circle will expand along with the rest of the metal; so the circle expands. Cutting the metal where the circle is makes clear to us that the hole increases in diameter.

**FIGURE 13–10** Example 13–4.

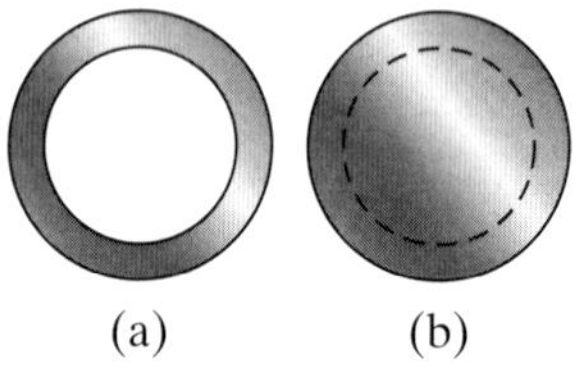

**EXAMPLE 13–5** **Ring on a rod.** An iron ring is to fit snugly on a cylindrical iron rod. At 20°C, the diameter of the rod is 6.445 cm and the inside diameter of the ring is 6.420 cm. To slip over the rod, the ring must be slightly larger than the rod diameter by about 0.008 cm. To what temperature must the ring be brought if its hole is to be large enough so it will slip over the rod?

**APPROACH** The hole in the ring must be increased from a diameter of 6.420 cm to 6.445 cm + 0.008 cm = 6.453 cm. The ring must be heated since the hole diameter will increase linearly with temperature (as in Example 13–4).

**SOLUTION** We solve for $\Delta T$ in Eq. 13–1a and find

$$\Delta T = \frac{\Delta L}{\alpha L_0} = \frac{6.453\text{ cm} - 6.420\text{ cm}}{(12 \times 10^{-6}/\text{C}°)(6.420\text{ cm})} = 430\text{ C}°.$$

So it must be raised at least to $T = (20°\text{C} + 430\text{ C}°) = 450°\text{C}$.

**NOTE** In doing Problems, don't forget the last step, adding in the initial temperature (20°C here).

**CONCEPTUAL EXAMPLE 13–6** **Opening a tight jar lid.** When the lid of a glass jar is tight, holding the lid under hot water for a short time will often make it easier to open. Why?

PHYSICS APPLIED
*Opening a tight lid*

**RESPONSE** The lid may be struck by the hot water more directly than the glass and so expand sooner. But even if not, metals generally expand more than glass for the same temperature change ($\alpha$ is greater—see Table 13–1).

## Volume Expansion

The change in *volume* of a material which undergoes a temperature change is given by a relation similar to Eq. 13–1a, namely,

$$\Delta V = \beta V_0 \, \Delta T, \tag{13–2}$$

*Volume expansion*

where $\Delta T$ is the change in temperature, $V_0$ is the original volume, $\Delta V$ is the change in volume, and $\beta$ is the *coefficient of volume expansion*. The units of $\beta$ are $(\text{C}°)^{-1}$.

Values of $\beta$ for various materials are given in Table 13–1. Notice that for solids, $\beta$ is normally equal to approximately $3\alpha$ (work Problem 19 to see why). For solids that are not isotropic (that is, not having the same properties in all directions), the relation $\beta \approx 3\alpha$ is not valid. (Note that linear expansion has no meaning for liquids and gases since they do not have fixed shapes.)

*$\beta \approx 3\alpha$*

**EXAMPLE 13–7** **Gas tank in the sun.** The 70-L steel gas tank of a car is filled to the top with gasoline at 20°C. The car sits in the sun and the tank reaches a temperature of 40°C (104°F). How much gasoline do you expect to overflow from the tank?

PHYSICS APPLIED
*Gas tank overflow*

**APPROACH** Both the gasoline and the tank expand as the temperature increases, and we assume they do so linearly as described by Eq. 13–2. The volume of overflowing gasoline equals the volume increase of the gasoline minus the increase in volume of the tank.

**SOLUTION** The gasoline expands by

$$\Delta V = \beta V_0 \, \Delta T = \left(950 \times 10^{-6}\,\text{C}°^{-1}\right)(70\text{ L})(40°\text{C} - 20°\text{C}) = 1.3\text{ L}.$$

The tank also expands. We can think of it as a steel shell that undergoes volume expansion $\left(\beta \approx 3\alpha = 36 \times 10^{-6}\,\text{C}°^{-1}\right)$. If the tank were solid, the surface layer (the shell) would expand just the same. Thus the tank increases in volume by

$$\Delta V = \left(36 \times 10^{-6}\,\text{C}°^{-1}\right)(70\text{ L})(40°\text{C} - 20°\text{C}) = 0.050\text{ L},$$

so the tank expansion has little effect. More than a liter of gas could spill out.

**NOTE** Want to save a few pennies? Fill your gas tank when it is cool and the gas is denser—more molecules for the same price. But don't fill the tank all the way.

Equations 13–1 and 13–2 are accurate only if $\Delta L$ (or $\Delta V$) is small compared to $L_0$ (or $V_0$). This is of particular concern for liquids and even more so for gases because of the large values of $\beta$. Furthermore, $\beta$ itself varies substantially with temperature for gases. Therefore, a better description of volume changes for gases is needed, as we will discuss starting in Section 13–6.

## Anomalous Behavior of Water Below 4°C

*Water is unusual: it contracts when warmed from 0°C to 4°C*

**PHYSICS APPLIED**
*Life under ice*

Most substances expand more or less uniformly with an increase in temperature, as long as no phase change occurs. Water, however, does not follow the usual pattern. If water at 0°C is heated, it actually *decreases* in volume until it reaches 4°C. Above 4°C water behaves normally and expands in volume as the temperature is increased, Fig. 13–11. Water thus has its greatest density at 4°C. This anomalous behavior of water is of great importance for the survival of aquatic life during cold winters. When the water in a lake or river is above 4°C and begins to cool by contact with cold air, the water at the surface sinks because of its greater density. It is replaced by warmer water from below. This mixing continues until the temperature reaches 4°C. As the surface water cools further, it remains on the surface because it is less dense than the 4°C water below. Water then freezes first at the surface, and the ice remains on the surface since ice (specific gravity = 0.917) is less dense than water. The water at the bottom remains liquid unless it is so cold that the whole body of water freezes. If water were like most substances, becoming more dense as it cools, the water at the bottom of a lake would be frozen first. Lakes would freeze solid more easily since circulation would bring the warmer water to the surface to be efficiently cooled. The complete freezing of a lake would cause severe damage to its plant and animal life. Because of the unusual behavior of water below 4°C, it is rare for any large body of water to freeze completely, and this is helped by the layer of ice on the surface which acts as an insulator to reduce the flow of heat out of the water into the cold air above. Without this peculiar but wonderful property of water, life on this planet as we know it might not have been possible.

Not only does water expand as it cools from 4°C to 0°C, it expands even more as it freezes to ice. This is why ice cubes float in water and pipes break when water inside them freezes.

**FIGURE 13–11** Behavior of water as a function of temperature near 4°C. (a) Volume of 1.00000 gram of water as a function of temperature. (b) Density vs. temperature. [Note the breaks in each axis.]

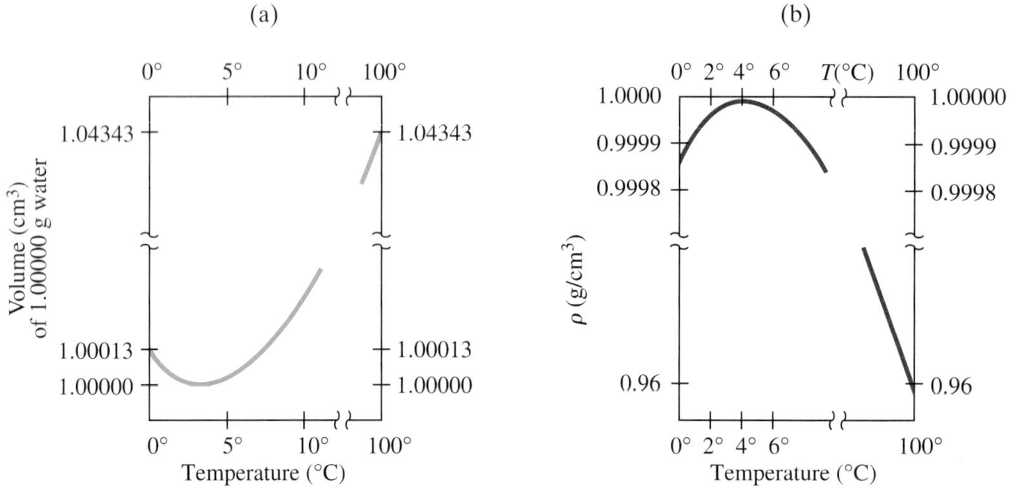

## * 13–5 Thermal Stresses

In many situations, such as in buildings and roads, the ends of a beam or slab of material are rigidly fixed, which greatly limits expansion or contraction. If the temperature should change, large compressive or tensile stresses, called *thermal stresses*, will occur. The magnitude of such stresses can be calculated using the concept of elastic modulus developed in Chapter 9. To calculate the internal stress, we can think of this process as occurring in two steps. The beam tries to expand (or contract) by an amount $\Delta L$ given by Eq. 13–1; secondly, the solid in contact with the beam exerts a force to compress (or expand) it, keeping it at its original length. The force $F$ required is given by Eq. 9–4:

$$\Delta L = \frac{1}{E}\frac{F}{A}L_0,$$

where $E$ is Young's modulus for the material. To calculate the internal stress, $F/A$, we then set $\Delta L$ in Eq. 13–1a equal to $\Delta L$ in the equation above and find

$$\alpha L_0\,\Delta T = \frac{1}{E}\frac{F}{A}L_0.$$

Hence, the stress

$$\frac{F}{A} = \alpha E\,\Delta T.$$

**EXAMPLE 13–8** **Stress in concrete on a hot day.** A highway is to be made of blocks of concrete 10 m long placed end to end with no space between them to allow for expansion. If the blocks were placed at a temperature of 10°C, what compressive stress would occur if the temperature reached 40°C? The contact area between each block is $0.20\,\mathrm{m}^2$. Will fracture occur?

PHYSICS APPLIED
*Highway buckling*

**APPROACH** We use the expression for the stress $F/A$ we just derived, and find the value of $E$ from Table 9–1. To see if fracture occurs, we compare this stress to the ultimate strength of concrete in Table 9–2.

**SOLUTION**

$$\frac{F}{A} = \alpha\,E\,\Delta T = \left(12\times10^{-6}/\mathrm{C}^\circ\right)\left(20\times10^{9}\,\mathrm{N/m^2}\right)(30\,\mathrm{C}^\circ) = 7.2\times10^{6}\,\mathrm{N/m^2}.$$

This stress is not far from the ultimate strength of concrete under compression (Table 9–2) and exceeds it for tension and shear. If the concrete is not perfectly aligned, part of the force will act in shear, and fracture is likely. This is why soft spacers or expansion joints (Fig. 13–3) are used in concrete sidewalks, highways, and bridges.

## 13–6 The Gas Laws and Absolute Temperature

Equation 13–2 is not very useful for describing the expansion of a gas, partly because the expansion can be so great, and partly because gases generally expand to fill whatever container they are in. Indeed, Eq. 13–2 is meaningful only if the pressure is kept constant. The volume of a gas depends very much on the pressure as well as on the temperature. It is therefore valuable to determine a relation between the volume, the pressure, the temperature, and the mass of a gas. Such a relation is called an **equation of state**. (By the word *state*, we mean the physical condition of the system.)

If the state of a system is changed, we will always wait until the pressure and temperature have reached the same values throughout. We thus consider only **equilibrium states** of a system—when the variables that describe it (such as temperature and pressure) are the same throughout the system and are not changing in time. We also note that the results of this Section are accurate only for gases that are not too dense (the pressure is not too high, on the order of an atmosphere or so) and not close to the liquefaction (boiling) point.

For a given quantity of gas it is found experimentally that, to a good approximation, *the volume of a gas is inversely proportional to the absolute pressure applied to it when the temperature is kept constant.* That is,

*Boyle's law*

$$V \propto \frac{1}{P}, \qquad \text{[constant } T\text{]}$$

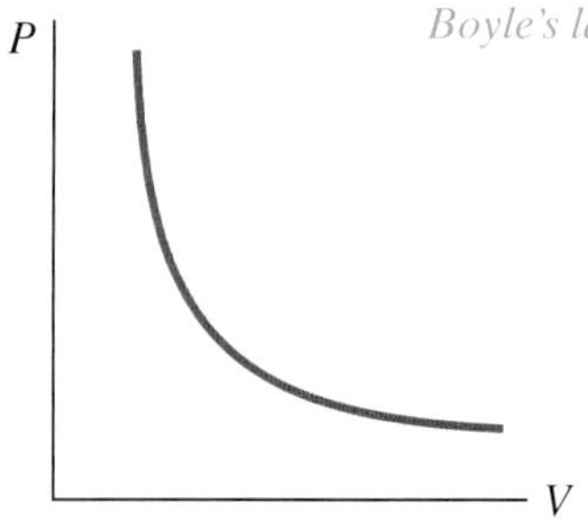


**FIGURE 13–12** Pressure vs. volume of a fixed amount of gas at a constant temperature, showing the inverse relationship as given by Boyle's law: as the pressure decreases, the volume increases.

where $P$ is the absolute pressure (*not* "gauge pressure"—see Section 10–4). For example, if the pressure on a gas is doubled, the volume is reduced to half its original volume. This relation is known as **Boyle's law**, after Robert Boyle (1627–1691), who first stated it on the basis of his own experiments. A graph of $P$ vs. $V$ for a fixed temperature is shown in Fig. 13–12. Boyle's law can also be written

$$PV = \text{constant.} \qquad \text{[constant } T\text{]}$$

That is, at constant temperature, if either the pressure or volume of the gas is allowed to vary, the other variable also changes so that the product $PV$ remains constant.

Temperature also affects the volume of a gas, but a quantitative relationship between $V$ and $T$ was not found until more than a century after Boyle's work. The Frenchman Jacques Charles (1746–1823) found that when the pressure is not too high and is kept constant, the volume of a gas increases with temperature at a nearly constant rate, as in Fig. 13–13a. However, all gases liquefy at low temperatures (for example, oxygen liquefies at −183°C), so the graph cannot be extended below the liquefaction point. Nonetheless, the graph is essentially a straight line and if projected to lower temperatures, as shown by the dashed line, it crosses the axis at about −273°C.

Such a graph can be drawn for any gas, and the straight line always projects back to −273°C at zero volume. This seems to imply that if a gas could be cooled to −273°C, it would have zero volume, and at lower temperatures a negative volume, which makes no sense. It could be argued that −273°C is the lowest temperature possible; indeed, many other more recent experiments indicate that this is so. This temperature is called the **absolute zero** of temperature. Its value has been determined to be −273.15°C.

*Absolute zero*

**FIGURE 13–13** Volume of a fixed amount of gas as a function of (a) Celsius temperature, and (b) Kelvin temperature, when the pressure is kept constant.

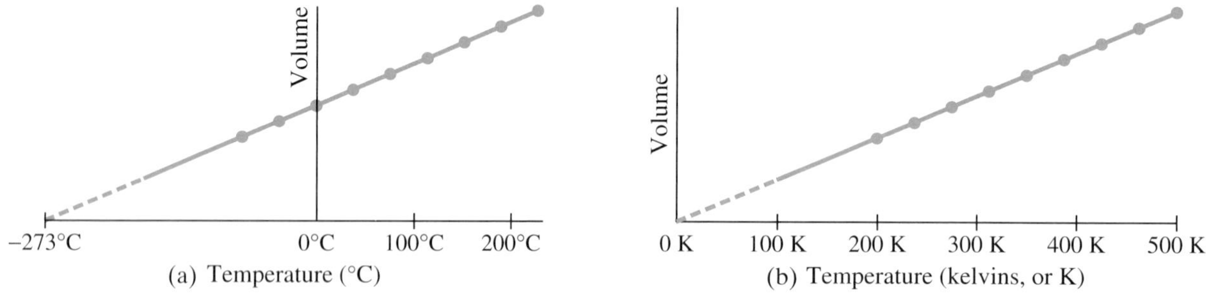


*Kelvin scale*

Absolute zero forms the basis of a temperature scale known as the **absolute scale** or **Kelvin scale**, and it is used extensively in scientific work. On this scale the temperature is specified as degrees Kelvin or, preferably, simply as *kelvins* (K) without the degree sign. The intervals are the same as for the Celsius scale, but the zero on this scale (0 K) is chosen as absolute zero. Thus the freezing point of water (0°C) is 273.15 K, and the boiling point of water is 373.15 K. Indeed, any temperature on the Celsius scale can be changed to kelvins by adding 273.15 to it:

*Conversion between Kelvin (absolute) and Celsius scales*

$$T(\text{K}) = T(^\circ\text{C}) + 273.15.$$

Now let us look at Fig. 13–13b, where the graph of the volume of a gas versus absolute temperature is a straight line that passes through the origin. Thus, to a good approximation, *the volume of a given amount of gas is directly proportional to the absolute temperature when the pressure is kept constant.* This is known as **Charles's law**, and is written

$$V \propto T. \qquad \text{[constant } P\text{]}$$

*Charles's law*

A third gas law, known as **Gay-Lussac's law**, after Joseph Gay-Lussac (1778–1850), states that *at constant volume, the absolute pressure of a gas is directly proportional to the absolute temperature*:

$$P \propto T. \qquad \text{[constant } V\text{]}$$

*Gay-Lussac's law*

A familiar example is that a closed jar or an aerosol can thrown into a hot fire will explode due to the increase in gas pressure inside that results from the temperature increase.

The laws of Boyle, Charles, and Gay-Lussac are not really laws in the sense that we use this term today (precise, deep, wide-ranging validity). They are really only approximations that are accurate for real gases only as long as the pressure and density of the gas are not too high, and the gas is not too close to liquefaction (condensation). The term *law* applied to these three relationships has become traditional, however, so we have stuck with that usage.

CONCEPTUAL EXAMPLE 13–9 **Don't throw a closed glass jar into a campfire.** What can happen if you did throw an empty glass jar, with lid on tight, into a fire, and why?

**RESPONSE** The inside of the jar is not empty. It is filled with air. As the fire heats the air inside, its temperature rises. The volume of the glass jar changes only slightly due to the heating. According to Gay-Lussac's law the pressure $P$ of the air inside the jar can increase dramatically, enough to cause the jar to explode, throwing glass pieces outward.

## 13–7 The Ideal Gas Law

The gas laws of Boyle, Charles, and Gay-Lussac were obtained by means of a technique that is very useful in science: namely, holding one or more variables constant to see clearly the effects on one variable due to changing one other variable. These laws can now be combined into a single more general relation between the absolute pressure, volume, and absolute temperature of a fixed quantity of gas:

$$PV \propto T.$$

This relation indicates how any of the quantities $P$, $V$, or $T$ will vary when the other two quantities change. This relation reduces to Boyle's, Charles's, or Gay-Lussac's law when either the temperature, the pressure, or the volume, respectively, is held constant.

Finally, we must incorporate the effect of the amount of gas present. Anyone who has blown up a balloon knows that the more air forced into the balloon, the bigger it gets (Figure 13–14). Indeed, careful experiments show that at constant temperature and pressure, the volume $V$ of an enclosed gas increases in direct proportion to the mass $m$ of gas present. Hence we write

$$PV \propto mT.$$

This proportion can be made into an equation by inserting a constant of proportionality. Experiment shows that this constant has a different value for different gases. However, the constant of proportionality turns out to be the same for all gases if, instead of the mass $m$, we use the number of *moles*.

**FIGURE 13–14** Blowing up a balloon means putting more air (more air molecules) into the balloon, which increases its volume. The pressure is nearly constant (atmospheric) except for the small effect of the balloon's elasticity.

*Mole (unit for amount of a substance)*

One **mole** (abbreviated mol) is defined as the amount of substance that contains as many atoms or molecules as there are in precisely 12 grams of carbon 12 (whose atomic mass is exactly 12 u). A simpler but equivalent definition is this: 1 mol is that number of grams of a substance numerically equal to the molecular mass (Section 13–1) of the substance. For example, the molecular mass of hydrogen gas ($H_2$) is 2.0 u (since each molecule contains two atoms of hydrogen and each atom has an atomic mass of 1.0 u). Thus 1 mol of $H_2$ has a mass of 2.0 g. Similarly, 1 mol of neon gas has a mass of 20 g, and 1 mol of $CO_2$ has a mass of $[12 + (2 \times 16)] = 44\text{ g}$ since oxygen has atomic mass of 16 (see periodic Table inside the rear cover). The mole is the official unit of amount of substance in the SI system. In general, the number of moles, $n$, in a given sample of a pure substance is equal to the mass of the sample in grams divided by the molecular mass specified as grams per mole:

$$n\,(\text{mol}) = \frac{\text{mass (grams)}}{\text{molecular mass (g/mol)}}.$$

For example, the number of moles in 132 g of $CO_2$ (molecular mass 44 u) is

$$n = \frac{132\text{ g}}{44\text{ g/mol}} = 3.0\text{ mol}.$$

We can now write the proportion discussed above as an equation:

*IDEAL GAS LAW*

$$PV = nRT, \qquad \textbf{(13–3)}$$

where $n$ represents the number of moles and $R$ is the constant of proportionality. $R$ is called the **universal gas constant** because its value is found experimentally to be the same for all gases. The value of $R$, in several sets of units (only the first is the proper SI unit), is

*Universal gas constant (in various units)*

$$\begin{aligned} R &= 8.314\text{ J/(mol}\cdot\text{K)} \qquad \text{[SI units]} \\ &= 0.0821\text{ (L}\cdot\text{atm)/(mol}\cdot\text{K)} \\ &= 1.99\text{ calories/(mol}\cdot\text{K)}.^{\dagger} \end{aligned}$$

Equation 13–3 is called the **ideal gas law**, or the **equation of state for an ideal gas**. We use the term "ideal" because real gases do not follow Eq. 13–3 precisely, particularly at high pressure (and density) or when the gas is near the liquefaction point (= boiling point). However, at pressures less than an atmosphere or so, and when $T$ is not close to the liquefaction point of the gas, Eq. 13–3 is quite accurate and useful for real gases.

**CAUTION** *Always give T in kelvins and P as absolute, not gauge, pressure*

Always remember, when using the ideal gas law, that temperatures must be given in kelvins (K) and that the pressure $P$ must always be *absolute* pressure, not gauge pressure (Section 10–4).

## 13–8 Problem Solving with the Ideal Gas Law

The ideal gas law is an extremely useful tool, and we now consider some Examples. We will often refer to "standard conditions" or "standard temperature and pressure" (STP), which means:

*STP = 273 K, 1 atm*

$$T = 273\text{ K }(0^\circ\text{C}) \text{ and } P = 1.00\text{ atm} = 1.013 \times 10^5\text{ N/m}^2 = 101.3\text{ kPa}.$$

**EXAMPLE 13–10** **Volume of one mol at STP.** Determine the volume of 1.00 mol of any gas, assuming it behaves like an ideal gas, at STP.

**APPROACH** We use the ideal gas law, solving for $V$.

**SOLUTION** We solve for $V$ in Eq. 13–3:

$$V = \frac{nRT}{P} = \frac{(1.00\text{ mol})(8.314\text{ J/mol}\cdot\text{K})(273\text{ K})}{(1.013 \times 10^5\text{ N/m}^2)} = 22.4 \times 10^{-3}\text{ m}^3.$$

*1 mol of gas at STP has V = 22.4 L*

Since 1 liter is $1000\text{ cm}^3 = 1 \times 10^{-3}\text{ m}^3$, 1 mol of any gas has $V = 22.4\text{ L}$ at STP.

† Calories will be defined in Section 14–1; sometimes it is useful to use $R$ as given in terms of calories.

The value of 22.4 L for the volume of 1 mol of an ideal gas at STP is worth remembering, for it sometimes makes calculation simpler.

**EXERCISE B** What is the volume of 1.00 mol of ideal gas at 20°C?

**EXAMPLE 13–11** **Helium balloon.** A helium party balloon, assumed to be a perfect sphere, has a radius of 18.0 cm. At room temperature (20°C), its internal pressure is 1.05 atm. Find the number of moles of helium in the balloon and the mass of helium needed to inflate the balloon to these values.

**APPROACH** We can use the ideal gas law to find $n$, since we are given $P$ and $T$, and can find $V$ from the given radius.

**SOLUTION** We get the volume $V$ from the formula for a sphere:

$$V = \tfrac{4}{3}\pi r^3 = \tfrac{4}{3}\pi\,(0.180\text{ m})^3 = 0.0244\text{ m}^3.$$

The pressure is given as $1.05\text{ atm} = 1.064 \times 10^5\text{ N/m}^2$. The temperature must be expressed in kelvins, so we change 20°C to $(20 + 273)\text{K} = 293\text{ K}$. Finally, we choose the value of $R$ to be $R = 8.314\text{ J/(mol}\cdot\text{K)}$ because we are using SI units. Thus

$$n = \frac{PV}{RT} = \frac{(1.064 \times 10^5\text{ N/m}^2)(0.0244\text{ m}^3)}{(8.314\text{ J/mol}\cdot\text{K})(293\text{ K})} = 1.066\text{ mol}.$$

The mass of helium (atomic mass = 4.00 g/mol as given in Appendix B or the periodic Table) can be obtained from

$$\text{mass} = n \times \text{molecular mass} = (1.066\text{ mol})(4.00\text{ g/mol}) = 4.26\text{ g}.$$

**EXAMPLE 13–12** **ESTIMATE** **Mass of air in a room.** Estimate the mass of air in a room whose dimensions are $5\text{ m} \times 3\text{ m} \times 2.5\text{ m}$ high, at STP.

PHYSICS APPLIED
*Mass (and weight) of the air in a room*

**APPROACH** First we determine the number of moles $n$ using the given volume. Then we can multiply by the mass of one mole to get the total mass.

**SOLUTION** Example 13–10 told us that 1 mol at 0°C has a volume of 22.4 L. The room's volume is $5\text{ m} \times 3\text{ m} \times 2.5\text{ m}$, so

$$n = \frac{(5\text{ m})(3\text{ m})(2.5\text{ m})}{22.4 \times 10^{-3}\text{ m}^3} \approx 1700\text{ mol}.$$

Air is a mixture of about 20% oxygen $(O_2)$ and 80% nitrogen $(N_2)$. The molecular masses are $2 \times 16\text{ u} = 32\text{ u}$ and $2 \times 14\text{ u} = 28\text{ u}$, respectively, for an average of about 29 u. Thus, 1 mol of air has a mass of about $29\text{ g} = 0.029\text{ kg}$, so our room has a mass of air

$$m \approx (1700\text{ mol})(0.029\text{ kg/mol}) \approx 50\text{ kg}.$$

**NOTE** That is roughly 100 lbs of air!

**EXERCISE C** At 20°C, would there be more or less air mass in a room than at 0°C?

Frequently, volume is specified in liters and pressure in atmospheres. Rather than convert these to SI units, we can instead use the value of $R$ given in Section 13–7 as $0.0821\text{ L}\cdot\text{atm/mol}\cdot\text{K}$.

In many situations it is not necessary to use the value of $R$ at all. For example, many problems involve a change in the pressure, temperature, and

➡ PROBLEM SOLVING

*Using the ideal gas law as a ratio*

volume of a fixed amount of gas. In this case, $PV/T = nR =$ constant, since $n$ and $R$ remain constant. If we now let $P_1$, $V_1$, and $T_1$ represent the appropriate variables initially, and $P_2, V_2, T_2$ represent the variables after the change is made, then we can write

$$\frac{P_1 V_1}{T_1} = \frac{P_2 V_2}{T_2}.$$

If we know any five of the quantities in this equation, we can solve for the sixth. Or, if one of the three variables is constant ($V_1 = V_2$, or $P_1 = P_2$, or $T_1 = T_2$) then we can use this equation to solve for one unknown when given the other three quantities.

PHYSICS APPLIED

*Pressure in a hot tire*

**FIGURE 13–15** Example 13–13.

➡ PROBLEM SOLVING

*Do not use gauge pressure or C° in the ideal gas law*

**EXAMPLE 13–13** **Check tires cold.** An automobile tire is filled (Fig. 13–15) to a gauge pressure of 200 kPa at 10°C. After a drive of 100 km, the temperature within the tire rises to 40°C. What is the pressure within the tire now?

**APPROACH** We don't know the number of moles of gas, or the volume of the tire, but we assume they are constant. We use the ratio form of the ideal gas law.

**SOLUTION** Since $V_1 = V_2$, then

$$\frac{P_1}{T_1} = \frac{P_2}{T_2}.$$

This is, incidentally, a statement of Gay-Lussac's law. Since the pressure given is the gauge pressure (Section 10–4), we must add atmospheric pressure (= 101 kPa) to get the absolute pressure $P_1 = (200\,\text{kPa} + 101\,\text{kPa}) = 301\,\text{kPa}$. We convert temperatures to kelvins by adding 273 and solve for $P_2$:

$$P_2 = P_1\left(\frac{T_2}{T_1}\right) = \left(3.01 \times 10^5\,\text{Pa}\right)\left(\frac{313\,\text{K}}{283\,\text{K}}\right) = 333\,\text{kPa}.$$

Subtracting atmospheric pressure, we find the resulting gauge pressure to be 232 kPa, which is a 16% increase. This Example shows why car manuals suggest checking tire pressure when the tires are cold.

**NOTE** When using the ideal gas law, temperatures must be given in kelvins (K) and the pressure $P$ must always be *absolute* pressure, not gauge pressure.

## 13–9 Ideal Gas Law in Terms of Molecules: Avogadro's Number

The fact that the gas constant, $R$, has the same value for all gases is a remarkable reflection of simplicity in nature. It was first recognized, although in a slightly different form, by the Italian scientist Amedeo Avogadro (1776–1856). Avogadro stated that *equal volumes of gas at the same pressure and temperature contain equal numbers of molecules*. This is sometimes called **Avogadro's hypothesis**. That this is consistent with $R$ being the same for all gases can be seen as follows. First of all, from Eq. 13–3 we see that for the same number of moles, $n$, and the same pressure and temperature, the volume will be the same for all gases as long as $R$ is the same. Second, the number of molecules in 1 mole is the same for all gases.† Thus Avogadro's hypothesis is equivalent to $R$ being the same for all gases.

*Avogadro's hypothesis*

The number of molecules in one mole of any pure substance is known as **Avogadro's number**, $N_A$. Although Avogadro conceived the notion, he was not able to actually determine the value of $N_A$. Indeed, precise measurements were not done until the twentieth century.

†For example, the molecular mass of $H_2$ gas is 2.0 atomic mass units (u), whereas that of $O_2$ gas is 32.0 u. Thus 1 mol of $H_2$ has a mass of 0.0020 kg and 1 mol of $O_2$ gas, 0.0320 kg. The number of molecules in a mole is equal to the total mass $M$ of a mole divided by the mass $m$ of one molecule; since this ratio $(M/m)$ is the same for all gases by definition of the mole, a mole of any gas must contain the same number of molecules.

A number of methods have been devised to measure $N_A$, and the accepted value today is

$$N_A = 6.02 \times 10^{23}. \qquad \text{[molecules/mole]}$$

*Avogadro's number*

Since the total number of molecules, $N$, in a gas is equal to the number per mole times the number of moles $(N = nN_A)$, the ideal gas law, Eq. 13–3, can be written in terms of the number of molecules present:

$$PV = nRT = \frac{N}{N_A}RT,$$

or

$$PV = NkT, \qquad \textbf{(13–4)}$$

*IDEAL GAS LAW (in terms of molecules)*

where $k = R/N_A$ is called **Boltzmann's constant** and has the value

$$k = \frac{R}{N_A} = \frac{8.314\ \text{J/mol}\cdot\text{K}}{6.02 \times 10^{23}/\text{mol}} = 1.38 \times 10^{-23}\ \text{J/K}.$$

*Boltzmann's constant*

**EXAMPLE 13–14 Hydrogen atom mass.** Use Avogadro's number to determine the mass of a hydrogen atom.

**APPROACH** The mass of one atom equals the mass of 1 mol divided by the number of atoms in 1 mol, $N_A$.

**SOLUTION** One mole of hydrogen atoms (atomic mass = 1.008 u, Section 13–1 or Appendix B) has a mass of $1.008 \times 10^{-3}$ kg and contains $6.02 \times 10^{23}$ atoms. Thus one atom has a mass

$$m = \frac{1.008 \times 10^{-3}\ \text{kg}}{6.02 \times 10^{23}} = 1.67 \times 10^{-27}\ \text{kg}.$$

**NOTE** Historically, the reverse process was one method used to obtain $N_A$: that is, a precise value of $N_A$ can be obtained from a precise measurement of the mass of the hydrogen atom.

**EXAMPLE 13–15 ESTIMATE How many molecules in one breath?** Estimate how many molecules you breathe in with a 1.0-L breath of air.

**PHYSICS APPLIED**
*Molecules in a breath*

**APPROACH** We determine what fraction of a mole 1.0 L is using the result of Example 13–10 that 1 mole has a volume of 22.4 L at STP, and then multiply that by $N_A$ to get the number of molecules in this number of moles.

**SOLUTION** One mole corresponds to 22.4 L at STP, so 1.0 L of air is $(1.0\ \text{L})/(22.4\ \text{L/mol}) = 0.045$ mol. Then 1.0 L of air contains

$$(0.045\ \text{mol})(6.02 \times 10^{23}\ \text{molecules/mole}) \approx 3 \times 10^{22}\ \text{molecules}.$$

## 13–10 Kinetic Theory and the Molecular Interpretation of Temperature

The analysis of matter in terms of atoms in continuous random motion is called the **kinetic theory**. We now investigate the properties of a gas from the point of view of kinetic theory, which is based on the laws of classical mechanics. But to apply Newton's laws to each of the vast number of molecules in a gas ($>10^{25}/\text{m}^3$ at STP) is far beyond the capability of any present computer. Instead we take a statistical approach and determine averages of certain quantities, and these averages correspond to macroscopic variables. We will, of course, demand that our microscopic description correspond to the macroscopic properties of gases; otherwise our theory would be of little value. Most importantly, we will arrive at an important relation between the average kinetic energy of molecules in a gas and the absolute temperature.

We make the following assumptions about the molecules in a gas. These assumptions reflect a simple view of a gas, but nonetheless the results they predict correspond well to the essential features of real gases that are at low pressures and far from the liquefaction point. Under these conditions real gases follow the ideal gas law quite closely, and indeed the gas we now describe is referred to as an **ideal gas**. The assumptions, which represent the basic postulates of the kinetic theory, are:

*Postulates of kinetic theory*

1. There are a large number of molecules, $N$, each of mass $m$, moving in random directions with a variety of speeds. This assumption is in accord with our observation that a gas fills its container and, in the case of air on Earth, is kept from escaping only by the force of gravity.
2. The molecules are, on the average, far apart from one another. That is, their average separation is much greater than the diameter of each molecule.
3. The molecules are assumed to obey the laws of classical mechanics, and are assumed to interact with one another only when they collide. Although molecules exert weak attractive forces on each other between collisions, the potential energy associated with these forces is small compared to the kinetic energy, and we ignore it for now.
4. Collisions with another molecule or the wall of the vessel are assumed to be perfectly elastic, like the collisions of perfectly elastic billiard balls (Chapter 7). We assume the collisions are of very short duration compared to the time between collisions. Then we can ignore the potential energy associated with collisions in comparison to the kinetic energy between collisions.

*Boyle's law explained*

We can see immediately how this kinetic view of a gas can explain Boyle's law (Section 13–6). The pressure exerted on a wall of a container of gas is due to the constant bombardment of molecules. If the volume is reduced by (say) half, the molecules are closer together and twice as many will be striking a given area of the wall per second. Hence we expect the pressure to be twice as great, in agreement with Boyle's law.

**FIGURE 13–16** (a) Molecules of a gas moving about in a rectangular container. (b) Arrows indicate the momentum of one molecule as it rebounds from the end wall.

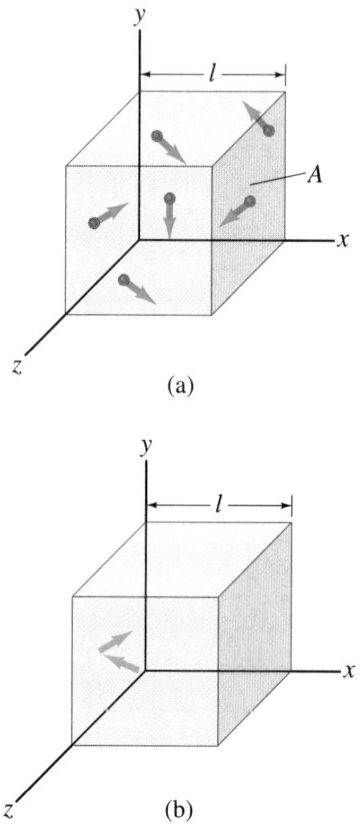


Now let us calculate quantitatively the pressure a gas exerts on its container as based on kinetic theory. We imagine that the molecules are inside a rectangular container (at rest) whose ends have area $A$ and whose length is $l$, as shown in Fig. 13–16a. The pressure exerted by the gas on the walls of its container is, according to our model, due to the collisions of the molecules with the walls. Let us focus our attention on the wall, of area $A$, at the left end of the container and examine what happens when one molecule strikes this wall, as shown in Fig. 13–16b. This molecule exerts a force on the wall, and according to Newton's third law the wall exerts an equal and opposite force back on the molecule. The magnitude of this force on the molecule, according to Newton's second law, is equal to the molecule's rate of change of momentum, $F = \Delta(mv)/\Delta t$ (Eq. 7–2). Assuming the collision is elastic, only the $x$ component of the molecule's momentum changes, and it changes from $-mv_x$ (it is moving in the negative $x$ direction) to $+mv_x$. Thus the change in the molecule's momentum, $\Delta(mv)$, which is the final momentum minus the initial momentum, is

$$\Delta(mv) = mv_x - (-mv_x) = 2mv_x$$

for one collision. This molecule will make many collisions with the wall, each separated by a time $\Delta t$, which is the time it takes the molecule to travel across the container and back again, a distance ($x$ component) equal to $2l$. Thus $2l = v_x\,\Delta t$, or

$$\Delta t = \frac{2l}{v_x}.$$

The time $\Delta t$ between collisions is very small, so the number of collisions per second is very large. Thus the average force—averaged over many collisions—

will be equal to the momentum change during one collision divided by the time between collisions (Newton's second law):

$$F = \frac{\Delta(mv)}{\Delta t} = \frac{2mv_x}{2l/v_x} = \frac{mv_x^2}{l}. \qquad \text{[due to one molecule]}$$

During its passage back and forth across the container, the molecule may collide with the tops and sides of the container, but this does not alter its $x$ component of momentum and thus does not alter our result. It may also collide with other molecules, which may change its $v_x$. However, any loss (or gain) of momentum is acquired by other molecules, and because we will eventually sum over all the molecules, this effect will be included. So our result above is not altered.

The actual force due to one molecule is intermittent, but because a huge number of molecules are striking the wall per second, the force is, on average, nearly constant. To calculate the force due to *all* the molecules in the container, we have to add the contributions of each. Thus the net force on the wall is

$$F = \frac{m}{l}\left(v_{x1}^2 + v_{x2}^2 + \cdots + v_{xN}^2\right),$$

where $v_{x1}$ means $v_x$ for molecule number 1 (we arbitrarily assign each molecule a number) and the sum extends over the total number of molecules $N$ in the container. The average value of the square of the $x$ component of velocity is

$$\overline{v_x^2} = \frac{v_{x1}^2 + v_{x2}^2 + \cdots + v_{xN}^2}{N}. \tag{13–5}$$

Thus we can write the force as

$$F = \frac{m}{l} N\overline{v_x^2}.$$

We know that the square of any vector is equal to the sum of the squares of its components (theorem of Pythagoras). Thus $v^2 = v_x^2 + v_y^2 + v_z^2$ for any velocity $v$. Taking averages, we obtain

$$\overline{v^2} = \overline{v_x^2} + \overline{v_y^2} + \overline{v_z^2}.$$

Since the velocities of the molecules in our gas are assumed to be random, there is no preference to one direction or another. Hence

$$\overline{v_x^2} = \overline{v_y^2} = \overline{v_z^2}.$$

Combining this relation with the one just above, we get

$$\overline{v^2} = 3\overline{v_x^2}.$$

We substitute this into the equation for net force $F$:

$$F = \frac{m}{l} N \frac{\overline{v^2}}{3}.$$

The pressure on the wall is then

$$P = \frac{F}{A} = \tfrac{1}{3}\frac{Nm\overline{v^2}}{Al}$$

or

$$P = \tfrac{1}{3}\frac{Nm\overline{v^2}}{V}, \tag{13–6}$$

*Pressure in a gas*

where $V = lA$ is the volume of the container. This is the result we were seeking, the pressure exerted by a gas on its container expressed in terms of molecular properties.

Equation 13–6, $P = \frac{1}{3}N m\overline{v^2}/V$, can be rewritten in a clearer form by multiplying both sides by $V$ and rearranging the right-hand side:

$$PV = \tfrac{2}{3}N\left(\tfrac{1}{2}m\overline{v^2}\right). \qquad \textbf{(13–7)}$$

The quantity $\frac{1}{2}m\overline{v^2}$ is the average kinetic energy $(\overline{\text{KE}})$ of the molecules in the gas. If we compare Eq. 13–7 with Eq. 13–4, the ideal gas law $PV = NkT$, we see that the two agree if

*TEMPERATURE RELATED TO AVERAGE KINETIC ENERGY OF MOLECULES*

$$\tfrac{2}{3}\left(\tfrac{1}{2}m\overline{v^2}\right) = kT,$$

or

$$\overline{\text{KE}} = \tfrac{1}{2}m\overline{v^2} = \tfrac{3}{2}kT. \qquad \text{[ideal gas]}\ \textbf{(13–8)}$$

This equation tells us that

> **the average translational kinetic energy of molecules in random motion in an ideal gas is directly proportional to the absolute temperature of the gas.**

The higher the temperature, according to kinetic theory, the faster the molecules are moving on the average. This relation is one of the triumphs of the kinetic theory.

**EXAMPLE 13–16** **Molecular kinetic energy.** What is the average translational kinetic energy of molecules in an ideal gas at 37°C?

**APPROACH** We use the absolute temperature in Eq. 13–8.

**SOLUTION** We change 37°C to 310 K and insert into Eq. 13–8:

$$\overline{\text{KE}} = \tfrac{3}{2}kT = \tfrac{3}{2}\left(1.38 \times 10^{-23}\,\text{J/K}\right)(310\,\text{K}) = 6.42 \times 10^{-21}\,\text{J}.$$

**NOTE** A mole of molecules would have a total translational kinetic energy equal to $\left(6.42 \times 10^{-21}\,\text{J}\right)\left(6.02 \times 10^{23}\right) = 3900\,\text{J}$, which equals the kinetic energy of a 1-kg stone traveling faster than 85 m/s.

Equation 13–8 holds not only for gases, but also applies reasonably accurately to liquids and solids. Thus the result of Example 13–16 would apply to molecules within living cells at body temperature (37°C).

*Root-mean-square (rms) speed*

We can use Eq. 13–8 to calculate how fast molecules are moving on the average. Notice that the average in Eqs. 13–5 through 13–8 is over the *square* of the speed. The square root of $\overline{v^2}$ is called the **root-mean-square** speed, $v_{\text{rms}}$ (since we are taking the square *root* of the *mean* of the *square* of the speed):

*rms speed of molecules*

$$v_{\text{rms}} = \sqrt{\overline{v^2}} = \sqrt{\frac{3kT}{m}}. \qquad \textbf{(13–9)}$$

**EXAMPLE 13–17** **Speeds of air molecules.** What is the rms speed of air molecules ($O_2$ and $N_2$) at room temperature (20°C)?

**APPROACH** To obtain $v_{\text{rms}}$, we need the masses of $O_2$ and $N_2$ molecules and then apply Eq. 13–9 to oxygen and nitrogen separately, since they have different masses.

**SOLUTION** The masses of one molecule of $O_2$ (molecular mass = 32 u) and $N_2$ (molecular mass = 28 u) are (where $1\,\text{u} = 1.66 \times 10^{-27}\,\text{kg}$)

$$m(O_2) = (32)\left(1.66 \times 10^{-27}\,\text{kg}\right) = 5.3 \times 10^{-26}\,\text{kg},$$
$$m(N_2) = (28)\left(1.66 \times 10^{-27}\,\text{kg}\right) = 4.6 \times 10^{-26}\,\text{kg}.$$

Thus, for oxygen

$$v_{\text{rms}} = \sqrt{\frac{3kT}{m}} = \sqrt{\frac{(3)\left(1.38 \times 10^{-23}\,\text{J/K}\right)(293\,\text{K})}{\left(5.3 \times 10^{-26}\,\text{kg}\right)}} = 480\,\text{m/s},$$

and for nitrogen the result is $v_{\text{rms}} = 510\,\text{m/s}$. These speeds† are more than 1700 km/h or 1000 mi/h.

†The speed $v_{\text{rms}}$ is a magnitude only. The *velocity* of molecules averages to zero: the velocity has direction, and as many molecules move to the right as to the left.

**EXERCISE D** What speed would a 1-gram paper clip have if it had the same KE as a molecule of Example 13–17?

Equation 13–8, $\overline{\text{KE}} = \frac{3}{2}kT$, implies that as the temperature approaches absolute zero, the kinetic energy of molecules approaches zero. Modern quantum theory, however, tells us this is not quite so. Instead, as absolute zero is approached, the kinetic energy approaches a very small nonzero minimum value. Even though all real gases become liquid or solid near 0 K, molecular motion does not cease, even at absolute zero.

## * 13–11 Distribution of Molecular Speeds

The molecules in a gas are assumed to be in random motion, which means that many molecules have speeds less than the rms speed and others have greater speeds. In 1859, James Clerk Maxwell (1831–1879) derived, on the basis of kinetic theory, that the speeds of molecules in a gas are distributed according to the graph shown in Fig. 13–17. This is known as the **Maxwell distribution of speeds.**† The speeds vary from zero to many times the rms speed, but as the graph shows, most molecules have speeds that are not far from the average. Less than 1% of the molecules exceed four times $v_{\text{rms}}$.

*Maxwell distribution of speeds of molecules in a gas*

Experiments to determine the distribution in real gases, starting in the 1920s, confirmed with considerable accuracy the Maxwell distribution and the direct proportion between average kinetic energy and absolute temperature, Eq. 13–8.

Figure 13–18 shows the Maxwell distribution for two different temperatures; just as $v_{\text{rms}}$ increases with temperature, so the whole distribution curve shifts to the right at higher temperatures. This Figure illustrates how kinetic theory can explain why many chemical reactions, including those in biological cells, take place more rapidly as the temperature increases. Two molecules may chemically react only if their kinetic energy is above some minimum value (called the *activation energy*), $E_{\text{A}}$, so that when they collide, they penetrate into each other somewhat. Figure 13–18 shows that at a higher temperature, many more molecules have a speed and kinetic energy KE above the needed threshold $E_{\text{A}}$.

PHYSICS APPLIED
*How chemical reactions depend on temperature*

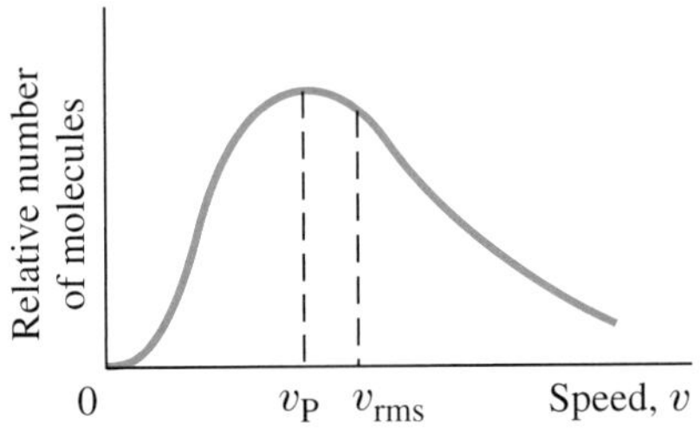


**FIGURE 13–17** Distribution of speeds of molecules in an ideal gas. Note that $v_{\text{rms}}$ is not at the peak of the curve (that speed is called the "most probable speed," $v_{\text{P}}$). This is because the curve is skewed to the right: it is not symmetrical.

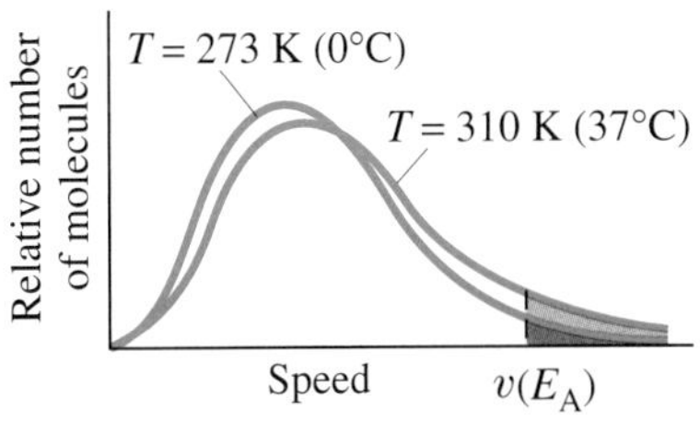


**FIGURE 13–18** Distribution of molecular speeds for two different temperatures.

## * 13–12 Real Gases and Changes of Phase

The ideal gas law is an accurate description of the behavior of a real gas as long as the pressure is not too high and as long as the temperature is far from the liquefaction point. But what happens when these two criteria are not satisfied? First we discuss real gas behavior and then we examine how kinetic theory can help us understand this behavior.

†Mathematically, the distribution is given by $\Delta N = Cv^2 \exp(-\frac{1}{2}mv^2/kT)\Delta v$, where $\Delta N$ is the number of molecules with speed between $v$ and $v + \Delta v$, $C$ is a constant, and exp means the expression in parentheses is an exponent on the natural number $e = 2.718\ldots$.

*PV diagram*

Let us look at a graph of pressure plotted against volume for a given amount of gas. On such a "*PV* diagram," Fig. 13–19, each point represents an equilibrium state of the given substance. The various curves (labeled A, B, C, and D) show how the pressure varies as the volume is changed at constant temperature for several different values of the temperature. The dashed curve A′ represents the behavior of a gas as predicted by the ideal gas law; that is, $PV = \text{constant}$. The solid curve A represents the behavior of a real gas at the same temperature. Notice that at high pressure, the volume of a real gas is less than that predicted by the ideal gas law. The curves B and C in Fig. 13–19 represent the gas at successively lower temperatures, and we see that the behavior deviates even more from the curves predicted by the ideal gas law (for example, B′), and the deviation is greater the closer the gas is to liquefying.

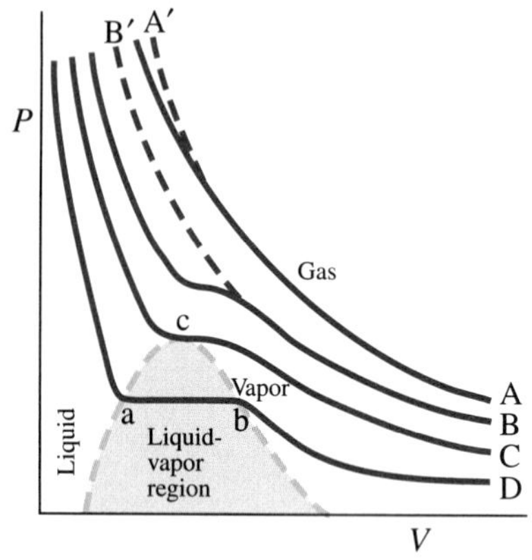


**FIGURE 13–19** *PV* diagram for a real substance. Curves A, B, C, and D represent the same gas at different fixed temperatures ($T_A > T_B > T_C > T_D$).

To explain this, we note that at higher pressure we expect the molecules to be closer together. And, particularly at lower temperatures, the potential energy associated with the attractive forces between the molecules (which we ignored before) is no longer negligible compared to the now reduced kinetic energy of the molecules. These attractive forces tend to pull the molecules closer together so at a given pressure, the volume is less than expected from the ideal gas law. At still lower temperatures, these forces cause liquefaction, and the molecules become very close together.

Curve D represents the situation when liquefaction occurs. At low pressure on curve D (on the right in Fig. 13–19), the substance is a gas and occupies a large volume. As the pressure is increased, the volume decreases until point b is reached. Beyond b, the volume decreases with no change in pressure; the substance is gradually changing from the gas to the liquid phase. At point a, all of the substance has changed to liquid. Further increase in pressure reduces the volume only slightly—liquids are nearly incompressible—so on the left the curve is very steep as shown. The shaded area under the dashed line represents the region where the gas and liquid phases exist together in equilibrium.

*Critical point*

Curve C in Fig. 13–19 represents the behavior of the substance at its **critical temperature**; the point c (the one point where this curve is horizontal) is called the **critical point**. At temperatures less than the critical temperature (and this is the definition of the term), a gas will change to the liquid phase if sufficient pressure is applied. Above the critical temperature, no amount of pressure can cause a gas to change phase and become a liquid: no liquid surface forms. The critical temperatures for various gases are given in Table 13–2. Scientists tried for many years to liquefy oxygen without success. Only after the discovery of the critical point was it realized that oxygen can be liquefied only if first cooled below its critical temperature of −118°C.

*Vapor vs. gas*

Often a distinction is made between the terms "gas" and "vapor": a substance below its critical temperature in the gaseous state is called a **vapor**; above the critical temperature, it is called a **gas**.

*Phase diagram (PT)*

The behavior of a substance can be diagrammed not only on a *PV* diagram but also on a *PT* diagram. A *PT* diagram, often called a **phase diagram**, is

**TABLE 13–2 Critical Temperatures and Pressures**

| Substance | Critical Temperature °C | Critical Temperature K | Critical Pressure (atm) |
|---|---|---|---|
| Water | 374 | 647 | 218 |
| $CO_2$ | 31 | 304 | 72.8 |
| Oxygen | −118 | 155 | 50 |
| Nitrogen | −147 | 126 | 33.5 |
| Hydrogen | −239.9 | 33.3 | 12.8 |
| Helium | −267.9 | 5.3 | 2.3 |

particularly convenient for comparing the different phases of a substance. Figure 13–20 is the phase diagram for water. The curve labeled *l-v* represents those points where the liquid and vapor phases are in equilibrium—it is thus a graph of the boiling point versus pressure. Note that the curve correctly shows that at a pressure of 1 atm the boiling point is 100°C and that the boiling point is lowered for a decreased pressure. The curve *s-l* represents points where solid and liquid exist in equilibrium and thus is a graph of the freezing point versus pressure. At 1 atm, the freezing point of water is 0°C, as shown. Notice also in Fig. 13–20 that at a pressure of 1 atm, the substance is in the liquid phase if the temperature is between 0°C and 100°C, but is in the solid or vapor phase if the temperature is below 0°C or above 100°C. The curve labeled *s-v* is the *sublimation point* versus pressure curve. **Sublimation** refers to the process whereby at low pressures a solid changes directly into the vapor phase without passing through the liquid phase. For water, sublimation occurs if the pressure of the water vapor is less than 0.0060 atm. Carbon dioxide, which in the solid phase is called dry ice, sublimates even at atmospheric pressure.

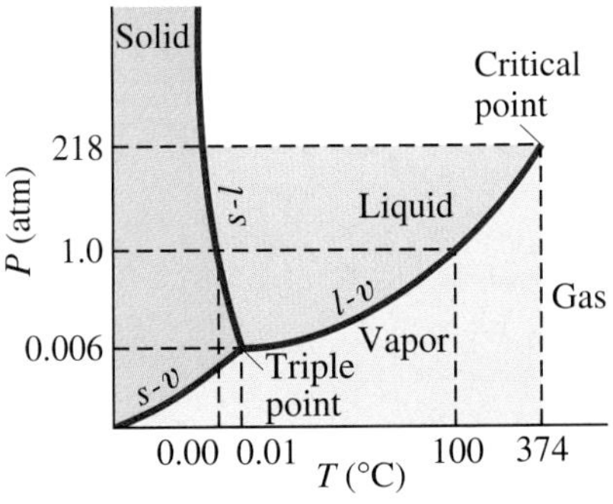


**FIGURE 13–20** Phase diagram for water (note that the scales are not linear).

*Triple point*

The intersection of the three curves (in Fig. 13–20) is the **triple point**. For water this occurs at $T = 273.16\text{ K}$ and $P = 6.03 \times 10^{-3}\text{ atm}$. It is only at the triple point that the three phases can exist together in equilibrium. Because the triple point corresponds to a unique value of temperature and pressure, it is precisely reproducible and is often used as a point of reference. For example, the standard of temperature is usually specified as exactly 273.16 K at the triple point of water, rather than 273.15 K at the freezing point of water at 1 atm.

**FIGURE 13–21** Phase diagram for carbon dioxide.

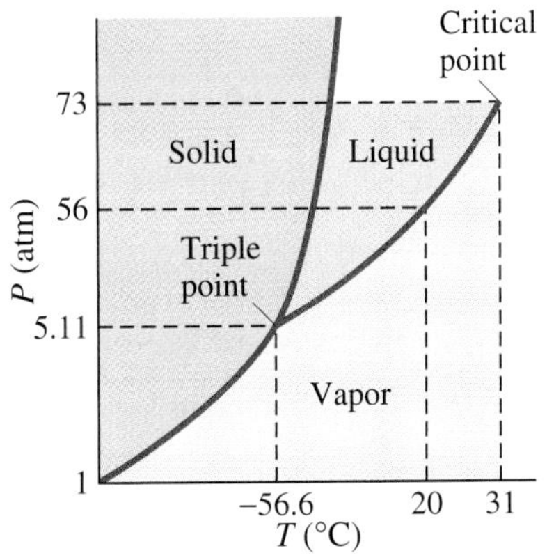


Notice that the *s-l* curve for water slopes upward to the left. This is true only of substances that *expand* upon freezing: at a higher pressure, a lower temperature is needed to cause the liquid to freeze. More commonly, substances contract upon freezing and the *s-l* curve slopes upward to the right, as shown for carbon dioxide $(CO_2)$ in Fig. 13–21.

*Superfluidity*

The phase transitions we have been discussing are the common ones. Some substances, however, can exist in several forms in the solid phase. A transition from one phase to another occurs at a particular temperature and pressure, just like ordinary phase changes. For example, ice has been observed in at least eight forms at very high pressure. Ordinary helium has two distinct liquid phases, called helium I and II. They exist only at temperatures within a few degrees of absolute zero. Helium II exhibits very unusual properties referred to as **superfluidity**. It has essentially zero viscosity and exhibits strange properties such as climbing up the sides of an open container.

## * 13–13 Vapor Pressure and Humidity

### Evaporation

If a glass of water is left out overnight, the water level will have dropped by morning. We say the water has evaporated, meaning that some of the water has changed to the vapor or gas phase.

*Evaporation*

This process of **evaporation** can be explained on the basis of kinetic theory. The molecules in a liquid move past one another with a variety of speeds that follow, approximately, the Maxwell distribution. There are strong attractive forces between these molecules, which is what keeps them close together in the liquid phase. A molecule near the surface of the liquid may, because of its speed, leave the liquid momentarily. But just as a rock thrown into the air returns to the Earth, so the attractive forces of the other molecules can pull the vagabond molecule back to the liquid surface—that is, if its velocity is not too large. A molecule with a high enough velocity, however, will escape the liquid entirely, like a rocket escaping the Earth, and become part of the gas phase. Only those molecules that have kinetic energy above a particular value can escape to the gas phase. We have already seen that kinetic theory predicts that the relative number of molecules with kinetic energy above a particular value (such as $E_A$ in Fig. 13–18) increases with temperature. This is in accord with the well-known observation that the evaporation rate is greater at higher temperatures.

PHYSICS APPLIED
*Evaporation cools*

Because it is the fastest molecules that escape from the surface, the average speed of those remaining is less. When the average speed is less, the absolute temperature is less. Thus kinetic theory predicts that *evaporation is a cooling process*. You have no doubt noticed this effect when you stepped out of a warm shower and felt cold as the water on your body began to evaporate; and after working up a sweat on a hot day, even a slight breeze makes you feel cool through evaporation.

## Vapor Pressure

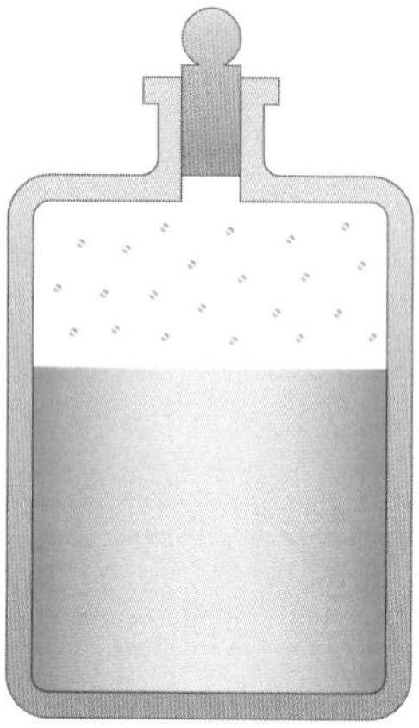

FIGURE 13–22 Vapor appears above a liquid in a closed container.

Air normally contains water vapor (water in the gas phase), and it comes mainly from evaporation. To look at this process in a little more detail, consider a closed container that is partially filled with water (or another liquid) and from which the air has been removed (Fig. 13–22). The fastest moving molecules quickly evaporate into the empty space above the liquid's surface. As they move about, some of these molecules strike the liquid surface and again become part of the liquid phase: this is called **condensation**. The number of molecules in the vapor increases until a point is reached when the number of molecules returning to the liquid equals the number leaving in the same time interval. Equilibrium then exists, and the space above the liquid surface is said to be *saturated*. The pressure of the vapor when it is saturated is called the **saturated vapor pressure** (or sometimes simply the vapor pressure).

The saturated vapor pressure does not depend on the volume of the container. If the volume above the liquid were reduced suddenly, the density of molecules in the vapor phase would be increased temporarily. More molecules would then be striking the liquid surface per second. There would be a net flow of molecules back to the liquid phase until equilibrium was again reached, and this would occur at the same value of the saturated vapor pressure, as long as the temperature had not changed.

The saturated vapor pressure of any substance depends on the temperature. At higher temperatures, more molecules have sufficient kinetic energy to break from the liquid surface into the vapor phase. Hence equilibrium will be reached at a higher pressure. The saturated vapor pressure of water at various temperatures is given in Table 13–3. Notice that even solids—for example, ice—have a measurable saturated vapor pressure.

**TABLE 13–3 Saturated Vapor Pressure of Water**

| Temperature (°C) | Saturated Vapor Pressure: torr (= mm-Hg) | Saturated Vapor Pressure: Pa (= $N/m^2$) |
|---|---|---|
| −50 | 0.030 | 4.0 |
| −10 | 1.95 | $2.60 \times 10^2$ |
| 0 | 4.58 | $6.11 \times 10^2$ |
| 5 | 6.54 | $8.72 \times 10^2$ |
| 10 | 9.21 | $1.23 \times 10^3$ |
| 15 | 12.8 | $1.71 \times 10^3$ |
| 20 | 17.5 | $2.33 \times 10^3$ |
| 25 | 23.8 | $3.17 \times 10^3$ |
| 30 | 31.8 | $4.24 \times 10^3$ |
| 40 | 55.3 | $7.37 \times 10^3$ |
| 50 | 92.5 | $1.23 \times 10^4$ |
| 60 | 149 | $1.99 \times 10^4$ |
| 70† | 234 | $3.12 \times 10^4$ |
| 80 | 355 | $4.73 \times 10^4$ |
| 90 | 526 | $7.01 \times 10^4$ |
| 100‡ | 760 | $1.01 \times 10^5$ |
| 120 | 1489 | $1.99 \times 10^5$ |
| 150 | 3570 | $4.76 \times 10^5$ |

† Boiling point on summit of Mt. Everest.
‡ Boiling point at sea level.

In everyday situations, evaporation from a liquid takes place into the air above it rather than into a vacuum. This does not materially alter the discussion above relating to Fig. 13–22. Equilibrium will still be reached when there are sufficient molecules in the gas phase that the number reentering the liquid equals the number leaving. The concentration of particular molecules (such as water) in the gas phase is not affected by the presence of air, although collisions with air molecules may lengthen the time needed to reach equilibrium. Thus equilibrium occurs at the same value of the saturated vapor pressure as if air weren't there.

If the container is large or is not closed, all the liquid may evaporate before saturation is reached. And if the container is not sealed—as, for example, a room in your house—it is not likely that the air will become saturated with water vapor (unless it is raining outside).

## Boiling

The saturated vapor pressure of a liquid increases with temperature. When the temperature is raised to the point where the saturated vapor pressure at that temperature equals the external pressure, **boiling** occurs (Fig. 13–23). As the boiling point is approached, tiny bubbles tend to form in the liquid, which indicate a change from the liquid to the gas phase. However, if the vapor pressure inside the bubbles is less than the external pressure, the bubbles immediately are crushed. As the temperature is increased, the saturated vapor pressure inside a bubble eventually becomes equal to or exceeds the external air pressure. The bubble will then not collapse but can rise to the surface. Boiling has then begun. *A liquid boils when its saturated vapor pressure equals the external pressure*. This occurs for water at a pressure of 1 atm (760 torr) at 100°C, as can be seen from Table 13–3.

*At boiling, saturated vapor pressure equals external pressure*

The boiling point of a liquid clearly depends on the external pressure. At high elevations, the boiling point of water is somewhat less than at sea level since the air pressure is less up there. For example, on the summit of Mt. Everest (8850 m) the air pressure is about one-third of what it is at sea level, and from Table 13–3 we can see that water will boil at about 70°C. Cooking food by boiling takes longer at high elevations, since the temperature is less. Pressure cookers, however, reduce cooking time, because they build up a pressure as high as 2 atm, allowing higher boiling temperatures to be attained.

**FIGURE 13–23** Boiling: bubbles of water vapor float upward from the bottom (where the temperature is highest).

## Partial Pressure and Humidity

When we refer to the weather as being dry or humid, we are referring to the water vapor content of the air. In a gas such as air, which is a mixture of several types of gases, the total pressure is the sum of the *partial pressures* of each gas present.[†] By **partial pressure**, we mean the pressure each gas would exert if it alone were present. The partial pressure of water in the air can be as low as zero and can vary up to a maximum equal to the saturated vapor pressure of water at the given temperature. Thus, at 20°C, the partial pressure of water cannot exceed 17.5 torr (see Table 13–3). The **relative humidity** is defined as the ratio of the partial pressure of water vapor to the saturated vapor pressure at a given temperature. It is usually expressed as a percentage:

*Relative humidity*

$$\text{Relative humidity} = \frac{\text{partial pressure of } H_2O}{\text{saturated vapor pressure of } H_2O} \times 100\%.$$

Thus, when the humidity is close to 100%, the air holds nearly all the water vapor it can.

**EXAMPLE 13–18** **Relative humidity.** On a particular hot day, the temperature is 30°C and the partial pressure of water vapor in the air is 21.0 torr. What is the relative humidity?

**APPROACH** From Table 13–3, we see that the saturated vapor pressure of water at 30°C is 31.8 torr.

**SOLUTION** The relative humidity is thus

$$\frac{21.0\ \text{torr}}{31.8\ \text{torr}} \times 100\% = 66\%.$$

PHYSICS APPLIED
*Humidity and comfort*

Humans are sensitive to humidity. A relative humidity of 40–50% is generally optimum for both health and comfort. High humidity, particularly on a hot day, reduces the evaporation of moisture from the skin, which is one of the body's vital mechanisms for regulating body temperature. Very low humidity, on the other hand, can dry the skin and mucous membranes.

[†]For example, 78% (by volume) of air molecules are nitrogen and 21% oxygen, with much smaller amounts of water vapor, argon, and other gases. At an air pressure of 1 atm, oxygen exerts a partial pressure of 0.21 atm and nitrogen 0.78 atm.

PHYSICS APPLIED

*Weather*

Air is saturated with water vapor when the partial pressure of water in the air is equal to the saturated vapor pressure at that temperature. If the partial pressure of water exceeds the saturated vapor pressure, the air is said to be **supersaturated**. This situation can occur when a temperature decrease occurs. For example, suppose the temperature is 30°C and the partial pressure of water is 21 torr, which represents a humidity of 66% as we saw in Example 13–18. Suppose now that the temperature falls to, say, 20°C, as might happen at nightfall. From Table 13–3 we see that the saturated vapor pressure of water at 20°C is 17.5 torr. Hence the relative humidity would be greater than 100%, and the supersaturated air cannot hold this much water. The excess water may condense and appear as dew, or as fog or rain (Fig. 13–24).

**FIGURE 13–24** Fog or mist settling over a low-lying village where the temperature has dropped below the dew point.

When air containing a given amount of water is cooled, a temperature is reached where the partial pressure of water equals the saturated vapor pressure. This is called the **dew point**. Measurement of the dew point is the most accurate means of determining the relative humidity. One method uses a polished metal surface in contact with air, which is gradually cooled down. The temperature at which moisture begins to appear on the surface is the dew point, and the partial pressure of water can then be obtained from saturated vapor pressure tables. If, for example, on a given day the temperature is 20°C and the dew point is 5°C, then the partial pressure of water (Table 13–3) in the 20°C air was 6.54 torr, whereas its saturated vapor pressure was 17.5 torr; hence the relative humidity was $6.54/17.5 = 37\%$.

## * 13–14 Diffusion

If you carefully place a few drops of food coloring in a container of water as in Fig. 13–25, you will find that the color spreads throughout the water. The process may take several hours (assuming you don't shake the glass), but eventually the color will become uniform. This mixing, known as **diffusion**, is further evidence for the random movement of molecules. Diffusion occurs in gases too. Common examples include perfume or smoke diffusing in air, including the odor of something cooking, although convection (moving air currents) often plays a greater role in spreading odors than does diffusion. Diffusion depends on *concentration*, by which we mean the number of molecules or moles per unit volume. In general, *the diffusing substance moves from a region where its concentration is high to one where its concentration is low.*

*Diffusion occurs from high to low concentration*

Diffusion can be readily understood on the basis of kinetic theory and the random motion of molecules. Consider a tube of cross-sectional area $A$ containing molecules in a higher concentration on the left than on the right,

**FIGURE 13–25** A few drops of food coloring spreads slowly throughout the water, eventually becoming uniform.

(a) (b) (c)

Fig. 13–26. We assume the molecules are in random motion. Yet there will be a net flow of molecules to the right. To see why this is true, let us consider the small section of tube of length $\Delta x$ as shown. Molecules from both regions 1 and 2 cross into this central section as a result of their random motion. The more molecules there are in a region, the more will strike a given area or cross a boundary. Since there is a greater concentration of molecules in region 1 than in region 2, more molecules cross into the central section from region 1 than from region 2. There is, then, a net flow of molecules from left to right, from high concentration toward low concentration. The net flow becomes zero only when the concentrations become equal.

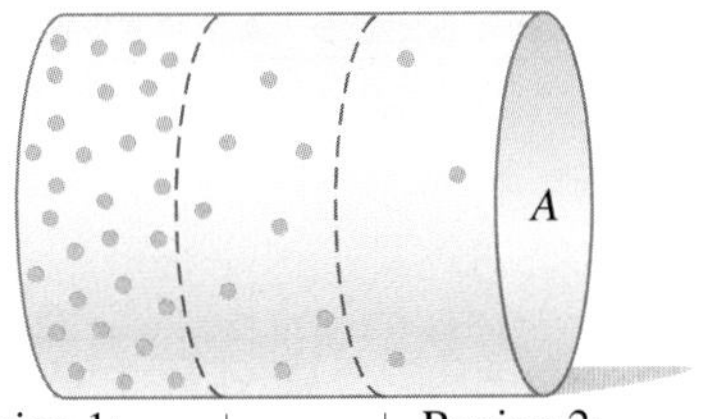


**FIGURE 13–26** Diffusion occurs from a region of high concentration to one of lower concentration. (Only one type of molecule is shown.)

You might expect that the greater the difference in concentration, the greater the flow rate. Indeed, the rate of diffusion, $J$ (number of molecules or moles or kg per second), is directly proportional to the change in concentration per unit distance, $(C_1 - C_2)/\Delta x$ (which is called the **concentration gradient**), and to the cross-sectional area $A$ (see Fig. 13–26):

*Diffusion equation*

$$J = DA\frac{C_1 - C_2}{\Delta x}. \qquad \textbf{(13–10)}$$

$D$ is a constant of proportionality called the **diffusion constant**. Equation 13–10 is known as the **diffusion equation**, or **Fick's law**. If the concentrations are given in $\text{mol/m}^3$, then $J$ is the number of moles passing a given point per second. If the concentrations are given in $\text{kg/m}^3$, then $J$ is the mass movement per second (kg/s). The length $\Delta x$ is given in meters. The values of $D$ for a variety of substances are given in Table 13–4.

**EXAMPLE 13–19 ESTIMATE Diffusion of ammonia in air.** To get an idea of the time required for diffusion, estimate how long it might take for ammonia $(NH_3)$ to be detected 10 cm from a bottle after it is opened, assuming only diffusion is occurring.

PHYSICS APPLIED

*Diffusion time*

**APPROACH** This will be an order-of-magnitude calculation. The rate of diffusion $J$ can be set equal to the number of molecules $N$ diffusing across area $A$ in a time $t$: $J = N/t$. Then the time $t = N/J$, where $J$ is given by Eq. 13–10. We will have to make some assumptions and rough approximations about concentrations to use Eq. 13–10.

**SOLUTION** Using Eq. 13–10, we get

$$t = \frac{N}{J} = \frac{N}{DA}\frac{\Delta x}{\Delta C}.$$

The average concentration (midway between bottle and nose) can be approximated by $\overline{C} \approx N/V$, where $V$ is the volume over which the molecules move and is roughly of the order of $V \approx A\,\Delta x$, where $\Delta x$ is $10\text{ cm} = 0.10\text{ m}$. We substitute $N = \overline{C}V = \overline{C}A\,\Delta x$ into the above equation:

$$t \approx \frac{(\overline{C}A\,\Delta x)\Delta x}{DA\,\Delta C} = \frac{\overline{C}}{\Delta C}\frac{(\Delta x)^2}{D}.$$

The concentration of ammonia is high near the bottle and low near the detecting nose, so $\overline{C} \approx \Delta C/2$, or $(\overline{C}/\Delta C) \approx \frac{1}{2}$. Since $NH_3$ molecules have a size somewhere between $H_2$ and $O_2$, from Table 13–4 we can estimate $D \approx 4 \times 10^{-5}\,\text{m}^2/\text{s}$. Then

$$t \approx \frac{1}{2}\frac{(0.10\text{ m})^2}{(4 \times 10^{-5}\,\text{m}^2/\text{s})} \approx 100\text{ s},$$

or about a minute or two.

**NOTE** This result seems rather long from experience, suggesting that air currents (convection) are more important than diffusion for transmitting odors.

**TABLE 13–4 Diffusion Constants, $D$ (20°C, 1 atm)**

| Diffusing Molecules | Medium | $D$ ($\text{m}^2/\text{s}$) |
|---|---|---|
| $H_2$ | Air | $6.3 \times 10^{-5}$ |
| $O_2$ | Air | $1.8 \times 10^{-5}$ |
| $O_2$ | Water | $100 \times 10^{-11}$ |
| Blood hemoglobin | Water | $6.9 \times 10^{-11}$ |
| Glycine (an amino acid) | Water | $95 \times 10^{-11}$ |
| DNA (mass $6 \times 10^6$ u) | Water | $0.13 \times 10^{-11}$ |

**PHYSICS APPLIED**

*Diffusion in living organisms*

Diffusion is extremely important for living organisms. For example, molecules produced in certain chemical reactions within cells diffuse to other areas where they take part in other reactions.

Gas diffusion is important too. Plants require carbon dioxide for photosynthesis. The $CO_2$ diffuses into leaves from the outside air through tiny openings (stomata). As $CO_2$ is utilized by the cells, its concentration drops below that in the air outside, and more diffuses inward. Water vapor and oxygen produced by the cells diffuse outward into the air.

Animals also exchange oxygen and $CO_2$ with the environment. Oxygen is required for energy-producing reactions and must diffuse into cells. $CO_2$ is produced as an end product of many metabolic reactions and must diffuse out of cells. But diffusion is slow over longer distances, so only the smallest organisms in the animal world could survive without having developed complex respiratory and circulatory systems. In humans, oxygen is taken into the lungs, where it diffuses short distances across lung tissue and into the blood. Then the blood circulates it to cells throughout the body. The blood also carries $CO_2$ produced by the cells back to the lungs, where it diffuses outward.

## Summary

The atomic theory of matter postulates that all matter is made up of tiny entities called **atoms**, which are typically $10^{-10}$ m in diameter.

**Atomic** and **molecular masses** are specified on a scale where ordinary carbon ($^{12}C$) is arbitrarily given the value 12.0000 u (atomic mass units).

The distinction between solids, liquids, and gases can be attributed to the strength of the attractive forces between the atoms or molecules and to their average speed.

**Temperature** is a measure of how hot or cold something is. **Thermometers** are used to measure temperature on the **Celsius** (°C), **Fahrenheit** (°F), and **Kelvin** (K) scales. Two standard points on each scale are the freezing point of water (0°C, 32°F, 273.15 K) and the boiling point of water (100°C, 212°F, 373.15 K). A one-kelvin change in temperature equals a change of one Celsius degree or $\frac{9}{5}$ Fahrenheit degrees. Kelvins are related to °C by

$$T(\text{K}) = T(°\text{C}) + 273.15.$$

The change in length, $\Delta L$, of a solid, when its temperature changes by an amount $\Delta T$, is directly proportional to the temperature change and to its original length $L_0$. That is,

$$\Delta L = \alpha L_0 \, \Delta T, \qquad \textbf{(13–1a)}$$

where $\alpha$ is the *coefficient of linear expansion*.

The change in volume of most solids, liquids, and gases is proportional to the temperature change and to the original volume $V_0$:

$$\Delta V = \beta V_0 \, \Delta T. \qquad \textbf{(13–2)}$$

The *coefficient of volume expansion*, $\beta$, is approximately equal to $3\alpha$ for uniform solids.

Water is unusual because, unlike most materials whose volume increases with temperature, its volume actually decreases as the temperature increases in the range from 0°C to 4°C.

The **ideal gas law**, or **equation of state for an ideal gas**, relates the pressure $P$, volume $V$, and temperature $T$ (in kelvins) of $n$ moles of gas by

$$PV = nRT, \qquad \textbf{(13–3)}$$

where $R = 8.314 \text{ J/mol}\cdot\text{K}$ for all gases. Real gases obey the ideal gas law quite accurately if they are not at too high a pressure or near their liquefaction point.

One **mole** of a substance is defined as the number of grams which is numerically equal to the atomic or molecular mass.

**Avogadro's number**, $N_A = 6.02 \times 10^{23}$, is the number of atoms or molecules in 1 mol of any pure substance.

The ideal gas law can be written in terms of the number of molecules $N$ in the gas as

$$PV = NkT, \qquad \textbf{(13–4)}$$

where $k = R/N_A = 1.38 \times 10^{-23}$ J/K is Boltzmann's constant.

According to the **kinetic theory** of gases, which is based on the idea that a gas is made up of molecules that are moving rapidly and randomly, the average kinetic energy of molecules is proportional to the Kelvin temperature $T$:

$$\overline{\text{KE}} = \tfrac{1}{2} m\overline{v^2} = \tfrac{3}{2} kT, \qquad \textbf{(13–8)}$$

where $k$ is Boltzmann's constant. At any moment, there exists a wide distribution of molecular speeds within a gas.

[*The behavior of real gases at high pressure, and/or near their liquefaction point, deviates from the ideal gas law, due to molecular size and the attractive forces between molecules. Below the **critical temperature**, a gas can change to a liquid if sufficient pressure is applied; but if the temperature is higher than the critical temperature, no amount of pressure will cause a liquid surface to form. The **triple point** of a substance is that unique temperature and pressure at which all three phases—solid, liquid, and gas—can coexist in equilibrium.]

[***Evaporation** of a liquid is the result of the fastest moving molecules escaping from the surface. **Saturated vapor pressure** refers to the pressure of the vapor above a liquid when the two phases are in equilibrium. The vapor pressure of a substance at its boiling point is equal to atmospheric pressure. **Relative humidity** of air at a given place is the ratio of the partial pressure of water vapor in the air to the saturated vapor pressure at that temperature; it is usually expressed as a percentage.]

[***Diffusion** is the process whereby molecules of a substance move (on average) from one area to another because of a difference in that substance's concentration.]

# Questions

1. Which has more atoms: 1 kg of iron or 1 kg of aluminum? See the Periodic Table or Appendix B.

2. Name several properties of materials that could be exploited to make a thermometer.

3. Which is larger, 1 C° or 1 F°?

*4. If system A is in thermal equilibrium with system B, but B is not in thermal equilibrium with system C, what can you say about the temperatures of A, B, and C?

5. A flat bimetallic strip consists of aluminum riveted to a strip of iron. When heated, the strip will bend. Which metal will be on the outside of the curve? [*Hint*: See Table 13–1.] Why?

6. In the relation $\Delta L = \alpha L_0 \Delta T$, should $L_0$ be the initial length, the final length, or does it matter? Explain.

7. The units for the coefficient of linear expansion $\alpha$ are $(\text{C}^\circ)^{-1}$, and there is no mention of a length unit such as meters. Would the expansion coefficient change if we used feet or millimeters instead of meters? Explain.

8. Figure 13–27 shows a diagram of a simple *thermostat* used to control a furnace (or other heating or cooling system). The bimetallic strip consists of two strips of different metals bonded together. The electric switch is a glass vessel containing liquid mercury that conducts electricity when it can flow to touch both contact wires. Explain how this device controls the furnace and how it can be set at different temperatures.

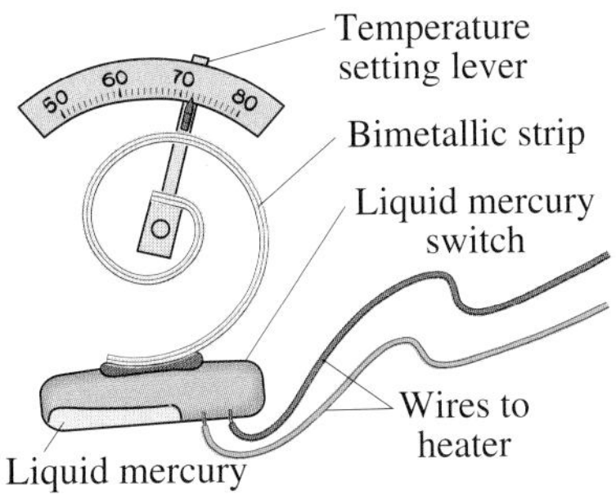


**FIGURE 13–27** A thermostat (Question 8).

9. Long steam pipes that are fixed at the ends often have a section in the shape of a U. Why?

10. A flat, uniform cylinder of lead floats in mercury at 0°C. Will the lead float higher or lower when the temperature is raised? Explain.

11. When a cold mercury-in-glass thermometer is first placed in a hot tub of water, the mercury initially descends a bit and then rises. Explain.

12. A glass container may break if one part of it is heated or cooled more rapidly than adjacent parts. Explain.

13. The principal virtue of Pyrex glass is that its coefficient of linear expansion is much smaller than that for ordinary glass (Table 13–1). Explain why this gives rise to the increased heat resistance of Pyrex.

14. Will a grandfather clock, accurate at 20°C, run fast or slow on a hot day (30°C)? Explain. The clock uses a pendulum supported on a long, thin brass rod.

15. Freezing a can of soda will cause its bottom and top to bulge so badly the can will not stand up. What has happened?

16. When a gas is rapidly compressed (say, by pushing down a piston), its temperature increases. When a gas expands against a piston, it cools. Explain these changes in temperature using the kinetic theory, in particular noting what happens to the momentum of molecules when they strike the moving piston.

17. Will the buoyant force on an aluminum sphere submerged in water increase or decrease if the temperature is increased from 20°C to 40°C? Explain.

18. Explain in words how Charles's law follows from kinetic theory and the relation between average kinetic energy and the absolute temperature.

19. Explain in words how Gay-Lussac's law follows from kinetic theory.

20. As you go higher in the Earth's atmosphere, the ratio of $N_2$ molecules to $O_2$ molecules increases. Why?

* 21. Escape velocity for the Earth refers to the minimum speed an object must have to leave the Earth and never return. The escape velocity for the Moon is about one-fifth what it is for the Earth due to the Moon's smaller mass. Explain why the Moon has practically no atmosphere.

* 22. Alcohol evaporates more quickly than water at room temperature. What can you infer about the molecular properties of one relative to the other?

* 23. Explain why a hot humid day is far more uncomfortable than a hot dry day at the same temperature.

* 24. Is it possible to boil water at room temperature (20°C) without heating it? Explain.

* 25. Consider two days when the air temperature is the same but the humidity is different. Which is more dense, the dry air or the humid air at the same $T$? Explain.

* 26. Explain why it is dangerous to open the radiator cap of an overheated automobile engine.

* 27. Why does exhaled air appear as a little white cloud in the winter (Fig. 13–28)?

**FIGURE 13–28** Question 27.

## Problems

### 13–1 Atomic Theory

1. (I) How many atoms are there in a 3.4-gram copper penny?
2. (I) How does the number of atoms in a 26.5-gram gold ring compare to the number in a silver ring of the same mass?

### 13–2 Temperature and Thermometers

3. (I) (*a*) "Room temperature" is often taken to be 68°F. What is this on the Celsius scale? (*b*) The temperature of the filament in a lightbulb is about 1800°C. What is this on the Fahrenheit scale?
4. (I) Among the highest and lowest temperatures recorded are 136°F in the Libyan desert and −129°F in Antarctica. What are these temperatures on the Celsius scale?
5. (I) (*a*) 15° below zero on the Celsius scale is what Fahrenheit temperature? (*b*) 15° below zero on the Fahrenheit scale is what Celsius temperature?
6. (II) In an alcohol-in-glass thermometer, the alcohol column has length 11.82 cm at 0.0°C and length 22.85 cm at 100.0°C. What is the temperature if the column has length (*a*) 16.70 cm, and (*b*) 20.50 cm?

### 13–4 Thermal Expansion

7. (I) A concrete highway is built of slabs 12 m long (20°C). How wide should the expansion cracks between the slabs be (at 20°C) to prevent buckling if the range of temperature is −30°C to +50°C?
8. (I) Super Invar™, an alloy of iron and nickel, is a strong material with a very low coefficient of linear expansion $\left[0.2 \times 10^{-6}\,(\mathrm{C}°)^{-1}\right]$. A 2.0-m-long tabletop made of this alloy is used for sensitive laser measurements where extremely high tolerances are required. How much will this table expand along its length if the temperature increases 5.0 C°? Compare to tabletops made of steel.
9. (I) The Eiffel Tower (Fig. 13–29) is built of wrought iron approximately 300 m tall. Estimate how much its height changes between July (average temperature of 25°C) and January (average temperature of 2°C). Ignore the angles of the iron beams, and treat the tower as a vertical beam.

**FIGURE 13–29**
Problem 9.
The Eiffel Tower in Paris.

10. (II) To make a secure fit, rivets that are larger than the rivet hole are often used and the rivet is cooled (usually in dry ice) before it is placed in the hole. A steel rivet 1.871 cm in diameter is to be placed in a hole 1.869 cm in diameter at 20°C. To what temperature must the rivet be cooled if it is to fit in the hole?
11. (II) The density of water at 4°C is $1.00 \times 10^3\,\mathrm{kg/m^3}$. What is water's density at 94°C?
12. (II) A quartz sphere is 8.75 cm in diameter. What will be its change in volume if it is heated from 30°C to 200°C?
13. (II) An ordinary glass is filled to the brim with 350.0 mL of water at 100.0°C. If the temperature decreased to 20.0°C, how much water could be added to the glass?
14. (II) It is observed that 55.50 mL of water at 20°C completely fills a container to the brim. When the container and the water are heated to 60°C, 0.35 g of water is lost. (*a*) What is the coefficient of volume expansion of the container? (*b*) What is the most likely material of the container? The density of water at 60°C is 0.98324 g/mL.
15. (II) (*a*) A brass plug is to be placed in a ring made of iron. At 20°C, the diameter of the plug is 8.753 cm and that of the inside of the ring is 8.743 cm. They must both be brought to what common temperature in order to fit? (*b*) What if the plug were iron and the ring brass?
16. (II) If a fluid is contained in a long, narrow vessel so it can expand in essentially one direction only, show that the effective coefficient of linear expansion $\alpha$ is approximately equal to the coefficient of volume expansion $\beta$.
17. (II) (*a*) Show that the change in the density $\rho$ of a substance, when the temperature changes by $\Delta T$, is given by $\Delta\rho = -\beta\rho\,\Delta T$. (*b*) What is the fractional change in density of a lead sphere whose temperature decreases from 25°C to −40°C?
18. (II) A uniform rectangular plate of length $l$ and width $w$ has coefficient of linear expansion $\alpha$. Show that, if we neglect very small quantities, the change in area of the plate due to a temperature change $\Delta T$ is $\Delta A = 2\alpha l w\,\Delta T$. See Fig. 13–30.

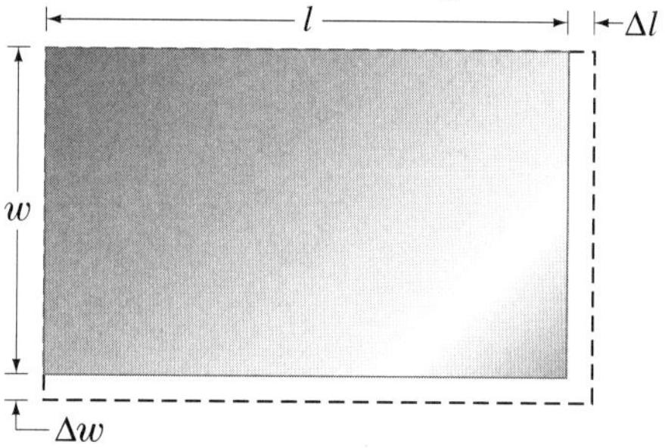


**FIGURE 13–30**
Problem 18.
A rectangular plate is heated.

19. (III) Show that for an isotropic solid, $\beta = 3\alpha$, if the amount of expansion is small. $\beta$ and $\alpha$ are the coefficients of volume and linear expansion, respectively. [*Hint*: Consider a cubical solid, and neglect very small quantities. See also Problem 18 and Fig. 13–30.]
20. (III) The pendulum in a grandfather clock is made of brass and keeps perfect time at 17°C. How much time is gained or lost in a year if the clock is kept at 25°C? (Assume the frequency dependence on length for a simple pendulum applies.)
21. (III) (*a*) The tube of a mercury thermometer has an inside diameter of 0.140 mm. The bulb has a volume of $0.255\,\mathrm{cm^3}$. How far will the thread of mercury move when the temperature changes from 11.5°C to 33.0°C? Take into account expansion of the Pyrex glass. (*b*) Determine a formula for the change in length of the mercury column in terms of relevant variables. Ignore tube volume compared to bulb volume.
22. (III) A 23.4-kg solid aluminum cylindrical wheel of radius 0.41 m is rotating about its axle on frictionless bearings with angular velocity $\omega = 32.8\,\mathrm{rad/s}$. If its temperature is now raised from 20.0°C to 75.0°C, what is the fractional change in $\omega$?

## * 13–5 Thermal Stresses

* 23. (II) An aluminum bar has the desired length when at 15°C. How much stress is required to keep it at this length if the temperature increases to 35°C?

* 24. (II) (*a*) A horizontal steel I-beam of cross-sectional area $0.041\ m^2$ is rigidly connected to two vertical steel girders. If the beam was installed when the temperature was 30°C, what stress is developed in the beam when the temperature drops to −30°C? (*b*) Is the ultimate strength of the steel exceeded? (*c*) What stress is developed if the beam is concrete and has a cross-sectional area of $0.13\ m^2$? Will it fracture?

* 25. (III) A barrel of diameter 134.122 cm at 20°C is to be enclosed by an iron band. The circular band has an inside diameter of 134.110 cm at 20°C. It is 7.4 cm wide and 0.65 cm thick. (*a*) To what temperature must the band be heated so that it will fit over the barrel? (*b*) What will be the tension in the band when it cools to 20°C?

## 13–6 Gas Laws; Absolute Temperature

26. (I) What are the following temperatures on the Kelvin scale: (*a*) 86°C, (*b*) 78°F, (*c*) −100°C, (*d*) 5500°C, (*e*) −459°F?

27. (I) Absolute zero is what temperature on the Fahrenheit scale?

28. (II) Typical temperatures in the interior of the Earth and Sun are about 4000°C and $15 \times 10^6$ °C, respectively. (*a*) What are these temperatures in kelvins? (*b*) What percent error is made in each case if a person forgets to change °C to K?

## 13–7 and 13–8 Ideal Gas Law

29. (I) If $3.00\ m^3$ of a gas initially at STP is placed under a pressure of 3.20 atm, the temperature of the gas rises to 38.0°C. What is the volume?

30. (I) In an internal combustion engine, air at atmospheric pressure and a temperature of about 20°C is compressed in the cylinder by a piston to $\frac{1}{9}$ of its original volume (compression ratio = 9.0). Estimate the temperature of the compressed air, assuming the pressure reaches 40 atm.

31. (II) Calculate the density of oxygen at STP using the ideal gas law.

32. (II) A storage tank contains 21.6 kg of nitrogen ($N_2$) at an absolute pressure of 3.65 atm. What will the pressure be if the nitrogen is replaced by an equal mass of $CO_2$?

33. (II) A storage tank at STP contains 18.5 kg of nitrogen ($N_2$). (*a*) What is the volume of the tank? (*b*) What is the pressure if an additional 15.0 kg of nitrogen is added without changing the temperature?

34. (II) If 18.75 mol of helium gas is at 10.0°C and a gauge pressure of 0.350 atm, (*a*) calculate the volume of the helium gas under these conditions. (*b*) Calculate the temperature if the gas is compressed to precisely half the volume at a gauge pressure of 1.00 atm.

35. (II) What is the pressure inside a 35.0-L container holding 105.0 kg of argon gas at 385 K?

36. (II) A tank contains 26.0 kg of $O_2$ gas at a gauge pressure of 8.70 atm. If the oxygen is replaced by helium, how many kilograms of the latter will be needed to produce a gauge pressure of 7.00 atm?

37. (II) A hot-air balloon achieves its buoyant lift by heating the air inside the balloon, which makes it less dense than the air outside. Suppose the volume of a balloon is $1800\ m^3$ and the required lift is 2700 N (rough estimate of the weight of the equipment and passenger). Calculate the temperature of the air inside the balloon which will produce the required lift. Assume that the outside air temperature is 0°C and that air is an ideal gas under these conditions. What factors limit the maximum altitude attainable by this method for a given load? (Neglect variables like wind.)

38. (II) A tire is filled with air at 15°C to a gauge pressure of 220 kPa. If the tire reaches a temperature of 38°C, what fraction of the original air must be removed if the original pressure of 220 kPa is to be maintained?

39. (II) If 61.5 L of oxygen at 18.0°C and an absolute pressure of 2.45 atm are compressed to 48.8 L and at the same time the temperature is raised to 50.0°C, what will the new pressure be?

40. (III) A helium-filled balloon escapes a child's hand at sea level and 20.0°C. When it reaches an altitude of 3000 m, where the temperature is 5.0°C and the pressure is only 0.70 atm, how will its volume compare to that at sea level?

## 13–9 Ideal Gas Law in Terms of Molecules; Avogadro's Number

41. (I) Calculate the number of molecules/$m^3$ in an ideal gas at STP.

42. (I) How many moles of water are there in 1.000 L? How many molecules?

43. (II) Estimate the number of (*a*) moles, and (*b*) molecules of water in all the Earth's oceans. Assume water covers 75% of the Earth to an average depth of 3 km.

44. (II) A cubic box of volume $5.1 \times 10^{-2}\ m^3$ is filled with air at atmospheric pressure at 20°C. The box is closed and heated to 180°C. What is the net force on each side of the box?

45. (III) Estimate how many molecules of air are in each 2.0-L breath you inhale that were also in the last breath Galileo took. [*Hint*: Assume the atmosphere is about 10 km high and of constant density.]

## 13–10 Molecular Interpretation of Temperature

46. (I) (*a*) What is the average translational kinetic energy of an oxygen molecule at STP? (*b*) What is the total translational kinetic energy of 2.0 mol of $O_2$ molecules at 20°C?

47. (I) Calculate the rms speed of helium atoms near the surface of the Sun at a temperature of about 6000 K.

48. (I) By what factor will the rms speed of gas molecules increase if the temperature is increased from 0°C to 100°C?

49. (I) A gas is at 20°C. To what temperature must it be raised to double the rms speed of its molecules?

50. (I) Twelve molecules have the following speeds, given in units of km/s: 6, 2, 4, 6, 0, 4, 1, 8, 5, 3, 7, and 8. Calculate the rms speed.

51. (II) The rms speed of molecules in a gas at 20.0°C is to be increased by 1.0%. To what temperature must it be raised?

52. (II) If the pressure of a gas is doubled while its volume is held constant, by what factor does $v_{rms}$ change?

53. (II) Show that the rms speed of molecules in a gas is given by $v_{\text{rms}} = \sqrt{3P/\rho}$, where $P$ is the pressure in the gas, and $\rho$ is the gas density.

54. (II) Show that for a mixture of two gases at the same temperature, the ratio of their rms speeds is equal to the inverse ratio of the square roots of their molecular masses.

55. (II) What is the rms speed of nitrogen molecules contained in an 8.5-m$^3$ volume at 2.1 atm if the total amount of nitrogen is 1300 mol?

56. (II) Calculate (*a*) the rms speed of an oxygen molecule at 0°C and (*b*) determine how many times per second it would move back and forth across a 7.0-m-long room on the average, assuming it made very few collisions with other molecules.

57. (II) What is the average distance between nitrogen molecules at STP?

58. (II) (*a*) Estimate the rms speed of an amino acid whose molecular mass is 89 u in a living cell at 37°C. (*b*) What would be the rms speed of a protein of molecular mass 50,000 u at 37°C?

59. (II) Show that the pressure $P$ of a gas can be written $P = \frac{1}{3}\rho v^2$, where $\rho$ is the density of the gas and $v$ is the rms speed of the molecules.

60. (III) The two isotopes of uranium, $^{235}U$ and $^{238}U$ (the superscripts refer to their atomic mass), can be separated by a gas-diffusion process by combining them with fluorine to make the gaseous compound $UF_6$. Calculate the ratio of the rms speeds of these molecules for the two isotopes, at constant $T$.

### * 13–12 Real Gases; Phase Changes

* 61. (I) (*a*) At atmospheric pressure, in what phases can $CO_2$ exist? (*b*) For what range of pressures and temperatures can $CO_2$ be a liquid? Refer to Fig. 13–21.

* 62. (I) Water is in which phase when the pressure is 0.01 atm and the temperature is (*a*) 90°C, (*b*) −20°C?

### * 13–13 Vapor Pressure; Humidity

* 63. (I) What is the dew point (approximately) if the humidity is 50% on a day when the temperature is 25°C?

* 64. (I) What is the air pressure at a place where water boils at 90°C?

* 65. (I) If the air pressure at a particular place in the mountains is 0.72 atm, estimate the temperature at which water boils.

* 66. (I) What is the temperature on a day when the partial pressure of water is 530 Pa and the relative humidity is 40%?

* 67. (I) What is the partial pressure of water on a day when the temperature is 25°C and the relative humidity is 35%?

* 68. (I) What is the approximate pressure inside a pressure cooker if the water is boiling at a temperature of 120°C? Assume no air escaped during the heating process, which started at 20°C.

* 69. (II) If the humidity in a room of volume 680 m$^3$ at 25°C is 80%, what mass of water can still evaporate from an open pan?

* 70. (III) Air that is at its dew point of 5°C is drawn into a building where it is heated to 25°C. What will be the relative humidity at this temperature? Assume constant pressure of 1.0 atm. Take into account the expansion of the air.

### * 13–14 Diffusion

* 71. (II) Estimate the time needed for a glycine molecule (see Table 13–4) to diffuse a distance of 15 $\mu$m in water at 20°C if its concentration varies over that distance from 1.00 mol/m$^3$ to 0.40 mol/m$^3$. Compare this "speed" to its rms (thermal) speed. The molecular mass of glycine is about 75 u.

* 72. (II) Oxygen diffuses from the surface of insects to the interior through tiny tubes called tracheae. An average trachea is about 2 mm long and has cross-sectional area of $2 \times 10^{-9}$ m$^2$. Assuming the concentration of oxygen inside is half what it is outside in the atmosphere, (*a*) show that the concentration of oxygen in the air (assume 21% is oxygen) at 20°C is about 8.7 mol/m$^3$, then (*b*) calculate the diffusion rate $J$, and (*c*) estimate the average time for a molecule to diffuse in. Assume the diffusion constant is $1 \times 10^{-5}$ m$^2$/s.

## General Problems

73. A precise steel tape measure has been calibrated at 20°C. At 34°C, (*a*) will it read high or low, and (*b*) what will be the percentage error?

74. A Pyrex measuring cup was calibrated at normal room temperature. How much error will be made in a recipe calling for 300 mL of cool water, if the water and the cup are hot, at 80°C, instead of at 20°C? Neglect the glass expansion.

75. The gauge pressure in a helium gas cylinder is initially 28 atm. After many balloons have been blown up, the gauge pressure has decreased to 5 atm. What fraction of the original gas remains in the cylinder?

76. Estimate the number of air molecules in a room of length 6.5 m, width 3.1 m, and height 2.5 m. Assume the temperature is 22°C. How many moles does that correspond to?

77. In outer space the density of matter is about one atom per cm$^3$, mainly hydrogen atoms, and the temperature is about 2.7 K. Calculate the rms speed of these hydrogen atoms, and the pressure (in atmospheres).

78. The lowest pressure attainable using the best available vacuum techniques is about $10^{-12}$ N/m$^2$. At such a pressure, how many molecules are there per cm$^3$ at 0°C?

79. If a scuba diver fills his lungs to full capacity of 5.5 L when 10 m below the surface, to what volume would his lungs expand if he quickly rose to the surface? Is this advisable?

80. A space vehicle returning from the Moon enters Earth's atmosphere at a speed of about 40,000 km/h. Molecules (assume nitrogen) striking the nose of the vehicle with this speed correspond to what temperature? (Because of this high temperature, the nose of a space vehicle must be made of special materials; indeed, part of it does vaporize, and this is seen as a bright blaze upon reentry.)

81. The temperature of an ideal gas is increased from 110°C to 360°C while the volume and the number of moles stay constant. By what factor does the pressure change? By what factor does $v_{\text{rms}}$ change?

82. A house has a volume of $770\text{ m}^3$. (*a*) What is the total mass of air inside the house at 20°C? (*b*) If the temperature drops to −10°C, what mass of air enters or leaves the house?

83. From the known value of atmospheric pressure at the surface of the Earth, estimate the total number of air molecules in the Earth's atmosphere.

84. What is the rms speed of nitrogen molecules contained in a $7.6\text{-m}^3$ volume at 4.2 atm if the total amount of nitrogen is 1800 mol?

85. A standard cylinder of oxygen used in a hospital has gauge pressure = 2000 psi (13,800 kPa) and volume = 16 L $(0.016\text{ m}^3)$ at $T = 295$ K. How long will the cylinder last if the flow rate, measured at atmospheric pressure, is constant at 2.4 L/min?

86. An iron cube floats in a bowl of liquid mercury at 0°C. (*a*) If the temperature is raised to 25°C, will the cube float higher or lower in the mercury? (*b*) By what percent will the fraction of volume submerged change?

87. The density of gasoline at 0°C is $0.68 \times 10^3\text{ kg/m}^3$. What is the density on a hot day, when the temperature is 38°C? What is the percentage change?

88. If a steel band were to fit snugly around the Earth's equator at 25°C, but then was heated to 45°C, how high above the Earth would the band be (assume equal everywhere)?

89. A brass lid screws tightly onto a glass jar at 20°C. To help open the jar, it can be placed into a bath of hot water. After this treatment, the temperatures of the lid and the jar are both 60°C. The inside diameter of the lid is 8.0 cm at 20°C. Find the size of the gap (difference in radius) that develops by this procedure.

90. The first length standard, adopted in the $18^{\text{th}}$ century, was a platinum bar with two very fine marks separated by what was defined to be exactly 1 m. If this standard bar was to be accurate to within $\pm 1.0\,\mu$m, how carefully would the trustees have needed to control the temperature? The coefficient of linear expansion for platinum is $9 \times 10^{-6}\,\text{C°}^{-1}$.

91. A scuba tank, when fully charged, has a pressure of 195 atm at 20°C. The volume of the tank is 11.3 L. (*a*) What would the volume of the air be at 1.00 atm and at the same temperature? (*b*) Before entering the water, a person consumes 2.0 L of air in each breath, and breathes 12 times a minute. At this rate, how long would the tank last? (*c*) At a depth of 20.0 m of sea water and temperature of 10°C, how long would the same tank last assuming the breathing rate does not change?

92. The escape speed from the Earth is $1.12 \times 10^4$ m/s, so a gas molecule travelling away from Earth near the outer boundary of the Earth's atmosphere would, at this speed, be able to escape from the Earth's gravitational field. At what temperature is the average speed of (*a*) oxygen molecules, and (*b*) helium atoms equal to $1.12 \times 10^4$ m/s? (*c*) Can you see why our atmosphere contains oxygen but not helium?

93. A 1.0-kg trash-can lid is suspended against gravity by tennis balls thrown vertically upward at it. How many tennis balls per second must rebound from the lid elastically, assuming they have a mass of 0.060 kg and are thrown at 12 m/s?

94. A scuba diver releases a 3.00-cm-diameter (spherical) bubble of air from a depth of 14.0 m in a lake. Assume the temperature is constant at 298 K, and the air behaves as a perfect gas. How large is the bubble when it reaches the surface?

* 95. Calculate the total water vapor pressure in the air on the following two days: (*a*) a hot summer day, with the temperature 30°C and the relative humidity at 40%; (*b*) a cold winter day, with the temperature 5°C and the relative humidity at 80%.

* 96. A sauna has $7.0\text{ m}^3$ of air volume, and the temperature is 90°C. The air is perfectly dry. How much water (in kg) should be evaporated if we want to increase the relative humidity from 0% to 10%? (See Table 13–3.)

* 97. Estimate the percent difference in the density of iron at STP, and when it is a solid deep in the Earth where the temperature is 2000°C and under 5000 atm of pressure. Assume the bulk modulus $(90 \times 10^9\text{ N/m}^2)$ and the coefficient of volume expansion do not vary with temperature and are the same as at STP.

* 98. (*a*) Use the ideal gas law to show that, for an ideal gas at constant pressure, the coefficient of volume expansion is equal to $\beta = 1/T$, where $T$ is the temperature in kelvins. Compare to Table 13–1 for gases at $T = 293$ K. (*b*) Show that the bulk modulus (Section 9–5) for an ideal gas held at constant temperature is $B = P$, where $P$ is the pressure.

* 99. In humid climates, people constantly *dehumidify* their cellars to prevent rot and mildew. If the cellar in a house (kept at 20°C) has $95\text{ m}^2$ of floor space and a ceiling height of 2.8 m, what is the mass of water that must be removed from it to drop the humidity from 95% to a more reasonable 30%?

## Answers to Exercises

**A:** −40°C = −40°F.
**B:** 24.0 L.
**C:** Less.
**D:** $3.5 \times 10^{-9}$ m/s.

When it is cold, warm clothes act as insulators to reduce heat loss from the body to the outside by conduction and convection. Heat radiation from a campfire can warm you and your clothes. The fire can also transfer energy directly by heat conduction to what you are cooking. Heat, like work, represents a transfer of energy. Heat is defined as a transfer of energy due to a difference of temperature. Another useful concept is the internal energy $U$, which is the sum total of all the energies of the molecules of the system.

CHAPTER 14

# Heat

When a pot of cold water is placed on a hot burner of a stove, the temperature of the water increases. We say that heat "flows" from the hot burner to the cold water. When two objects at different temperatures are put in contact, heat spontaneously flows from the hotter one to the colder one. The spontaneous flow of heat is in the direction tending to equalize the temperature. If the two objects are kept in contact long enough for their temperatures to become equal, the objects are said to be in thermal equilibrium, and there is no further heat flow between them. For example, when a fever thermometer is first placed in your mouth, heat flows from your mouth to the thermometer. When the thermometer reaches the same temperature as the inside of your mouth, the thermometer and your mouth are then in equilibrium, and no more heat flows.

Heat and temperature are often confused. They are very different concepts, and in this Chapter we will make a clear distinction between them. We begin by defining and using the concept of heat. We also discuss how heat is used in calorimetry, how it is involved in changes of state of matter, and the processes of heat transfer—conduction, convection, and radiation.

## 14–1 Heat as Energy Transfer

We use the term "heat" in everyday life as if we knew what we meant. But the term is often used inconsistently, so it is important for us to define heat clearly, and to clarify the phenomena and concepts related to heat.

We commonly speak of the flow of heat—heat flows from a stove burner to a pot of soup, from the Sun to the Earth, from a person's mouth into a fever thermometer. Heat flows spontaneously from an object at higher temperature to one at lower temperature. Indeed, an eighteenth-century model of heat pictured heat flow as movement of a fluid substance called *caloric*. However, the caloric fluid was never able to be detected. In the nineteenth century, it was found that the various phenomena associated with heat could be described consistently using a new model that views heat as being akin to work, as we will discuss in a moment. First we note that a common unit for heat, still in use today, is named after caloric. It is called the **calorie** (cal) and is defined as *the amount of heat necessary to raise the temperature of 1 gram of water by 1 Celsius degree.* [To be precise, the particular temperature range from 14.5°C to 15.5°C is specified because the heat required is very slightly different at different temperatures. The difference is less than 1% over the range 0 to 100°C, and we will ignore it for most purposes.] More often used than the calorie is the **kilocalorie** (kcal), which is 1000 calories. Thus *1 kcal is the heat needed to raise 1 kg of water by 1 C°.* Often a kilocalorie is called a **Calorie** (with a capital C), and it is by this unit that the energy value of food is specified. In the British system of units, heat is measured in British thermal units (Btu). One Btu is defined as the heat needed to raise the temperature of 1 lb of water by 1 F°. It can be shown (Problem 4) that 1 Btu = 0.252 kcal = 1055 J.

CAUTION
*Heat is not a fluid*

*The calorie (unit)*

*Kilocalorie (= dietary Calorie)*

*BTU*

The idea that heat is related to energy was pursued by a number of scientists in the 1800s, particularly by an English brewer, James Prescott Joule (1818–1889). Joule and others performed a number of experiments that were crucial for establishing our present-day view that heat, like work, represents a transfer of energy. One of Joule's experiments is shown (simplified) in Fig. 14–1. The falling weight causes the paddle wheel to turn. The friction between the water and the paddle wheel causes the temperature of the water to rise slightly (barely measurable, in fact, by Joule). The same temperature rise could also be obtained by heating the water on a hot stove. In this and many other experiments (some involving electrical energy), Joule determined that a given amount of work done was always equivalent to a particular amount of heat input. Quantitatively, 4.186 joules (J) of work was found to be equivalent to 1 calorie (cal) of heat. This is known as the **mechanical equivalent of heat**:

$$4.186\text{ J} = 1\text{ cal};$$
$$4.186\text{ kJ} = 1\text{ kcal}.$$

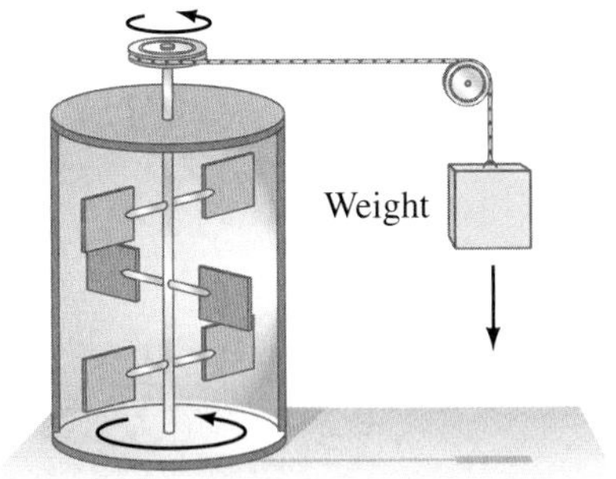


**FIGURE 14–1** Joule's experiment on the mechanical equivalent of heat.

*Mechanical equivalent of heat*

As a result of these and other experiments, scientists came to interpret heat not as a substance, and not exactly as a form of energy. Rather, heat refers to a *transfer of energy*: when heat flows from a hot object to a cooler one, it is energy that is being transferred from the hot to the cold object. Thus, **heat** is *energy transferred from one object to another because of a difference in temperature.* In SI units, the unit for heat, as for any form of energy, is the joule. Nonetheless, calories and kcal are still sometimes used. Today the calorie is *defined* in terms of the joule (via the mechanical equivalent of heat, above), rather than in terms of the properties of water, as given previously. The latter is still handy to remember: 1 cal raises 1 g of water by 1 C°, or 1 kcal raises 1 kg of water by 1 C°.

*Heat defined: energy transferred because of a $\Delta T$*

Whenever we use the word "heat," we mean an energy transfer from one place or object to another at a lower temperature.

CAUTION
*Heat refers to a transfer of energy—not to energy itself*

Joule's result was crucial because it extended the work-energy principle to include processes involving heat. It also led to the establishment of the law of conservation of energy, which we shall discuss more fully in the next Chapter.

PHYSICS APPLIED
*Working off Calories*

**EXAMPLE 14–1 ESTIMATE Working off the extra Calories.** Suppose you throw caution to the wind and eat too much ice cream and cake on the order of 500 Calories. To compensate, you want to do an equivalent amount of work climbing stairs or a mountain. How much total height must you climb? For this calculation, take your mass to be about 60 kg.

**APPROACH** The work $W$ you need to do in climbing stairs equals the change in gravitational potential energy: $W = \Delta PE = mgh$, where $h$ is the vertical height climbed.

**SOLUTION** 500 Calories is 500 kcal, which in joules is

$$(500\text{ kcal})(4.186 \times 10^3\text{ J/kcal}) = 2.1 \times 10^6\text{ J}.$$

The work done to climb a vertical height $h$ is $W = mgh$. We solve for $h$:

$$h = \frac{W}{mg} = \frac{2.1 \times 10^6\text{ J}}{(60\text{ kg})(9.80\text{ m/s}^2)} = 3600\text{ m}.$$

This is a huge elevation change (over 11,000 ft).

**NOTE** The human body does not transform energy with 100% efficiency—it is more like 20% efficient. As we'll discuss in the next Chapter, some energy is always "wasted," so you would actually have to climb only about $(0.2)(3600\text{ m}) \approx 700\text{ m}$, which is still a lot (about 2300 ft of elevation gain).

## 14–2 Internal Energy

*Internal energy*

The sum total of all the energy of all the molecules in an object is called its **internal energy**. (Sometimes **thermal energy** is used to mean the same thing.) We introduce the concept of internal energy now since it will help clarify ideas about heat.

### Distinguishing Temperature, Heat, and Internal Energy

CAUTION
*Distinguish heat from internal energy and from temperature*

Using the kinetic theory, we can make a clear distinction between temperature, heat, and internal energy. Temperature (in kelvins) is a measure of the *average* kinetic energy of individual molecules. Internal energy refers to the *total* energy of all the molecules in the object. (Thus two equal-mass hot ingots of iron may have the same temperature, but two of them have twice as much thermal energy as one does.) Heat, finally, refers to a *transfer* of energy from one object to another because of a difference in temperature.

CAUTION
*Direction of heat flow depends on temperature (not on amount of internal energy)*

Notice that the direction of heat flow between two objects depends on their temperatures, not on how much internal energy each has. Thus, if 50 g of water at 30°C is placed in contact (or mixed) with 200 g of water at 25°C, heat flows *from* the water at 30°C *to* the water at 25°C even though the internal energy of the 25°C water is much greater because there is so much more of it.

### Internal Energy of an Ideal Gas

Let us calculate the internal energy of $n$ moles of an ideal monatomic (one atom per molecule) gas. The internal energy, $U$, is the sum of the translational kinetic energies of all the atoms. This sum is just equal to the average kinetic energy per molecule times the total number of molecules, $N$:

$$U = N(\tfrac{1}{2}m\overline{v^2}).$$

Using Eq. 13–8, $\overline{\text{KE}} = \frac{1}{2}m\overline{v^2} = \frac{3}{2}kT$, we can write this as

$$U = \tfrac{3}{2}NkT$$

or (recall Section 13–9)

$$U = \tfrac{3}{2}nRT, \qquad \text{[ideal monatomic gas]} \quad \textbf{(14–1)}$$

*Internal energy of ideal monatomic gas*

where $n$ is the number of moles. Thus, the internal energy of an ideal gas depends only on temperature and the number of moles of gas.

If the gas molecules contain more than one atom, then the rotational and vibrational energy of the molecules (Fig. 14–2) must also be taken into account. The internal energy will be greater at a given temperature than for a monatomic gas, but it will still be a function only of temperature for an ideal gas.

The internal energy of real gases also depends mainly on temperature, but where real gases deviate from ideal gas behavior, their internal energy depends also somewhat on pressure and volume (due to atomic potential energy).

The internal energy of liquids and solids is quite complicated, for it includes electrical potential energy associated with the forces (or "chemical" bonds) between atoms and molecules.

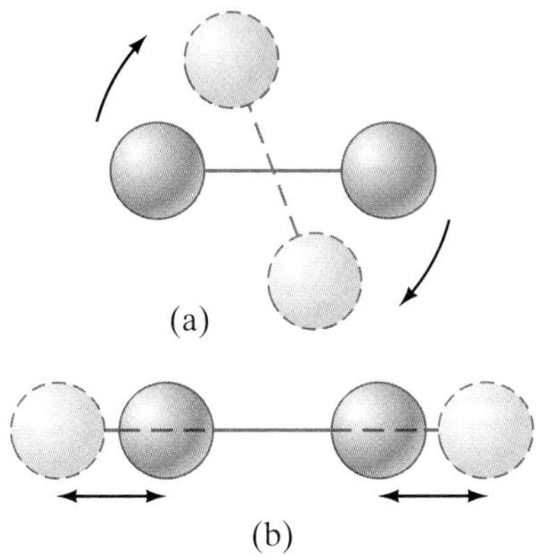


**FIGURE 14–2** Besides translational kinetic energy, molecules can have (a) rotational kinetic energy, and (b) vibrational energy (both kinetic and potential).

## 14–3 Specific Heat

If heat flows into an object, the object's temperature rises (assuming no phase change). But how much does the temperature rise? That depends. As early as the eighteenth century, experimenters had recognized that the amount of heat $Q$ required to change the temperature of a given material is proportional to the mass $m$ of the material present and to the temperature change $\Delta T$. This remarkable simplicity in nature can be expressed in the equation

*Relation between heat transfer and temperature change*

$$Q = mc\,\Delta T, \qquad \textbf{(14–2)}$$

where $c$ is a quantity characteristic of the material called its **specific heat**. Because $c = Q/m\,\Delta T$, specific heat is specified in units of $\text{J/kg}\cdot\text{C}^\circ$ (the proper SI unit) or $\text{kcal/kg}\cdot\text{C}^\circ$. For water at 15°C and a constant pressure of 1 atm, $c = 4.19 \times 10^3\ \text{J/kg}\cdot\text{C}^\circ$ or $1.00\ \text{kcal/kg}\cdot\text{C}^\circ$, since, by definition of the cal and the joule, it takes 1 kcal of heat to raise the temperature of 1 kg of water by 1 C°. Table 14–1 gives the values of specific heat for other substances at 20°C. The values of $c$ depend to some extent on temperature (as well as slightly on pressure), but for temperature changes that are not too great, $c$ can often be considered constant.

*Specific heat*

**TABLE 14–1 Specific Heats**
**(at 1 atm constant pressure and 20°C unless otherwise stated)**

| **Substance** | **Specific Heat, c** kcal/kg · C° (= cal/g · C°) | J/kg · C° |
|---|---|---|
| Aluminum | 0.22 | 900 |
| Alcohol (ethyl) | 0.58 | 2400 |
| Copper | 0.093 | 390 |
| Glass | 0.20 | 840 |
| Iron or steel | 0.11 | 450 |
| Lead | 0.031 | 130 |
| Marble | 0.21 | 860 |
| Mercury | 0.033 | 140 |
| Silver | 0.056 | 230 |
| Wood | 0.4 | 1700 |
| Water | | |
| Ice (−5°C) | 0.50 | 2100 |
| Liquid (15°C) | 1.00 | 4186 |
| Steam (110°C) | 0.48 | 2010 |
| Human body (average) | 0.83 | 3470 |
| Protein | 0.4 | 1700 |

**EXAMPLE 14–2 How heat transferred depends on specific heat.** (*a*) How much heat input is needed to raise the temperature of an empty 20-kg vat made of iron from 10°C to 90°C? (*b*) What if the vat is filled with 20 kg of water?

**APPROACH** We apply Eq. 14–2 to the different materials involved.

**SOLUTION** (*a*) Our system is the iron vat alone. From Table 14–1, the specific heat of iron is $450\ \text{J/kg}\cdot\text{C}^\circ$. The change in temperature is $(90°\text{C} - 10°\text{C}) = 80\ \text{C}^\circ$. Thus,

$$Q = mc\,\Delta T = (20\ \text{kg})(450\ \text{J/kg}\cdot\text{C}^\circ)(80\ \text{C}^\circ) = 7.2 \times 10^5\ \text{J} = 720\ \text{kJ}.$$

(*b*) Our system is the vat plus the water. The water alone would require

$$Q = mc\,\Delta T = (20\ \text{kg})(4186\ \text{J/kg}\cdot\text{C}^\circ)(80\ \text{C}^\circ) = 6.7 \times 10^6\ \text{J} = 6700\ \text{kJ},$$

or almost 10 times what an equal mass of iron requires. The total, for the vat plus the water, is $720\ \text{kJ} + 6700\ \text{kJ} = 7400\ \text{kJ}$.

**NOTE** In (*b*), the iron vat and the water underwent the same temperature change, $\Delta T = 80\ \text{C}^\circ$, but their specific heats are different.

If the iron vat in part (*a*) of Example 14–2 had been *cooled* from 90°C to 10°C, 720 kJ of heat would have flowed *out* of the iron. In other words, Eq. 14–2 is valid for heat flow either in or out, with a corresponding increase or decrease in temperature. We saw in part (*b*) that water requires almost 10 times as much heat as an equal mass of iron to make the same temperature change. Water has one of the highest specific heats of all substances, which makes it an ideal substance for hot-water space-heating systems and other uses that require a minimal drop in temperature for a given amount of heat transfer. It is the water content, too, that causes the apples rather than the crust in hot apple pie to burn our tongues, through heat transfer.

*Practical effects of water's high specific heat*

**CONCEPTUAL EXAMPLE 14–3** **A very hot frying pan.** You accidentally let an empty iron frying pan get very hot on the stove (200°C or even more). What happens when you dunk it into a few inches of cool water in the bottom of the sink? Will the final temperature be midway between the initial temperatures of the water and pan? Will the water start boiling? Assume the mass of water is roughly the same as the mass of the frying pan.

**RESPONSE** Experience may tell you that the water warms up—perhaps by as much as 10 or 20 degrees. The water doesn't come close to boiling. The water's temperature increase is a lot less than the frying pan's temperature decrease. Why? Because the mass of water is roughly equal to that of the pan, and iron has a specific heat nearly 10 times smaller than that of water (Table 14–1). As heat leaves the frying pan and enters the water, the iron pans' temperature change will be about 10 times greater than that of the water. If, instead, you let a few drops of water fall onto the hot pan, that very small mass of water will sizzle and boil away (the pan's mass may be hundreds of times larger than that of the water).

## * Specific Heats for Gases

Specific heats for gases are more complicated than for solids and liquids, which change in volume only slightly with a change in temperature (Section 13–4). Gases change strongly in volume with a change in temperature at constant pressure, as we saw in Chapter 13 with the gas laws; or, if kept at constant volume, the pressure in a gas changes strongly with temperature. The specific heat of a gas depends very much on how the process of changing its temperature is carried out. Most commonly, we deal with the specific heats of gases kept (a) at constant pressure $(c_p)$ or (b) at constant volume $(c_V)$. Some values are given in Table 14–2, where we see that $c_p$ is always greater than $c_V$. For liquids and solids, this distinction is usually negligible. More details are given in Appendix D on molecular specific heats and the equipartition of energy.

**TABLE 14–2**
**Specific Heats of Gases**
**(kcal/kg · C°)**

| Gas | $c_p$ (constant pressure) | $c_V$ (constant volume) |
|---|---|---|
| Steam (100°C) | 0.482 | 0.350 |
| Oxygen | 0.218 | 0.155 |
| Helium | 1.15 | 0.75 |
| Carbon dioxide | 0.199 | 0.153 |
| Nitrogen | 0.248 | 0.177 |

## 14–4 Calorimetry—Solving Problems

*Systems*

In discussing heat and thermodynamics, we shall often refer to particular systems. As already mentioned in earlier Chapters, a **system** is any object or set of objects that we wish to consider. Everything else in the universe we will refer to as its "environment" or the "surroundings." There are several categories of systems. A **closed system** is one for which no mass enters or leaves (but energy may be exchanged with the environment). In an **open system**, mass may enter or leave (as may energy). Many (idealized) systems we study in physics are closed systems. But many systems, including plants and animals, are open systems since they exchange materials (food, oxygen, waste products) with the environment. A closed system is said to be **isolated** if no energy in any form passes across its boundaries; otherwise it is not isolated.

When different parts of an isolated system are at different temperatures, heat will flow (energy is transferred) from the part at higher temperature to the part at lower temperature—that is, within the system. If the system is completely isolated, no energy is transferred into or out of it. So the *conservation of energy* again plays an important role for us: the heat lost by one part of the system is equal to the heat gained by the other part:

$$\text{heat lost} = \text{heat gained}$$

*Energy conservation*

or

$$\text{energy out of one part} = \text{energy into another part.}$$

These simple relations are very useful. Let us take an Example.

**EXAMPLE 14–4 The cup cools the tea.** If 200 cm$^3$ of tea at 95°C is poured into a 150-g glass cup initially at 25°C (Fig. 14–3), what will be the common final temperature $T$ of the tea and cup when equilibrium is reached, assuming no heat flows to the surroundings?

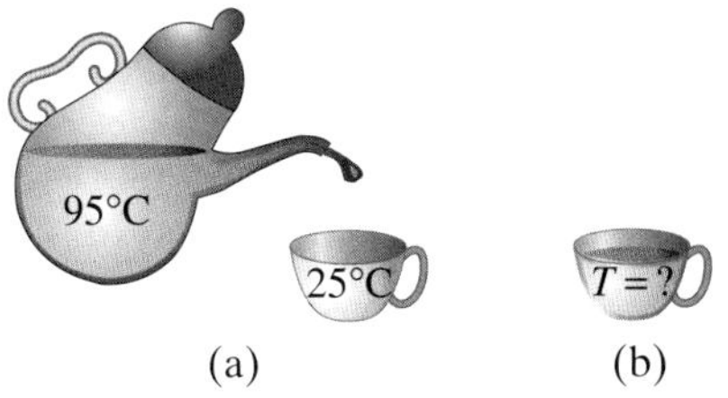


**FIGURE 14–3** Example 14–4.

**APPROACH** We apply conservation of energy to our system of tea plus cup, which we are assuming is isolated: all of the heat that leaves the tea flows into the cup. We can use the specific heat equation, Eq. 14–2, to determine how the heat flow is related to the temperature changes.

**SOLUTION** Since tea is mainly water, its specific heat is 4186 J/kg·C° (Table 14–1), and its mass $m$ is its density times its volume $(V = 200\,\text{cm}^3 = 200 \times 10^{-6}\,\text{m}^3)$: $m = \rho V = (1.0 \times 10^3\,\text{kg/m}^3)(200 \times 10^{-6}\,\text{m}^3) = 0.20\,\text{kg}$. We use Eq. 14–2, apply conservation of energy, and let $T$ be the as yet unknown final temperature:

$$\text{heat lost by tea} = \text{heat gained by cup}$$
$$m_{\text{tea}}\, c_{\text{tea}}(95^\circ\text{C} - T) = m_{\text{cup}}\, c_{\text{cup}}(T - 25^\circ\text{C}).$$

Putting in numbers and using Table 14–1 ($c_{\text{cup}} = 840\,\text{J/kg}\cdot\text{C}^\circ$ for glass), we solve for $T$, and find

$$(0.20\,\text{kg})(4186\,\text{J/kg}\cdot\text{C}^\circ)(95^\circ\text{C} - T) = (0.15\,\text{kg})(840\,\text{J/kg}\cdot\text{C}^\circ)(T - 25^\circ\text{C})$$
$$79{,}500\,\text{J} - (837\,\text{J/C}^\circ)T = (126\,\text{J/C}^\circ)T - 3150\,\text{J}$$
$$T = 86^\circ\text{C}.$$

The tea drops in temperature by 9 C° by coming into equilibrium with the cup.

**NOTE** The cup increases in temperature by $86^\circ\text{C} - 25^\circ\text{C} = 61\,\text{C}^\circ$. Its much greater change in temperature (compared with that of the tea water) is due to its much smaller specific heat compared to that of water.

**NOTE** In this calculation, the $\Delta T$ (of Eq. 14–2, $Q = mc\,\Delta T$) is a positive quantity on both sides of our conservation of energy equation. On the left is "heat lost" and $\Delta T$ is the initial minus the final temperature $(95^\circ\text{C} - T)$, whereas on the right is "heat gained" and $\Delta T$ is the final minus the initial temperature. But consider this alternate approach.

**CAUTION**

*When using heat lost = heat gained, $\Delta T$ is positive on both sides*

***Alternate Solution*** We can set up this Example (and others) by a different approach. We can write that the total heat transferred into or out of the isolated system is zero:

$$\Sigma Q = 0.$$

**PROBLEM SOLVING**

*Alternate approach: $\Sigma Q = 0$*

Then each term is written as $Q = mc(T_{\text{f}} - T_{\text{i}})$, and $\Delta T = T_{\text{f}} - T_{\text{i}}$ is always the final minus the initial temperature, and each $\Delta T$ can be positive or negative. In the present Example:

$$\Sigma Q = m_{\text{cup}}\, c_{\text{cup}}(T - 25^\circ\text{C}) + m_{\text{tea}}\, c_{\text{tea}}(T - 95^\circ\text{C}) = 0.$$

The second term is negative because $T$ will be less than 95°C. Solving the algebra gives the same result.

The exchange of energy, as exemplified in Example 14–4, is the basis for a technique known as **calorimetry**, which is the quantitative measurement of heat

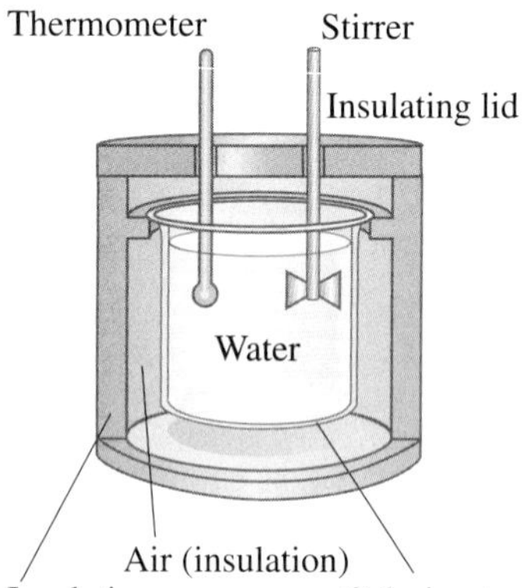


**FIGURE 14–4** Simple water calorimeter.

exchange. To make such measurements, a **calorimeter** is used; a simple water calorimeter is shown in Fig. 14–4. It is very important that the calorimeter be well insulated so that almost no heat is exchanged with the surroundings. One important use of the calorimeter is in the determination of specific heats of substances. In the technique known as the "method of mixtures," a sample of a substance is heated to a high temperature, which is accurately measured, and then quickly placed in the cool water of the calorimeter. The heat lost by the sample will be gained by the water and the calorimeter cup. By measuring the final temperature of the mixture, the specific heat can be calculated, as illustrated in the following Example.

**EXAMPLE 14–5** **Unknown specific heat determined by calorimetry.** An engineer wishes to determine the specific heat of a new metal alloy. A 0.150-kg sample of the alloy is heated to 540°C. It is then quickly placed in 400 g of water at 10.0°C, which is contained in a 200-g aluminum calorimeter cup. (We do not need to know the mass of the insulating jacket since we assume the air space between it and the cup insulates it well, so that its temperature does not change significantly.) The final temperature of the system is 30.5°C. Calculate the specific heat of the alloy.

**APPROACH** We apply conservation of energy to our system, which we take to be the alloy sample, the water, and the calorimeter cup. We assume this system is isolated, so the energy lost by the hot alloy equals the energy gained by the water and calorimeter cup.

**SOLUTION** The heat lost equals the heat gained:

$$\begin{pmatrix}\text{heat lost}\\ \text{by alloy}\end{pmatrix} = \begin{pmatrix}\text{heat gained}\\ \text{by water}\end{pmatrix} + \begin{pmatrix}\text{heat gained by}\\ \text{calorimeter cup}\end{pmatrix}$$

$$m_{\text{a}}c_{\text{a}}\,\Delta T_{\text{a}} = m_{\text{w}}c_{\text{w}}\,\Delta T_{\text{w}} + m_{\text{cal}}c_{\text{cal}}\,\Delta T_{\text{cal}}$$

where the subscripts a, w, and cal refer to the alloy, water, and calorimeter, respectively, and each $\Delta T > 0$. When we put in values and use Table 14–1, this equation becomes

$$\begin{aligned}(0.150\,\text{kg})(c_{\text{a}})(540^\circ\text{C} - 30.5^\circ\text{C}) &= (0.40\,\text{kg})(4186\,\text{J/kg}\cdot\text{C}^\circ)(30.5^\circ\text{C} - 10.0^\circ\text{C})\\ &\quad + (0.20\,\text{kg})(900\,\text{J/kg}\cdot\text{C}^\circ)(30.5^\circ\text{C} - 10.0^\circ\text{C})\\ 76.4\,c_{\text{a}} &= (34{,}300 + 3700)\,\text{J/kg}\cdot\text{C}^\circ\\ c_{\text{a}} &= 500\,\text{J/kg}\cdot\text{C}^\circ.\end{aligned}$$

In making this calculation, we have ignored any heat transferred to the thermometer and the stirrer (which is used to quicken the heat transfer process and thus reduce heat loss to the outside). It can be taken into account by adding additional terms to the right side of the above equation and will result in a slight correction to the value of $c_{\text{a}}$ (see Problem 14).

**PROBLEM SOLVING**
*Be sure to consider all possible sources of energy transfer*

In all Examples and Problems of this sort, be sure to include *all* objects that gain or lose heat (within reason). On the "heat loss" side here, it is only the hot metal alloy. On the "heat gain" side, it is both the water and the aluminum calorimeter cup. For simplicity, we have ignored very small masses, such as the thermometer and the stirrer, which will affect the energy balance only very slightly.

**PHYSICS APPLIED**
*Measuring Calorie content*

A **bomb calorimeter** is used to measure the thermal energy released when a substance burns. Important applications are the burning of foods to determine their Calorie content, and the burning of seeds and other substances to determine their "energy content," or heat of combustion. A carefully weighed sample of the substance, together with an excess amount of oxygen at high pressure, is placed in a sealed container (the "bomb"). The bomb is placed in the water of the calorimeter and a fine wire passing into the bomb is then heated briefly, which causes the mixture to ignite. The energy released in the burning process is gained by the water and the bomb.

**EXAMPLE 14–6** **Measuring the energy content of a cookie.** Determine the energy content of 100 g of Fahlgren's fudge cookies from the following measurements. A 10-g sample of a cookie is allowed to dry before putting it in a bomb calorimeter. The aluminum bomb has a mass of 0.615 kg and is placed in 2.00 kg of water contained in an aluminum calorimeter cup of mass 0.524 kg. The initial temperature of the system is 15.0°C, and its temperature after ignition is 36.0°C.

**APPROACH** We apply energy conservation to our system, which we assume is isolated and consists of the cookie sample, the bomb, the calorimeter cup, and the water.

**SOLUTION** In this case, the heat $Q$ released in the burning of the cookie is absorbed by the system of bomb, calorimeter, and water:

$$\begin{aligned} Q &= \left(m_{\mathrm{w}} c_{\mathrm{w}} + m_{\mathrm{cal}} c_{\mathrm{cal}} + m_{\mathrm{bomb}} c_{\mathrm{bomb}}\right) \Delta T \\ &= \left[(2.00\,\mathrm{kg})(1.0\,\mathrm{kcal/kg \cdot C^\circ}) + (0.524\,\mathrm{kg})(0.22\,\mathrm{kcal/kg \cdot C^\circ})\right. \\ &\quad \left. + (0.615\,\mathrm{kg})(0.22\,\mathrm{kcal/kg \cdot C^\circ})\right][36.0^\circ\mathrm{C} - 15.0^\circ\mathrm{C}] = 47\,\mathrm{kcal}. \end{aligned}$$

In joules, $Q = (47\,\mathrm{kcal})(4186\,\mathrm{J/kcal}) = 197\,\mathrm{kJ}$. Since 47 kcal is released in the burning of 10 g of cookie, a 100-g portion would contain 470 food Calories, or 1970 kJ.

## 14–5 Latent Heat

When a material changes phase from solid to liquid, or from liquid to gas (see also Section 13–12), a certain amount of energy is involved in this **change of phase**. For example, let us trace what happens when a 1.0-kg block of ice at −40°C is heated at a slow steady rate until all the ice has changed to water, then the (liquid) water is heated to 100°C and changed to steam above 100°C, all at 1 atm pressure. As shown in the graph of Fig. 14–5, as the ice is heated, its temperature rises at a rate of about 2 C°/kcal of heat added (since for ice, $c \approx 0.50\,\mathrm{kcal/kg \cdot C^\circ}$). However, when 0°C is reached, the temperature stops increasing even though heat is still being added. The ice gradually changes to water in the liquid state, with no change in temperature. After about 40 kcal has been added at 0°C, half the ice remains and half has changed to water. After about 80 kcal, or 330 kJ, has been added, all the ice has changed to water, still at 0°C. Continued addition of heat causes the water's temperature to again increase, now at a rate of 1 C°/kcal. When 100°C is reached, the temperature again remains constant as the heat added changes the liquid water to vapor (steam). About 540 kcal (2260 kJ) is required to change the 1.0 kg of water completely to steam, after which the graph rises again, indicating that the temperature of the steam rises as heat is added.

**FIGURE 14–5** Temperature as a function of the heat added to bring 1.0 kg of ice at −40°C to steam above 100°C.

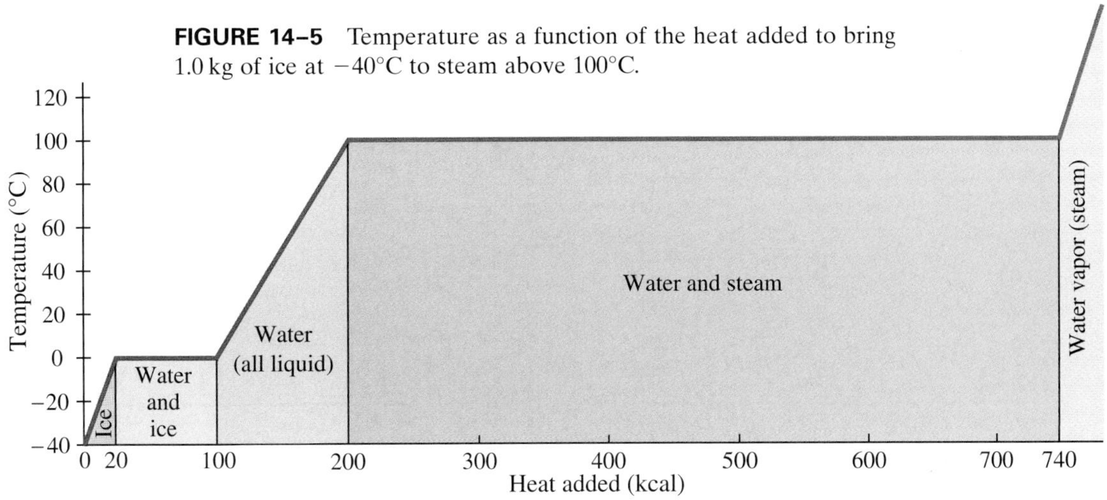

FIGURE 14–5 (repeated) Temperature as a function of the heat added to bring 1.0 kg of ice at −40°C to steam above 100°C.

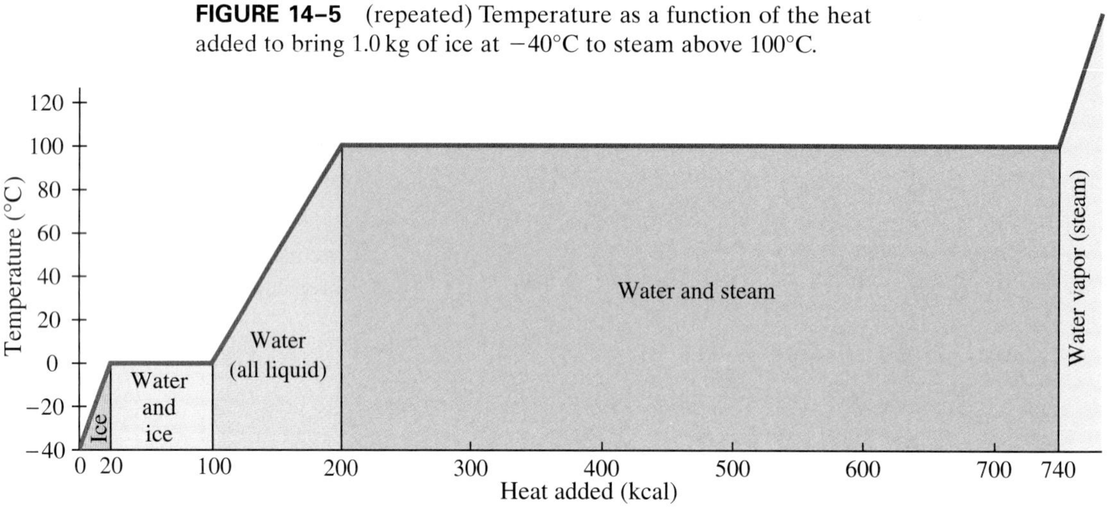


*Heat of fusion*

*Heat of vaporization*

*Latent heat*

The heat required to change 1.0 kg of a substance from the solid to the liquid state is called the **heat of fusion**; it is denoted by $L_F$. The heat of fusion of water is 79.7 kcal/kg or, in proper SI units, 333 kJ/kg $(= 3.33 \times 10^5\ \text{J/kg})$. The heat required to change a substance from the liquid to the vapor phase is called the **heat of vaporization**, $L_V$. For water it is 539 kcal/kg or 2260 kJ/kg. Other substances follow graphs similar to Fig. 14–5, although the melting-point and boiling-point temperatures are different, as are the specific heats and heats of fusion and vaporization. Values for the heats of fusion and vaporization, which are also called the **latent heats**, are given in Table 14–3 for a number of substances.

The heats of vaporization and fusion also refer to the amount of heat *released* by a substance when it changes from a gas to a liquid, or from a liquid to a solid. Thus, steam releases 2260 kJ/kg when it changes to water, and water releases 333 kJ/kg when it becomes ice.

The heat involved in a change of phase depends not only on the latent heat but also on the total mass of the substance. That is,

*Change of phase*

$$Q = mL, \tag{14–3}$$

where $L$ is the latent heat of the particular process and substance, $m$ is the mass of the substance, and $Q$ is the heat added or released during the phase change. For example, when 5.00 kg of water freezes at 0°C, $(5.00\ \text{kg})(3.33 \times 10^5\ \text{J/kg}) = 1.67 \times 10^6\ \text{J}$ of energy is released.

**TABLE 14–3 Latent Heats (at 1 atm)**

| Substance | Melting Point (°C) | Heat of Fusion | | Boiling Point (°C) | Heat of Vaporization | |
|---|---|---|---|---|---|---|
| | | kcal/kg† | kJ/kg | | kcal/kg† | kJ/kg |
| Oxygen | −218.8 | 3.3 | 14 | −183 | 51 | 210 |
| Nitrogen | −210.0 | 6.1 | 26 | −195.8 | 48 | 200 |
| Ethyl alcohol | −114 | 25 | 104 | 78 | 204 | 850 |
| Ammonia | −77.8 | 8.0 | 33 | −33.4 | 33 | 137 |
| Water | 0 | 79.7 | 333 | 100 | 539 | 2260 |
| Lead | 327 | 5.9 | 25 | 1750 | 208 | 870 |
| Silver | 961 | 21 | 88 | 2193 | 558 | 2300 |
| Iron | 1808 | 69.1 | 289 | 3023 | 1520 | 6340 |
| Tungsten | 3410 | 44 | 184 | 5900 | 1150 | 4800 |

† Numerical values in kcal/kg are the same in cal/g.

Calorimetry sometimes involves a change of state, as the following Examples show. Indeed, latent heats are often measured using calorimetry.

**EXAMPLE 14–7** **Making ice.** How much energy does a freezer have to remove from 1.5 kg of water at 20°C to make ice at −12°C?

**APPROACH** We need to calculate the total energy removed by adding the heat outflow (1) to reduce the water from 20°C to 0°C, (2) to change it to ice at 0°C, and (3) to lower the ice from 0°C to −12°C.

**SOLUTION** The heat $Q$ that needs to be removed from the 1.5 kg of water is

$$\begin{aligned} Q &= mc_{\mathrm{w}}(20^\circ\mathrm{C} - 0^\circ\mathrm{C}) + mL_{\mathrm{F}} + mc_{\mathrm{ice}}[0^\circ - (-12^\circ\mathrm{C})] \\ &= (1.5\,\mathrm{kg})(4186\,\mathrm{J/kg\cdot C^\circ})(20\,\mathrm{C^\circ}) + (1.5\,\mathrm{kg})(3.33 \times 10^5\,\mathrm{J/kg}) \\ &\quad + (1.5\,\mathrm{kg})(2100\,\mathrm{J/kg\cdot C^\circ})(12\,\mathrm{C^\circ}) \\ &= 6.6 \times 10^5\,\mathrm{J} = 660\,\mathrm{kJ}. \end{aligned}$$

**EXAMPLE 14–8** **ESTIMATE** **Will all the ice melt?** At a reception, a 0.50-kg chunk of ice at −10°C is placed in 3.0 kg of "iced" tea at 20°C. At what temperature and in what phase will the final mixture be? The tea can be considered as water. Ignore any heat flow to the surroundings, including the container.

**APPROACH** Before we can write down an equation applying conservation of energy, we must first check to see if the final state will be all ice, a mixture of ice and water at 0°C, or all water. To bring the 3.0 kg of water at 20°C down to 0°C would require an energy release of

**PROBLEM SOLVING**
*First determine (or estimate) the final state*

$$m_{\mathrm{w}}c_{\mathrm{w}}(20^\circ\mathrm{C} - 0^\circ\mathrm{C}) = (3.0\,\mathrm{kg})(4186\,\mathrm{J/kg\cdot C^\circ})(20\,\mathrm{C^\circ}) = 250\,\mathrm{kJ}.$$

On the other hand, to raise the ice from −10°C to 0°C would require

$$m_{\mathrm{ice}}c_{\mathrm{ice}}[0^\circ\mathrm{C} - (-10^\circ\mathrm{C})] = (0.50\,\mathrm{kg})(2100\,\mathrm{J/kg\cdot C^\circ})(10\,\mathrm{C^\circ}) = 10.5\,\mathrm{kJ},$$

and to change the ice to water at 0°C would require

$$m_{\mathrm{ice}}L_{\mathrm{F}} = (0.50\,\mathrm{kg})(333\,\mathrm{kJ/kg}) = 167\,\mathrm{kJ},$$

for a total of $10.5\,\mathrm{kJ} + 167\,\mathrm{kJ} = 177\,\mathrm{kJ}$. This is not enough energy to bring the 3.0 kg of water at 20°C down to 0°C, so we know that the mixture must end up all water, somewhere between 0°C and 20°C.

**SOLUTION** To determine the final temperature $T$, we apply conservation of energy and write

*Then determine the final temperature*

$$\text{heat gain} = \text{heat loss}$$

$$\begin{pmatrix}\text{heat to raise}\\ \text{0.50 kg of ice}\\ \text{from } -10^\circ\text{C}\\ \text{to } 0^\circ\text{C}\end{pmatrix} + \begin{pmatrix}\text{heat to change}\\ \text{0.50 kg}\\ \text{of ice}\\ \text{to water}\end{pmatrix} + \begin{pmatrix}\text{heat to raise}\\ \text{0.50 kg of water}\\ \text{from } 0^\circ\text{C}\\ \text{to } T\end{pmatrix} = \begin{pmatrix}\text{heat lost by}\\ \text{3.0 kg of}\\ \text{water cooling}\\ \text{from } 20^\circ\text{C to } T\end{pmatrix}.$$

Using some of the results from above, we obtain

$$\begin{aligned} 10.5\,\mathrm{kJ} + 167\,\mathrm{kJ} + (0.50\,\mathrm{kg})(4186\,\mathrm{J/kg\cdot C^\circ})(T - 0^\circ\mathrm{C}) \\ = (3.0\,\mathrm{kg})(4186\,\mathrm{J/kg\cdot C^\circ})(20^\circ\mathrm{C} - T). \end{aligned}$$

Solving for $T$ we obtain

$$T = 5.0^\circ\mathrm{C}.$$

**EXERCISE A** How much more ice at −10°C would be needed in Example 14–8 to bring the tea down to 0°C, while just melting all the ice?

## PROBLEM SOLVING Calorimetry

1. Be sure you have sufficient information to apply energy conservation. Ask yourself: **is the system isolated** (or very nearly so, enough to get a good estimate)? Do we know or can we calculate all significant sources of energy transfer?
2. Apply **conservation of energy**:

   heat gained = heat lost.

   For each substance in the system, a heat (energy) term will appear on either the left or right side of this equation. [Alternatively, use $\Sigma Q = 0$.]
3. If **no phase changes** occur, each term in the energy conservation equation (above) will have the form

   $$Q(\text{gain}) = mc(T_f - T_i)$$

   or

   $$Q(\text{lost}) = mc(T_i - T_f)$$

   where $T_i$ and $T_f$ are the initial and final temperatures of the substance, and $m$ and $c$ are its mass and specific heat, respectively.
4. If **phase changes** do or might occur, there may be terms in the energy conservation equation of the form $Q = mL$, where $L$ is the latent heat. But *before* applying energy conservation, determine (or estimate) in which phase the final state will be, as we did in Example 14–8 by calculating the different contributing values for heat $Q$.
5. Be sure each term appears on the correct side of the **energy equation** (heat gained or heat lost) and that each $\Delta T$ is positive.
6. Note that when the system reaches thermal **equilibrium**, the final **temperature** of each substance will have the *same* value. There is only one $T_f$.
7. **Solve** your energy equation for the unknown.

**EXAMPLE 14–9** **Determining a latent heat.** The specific heat of liquid mercury is $140\,\text{J/kg}\cdot\text{C}^\circ$. When 1.0 kg of solid mercury at its melting point of $-39^\circ\text{C}$ is placed in a 0.50-kg aluminum calorimeter filled with 1.2 kg of water at 20.0°C, the final temperature of the combination is found to be 16.5°C. What is the heat of fusion of mercury in J/kg?

**APPROACH** We follow the Problem Solving Box explicitly.

**SOLUTION**

1. **Is the system isolated?** The mercury is placed in a calorimeter, which, by definition, is well insulated. Our isolated system is the calorimeter, the water, and the mercury.
2. **Conservation of energy.** The heat gained by the mercury = the heat lost by the water and calorimeter.

3 and **4. Phase changes.** There is a phase change, plus we use specific heat equations. The heat gained by the mercury (Hg) includes a term representing the melting of the Hg:

$$Q(\text{melt solid Hg}) = m_{\text{Hg}} L_{\text{Hg}},$$

plus a term representing the heating of the liquid Hg from $-39^\circ\text{C}$ to $+16.5^\circ\text{C}$:

$$\begin{aligned} Q(\text{heat liquid Hg}) &= m_{\text{Hg}} c_{\text{Hg}}[16.5^\circ\text{C} - (-39^\circ\text{C})] \\ &= (1.0\,\text{kg})(140\,\text{J/kg}\cdot\text{C}^\circ)(55.5\,\text{C}^\circ) = 7770\,\text{J}. \end{aligned}$$

All of this heat gained by the mercury is obtained from the water and calorimeter, which cool down:

$$\begin{aligned} Q_{\text{cal}} + Q_{\text{H}_2\text{O}} &= m_{\text{cal}} c_{\text{cal}}(20.0^\circ\text{C} - 16.5^\circ\text{C}) + m_{\text{H}_2\text{O}} c_{\text{H}_2\text{O}}(20.0^\circ\text{C} - 16.5^\circ\text{C}) \\ &= (0.50\,\text{kg})(900\,\text{J/kg}\cdot\text{C}^\circ)(3.5\,\text{C}^\circ) + (1.2\,\text{kg})(4186\,\text{J/kg}\cdot\text{C}^\circ)(3.5\,\text{C}^\circ) \\ &= 19{,}200\,\text{J}. \end{aligned}$$

5. **Energy equation.** The conservation of energy tells us the heat lost by the water and calorimeter cup must equal the heat gained by the mercury:

   $$Q_{\text{cal}} + Q_{\text{H}_2\text{O}} = Q(\text{melt solid Hg}) + Q(\text{heat liquid Hg})$$

   or

   $$19{,}200\,\text{J} = m_{\text{Hg}} L_{\text{Hg}} + 7770\,\text{J}.$$
6. **Equilibrium temperature.** It is given as 16.5°C, and we already used it.

7. **Solve.** The only unknown in our energy equation (point 5) is $L_{Hg}$, the latent heat of fusion (or melting) of mercury. We solve for it, putting in $m_{Hg} = 1.0$ kg:

$$L_{Hg} = \frac{19{,}200\text{ J} - 7770\text{ J}}{1.0\text{ kg}} = 11{,}400\text{ J/kg} \approx 11\text{ kJ/kg},$$

where we rounded off to 2 significant figures.

## Evaporation

The latent heat to change a liquid to a gas is needed not only at the boiling point. Water can change from the liquid to the gas phase even at room temperature. This process is called **evaporation** (see also Section 13–13). The value of the heat of vaporization of water increases slightly with a decrease in temperature: at 20°C, for example, it is 2450 kJ/kg (585 kcal/kg) compared to 2260 kJ/kg (= 539 kcal/kg) at 100°C. When water evaporates, the remaining liquid cools, because the energy required (the latent heat of vaporization) comes from the water itself; so its internal energy, and therefore its temperature, must drop.[†]

PHYSICS APPLIED
*Body temperature*

Evaporation of water from the skin is one of the most important methods the body uses to control its temperature. When the temperature of the blood rises slightly above normal, the hypothalamus region of the brain detects this temperature increase and sends a signal to the sweat glands to increase their production. The energy (latent heat) required to vaporize this water comes from the body, and hence the body cools.

## Kinetic Theory of Latent Heats

We can make use of kinetic theory to see why energy is needed to melt or vaporize a substance. At the melting point, the latent heat of fusion does not act to increase the average kinetic energy (and the temperature) of the molecules in the solid, but instead is used to overcome the potential energy associated with the forces between the molecules. That is, work must be done against these attractive forces to break the molecules loose from their relatively fixed positions in the solid so they can freely roll over one another in the liquid phase. Similarly, energy is required for molecules held close together in the liquid phase to escape into the gaseous phase. This process is a more violent reorganization of the molecules than is melting (the average distance between the molecules is greatly increased), and hence the heat of vaporization is generally much greater than the heat of fusion for a given substance.

# 14–6 Heat Transfer: Conduction

*Three methods of heat transfer*

Heat transfer from one place or object to another occurs in three different ways: by *conduction, convection*, and *radiation*. We now discuss each of these in turn; but in practical situations, any two or all three may be operating at the same time. This Section deals with conduction.

When a metal poker is put in a hot fire, or a silver spoon is placed in a hot bowl of soup, the end that you hold soon becomes hot as well, even though it is not directly in contact with the source of heat. We say that heat has been *conducted* from the hot end to the cold end.

Heat **conduction** in many materials can be visualized as being carried out via molecular collisions. As one end of an object is heated, the molecules there move faster and faster. As they collide with their slower-moving neighbors, they transfer some of their kinetic energy to these molecules, whose speeds thus increase. These in turn transfer some of their energy by collision with molecules still farther along the object. Thus the kinetic energy of thermal motion is transferred by molecular collision along the object. In metals, according to modern theory, it is collisions of free electrons within the metal that are visualized as being mainly responsible for conduction.

[†] According to kinetic theory, evaporation is a cooling process because it is the fastest-moving molecules that escape from the surface (Section 13–13). Hence the average speed of the remaining molecules is less, so by Eq. 13–8 the temperature is less.

**FIGURE 14–6** Heat conduction between areas at temperatures $T_1$ and $T_2$. If $T_1$ is greater than $T_2$, the heat flows to the right; the rate is given by Eq. 14–4.

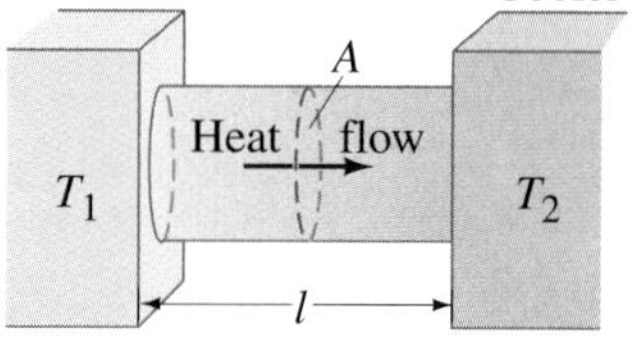


*Rate of heat flow by conduction*

Heat conduction from one point to another takes place only if there is a difference in temperature between the two points. Indeed, it is found experimentally that the rate of heat flow through a substance is proportional to the difference in temperature between its ends. The rate of heat flow also depends on the size and shape of the object. To investigate this quantitatively, let us consider the heat flow through a uniform cylinder, as illustrated in Fig. 14–6. It is found experimentally that the heat flow $Q$ over a time interval $t$ is given by the relation

$$\frac{Q}{t} = kA\frac{T_1 - T_2}{l} \tag{14–4}$$

where $A$ is the cross-sectional area of the object, $l$ is the distance between the two ends, which are at temperatures $T_1$ and $T_2$, and $k$ is a proportionality constant called the **thermal conductivity** which is characteristic of the material. From Eq. 14–4, we see that the rate of heat flow (units of J/s) is directly proportional to the cross-sectional area and to the temperature gradient† $(T_1 - T_2)/l$.

**TABLE 14–4 Thermal Conductivities**

| Substance | Thermal Conductivity, $k$: kcal/(s·m·C°) | J/(s·m·C°) |
|---|---|---|
| Silver | $10 \times 10^{-2}$ | 420 |
| Copper | $9.2 \times 10^{-2}$ | 380 |
| Aluminum | $5.0 \times 10^{-2}$ | 200 |
| Steel | $1.1 \times 10^{-2}$ | 40 |
| Ice | $5 \times 10^{-4}$ | 2 |
| Glass | $2.0 \times 10^{-4}$ | 0.84 |
| Brick | $2.0 \times 10^{-4}$ | 0.84 |
| Concrete | $2.0 \times 10^{-4}$ | 0.84 |
| Water | $1.4 \times 10^{-4}$ | 0.56 |
| Human tissue | $0.5 \times 10^{-4}$ | 0.2 |
| Wood | $0.3 \times 10^{-4}$ | 0.1 |
| Fiberglass | $0.12 \times 10^{-4}$ | 0.048 |
| Cork | $0.1 \times 10^{-4}$ | 0.042 |
| Wool | $0.1 \times 10^{-4}$ | 0.040 |
| Goose down | $0.06 \times 10^{-4}$ | 0.025 |
| Polyurethane | $0.06 \times 10^{-4}$ | 0.024 |
| Air | $0.055 \times 10^{-4}$ | 0.023 |

The thermal conductivities, $k$, for a variety of substances are given in Table 14–4. Substances for which $k$ is large conduct heat rapidly and are said to be good **conductors**. Most metals fall in this category, although there is a wide range even among them, as you may observe by holding the ends of a silver spoon and a stainless-steel spoon immersed in the same hot cup of soup. Substances for which $k$ is small, such as wool, fiberglass, polyurethane, and goose down, are poor conductors of heat and are therefore good **insulators**. The relative magnitudes of $k$ can explain simple phenomena such as why a tile floor is much colder on the feet than a rug-covered floor at the same temperature. Tile is a better conductor of heat than the rug; heat that flows from your foot to the rug is not conducted away rapidly, so the rug's surface quickly warms up to the temperature of your foot and feels good. But the tile conducts the heat away rapidly and thus can take more heat from your foot quickly, so your foot's surface temperature drops.

*Why rugs feel warmer than tile*

PHYSICS APPLIED

*Heat loss through windows*

**EXAMPLE 14–10 Heat loss through windows.** A major source of heat loss from a house is through the windows. Calculate the rate of heat flow through a glass window 2.0 m × 1.5 m in area and 3.2 mm thick, if the temperatures at the inner and outer surfaces are 15.0°C and 14.0°C, respectively (Fig. 14–7).

**APPROACH** Heat flows by conduction through the 3.2-mm thickness of glass from the higher inside temperature to the lower outside temperature. We use the heat conduction equation, Eq. 14–4.

**SOLUTION** Here $A = (2.0\,\text{m})(1.5\,\text{m}) = 3.0\,\text{m}^2$ and $l = 3.2 \times 10^{-3}\,\text{m}$. Using Table 14–4 to get $k$, we have

$$\frac{Q}{t} = kA\frac{T_1 - T_2}{l} = \frac{(0.84\,\text{J/s}\cdot\text{m}\cdot\text{C}^\circ)(3.0\,\text{m}^2)(15.0^\circ\text{C} - 14.0^\circ\text{C})}{(3.2 \times 10^{-3}\,\text{m})}$$
$$= 790\,\text{J/s}.$$

**NOTE** This rate of heat flow is equivalent to $(790\,\text{J/s})/(4.19 \times 10^3\,\text{J/kcal}) = 0.19\,\text{kcal/s}$, or $(0.19\,\text{kcal/s}) \times (3600\,\text{s/h}) = 680\,\text{kcal/h}$.

**FIGURE 14–7** Example 14–10.

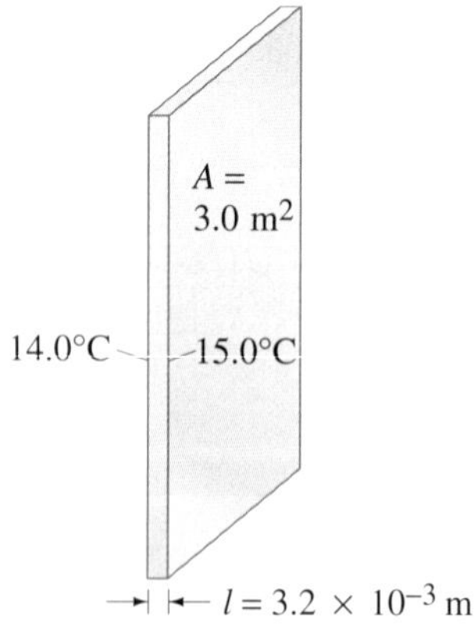


†Equation 14–4 is quite similar to the relations describing diffusion (Section 13–14) and the flow of fluids through a pipe (Section 10–12). In those cases, the flow of matter was found to be proportional to the concentration gradient $(C_1 - C_2)/l$, or to the pressure gradient $(P_1 - P_2)/l$. This close similarity is one reason we speak of the "flow" of heat. Yet we must keep in mind that no substance is flowing in this case—it is energy that is being transferred.

You might notice in Example 14–10 that 15°C is not very warm for the living room of a house. The room itself may indeed be much warmer, and the outside might be colder than 14°C. But the temperatures of 15°C and 14°C were specified as those at the window surfaces, and there is usually a considerable drop in temperature of the air in the vicinity of the window both on the inside and the outside. That is, the layer of air on either side of the window acts as an insulator, and normally the major part of the temperature drop between the inside and outside of the house takes place across the air layer. If there is a heavy wind, the air outside a window will constantly be replaced with cold air; the temperature gradient across the glass will be greater and there will be a much greater rate of heat loss. Increasing the width of the air layer, such as using two panes of glass separated by an air gap, will reduce the heat loss more than simply increasing the glass thickness, since the thermal conductivity of air is much less than that for glass.

*Wind can cause much greater heat loss*

PHYSICS APPLIED
*Thermal windows*

The insulating properties of clothing come from the insulating properties of air. Without clothes, our bodies would heat the air in contact with the skin and would soon become reasonably comfortable because air is a very good insulator. But since air moves—there are breezes and drafts, and people move about—the warm air would be replaced by cold air, thus increasing the temperature difference and the heat loss from the body. Clothes keep us warm by trapping air so it cannot move readily. It is not the cloth that insulates us, but the air that the cloth traps. Goose down is a very good insulator because even a small amount of it fluffs up and traps a great amount of air.

PHYSICS APPLIED
*Clothes insulate by trapping an air layer*

**EXERCISE B** Explain why drapes in front of a window reduce heat loss from a house.

### *R*-values for Building Materials

PHYSICS APPLIED
*R-values of thermal insulation*

For practical purposes the thermal properties of building materials, particularly when considered as insulation, are usually specified by *R*-values (or "thermal resistance"), defined for a given thickness $l$ of material as:

$$R = \frac{l}{k}.$$

The *R*-value of a given piece of material combines the thickness $l$ and the thermal conductivity $k$ in one number. In the United States, *R*-values are given in British units as $\mathrm{ft^2 \cdot h \cdot F^\circ/Btu}$ (for example, *R*-19 means $R = 19\,\mathrm{ft^2 \cdot h \cdot F^\circ/Btu}$). Table 14–5 gives *R*-values for some common building materials: note that *R*-values increase directly with material thickness. For example, 2 inches of fiberglass is *R*-6, half that for 4 inches (= *R*-12; see Table 14–5).

**TABLE 14–5 *R*-values**

| Material | Thickness | *R*-value ($\mathrm{ft^2 \cdot h \cdot F^\circ/Btu}$) |
|---|---|---|
| Glass | $\frac{1}{8}$ inch | 1 |
| Brick | $3\frac{1}{2}$ inches | 0.6–1 |
| Plywood | $\frac{1}{2}$ inch | 0.6 |
| Fiberglass insulation | 4 inches | 12 |

## 14–7 Heat Transfer: Convection

Although liquids and gases are generally not very good conductors of heat, they can transfer heat quite rapidly by convection. **Convection** is the process whereby heat flows by the mass movement of molecules from one place to another. Whereas conduction involves molecules (and/or electrons) moving only over small distances and colliding, convection involves the movement of large numbers of molecules over large distances.

A forced-air furnace, in which air is heated and then blown by a fan into a room, is an example of *forced convection. Natural convection* occurs as well, and one familiar example is that hot air rises. For instance, the air above a radiator (or other type of heater) expands as it is heated (Chapter 13), and hence its density decreases. Because its density is less than that of the surrounding cooler air, it rises, just as a log submerged in water floats upward because its density is less than that of water. Warm or cold ocean currents, such as the balmy Gulf Stream, represent natural convection on a global scale. Wind is another example of convection, and weather in general is a result of convective air currents.

PHYSICS APPLIED
*Ocean currents and wind*

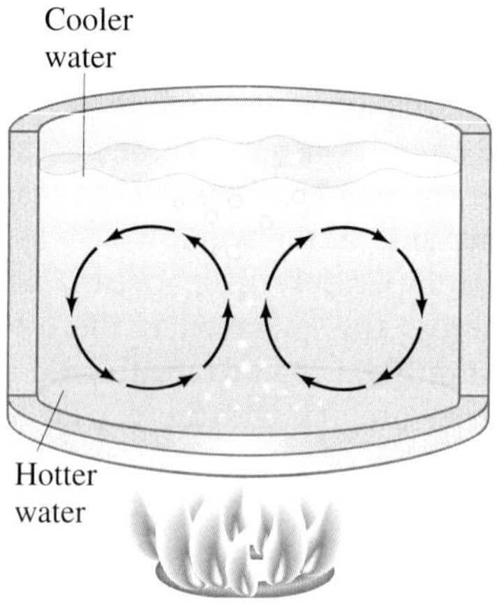


**FIGURE 14–8** Convection currents in a pot of water being heated on a stove.

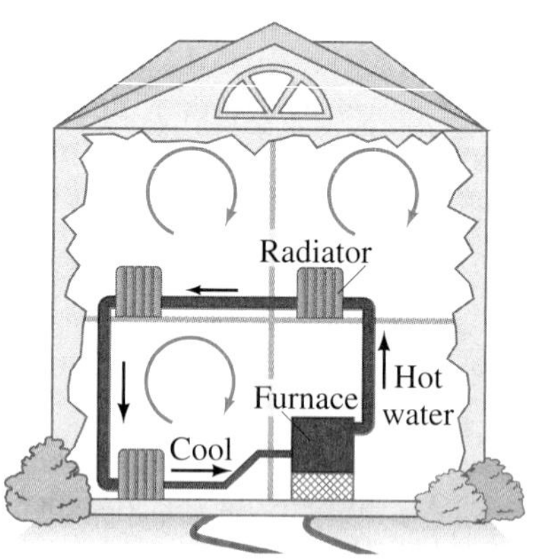


**FIGURE 14–9** Convection plays a role in heating a house. The circular arrows show the convective air currents in the rooms.

When a pot of water is heated (Fig. 14–8), convection currents are set up as the heated water at the bottom of the pot rises because of its reduced density. That heated water is replaced by cooler water from above. This principle is used in many heating systems, such as the hot-water radiator system shown in Fig. 14–9. Water is heated in the furnace, and as its temperature increases, it expands and rises as shown. This causes the water to circulate in the heating system. Hot water then enters the radiators, heat is transferred by conduction to the air, and the cooled water returns to the furnace. Thus, the water circulates because of convection; pumps are sometimes used to improve circulation. The air throughout the room also becomes heated as a result of convection. The air heated by the radiators rises and is replaced by cooler air, resulting in convective air currents, as shown by the green arrows in Fig. 14–9.

PHYSICS APPLIED
*House heating via convection*

Other types of furnaces also depend on convection. Hot-air furnaces with registers (openings) near the floor often do not have fans but depend on natural convection, which can be appreciable. In other systems, a fan is used. In either case, it is important that cold air can return to the furnace so that convective currents circulate throughout the room if the room is to be uniformly heated.

PHYSICS APPLIED
*Convection on steep hiking trails*

Another example of convection and its effects is given in the following excerpt from "The Winds of Yosemite Valley"† by the early environmentalist François Matthes:

> It happens to be so ordained in nature that the sun shall heat the ground more rapidly than the air. And so it comes that every slope or hillside basking in the morning sun soon becomes itself a source of heat. It gradually warms the air immediately over it, and the latter, becoming lighter, begins to rise. But not vertically upward, for above it is still the cool air pressing down. Up along the warm slope it ascends, much as shown by the arrows in the accompanying diagram [Fig. 14–10a]. Few visitors to the valley but will remember toiling up some never ending zigzags on a hot and breathless day, with the sun on their backs and their own dust floating upward with them in an exasperating, choking cloud. Perhaps they thought it was simply their misfortune that the dust should happen to rise on that particular day. It always does on a sun-warmed slope.
>
> But again, memories may arise of another occasion when, on coming down a certain trail the dust ever descended with the travelers, wafting down upon them from zigzag to zigzag as if with malicious pleasure. That, however, undoubtedly happened on the shady side of the valley. For there the conditions are exactly reversed. When the sun leaves a slope the latter begins at once to lose its heat by radiation, and in a short time is colder than the air. The layer next to the ground then gradually chills by contact, and, becoming heavier as it condenses, begins to creep down along the slope [Fig. 14–10b]. There is, thus,

**FIGURE 14–10** Convection on a hiking trail: (a) upward movement of air in the morning because it is heated; (b) downward movement in the evening because the air is cooled.

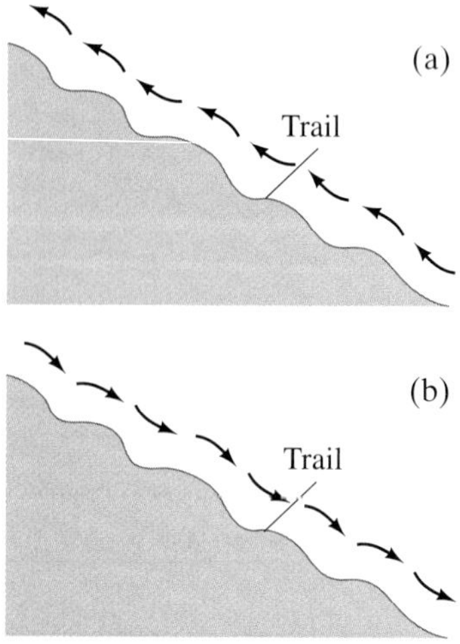


†Reprinted from the *Sierra Club Bulletin*, June 1911, pp. 91–92.

normally a warm updraft on a sunlit slope and a cold downdraft on a shaded slope—and that rule one may depend on almost any day in a windless region like the Yosemite. Indeed, one might readily take advantage of it and plan his trips so as to have a dust-free journey.

The human body produces a great deal of thermal energy. Of the food energy transformed within the body, at best 20% is used to do work, so over 80% appears as thermal energy. During light activity, for example, if this thermal energy were not dissipated, the body temperature would rise about 3 C° per hour. Clearly, the heat generated by the body must be transferred to the outside. Is the heat transferred by conduction? The temperature of the skin in a comfortable environment is 33 to 35°C, whereas the interior of the body is at 37°C. A simple calculation (see Problem 55) shows that, because of this small temperature difference, plus the low thermal conductivity of tissue, direct conduction is responsible for very little of the heat that must be dissipated. Instead, the heat is carried to the surface by the blood. In addition to all its other important responsibilities, blood acts as a convective fluid to transfer heat to just beneath the surface of the skin. It is then conducted (over a very short distance) to the surface. Once at the surface, the heat is transferred to the environment by convection, evaporation, and radiation (see Section 14–8).

PHYSICS APPLIED
*Body heat: convection by blood*

## 14–8 Heat Transfer: Radiation

Convection and conduction require the presence of matter as a medium to carry the heat from the hotter to the colder region. But a third type of heat transfer occurs without any medium at all. All life on Earth depends on the transfer of energy from the Sun, and this energy is transferred to the Earth over empty (or nearly empty) space. This form of energy transfer is heat—since the Sun's surface temperature is much higher (6000 K) than Earth's—and is referred to as **radiation** (Fig. 14–11). The warmth we receive from a fire is mainly radiant energy. (Most of the air heated by a fire in a fireplace rises by convection up the chimney and does not reach us.)

**FIGURE 14–11** The Sun's surface radiates at 6000 K—much higher than the Earth's surface.

As we shall see in later Chapters, radiation consists essentially of electromagnetic waves. Suffice it to say for now that radiation from the Sun consists of visible light plus many other wavelengths that the eye is not sensitive to, including infrared (IR) radiation, which is mainly responsible for heating the Earth.

The rate at which an object radiates energy has been found to be proportional to the fourth power of the Kelvin temperature, $T$. That is, a body at 2000 K, as compared to one at 1000 K, radiates energy at a rate $2^4 = 16$ times as much. The rate of radiation is also proportional to the area $A$ of the emitting object, so the rate at which energy leaves the object, $\Delta Q/\Delta t$, is

$$\frac{\Delta Q}{\Delta t} = e\sigma A T^4. \qquad \textbf{(14–5)}$$

*Radiation $\propto T^4$*

This is called the **Stefan-Boltzmann equation**, and $\sigma$ is a universal constant called the **Stefan-Boltzmann constant** which has the value

$$\sigma = 5.67 \times 10^{-8}\,\mathrm{W/m^2 \cdot K^4}.$$

*Stefan-Boltzmann constant*

The factor $e$, called the **emissivity**, is a number between 0 and 1 that is characteristic of the surface of the radiating material. Very black surfaces, such as charcoal, have emissivity close to 1, whereas shiny metal surfaces have $e$ close to zero and thus emit correspondingly less radiation. The value of $e$ depends somewhat on the temperature of the body.

*Emissivity*

Not only do shiny surfaces emit less radiation, but they absorb little of the radiation that falls upon them (most is reflected). Black and very dark objects, on the other hand, absorb nearly all the radiation that falls on them—which is why light-colored clothing is usually preferable to dark clothing on a hot day. Thus, **a good absorber is also a good emitter**.

PHYSICS APPLIED
*Dark vs. light clothing*

*Good absorber is good emitter*

Any object not only emits energy by radiation but also absorbs energy radiated by other bodies. If an object of emissivity $e$ and area $A$ is at a temperature $T_1$, it radiates energy at a rate $e\sigma AT_1^4$. If the object is surrounded by an environment at temperature $T_2$, the rate at which the surroundings radiate energy is proportional to $T_2^4$, and the rate that energy is absorbed by the object is proportional to $T_2^4$. The *net* rate of radiant heat flow from the object is given by the equation

*Net flow rate of heat radiation*

$$\frac{\Delta Q}{\Delta t} = e\sigma A\left(T_1^4 - T_2^4\right), \tag{14–6}$$

where $A$ is the surface area of the object, $T_1$ its temperature and $e$ its emissivity (at temperature $T_1$), and $T_2$ is the temperature of the surroundings. Notice in this equation that the rate of heat absorption by an object was taken to be $e\sigma AT_2^4$; that is, the proportionality constant is the same for both emission and absorption. This must be true to correspond with the experimental fact that equilibrium between the object and its surroundings is reached when they come to the same temperature. That is, $\Delta Q/\Delta t$ must equal zero when $T_1 = T_2$, so the coefficients of emission and absorption terms must be the same. This confirms the idea that a good emitter is a good absorber.

Because both the object and its surroundings radiate energy, there is a net transfer of energy from one to the other unless everything is at the same temperature. From Eq. 14–6 it is clear that if $T_1 > T_2$, the net flow of heat is from the object to the surroundings, so the object cools. But if $T_1 < T_2$, the net heat flow is from the surroundings into the object, and its temperature rises. If different parts of the surroundings are at different temperatures, Eq. 14–6 becomes more complicated.

**PHYSICS APPLIED**
*The body's radiative heat loss*

**EXAMPLE 14–11 ESTIMATE Cooling by radiation.** An athlete is sitting unclothed in a locker room whose dark walls are at a temperature of 15°C. Estimate the rate of heat loss by radiation, assuming a skin temperature of 34°C and $e = 0.70$. Take the surface area of the body not in contact with the chair to be 1.5 m$^2$.

**APPROACH** We can make a rough estimate using the given assumptions and Eq. 14–6, for which we must use Kelvin temperatures.

**SOLUTION** We have

**PROBLEM SOLVING**
*Must use the Kelvin temperature*

$$\begin{aligned}\frac{\Delta Q}{\Delta t} &= e\sigma A\left(T_1^4 - T_2^4\right) \\ &= (0.70)\left(5.67 \times 10^{-8}\,\mathrm{W/m^2 \cdot K^4}\right)\left(1.5\,\mathrm{m^2}\right)\left[(307\,\mathrm{K})^4 - (288\,\mathrm{K})^4\right] \\ &= 120\,\mathrm{W}.\end{aligned}$$

**NOTE** The "output" of this resting person is a bit more than what a 100-W lightbulb uses.

**PHYSICS APPLIED**
*Room comfort*

A resting person naturally produces heat internally at a rate of about 100 W (Chapter 15), less than the heat loss by radiation as calculated in this Example. Hence, the person's temperature would drop, causing considerable discomfort. The body responds to excessive heat loss by increasing its metabolic rate (Section 15–3), and shivering is one method by which the body increases its metabolism. Naturally, clothes help a lot. Example 14–11 illustrates that a person may be uncomfortable even if the temperature of the air is, say, 25°C, which is quite a warm room. If the walls or floor are cold, radiation to them occurs no matter how warm the air is. Indeed, it is estimated that radiation accounts for about 50% of the heat loss from a sedentary person in a normal room. Rooms are most comfortable when the walls and floor are warm and the air is not so warm. Floors and walls can be heated by means of hot-water conduits or electric heating elements. Such first-rate heating systems are becoming more common today, and it is interesting to note that 2000 years ago

*Temperature of walls and surroundings, not only the air, affects comfort*

the Romans, even in houses in the remote province of Great Britain, made use of hot-water and steam conduits in the floor to heat their houses.

**EXAMPLE 14–12 ESTIMATE** **Two teapots.** A ceramic teapot ($e = 0.70$) and a shiny one ($e = 0.10$) each hold 0.75 L of tea at 95°C. (*a*) Estimate the rate of heat loss from each, and (*b*) estimate the temperature drop after 30 min for each. Consider only radiation, and assume the surroundings are at 20°C.

**APPROACH** We are given all the information necessary to calculate the heat loss due to radiation, except for the area. The teapot holds 0.75 L, and we can approximate it as a cube 10 cm on a side (volume = 1.0 L), with five sides exposed. To estimate the temperature drop in (*b*), we use the concept of specific heat and ignore the contribution of the pots compared to that of the water.

**SOLUTION** (*a*) The teapot, approximated by a cube 10 cm on a side with five sides exposed, has a surface area of about $5 \times (0.1\,\text{m})^2 = 5 \times 10^{-2}\,\text{m}^2$. The rate of heat loss would be about

$$\begin{aligned}\frac{\Delta Q}{\Delta t} &= e\sigma A\left(T_1^4 - T_2^4\right)\\ &= e\left(5.67 \times 10^{-8}\,\text{W/m}^2\cdot\text{K}^4\right)\left(5 \times 10^{-2}\,\text{m}^2\right)\left[(368\,\text{K})^4 - (293\,\text{K})^4\right]\\ &\approx e(30)\ \text{W},\end{aligned}$$

or about 20 W for the ceramic pot ($e = 0.70$) and 3 W for the shiny one ($e = 0.10$).

(*b*) To estimate the temperature drop, we use the specific heat of water and ignore the contribution of the pots. The mass of 0.75 L of water is 0.75 kg. (Recall that $1.0\,\text{L} = 1000\,\text{cm}^3 = 1 \times 10^{-3}\,\text{m}^3$ and $\rho = 1000\,\text{kg/m}^3$.) Using Eq. 14–2 and Table 14–1, we get

$$\frac{\Delta Q}{\Delta t} = mc\,\frac{\Delta T}{\Delta t}.$$

Then

$$\frac{\Delta T}{\Delta t} = \frac{\Delta Q/\Delta t}{mc} \approx \frac{e(30)\ \text{J/s}}{(0.75\,\text{kg})\left(4.186 \times 10^3\,\text{J/kg}\cdot\text{C}^\circ\right)} = e(0.01)\ \text{C}^\circ/\text{s}.$$

After 30 min (1800 s), $\Delta T = e(0.01\,\text{C}^\circ/\text{s})\Delta t = e(0.01\,\text{C}^\circ/\text{s})(1800\,\text{s}) = 18e\,\text{C}^\circ$, or about 12 C° for the ceramic pot ($e = 0.70$) and about 2 C° for the shiny one ($e = 0.10$). The shiny one clearly has an advantage, at least as far as radiation is concerned.

**NOTE** Convection and conduction could play a greater role than radiation.

Heating of an object by radiation from the Sun cannot be calculated using Eq. 14–6 since this equation assumes a uniform temperature, $T_2$, of the environment surrounding the object, whereas the Sun is essentially a point source. Hence the Sun must be treated as a separate source of energy. Heating by the Sun is calculated using the fact that about 1350 J of energy strikes the atmosphere of the Earth from the Sun per second per square meter of area at right angles to the Sun's rays. This number, $1350\,\text{W/m}^2$, is called the **solar constant**. The atmosphere may absorb as much as 70% of this energy before it reaches the ground, depending on the cloud cover. On a clear day, about $1000\,\text{W/m}^2$ reaches the Earth's surface. An object of emissivity $e$ with area $A$ facing the Sun absorbs energy from the Sun at a rate, in watts, of about

PHYSICS APPLIED

*Radiation from the Sun*

*Solar constant*

$$\frac{\Delta Q}{\Delta t} = \left(1000\,\text{W/m}^2\right)eA\cos\theta, \qquad \textbf{(14–7)}$$

where $\theta$ is the angle between the Sun's rays and a line perpendicular to the area $A$ (Fig. 14–12). That is, $A\cos\theta$ is the "effective" area, at right angles to the Sun's rays.

**FIGURE 14–12** Radiant energy striking a body at an angle $\theta$.

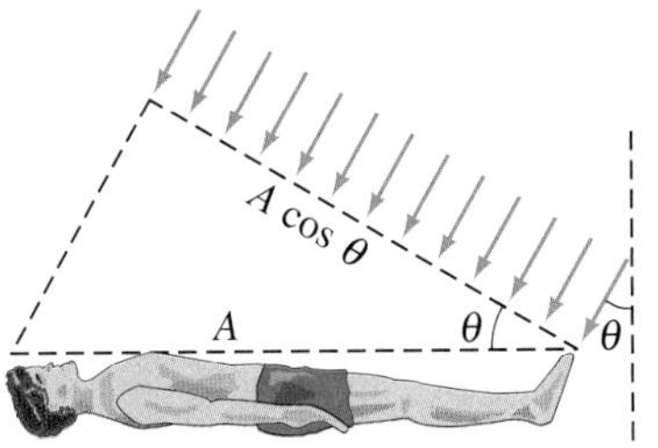

The explanation for the **seasons** and the polar ice caps (see Fig. 14–13) depends on this $\cos\theta$ factor in Eq. 14–7. The seasons are *not* a result of how close the Earth is to the Sun—in fact, in the Northern Hemisphere, summer occurs when the Earth is farthest from the Sun. It is the angle (i.e., $\cos\theta$) that really matters. Furthermore, the reason the Sun heats the Earth more at midday than at sunrise or sunset is also related to this $\cos\theta$ factor.

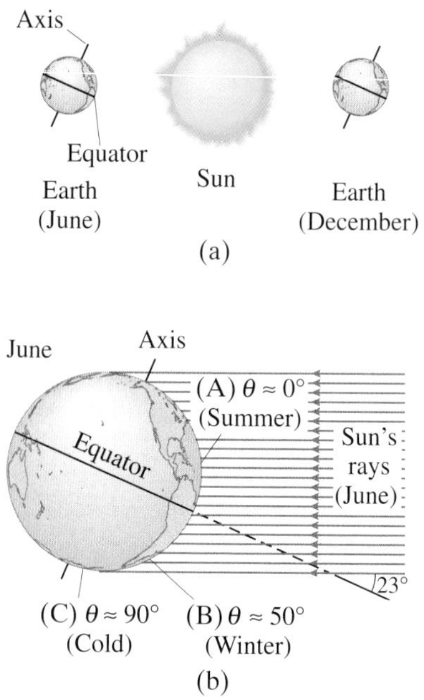


**FIGURE 14–13** (a) Earth's seasons arise from the $23\frac{1}{2}°$ angle Earth's axis makes with its orbit around the Sun. (b) June sunlight makes an angle of about 23° with the equator. Thus $\theta$ in the southern United States (A) is near 0° (direct summer sunlight), whereas in the Southern Hemisphere (B), $\theta$ is 50° or 60°, and less heat can be absorbed—hence it is winter. Near the poles (C), there is never strong direct sunlight; $\cos\theta$ varies from about $\frac{1}{2}$ in summer to 0 in winter; so with little heating, ice can form.

**EXAMPLE 14–13 ESTIMATE** **Getting a tan—energy absorption.** What is the rate of energy absorption from the Sun by a person lying flat on the beach on a clear day if the Sun makes a 30° angle with the vertical? Assume that $e = 0.70$ and that $1000\ \text{W/m}^2$ reaches the Earth's surface.

**APPROACH** We use Eq. 14–7 and estimate a typical human to be roughly 2 m tall by 0.4 m wide, so $A \approx (2\ \text{m})(0.4\ \text{m}) = 0.8\ \text{m}^2$.

**SOLUTION** Since $\cos 30° = 0.866$, we have

$$\frac{\Delta Q}{\Delta t} = \left(1000\ \text{W/m}^2\right) eA\cos\theta$$

$$= \left(1000\ \text{W/m}^2\right)(0.70)\left(0.8\ \text{m}^2\right)(0.866) = 500\ \text{W}.$$

**NOTE** If a person wears light-colored clothing, $e$ is much smaller, so the energy absorbed is less.

An interesting application of thermal radiation to diagnostic medicine is **thermography**. A special instrument, the thermograph, scans the body, measuring the intensity of radiation from many points and forming a picture that resembles an X-ray (Fig. 14–14). Areas where metabolic activity is high, such as in tumors, can often be detected on a thermogram as a result of their higher temperature and consequent increased radiation.

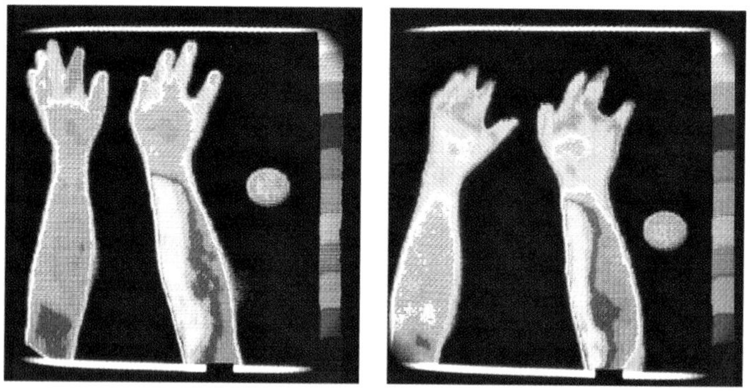


**FIGURE 14–14** Thermograms of a healthy person's arms and hands (a) before and (b) after smoking a cigarette, showing a temperature decrease due to impaired blood circulation associated with smoking. The thermograms have been color-coded according to temperature; the scale on the right goes from blue (cold) to white (hot).

PHYSICS APPLIED

*Astronomy—size of a star*

**EXAMPLE 14–14 ESTIMATE** **Star radius.** The giant star Betelgeuse emits radiant energy at a rate $10^4$ times greater than our Sun, whereas its surface temperature is only half (2900 K) that of our Sun. Estimate the radius of Betelgeuse, assuming $e = 1$. The Sun's radius is $r_S = 7 \times 10^8$ m.

**APPROACH** We assume both Betelgeuse and the Sun are spherical, with surface area $4\pi r^2$.

**SOLUTION** We solve Eq. 14–5 for $A$:

$$4\pi r^2 = A = \frac{(\Delta Q/\Delta t)}{e\sigma T^4}.$$

Then

$$\frac{r_B^2}{r_S^2} = \frac{(\Delta Q/\Delta t)_B}{(\Delta Q/\Delta t)_S} \cdot \frac{T_S^4}{T_B^4} = \left(10^4\right)\left(2^4\right) = 16 \times 10^4.$$

Hence $r_B = \sqrt{16 \times 10^4}\, r_S = (400)\left(7 \times 10^8\ \text{m}\right) \approx 3 \times 10^{11}$ m. If Betelgeuse were our Sun, it would envelop us (Earth is $1.5 \times 10^{11}$ m from the Sun).

## Summary

**Internal energy**, $U$, refers to the total energy of all the molecules in an object. For an ideal monatomic gas,

$$U = \tfrac{3}{2}NkT = \tfrac{3}{2}nRT \qquad \textbf{(14–1)}$$

where $N$ is the number of molecules or $n$ is the number of moles.

**Heat** refers to the transfer of energy from one object to another because of a difference of temperature. Heat is thus measured in energy units, such as joules.

Heat and internal energy are also sometimes specified in calories or kilocalories (kcal), where

$$1\text{ kcal} = 4.186\text{ kJ}$$

is the amount of heat needed to raise the temperature of 1 kg of water by 1 C°.

The **specific heat**, $c$, of a substance is defined as the energy (or heat) required to change the temperature of unit mass of substance by 1 degree; as an equation,

$$Q = mc\,\Delta T, \qquad \textbf{(14–2)}$$

where $Q$ is the heat absorbed or given off, $\Delta T$ is the temperature increase or decrease, and $m$ is the mass of the substance.

When heat flows between parts of an isolated system, conservation of energy tells us that the heat gained by one part of the system is equal to the heat lost by the other part of the system. This is the basis of **calorimetry**, which is the quantitative measurement of heat exchange.

Exchange of energy occurs, without a change in temperature, whenever a substance changes phase. The **heat of fusion** is the heat required to melt 1 kg of a solid into the liquid phase; it is also equal to the heat given off when the substance changes from liquid to solid. The **heat of vaporization** is the energy required to change 1 kg of a substance from the liquid to the vapor phase; it is also the energy given off when the substance changes from vapor to liquid.

Heat is transferred from one place (or object) to another in three different ways: conduction, convection, and radiation.

In **conduction**, energy is transferred from molecules or electrons with higher kinetic energy to lower-KE neighbors when they collide.

**Convection** is the transfer of energy by the mass movement of molecules over considerable distances.

**Radiation**, which does not require the presence of matter, is energy transfer by electromagnetic waves, such as from the Sun. All objects radiate energy in an amount that is proportional to the fourth power of their Kelvin temperature $(T^4)$ and to their surface area. The energy radiated (or absorbed) also depends on the nature of the surface (dark surfaces absorb and radiate more than do bright shiny ones), which is characterized by the emissivity, $e$.

Radiation from the Sun arrives at the surface of the Earth on a clear day at a rate of about $1000\text{ W/m}^2$.

## Questions

1. What happens to the work done when a jar of orange juice is vigorously shaken?
2. When a hot object warms a cooler object, does temperature flow between them? Are the temperature changes of the two objects equal?
3. (*a*) If two objects of different temperatures are placed in contact, will heat naturally flow from the object with higher internal energy to the object with lower internal energy? (*b*) Is it possible for heat to flow even if the internal energies of the two objects are the same? Explain.
4. In warm regions where tropical plants grow but the temperature may drop below freezing a few times in the winter, the destruction of sensitive plants due to freezing can be reduced by watering them in the evening. Explain.
5. The specific heat of water is quite large. Explain why this fact makes water particularly good for heating systems (that is, hot-water radiators).
6. Why does water in a metal canteen stay cooler if the cloth jacket surrounding the canteen is kept moist?
7. Explain why burns caused by steam on the skin are often more severe than burns caused by water at 100°C.
8. Explain why water cools (its temperature drops) when it evaporates, using the concepts of latent heat and internal energy.
9. Will potatoes cook faster if the water is boiling faster?
10. Does an ordinary electric fan cool the air? Why or why not? If not, why use it?
11. Very high in the Earth's atmosphere, the temperature can be 700°C. Yet an animal there would freeze to death rather than roast. Explain.
12. Explorers on failed Arctic expeditions have survived by covering themselves with snow. Why would they do that?
13. Why is wet sand at the beach cooler to walk on than dry sand?
14. If you hear that an object has "high heat content," does that mean that its temperature is high? Explain.
15. When hot-air furnaces are used to heat a house, why is it important that there be a vent for air to return to the furnace? What happens if this vent is blocked by a bookcase?
16. Ceiling fans are sometimes reversible, so that they drive the air down in one season and pull it up in another season. Which way should you set the fan for summer? For winter?
17. Down sleeping bags and parkas are often specified as so many inches or centimeters of *loft*, the actual thickness of the garment when it is fluffed up. Explain.
18. Microprocessor chips have a "heat sink" glued on top that looks like a series of fins. Why is it shaped like that?
19. Sea breezes are often encountered on sunny days at the shore of a large body of water. Explain in light of the fact that the temperature of the land rises more rapidly than that of the nearby water.
20. The floor of a house on a foundation under which the air can flow is often cooler than a floor that rests directly on the ground (such as a concrete slab foundation). Explain.
21. A 22°C day is warm, while a swimming pool at 22°C feels cool. Why?
22. Explain why air temperature readings are always taken with the thermometer in the shade.
23. A premature baby in an incubator can be dangerously cooled even when the air temperature in the incubator is warm. Explain.

24. Why is the liner of a thermos bottle silvered (Fig. 14–15), and why does it have a vacuum between its two walls?

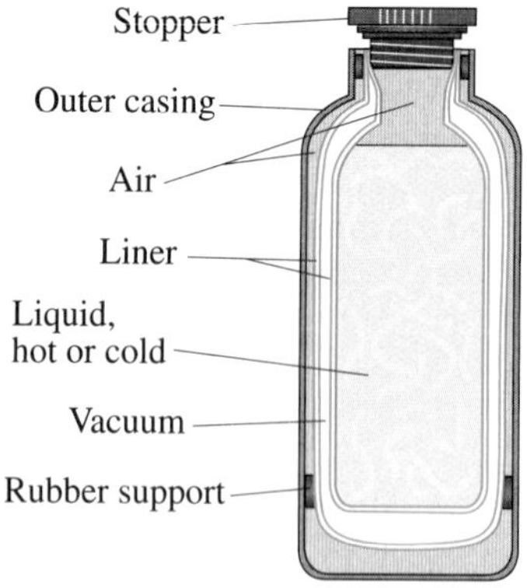


**FIGURE 14–15**
Question 24.

25. Imagine you have a wall that is very well insulated—it has a very high thermal resistance, $R_1$. Now you place a window in the wall that has a relatively low $R$-value, $R_2$. What has happened to the overall $R$-value of the wall plus window, compared to $R_1$ and $R_2$? [*Hint*: The temperature *difference* across the wall is still the same everywhere.]

26. Heat loss occurs through windows by the following processes: (1) ventilation around edges; (2) through the frame, particularly if it is metal; (3) through the glass panes; and (4) radiation. (*a*) For the first three, what is (are) the mechanism(s): conduction, convection, or radiation? (*b*) Heavy curtains reduce which of these heat losses? Explain in detail.

27. A piece of wood lying in the Sun absorbs more heat than a piece of shiny metal. Yet the wood feels less hot than the metal when you pick it up. Explain.

28. The Earth cools off at night much more quickly when the weather is clear than when cloudy. Why?

29. An "emergency blanket" is a thin shiny (metal coated) plastic foil. Explain how it can help to keep an immobile person warm.

30. Explain why cities situated by the ocean tend to have less extreme temperatures than inland cities at the same latitude.

# Problems

## 14–1 Heat as Energy Transfer

1. (I) How much heat (in joules) is required to raise the temperature of 30.0 kg of water from 15°C to 95°C?

2. (I) To what temperature will 7700 J of heat raise 3.0 kg of water that is initially at 10.0°C?

3. (II) An average active person consumes about 2500 Cal a day. (*a*) What is this in joules? (*b*) What is this in kilowatt-hours? (*c*) Your power company charges about a dime per kilowatt-hour. How much would your energy cost per day if you bought it from the power company? Could you feed yourself on this much money per day?

4. (II) A British thermal unit (Btu) is a unit of heat in the British system of units. One Btu is defined as the heat needed to raise 1 lb of water by 1 F°. Show that

$$1 \text{ Btu} = 0.252 \text{ kcal} = 1055 \text{ J}.$$

5. (II) A water heater can generate 32,000 kJ/h. How much water can it heat from 15°C to 50°C per hour?

6. (II) A small immersion heater is rated at 350 W. Estimate how long it will take to heat a cup of soup (assume this is 250 mL of water) from 20°C to 60°C.

7. (II) How many kilocalories are generated when the brakes are used to bring a 1200-kg car to rest from a speed of 95 km/h?

## 14–3 and 14–4 Specific Heat; Calorimetry

8. (I) An automobile cooling system holds 16 L of water. How much heat does it absorb if its temperature rises from 20°C to 90°C?

9. (I) What is the specific heat of a metal substance if 135 kJ of heat is needed to raise 5.1 kg of the metal from 18.0°C to 31.5°C?

10. (II) Samples of copper, aluminum, and water experience the same temperature rise when they absorb the same amount of heat. What is the ratio of their masses? [*Hint*: See Table 14–1.]

11. (II) A 35-g glass thermometer reads 21.6°C before it is placed in 135 mL of water. When the water and thermometer come to equilibrium, the thermometer reads 39.2°C. What was the original temperature of the water?

12. (II) What will be the equilibrium temperature when a 245-g block of copper at 285°C is placed in a 145-g aluminum calorimeter cup containing 825 g of water at 12.0°C?

13. (II) A hot iron horseshoe (mass = 0.40 kg), just forged (Fig. 14–16), is dropped into 1.35 L of water in a 0.30-kg iron pot initially at 20.0°C. If the final equilibrium temperature is 25.0°C, estimate the initial temperature of the hot horseshoe.

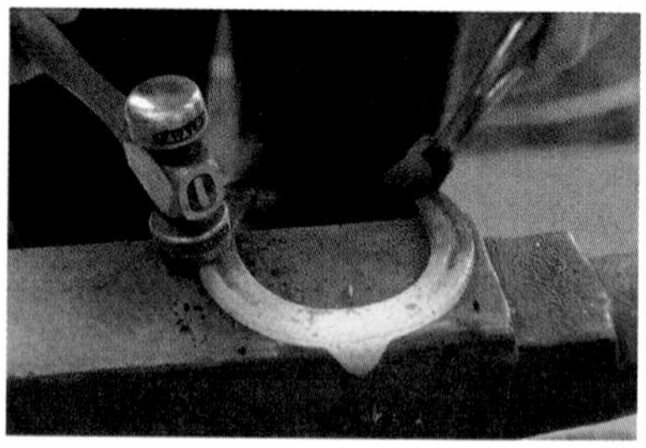

**FIGURE 14–16**
Problem 13.

14. (II) A 215-g sample of a substance is heated to 330°C and then plunged into a 105-g aluminum calorimeter cup containing 165 g of water and a 17-g glass thermometer at 12.5°C. The final temperature is 35.0°C. What is the specific heat of the substance? (Assume no water boils away.)

15. (II) How long does it take a 750-W coffeepot to bring to a boil 0.75 L of water initially at 8.0°C? Assume that the part of the pot which is heated with the water is made of 360 g of aluminum, and that no water boils away.

16. (II) Estimate the Calorie content of 75 g of candy from the following measurements. A 15-g sample of the candy is allowed to dry before putting it in a bomb calorimeter. The aluminum bomb has a mass of 0.725 kg and is placed in 2.00 kg of water contained in an aluminum calorimeter cup of mass 0.624 kg. The initial temperature of the mixture is 15.0°C, and its temperature after ignition is 53.5°C.

17. (II) When a 290-g piece of iron at 180°C is placed in a 95-g aluminum calorimeter cup containing 250 g of glycerin at 10°C, the final temperature is observed to be 38°C. Estimate the specific heat of glycerin.

18. (II) The 1.20-kg head of a hammer has a speed of 6.5 m/s just before it strikes a nail (Fig. 14–17) and is brought to rest. Estimate the temperature rise of a 14-g iron nail generated by 10 such hammer blows done in quick succession. Assume the nail absorbs all the energy.

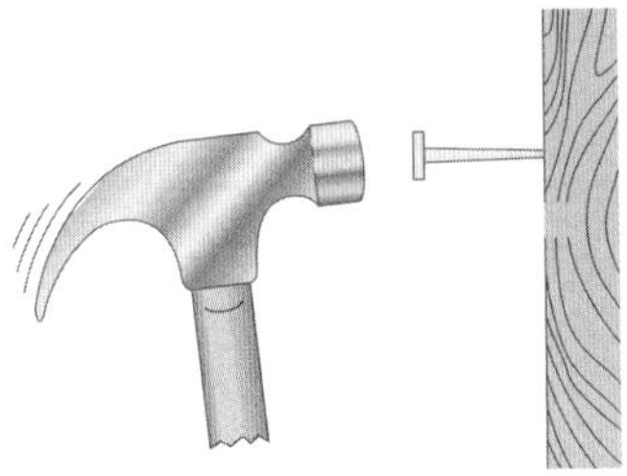

**FIGURE 14–17** Problem 18.

19. (II) A 0.095-kg aluminium sphere is dropped from the roof of a 45-m-high building. If 65% of the thermal energy produced when it hits the ground is absorbed by the sphere, what is its temperature increase?

20. (II) The *heat capacity, C*, of an object is defined as the amount of heat needed to raise its temperature by 1 C°. Thus, to raise the temperature by $\Delta T$ requires heat $Q$ given by

$$Q = C\,\Delta T.$$

(*a*) Write the heat capacity $C$ in terms of the specific heat, $c$, of the material. (*b*) What is the heat capacity of 1.0 kg of water? (*c*) Of 25 kg of water?

### 14–5 Latent Heat

21. (I) How much heat is needed to melt 16.50 kg of silver that is initially at 20°C?

22. (I) During exercise, a person may give off 180 kcal of heat in 30 min by evaporation of water from the skin. How much water has been lost?

23. (I) If $2.80 \times 10^5$ J of energy is supplied to a flask of liquid oxygen at −183°C, how much oxygen can evaporate?

24. (II) A 30-g ice cube at its melting point is dropped into an insulated container of liquid nitrogen. How much nitrogen evaporates if it is at its boiling point of 77 K and has a latent heat of vaporization of 200 kJ/kg? Assume for simplicity that the specific heat of ice is a constant and is equal to its value near its melting point.

25. (II) A cube of ice is taken from the freezer at −8.5°C and placed in a 95-g aluminum calorimeter filled with 310 g of water at room temperature of 20.0°C. The final situation is observed to be all water at 17.0°C. What was the mass of the ice cube?

26. (II) An iron boiler of mass 230 kg contains 830 kg of water at 18°C. A heater supplies energy at the rate of 52,000 kJ/h. How long does it take for the water (*a*) to reach the boiling point, and (*b*) to all have changed to steam?

27. (II) In a hot day's race, a bicyclist consumes 8.0 L of water over the span of four hours. Making the approximation that all of the cyclist's energy goes into evaporating this water as sweat, how much energy in kcal did the rider use during the ride? (Since the efficiency of the rider is only about 20%, most of the energy consumed does go to heat, so our approximation is not far off.)

28. (II) What mass of steam at 100°C must be added to 1.00 kg of ice at 0°C to yield liquid water at 20°C?

29. (II) The specific heat of mercury is 138 J/kg·C°. Determine the latent heat of fusion of mercury using the following calorimeter data: 1.00 kg of solid Hg at its melting point of −39.0°C is placed in a 0.620-kg aluminum calorimeter with 0.400 kg of water at 12.80°C; the resulting equilibrium temperature is 5.06°C.

30. (II) A 70-g bullet traveling at 250 m/s penetrates a block of ice at 0°C and comes to rest within the ice. Assuming that the temperature of the bullet doesn't change appreciably, how much ice is melted as a result of the collision?

31. (II) A 54.0-kg ice-skater moving at 6.4 m/s glides to a stop. Assuming the ice is at 0°C and that 50% of the heat generated by friction is absorbed by the ice, how much ice melts?

32. (II) At a crime scene, the forensic investigator notes that the 8.2-g lead bullet that was stopped in a doorframe apparently melted completely on impact. Assuming the bullet was fired at room temperature (20°C), what does the investigator calculate as the *minimum* muzzle velocity of the gun?

### 14–6 to 14–8 Conduction, Convection, Radiation

33. (I) One end of a 33-cm-long aluminum rod with a diameter of 2.0 cm is kept at 460°C, and the other is immersed in water at 22°C. Calculate the heat conduction rate along the rod.

34. (I) Calculate the rate of heat flow by conduction in Example 14–10, assuming that there are strong gusty winds and the external temperature is −5°C.

35. (I) (*a*) How much power is radiated by a tungsten sphere (emissivity $e = 0.35$) of radius 22 cm at a temperature of 25°C? (*b*) If the sphere is enclosed in a room whose walls are kept at −5°C, what is the *net* flow rate of energy out of the sphere?

36. (II) *Heat conduction to skin*. Suppose 200 W of heat flows by conduction from the blood capillaries beneath the skin to the body's surface area of 1.5 m². If the temperature difference is 0.50 C°, estimate the average distance of capillaries below the skin surface.

37. (II) Two rooms, each a cube 4.0 m per side, share a 12-cm-thick brick wall. Because of a number of 100-W lightbulbs in one room, the air is at 30°C, while in the other room it is at 10°C. How many of the 100-W bulbs are needed to maintain the temperature difference across the wall?

38. (II) How long does it take the Sun to melt a block of ice at 0°C with a flat horizontal area 1.0 m² and thickness 1.0 cm? Assume that the Sun's rays make an angle of 30° with the vertical and that the emissivity of ice is 0.050.

39. (II) A copper rod and an aluminum rod of the same length and cross-sectional area are attached end to end (Fig. 14–18). The copper end is placed in a furnace maintained at a constant temperature of 250°C. The aluminum end is placed in an ice bath held at constant temperature of 0.0°C. Calculate the temperature at the point where the two rods are joined.

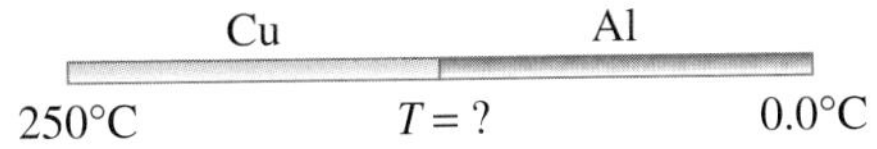


**FIGURE 14–18** Problem 39.

40. (II) (*a*) Using the solar constant, estimate the rate at which the whole Earth receives energy from the Sun. (*b*) Assume the Earth radiates an equal amount back into space (that is, the Earth is in equilibrium). Then, assuming the Earth is a perfect emitter ($e = 1.0$), estimate its average surface temperature.

41. (II) A 100-W lightbulb generates 95 W of heat, which is dissipated through a glass bulb that has a radius of 3.0 cm and is 1.0 mm thick. What is the difference in temperature between the inner and outer surfaces of the glass?

42. (III) Suppose the insulating qualities of the wall of a house come mainly from a 4.0-in. layer of brick and an *R*-19 layer of insulation, as shown in Fig. 14–19. What is the total rate of heat loss through such a wall, if its total area is 240 ft$^2$ and the temperature difference across it is 12 F°?

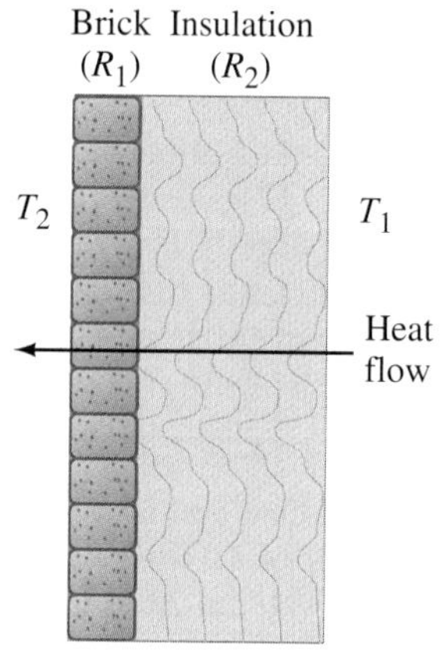


**FIGURE 14–19** Two layers insulating a wall. Problem 42.

43. (III) A double-glazed window has two panes of glass separated by an air space, Fig. 14–20. (*a*) Show that the rate of heat flow through such a window by conduction is given by

$$\frac{Q}{t} = \frac{A(T_2 - T_1)}{l_1/k_1 + l_2/k_2 + l_3/k_3},$$

where $k_1$, $k_2$, and $k_3$ are the thermal conductivities for glass, air, and glass, respectively. (*b*) Generalize this expression for any number of materials placed next to one another.

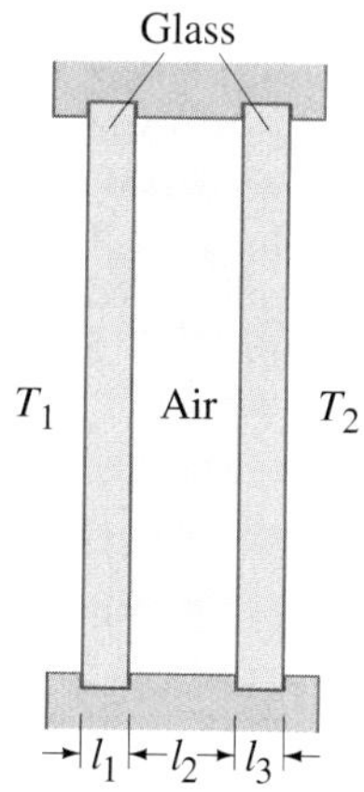


**FIGURE 14–20** Problem 43.

44. (III) Approximately how long should it take 11.0 kg of ice at 0°C to melt when it is placed in a carefully sealed Styrofoam ice chest of dimensions 25 cm × 35 cm × 55 cm whose walls are 1.5 cm thick? Assume that the conductivity of Styrofoam is double that of air and that the outside temperature is 32°C.

## General Problems

45. A soft-drink can contains about 0.20 kg of liquid at 5°C. Drinking this liquid can actually consume some of the fat in the body, since energy is needed to warm the water to body temperature (37°C). How many food Calories should the drink have so that it is in perfect balance with the heat needed to warm the liquid?

46. If coal gives off 30 MJ/kg when it is burned, how much coal would be needed to heat a house that requires $2.0 \times 10^5$ MJ for the whole winter? Assume that 30% of the heat is lost up the chimney.

47. To get an idea of how much thermal energy is contained in the world's oceans, estimate the heat liberated when a cube of ocean water, 1 km on each side, is cooled by 1 K. (Approximate the ocean water as pure water for this estimate.)

48. A 15-g lead bullet is tested by firing it into a fixed block of wood with a mass of 1.05 kg. The block and imbedded bullet together absorb all the heat generated. After thermal equilibrium has been reached, the system has a temperature rise measured as 0.020 C°. Estimate the entering speed of the bullet.

49. (*a*) Find the total power radiated into space by the Sun, assuming it to be a perfect emitter at $T = 5500$ K. The Sun's radius is $7.0 \times 10^8$ m. (*b*) From this, determine the power per unit area arriving at the Earth, $1.5 \times 10^{11}$ m away (Fig. 14–21).

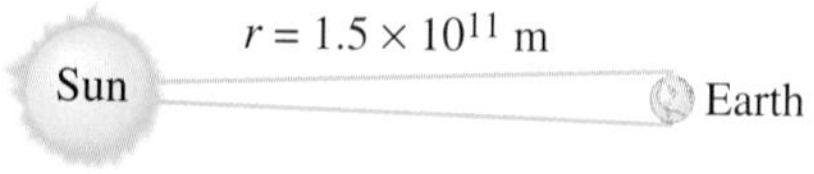


**FIGURE 14–21** Problem 49.

50. During light activity, a 70-kg person may generate 200 kcal/h. Assuming that 20% of this goes into useful work and the other 80% is converted to heat, calculate the temperature rise of the body after 1.00 h if none of this heat were transferred to the environment.

51. A 340-kg marble boulder rolls off the top of a cliff and falls a vertical height of 140 m before striking the ground. Estimate the temperature rise of the rock if 50% of the heat generated remains in the rock.

52. A 2.3-kg lead ball is dropped into a 2.5-L insulated pail of water initially at 20.0°C. If the final temperature of the water–lead combination is 28.0°C, what was the initial temperature of the lead ball?

53. A mountain climber wears a goose down jacket 3.5 cm thick with total surface area 1.2 m$^2$. The temperature at the surface of the clothing is −20°C and at the skin is 34°C. Determine the rate of heat flow by conduction through the jacket (*a*) assuming it is dry and the thermal conductivity $k$ is that of down, and (*b*) assuming the jacket is wet, so $k$ is that of water and the jacket has matted to 0.50 cm thickness.

54. A marathon runner has an average metabolism rate of about 950 kcal/h during a race. If the runner has a mass of 55 kg, estimate how much water she would lose to evaporation from the skin for a race that lasts 2.5 h.

55. Estimate the rate at which heat can be conducted from the interior of the body to the surface. Assume that the thickness of tissue is 4.0 cm, that the skin is at 34°C and the interior at 37°C, and that the surface area is 1.5 m$^2$. Compare this to the measured value of about 230 W that must be dissipated by a person working lightly. This clearly shows the necessity of convective cooling by the blood.

56. A house has well-insulated walls 17.5 cm thick (assume conductivity of air) and area $410\,m^2$, a roof of wood 6.5 cm thick and area $280\,m^2$, and uncovered windows 0.65 cm thick and total area $33\,m^2$. (*a*) Assuming that heat is lost only by conduction, calculate the rate at which heat must be supplied to this house to maintain its inside temperature at 23°C if the outside temperature is −10°C. (*b*) If the house is initially at 10°C, estimate how much heat must be supplied to raise the temperature to 23°C within 30 min. Assume that only the air needs to be heated and that its volume is $750\,m^3$. (*c*) If natural gas costs \$0.080 per kilogram and its heat of combustion is $5.4 \times 10^7\,J/kg$, how much is the monthly cost to maintain the house as in part (*a*) for 24 h each day, assuming 90% of the heat produced is used to heat the house? Take the specific heat of air to be 0.24 kcal/kg·C°.

57. A 15-g lead bullet traveling at 220 m/s passes through a thin wall and emerges at a speed of 160 m/s. If the bullet absorbs 50% of the heat generated, (*a*) what will be the temperature rise of the bullet? (*b*) If the bullet's initial temperature was 20°C, will any of the bullet melt, and if so, how much?

58. A leaf of area $40\,cm^2$ and mass $4.5 \times 10^{-4}\,kg$ directly faces the Sun on a clear day. The leaf has an emissivity of 0.85 and a specific heat of 0.80 kcal/kg·K. (*a*) Estimate the rate of rise of the leaf's temperature. (*b*) Calculate the temperature the leaf would reach if it lost all its heat by radiation to the surroundings at 20°C. (*c*) In what other ways can the heat be dissipated by the leaf?

59. Using the result of part (*a*) in Problem 58, take into account radiation from the leaf to calculate how much water must be transpired (evaporated) by the leaf per hour to maintain a temperature of 35°C.

60. An iron meteorite melts when it enters the Earth's atmosphere. If its initial temperature was −125°C outside of Earth's atmosphere, calculate the minimum velocity the meteorite must have had before it entered Earth's atmosphere.

61. The temperature within the Earth's crust increases about 1.0 C° for each 30 m of depth. The thermal conductivity of the crust is 0.80 W/C°·m. (*a*) Determine the heat transferred from the interior to the surface for the entire Earth in 1 day. (*b*) Compare this heat to the amount of energy incident on the Earth in 1 day due to radiation from the Sun.

62. In a typical game of squash (Fig. 14–22), two people hit a soft rubber ball at a wall until they are about to drop due to dehydration and exhaustion. Assume that the ball hits the wall at a velocity of 22 m/s and bounces back with a velocity of 12 m/s, and that the kinetic energy lost in the process heats the ball. What will be the temperature increase of the ball after one bounce? (The specific heat of rubber is about 1200 J/kg·C°.)

**FIGURE 14–22** Problem 62.

63. What will be the final result when equal masses of ice at 0°C and steam at 100°C are mixed together?

64. In a cold environment, a person can lose heat by conduction and radiation at a rate of about 200 W. Estimate how long it would take for the body temperature to drop from 36.6°C to 35.6°C if metabolism were nearly to stop. Assume a mass of 70 kg. (See Table 14–1.)

65. After a hot shower and dishwashing, there is "no hot water" left in the 50-gal (185-L) water heater. This suggests that the tank has emptied and refilled with water at roughly 10°C. (*a*) How much energy does it take to reheat the water to 50°C? (*b*) How long would it take if the heater output is 9500 W?

66. The temperature of the glass surface of a 60-W lightbulb is 65°C when the room temperature is 18°C. Estimate the temperature of a 150-W lightbulb with a glass bulb the same size. Consider only radiation, and assume that 90% of the energy is emitted as heat.

## Answers to Exercises

**A:** 0.21 kg.

**B:** The drapes trap a layer of air between the outside wall and the room, which acts as an excellent insulator.

Thermodynamics is the study of heat and work. Heat is a transfer of energy due to a difference of temperature; work is a transfer of energy by mechanical means, not due to a temperature difference. The first law of thermodynamics is a general statement of energy conservation: the heat $Q$ added to a system minus the net work $W$ done by the system equals the change in internal energy $\Delta U$ of the system: $\Delta U = Q - W$. The photos show two uses for a heat engine: a modern coal-burning power plant, and an old steam locomotive. Both produce steam which does work—on turbines to generate electricity, and on a piston that moves linkage to turn locomotive wheels. The efficiency of any engine is limited by nature as described in the second law of thermodynamics. This great law is best stated in terms of a quantity called entropy, which is *not* conserved, but instead is constrained always to increase in any real process. Entropy is a measure of disorder. The second law of thermodynamics tells us that as time moves forward, the disorder in the universe increases.

CHAPTER 15

# The Laws of Thermodynamics

**Thermodynamics** is the name we give to the study of processes in which energy is transferred as heat and as work.

In Chapter 6 we saw that work is done when energy is transferred from one object to another by mechanical means. In Chapter 14 we saw that heat is a transfer of energy from one object to a second one at a lower temperature. Thus, heat is much like work. To distinguish them, *heat* is defined as a *transfer of energy due to a difference in temperature*, whereas work is a transfer of energy that is not due to a temperature difference.

*Heat distinguished from work*

In discussing thermodynamics, we often refer to particular systems. A **system** is any object or set of objects that we wish to consider (see Section 14–4). Everything else in the universe will be referred to as the "environment" or the "surroundings."

In this Chapter, we examine the two great laws of thermodynamics. The first law of thermodynamics relates work and heat transfers to the change in internal energy of a system, and is a general statement of the conservation of energy. The second law of thermodynamics expresses limits on the ability to do useful work, and is often stated in terms of *entropy*, which is a measure of disorder. Besides these two great laws, we also discuss some important related practical devices: heat engines, refrigerators, heat pumps, and air conditioners.

## 15–1 The First Law of Thermodynamics

In Section 14–2, we defined the internal energy of a system as the sum total of all the energy of the molecules of the system. We would expect that the internal energy of a system would be increased if work was done on the system, or if heat were added to it. Similarly the internal energy would be decreased if heat flowed out of the system or if work were done by the system on something in the surroundings.

Thus it is reasonable to extend the work-energy principle and propose an important law: the change in internal energy of a closed system, $\Delta U$, will be equal to the energy added to the system by heating minus the work done by the system on the surroundings. In equation form we write

*FIRST LAW OF THERMODYNAMICS*

$$\Delta U = Q - W \tag{15–1}$$

*Heat added is +*
*Heat lost is −*
*Work on system is −*
*Work by system is +*

where $Q$ is the net heat *added* to the system and $W$ is the net work done *by* the system. We must be careful and consistent in following the sign conventions for $Q$ and $W$. Because $W$ in Eq. 15–1 is the work done *by* the system, then if work is done *on* the system, $W$ will be negative and $U$ will increase. Similarly, $Q$ is positive for heat added to the system, so if heat leaves the system, $Q$ is negative.

Equation 15–1 is known as the **first law of thermodynamics**. It is one of the great laws of physics, and its validity rests on experiments (such as Joule's) to which no exceptions have been seen. Since $Q$ and $W$ represent energy transferred into or out of the system, the internal energy changes accordingly. Thus, the first law of thermodynamics is a great and broad statement of the *law of conservation of energy*.

*First law of thermodynamics is conservation of energy*

It is worth noting that the conservation of energy law was not formulated until the nineteenth century, for it depended on the interpretation of heat as a transfer of energy.

A given system at any moment is in a particular state and can be said to have a certain amount of internal energy, $U$. But a system does not "have" a certain amount of heat or work. Rather, when work is done on a system (such as compressing a gas), or when heat is added or removed from a system, the state of the system *changes*. Thus, work and heat are involved in *thermodynamic processes* that can change the system from one state to another; they are not characteristic of the state itself. Quantities which describe the state of a system, such as internal energy $U$, pressure $P$, volume $V$, temperature $T$, and mass $m$ or number of moles $n$, are called **state variables**. $Q$ and $W$ are *not* state variables.

*Internal energy is a property of the system; work and heat are not*

**EXAMPLE 15–1** **Using the first law.** 2500 J of heat is added to a system, and 1800 J of work is done on the system. What is the change in internal energy of the system?

**APPROACH** We apply the first law of thermodynamics, Eq. 15–1, to our system.

**SOLUTION** The heat added to the system is $Q = 2500\,\text{J}$. The work $W$ done *by* the system is $-1800\,\text{J}$. Why the minus sign? Because 1800 J done *on* the system (as given) equals $-1800\,\text{J}$ done *by* the system, and it is the latter we need to put in Eq. 15–1 by the sign conventions given above. Hence

$$\Delta U = 2500\,\text{J} - (-1800\,\text{J}) = 2500\,\text{J} + 1800\,\text{J} = 4300\,\text{J}.$$

You may have intuitively thought that the 2500 J and the 1800 J would need to be added together, since both refer to energy added to the system. You would have been right.

**NOTE** We did this calculation in detail to emphasize the importance of keeping careful track of signs.

**EXERCISE A** What would be the internal energy change in Example 15–1 if 2500 J of heat is added to the system and 1800 J of work is done *by* the system (i.e., as output)?

## * The First Law of Thermodynamics Extended

To be really complete about the first law, consider a system that is moving, so it has kinetic energy KE, and suppose there is also potential energy PE. Then the first law of thermodynamics would have to include these terms and would be written as

$$\Delta \text{KE} + \Delta \text{PE} + \Delta U = Q - W. \qquad \textbf{(15–2)}$$

**EXAMPLE 15–2** **Kinetic energy transformed to thermal energy.** A 3.0-g bullet traveling at a speed of 400 m/s enters a tree and exits the other side with a speed of 200 m/s. Where did the bullet's lost KE go, and what was the energy transferred?

**APPROACH** Take the bullet and tree as our system. No potential energy is involved. No work is done on (or by) the system by outside forces, nor is any heat added because no energy was transferred to or from the system due to a temperature difference. Thus the kinetic energy gets transformed into internal energy of the bullet and tree.

**SOLUTION** From the first law of thermodynamics as given in Eq. 15–2, we are given $Q = W = \Delta\text{PE} = 0,$ so we have

$$\Delta \text{KE} + \Delta U = 0$$

or

$$\Delta U = -\Delta\text{KE} = -(\text{KE}_\text{f} - \text{KE}_\text{i}) = \tfrac{1}{2}m(v_\text{i}^2 - v_\text{f}^2)$$
$$= \tfrac{1}{2}(3.0 \times 10^{-3}\,\text{kg})\left[(400\,\text{m/s})^2 - (200\,\text{m/s})^2\right] = 180\,\text{J}.$$

**NOTE** The internal energy of the bullet and tree both increase, as both experience a rise in temperature. If we had chosen the bullet alone as our system, work would be done on it and heat transfer would occur.

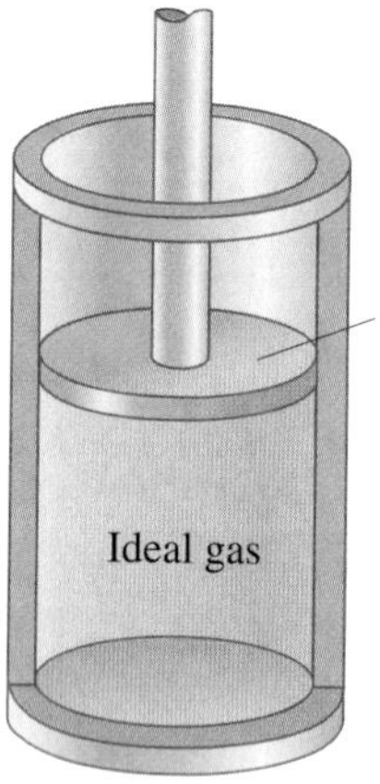


**FIGURE 15–1** An ideal gas in a cylinder fitted with a movable piston.

## 15–2 Thermodynamic Processes and the First Law

Let us analyze some thermodynamic processes in light of the first law of thermodynamics. To begin, we choose a very simple system: a fixed mass of an ideal gas enclosed in a container fitted with a movable piston as shown in Fig. 15–1.

*Isothermal process ($\Delta T = 0$)*

First we consider an idealized process that is carried out at constant temperature. Such a process is called an **isothermal** process (from the Greek meaning "same temperature"). If an isothermal process is carried out on our ideal gas, then $PV = nRT$ (Eq. 13–3) becomes $PV =$ constant. Thus the process follows a curve like AB on the $PV$ diagram shown in Fig. 15–2, which is a curve for $PV =$ constant (as in Fig. 13–12). Each point on the curve, such as point A, represents a state of the system—that is, its pressure $P$ and volume $V$ at a given moment. At a lower temperature, another isothermal process would be represented by a curve like A′B′ in Fig. 15–2 (the product $PV = nRT =$ constant is less when $T$ is less). The curves shown in Fig. 15–2 are referred to as *isotherms*.

*Heat reservoir*

**FIGURE 15–2** *PV* diagram for an ideal gas undergoing isothermal processes at two different temperatures.

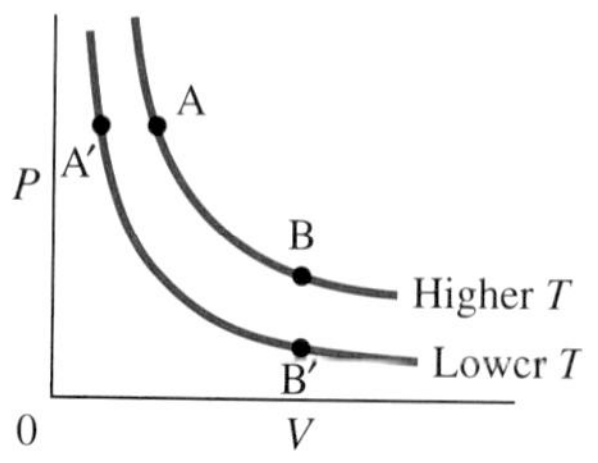


We assume that the gas is in contact with a **heat reservoir** (a body whose mass is so large that, ideally, its temperature does not change significantly when heat is exchanged with our system). We also assume that the process of compression (volume decrease) or expansion (volume increase) is done very slowly to make certain that all of the gas stays in equilibrium at the same constant temperature. If the gas is initially in a state represented by point A in Fig. 15–2, and an amount of heat $Q$ is added to the system, the pressure and volume will change and the state of the system will be represented by another point, B, on the diagram. If the temperature is to remain constant, the gas must expand and do an amount of work $W$ on the environment (it exerts a force on the piston in Fig. 15–1 and moves it through a distance). The temperature is kept constant so, from Eq. 14–1, the internal energy does not change: $\Delta U = \tfrac{3}{2}nR\,\Delta T = 0.$ Hence, by the first law of thermodynamics (Eq. 15–1), $\Delta U = Q - W = 0,$ so $W = Q$: the work done by the gas in an isothermal process equals the heat added to the gas.

*Isothermal process (ideal gas): $T =$ constant, $\Delta U = 0$, $Q = W$*

An **adiabatic** process is one in which no heat is allowed to flow into or out of the system: $Q = 0$. This situation can occur if the system is extremely well insulated, or the process happens so quickly that heat—which flows slowly—has no time to flow in or out. The very rapid expansion of gases in an internal combustion engine is one example of a process that is very nearly adiabatic. A slow adiabatic expansion of an ideal gas follows a curve like that labeled AC in Fig. 15–3. Since $Q = 0$, we have from Eq. 15–1 that $\Delta U = -W$. That is, the internal energy decreases if the gas expands; hence the temperature decreases as well (because $\Delta U = \frac{3}{2}nR\,\Delta T$). This is evident in Fig. 15–3 where the product $PV\ (= nRT)$ is less at point C than at point B (curve AB is for an isothermal process, for which $\Delta U = 0$ and $\Delta T = 0$). In the reverse operation, an adiabatic compression (going from C to A, for example), work is done *on* the gas, and hence the internal energy increases and the temperature rises. In a diesel engine, the fuel–air mixture is rapidly compressed adiabatically by a factor of 15 or more; the temperature rise is so great that the mixture ignites spontaneously.

*Adiabatic process ($Q = 0$)*

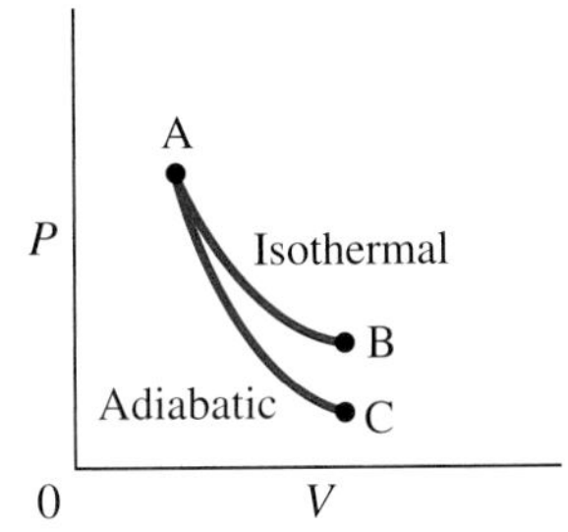


**FIGURE 15–3** *PV* diagram for adiabatic (AC) and isothermal (AB) processes on an ideal gas.

Isothermal and adiabatic processes are just two possible processes that can occur. Two other simple thermodynamic processes are illustrated on the *PV* diagrams of Fig. 15–4: (*a*) an **isobaric** process is one in which the pressure is kept constant, so the process is represented by a straight horizontal line on the *PV* diagram (Fig. 15–4a); (*b*) an **isovolumetric** or *isochoric* process is one in which the volume does not change (Fig. 15–4b). In these, and in all other processes, the first law of thermodynamics holds.

*Isobaric process: $P$ = constant, $W = P\,\Delta V$*

*Isovolumetric process: $V$ = constant, $W = 0$*

**FIGURE 15–4** (a) Isobaric ("same pressure") process. (b) Isovolumetric ("same volume") process.

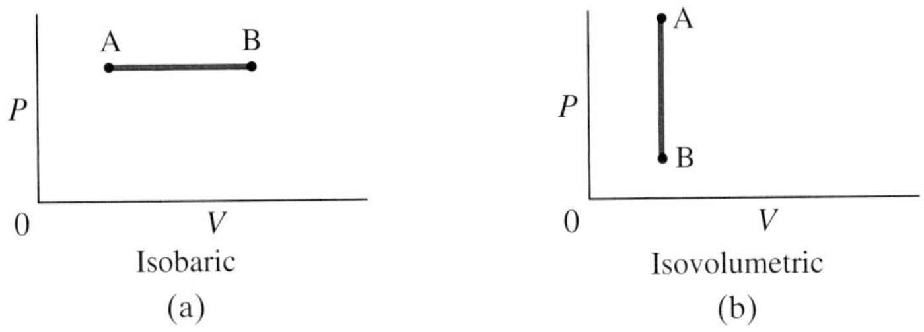


**FIGURE 15–5** Work is done on the piston when the gas expands, moving the piston a distance *d*.

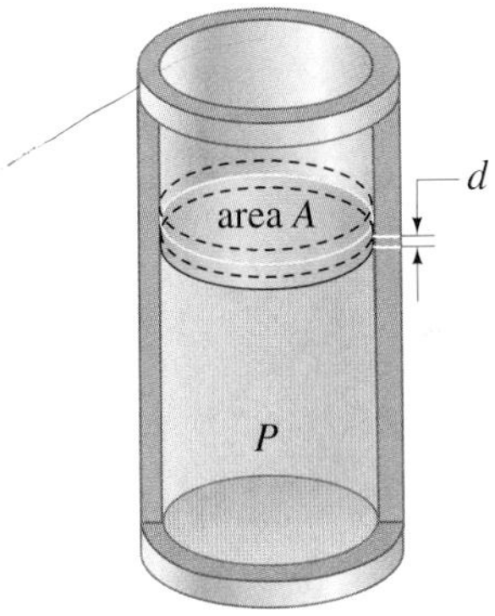


It is often valuable to calculate the work done in a process. If the pressure is kept constant during a process (isobaric), the work done is easily calculated. For example, if the gas in Fig. 15–5 expands slowly against the piston, the work done by the gas to raise the piston is the force $F$ times the distance $d$. But the force is just the pressure $P$ of the gas times the area $A$ of the piston, $F = PA$. Thus,

$$W = Fd = PAd.$$

Because $Ad = \Delta V$, the change in volume of the gas, then

*Work done in volume changes*

$$W = P\,\Delta V. \qquad \text{[constant pressure]} \quad \textbf{(15–3)}$$

Equation 15–3 also holds if the gas is *compressed* at constant pressure, in which case $\Delta V$ is negative (since $V$ decreases); $W$ is then negative, which indicates that work is done *on* the gas. Equation 15–3 is also valid for liquids and solids, as long as the pressure is constant during the process.

In an isovolumetric process (Fig. 15–4b) the volume does not change, so no work is done, $W = 0$.

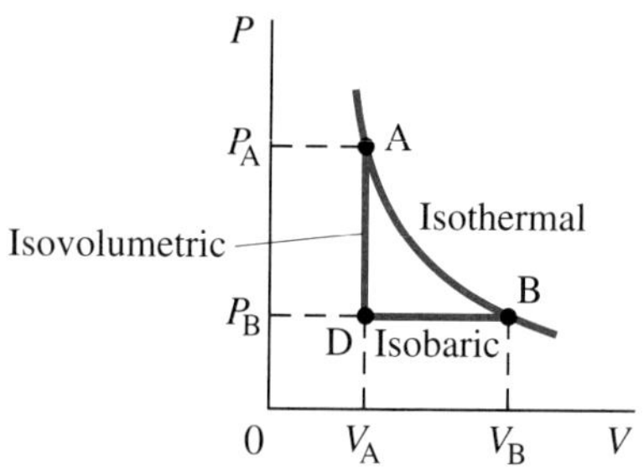


**FIGURE 15–6** *PV* diagram for different processes (see the text), where the system changes from A to B.

Figure 15–6 shows the isotherm AB we saw in Fig. 15–2 as well as another possible process represented by the path ADB. In going from A to D, the gas does no work since the volume does not change. But in going from D to B, the gas does work equal to $P_B(V_B - V_A)$, and this is the total work done in the process ADB.

*Work = area under PV curve*

If the pressure varies during a process, such as for the isothermal process AB in Fig. 15–2, Eq. 15–3 cannot be used directly to determine the work. A rough estimate can be obtained, however, by using an "average" value for $P$ in Eq. 15–3. More accurately, the work done is equal to the area under the *PV* curve. This is obvious when the pressure is constant: as Fig. 15–7a shows, the shaded area is just $P_B(V_B - V_A)$, and this is the work done. Similarly, the work done during an isothermal process is equal to the shaded area shown in Fig. 15–7b. The calculation of work done in this case can be carried out using calculus, or by estimating the area on graph paper.

**FIGURE 15–7** Work done by a gas is equal to the area under the *PV* curve.

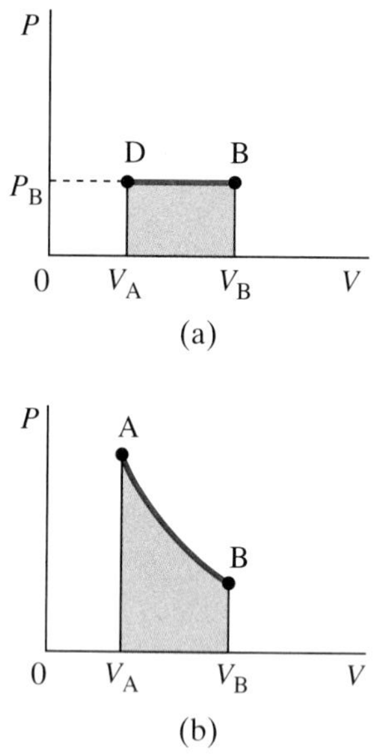


**CONCEPTUAL EXAMPLE 15–3** **Work in isothermal and adiabatic processes.** In Fig. 15–3 we saw the *PV* diagrams for a gas expanding in two ways, isothermally and adiabatically. The initial volume $V_A$ was the same in each case, and the final volumes were the same $(V_B = V_C)$. In which process was more work done by the gas?

**RESPONSE** Our system is the gas. More work was done by the gas in the isothermal process, which we can see in two simple ways by looking at Fig. 15–3. First, the "average" pressure was higher during the isothermal process AB, so $W = P_{av}\,\Delta V$ was greater ($\Delta V$ is the same for both processes). Second, we can look at the area under each curve: the area under curve AB, which represents the work done, was greater (since curve AB is higher) than that under AC.

**EXERCISE B** Is the work done by the gas in process ADB of Fig. 15–6 greater than, less than, or equal to the work done in the isothermal process AB?

**CONCEPTUAL EXAMPLE 15–4** **Simple adiabatic process.** Here is an example of an adiabatic process that you can do with just a rubber band. Hold a thin rubber band loosely with two hands and gauge its temperature with your lips. Stretch the rubber band suddenly and again touch it lightly to your lips. You should notice an increase in temperature. Explain clearly why the temperature increases.

**RESPONSE** Stretching the rubber band *suddenly* makes the process adiabatic because there is no time for heat to enter or leave the system (the rubber band), so $Q = 0$. You do work on the system, representing an energy input, so $W$ is negative in Eq. 15–1 $(\Delta U = Q - W)$. Hence $\Delta U$ must be positive. An increase in internal energy corresponds to an increase in temperature (for an ideal gas it is given by Eq. 14–1).

Table 15–1 gives a brief summary of the processes we have discussed.

**TABLE 15–1 Simple Thermodynamic Processes and the First Law**

| Process | What is constant: | The first law predicts: |
|---|---|---|
| Isothermal | $T$ = constant | $\Delta T = 0$ makes $\Delta U = 0$, so $Q = W$ |
| Isobaric | $P$ = constant | $Q = \Delta U + W = \Delta U + P\,\Delta V$ |
| Isovolumetric | $V$ = constant | $\Delta V = 0$ makes $W = 0$, so $Q = \Delta U$ |
| Adiabatic | $Q = 0$ | $\Delta U = -W$ |

**EXAMPLE 15–5** **First law in isobaric and isovolumetric processes.** An ideal gas is slowly compressed at a constant pressure of 2.0 atm from 10.0 L to 2.0 L. This process is represented in Fig. 15–8 as the path B to D. (In this process, some heat flows out of the gas and the temperature drops.) Heat is then added to the gas, holding the volume constant, and the pressure and temperature are allowed to rise (line DA) until the temperature reaches its original value $(T_A = T_B)$. Calculate $(a)$ the total work done by the gas in the process BDA, and $(b)$ the total heat flow into the gas.

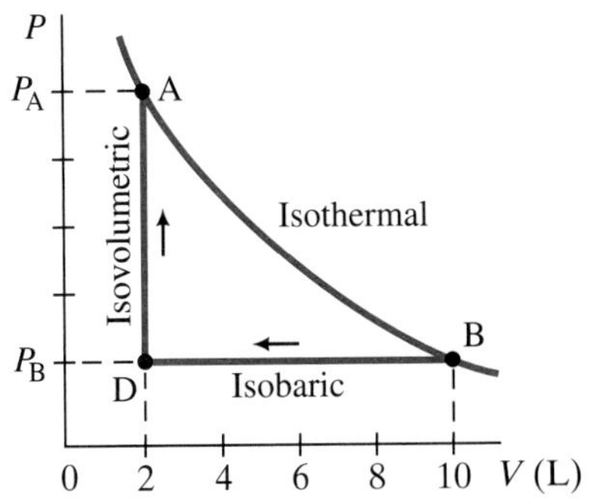


**FIGURE 15–8** Example 15–5.

**APPROACH** $(a)$ Work is done only in the compression process BD. In process DA, the volume is constant so $\Delta V = 0$ and no work is done (Eq. 15–3). $(b)$ We use the first law of thermodynamics, Eq. 15–1.

**SOLUTION** $(a)$ During the compression BD, the pressure is 2.0 atm = $2(1.01 \times 10^5\,\text{N/m}^2)$ and the change in volume is

$$\Delta V = \left(2.0 \times 10^{-3}\,\text{m}^3\right) - \left(10.0 \times 10^{-3}\,\text{m}^3\right) = -8.0 \times 10^{-3}\,\text{m}^3.$$

Then the work done is

$$W = P\,\Delta V = \left(2.02 \times 10^5\,\text{N/m}^2\right)\left(-8.0 \times 10^{-3}\,\text{m}^3\right) = -1.6 \times 10^3\,\text{J}.$$

The total work done by the gas is $-1.6 \times 10^3$ J, where the minus sign means that $+1.6 \times 10^3$ J of work is done *on* the gas.

$(b)$ Because the temperature at the beginning and at the end of process BDA is the same, there is no change in internal energy: $\Delta U = 0$. From the first law of thermodynamics we have

$$0 = \Delta U = Q - W,$$

so

$$Q = W = -1.6 \times 10^3\,\text{J}.$$

Since $Q$ is negative, 1600 J of heat flows out of the gas for the whole process, BDA.

**EXERCISE C** In Example 15–5, if the heat lost from the gas in the process BD is $8.4 \times 10^3$ J, what is the change in internal energy of the gas during process BD?

## Additional Examples

**EXAMPLE 15–6** **Work done in an engine.** In an engine, 0.25 moles of an ideal monatomic gas in the cylinder expands rapidly and adiabatically against the piston. In the process, the temperature of the gas drops from 1150 K to 400 K. How much work does the gas do?

**APPROACH** We take the gas as our system (the piston is part of the surroundings). The pressure is not constant, so we can't use Eq. 15–3. Instead, we can use the first law of thermodynamics because we can determine $\Delta U$ given $Q = 0$ (the process is adiabatic).

**SOLUTION** We determine $\Delta U$ from Eq. 14–1 for the internal energy of an ideal monatomic gas:

$$\begin{aligned}\Delta U = U_f - U_i &= \tfrac{3}{2}nR(T_f - T_i)\\ &= \tfrac{3}{2}(0.25\,\text{mol})(8.314\,\text{J/mol}\cdot\text{K})(400\,\text{K} - 1150\,\text{K})\\ &= -2300\,\text{J}.\end{aligned}$$

Then, from the first law of thermodynamics, Eq. 15–1,

$$W = Q - \Delta U = 0 - (-2300\,\text{J}) = 2300\,\text{J}.$$

**EXAMPLE 15–7** **$\Delta U$ for boiling water to steam.** Determine the change in internal energy of 1.00 liter of water (mass 1.00 kg) at 100°C when it is fully boiled from liquid to gas, which results in 1671 liters of steam at 100°C. Assume the process is done at atmospheric pressure.

**APPROACH** Our system is the water. The heat required here does not result in a temperature change; rather, a change in phase occurs. We can determine the heat $Q$ required using the latent heat of water, as in Section 14–5. Work too will be done: $W = P\,\Delta V$. The first law of thermodynamics will then give us $\Delta U$.

**SOLUTION** The latent heat of vaporization of water (Table 14–3) is $L_V = 22.6 \times 10^5\ \mathrm{J/kg}$. So the heat input required for this process is

$$Q = mL = (1.00\ \mathrm{kg})(22.6 \times 10^5\ \mathrm{J/kg}) = 22.6 \times 10^5\ \mathrm{J}.$$

The work done by the water is (Eq. 15–3)

$$W = P\,\Delta V = (1.01 \times 10^5\ \mathrm{N/m^2})\left[(1671 \times 10^{-3}\ \mathrm{m^3}) - (1 \times 10^{-3}\ \mathrm{m^3})\right] = 1.69 \times 10^5\ \mathrm{J},$$

where we used $1\ \mathrm{atm} = 1.01 \times 10^5\ \mathrm{N/m^2}$ and $1\ \mathrm{L} = 10^3\ \mathrm{cm^3} = 10^{-3}\ \mathrm{m^3}$. Then

$$\Delta U = Q - W = (22.6 \times 10^5\ \mathrm{J}) - (1.7 \times 10^5\ \mathrm{J}) = 20.9 \times 10^5\ \mathrm{J}.$$

**NOTE** Most of the heat added goes to increasing the internal energy of the water (increasing molecular energy to overcome the attraction that held the molecules close together in the liquid state). Only a small part ($< 10\%$) goes into doing work.

**EXERCISE D** Equation 14–1, $U = \frac{3}{2}nRT$, tells us that $\Delta U = 0$ in Example 15–7 because $\Delta T = 0$. Yet we determined that $\Delta U = 21 \times 10^5\ \mathrm{J}$. What is wrong?

## * 15–3 Human Metabolism and the First Law

PHYSICS APPLIED
*Energy in the human body*

Human beings and other animals do work. Work is done when a person walks or runs, or lifts a heavy object. Work requires energy. Energy is also needed for growth—to make new cells, and to replace old cells that have died. A great many energy-transforming processes occur within an organism, and they are referred to as *metabolism*.

We can apply the first law of thermodynamics,

$$\Delta U = Q - W,$$

to an organism: say, the human body. Work $W$ is done by the body in its various activities; if this is not to result in a decrease in the body's internal energy (and temperature), energy must somehow be added to compensate. The body's internal energy is not maintained by a flow of heat $Q$ into the body, however. Normally, the body is at a higher temperature than its surroundings, so heat usually flows *out* of the body. Even on a very hot day when heat is absorbed, the body has no way of utilizing this heat to support its vital processes. What then is the source of energy that allows us to do work? It is the internal energy (chemical potential energy) stored in foods (Fig. 15–9). In a closed system, the internal energy changes only as a result of heat flow or work done. In an open system, such as a human, internal energy itself can flow into or out of the system. When we eat food, we are bringing internal energy into our bodies directly, which thus increases the total internal energy $U$ in our bodies. This energy eventually goes into work and heat flow from the body according to the first law.

**FIGURE 15–9** Bike rider getting an input of energy.

The metabolic rate is the rate at which internal energy is transformed within the body. It is usually specified in kcal/h or in watts. Typical metabolic rates for a variety of human activities are given in Table 15–2 for an "average" 65-kg adult.

**TABLE 15–2 Metabolic Rates (65-kg human)**

| Activity | Metabolic Rate (approximate) kcal/h | watts |
|---|---|---|
| Sleeping | 60 | 70 |
| Sitting upright | 100 | 115 |
| Light activity (eating, dressing, household chores) | 200 | 230 |
| Moderate work (tennis, walking) | 400 | 460 |
| Running (15 km/h) | 1000 | 1150 |
| Bicycling (race) | 1100 | 1270 |

**EXAMPLE 15–8** **Energy transformation in the body.** How much energy is transformed in 24 h by a 65-kg person who spends 8.0 h sleeping, 1.0 h at moderate physical labor, 4.0 h in light activity, and 11.0 h working at a desk or relaxing?

**APPROACH** The energy transformed during each activity equals the metabolic rate (Table 15–2) multiplied by the time.

**SOLUTION** Table 15–2 gives the metabolic rate in watts (J/s). Since there are 3600 s in an hour, the total energy transformed is

$$\left[\begin{array}{l}(8.0\,\mathrm{h})(70\,\mathrm{J/s}) + (1.0\,\mathrm{h})(460\,\mathrm{J/s}) \\ \quad + (4.0\,\mathrm{h})(230\,\mathrm{J/s}) + (11.0\,\mathrm{h})(115\,\mathrm{J/s})\end{array}\right](3600\,\mathrm{s/h}) = 1.15 \times 10^7\,\mathrm{J}.$$

**NOTE** Since $4.186 \times 10^3\,\mathrm{J} = 1\,\mathrm{kcal}$, this is equivalent to 2800 kcal; a food intake of 2800 Cal would compensate for this energy output. A 65-kg person who wanted to lose weight would have to eat less than 2800 Cal a day, or increase his or her level of activity.

## 15–4 The Second Law of Thermodynamics—Introduction

The first law of thermodynamics states that energy is conserved. There are, however, many processes we can imagine that conserve energy but are not observed to occur in nature. For example, when a hot object is placed in contact with a cold object, heat flows from the hotter one to the colder one, never spontaneously the reverse. If heat were to leave the colder object and pass to the hotter one, energy could still be conserved. Yet it doesn't happen spontaneously.† As a second example, consider what happens when you drop a rock and it hits the ground. The initial potential energy of the rock changes to kinetic energy as the rock falls. When the rock hits the ground, this energy in turn is transformed into internal energy of the rock and the ground in the vicinity of the impact; the molecules move faster and the temperature rises slightly. But have you seen the reverse happen—a rock at rest on the ground suddenly rise up in the air because the thermal energy of molecules is transformed into kinetic energy of the rock as a whole? Energy could be conserved in this process, yet we never see it happen.

There are many other examples of processes that occur in nature but whose reverse does not. Here are two more. (1) If you put a layer of salt in a jar and cover it with a layer of similar-sized grains of pepper, when you shake it you get a thorough mixture. But no matter how long you shake it, the mixture does not separate into two layers again. (2) Coffee cups and glasses break spontaneously if you drop them. But they don't go back together spontaneously (Fig. 15–10).

The first law of thermodynamics (conservation of energy) would not be violated if any of these processes occurred in reverse. To explain this lack of reversibility, scientists in the latter half of the nineteenth century formulated a new principle known as the second law of thermodynamics.

† By spontaneously, we mean by itself without input of work of some sort. (A refrigerator does move heat from a cold environment to a warmer one, but only by doing work.)

(a) Initial state. (b) Later: cup reassembles and rises up. (c) Later still: cup lands on table.

**FIGURE 15–10** Have you ever observed this process, a broken cup spontaneously reassembling and rising up onto a table?

The **second law of thermodynamics** is a statement about which processes occur in nature and which do not. It can be stated in a variety of ways, all of which are equivalent. One statement, due to R. J. E. Clausius (1822–1888), is that

*SECOND LAW OF THERMODYNAMICS (Clausius statement)*

**heat can flow spontaneously from a hot object to a cold object; heat will not flow spontaneously from a cold object to a hot object.**

Since this statement applies to one particular process, it is not obvious how it applies to other processes. A more general statement is needed that will include other possible processes in a more obvious way.

*Heat engine*

The development of a general statement of the second law of thermodynamics was based partly on the study of heat engines. A **heat engine** is any device that changes thermal energy into mechanical work, such as steam engines and automobile engines. We now examine heat engines, both from a practical point of view and to show their importance in developing the second law of thermodynamics.

## 15–5 Heat Engines

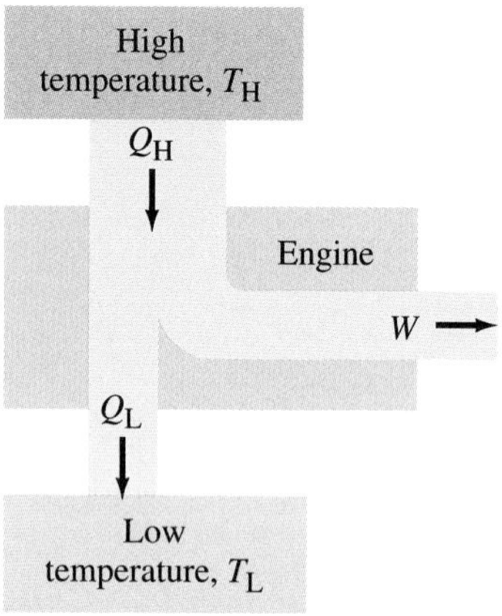


**FIGURE 15–11** Schematic diagram of energy transfers for a heat engine.

It is easy to produce thermal energy by doing work—for example, by simply rubbing your hands together briskly, or indeed by any frictional process. But to get work from thermal energy is more difficult, and a practical device to do this was invented only about 1700 with the development of the steam engine.

The basic idea behind any heat engine is that mechanical energy can be obtained from thermal energy only when heat is allowed to flow from a high temperature to a low temperature. In the process, some of the heat can then be transformed to mechanical work, as diagrammed schematically in Fig. 15–11. We will be interested only in engines that run in a repeating *cycle* (that is, the system returns repeatedly to its starting point) and thus can run continuously. In each cycle the change in internal energy of the system is $\Delta U = 0$ because it returns to the starting state. Thus a heat input $Q_H$ at a high temperature $T_H$ is partly transformed into work $W$ and partly exhausted as heat $Q_L$ at a lower temperature $T_L$ (Fig. 15–11). By conservation of energy, $Q_H = W + Q_L$. The high and low temperatures, $T_H$ and $T_L$, are called the **operating temperatures** of the engine. Note carefully that we are now using a new sign convention: we take $Q_H$, $Q_L$, and $W$ as always positive. The direction of each energy transfer is found from the applicable diagram, such as Fig. 15–11.

**CAUTION**
*New sign convention:* $Q_H > 0, Q_L > 0, W > 0$

### Steam Engine and Internal Combustion Engine

**PHYSICS APPLIED**
*Engines*

The operation of a steam engine is illustrated in Fig. 15–12. Steam engines are of two main types, each making use of steam heated by combustion of coal, oil,

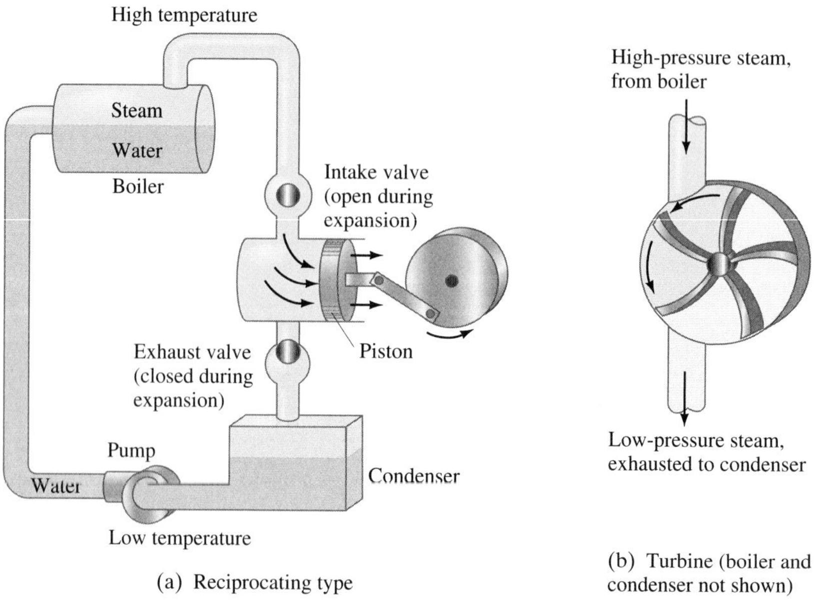


**FIGURE 15–12** Steam engines.

gas, or nuclear energy. In the so-called reciprocating type, Fig. 15–12a, the heated steam passes through the intake valve and expands against a piston, forcing it to move. As the piston returns to its original position, it forces the gases out the exhaust valve. In a steam turbine, Fig. 15–12b, everything is essentially the same, except that the reciprocating piston is replaced by a rotating turbine that resembles a paddlewheel with many sets of blades. Most of our electricity today is generated using steam turbines.† The material that is heated and cooled, steam in this case, is called the **working substance**. In a steam engine, the high temperature is obtained by burning coal, oil, or other fuel to heat the steam.

In an internal combustion engine (used in most automobiles), the high temperature is achieved by burning the gasoline–air mixture in the cylinder itself (ignited by the spark plug), as described in Fig. 15–13.

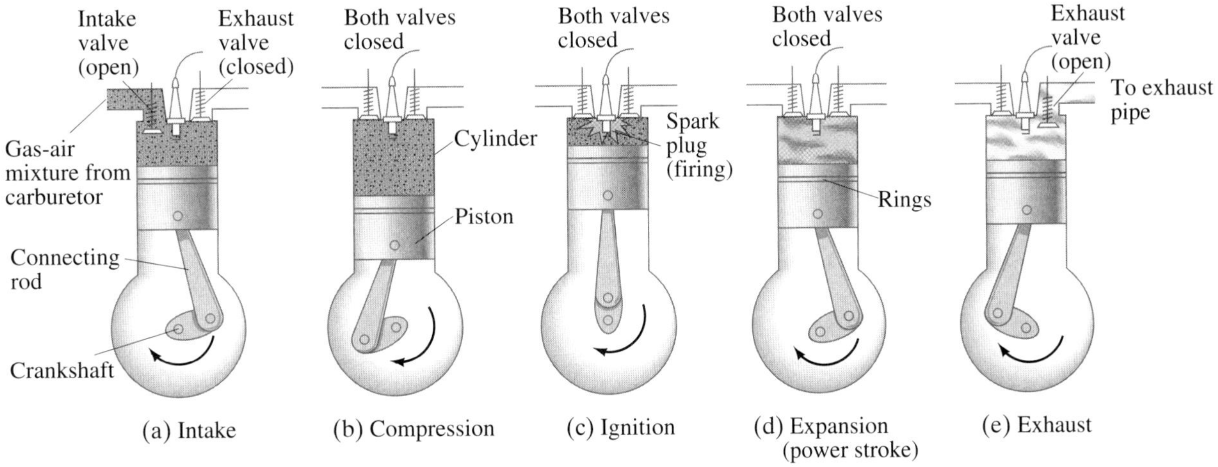


**FIGURE 15–13** Four-stroke-cycle internal combustion engine: (a) the gasoline–air mixture flows into the cylinder as the piston moves down; (b) the piston moves upward and compresses the gas; (c) the brief instant when firing of the spark plug ignites the highly compressed gasoline–air mixture, raising it to a high temperature; (d) the gases, now at high temperature and pressure, expand against the piston in this, the power stroke; (e) the burned gases are pushed out to the exhaust pipe; when the piston reaches the top, the exhaust valve closes and the intake valve opens, and the whole cycle repeats. (a), (b), (d), and (e) are the four strokes of the cycle.

## Why a $\Delta T$ Is Needed to Drive a Heat Engine

To see why a *temperature difference* is required to run an engine, let us examine the steam engine. In the reciprocating engine, for example, suppose there were no condenser or pump (Fig. 15–12a), and that the steam was at the same temperature throughout the system. This would mean that the pressure of the gas being exhausted would be the same as that on intake. Thus, although work would be done by the gas *on* the piston when it expanded, an equal amount of work would have to be done *by* the piston to force the steam out the exhaust; hence, no net work would be done. In a real engine, the exhausted gas is cooled to a lower temperature and condensed so that the exhaust pressure is less than the intake pressure. Thus, although the piston must do work on the gas to expel it on the exhaust stroke, it is less than the work done by the gas on the piston during the intake. So a net amount of work can be obtained—but only if there is a difference of temperature. Similarly, in the gas turbine if the gas isn't cooled, the pressure on each side of the blades would be the same. By cooling the gas on the exhaust side, the pressure on the back side of the blade is less and hence the turbine turns.

†Even nuclear power plants utilize steam turbines; the nuclear fuel—uranium—merely serves as fuel to heat the steam.

## Efficiency

The **efficiency**, $e$, of any heat engine can be defined as the ratio of the work it does, $W$, to the heat input at the high temperature, $Q_H$ (Fig. 15–11):

$$e = \frac{W}{Q_H}.$$

This is a sensible definition since $W$ is the output (what you get from the engine), whereas $Q_H$ is what you put in and pay for in burned fuel. Since energy is conserved, the heat input $Q_H$ must equal the work done plus the heat that flows out at the low temperature $(Q_L)$:

$$Q_H = W + Q_L.$$

Thus $W = Q_H - Q_L$, and the efficiency of an engine is

*Efficiency of any heat engine*

$$e = \frac{W}{Q_H} \qquad \textbf{(15–4a)}$$

$$= \frac{Q_H - Q_L}{Q_H} = 1 - \frac{Q_L}{Q_H}. \qquad \textbf{(15–4b)}$$

To give the efficiency as a percent, we multiply Eq. 15–4 by 100. Note that $e$ could be 1.0 (or 100%) only if $Q_L$ were zero—that is, only if no heat were exhausted to the environment.

**EXAMPLE 15–9** **Car efficiency.** An automobile engine has an efficiency of 20% and produces an average of 23,000 J of mechanical work per second during operation. (*a*) How much heat input is required, and (*b*) how much heat is discharged as waste heat from this engine, per second?

**APPROACH** We want to find the heat input $Q_H$ as well as the heat output $Q_L$, given $W = 23{,}000\text{ J}$ each second and an efficiency $e = 0.20$. We can use the definition of efficiency, Eq. 15–4 in its various forms, to find first $Q_H$ and then $Q_L$.

**SOLUTION** (*a*) From Eq. 15–4, $e = W/Q_H$, we solve for $Q_H$:

$$Q_H = \frac{W}{e} = \frac{23{,}000\text{ J}}{0.20}$$
$$= 1.15 \times 10^5\text{ J} = 115\text{ kJ}.$$

The engine requires $115\text{ kJ/s} = 115\text{ kW}$ of heat input.

(*b*) We now use the last part of Eq. 15–4 $(e = 1 - Q_L/Q_H)$ to solve for $Q_L$:

$$\frac{Q_L}{Q_H} = 1 - e$$

so

$$Q_L = (1 - e)Q_H = (0.80)115\text{ kJ}$$
$$= 92\text{ kJ}.$$

The engine discharges heat to the environment at a rate of $92\text{ kJ/s} = 92\text{ kW}$.

**NOTE** Of the 115 kJ that enters the engine per second, only 23 kJ does useful work whereas 92 kJ is wasted as heat output.

**NOTE** The problem was stated in terms of energy per unit time. We could just as well have stated it in terms of power, since $1\text{ J/s} = 1\text{ W}$.

## Carnot Engine

To see how to increase efficiency, the French scientist Sadi Carnot (1796–1832) examined the characteristics of an ideal engine (now called a **Carnot engine**). No Carnot engine actually exists, but as a theoretical idea it played an important role in the development of thermodynamics.

*Carnot (ideal) engine*

The idealized Carnot engine consisted of four processes done in a cycle, two of which are adiabatic ($Q = 0$) and two are isothermal ($\Delta T = 0$). This idealized cycle is shown in Fig. 15–14. Each of the processes was considered to be done **reversibly**. That is, each of the processes (say, during expansion of the gases against a piston) was done so slowly that the process could be considered a series of equilibrium states, and the whole process could be done in reverse with no change in the magnitude of work done or heat exchanged. A real process, on the other hand, would occur more quickly; there would be turbulence in the gas, friction would be present, and so on. Because of these factors, a real process cannot be done precisely in reverse—the turbulence would be different and the heat lost to friction would not reverse itself. Thus, real processes are **irreversible**.

**FIGURE 15–14** The Carnot cycle. Heat engines work in a cycle, and the cycle for the Carnot engine begins at point a on this $PV$ diagram. (1) The gas is first expanded isothermally, with the addition of heat $Q_H$, along the path ab at temperature $T_H$. (2) Next the gas expands adiabatically from b to c—no heat is exchanged, but the temperature drops to $T_L$. (3) The gas is then compressed at constant temperature $T_L$, path cd, and heat $Q_L$ flows out. (4) Finally, the gas is compressed adiabatically, path da, back to its original state.

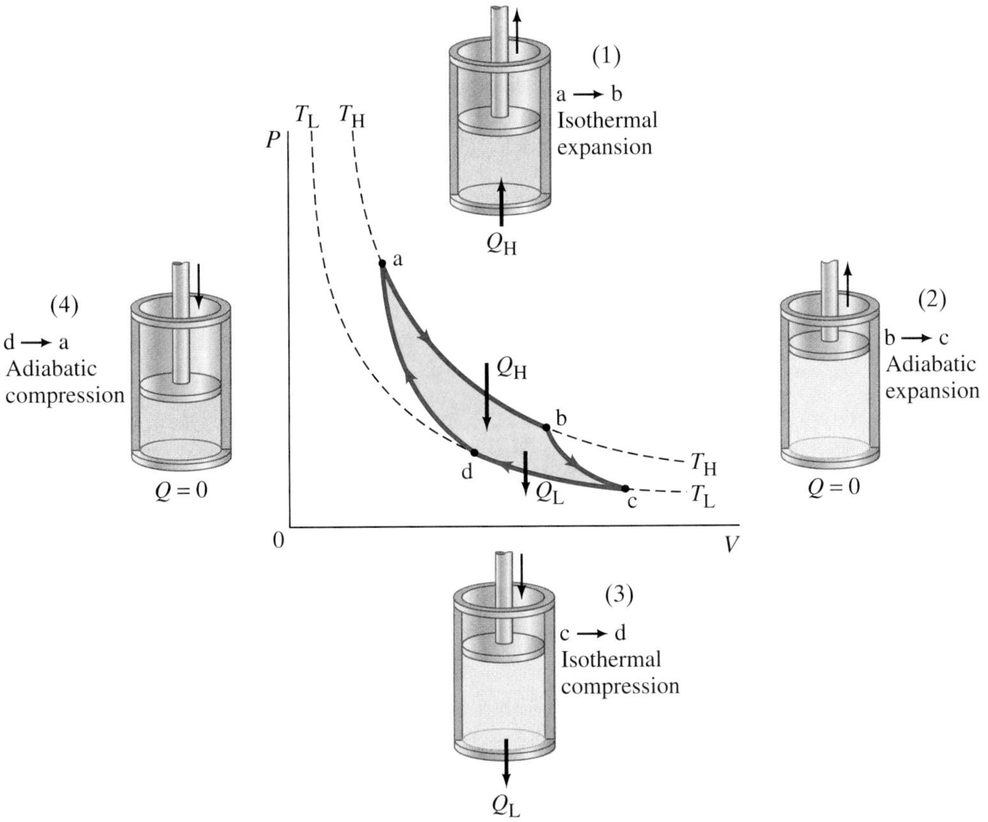

Carnot showed that for an ideal reversible engine, the heats $Q_H$ and $Q_L$ are proportional to the operating temperatures $T_H$ and $T_L$ (in kelvins), so the efficiency can be written as

*Carnot (ideal) efficiency*

$$e_{ideal} = \frac{T_H - T_L}{T_H} = 1 - \frac{T_L}{T_H}. \quad \begin{bmatrix}\text{Carnot (ideal)}\\ \text{efficiency}\end{bmatrix} \quad \textbf{(15–5)}$$

Equation 15–5 expresses the fundamental upper limit to the efficiency. Real engines always have an efficiency lower than this because of losses due to friction and the like. Real engines that are well designed reach 60 to 80% of the Carnot efficiency.

**EXAMPLE 15–10** **Steam engine efficiency.** A steam engine operates between 500°C and 270°C. What is the maximum possible efficiency of this engine?

**APPROACH** The maximum possible efficiency is the idealized Carnot efficiency, Eq. 15–5. We must use kelvin temperatures.

**SOLUTION** We first change the temperature to kelvins by adding 273 to the given Celsius temperatures: $T_H = 773\text{ K}$ and $T_L = 543\text{ K}$. Then

$$e_{ideal} = 1 - \frac{543}{773} = 0.30.$$

To get the efficiency in percent, we multiply by 100. Thus, the maximum (or Carnot) efficiency is 30%. Realistically, an engine might attain 0.70 of this value, or 21%.

**NOTE** In this Example the exhaust temperature is still rather high, 270°C. Steam engines are often arranged in series so that the exhaust of one engine is used as intake by a second or third engine.

**EXAMPLE 15–11** **A phony claim?** An engine manufacturer makes the following claims: An engine's heat input per second is 9.0 kJ at 435 K. The heat output per second is 4.0 kJ at 285 K. Do you believe these claims?

**APPROACH** The engine's efficiency can be calculated from the definition, Eq. 15–4. It must be less than the maximum possible, Eq. 15–5.

**SOLUTION** The claimed efficiency of the engine is

$$e = \frac{Q_H - Q_L}{Q_H} = \frac{9.0\text{ kJ} - 4.0\text{ kJ}}{9.0\text{ kJ}} = 0.56.$$

However, the maximum possible efficiency is given by the Carnot efficiency, Eq. 15–5:

$$e_{ideal} = \frac{T_H - T_L}{T_H} = \frac{435\text{ K} - 285\text{ K}}{435\text{ K}} = 0.34.$$

The manufacturer's claims violate the second law of thermodynamics and cannot be believed.

It is quite clear from Eq. 15–5 that at normal temperatures, a 100% efficient engine is not possible. Only if the exhaust temperature, $T_L$, were at absolute zero could 100% efficiency be obtained. But reaching absolute zero is a practical (as well as theoretical) impossibility.†

†Careful experimentation suggests that absolute zero is unattainable. This result is known as the **third law of thermodynamics**.

Because no engine can be 100% efficient, we can say that

> **no device is possible whose sole effect is to transform a given amount of heat completely into work.**

*SECOND LAW OF THERMODYNAMICS (Kelvin-Planck statement)*

This is known as the **Kelvin-Planck statement of the second law of thermodynamics**. Figure 15–15 diagrams the ideal perfect heat engine, which does not exist.

If the second law were not true, so that a perfect engine could be built, rather remarkable things could happen. For example, if the engine of a ship did not need a low-temperature reservoir to exhaust heat into, the ship could sail across the ocean using the vast resources of the internal energy of the ocean water. Indeed, we would have no fuel problems at all!

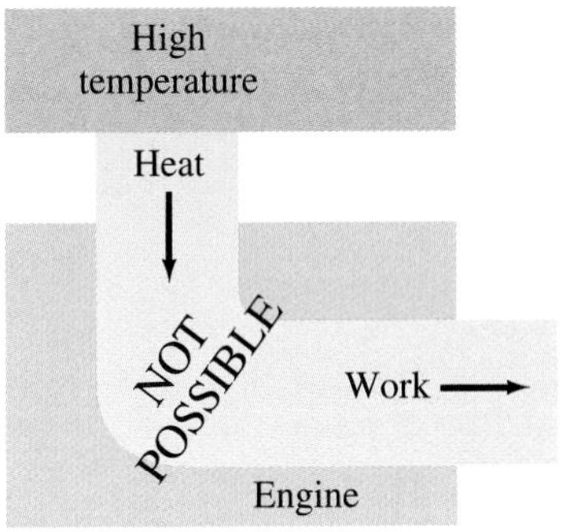


**FIGURE 15–15** Diagram of an impossible perfect heat engine in which all heat input is used to do work.

## 15–6 Refrigerators, Air Conditioners, and Heat Pumps

The operating principle of refrigerators, air conditioners, and heat pumps is just the reverse of a heat engine. Each operates to transfer heat *out* of a cool environment into a warm environment. As diagrammed in Fig. 15–16, by doing work $W$, heat is taken from a low-temperature region, $T_L$ (such as inside a refrigerator), and a greater amount of heat is exhausted at a high temperature, $T_H$ (the room). You can often feel this heat blowing out beneath a refrigerator. The work $W$ is usually done by an electric compressor motor which compresses a fluid, as illustrated in Fig. 15–17.

**FIGURE 15–16** Schematic diagram of energy transfers for a refrigerator or air conditioner.

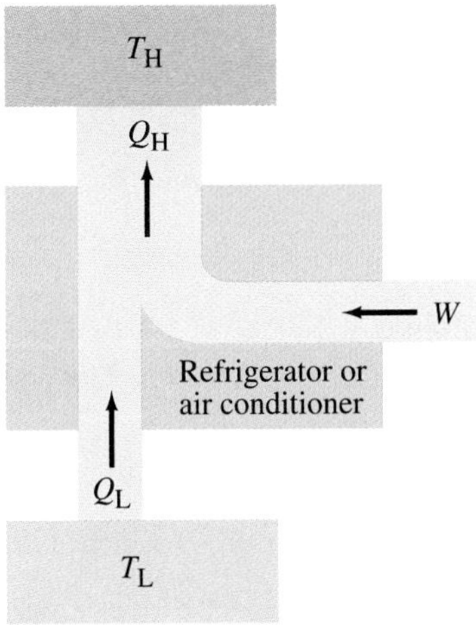


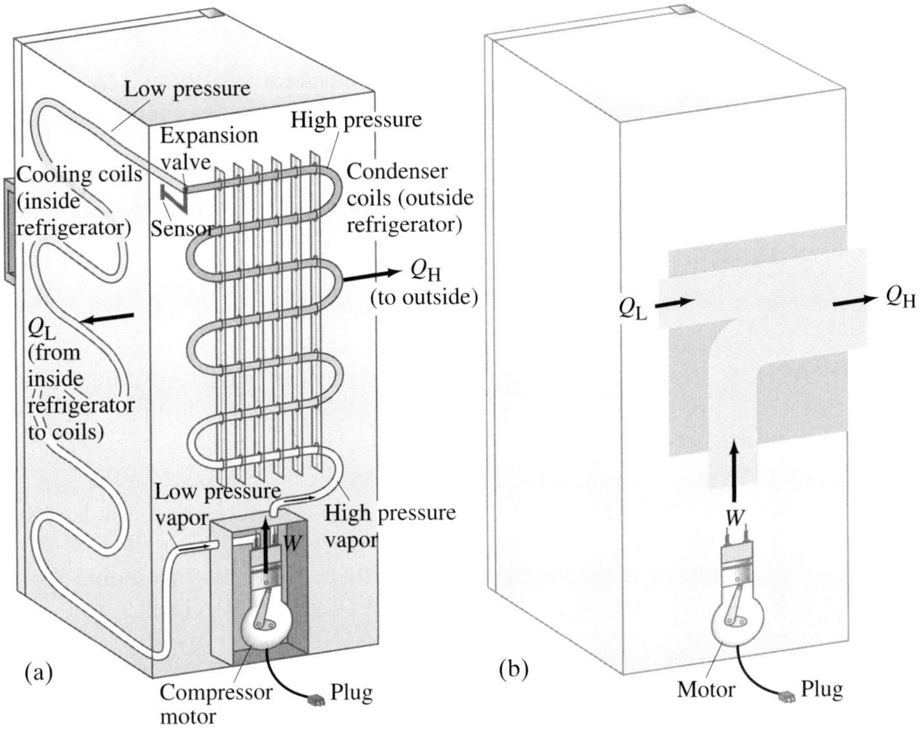


**FIGURE 15–17** (a) Typical refrigerator system. The electric compressor motor forces a gas at high pressure through a heat exchanger (condenser) on the rear outside wall of the refrigerator, where $Q_H$ is given off, and the gas cools to become liquid. The liquid passes from a high-pressure region, via a valve, to low-pressure tubes on the inside walls of the refrigerator; the liquid evaporates at this lower pressure and thus absorbs heat ($Q_L$) from the inside of the refrigerator. The fluid returns to the compressor, where the cycle begins again. (b) Schematic diagram, like Fig. 15–16.

PHYSICS APPLIED
*Refrigerator*

A perfect **refrigerator**—one in which no work is required to take heat from the low-temperature region to the high-temperature region—is not possible. This is the **Clausius statement of the second law of thermodynamics**, already mentioned in Section 15–4: it can be stated formally as

*SECOND LAW OF THERMODYNAMICS (Clausius statement)*

**no device is possible whose sole effect is to transfer heat from one system at a temperature $T_L$ into a second system at a higher temperature $T_H$.**

To make heat flow from a low-temperature object (or system) to one at a higher temperature, work must be done. Thus, *there can be no perfect refrigerator.*

The **coefficient of performance** (COP) of a refrigerator is defined as the heat $Q_L$ removed from the low-temperature area (inside a refrigerator) divided by the work $W$ done to remove the heat (Fig. 15–16):

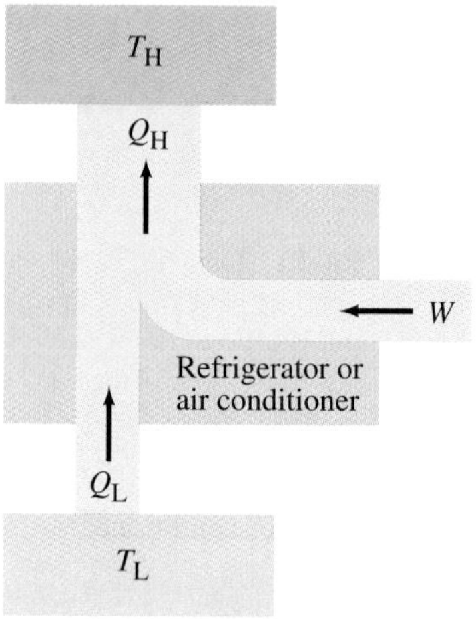


**FIGURE 15–16** (repeated) Schematic diagram of energy transfers for a refrigerator or air conditioner.

$$\text{COP} = \frac{Q_L}{W}. \quad \begin{bmatrix}\text{refrigerator and}\\ \text{air conditioner}\end{bmatrix} \quad \textbf{(15–6a)}$$

This makes sense since the more heat, $Q_L$, that can be removed from inside the refrigerator for a given amount of work, the better (more efficient) the refrigerator is. Energy is conserved, so from the first law of thermodynamics we can write $Q_L + W = Q_H$, or $W = Q_H - Q_L$ (see Fig. 15–16). Then Eq. 15–6a becomes

$$\text{COP} = \frac{Q_L}{W} = \frac{Q_L}{Q_H - Q_L}. \quad \begin{bmatrix}\text{refrigerator and}\\ \text{air conditioner}\end{bmatrix} \quad \textbf{(15–6b)}$$

For an ideal refrigerator (not a perfect one, which is impossible), the best one could do would be

$$\text{COP}_{\text{ideal}} = \frac{T_L}{T_H - T_L}, \quad \begin{bmatrix}\text{refrigerator and}\\ \text{air conditioner}\end{bmatrix} \quad \textbf{(15–6c)}$$

analagous to an ideal (Carnot) engine (Eq. 15–5).

PHYSICS APPLIED
*Air conditioner*

An **air conditioner** works very much like a refrigerator, although the actual construction details are different: an air conditioner takes heat $Q_L$ from inside a room or building at a low temperature, and deposits heat $Q_H$ outside to the environment at a higher temperature. Equations 15–6 also describe the coefficient of performance for an air conditioner.

**EXAMPLE 15–12** **Making ice.** A freezer has a COP of 3.8 and uses 200 W of power. How long would it take to freeze an ice-cube tray that contains 600 g of water at 0°C?

**APPROACH** In Eq. 15–6b, $Q_L$ is the heat that must be transferred out of the water so it will become ice. To determine $Q_L$, we use the latent heat of fusion of water and Eq. 14–3, $Q = mL$.

**SOLUTION** From Table 14–3, $L = 333\,\text{kJ/kg}$. Hence $Q = mL = (0.600\,\text{kg})(3.33 \times 10^5\,\text{J/kg}) = 2.0 \times 10^5\,\text{J}$ is the total energy that needs to be removed from the water. The freezer does work at the rate of $200\,\text{W} = 200\,\text{J/s} = W/t$, which is the work $W$ it can do in $t$ seconds. We solve for $t$: $t = W/(200\,\text{J/s})$. For $W$, we use Eq. 15–6b: $W = Q_L/\text{COP}$. Thus

$$t = \frac{W}{200\,\text{J/s}} = \frac{Q_L/\text{COP}}{200\,\text{J/s}} = \frac{2.0 \times 10^5\,\text{J}}{(3.8)(200\,\text{J/s})} = 260\,\text{s},$$

or about $4\frac{1}{2}$ min.

Heat naturally flows from high temperature to low temperature. Refrigerators and air conditioners do work to accomplish the opposite: to make heat flow from cold to hot. We might say they "pump" heat from cold areas to hotter areas, against the natural tendency of heat to flow from hot to cold, just as water can be pumped uphill, against the natural tendency to flow downhill. The term

**heat pump** is usually reserved for a device that can heat a house in winter by using an electric motor that does work $W$ to take heat $Q_L$ from the outside at low temperature and delivers heat $Q_H$ to the warmer inside of the house; see Fig. 15–18. As in a refrigerator, there is an indoor and an outdoor heat exchanger (coils of the refrigerator) and an electric compressor motor. The operating principle is like that for a refrigerator or air conditioner; but the objective of a heat pump is to heat (deliver $Q_H$), rather than to cool (remove $Q_L$). Thus, the coefficient of performance of a heat pump is defined differently than for an air conditioner because it is the heat $Q_H$ delivered to the inside of the house that is important now:

PHYSICS APPLIED
*Heat pump*

$$\text{COP} = \frac{Q_H}{W}. \qquad \text{[Heat pump]} \quad \textbf{(15–7)}$$

The COP is necessarily greater than 1. Most heat pumps can be "turned around" and used as air conditioners in the summer.

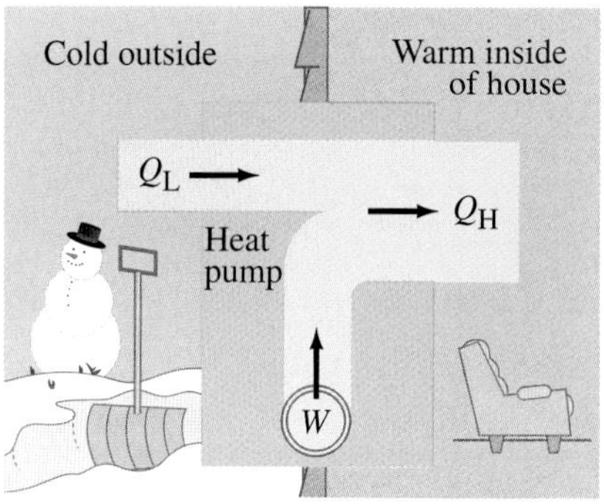


**FIGURE 15–18** A heat pump uses an electric motor to "pump" heat from the cold outside to the warm inside of a house.

**EXAMPLE 15–13 Heat pump.** A heat pump has a coefficient of performance of 3.0 and is rated to do work at 1500 W. (*a*) How much heat can it add to a room per second? (*b*) If the heat pump were turned around to act as an air conditioner in the summer, what would you expect its coefficient of performance to be, assuming all else stays the same?

**APPROACH** We use the definitions of coefficient of performance, which are different for the two devices in (*a*) and (*b*).

**SOLUTION** (*a*) We use Eq. 15–7 for the heat pump, and, since our device does 1500 J of work per second, it can pour heat into the room at a rate of

$$Q_H = \text{COP} \times W = 3.0 \times 1500\,\text{J} = 4500\,\text{J}$$

per second, or at a rate of 4500 W.

(*b*) If our device is turned around in summer, it can take heat $Q_L$ from inside the house, doing 1500 J of work per second to then dump $Q_H = 4500\,\text{J}$ per second to the hot outside. Energy is conserved, so $Q_L + W = Q_H$ (see Fig. 15–18, but reverse the inside and outside of the house). Then

$$Q_L = Q_H - W = 4500\,\text{J} - 1500\,\text{J} = 3000\,\text{J}.$$

The coefficient of performance as an air conditioner would thus be (Eq. 15–6a)

$$\text{COP} = \frac{Q_L}{W} = \frac{3000\,\text{J}}{1500\,\text{J}} = 2.0.$$

**NOTE** The coefficients of performance are defined differently for heat pumps and air conditioners.

CAUTION
*Heat pumps and air conditioners have different COP definitions*

A good heat pump can sometimes be a money saver and an energy saver, depending on the cost of the unit and installation, etc. Compare, for example, our heat pump in Example 15–13 to, say, a 1500-W electric heater. We plug the latter into the wall, it draws 1500 W of electricity and delivers 1500 W of heat to the room. Our heat pump when plugged into the wall also draws 1500 W of electricity (which is what we pay for), but it delivers 4500 W of heat!

## * SEER Rating

Cooling devices such as refrigerators and air conditioners are often given a rating known as SEER (Seasonal Energy Efficiency Ratio), which is defined as

$$\text{SEER} = \frac{\text{(heat removed in Btu)}}{\text{(electrical input in watt-hours)}},$$

PHYSICS APPLIED
*SEER rating*

as measured by averaging over varying (seasonal) conditions. The definition of the SEER is basically the same as the COP except for the (unfortunate) mixed units. Given that $1\,\text{Btu} = 1055\,\text{J}$ (see Section 14–1 and Problem 4 in Chapter 14), then a $\text{SEER} = 1$ is a COP equal to $(1\,\text{Btu}/1\,\text{W}\cdot\text{h}) = (1055\,\text{J})/(1\,\text{J/s} \times 3600\,\text{s}) = 0.29$. A $\text{COP} = 1$ is a $\text{SEER} = 1/0.29 = 3.4$.

## 15–7 Entropy and the Second Law of Thermodynamics

We have seen several aspects of the second law of thermodynamics; and the different statements of it that we have discussed can be shown to be completely equivalent. But what we really need is a general statement of the second law of thermodynamics. It was not until the latter half of the nineteenth century that the *second law of thermodynamics* was finally stated in a general way—namely, in terms of a quantity called **entropy**, introduced by Clausius in the 1860s. Entropy, unlike heat, is a function of the state of a system. That is, a system in a given state has a temperature, a volume, a pressure, and so on, and also has a particular value of entropy. In the next Section, we will see that entropy can be interpreted as a measure of the order or disorder of a system.

*Entropy*

When we deal with entropy—as with potential energy—it is the *change* in entropy during a process that is important, not the absolute amount. According to Clausius, the change in entropy $S$ of a system, when an amount of heat $Q$ is *added* to it by a reversible† process at constant temperature, is given by

*Entropy change*

$$\Delta S = \frac{Q}{T}, \tag{15–8}$$

where $T$ is the kelvin temperature.

**EXAMPLE 15–14 Entropy change in melting.** An ice cube of mass 56 g is taken from a storage compartment at 0°C and placed in a paper cup. After a few minutes, exactly half of the mass of the ice cube has melted, becoming water at 0°C. Find the change in entropy of the ice/water.

**APPROACH** We consider the 56 g of water, initially in the form of ice, as our system. To determine the entropy change, we first must find the heat needed to melt the ice, which we do using the latent heat of fusion of water, $L = 333\,\mathrm{kJ/kg}$ (Section 14–5).

**SOLUTION** The heat required to melt 28 g of ice (half of the 56-g ice cube) is

$$Q = mL = (0.028\,\mathrm{kg})(333\,\mathrm{kJ/kg}) = 9.3\,\mathrm{kJ}.$$

The temperature remains constant in our process, so we can find the change in entropy from Eq. 15–8:

$$\Delta S = \frac{Q}{T} = \frac{9.3\,\mathrm{kJ}}{273\,\mathrm{K}} = 34\,\mathrm{J/K}.$$

**NOTE** The change in entropy of the surroundings (cup, air) has not been computed.

The temperature in Example 15–14 was constant, so the calculation was easy. If the temperature varies during a process, a summation of the heat flow over the changing temperature can often be calculated using calculus or a computer. However, if the temperature change is not too great, a reasonable approximation can be made using the average value of the temperature, as indicated in the next Example.

**EXAMPLE 15–15 ESTIMATE Entropy change when mixing water.** A sample of 50.0 kg of water at 20.00°C is mixed with 50.0 kg of water at 24.00°C. Estimate the change in entropy.

**APPROACH** The final temperature of the mixture will be 22.00°C, since we started with equal amounts of water. We use the specific heat of water and the methods of calorimetry (Sections 14–3 and 14–4) to determine the heat transferred. Then we use the average temperature of each sample of water to estimate the entropy change ($\Delta Q/T$).

†Real processes are irreversible. Because entropy is a state variable, the change in entropy $\Delta S$ for an irreversible process can be determined by calculating $\Delta S$ for a reversible process between the same two states.

**SOLUTION** A quantity of heat,

$$Q = mc\,\Delta T = (50.0\text{ kg})(4186\text{ J/kg}\cdot\text{C}^\circ)(2.00\text{ C}^\circ) = 4.186 \times 10^5\text{ J},$$

flows out of the hot water as it cools down from 24°C to 22°C, and this heat flows into the cold water as it warms from 20°C to 22°C. The total change in entropy, $\Delta S$, will be the sum of the changes in entropy of the hot water, $\Delta S_H$, and that of the cold water, $\Delta S_C$:

$$\Delta S = \Delta S_H + \Delta S_C.$$

We estimate entropy changes by writing $\Delta S = Q/T_{av}$, where $T_{av}$ is an "average" temperature for each process, which ought to give a reasonable estimate since the temperature change is small. For the hot water we use an average temperature of 23°C (296 K), and for the cold water an average temperature of 21°C (294 K). Thus

$$\Delta S_H \approx -\frac{4.186 \times 10^5\text{ J}}{296\text{ K}} = -1414\text{ J/K}$$

which is negative because this heat flows out, whereas heat is added to the cold water:

$$\Delta S_C \approx \frac{4.186 \times 10^5\text{ J}}{294\text{ K}} = 1424\text{ J/K}.$$

Note that the entropy of the hot water $(S_H)$ decreases since heat flows out of the hot water. But the entropy of the cold water $(S_C)$ increases by a greater amount. The total change in entropy is

$$\Delta S = \Delta S_H + \Delta S_C \approx -1414\text{ J/K} + 1424\text{ J/K} \approx 10\text{ J/K}.$$

In Example 15–15, we saw that although the entropy of one part of the system decreased, the entropy of the other part increased by a greater amount; the net change in entropy of the whole system was positive. This result, which we have calculated for a specific case in Example 15–15, has been found to hold in all other cases tested. That is, the total entropy of an isolated system is found to increase in all natural processes. The second law of thermodynamics can be stated in terms of entropy as follows: *The entropy of an isolated system never decreases. It can only stay the same or increase.* Entropy can remain the same only for an idealized (reversible) process. For any real process, the change in entropy $\Delta S$ is greater than zero:

*Entropy of an isolated system never decreases*

$$\Delta S > 0. \tag{15–9}$$

If the system is not isolated, then the change in entropy of the system, $\Delta S_s$, plus the change in entropy of the environment, $\Delta S_{env}$, must be greater than or equal to zero:

$$\Delta S = \Delta S_s + \Delta S_{env} \geq 0. \tag{15–10}$$

Only idealized processes have $\Delta S = 0$. Real processes have $\Delta S > 0$. This, then, is the *general statement of the second law of thermodynamics*:

> **the total entropy of any system plus that of its environment increases as a result of any natural process.**

*SECOND LAW OF THERMODYNAMICS (general statement)*

Although the entropy of one part of the universe may decrease in any process (see Example 15–15), the entropy of some other part of the universe always increases by a greater amount, so the total entropy always increases.

Now that we finally have a quantitative general statement of the second law of thermodynamics, we can see that it is an unusual law. It differs considerably from other laws of physics, which are typically equalities (such as $F = ma$) or conservation laws (such as for energy and momentum). The second law of thermodynamics introduces a new quantity, the entropy $S$, but does not tell us it is conserved. Quite the opposite. Entropy is *not* conserved in natural processes; it always increases in time.

## 15–8 Order to Disorder

The concept of entropy, as we have discussed it so far, may seem rather abstract. To get a feel for the concept of entropy, we can relate it to the more ordinary concepts of *order* and *disorder*. In fact, the entropy of a system can be considered a *measure of the disorder of the system*. Then the second law of thermodynamics can be stated simply as:

*SECOND LAW OF THERMODYNAMICS (general statement)*

**Natural processes tend to move toward a state of greater disorder.**

Exactly what we mean by disorder may not always be clear, so we now consider a few examples. Some of these will show us how this very general statement of the second law applies beyond what we usually consider as thermodynamics.

Let us look at the simple processes mentioned in Section 15–4. First, a jar containing separate layers of salt and pepper is more orderly than a jar in which the salt and pepper are all mixed up. Shaking a jar containing separate layers results in a mixture, and no amount of shaking brings the orderly layers back again. The natural process is from a state of relative order (layers) to one of relative disorder (a mixture), not the reverse. That is, disorder increases. Second, a solid coffee cup is a more "orderly" and useful object than the pieces of a broken cup. Cups break when they fall, but they do not spontaneously mend themselves (as faked in Fig 15–10). Again, the normal course of events is an increase of disorder.

When a hot object is put in contact with a cold object, heat flows from the high temperature to the low until the two objects reach the same intermediate temperature. At the beginning of the process we can distinguish two classes of molecules: those with a high average kinetic energy (the hot object), and those with a low average kinetic energy (the cooler object). After the process in which heat flows, all the molecules are in one class with the same average kinetic energy; we no longer have the more orderly arrangement of molecules in two classes. Order has gone to disorder. Furthermore, the separate hot and cold objects could serve as the hot- and cold-temperature regions of a heat engine, and thus could be used to obtain useful work. But once the two objects are put in contact and reach the same temperature, no work can be obtained. Disorder has increased, since a system that has the ability to perform work must surely be considered to have a higher order than a system no longer able to do work.

When a stone falls to the ground, its kinetic energy is transformed to thermal energy. (We noted earlier that the reverse never happens: a stone never absorbs thermal energy and rises into the air of its own accord.) This is another example of order changing to disorder. Thermal energy is associated with the disorderly random motion of molecules, but the molecules in the falling stone all have the same velocity downward in addition to their own random velocities. Thus, the more orderly kinetic energy of the stone is changed to disordered thermal energy when the stone strikes the ground. Disorder increases in this process, as it does in all processes that occur in nature.

## 15–9 Unavailability of Energy; Heat Death

In the process of heat conduction from a hot object to a cold one, we have seen that entropy increases and that order goes to disorder. The separate hot and cold objects could serve as the high- and low-temperature regions for a heat engine and thus could be used to obtain useful work. But after the two objects are put in contact with each other and reach the same uniform temperature, no work can be obtained from them. With regard to being able to do useful work, order has gone to disorder in this process.

The same can be said about a falling rock that comes to rest upon striking the ground. Before hitting the ground, all the kinetic energy of the rock could have been used to do useful work. But once the rock's mechanical kinetic energy becomes thermal energy, doing useful work is no longer possible.

Both these examples illustrate another important aspect of the second law of thermodynamics:

> **in any natural process, some energy becomes unavailable to do useful work.**

In any process, no energy is ever lost (it is always conserved). Rather, energy becomes less useful—it can do less useful work. As time goes on, **energy is degraded**, in a sense; it goes from more orderly forms (such as mechanical) eventually to the least orderly form, internal, or thermal, energy. Entropy is a factor here because the amount of energy that becomes unavailable to do work is proportional to the change in entropy during any process.

*Energy degradation*

A natural outcome of this degradation of energy is the prediction that as time goes on, the universe will approach a state of maximum disorder. Matter will become a uniform mixture, and heat will have flowed from high-temperature regions to low-temperature regions until the whole universe is at one temperature. No work can then be done. All the energy of the universe will have become degraded to thermal energy. All change will cease. This prediction, called the **heat death** of the universe, has been much discussed by philosophers. The tendency toward this final state would seem an inevitable consequence of the second law of thermodynamics, although it would lie very far in the future.

*"Heat death"*

## * 15–10 Evolution and Growth; "Time's Arrow"

PHYSICS APPLIED

*Biological evolution*

An interesting example of the increase in entropy relates to biological evolution and to growth of organisms. Clearly, a human being is a highly ordered organism. The theory of evolution describes the process from the early macromolecules and simple forms of life to *Homo sapiens*, which is a process of increasing order. So, too, the development of an individual from a single cell to a grown person is a process of increasing order. Do these processes violate the second law of thermodynamics? No, they do not. In the processes of evolution and growth, and even during the mature life of an individual, waste products are eliminated. These small molecules that remain as a result of metabolism are simple molecules without much order. Thus they represent relatively higher disorder or entropy. Indeed, the total entropy of the molecules cast aside by organisms during the processes of evolution and growth is greater than the decrease in entropy associated with the order of the growing individual or evolving species.

Another aspect of the second law of thermodynamics is that it tells us in which *direction* processes go. If you were to see a film being run backward, you would undoubtedly be able to tell that it *was* run backward. For you would see odd occurrences, such as a broken coffee cup rising from the floor and reassembling on a table, or a torn balloon suddenly becoming whole again and filled with air. We know these things don't happen in real life; they are processes in which order increases—or entropy decreases. They violate the second law of thermodynamics. When watching a movie (or imagining that time could go backward), we are tipped off to a reversal of time by observing whether entropy (and disorder) is increasing or decreasing. Hence, entropy has been called **time's arrow**, for it can tell us in which direction time is going.

## * 15–11 Statistical Interpretation of Entropy and the Second Law

The ideas of entropy and disorder are made clearer with the use of a statistical or probabilistic analysis of the molecular state of a system. This statistical approach, which was first applied toward the end of the nineteenth century by Ludwig Boltzmann (1844–1906), makes a clear distinction between the "macrostate" and the "microstate" of a system. The **microstate** of a system would be specified in giving the position and velocity of every particle (or molecule). The **macrostate** of a system is specified by giving the macroscopic properties of the system—the temperature, pressure, number of moles, and so on. In reality, we can know only the macrostate of a system. There are generally far too many molecules in a system to be able to know the velocity and position of every one at a given moment. Nonetheless, it is important to recognize that a great many different microstates can correspond to the *same* macrostate.

Let us take a very simple example. Suppose you repeatedly shake four coins in your hand and drop them on a table. Specifying the number of heads and the number of tails that appear on a given throw is the macrostate of this system. Specifying each coin as being a head or a tail is the microstate of the system. In the following Table we see how many microstates correspond to each macrostate:

| Macrostate | Possible Microstates (H = heads, T = tails) | Number of Microstates |
|---|---|---|
| 4 heads | H H H H | 1 |
| 3 heads, 1 tail | H H H T, H H T H, H T H H, T H H H | 4 |
| 2 heads, 2 tails | H H T T, H T H T, T H H T, H T T H, T H T H, T T H H | 6 |
| 1 head, 3 tails | T T T H, T T H T, T H T T, H T T T | 4 |
| 4 tails | T T T T | 1 |

*Probabilities*

A basic assumption behind the statistical approach is that *each microstate is equally probable*. Thus the number of microstates that give the same macrostate corresponds to the relative probability of that macrostate occurring. The macrostate of two heads and two tails is the most probable one in our case of tossing four coins; out of the total of 16 possible microstates, six correspond to two heads and two tails, so the probability of throwing two heads and two tails is 6 out of 16, or 38%. The probability of throwing one head and three tails is 4 out of 16, or 25%. The probability of four heads is only 1 in 16, or 6%. If you threw the coins 16 times, you might not find that two heads and two tails appear exactly 6 times, or four tails exactly once. These are only probabilities or averages. But if you made 1600 throws, very nearly 38% of them would be two heads and two tails. The greater the number of tries, the closer the percentages are to the calculated probabilities.

If we toss more coins—say, 100 all at the same time—the relative probability of throwing all heads (or all tails) is greatly reduced. There is only one microstate corresponding to all heads. For 99 heads and 1 tail, there are 100 microstates since each of the coins could be the one tail. The relative probabilities for other macrostates are given in Table 15–3. About $10^{30}$ microstates are possible.† Thus the relative probability of finding all heads is 1 in $10^{30}$, an incredibly unlikely event! The probability of obtaining 50 heads and 50 tails (see Table 15–3) is $\left(1.0 \times 10^{29}\right)/10^{30} = 0.10$, or 10%. The probability of obtaining anything between 45 and 55 heads is 90%.

Thus we see that as the number of coins increases, the probability of obtaining the most orderly arrangement (all heads or all tails) becomes extremely unlikely. The least orderly arrangement (half heads, half tails) is the most probable, and the probability of being within, say, 5% of the most probable

†Each coin has two possibilities, heads or tails. Then the possible number of microstates is $2 \times 2 \times 2 \times \cdots = 2^{100} = 1.27 \times 10^{30}$ (using a calculator or logarithms).

**TABLE 15–3**
**Probabilities of Various Macrostates for 100 Coin Tosses**

| Macrostate | | Number of | |
|---|---|---|---|
| heads | tails | microstates | Probability |
| 100 | 0 | 1 | $8.0 \times 10^{-31}$ |
| 99 | 1 | $1.0 \times 10^{2}$ | $8.0 \times 10^{-29}$ |
| 90 | 10 | $1.7 \times 10^{13}$ | $1.0 \times 10^{-17}$ |
| 80 | 20 | $5.4 \times 10^{20}$ | $4.0 \times 10^{-10}$ |
| 60 | 40 | $1.4 \times 10^{28}$ | 0.01 |
| 55 | 45 | $6.1 \times 10^{28}$ | 0.05 |
| 50 | 50 | $1.0 \times 10^{29}$ | 0.08 |
| 45 | 55 | $6.1 \times 10^{28}$ | 0.05 |
| 40 | 60 | $1.4 \times 10^{28}$ | 0.01 |
| 20 | 80 | $5.4 \times 10^{20}$ | $4.0 \times 10^{-10}$ |
| 10 | 90 | $1.7 \times 10^{13}$ | $1.0 \times 10^{-17}$ |
| 1 | 99 | $1.0 \times 10^{2}$ | $8.0 \times 10^{-29}$ |
| 0 | 100 | 1 | $8.0 \times 10^{-31}$ |

arrangement greatly increases as the number of coins increases. These same ideas can be applied to the molecules of a system. For example, the most probable state of a gas (say, the air in a room) is one in which the molecules take up the whole space and move about randomly; this corresponds to the Maxwellian distribution, Fig. 15–19a (and see Chapter 13). On the other hand, the very orderly arrangement of all the molecules located in one corner of the room and all moving with the same velocity (Fig. 15–19b) is extremely unlikely.

From these examples, it is clear that probability is directly related to disorder and hence to entropy. That is, the most probable state is the one with greatest entropy, or greatest disorder and randomness.

*Entropy in terms of probability*

In terms of probability, the second law of thermodynamics—which tells us that entropy increases in any process—reduces to the statement that those processes occur which are most probable. The second law thus becomes a trivial statement. However, there is an additional element now. The second law in terms of probability does not *forbid* a decrease in entropy. Rather, it says the probability is extremely low. It is not impossible that salt and pepper should separate spontaneously into layers, or that a broken teacup should mend itself. It is even possible that a lake should freeze over on a hot summer day (that is, for heat to flow out of the cold lake into the warmer surroundings). But the probability for such events occurring is miniscule. In our coin examples, we saw that increasing the number of coins from 4 to 100 drastically reduced the probability of large deviations from the average, or most probable, arrangement. In ordinary systems, we are dealing not with 100 molecules, but with incredibly large numbers of molecules: in 1 mole alone there are $6 \times 10^{23}$ molecules. Hence the probability of deviation far from the average is incredibly tiny. For example, it has been calculated that the probability that a stone resting on the ground could transform 1 cal of thermal energy into mechanical energy and rise up into the air is much less likely than the probability that a group of monkeys typing randomly would by chance produce the complete works of Shakespeare.

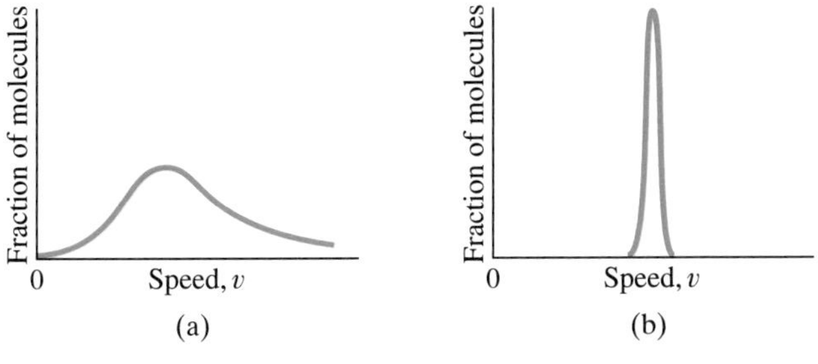


**FIGURE 15–19** (a) Most probable distribution of molecular speeds in a gas (Maxwellian, or random); (b) orderly, but highly unlikely, distribution of speeds in which all molecules have nearly the same speed.

(a) (b) (c)

**FIGURE 15–20** (a) An array of mirrors focuses sunlight on a boiler to produce steam at a solar energy installation. (b) A fossil-fuel steam plant. (c) Large cooling towers at an electric generating plant.

**FIGURE 15–21** Mechanical or heat energy is transformed to electric energy with a turbine and generator.

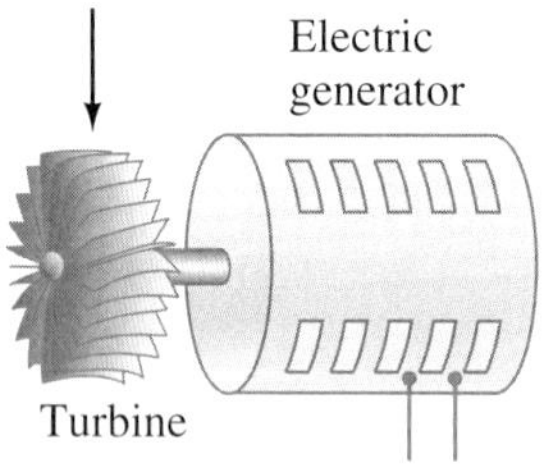


PHYSICS APPLIED

*Heat engines and thermal pollution*

## * 15–12 Thermal Pollution and Global Warming

Much of the energy we utilize in everyday life—from motor vehicles to most of the electricity produced by power plants—makes use of a heat engine. Electricity produced by falling water at dams, by windmills, or by solar cells (Fig. 15–20a) does not involve a heat engine. But over 90% of the electric energy produced in the U.S. is generated at fossil-fuel steam plants (coal, oil, or gas—see Fig. 15–20b), and they make use of a heat engine (essentially steam engines). In electric power plants, the steam drives the turbines and generators (Fig. 15–21) whose output is electric energy. The various means to turn the turbine are discussed briefly in Table 15–4, along with some of the advantages and disadvantages of each. Even nuclear power plants use nuclear fuel to run a steam engine.

The heat output $Q_L$ from every heat engine, from power plants to cars, is referred to as **thermal pollution** because this heat $(Q_L)$ must be absorbed by the environment—such as by water from rivers or lakes, or by the air using large cooling towers (Fig. 15–20c). This heat raises the temperature of the cooling water, altering the natural ecology of aquatic life (largely because warmer water holds less oxygen). In the case of air cooling towers, the output heat $Q_L$ raises the temperature of the atmosphere, which affects the weather.

**Air pollution**—by which we mean the chemicals released in the burning of fossil fuels in cars, power plants, and industrial furnaces—gives rise to smog and other problems. One big problem is the buildup of $CO_2$ in the Earth's atmosphere due to the burning of fossil fuels. This $CO_2$ absorbs some of the infrared radiation that the Earth naturally emits (Section 14–8), causing **global warming**, a serious problem that can be addressed by limiting the burning of fossil fuels.

Thermal pollution, however, is unavoidable. Engineers can try to design and build engines that are more efficient, but they cannot surpass the Carnot efficiency and must live with $T_L$ being at best the ambient temperature of water or air. The second law of thermodynamics tells us the limit imposed by nature. What we can do, in the light of the second law of thermodynamics, is use less energy and conserve our fuel resources.

## TABLE 15–4 Electric Energy Resources

| Form of Electric Energy Production | % of Production (approx.) | | Advantages | Disadvantages |
|---|---|---|---|---|
| | U.S. | World | | |
| **Fossil-fuel steam plants:** burn coal, oil, or natural gas to boil water, producing high-pressure steam that turns a turbine of a generator (Figs. 15–12b, 15–21); uses heat engine. | 87 | 86 | We know how to build them; for now relatively inexpensive. | Air pollution; thermal pollution; limited efficiency; land devastation from extraction of raw materials (mining); global warming; accidents such as oil spills at sea; limited fuel supply (estimates range from a couple of decades to a few centuries). |
| **Nuclear energy:** | | | | |
| **Fission:** nuclei of uranium or plutonium atoms split ("fission") with release of energy (Chapter 31) that heats steam; uses heat engine. | 8 | 6 | Normally almost no air pollution; less contribution to global warming; relatively inexpensive.  | Thermal pollution; accidents can release damaging radioactivity; difficult disposal of radioactive by-products; possible diversion of nuclear material by terrorists; limited fuel supply. |
| **Fusion:** energy released when isotopes of hydrogen (or other small nuclei) combine or "fuse" (Chapter 31). | 0 | 0 | Relatively "clean"; vast fuel supply (hydrogen in water molecules in oceans); less contribution to global warming. | Not yet workable. |
| **Hydroelectric:** Falling water turns turbines at the base of a dam.  | 4 | 7 | No heat engine needed; no air, water, or thermal pollution; relatively inexpensive; high efficiency; dams can control flooding. | Reservoirs behind dams inundate scenic land or canyons; dams block upstream migration of salmon and other fish for reproduction; few locations remain for new dams; drought. |
| **Geothermal:** natural steam from inside the Earth comes to the surface (hot springs, geysers, steam vents); or cold water passed down into contact with hot, dry rock is heated to steam. | $<1$ | $<1$ | No heat engine needed; little air pollution; good efficiency; relatively inexpensive and "clean." | Few appropriate sites; small production; mineral content of spent hot water can pollute. |
| **Wind power:** 3-kW to 5-MW windmills (vanes up to 50 m wide) turn a generator.  | $<1$ | $<1$ | No heat engine; no air, water or thermal pollution; relatively inexpensive. | Large array of big windmills might affect weather and be eyesores; hazardous to migratory birds; winds not always strong. |
| **Solar energy:** | $<0.1$ | $<1$ | | |
| **Active solar heating:** rooftop solar panels absorb the Sun's rays, which heat water in tubes for space heating and hot water supply. | | | No heat engine needed; no air or thermal pollution; unlimited fuel supply.  | Space limitations; may require back-up; relatively expensive; less effective when cloudy. |
| **Passive solar heating:** architectural devices—windows along southern exposure, sunshade over windows to keep Sun's rays out in summer. | | | No heat engine needed; no air or thermal pollution; relatively inexpensive. | Almost none, but other methods needed too. 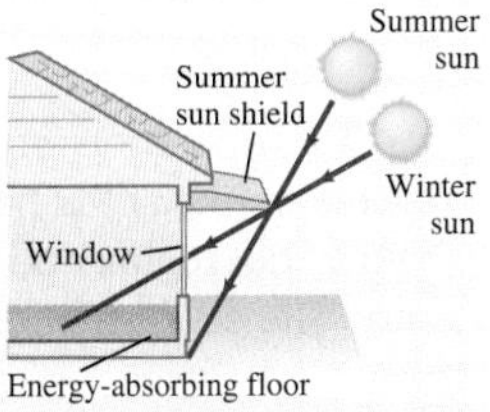  |
| **Solar cells (photovoltaic cells):** convert sunlight directly into electricity without use of heat engine. | | | No heat engine; thermal, air, and water pollution very low; good efficiency (>30% and improving). | Expensive; chemical pollution at manufacture; large land area needed as Sun's energy not concentrated. |

## PROBLEM SOLVING Thermodynamics

1. Define the **system** you are dealing with; distinguish the system under study from its surroundings.
2. When applying the first law of thermodynamics, be careful of **signs** associated with **work** and **heat**. In the first law, work done *by* the system is positive; work done *on* the system is negative. Heat *added* to the system is positive, but heat *removed* from it is negative. With heat engines, we usually consider the heat intake, the heat exhausted, and the work done as positive.
3. Watch the **units** used for work and heat; work is most often expressed in joules, and heat can be in calories, kilocalories, or joules. Be consistent: choose only one unit for use throughout a given problem.
4. **Temperatures** must generally be expressed in kelvins; temperature *differences* may be expressed in C° or K.
5. **Efficiency** (or coefficient of performance) is a ratio of two energy transfers: useful output divided by required input. Efficiency (but *not* coefficient of performance) is always less than 1 in value, and hence is often stated as a percentage.
6. The **entropy** of a system increases when heat is added to the system, and decreases when heat is removed. If heat is transferred from system A to system B, the change in entropy of A is negative and the change in entropy of B is positive.

## Summary

The **first law of thermodynamics** states that the change in internal energy $\Delta U$ of a system is equal to the heat *added* to the system, $Q$, minus the work done *by* the system, $W$:

$$\Delta U = Q - W. \quad \textbf{(15–1)}$$

This is a statement of the conservation of energy, and is found to hold for all types of processes.

An **isothermal** process is a process carried out at constant temperature.

In an **adiabatic** process, no heat is exchanged ($Q = 0$).

The work $W$ done by a gas at constant pressure $P$ is given by

$$W = P\,\Delta V, \quad \textbf{(15–3)}$$

where $\Delta V$ is the change in volume of the gas.

A **heat engine** is a device for changing thermal energy, by means of heat flow between two temperatures, into useful work.

The **efficiency** $e$ of a heat engine is defined as the ratio of the work $W$ done by the engine to the heat input $Q_H$. Because of conservation of energy, the work output equals $Q_H - Q_L$, where $Q_L$ is the heat exhausted at low temperature to the environment; hence

$$e = \frac{W}{Q_H} = 1 - \frac{Q_L}{Q_H}. \quad \textbf{(15–4)}$$

The *upper limit* on the efficiency (the *Carnot efficiency*) can be written in terms of the higher and lower operating temperatures (in kelvins) of the engine, $T_H$ and $T_L$, as

$$e_{ideal} = 1 - \frac{T_L}{T_H}. \quad \textbf{(15–5)}$$

The operation of **refrigerators** and **air conditioners** is the reverse of that of a heat engine: work is done to extract heat from a cool region and exhaust it to a region at a higher temperature. The coefficient of performance (COP) for either is

$$\text{COP} = \frac{Q_L}{W}, \quad \left[\begin{array}{c}\text{refrigerator or}\\ \text{air conditioner}\end{array}\right] \quad \textbf{(15–6a)}$$

where $W$ is the work needed to remove heat $Q_L$ from the area with the low temperature.

A **heat pump** does work $W$ to bring heat $Q_L$ from the cold outside and deliver heat $Q_H$ to warm the interior. The coefficient of performance of a heat pump is

$$\text{COP} = \frac{Q_H}{W}. \quad \text{[heat pump]} \quad \textbf{(15–7)}$$

The **second law of thermodynamics** can be stated in several equivalent ways:

(a) heat flows spontaneously from a hot object to a cold one, but not the reverse;

(b) there can be no 100% efficient heat engine—that is, one that can change a given amount of heat completely into work;

(c) natural processes tend to move toward a state of greater disorder or greater **entropy**.

Statement (*c*) is the most general statement of the second law of thermodynamics, and can be restated as: the total entropy, $S$, of any system plus that of its environment increases as a result of any natural process:

$$\Delta S > 0. \quad \textbf{(15–9)}$$

The change in entropy in a process that transfers heat $Q$ at a constant temperature $T$ is

$$\Delta S = \frac{Q}{T}. \quad \textbf{(15–8)}$$

Entropy is a quantitative measure of the disorder of a system.

As time goes on, energy is degraded to less useful forms—that is, it is less available to do useful work.

[*The second law of thermodynamics tells us in which direction processes tend to go, so entropy is called "time's arrow."]

[*All heat engines give rise to **thermal pollution** because they exhaust heat to the environment.]

# Questions

1. What happens to the internal energy of water vapor in the air that condenses on the outside of a cold glass of water? Is work done or heat exchanged? Explain.
2. Use the conservation of energy to explain why the temperature of a gas increases when it is quickly compressed, whereas the temperature decreases when the gas expands.
3. In an isothermal process, 3700 J of work is done by an ideal gas. Is this enough information to tell how much heat has been added to the system? If so, how much?
4. Is it possible for the temperature of a system to remain constant even though heat flows into or out of it? If so, give one or two examples.
5. Explain why the temperature of a gas increases when it is adiabatically compressed.
6. Can mechanical energy ever be transformed completely into heat or internal energy? Can the reverse happen? In each case, if your answer is no, explain why not; if yes, give one or two examples.
7. Can you warm a kitchen in winter by leaving the oven door open? Can you cool the kitchen on a hot summer day by leaving the refrigerator door open? Explain.
8. Would a definition of heat engine efficiency as $e = W/Q_L$ be useful? Explain.
9. What plays the role of high-temperature and low-temperature areas in (*a*) an internal combustion engine, and (*b*) a steam engine?
10. Which will give the greater improvement in the efficiency of a Carnot engine, a 10 C° increase in the high-temperature reservoir, or a 10 C° decrease in the low-temperature reservoir? Explain.
11. The oceans contain a tremendous amount of thermal (internal) energy. Why, in general, is it not possible to put this energy to useful work?
12. A gas is allowed to expand (*a*) adiabatically and (*b*) isothermally. In each process, does the entropy increase, decrease, or stay the same? Explain.
13. A gas can expand to twice its original volume either adiabatically or isothermally. Which process would result in a greater change in entropy? Explain.
14. Give three examples, other than those mentioned in this Chapter, of naturally occurring processes in which order goes to disorder. Discuss the observability of the reverse process.
15. Which do you think has the greater entropy, 1 kg of solid iron or 1 kg of liquid iron? Why?
16. (*a*) What happens if you remove the lid of a bottle containing chlorine gas? (*b*) Does the reverse process ever happen? Why or why not? (*c*) Can you think of two other examples of irreversibility?
17. You are asked to test a machine that the inventor calls an "in-room air conditioner": a big box, standing in the middle of the room, with a cable that plugs into a power outlet. When the machine is switched on, you feel a stream of cold air coming out of it. How do you know that this machine cannot cool the room?
18. Think up several processes (other than those already mentioned) that would obey the first law of thermodynamics, but, if they actually occurred, would violate the second law.
19. Suppose a lot of papers are strewn all over the floor; then you stack them neatly. Does this violate the second law of thermodynamics? Explain.
20. The first law of thermodynamics is sometimes whimsically stated as, "You can't get something for nothing," and the second law as, "You can't even break even." Explain how these statements could be equivalent to the formal statements.

* 21. Entropy is often called "time's arrow" because it tells us in which direction natural processes occur. If a movie were run backward, name some processes that you might see that would tell you that time was "running backward."

* 22. Living organisms, as they grow, convert relatively simple food molecules into a complex structure. Is this a violation of the second law of thermodynamics?

# Problems

### 15–1 and 15–2 First Law of Thermodynamics

1. (I) An ideal gas expands isothermally, performing $3.40 \times 10^3$ J of work in the process. Calculate (*a*) the change in internal energy of the gas, and (*b*) the heat absorbed during this expansion.
2. (I) A gas is enclosed in a cylinder fitted with a light frictionless piston and maintained at atmospheric pressure. When 1400 kcal of heat is added to the gas, the volume is observed to increase slowly from $12.0\ \text{m}^3$ to $18.2\ \text{m}^3$. Calculate (*a*) the work done by the gas and (*b*) the change in internal energy of the gas.
3. (I) One liter of air is cooled at constant pressure until its volume is halved, and then it is allowed to expand isothermally back to its original volume. Draw the process on a *PV* diagram.
4. (I) Sketch a *PV* diagram of the following process: 2.0 L of ideal gas at atmospheric pressure are cooled at constant pressure to a volume of 1.0 L, and then expanded isothermally back to 2.0 L, whereupon the pressure is increased at constant volume until the original pressure is reached.
5. (II) A 1.0-L volume of air initially at 4.5 atm of (absolute) pressure is allowed to expand isothermally until the pressure is 1.0 atm. It is then compressed at constant pressure to its initial volume, and lastly is brought back to its original pressure by heating at constant volume. Draw the process on a *PV* diagram, including numbers and labels for the axes.
6. (II) The pressure in an ideal gas is cut in half slowly, while being kept in a container with rigid walls. In the process, 265 kJ of heat left the gas. (*a*) How much work was done during this process? (*b*) What was the change in internal energy of the gas during this process?

7. (II) In an engine, an almost ideal gas is compressed adiabatically to half its volume. In doing so, 1850 J of work is done on the gas. (*a*) How much heat flows into or out of the gas? (*b*) What is the change in internal energy of the gas? (*c*) Does its temperature rise or fall?

8. (II) An ideal gas expands at a constant total pressure of 3.0 atm from 400 mL to 660 mL. Heat then flows out of the gas at constant volume, and the pressure and temperature are allowed to drop until the temperature reaches its original value. Calculate (*a*) the total work done by the gas in the process, and (*b*) the total heat flow into the gas.

9. (II) One and one-half moles of an ideal monatomic gas expand adiabatically, performing 7500 J of work in the process. What is the change in temperature of the gas during this expansion?

10. (II) Consider the following two-step process. Heat is allowed to flow out of an ideal gas at constant volume so that its pressure drops from 2.2 atm to 1.4 atm. Then the gas expands at constant pressure, from a volume of 6.8 L to 9.3 L, where the temperature reaches its original value. See Fig. 15–22. Calculate (*a*) the total work done by the gas in the process, (*b*) the change in internal energy of the gas in the process, and (*c*) the total heat flow into or out of the gas.

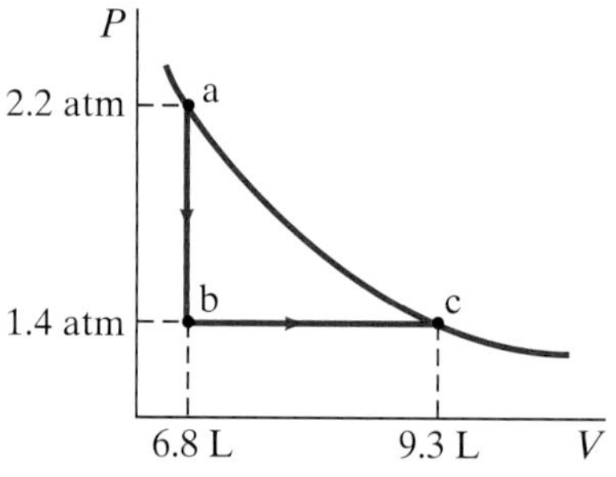


**FIGURE 15–22** Problem 10.

11. (II) The *PV* diagram in Fig. 15–23 shows two possible states of a system containing 1.35 moles of a monatomic ideal gas. ($P_1 = P_2 = 455\ \mathrm{N/m^2}$, $V_1 = 2.00\ \mathrm{m^3}$, $V_2 = 8.00\ \mathrm{m^3}$.) (*a*) Draw the process which depicts an isobaric expansion from state 1 to state 2, and label this process A. (*b*) Find the work done by the gas and the change in internal energy of the gas in process A. (*c*) Draw the two-step process which depicts an isothermal expansion from state 1 to the volume $V_2$, followed by an isovolumetric increase in temperature to state 2, and label this process B. (*d*) Find the change in internal energy of the gas for the two-step process B.

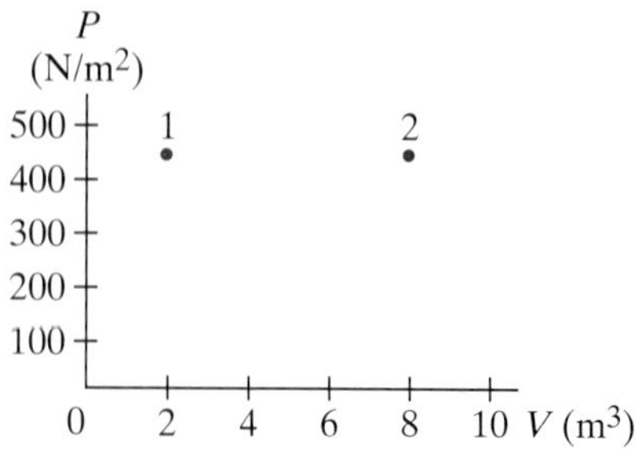


**FIGURE 15–23** Problem 11.

12. (III) When a gas is taken from a to c along the curved path in Fig. 15–24, the work done by the gas is $W = -35$ J and the heat added to the gas is $Q = -63$ J. Along path abc, the work done is $W = -48$ J. (*a*) What is $Q$ for path abc? (*b*) If $P_c = \frac{1}{2}P_b$, what is $W$ for path cda? (*c*) What is $Q$ for path cda? (*d*) What is $U_a - U_c$? (*e*) If $U_d - U_c = 5$ J, what is $Q$ for path da?

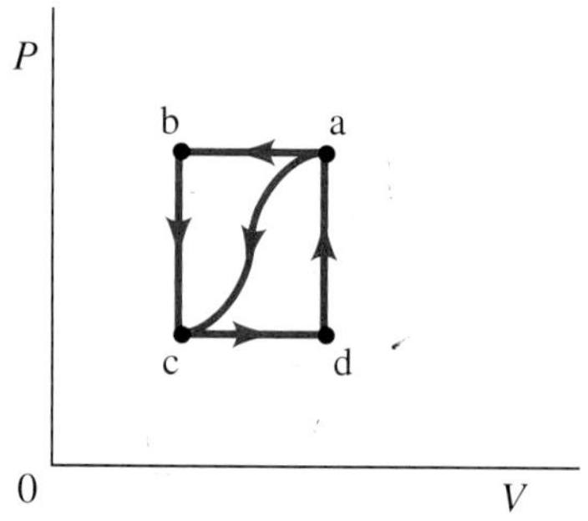


**FIGURE 15–24** Problems 12 and 13.

13. (III) In the process of taking a gas from state a to state c along the curved path shown in Fig. 15–24, 80 J of heat leaves the system and 55 J of work is done *on* the system. (*a*) Determine the change in internal energy, $U_a - U_c$. (*b*) When the gas is taken along the path cda, the work done by the gas is $W = 38$ J. How much heat $Q$ is added to the gas in the process cda? (*c*) If $P_a = 2.5P_d$, how much work is done by the gas in the process abc? (*d*) What is $Q$ for path abc? (*e*) If $U_a - U_b = 10$ J, what is $Q$ for the process bc? Here is a summary of what is given:

$$Q_{a\to c} = -80\ \mathrm{J}$$
$$W_{a\to c} = -55\ \mathrm{J}$$
$$W_{cda} = 38\ \mathrm{J}$$
$$U_a - U_b = 10\ \mathrm{J}$$
$$P_a = 2.5P_d.$$

## * 15–3 Human Metabolism

* 14. (I) How much energy would the person of Example 15–8 transform if instead of working 11.0 h she took a noontime break and ran for 1.0 h?

* 15. (I) Calculate the average metabolic rate of a person who sleeps 8.0 h, sits at a desk 8.0 h, engages in light activity 4.0 h, watches television 2.0 h, plays tennis 1.5 h, and runs 0.5 h daily.

* 16. (II) A person decides to lose weight by sleeping one hour less per day, using the time for light activity. How much weight (or mass) can this person expect to lose in 1 year, assuming no change in food intake? Assume that 1 kg of fat stores about 40,000 kJ of energy.

## 15–5 Heat Engines

17. (I) A heat engine exhausts 8200 J of heat while performing 3200 J of useful work. What is the efficiency of this engine?

18. (I) A heat engine does 9200 J of work per cycle while absorbing 22.0 kcal of heat from a high-temperature reservoir. What is the efficiency of this engine?

19. (I) What is the maximum efficiency of a heat engine whose operating temperatures are 580°C and 380°C?

20. (I) The exhaust temperature of a heat engine is 230°C. What must be the high temperature if the Carnot efficiency is to be 28%?

21. (II) A nuclear power plant operates at 75% of its maximum theoretical (Carnot) efficiency between temperatures of 625°C and 350°C. If the plant produces electric energy at the rate of 1.3 GW, how much exhaust heat is discharged per hour?

22. (II) It is not necessary that a heat engine's hot environment be hotter than ambient temperature. Liquid nitrogen (77 K) is about as cheap as bottled water. What would be the efficiency of an engine that made use of heat transferred from air at room temperature (293 K) to the liquid nitrogen "fuel" (Fig. 15–25)?

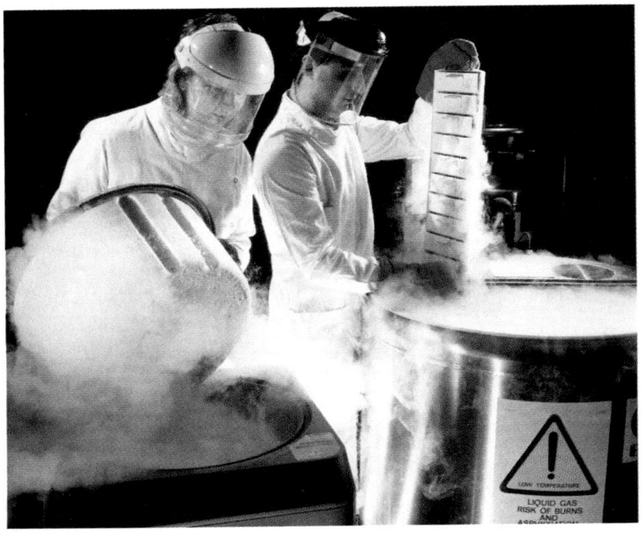

**FIGURE 15–25** Problem 22.

23. (II) A Carnot engine performs work at the rate of 440 kW while using 680 kcal of heat per second. If the temperature of the heat source is 570°C, at what temperature is the waste heat exhausted?

24. (II) A Carnot engine's operating temperatures are 210°C and 45°C. The engine's power output is 950 W. Calculate the rate of heat output.

25. (II) A certain power plant puts out 550 MW of electric power. Estimate the heat discharged per second, assuming that the plant has an efficiency of 38%.

26. (II) A heat engine utilizes a heat source at 550°C and has an ideal (Carnot) efficiency of 28%. To increase the ideal efficiency to 35%, what must be the temperature of the heat source?

27. (II) A heat engine exhausts its heat at 350°C and has a Carnot efficiency of 39%. What exhaust temperature would enable it to achieve a Carnot efficiency of 49%?

28. (III) At a steam power plant, steam engines work in pairs, the output of heat from one being the approximate heat input of the second. The operating temperatures of the first are 670°C and 440°C, and of the second 430°C and 290°C. If the heat of combustion of coal is $2.8 \times 10^7$ J/kg, at what rate must coal be burned if the plant is to put out 1100 MW of power? Assume the efficiency of the engines is 60% of the ideal (Carnot) efficiency.

## 15–6 Refrigerators, Air Conditioners, Heat Pumps

29. (I) The low temperature of a freezer cooling coil is −15°C, and the discharge temperature is 30°C. What is the maximum theoretical coefficient of performance?

30. (II) An ideal refrigerator-freezer operates with a COP = 7.0 in a 24°C room. What is the temperature inside the freezer?

31. (II) A restaurant refrigerator has a coefficient of performance of 5.0. If the temperature in the kitchen outside the refrigerator is 29°C, what is the lowest temperature that could be obtained inside the refrigerator if it were ideal?

32. (II) A heat pump is used to keep a house warm at 22°C. How much work is required of the pump to deliver 2800 J of heat into the house if the outdoor temperature is (*a*) 0°C, (*b*) −15°C? Assume ideal (Carnot) behavior.

33. (II) What volume of water at 0°C can a freezer make into ice cubes in 1.0 hour, if the coefficient of performance of the cooling unit is 7.0 and the power input is 1.0 kilowatt?

34. (II) An ideal (Carnot) engine has an efficiency of 35%. If it were possible to run it backward as a heat pump, what would be its coefficient of performance?

## 15–7 Entropy

35. (I) What is the change in entropy of 250 g of steam at 100°C when it is condensed to water at 100°C?

36. (I) One kilogram of water is heated from 0°C to 100°C. Estimate the change in entropy of the water.

37. (I) What is the change in entropy of 1.00 $m^3$ of water at 0°C when it is frozen to ice at 0°C?

38. (II) If 1.00 $m^3$ of water at 0°C is frozen and cooled to −10°C by being in contact with a great deal of ice at −10°C, what would be the total change in entropy of the process?

39. (II) A 10.0-kg box having an initial speed of 3.0 m/s slides along a rough table and comes to rest. Estimate the total change in entropy of the universe. Assume all objects are at room temperature (293 K).

40. (II) A falling rock has kinetic energy KE just before striking the ground and coming to rest. What is the total change in entropy of the rock plus environment as a result of this collision?

41. (II) An aluminum rod conducts 7.50 cal/s from a heat source maintained at 240°C to a large body of water at 27°C. Calculate the rate entropy increases per unit time in this process.

42. (II) 1.0 kg of water at 30°C is mixed with 1.0 kg of water at 60°C in a well-insulated container. Estimate the net change in entropy of the system.

43. (II) A 3.8-kg piece of aluminum at 30°C is placed in 1.0 kg of water in a Styrofoam container at room temperature (20°C). Calculate the approximate net change in entropy of the system.

44. (III) A real heat engine working between heat reservoirs at 970 K and 650 K produces 550 J of work per cycle for a heat input of 2200 J. (*a*) Compare the efficiency of this real engine to that of an ideal (Carnot) engine. (*b*) Calculate the total entropy change of the universe per cycle of the real engine. (*c*) Calculate the total entropy change of the universe per cycle of a Carnot engine operating between the same two temperatures.

## * 15–11 Statistical Interpretation

* 45. (II) Calculate the probabilities, when you throw two dice, of obtaining (*a*) a 5, and (*b*) an 11.

* 46. (II) Rank the following five-card hands in order of increasing probability: (*a*) four aces and a king; (*b*) six of hearts, eight of diamonds, queen of clubs, three of hearts, jack of spades; (*c*) two jacks, two queens, and an ace; and (*d*) any hand having no two equal-value cards. Discuss your ranking in terms of microstates and macrostates.

* 47. (II) Suppose that you repeatedly shake six coins in your hand and drop them on the floor. Construct a table showing the number of microstates that correspond to each macrostate. What is the probability of obtaining (*a*) three heads and three tails, and (*b*) six heads?

## * 15–12 Energy Resources

* 48. (I) Solar cells (Fig. 15–26) can produce about 40 W of electricity per square meter of surface area if directly facing the Sun. How large an area is required to supply the needs of a house that requires 22 kWh/day? Would this fit on the roof of an average house? (Assume the Sun shines about 9 h/day.)

**FIGURE 15–26** Problem 48.

* 49. (II) Energy may be stored for use during peak demand by pumping water to a high reservoir when demand is low and then releasing it to drive turbines when needed. Suppose water is pumped to a lake 135 m above the turbines at a rate of $1.00 \times 10^5$ kg/s for 10.0 h at night. (*a*) How much energy (kWh) is needed to do this each night? (*b*) If all this energy is released during a 14-h day, at 75% efficiency, what is the average power output?

* 50. (II) Water is stored in an artificial lake created by a dam (Fig. 15–27). The water depth is 45 m at the dam, and a steady flow rate of 35 $m^3/s$ is maintained through hydroelectric turbines installed near the base of the dam. How much electrical power can be produced?

**FIGURE 15–27** Problem 50.

# General Problems

51. An inventor claims to have designed and built an engine that produces 1.50 MW of usable work while taking in 3.00 MW of thermal energy at 425 K, and rejecting 1.50 MW of thermal energy at 215 K. Is there anything fishy about his claim? Explain.

52. When $5.30 \times 10^5$ J of heat is added to a gas enclosed in a cylinder fitted with a light frictionless piston maintained at atmospheric pressure, the volume is observed to increase from 1.9 $m^3$ to 4.1 $m^3$. Calculate (*a*) the work done by the gas, and (*b*) the change in internal energy of the gas. (*c*) Graph this process on a *PV* diagram.

53. A 4-cylinder gasoline engine has an efficiency of 0.25 and delivers 220 J of work per cycle per cylinder. When the engine fires at 45 cycles per second, (*a*) what is the work done per second? (*b*) What is the total heat input per second from the fuel? (*c*) If the energy content of gasoline is 35 MJ per liter, how long does one liter last?

54. A "Carnot" refrigerator (the reverse of a Carnot engine) absorbs heat from the freezer compartment at a temperature of −17°C and exhausts it into the room at 25°C. (*a*) How much work must be done by the refrigerator to change 0.50 kg of water at 25°C into ice at −17°C? (*b*) If the compressor output is 210 W, what minimum time is needed to accomplish this?

55. It has been suggested that a heat engine could be developed that made use of the temperature difference between water at the surface of the ocean and that several hundred meters deep. In the tropics, the temperatures may be 27°C and 4°C, respectively. (*a*) What is the maximum efficiency such an engine could have? (*b*) Why might such an engine be feasible in spite of the low efficiency? (*c*) Can you imagine any adverse environmental effects that might occur?

56. Two 1100-kg cars are traveling 95 km/h in opposite directions when they collide and are brought to rest. Estimate the change in entropy of the universe as a result of this collision. Assume $T = 20°C$.

57. A 120-g insulated aluminum cup at 15°C is filled with 140 g of water at 50°C. After a few minutes, equilibrium is reached. (*a*) Determine the final temperature, and (*b*) estimate the total change in entropy.

* 58. (*a*) What is the coefficient of performance of an ideal heat pump that extracts heat from 6°C air outside and deposits heat inside your house at 24°C? (*b*) If this heat pump operates on 1200 W of electrical power, what is the maximum heat it can deliver into your house each hour?

59. The burning of gasoline in a car releases about $3.0 \times 10^4$ kcal/gal. If a car averages 41 km/gal when driving 90 km/h, which requires 25 hp, what is the efficiency of the engine under those conditions?

60. A Carnot engine has a lower operating temperature $T_L = 20°C$ and an efficiency of 30%. By how many kelvins should the high operating temperature $T_H$ be increased to achieve an efficiency of 40%?

61. Calculate the work done by an ideal gas in going from state A to state C in Fig. 15–28 for each of the following processes: (*a*) ADC, (*b*) ABC, and (*c*) AC directly.

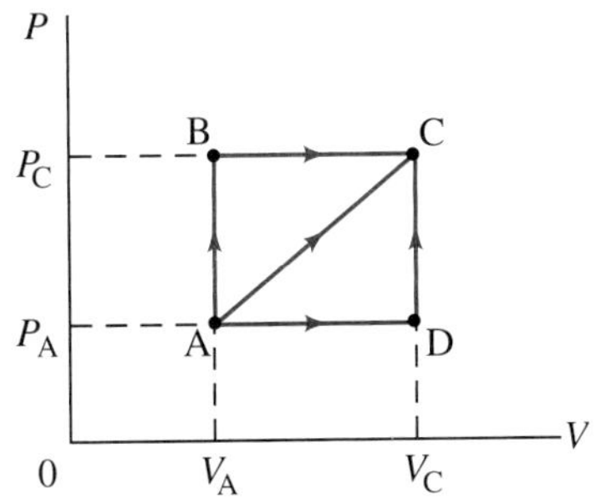


**FIGURE 15–28** Problem 61.

62. A 33% efficient power plant puts out 850 MW of electrical power. Cooling towers are used to take away the exhaust heat. (*a*) If the air temperature is allowed to rise 7.0 C°, estimate what volume of air ($km^3$) is heated per day. Will the local climate be heated significantly? (*b*) If the heated air were to form a layer 200 m thick, estimate how large an area it would cover for 24 h of operation. Assume the air has density 1.2 kg/m$^3$ and that its specific heat is about 1.0 kJ/kg·C° at constant pressure.

63. Suppose a power plant delivers energy at 980 MW using steam turbines. The steam goes into the turbines superheated at 625 K and deposits its unused heat in river water at 285 K. Assume that the turbine operates as an ideal Carnot engine. (*a*) If the river flow rate is 37 m$^3$/s, estimate the average temperature increase of the river water immediately downstream from the power plant. (*b*) What is the entropy increase per kilogram of the downstream river water in J/kg·K?

64. A 100-hp car engine operates at about 15% efficiency. Assume the engine's water temperature of 85°C is its cold-temperature (exhaust) reservoir and 495°C is its thermal "intake" temperature (the temperature of the exploding gas–air mixture). (*a*) What is the ratio of its efficiency relative to its maximum possible (Carnot) efficiency? (*b*) Estimate how much power (in watts) goes into moving the car, and how much heat, in joules and in kcal, is exhausted to the air in 1.0 h.

65. An ideal gas is placed in a tall cylindrical jar of cross-sectional area 0.080 m$^2$. A frictionless 0.10-kg movable piston is placed vertically into the jar such that the piston's weight is supported by the gas pressure in the jar. When the gas is heated (at constant pressure) from 25°C to 55°C, the piston rises 1.0 cm. How much heat was required for this process? Assume atmospheric pressure outside.

66. Metabolizing 1.0 kg of fat results in about $3.7 \times 10^7$ J of internal energy in the body. (*a*) In one day, how much fat does the body burn to maintain the body temperature of a person staying in bed and metabolizing at an average rate of 95 W? (*b*) How long would it take to burn 1.0-kg of fat this way assuming there is no food intake?

67. An ideal air conditioner keeps the temperature inside a room at 21°C when the outside temperature is 32°C. If 5.3 kW of power enters a room through the windows in the form of direct radiation from the Sun, how much electrical power would be saved if the windows were shaded so that the amount of radiation were reduced to 500 W?

68. A dehumidifier is essentially a "refrigerator with an open door." The humid air is pulled in by a fan and guided to a cold coil, where the temperature is less than the dew point, and some of the air's water condenses. After this water is extracted, the air is warmed back to its original temperature and sent into the room. In a well-designed dehumidifier, the heat is exchanged between the incoming and outgoing air. This way the heat that is removed by the refrigerator coil mostly comes from the condensation of water vapor to liquid. Estimate how much water is removed in 1.0 h by an ideal dehumidifier, if the temperature of the room is 25°C, the water condenses at 8°C, and the dehumidifier does work at the rate of 600 W of electrical power.

## Answers to Exercises

**A:** 700 J.

**B:** Less.

**C:** $-6.8 \times 10^3$ J.

**D:** Equation 14–1 applies only to an ideal monatomic gas, not to liquid water.

Photo of Lino Lacedelli on the summit of K2 taken by Achille Compagnoni on July 31, 1954, recording the first ascent of the world's second highest peak (shown on the cover of this book) and considered the most difficult of the world's tallest mountains, the 8000 m peaks. See Table 1-6 and Example 1-3. It was 23 years before K2 was climbed for the second time.

This comb has acquired a static electric charge, either from passing through hair, or being rubbed by a cloth or paper towel. The electrical charge on the comb induces a polarization (separation of charge) in scraps of paper, and thus attracts them.

Our introduction to electricity in this Chapter covers conductors and insulators, and Coulomb's law which relates the force between two point charges as a function of their distance apart. We also introduce the powerful concept of electric field.

CHAPTER 16

# Electric Charge and Electric Field

The word "electricity" may evoke an image of complex modern technology: lights, motors, electronics, and computers. But the electric force is thought to play an even deeper role in our lives. According to atomic theory, electric forces between atoms and molecules hold them together to form liquids and solids, and electric forces are also involved in the metabolic processes that occur within our bodies. Many of the forces we have dealt with so far, such as elastic forces, the normal force, and friction and other contact forces (pushes and pulls), are now considered to result from electric forces acting at the atomic level. Gravity, on the other hand, is a separate force.†

The earliest studies on electricity date back to the ancients, but it has been only in the past two centuries that electricity was studied in detail. We will discuss the development of ideas about electricity, including practical devices, as well as the relation to magnetism, in the next seven Chapters.

†As we discussed in Section 5–10, physicists in the twentieth century came to recognize four different fundamental forces in nature: (1) gravitational force, (2) electromagnetic force (we will see later that electric and magnetic forces are intimately related), (3) strong nuclear force, and (4) weak nuclear force. The last two forces operate at the level of the nucleus of an atom. Recent theory has combined the electromagnetic and weak nuclear forces so they are now considered to have a common origin known as the electroweak force. We will discuss these forces in later Chapters.

(a) (b)

**FIGURE 16–1** (a) Rub a plastic ruler and (b) bring it close to some tiny pieces of paper.

## 16–1 Static Electricity; Electric Charge and Its Conservation

The word *electricity* comes from the Greek word *elektron*, which means "amber." Amber is petrified tree resin, and the ancients knew that if you rub a piece of amber with a cloth, the amber attracts small pieces of leaves or dust. A piece of hard rubber, a glass rod, or a plastic ruler rubbed with a cloth will also display this "amber effect," or **static electricity** as we call it today. You can readily pick up small pieces of paper with a plastic comb or ruler that you've just vigorously rubbed with even a paper towel. See the photo on the previous page and Fig. 16–1. You have probably experienced static electricity when combing your hair or when taking a synthetic blouse or shirt from a clothes dryer. And you may have felt a shock when you touched a metal doorknob after sliding across a car seat or walking across a nylon carpet. In each case, an object becomes "charged" as a result of rubbing, and is said to possess a net **electric charge**.

**FIGURE 16–2** Like charges repel one another; unlike charges attract.

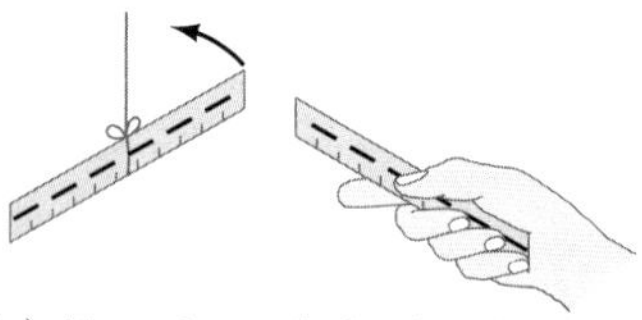

(a) Two charged plastic rulers repel

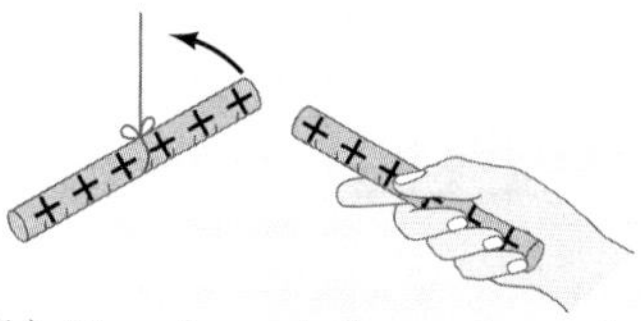

(b) Two charged glass rods repel

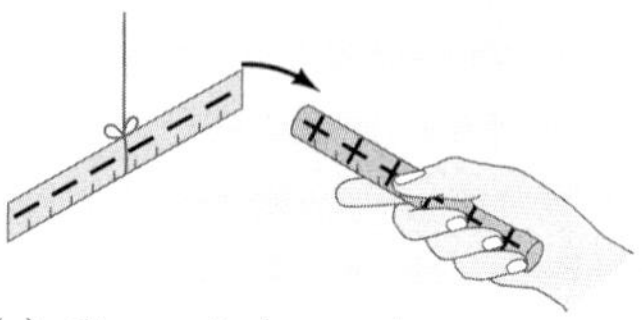

(c) Charged glass rod attracts charged plastic ruler

Is all electric charge the same, or is there more than one type? In fact, there are *two* types of electric charge, as the following simple experiments show. A plastic ruler suspended by a thread is vigorously rubbed with a cloth to charge it. When a second plastic ruler, which has also been charged in the same way, is brought close to the first, it is found that the one ruler *repels* the other. This is shown in Fig. 16–2a. Similarly, if a rubbed glass rod is brought close to a second charged glass rod, again a repulsive force is seen to act, Fig. 16–2b. However, if the charged glass rod is brought close to the charged plastic ruler, it is found that they *attract* each other, Fig. 16–2c. The charge on the glass must therefore be different from that on the plastic. Indeed, it is found experimentally that all charged objects fall into one of two categories. Either they are attracted to the plastic and repelled by the glass; or they are repelled by the plastic and attracted to the glass. Thus there seem to be two, and only two, types of electric charge. Each type of charge repels the same type but attracts the opposite type. That is: **unlike charges attract; like charges repel**.

*Like charges repel; unlike charges attract*

The two types of electric charge were referred to as *positive* and *negative* by the American statesman, philosopher, and scientist Benjamin Franklin (1706–1790). The choice of which name went with which type of charge was arbitrary. Franklin's choice set the charge on the rubbed glass rod to be positive charge, so the charge on a rubbed plastic ruler (or amber) is called negative charge. We still follow this convention today.

Franklin argued that whenever a certain amount of charge is produced on one object, an equal amount of the opposite type of charge is produced on another object. The positive and negative are to be treated *algebraically*, so during any process, the net change in the amount of charge produced is zero. For example, when a plastic ruler is rubbed with a paper towel, the plastic acquires a negative charge and the towel acquires an equal amount of positive charge. The charges are separated, but the sum of the two is zero.

This is an example of a law that is now well established: the **law of conservation of electric charge**, which states that

**the net amount of electric charge produced in any process is zero;**

or, said another way,

**no net electric charge can be created or destroyed.**

LAW OF CONSERVATION OF ELECTRIC CHARGE

If one object (or a region of space) acquires a positive charge, then an equal amount of negative charge will be found in neighboring areas or objects. No violations have ever been found, and this conservation law is as firmly established as those for energy and momentum.

## 16–2 Electric Charge in the Atom

Only within the past century has it become clear that an understanding of electricity originates inside the atom itself. In later Chapters we will discuss atomic structure and the ideas that led to our present view of the atom in more detail. But it will help our understanding of electricity if we discuss it briefly now.

*Electrons, protons, neutrons*

A simplified model of an atom shows it as having a tiny but heavy, positively charged nucleus surrounded by one or more negatively charged electrons (Fig. 16–3). The nucleus contains protons, which are positively charged, and neutrons, which have no net electric charge. All protons and all electrons have exactly the same magnitude of electric charge; but their signs are opposite. Hence neutral atoms, having no net charge, contain equal numbers of protons and electrons. Sometimes, an atom may lose one or more of its electrons, or may gain extra electrons, in which case it will have a net positive or negative charge and is called an **ion**.

*Ion*

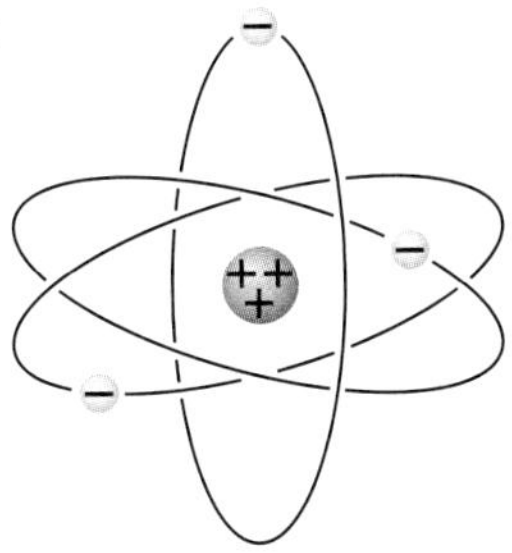

**FIGURE 16–3** Simple model of the atom.

In solid materials the nuclei tend to remain close to fixed positions, whereas some of the electrons may move quite freely. When an object is *neutral*, it contains equal amounts of positive and negative charge. The charging of a solid object by rubbing can be explained by the transfer of electrons from one object to the other. When a plastic ruler becomes negatively charged by rubbing with a paper towel, the transfer of electrons from the towel to the plastic leaves the towel with a positive charge equal in magnitude to the negative charge acquired by the plastic. In liquids and gases, nuclei or ions can move as well as electrons.

*Polar molecule*

Normally when objects are charged by rubbing, they hold their charge only for a limited time and eventually return to the neutral state. Where does the charge go? Usually the charge "leaks off" onto water molecules in the air. This is because water molecules are **polar**—that is, even though they are neutral, their charge is not distributed uniformly, Fig. 16–4. Thus the extra electrons on, say, a charged plastic ruler can "leak off" into the air because they are attracted to the positive end of water molecules. A positively charged object, on the other hand, can be neutralized by transfer of loosely held electrons from water molecules in the air. On dry days, static electricity is much more noticeable since the air contains fewer water molecules to allow leakage. On humid or rainy days, it is difficult to make any object hold a net charge for long.

**FIGURE 16–4** Diagram of a water molecule. Because it has opposite charges on different ends, it is called a "polar" molecule.

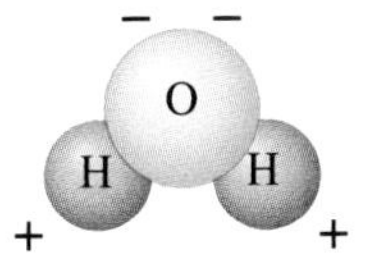


## 16–3 Insulators and Conductors

Suppose we have two metal spheres, one highly charged and the other electrically neutral (Fig. 16–5a). If we now place a metal object, such as a nail, so that it touches both spheres (Fig. 16–5b), the previously uncharged sphere quickly becomes charged. If, instead, we had connected the two spheres by a wooden rod or a piece of rubber (Fig. 16–5c), the uncharged ball would not become noticeably charged. Materials like the iron nail are said to be **conductors** of electricity, whereas wood and rubber are **nonconductors** or **insulators**.

*Conductors and insulators*

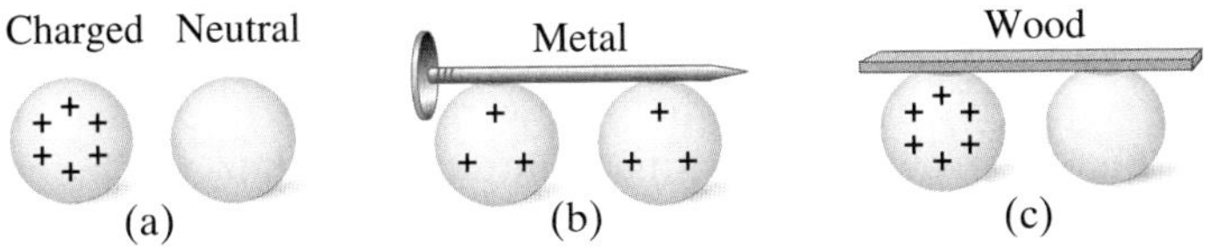


**FIGURE 16–5** (a) A charged metal sphere and a neutral metal sphere. (b) The two spheres connected by a conductor (a metal nail), which conducts charge from one sphere to the other. (c) The two spheres connected by an insulator (wood); almost no charge is conducted.

*Metals are good conductors*

Metals are generally good conductors, whereas most other materials are insulators (although even insulators conduct electricity very slightly). Nearly all natural materials fall into one or the other of these two quite distinct categories. However, a few materials (notably silicon and germanium) fall into an intermediate category known as **semiconductors**.

From the atomic point of view, the electrons in an insulating material are bound very tightly to the nuclei. In a good conductor, on the other hand, some of the electrons are bound very loosely and can move about freely within the material (although they cannot *leave* the object easily) and are often referred to as *free electrons* or *conduction electrons*. When a positively charged object is brought close to or touches a conductor, the free electrons in the conductor are attracted by this positively charged object and move quickly toward it. On the other hand, the free electrons move swiftly away from a negatively charged object that is brought close. In a semiconductor, there are many fewer free electrons, and in an insulator, almost none.

## 16–4 Induced Charge; the Electroscope

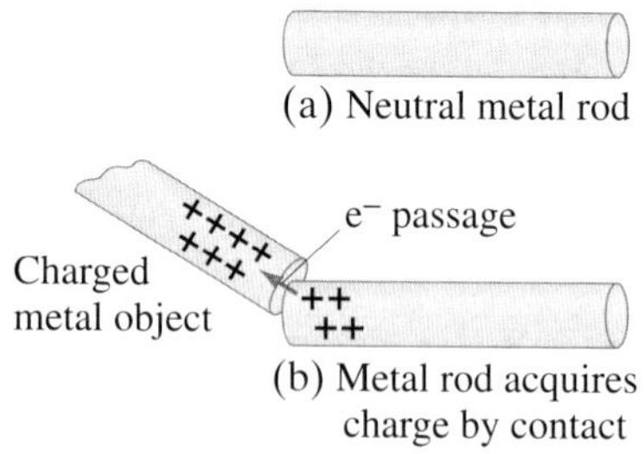


**FIGURE 16–6** A neutral metal rod in (a) will acquire a positive charge if placed in contact (b) with a positively charged metal object. (Electrons move as shown by the orange arrow.) This is called charging by conduction.

Suppose a positively charged metal object is brought close to an uncharged metal object. If the two touch, the free electrons in the neutral one are attracted to the positively charged object and some will pass over to it, Fig. 16–6. Since the second object, originally neutral, is now missing some of its negative electrons, it will have a net positive charge. This process is called "charging by conduction," or "by contact," and the two objects end up with the same sign of charge.

Now suppose a positively charged object is brought close to a neutral metal rod, but does not touch it. Although the free electrons of the metal rod do not leave the rod, they still move within the metal toward the external positive charge, leaving a positive charge at the opposite end of the rod (Fig. 16–7). A charge is said to have been *induced* at the two ends of the metal rod. No net charge has been created in the rod: charges have merely been *separated*. The net charge on the metal rod is still zero. However, if the metal is broken into two pieces, we would have two charged objects: one charged positively and one charged negatively.

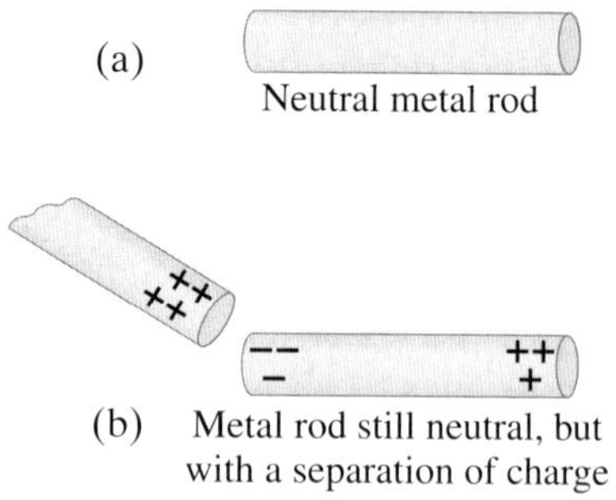


**FIGURE 16–7** Charging by induction.

**FIGURE 16–8** Inducing a charge on an object connected to ground.

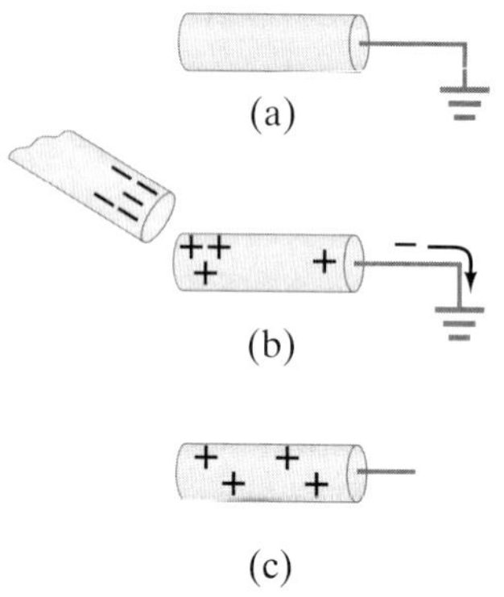


Another way to induce a net charge on a metal object is to first connect it with a conducting wire to the ground (or a conducting pipe leading into the ground) as shown in Fig. 16–8a (the symbol ⏚ means connected to "ground"). The object is then said to be "grounded" or "earthed." The Earth, because it is so large and can conduct, easily accepts or gives up electrons; hence it acts like a reservoir for charge. If a charged object—say negative this time—is brought up close to the metal object, free electrons in the metal are repelled and many of them move down the wire into the Earth, Fig. 16–8b. This leaves the metal positively charged. If the wire is now cut, the metal object will have a positive induced charge on it (Fig. 16–8c). If the wire were cut after the negative object is moved away, the electrons would all have moved back into the metal object and it would be neutral.

Charge separation can also be done in nonconductors. If you bring a positively charged object close to a neutral nonconductor as shown in Fig. 16–9, almost no electrons can move about freely within the nonconductor. But they can move slightly within their own atoms and molecules. Each oval in Fig. 16–9 represents a molecule (not to scale); the negatively charged electrons, attracted to the external positive charge, tend to move in its direction within their molecules. Because the negative charges in the nonconductor are nearer to the external positive charge, the nonconductor as a whole is attracted to the external positive charge (see the Chapter-opening photo, p. 439).

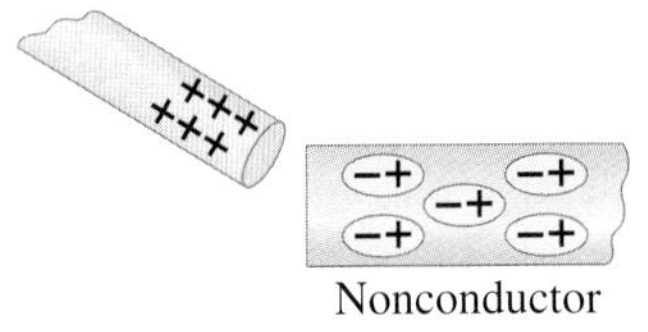


**FIGURE 16–9** A charged object brought near an insulator causes a charge separation within the insulator's molecules.

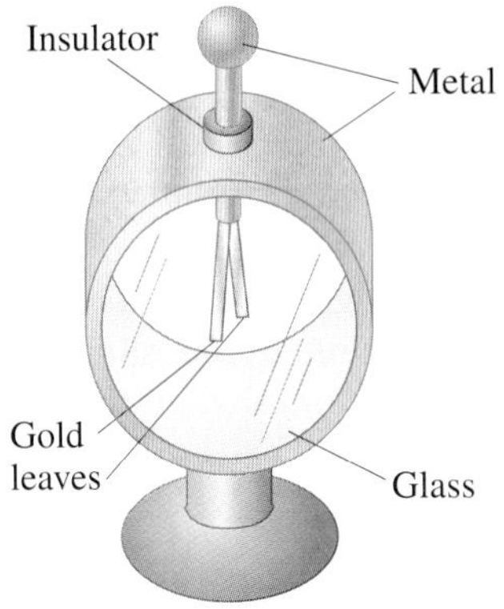


**FIGURE 16–10** Electroscope.

An **electroscope** is a device that can be used for detecting charge. As shown in Fig. 16–10, inside of a case are two movable metal leaves, often made of gold. (Sometimes only one leaf is movable.) The leaves are connected by a conductor to a metal knob on the outside of the case, but are insulated from the case itself. If a positively charged object is brought close to the knob, a separation of charge is induced: electrons are attracted up into the knob, leaving the leaves positively charged, Fig. 16–11a. The two leaves repel each other as shown, because they are both positively charged. If, instead, the knob is charged by conduction, the whole apparatus acquires a net charge as shown in Fig. 16–11b. In either case, the greater the amount of charge, the greater the separation of the leaves.

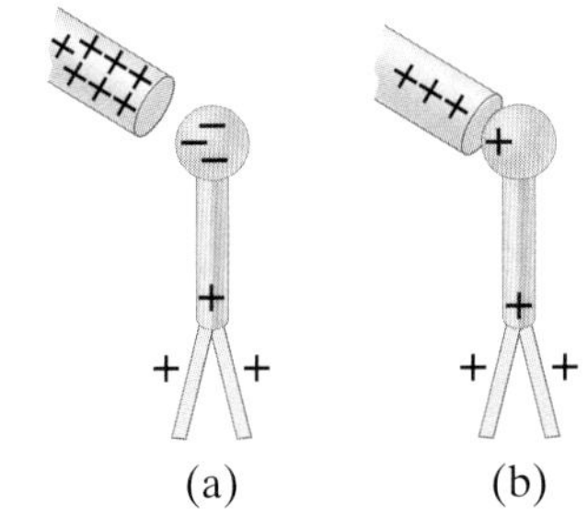


**FIGURE 16–11** Electroscope charged (a) by induction, (b) by conduction.

Note that you cannot tell the sign of the charge in this way, since negative charge will cause the leaves to separate just as much as an equal amount of positive charge; in either case, the two leaves repel each other. An electroscope can, however, be used to determine the sign of the charge if it is first charged by conduction, say, negatively, as in Fig. 16–12a. Now if a negative object is brought close, as in Fig. 16–12b, more electrons are induced to move down into the leaves and they separate further. If a positive charge is brought close instead, the electrons are induced to flow upward, leaving the leaves less negative and their separation is reduced, Fig. 16–12c.

The electroscope was much used in the early studies of electricity. The same principle, aided by some electronics, is used in much more sensitive modern **electrometers**.

*Electrometer*

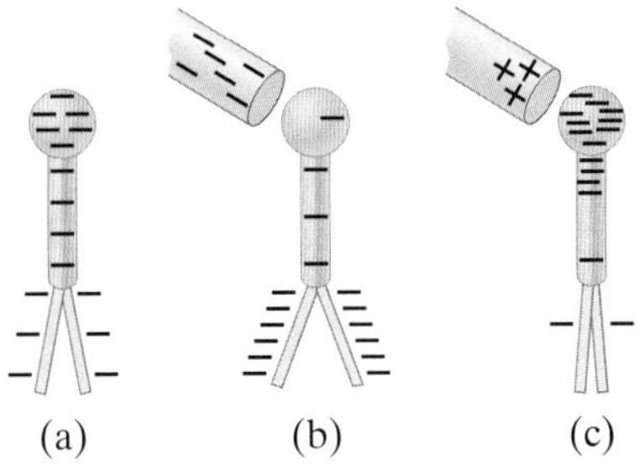


**FIGURE 16–12** A previously charged electroscope can be used to determine the sign of a charged object.

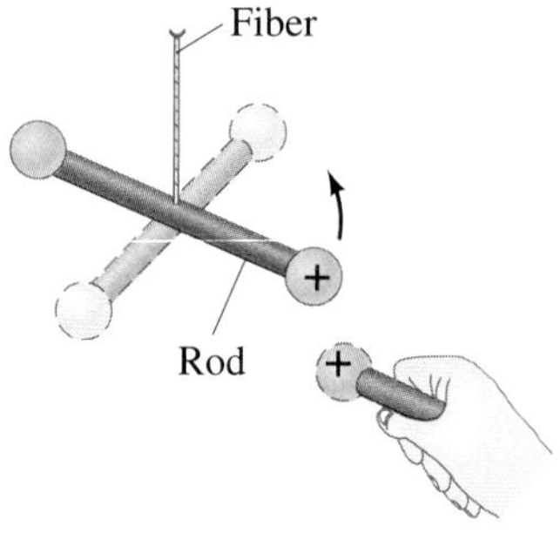


**FIGURE 16–13** Principle of Coulomb's apparatus. It is similar to Cavendish's, which was used for the gravitational force. When an external charged sphere is placed close to the charged one on the suspended bar, the bar rotates slightly. The suspending fiber resists the twisting motion, and the angle of twist is proportional to the force applied. With this apparatus, Coulomb investigated how the electric force varies as a function of the magnitude of the charges and of the distance between them.

## 16–5 Coulomb's Law

We have seen that an electric charge exerts a force of attraction or repulsion on other electric charges. What factors affect the magnitude of this force? To find an answer, the French physicist Charles Coulomb (1736–1806) investigated electric forces in the 1780s using a torsion balance (Fig. 16–13) much like that used by Cavendish for his studies of the gravitational force (Chapter 5).

Precise instruments for the measurement of electric charge were not available in Coulomb's time. Nonetheless, Coulomb was able to prepare small spheres with different magnitudes of charge in which the *ratio* of the charges was known.† Although he had some difficulty with induced charges, Coulomb was able to argue that the force one tiny charged object exerted on a second tiny charged object is directly proportional to the charge on each of them. That is, if the charge on either one of the objects was doubled, the force was doubled; and if the charge on both of the objects was doubled, the force increased to four times the original value. This was the case when the distance between the two charges remained the same. If the distance between them was allowed to increase, he found that the force decreased with the *square of the distance* between them. That is, if the distance was doubled, the force fell to one-fourth of its original value. Thus, Coulomb concluded, the force one small charged object exerts on a second one is proportional to the product of the magnitude of the charge on one, $Q_1$, times the magnitude of the charge on the other, $Q_2$, and inversely proportional to the square of the distance $r$ between them (Fig. 16–14). As an equation, we can write **Coulomb's law** as

COULOMB'S LAW

$$F = k\frac{Q_1 Q_2}{r^2}, \qquad \text{[magnitudes]} \qquad \textbf{(16–1)}$$

where $k$ is a proportionality constant.‡

Force direction

Coulomb's law, Eq. 16–1, gives the *magnitude* of the electric force that either object exerts on the other. The *direction* of the electric force *is always along the line joining the two objects*. If the two charges have the same sign, the force on either object is directed away from the other (they repel each other). If the two charges have opposite signs, the force on one is directed toward the other (they attract). See Fig. 16–15. Notice that the force one charge exerts on the second is equal but opposite to that exerted by the second on the first, in accord with Newton's third law.

**FIGURE 16–14** Coulomb's law, Eq. 16–1, gives the force between two point charges, $Q_1$ and $Q_2$, a distance $r$ apart.

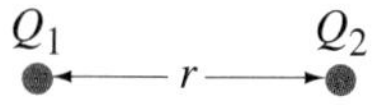


†Coulomb reasoned that if a charged conducting sphere is placed in contact with an identical uncharged sphere, the charge on the first would be shared equally by the two of them because of symmetry. He thus had a way to produce charges equal to $\frac{1}{2}, \frac{1}{4}$, and so on, of the original charge.

‡The validity of Coulomb's law today rests on precision measurements that are much more sophisticated than Coulomb's original experiment. The exponent, 2, in Coulomb's law has been shown to be accurate to 1 part in $10^{16}$ [that is, $2 \pm (1 \times 10^{-16})$].

**FIGURE 16–15** Direction of the force depends on whether the charges have the same sign as in (a) and (b), or opposite signs (c).

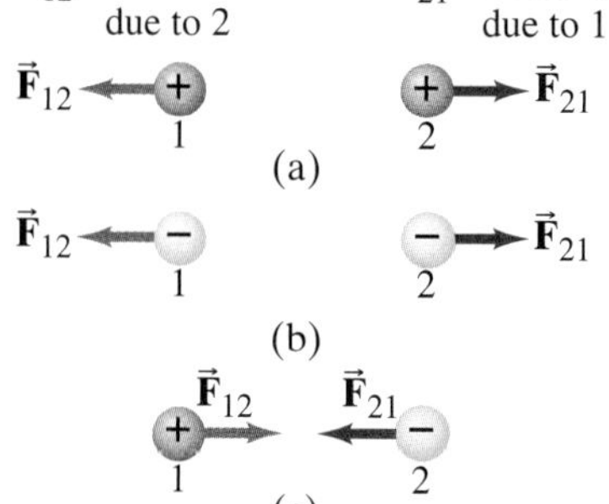

The SI unit of charge is the **coulomb** (C).† The precise definition of the coulomb today is in terms of electric current and magnetic field, and will be discussed later (Section 20–6). In SI units, $k$ has the value

*Unit for charge: the coulomb*

$$k = 8.988 \times 10^9\,\mathrm{N \cdot m^2/C^2}$$

or, when we only need two significant figures,

$$k \approx 9.0 \times 10^9\,\mathrm{N \cdot m^2/C^2}.$$

Thus, 1 C is that amount of charge which, if placed on each of two point objects that are 1.0 m apart, will result in each object exerting a force of $(9.0 \times 10^9\,\mathrm{N \cdot m^2/C^2})(1.0\,\mathrm{C})(1.0\,\mathrm{C})/(1.0\,\mathrm{m})^2 = 9.0 \times 10^9\,\mathrm{N}$ on the other. This would be an enormous force, equal to the weight of almost a million tons. We don't normally encounter charges as large as a coulomb.

Charges produced by rubbing ordinary objects (such as a comb or plastic ruler) are typically around a microcoulomb $(1\,\mu\mathrm{C} = 10^{-6}\,\mathrm{C})$ or less. Objects that carry a positive charge have a deficit of electrons, whereas negatively charged objects have an excess of electrons. The charge on one electron has been determined to have a magnitude of about $1.602 \times 10^{-19}$ C, and is negative. This is the smallest charge found in nature,‡ and because it is fundamental, it is given the symbol $e$ and is often referred to as the *elementary charge*:

*Charge on electron (the elementary charge)*

$$e = 1.602 \times 10^{-19}\,\mathrm{C}.$$

Note that $e$ is defined as a positive number, so the charge on the electron is $-e$. (The charge on a proton, on the other hand, is $+e$.) Since an object cannot gain or lose a fraction of an electron, the net charge on any object must be an integral multiple of this charge. Electric charge is thus said to be **quantized** (existing only in discrete amounts: $1e$, $2e$, $3e$, etc.). Because $e$ is so small, however, we normally don't notice this discreteness in macroscopic charges ($1\,\mu\mathrm{C}$ requires about $10^{13}$ electrons), which thus seem continuous.

*Electric charge is quantized*

Coulomb's law looks a lot like the *law of universal gravitation*, $F = G\,m_1 m_2/r^2$, which expresses the gravitational force a mass $m_1$ exerts on a mass $m_2$ (Eq. 5–4). Both are inverse square laws $(F \propto 1/r^2)$. Both also have a proportionality to a property of each object—mass for gravity, electric charge for electricity. And both act over a distance (that is, there is no need for contact). A major difference between the two laws is that gravity is always an attractive force, whereas the electric force can be either attractive or repulsive. Electric charge comes in two types, positive and negative; gravitational mass is only positive.

*Coulomb's law and the law of universal gravitation*

The constant $k$ in Eq. 16–1 is often written in terms of another constant, $\epsilon_0$, called the **permittivity of free space**. It is related to $k$ by $k = 1/4\pi\epsilon_0$. Coulomb's law can then be written

$$F = \frac{1}{4\pi\epsilon_0}\frac{Q_1 Q_2}{r^2}, \qquad \textbf{(16–2)}$$

*COULOMB'S LAW (in terms of $\epsilon_0$)*

where

$$\epsilon_0 = \frac{1}{4\pi k} = 8.85 \times 10^{-12}\,\mathrm{C^2/N \cdot m^2}.$$

Equation 16–2 looks more complicated than Eq. 16–1, but other fundamental equations we haven't seen yet are simpler in terms of $\epsilon_0$ rather than $k$. It doesn't matter which form we use since Eqs. 16–1 and 16–2 are equivalent. (The latest precise values of $e$ and $\epsilon_0$ are given inside the front cover.)

[Our convention for units, such as $\mathrm{C^2/N \cdot m^2}$ for $\epsilon_0$, means $\mathrm{m^2}$ is in the denominator. That is, $\mathrm{C^2/N \cdot m^2}$ does *not* mean $(\mathrm{C^2/N}) \cdot \mathrm{m^2} = \mathrm{C^2 \cdot m^2/N}$. (Otherwise we would have written it that way.)]

*Writing units*

†In the once common cgs system of units, $k$ is set equal to 1, and the unit of electric charge is called the *electrostatic unit* (esu) or the statcoulomb. One esu is defined as that charge, on each of two point objects 1 cm apart, that gives rise to a force of 1 dyne.

‡According to the standard model of elementary particle physics, subnuclear particles called quarks (Chapter 32) have a smaller charge than that on the electron, equal to $\frac{1}{3}e$ or $\frac{2}{3}e$. Quarks have not been detected directly as isolated objects, and theory indicates that free quarks may not be detectable.

Equations 16–1 and 16–2 apply to objects whose size is much smaller than the distance between them. Ideally, it is precise for **point charges** (spatial size negligible compared to other distances). For finite-sized objects, it is not always clear what value to use for $r$, particularly since the charge may not be distributed uniformly on the objects. If the two objects are spheres and the charge is known to be distributed uniformly on each, then $r$ is the distance between their centers.

*Point charge*

Coulomb's law describes the force between two charges when they are at rest. Additional forces come into play when charges are in motion, and these will be discussed in later Chapters. In this Chapter we discuss only charges at rest, the study of which is called **electrostatics**.

**PROBLEM SOLVING**
*Use magnitudes in Coulomb's law; find force direction from signs of charges*

When calculating with Coulomb's law, we usually ignore the signs of the charges and determine the direction of a force separately based on whether the force is attractive or repulsive.

**EXAMPLE 16–1** **Electric force on electron by proton.** Determine the magnitude and direction of the electric force on the electron of a hydrogen atom exerted by the single proton $(Q_2 = +e)$ that is the atom's nucleus. Assume the average distance between the revolving electron and the proton is $r = 0.53 \times 10^{-10}$ m, Fig. 16–16.

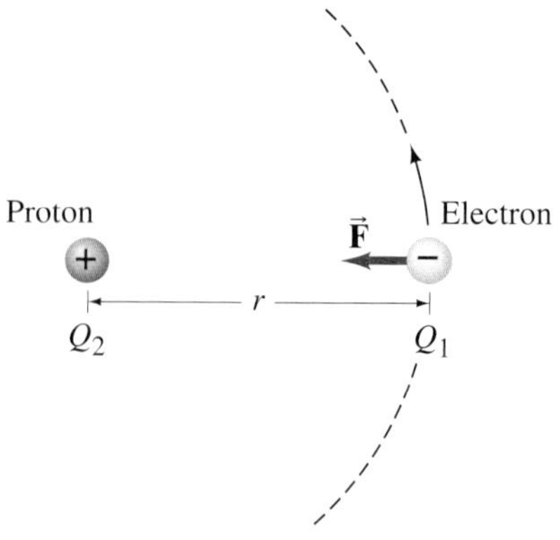

**FIGURE 16–16** Example 16–1.

**APPROACH** To find the force magnitude we use Coulomb's law, $F = kQ_1Q_2/r^2$ (Eq. 16–1), with $r = 0.53 \times 10^{-10}$ m. The electron and proton have the same magnitude of charge, $e$, so $Q_1 = Q_2 = 1.6 \times 10^{-19}$ C.

**SOLUTION** The magnitude of the force is

$$F = k\frac{Q_1Q_2}{r^2} = \frac{(9.0 \times 10^9\,\mathrm{N\cdot m^2/C^2})(1.6 \times 10^{-19}\,\mathrm{C})(1.6 \times 10^{-19}\,\mathrm{C})}{(0.53 \times 10^{-10}\,\mathrm{m})^2}$$
$$= 8.2 \times 10^{-8}\,\mathrm{N}.$$

The direction of the force on the electron is toward the proton, because the charges have opposite signs and the force is attractive.

**CONCEPTUAL EXAMPLE 16–2** **Which charge exerts the greater force?** Two positive point charges, $Q_1 = 50\,\mu$C and $Q_2 = 1\,\mu$C, are separated by a distance $l$, Fig. 16–17. Which is larger in magnitude, the force that $Q_1$ exerts on $Q_2$, or the force that $Q_2$ exerts on $Q_1$?

**FIGURE 16–17** Example 16–2.

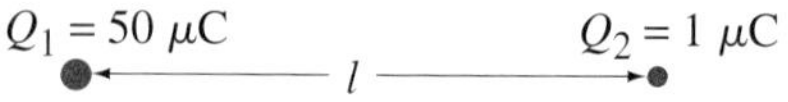


**RESPONSE** From Coulomb's law, the force on $Q_1$ exerted by $Q_2$ is

$$F_{12} = k\frac{Q_1Q_2}{l^2}.$$

The force on $Q_2$ exerted by $Q_1$ is

$$F_{21} = k\frac{Q_2Q_1}{l^2}$$

which is the same magnitude. The equation is symmetric with respect to the two charges, so $F_{21} = F_{12}$. Newton's third law also tells us that these two forces must have equal magnitude.

**EXERCISE A** In Example 16–2, how is the direction of $F_{12}$ related to the direction of $F_{21}$?

**EXERCISE B** What is the magnitude of $F_{12}$ (and $F_{21}$) in Example 16–2 if $l = 30$ cm?

It is very important to keep in mind that Coulomb's law, Eq. 16–1 or 16–2, gives the force on a charge due to only *one* other charge. If several (or many) charges are present, the *net force on any one of them will be the vector sum of the forces on that charge due to each of the others*. This **principle of superposition** is based on experiment, and tells us that electric force vectors add like any other vector. For example, if you have a system of four charges, the net force on charge 1, say, is the sum of the forces exerted on charge 1 by charges 2, 3, and 4. The magnitudes of these three forces are determined from Coulomb's law, and then are added vectorially.

*Superposition principle: electric forces add as vectors*

## 16–6 Solving Problems Involving Coulomb's Law and Vectors

The electric force between charged particles at rest (sometimes referred to as the **electrostatic force** or as the **Coulomb force**) is, like all forces, a vector: it has both magnitude and direction. When several forces act on an object (call them $\vec{\mathbf{F}}_1$, $\vec{\mathbf{F}}_2$, etc.), the net force $\vec{\mathbf{F}}_{\text{net}}$ on the object is the vector sum of all the forces acting on it:

$$\vec{\mathbf{F}}_{\text{net}} = \vec{\mathbf{F}}_1 + \vec{\mathbf{F}}_2 + \cdots.$$

As we just saw, this is the principle of superposition for forces. We studied how to add vectors in Chapter 3; then in Chapter 4 we used the rules for adding vectors to obtain the net force on an object by adding the different vector forces acting on it. It might be a good idea now to review Sections 3–2, 3–3, 3–4, as well as Section 4–9 on general problem-solving techniques. Here is a brief review of vectors.

FIGURE 16–18 Review of vector addition.

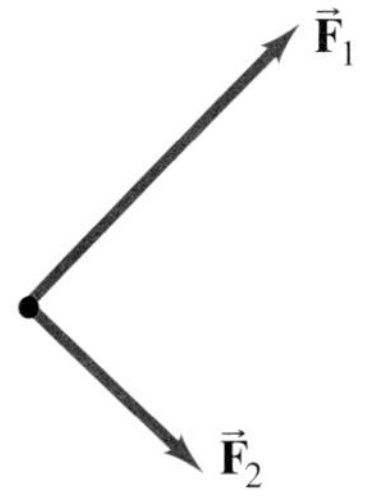


(a) Two forces acting on an object.

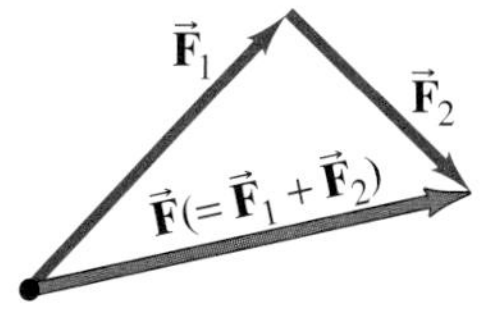


(b) The total, or net, force is $\vec{\mathbf{F}} = \vec{\mathbf{F}}_1 + \vec{\mathbf{F}}_2$ by the tail-to-tip method of adding vectors.

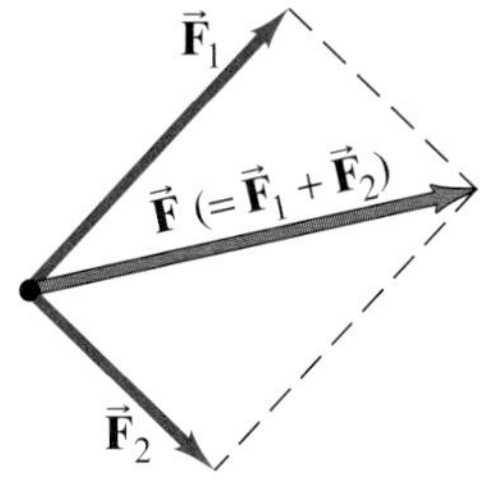


(c) $\vec{\mathbf{F}} = \vec{\mathbf{F}}_1 + \vec{\mathbf{F}}_2$ by the parallelogram method.

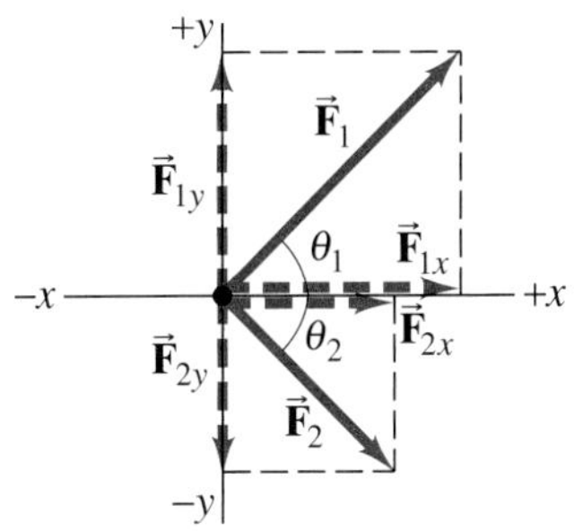


(d) $\vec{\mathbf{F}}_1$ and $\vec{\mathbf{F}}_2$ resolved into their $x$ and $y$ components.

### Vector Addition Review

Suppose two vector forces, $\vec{\mathbf{F}}_1$ and $\vec{\mathbf{F}}_2$, act on an object (Fig. 16–18a). They can be added using the tail-to-tip method (Fig. 16–18b) or by the parallelogram method (Fig. 16–18c), as discussed in Section 3–2. These two methods are useful for *understanding* a given problem (for getting a picture in your mind of what is going on), but for *calculating* the direction and magnitude of the resultant sum, it is more precise to use the method of adding components. Figure 16–18d shows the components of our forces $\vec{\mathbf{F}}_1$ and $\vec{\mathbf{F}}_2$ resolved into components along chosen $x$ and $y$ axes (for more details, see Section 3–4). From the definitions of the trigonometric functions (Figs. 3–11 and 3–12), we have

$$F_{1x} = F_1 \cos\theta_1 \qquad F_{2x} = F_2 \cos\theta_2$$
$$F_{1y} = F_1 \sin\theta_1 \qquad F_{2y} = -F_2 \sin\theta_2.$$

We add up the $x$ and $y$ components separately to obtain the components of the resultant force $\vec{\mathbf{F}}$, which are

$$F_x = F_{1x} + F_{2x} = F_1\cos\theta_1 + F_2\cos\theta_2,$$
$$F_y = F_{1y} + F_{2y} = F_1\sin\theta_1 - F_2\sin\theta_2.$$

The magnitude of the resultant (or *net*) force $\vec{\mathbf{F}}$ is

$$F = \sqrt{F_x^2 + F_y^2}.$$

The direction of $\vec{\mathbf{F}}$ is specified by the angle $\theta$ that $\vec{\mathbf{F}}$ makes with the $x$ axis, which is given by

$$\tan\theta = \frac{F_y}{F_x}.$$

## Adding Electric Forces; Principle of Superposition

When dealing with several charges, it is helpful to use double subscripts on each of the forces involved. The first subscript refers to the particle *on* which the force acts; the second refers to the particle that exerts the force. For example, if we have three charges, $\vec{\mathbf{F}}_{31}$ means the force exerted *on* particle 3 *by* particle 1.

As in all problem solving, it is very important to draw a diagram, in particular a free-body diagram (Chapter 4) for each object, showing all the forces acting on that object. In applying Coulomb's law, we can deal with charge magnitudes only (leaving out minus signs) to get the magnitude of each force. Then determine separately the direction of the force physically (along the line joining the two particles: like charges repel, unlike charges attract), and show the force on the diagram. Finally, add all the forces on one object together as vectors to obtain the net force on that object.

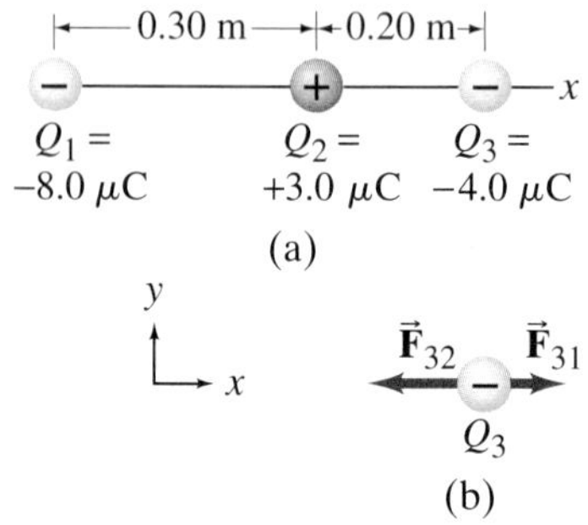


**FIGURE 16–19** Example 16–3.

**EXAMPLE 16–3** **Three charges in a line.** Three charged particles are arranged in a line, as shown in Fig. 16–19a. Calculate the net electrostatic force on particle 3 (the $-4.0\ \mu C$ on the right) due to the other two charges.

**APPROACH** The net force on particle 3 is the vector sum of the force $\vec{\mathbf{F}}_{31}$ exerted on 3 by particle 1 and the force $\vec{\mathbf{F}}_{32}$ exerted on 3 by particle 2: $\vec{\mathbf{F}} = \vec{\mathbf{F}}_{31} + \vec{\mathbf{F}}_{32}$.

**SOLUTION** The magnitudes of these two forces are obtained using Coulomb's law, Eq. 16–1:

$$F_{31} = k\frac{Q_3 Q_1}{r_{31}^2} = \frac{(9.0 \times 10^9\,\mathrm{N\cdot m^2/C^2})(4.0 \times 10^{-6}\,\mathrm{C})(8.0 \times 10^{-6}\,\mathrm{C})}{(0.50\,\mathrm{m})^2} = 1.2\,\mathrm{N},$$

where $r_{31} = 0.50\,\mathrm{m}$ is the distance from $Q_3$ to $Q_1$. Similarly,

$$F_{32} = k\frac{Q_3 Q_2}{r_{32}^2} = \frac{(9.0 \times 10^9\,\mathrm{N\cdot m^2/C^2})(4.0 \times 10^{-6}\,\mathrm{C})(3.0 \times 10^{-6}\,\mathrm{C})}{(0.20\,\mathrm{m})^2} = 2.7\,\mathrm{N}.$$

Since we were calculating the magnitudes of the forces, we omitted the signs of the charges. But we must be aware of them to get the direction of each force. Let the line joining the particles be the $x$ axis, and we take it positive to the right. Then, because $\vec{\mathbf{F}}_{31}$ is repulsive and $\vec{\mathbf{F}}_{32}$ is attractive, the directions of the forces are as shown in Fig. 16–19b: $F_{31}$ points in the positive $x$ direction and $F_{32}$ points in the negative $x$ direction. The net force on particle 3 is then

$$F = -F_{32} + F_{31} = -2.7\,\mathrm{N} + 1.2\,\mathrm{N} = -1.5\,\mathrm{N}.$$

The magnitude of the net force is 1.5 N, and it points to the left.

**NOTE** Charge $Q_1$ acts on charge $Q_3$ just as if $Q_2$ were not there (this is the principle of superposition). That is, the charge in the middle, $Q_2$, in no way blocks the effect of charge $Q_1$ acting on $Q_3$. Naturally, $Q_2$ exerts its own force on $Q_3$.

**CAUTION**

*Each charge exerts its own force. No charge blocks the effect of the others*

**EXERCISE C** Determine the net force on $Q_1$ in Fig. 16–19a.

**EXAMPLE 16–4** **Electric force using vector components.** Calculate the net electrostatic force on charge $Q_3$ shown in Fig. 16–20a due to the charges $Q_1$ and $Q_2$.

**APPROACH** We use Coulomb's law to find the magnitudes of the individual forces. The direction of each force will be along the line connecting $Q_3$ to $Q_1$ or $Q_2$. The forces $\vec{\mathbf{F}}_{31}$ and $\vec{\mathbf{F}}_{32}$ have the directions shown in Fig. 16–20a, since $Q_1$ exerts an attractive force on $Q_3$, and $Q_2$ exerts a repulsive force. The forces $\vec{\mathbf{F}}_{31}$ and $\vec{\mathbf{F}}_{32}$ are *not* along the same line, so to find the resultant force on $Q_3$ we resolve $\vec{\mathbf{F}}_{31}$ and $\vec{\mathbf{F}}_{32}$ into $x$ and $y$ components and perform the vector addition.

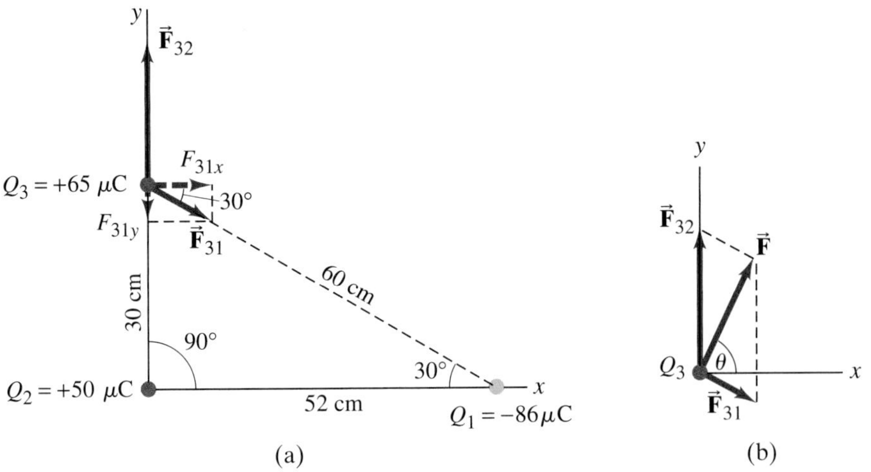


**FIGURE 16–20** Determining the forces for Example 16–4. (a) The directions of the individual forces are as shown because $\vec{F}_{32}$ is repulsive (the force on $Q_3$ is in the direction away from $Q_2$ because $Q_3$ and $Q_2$ are both positive) whereas $\vec{F}_{31}$ is attractive ($Q_3$ and $Q_1$ have opposite signs), so $\vec{F}_{31}$ points toward $Q_1$. (b) Adding $\vec{F}_{32}$ to $\vec{F}_{31}$ to obtain the net force $\vec{F}$.

**SOLUTION** The magnitudes of $\vec{F}_{31}$ and $\vec{F}_{32}$ are (ignoring signs of the charges since we know the directions)

$$F_{31} = k\frac{Q_3Q_1}{r_{31}^2} = \frac{(9.0\times10^9\,\mathrm{N\cdot m^2/C^2})(6.5\times10^{-5}\,\mathrm{C})(8.6\times10^{-5}\,\mathrm{C})}{(0.60\,\mathrm{m})^2} = 140\,\mathrm{N},$$

$$F_{32} = k\frac{Q_3Q_2}{r_{32}^2} = \frac{(9.0\times10^9\,\mathrm{N\cdot m^2/C^2})(6.5\times10^{-5}\,\mathrm{C})(5.0\times10^{-5}\,\mathrm{C})}{(0.30\,\mathrm{m})^2} = 330\,\mathrm{N}.$$

We resolve $\vec{F}_{31}$ into its components along the $x$ and $y$ axes, as shown in Fig. 16–20a:

$$F_{31x} = F_{31}\cos30° = (140\,\mathrm{N})\cos30° = 120\,\mathrm{N},$$
$$F_{31y} = -F_{31}\sin30° = -(140\,\mathrm{N})\sin30° = -70\,\mathrm{N}.$$

The force $\vec{F}_{32}$ has only a $y$ component. So the net force $\vec{F}$ on $Q_3$ has components

$$F_x = F_{31x} = 120\,\mathrm{N},$$
$$F_y = F_{32} + F_{31y} = 330\,\mathrm{N} - 70\,\mathrm{N} = 260\,\mathrm{N}.$$

The magnitude of the net force is

$$F = \sqrt{F_x^2 + F_y^2} = \sqrt{(120\,\mathrm{N})^2 + (260\,\mathrm{N})^2} = 290\,\mathrm{N};$$

and it acts at an angle $\theta$ (see Fig. 16–20b) given by

$$\tan\theta = \frac{F_y}{F_x} = \frac{260\,\mathrm{N}}{120\,\mathrm{N}} = 2.2,$$

so $\theta = \tan^{-1}(2.2) = 65°$.

**NOTE** Because $\vec{F}_{31}$ and $\vec{F}_{32}$ are not along the same line, the magnitude of $\vec{F}_3$ is not equal to the sum (or difference as in Example 16–3) of the separate magnitudes. That is, $F_3$ is not equal to $F_{31} + F_{32}$; nor does it equal $F_{32} - F_{31}$. Instead we had to do vector addition.

**FIGURE 16–21** Example 16–5 and Exercise D: $Q_4$ exerts force $(\vec{F}_{34})$ that makes the net force on $Q_3$ zero.

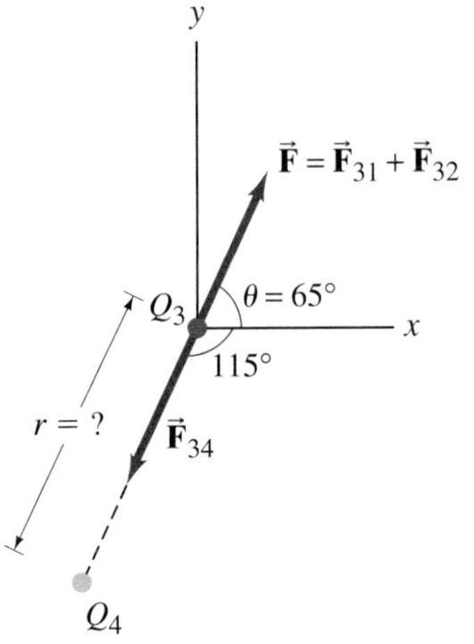


CONCEPTUAL EXAMPLE 16–5 **Make the force on $Q_3$ zero.** In Fig. 16–20, where could you place a fourth charge, $Q_4 = -50\,\mu\mathrm{C}$, so that the net force on $Q_3$ would be zero?

**RESPONSE** By the principle of superposition, we need a force in exactly the opposite direction to the resultant $\vec{F}$ due to $Q_2$ and $Q_1$ that we calculated in Example 16–4, Fig. 16–20b. Our force must have magnitude 290 N, and must point down and to the left of $Q_3$ in Fig. 16–20b. So $Q_4$ must be along this line. See Fig. 16–21.

**EXERCISE D** In Example 16–5, what distance $r$ must $Q_4$ be from $Q_3$?

**EXERCISE E** (*a*) Consider two point charges of the same magnitude but opposite sign ($+Q$ and $-Q$), which are fixed a distance $d$ apart. Can you find a location where a third positive charge $Q$ could be placed so that the net electric force on this third charge is zero? (*b*) What if the first two charges were both $+Q$?

## 16–7 The Electric Field

Many common forces might be referred to as "contact forces," such as your hands pushing or pulling a cart, or a tennis racket hitting a tennis ball.

In contrast, both the gravitational force and the electrical force act over a distance: there is a force between two objects even when the objects are not touching. The idea of a force *acting at a distance* was a difficult one for early thinkers. Newton himself felt uneasy with this idea when he published his law of universal gravitation. A helpful way to look at the situation uses the idea of the **field**, developed by the British scientist Michael Faraday (1791–1867). In the electrical case, according to Faraday, an *electric field* extends outward from every charge and permeates all of space (Fig. 16–22). If a second charge (call it $Q_2$) is placed near the first charge, it feels a force exerted by the electric field that is there (say, at point P in Fig. 16–22). The electric field at point P is considered to interact directly with charge $Q_2$ to produce the force on $Q_2$.

*Field*

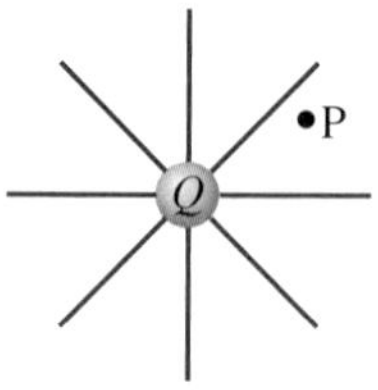


**FIGURE 16–22** An electric field surrounds every charge. P is an arbitrary point.

We can in principle investigate the electric field surrounding a charge or group of charges by measuring the force on a small positive **test charge**. By a test charge we mean a charge so small that the force it exerts does not significantly alter the distribution of those other charges that create the field. If a tiny positive test charge $q$ is placed at various locations in the vicinity of a single positive charge $Q$ as shown in Fig. 16–23 (points a, b, c), the force exerted on $q$ is as shown. The force at b is less than at a because b's distance from $Q$ is greater (Coulomb's law); and the force at c is smaller still. In each case, the force on $q$ is directed radially away from $Q$. The electric field is defined in terms of the force on such a positive test charge. In particular, the **electric field**, $\vec{\mathbf{E}}$, at any point in space is defined as the force $\vec{\mathbf{F}}$ exerted on a tiny positive test charge placed at that point divided by the magnitude of the test charge $q$:

*Test charge*

**FIGURE 16–23** Force exerted by charge $+Q$ on a small test charge, $q$, placed at points a, b, and c.

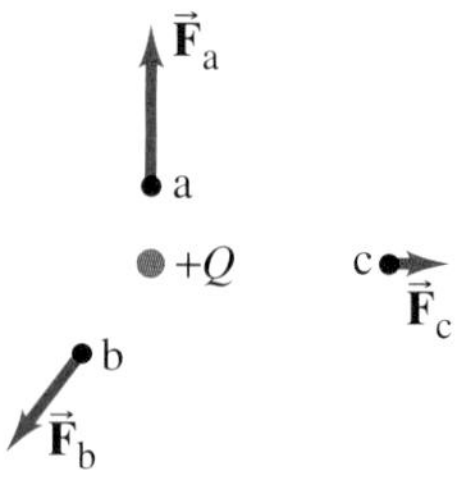


*Definition of electric field*

$$\vec{\mathbf{E}} = \frac{\vec{\mathbf{F}}}{q}. \tag{16–3}$$

More precisely, $\vec{\mathbf{E}}$ is defined as the limit of $\vec{\mathbf{F}}/q$ as $q$ is taken smaller and smaller, approaching zero. That is, $q$ is so tiny that it exerts essentially no force on the other charges which created the field. From this definition (Eq. 16–3), we see that the electric field at any point in space is a vector whose direction is the direction of the force on a tiny positive test charge at that point, and whose magnitude is the *force per unit charge*. Thus $\vec{\mathbf{E}}$ has SI units of newtons per coulomb (N/C).

*$\vec{\mathbf{E}}$ is a vector*

The reason for defining $\vec{\mathbf{E}}$ as $\vec{\mathbf{F}}/q$ (with $q \rightarrow 0$) is so that $\vec{\mathbf{E}}$ does not depend on the magnitude of the test charge $q$. This means that $\vec{\mathbf{E}}$ describes only the effect of the charges creating the electric field at that point.

The electric field at any point in space can be measured, based on the definition, Eq. 16–3. For simple situations involving one or several point charges, we can calculate $\vec{\mathbf{E}}$. For example, the electric field at a distance $r$ from a single point charge $Q$ would have magnitude

$$E = \frac{F}{q} = \frac{kqQ/r^2}{q}$$

*Electric field due to one point charge*

$$E = k\frac{Q}{r^2}; \qquad \text{[single point charge]} \tag{16–4a}$$

or, in terms of $\epsilon_0$ as in Eq. 16–2 ($k = 1/4\pi\epsilon_0$):

$$E = \frac{1}{4\pi\epsilon_0}\frac{Q}{r^2}. \qquad \text{[single point charge]} \tag{16–4b}$$

Notice that $E$ is independent of the test charge $q$—that is, $E$ depends only on the charge $Q$ which produces the field, and not on the value of the test charge $q$. Equations 16–4 are referred to as the electric field form of Coulomb's law.

If we are given the electric field $\vec{\mathbf{E}}$ at a given point in space, then we can calculate the force $\vec{\mathbf{F}}$ on any charge $q$ placed at that point by writing (see Eq. 16–3):

$$\vec{\mathbf{F}} = q\vec{\mathbf{E}}. \qquad \textbf{(16–5)}$$

This is valid even if $q$ is not small as long as $q$ does not cause the charges creating $\vec{\mathbf{E}}$ to move. If $q$ is positive, $\vec{\mathbf{F}}$ and $\vec{\mathbf{E}}$ point in the same direction. If $q$ is negative, $\vec{\mathbf{F}}$ and $\vec{\mathbf{E}}$ point in opposite directions. See Fig. 16–24.

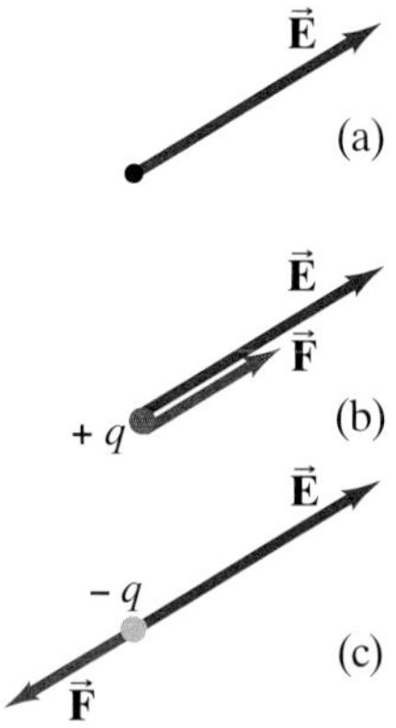


**FIGURE 16–24** (a) Electric field at a given point in space. (b) Force on a positive charge at that point. (c) Force on a negative charge at that point.

PHYSICS APPLIED
*Photocopier*

**EXAMPLE 16–6** **Photocopy machine.** A photocopy machine works by arranging positive charges (in the pattern to be copied) on the surface of a drum, then gently sprinkling negatively charged dry toner (ink) particles onto the drum. The toner particles temporarily stick to the pattern on the drum (Fig. 16–25) and are later transferred to paper and "melted" to produce the copy. Suppose each toner particle has a mass of $9.0 \times 10^{-16}$ kg and carries an average of 20 extra electrons to provide an electric charge. Assuming that the electric force on a toner particle must exceed twice its weight in order to ensure sufficient attraction, compute the required electric field strength near the surface of the drum.

**APPROACH** The electric force on a toner particle of charge $q = 20e$ is $F = qE$, where $E$ is the needed electric field. This force needs to be at least as great as twice the weight ($mg$) of the particle.

**SOLUTION** The minimum value of electric field satisfies the relation

$$qE = 2mg$$

where $q = 20e$. Hence

$$E = \frac{2mg}{q} = \frac{2(9.0 \times 10^{-16}\,\text{kg})(9.8\,\text{m/s}^2)}{20(1.6 \times 10^{-19}\,\text{C})} = 5.5 \times 10^3\,\text{N/C}.$$

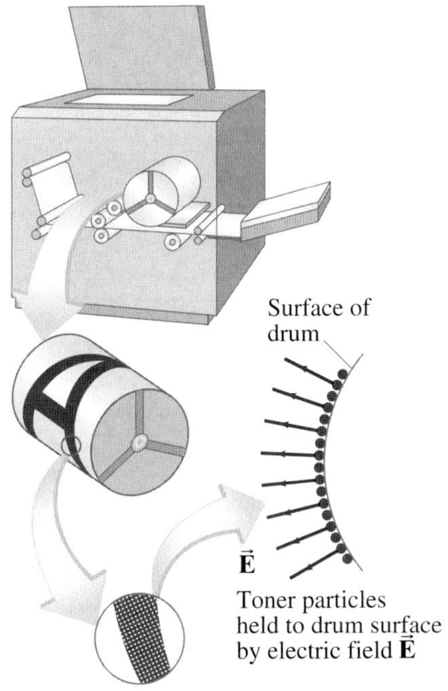


**FIGURE 16–25** Example 16–6.

**EXAMPLE 16–7** **Electric field of a single point charge.** Calculate the magnitude and direction of the electric field at a point P which is 30 cm to the right of a point charge $Q = -3.0 \times 10^{-6}$ C.

**APPROACH** The magnitude of the electric field due to a single point charge is given by Eq. 16–4. The direction is found using the sign of the charge $Q$.

**SOLUTION** The magnitude of the electric field is:

$$E = k\frac{Q}{r^2} = \frac{(9.0 \times 10^9\,\text{N}\cdot\text{m}^2/\text{C}^2)(3.0 \times 10^{-6}\,\text{C})}{(0.30\,\text{m})^2} = 3.0 \times 10^5\,\text{N/C}.$$

The direction of the electric field is *toward* the charge $Q$, to the left as shown in Fig. 16–26a, since we defined the direction as that of the force on a positive test charge which here would be attractive. If $Q$ had been positive, the electric field would have pointed away, as in Fig. 16–26b.

**NOTE** There is no electric charge at point P. But there is an electric field there. The only real charge is $Q$.

**FIGURE 16–26** Example 16–7. Electric field at point P (a) due to a negative charge $Q$, and (b) due to a positive charge $Q$, each 30 cm from P.

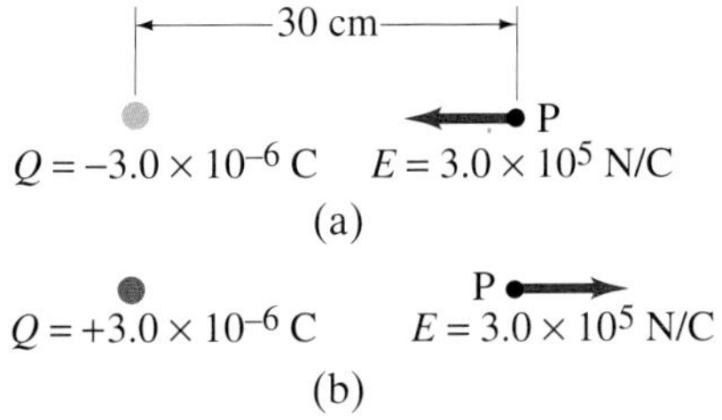


This Example illustrates a general result: The electric field $\vec{\mathbf{E}}$ due to a positive charge points away from the charge, whereas $\vec{\mathbf{E}}$ due to a negative charge points toward that charge.

**EXERCISE F** What is the magnitude and the direction of the electric field due to a $+2.5\,\mu$C charge at a point 50 cm below it?

*Superposition principle for electric fields*

If the electric field at a given point in space is due to more than one charge, the individual fields (call them $\vec{\mathbf{E}}_1$, $\vec{\mathbf{E}}_2$, etc.) due to each charge are added vectorially to get the total field at that point:

$$\vec{\mathbf{E}} = \vec{\mathbf{E}}_1 + \vec{\mathbf{E}}_2 + \cdots.$$

The validity of this **superposition principle** for electric fields is fully confirmed by experiment.

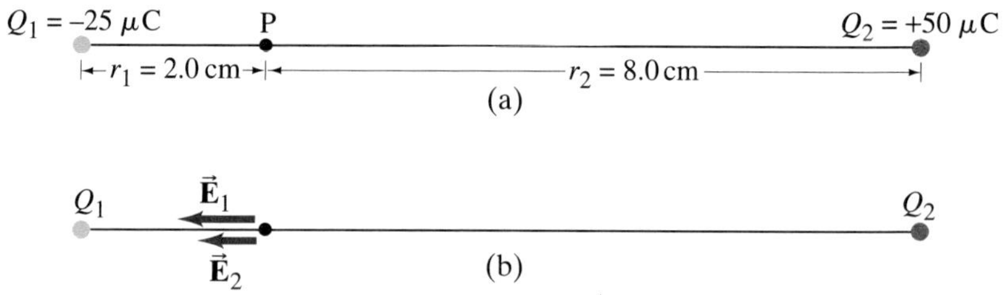


**FIGURE 16–27** Example 16–8. In (b), we don't know the relative lengths of $\vec{\mathbf{E}}_1$ and $\vec{\mathbf{E}}_2$ until we do the calculation.

**EXAMPLE 16–8** ***E* at a point between two charges.** Two point charges are separated by a distance of 10.0 cm. One has a charge of $-25\ \mu C$ and the other $+50\ \mu C$. (*a*) Determine the direction and magnitude of the electric field at a point P between the two charges that is 2.0 cm from the negative charge (Fig. 16–27a). (*b*) If an electron (mass $= 9.11 \times 10^{-31}$ kg) is placed at rest at P and then released, what will be its initial acceleration (direction and magnitude)?

**APPROACH** The electric field at P will be the vector sum of the fields created separately by $Q_1$ and $Q_2$. The field due to the negative charge $Q_1$ points toward $Q_1$, and the field due to the positive charge $Q_2$ points away from $Q_2$. Thus both fields point to the left as shown in Fig. 16–27b, and we can add the magnitudes of the two fields together algebraically, ignoring the signs of the charges. In (*b*) we use Newton's second law ($F = ma$) to determine the acceleration, where $F = qE$ (Eq. 16–5).

**SOLUTION** (*a*) Each field is due to a point charge as given by Eq. 16–4, $E = kQ/r^2$. The total field is

$$\begin{aligned} E &= k\frac{Q_1}{r_1^2} + k\frac{Q_2}{r_2^2} = k\left(\frac{Q_1}{r_1^2} + \frac{Q_2}{r_2^2}\right) \\ &= \left(9.0 \times 10^9\ \mathrm{N\cdot m^2/C^2}\right)\left(\frac{25 \times 10^{-6}\ \mathrm{C}}{(2.0 \times 10^{-2}\ \mathrm{m})^2} + \frac{50 \times 10^{-6}\ \mathrm{C}}{(8.0 \times 10^{-2}\ \mathrm{m})^2}\right) \\ &= 6.3 \times 10^8\ \mathrm{N/C}. \end{aligned}$$

(*b*) The electric field points to the left, so the electron will feel a force to the *right* since it is negatively charged. Therefore the acceleration $a = F/m$ (Newton's second law) will be to the right. The force on a charge $q$ in an electric field $E$ is $F = qE$ (Eq. 16–5). Hence the magnitude of the electron's initial acceleration is

$$a = \frac{F}{m} = \frac{qE}{m} = \frac{\left(1.60 \times 10^{-19}\ \mathrm{C}\right)\left(6.3 \times 10^8\ \mathrm{N/C}\right)}{9.11 \times 10^{-31}\ \mathrm{kg}} = 1.1 \times 10^{20}\ \mathrm{m/s^2}.$$

**NOTE** By carefully considering the directions of *each* field ($\vec{\mathbf{E}}_1$ and $\vec{\mathbf{E}}_2$) before doing any calculations, we made sure our calculation could be done simply and correctly.

**EXERCISE G** Given the same two charges $Q_1$ and $Q_2$ as in Fig. 16–27, determine the direction of each of the component electric fields $\vec{\mathbf{E}}_1$ and $\vec{\mathbf{E}}_2$, as well as of the total electric field for two positions: (*a*) a point just slightly to the left of $Q_1$, and (*b*) a point slightly to the right of $Q_2$. (*Hint*: Remember the $1/r^2$ factor).

**EXAMPLE 16–9** ***E* above two point charges.** Calculate the total electric field (*a*) at point A and (*b*) at point B in Fig. 16–28 due to both charges, $Q_1$ and $Q_2$.

**APPROACH** The calculation is much like that of Example 16–4, except now we are dealing with electric fields instead of force. The electric field at point A is the vector sum of the fields $\vec{\mathbf{E}}_{A1}$ due to $Q_1$, and $\vec{\mathbf{E}}_{A2}$ due to $Q_2$. We find the magnitude of the field produced by each point charge, then we add their components to find the total field at point A. We do the same for point B.

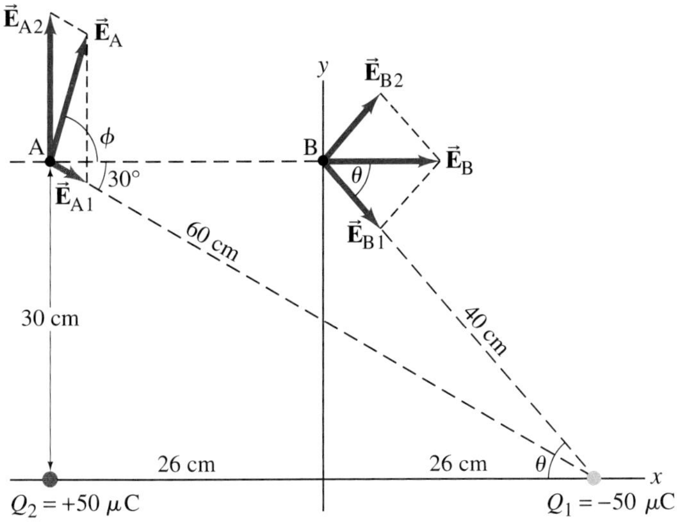


**FIGURE 16–28** Calculation of the electric field at points A and B for Example 16–9.

**SOLUTION** (*a*) The magnitude of the electric field produced at point A by each of the charges $Q_1$ and $Q_2$ is given by $E = kQ/r^2$, so

$$E_{A1} = \frac{(9.0 \times 10^9\,\mathrm{N\cdot m^2/C^2})(50 \times 10^{-6}\,\mathrm{C})}{(0.60\,\mathrm{m})^2} = 1.25 \times 10^6\,\mathrm{N/C},$$

$$E_{A2} = \frac{(9.0 \times 10^9\,\mathrm{N\cdot m^2/C^2})(50 \times 10^{-6}\,\mathrm{C})}{(0.30\,\mathrm{m})^2} = 5.0 \times 10^6\,\mathrm{N/C}.$$

➡ **PROBLEM SOLVING**

*Ignore signs of charges and determine direction physically, showing directions on diagram*

The direction of $E_{A1}$ points from A toward $Q_1$ (negative charge), whereas $E_{A2}$ points from A away from $Q_2$, as shown; so the total electric field at A, $\vec{\mathbf{E}}_A$, has components

$$E_{Ax} = E_{A1}\cos 30° = 1.1 \times 10^6\,\mathrm{N/C},$$

$$E_{Ay} = E_{A2} - E_{A1}\sin 30° = 4.4 \times 10^6\,\mathrm{N/C}.$$

Thus the magnitude of $\vec{\mathbf{E}}_A$ is

$$E_A = \sqrt{(1.1)^2 + (4.4)^2} \times 10^6\,\mathrm{N/C} = 4.5 \times 10^6\,\mathrm{N/C},$$

and its direction is $\phi$ given by $\tan\phi = E_{Ay}/E_{Ax} = 4.4/1.1 = 4.0$, so $\phi = 76°$.

(*b*) Because B is equidistant (40 cm by the Pythagorean theorem) from the two equal charges, the magnitudes of $E_{B1}$ and $E_{B2}$ are the same; that is,

➡ **PROBLEM SOLVING**

*Use symmetry to save work, when possible*

$$E_{B1} = E_{B2} = \frac{kQ}{r^2} = \frac{(9.0 \times 10^9\,\mathrm{N\cdot m^2/C^2})(50 \times 10^{-6}\,\mathrm{C})}{(0.40\,\mathrm{m})^2}$$
$$= 2.8 \times 10^6\,\mathrm{N/C}.$$

Also, because of the symmetry, the $y$ components are equal and opposite, and so cancel out. Hence the total field $E_B$ is horizontal and equals $E_{B1}\cos\theta + E_{B2}\cos\theta = 2E_{B1}\cos\theta$. From the diagram, $\cos\theta = 26\,\mathrm{cm}/40\,\mathrm{cm} = 0.65$. Then

$$E_B = 2E_{B1}\cos\theta = 2(2.8 \times 10^6\,\mathrm{N/C})(0.65)$$
$$= 3.6 \times 10^6\,\mathrm{N/C},$$

and the direction of $\vec{\mathbf{E}}_B$ is along the $+x$ direction.

**NOTE** We could have done part (*b*) in the same way we did part (*a*). But symmetry allowed us to solve the problem with less effort.

## PROBLEM SOLVING Electrostatics: Electric Forces and Electric Fields

Solving electrostatics problems follows, to a large extent, the general problem-solving procedure discussed in Section 4–9. Whether you use electric field or electrostatic forces, the procedure is similar:

1. **Draw** a careful **diagram**—namely, a free-body diagram for each object, showing all the forces acting on that object, or showing the electric field at a point due to all significant charges present. Determine the **direction** of each force or electric field physically: like charges repel each other, unlike charges attract; fields point away from a + charge, and toward a − charge. Show and label each vector force or field on your diagram.
2. **Apply Coulomb's law** to calculate the magnitude of the force that each contributing charge exerts on a charged object, or the magnitude of the electric field at a point. Deal only with magnitudes of charges (leaving out minus signs), and obtain the magnitude of each force or electric field.
3. **Add vectorially** all the forces on an object, or the contributing fields at a point, to get the resultant. Use **symmetry** (say, in the geometry) whenever possible.

Let us see how this Problem Solving Box can be applied to Example 16–9, part (*b*).

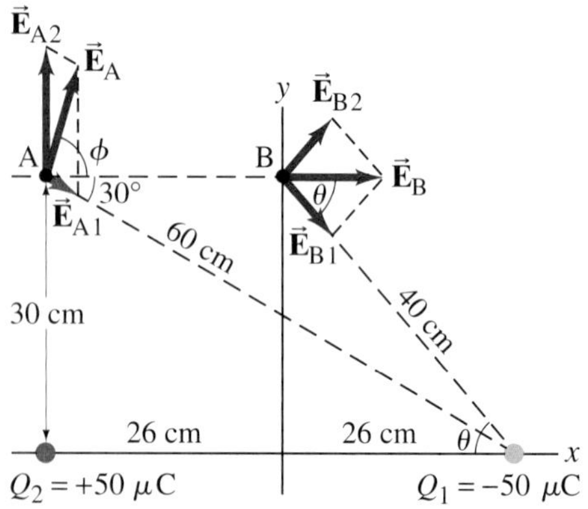


**FIGURE 16–28** (repeated) Calculation of the electric field at points A and B for Example 16–9.

**EXAMPLE 16–9 Repeated.** Calculate the total electric field at point B in Fig. 16–28 due to both charges, $Q_1$ and $Q_2$.

**APPROACH and SOLUTION**

1. **Draw** a careful **diagram**. The **directions** of the electric fields $\vec{\mathbf{E}}_{B1}$ and $\vec{\mathbf{E}}_{B2}$, as well as the net field $\vec{\mathbf{E}}_B$, are shown in Fig. 16–28. $\vec{\mathbf{E}}_{B2}$ points away from the positive charge $Q_2$; $\vec{\mathbf{E}}_{B1}$ points toward the negative charge $Q_1$.
2. **Apply Coulomb's law** to find the magnitudes of the contributing electric fields. Because B is equidistant (40 cm by the Pythagorean theorem) from the two equal charges, the magnitudes of $E_{B1}$ and $E_{B2}$ are the same; that is,

$$E_{B1} = E_{B2} = \frac{kQ}{r^2} = \frac{(9.0 \times 10^9\,\mathrm{N\cdot m^2/C^2})(50 \times 10^{-6}\,\mathrm{C})}{(0.40\,\mathrm{m})^2}$$
$$= 2.8 \times 10^6\,\mathrm{N/C}.$$

3. **Add vectorially**, and use **symmetry** when possible. The $y$ components of $\vec{\mathbf{E}}_{B1}$ and $\vec{\mathbf{E}}_{B2}$ are equal and opposite. Because of this symmetry, the total field $E_B$ is horizontal and equals $E_{B1}\cos\theta + E_{B2}\cos\theta = 2E_{B1}\cos\theta$. From Fig. 16–28, $\cos\theta = 26\,\mathrm{cm}/40\,\mathrm{cm} = 0.65$. Then

$$E_B = 2E_{B1}\cos\theta = 2(2.8 \times 10^6\,\mathrm{N/C})(0.65)$$
$$= 3.6 \times 10^6\,\mathrm{N/C},$$

and the direction of $\vec{\mathbf{E}}_B$ is along the $+x$ direction.

**NOTE** Part (*a*) of Example 16–9 exhibited no useful symmetry.

**FIGURE 16–29** Electric field vector, shown at three points, due to a single point charge $Q$. (Compare to Fig. 16–23.)

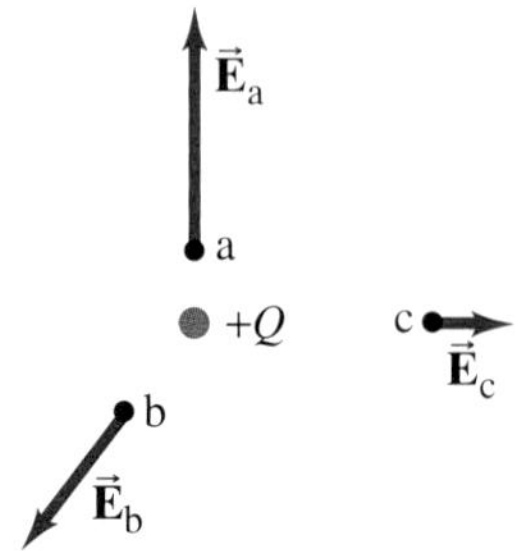


## 16–8 Field Lines

Since the electric field is a vector, it is sometimes referred to as a *vector field*. We could indicate the electric field with arrows at various points in a given situation, such as at a, b, and c in Fig. 16–29. The directions of $\vec{\mathbf{E}}_a$, $\vec{\mathbf{E}}_b$, and $\vec{\mathbf{E}}_c$ are the same as for the forces shown earlier in Fig. 16–23, but the lengths (magnitudes) are different since we divide $F$ by $q$ to get $E$. However, the relative lengths of $\vec{\mathbf{E}}_a$, $\vec{\mathbf{E}}_b$, and $\vec{\mathbf{E}}_c$ are the same as for the forces since we divide by the same $q$ each time. To indicate the electric field in such a way at *many* points, however, would result in many arrows, which would quickly become confusing. To avoid this, we use another technique, that of field lines.

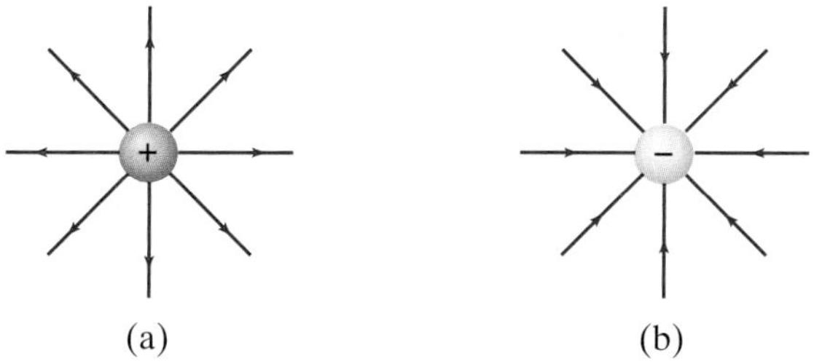


**FIGURE 16–30** Electric field lines (a) near a single positive point charge, (b) near a single negative point charge.

*Electric field lines*

To visualize the electric field, we draw a series of lines to indicate the direction of the electric field at various points in space. These **electric field lines** (sometimes called *lines of force*) are drawn so that they indicate the direction of the force due to the given field on a positive test charge. The lines of force due to a single isolated positive charge are shown in Fig. 16–30a and for a single isolated negative charge in Fig. 16–30b. In part (a) the lines point radially outward from the charge, and in part (b) they point radially inward toward the charge because that is the direction the force would be on a positive test charge in each case (as in Fig. 16–26). Only a few representative lines are shown. We could just as well draw lines in between those shown since the electric field exists there as well. We can draw the lines so that the *number of lines starting on a positive charge, or ending on a negative charge, is proportional to the magnitude of the charge*. Notice that nearer the charge, where the electric field is greater $\left(F \propto 1/r^2\right)$, the lines are closer together. This is a general property of electric field lines: *the closer together the lines are, the stronger the electric field in that region*. In fact, field lines can be drawn so that the number of lines crossing unit area perpendicular to $\vec{\mathbf{E}}$ is proportional to the magnitude of the electric field.

**FIGURE 16–31** Electric field lines for four arrangements of charges.

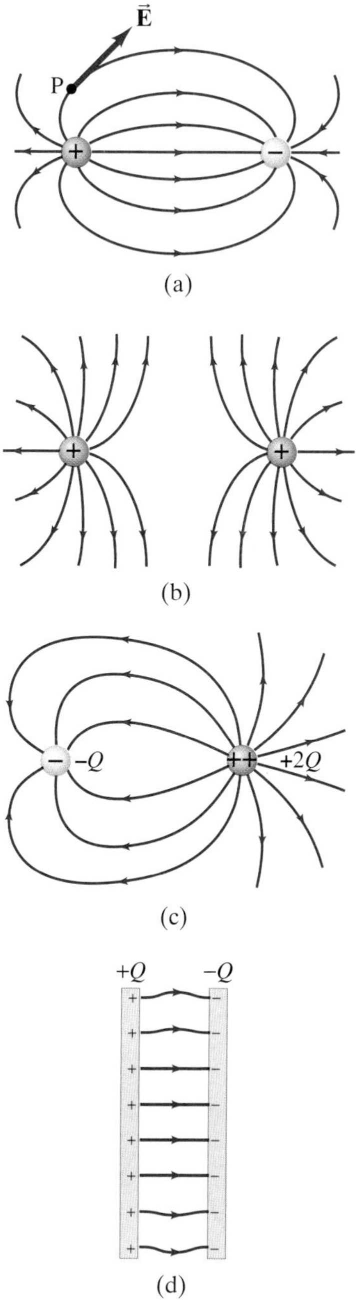


Figure 16–31a shows the electric field lines due to two equal charges of opposite sign, a combination known as an **electric dipole**. The electric field lines are curved in this case and are directed from the positive charge to the negative charge. The direction of the electric field at any point is tangent to the field line at that point as shown by the vector arrow $\vec{\mathbf{E}}$ at point P. To satisfy yourself that this is the correct pattern for the electric field lines, you can make a few calculations such as those done in Example 16–9 for just this case (see Fig. 16–28). Figure 16–31b shows the electric field lines for two equal positive charges, and Fig. 16–31c for unequal charges, $+2Q$ and $-Q$. Note that twice as many lines leave $+2Q$ as enter $-Q$ (number of lines is proportional to magnitude of $Q$). Finally, in Fig. 16–31d, we see the field between two parallel plates carrying equal but opposite charges. Notice that the electric field lines between the two plates start out perpendicular to the surface of the metal plates (we'll see why this is true in the next Section) and go directly from one plate to the other, as we expect because a positive test charge placed between the plates would feel a strong repulsion from the positive plate and a strong attraction to the negative plate. The field lines between two close plates are parallel and equally spaced in the central region, but fringe outward near the edges. Thus, in the central region, the electric field has the same magnitude at all points, and we can write

$$E = \text{constant.} \qquad \left[\begin{array}{l}\text{between two closely spaced,}\\ \text{oppositely charged, parallel plates}\end{array}\right] \qquad \textbf{(16–6)}$$

The fringing of the field near the edges can often be ignored, particularly if the separation of the plates is small compared to their size.†

†The magnitude of the constant electric field between two parallel plates is given by $E = Q/\epsilon_0 A$, where $Q$ is the magnitude of the charge on each plate and $A$ is the area of one plate. We show this in the optional Section 16–10 on Gauss's law.

We summarize the properties of field lines as follows:

1. Electric field lines indicate the direction of the electric field; the field points in the direction tangent to the field line at any point.
2. The lines are drawn so that the magnitude of the electric field, $E$, is proportional to the number of lines crossing unit area perpendicular to the lines. The closer together the lines, the stronger the field.
3. Electric field lines start on positive charges and end on negative charges; and the number starting or ending is proportional to the magnitude of the charge.

Also note that field lines never cross. Why not? Because it would not make sense for the electric field to have two directions at the same point.

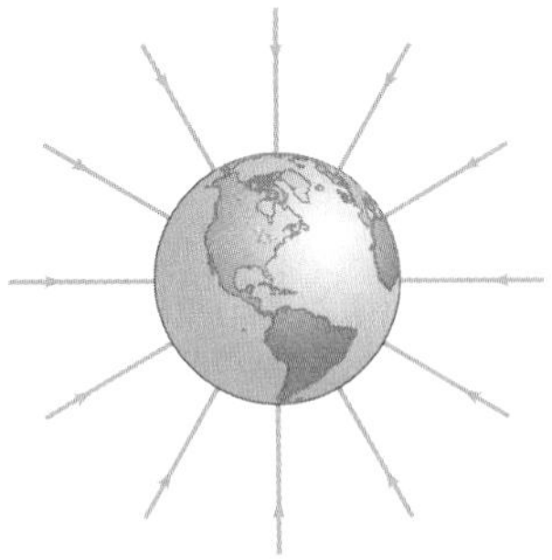

**FIGURE 16–32** The Earth's gravitational field, which at any point is directed toward the Earth's center (the force on any mass points toward the Earth's center).

### Gravitational Field

The field concept can also be applied to the gravitational force. Thus we can say that a **gravitational field** exists for every object that has mass. One object attracts another by means of the gravitational field. The Earth, for example, can be said to possess a gravitational field (Fig. 16–32) which is responsible for the gravitational force on objects. The *gravitational field* is defined as the *force per unit mass*. The magnitude of the Earth's gravitational field at any point above the Earth's surface is thus $(GM_E/r^2)$, where $M_E$ is the mass of the Earth, $r$ is the distance of the point from the Earth's center, and $G$ is the gravitational constant (Chapter 5). At the Earth's surface, $r$ is the radius of the Earth and the gravitational field is equal to $g$, the acceleration due to gravity. Beyond the Earth, the gravitational field can be calculated at any point as a sum of terms due to Earth, Sun, Moon, and other bodies that contribute significantly.

## 16–9 Electric Fields and Conductors

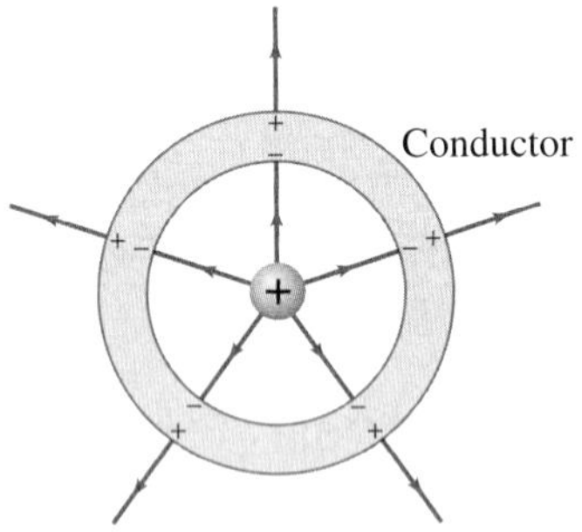


**FIGURE 16–33** A charge inside a neutral spherical metal shell induces charge on its surfaces. The electric field exists even beyond the shell but not within the conductor itself.

We now discuss some properties of conductors. First, *the electric field inside a conductor is zero in the static situation*—that is, when the charges are at rest. If there were an electric field within a conductor, there would be a force on the free electrons. The electrons would move until they reached positions where the electric field, and therefore the electric force on them, did become zero.

This reasoning has some interesting consequences. For one, *any net charge on a conductor distributes itself on the surface.* For a negatively charged conductor, you can imagine that the negative charges repel one another and race to the surface to get as far from one another as possible. Another consequence is the following. Suppose that a positive charge $Q$ is surrounded by an isolated uncharged metal conductor whose shape is a spherical shell, Fig. 16–33. Because there can be no field within the metal, the lines leaving the central positive charge must end on negative charges on the inner surface of the metal. Thus an equal amount of negative charge, $-Q$, is induced on the inner surface of the spherical shell. Then, since the shell is neutral, a positive charge of the same magnitude, $+Q$, must exist on the outer surface of the shell. Thus, although no field exists in the metal itself, an electric field exists outside of it, as shown in Fig. 16–33, as if the metal were not even there.

**FIGURE 16–34** If the electric field $\vec{\mathbf{E}}$ at the surface of a conductor had a component parallel to the surface, $\vec{\mathbf{E}}_{\parallel}$, the latter would accelerate electrons into motion. In the static case, $\vec{\mathbf{E}}_{\parallel}$ must be zero, and the electric field must be perpendicular to the conductor's surface: $\vec{\mathbf{E}} = \vec{\mathbf{E}}_{\perp}$.

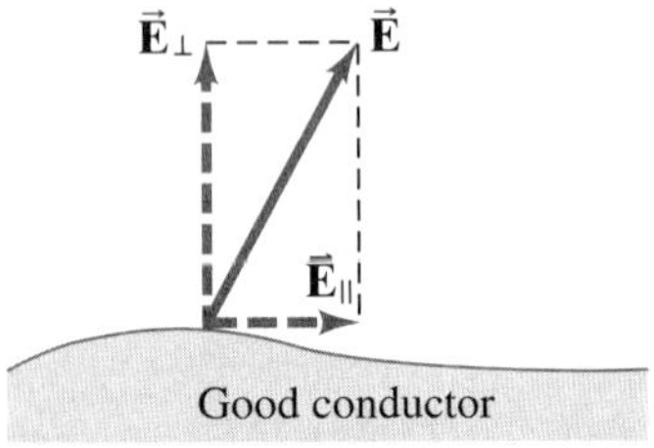


A related property of static electric fields and conductors is that *the electric field is always perpendicular to the surface outside of a conductor.* If there were a component of $\vec{\mathbf{E}}$ parallel to the surface (Fig. 16–34), it would exert a force on free electrons at the surface, causing the electrons to move along the surface until they reached positions where no net force was exerted on them parallel to the surface—that is, until the electric field was perpendicular to the surface.

These properties apply only to conductors. Inside a nonconductor, which does not have free electrons, a static electric field can exist as we will see in the next Chapter. Also, the electric field outside a nonconductor does not necessarily make an angle of 90° to the surface.

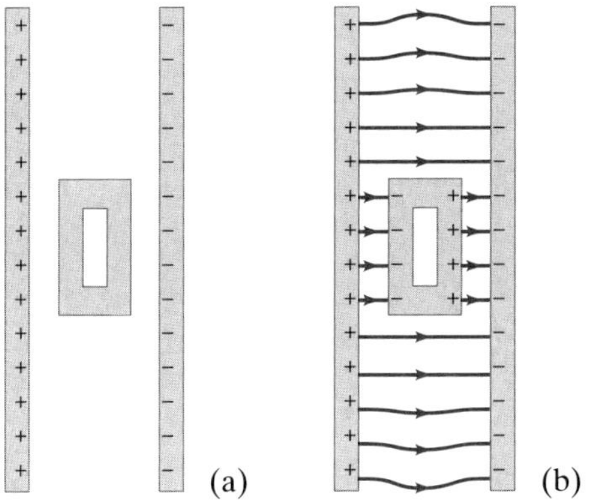


**FIGURE 16–35** Example 16–10.

**FIGURE 16–36** A strong electric field exists in the vicinity of this "Faraday cage," so strong that stray electrons in the atmosphere are accelerated to the KE needed to knock electrons out of air atoms, causing an avalanche of charge which flows to (or from) the metal cage. Yet the person inside the cage is not affected.

CONCEPTUAL EXAMPLE 16–10 **Shielding, and safety in a storm.** A neutral hollow metal box is placed between two parallel charged plates as shown in Fig. 16–35a. What is the field like inside the box?

**RESPONSE** If our metal box had been solid, and not hollow, free electrons in the box would have redistributed themselves along the surface until all their individual fields would have canceled each other inside the box. The net field inside the box would have been zero. For a hollow box, the external field is not changed since the electrons in the metal can move just as freely as before to the surface. Hence the field inside the hollow metal box is also zero, and the field lines are something like those shown in Fig. 16–35b. A conducting box used in this way is an effective device for shielding delicate instruments and electronic circuits from unwanted external electric fields. We also can see that a relatively safe place to be during a lightning storm is inside a car, surrounded by metal. See also Fig. 16–36, where a person inside a porous "cage" is protected from a strong electric discharge.

PHYSICS APPLIED
*Electrical shielding*

## * 16–10 Gauss's Law

An important relation in electricity is Gauss's law, developed by the great mathematician Karl Friedrich Gauss (1777–1855). It relates electric charge and electric field, and is a more general and elegant version of Coulomb's law.

Gauss's law involves the concept of **electric flux**, which refers to the electric field passing through a given area. For a uniform electric field $\vec{\mathbf{E}}$ passing through an area $A$, as shown in Fig. 16–37a, the electric flux $\Phi_E$ is defined as

$$\Phi_E = EA\cos\theta,$$

where $\theta$ is the angle between the electric field direction and a line drawn perpendicular to the area. The flux can be written equivalently as

$$\Phi_E = E_\perp A = EA_\perp, \qquad \textbf{(16–7)}$$

where $E_\perp = E\cos\theta$ is the component of $\vec{\mathbf{E}}$ perpendicular to the area (Fig. 16–37b) and, similarly, $A_\perp = A\cos\theta$ is the projection of the area $A$ perpendicular to the field $\vec{\mathbf{E}}$ (Fig. 16–37c).

Electric flux has a simple intuitive interpretation in terms of field lines. We mentioned in Section 16–8 that field lines can always be drawn so that the number ($N$) passing through unit area perpendicular to the field $(A_\perp)$ is proportional to the magnitude of the field ($E$): that is, $E \propto N/A_\perp$. Hence,

$$N \propto EA_\perp = \Phi_E, \qquad \textbf{(16–8)}$$

so the flux through an area is proportional to the number of lines passing through that area.

**FIGURE 16–37** (a) A uniform electric field $\vec{\mathbf{E}}$ passing through a flat area $A$. (b) $E_\perp = E\cos\theta$ is the component of $\vec{\mathbf{E}}$ perpendicular to the plane of area $A$. (c) $A_\perp = A\cos\theta$ is the projection (dashed) of the area $A$ perpendicular to the field $\vec{\mathbf{E}}$.

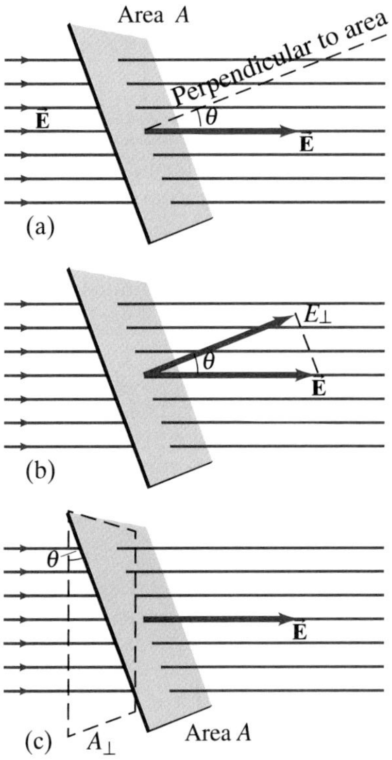

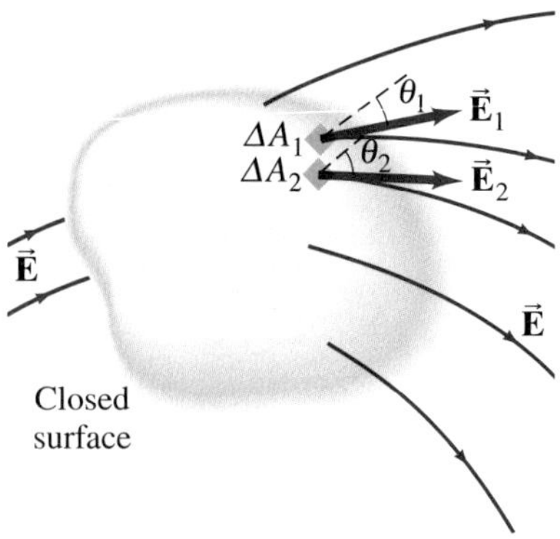


**FIGURE 16–38** Electric field lines passing through a closed surface. The surface is divided up into many tiny areas, $\Delta A_1, \Delta A_2, \cdots$, and so on, of which only two are shown.

Gauss's law involves the *total* flux through a closed surface—a surface of any shape that encloses a volume of space. For any such surface, such as that shown in Fig. 16–38, we divide the surface up into many tiny areas, $\Delta A_1, \Delta A_2, \Delta A_3, \cdots$, and so on. We make the division so that each $\Delta A$ is small enough that it can be considered flat and so that the electric field can be considered constant within each $\Delta A$. Then the *total* flux through the entire surface is the sum over all the individual fluxes through each of the tiny areas:

$$\Phi_E = E_1\,\Delta A_1 \cos\theta_1 + E_2\,\Delta A_2 \cos\theta_2 + \cdots$$
$$= \sum E\,\Delta A \cos\theta = \sum E_\perp\,\Delta A,$$

where the symbol $\Sigma$ means "sum of." We saw in Section 16–8 that the number of field lines starting on a positive charge or ending on a negative charge is proportional to the magnitude of the charge. Hence, the *net* number of lines $N$ pointing out of any closed surface (number of lines pointing out minus the number pointing in) must be proportional to the net charge enclosed by the surface, $Q_{\text{encl}}$. But from Eq. 16–8, we have that the net number of lines $N$ is proportional to the total flux $\Phi_E$. Therefore,

$$\Phi_E = \sum_{\substack{\text{closed}\\ \text{surface}}} E_\perp\,\Delta A \propto Q_{\text{encl}}.$$

The constant of proportionality is $1/\epsilon_0$, consistent with Coulomb's law, so we have

GAUSS'S LAW

$$\sum_{\substack{\text{closed}\\ \text{surface}}} E_\perp\,\Delta A = \frac{Q_{\text{encl}}}{\epsilon_0}, \tag{16–9}$$

where the sum ($\Sigma$) is over any closed surface, and $Q_{\text{encl}}$ is the net charge enclosed within that surface. This is **Gauss's law**.

Coulomb's law and Gauss's law can be used to determine the electric field due to a given (static) charge distribution. Gauss's law is useful when the charge distribution is simple and symmetrical. However, we must choose the closed "gaussian" surface very carefully so we can determine $\vec{\mathbf{E}}$. We normally choose a surface that has just the symmetry needed so that $E$ will be constant on all or on parts of its surface.

**EXAMPLE 16–11 Charged spherical shell.** A thin spherical shell of radius $r_0$ possesses a total net charge $Q$ that is uniformly distributed on it, Fig. 16–39. Determine the electric field at points (*a*) outside the shell, and (*b*) inside the shell.

**FIGURE 16–39** Cross-sectional drawing of a thin spherical shell of radius $r_0$, carrying a net charge $Q$ uniformly distributed. $A_1$ and $A_2$ represent two gaussian surfaces we use to determine $\vec{\mathbf{E}}$. Example 16–11.

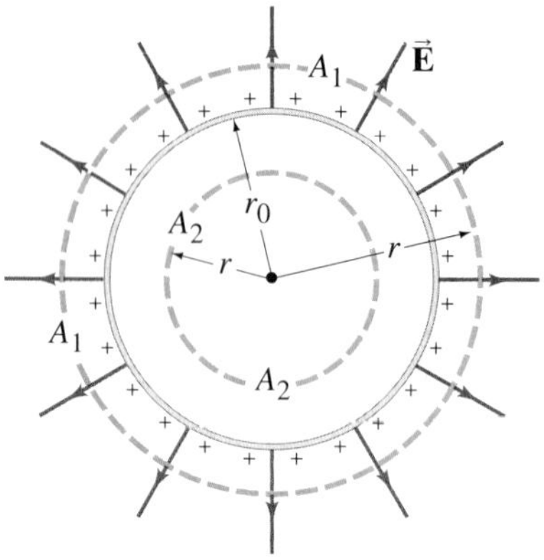


**APPROACH** Because the charge is distributed symmetrically, the electric field must be symmetric. Thus the field outside the shell must be directed radially outward (inward if $Q < 0$) and must depend only on $r$.

**SOLUTION** (*a*) The electric field will have the same magnitude at all points on an imaginary gaussian surface, if we choose it as a sphere of radius $r$ $(r > r_0)$ concentric with the shell, and shown in Fig. 16–39 as the dashed circle $A_1$. Because $\vec{\mathbf{E}}$ is perpendicular to this surface, Gauss's law gives (with $Q_{\text{encl}} = Q$ in Eq. 16–9)

$$\sum E_\perp\,\Delta A = E\sum \Delta A = E(4\pi r^2) = \frac{Q}{\epsilon_0},$$

where $4\pi r^2$ is the surface area of our sphere (Gaussian surface) of radius $r$. Thus

$$E = \frac{1}{4\pi\epsilon_0}\frac{Q}{r^2}. \qquad [r > r_0]$$

Thus the field outside a uniformly charged spherical shell is the same as if all the charge were concentrated at the center as a point charge.

(*b*) Inside the shell, the field must also be symmetric. So $E$ must again have the same value at all points on a spherical gaussian surface ($A_2$ in Fig. 16–39) concentric with the shell. Thus, $E$ can be factored out of the sum and, with $Q_{encl} = 0$ since the charge inside the surface is zero, we have

$$\sum E_{\perp}\,\Delta A = E\sum \Delta A = E\left(4\pi r^2\right) = \frac{Q_{encl}}{\epsilon_0} = 0.$$

Hence

$$E = 0 \qquad \left[r < r_0\right]$$

inside a uniform spherical shell of charge.

The useful results of Example 16–11 also apply to a uniform *solid* spherical conductor that is charged, since all the charge would lie in a thin layer at the surface (Section 16–9).

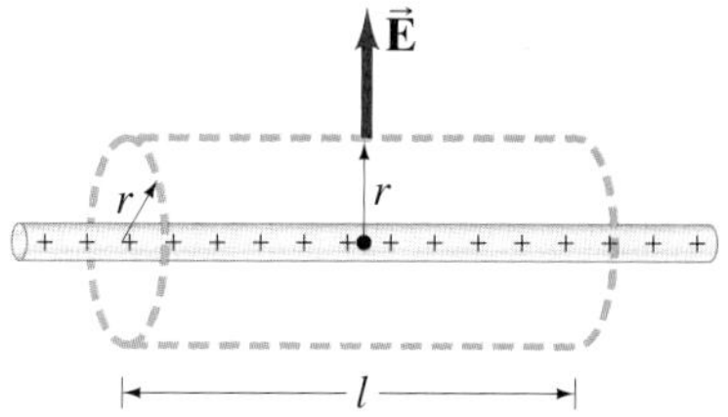


**FIGURE 16–40** Calculation of $\vec{\mathbf{E}}$ due to a very long line of charge, Exercise H, where the cylinder shown (dashed) is the gaussian surface.

**EXERCISE H** A very long, straight wire possesses a uniform charge per unit length, $Q/L$. Show that the electric field at points near (but outside) the wire, far from the ends, is given by

$$E = \frac{1}{2\pi\epsilon_0 r}\frac{Q}{L}$$

using the cylindrical gaussian surface shown (dashed) in Fig. 16–40. [*Hint:* there is no electric flux through the flat ends of the cylinder.]

**EXAMPLE 16–12** ***E* at surface of conductor.** Show that the electric field just outside the surface of any good conductor of arbitrary shape is given by

$$E = \frac{\sigma}{\epsilon_0},$$

where $\sigma$ is the surface charge density $(Q/A)$ on the conductor at that point.

**APPROACH** We choose as our gaussian surface a small cylindrical box, very small in height so that one of its circular ends is just above the conductor (Fig. 16–41). The other end is just below the conductor's surface, and the sides are perpendicular to it.

**SOLUTION** The electric field is zero inside a conductor and is perpendicular to the surface just outside it (Section 16–9), so electric flux passes only through the outside end of our cylindrical box; no flux passes through the short sides or inside end. We choose the area $A$ (of the flat cylinder end above the conductor surface) small enough so that $E$ is essentially uniform over it. Then Gauss's law gives

$$\sum E_{\perp}\,\Delta A = EA = \frac{Q_{encl}}{\epsilon_0} = \frac{\sigma A}{\epsilon_0},$$

so that

$$E = \frac{\sigma}{\epsilon_0}. \qquad \text{[at surface of conductor]}$$

This useful result applies for any shape conductor, including a large, uniformly charged flat sheet: the electric field will be constant and equal to $\sigma/\epsilon_0$.

**FIGURE 16–41** Electric field near the surface of a conductor. Two small cylindrical boxes are shown dashed. Either one can serve as our gaussian surface. Example 16–12.

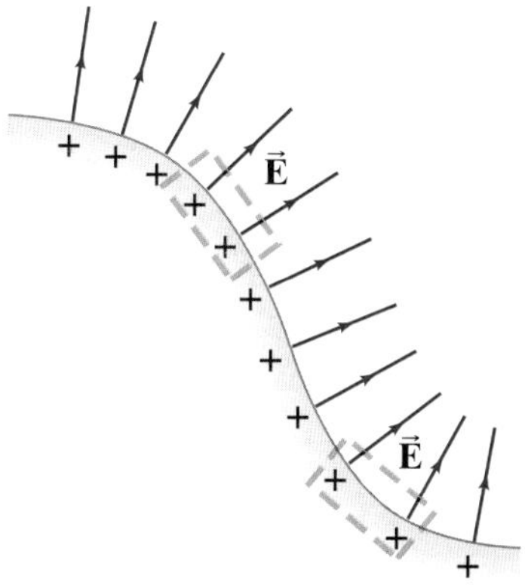


This last Example also gives us the field between the two parallel plates we discussed in Fig. 16–31d. If the plates are large compared to their separation, then the field lines are perpendicular to the plates and, except near the edges, they are parallel to each other. Therefore the electric field (see Fig. 16–42, which shows the same gaussian surface as Fig. 16–41) is also

$$E = \frac{\sigma}{\epsilon_0} = \frac{Q/A}{\epsilon_0}, \qquad \left[\begin{array}{l}\text{between two closely spaced}\\ \text{oppositely charged parallel plates}\end{array}\right] \qquad \textbf{(16–10)}$$

where $Q = \sigma A$ is the charge on one of the plates.

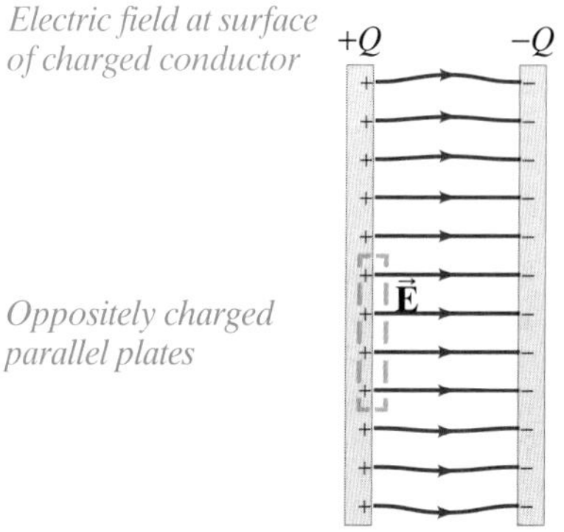


**FIGURE 16–42** The electric field between two parallel plates is uniform and equal to $E = \sigma/\epsilon_0$.

# * 16–11 Electric Forces in Molecular Biology: DNA Structure and Replication

PHYSICS APPLIED
*Inside a cell: Kinetic theory plus electrostatic force*

The study of the structure and functioning of a living cell at the molecular level is known as molecular biology. It is an important area for application of physics. Since the interior of a cell is mainly water, we can imagine it as a vast sea of molecules continually in motion (as in kinetic theory, Chapter 13), colliding with one another with various amounts of kinetic energy. These molecules interact with one another in various ways—chemical reactions (making and breaking of bonds between atoms) and more brief interactions or unions that occur because of *electrostatic attraction* between molecules.

The many processes that occur within the cell are now considered to be the result of *random ("thermal") molecular motion plus the ordering effect of the electrostatic force*. We use these ideas now to analyze some basic cellular processes involving macromolecules (large molecules). The picture we present here has not been seen "in action." Rather, it is a model of what happens based on presently accepted physical theories and experimental results.

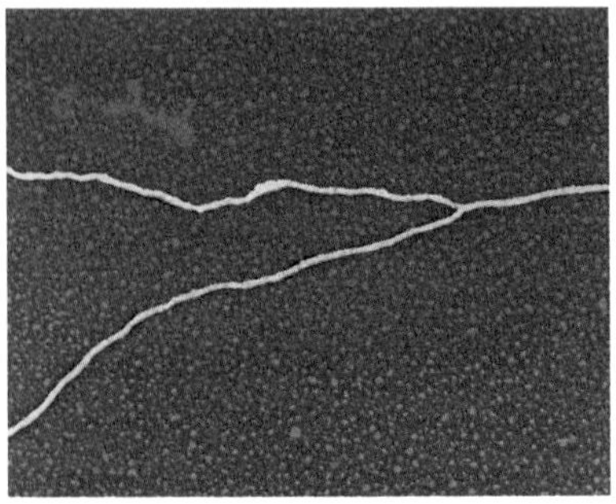

**FIGURE 16–43** DNA replicating in a human HeLa cancer cell. This is a false-color image made by a transmission electron microscope (TEM; discussed in Chapter 27).

PHYSICS APPLIED
*DNA structure*

The genetic information that is passed on from generation to generation in all living cells is contained in the chromosomes, which are made up of genes. Each gene contains the information needed to produce a particular type of protein molecule. The genetic information contained in a gene is built into the principal molecule of a chromosome, DNA (deoxyribonucleic acid), Fig. 16–43. DNA molecules are made up of many small molecules known as nucleotide bases. There are four types of nucleotide bases in DNA: adenine (A), cytosine (C), guanine (G), and thymine (T).

The DNA of a chromosome generally consists of two long DNA strands wrapped about one another in the shape of a "double helix." The genetic information is contained in the specific order of the four bases (A, C, G, T) along the strand. As shown in Fig. 16–44, the two strands are attracted by electrostatic forces—that is, by the attraction of positive charges to negative charges. We see in Fig. 16–44a that an A (adenine) on one strand is always opposite a T on the

(a)

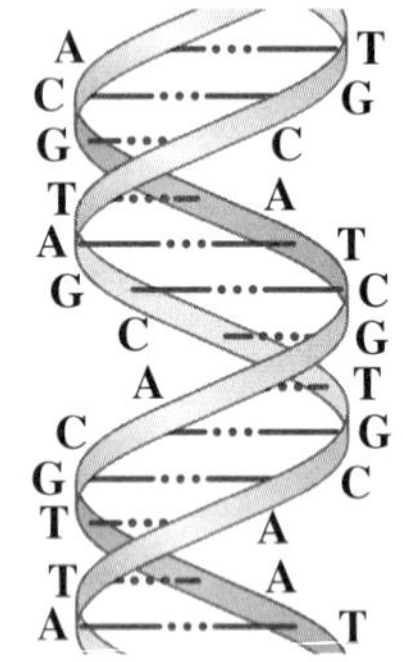


(b)

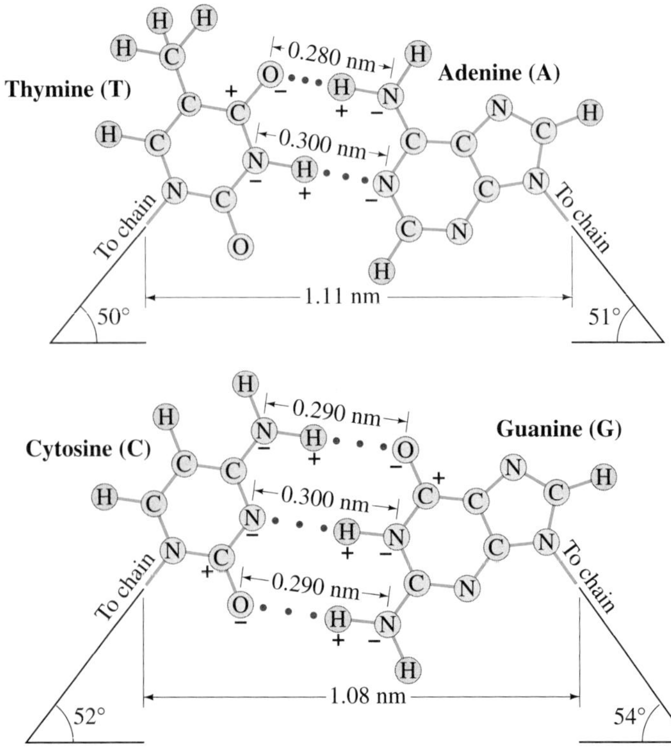


**FIGURE 16–44** (a) Section of a DNA double helix. (b) "Close-up" view of the helix, showing how A and T attract each other and how G and C attract each other through electrostatic forces. The + and − signs indicated on certain atoms represent net charges, usually a fraction of *e*, due to uneven sharing of electrons. The red dots indicate the electrostatic attraction (often called a "weak bond" or "hydrogen bond"). Note that there are two weak bonds between A and T, and three between C and G.

other strand; similarly, a G is always opposite a C. This important ordering effect occurs because the shapes of A, T, C, and G are such that a T fits closely only into an A, and a G into a C; and only in the case of this close proximity of the charged portions is the electrostatic force great enough to hold them together even for a short time (Fig. 16–44b), forming what are referred to as "weak bonds." The electrostatic force between A and T, and between C and G, exists because these molecules have charged parts. These charges are due to some electrons in each of these molecules spending more time orbiting one atom than another. For example, the electron normally on the H atom of adenine (upper part of Fig. 16–44b) spends some of its time orbiting the adjacent N atom (more on this in Chapter 29), so the N has a net negative charge and the H a positive charge. This $H^+$ atom of adenine† is then attracted to the $O^-$ atom of thymine. These net + and − charges usually have magnitudes of a fraction of $e$ (charge on the electron) such as $0.2e$ or $0.4e$.

How does the arrangement shown in Fig. 16–44 come about? It occurs when the DNA replicates (duplicates) itself just before cell division. Indeed, the arrangement of A opposite T and G opposite C is crucial for ensuring that the genetic information is passed on accurately to the next generation. The process of replication is shown in a simplified form in Fig. 16–45. The two strands of DNA separate (with the help of enzymes, which also operate via the electrostatic force), leaving the charged parts of the bases exposed. Once replication starts, let us see how the correct order of bases occurs by focusing our attention on the G molecule indicated by the arrow on the lowest strand in Fig. 16–45. There are many unattached nucleotide bases of all four kinds bouncing around in the cellular fluid. The only one of the four bases that will experience attraction to our G, if it bounces close to it, will be a C. The charges on the other three bases are not arranged so that they can get close to those on the G, and thus there will be no significant attractive force exerted on them—remember that the force decreases rapidly with distance $(\propto 1/r^2)$. Because the G does not attract an A, T, or G appreciably, an A, T, or G will be knocked away by collisions with other molecules before enzymes can attach it to the growing chain (number 3). But the electrostatic force will often hold a C opposite our G long enough so that an enzyme can attach the C to the growing end of the new chain.

PHYSICS APPLIED

*DNA replication*

Thus we see that electrostatic forces are responsible for selecting the bases in the proper order during replication, so the genetic information is passed on accurately to the next generation. Note in Fig. 16–45 that the new number 4 strand has the same order of bases as the old number 1 strand; and the new number 3 strand is the same as the old number 2. So the two new double helixes, 1–3 and 2–4, are identical to the original 1–2 helix.

†When $H^+$ is involved, the weak bond it can make with a nearby negative charge, such as $O^-$, is relatively strong among weak bonds (partly because $H^+$ is so small) and is referred to as a "hydrogen bond" (Section 29–3).

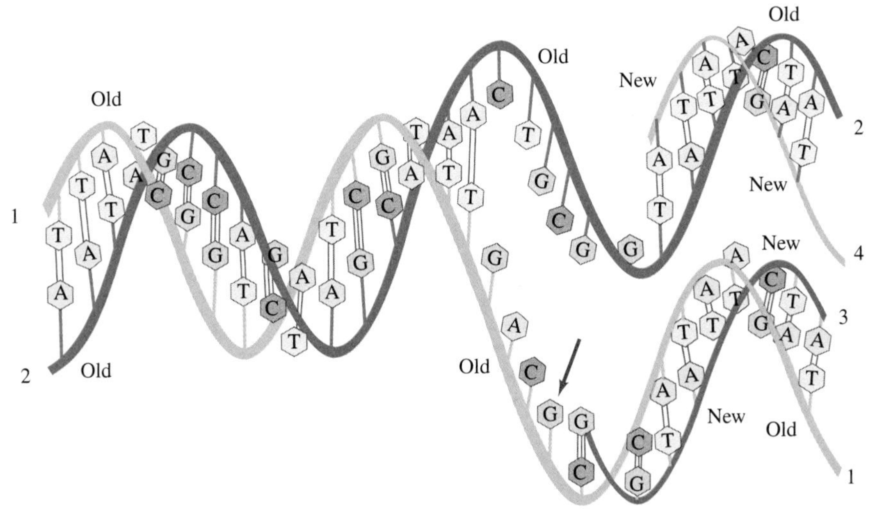


**FIGURE 16–45** Replication of DNA.

This process of DNA replication is often presented as if it occurred in clockwork fashion—as if each molecule knew its role and went to its assigned place, like bees in a hive. But this is not the case. The forces of attraction between the electric charges of the molecules are rather weak and become significant only when the molecules can come close together and several "weak bonds" can be made. Indeed, if the shapes are not just right, there is almost no electrostatic attraction, which is why there are few mistakes. Thus, out of the random motion of the molecules, the electrostatic force acts to bring order out of chaos.

Another outcome of the random (thermal) velocities of molecules in the cell (kinetic theory) relates to *cloning*. Even at the level of *E. coli* bacteria, when a cell divides, the two new bacteria have nearly identical DNA. Even if the DNA were perfectly identical, the two bacteria would not end up behaving in the same way. The cells are *not* identical because (via kinetic theory) long protein, DNA, and RNA molecules get bumped into different shapes, and even the expression of genes can thus be different. Furthermore, loosely held parts of large molecules such as a methyl group ($CH_3$) can be knocked off by a particularly strong collision with another molecule in the cellular fluid. Hence, cloned organisms are not identical, even if their DNA were identical. Indeed, there can not really be genetic determinism.

## * 16–12 Photocopy Machines and Computer Printers Use Electrostatics

PHYSICS APPLIED
*Photocopy machines*

Photocopy machines and laser printers make use of electrostatic attraction to print an image of the original. They each use a different technique to project the image onto a special cylindrical drum. In a *photocopier*, lenses and mirrors focus an image of the original sheet of paper onto the drum, much like a camera lens† focuses an image on film. The drum is typically made of aluminum, a good conductor, and its surface is coated with a thin layer of selenium. Selenium is a material that has the interesting property (called "photoconductivity") of being an electrical nonconductor in the dark, but becoming a conductor when exposed to light.

Step 1 in photocopying is the placing of a uniform positive charge on the drum's selenium layer by a charged rod or roller. This is done in the dark. In step 2, the image to be copied or printed is projected onto the drum. For simplicity, let us assume the image is a dark letter A on a white background (as on the page of a book) as shown in Fig. 16–46. The letter A on the drum is dark, but all around it is light. At all these light places, the selenium becomes conducting and electrons flow in from the aluminum beneath, neutralizing those positive areas. In the dark areas of the letter A, the selenium is nonconducting and so retains a positive charge, Fig. 16–46.

In step 3, a fine dark powder known as *toner* is given a negative charge, and brushed on the drum as it rotates. The negatively charged toner particles are attracted to the positive areas on the drum (the A in our case) and stick only there. In step 4, as the drum continues to rotate, it presses against a piece

†Cameras are discussed in Section 25–1, and images by lenses and mirrors in Chapter 23.

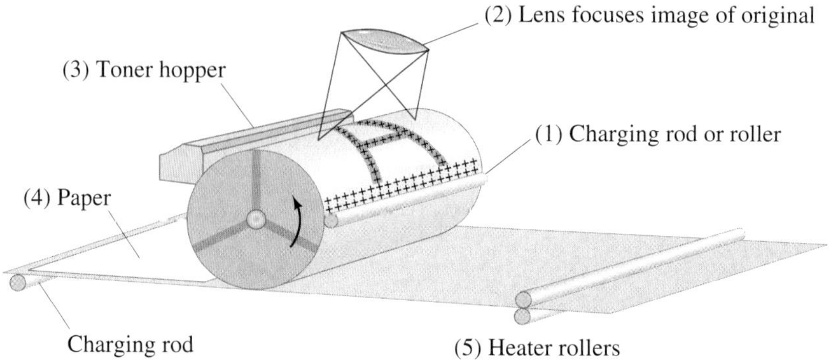


**FIGURE 16–46** Inside a photocopy machine: (1) the selenium drum is given a + charge; (2) the lens focuses image on drum—only dark spots stay charged; (3) toner particles (negatively charged) are attracted to positive areas on drum; (4) the image is transferred to paper; (5) heat binds the image to the paper.

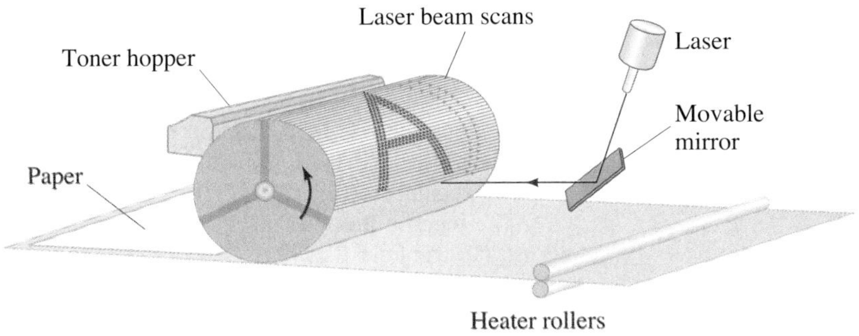


**FIGURE 16–47** Inside a laser printer: A movable mirror sweeps the laser beam in horizontal lines across the drum.

of paper which has been positively charged more strongly than the selenium, so the toner particles are transferred to the paper, forming the final image. Finally, step 5, the paper is heated to fix the toner particles firmly on the paper.

In a color copier (or printer), this process is repeated for each color—black, cyan (blue), magenta (red), and yellow. Combining these four colors in different proportions produces any desired color.

PHYSICS APPLIED
*Laser printer*

A *laser printer*, on the other hand, does not use a hard copy original but instead accepts a computer output which programs the intensity of a laser beam. The process is much the same as for a photocopier, involving a selenium-coated drum and toner powder, but the formation of the image onto the drum is different. The thin beam of light from a laser is focused by lenses to a fine point. By means of a movable mirror, the laser beam is scanned from side to side across the drum in a series of horizontal lines, each line just below the previous line. As the beam sweeps across the drum, the intensity of the beam is varied (by the computer output), being strong for a point that is meant to be white or bright, and weak or zero for points that are meant to come out dark. After one sweep, the drum rotates very slightly, and another horizontal sweep is made, and then another and another, Fig. 16–47. As the drum turns, a complete image is formed on it. The light parts of the selenium become conducting and lose their electric charge, and the toner sticks only to the dark, electrically charged areas. The drum then transfers the image to paper, as in a photocopier.

PHYSICS APPLIED
*Inkjet printer*

An inkjet printer does not use a drum. Instead nozzles spray tiny droplets of ink directly at the paper. The nozzles are swept across the paper, each sweep just above the previous one as the paper moves down. On each sweep, the ink makes dots on the paper, except for those points where no ink is desired, as directed by the computer. The image consists of a huge number of very tiny dots. The quality or resolution of a printer is usually specified in dots per inch (dpi) in each (linear) direction.

## Summary

There are two kinds of **electric charge**, positive and negative. These designations are to be taken algebraically—that is, any charge is plus or minus so many coulombs (C), in SI units.

Electric charge is **conserved**: if a certain amount of one type of charge is produced in a process, an equal amount of the opposite type is also produced; thus the *net* charge produced is zero.

According to the atomic theory, electricity originates in the atom, which consists of a positively charged nucleus surrounded by negatively charged electrons. Each electron has a charge $-e = -1.6 \times 10^{-19}$ C.

Electric **conductors** are those materials in which many electrons are relatively free to move, whereas electric **insulators** are those in which very few electrons are free to move.

An object is negatively charged when it has an excess of electrons, and positively charged when it has less than its balanced number of electrons. The net charge on any object is zero or a whole number times $+e$ or $-e$. That is, charge is **quantized**.

An object can become charged by rubbing (in which electrons are transferred from one material to another), by conduction (which is transfer of charge from one charged object to another by touching), or by induction (the separation of charge within an object because of the close approach of another charged object but without touching).

Electric charges exert a force on each other. If two charges are of opposite types, one positive and one negative, they each exert an attractive force on the other. If the two charges are the same type, each repels the other.

The magnitude of the force one point charge exerts on another is proportional to the product of their charges, and inversely proportional to the square of the distance between them:

$$F = k\frac{Q_1 Q_2}{r^2}; \qquad \textbf{(16–1)}$$

this is **Coulomb's law**. In SI units, $k$ is often written as $1/4\pi\epsilon_0$.

We think of an **electric field** as existing in space around any charge or group of charges. The force on another charged object is then said to be due to the electric field present at its location.

The *electric field*, $\vec{\mathbf{E}}$, at any point in space due to one or more charges, is defined as the force per unit charge that would act on a positive test charge $q$ placed at that point:

$$\vec{\mathbf{E}} = \frac{\vec{\mathbf{F}}}{q}. \qquad \textbf{(16–3)}$$

The magnitude of the electric field a distance $r$ from a point charge $Q$ is

$$E = k\frac{Q}{r^2}. \qquad \textbf{(16–4a)}$$

The total electric field at a point in space is equal to the vector sum of the individual fields due to each contributing charge (**principle of superposition**).

Electric fields are represented by **electric field lines** that start on positive charges and end on negative charges. Their direction indicates the direction the force would be on a tiny positive test charge placed at a point. The lines can be drawn so that the number per unit area is proportional to the magnitude of $E$.

The static electric field inside a good conductor is zero, and the electric field lines just outside a charged conductor are perpendicular to its surface.

[*The **electric flux** passing through a small area $A$ for a uniform electric field $\vec{\mathbf{E}}$ is

$$\Phi_E = E_\perp A, \qquad \textbf{(16–7)}$$

where $E_\perp$ is the component of $\vec{\mathbf{E}}$ perpendicular to the surface. The flux through a surface is proportional to the number of field lines passing through it.]

[***Gauss's law** states that the total flux summed over any closed surface (considered as made up of many small areas $\Delta A$) is equal to the net charge $Q_{\text{encl}}$ enclosed by the surface divided by $\epsilon_0$:

$$\sum_{\substack{\text{closed}\\\text{surface}}} E_\perp \, \Delta A = \frac{Q_{\text{encl}}}{\epsilon_0}. \qquad \textbf{(16–9)}$$

Gauss's law can be used to determine the electric field due to given charge distributions, but its usefulness is mainly limited to cases where the charge distribution displays much symmetry. The real importance of Gauss's law is that it is a general and elegant statement of the relation between electric charge and electric field.]

[*In the replication of DNA, the electrostatic force plays a crucial role in selecting the proper molecules so that the genetic information is passed on accurately from generation to generation.]

# Questions

1. If you charge a pocket comb by rubbing it with a silk scarf, how can you determine if the comb is positively or negatively charged?
2. Why does a shirt or blouse taken from a clothes dryer sometimes cling to your body?
3. Explain why fog or rain droplets tend to form around ions or electrons in the air.
4. A positively charged rod is brought close to a neutral piece of paper, which it attracts. Draw a diagram showing the separation of charge and explain why attraction occurs.
5. Why does a plastic ruler that has been rubbed with a cloth have the ability to pick up small pieces of paper? Why is this difficult to do on a humid day?
6. Contrast the *net charge* on a conductor to the "free charges" in the conductor.
7. Figures 16–7 and 16–8 show how a charged rod placed near an uncharged metal object can attract (or repel) electrons. There are a great many electrons in the metal, yet only some of them move as shown. Why not all of them?
8. When an electroscope is charged, its two leaves repel each other and remain at an angle. What balances the electric force of repulsion so that the leaves don't separate further?
9. The form of Coulomb's law is very similar to that for Newton's law of universal gravitation. What are the differences between these two laws? Compare also gravitational mass and electric charge.
10. We are not normally aware of the gravitational or electric force between two ordinary objects. What is the reason in each case? Give an example where we are aware of each one and why.
11. Is the electric force a conservative force? Why or why not? (See Chapter 6.)
12. When a charged ruler attracts small pieces of paper, sometimes a piece jumps quickly away after touching the ruler. Explain.
13. Explain why the test charges we use when measuring electric fields must be small.
14. When determining an electric field, must we use a *positive* test charge, or would a negative one do as well? Explain.
15. Draw the electric field lines surrounding two negative electric charges a distance $l$ apart.
16. Assume that the two opposite charges in Fig. 16–31a are 12.0 cm apart. Consider the magnitude of the electric field 2.5 cm from the positive charge. On which side of this charge—top, bottom, left, or right—is the electric field the strongest? The weakest? Explain.

**17.** Consider the electric field at points A, B, and C in Fig. 16–48. First draw an arrow at each point indicating the direction of the net force that a positive test charge would experience if placed at that point, then list the points in order of *decreasing* field strength (strongest first).

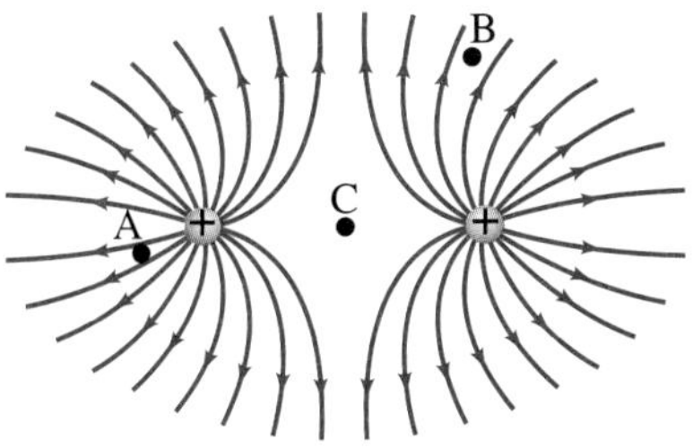


**FIGURE 16–48** Question 17.

**18.** Why can electric field lines never cross?

**19.** Show, using the three rules for field lines given in Section 16–8, that the electric field lines starting or ending on a single point charge must be symmetrically spaced around the charge.

**20.** Given two point charges $Q$ and $2Q$, a distance $l$ apart, is there a point along the straight line that passes through them where $E = 0$ when their signs are (*a*) opposite, (*b*) the same? If yes, state roughly where this point will be.

**21.** Consider a small positive test charge located on an electric field line at some point, such as point P in Fig. 16–31a. Is the direction of the velocity and/or acceleration of the test charge along this line? Discuss.

**22.** Sketch the electric field lines for a uniform line of charge which is infinitely long. (*Hint*: Use symmetry.) Is the electric field uniform in strength?

* **23.** If the electric flux through a closed surface is zero, is the electric field necessarily zero at all points on the surface? Explain. What about the converse: If $\vec{\mathbf{E}} = 0$ at all points on the surface is the flux through the surface zero?

* **24.** A point charge is surrounded by a spherical gaussian surface of radius $r$. If the sphere is replaced by a cube of side $r$, will $\Phi_E$ be larger, smaller, or the same? Explain.

## Problems

### 16–5 and 16–6 Coulomb's Law

[1 mC = $10^{-3}$ C, 1 $\mu$C = $10^{-6}$ C, 1 nC = $10^{-9}$ C.]

1. (I) Calculate the magnitude of the force between two 3.60-$\mu$C point charges 9.3 cm apart.
2. (I) How many electrons make up a charge of $-30.0\,\mu$C?
3. (I) What is the magnitude of the electric force of attraction between an iron nucleus ($q = +26e$) and its innermost electron if the distance between them is $1.5 \times 10^{-12}$ m?
4. (I) What is the repulsive electrical force between two protons $5.0 \times 10^{-15}$ m apart from each other in an atomic nucleus?
5. (I) What is the magnitude of the force a $+25\,\mu$C charge exerts on a +3.0 mC charge 35 cm away?
6. (II) Two charged dust particles exert a force of $3.2 \times 10^{-2}$ N on each other. What will be the force if they are moved so they are only one-eighth as far apart?
7. (II) Two charged spheres are 8.45 cm apart. They are moved, and the force on each of them is found to have been tripled. How far apart are they now?
8. (II) A person scuffing her feet on a wool rug on a dry day accumulates a net charge of $-42\,\mu$C. How many excess electrons does she get, and by how much does her mass increase?
9. (II) What is the total charge of all the electrons in 1.0 kg of $H_2O$?
10. (II) Compare the electric force holding the electron in orbit $\left(r = 0.53 \times 10^{-10}\text{ m}\right)$ around the proton nucleus of the hydrogen atom, with the gravitational force between the same electron and proton. What is the ratio of these two forces?
11. (II) Two positive point charges are a fixed distance apart. The sum of their charges is $Q_T$. What charge must each have in order to (*a*) maximize the electric force between them, and (*b*) minimize it?
12. (II) Particles of charge +75, +48, and $-85\,\mu$C are placed in a line (Fig. 16–49). The center one is 0.35 m from each of the others. Calculate the net force on each charge due to the other two.

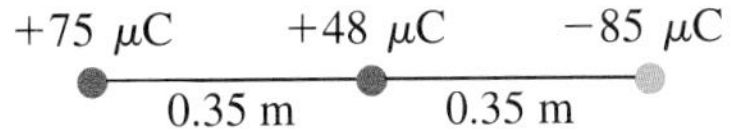


**FIGURE 16–49** Problem 12.

13. (II) Three positive particles of equal charge, $+11.0\,\mu$C, are located at the corners of an equilateral triangle of side 15.0 cm (Fig. 16–50). Calculate the magnitude and direction of the net force on each particle.

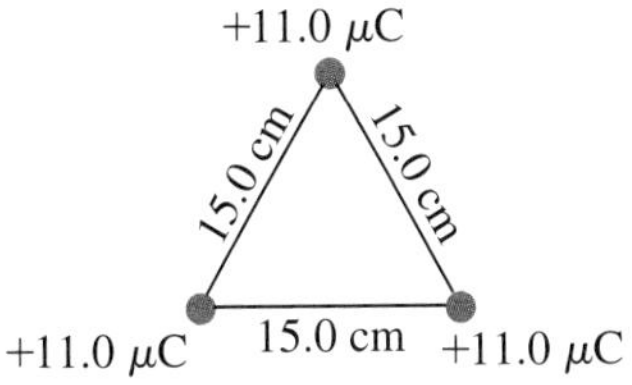


**FIGURE 16–50** Problem 13.

14. (II) A charge of 6.00 mC is placed at each corner of a square 0.100 m on a side. Determine the magnitude and direction of the force on each charge.
15. (II) Repeat Problem 14 for the case when two of the positive charges, on opposite corners, are replaced by negative charges of the same magnitude (Fig. 16–51).

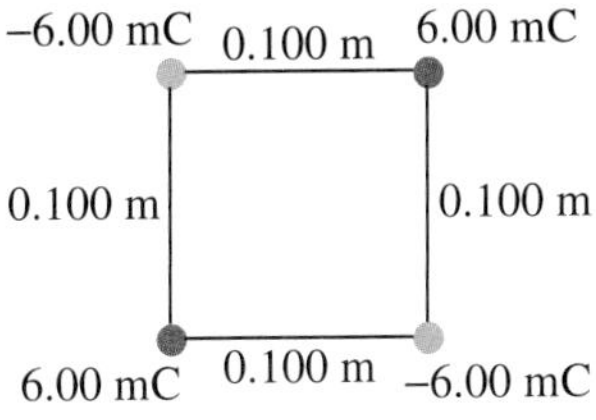


**FIGURE 16–51** Problem 15.

16. (II) At each corner of a square of side $l$ there are point charges of magnitude $Q$, $2Q$, $3Q$, and $4Q$ (Fig. 16–52). Determine the force on (*a*) the charge $2Q$, and (*b*) the charge $3Q$, due to the other three charges.

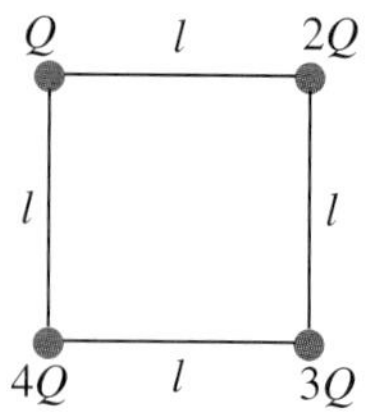


**FIGURE 16–52** Problem 16.

17. (II) Three charged particles are placed at the corners of an equilateral triangle of side 1.20 m (Fig. 16–53). The charges are $+4.0\,\mu C$, $-8.0\,\mu C$, and $-6.0\,\mu C$. Calculate the magnitude and direction of the net force on each due to the other two.

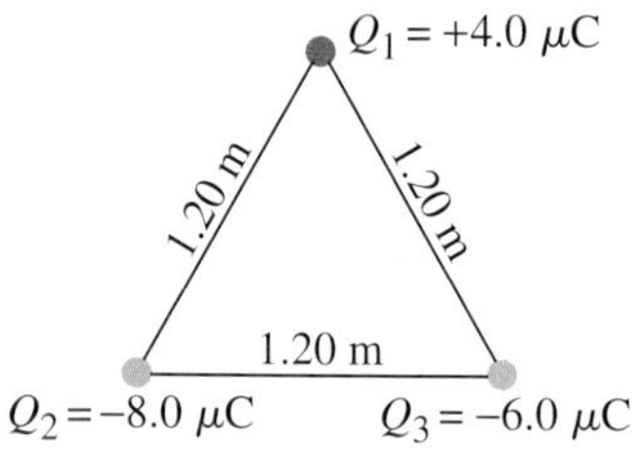


**FIGURE 16–53** Problem 17.

18. (III) Two point charges have a total charge of $560\,\mu C$. When placed 1.10 m apart, the force each exerts on the other is 22.8 N and is repulsive. What is the charge on each?

19. (III) Two charges, $-Q_0$ and $-3Q_0$, are a distance $l$ apart. These two charges are free to move but do not because there is a third charge nearby. What must be the charge and placement of the third charge for the first two to be in equilibrium?

20. (III) A $+4.75\,\mu C$ and a $-3.55\,\mu C$ charge are placed 18.5 cm apart. Where can a third charge be placed so that it experiences no net force?

21. (III) Two small nonconducting spheres have a total charge of $90.0\,\mu C$. (*a*) When placed 1.06 m apart, the force each exerts on the other is 12.0 N and is repulsive. What is the charge on each? (*b*) What if the force were attractive?

22. (III) A charge $Q$ is transferred from an initially uncharged plastic ball to an identical ball 12 cm away. The force of attraction is then 17 mN. How many electrons were transferred from one ball to the other?

### 16–7 and 16–8 Electric Field, Field Lines

23. (I) What are the magnitude and direction of the electric force on an electron in a uniform electric field of strength 2360 N/C that points due east?

24. (I) A proton is released in a uniform electric field, and it experiences an electric force of $3.75 \times 10^{-14}$ N toward the south. What are the magnitude and direction of the electric field?

25. (I) A downward force of 8.4 N is exerted on a $-8.8\,\mu C$ charge. What are the magnitude and direction of the electric field at this point?

26. (I) What are the magnitude and direction of the electric field 20.0 cm directly above an isolated $33.0 \times 10^{-6}$ C charge?

27. (II) What is the magnitude of the acceleration experienced by an electron in an electric field of 750 N/C? How does the direction of the acceleration depend on the direction of the field at that point?

28. (II) What are the magnitude and direction of the electric field at a point midway between a $-8.0\,\mu C$ and a $+7.0\,\mu C$ charge 8.0 cm apart? Assume no other charges are nearby.

29. (II) Draw, approximately, the electric field lines about two point charges, $+Q$ and $-3Q$, which are a distance $l$ apart.

30. (II) What is the electric field strength at a point in space where a proton $(m = 1.67 \times 10^{-27}\,\text{kg})$ experiences an acceleration of 1 million "$g$'s"?

31. (II) An electron is released from rest in a uniform electric field and accelerates to the north at a rate of $115\,\text{m/s}^2$. What are the magnitude and direction of the electric field?

32. (II) The electric field midway between two equal but opposite point charges is 745 N/C, and the distance between the charges is 16.0 cm. What is the magnitude of the charge on each?

33. (II) Calculate the electric field at the center of a square 52.5 cm on a side if one corner is occupied by a $+45.0\,\mu C$ charge and the other three are occupied by $-27.0\,\mu C$ charges.

34. (II) Calculate the electric field at one corner of a square 1.00 m on a side if the other three corners are occupied by $2.25 \times 10^{-6}$ C charges.

35. (II) Determine the direction and magnitude of the electric field at the point P in Fig. 16–54. The charges are separated by a distance $2a$, and point P is a distance $x$ from the midpoint between the two charges. Express your answer in terms of $Q$, $x$, $a$, and $k$.

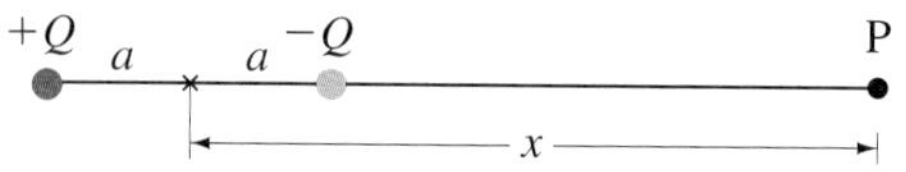


**FIGURE 16–54** Problem 35.

36. (II) Two point charges, $Q_1 = -25\,\mu C$ and $Q_2 = +50\,\mu C$, are separated by a distance of 12 cm. The electric field at the point P (see Fig. 16–55) is zero. How far from $Q_1$ is P?

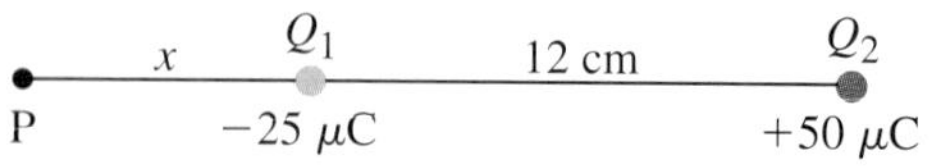


**FIGURE 16–55** Problem 36.

37. (II) (*a*) Determine the electric field $\vec{\mathbf{E}}$ at the origin 0 in Fig. 16–56 due to the two charges at A and B. (*b*) Repeat, but let the charge at B be reversed in sign.

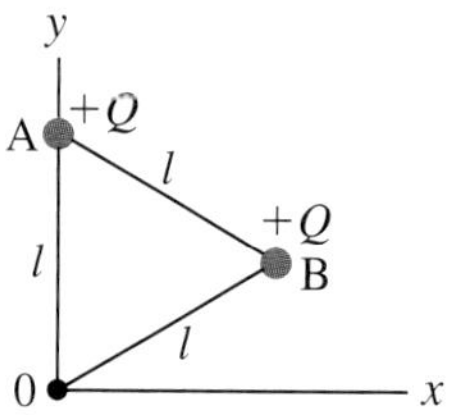


**FIGURE 16–56** Problem 37.

38. (II) Use Coulomb's law to determine the magnitude and direction of the electric field at points A and B in Fig. 16–57 due to the two positive charges ($Q = 7.0\,\mu\text{C}$) shown. Are your results consistent with Fig. 16–31b?

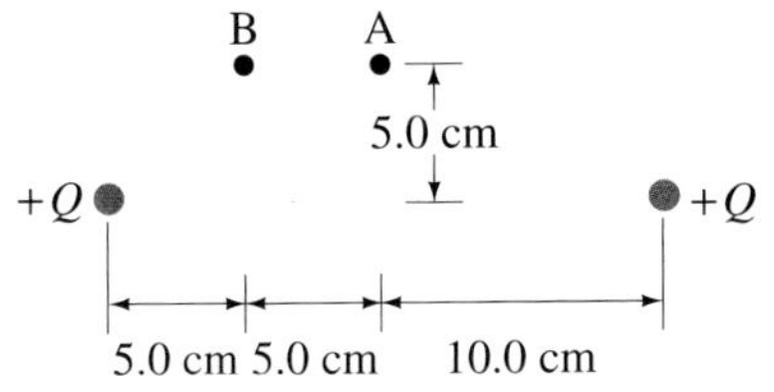


**FIGURE 16–57** Problem 38.

39. (II) You are given two unknown point charges, $Q_1$ and $Q_2$. At a point on the line joining them, one-third of the way from $Q_1$ to $Q_2$, the electric field is zero (Fig. 16–58). What is the ratio $Q_1/Q_2$?

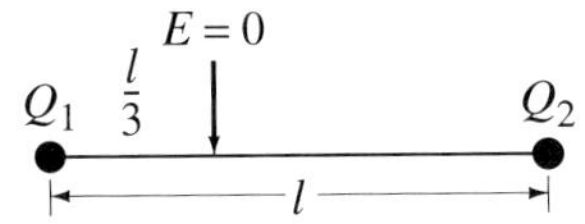


**FIGURE 16–58** Problem 39.

40. (III) Determine the direction and magnitude of the electric field at the point P shown in Fig. 16–59. The two charges are separated by a distance of $2a$. Point P is on the perpendicular bisector of the line joining the charges, a distance $x$ from the midpoint between them. Express your answers in terms of $Q$, $x$, $a$, and $k$.

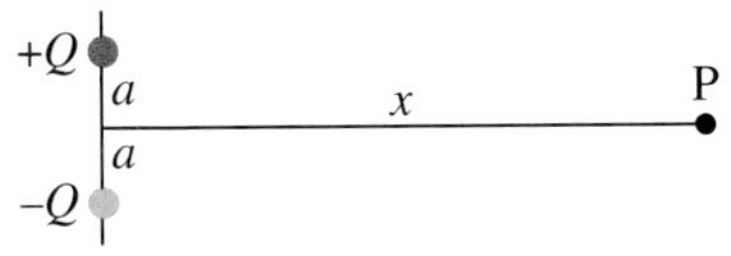


**FIGURE 16–59** Problem 40.

41. (III) An electron (mass $m = 9.11 \times 10^{-31}$ kg) is accelerated in the uniform field $\vec{\mathbf{E}}$ ($E = 1.45 \times 10^4\,\text{N/C}$) between two parallel charged plates. The separation of the plates is 1.10 cm. The electron is accelerated from rest near the negative plate and passes through a tiny hole in the positive plate, Fig. 16–60. (a) With what speed does it leave the hole? (b) Show that the gravitational force can be ignored.

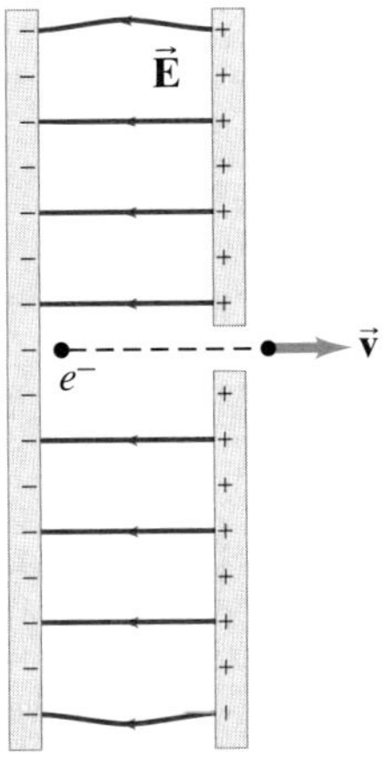


**FIGURE 16–60** Problem 41.

42. (III) An electron moving to the right at 1.0% the speed of light enters a uniform electric field parallel to its direction of motion. If the electron is to be brought to rest in the space of 4.0 cm, (a) what direction is required for the electric field, and (b) what is the strength of the field?

## * 16–10 Gauss's Law

* 43. (I) The total electric flux from a cubical box 28.0 cm on a side is $1.45 \times 10^3\,\text{N}\cdot\text{m}^2/\text{C}$. What charge is enclosed by the box?

* 44. (II) A flat circle of radius 18 cm is placed in a uniform electric field of magnitude $5.8 \times 10^2\,\text{N/C}$. What is the electric flux through the circle when its face is (a) perpendicular to the field lines, (b) at 45° to the field lines, and (c) parallel to the field lines?

* 45. (II) In Fig. 16–61, two objects, $O_1$ and $O_2$, have charges $+1.0\,\mu\text{C}$ and $-2.0\,\mu\text{C}$, respectively, and a third object, $O_3$, is electrically neutral. (a) What is the electric flux through the surface $A_1$ that encloses all three objects? (b) What is the electric flux through the surface $A_2$ that encloses the third object only?

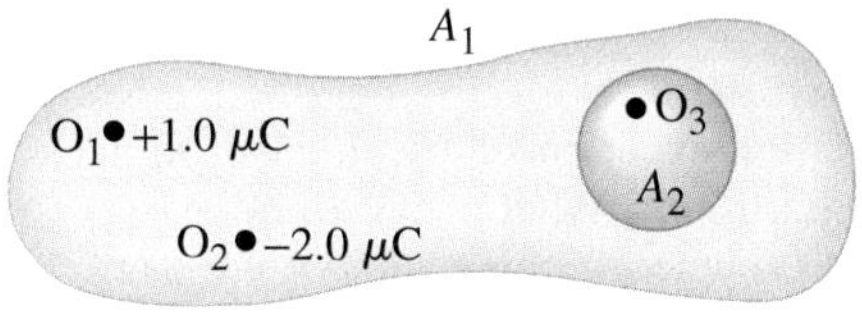


**FIGURE 16–61** Problem 45.

* 46. (II) A cube of side $l$ is placed in a uniform field $E = 6.50 \times 10^3\,\text{N/C}$ with edges parallel to the field lines. (a) What is the net flux through the cube? (b) What is the flux through each of its six faces?

* 47. (II) The electric field between two square metal plates is 130 N/C. The plates are 1.0 m on a side and are separated by 3.0 cm. What is the charge on each plate (assume equal and opposite)? Neglect edge effects.

* 48. (II) The field just outside a 3.50-cm-radius metal ball is $2.75 \times 10^2\,\text{N/C}$ and points toward the ball. What charge resides on the ball?

* 49. (II) A solid metal sphere of radius 3.00 m carries a total charge of $-3.50\,\mu\text{C}$. What is the magnitude of the electric field at a distance from the sphere's center of (a) 0.15 m, (b) 2.90 m, (c) 3.10 m, and (d) 6.00 m? (e) How would the answers differ if the sphere were a thin shell?

* 50. (III) A point charge $Q$ rests at the center of an uncharged thin spherical conducting shell. (See Fig. 16–33.) What is the electric field $E$ as a function of $r$ (a) for $r$ less than the inner radius of the shell, (b) inside the shell, and (c) beyond the shell? (d) Does the shell affect the field due to $Q$ alone? Does the charge $Q$ affect the shell?

## * 16–11 DNA

* 51. (III) The two strands of the helix-shaped DNA molecule are held together by electrostatic forces as shown in Fig. 16–44. Assume that the net average charge (due to electron sharing) indicated on H and N atoms is $0.2e$ and on the indicated C and O atoms is $0.4e$. Assume also that atoms on each molecule are separated by $1.0 \times 10^{-10}$ m. Estimate the net force between (a) a thymine and an adenine; and (b) a cytosine and a guanine. For each bond (red dots) consider only the three atoms in a line (two atoms on one molecule, one atom on the other). (c) Estimate the total force for a DNA molecule containing $10^5$ pairs of such molecules.

## General Problems

52. How close must two electrons be if the electric force between them is equal to the weight of either at the Earth's surface?

53. A 3.0-g copper penny has a positive charge of $38\,\mu\text{C}$. What fraction of its electrons has it lost?

54. A proton $(m = 1.67 \times 10^{-27}\,\text{kg})$ is suspended at rest in a uniform electric field $\vec{\mathbf{E}}$. Take into account gravity at the Earth's surface, and determine $\vec{\mathbf{E}}$.

55. Measurements indicate that there is an electric field surrounding the Earth. Its magnitude is about 150 N/C at the Earth's surface and points inward toward the Earth's center. What is the magnitude of the electric charge on the Earth? Is it positive or negative? [*Hint*: the electric field outside a uniformly charged sphere is the same as if all the charge were concentrated at its center.]

56. (*a*) Given the local electric field of 150 N/C, what is the acceleration experienced by an electron near the surface of the Earth? (*b*) What about a proton? (*c*) Calculate the ratio of each acceleration to $g = 9.8\,\text{m/s}^2$.

57. A water droplet of radius 0.018 mm remains stationary in the air. If the downward-directed electric field of the Earth is 150 N/C, how many excess electron charges must the water droplet have?

58. Estimate the net force between the CO group and the HN group shown in Fig. 16–62. The C and O have charges $\pm 0.40e$, and the H and N have charges $\pm 0.20e$, where $e = 1.6 \times 10^{-19}\,\text{C}$. [*Hint*: do not include the "internal" forces between C and O, or between H and N.]

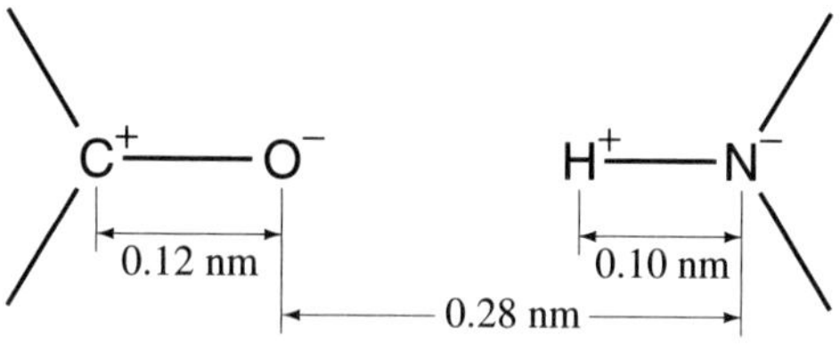


**FIGURE 16–62** Problem 58.

59. In a simple model of the hydrogen atom, the electron revolves in a circular orbit around the proton with a speed of $1.1 \times 10^6\,\text{m/s}$. Determine the radius of the electron's orbit. [*Hint*: see Chapter 5 on circular motion.]

60. Suppose that electrical attraction, rather than gravity, were responsible for holding the Moon in orbit around the Earth. If equal and opposite charges $Q$ were placed on the Earth and the Moon, what should be the value of $Q$ to maintain the present orbit? Use these data: mass of Earth $= 5.98 \times 10^{24}\,\text{kg}$, mass of Moon $= 7.35 \times 10^{22}\,\text{kg}$, radius of orbit $= 3.84 \times 10^8\,\text{m}$. Treat the Earth and Moon as point particles.

61. An electron with speed $v_0 = 21.5 \times 10^6\,\text{m/s}$ is traveling parallel to an electric field of magnitude $E = 11.4 \times 10^3\,\text{N/C}$. (*a*) How far will the electron travel before it stops? (*b*) How much time will elapse before it returns to its starting point?

62. A positive point charge $Q_1 = 2.5 \times 10^{-5}\,\text{C}$ is fixed at the origin of coordinates, and a negative charge $Q_2 = -5.0 \times 10^{-6}\,\text{C}$ is fixed to the $x$ axis at $x = +2.0\,\text{m}$. Find the location of the place(s) along the $x$ axis where the electric field due to these two charges is zero.

63. A small lead sphere is encased in insulating plastic and suspended vertically from an ideal spring ($k = 126\,\text{N/m}$) above a lab table, Fig. 16–63. The total mass of the coated sphere is 0.800 kg, and its center lies 15.0 cm above the tabletop when in equilibrium. The sphere is pulled down 5.00 cm below equilibrium, an electric charge $Q = -3.00 \times 10^{-6}\,\text{C}$ is deposited on it and then it is released. Using what you know about harmonic oscillation, write an expression for the electric field strength as a function of time that would be measured at the point on the tabletop (P) directly below the sphere.

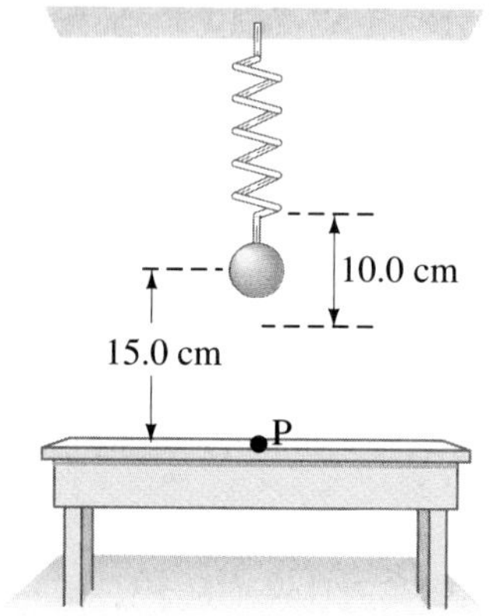


**FIGURE 16–63** Problem 63.

64. A large electroscope is made with "leaves" that are 78-cm-long wires with tiny 24-g spheres at the ends. When charged, nearly all the charge resides on the spheres. If the wires each make a 30° angle with the vertical (Fig. 16–64), what total charge $Q$ must have been applied to the electroscope? Ignore the mass of the wires.

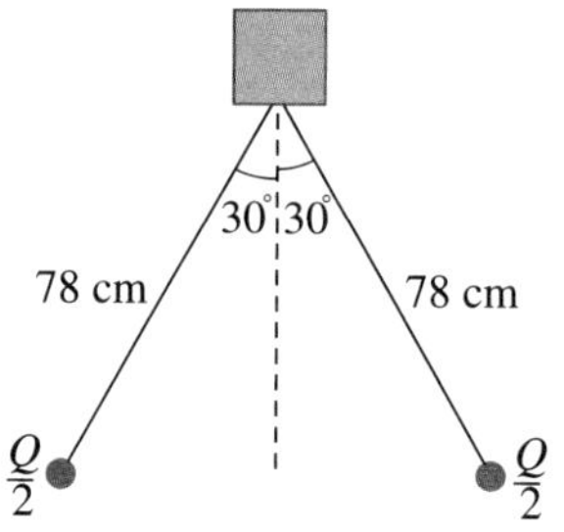


**FIGURE 16–64** Problem 64.

65. Dry air will break down and generate a spark if the electric field exceeds about $3 \times 10^6\,\text{N/C}$. How much charge could be packed onto a green pea (diameter 0.75 cm) before the pea spontaneously discharges? [*Hint*: Eqs. 16–4 work outside a sphere if $r$ is measured from its center.]

66. Two point charges, $Q_1 = -6.7\,\mu\text{C}$ and $Q_2 = 1.8\,\mu\text{C}$ are located between two oppositely charged parallel plates, as shown in Fig. 16–65. The two charges are separated by a distance of $x = 0.34\,\text{m}$. Assume that the electric field produced by the charged plates is uniform and equal to $E = 73{,}000\,\text{N/C}$. Calculate the net electrostatic force on $Q_1$ and give its direction.

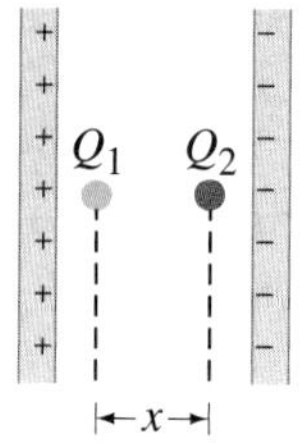


**FIGURE 16–65** Problem 66.

67. A point charge ($m = 1.0\,\text{g}$) at the end of an insulating string of length 55 cm is observed to be in equilibrium in a uniform horizontal electric field of 12,000 N/C, when the pendulum's position is as shown in Fig. 16–66, with the charge 12 cm above the lowest (vertical) position. If the field points to the right in Fig. 16–66, determine the magnitude and sign of the point charge.

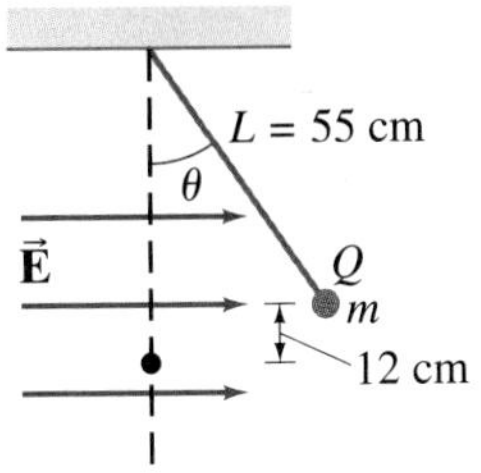

**FIGURE 16–66** Problem 67.

68. A point charge of mass 0.210 kg, and net charge $+0.340\,\mu\text{C}$, hangs at rest at the end of an insulating string above a large sheet of charge. The horizontal sheet of uniform charge creates a uniform vertical electric field in the vicinity of the point charge. The tension in the string is measured to be 5.67 N. Calculate the magnitude and direction of the electric field due to the sheet of charge (Fig. 16–67).

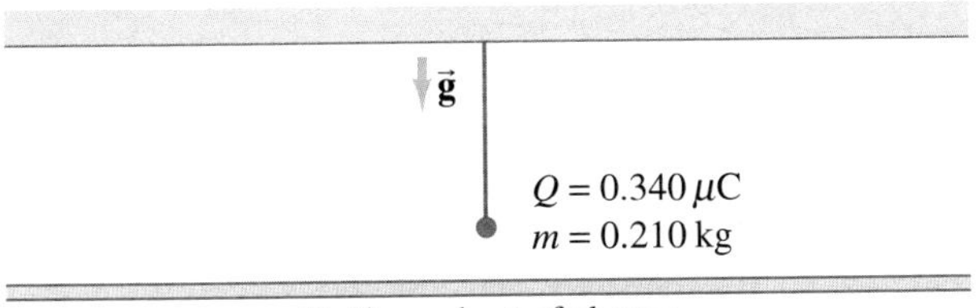

**FIGURE 16–67** Problem 68.

69. What is the total charge of all the electrons in a 15-kg bar of aluminum? What is the net charge of the bar? (Aluminum has 13 electrons per atom and an atomic mass of 27 u.)

70. Two small, identical conducting spheres A and B are a distance $R$ apart; each carries the same charge $Q$. (*a*) What is the force sphere B exerts on sphere A? (*b*) An identical sphere with zero charge, sphere C, makes contact with sphere B and is then moved very far away. What is the net force now acting on sphere A? (*c*) Sphere C next makes contact with sphere A and is then moved far away. What is the force on sphere A in this third case?

71. Given the two charges shown in Fig. 16–68, at what position(s) $x$ is the electric field zero? Is the field zero at any other points, not on the $x$ axis?

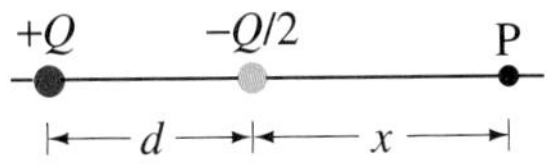

**FIGURE 16–68** Problem 71.

72. Two point charges, $+Q$ and $-Q$ of mass $m$, are placed on the ends of a massless rod of length $L$, which is fixed to a table by a pin through its center. If the apparatus is then subjected to a uniform electric field $E$ parallel to the table and perpendicular to the rod, find the net torque on the system of rod plus charges.

73. Four equal positive point charges, each of charge $8.0\,\mu\text{C}$, are at the corners of a square of side 9.2 cm. What charge should be placed at the center of the square so that all charges are at equilibrium? Is this a stable or unstable equilibrium (Section 9–4) in the plane?

## Answers to Exercises

**A:** Opposite.

**B:** 5 N.

**C:** 1.2 N, to the right.

**D:** 0.32 m.

**E:** (*a*) No; (*b*) yes, midway between them.

**F:** $9.0 \times 10^4\,\text{N/C}$, vertically down.

**G:** (*a*) $\vec{\mathbf{E}}_1$ right; $\vec{\mathbf{E}}_2$ left; $\vec{\mathbf{E}}$ right;
(*b*) $\vec{\mathbf{E}}_1$ left; $\vec{\mathbf{E}}_2$ right; $\vec{\mathbf{E}}$ right.

**H:** $\sum E_{\perp}\,\Delta A = E\sum \Delta A = E(2\pi r L) = \dfrac{Q_{\text{encl}}}{\epsilon_0}$,

so $E = \dfrac{1}{2\pi\epsilon_0}\dfrac{Q}{r}\dfrac{}{}\!\!\dfrac{1}{L}$.

A huge amount of electric potential energy can be stored in clouds. In lightning, the voltage (= potential difference = $\Delta$PE per charge) between the clouds and the Earth can be a hundred million volts. The electric field is related to the potential difference per unit length, and if it becomes high enough inside the cloud, electrons can reach a KE large enough to knock electrons out of atoms. The air becomes a conductor as the freed electrons and ionized atoms flow rapidly, colliding with more atoms, and causing more ionization. The massive flow of charge reduces the potential difference, and the "discharge" ceases. The ions and electrons recombine to form atoms. The light we see comes from electrons returning to lower states inside the atoms.

We discuss voltage and its relation to electric field, as well as electric energy storage, capacitors, and applications such as the cathode ray tube and ECG.

CHAPTER 17

# Electric Potential

We saw in Chapter 6 that the concept of energy was extremely valuable in dealing with the subject of mechanics. For one thing, energy is a conserved quantity and is thus an important tool for understanding nature. Furthermore, we saw that many Problems could be solved using the energy concept even though a detailed knowledge of the forces involved was not possible, or when a calculation involving Newton's laws would have been too difficult.

The energy point of view can be used in electricity, and it is especially useful. It not only extends the law of conservation of energy, but it gives us another way to view electrical phenomena. Energy is also a tool in solving Problems more easily in many cases than by using forces and electric fields.

## 17–1 Electric Potential Energy and Potential Difference

### Electric Potential Energy

To apply conservation of energy, we need to define electric potential energy as for other types of potential energy. As we saw in Chapter 6, potential energy can be defined only for a conservative force. The work done by a conservative force in moving an object between any two positions is independent of the path taken. The electrostatic force between any two charges (Eq. 16–1, $F = kQ_1Q_2/r^2$) is conservative since the dependence is on position just like the gravitational force, which is conservative. Hence we can define potential energy PE for the electrostatic force.

We saw in Chapter 6 that the change in potential energy between two points a and b equals the negative of the work done by the conservative force to move an object from a to b: $\Delta\text{PE} = -W$.

Thus we define the change in electric potential energy, $\text{PE}_b - \text{PE}_a$, when a point charge $q$ moves from some point a to another point b, as the negative of the work done by the electric force to move the charge from a to b. For example, consider the electric field between two equally but oppositely charged parallel plates; we assume their separation is small compared to their width and height, so the field $\vec{\mathbf{E}}$ will be uniform over most of the region, Fig. 17–1. Now consider a tiny positive point charge $q$ placed at point a very near the positive plate as shown. This charge $q$ is so small it doesn't affect $\vec{\mathbf{E}}$. If this charge $q$ at point a is released, the electric force will do work on the charge and accelerate it toward the negative plate. The work $W$ done by the electric field $E$ to move the charge a distance $d$ is

$$W = Fd = qEd$$

where we used Eq. 16–5, $F = qE$. The change in electric potential energy equals the negative of the work done by the electric force:

$$\text{PE}_b - \text{PE}_a = -qEd \qquad [\text{uniform } \vec{\mathbf{E}}] \qquad \textbf{(17–1)}$$

for this case of uniform electric field $\vec{\mathbf{E}}$. In the case illustrated, the potential energy decreases ($\Delta\text{PE}$ is negative); and as the charged particle accelerates from point a to point b in Fig. 17–1, the particle's kinetic energy KE increases—by an equal amount. In accord with the conservation of energy, electric potential energy is transformed into kinetic energy, and the total energy is conserved. Note that the positive charge $q$ has its greatest potential energy at point a, near the positive plate.† The reverse is true for a negative charge: its potential energy is greatest near the negative plate.

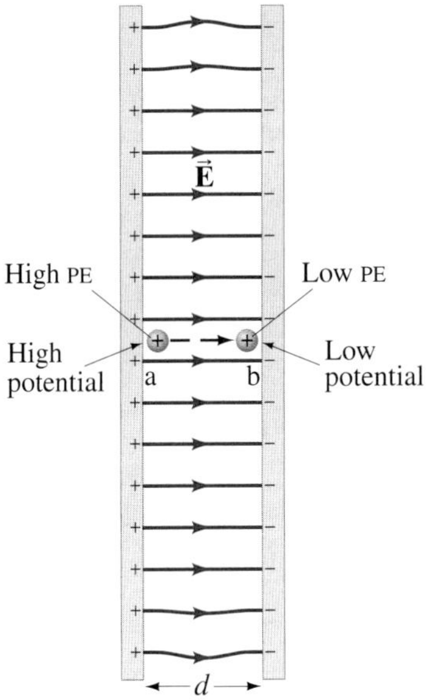

**FIGURE 17–1** Work is done by the electric field in moving the positive charge from position a to position b.

## Electric Potential and Potential Difference

In Chapter 16, we found it useful to define the electric field as the force per unit charge. Similarly, it is useful to define the **electric potential** (or simply the **potential** when "electric" is understood) as the *electric potential energy per unit charge*. Electric potential is given the symbol $V$. If a positive test charge $q$ has electric potential energy $\text{PE}_a$ at some point a (relative to some zero potential energy), the electric potential $V_a$ at this point is

*Potential is potential energy per unit charge*

$$V_a = \frac{\text{PE}_a}{q}. \qquad \textbf{(17–2a)}$$

*Potential difference*

As we discussed in Chapter 6, only differences in potential energy are physically meaningful. Hence only the **difference in potential**, or the **potential difference**, between two points a and b (such as between a and b in Fig. 17–1) is measurable. When the electric force does positive work on a charge, the kinetic energy increases and the potential energy decreases. The difference in potential energy, $\text{PE}_b - \text{PE}_a$, is equal to the negative of the work, $W_{ba}$, done by the electric field to move the charge from a to b; so the potential difference $V_{ba}$ is

$$V_{ba} = V_b - V_a = \frac{\text{PE}_b - \text{PE}_a}{q} = -\frac{W_{ba}}{q}. \qquad \textbf{(17–2b)}$$

Note that electric potential, like electric field, does not depend on our test charge $q$. $V$ depends on the other charges that create the field, not on $q$; $q$ acquires potential energy by being in the potential $V$ due to the other charges.

We can see from our definition that the positive plate in Fig. 17–1 is at a higher potential than the negative plate. Thus a positively charged object moves naturally from a high potential to a low potential. A negative charge does the reverse.

†At this point the charge has its greatest ability to do work (on some other object or system).

*Unit of potential difference: the volt (1 V = 1 J/C)*

The unit of electric potential, and of potential difference, is joules/coulomb and is given a special name, the **volt**, in honor of Alessandro Volta (1745–1827) who is best known for inventing the electric battery. The volt is abbreviated V, so $1\,\mathrm{V} = 1\,\mathrm{J/C}$. Potential difference, since it is measured in volts, is often referred to as **voltage**.

*Voltage = potential difference*

*V = 0 chosen arbitrarily*

If we wish to speak of the potential $V_a$ at some point a, we must be aware that $V_a$ depends on where the potential is chosen to be zero. The zero for electric potential in a given situation can be chosen arbitrarily, just as for potential energy, because only differences in potential energy can be measured. Often the ground, or a conductor connected directly to the ground (the Earth), is taken as zero potential, and other potentials are given with respect to ground. (Thus, a point where the voltage is 50 V is one where the difference of potential between it and ground is 50 V.) In other cases, as we shall see, we may choose the potential to be zero at an infinite distance ($r = \infty$).

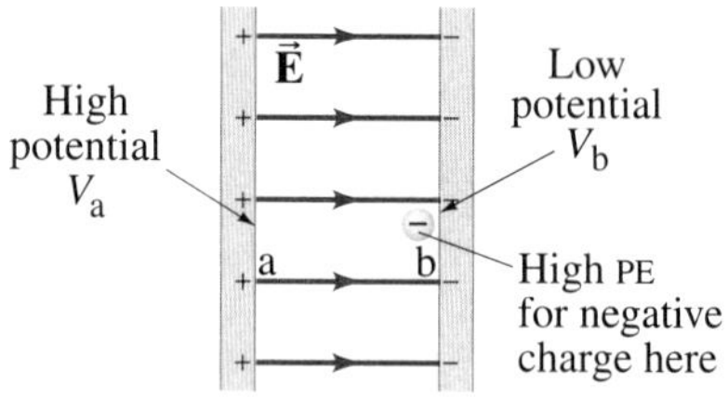


**FIGURE 17–2** Central part of Fig. 17–1, showing a negative point charge near the negative plate. Conceptual Example 17–1.

**CONCEPTUAL EXAMPLE 17–1** **A negative charge.** Suppose a negative charge, such as an electron, is placed near the negative plate in Fig. 17–1, at point b, shown here in Fig. 17–2. If the electron is free to move, will its electric potential energy increase or decrease? How will the electric potential change?

**RESPONSE** An electron released at point b will move toward the positive plate. As the electron moves toward the positive plate, its potential energy *decreases* as its kinetic energy gets larger. But note that the electron moves from point b at low potential to point a at higher potential: $\Delta V = V_a - V_b > 0$. (The potentials $V_a$ and $V_b$ are due to the charges on the plates, not due to the electron.)

**NOTE** A positive charge placed near the negative plate at b would not be accelerated. A positive charge tends to move from high potential to low.

**CAUTION**

*A negative charge has high PE when potential V is low*

Because the electric potential difference is defined as the potential energy difference per unit charge, then the change in potential energy of a charge $q$ when moved between two points a and b is

*Electric potential and potential energy*

$$\mathrm{PE_b} - \mathrm{PE_a} = q(V_b - V_a) = qV_{ba}. \qquad \textbf{(17–3)}$$

That is, if an object with charge $q$ moves through a potential difference $V_{ba}$, its potential energy changes by an amount $qV_{ba}$. For example, if the potential difference between the two plates in Fig. 17–1 is 6 V, then a +1 C charge moved (say by an external force) from b to a will gain $(1\,\mathrm{C})(6\,\mathrm{V}) = 6\,\mathrm{J}$ of electric potential energy. (And it will lose 6 J of electric potential energy if it moves from a to b.) Similarly, a +2 C charge will gain 12 J, and so on. Thus, electric potential difference is a measure of how much energy an electric charge can acquire in a given situation. And, since energy is the ability to do work, the electric potential difference is also a measure of how much work a given charge can do. The exact amount depends both on the potential difference and on the charge.

*Potential likened to height of a cliff*

To better understand electric potential, let's make a comparison to the gravitational case when a rock falls from the top of a cliff. The greater the height, $h$, of a cliff, the more potential energy ($= mgh$) the rock has at the top of the cliff, relative to the bottom, and the more kinetic energy it will have when it reaches the bottom. The actual amount of kinetic energy it will acquire, and the amount of work it can do, depends both on the height of the cliff and the mass $m$ of the rock. A large rock and a small rock can be at the same height $h$ (Fig. 17–3a) and thus have the same "gravitational potential," but the larger rock has the greater potential energy (it has more mass). The electrical case is similar (Fig. 17–3b): the potential energy change, or the work that can be done, depends both on the potential difference (corresponding to the height of the cliff) and on the charge (corresponding to mass), Eq. 17–3. But note a significant difference: electric charge comes in two types, + and −, whereas gravitational mass is always +.

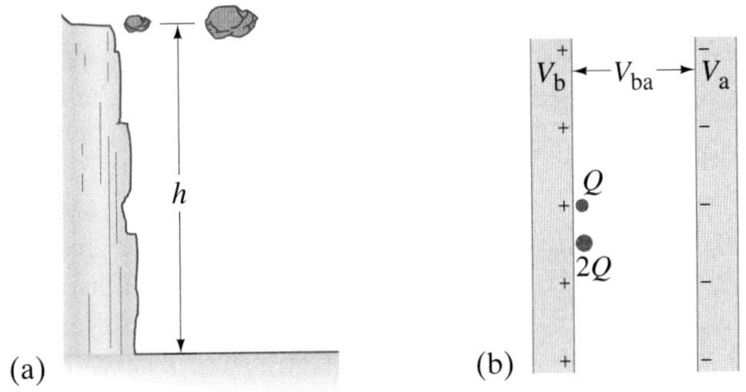


**FIGURE 17–3** (*a*) Two rocks are at the same height. The larger rock has more potential energy. (*b*) Two charges have the same electric potential. The $2Q$ charge has more potential energy.

Practical sources of electrical energy such as batteries and electric generators are meant to maintain a potential difference. The actual amount of energy transformed by such a device depends on how much charge flows, as well as the potential difference (Eq. 17–3). For example, consider an automobile headlight connected to a 12.0-V battery. The amount of energy transformed (into light and thermal energy) is proportional to how much charge flows, which in turn depends on how long the light is on. If over a given period of time 5.0 C of charge flows through the light, the total energy transformed is $(5.0\text{ C})(12.0\text{ V}) = 60\text{ J}$. If the headlight is left on twice as long, 10.0 C of charge will flow and the energy transformed is $(10.0\text{ C})(12.0\text{ V}) = 120\text{ J}$.

Table 17–1 presents some typical voltages.

**TABLE 17–1 Some Typical Potential Differences (Voltages)**

| Source | Voltage (approx.) |
|---|---|
| Thundercloud to ground | $10^8$ V |
| High-voltage power line | $10^5$–$10^6$ V |
| Power supply for TV tube | $10^4$ V |
| Automobile ignition | $10^4$ V |
| Household outlet | $10^2$ V |
| Automobile battery | 12 V |
| Flashlight battery | 1.5 V |
| Resting potential across nerve membrane | $10^{-1}$ V |
| Potential changes on skin (EKG and EEG) | $10^{-4}$ V |

**EXAMPLE 17–2** **Electron in TV tube.** Suppose an electron in the picture tube of a television set is accelerated from rest through a potential difference $V_b - V_a = V_{ba} = +5000\text{ V}$ (Fig. 17–4). (*a*) What is the change in electric potential energy of the electron? (*b*) What is the speed of the electron $(m = 9.1 \times 10^{-31}\text{ kg})$ as a result of this acceleration?

**APPROACH** The electron, accelerated toward the positive plate, will decrease in potential energy by an amount $\Delta\text{PE} = qV_{ba}$ (Eq. 17–3). The loss in potential energy will equal its gain in kinetic energy (energy conservation).

**SOLUTION** (*a*) The charge on an electron is $q = -e = -1.6 \times 10^{-19}\text{ C}$. Therefore its change in potential energy is

$$\Delta\text{PE} = qV_{ba} = (-1.6 \times 10^{-19}\text{ C})(+5000\text{ V}) = -8.0 \times 10^{-16}\text{ J}.$$

The minus sign indicates that the potential energy decreases. The potential difference, $V_{ba}$, has a positive sign since the final potential $V_b$ is higher than the initial potential $V_a$; negative electrons are attracted toward a positive electrode and repelled away from a negative electrode.

(*b*) The potential energy lost by the electron becomes kinetic energy KE. From conservation of energy (Eq. 6–11a), $\Delta\text{KE} + \Delta\text{PE} = 0$, so

$$\Delta\text{KE} = -\Delta\text{PE}$$
$$\tfrac{1}{2}mv^2 - 0 = -q(V_b - V_a) = -qV_{ba},$$

where the initial kinetic energy is zero since we are given that the electron started from rest. We solve for $v$:

$$v = \sqrt{-\frac{2qV_{ba}}{m}} = \sqrt{-\frac{2(-1.6 \times 10^{-19}\text{ C})(5000\text{ V})}{9.1 \times 10^{-31}\text{ kg}}} = 4.2 \times 10^7\text{ m/s}.$$

**NOTE** The potential energy doesn't depend on the mass, only on the charge and voltage. The speed *does* depend on $m$.

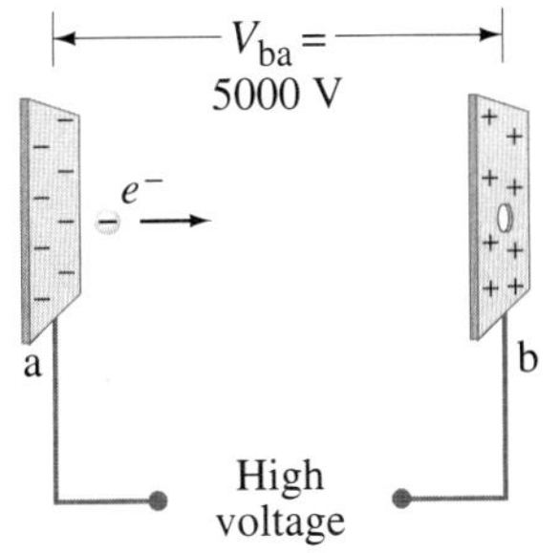


**FIGURE 17–4** Electron accelerated in TV picture tube. Example 17–2.

**EXERCISE A** Instead of the electron in Example 17–2, suppose a proton $(m = 1.67 \times 10^{-27}\text{ kg})$ was accelerated from rest by a potential difference $V_{ba} = -5000\text{ V}$. What would be the proton's (*a*) change in PE, and (*b*) final speed?

## 17–2 Relation between Electric Potential and Electric Field

The effects of any charge distribution can be described either in terms of electric field or in terms of electric potential. Electric potential is often easier to use since it is a scalar, whereas electric field is a vector. There is an intimate connection between the potential and the field. Let us consider the case of a uniform electric field, such as that between the parallel plates of Fig. 17–1 whose difference of potential is $V_{ba}$. The work done by the electric field to move a positive charge $q$ from a to b is equal to the negative of the change in potential energy (Eq. 17–2b), so

$$W = -q(V_b - V_a) = -qV_{ba}.$$

We can also write the work done as the force times distance, where the force on $q$ is $F = qE$, so

$$W = Fd = qEd,$$

where $d$ is the distance (parallel to the field lines) between points a and b. We now set these two expressions for $W$ equal and find $qV_{ba} = -qEd$, or

*V related to uniform E*

$$V_{ba} = -Ed. \qquad [E \text{ uniform}] \quad \textbf{(17–4a)}$$

If we solve for $E$, we find

$$E = -\frac{V_{ba}}{d}. \qquad [E \text{ uniform}] \quad \textbf{(17–4b)}$$

*Units for E: 1 N/C = 1 V/m*

From Eq. 17–4b we see that the units for electric field can be written as volts per meter (V/m) as well as newtons per coulomb (N/C). These are equivalent in general, since 1 N/C = 1 N·m/C·m = 1 J/C·m = 1 V/m. The minus sign in Eq. 17–4b tells us that $\vec{\mathbf{E}}$ points in the direction of decreasing potential $V$.

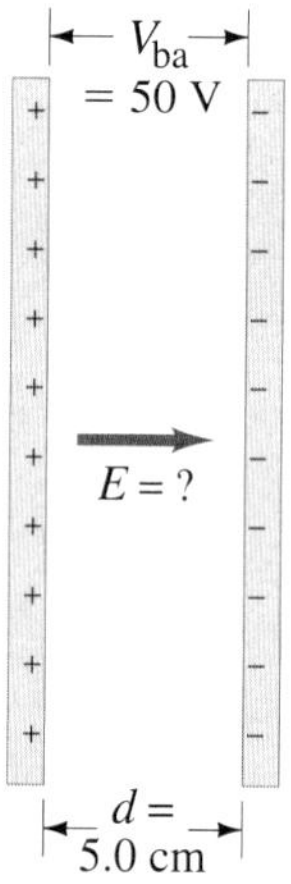


**FIGURE 17–5** Example 17–3.

**EXAMPLE 17–3 Electric field obtained from voltage.** Two parallel plates are charged to produce a potential difference of 50 V. If the separation between the plates is 0.050 m, calculate the magnitude of the electric field in the space between the plates (Fig. 17–5).

**APPROACH** We apply Eq. 17–4b to obtain the magnitude of $E$, assumed uniform.

**SOLUTION** The magnitude of the electric field is

$$E = V_{ba}/d = (50\,\text{V}/0.050\,\text{m}) = 1000\,\text{V/m}.$$

**NOTE** Equations 17–4 apply only for a uniform electric field. The general relationship between $\vec{\mathbf{E}}$ and $V$ is more complicated.

### * General Relation between $\vec{\mathbf{E}}$ and $V$

In a region where $\vec{\mathbf{E}}$ is not uniform, the connection between $\vec{\mathbf{E}}$ and $V$ takes on a different form than Eqs. 17–4. In general, it is possible to show that the electric field in a given direction at any point in space is equal to the *rate at which the electric potential decreases over distance in that direction.* For example, the $x$ component of the electric field is given by $E_x = -\Delta V/\Delta x$, where $\Delta V$ is the change in potential over the very short distance $\Delta x$.

## 17–3 Equipotential Lines

The electric potential can be represented diagrammatically by drawing **equipotential lines** or, in three dimensions, **equipotential surfaces**. An equipotential surface is one on which all points are at the same potential. That is, the potential difference between any two points on the surface is zero, and no work is required to move a charge from one point to another on an equipotential surface. An *equipotential surface must be perpendicular to the electric field* at any point. If this were not so—that is, if there were a component of $\vec{\mathbf{E}}$ parallel to the surface—it would require work to move the charge along the surface against this component of $\vec{\mathbf{E}}$; and this would contradict the idea that it is an *equi*potential surface.

*Equipotentials ⊥ $\vec{\mathbf{E}}$*

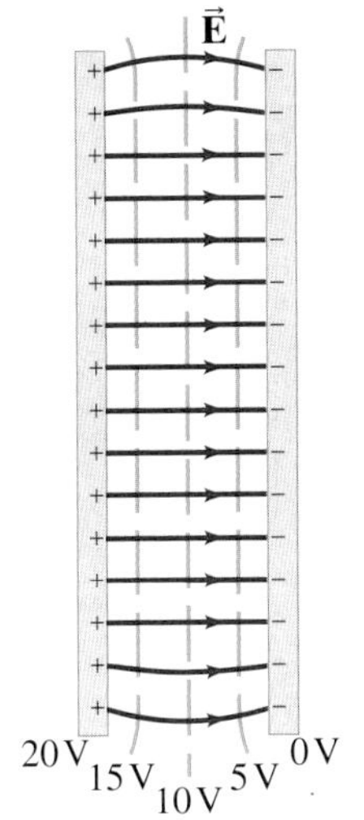


**FIGURE 17–6** Equipotential lines (the green dashed lines) between two charged parallel plates are always perpendicular to the electric field (solid red lines).

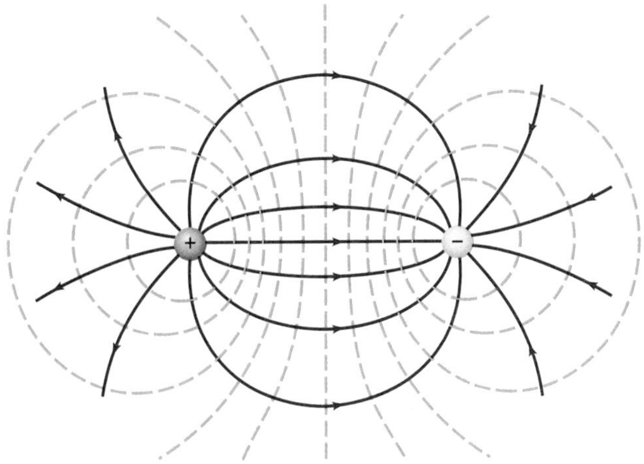

**FIGURE 17–7** Equipotential lines (green, dashed) are always perpendicular to the electric field lines (solid red), shown here for two equal but oppositely charged particles (an "electric dipole").

The fact that the electric field lines and equipotential surfaces are mutually perpendicular helps us locate the equipotentials when the electric field lines are known. In a normal two-dimensional drawing, we show equipotential *lines*, which are the intersections of equipotential surfaces with the plane of the drawing. In Fig. 17–6, a few of the equipotential lines are drawn (dashed green lines) for the electric field (red lines) between two parallel plates at a potential difference of 20 V. The negative plate is arbitrarily chosen to be zero volts and the potential of each equipotential line is indicated. Note that $\vec{\mathbf{E}}$ points toward lower values of $V$. The equipotential lines for the case of two equal but oppositely charged particles are shown in Fig. 17–7 as green dashed lines. (This combination of equal + and − charges is called an "electric dipole," as we saw in Section 16–8; see Fig. 16–31a.)

Unlike electric field lines, which start and end on electric charges, equipotential lines and surfaces are always continuous and never end, and so continue beyond the borders of Figs. 17–6 and 17–7. A useful analogy is a topographic map: the contour lines are essentially gravitational equipotential lines (Fig. 17–8).

We saw in Section 16–9 that there can be no electric field within a conductor in the static case, for otherwise the free electrons would feel a force and would move. Indeed *a conductor must be entirely at the same potential in the static case*, and the surface of a conductor is then an equipotential surface. (If it weren't, the free electrons at the surface would move, since whenever there is a potential difference between two points, work can be done on charged particles to move them.) This is fully consistent with our result, discussed earlier, that the electric field at the surface of a conductor must be perpendicular to the surface.

*Conductors are equipotential surfaces*

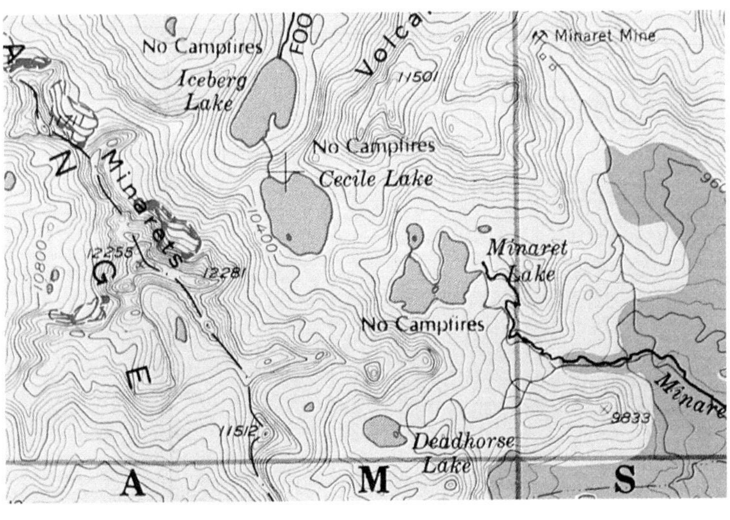


**FIGURE 17–8** A topographic map (here, a portion of the Sierra Nevada in California) shows continuous contour lines, each of which is at a fixed height above sea level. Here they are at 80-ft (25-m) intervals. If you walk along one contour line, you neither climb nor descend. If you cross lines, and especially if you climb perpendicular to the lines, you will be changing your gravitational potential (rapidly, if the lines are close together).

## 17–4 The Electron Volt, a Unit of Energy

The joule is a very large unit for dealing with energies of electrons, atoms, or molecules. For this purpose, the unit **electron volt** (eV) is used. One electron volt is defined as the energy acquired by a particle carrying a charge whose magnitude equals that on the electron ($q = e$) as a result of moving through a potential difference of 1 V. Since the charge on an electron has magnitude $1.6 \times 10^{-19}$ C, and since the change in potential energy equals $qV$, 1 eV is equal to $(1.6 \times 10^{-19}\,\text{C})(1.0\,\text{V}) = 1.6 \times 10^{-19}\,\text{J}$:

*Electron volt (unit)*

$$1\,\text{eV} = 1.6 \times 10^{-19}\,\text{J}.$$

An electron that accelerates through a potential difference of 1000 V will lose 1000 eV of potential energy and will thus gain 1000 eV, or 1 keV (kiloelectron volt) of kinetic energy. On the other hand, if a particle with a charge equal to twice the magnitude of the charge on the electron $(= 2e = 3.2 \times 10^{-19}\,\text{C})$ moves through a potential difference of 1000 V, its energy will change by 2000 eV.

Although the electron volt is handy for *stating* the energies of molecules and elementary particles, it is *not* a proper SI unit. For calculations, electron volts should be converted to joules using the conversion factor just given. In Example 17–2, for example, the electron acquired a kinetic energy of $8.0 \times 10^{-16}$ J. We normally would quote this energy as 5000 eV $(= 8.0 \times 10^{-16}\,\text{J}/1.6 \times 10^{-19}\,\text{J/eV})$. But when determining the speed of a particle in SI units, we must use the KE in joules (J).

## 17–5 Electric Potential Due to Point Charges

The electric potential at a distance $r$ from a single point charge $Q$ can be derived from the expression for its electric field (Eq. 16–4) using calculus. The potential in this case is usually taken to be zero at infinity ($\infty$); this is also where the electric field $(E = kQ/r^2)$ is zero. The result is

*Electric potential of a point charge ($V = 0$ at $r = \infty$)*

$$V = k\frac{Q}{r} = \frac{1}{4\pi\epsilon_0}\frac{Q}{r}, \qquad \text{[single point charge]} \quad \textbf{(17–5)}$$

where $k = 8.99 \times 10^9\,\text{N}\cdot\text{m}^2/\text{C}^2$. We can think of $V$ here as representing the *absolute potential* at a distance $r$ from the charge $Q$, where $V = 0$ at $r = \infty$, or we can think of $V$ as the potential difference between $r$ and infinity. Notice that the potential $V$ decreases with the first power of the distance, whereas the electric field (Eq. 16–4) decreases as the *square* of the distance. The potential near a positive charge is large and positive, and it decreases toward zero at very large distances. The potential near a negative charge is negative and increases toward zero at large distances (Fig. 17–9).

**CAUTION**

*$V \propto \frac{1}{r}$, $E \propto \frac{1}{r^2}$ for a point charge*

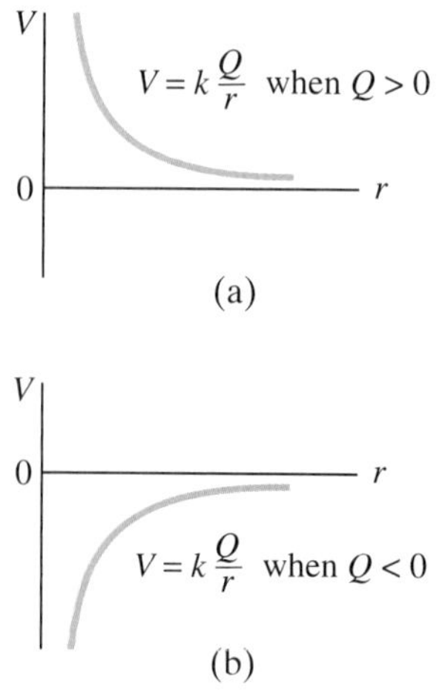


**FIGURE 17–9** Potential $V$ as a function of distance $r$ from a single point charge $Q$ when the charge is ($a$) positive, ($b$) negative.

**EXAMPLE 17–4 Potential due to a positive or a negative charge.** Determine the potential at a point 0.50 m (*a*) from a $+20\,\mu C$ point charge, (*b*) from a $-20\,\mu C$ point charge.

**APPROACH** The potential due to a point charge is given by Eq. 17–5, $V = kQ/r$.

**SOLUTION** (*a*) At a distance of 0.50 m from a positive $20\,\mu C$ charge, the potential is

$$V = k\frac{Q}{r}$$

$$= (9.0 \times 10^9\,N\cdot m^2/C^2)\left(\frac{20 \times 10^{-6}\,C}{0.50\,m}\right) = 3.6 \times 10^5\,V.$$

(*b*) For the negative charge,

$$V = (9.0 \times 10^9\,N\cdot m^2/C^2)\left(\frac{-20 \times 10^{-6}\,C}{0.50\,m}\right) = -3.6 \times 10^5\,V.$$

**NOTE** Potential can be positive or negative. In contrast to calculations of electric field magnitudes, for which we usually ignore the sign of the charges, it is important to include a charge's sign when we find electric potential.

PROBLEM SOLVING

*Keep track of charge signs for electric potential*

**EXAMPLE 17–5 Work done to bring two positive charges close together.** What minimum work must be done by an external force to bring a charge $q = 3.00\,\mu C$ from a great distance away (take $r = \infty$) to a point 0.500 m from a charge $Q = 20.0\,\mu C$?

**APPROACH** To find the work we cannot simply multiply the force times distance because the force is not constant. Instead we can set the change in potential energy equal to the (positive of the) work required of an *external* force (Chapter 6), and Eq. 17–3: $W = \Delta PE = q(V_b - V_a)$. We get the potentials $V_b$ and $V_a$ using Eq. 17–5.

CAUTION

*We cannot use $W = Fd$ if $F$ is not constant*

**SOLUTION** The work required is equal to the change in potential energy:

$$W = q(V_b - V_a) = q\left(\frac{kQ}{r_b} - \frac{kQ}{r_a}\right),$$

where $r_b = 0.500\,m$ and $r_a = \infty$. The right-hand term within the parentheses is zero $(1/\infty = 0)$ so

$$W = (3.00 \times 10^{-6}\,C)\frac{(8.99 \times 10^9\,N\cdot m^2/C^2)(2.00 \times 10^{-5}\,C)}{(0.500\,m)} = 1.08\,J.$$

**NOTE** We could not use Eqs. 17–4 here because they apply *only* to uniform fields. But we did use Eq. 17–3 because it is always valid.

**EXERCISE B** What work is required to bring a charge $q = 3.00\,\mu C$ originally a distance of 1.50 m from a charge $Q = 20.0\,\mu C$ until it is 0.50 m away?

To determine the electric field at points near a collection of two or more point charges requires adding up the electric fields due to each charge. Since the electric field is a vector, this can be time consuming or complicated. To find the electric potential at a point due to a collection of point charges is far easier, since the electric potential is a scalar, and hence you only need to add numbers together without concern for direction. This is a major advantage in using electric potential for solving Problems. We do have to include the signs of charges, however.

*Potentials add as scalars (fields add as vectors)*

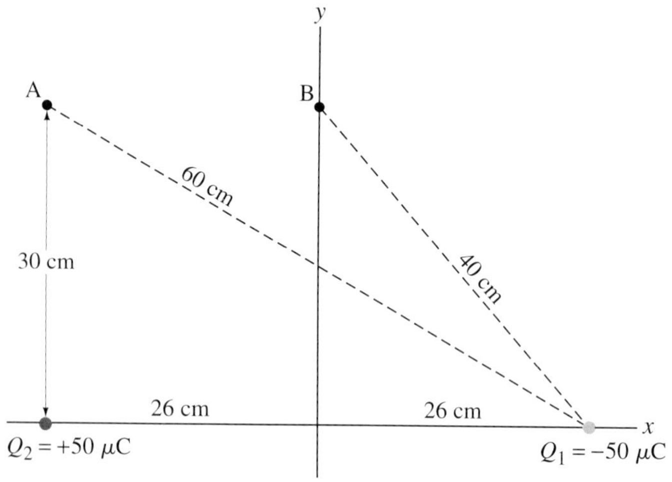


**FIGURE 17–10** Example 17–6. (See also Example 16–9, Fig. 16–28.)

**EXAMPLE 17–6** **Potential above two charges.** Calculate the electric potential (*a*) at point A in Fig. 17–10 due to the two charges shown, and (*b*) at point B. [This is the same situation as Example 16–9, Fig. 16–28, where we calculated the electric field at these points.]

**CAUTION**
*Potential is a scalar and has no components*

**APPROACH** The total potential at point A (or at point B) is the sum of the potentials at that point due to each of the two charges $Q_1$ and $Q_2$. The potential due to each single charge is given by Eq. 17–5. We do not have to worry about directions because electric potential is a scalar quantity. But we do have to keep track of the signs of charges.

**SOLUTION** (*a*) We add the potentials at point A due to the each charge $Q_1$ and $Q_2$, and we use Eq. 17–5 for each:

$$\begin{aligned} V_A &= V_{A2} + V_{A1} \\ &= k\frac{Q_2}{r_{2A}} + k\frac{Q_1}{r_{1A}} \end{aligned}$$

where $r_{1A} = 60\,\text{cm}$ and $r_{2A} = 30\,\text{cm}$. Then

$$\begin{aligned} V_A &= \frac{(9.0 \times 10^9\,\text{N}\cdot\text{m}^2/\text{C}^2)(5.0 \times 10^{-5}\,\text{C})}{0.30\,\text{m}} \\ &\quad + \frac{(9.0 \times 10^9\,\text{N}\cdot\text{m}^2/\text{C}^2)(-5.0 \times 10^{-5}\,\text{C})}{0.60\,\text{m}} \\ &= 1.50 \times 10^6\,\text{V} - 0.75 \times 10^6\,\text{V} \\ &= 7.5 \times 10^5\,\text{V}. \end{aligned}$$

(*b*) At point B, $r_{1B} = r_{2B} = 0.40\,\text{m}$, so

$$\begin{aligned} V_B &= V_{B2} + V_{B1} \\ &= \frac{(9.0 \times 10^9\,\text{N}\cdot\text{m}^2/\text{C}^2)(5.0 \times 10^{-5}\,\text{C})}{0.40\,\text{m}} \\ &\quad + \frac{(9.0 \times 10^9\,\text{N}\cdot\text{m}^2/\text{C}^2)(-5.0 \times 10^{-5}\,\text{C})}{0.40\,\text{m}} \\ &= 0\,\text{V}. \end{aligned}$$

**NOTE** The two terms in the sum in (*b*) cancel for any point equidistant from $Q_1$ and $Q_2$ $(r_{1B} = r_{2B})$. Thus the potential will be zero everywhere on the plane equidistant between the two charges. This plane is an equipotential surface with $V = 0$.

Simple summations like these can easily be performed for any number of point charges.

**CONCEPTUAL EXAMPLE 17–7** **Potential energies.** Consider the three pairs of charges, $Q_1$ and $Q_2$, in Fig. 17–11. (*a*) Which set has a positive potential energy? (*b*) Which set has the most negative potential energy? (*c*) Which set requires the most work to separate the charges to infinity? Assume the charges all have the same magnitude.

**RESPONSE** The potential energy equals the work required to bring the two charges near each other, starting at a great distance ($\infty$). Assume the left (+) charge is already there. To bring a second charge close to the first from a great distance away ($\infty$) requires work

$$W = Q_2 V_{\text{ba}} = k\frac{Q_1 Q_2}{r}$$

where $r$ is the final distance between them. Thus the potential energy of the two charges is

$$\text{PE} = k\frac{Q_1 Q_2}{r}.$$

(*a*) Set (iii) has a positive potential energy because the charges have the same sign. (*b*) Set (i) has the most negative potential energy because the charges are of opposite sign and their separation is less than that for set (ii). That is, $r$ is smaller for (i). (*c*) Set (i) will require the most work for separation to infinity. The more negative the potential energy, the more work required to separate the charges and bring the PE up to zero ($r = \infty$).

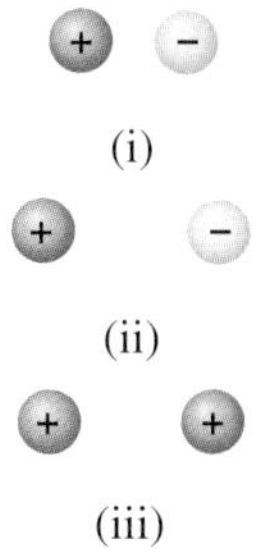


**FIGURE 17–11** Example 17–7.

## * 17–6 Potential Due to Electric Dipole; Dipole Moment

Two equal point charges $Q$, of opposite sign, separated by a distance $l$, are called an **electric dipole**. The electric field lines and equipotential surfaces for a dipole were shown in Fig. 17–7. Because electric dipoles occur often in physics, as well as in other fields such as molecular biology, it is useful to examine them more closely.

The electric potential at an arbitrary point P due to a dipole, Fig. 17–12, is the sum of the potentials due to each of the two charges:

$$V = \frac{kQ}{r} + \frac{k(-Q)}{r + \Delta r} = kQ\left(\frac{1}{r} - \frac{1}{r + \Delta r}\right) = kQ\frac{\Delta r}{r(r + \Delta r)},$$

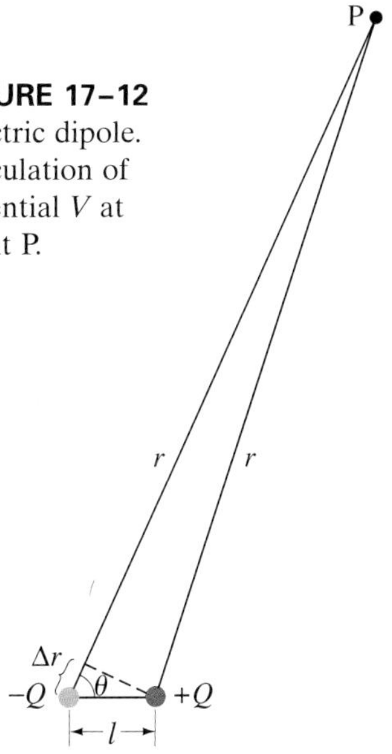


**FIGURE 17–12** Electric dipole. Calculation of potential $V$ at point P.

where $r$ is the distance from P to the positive charge and $r + \Delta r$ is the distance to the negative charge. This equation becomes simpler if we consider points P whose distance from the dipole is much larger than the separation of the two charges—that is, for $r \gg l$. From the diagram we see that $\Delta r \approx l\cos\theta$; since $r \gg \Delta r = l\cos\theta$, we can neglect $\Delta r$ in the denominator as compared to $r$. Then we obtain

$$V \approx \frac{kQl\cos\theta}{r^2}. \qquad [\text{dipole}; r \gg l] \quad \textbf{(17–6a)}$$

*Potential far from a dipole*

We see that the potential decreases as the *square* of the distance from the dipole, whereas for a single point charge the potential decreases with the first power of the distance (Eq. 17–5). It is not surprising that the potential should fall off faster for a dipole; for when you are far from a dipole, the two equal but opposite charges appear so close together as to tend to neutralize each other.

The product $Ql$ in Eq. 17–6a is referred to as the **dipole moment**, $p$, of the dipole. Equation 17–6a in terms of the dipole moment is

*Dipole moment $p = Ql$*

$$V \approx \frac{kp\cos\theta}{r^2}. \qquad [\text{dipole}; r \gg l] \quad \textbf{(17–6b)}$$

A dipole moment has units of coulomb-meters (C·m), although for molecules a smaller unit called a *debye* is sometimes used: 1 debye $= 3.33 \times 10^{-30}$ C·m.

PHYSICS APPLIED
*Dipoles in molecular biology*

**TABLE 17–2 Dipole Moments of Selected Molecules**

| Molecule | Dipole Moment (C · m) |
|---|---|
| $H_2^{(+)}O^{(-)}$ | $6.1 \times 10^{-30}$ |
| $H^{(+)}Cl^{(-)}$ | $3.4 \times 10^{-30}$ |
| $N^{(-)}H_3^{(+)}$ | $5.0 \times 10^{-30}$ |
| $>N^{(-)}—H^{(+)}$ | $\approx 3.0 \times 10^{-30}$‡ |
| $>C^{(+)}=O^{(-)}$ | $\approx 8.0 \times 10^{-30}$‡ |

‡These last two groups often appear on larger molecules; hence the value for the dipole moment will vary somewhat, depending on the rest of the molecule.

In many molecules, even though they are electrically neutral, the electrons spend more time in the vicinity of one atom than another, which results in a separation of charge. Such molecules have a dipole moment and are called **polar molecules**. We already saw that water (Fig. 16–4) is a polar molecule, and we have encountered others in our discussion of molecular biology (Section 16–11). Table 17–2 gives the dipole moments for several molecules. The + and − signs indicate on which atoms these charges lie. The last two entries are a part of many organic molecules and play an important role in molecular biology.

## 17–7 Capacitance

PHYSICS APPLIED
*Uses of capacitors*

A **capacitor** is a device that can store electric charge, and consists of two conducting objects (usually plates or sheets) placed near each other but not touching. Capacitors are widely used in electronic circuits. They store charge which can later be released, as in a camera flash, and as energy backup in computers if the power fails. Capacitors block surges of charge and energy to protect circuits. Very tiny capacitors serve as memory for the "ones" and "zeroes" of the binary code in the random access memory (RAM) of computers. Capacitors serve many other applications as well, some of which we will discuss.

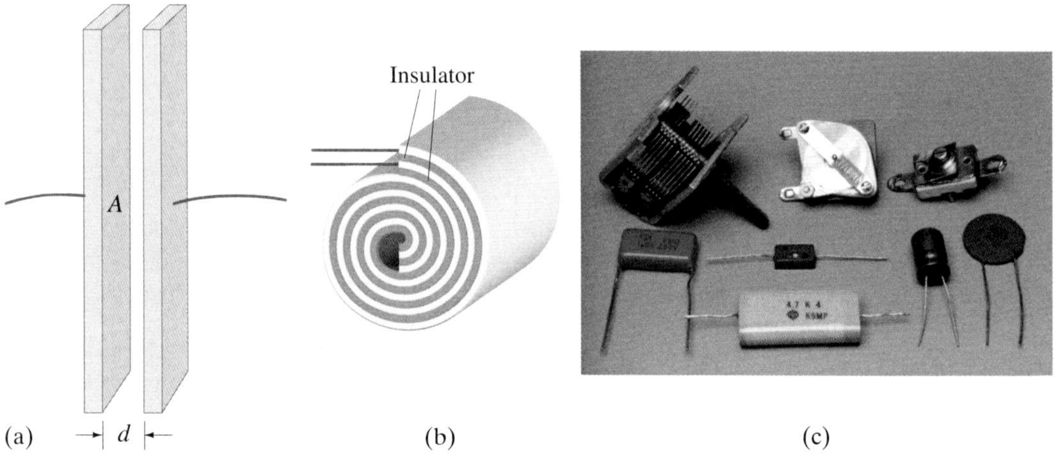


**FIGURE 17–13** Capacitors: diagrams of (*a*) parallel plate, (*b*) cylindrical (rolled up parallel plate). (*c*) Photo of some real capacitors.

A simple capacitor consists of a pair of parallel plates of area $A$ separated by a small distance $d$ (Fig. 17–13a). Often the two plates are rolled into the form of a cylinder with paper or other insulator separating the plates, Fig. 17–13b; Fig. 17–13c is a photo of some actual capacitors used for various applications. In a diagram, the symbol

⊣⊢ [capacitor symbol]

represents a capacitor. Another symbol for a capacitor you may encounter is ⊣(⊢. A battery, which is a source of voltage, is indicated by the symbol

+⊣|⊢− [battery symbol]

with unequal arms.

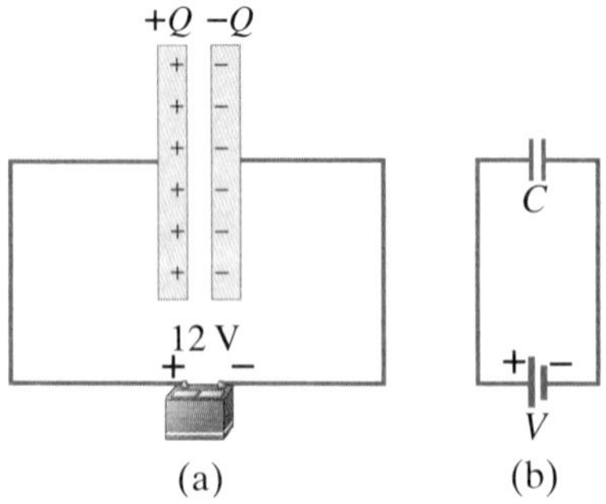


**FIGURE 17–14** (*a*) Parallel-plate capacitor connected to a battery. (*b*) Same circuit shown using symbols.

If a voltage is applied across a capacitor by connecting the capacitor to a battery with conducting wires as in Fig. 17–14, the two plates quickly become charged: one plate acquires a negative charge, the other an equal amount of positive charge. Each battery terminal and the plate of the capacitor connected to it are at the same potential; hence the full battery voltage appears across the capacitor. For a given capacitor, it is found that the amount of charge $Q$ acquired by each plate is proportional to the magnitude of the potential difference $V$ between them:

*Capacitance*

$$Q = CV. \qquad \textbf{(17–7)}$$

The constant of proportionality, $C$, in Eq. 17–7 is called the **capacitance** of the capacitor. The unit of capacitance is coulombs per volt, and this unit is called a **farad** (F). Common capacitors have capacitance in the range of 1 pF (picofarad $= 10^{-12}$ F) to $10^3\,\mu$F (microfarad $= 10^{-6}$ F). The relation, Eq. 17–7, was first suggested by Volta in the late eighteenth century.

*Unit of capacitance: the farad* ($1\text{ F} = 1\text{ C/V}$)

From here on, we will use simply $V$ (in italics) to represent a potential difference, such as that produced by a battery, rather than $V_{ba}$ or $V_b - V_a$ as previously. (Be sure not to confuse italic $V$ and $C$ which stand for voltage and capacitance, with non-italic V and C which stand for the units volts and coulombs.)

**CAUTION**

*$V$ = potential difference from here on*

The capacitance $C$ does not in general depend on $Q$ or $V$. Its value depends only on the size, shape, and relative position of the two conductors, and also on the material that separates them. For a parallel-plate capacitor whose plates have area $A$ and are separated by a distance $d$ of air (Fig. 17–13a), the capacitance is given by

*Capacitance depends only on physical characteristics of the capacitor,* not *on $Q$ or $V$*

$$C = \epsilon_0 \frac{A}{d}. \qquad \text{[parallel-plate capacitor]} \qquad \textbf{(17–8)}$$

We see that $C$ depends only on geometric factors, $A$ and $d$, and not on $Q$ or $V$. We derive this useful relation in the optional subsection on the next page. The constant $\epsilon_0$ is the *permittivity of free space*, which, as we saw in Chapter 16, has the value $8.85 \times 10^{-12}\,\text{C}^2/\text{N}\cdot\text{m}^2$.

**EXAMPLE 17–8 Capacitor calculations.** ($a$) Calculate the capacitance of a parallel-plate capacitor whose plates are 20 cm × 3.0 cm and are separated by a 1.0-mm air gap. ($b$) What is the charge on each plate if a 12-V battery is connected across the two plates? ($c$) What is the electric field between the plates? ($d$) Estimate the area of the plates needed to achieve a capacitance of 1 F, given the same air gap $d$.

**APPROACH** The capacitance is found by using Eq. 17–8, $C = \epsilon_0 A/d$. The charge on each plate is obtained from the definition of capacitance, Eq. 17–7, $Q = CV$. The electric field is uniform, so we can use Eq. 17–4b for the magnitude $E = V/d$. In ($d$) we use Eq. 17–8 again.

**SOLUTION** ($a$) The area $A = (20 \times 10^{-2}\,\text{m})(3.0 \times 10^{-2}\,\text{m}) = 6.0 \times 10^{-3}\,\text{m}^2$ The capacitance $C$ is then

$$C = \epsilon_0 \frac{A}{d} = (8.85 \times 10^{-12}\,\text{C}^2/\text{N}\cdot\text{m}^2)\frac{6.0 \times 10^{-3}\,\text{m}^2}{1.0 \times 10^{-3}\,\text{m}} = 53\text{ pF}.$$

($b$) The charge on each plate is

$$Q = CV = (53 \times 10^{-12}\,\text{F})(12\,\text{V}) = 6.4 \times 10^{-10}\,\text{C}.$$

($c$) From Eq. 17–4b for a uniform electric field, the magnitude of $E$ is

$$E = \frac{V}{d} = \frac{12\,\text{V}}{1.0 \times 10^{-3}\,\text{m}} = 1.2 \times 10^4\,\text{V/m}.$$

($d$) We solve for $A$ in Eq. 17–8 and substitute $C = 1.0$ F and $d = 1.0$ mm to find that we need plates with an area

$$A = \frac{Cd}{\epsilon_0} \approx \frac{(1\,\text{F})(1.0 \times 10^{-3}\,\text{m})}{(9 \times 10^{-12}\,\text{C}^2/\text{N}\cdot\text{m}^2)} \approx 10^8\,\text{m}^2.$$

**NOTE** This is the area of a square $10^4$ m or 10 km on a side. That is the size of a city like San Francisco or Boston! Large capacitance capacitors will not be simple parallel plates.

Not long ago, a capacitance greater than $1\,\mu$F was unusual. Today capacitors are available that are 1 or 2 F, yet they are just a few cm on a side. Such capacitors are used as power backups, for example, in computer memory and electronics where the time and date can be maintained through tiny charge flow.

**PHYSICS APPLIED**

*Capacitor as power backup*

*Very high capacitance*

Such high capacitance capacitors can be made of "activated" carbon which has very high porosity, so that the surface area is very large; one-tenth of a gram of activated carbon can have a surface area of $100\,m^2$. Furthermore, the equal and opposite charges can exist in an electric "double layer" only about $10^{-9}$ m thick.

PHYSICS APPLIED

*Computer keys*

One type of computer keyboard operates by capacitance. As shown in Fig. 17–15, each key is connected to the upper plate of a capacitor. The upper plate moves down when the key is pressed, reducing the spacing between the capacitor plates, and increasing the capacitance (Eq. 17–8: smaller $d$, larger $C$). The *change* in capacitance becomes an electric signal that is detected by an electronic circuit.

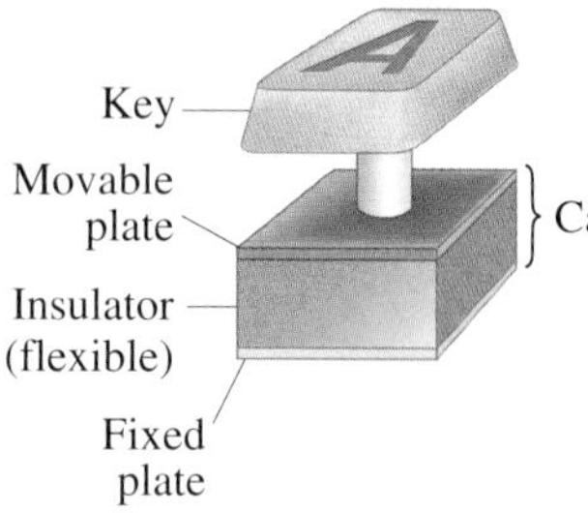


**FIGURE 17–15** Key of a computer keyboard. Pressing the key reduces the capacitor spacing, thus increasing the capacitance which can be detected electronically.

**EXERCISE C** Two circular plates of radius 5.0 cm are separated by a 0.10-mm air gap. What is the magnitude of the charge on each plate when connected to a 12-V battery?

### * Derivation of Capacitance for Parallel-Plate Capacitor

Equation 17–8 is readily derived using the result from Section 16–10 on Gauss's law, namely that the electric field between two parallel plates is given by Eq. 16–10:

$$E = \frac{Q/A}{\epsilon_0}.$$

We combine this with Eq. 17–4a magnitudes, $V = Ed$, to obtain

$$V = \left(\frac{Q}{A\epsilon_0}\right)d.$$

Then, from Eq. 17–7, the definition of capacitance,

$$C = \frac{Q}{V} = \frac{Q}{(Q/A\epsilon_0)d} = \epsilon_0 \frac{A}{d}$$

which is Eq. 17–8.

## 17–8 Dielectrics

In most capacitors there is an insulating sheet of material, such as paper or plastic, called a **dielectric** between the plates. This serves several purposes. First, dielectrics do not break down (allowing electric charge to flow) as readily as air, so higher voltages can be applied without charge passing across the gap. Furthermore, a dielectric allows the plates to be placed closer together without touching, thus allowing an increased capacitance because $d$ is less in Eq. 17–8. Thirdly, it is found experimentally that if the dielectric fills the space between the two conductors, it increases the capacitance by a factor $K$, known as the **dielectric constant**. Thus, for a parallel-plate capacitor,

*Dielectric constant*

*Parallel-plate capacitor with dielectric*

$$C = K\epsilon_0 \frac{A}{d}. \qquad \textbf{(17–9)}$$

This can also be written

$$C = \epsilon \frac{A}{d},$$

where

$$\epsilon = K\epsilon_0$$

is called the **permittivity** of the material.

The values of the dielectric constant for various materials are given in Table 17–3. Also shown in Table 17–3 is the **dielectric strength**, the maximum electric field before breakdown (charge flow) occurs.

**CONCEPTUAL EXAMPLE 17–9** **Inserting a dielectric at constant $V$.** An airfilled capacitor consisting of two parallel plates separated by a distance $d$ is connected to a battery of voltage $V$ and acquires a charge $Q$. While it is still connected to the battery, a slab of dielectric material with $K = 3$ is inserted between the plates of the capacitor. Will $Q$ increase, decrease, or stay the same?

**RESPONSE** Since the capacitor remains connected to the battery, the voltage stays constant and equal to the battery voltage $V$. The capacitance $C$ increases when the dielectric material is inserted because $K$ in Eq. 17–9 has increased. From the relation $Q = CV$, if $V$ stays constant, but $C$ increases, $Q$ must increase as well. As the dielectric is inserted, more charge will be pulled from the battery and deposited onto the plates of the capacitor as its capacitance increases.

**EXERCISE D** If the dielectric in Example 17–9 fills the space between the plates, by what factor does ($a$) the capacitance change, ($b$) the charge on each plate change?

**CONCEPTUAL EXAMPLE 17–10** **Inserting a dielectric into an isolated capacitor.** Suppose the airfilled capacitor of Example 17–9 is charged (to $Q$) and then disconnected from the battery. Next a dielectric is inserted between the plates. Will $Q$, $C$, or $V$ change?

**RESPONSE** The charge $Q$ remains the same—the capacitor is isolated, so there is nowhere for the charge to go. The capacitance increases as a result of inserting the dielectric (Eq. 17–9). The voltage across the capacitor also changes—it *decreases* because, by Eq. 17–7, $Q = CV$, so $V = Q/C$; if $Q$ stays constant and $C$ increases (it is in the denominator), then $V$ decreases.

**TABLE 17–3 Dielectric constants** (at 20°C)

| Material | Dielectric constant K | Dielectric strength (V/m) |
|---|---|---|
| Vacuum | 1.0000 | |
| Air (1 atm) | 1.0006 | $3 \times 10^6$ |
| Paraffin | 2.2 | $10 \times 10^6$ |
| Polystyrene | 2.6 | $24 \times 10^6$ |
| Vinyl (plastic) | 2–4 | $50 \times 10^6$ |
| Paper | 3.7 | $15 \times 10^6$ |
| Quartz | 4.3 | $8 \times 10^6$ |
| Oil | 4 | $12 \times 10^6$ |
| Glass, Pyrex | 5 | $14 \times 10^6$ |
| Rubber, neoprene | 6.7 | $12 \times 10^6$ |
| Porcelain | 6–8 | $5 \times 10^6$ |
| Mica | 7 | $150 \times 10^6$ |
| Water (liquid) | 80 | |
| Strontium titanate | 300 | $8 \times 10^6$ |

## * Molecular Description of Dielectrics

Let us examine, from the molecular point of view, why the capacitance of a capacitor should be larger when a dielectric is between the plates. A capacitor whose plates are separated by an air gap has a charge $+Q$ on one plate and $-Q$ on the other (Fig. 17–16a). Assume it is isolated (not connected to a battery) so charge cannot flow to or from the plates. The potential difference between the plates, $V_0$, is given by Eq. 17–7:

$$Q = C_0 V_0,$$

where the subscripts refer to air between the plates. Now we insert a dielectric between the plates (Fig. 17–16b). Because of the electric field between the capacitor plates, the dielectric molecules will tend to become oriented as shown in Fig. 17–16b. If the dielectric molecules are *polar*, the positive end is attracted to the negative plate and vice versa. Even if the dielectric molecules are not polar, electrons within them will tend to move slightly toward the positive capacitor plate, so the effect is the same. The net effect of the aligned dipoles is a net negative charge on the outer edge of the dielectric facing the positive plate, and a net positive charge on the opposite side, as shown in Fig. 17–16c.

Some of the electric field lines, then, do not pass through the dielectric but instead end on charges induced on the surface of the dielectric as shown in Fig. 17–16c. Hence the electric field within the dielectric is less than in air. That is, the electric field between the capacitor plates, assumed filled by the dielectric, has been reduced by some factor $K$. The voltage across the capacitor is reduced by the same factor $K$ because $V = Ed$ (Eq. 17–4) and hence, by Eq. 17–7, $Q = CV$, the capacitance $C$ must increase by that same factor $K$ to keep $Q$ constant.

**FIGURE 17–16** Molecular view of the effects of a dielectric.

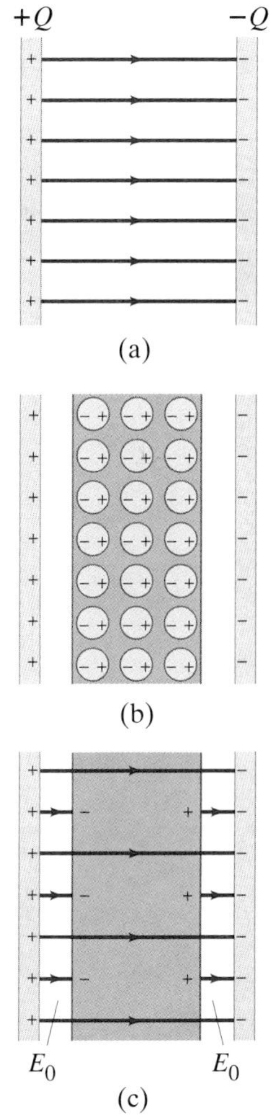

## 17–9 Storage of Electric Energy

A charged capacitor stores electric energy by separating + and − charges. The energy stored in a capacitor will be equal to the work done to charge it. The net effect of charging a capacitor is to remove charge from one plate and add it to the other plate. This is what a battery does when it is connected to a capacitor. Initially, when the capacitor is uncharged, no work is required to move the first bit of charge over. As more charge is transferred, work is needed to move charge against the increasing voltage $V$. The work needed to add a small amount of charge $\Delta q$, when a potential difference $V$ is across the plates, is $\Delta W = V\,\Delta q$. The total work needed to move total charge $Q$ is equivalent to moving all the charge $Q$ across a voltage equal to the *average* voltage during the process. (This is just like calculating the work done to compress a spring, Section 6–4, page 147.) The average voltage is $(V_f - 0)/2 = V_f/2$, where $V_f$ is the final voltage; so the work to move the total charge $Q$ from one plate to the other is

$$W = Q\frac{V_f}{2}.$$

Thus we can say that the electric potential energy, PE, stored in a capacitor is

$$\text{PE} = \text{energy} = \tfrac{1}{2}QV,$$

where $V$ is the potential difference between the plates (we have dropped the subscript), and $Q$ is the charge on each plate. Since $Q = CV$, we can also write

*Energy stored in capacitor*

$$\text{PE} = \tfrac{1}{2}QV = \tfrac{1}{2}CV^2 = \tfrac{1}{2}\frac{Q^2}{C}. \qquad \textbf{(17–10)}$$

PHYSICS APPLIED

*Camera flash*

**EXAMPLE 17–11** **Energy stored in a capacitor.** A camera flash unit (Fig. 17–17) stores energy in a 150-$\mu$F capacitor at 200 V. How much electric energy can be stored?

**APPROACH** We use Eq. 17–10 in the form $\text{PE} = \tfrac{1}{2}CV^2$ because we are given $C$ and $V$.

**SOLUTION** The energy stored is

$$\text{PE} = \tfrac{1}{2}CV^2 = \tfrac{1}{2}(150 \times 10^{-6}\,\text{F})(200\,\text{V})^2 = 3.0\,\text{J}.$$

**NOTE** If this energy could be released in $\frac{1}{1000}$ of a second $(10^{-3}\,\text{s})$, the power output would be equivalent to 3000 W.

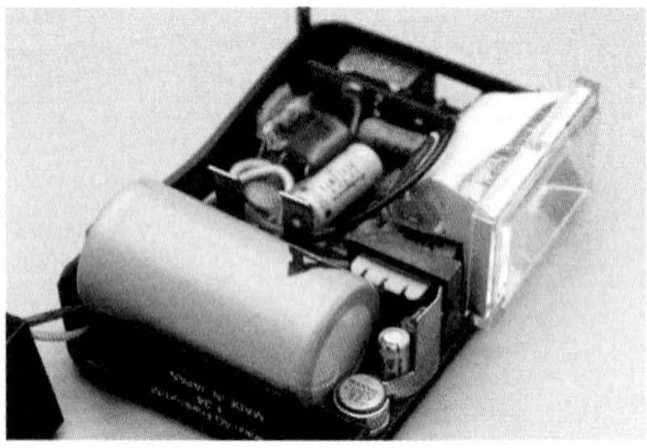

**FIGURE 17–17** A camera flash unit.

**EXERCISE E** A capacitor stores 0.50 J of energy at 9.0 V. What is its capacitance?

**CONCEPTUAL EXAMPLE 17–12** **Capacitor plate separation increased.** A parallel-plate capacitor carries charge $Q$ and is then disconnected from a battery. The two plates are initially separated by a distance $d$. Suppose the plates are pulled apart until the separation is $2d$. How has the energy stored in this capacitor changed?

**RESPONSE** If we increase the plate separation $d$, we decrease the capacitance according to Eq. 17–8, $C = \epsilon_0 A/d$, by a factor of 2. The charge $Q$ hasn't changed. So according to Eq. 17–10, where we choose the form $\text{PE} = \tfrac{1}{2}Q^2/C$ because we know $Q$ is the same and $C$ has been halved, the reduced $C$ means the PE stored increases by a factor of 2.

**NOTE** We can see why the energy stored increases from a physical point of view: the two plates are charged equal and opposite, so they attract each other. If we pull them apart, we must do work, so we raise their potential energy.

It is useful to think of the energy stored in a capacitor as being stored in the electric field between the plates. As an example let us calculate the energy stored in a parallel-plate capacitor in terms of the electric field.

We have seen that the electric field $\vec{\mathbf{E}}$ between two close parallel plates is nearly uniform and its magnitude is related to the potential difference by $V = Ed$ (Eq. 17–4), where $d$ is the separation. Also, Eq. 17–8 tells us $C = \epsilon_0 A/d$ for a parallel-plate capacitor. Thus

$$\text{PE} = \tfrac{1}{2}CV^2 = \frac{1}{2}\left(\frac{\epsilon_0 A}{d}\right)(E^2d^2)$$
$$= \tfrac{1}{2}\epsilon_0 E^2 Ad.$$

The quantity $Ad$ is the volume between the plates in which the electric field $E$ exists. If we divide both sides of this equation by the volume, we obtain an expression for the energy per unit volume or **energy density**:

$$\text{energy density} = \frac{\text{PE}}{\text{volume}} = \tfrac{1}{2}\epsilon_0 E^2. \qquad \textbf{(17–11)}$$

*Energy stored per unit volume in electric field*

The *electric energy stored per unit volume in any region of space is proportional to the square of the electric field* in that region. We derived Eq. 17–11 for the special case of a parallel-plate capacitor. But it can be shown to be true for any region of space where there is an electric field. Indeed, we will use this result when we discuss electromagnetic radiation (Chapter 22).

## Health Effects

PHYSICS APPLIED

*Avoid a shock or burn*

*Heart defibrillator*

The energy stored in a large capacitance can do harm, giving you a burn or a shock. One reason you are warned not to touch a circuit, or the inside of electronic devices, is because capacitors may still be carrying charge even if the external power has been turned off.

On the other hand, the basis of a heart *defibrillator* is a capacitor charged to a high voltage. A heart attack can be characterized by fast irregular beating of the heart, known as *ventricular* (or *cardiac*) *fibrillation*. The heart then does not pump blood to the rest of the body properly, and if it lasts for long, death results. A sudden, brief jolt of charge through the heart from a defibrillator can cause complete heart stoppage, sometimes followed by a resumption of normal beating. The defibrillator capacitor is charged to a voltage typically of a few thousand volts, and is allowed to discharge very rapidly through the heart via a pair of wide contacts known as "paddles" that spread out the current over the chest (Fig. 17–18).

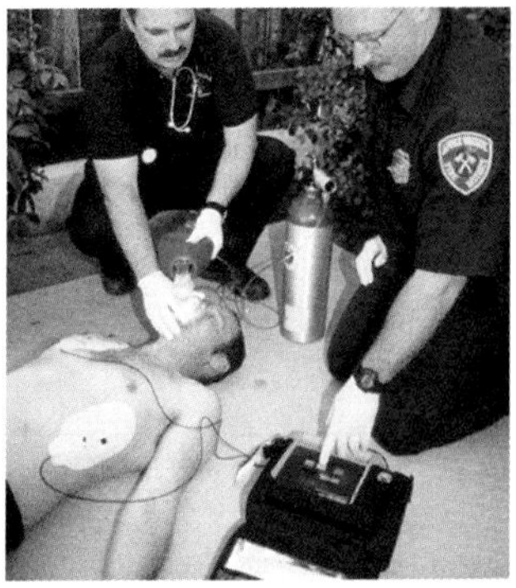

**FIGURE 17–18** Heart defibrillator.

## *17–10 Cathode Ray Tube: TV and Computer Monitors, Oscilloscope

An important device that makes use of voltage, and that allows us to "visualize" how a voltage changes in time, is the *cathode ray tube* (CRT). A CRT used in this way is an *oscilloscope*. The CRT has also been used for many years as the picture tube of television sets and computer monitors, although LCD and other screens are becoming popular.

The operation of a CRT depends on the phenomenon of **thermionic emission**, discovered by Thomas Edison (1847–1931). Consider two small plates (electrodes) inside an evacuated "bulb" or "tube" as shown in Fig. 17–19, to which is applied a potential difference. The negative electrode is called the **cathode**, the positive one the **anode**. If the negative cathode is heated (usually by an electric current, as in a lightbulb) so that it becomes hot and glowing, it is found that negative charge leaves the cathode and flows to the positive anode. These negative charges are now called electrons, but originally they were called **cathode rays** since they seemed to come from the cathode (see Section 27–1 on the discovery of the electron).

**FIGURE 17–19** If the cathode inside the evacuated glass tube is heated to glowing (by an electric current, not shown), negatively charged "cathode rays" (electrons) are "boiled off" and flow across to the anode (+), to which they are attracted.

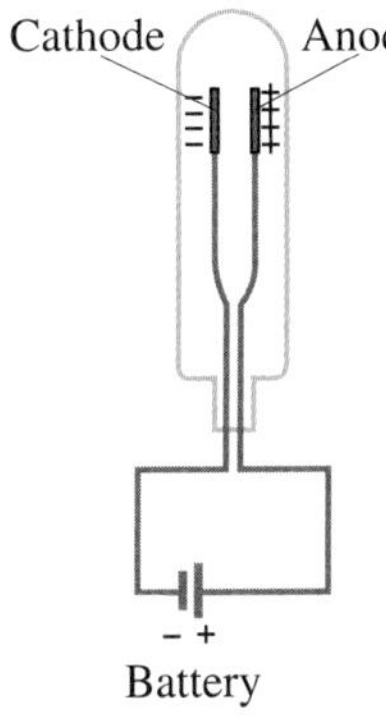

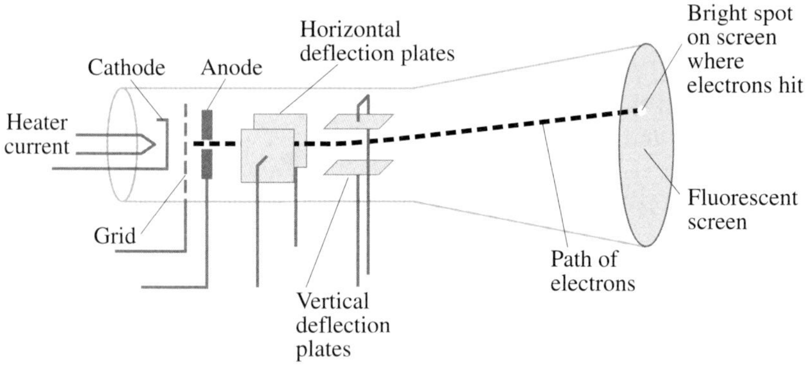


**FIGURE 17–20** A cathode-ray tube. Magnetic deflection coils are often used in place of the electric deflection plates shown here. The relative positions of the elements have been exaggerated for clarity.

PHYSICS APPLIED
*CRT*

The **cathode ray tube** (CRT) derives its name from the fact that inside an evacuated glass tube, a beam of cathode rays (electrons) is directed to various parts of a screen to produce a "picture." A simple CRT is diagrammed in Fig. 17–20. Electrons emitted by the heated cathode are accelerated by a high voltage (5000–50,000 V) applied between the anode and cathode. The electrons pass out of this "electron gun" through a small hole in the anode. The inside of the tube face is coated with a fluorescent material that glows when struck by electrons. A tiny bright spot is thus visible where the electron beam strikes the screen. Two horizontal and two vertical plates can deflect the beam of electrons when a voltage is applied to them. The electrons are deflected toward whichever plate is positive. By varying the voltage on the deflection plates, the bright spot can be placed at any point on the screen. Many CRTs use magnetic deflection coils (Chapter 20) instead of electric plates.

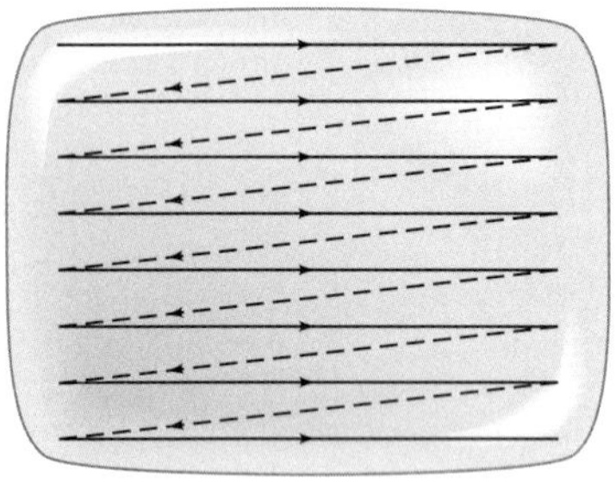

**FIGURE 17–21** Electron beam sweeps across a television screen in a succession of horizontal lines. Each horizontal sweep is made by varying the voltage on the horizontal deflection plates. Then the electron beam is moved down a short distance by a change in voltage on the vertical deflection plates, and the process is repeated.

PHYSICS APPLIED
*TV and computer monitors*

In the picture tube or monitor for a computer or television set, the electron beam is made to sweep over the screen in the manner shown in Fig. 17–21 by changing voltages applied to the deflection plates. For standard television in the United States, 525 lines constitutes a complete sweep in $\frac{1}{30}$ s, over the entire screen. High-definition TV provides more than double this number of lines, giving greater picture sharpness. We see a picture because the image is retained by the fluorescent screen and by our eyes for about $\frac{1}{20}$ s. The picture we see consists of the varied brightness of the spots on the screen, controlled by the grid (a "porous" electrode, such as a wire grid, that allows passage of electrons). The grid limits the flow of electrons by means of the voltage (the "video signal") applied to it: the more negative this voltage, the more electrons are repelled and the fewer pass through. This video signal sent out by the TV station, and received by the TV set, is accompanied by signals that synchronize the grid voltage to the horizontal and vertical sweeps.

PHYSICS APPLIED
*Oscilloscope*

An **oscilloscope** is a device for amplifying, measuring, and visually observing an electrical signal (a "signal" is usually a time-varying voltage) on the screen of a CRT. The electron beam is swept horizontally at a uniform rate in time by the horizontal deflection plates. The signal to be displayed is applied (after amplification) to the vertical deflection plates. The visible "trace" on the screen, which could be an electrocardiogram (Fig. 17–22), or a signal from an experiment on nerve conduction, is a plot of the signal voltage (vertically) versus time (horizontally).

**FIGURE 17–22** An electrocardiogram (ECG) trace displayed on a CRT.

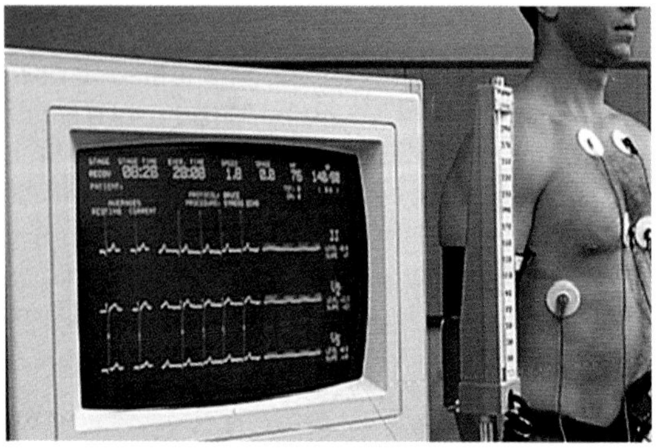

## * 17–11 The Electrocardiogram (ECG or EKG)

Each time the heart beats, changes in electrical potential occur on its surface that can be detected using metal contacts, called "electrodes," which are attached to the skin. The changes in potential are small, on the order of millivolts (mV), and must be amplified. They are displayed with a chart recorder on paper, or on a monitor (CRT), as in Fig. 17–22. An **electrocardiogram** (EKG or ECG) is the record of the potential changes for a given person's heart. An example is shown in Fig. 17–23. The instrument itself is called an electrocardiograph. We are not so interested now in the electronics, but in the source of these potential changes and their relation to heart activity.

PHYSICS APPLIED
*Electrocardiogram*

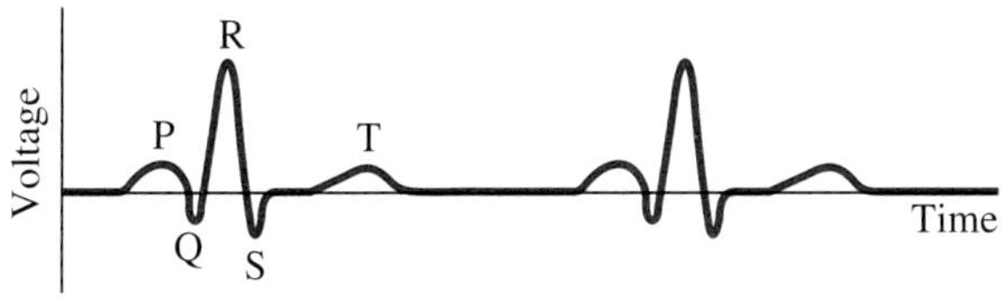


**FIGURE 17–23** Typical ECG. Two heart beats are shown.

Both muscle and nerve cells have an electric dipole layer across the cell wall. That is, in the normal situation there is a net positive charge on the exterior surface and a net negative charge on the interior surface, as shown in Fig. 17–24a. The amount of charge depends on the size of the cell, but is approximately $10^{-3}\ \mathrm{C/m^2}$ of surface. For a cell whose surface area is $10^{-5}\ \mathrm{m^2}$, the total charge on either surface is thus $\approx 10^{-8}$ C. Just before the contraction of heart muscles, changes occur in the cell wall, so that positive ions on the exterior of the cell are able to pass through the wall and neutralize those on the inside, or even make the inside surface slightly positive compared to the exterior, as shown in Fig. 17–24b. This "depolarization" starts at one end of the cell and progresses toward the opposite end, as indicated by the arrow, until the whole muscle is depolarized; the muscle then repolarizes to its original state (Fig. 17–24a), all in less than a second. Figure 17–24c shows rough graphs of the potential $V$ as a function of time at the two points P and P′ (on either side of this cell) as the depolarization moves across the cell. The path of depolarization within the heart as a whole is more complicated, and produces the complex potential difference as a function of time of Fig. 17–23.

It is standard procedure to divide a typical electrocardiogram into regions corresponding to the various deflections (or "waves"), as shown in Fig. 17–23. Each of the deflections corresponds to the activity of a particular part of the heart beat (Fig. 10–42). The P wave corresponds to contraction of the atria. The QRS group corresponds to contraction of the ventricles as the depolarization follows a very complicated path. The T wave corresponds to recovery (repolarization) of the heart in preparation for the next cycle.

Electrocardiograms make use of three basic electrodes, one placed on either side of the heart on the hands, and one on the left foot. Sometimes six additional electrodes are placed at other locations. The measurement of so many potential differences provides additional information (some of it redundant), since the heart is a three-dimensional object and depolarization takes place in all three dimensions. A complete electrocardiogram may include as many as 12 graphs.

The ECG is a powerful tool in identifying heart defects. For example, the right side of the heart enlarges if the right ventricle must push against an abnormally large load (as when blood vessels become hardened or clogged). This problem is readily observed on an ECG, since the S wave becomes very large (negatively). *Infarcts*, which are dead regions of the heart muscle that result from heart attacks, are also detected on an ECG because they reflect the depolarization wave.

**FIGURE 17–24** Heart muscle cell showing (*a*) charge dipole layer in resting state; (*b*) depolarization of cell progressing as muscle begins to contract; and (*c*) potential $V$ at points P and P′ as a function of time.

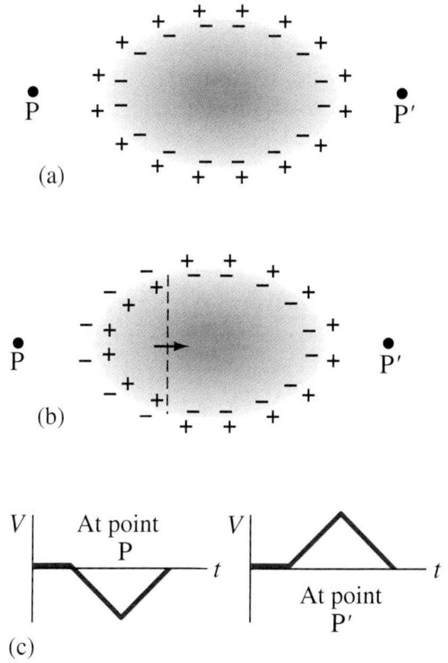

## Summary

The **electric potential** $V$ at any point in space is defined as the electric potential energy per unit charge:

$$V_a = \frac{\text{PE}_a}{q}. \qquad \textbf{(17–2a)}$$

The **electric potential difference** between any two points is defined as the work done to move a 1 C electric charge between the two points. Potential difference is measured in volts (1 V = 1 J/C) and is sometimes referred to as **voltage**.

The change in potential energy when a charge $q$ moves through a potential difference $V_{ba}$ is

$$\Delta\text{PE} = qV_{ba}. \qquad \textbf{(17–3)}$$

The potential difference $V_{ba}$ between two points a and b where a uniform electric field $E$ exists is given by

$$V_{ba} = -Ed, \qquad \textbf{(17–4a)}$$

where $d$ is the distance between the two points.

An **equipotential line** or **surface** is all at the same potential, and is perpendicular to the electric field at all points.

The electric potential at a position P due to a single point charge $Q$, relative to zero potential at infinity, is given by

$$V = \frac{kQ}{r}, \qquad \textbf{(17–5)}$$

where $r$ is the distance from $Q$ to the position P.

[*The potential due to an **electric dipole** drops off as $1/r^2$. The **dipole moment** is $p = Ql$, where $l$ is the distance between the two equal but opposite charges of magnitude $Q$.]

A **capacitor** is a device used to store charge (and electric energy), and consists of two nontouching conductors. The two conductors can hold equal and opposite charges, of magnitude $Q$, and the ratio of this charge to the potential difference $V$ between the conductors is called the **capacitance**, $C$:

$$C = \frac{Q}{V}, \quad \text{or} \quad Q = CV. \qquad \textbf{(17–7)}$$

The capacitance of a parallel-plate capacitor is proportional to the area of each plate and inversely proportional to their separation:

$$C = \epsilon_0 \frac{A}{d}. \qquad \textbf{(17–8)}$$

The space between the two conductors of a capacitor contains a nonconducting material such as air, paper, or plastic; these materials are referred to as **dielectrics**, and the capacitance is proportional to a property of dielectrics called the **dielectric constant**, $K$ (nearly equal to 1 for air).

A charged capacitor stores an amount of electric energy given by

$$\text{PE} = \tfrac{1}{2}QV = \tfrac{1}{2}CV^2 = \tfrac{1}{2}\frac{Q^2}{C}. \qquad \textbf{(17–10)}$$

This energy can be thought of as stored in the electric field between the plates.

The energy stored in any electric field $E$ has a density (energy per unit volume) of

$$\frac{\text{PE}}{\text{volume}} = \tfrac{1}{2}\epsilon_0 E^2. \qquad \textbf{(17–11)}$$

[*Television and computer monitors traditionally use a **cathode ray tube** (CRT) that accelerates electrons by high voltage, and sweeps them across the screen in a regular way using deflection plates.]

[*An **electrocardiogram** (EKG or ECG) records the millivolt potential changes of each heart beat as the cells depolarize and repolarize, and displays these changes on a monitor screen or chart recorder printout.]

## Questions

**1.** If two points are at the same potential, does this mean that no work is done in moving a test charge from one point to the other? Does this imply that no force need be exerted? Explain.

**2.** If a negative charge is initially at rest in an electric field, will it move toward a region of higher potential or lower potential? What about a positive charge? How does the potential energy of the charge change in each instance?

**3.** State clearly the difference (*a*) between electric potential and electric field, (*b*) between electric potential and electric potential energy.

**4.** An electron is accelerated by a potential difference of, say, 0.10 V. How much greater would its final speed be if it is accelerated with four times as much voltage? Explain.

**5.** Is there a point along the line joining two equal positive charges where the electric field is zero? Where the electric potential is zero? Explain.

**6.** Can a particle ever move from a region of low electric potential to one of high potential and yet have its electric potential energy decrease? Explain.

**7.** Compare the kinetic energy gained by a proton ($q = +e$) to the energy gained by an alpha particle ($q = +2e$) accelerated by the same voltage $V$.

**8.** If $V = 0$ at a point in space, must $\vec{\mathbf{E}} = 0$ there? If $\vec{\mathbf{E}} = 0$ at some point, must $V = 0$ at that point? Explain. Give examples for each.

**9.** Can two equipotential lines cross? Explain.

**10.** Draw in a few equipotential lines in Fig. 16–31b.

* **11.** What can you say about the electric field in a region of space that has the same potential throughout?

**12.** A satellite orbits the Earth along a gravitational equipotential line. What shape must the orbit be?

**13.** When dealing with practical devices, we often take the ground (the Earth) to be 0 V. If, instead, we said the ground was −10 V, how would this affect (*a*) the potential $V$, and (*b*) the electric field $E$, at other points?

**14.** When a battery is connected to a capacitor, why do the two plates acquire charges of the same magnitude? Will this be true if the two conductors are different sizes or shapes?

**15.** We have seen that the capacitance $C$ depends on the size, shape, and position of the two conductors, as well as on the dielectric constant $K$. What then did we mean when we said that $C$ is a constant in Eq. 17–7?

## Problems

### 17–1 to 17–4 Electric Potential

1. (I) How much work does the electric field do in moving a $-7.7\,\mu C$ charge from ground to a point whose potential is $+55$ V higher?

2. (I) How much work does the electric field do in moving a proton from a point with a potential of $+125$ V to a point where it is $-55$ V? Express your answer both in joules and electron volts.

3. (I) How much kinetic energy will an electron gain (in joules and eV) if it accelerates through a potential difference of 23,000 V in a TV picture tube?

4. (I) An electron acquires $7.45 \times 10^{-16}$ J of kinetic energy when it is accelerated by an electric field from plate A to plate B. What is the potential difference between the plates, and which plate is at the higher potential?

5. (I) How strong is the electric field between two parallel plates 5.8 mm apart if the potential difference between them is 220 V?

6. (I) An electric field of 640 V/m is desired between two parallel plates 11.0 mm apart. How large a voltage should be applied?

7. (I) The electric field between two parallel plates connected to a 45-V battery is 1500 V/m. How far apart are the plates?

8. (I) What potential difference is needed to give a helium nucleus ($Q = 2e$) 65.0 keV of kinetic energy?

9. (II) Two parallel plates, connected to a 200-V power supply, are separated by an air gap. How small can the gap be if the air is not to become conducting by exceeding its breakdown value of $E = 3 \times 10^6$ V/m?

10. (II) The work done by an external force to move a $-8.50\,\mu C$ charge from point a to point b is $15.0 \times 10^{-4}$ J. If the charge was started from rest and had $4.82 \times 10^{-4}$ J of kinetic energy when it reached point b, what must be the potential difference between a and b?

11. (II) What is the speed of an electron with kinetic energy (*a*) 750-eV, and (*b*) 3.2-keV?

12. (II) What is the speed of a proton whose kinetic energy is 3.2 keV?

13. (II) An alpha particle (which is a helium nucleus, $Q = +2e$, $m = 6.64 \times 10^{-27}$ kg) is emitted in a radioactive decay with KE $= 5.53$ MeV. What is its speed?

### 17–5 Potential Due to Point Charges

14. (I) What is the electric potential 15.0 cm from a $4.00\,\mu C$ point charge?

15. (I) A point charge $Q$ creates an electric potential of $+125$ V at a distance of 15 cm. What is $Q$?

16. (II) A $+35\,\mu C$ point charge is placed 32 cm from an identical $+35\,\mu C$ charge. How much work would be required to move a $+0.50\,\mu C$ test charge from a point midway between them to a point 12 cm closer to either of the charges?

17. (II) Draw a conductor in the shape of a football. This conductor carries a net negative charge, $-Q$. Draw in a dozen electric field lines and two equipotential lines.

18. (II) (*a*) What is the electric potential a distance of $2.5 \times 10^{-15}$ m away from a proton? (*b*) What is the electric potential energy of a system that consists of two protons $2.5 \times 10^{-15}$ m apart—as might occur inside a typical nucleus?

19. (II) Three point charges are arranged at the corners of a square of side $L$ as shown in Fig. 17–25. What is the potential at the fourth corner (point A), taking $V = 0$ at a great distance?

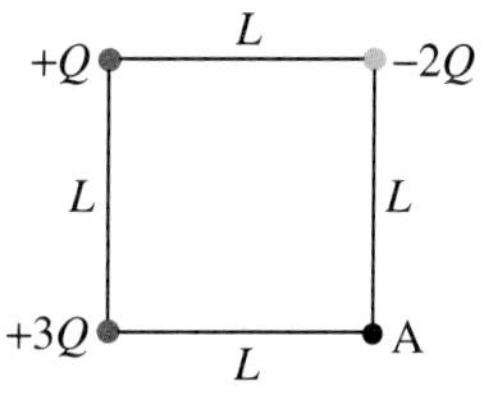


**FIGURE 17–25** Problem 19.

20. (II) An electron starts from rest 32.5 cm from a fixed point charge with $Q = -0.125\,\mu C$. How fast will the electron be moving when it is very far away?

21. (II) Two identical $+9.5\,\mu C$ point charges are initially 3.5 cm from each other. If they are released at the same instant from rest, how fast will each be moving when they are very far away from each other? Assume they have identical masses of 1.0 mg.

22. (II) Two point charges, $3.0\,\mu C$ and $-2.0\,\mu C$, are placed 5.0 cm apart on the $x$ axis. At what points along the $x$ axis is (*a*) the electric field zero and (*b*) the potential zero? Let $V = 0$ at $r = \infty$.

23. (II) How much work must be done to bring three electrons from a great distance apart to $1.0 \times 10^{-10}$ m from one another (at the corners of an equilateral triangle)?

24. (II) Consider point a which is 72 cm north of a $-3.8\,\mu C$ point charge, and point b which is 88 cm west of the charge (Fig. 17–26). Determine (*a*) $V_{ba} = V_b - V_a$ and (*b*) $\vec{\mathbf{E}}_b - \vec{\mathbf{E}}_a$ (magnitude and direction).

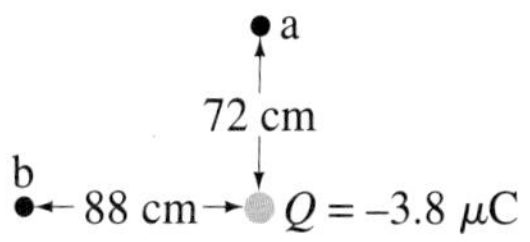


**FIGURE 17–26** Problem 24.

25. (III) How much voltage must be used to accelerate a proton (radius $1.2 \times 10^{-15}$ m) so that it has sufficient energy to just penetrate a silicon nucleus? A silicon nucleus has a charge of $+14e$, and its radius is about $3.6 \times 10^{-15}$ m. Assume the potential is that for point charges.

26. (III) Two equal but opposite charges are separated by a distance $d$, as shown in Fig. 17–27. Determine a formula for $V_{BA} = V_B - V_A$ for points B and A on the line between the charges.

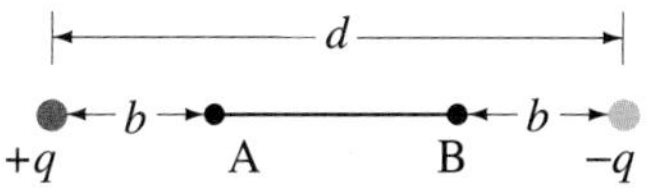


**FIGURE 17–27** Problem 26.

27. (III) In the Bohr model of the hydrogen atom, an electron orbits a proton (the nucleus) in a circular orbit of radius $0.53 \times 10^{-10}$ m. (*a*) What is the electric potential at the electron's orbit due to the proton? (*b*) What is the kinetic energy of the electron? (*c*) What is the total energy of the electron in its orbit? (*d*) What is the *ionization energy*—that is, the energy required to remove the electron from the atom and take it to $r = \infty$, at rest? Express the results of parts b, c and d in joules and eV.

### * 17–6 Electric Dipoles

* 28. (I) An electron and a proton are $0.53 \times 10^{-10}$ m apart. What is their dipole moment if they are at rest?

* 29. (II) Calculate the electric potential due to a dipole whose dipole moment is $4.8 \times 10^{-30}\,\mathrm{C \cdot m}$ at a point $1.1 \times 10^{-9}$ m away if this point is (*a*) along the axis of the dipole nearer the positive charge; (*b*) 45° above the axis but nearer the positive charge; (*c*) 45° above the axis but nearer the negative charge.

* 30. (III) The dipole moment, considered as a vector, points from the negative to the positive charge. The water molecule, Fig. 17–28, has a dipole moment $\vec{\mathbf{p}}$ which can be considered as the vector sum of the two dipole moments, $\vec{\mathbf{p}}_1$ and $\vec{\mathbf{p}}_2$, as shown. The distance between each H and the O is about $0.96 \times 10^{-10}$ m. The lines joining the center of the O atom with each H atom make an angle of 104°, as shown, and the net dipole moment has been measured to be $p = 6.1 \times 10^{-30}\,\mathrm{C \cdot m}$. Determine the charge $q$ on each H atom.

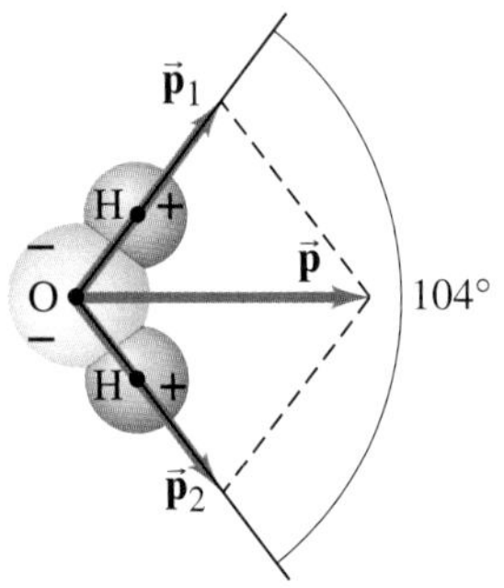


**FIGURE 17–28** Problem 30.

### 17–7 Capacitance

31. (I) The two plates of a capacitor hold $+2500\,\mu\mathrm{C}$ and $-2500\,\mu\mathrm{C}$ of charge, respectively, when the potential difference is 850 V. What is the capacitance?

32. (I) A 9500-pF capacitor holds plus and minus charges of $16.5 \times 10^{-8}$ C. What is the voltage across the capacitor?

33. (I) The potential difference between two short sections of parallel wire in air is 120 V. They carry equal and opposite charge of magnitude 95 pC. What is the capacitance of the two wires?

34. (I) How much charge flows from each terminal of a 12.0-V battery when it is connected to a $7.00\text{-}\mu\mathrm{F}$ capacitor?

35. (I) A 0.20-F capacitor is desired. What area must the plates have if they are to be separated by a 2.2-mm air gap?

36. (II) The charge on a capacitor increases by $18\,\mu\mathrm{C}$ when the voltage across it increases from 97 V to 121 V. What is the capacitance of the capacitor?

37. (II) An electric field of $8.50 \times 10^{5}$ V/m is desired between two parallel plates, each of area $35.0\,\mathrm{cm}^2$ and separated by 2.45 mm of air. What charge must be on each plate?

38. (II) If a capacitor has opposite $5.2\,\mu\mathrm{C}$ charges on the plates, and an electric field of 2.0 kV/mm is desired between the plates, what must each plate's area be?

39. (II) How strong is the electric field between the plates of a $0.80\text{-}\mu\mathrm{F}$ air-gap capacitor if they are 2.0 mm apart and each has a charge of $72\,\mu\mathrm{C}$?

40. (III) A $7.7\text{-}\mu\mathrm{F}$ capacitor is charged by a 125-V battery (Fig. 17–29a) and then is disconnected from the battery. When this capacitor ($C_1$) is then connected (Fig. 17–29b) to a second (initially uncharged) capacitor, $C_2$, the final voltage on each capacitor is 15 V. What is the value of $C_2$? [*Hint*: charge is conserved.]

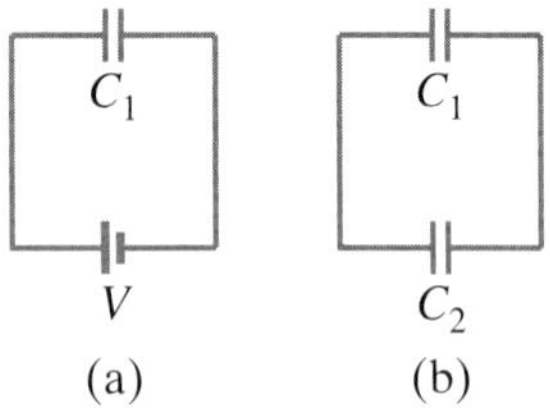


**FIGURE 17–29** Problems 40 and 52.

41. (III) A $2.50\text{-}\mu\mathrm{F}$ capacitor is charged to 857 V and a $6.80\text{-}\mu\mathrm{F}$ capacitor is charged to 652 V. These capacitors are then disconnected from their batteries. Next the positive plates are connected to each other and the negative plates are connected to each other. What will be the potential difference across each and the charge on each? [*Hint*: charge is conserved.]

### 17–8 Dielectrics

42. (I) What is the capacitance of two square parallel plates 5.5 cm on a side that are separated by 1.8 mm of paraffin?

43. (I) What is the capacitance of a pair of circular plates with a radius of 5.0 cm separated by 3.2 mm of mica?

44. (II) A 3500-pF air-gap capacitor is connected to a 22-V battery. If a piece of mica is placed between the plates, how much charge will flow from the battery?

* 45. (II) The electric field between the plates of a paper-separated ($K = 3.75$) capacitor is $8.24 \times 10^{4}$ V/m. The plates are 1.95 mm apart, and the charge on each plate is $0.775\,\mu\mathrm{C}$. Determine the capacitance of this capacitor and the area of each plate.

### 17–9 Electric Energy Storage

46. (I) 650 V is applied to a 2200-pF capacitor. How much energy is stored?

47. (I) A cardiac defibrillator is used to shock a heart that is beating erratically. A capacitor in this device is charged to 5.0 kV and stores 1200 J of energy. What is its capacitance?

48. (II) How much energy is stored by the electric field between two square plates, 8.0 cm on a side, separated by a 1.5-mm air gap? The charges on the plates are equal and opposite and of magnitude $420\,\mu\mathrm{C}$.

49. (II) A homemade capacitor is assembled by placing two 9-in. pie pans 5 cm apart and connecting them to the opposite terminals of a 9-V battery. Estimate (*a*) the capacitance, (*b*) the charge on each plate, (*c*) the electric field halfway between the plates, and (*d*) the work done by the battery to charge the plates. (*e*) Which of the above values change if a dielectric is inserted?

50. (II) A parallel-plate capacitor has fixed charges $+Q$ and $-Q$. The separation of the plates is then doubled. (*a*) By what factor does the energy stored in the electric field change? (*b*) How much work must be done in doubling the plate separation from $d$ to $2d$? The area of each plate is $A$.

51. (II) How does the energy stored in a capacitor change if (*a*) the potential difference is doubled, and (*b*) the charge on each plate is doubled, as the capacitor remains connected to a battery?

52. (III) A 2.70-$\mu$F capacitor is charged by a 12.0-V battery. It is disconnected from the battery and then connected to an uncharged 4.00-$\mu$F capacitor (Fig. 17–29). Determine the total stored energy (*a*) before the two capacitors are connected, and (*b*) after they are connected. (*c*) What is the change in energy?

### * 17–10 Cathode Ray Tube

* 53. (III) In a given CRT, electrons are accelerated horizontally by 7.0 kV. They then pass through a uniform electric field $E$ for a distance of 2.8 cm, which deflects them upward so they reach the screen top 22 cm away, 11 cm above the center. Estimate the value of $E$.

* 54. (III) Electrons are accelerated by 6.0 kV in a CRT. The screen is 30 cm wide and is 34 cm from the 2.6-cm-long deflection plates. Over what range must the horizontally deflecting electric field vary to sweep the beam fully across the screen?

## General Problems

55. An electron starting from rest acquires 6.3 keV of KE in moving from point A to point B. (*a*) How much KE would a proton acquire, starting from rest at B and moving to point A? (*b*) Determine the ratio of their speeds at the end of their respective trajectories.

56. A lightning flash transfers 4.0 C of charge and 4.2 MJ of energy to the Earth. (*a*) Across what potential difference did it travel? (*b*) How much water could this boil and vaporize, starting from room temperature?

57. There is an electric field near the Earth's surface whose magnitude is about 150 V/m. How much energy is stored per cubic meter in this field?

58. In a television picture tube, electrons are accelerated by thousands of volts through a vacuum. If a television set were laid on its back, would electrons be able to move upward against the force of gravity? What potential difference, acting over a distance of 3.0 cm, would be needed to balance the downward force of gravity so that an electron would remain stationary? Assume that the electric field is uniform.

59. A huge 4.0-F capacitor has enough stored energy to heat 2.5 kg of water from 21° C to 95° C. What is the potential difference across the plates?

60. An uncharged capacitor is connected to a 24.0-V battery until it is fully charged, after which it is disconnected from the battery. A slab of paraffin is then inserted between the plates. What will now be the voltage between the plates?

61. Dry air will break down if the electric field exceeds $3.0 \times 10^6$ V/m. What amount of charge can be placed on a parallel-plate capacitor if the area of each plate is 56 cm$^2$?

62. Three charges are at the corners of an equilateral triangle (side $L$) as shown in Fig. 17–30. Determine the potential at the midpoint of each of the sides.

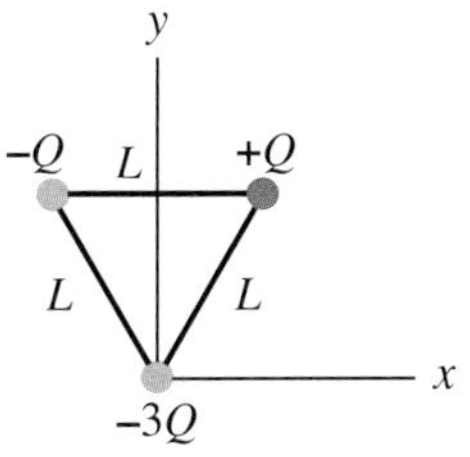


**FIGURE 17–30** Problem 62.

63. A 3.4 $\mu$C and a −2.6 $\mu$C charge are placed 1.6 cm apart. At what points along the line joining them is (*a*) the electric field zero, and (*b*) the electric potential zero?

64. A 2600-pF air-gap capacitor is connected to a 9.0-V battery. If a piece of Pyrex glass is placed between the plates, how much charge will then flow from the battery?

65. An electron is accelerated horizontally from rest in a television picture tube by a potential difference of 5500 V. It then passes between two horizontal plates 6.5 cm long and 1.3 cm apart that have a potential difference of 250 V (Fig. 17–31). At what angle $\theta$ will the electron be traveling after it passes between the plates?

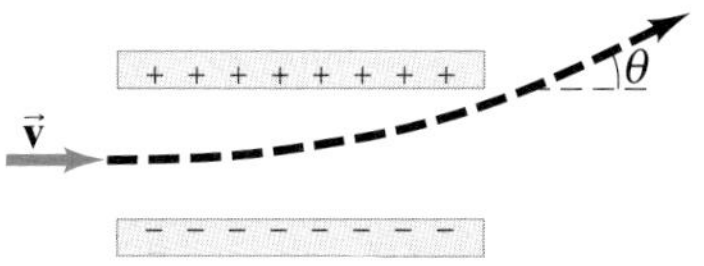


**FIGURE 17–31** Problem 65.

66. A capacitor of capacitance $C_1$ carries a charge $Q_0$. It is then connected directly to a second, uncharged, capacitor of capacitance $C_2$, as shown in Fig. 17–32. What charge will each carry now? What will be the potential difference across each?

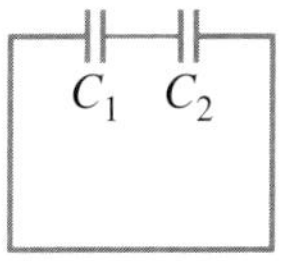


**FIGURE 17–32** Problem 66.

67. To get an idea how big a farad is, suppose you want to make a 1-F air-filled parallel-plate capacitor for a circuit you are building. To make it a reasonable size, suppose you limit the plate area to 1.0 cm$^2$. What would the gap have to be between the plates? Is this practically achievable?

68. Near the surface of the Earth there is an electric field of about 150 V/m which points downward. Two identical balls with mass $m = 0.540$ kg are dropped from a height of 2.00 m, but one of the balls is positively charged with $q_1 = 650\ \mu$C, and the second is negatively charged with $q_2 = -650\ \mu$C. Use conservation of energy to determine the difference in the speed of the two balls when they hit the ground. (Neglect air resistance.)

69. The power supply for a pulsed nitrogen laser has a 0.050-$\mu$F capacitor with a maximum voltage rating of 30 kV. (*a*) Estimate how much energy could be stored in this capacitor. (*b*) If 12% of this stored electrical energy is converted to light energy in a pulse that is 8.0 microseconds long, what is the power of the laser pulse?

70. In lightning storms, the potential difference between the Earth and the bottom of the thunderclouds can be as high as 35,000,000 V. The bottoms of the thunderclouds are typically 1500 m above the Earth, and can have an area of 110 km$^2$. Modeling the Earth–cloud system as a huge capacitor, calculate (*a*) the capacitance of the Earth–cloud system, (*b*) the charge stored in the "capacitor," and (*c*) the energy stored in the "capacitor."

71. In a photocell, ultraviolet (UV) light provides enough energy to some electrons in barium metal to eject them from a surface at high speed. See Fig. 17–33. To measure the maximum energy of the electrons, another plate above the barium surface is kept at a negative enough potential that the emitted electrons are slowed down and stopped, and return to the barium surface. If the plate voltage is $-3.02$ V (compared to the barium) when the fastest electrons are stopped, what was the speed of these electrons when they were emitted?

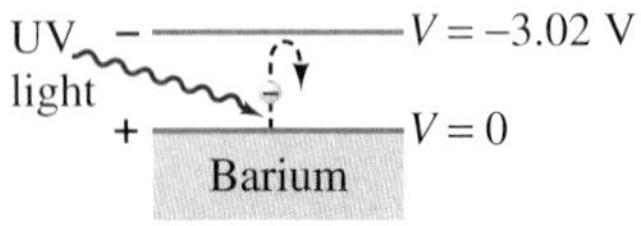


**FIGURE 17–33** Problem 71.

72. A +33 $\mu$C point charge is placed 36 cm from an identical +33 $\mu$C charge. A $-1.5$ $\mu$C charge is moved from point a to point b in Fig. 17–34. What is the change in potential energy?

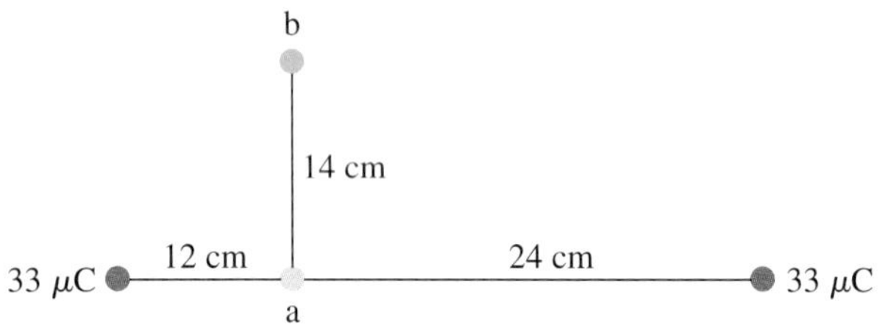


**FIGURE 17–34** Problem 72.

73. A capacitor is made from two 1.1-cm-diameter coins separated by a 0.15-mm-thick piece of paper ($K = 3.7$). A 12-V battery is connected to the capacitor. How much charge is on each coin?

74. A +4.5 $\mu$C charge is 23 cm to the right of a $-8.2$ $\mu$C charge. At the midpoint between the two charges, (*a*) what are the potential and (*b*) the electric field?

75. A parallel-plate capacitor with plate area 2.0 cm$^2$ and air-gap separation 0.50 mm is connected to a 12-V battery, and fully charged. The battery is then disconnected. (*a*) What is the charge on the capacitor? (*b*) The plates are now pulled to a separation of 0.75 mm. What is the charge on the capacitor now? (*c*) What is the potential difference across the plates now? (*d*) How much work was required to pull the plates to their new separation?

76. A 2.5-$\mu$F capacitor is fully charged by a 6.0-V battery. The battery is then disconnected. The capacitor is not ideal and the charge slowly leaks out from the plates. The next day, the capacitor has lost half its stored energy. Calculate the amount of charge lost.

77. Two point charges are fixed 4.0 cm apart from each other. Their charges are $Q_1 = Q_2 = 5.0\,\mu$C, and their masses are $m_1 = 1.5$ mg and $m_2 = 2.5$ mg. (*a*) If $Q_1$ is released from rest, what will be its speed after a very long time? (*b*) If both charges are released from rest at the same time, what will be the speed of $Q_1$ after a very long time?

78. Two charges are placed as shown in Fig. 17–35 with $q_1 = 1.5\,\mu$C and $q_2 = -3.3\,\mu$C. Find the potential difference between points A and B.

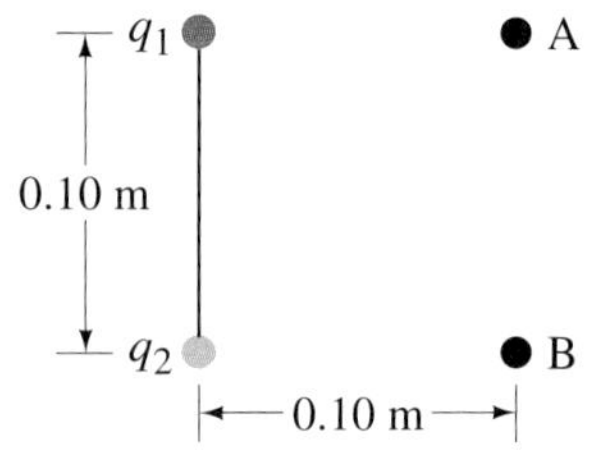


**FIGURE 17–35** Problem 78.

## Answers to Exercises

**A:** (*a*) $-8.0 \times 10^{-16}$ J; (*b*) $9.8 \times 10^5$ m/s.
**B:** 0.72 J.
**C:** $8.3 \times 10^{-9}$ C.
**D:** (*a*) 3 times greater; (*b*) 3 times greater.
**E:** 12 mF.

The glow of the thin wire filament of a lightbulb is caused by the electric current passing through it. Electric energy is transformed to thermal energy (via collisions between moving electrons and atoms of the wire), which causes the wire's temperature to become so high that it glows. Electric current and electric power in electric circuits are of basic importance in everyday life. We examine both dc and ac in this Chapter, and include the microscopic analysis of electric current.

CHAPTER 18

# Electric Currents

In the previous two Chapters we have been studying static electricity: electric charges at rest. In this Chapter we begin our study of charges in motion, and we call a flow of charge an electric current.

In everyday life we are familiar with electric currents in wires and other conductors. Indeed, most practical electrical devices depend on electric current: current through a lightbulb, current in the heating element of a stove or electric heater, and of course currents in electronic devices. Electric currents can exist in conductors such as wires, and also in other devices such as the CRT of a television or computer monitor whose charged electrons flow through space (Section 17–10).

In electrostatic situations, we saw in Section 16–9 that the electric field must be zero inside a conductor (if it weren't, the charges would move). But when charges are *moving* in a conductor, there usually *is* an electric field in the conductor. Indeed, an electric field is needed to set charges into motion, and to keep them in motion in any normal conductor. We can control the flow of charge using electric fields and electric potential (voltage), concepts we have just been discussing. In order to have a current in a wire, a potential difference is needed, which can be provided by a battery.

**FIGURE 18–1** Alessandro Volta. In this portrait, Volta exhibits his battery to Napoleon in 1801.

We first look at electric current from a macroscopic point of view: that is, current as measured in a laboratory. Later in the Chapter we look at currents from a microscopic (theoretical) point of view as a flow of electrons in a wire.

Until the year 1800, the technical development of electricity consisted mainly of producing a static charge by friction. It all changed in 1800 when Alessandro Volta (1745–1827; Fig. 18–1) invented the electric battery, and with it produced the first steady flow of electric charge—that is, a steady electric current.

## 18–1 The Electric Battery

The events that led to the discovery of the battery are interesting. For not only was this an important discovery, but it also gave rise to a famous scientific debate.

In the 1780s, Luigi Galvani (1737–1798), professor at the University of Bologna, carried out a series of experiments on the contraction of a frog's leg muscle through electricity produced by static electricity. Galvani found that the muscle also contracted when dissimilar metals were inserted into the frog. Galvani believed that the source of the electric charge was in the frog muscle or nerve itself, and that the metal merely transmitted the charge to the proper points. When he published his work in 1791, he termed this charge "animal electricity." Many wondered, including Galvani himself, if he had discovered the long-sought "life-force."

Volta, at the University of Pavia 200 km away, was skeptical of Galvani's results, and came to believe that the source of the electricity was not in the animal itself, but rather in the *contact between the dissimilar metals*. Volta realized that a moist conductor, such as a frog muscle or moisture at the contact point of two dissimilar metals, was necessary in the circuit if it was to be effective. He also saw that the contracting frog muscle was a sensitive instrument for detecting electric "tension" or "electromotive force" (his words for what we now call potential), in fact more sensitive than the best available electroscopes that he and others had developed.†

**FIGURE 18–2** A voltaic battery, from Volta's original publication.

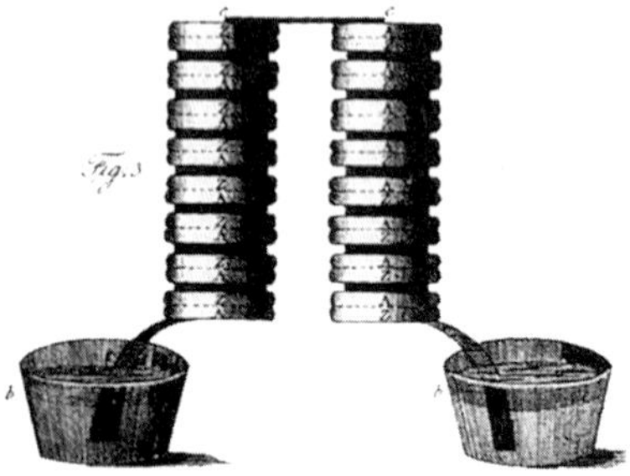

Volta's research found that certain combinations of metals produced a greater effect than others, and, using his measurements, he listed them in order of effectiveness. (This "electrochemical series" is still used by chemists today.) He also found that carbon could be used in place of one of the metals.

Volta then conceived his greatest contribution to science. Between a disc of zinc and one of silver, he placed a piece of cloth or paper soaked in salt solution or dilute acid and piled a "battery" of such couplings, one on top of another, as shown in Fig. 18–2. This "pile" or "battery" produced a much increased potential difference. Indeed, when strips of metal connected to the two ends of the pile were brought close, a spark was produced. Volta had designed and built the first electric battery; he published his discovery in 1800.

### Electric Cells and Batteries

A battery produces electricity by transforming chemical energy into electrical energy. Today a great variety of electric cells and batteries are available, from flashlight batteries to the storage battery of a car. The simplest batteries contain two plates or rods made of dissimilar metals (one can be carbon) called

*Electrodes*

**electrodes**. The electrodes are immersed in a solution, such as a dilute acid, called the **electrolyte**. Such a device is properly called an **electric cell**, and several cells connected together is a **battery**, although today even a single cell is

†Volta's most sensitive electroscope (see Section 16–4 and Fig. 16–10) measured about 40 V per degree (angle of leaf separation). Nonetheless, he was able to estimate the potential differences produced by dissimilar metals in contact: for a silver–zinc contact he got about 0.7 V, remarkably close to today's value of 0.78 V.

called a battery. The chemical reactions involved in most electric cells are quite complicated. Here we describe how one very simple cell works, emphasizing the physical aspects.

The cell shown in Fig. 18–3 uses dilute sulfuric acid as the electrolyte. One of the electrodes is made of carbon, the other of zinc. That part of each electrode outside the solution is called the **terminal**, and connections to wires and circuits are made here. The acid tends to dissolve the zinc electrode. Each zinc atom leaves two electrons behind on the electrode and enters the solution as a positive ion. The zinc electrode thus acquires a negative charge. As the electrolyte becomes positively charged, electrons are pulled off the carbon electrode. Thus the carbon electrode becomes positively charged. Because there is an opposite charge on the two electrodes, there is a potential difference between the two terminals.

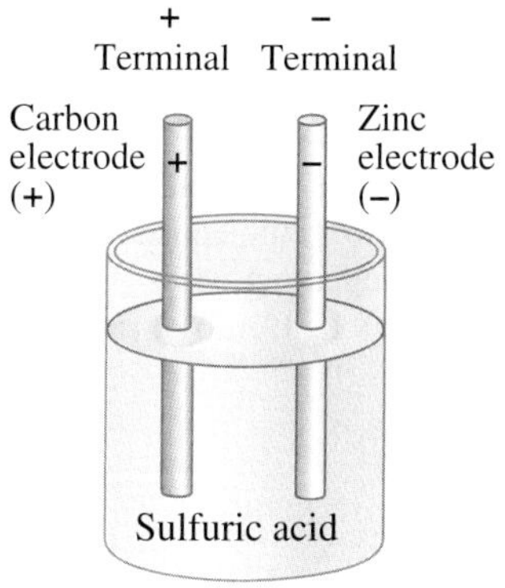


**FIGURE 18–3** Simple electric cell.

In a cell whose terminals are not connected, only a small amount of the zinc is dissolved, for as the zinc electrode becomes increasingly negative, any new positive zinc ions produced are attracted back to the electrode. Thus, a particular potential difference (or voltage) is maintained between the two terminals. If charge is allowed to flow between the terminals, say, through a wire (or a lightbulb), then more zinc can be dissolved. After a time, one or the other electrode is used up and the cell becomes "dead."

*Batteries produce potential difference (voltage)*

The voltage that exists between the terminals of a battery depends on what the electrodes are made of and their relative ability to be dissolved or give up electrons.

When two or more cells are connected so that the positive terminal of one is connected to the negative terminal of the next, they are said to be connected in *series* and their voltages add up. Thus, the voltage between the ends of two 1.5-V flashlight batteries connected in series is 3.0 V, whereas the six 2-V cells of an automobile storage battery give 12 V. Figure 18–4a shows a diagram of a common "dry cell" or "flashlight battery" used in portable radios and CD players, flashlights, etc., and Fig. 18–4b shows two smaller ones in series, connected to a flashlight bulb. A lightbulb consists of a thin, coiled wire (filament) inside an evacuated glass bulb, as shown in Fig. 18–5 and in the large photo opening this Chapter, page 493. The filament gets hot and glows when charge passes through it.

**FIGURE 18–4** (a) Diagram of an ordinary dry cell (like a D-cell or AA). The cylindrical zinc cup is covered on the sides; its flat bottom is the negative terminal. (b) Two dry cells (AA type) connected in series. Note that the positive terminal of one cell pushes against the negative terminal of the other.

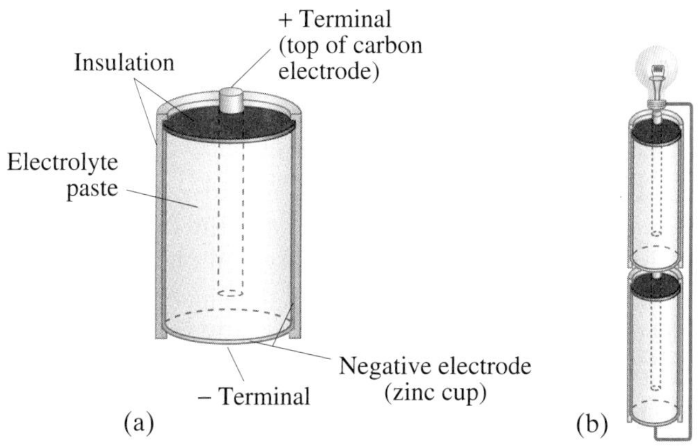


**FIGURE 18–5** A lightbulb: the fine wire of the filament becomes so hot that it glows. This type of lightbulb is called an incandescent bulb (as compared, say, to a fluorescent bulb).

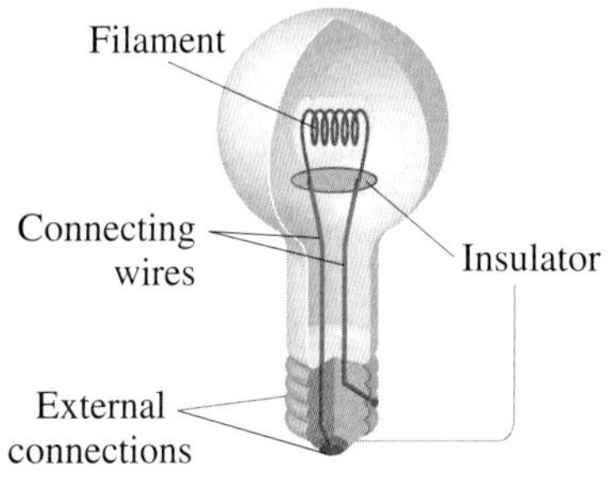

**FIGURE 18–6** (a) A simple electric circuit. (b) Schematic drawing of the same circuit, consisting of a battery, connecting wires (thick gray lines), and a lightbulb or other device.

## 18–2 Electric Current

The purpose of a battery is to produce a potential difference, which can then make charges move. When a continuous conducting path is connected between the terminals of a battery, we have an electric **circuit**, Fig. 18–6a. On any diagram of a circuit, as in Fig. 18–6b, we use the symbol

*Electric circuit*

*Battery symbol*

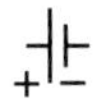 [battery symbol]

to represent a battery. The device connected to the battery could be a lightbulb, a heater, a radio, or whatever. When such a circuit is formed, charge can flow through the wires of the circuit, from one terminal of the battery to the other, as long as the conducting path is continuous. Any flow of charge such as this is called an **electric current**.

More precisely, the electric current in a wire is defined as the net amount of charge that passes through the wire's full cross section at any point per unit time. Thus, the current $I$ is defined as

*Electric current*

$$I = \frac{\Delta Q}{\Delta t}, \tag{18–1}$$

where $\Delta Q$ is the amount of charge that passes through the conductor at any location during the time interval $\Delta t$.

*Unit of electric current: the ampere (1 A = 1 C/s)*

Electric current is measured in coulombs per second; this is given a special name, the **ampere** (abbreviated amp or A), after the French physicist André Ampère (1775–1836). Thus, $1\ \text{A} = 1\ \text{C/s}$. Smaller units of current are often used, such as the milliampere $(1\ \text{mA} = 10^{-3}\ \text{A})$ and microampere $(1\ \mu\text{A} = 10^{-6}\ \text{A})$.

*Circuits: complete or open*

A current can flow in a circuit only if there is a *continuous* conducting path. We then have a **complete circuit**. If there is a break in the circuit, say, a cut wire, we call it an **open circuit** and no current flows. In any single circuit, with only a single path for current to follow such as in Fig. 18–6b, a steady current at any instant is the same at one point (say, point A) as at any other point (such as B). This follows from the conservation of electric charge: charge doesn't disappear. A battery does not create (or destroy) any net charge, nor does a lightbulb absorb or destroy charge.

**CAUTION**
*A battery does not create charge; a lightbulb does not destroy charge*

**EXAMPLE 18–1** **Current is flow of charge.** A steady current of 2.5 A exists in a wire for 4.0 min. (*a*) How much total charge passed by a given point in the circuit during those 4.0 min? (*b*) How many electrons would this be?

**APPROACH** Current is flow of charge per unit time, Eq. 18–1, so the amount of charge passing a point is the product of the current and the time interval. To get the number of electrons (*b*), we divide by the charge on one electron.

**SOLUTION** (*a*) Since the current was 2.5 A, or 2.5 C/s, then in 4.0 min (= 240 s) the total charge that flowed past a given point in the wire was, from Eq. 18–1,

$$\Delta Q = I\,\Delta t = (2.5\ \text{C/s})(240\ \text{s}) = 600\ \text{C}.$$

(*b*) The charge on one electron is $1.60 \times 10^{-19}$ C, so 600 C would consist of

$$\frac{600\ \text{C}}{1.6 \times 10^{-19}\ \text{C/electron}} = 3.8 \times 10^{21}\ \text{electrons}.$$

**EXERCISE A** If 1 million electrons per second pass a point in a wire, what is the current in amps?

**CONCEPTUAL EXAMPLE 18–2** **How to connect a battery.** What is wrong with each of the schemes shown in Fig. 18–7 for lighting a flashlight bulb with a flashlight battery and a single wire?

**RESPONSE** (*a*) There is no closed path for charge to flow around. Charges might briefly start to flow from the battery toward the lightbulb, but there they run into a "dead end," and the flow would immediately come to a stop.
(*b*) Now there is a closed path passing to and from the lightbulb; but the wire touches only one battery terminal, so there is no potential difference in the circuit to make the charge move.
(*c*) Nothing is wrong here. This is a complete circuit: charge can flow out from one terminal of the battery, through the wire and the bulb, and into the other terminal. This scheme will light the bulb.

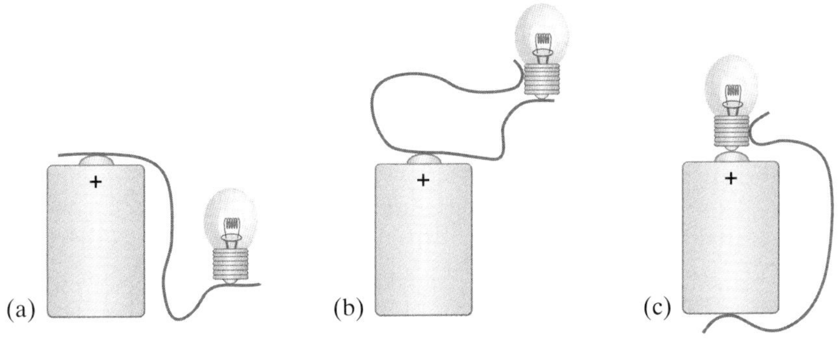


**FIGURE 18–7** Example 18–2.

*Grounds, and complete circuits*

In many real circuits, wires are connected to a common conductor to provide continuity. This common conductor is called **ground**, usually represented as ⏚, and really is connected to the ground in a building or house. In a car, one terminal of the battery is called "ground," but is not connected to the ground—it is connected to the frame of the car, as is one connection to each lightbulb and other devices. Thus the car frame is a conductor in each circuit, ensuring a continuous path for charge flow.

We saw in Chapter 16 (Section 16–3) that conductors contain many free electrons. Thus, if a continuous conducting wire is connected to the terminals of a battery, negatively charged electrons flow in the wire. When the wire is first connected, the potential difference between the terminals of the battery sets up an electric field inside the wire† and parallel to it. Free electrons at one end of the wire are attracted into the positive terminal, and at the same time other electrons leave the negative terminal of the battery and enter the wire at the other end. There is a continuous flow of electrons throughout the wire that begins as soon as the wire is connected to *both* terminals. However, when the conventions of positive and negative charge were invented two centuries ago, it was assumed that positive charge flowed in a wire. For nearly all purposes, positive charge flowing in one direction is exactly equivalent to negative charge flowing in the opposite direction, as shown in Fig. 18–8. Today, we still use the historical convention of positive charge flow when discussing the direction of a current. So when we speak of the current direction in a circuit, we mean the direction positive charge would flow. This is sometimes referred to as **conventional current**. When we want to speak of the direction of electron flow, we will specifically state it is the electron current. In liquids and gases, both positive and negative charges (ions) can move.

**FIGURE 18–8** Conventional current from + to − is equivalent to a negative electron flow from − to +.

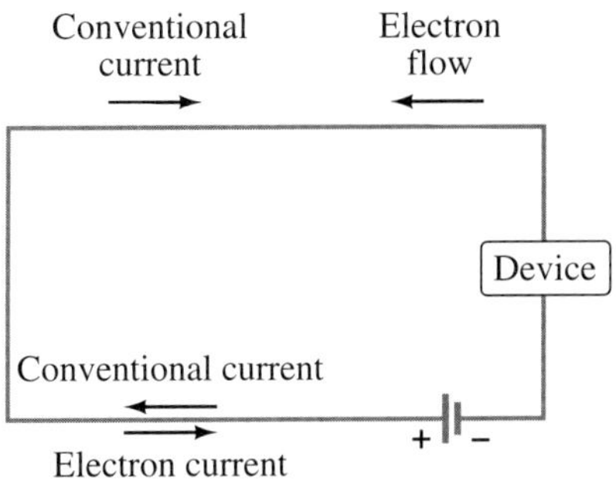


**CAUTION**

*Distinguish conventional current from electron flow*

†This does not contradict what was said in Section 16–9 that in the *static* case, there can be no electric field within a conductor since otherwise the charges would move. Indeed, when there is an electric field in a conductor, charges do move, and we get an electric current.

## 18–3 Ohm's Law: Resistance and Resistors

To produce an electric current in a circuit, a difference in potential is required. One way of producing a potential difference along a wire is to connect its ends to the opposite terminals of a battery. It was Georg Simon Ohm (1787–1854) who established experimentally that the current in a metal wire is proportional to the potential difference $V$ applied to its two ends:

$$I \propto V.$$

If, for example, we connect a wire to a 6-V battery, the current in the wire will be twice what it would be if the wire were connected to a 3-V battery. It is also found that reversing the sign of the voltage does not affect the magnitude of the current.

*Water analogy*

A useful analogy compares the flow of electric charge in a wire to the flow of water in a river, or in a pipe, acted on by gravity. If the river or pipe is nearly level, the flow rate is small. But if one end is somewhat higher than the other, the flow rate—or current—is greater. The greater the difference in height, the swifter the current. We saw in Chapter 17 that electric potential is analogous, in the gravitational case, to the height of a cliff. This applies in the present case to the height through which the fluid flows. Just as an increase in height can cause a greater flow of water, so a greater electric potential difference, or voltage, causes a greater electric current.

Exactly how large the current is in a wire depends not only on the voltage, but also on the resistance the wire offers to the flow of electrons. The walls of a pipe, or the banks of a river and rocks in the middle, offer resistance to the current. Similarly, electron flow is impeded because of interactions with the atoms of the wire. The higher this resistance, the less the current for a given voltage $V$. We then define electrical *resistance* so that the current is inversely proportional to the resistance: that is,

$$R = \frac{V}{I} \qquad \textbf{(18–2a)}$$

where $R$ is the **resistance** of a wire or other device, $V$ is the potential difference applied across the wire or device, and $I$ is the current through it. Equation 18–2a is often written as

*OHM'S "LAW"*

$$V = IR. \qquad \textbf{(18–2b)}$$

As mentioned above, Ohm found experimentally that in metal conductors $R$ is a constant independent of $V$, a result known as **Ohm's law**. Equation 18–2b, $V = IR$, is itself sometimes called Ohm's law, but only when referring to materials or devices for which $R$ is a constant independent of $V$. But $R$ is not a constant for many substances other than metals, nor for devices such as diodes, vacuum tubes, transistors, and so on. Thus Ohm's "law" is not a fundamental law, but rather a description of a certain class of materials: metal conductors. Materials or devices that do not follow Ohm's law ($R$ = constant) are said to be *nonohmic*. See Fig. 18–9.

*Unit of electrical resistance: the ohm* ($1\,\Omega = 1\,\text{V/A}$)

The unit for resistance is called the **ohm** and is abbreviated $\Omega$ (Greek capital letter omega). Because $R = V/I$, we see that $1.0\,\Omega$ is equivalent to $1.0\,\text{V/A}$.

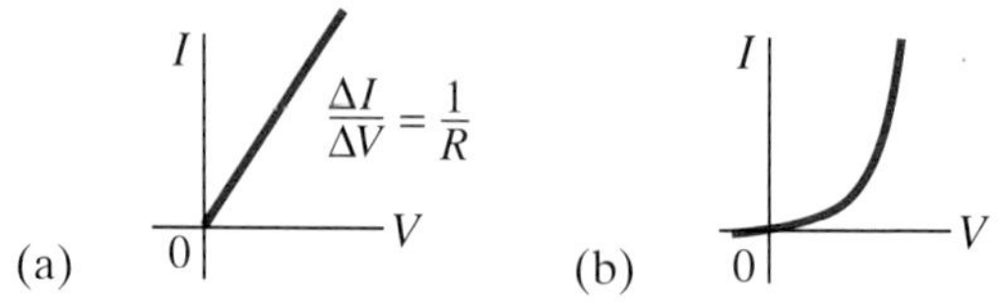


**FIGURE 18–9** Graphs of current vs. voltage for (a) a metal conductor which obeys Ohm's law, and (b) for a nonohmic device, in this case a semiconductor diode.

**EXAMPLE 18–3** **Flashlight bulb resistance.** A small flashlight bulb (Fig. 18–10) draws 300 mA from its 1.5-V battery. (*a*) What is the resistance of the bulb? (*b*) If the battery becomes weak and the voltage drops to 1.2 V, how would the current change?

**APPROACH** We can apply Ohm's law to the bulb, where the voltage applied across it is the battery voltage.

**SOLUTION** (*a*) We change 300 mA to 0.30 A and use Eq. 18–2:

$$R = \frac{V}{I} = \frac{1.5\text{ V}}{0.30\text{ A}} = 5.0\ \Omega.$$

(*b*) If the resistance stays the same, the current would be

$$I = \frac{V}{R} = \frac{1.2\text{ V}}{5.0\ \Omega} = 0.24\text{ A} = 240\text{ mA},$$

or a decrease of 60 mA.

**NOTE** With the smaller current in b, the bulb filament's temperature would be lower and the bulb less bright. Also, resistance does depend on temperature (Section 18–4), so our calculation is only a rough approximation.

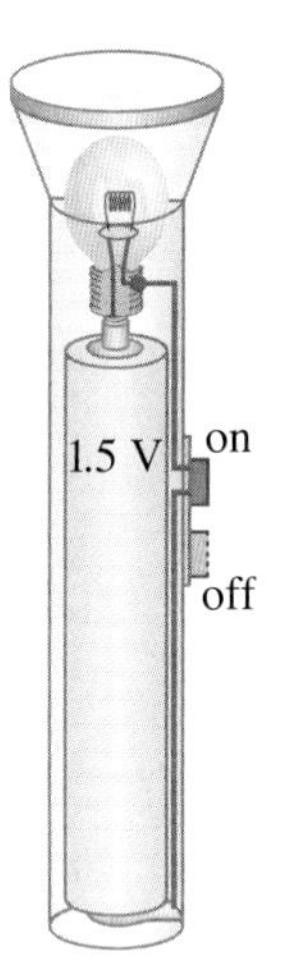


**FIGURE 18–10** Flashlight (Example 18–3). Note how the circuit is completed along the side strip.

**EXERCISE B** What is the resistance of a lightbulb if 0.50 A flows through it when 120 V is connected across it?

All electric devices, from heaters to lightbulbs to stereo amplifiers, offer resistance to the flow of current. The filaments of lightbulbs (Fig. 18–5) and electric heaters are special types of wires whose resistance results in their becoming very hot. Generally, the connecting wires have very low resistance in comparison to the resistance of the wire filaments or coils, so the wires usually have a minimal effect on the magnitude of the current. In many circuits, particularly in electronic devices, **resistors** are used to control the amount of current. Resistors have resistances ranging from less than an ohm to millions of ohms (see Figs. 18–11 and 18–12). The main types are "wire-wound" resistors which consist of a coil of fine wire, "composition" resistors which are usually made of carbon, and thin carbon or metal films.

**FIGURE 18–11** Photo of resistors (striped), plus other devices on a circuit board.

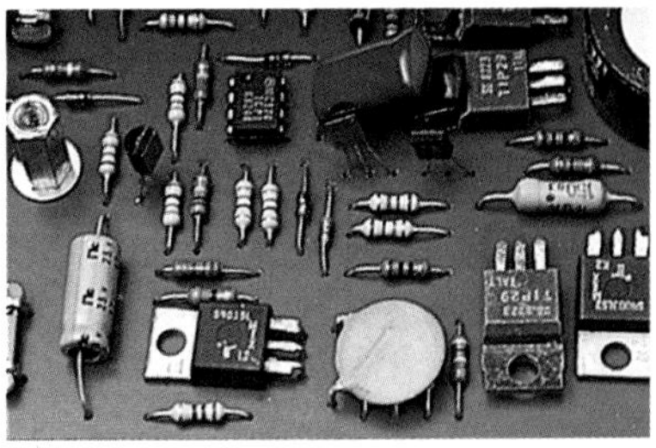

When we draw a diagram of a circuit, we use the symbol

 [resistor symbol]

*Resistor symbol*

to indicate a resistance. Wires whose resistance is negligible, however, are shown simply as straight lines.

**Resistor Color Code**

| Color | Number | Multiplier | Tolerance |
|---|---|---|---|
| Black | 0 | 1 | |
| Brown | 1 | $10^1$ | |
| Red | 2 | $10^2$ | |
| Orange | 3 | $10^3$ | |
| Yellow | 4 | $10^4$ | |
| Green | 5 | $10^5$ | |
| Blue | 6 | $10^6$ | |
| Violet | 7 | $10^7$ | |
| Gray | 8 | $10^8$ | |
| White | 9 | $10^9$ | |
| Gold | | $10^{-1}$ | 5% |
| Silver | | $10^{-2}$ | 10% |
| No color | | | 20% |

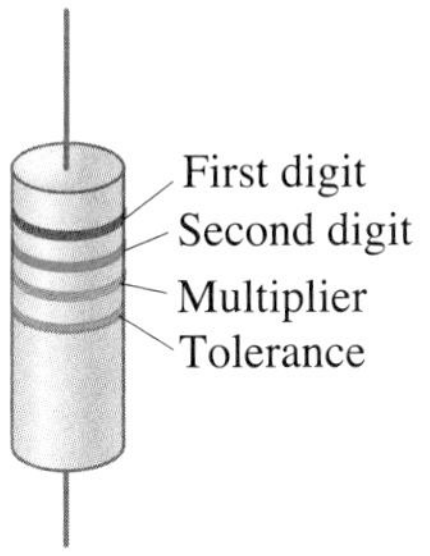


**FIGURE 18–12** The resistance value of a given resistor is written on the exterior, or may be given as a color code as shown above and in the Table: the first two colors represent the first two digits in the value of the resistance, the third color represents the power of ten that it must be multiplied by, and the fourth is the manufactured tolerance. For example, a resistor whose four colors are red, green, yellow, and silver has a resistance of $25 \times 10^4\ \Omega = 250{,}000\ \Omega = 250\text{ k}\Omega$, plus or minus 10%.

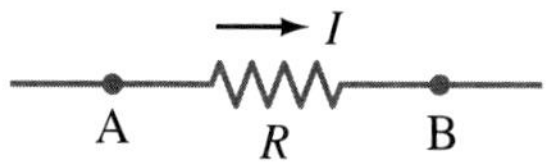


**FIGURE 18–13** Example 18–4.

**CONCEPTUAL EXAMPLE 18–4** **Current and potential.** Current $I$ enters a resistor $R$ as shown in Fig. 18–13. (*a*) Is the potential higher at point A or at point B? (*b*) Is the current greater at point A or at point B?

**RESPONSE** (*a*) Positive charge always flows from + to −, from high potential to low potential. Think again of the gravitational analogy: a mass will fall down from high gravitational potential to low. So for positive current $I$, point A is at a higher potential than point B.
(*b*) Conservation of charge requires that whatever charge flows into the resistor at point A, an equal amount of charge emerges at point B. Charge or current does not get "used up" by a resistor, just as an object that falls through a gravitational potential difference does not gain or lose mass. So the current is the same at A and B.

*Voltage "drop"*

An electric potential decrease, as from point A to point B in Example 18–4, is often called a **potential drop** or a **voltage drop**.

## Some Helpful Clarifications

**CAUTION** *Voltage is applied* across *a device; current passes* through *a device*

Here we briefly summarize some possible misunderstandings and clarifications. Batteries do not put out a constant current. Instead, batteries are intended to maintain a constant potential difference, or very nearly so. (Details in the next Chapter). Thus a battery should be considered a source of voltage. The voltage is applied *across* a wire or device.

Electric current passes *through* a wire or device (connected to a battery), and its magnitude depends on that device's resistance. The resistance is a *property* of the wire or device. The voltage, on the other hand, is external to the wire or device, and is applied across the two ends of the wire or device. The current through the device might be called the "response": the current increases if the voltage increases or the resistance decreases, as $I = V/R$.

Current is *not* a vector, even though current does have a direction. In a wire, the current is always parallel to the wire, no matter how the wire curves, just like water in a pipe. The direction of conventional (positive) current is from high potential (+) toward lower potential (−).

**CAUTION** *Current is not consumed*

Current and charge do not increase or decrease or get "used up" when going through a wire or other device. The amount of charge that goes in at one end comes out at the other end.

# 18–4 Resistivity

It is found experimentally that the resistance $R$ of any wire is directly proportional to its length $L$ and inversely proportional to its cross-sectional area $A$. That is,

$$R = \rho \frac{L}{A}, \qquad \textbf{(18–3)}$$

*Resistivity (units = Ω·m)*

where $\rho$, the constant of proportionality, is called the **resistivity** and depends on the material used. Typical values of $\rho$, whose units are $\Omega \cdot \mathrm{m}$ (see Eq. 18–3), are given for various materials in the middle column of Table 18–1. The values depend somewhat on purity, heat treatment, temperature, and other factors. Notice that silver has the lowest resistivity and is thus the best conductor (although it is expensive). Copper is close, and much less expensive, which is why most wires are made of copper. Aluminum, although it has a higher resistivity, is much less dense than copper; it is thus preferable to copper in some situations, such as for transmission lines, because its resistance for the same weight is less than that for copper.

**TABLE 18–1 Resistivity and Temperature Coefficients (at 20°C)**

| Material | Resistivity, $\rho$ ($\Omega \cdot$ m) | Temperature Coefficient, $\alpha$ $(\mathrm{C}^\circ)^{-1}$ |
|---|---|---|
| *Conductors* | | |
| Silver | $1.59 \times 10^{-8}$ | 0.0061 |
| Copper | $1.68 \times 10^{-8}$ | 0.0068 |
| Gold | $2.44 \times 10^{-8}$ | 0.0034 |
| Aluminum | $2.65 \times 10^{-8}$ | 0.00429 |
| Tungsten | $5.6 \times 10^{-8}$ | 0.0045 |
| Iron | $9.71 \times 10^{-8}$ | 0.00651 |
| Platinum | $10.6 \times 10^{-8}$ | 0.003927 |
| Mercury | $98 \times 10^{-8}$ | 0.0009 |
| Nichrome (Ni, Fe, Cr alloy) | $100 \times 10^{-8}$ | 0.0004 |
| *Semiconductors*† | | |
| Carbon (graphite) | $(3–60) \times 10^{-5}$ | −0.0005 |
| Germanium | $(1–500) \times 10^{-3}$ | −0.05 |
| Silicon | 0.1–60 | −0.07 |
| *Insulators* | | |
| Glass | $10^{9} - 10^{12}$ | |
| Hard rubber | $10^{13} - 10^{15}$ | |

† Values depend strongly on the presence of even slight amounts of impurities.

**EXAMPLE 18–5 Speaker wires.** Suppose you want to connect your stereo to remote speakers (Fig. 18–14). (*a*) If each wire must be 20 m long, what diameter copper wire should you use to keep the resistance less than 0.10 Ω per wire? (*b*) If the current to each speaker is 4.0 A, what is the potential difference, or voltage drop, across each wire?

**APPROACH** We solve Eq. 18–3 to get the area $A$, from which we can calculate the wire's radius using $A = \pi r^2$. The diameter is $2r$. In (*b*) we can use Ohm's law, $V = IR$.

**SOLUTION** (*a*) We solve Eq. 18–3 for the area $A$ and find $\rho$ for copper in Table 18–1:

$$A = \rho \frac{L}{R} = \frac{(1.68 \times 10^{-8}\,\Omega \cdot \mathrm{m})(20\,\mathrm{m})}{(0.10\,\Omega)} = 3.4 \times 10^{-6}\,\mathrm{m}^2.$$

The cross-sectional area $A$ of a circular wire is $A = \pi r^2$. The radius must then be at least

$$r = \sqrt{\frac{A}{\pi}} = 1.04 \times 10^{-3}\,\mathrm{m} = 1.04\,\mathrm{mm}.$$

The diameter is twice the radius and so must be at least $2r = 2.1$ mm.

(*b*) From $V = IR$ we find that the voltage drop across each wire is

$$V = IR = (4.0\,\mathrm{A})(0.10\,\Omega) = 0.40\,\mathrm{V}.$$

**NOTE** The voltage drop across the wires reduces the voltage that reaches the speakers from the stereo amplifier, thus reducing the sound level a bit.

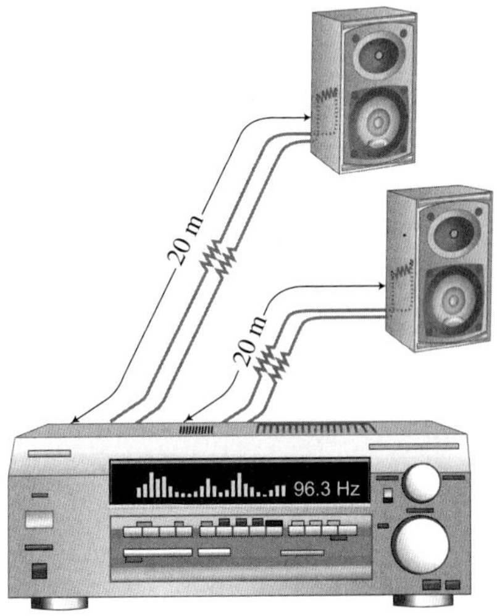


**FIGURE 18–14** Example 18–5.

**CONCEPTUAL EXAMPLE 18–6 Stretching changes resistance.** A wire of resistance $R$ is stretched uniformly until it is twice its original length. What happens to its resistance?

**RESPONSE** If the length $L$ doubles, then the cross-sectional area $A$ is halved, because the volume ($V = AL$) of the wire remains the same. From Eq. 18–3 we see that the resistance would increase by a factor of four $(2/\frac{1}{2} = 4)$.

**EXERCISE C** Copper wires in houses typically have a diameter of about 1.5 mm. How long a wire would have a 1.0-Ω resistance?

## * Temperature Dependence of Resistivity

The resistivity of a material depends somewhat on temperature. In general, the resistance of metals increases with temperature. This is not surprising, for at higher temperatures, the atoms are moving more rapidly and are arranged in a less orderly fashion. So they might be expected to interfere more with the flow of electrons. If the temperature change is not too great, the resistivity of metals usually increases nearly linearly with temperature. That is,

*Effect of temperature on resistivity*

$$\rho_T = \rho_0[1 + \alpha(T - T_0)] \qquad \textbf{(18–4)}$$

where $\rho_0$ is the resistivity at some reference temperature $T_0$ (such as 0°C or 20°C), $\rho_T$ is the resistivity at a temperature $T$, and $\alpha$ is the *temperature coefficient of resistivity*. Values for $\alpha$ are given in Table 18–1. Note that the temperature coefficient for semiconductors can be negative. Why? It seems that at higher temperatures, some of the electrons that are normally not free in a semiconductor become free and can contribute to the current. Thus, the resistance of a semiconductor can decrease with an increase in temperature, although this is not always the case.

PHYSICS APPLIED
*Resistance thermometer*

**EXAMPLE 18–7** **Resistance thermometer.** The variation in electrical resistance with temperature can be used to make precise temperature measurements. Platinum is commonly used since it is relatively free from corrosive effects and has a high melting point. Suppose at 20.0°C the resistance of a platinum resistance thermometer is 164.2 Ω. When placed in a particular solution, the resistance is 187.4 Ω. What is the temperature of this solution?

**APPROACH** Since the resistance $R$ is directly proportional to the resistivity $\rho$, we can combine Eq. 18–3 with Eq. 18–4 to find $R$ as a function of temperature $T$, and then solve that equation for $T$.

**SOLUTION** We multiply Eq. 18–4 by $(L/A)$ to obtain (see also Eq. 18–3)

$$R = R_0[1 + \alpha(T - T_0)].$$

Here $R_0 = \rho_0 L/A$ is the resistance of the wire at $T_0 = 20.0°\text{C}$. We solve this equation for $T$ and find (see Table 18–1 for $\alpha$)

$$T = T_0 + \frac{R - R_0}{\alpha R_0} = 20.0°\text{C} + \frac{187.4\,\Omega - 164.2\,\Omega}{(3.927 \times 10^{-3}(\text{C}°)^{-1})(164.2\,\Omega)} = 56.0°\text{C}.$$

**NOTE** Resistance thermometers have the advantage that they can be used at very high or low temperatures where gas or liquid thermometers would be useless.

**NOTE** More convenient for some applications is a *thermistor* (Fig. 18–15), which consists of a metal oxide or semiconductor whose resistance also varies in a repeatable way with temperature. Thermistors can be made quite small and respond very quickly to temperature changes.

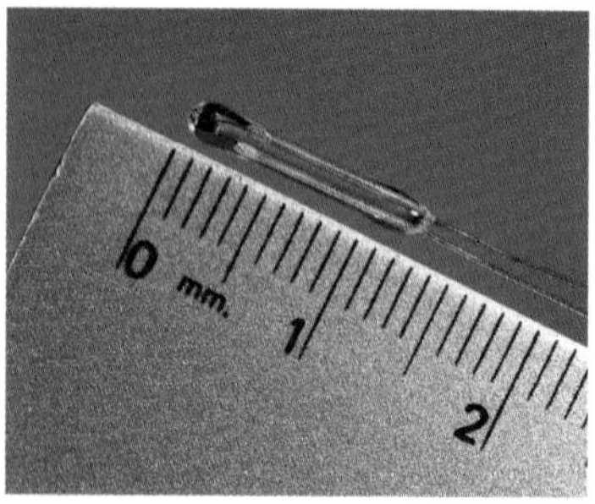


**FIGURE 18–15** A thermistor shown next to a millimeter ruler for scale.

The value of $\alpha$ in Eq. 18–4 itself can depend on temperature, so it is important to check the temperature range of validity of any value (say, in a handbook of physical data). If the temperature range is wide, Eq. 18–4 is not adequate and terms proportional to the square and cube of the temperature are needed, but they are generally very small except when $T - T_0$ is large.

## 18–5 Electric Power

Electric energy is useful to us because it can be easily transformed into other forms of energy. Motors transform electric energy into mechanical energy, and are examined in Chapter 20.

In other devices such as electric heaters, stoves, toasters, and hair dryers, electric energy is transformed into thermal energy in a wire resistance known as a "heating element." And in an ordinary lightbulb, the tiny wire filament

(Fig. 18–5 and Chapter opening photo) becomes so hot it glows; only a few percent of the energy is transformed into visible light, and the rest, over 90%, into thermal energy. Lightbulb filaments and heating elements (Fig. 18–16) in household appliances have resistances typically of a few ohms to a few hundred ohms.

Electric energy is transformed into thermal energy or light in such devices, and there are many collisions between the moving electrons and the atoms of the wire. In each collision, part of the electron's kinetic energy is transferred to the atom with which it collides. As a result, the kinetic energy of the wire's atoms increases and hence the temperature of the wire element increases. The increased thermal energy can be transferred as heat by conduction and convection to the air in a heater or to food in a pan, by radiation to bread in a toaster, or radiated as light.

**FIGURE 18–16** Coiled heating element of an electric space heater glows because of energy transformed by electric current.

To find the power transformed by an electric device, recall that the energy transformed when a charge $Q$ moves through a potential difference $V$ is $QV$ (Eq. 17–3). Then the power $P$, which is the rate energy is transformed, is

$$P = \frac{\text{energy transformed}}{\text{time}} = \frac{QV}{t}.$$

The charge that flows per second, $Q/t$, is simply the electric current $I$. Thus we have

$$P = IV. \qquad \textbf{(18–5)}$$

*Electric power (general)*

This general relation gives us the power transformed by any device, where $I$ is the current passing through it and $V$ is the potential difference across it. It also gives the power delivered by a source such as a battery. The SI unit of electric power is the same as for any kind of power, the **watt** (1 W = 1 J/s).

The rate of energy transformation in a resistance $R$ can be written in two other ways, starting with the general relation $P = IV$ and substituting in $V = IR$:

$$P = IV = I(IR) = I^2R \qquad \textbf{(18–6a)}$$

$$P = IV = \left(\frac{V}{R}\right)V = \frac{V^2}{R}. \qquad \textbf{(18–6b)}$$

*Electric power (in resistance R)*

Equations 18–6a and b apply only to resistors, whereas Eq. 18–5, $P = IV$, applies to any device, including a resistor.

**EXAMPLE 18–8** **Headlights.** Calculate the resistance of a 40-W automobile headlight designed for 12 V (Fig. 18–17).

**APPROACH** We are given the power and the potential difference across the headlight, so we solve Eq. 18–6b for $R$.

**SOLUTION** Given $P = 40\text{ W}$ and $V = 12\text{ V}$, and solving Eq. 18–6b for $R$, we obtain

$$R = \frac{V^2}{P} = \frac{(12\text{ V})^2}{(40\text{ W})} = 3.6\ \Omega.$$

**NOTE** This is the resistance when the bulb is burning brightly at 40 W. When the bulb is cold, the resistance is much lower, as we saw in Eq. 18–4. Since the current is high when the resistance is low, lightbulbs burn out most often when first turned on.

**PHYSICS APPLIED**
*Why lightbulbs burn out when first turned on*

**FIGURE 18–17** Example 18–8.

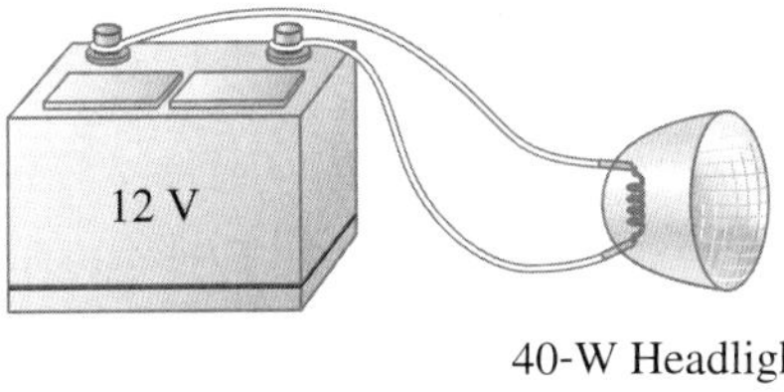

**CAUTION**

*You pay for energy, which is power × time, not for power*

*Kilowatt-hour (energy unit used by energy companies)*

It is energy, not power, that you pay for on your electric bill. Since power is the *rate* energy is transformed, the total energy used by any device is simply its power consumption multiplied by the time it is on. If the power is in watts and the time is in seconds, the energy will be in joules since $1\text{ W} = 1\text{ J/s}$. Electric companies usually specify the energy with a much larger unit, the **kilowatt-hour** (kWh). One $\text{kWh} = (1000\text{ W})(3600\text{ s}) = 3.60 \times 10^6\text{ J}$.

**EXAMPLE 18–9 Electric heater.** An electric heater draws a steady 15.0 A on a 120-V line. How much power does it require and how much does it cost per month (30 days) if it operates 3.0 h per day and the electric company charges 9.2 cents per kWh?

**APPROACH** Given the current and voltage, we use Eq. 18–5 to find the power. We multiply the power (in kW) by the time (h) used in a month to find the energy transformed in a month, and then multiply by the cost per energy unit, $0.092 per kWh, to get the cost per month.

**SOLUTION** The power is

$$\begin{aligned} P = IV &= (15.0\text{ A})(120\text{ V}) \\ &= 1800\text{ W} \end{aligned}$$

or 1.80 kW. The time (in hours) the heater is used per month is $(3.0\text{ h/d})(30\text{ d}) = 90\text{ h}$, which at 9.2¢/kWh would cost $(1.80\text{ kW})(90\text{ h})(\$0.092/\text{kWh}) = \$15$.

**NOTE** Household current is actually alternating (ac), but our solution is still valid assuming the given values for $V$ and $I$ are the proper averages (rms) as discussed in Section 18–7.

**PHYSICS APPLIED**

*Lightning*

**FIGURE 18–18** Example 18–10: a lightning bolt.

**EXAMPLE 18–10 ESTIMATE Lightning bolt.** Lightning is a spectacular example of electric current in a natural phenomenon (Fig. 18–18). There is much variability to lightning bolts, but a typical event can transfer $10^9$ J of energy across a potential difference of perhaps $5 \times 10^7$ V during a time interval of about 0.2 s. Use this information to estimate (*a*) the total amount of charge transferred between cloud and ground, (*b*) the current in the lightning bolt, and (*c*) the average power delivered over the 0.2 s.

**APPROACH** We estimate the charge $Q$, recalling that potential energy change equals the potential difference $V_{ba}$ times the charge $Q$, Eq. 17–3. We equate $\Delta\text{PE}$ with the energy transferred, $\Delta\text{PE} \approx 10^9$ J. Next, the current $I$ is $Q/t$ (Eq. 18–1) and the power $P$ is energy/time.

**SOLUTION** (*a*) From Eq. 17–3, the energy transformed is $\Delta\text{PE} = QV_{ba}$. We solve for $Q$:

$$Q = \frac{\Delta\text{PE}}{V_{ba}} \approx \frac{10^9\text{ J}}{5 \times 10^7\text{ V}} = 20\text{ coulombs}.$$

(*b*) The current during the 0.2 s is about

$$I = \frac{Q}{t} \approx \frac{20\text{ C}}{0.2\text{ s}} = 100\text{ A}.$$

(*c*) The average power delivered is

$$P = \frac{\text{energy}}{\text{time}} = \frac{10^9\text{ J}}{0.2\text{ s}} = 5 \times 10^9\text{ W} = 5\text{ GW}.$$

We can also use Eq. 18–5:

$$P = IV = (100\text{ A})(5 \times 10^7\text{ V}) = 5\text{ GW}.$$

**NOTE** Since most lightning bolts consist of several stages, it is possible that individual parts could carry currents much higher than the 100 A calculated above.

**EXERCISE D** Since $1\,\text{kWh} = 3.6 \times 10^6\,\text{J}$, how much mass must be lifted against gravity through one meter to do the equivalent amount of work?

## 18–6 Power in Household Circuits

The electric wires that carry electricity to lights and other electric appliances have some resistance, although usually it is quite small. Nonetheless, if the current is large enough, the wires will heat up and produce thermal energy at a rate equal to $I^2R$, where $R$ is the wire's resistance. One possible hazard is that the current-carrying wires in the wall of a building may become so hot as to start a fire. Thicker wires have less resistance (see Eq. 18–3) and thus can carry more current without becoming too hot. When a wire carries more current than is safe, it is said to be "overloaded." To prevent overloading, *fuses* or *circuit breakers* are installed in circuits. They are basically switches (Fig. 18–19) that open the circuit when the current exceeds some particular value. A 20-A fuse or circuit breaker, for example, opens when the current passing through it exceeds 20 A. If a circuit repeatedly burns out a fuse or opens a circuit breaker, there are two possibilities: there may be too many devices drawing current in that circuit; or there is a fault somewhere, such as a "short." A short, or "short circuit," means that two wires have touched that should not have (perhaps because the insulation has worn through) so the path of the current is shortened. The resistance of the circuit is then very small, so the current will be very large. Short circuits should be remedied immediately.

PHYSICS APPLIED
*Safety—wires getting hot*

*Fuses, circuit breakers, and shorts*

**FIGURE 18–19** (a) Fuses. When the current exceeds a certain value, the metallic ribbon melts and the circuit opens. Then the fuse must be replaced. (b) One type of circuit breaker. The electric current passes through a bimetallic strip. When the current exceeds a safe level, the heating of the bimetallic strip causes the strip to bend so far to the left that the notch in the spring-loaded metal strip drops down over the end of the bimetallic strip; (c) the circuit then opens at the contact points (one is attached to the metal strip) and the outside switch is also flipped. As soon as the bimetallic strip cools down, it can be reset using the outside switch. Magnetic-type circuit breakers are discussed in Chapters 20 and 21.

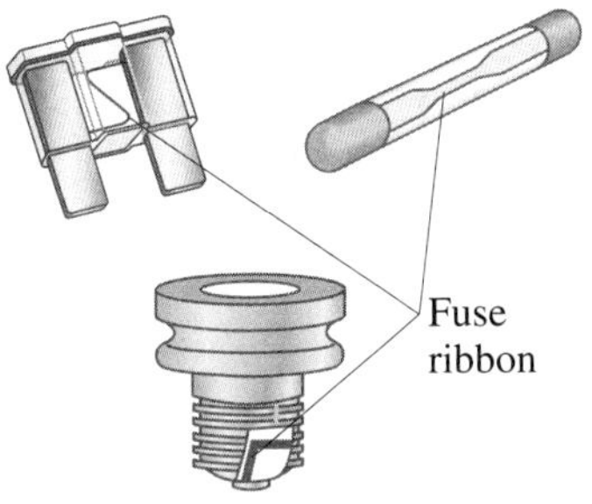


(a) Types of fuses

PHYSICS APPLIED
*Fuses and circuit breakers*

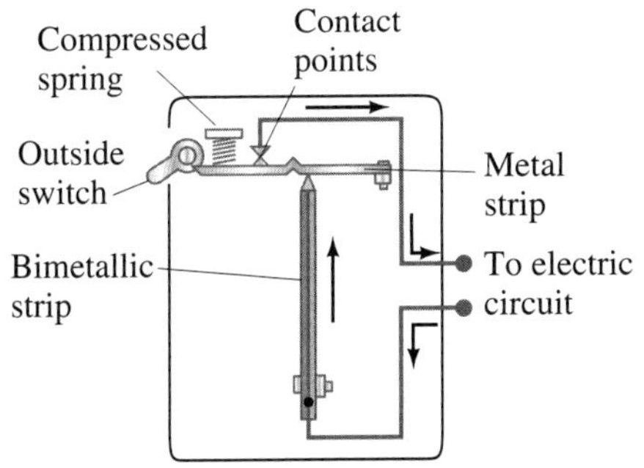


(b) Circuit breaker (closed)

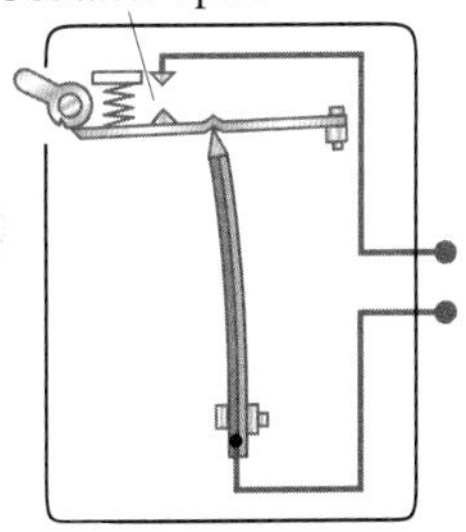


(c) Circuit breaker (open)

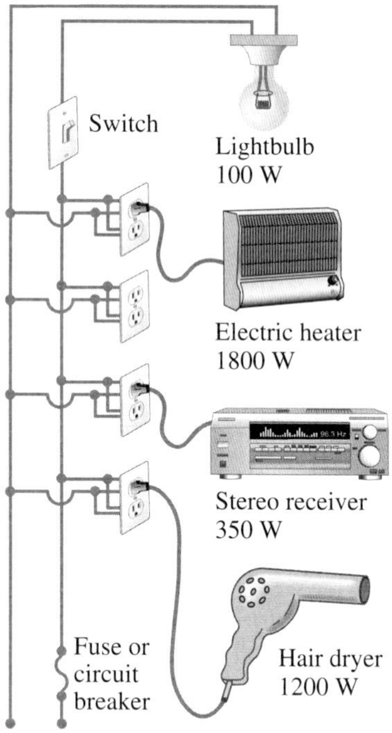


**FIGURE 18–20** Connection of household appliances.

PHYSICS APPLIED

*Proper fuses and shorts*

PHYSICS APPLIED

*Extension cords and possible danger*

Household circuits are designed with the various devices connected so that each receives the standard voltage (usually 120 V in the United States) from the electric company (Fig. 18–20). Circuits with the devices arranged as in Fig. 18–20 are called *parallel circuits*, as we will discuss in the next Chapter. When a fuse blows or circuit breaker opens, it is important to check the total current being drawn on that circuit, which is the sum of the currents in each device.

**EXAMPLE 18–11** **Will a fuse blow?** Determine the total current drawn by all the devices in the circuit of Fig. 18–20.

**APPROACH** Each device has the same 120-V voltage across it. The current each draws from the source is found from $I = P/V$, Eq. 18–5.

**SOLUTION** The circuit in Fig. 18–20 draws the following currents: the lightbulb draws $I = P/V = 100\,\mathrm{W}/120\,\mathrm{V} = 0.8\,\mathrm{A}$; the heater draws $1800\,\mathrm{W}/120\,\mathrm{V} = 15.0\,\mathrm{A}$; the stereo draws a maximum of $350\,\mathrm{W}/120\,\mathrm{V} = 2.9\,\mathrm{A}$; and the hair dryer draws $1200\,\mathrm{W}/120\,\mathrm{V} = 10.0\,\mathrm{A}$. The total current drawn, if all devices are used at the same time, is

$$0.8\,\mathrm{A} + 15.0\,\mathrm{A} + 2.9\,\mathrm{A} + 10.0\,\mathrm{A} = 28.7\,\mathrm{A}.$$

**NOTE** The heater draws as much current as 18 100-W lightbulbs. For safety, the heater should probably be on a circuit by itself.

If the circuit in Fig. 18–20 is designed for a 20-A fuse, the fuse should blow, and we hope it will, to prevent overloaded wires from getting hot enough to start a fire. Something will have to be turned off to get this circuit below 20 A. (Houses and apartments usually have several circuits, each with its own fuse or circuit breaker; try moving one of the devices to another circuit.) If the circuit is designed with heavier wire and a 30-A fuse, the fuse shouldn't blow—if it does, a short may be the problem. (The most likely place for a short is in the cord of one of the devices.) Proper fuse size is selected according to the wire used to supply the current; a properly rated fuse should *never* be replaced by a higher-rated one. A fuse blowing or a circuit breaker opening is acting like a switch, making an "open circuit." By an open circuit, we mean that there is no longer a complete conducting path, so no current can flow; it is as if $R = \infty$.

**EXERCISE E** Your 1800-W portable electric heater is too far from your desk to warm your feet. Its cord is too short, so you plug it into an extension cord rated at 11 A. Why is this dangerous?

## 18–7 Alternating Current

*DC and AC*

**FIGURE 18–21** (a) Direct current. (b) Alternating current.

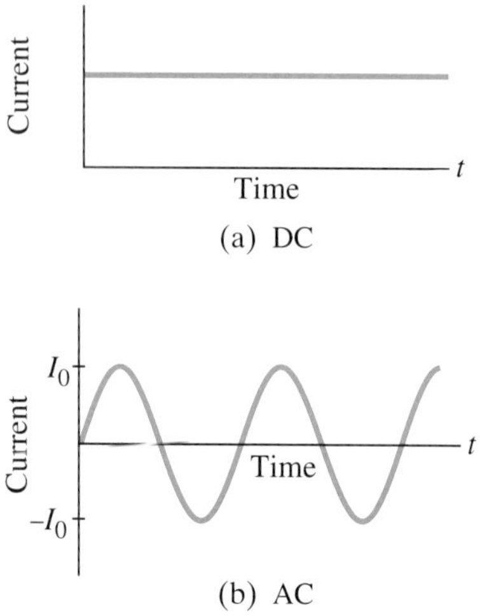


When a battery is connected to a circuit, the current moves steadily in one direction. This is called a **direct current**, or **dc**. Electric generators at electric power plants, however, produce **alternating current**, or **ac**. (Sometimes capital letters are used, DC and AC.) An alternating current reverses direction many times per second and is commonly sinusoidal, as shown in Fig. 18–21. The electrons in a wire first move in one direction and then in the other. The current supplied to homes and businesses by electric companies is ac throughout virtually the entire world. We will discuss and analyze ac circuits in detail in Chapter 21. But because ac circuits are so common in real life, we will discuss some of their basic aspects here.

The voltage produced by an ac electric generator is sinusoidal, as we shall see later. The current it produces is thus sinusoidal (Fig. 18–21b). We can write the voltage as a function of time as

$$V = V_0 \sin 2\pi f t = V_0 \sin \omega t.$$

The potential $V$ oscillates between $+V_0$ and $-V_0$, and $V_0$ is referred to as the **peak voltage**. The frequency $f$ is the number of complete oscillations made per second, and $\omega = 2\pi f$. In most areas of the United States and Canada, $f$ is

60 Hz (the unit "hertz," as we saw in Chapter 11, means cycles per second). In many countries, 50 Hz is used.

Equation 18–2, $V = IR$, works also for ac: if a voltage $V$ exists across a resistance $R$, then the current $I$ through the resistance is

$$I = \frac{V}{R} = \frac{V_0}{R}\sin\omega t = I_0 \sin\omega t. \qquad \textbf{(18–7)}$$

The quantity $I_0 = V_0/R$ is the **peak current**. The current is considered positive when the electrons flow in one direction and negative when they flow in the opposite direction. It is clear from Fig. 18–21b that an alternating current is as often positive as it is negative. Thus, the average current is zero. This does not mean, however, that no power is needed or that no heat is produced in a resistor. Electrons do move back and forth, and do produce heat. Indeed, the power transformed in a resistance $R$ at any instant is

$$P = I^2R = I_0^2 R \sin^2\omega t.$$

Because the current is squared, we see that the power is always positive, as graphed in Fig. 18–22. The quantity $\sin^2\omega t$ varies between 0 and 1; and it is not too difficult to show that its average value is $\frac{1}{2}$, as indicated in Fig. 18–22. Thus, the *average power* transformed, $\overline{P}$, is

$$\overline{P} = \tfrac{1}{2} I_0^2 R.$$

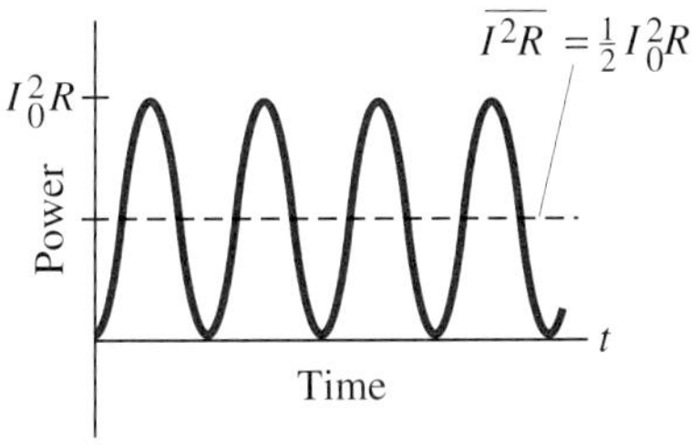

**FIGURE 18–22** Power transformed in a resistor in an ac circuit.

Since power can also be written $P = V^2/R = (V_0^2/R)\sin^2\omega t$, we also have that the average power is

$$\overline{P} = \frac{1}{2}\frac{V_0^2}{R}.$$

The average or mean value of the *square* of the current or voltage is thus what is important for calculating average power: $\overline{I^2} = \frac{1}{2}I_0^2$ and $\overline{V^2} = \frac{1}{2}V_0^2$. The square root of each of these is the **rms** (root-mean-square) value of the current or voltage:

$$I_{rms} = \sqrt{\overline{I^2}} = \frac{I_0}{\sqrt{2}} = 0.707 I_0, \qquad \textbf{(18–8a)}$$

*rms current*

$$V_{rms} = \sqrt{\overline{V^2}} = \frac{V_0}{\sqrt{2}} = 0.707 V_0. \qquad \textbf{(18–8b)}$$

*rms voltage*

The rms values of $V$ and $I$ are sometimes called the *effective values*. They are useful because they can be substituted directly into the power formulas, Eqs. 18–5 and 18–6, to get the average power:

$$\overline{P} = I_{rms}V_{rms} \qquad \textbf{(18–9a)}$$

$$\overline{P} = \tfrac{1}{2}I_0^2R = I_{rms}^2R \qquad \textbf{(18–9b)}$$

$$\overline{P} = \frac{1}{2}\frac{V_0^2}{R} = \frac{V_{rms}^2}{R}. \qquad \textbf{(18–9c)}$$

Thus, a direct current whose values of $I$ and $V$ equal the rms values of $I$ and $V$ for an alternating current will produce the same power. Hence it is usually the rms value of current that is specified or measured. For example, in the United States and Canada, standard line voltage† is 120-V ac. The 120 V is $V_{rms}$; the peak voltage $V_0$ is

$$V_0 = \sqrt{2}\,V_{rms} = 170\text{ V}.$$

In much of the world (Europe, Australia, Asia) the rms voltage is 240 V, so the peak voltage is 340 V.

†The line voltage can vary, depending on the total load; the frequency of 60 Hz or 50 Hz, however, remains extremely steady.

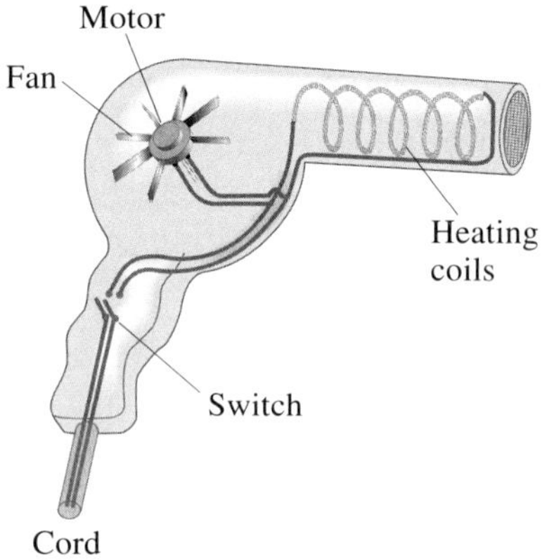


**FIGURE 18–23** A hair dryer. Most of the current goes through the heating coils, a pure resistance; a small part goes to the motor to turn the fan. Example 18–12.

**EXAMPLE 18–12** **Hair dryer.** (*a*) Calculate the resistance and the peak current in a 1000-W hair dryer (Fig. 18–23) connected to a 120-V line. (*b*) What happens if it is connected to a 240-V line in Britain?

**APPROACH** We are given $\overline{P}$ and $V_{\rm rms}$, so $I_{\rm rms} = \overline{P}/V_{\rm rms}$ (Eq. 18–9a or 18–5), and $I_0 = \sqrt{2}\, I_{\rm rms}$. Then we find $R$ from $V = IR$.

**SOLUTION** (*a*) We solve Eq. 18–9a for the rms current:

$$I_{\rm rms} = \frac{\overline{P}}{V_{\rm rms}} = \frac{1000\ \text{W}}{120\ \text{V}} = 8.33\ \text{A}.$$

Then

$$I_0 = \sqrt{2}\, I_{\rm rms} = 11.8\ \text{A}.$$

The resistance is

$$R = \frac{V_{\rm rms}}{I_{\rm rms}} = \frac{120\ \text{V}}{8.33\ \text{A}} = 14.4\ \Omega.$$

The resistance could equally well be calculated using peak values:

$$R = \frac{V_0}{I_0} = \frac{170\ \text{V}}{11.8\ \text{A}} = 14.4\ \Omega.$$

(*b*) When connected to a 240-V line, more current would flow and the resistance would change with the increased temperature (Section 18–4). But let us make an estimate of the power transformed based on the same 14.4-Ω resistance. The average power would be

$$\overline{P} = \frac{V_{\rm rms}^2}{R} = \frac{(240\ \text{V})^2}{(14.4\ \Omega)} = 4000\ \text{W}.$$

This is four times the dryer's power rating and would undoubtedly melt the heating element or the wire coils of the motor.

**EXAMPLE 18–13** **Stereo power.** Each channel of a stereo receiver is capable of an average power output of 100 W into an 8-Ω loudspeaker (see Fig. 18–14). What are the rms voltage and the rms current fed to the speaker (*a*) at the maximum power of 100 W, and (*b*) at 1.0 W when the volume is turned down?

**APPROACH** We assume that the loudspeaker can be treated as a simple resistance (not quite true—see Chapter 21) with $R = 8.0\ \Omega$. We are given the power $P$, so we can determine $V_{\rm rms}$ and $I_{\rm rms}$ using the power equations, Eqs. 18–9.

**SOLUTION** (*a*) We solve Eq. 18–9c for $V_{\rm rms}$ and set $\overline{P} = 100\ \text{W}$ (at the maximum):

$$V_{\rm rms} = \sqrt{\overline{P}R} = \sqrt{(100\ \text{W})(8.0\ \Omega)} = 28\ \text{V}.$$

Next we solve Eq. 18–9b for $I_{\rm rms}$ and obtain

$$I_{\rm rms} = \sqrt{\frac{\overline{P}}{R}} = \sqrt{\frac{100\ \text{W}}{8.0\ \Omega}} = 3.5\ \text{A}.$$

Or we could use Ohm's law ($V = IR$):

$$I_{\rm rms} = \frac{V_{\rm rms}}{R} = \frac{28\ \text{V}}{8.0\ \Omega} = 3.5\ \text{A}.$$

(*b*) At $\overline{P} = 1.0\ \text{W}$,

$$V_{\rm rms} = \sqrt{(1.0\ \text{W})(8.0\ \Omega)} = 2.8\ \text{V}$$

$$I_{\rm rms} = \frac{2.8\ \text{V}}{8.0\ \Omega} = 0.35\ \text{A}.$$

**EXERCISE F** What would be the rms voltage and rms current of the stereo in Example 18–13 if the 100 W was connected to a loudspeaker rated at 4 Ω?

This Section has given a brief introduction to the simpler aspects of alternating currents. We will discuss ac circuits in more detail in Chapter 21. In Chapter 19 we will deal with the details of dc circuits only.

## * 18–8 Microscopic View of Electric Current

It can be useful to analyze a simple model of electric current at the microscopic level of atoms and electrons. In a conducting wire, for example, we can imagine the free electrons as moving about randomly at high speeds, bouncing off the atoms of the wire (somewhat like the molecules of a gas—Sections 13–9 to 13–11). When an electric field exists in the wire (Fig. 18–24) due to a potential difference applied between its ends, the electrons feel a force and initially begin to accelerate. But they soon reach a more or less steady average speed (due to collisions with atoms in the wire), known as their **drift speed**, $v_d$. The drift speed is normally very much smaller than the electrons' average random speed.

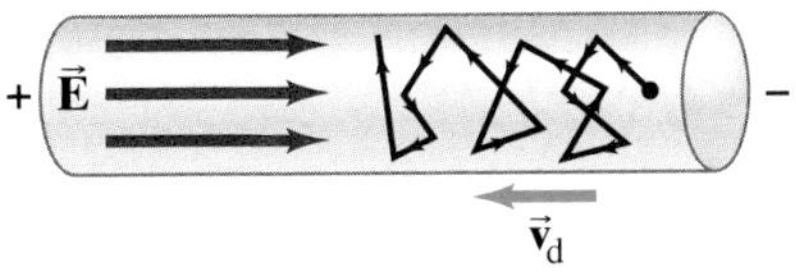


**FIGURE 18–24** Electric field $\vec{E}$ in a wire gives electrons in random motion a drift speed $v_d$.

*Drift speed*

We can relate $v_d$ to the macroscopic current $I$ in the wire. In a time $\Delta t$, the electrons will travel a distance $l = v_d \Delta t$ on average. Suppose the wire has cross-sectional area $A$. Then in time $\Delta t$, all electrons in a volume $V = Al = Av_d \Delta t$ will pass through the cross section $A$ of wire, as shown in Fig. 18–25. If there are $n$ free electrons (each of charge $e$) per unit volume, then the total number of electrons is $N = nV$ ($V$ is volume, not voltage) and the total charge $\Delta Q$ that passes through the area $A$ in a time $\Delta t$ is

**FIGURE 18–25** Electrons in the volume $Al$ will all pass through the cross section indicated in a time $\Delta t$, where $l = v_d \Delta t$.

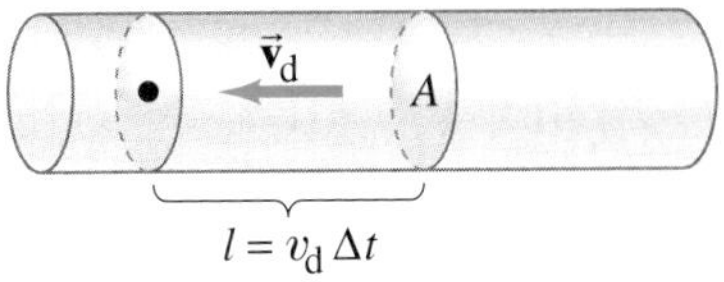


$$\begin{aligned}\Delta Q &= (\text{number of charges, } N) \times (\text{charge per particle}) \\ &= (nV)(e) = (nAv_d \Delta t)(e).\end{aligned}$$

The current $I$ in the wire is thus

$$I = \frac{\Delta Q}{\Delta t} = neAv_d. \tag{18–10}$$

*Current (microscopic variables)*

**EXAMPLE 18–14 Electron speeds in a wire.** A copper wire, 3.2 mm in diameter, carries a 5.0-A current. Determine the drift speed of the free electrons. Assume that one electron per Cu atom is free to move (the others remain bound to the atom).

**APPROACH** We can apply Eq. 18–10 to find the drift speed if we can determine the number $n$ of free electrons per unit volume. Since we assume there is one free electron per atom, the density of free electrons, $n$, is the same as the density of Cu atoms. The atomic mass of Cu is 63.5 u (see Periodic Table inside the back cover), so 63.5 g of Cu contains one mole or $6.02 \times 10^{23}$ free electrons. We then use the mass density of copper (Table 10–1), $\rho_D = 8.9 \times 10^3\,\text{kg/m}^3$, to find the volume of this amount of copper, and then $n = N/V$. (We use $\rho_D$ to distinguish it here from $\rho$ for resistivity.)

**SOLUTION** The mass density $\rho_D = m/V$ is related to the number of free electrons per unit volume, $n = N/V$, by

$$\begin{aligned}n = \frac{N}{V} = \frac{N}{m/\rho_D} &= \frac{N\,(1\text{ mole})}{m\,(1\text{ mole})}\rho_D \\ &= \left(\frac{6.02 \times 10^{23}\text{ electrons}}{63.5 \times 10^{-3}\text{ kg}}\right)(8.9 \times 10^3\text{ kg/m}^3) \\ &= 8.4 \times 10^{28}\text{ m}^{-3}.\end{aligned}$$

The cross-sectional area of the wire is

$$A = \pi r^2 = (3.14)(1.6 \times 10^{-3}\text{ m})^2 = 8.0 \times 10^{-6}\text{ m}^2.$$

Then, by Eq. 18–10, the drift speed is

$$\begin{aligned}v_d = \frac{I}{neA} &= \frac{5.0\text{ A}}{(8.4 \times 10^{28}\text{ m}^{-3})(1.6 \times 10^{-19}\text{ C})(8.0 \times 10^{-6}\text{ m}^2)} \\ &= 4.7 \times 10^{-5}\text{ m/s},\end{aligned}$$

which is only about 0.05 mm/s.

**NOTE** We can compare this drift speed to the actual speed of free electrons bouncing around inside the metal like molecules in a gas, calculated to be about $1.6 \times 10^6$ m/s at 20°C.

The drift speed of electrons in a wire is very slow, only about 0.05 mm/s for Example 18–14, which means it takes an electron about $20 \times 10^3$ s, or $5\frac{1}{2}$ h, to travel only 1 m. This is not, however, how fast "electricity travels": when you flip a light switch, the light—even if many meters away—goes on nearly instantaneously because electric fields travel essentially at the speed of light $(3 \times 10^8\ \mathrm{m/s})$. We can think of electrons in a wire as being like a pipe full of water: when a little water enters one end of the pipe, almost immediately some water comes out the other end.

*Electricity's "speed"*

## * 18–9 Superconductivity

At very low temperatures, well below 0°C, the resistivity (Section 18–4) of certain metals and certain compounds or alloys becomes zero as measured by the highest-precision techniques. Materials in such a state are said to be **superconducting**. This phenomenon was first observed by H. K. Onnes (1853–1926) in 1911 when he cooled mercury below 4.2 K (−269°C). He found that at this temperature, the resistance of mercury suddenly dropped to zero. In general, superconductors become superconducting only below a certain *transition temperature* or *critical temperature*, $T_C$, which is usually within a few degrees of absolute zero. Current in a ring-shaped superconducting material has been observed to flow for years in the absence of a potential difference, with no measurable decrease. Measurements show that the resistivity $\rho$ of superconductors is less than $4 \times 10^{-25}\ \Omega\cdot\mathrm{m}$, which is over $10^{16}$ times smaller than that for copper, and is considered to be zero in practice. See Fig. 18–26.

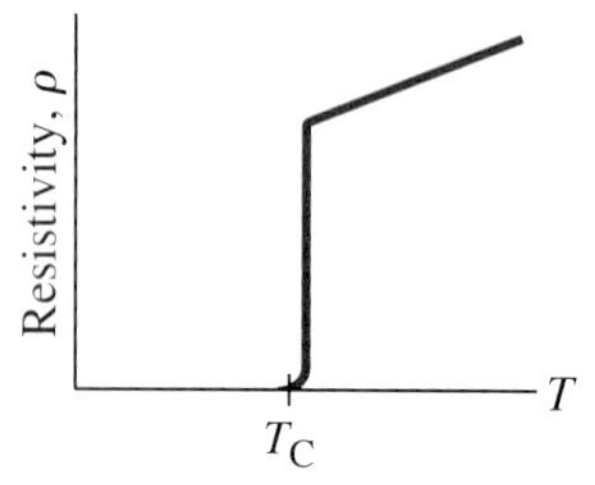


**FIGURE 18–26** A superconducting material has zero resistivity when its temperature is below $T_C$, its "critical temperature." At $T_C$, the resistivity jumps to a "normal" non-zero value and increases with temperature as most materials do (Eq. 18–4).

Much research has been done on superconductivity to try to understand why it occurs, and to find materials that superconduct at higher, more accessible temperatures to reduce the cost and inconvenience of refrigeration at the required very low temperature. Before 1986 the highest temperature at which a material was found to superconduct was 23 K, and this required liquid helium to keep the material cold. In 1987, a compound of yttrium, barium, copper, and oxygen (YBCO) was developed that can be superconducting at 90 K. Since this is above the boiling temperature of liquid nitrogen, 77 K, liquid nitrogen is sufficiently cold to keep the material superconducting. This was an important breakthrough since liquid nitrogen is much more easily and cheaply obtained than is the liquid helium needed for conventional superconductors. Since then, superconductivity at temperatures as high as 160 K have been reported, though in fragile compounds.

*High-temperature superconductors*

Considerable research is being done to develop high-$T_C$ superconductors as wires that can carry currents strong enough to be practical. Most applications today use a bismuth-strontium-calcium-copper oxide, known (for short) as BSCCO. A major problem is how to make a useable, bendable wire out of the BSCCO, which is very brittle. One solution is to embed tiny filaments of the high-$T_C$ superconductor in a metal alloy matrix with the superconducting wire wrapped around a tube carrying liquid nitrogen to keep the BSCCO below $T_C$. The wire can not be resistanceless, because of the silver connections, but the resistance is much less than that of a conventional copper cable.

## * 18–10 Electrical Conduction in the Human Nervous System

An interesting example of the flow of electric charge is the human nervous system, which provides us with the means for being aware of the world, for communication within the body, and for controlling the body's muscles. Although the detailed functioning of the hugely complex nervous system is still not well understood, we do have a reasonable understanding of how messages are transmitted within the nervous system: they are electrical signals passing along the basic element of the nervous system, the *neuron*.

Neurons are living cells of unusual shape (Fig. 18–27). Attached to the main cell body are several small appendages known as *dendrites* and a long tail called the *axon*. Signals are received by the dendrites and are propagated along the axon. When a signal reaches the nerve endings, it is transmitted to the next neuron or to a muscle at a connection called a *synapse*. (Some neurons have separate cells, called Schwann cells, wrapped around their axons; they form a layered sheath called a myelin sheath and help to insulate neurons from one another.)

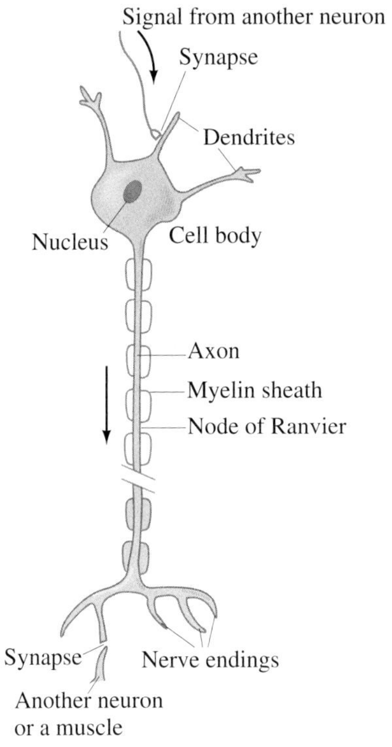


**FIGURE 18–27** A simplified sketch of a typical neuron.

Neurons serve in three capacities. "Sensory neurons" carry messages from the eyes, ears, skin, and other organs to the central nervous system, which consists of the brain and spinal cord. "Motor neurons" carry signals from the central nervous system to particular muscles and can signal them to contract. These two types of neuron make up the "peripheral nervous system" as distinguished from the central nervous system. The third type of neuron is the "interneuron," which transmits signals between neurons. Interneurons are in the brain and spinal column, and often are connected in an incredibly complex array.

A neuron, before transmitting an electrical signal, is in the so-called "resting state." Like nearly all living cells, neurons have a net positive charge on the outer surface of the cell membrane and a negative charge on the inner surface, as mentioned in Section 17–11 with regard to heart muscles and the ECG. This difference in charge, or "dipole layer," means that a potential difference exists across the cell membrane. When a neuron is not transmitting a signal, this "resting potential," normally stated as

$$V_{\text{inside}} - V_{\text{outside}},$$

is typically $-60\,\text{mV}$ to $-90\,\text{mV}$, depending on the type of organism. The most common ions in a cell are $K^+$, $Na^+$, and $Cl^-$. There are large differences in the concentrations of these ions inside and outside a cell, as indicated by the typical values given in Table 18–2. Other ions are also present, so the fluids both inside and outside the axon are electrically neutral. Because of the differences in concentration, there is a tendency for ions to diffuse across the membrane (see Section 13–14 on diffusion). However, in the resting state the cell membrane prevents any net flow of $Na^+$ (through a mechanism of "active pumping" of $Na^+$ out of the cell). But it does allow the flow of $Cl^-$ ions, and less so of $K^+$ ions, and it is these two ions that produce the dipole charge layer on the membrane. Because there is a greater concentration of $K^+$ inside the cell than outside, more $K^+$ ions tend to diffuse outward across the membrane than diffuse inward. A $K^+$ ion that passes through the membrane becomes attached to the outer surface of the membrane, and leaves behind an equal negative charge that lies on the inner surface of the membrane (Fig. 18–28). The fluids themselves remain neutral. Indeed, what keeps the ions on the membrane is their attraction for each other across the membrane. Independent of this process, $Cl^-$ ions tend to diffuse *into* the cell since their concentration outside is higher. Both $K^+$ and $Cl^-$ diffusion tends to charge the interior surface of the membrane negatively and the outside positively. As charge accumulates on the membrane surface, it becomes increasingly difficult for more ions to diffuse: $K^+$ ions trying to move outward, for example, are repelled by the positive charge already there. Equilibrium is reached when the tendency to diffuse because of the concentration difference is just balanced by the electrical potential difference across the membrane. The greater the concentration difference, the greater the potential difference across the membrane, which, as mentioned above, is in the range $-60\,\text{mV}$ to $-90\,\text{mV}$.

**TABLE 18–2**
**Concentrations of Ions Inside and Outside a Typical Axon**

| | Concentration inside axon ($\text{mol/m}^3$) | Concentration outside axon ($\text{mol/m}^3$) |
|---|---|---|
| $K^+$ | 140 | 5 |
| $Na^+$ | 15 | 140 |
| $Cl^-$ | 9 | 125 |

**FIGURE 18–28** How a dipole layer of charge forms on a cell membrane.

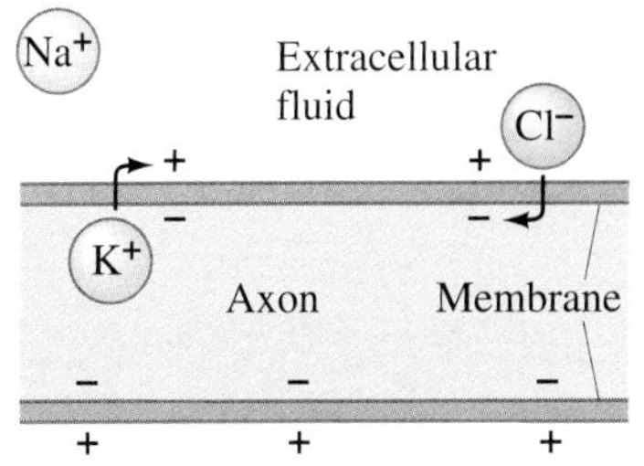

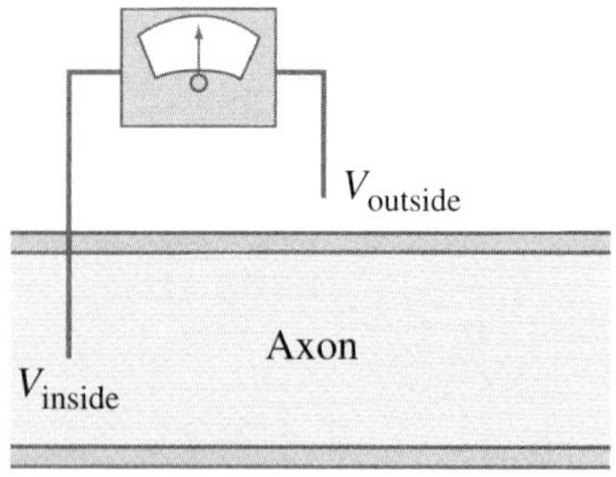


**FIGURE 18–29** Measuring the potential difference between the inside and outside of a nerve cell.

The most important aspect of a neuron is not that it has a resting potential (most cells do), but rather that it can respond to a stimulus and conduct an electrical signal along its length. A nerve can be stimulated in various ways. The stimulus could be thermal (when you touch a hot stove) or chemical (as in taste buds); it could be pressure (as on the skin or at the eardrum), or light (as in the eye); or it could be the electric stimulus of a signal coming from the brain or another neuron. In the laboratory, the stimulus is usually electrical and is applied by a tiny probe at some point on the neuron. If the stimulus exceeds some threshold, a voltage pulse will travel down the axon. This voltage pulse can be detected at a point on the axon using a voltmeter or an oscilloscope connected as in Fig. 18–29. This voltage pulse has the shape shown in Fig. 18–30, and is called an **action potential**. As can be seen, the potential increases from a resting potential of about $-70\,\text{mV}$ and becomes a positive $30\,\text{mV}$ or $40\,\text{mV}$. The action potential lasts for about 1 ms and travels down an axon with a speed of $30\,\text{m/s}$ to $150\,\text{m/s}$. When an action potential is stimulated, the nerve is said to have "fired."

**FIGURE 18–30** Action potential.

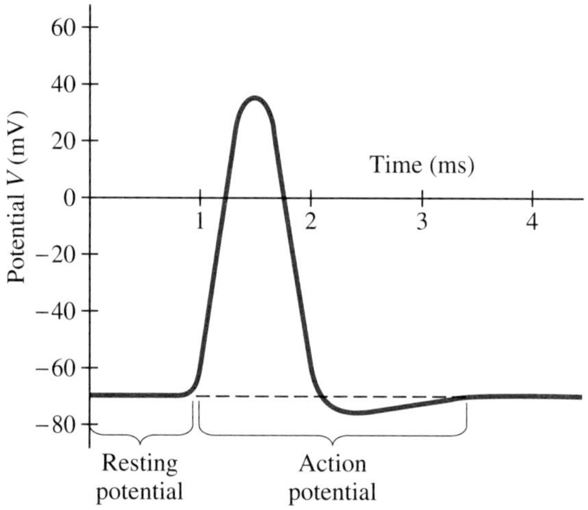


**FIGURE 18–31** Propagation of an action potential along an axon membrane.

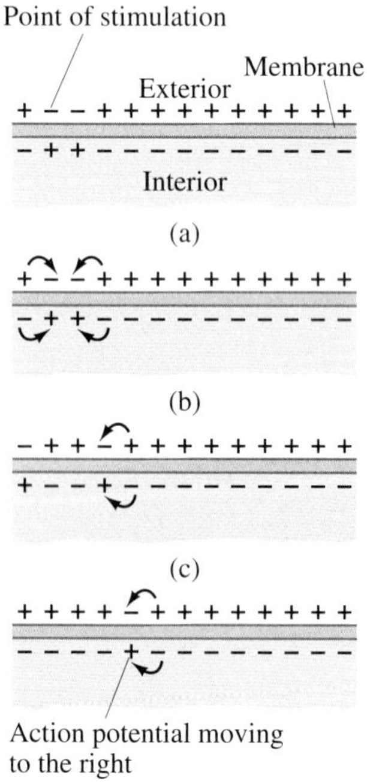


What causes the action potential? Apparently, the cell membrane has the ability to alter its permeability properties. At the point where the stimulus occurs, the membrane suddenly becomes much more permeable to $Na^+$ than to $K^+$ and $Cl^-$ ions. Thus, $Na^+$ ions rush into the cell and the inner surface of the wall becomes positively charged, and the potential difference quickly swings positive ($\approx +30\,\text{mV}$ in Fig. 18–30). Just as suddenly, the membrane returns to its original characteristics: it becomes impermeable to $Na^+$ and in fact pumps out $Na^+$ ions. The diffusion of $Cl^-$ and $K^+$ ions again predominates and the original resting potential is restored ($-70\,\text{mV}$ in Fig. 18–30).

What causes the action potential to travel along the axon? The action potential occurs at the point of stimulation, as shown in Fig. 18–31a. The membrane momentarily is positive on the inside and negative on the outside at this point. Nearby charges are attracted toward this region, as shown in Fig. 18–31b. The potential in these adjacent regions then drops, causing an action potential there. Thus, as the membrane returns to normal at the original point, nearby it experiences an action potential, so the action potential moves down the axon (Figs. 18–31c and d).

You may wonder if the number of ions that pass through the membrane would significantly alter the concentrations. The answer is no; and we can show why by treating the axon as a capacitor in the following Example.

**EXAMPLE 18–15 ESTIMATE Capacitance of an axon.** (*a*) Do an order-of-magnitude estimate for the capacitance of an axon 10 cm long of radius 10 $\mu$m. The thickness of the membrane is about $10^{-8}$ m, and the dielectric constant is about 3. (*b*) By what factor does the concentration (number of ions per volume) of $Na^+$ ions in the cell change as a result of one action potential?

**APPROACH** We model the membrane of an axon as a cylindrically shaped parallel-plate capacitor, with opposite charges on each side. The separation of the "plates" is the thickness of the membrane, $d \approx 10^{-8}$ m. We first calculate the area of the cylinder and then can use Eq. 17–9, $C = K\epsilon_0 A/d$, to find the capacitance. In (*b*), we use the voltage change during one action potential to find the amount of charge moved across the membrane.

**SOLUTION** (*a*) The area $A$ is the area of a cylinder of radius $r$ and length $l$:

$$A = 2\pi r l \approx (6.28)(10^{-5}\,\text{m})(0.1\,\text{m}) \approx 6 \times 10^{-6}\,\text{m}^2.$$

From Eq. 17–9, we have

$$C = K\epsilon_0 \frac{A}{d} \approx (3)(8.85 \times 10^{-12}\,\text{C}^2/\text{N}\cdot\text{m}^2)\frac{6 \times 10^{-6}\,\text{m}^2}{10^{-8}\,\text{m}} \approx 10^{-8}\,\text{F}.$$

(*b*) Since the voltage changes from $-70$ mV to about $+30$ mV, the total change is about 100 mV. The amount of charge that moves is then

$$Q = CV \approx (10^{-8}\,\text{F})(0.1\,\text{V}) = 10^{-9}\,\text{C}.$$

Each ion carries a charge $e = 1.6 \times 10^{-19}\,\text{C}$, so the number of ions that flow per action potential is $Q/e = (10^{-9}\,\text{C})/(1.6 \times 10^{-19}\,\text{C}) \approx 10^{10}$. The volume of our cylindrical axon is

$$V = \pi r^2 l \approx (3)(10^{-5}\,\text{m})^2(0.1\,\text{m}) = 3 \times 10^{-11}\,\text{m}^3,$$

and the concentration of $Na^+$ ions inside the cell (Table 18–2) is $15\,\text{mol/m}^3 = 15 \times 6.02 \times 10^{23}\,\text{ions/m}^3 \approx 10^{25}\,\text{ions/m}^3$. Thus, the cell contains $(10^{25}\,\text{ions/m}^3) \times (3 \times 10^{-11}\,\text{m}^3) \approx 3 \times 10^{14}$ $Na^+$ ions. One action potential, then, will change the concentration of $Na^+$ ions by about $10^{10}/(3 \times 10^{14}) = \frac{1}{3} \times 10^{-4}$, or 1 part in 30,000. This tiny change would not be measurable.

Thus, even 1000 action potentials will not alter the concentration significantly. The sodium pump does not, therefore, have to remove $Na^+$ ions quickly after an action potential, but can operate slowly over time to maintain a relatively constant concentration.

The propagation of a nerve pulse as described here applies to an unmyelinated axon. Myelinated axons, on the other hand, are insulated from the extracellular fluid by the myelin sheath except at the nodes of Ranvier (see Fig. 18–27). An action potential cannot be generated where there is a myelin sheath. Once such a neuron is stimulated, the pulse will still travel along the membrane, but there is resistance and the pulse becomes smaller as it moves down the axon. Nonetheless, the weakened signal can still stimulate a full-fledged action potential when it reaches a node of Ranvier. Thus, the signal is repeatedly amplified at these points. Compare this to an unmyelinated neuron, in which the signal is continually amplified by repeated action potentials all along its length, requiring much more energy. Development of myelinated neurons can be seen as a significant evolutionary step, for it meant reliable transmission of nerve pulses with less energy expended. And the pulses travel more quickly, since ordinary conduction is faster than the repeated production of action potentials, whose speed depends on the flow of ions across the membrane.

# Summary

An electric **battery** serves as a source of nearly constant potential difference by transforming chemical energy into electric energy. A simple battery consists of two electrodes made of different metals immersed in a solution or paste known as an electrolyte.

**Electric current**, $I$, refers to the rate of flow of electric charge and is measured in **amperes** (A): 1 A equals a flow of 1 C/s past a given point.

The direction of **conventional current** is that of positive charge flow. In a wire, it is actually negatively charged electrons that move, so they flow in a direction opposite to the conventional current. A positive charge flow in one direction is almost always equivalent to a negative charge flow in the opposite direction. Positive conventional current always flows from a high potential to a low potential.

The **resistance** $R$ of a device is defined by the relation

$$V = IR, \tag{18–2}$$

where $I$ is the current in the device when a potential difference $V$ is applied across it. For materials such as metals, $R$ is a constant independent of $V$ (thus $I \propto V$), a result known as **Ohm's law**. Thus, the current $I$ coming from a battery of voltage $V$ depends on the resistance $R$ of the circuit connected to it.

Voltage is applied *across* a device or between the ends of a wire. Current passes *through* a wire or device. Resistance is a property *of* the wire or device.

The unit of resistance is the **ohm** ($\Omega$), where $1\,\Omega = 1\,\text{V/A}$. See Table 18–3.

**TABLE 18–3 Summary of Units**

| | |
|---|---|
| Current | $1\,\text{A} = 1\,\text{C/s}$ |
| Potential difference | $1\,\text{V} = 1\,\text{J/C}$ |
| Power | $1\,\text{W} = 1\,\text{J/s}$ |
| Resistance | $1\,\Omega = 1\,\text{V/A}$ |

The resistance $R$ of a wire is inversely proportional to its cross-sectional area $A$, and directly proportional to its length $l$ and to a property of the material called its resistivity:

$$R = \frac{\rho L}{A}. \tag{18–3}$$

The **resistivity**, $\rho$, increases with temperature for metals, but for semiconductors it may decrease.

The rate at which energy is transformed in a resistance $R$ from electric to other forms of energy (such as heat and light) is equal to the product of current and voltage. That is, the **power** transformed, measured in watts, is given by

$$P = IV, \tag{18–5}$$

which for resistors can be written as

$$P = I^2R = \frac{V^2}{R}. \tag{18–6}$$

The SI unit of power is the **watt** ($1\,\text{W} = 1\,\text{J/s}$).

The total electric energy transformed in any device equals the product of the power and the time during which the device is operated. In SI units, energy is given in joules ($1\,\text{J} = 1\,\text{W}\cdot\text{s}$), but electric companies use a larger unit, the **kilowatt-hour** ($1\,\text{kWh} = 3.6 \times 10^6\,\text{J}$).

Electric current can be **direct current (dc)**, in which the current is steady in one direction; or it can be **alternating current (ac)**, in which the current reverses direction at a particular frequency $f$, typically 60 Hz. Alternating currents are typically sinusoidal in time,

$$I = I_0 \sin \omega t, \tag{18–7}$$

where $\omega = 2\pi f$, and are produced by an alternating voltage.

The **rms** values of sinusoidally alternating currents and voltages are given by

$$I_{\text{rms}} = \frac{I_0}{\sqrt{2}} \quad \text{and} \quad V_{\text{rms}} = \frac{V_0}{\sqrt{2}}, \tag{18–8}$$

respectively, where $I_0$ and $V_0$ are the **peak** values. The power relationship, $P = IV = I^2R = V^2/R$, is valid for the average power in alternating currents when the rms values of $V$ and $I$ are used.

[*The current in a wire, at the microscopic level, is considered to be a slow **drift speed** of electrons, $v_d$. The current $I$ is given by

$$I = neAv_d, \tag{18–10}$$

where $n$ is the number of free electrons per unit volume, $e$ is the charge on an electron, and $A$ is the cross-sectional area of the wire.]

[*At very low temperatures certain materials become **superconducting**, which means their electrical resistance becomes zero.]

[*The human nervous system operates via electrical conduction: when a nerve "fires," an electrical signal travels as a voltage pulse known as an **action potential**.]

# Questions

1. What quantity is measured by a battery rating given in ampere-hours (A·h)?
2. When an electric cell is connected to a circuit, electrons flow away from the negative terminal in the circuit. But within the cell, electrons flow *to* the negative terminal. Explain.
3. When a flashlight is operated, what is being used up: battery current, battery voltage, battery energy, battery power, or battery resistance? Explain.
4. One terminal of a car battery is said to be connected to "ground." Since it is not really connected to the ground, what is meant by this expression?
5. When you turn on a water faucet, the water usually flows immediately. You don't have to wait for water to flow from the faucet valve to the spout. Why not? Is the same thing true when you connect a wire to the terminals of a battery?

6. Can a copper wire and an aluminum wire of the same length have the same resistance? Explain.

7. If the resistance of a small immersion heater (to heat water for tea or soup, Fig. 18–32) was increased, would it speed up or slow down the heating process? Explain.

**FIGURE 18–32** Question 7.

8. If a rectangular solid made of carbon has sides of lengths $a$, $2a$, and $3a$, how would you connect the wires from a battery so as to obtain ($a$) the least resistance, ($b$) the greatest resistance?

9. The equation $P = V^2/R$ indicates that the power dissipated in a resistor decreases if the resistance is increased, whereas the equation $P = I^2R$ implies the opposite. Is there a contradiction here? Explain.

10. What happens when a lightbulb burns out?

11. Explain why lightbulbs almost always burn out just as they are turned on and not after they have been on for some time.

12. Which draws more current, a 100-W lightbulb or a 75-W bulb? Which has the higher resistance?

13. Electric power is transferred over large distances at very high voltages. Explain how the high voltage reduces power losses in the transmission lines.

14. A 15-A fuse blows repeatedly. Why is it dangerous to replace this fuse with a 25-A fuse?

15. When electric lights are operated on low-frequency ac (say, 5 Hz), they flicker noticeably. Why?

16. Driven by ac power, the same electrons pass back and forth through your reading lamp over and over again. Explain why the light stays lit instead of going out after the first pass of electrons.

17. The heating element in a toaster is made of Nichrome wire. Immediately after the toaster is turned on, is the current ($I_{rms}$) in the wire increasing, decreasing, or staying constant? Explain.

18. Is current used up in a resistor? Explain.

19. Different lamps might have batteries connected in either of the two arrangements shown in Fig. 18–33. What would be the advantages of each scheme?

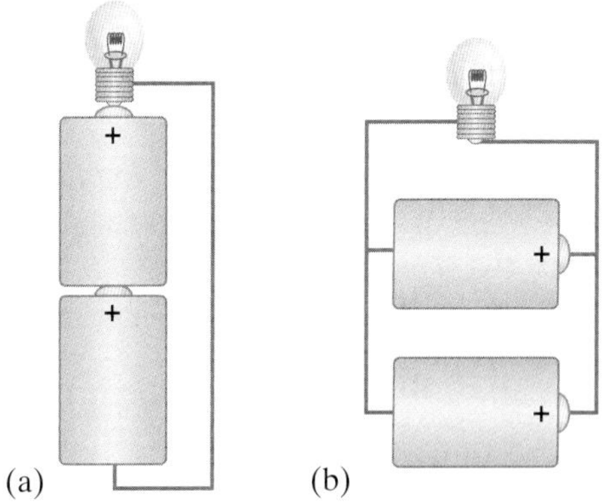


**FIGURE 18–33** Question 19.

## Problems

**18–2 and 18–3 Electric Current, Resistance, Ohms' Law**

(*Note:* The charge on one electron is $1.60 \times 10^{-19}$ C).

1. (I) A current of 1.30 A flows in a wire. How many electrons are flowing past any point in the wire per second?

2. (I) A service station charges a battery using a current of 6.7 A for 5.0 h. How much charge passes through the battery?

3. (I) What is the current in amperes if 1200 $Na^+$ ions flow across a cell membrane in 3.5 $\mu$s? The charge on the sodium is the same as on an electron, but positive.

4. (I) What is the resistance of a toaster if 120 V produces a current of 4.2 A?

5. (I) What voltage will produce 0.25 A of current through a 3800-Ω resistor?

6. (II) A hair dryer draws 7.5 A when plugged into a 120-V line. ($a$) What is its resistance? ($b$) How much charge passes through it in 15 min? (Assume direct current.)

7. (II) An electric clothes dryer has a heating element with a resistance of 9.6 Ω. ($a$) What is the current in the element when it is connected to 240 V? ($b$) How much charge passes through the element in 50 min?

8. (II) A 9.0-V battery is connected to a bulb whose resistance is 1.6 Ω. How many electrons leave the battery per minute?

9. (II) A bird stands on a dc electric transmission line carrying 2800 A (Fig. 18–34). The line has $2.5 \times 10^{-5}\,\Omega$ resistance per meter, and the bird's feet are 4.0 cm apart. What is the potential difference between the bird's feet?

**FIGURE 18–34** Problem 9.

10. (II) An electric device draws 6.50 A at 240 V. (*a*) If the voltage drops by 15%, what will be the current, assuming nothing else changes? (*b*) If the resistance of the device were reduced by 15%, what current would be drawn at 240 V?

11. (II) A 12-V battery causes a current of 0.60 A through a resistor. (*a*) What is its resistance, and (*b*) how many joules of energy does the battery lose in a minute?

### 18–4 Resistivity

12. (I) What is the diameter of a 1.00-m length of tungsten wire whose resistance is $0.32\,\Omega$?

13. (I) What is the resistance of a 3.5-m length of copper wire 1.5 mm in diameter?

14. (II) Calculate the ratio of the resistance of 10.0 m of aluminum wire 2.0 mm in diameter, to 20.0 m of copper wire 2.5 mm in diameter.

15. (II) Can a 2.5-mm-diameter copper wire have the same resistance as a tungsten wire of the same length? Give numerical details.

16. (II) A certain copper wire has a resistance of $10.0\,\Omega$. At what point along its length must the wire be cut so that the resistance of one piece is 4.0 times the resistance of the other? What is the resistance of each piece?

* 17. (II) How much would you have to raise the temperature of a copper wire (originally at 20°C) to increase its resistance by 15%?

* 18. (II) Estimate at what temperature copper will have the same resistivity as tungsten does at 20°C.

* 19. (II) A 100-W lightbulb has a resistance of about $12\,\Omega$ when cold (20°C) and $140\,\Omega$ when on (hot). Estimate the temperature of the filament when hot assuming an average temperature coefficient of resistivity $\alpha = 0.0060\,(\mathrm{C}^\circ)^{-1}$.

20. (II) Compute the voltage drop along a 26-m length of household no. 14 copper wire (used in 15-A circuits). The wire has diameter 1.628 mm and carries a 12-A current.

21. (II) A rectangular solid made of carbon has sides of lengths 1.0 cm, 2.0 cm, and 4.0 cm, lying along the *x*, *y*, and *z* axes, respectively (Fig. 18–35). Determine the resistance for current that passes through the solid in (*a*) the *x* direction, (*b*) the *y* direction, and (*c*) the *z* direction. Assume the resistivity is $\rho = 3.0 \times 10^{-5}\,\Omega\cdot\mathrm{m}$.

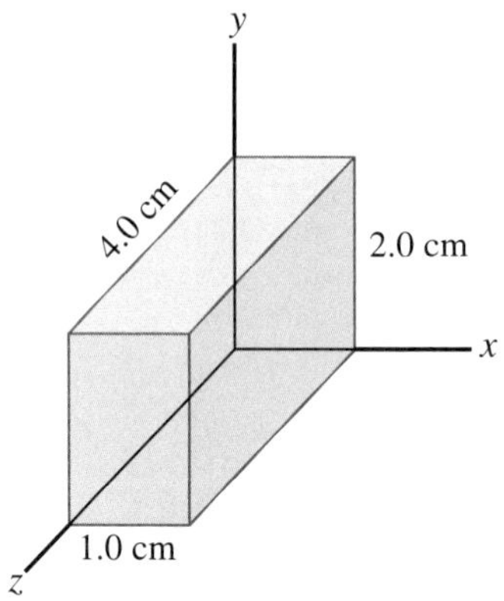


**FIGURE 18–35** Problem 21.

22. (II) Two aluminum wires have the same resistance. If one has twice the length of the other, what is the ratio of the diameter of the longer wire to the diameter of the shorter wire?

* 23. (II) A length of aluminum wire is connected to a precision 10.00-V power supply, and a current of 0.4212 A is precisely measured at 20.0°C. The wire is placed in a new environment of unknown temperature where the measured current is 0.3618 A. What is the unknown temperature?

24. (III) A 10.0-m length of wire consists of 5.0 m of copper followed by 5.0 m of aluminum, both of diameter 1.0 mm. A voltage difference of 85 mV is placed across the composite wire. (*a*) What is the total resistance (sum) of the two wires? (*b*) What is the current through the wire? (*c*) What are the voltages across the aluminum part and across the copper part?

* 25. (III) For some applications, it is important that the value of a resistance not change with temperature. For example, suppose you made a $4.70\text{-k}\Omega$ resistor from a carbon resistor and a Nichrome wire-wound resistor connected together so the total resistance is the sum of their separate resistances. What value should each of these resistors have (at 0°C) so that the combination is temperature independent?

### 18–5 and 18–6 Electric Power

26. (I) The heating element of an electric oven is designed to produce 3.3 kW of heat when connected to a 240-V source. What must be the resistance of the element?

27. (I) What is the maximum power consumption of a 3.0-V portable CD player that draws a maximum of 320 mA of current?

28. (I) What is the maximum voltage that can be applied across a $2.7\text{-k}\Omega$ resistor rated at $\frac{1}{4}$ watt?

29. (I) (*a*) Determine the resistance of, and current through, a 75-W lightbulb connected to its proper source voltage of 120 V. (*b*) Repeat for a 440-W bulb.

30. (II) A 115-V fish-tank heater is rated at 110 W. Calculate (*a*) the current through the heater when it is operating, and (*b*) its resistance?

31. (II) A 120-V hair dryer has two settings: 850 W and 1250 W. (*a*) At which setting do you expect the resistance to be higher? After making a guess, determine the resistance at (*b*) the lower setting; and (*c*) the higher setting.

32. (II) You buy a 75-W lightbulb in Europe, where electricity is delivered to homes at 240 V. If you use the lightbulb in the United States at 120 V (assume its resistance does not change), how bright will it be relative to 75-W 120-V bulbs? [*Hint*: assume roughly that brightness is proportional to power consumed.]

33. (II) How many kWh of energy does a 550-W toaster use in the morning if it is in operation for a total of 15 min? At a cost of 9.0 cents/kWh, estimate how much this would add to your monthly electric energy bill if you made toast four mornings per week.

34. (II) At $0.095 per kWh, what does it cost to leave a 25-W porch light on day and night for a year?

35. (II) An ordinary flashlight uses two D-cell 1.5-V batteries connected in series as in Fig. 18–4b (Fig. 18–36). The bulb draws 450 mA when turned on. (*a*) Calculate the resistance of the bulb and the power dissipated. (*b*) By what factor would the power increase if four D-cells in series were used with the same bulb? (Neglect heating effects of the filament.) Why shouldn't you try this?

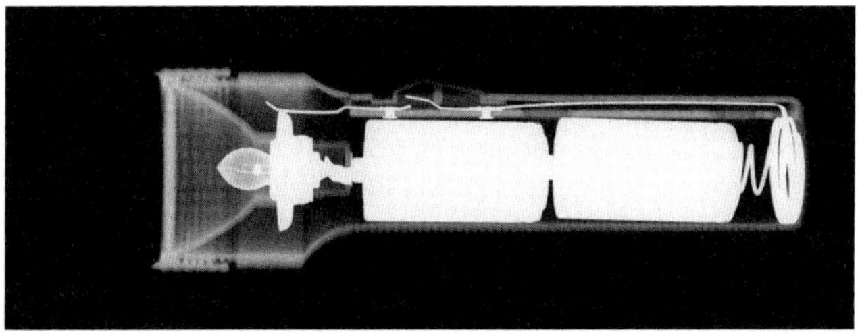

**FIGURE 18–36** Problem 35.

36. (II) What is the total amount of energy stored in a 12-V, 85-A·h car battery when it is fully charged?

37. (II) How many 100-W lightbulbs, connected to 120 V as in Fig. 18–20, can be used without blowing a 15-A fuse?

38. (II) An extension cord made of two wires of diameter 0.129 cm (no. 16 copper wire) and of length 2.7 m (9 ft) is connected to an electric heater which draws 15.0 A on a 120-V line. How much power is dissipated in the cord?

39. (II) A power station delivers 620 kW of power at 12,000 V to a factory through wires with total resistance 3.0 Ω. How much less power is wasted if the electricity is delivered at 50,000 V rather than 12,000 V?

40. (III) The current in an electromagnet connected to a 240-V line is 17.5 A. At what rate must cooling water pass over the coils if the water temperature is to rise by no more than 7.50 C°?

41. (III) A small immersion heater can be used in a car to heat a cup of water for coffee or tea. If the heater can heat 120 mL of water from 25°C to 95°C in 8.0 min, (*a*) approximately how much current does it draw from the car's 12-V battery, and (*b*) what is its resistance? Assume the manufacturer's claim of 60% efficiency.

### 18–7 Alternating Current

42. (I) Calculate the peak current in a 2.2-kΩ resistor connected to a 220-V rms ac source.

43. (I) An ac voltage, whose peak value is 180 V, is across a 330-Ω resistor. What are the rms and peak currents in the resistor?

44. (II) Estimate the resistance of the 120-$V_{rms}$ circuits in your house as seen by the power company, when (*a*) everything electrical is unplugged, and (*b*) there is a lone 75-W lightbulb burning.

45. (II) The peak value of an alternating current in a 1500-W device is 5.4 A. What is the rms voltage across it?

46. (II) An 1800-W arc welder is connected to a 660-$V_{rms}$ ac line. Calculate (*a*) the peak voltage and (*b*) the peak current.

47. (II) (*a*) What is the maximum instantaneous power dissipated by a 3.0-hp pump connected to a 240-$V_{rms}$ ac power source? (*b*) What is the maximum current passing through the pump?

48. (II) A heater coil connected to a 240-$V_{rms}$ ac line has a resistance of 34 Ω. (*a*) What is the average power used? (*b*) What are the maximum and minimum values of the instantaneous power?

### * 18–8 Microscopic View of Electric Current

* 49. (II) A 0.65-mm-diameter copper wire carries a tiny current of 2.3 μA. What is the electron drift speed in the wire?

* 50. (II) A 5.80-m length of 2.0-mm-diameter wire carries a 750-mA current when 22.0 mV is applied to its ends. If the drift speed is $1.7 \times 10^{-5}$ m/s, determine (*a*) the resistance $R$ of the wire, (*b*) the resistivity $\rho$, and (*c*) the number $n$ of free electrons per unit volume.

* 51. (III) At a point high in the Earth's atmosphere, $He^{2+}$ ions in a concentration of $2.8 \times 10^{12}/m^3$ are moving due north at a speed of $2.0 \times 10^6$ m/s. Also, a $7.0 \times 10^{11}/m^3$ concentration of $O_2^-$ ions is moving due south at a speed of $7.2 \times 10^6$ m/s. Determine the magnitude and direction of the net current passing through unit area $(A/m^2)$.

### * 18–10 Nerve Conduction

* 52. (I) What is the magnitude of the electric field across an axon membrane $1.0 \times 10^{-8}$ m thick if the resting potential is −70 mV?

* 53. (II) A neuron is stimulated with an electric pulse. The action potential is detected at a point 3.40 cm down the axon 0.0052 s later. When the action potential is detected 7.20 cm from the point of stimulation, the time required is 0.0063 s. What is the speed of the electric pulse along the axon? (Why are two measurements needed instead of only one?)

* 54. (III) Estimate how much energy is required to transmit one action potential along the axon of Example 18–15. [*Hint*: the energy to transmit one pulse is equivalent to the energy stored by charging the axon capacitance; see Section 17–9]. What minimum average power is required for $10^4$ neurons each transmitting 100 pulses per second?

* 55. (III) During an action potential, $Na^+$ ions move into the cell at a rate of about $3 \times 10^{-7}$ mol/m²·s. How much power must be produced by the "active $Na^+$ pumping" system to produce this flow against a +30-mV potential difference? Assume that the axon is 10 cm long and 20 μm in diameter.

# General Problems

56. How many coulombs are there in 1.00 ampere-hour?

57. What is the average current drawn by a 1.0-hp 120-V motor? (1 hp = 746 W.)

58. A person accidentally leaves a car with the lights on. If each of the two headlights uses 40 W and each of the two taillights 6 W, for a total of 92 W, how long will a fresh 12-V battery last if it is rated at 95 A·h? Assume the full 12 V appears across each bulb.

59. The heating element of a 110-V, 1500-W heater is 5.4 m long. If it is made of iron, what must its diameter be?

60. The *conductance* $G$ of an object is defined as the reciprocal of the resistance $R$; that is, $G = 1/R$. The unit of conductance is a *mho* (= $\text{ohm}^{-1}$), which is also called the *siemens* (S). What is the conductance (in siemens) of an object that draws 730 mA of current at 3.0 V?

61. A small city requires about 10 MW of power. Suppose that instead of using high-voltage lines to supply the power, the power is delivered at 120 V. Assuming a two-wire line of 0.50-cm-diameter copper wire, estimate the cost of the energy lost to heat per hour per meter. Assume the cost of electricity is about 10 cents per kWh.

62. (*a*) A particular household uses a 1.8-kW heater 3.0 h/day ("on" time), four 100-W lightbulbs 6.0 h/day, a 3.0-kW electric stove element for a total of 1.4 h/day, and miscellaneous power amounting to 2.0 kWh/day. If electricity costs \$0.105 per kWh, what will be their monthly bill (30 d)? (*b*) How much coal (which produces 7000 kcal/kg) must be burned by a 35%-efficient power plant to provide the yearly needs of this household?

63. A length of wire is cut in half and the two lengths are wrapped together side by side to make a thicker wire. How does the resistance of this new combination compare to the resistance of the original wire?

64. A 1200-W hair dryer is designed for 117 V. (*a*) What will be the percentage change in power output if the voltage drops to 105 V? Assume no change in resistance. (*b*) How would the actual change in resistivity with temperature affect your answer?

65. The wiring in a house must be thick enough so it does not become so hot as to start a fire. What diameter must a copper wire be if it is to carry a maximum current of 35 A and produce no more than 1.8 W of heat per meter of length?

66. Suppose a current is given by the equation $I = 1.80 \sin 210t$, where $I$ is in amperes and $t$ in seconds. (*a*) What is the frequency? (*b*) What is the rms value of the current? (*c*) If this is the current through a 42.0-Ω resistor, write the equation that describes the voltage as a function of time.

67. A microwave oven running at 65% efficiency delivers 950 W of energy per second to the interior. Find (*a*) the power drawn from the source, and (*b*) the current drawn. Assume a source voltage of 120 V.

68. A 1.00-Ω wire is stretched uniformly to 3.00 times its original length. What is its resistance now?

69. 220 V is applied to two different conductors made of the same material. One conductor is twice as long and twice the diameter of the second. What is the ratio of the power transformed in the first relative to the second?

70. An electric heater is used to heat a room of volume 62 $m^3$. Air is brought into the room at 5°C and is completely replaced twice per hour. Heat loss through the walls amounts to approximately 850 kcal/h. If the air is to be maintained at 20°C, what minimum wattage must the heater have? (The specific heat of air is about 0.17 kcal/kg·C°.)

71. A 2200-W oven is hooked to a 240-V source. (*a*) What is the resistance of the oven? (*b*) How long will it take to bring 120 mL of 15°C water to 100°C assuming 75% efficiency? (*c*) How much will this cost at 11 cents/kWh?

72. A projected electric vehicle makes use of storage batteries as its source of energy. Its mass is 1560 kg and it is powered by 24 batteries, each 12 V, 95 A·h. Assume that the car is driven on level roads at an average speed of 45 km/h, and the average friction force is 240 N. Assume 100% efficiency and neglect energy used for acceleration. No energy is consumed when the vehicle is stopped, since the engine doesn't need to idle. (*a*) Determine the horsepower required. (*b*) After approximately how many kilometers must the batteries be recharged?

73. A 12.5-Ω resistor is made from a coil of copper wire whose total mass is 18.0 g. What is the diameter of the wire, and how long is it?

74. A 100-W, 120-V lightbulb has a resistance of 12 Ω when cold (20°C) and 140 Ω when on (hot). Calculate its power consumption at (*a*) the instant it is turned on, and (*b*) after a few moments when it is hot.

* 75. The Tevatron accelerator at Fermilab (Illinois) is designed to carry an 11-mA beam of protons traveling at very nearly the speed of light ($3.0 \times 10^8$ m/s) around a ring 6300 m in circumference. How many protons are stored in the beam?

76. An air conditioner draws 12 A at 220-V ac. The connecting cord is copper wire with a diameter of 1.628 mm. (*a*) How much power does the air conditioner draw? (*b*) If the total length of wire is 15 m, how much power is dissipated in the wiring? (*c*) If no. 12 wire, with a diameter of 2.053 mm, was used instead, how much power would be dissipated? (*d*) Assuming that the air conditioner is run 12 h per day, how much money per month (30 days) would be saved by using no. 12 wire? Assume that the cost of electricity is 12 cents per kWh.

77. A fish-tank heater is rated at 95 W when connected to 120 V. The heating element is a coil of Nichrome wire. When uncoiled, the wire has a total length of 3.8 m. What is the diameter of the wire?

78. In an automobile, the system voltage varies from about 12 V when the car is off to about 13.8 V when the car is on and the charging system is in operation, a difference of 15%. By what percentage does the power delivered to the headlights vary as the voltage changes from 12 V to 13.8 V? Assume the headlight resistance remains constant.

79. Lightbulb A is rated at 120 V and 40 W for household applications. Lightbulb B is rated at 12 V and 40 W for automotive applications. (*a*) What is the current through each bulb? (*b*) What is the resistance of each bulb? (*c*) In one hour, how much charge passes through each bulb? (*d*) In one hour, how much energy does each bulb use? (*e*) Which bulb requires larger diameter wires to connect its power source and the bulb?

80. Copper wire of diameter 0.259 cm is used to connect a set of appliances at 120 V, which draw 2250 W of power total. (*a*) What power is wasted in 25.0 m of this wire? (*b*) What is your answer if wire of diameter 0.412 cm is used?

81. A copper pipe has an inside diameter of 3.00 cm and an outside diameter of 5.00 cm (Fig. 18–37). What is the resistance of 10.0 m of this pipe?

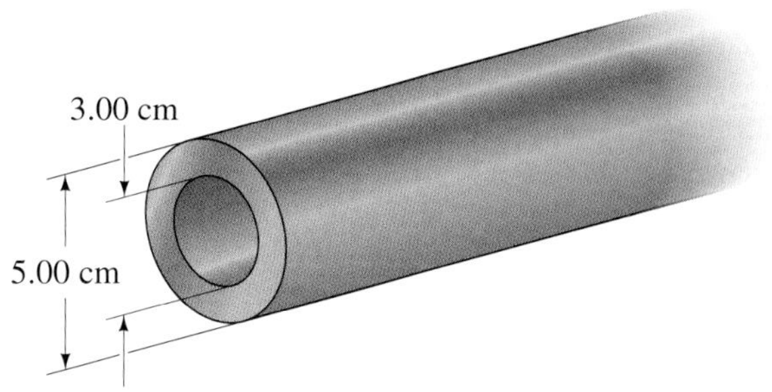


**FIGURE 18–37** Problem 81.

82. If a wire of resistance $R$ is stretched uniformly so that its length doubles, by what factor does the power dissipated in the wire change, assuming it remains hooked up to the same voltage source?

* 83. A tungsten filament used in a flashlight bulb operates at 0.20 A and 3.2 V. If its resistance at 20°C is 1.5 Ω, what is the temperature of the filament when the flashlight is on?

## Answers to Exercises

**A:** $1.6 \times 10^{-13}$ A.

**B:** 240 Ω.

**C:** 110 m.

**D:** 370,000 kg, or about 5000 people.

**E:** 1800 W at 120 V draws a 15-A current. The wires in the extension cord rated at 11 A could become hot enough to melt the insulation and cause a fire.

**F:** 20 V, 5.0 A.

This portable MP3-CD player contains circuits that are dc, at least in part. (The audio signal is ac.) The circuit diagram below shows a possible amplifier circuit for each stereo channel. Although the large triangle is an amplifier chip containing transistors (discussed in Chapter 29), the other circuit elements are ones we have met, resistors and capacitors, and we discuss them in circuits in this Chapter. We also discuss voltmeters and ammeters, and how they are built and used to make measurements.

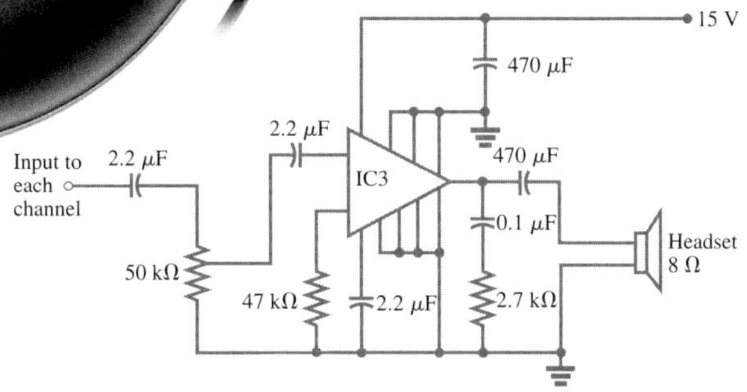


# CHAPTER 19

# DC Circuits

**TABLE 19–1 Symbols for Circuit Elements**

| Symbol | Device |
|---|---|
| ⊣⊢ | Battery |
| ⊣⊢ or ⊣( | Capacitor |
| –\/\/\/– | Resistor |
| —— | Wire with negligible resistance |
| –⁄– | Switch |
| ⏚ or ⏚ | Ground |

Electric circuits are basic parts of all electronic devices from radio and TV sets to computers and automobiles. Scientific measurements, from physics to biology and medicine, make use of electric circuits. In Chapter 18, we discussed the basic principles of electric current. Now we will apply these principles to analyze dc circuits involving combinations of batteries, resistors, and capacitors. We also study the operation of some useful instruments.†

When we draw a diagram for a circuit, we represent batteries, capacitors, and resistors by the symbols shown in Table 19–1. Wires whose resistance is negligible compared with other resistance in the circuit are drawn simply as straight lines. Some circuit diagrams show a ground symbol (⏚ or ⏚) which may mean a real connection to the ground, perhaps via a metal pipe, or it may simply mean a common connection, such as the frame of a car.

For the most part in this Chapter, except in Section 19–6 on *RC* circuits, we will be interested in circuits operating in their steady state. That is, we won't be looking at a circuit at the moment a change is made in it, such as when a battery or resistor is connected or disconnected, but rather a short time later when the currents have reached their steady values.

## 19–1 EMF and Terminal Voltage

To have current in an electric circuit, we need a device such as a battery or an electric generator that transforms one type of energy (chemical, mechanical, or light, for example) into electric energy. Such a device is called a **source** of **electromotive force** or of **emf**. (The term "electromotive force" is a misnomer since it does not refer to a "force" that is measured in newtons. Hence, to avoid confusion, we prefer to use the abbreviation, emf.) The *potential difference* between the terminals of such a source, when no current flows to an external circuit, is called the **emf** of the source. The symbol $\mathscr{E}$ is usually used for emf (don't confuse it with $E$ for electric field), and its unit is volts.

*emf defined*

†AC circuits that contain only a voltage source and resistors can be analyzed like the dc circuits in this Chapter. However, ac circuits that contain capacitors and other circuit elements are more complicated, and we discuss them in Chapter 21.

A battery is not a source of constant current—the current out of a battery varies according to the resistance in the circuit. A battery *is*, however, a nearly constant voltage source, but not perfectly constant as we now discuss. You may have noticed in your own experience that when a current is drawn from a battery, the potential difference (voltage) across its terminals drops below its rated emf. For example, if you start a car with the headlights on, you may notice the headlights dim. This happens because the starter draws a large current, and the battery voltage drops as a result. The voltage drop occurs because the chemical reactions in a battery cannot supply charge fast enough to maintain the full emf. For one thing, charge must move (within the electrolyte) between the electrodes of the battery, and there is always some hindrance to completely free flow. Thus, a battery itself has some resistance, which is called its **internal resistance**; it is usually designated $r$.

**CAUTION**

*Why battery voltage isn't perfectly constant*

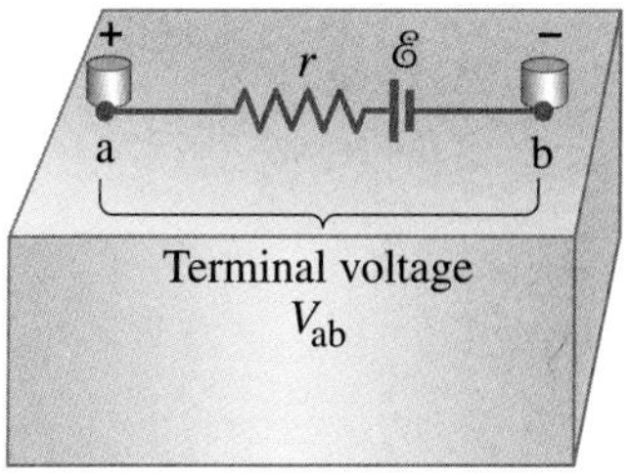


**FIGURE 19–1** Diagram for an electric cell or battery.

A real battery is modeled as if it were a perfect emf $\mathscr{E}$ in series with a resistor $r$, as shown in Fig. 19–1. Since this resistance $r$ is inside the battery, we can never separate it from the battery. The two points a and b in the diagram represent the two terminals of the battery. What we measure is the **terminal voltage** $V_{ab} = V_a - V_b$. When no current is drawn from the battery, the terminal voltage equals the emf, which is determined by the chemical reactions in the battery: $V_{ab} = \mathscr{E}$. However, when a current $I$ flows naturally from the battery there is an internal drop in voltage equal to $Ir$. Thus the terminal voltage (the actual voltage) is[†]

*Terminal voltage*

$$V_{ab} = \mathscr{E} - Ir. \tag{19–1}$$

For example, if a 12-V battery has an internal resistance of 0.1 Ω, then when 10 A flows from the battery, the terminal voltage is $12\text{ V} - (10\text{ A})(0.1\,\Omega) = 11\text{ V}$. The internal resistance of a battery is usually small. For example, an ordinary flashlight battery when fresh may have an internal resistance of perhaps 0.05 Ω. (However, as it ages and the electrolyte dries out, the internal resistance increases to many ohms.) Car batteries have lower internal resistance.

**EXAMPLE 19–1** **Battery with internal resistance.** A 65.0-Ω resistor is connected to the terminals of a battery whose emf is 12.0 V and whose internal resistance is 0.5 Ω, Fig. 19–2. Calculate (*a*) the current in the circuit, (*b*) the terminal voltage of the battery, $V_{ab}$, and (*c*) the power dissipated in the resistor $R$ and in the battery's internal resistance $r$.

**FIGURE 19–2** Example 19–1.

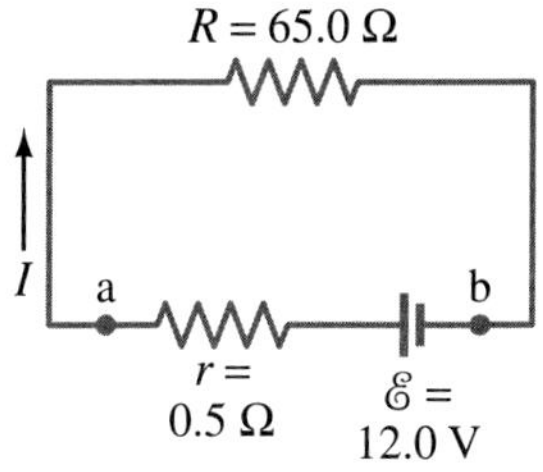


**APPROACH** We first consider the battery as a whole, which is shown in Fig. 19–2 as an emf $\mathscr{E}$ and internal resistance $r$ between points a and b. Then we apply $V = IR$ to the circuit itself.

**SOLUTION** (*a*) From Eq. 19–1, we have

$$V_{ab} = \mathscr{E} - Ir.$$

We apply Ohm's law (Eq. 18–2) to this battery and the resistance $R$ of the circuit: $V_{ab} = IR$. Hence $IR = \mathscr{E} - Ir$ or $\mathscr{E} = I(R + r)$, and so

$$I = \frac{\mathscr{E}}{R + r} = \frac{12.0\text{ V}}{65.0\,\Omega + 0.5\,\Omega} = \frac{12.0\text{ V}}{65.5\,\Omega} = 0.183\text{ A}.$$

(*b*) The terminal voltage is

$$V_{ab} = \mathscr{E} - Ir = 12.0\text{ V} - (0.183\text{ A})(0.5\,\Omega) = 11.9\text{ V}.$$

(*c*) The power dissipated (Eq. 18–6) in $R$ is

$$P_R = I^2R = (0.183\text{ A})^2(65.0\,\Omega) = 2.18\text{ W},$$

and in $r$ is

$$P_r = I^2r = (0.183\text{ A})^2(0.5\,\Omega) = 0.02\text{ W}.$$

**EXERCISE A** Repeat Example 19–1 assuming now that the resistance $R = 10.0\,\Omega$, whereas $\mathscr{E}$ and $r$ remain as before.

[†]When a battery is being charged, a current is forced to pass through it; we then have to write

$$V_{ab} = \mathscr{E} + Ir.$$

See Example 19–9 or Problem 24 and Fig. 19–44.

In much of what follows, unless stated otherwise, we assume that the battery's internal resistance is negligible, and that the battery voltage given is its terminal voltage, which we will usually write simply as $V$ rather than $V_{ab}$. And don't confuse $V$ (italic) for voltage and V (not italic) for the volt unit.

## 19–2 Resistors in Series and in Parallel

When two or more resistors are connected end to end along a single path as shown in Fig. 19–3a, they are said to be connected in **series**. The resistors could be simple resistors as were pictured in Fig. 18–11, or they could be lightbulbs (Fig. 19–3b), or heating elements, or other resistive devices. Any charge that passes through $R_1$ in Fig. 19–3a will also pass through $R_2$ and then $R_3$. Hence the same current $I$ passes through each resistor. (If it did not, this would imply that either charge was not conserved, or that charge was accumulating at some point in the circuit, which does not happen in the steady state.)

**FIGURE 19–3** (a) Resistances connected in series. (b) Resistances could be lightbulbs, or any other type of resistance. (c) Equivalent single resistance $R_{eq}$ that draws the same current: $R_{eq} = R_1 + R_2 + R_3$.

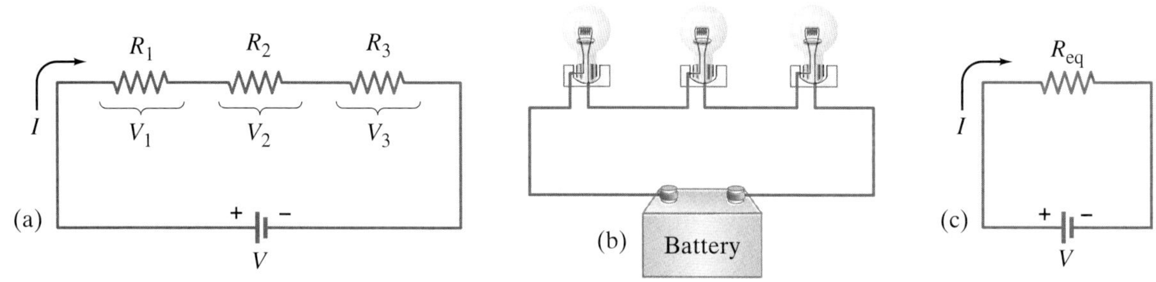


We let $V$ represent the potential difference (voltage) across all three resistors in Fig. 19–3a. We assume all other resistance in the circuit can be ignored, so $V$ equals the terminal voltage supplied by the battery. We let $V_1$, $V_2$, and $V_3$ be the potential differences across each of the resistors, $R_1$, $R_2$, and $R_3$, respectively. From Ohm's law, $V = IR$, we can write $V_1 = IR_1$, $V_2 = IR_2$, and $V_3 = IR_3$. Because the resistors are connected end to end, energy conservation tells us that the total voltage $V$ is equal to the sum of the voltages† across each resistor:

*Series circuit: voltages add; current the same in each R*

$$V = V_1 + V_2 + V_3 = IR_1 + IR_2 + IR_3. \quad \text{[series]} \quad \textbf{(19–2)}$$

Now let us determine the equivalent single resistance $R_{eq}$ that would draw the same current $I$ as our combination of three resistors in series; see Fig. 19–3c. Such a single resistance $R_{eq}$ would be related to $V$ by

$$V = IR_{eq}.$$

We equate this expression with Eq. 19–2, $V = I(R_1 + R_2 + R_3)$, and find

*Resistances in series*

$$R_{eq} = R_1 + R_2 + R_3. \quad \text{[series]} \quad \textbf{(19–3)}$$

This is, in fact, what we expect. When we put several resistances in series, the total or equivalent resistance is the sum of the separate resistances. (Sometimes we may also call it the "net resistance.") This sum applies to any number of resistances in series. Note that when you add more resistance to the circuit, the current through the circuit will decrease. For example, if a 12-V battery is connected to a 4-Ω resistor, the current will be 3 A. But if the 12-V battery is

†To see in more detail why this is true, note that an electric charge $q$ passing through $R_1$ loses an amount of potential energy equal to $qV_1$. In passing through $R_2$ and $R_3$, the potential energy PE decreases by $qV_2$ and $qV_3$, for a total $\Delta\text{PE} = qV_1 + qV_2 + qV_3$; this sum must equal the energy given to $q$ by the battery, $qV$, so that energy is conserved. Hence $qV = q(V_1 + V_2 + V_3)$, and so $V = V_1 + V_2 + V_3$, which is Eq. 19–2.

connected to three 4-Ω resistors in series, the total resistance is 12 Ω and the current through the entire circuit will be only 1 A.

Another simple way to connect resistors is in **parallel**, so that the current from the source splits into separate branches or paths, as shown in Fig. 19–4a. The wiring in houses and buildings is arranged so all electric devices are in parallel, as we already saw in Chapter 18, Fig. 18–20. With parallel wiring, if you disconnect one device (say, $R_1$ in Fig. 19–4a), the current to the other devices is not interrupted. Compare to a series circuit, where if one device (say, $R_1$ in Fig. 19–3a) is disconnected, the current *is* stopped to all the others..

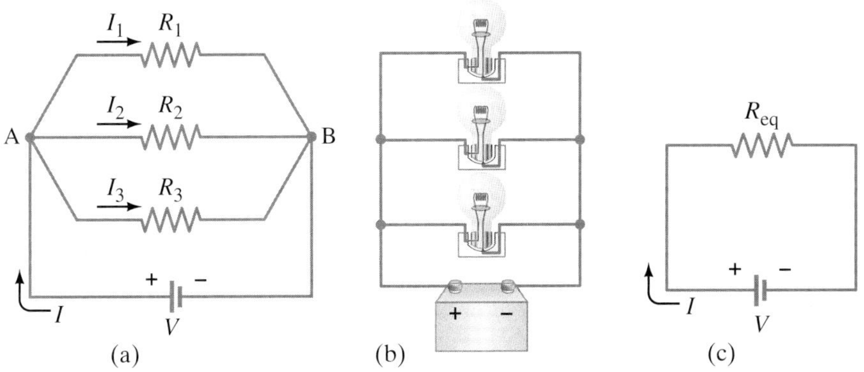


**FIGURE 19–4**
(a) Resistances connected in parallel.
(b) The resistances could be lightbulbs.
(c) The equivalent circuit with $R_{eq}$ obtained from Eq. 19–4:
$$\frac{1}{R_{eq}} = \frac{1}{R_1} + \frac{1}{R_2} + \frac{1}{R_3}.$$

In a parallel circuit, Fig. 19–4a, the total current $I$ that leaves the battery splits into three separate paths. We let $I_1$, $I_2$, and $I_3$ be the currents through each of the resistors, $R_1$, $R_2$, and $R_3$, respectively. Because *electric charge is conserved*, the current $I$ flowing into junction A (where the different wires or conductors meet, Fig. 19–4a) must equal the current flowing out of the junction. Thus

*Parallel circuit: currents add; voltage the same across each R*

$$I = I_1 + I_2 + I_3. \qquad \text{[parallel]}$$

When resistors are connected in parallel, each has the same voltage across it. (Indeed, any two points in a circuit connected by a wire of negligible resistance are at the same potential.) Hence the full voltage of the battery is applied to each resistor in Fig. 19–4a. Applying Ohm's law to each resistor, we have

$$I_1 = \frac{V}{R_1}, \quad I_2 = \frac{V}{R_2}, \quad \text{and} \quad I_3 = \frac{V}{R_3}.$$

Let us now determine what single resistor $R_{eq}$ (Fig. 19–4c) will draw the same current $I$ as these three resistances in parallel. This equivalent resistance $R_{eq}$ must satisfy Ohm's law too:

$$I = \frac{V}{R_{eq}}.$$

We now combine the equations above:

$$I = I_1 + I_2 + I_3,$$
$$\frac{V}{R_{eq}} = \frac{V}{R_1} + \frac{V}{R_2} + \frac{V}{R_3}.$$

When we divide out the $V$ from each term, we have

$$\frac{1}{R_{eq}} = \frac{1}{R_1} + \frac{1}{R_2} + \frac{1}{R_3}. \qquad \text{[parallel]} \quad \textbf{(19–4)}$$

*Resistances in parallel*

For example, suppose you connect two 4-Ω loudspeakers to a single set of output terminals of your stereo amplifier or receiver. (Ignore the other channel for a moment—our two speakers are both connected to the left channel, say.)

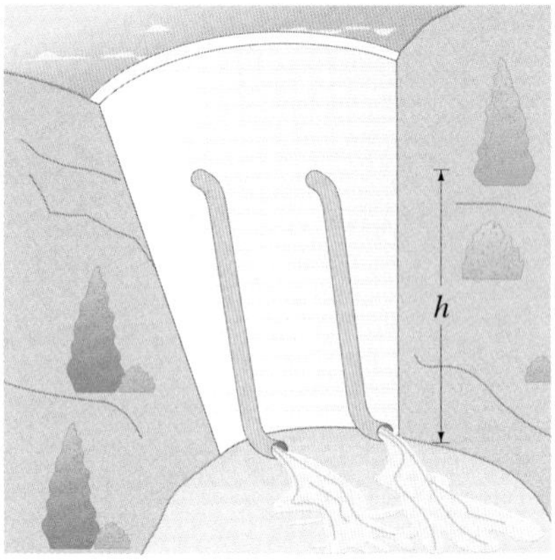


**FIGURE 19–5** Water pipes in parallel—analogy to electric currents in parallel.

The equivalent resistance of the two 4-Ω "resistors" in parallel is

$$\frac{1}{R_{eq}} = \frac{1}{4\,\Omega} + \frac{1}{4\,\Omega} = \frac{2}{4\,\Omega} = \frac{1}{2\,\Omega},$$

and so $R_{eq} = 2\,\Omega$. Thus the net (or equivalent) resistance is *less* than each single resistance. This may at first seem surprising. But remember that when you connect resistors in parallel, you are giving the current additional paths to follow. Hence the net resistance will be less.

An analogy may help here. Consider two identical pipes taking in water near the top of a dam and releasing it below as shown in Fig. 19–5. The gravitational potential difference, proportional to the height $h$, is the same for both pipes, just as the voltage is the same for parallel resistors. If both pipes are open, rather than only one, twice as much water will flow through. That is, with two equal pipes open, the net resistance to the flow of water will be reduced, by half, just as for electrical resistors in parallel. Note that if both pipes are closed, the dam offers infinite resistance to the flow of water. This corresponds in the electrical case to an open circuit—when the path is not continuous and no current flows—so the electrical resistance is infinite.

CONCEPTUAL EXAMPLE 19–2 **Series or parallel?** (*a*) The lightbulbs in Fig. 19–6 are identical and have identical resistance $R$. Which configuration produces more light? (*b*) Which way do you think the headlights of a car are wired?

**RESPONSE** (*a*) The equivalent resistance of the parallel circuit is found from Eq. 19–4, $1/R_{eq} = 1/R + 1/R = 2/R$. Thus $R_{eq} = R/2$. The parallel combination then has lower resistance $(= R/2)$ than the series combination $(R_{eq} = R + R = 2R)$. There will be more total current in the parallel configuration (2), since $I = V/R_{eq}$ and $V$ is the same for both circuits. The total power transformed, which is related to the light produced, is $P = IV$, so the greater current in (2) means more light produced.
(*b*) Headlights are wired in parallel (2), because if one bulb goes out, the other bulb can stay lit. If they were in series (1), when one bulb burned out (the filament broke), the circuit would be open and no current would flow, so even the good bulb would not light.

**FIGURE 19–6** Example 19–2.

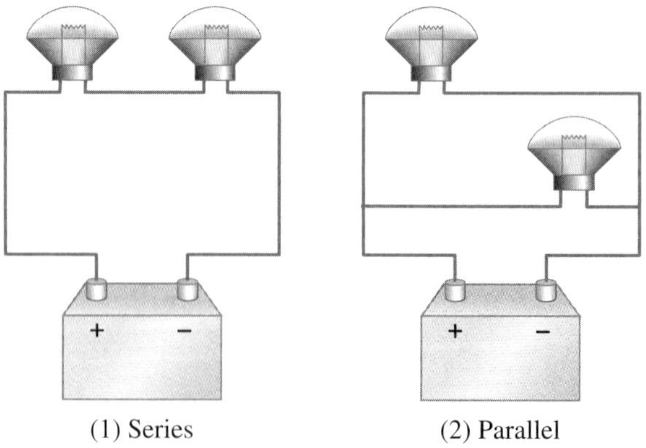


EXAMPLE 19–3 **Series and parallel resistors.** Two 100-Ω resistors are connected (*a*) in parallel, and (*b*) in series, to a 24.0-V battery. See Fig. 19–7. What is the current through each resistor and what is the equivalent resistance of each circuit?

**APPROACH** We use Ohm's law and the ideas just discussed for series and parallel connections to get the current in each case. We can also use Eqs. 19–3 and 19–4.

**SOLUTION** (*a*) Any given charge (or electron) can flow through only one or the other of the two resistors in Fig. 19–7a. Just as a river may break into two streams when going around an island, here too the total current $I$ from the battery (Fig. 19–7a) splits to flow through each resistor, so $I$ equals the sum of the separate currents through the two resistors:

$$I = I_1 + I_2.$$

The potential difference across each resistor is the battery voltage $V = 24.0\text{ V}$. Applying Ohm's law to each resistor gives

$$I = I_1 + I_2 = \frac{V}{R_1} + \frac{V}{R_2} = \frac{24.0\text{ V}}{100\,\Omega} + \frac{24.0\text{ V}}{100\,\Omega}$$
$$= 0.24\text{ A} + 0.24\text{ A} = 0.48\text{ A}.$$

The equivalent resistance is

$$R_{eq} = \frac{V}{I} = \frac{24.0\text{ V}}{0.48\text{ A}} = 50\,\Omega.$$

We could also have obtained this result from Eq. 19–4:

$$\frac{1}{R_{eq}} = \frac{1}{100\,\Omega} + \frac{1}{100\,\Omega} = \frac{2}{100\,\Omega} = \frac{1}{50\,\Omega},$$

so $R_{eq} = 50\,\Omega$.

(*b*) All the current that flows out of the battery passes first through $R_1$ and then $R_2$ since they lie along a single path, Fig. 19–7b. So the current $I$ is the same in both resistors; the potential difference $V$ across the battery equals the total change in potential across the two resistors:

$$V = V_1 + V_2.$$

Ohm's law gives

$$V = IR_1 + IR_2 = I(R_1 + R_2).$$

Hence

$$I = \frac{V}{R_1 + R_2} = \frac{24.0\text{ V}}{100\,\Omega + 100\,\Omega} = 0.120\text{ A}.$$

The equivalent resistance, using Eq. 19–3, is $R_{eq} = R_1 + R_2 = 200\,\Omega$. We could also get $R_{eq}$ by thinking from the point of view of the battery: the total resistance $R_{eq}$ must equal the battery voltage divided by the current it delivers:

$$R_{eq} = \frac{V}{I} = \frac{24.0\text{ V}}{0.120\text{ A}} = 200\,\Omega.$$

**NOTE** The voltage across $R_1$ is $V_1 = IR_1 = (0.120\text{ A})(100\,\Omega) = 12.0\text{ V}$, and that across $R_2$ is $V_2 = IR_2 = 12.0\text{ V}$, each being half of the battery voltage. A simple circuit like Fig. 19–7b is thus often called a simple **voltage divider**.

*Voltage divider*

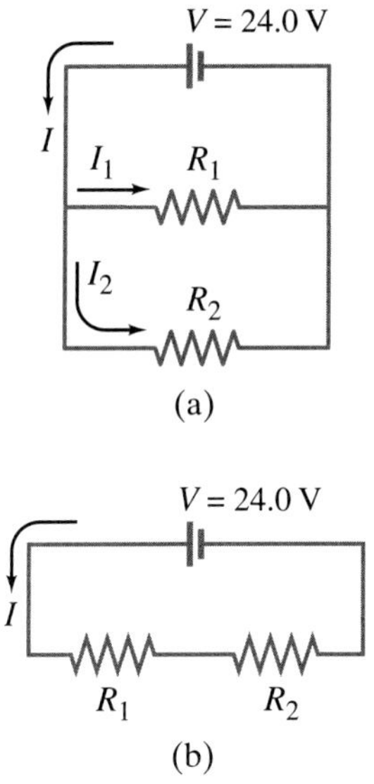

**FIGURE 19–7** Example 19–3.

**EXERCISE B** Design a voltage divider that would provide one-fifth (0.20) of the battery voltage across $R_2$. What is the ratio $R_1/R_2$?

Note that whenever a group of resistors is replaced by the equivalent resistance, current and voltage and power in the rest of the circuit are unaffected.

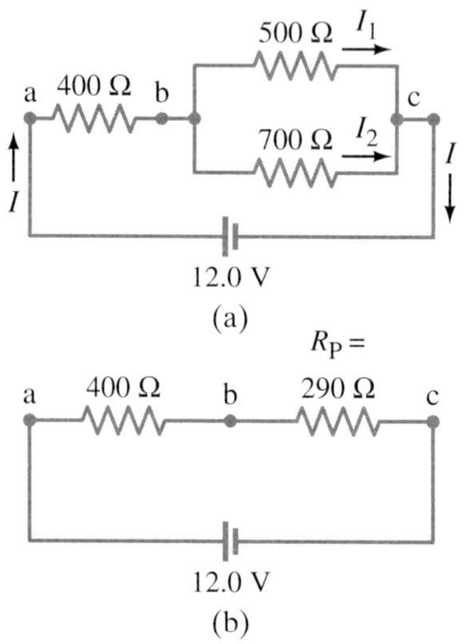


**FIGURE 19–8** (a) Circuit for Examples 19–4 and 19–5. (b) Equivalent circuit, showing the equivalent resistance of 290 Ω for the two parallel resistors in (a).

**EXAMPLE 19–4** **Circuit with series and parallel.** How much current is drawn from the battery shown in Fig. 19–8a?

**APPROACH** The current $I$ that flows out of the battery all passes through the 400-Ω resistor, but then it splits into $I_1$ and $I_2$ passing through the 500-Ω and 700-Ω resistors. The latter two resistors are in parallel with each other. We look for simplicity, something that we already know how to treat. So let's start by finding the equivalent resistance, $R_P$, of the parallel resistors, 500 Ω and 700 Ω. Then we can consider this $R_P$ to be in series with the 400-Ω resistor.

**SOLUTION** The equivalent resistance, $R_P$, of the 500-Ω and 700-Ω resistors in parallel is given by

$$\frac{1}{R_P} = \frac{1}{500\,\Omega} + \frac{1}{700\,\Omega} = 0.0020\,\Omega^{-1} + 0.0014\,\Omega^{-1} = 0.0034\,\Omega^{-1}.$$

**CAUTION**
*Remember to take the reciprocal*

This is $1/R_P$, so we take the reciprocal to find $R_P$. It is a common mistake to forget to take this reciprocal. Notice that the units of reciprocal ohms, $\Omega^{-1}$, are a reminder. Thus

$$R_P = \frac{1}{0.0034\,\Omega^{-1}} = 290\,\Omega.$$

This 290 Ω is the equivalent resistance of the two parallel resistors, and is in series with the 400-Ω resistor as shown in the equivalent circuit of Fig. 19–8b. To find the total equivalent resistance $R_{eq}$, we add the 400-Ω and 290-Ω resistances together, since they are in series, and find

$$R_{eq} = 400\,\Omega + 290\,\Omega = 690\,\Omega.$$

The total current flowing from the battery is then

$$I = \frac{V}{R_{eq}} = \frac{12.0\,\text{V}}{690\,\Omega} = 0.0174\,\text{A} \approx 17\,\text{mA}.$$

**NOTE** This $I$ is also the current flowing through the 400-Ω resistor, but not through the 500-Ω and 700-Ω resistors (both currents are less—see the next Example).

**NOTE** Complex resistor circuits can often be analyzed in this way, considering the circuit as a combination of series and parallel resistances.

**EXAMPLE 19–5** **Current in one branch.** What is the current through the 500-Ω resistor in Fig. 19–8a?

**APPROACH** We need to find the voltage across the 500-Ω resistor, which is the voltage between points b and c in Fig. 19–8a, and we call it $V_{bc}$. Once $V_{bc}$ is known, we can apply Ohm's law, $V = IR$, to get the current. First we find the voltage across the 400-Ω resistor, $V_{ab}$, since we know that 17 mA passes through it.

**SOLUTION** $V_{ab}$ can be found using $V = IR$:

$$V_{ab} = (0.0174\,\text{A})(400\,\Omega) = 7.0\,\text{V}.$$

Since the total voltage across the network of resistors is $V_{ac} = 12.0\,\text{V}$, then $V_{bc}$ must be $12.0\,\text{V} - 7.0\,\text{V} = 5.0\,\text{V}$. Then Ohm's law applied to the 500-Ω resistor tells us that the current $I_1$ through that resistor is

$$I_1 = \frac{5.0\,\text{V}}{500\,\Omega} = 1.0 \times 10^{-2}\,\text{A} = 10\,\text{mA}.$$

This is the answer we wanted. We can also calculate the current $I_2$ through the 700-Ω resistor since the voltage across it is also 5.0 V:

$$I_2 = \frac{5.0\,\text{V}}{700\,\Omega} = 7\,\text{mA}.$$

**NOTE** When $I_1$ combines with $I_2$ to form the total current $I$ (at point c in Fig. 19–8a), their sum is $10\,\text{mA} + 7\,\text{mA} = 17\,\text{mA}$. This is, of course, the total current $I$ as calculated in Example 19–4.

**CONCEPTUAL EXAMPLE 19–6** **Bulb brightness in a circuit.** The circuit shown in Fig. 19–9 has three identical lightbulbs, each of resistance $R$. (*a*) When switch S is closed, how will the brightness of bulbs A and B compare with that of bulb C? (*b*) What happens when switch S is opened? Use a minimum of mathematics in your answers.

**RESPONSE** (*a*) With switch S closed, the current that passes through bulb C must split into two equal parts when it reaches the junction leading to bulbs A and B. It splits into equal parts because the resistance of bulb A equals that of B. Thus, bulbs A and B each receive half of C's current; A and B will be equally bright, but they will be less bright than bulb C.
(*b*) When the switch S is open, no current can flow through bulb A, so it will be dark. We now have a simple one-loop series circuit, and we expect bulbs B and C to be equally bright. However, the equivalent resistance of this circuit ($= R + R$) is greater than that of the circuit with the switch closed. When we open the switch, we increase the resistance and reduce the current leaving the battery. Thus, bulb C will dim when we open the switch. Bulb B gets more current when the switch is open (you may have to use some mathematics here), and so it will be brighter than with the switch closed, and B will be as bright as C.

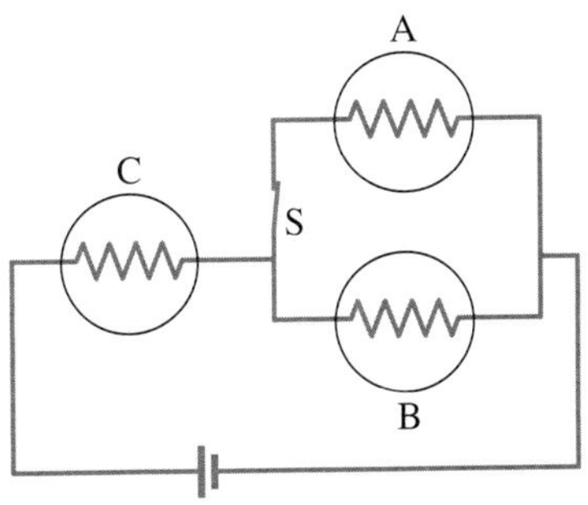


**FIGURE 19–9** Example 19–6, three identical lightbulbs. Each yellow circle with -WW- inside represents a lightbulb and its resistance.

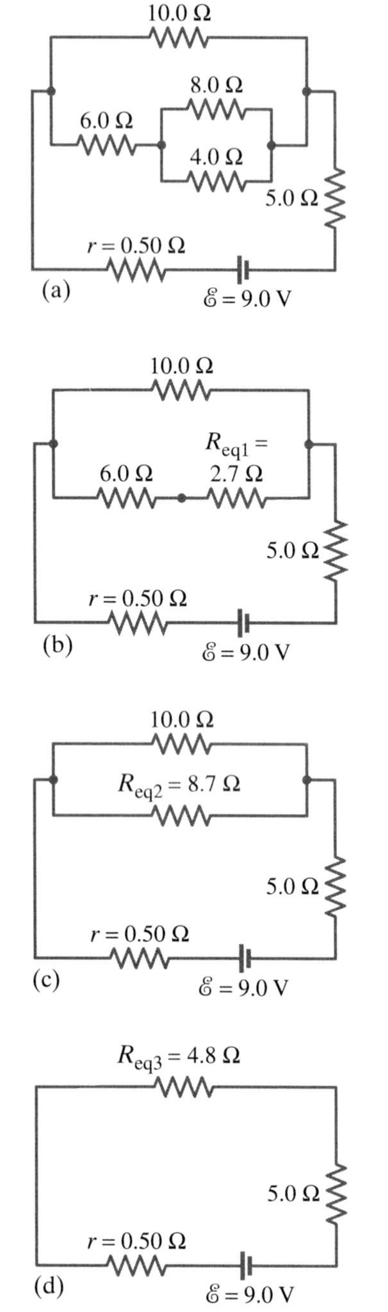


**FIGURE 19–10** Circuit for Example 19–7, where $r$ is the internal resistance of the battery.

**FIGURE 19–11** Currents can be calculated using Kirchhoff's rules.

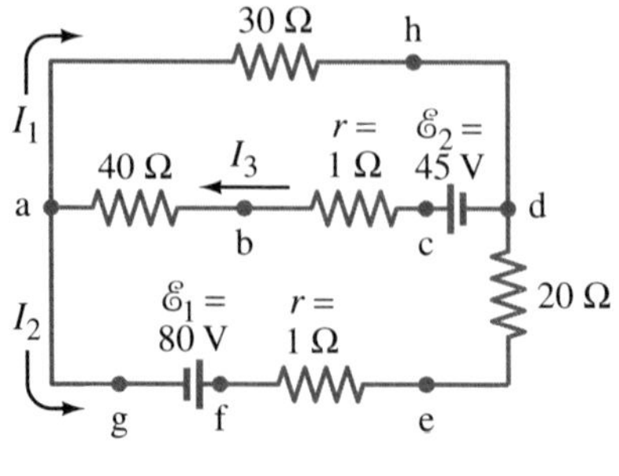


## Additional Example

**EXAMPLE 19–7** **Analyzing a circuit.** A 9.0-V battery whose internal resistance $r$ is 0.50 Ω is connected in the circuit shown in Fig. 19–10a. (*a*) How much current is drawn from the battery? (*b*) What is the terminal voltage of the battery? (*c*) What is the current in the 6.0-Ω resistor?

**APPROACH** To find the current out of the battery, we first need to determine the equivalent resistance $R_{eq}$ of the entire circuit, including $r$, which we do by identifying and isolating simple series or parallel combinations of resistors. Once we find $I$ from Ohm's law, $I = \mathscr{E}/R_{eq}$, we get the terminal voltage using $V_{ab} = \mathscr{E} - Ir$. For (*c*) we apply Ohm's law to the 6.0-Ω resistor.

**SOLUTION** (*a*) We want to determine the equivalent resistance of the circuit. But where do we start? We note that the 4.0-Ω and 8.0-Ω resistors are in parallel, and so have an equivalent resistance $R_{eq1}$ given by

$$\frac{1}{R_{eq1}} = \frac{1}{8.0\,\Omega} + \frac{1}{4.0\,\Omega} = \frac{3}{8.0\,\Omega};$$

so $R_{eq1} = 2.7\,\Omega$. This 2.7 Ω is in series with the 6.0-Ω resistor, as shown in the equivalent circuit of Fig. 19–10b. The net resistance of the lower arm of the circuit is then

$$R_{eq2} = 6.0\,\Omega + 2.7\,\Omega = 8.7\,\Omega,$$

as shown in Fig. 19–10c. The equivalent resistance $R_{eq3}$ of the 8.7-Ω and 10.0-Ω resistances in parallel is given by

$$\frac{1}{R_{eq3}} = \frac{1}{10.0\,\Omega} + \frac{1}{8.7\,\Omega} = 0.21\,\Omega^{-1},$$

so $R_{eq3} = \left(1/0.21\,\Omega^{-1}\right) = 4.8\,\Omega$. This 4.8 Ω is in series with the 5.0-Ω resistor and the 0.50-Ω internal resistance of the battery (Fig. 19–10d), so the total equivalent resistance $R_{eq}$ of the circuit is $R_{eq} = 4.8\,\Omega + 5.0\,\Omega + 0.50\,\Omega = 10.3\,\Omega$. Hence the current drawn is

$$I = \frac{\mathscr{E}}{R_{eq}} = \frac{9.0\,\text{V}}{10.3\,\Omega} = 0.87\,\text{A}.$$

(*b*) The terminal voltage of the battery is

$$V_{ab} = \mathscr{E} - Ir = 9.0\,\text{V} - (0.87\,\text{A})(0.50\,\Omega) = 8.6\,\text{V}.$$

(*c*) Now we can work back and get the current in the 6.0-Ω resistor. It must be the same as the current through the 8.7 Ω shown in Fig. 19–10c (why?). The voltage across that 8.7 Ω will be the emf of the battery minus the voltage drops across $r$ and the 5.0-Ω resistor: $V_{8.7} = 9.0\,\text{V} - (0.87\,\text{A})(0.50\,\Omega + 5.0\,\Omega)$. Applying Ohm's law, we get the current (call it $I'$)

$$I' = \frac{9.0\,\text{V} - (0.87\,\text{A})(0.50\,\Omega + 5.0\,\Omega)}{8.7\,\Omega} = 0.48\,\text{A}.$$

This is the current through the 6.0-Ω resistor.

## 19–3 Kirchhoff's Rules

In the last few Examples we have been able to find the currents in circuits by combining resistances in series and parallel, and using Ohm's law. This technique can be used for many circuits. However, some circuits are too complicated for that analysis. For example, we cannot find the currents in each part of the circuit shown in Fig. 19–11 simply by combining resistances as we did before.

To deal with such complicated circuits, we use Kirchhoff's rules, devised by G. R. Kirchhoff (1824–1887) in the mid-nineteenth century. There are two rules, and they are simply convenient applications of the laws of conservation of charge and energy. **Kirchhoff's first rule** or **junction rule** is based on the conservation of electric charge, and we already used it in deriving the rule for parallel resistors. It states that

*Junction rule (conservation of charge)*

**at any junction point, the sum of all currents entering the junction must equal the sum of all currents leaving the junction.**

That is, whatever charge goes in must come out. For example, at the junction point a in Fig. 19–11, $I_3$ is entering whereas $I_1$ and $I_2$ are leaving. Thus Kirchhoff's junction rule states that $I_3 = I_1 + I_2$. We already saw an instance of this in the NOTE at the end of Example 19–5.

**Kirchhoff's second rule** or **loop rule** is based on the conservation of energy. It states that

*Loop rule (conservation of energy)*

**the sum of the changes in potential around any closed path of a circuit must be zero.**

To see why this rule should hold, consider a rough analogy with the potential energy of a roller coaster on its track. When the roller coaster starts from the station, it has a particular potential energy. As it climbs the first hill, its potential energy increases and reaches a maximum at the top. As it descends the other side, its potential energy decreases and reaches a local minimum at the bottom of the hill. As the roller coaster continues on its path, its potential energy goes through more changes. But when it arrives back at the starting point, it has exactly as much potential energy as it had when it started at this point. Another way of saying this is that there was as much uphill as there was downhill.

Similar reasoning can be applied to an electric circuit. We will do the circuit of Fig. 19–11 shortly but first we consider the simpler circuit in Fig. 19–12. We have chosen it to be the same as the equivalent circuit of Fig. 19–8b already discussed. The current in this circuit is $I = (12.0\text{ V})/(690\,\Omega) = 0.0174\text{ A}$, as we calculated in Example 19–4. (We keep an extra digit in $I$ to reduce rounding errors.) The positive side of the battery, point e in Fig. 19–12a, is at a high potential compared to point d at the negative side of the battery. That is, point e is like the top of a hill for a roller coaster. We follow the current around the circuit starting at any point. We choose to start at point e and follow a positive test charge completely around this circuit. As we go, we note all changes in potential. When the test charge returns to point e, the potential will be the same as when we started (total change in potential around the circuit is zero). We plot the changes in potential around the circuit in Fig. 19–12b; point d is arbitrarily taken as zero.

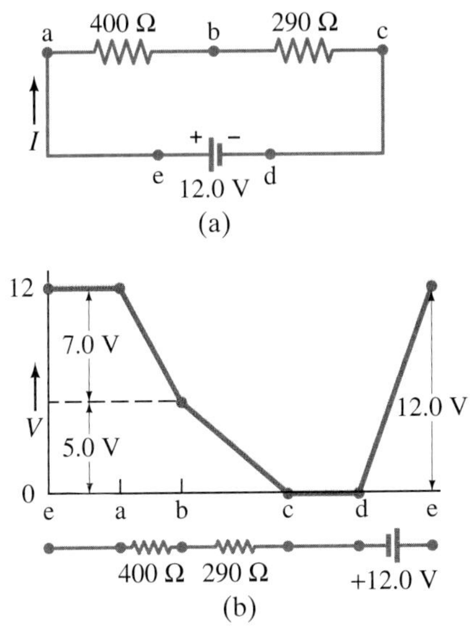


**FIGURE 19–12** Changes in potential around the circuit in (a) are plotted in (b).

As our positive test charge goes from point e to point a, there is no change in potential since there is no source of emf and we assume negligible resistance in the connecting wires. Next, as the charge passes through the 400-Ω resistor to get to point b, there is a decrease in potential of $V = IR = (0.0174\text{ A})(400\,\Omega) = 7.0\text{ V}$. The positive test charge is flowing "downhill" since it is heading toward the negative terminal of the battery, as indicated in the graph of Fig. 19–12b. Because this is a *decrease* in potential, we use a *negative* sign:

**PROBLEM SOLVING**

*Be consistent with signs when applying the loop rule*

$$V_{\text{ba}} = V_{\text{b}} - V_{\text{a}} = -7.0\text{ V}.$$

As the charge proceeds from b to c there is another potential decrease (a "voltage drop") of $(0.0174\text{ A}) \times (290\,\Omega) = 5.0\text{ V}$, and this too is a decrease in potential:

$$V_{\text{cb}} = -5.0\text{ V}.$$

There is no change in potential as our test charge moves from c to d as we assume negligible resistance in the wires. But when it moves from d, which is the negative or low potential side of the battery, to point e, which is the positive terminal (high potential side) of the battery, the potential *increases* by 12.0 V. That is,

$$V_{\text{ed}} = +12.0\text{ V}.$$

The sum of all the changes in potential around the circuit of Fig. 19–12 is

$$-7.0\text{ V} - 5.0\text{ V} + 12.0\text{ V} = 0.$$

This is exactly what Kirchhoff's loop rule said it would be.

## PROBLEM SOLVING Kirchhoff's Rules

1. **Label the current** in each separate branch of the given circuit with a different subscript, such as $I_1$, $I_2$, $I_3$ (see Fig. 19–11 or 19–13). Each current refers to a segment between two junctions. Choose the direction of each current, using an arrow. The direction can be chosen arbitrarily: if the current is actually in the opposite direction, it will come out with a minus sign in the solution.

2. **Identify the unknowns**. You will need as many independent equations as there are unknowns. You may write down more equations than this, but you will find that some of the equations will be redundant (that is, not be independent in the sense of providing new information). You may use $V = IR$ for each resistor, which sometimes will reduce the number of unknowns.

3. **Apply Kirchhoff's junction rule** at one or more junctions.

4. **Apply Kirchhoff's loop rule** for one or more loops: follow each loop in one direction only. Pay careful attention to subscripts, and to signs:
   (a) For a resistor, apply Ohm's law; the potential difference is negative (a decrease) if your chosen loop direction is the same as the chosen current direction through that resistor; the potential difference is positive (an increase) if your chosen loop direction is opposite to the chosen current direction.
   (b) For a battery, the potential difference is positive if your loop direction is from the negative terminal toward the positive terminal; the potential difference is negative if the loop direction is from the positive terminal toward the negative terminal.

5. **Solve the equations** algebraically for the unknowns. Be careful when manipulating equations not to err with signs. At the end, check your answers by plugging them into the original equations, or even by using any additional loop or junction rule equations not used previously.

**EXAMPLE 19–8** **Using Kirchhoff's rules.** Calculate the currents $I_1$, $I_2$, and $I_3$ in the three branches of the circuit in Fig. 19–13.

**APPROACH and SOLUTION**

1. **Label the currents** and their directions. Figure 19–13 uses the labels $I_1$, $I_2$, and $I_3$ for the current in the three separate branches. Since (positive) current tends to move away from the positive terminal of a battery, we choose $I_2$ and $I_3$ to have the directions shown in Fig. 19–13. The direction of $I_1$ is not obvious in advance, so we arbitrarily chose the direction indicated. If the current actually flows in the opposite direction, our answer will have a negative sign.

PROBLEM SOLVING
*Choose current directions arbitrarily*

2. **Identify the unknowns**. We have three unknowns and therefore we need three equations, which we get by applying Kirchhoff's junction and loop rules.

3. **Junction rule**: We apply Kirchhoff's junction rule to the currents at point a, where $I_3$ enters and $I_2$ and $I_1$ leave:

$$I_3 = I_1 + I_2. \qquad (a)$$

This same equation holds at point d, so we get no new information by writing an equation for point d.

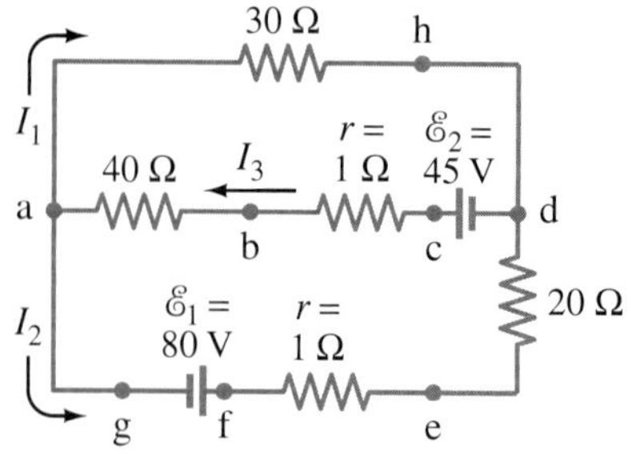


**FIGURE 19–13** Currents can be calculated using Kirchhoff's rules. See Example 19–8.

4. **Loop rule**: We apply Kirchhoff's loop rule to two different closed loops. First we apply it to the upper loop ahdcba. We start (and end) at point a. From a to h we have a potential decrease $V_{ha} = -(I_1)(30\,\Omega)$. From h to d there is no change, but from d to c the potential increases by 45 V: that is, $V_{cd} = +45\,\text{V}$. From c to a the potential decreases through the two resistances by an amount $V_{ac} = -(I_3)(40\,\Omega + 1\,\Omega) = -(41\,\Omega)I_3$. Thus we have $V_{ha} + V_{cd} + V_{ac} = 0$, or

$$-30I_1 + 45 - 41I_3 = 0, \qquad (b)$$

where we have omitted the units. For our second loop, we take the outer loop ahdefga. (We could have chosen the lower loop abcdefga instead.) Again we start at point a and have $V_{ha} = -(I_1)(30\,\Omega)$, and $V_{dh} = 0$. But when we take our positive test charge from d to e, it actually is going uphill, against the current—or at least against the *assumed* direction of the current, which is what counts in this calculation. Thus $V_{ed} = I_2(20\,\Omega)$ has a *positive* sign. Similarly, $V_{fe} = I_2(1\,\Omega)$. From f to g there is a decrease in potential of 80 V since we go from the high potential terminal of the battery to the low. Thus $V_{gf} = -80\,\text{V}$. Finally, $V_{ag} = 0$, and the sum of the potential changes around this loop is then

$$-30I_1 + (20 + 1)I_2 - 80 = 0. \qquad (c)$$

5. **Solve the equations**. We have three equations—labeled (*a*), (*b*), and (*c*)—and three unknowns. From Eq. (*c*) we have

$$I_2 = \frac{80 + 30I_1}{21} = 3.8 + 1.4I_1. \qquad (d)$$

From Eq. (*b*) we have

$$I_3 = \frac{45 - 30I_1}{41} = 1.1 - 0.73I_1. \qquad (e)$$

We substitute Eqs. (*d*) and (*e*) into Eq. (*a*):

$$I_1 = I_3 - I_2 = 1.1 - 0.73I_1 - 3.8 - 1.4I_1.$$

We solve for $I_1$, collecting terms:

$$3.1I_1 = -2.7$$
$$I_1 = -0.87\,\text{A}.$$

The negative sign indicates that the direction of $I_1$ is actually opposite to that initially assumed and shown in Fig. 19–13. Note that the answer automatically comes out in amperes because all values were in volts and ohms. From Eq. (*d*) we have

$$I_2 = 3.8 + 1.4I_1 = 3.8 + 1.4(-0.87) = 2.6\,\text{A},$$

and from Eq. (*e*)

$$I_3 = 1.1 - 0.73I_1 = 1.1 - 0.73(-0.87) = 1.7\,\text{A}.$$

This completes the solution.

**NOTE** The unknowns in different situations are not necessarily currents. It might be that the currents are given and we have to solve for unknown resistance or voltage.

**EXERCISE C** Write the equation for the lower loop abcdefga of Example 19–8 and show, assuming the currents calculated in this Example, that the potentials add to zero for this lower loop.

## * 19–4 EMFs in Series and in Parallel; Charging a Battery

When two or more sources of emf, such as batteries, are arranged in series as in Fig. 19–14a, the total voltage is the algebraic sum of their respective voltages. On the other hand, when a 20-V and a 12-V battery are connected oppositely, as shown in Fig. 19–14b, the net voltage $V_{ca}$ is 8 V (ignoring voltage drop across internal resistances). That is, a positive test charge moved from a to b gains in potential by 20 V, but when it passes from b to c it drops by 12 V. So the net change is 20 V − 12 V = 8 V. You might think that connecting batteries in reverse like this would be wasteful. For most purposes that would be true. But such a reverse arrangement is precisely how a battery charger works. In Fig. 19–14b, the 20-V source is charging up the 12-V battery. Because of its greater voltage, the 20-V source is forcing charge back into the 12-V battery: electrons are being forced into its negative terminal and removed from its positive terminal.

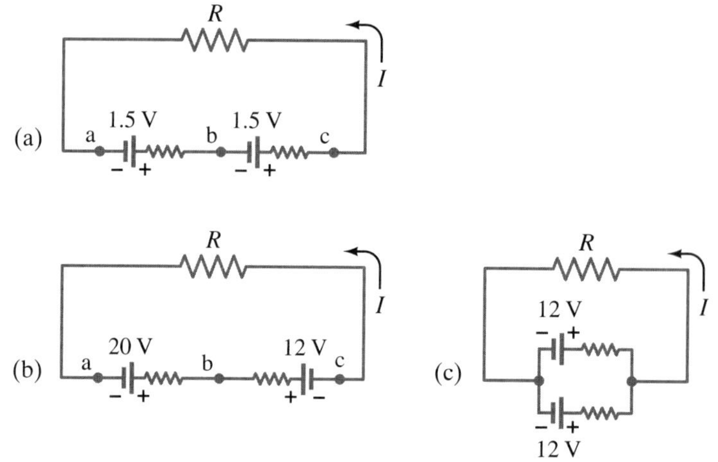


**FIGURE 19–14** Batteries in series (a) and (b), and in parallel (c).

An automobile alternator keeps the car battery charged in the same way. A voltmeter placed across the terminals of a (12-V) car battery with the engine running fairly fast can tell you whether or not the alternator is charging the battery. If it is, the voltmeter reads 13 or 14 V. If the battery is not being charged, the voltage will be 12 V, or less if the battery is discharging. Car batteries can be recharged, but other batteries may not be rechargeable, since the chemical reactions in many cannot be reversed. In such cases, the arrangement of Fig. 19–14b would simply waste energy.

Sources of emf can also be arranged in parallel, Fig. 19–14c, which is useful normally only if the emfs are the same. A parallel arrangement is not used to increase voltage, but rather to provide more energy when large currents are needed. Each of the cells in parallel has to produce only a fraction of the total current, so the energy loss due to internal resistance is less than for a single cell; and the batteries will go dead less quickly.

**FIGURE 19–15** Example 19–9, a jump start.

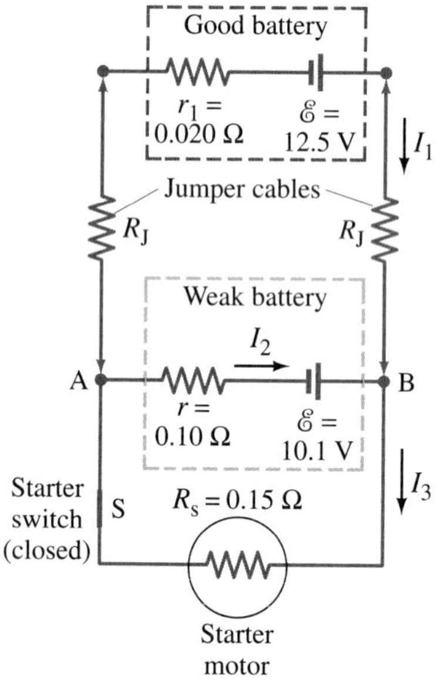


**EXAMPLE 19–9** **Jump starting a car.** A good car battery is being used to jump start a car with a weak battery. The good battery has an emf of 12.5 V and internal resistance 0.020 Ω. Suppose the weak battery has an emf of 10.1 V and internal resistance 0.10 Ω. Each copper jumper cable is 3.0 m long and 0.50 cm in diameter, and can be attached as shown in Fig. 19–15. Assume the starter motor can be represented as a resistor $R_s = 0.15\,\Omega$. Determine the current through the starter motor (*a*) if only the weak battery is connected to it, and (*b*) if the good battery is also connected, as shown in Fig. 19–15.

**APPROACH** We apply Kirchhoff's rules, but in (*b*) we will first need to determine the resistance of the jumper cables using their dimensions and the resistivity ($\rho = 1.68 \times 10^{-8}\,\Omega\cdot\text{m}$ for copper) as discussed in Section 18–4.

**SOLUTION** (*a*) The circuit with only the weak battery and no jumper cables is simple: an emf of 10.1 V connected to two resistances in series, $0.10\,\Omega + 0.15\,\Omega = 0.25\,\Omega$. Hence the current is $I = V/R = (10.1\text{ V})/(0.25\,\Omega) = 40\text{ A}$.
(*b*) We need to find the resistance of the jumper cables that connect the good battery. From Eq. 18–3, each has resistance $R_{\text{J}} = \rho L/A = (1.68 \times 10^{-8}\,\Omega\cdot\text{m})(3.0\text{ m})/(\pi)(0.25 \times 10^{-2}\text{ m})^2 = 0.0026\,\Omega$. Kirchhoff's loop rule for the full outside loop gives

$$12.5\text{ V} - I_1(2R_{\text{J}} + r_1) - I_3 R_{\text{S}} = 0$$
$$12.5\text{ V} - I_1(0.025\,\Omega) - I_3(0.15\,\Omega) = 0 \qquad (a)$$

since $(2R_{\text{J}} + r) = (0.0052\,\Omega + 0.020\,\Omega) = 0.025\,\Omega$.
The loop rule for the lower loop, including the weak battery and the starter, gives

$$10.1\text{ V} - I_3(0.15\,\Omega) - I_2(0.10\,\Omega) = 0. \qquad (b)$$

The junction rule at point B gives

$$I_1 + I_2 = I_3. \qquad (c)$$

We have three equations in three unknowns. From Eq. (*c*), $I_1 = I_3 - I_2$ and we substitute this into Eq. (*a*):

$$12.5\text{ V} - (I_3 - I_2)(0.025\,\Omega) - I_3(0.15\,\Omega) = 0,$$
$$12.5\text{ V} - I_3(0.175\,\Omega) + I_2(0.025\,\Omega) = 0.$$

Combining this last equation with (*b*) gives $I_3 = 71\text{ A}$, quite a bit better than in (*a*). The other currents are $I_2 = -5\text{A}$ and $I_1 = 76\text{A}$. Note that $I_2 = -5\text{A}$ is in the opposite direction from that assumed in Fig. 19–15. The terminal voltage of the weak 10.1-V battery is thus $V_{\text{BA}} = 10.1\text{ V} - (-5\text{ A})(0.10\,\Omega) = 10.6\text{ V}$.

**NOTE** The circuit shown in Fig. 19–15, without the starter motor, is how a battery can be charged. The stronger battery pushes charge back into the weaker battery.

**EXERCISE D** If the jumper cables of Example 19–9 were mistakenly connected in reverse, the positive terminal of each battery would be connected to the negative terminal of the other battery (Fig. 19–16). What would be the current $I$ even before the starter motor is engaged (the switch S in Fig. 19–16 is open)? Why could this cause the batteries to explode?

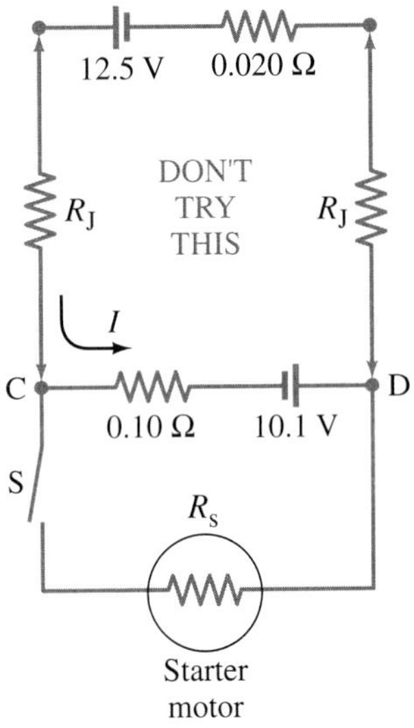


**FIGURE 19–16** Exercise D.

## 19–5 Circuits Containing Capacitors in Series and in Parallel

**FIGURE 19–17** Capacitors in parallel: $C_{\text{eq}} = C_1 + C_2 + C_3$.

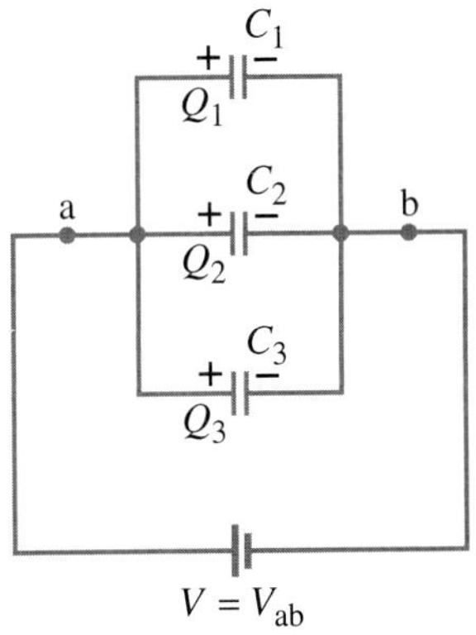


Just as resistors can be placed in series or in parallel in a circuit, so can capacitors (Chapter 17). We first consider a **parallel** connection as shown in Fig. 19–17. If a battery supplies a potential difference $V$ to points a and b, this same potential difference $V = V_{\text{ab}}$ exists across each of the capacitors. That is, since the left-hand plates of all the capacitors are connected by conductors, they all reach the same potential $V_{\text{a}}$ when connected to the battery; and the right-hand plates each reach potential $V_{\text{b}}$. Each capacitor plate acquires a charge given by $Q_1 = C_1 V$, $Q_2 = C_2 V$, and $Q_3 = C_3 V$. The total charge $Q$ that must leave the battery is then

$$Q = Q_1 + Q_2 + Q_3 = C_1 V + C_2 V + C_3 V.$$

Let us try to find a single equivalent capacitor that will hold the same charge $Q$ at the same voltage $V = V_{\text{ab}}$. It will have a capacitance $C_{\text{eq}}$ given by

$$Q = C_{\text{eq}} V.$$

Combining the two previous equations, we have

$$C_{\text{eq}} V = C_1 V + C_2 V + C_3 V = (C_1 + C_2 + C_3)V$$

or

$$C_{\text{eq}} = C_1 + C_2 + C_3. \qquad \text{[parallel]} \quad \textbf{(19–5)}$$

*Capacitors in parallel*

The net effect of connecting capacitors in parallel is thus to *increase* the capacitance. This makes sense because we are essentially increasing the area of the plates where charge can accumulate (see, for example, Eq. 17–8).

*Charge on each capacitor in series is the same*

Capacitors can also be connected in **series**: that is, end to end as shown in Fig. 19–18. A charge $+Q$ flows from the battery to one plate of $C_1$, and $-Q$ flows to one plate of $C_3$. The regions A and B between the capacitors were originally neutral, so the net charge there must still be zero. The $+Q$ on the left plate of $C_1$ attracts a charge of $-Q$ on the opposite plate. Because region A must have a zero net charge, there is $+Q$ on the left plate of $C_2$. The same considerations apply to the other capacitors, so we see the charge on each capacitor plate has the same magnitude $Q$. A single capacitor that could replace these three in series without affecting the circuit (that is, $Q$ and $V$ the same) would have a capacitance $C_{eq}$ where

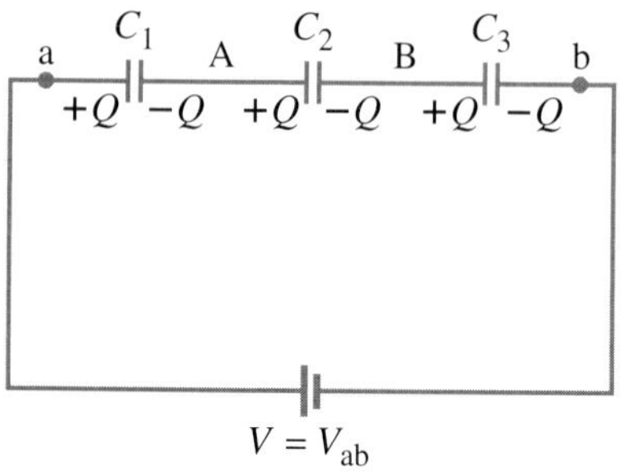


**FIGURE 19–18** Capacitors in series: $\frac{1}{C_{eq}} = \frac{1}{C_1} + \frac{1}{C_2} + \frac{1}{C_3}$.

$$Q = C_{eq}V.$$

The total voltage $V$ across the three capacitors in series must equal the sum of the voltages across each capacitor:

$$V = V_1 + V_2 + V_3.$$

We also have for each capacitor $Q = C_1V_1$, $Q = C_2V_2$, and $Q = C_3V_3$, so we substitute for $V$, $V_1$, $V_2$, and $V_3$ into the last equation and get

$$\frac{Q}{C_{eq}} = \frac{Q}{C_1} + \frac{Q}{C_2} + \frac{Q}{C_3} = Q\left(\frac{1}{C_1} + \frac{1}{C_2} + \frac{1}{C_3}\right)$$

or

*Capacitors in series (add as reciprocals)*

$$\frac{1}{C_{eq}} = \frac{1}{C_1} + \frac{1}{C_2} + \frac{1}{C_3}. \qquad \text{[series]} \quad \textbf{(19–6)}$$

**CAUTION**

*Formula for capacitors in series resembles formula for resistors in parallel*

Notice that the equivalent capacitance $C_{eq}$ is smaller than the smallest contributing capacitance. Notice also that the forms of the equations for capacitors in series or in parallel are the reverse of their counterparts for resistance. That is, the formula for capacitors in series resembles the formula for resistors in parallel.

**EXAMPLE 19–10** **Equivalent capacitance.** Determine the capacitance of a single capacitor that will have the same effect as the combination shown in Fig. 19–19a. Take $C_1 = C_2 = C_3 = C$.

**APPROACH** First we find the equivalent capacitance of $C_2$ and $C_3$ in parallel, and then consider that capacitance in series with $C_1$.

**SOLUTION** Capacitors $C_2$ and $C_3$ are connected in parallel, so they are equivalent to a single capacitor having capacitance

$$C_{23} = C_2 + C_3 = 2C.$$

This $C_{23}$ is in series with $C_1$, Fig. 19–19b, so the equivalent capacitance of the entire circuit, $C_{eq}$, is given by

$$\frac{1}{C_{eq}} = \frac{1}{C_1} + \frac{1}{C_{23}} = \frac{1}{C} + \frac{1}{2C} = \frac{3}{2C}.$$

**PROBLEM SOLVING**

*Remember to take the reciprocal*

Hence the equivalent capacitance of the entire combination is $C_{eq} = \frac{2}{3}C$, and it is smaller than any of the contributing capacitors, $C_1 = C_2 = C_3 = C$.

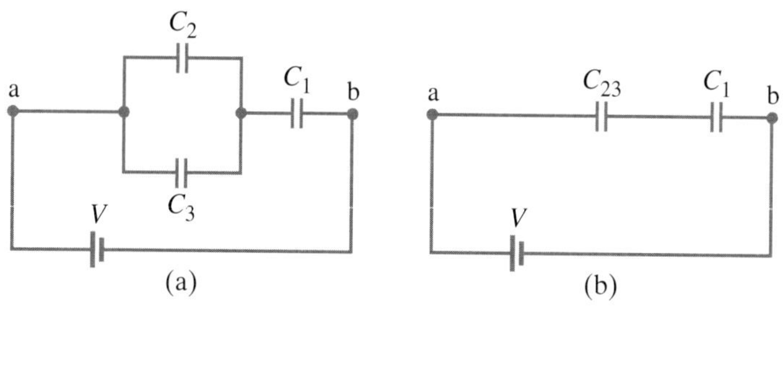


**FIGURE 19–19** Examples 19–10 and 19–11.

## * Additional Example—Calculating Charge and Voltage

**EXAMPLE 19–11** **Charge and voltage on capacitors.** Determine the charge on each capacitor in Fig. 19–19a of Example 19–10, and the voltage across each, assuming $C = 3.0\,\mu\text{F}$ and the battery voltage is $V = 4.0\,\text{V}$.

**APPROACH** We have to work "backward" through Example 19–10. That is, we find the charge $Q$ that leaves the battery, using the equivalent capacitance. Then we find the charge on each separate capacitor and the voltage across each. Each step uses Eq. 17–7, $Q = CV$.

**SOLUTION** The 4.0-V battery "thinks" it is connected to a capacitance $C_{eq} = \frac{2}{3}C = \frac{2}{3}(3.0\,\mu\text{F}) = 2.0\,\mu\text{F}$. Therefore the charge $Q$ that leaves the battery, by Eq. 17–7, is

$$Q = CV = (2.0\,\mu\text{F})(4.0\,\text{V}) = 8.0\,\mu\text{C}.$$

From Fig. 19–19a, this charge arrives at the negative plate of $C_1$, so $Q_1 = 8.0\,\mu\text{C}$. The charge $Q$ that leaves the positive plate is split evenly between $C_2$ and $C_3$ (symmetry: $C_2 = C_3$) and is $Q_2 = Q_3 = \frac{1}{2}Q = 4.0\,\mu\text{C}$. Also, the voltages across $C_2$ and $C_3$ have to be the same. The voltage across each capacitor is obtained using $V = Q/C$. So

$$V_1 = Q_1/C_1 = (8.0\,\mu\text{C})/(3.0\,\mu\text{F}) = 2.7\,\text{V}$$
$$V_2 = Q_2/C_2 = (4.0\,\mu\text{C})/(3.0\,\mu\text{F}) = 1.3\,\text{V}$$
$$V_3 = Q_3/C_3 = (4.0\,\mu\text{C})/(3.0\,\mu\text{F}) = 1.3\,\text{V}.$$

# 19–6 *RC* Circuits—Resistor and Capacitor in Series

*RC circuits*

Capacitors and resistors are often found together in a circuit. Such ***RC* circuits** are used to control a car's windshield wipers and the timing of traffic lights; they are used in camera flashes, in heart pacemakers, and many other electronic devices. In *RC* circuits, we are not so interested in the final "steady state" voltage and charge on the capacitor, but rather in how these variables change in time. A simple example is shown in Fig. 19–20a. We now analyze this *RC* circuit.

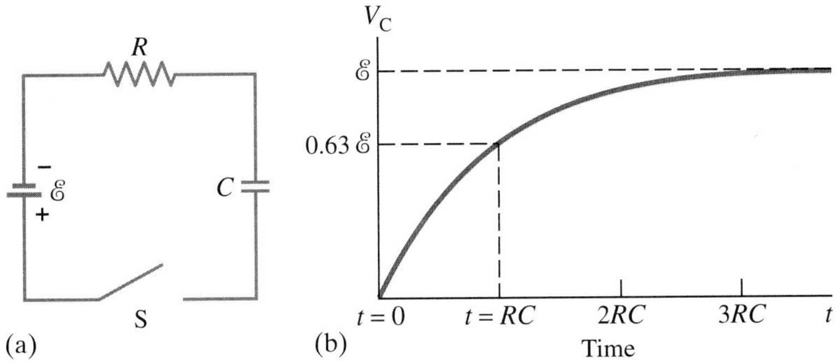


**FIGURE 19–20** For the *RC* circuit shown in (a), the voltage across the capacitor increases with time, as shown in (b), after the switch S is closed.

*Charging the capacitor*

When the switch S is closed, current immediately begins to flow through the circuit. Electrons will flow out from the negative terminal of the battery, through the resistor $R$, and accumulate on the upper plate of the capacitor. And electrons will flow into the positive terminal of the battery, leaving a positive charge on the other plate of the capacitor. As charge accumulates on the capacitor, the potential difference across it increases $(V = Q/C)$, and the current is reduced until eventually the voltage across the capacitor equals the emf of the battery, $\mathscr{E}$. There is then no potential difference across the resistor, and no further current flow. The potential difference across the capacitor, which is proportional to the charge on the capacitor ($V_C = Q/C$, Eq. 17–7), thus increases in time, as shown in Fig. 19–20b. The actual shape of this curve is a type of exponential. It is given by the formula†

$$V_C = \mathscr{E}(1 - e^{-t/RC}),$$

**CAUTION** *Don't confuse e for exponential with e for electron charge*

where we use the subscript C to remind us that $V_C$ is the voltage across the capacitor and is given here as a function of time $t$. [The constant $e$, known as the base for natural logarithms, has the value $e = 2.718\cdots$. Do not confuse this $e$ with $e$ for the charge on the electron.]

†The derivation uses calculus.

We can write a similar formula for the charge $Q\ (= CV_C)$ on the capacitor:

$$Q = Q_0\left(1 - e^{-t/RC}\right),$$

where $Q_0$ represents the maximum charge.

The product of the resistance $R$ times the capacitance $C$, which appears in the exponent, is called the **time constant** $\tau$ of the circuit:

*Time constant $\tau = RC$*

$$\tau = RC. \tag{19–7}$$

The time constant is a measure of how quickly the capacitor becomes charged. [The units of $RC$ are $\Omega \cdot \mathrm{F} = (\mathrm{V/A})(\mathrm{C/V}) = \mathrm{C/(C/s)} = \mathrm{s}$.] Specifically, it can be shown that the product $RC$ gives the time required for the capacitor's voltage (and charge) to reach 63% of the maximum. This can be checked† using any calculator with an $e^x$ key: $e^{-1} = 0.37$, so for $t = RC$, then $\left(1 - e^{-t/RC}\right) = \left(1 - e^{-1}\right) = (1 - 0.37) = 0.63$. In a circuit, for example, where $R = 200\,\mathrm{k\Omega}$ and $C = 3.0\,\mu\mathrm{F}$, the time constant is $\left(2.0 \times 10^5\,\Omega\right)\left(3.0 \times 10^{-6}\,\mathrm{F}\right) = 0.60\,\mathrm{s}$. If the resistance is much smaller, the time constant is much smaller and the capacitor becomes charged almost instantly. This makes sense, since a lower resistance will retard the flow of charge less. All circuits contain some resistance (if only in the connecting wires), so a capacitor can never be charged instantaneously when connected to a battery.

*Capacitor discharges*

The circuit just discussed involved the *charging* of a capacitor by a battery through a resistance. Now let us look at another situation: a capacitor is already charged (say, to a voltage $V_0$ and charge $Q_0$), and it is then allowed to *discharge* through a resistance $R$ as shown in Fig. 19–21a. (In this case there is no battery.) When the switch S is closed, charge begins to flow through resistor $R$ from one side of the capacitor toward the other side, until it is fully discharged. The voltage across the capacitor decreases, as shown in Fig. 19–21b. This "exponential decay" curve is given by

$$V_C = V_0 e^{-t/RC},$$

where $V_0$ is the initial voltage across the capacitor. The voltage falls 63% of the way to zero (to $0.37V_0$) in a time $\tau = RC$. Because the charge $Q$ on the capacitor is $Q = CV$, we can write

$$Q = Q_0 e^{-t/RC}$$

for a discharging capacitor, where $Q_0$ is the initial charge.

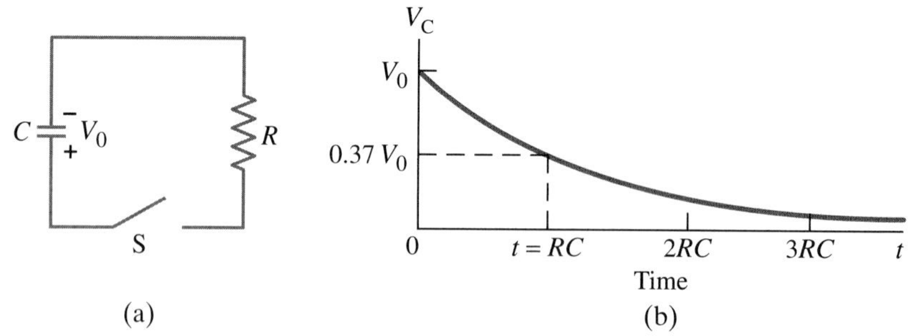


**FIGURE 19–21** For the $RC$ circuit shown in (a), the voltage $V_C$ on the capacitor decreases with time, as shown in (b), after the switch S is closed. The charge on the capacitor follows the same curve since $Q \propto V$.

**EXAMPLE 19–12 A discharging *RC* circuit.** If a charged capacitor, $C = 35\,\mu\mathrm{F}$, is connected to a resistance $R = 120\,\Omega$ as in Fig. 19–21a, how much time will elapse until the voltage falls to 10% of its original (maximum) value?

**APPROACH** The voltage across the capacitor decreases according to $V_C = V_0 e^{-t/RC}$. We set $V_C = 0.10V_0$ (10% of $V_0$), but first we need to calculate $\tau = RC$.

†More simply, since $e = 2.718\cdots$, then $e^{-1} = 1/e = 1/2.718 = 0.37$. Note that $e$ is the inverse operation to the natural logarithm ln: $\ln(e) = 1$, and $\ln\left(e^x\right) = x$.

**SOLUTION** The time constant for this circuit is given by

$$\tau = RC = (120\,\Omega)(35 \times 10^{-6}\,\text{F}) = 4.2 \times 10^{-3}\,\text{s}.$$

After a time $t$ the voltage across the capacitor will be

$$V_C = V_0\left(e^{-t/RC}\right).$$

We want to know the time $t$ for which $V_C = 0.10V_0$. We substitute into the above equation

$$0.10V_0 = V_0 e^{-t/RC}$$

so

$$e^{-t/RC} = 0.10.$$

The inverse operation to the exponential $e$ is the natural log, ln. Thus

$$\ln\left(e^{-t/RC}\right) = -\frac{t}{RC} = \ln 0.10 = -2.3.$$

Solving for $t$, we find the elapsed time is

$$t = 2.3(RC) = (2.3)\left(4.2 \times 10^{-3}\,\text{s}\right) = 9.7 \times 10^{-3}\,\text{s}$$

or 9.7 ms.

**NOTE** We can find the time for any specified voltage across a capacitor by using $t = RC \ln\left(V_0/V_C\right)$.

**EXERCISE E** For the same 35-$\mu$F capacitor as in Example 19–12, what value of resistance $R$ would produce a voltage reduction to 10% of $V_0$ in exactly 1.0 s?

CONCEPTUAL EXAMPLE 19–13 **Bulb in *RC* circuit.** In the circuit of Fig. 19–22, the capacitor is originally uncharged. Describe the behavior of the lightbulb from the instant switch S is closed until a long time later.

**RESPONSE** When the switch is first closed, the current in the circuit is high and the lightbulb burns brightly. As the capacitor charges, the voltage across the capacitor increases and the current is reduced, causing the lightbulb to dim. As the potential difference across the capacitor approaches the same voltage as the battery, the current decreases toward zero and the lightbulb goes out.

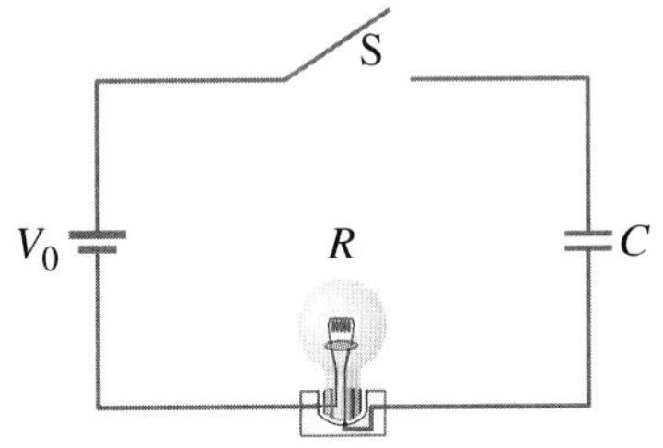


**FIGURE 19–22** Example 19–13.

## * Medical and Other Applications of *RC* Circuits

The charging and discharging in an *RC* circuit can be used to produce voltage pulses at a regular frequency. The charge on the capacitor increases to a particular voltage, and then discharges. A simple way of initiating the discharge of the capacitor is by the use of a gas-filled tube which has an electrical breakdown when the voltage across it reaches a certain value $V_0$. After the discharge is finished, the tube no longer conducts current and the recharging process repeats itself, starting at a lower voltage $V_0'$. Figure 19–23 shows a possible circuit, and the "sawtooth" voltage it produces.

PHYSICS APPLIED

*Sawtooth voltage: blinking flashers*

A simple blinker light can be an application of a sawtooth oscillator circuit. Here the emf is supplied by a battery; the neon bulb flashes on at a rate of perhaps 1 cycle per second. The main component of such a "flasher unit" is a moderately large capacitor.

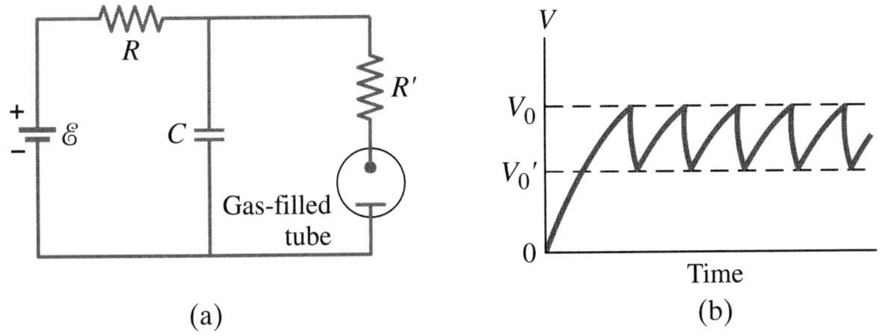


**FIGURE 19–23** (a) An *RC* circuit, coupled with a gas-filled tube as a switch, can produce a repeating "sawtooth" voltage, as shown in (b).

PHYSICS APPLIED
*Windshield wipers*

The intermittent windshield wipers of a car can also use an *RC* circuit. The *RC* time constant, which can be changed using a multi-positioned switch for different values of *R* with fixed *C*, determines the rate at which the wipers come on.

PHYSICS APPLIED
*Heart pacemaker*

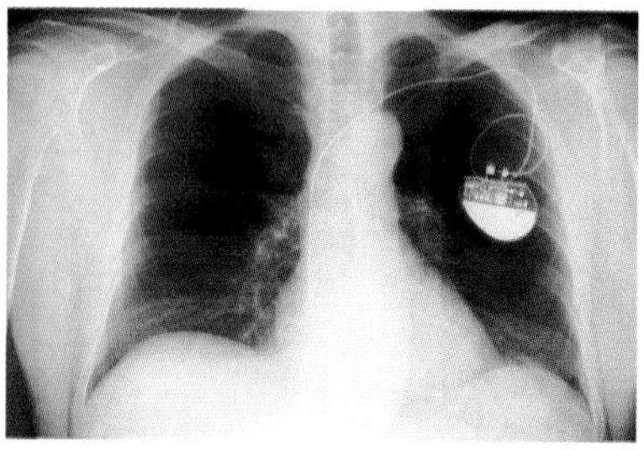

**FIGURE 19–24** Electronic battery-powered pacemaker can be seen on the rib cage in this X-ray.

An interesting medical use of an *RC* circuit is the electronic heart pacemaker, which can make a stopped heart start beating again by applying an electric stimulus through electrodes attached to the chest. The stimulus can be repeated at the normal heartbeat rate if necessary. The heart itself contains *pacemaker* cells, which send out tiny electric pulses at a rate of 60 to 80 per minute. These signals induce the start of each heartbeat. In some forms of heart disease, the natural pacemaker fails to function properly, and the heart loses its beat. Such patients use *electronic pacemakers* which produce a regular voltage pulse that starts and controls the frequency of the heartbeat. The electrodes are implanted in or near the heart (Fig. 19–24), and the circuit contains a capacitor and a resistor. The charge on the capacitor increases to a certain point and then discharges. Then it starts charging again. The pulsing rate depends on the values of *R* and *C*.

## 19–7 Electric Hazards

PHYSICS APPLIED
*Dangers of electricity*

Excess electric current can heat wires in buildings and cause fires, as discussed in Section 18–6. Electric current can also damage the human body or even be fatal. Electric current through the human body can cause damage in two ways: (1) Electric current heats tissue and can cause burns; (2) electric current stimulates nerves and muscles (whose operation, as we saw in Sections 17–11 and 18–10, is electrical), and we feel a "shock." The severity of a shock depends on the magnitude of the current, how long it acts, and through what part of the body it passes. A current passing through vital organs such as the heart or brain is especially serious for it can interfere with their operation.

Most people can "feel" a current of about 1 mA. Currents of a few mA cause pain but rarely cause much damage in a healthy person. Currents above 10 mA cause severe contraction of the muscles, and a person may not be able to release the source of the current (say, a faulty appliance or wire). Death from paralysis of the respiratory system can occur. Artificial respiration, however, can sometimes revive a victim. If a current above about 80 to 100 mA passes across the torso, so that a portion passes through the heart for more than a second or two, the heart muscles will begin to contract irregularly and blood will not be properly pumped. This condition is called *ventricular fibrillation*. If it lasts for long, death results. Strangely enough, if the current is much larger, on the order of 1 A, death by heart failure may be less likely,[†] but such currents can cause serious burns, especially if concentrated through a small area of the body.

The seriousness of a shock depends on the applied voltage and on the effective resistance of the body. Living tissue has low resistance since the fluid of cells contains ions that can conduct quite well. However, the outer layer of skin, when dry, offers high resistance and is thus protective. The effective resistance between two points on opposite sides of the body when the skin is dry is in the range of $10^4$ to $10^6\ \Omega$. But when the skin is wet, the resistance may be $10^3\ \Omega$ or less.

[†]Larger currents apparently bring the entire heart to a standstill. Upon release of the current, the heart returns to its normal rhythm. This may not happen when fibrillation occurs because, once started, it can be hard to stop. Fibrillation may also occur as a result of a heart attack or during heart surgery. A device known as a *defibrillator* (described in Section 17–9) can apply a brief high current to the heart, causing complete heart stoppage which is often followed by resumption of normal beating.

A person who is barefoot or wearing thin-soled shoes will be in good contact with the ground, and touching a 120-V line with a wet hand can result in a current

$$I = \frac{120\ \text{V}}{1000\ \Omega} = 120\ \text{mA}.$$

As we saw, this could be lethal.

A person who has received a shock has become part of a complete circuit. Figure 19–25 shows two ways the circuit might be completed when a person accidentally touches a "hot" electric wire—"hot" meaning a high potential such as 120 V (normal household voltage) relative to ground. The other side of building wiring is connected to ground—either by a wire connected to a buried conductor, or via a water pipe into the ground. In Fig. 19–25a, the current passes from the high-voltage wire, through the person, to the ground through his bare feet, and back along the ground (a fair conductor) to the ground terminal of the source. If the person stands on a good insulator—thick rubber-soled shoes or a dry wood floor—there will be much more resistance in the circuit and consequently much less current through the person. If the person stands with bare feet on the ground, or is in a bathtub, there is lethal danger because the resistance is much less and the current greater. In a bathtub (or swimming pool), not only are you wet, but the water is in contact with the drain pipe that leads to the ground. It is strongly recommended that you not touch anything electrical when wet or in bare feet.

In Fig. 19–25b, a person touches a faulty "hot" wire with one hand, and the other hand touches a sink faucet (connected to ground via the pipe). The current is particularly dangerous because it passes across the chest, through the heart and lungs. A rule of thumb: if one hand is touching something electrical, keep your other hand in your pocket (don't use it!), and wear thick rubber-soled shoes. It is also a good idea to remove metal jewelry, especially rings (your finger is usually moist under a ring).

You can come into contact with a hot wire by touching a bare wire whose insulation has worn off, or from a bare wire inside an appliance when you're tinkering with it. (Always unplug an electrical device before investigating[†] its insides!) Another possibility is that a wire inside a device may break or lose its insulation and come in contact with the case. If the case is metal, it will conduct electricity. A person could then suffer a severe shock merely by touching the case, as shown in Fig. 19–26b. To prevent an accident, metal cases are supposed to be connected directly to ground by a separate ground wire. Then if a "hot" wire touches the grounded case, a short circuit to ground immediately occurs internally, as shown in Fig. 19–26c, and most of the current passes through the low-resistance ground wire rather than through the person. Furthermore, the high current should open the fuse or circuit breaker.

[†] Even then you can get a bad shock from a capacitor that hasn't been discharged until you touch it.

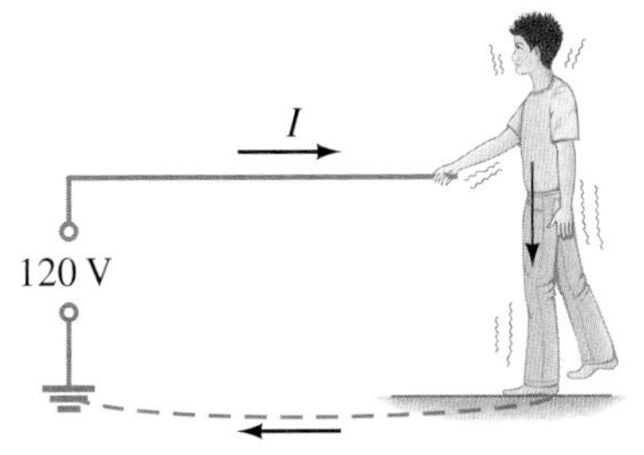


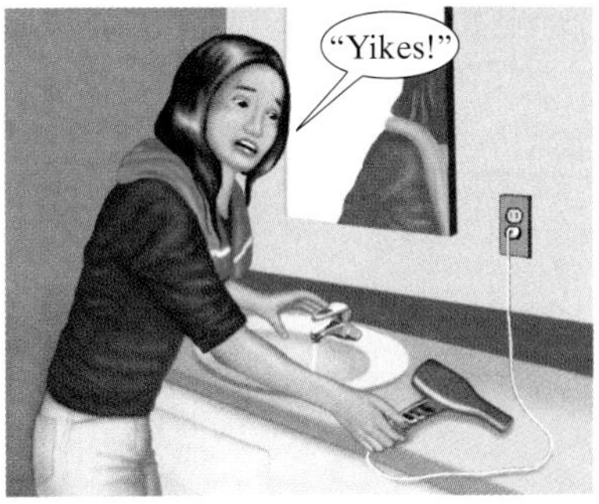


**FIGURE 19–25** A person receives an electric shock when the circuit is completed.

**CAUTION**

*Keep one hand in your pocket when other touches electricity*

**PHYSICS APPLIED**

*Grounding and shocks*

**FIGURE 19–26** (a) An electric oven operating normally with a 2-prong plug. (b) Short to the case with ungrounded case: shock. (c) Short to the case with the case grounded by a 3-prong plug.

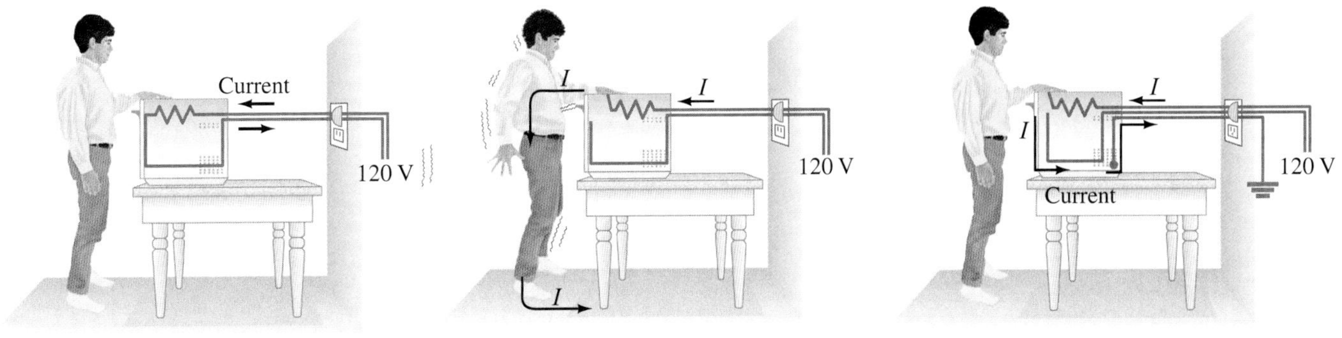

Grounding a metal case is done by a separate ground wire connected to the third (round) prong of a 3-prong plug (Fig. 19–27a). Never cut off the third prong of a plug—it could be deadly.

Why is a third wire needed? The 120 V is carried by the other two wires—one **hot** (120 V ac), the other **neutral**, which is itself grounded.[†] The third "dedicated" ground wire with the round prong may seem redundant. But it is protection for two reasons: (1) it protects against internal wiring that may have been done incorrectly; (2) the neutral wire carries normal current ("return" current from the 120 V) and it does have resistance; so there can be a voltage drop along it—normally small, but if connections are poor or corroded, or the plug is loose, the resistance could be large enough that you might feel that voltage if you touched the neutral wire some distance from its grounding point.

Some electrical devices come with only two wires, and the plug's two prongs are of different widths; the plug can be inserted only one way into the outlet so that the intended neutral (wider prong) in the device is connected to neutral in the wiring. For example, the screw threads of a lightbulb are meant to be connected to neutral (and the base contact to hot), to avoid shocks when changing a bulb in a possibly protruding socket. Devices with 2-prong plugs do *not* have their cases grounded; they are supposed to have double electric insulation. Take extra care anyway.

The insulation on a wire may be color coded. Hand-held meters may have red (hot) and black (ground) lead wires. But in a house, black is usually hot (or it may be red), whereas white is neutral and green is the dedicated ground. But beware: these color codes cannot always be trusted.

Normal circuit breakers (Sections 18–6 and 20–7) protect equipment and buildings from overload and fires. They protect humans only in some circumstances, such as the very high currents that result from a short, if they respond quickly enough. Ground fault circuit interrupters, described in Section 21–8, are designed to protect people from the much lower currents (10 mA to 100 mA) that are lethal but would not throw a 15-A circuit breaker or blow a 20-A fuse.

[†] In the U.S., three wires normally enter a house: two *hot* wires at 120 V each (which add together to 240 V for appliances or devices that run on 240 V) plus the grounded *neutral* (carrying return current for the two hots). See Fig. 19–28 below. The "dedicated" *ground* wire (non-current carrying) is a fourth wire that does not come from the electric company but enters the house from a nearby heavy stake in the ground or a buried metal pipe. The two hot wires can feed separate 120-V circuits in the house, so each 120-V circuit inside the house has only 3 wires as discussed in the text.

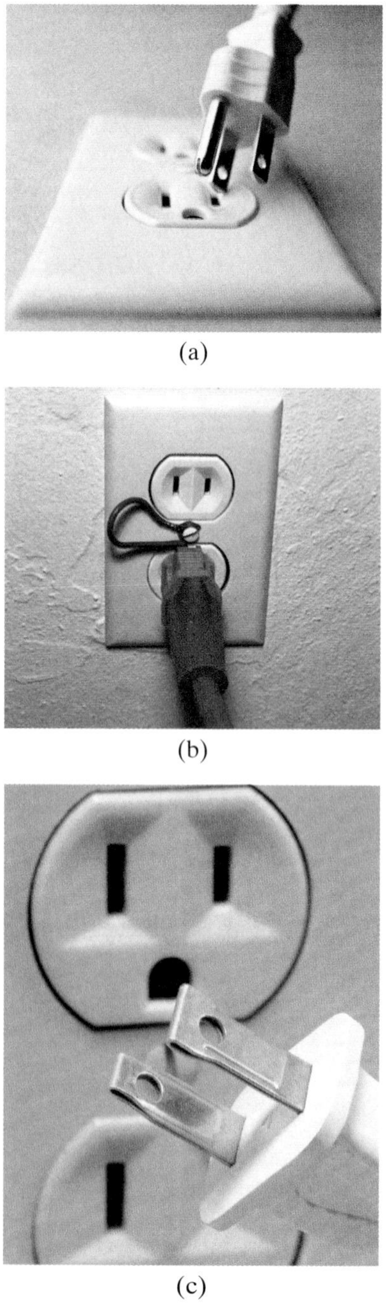


**FIGURE 19–27** (a) A 3-prong plug, and (b) an adapter (gray) for old fashioned 2-prong outlets—be sure to screw down the ground tab. (c) A polarized 2-prong plug.

**CAUTION**

*Black wire may be either ground or hot. Beware!*

**FIGURE 19–28** Four wires entering a typical house. The color codes for wires are not always as shown here—be careful!

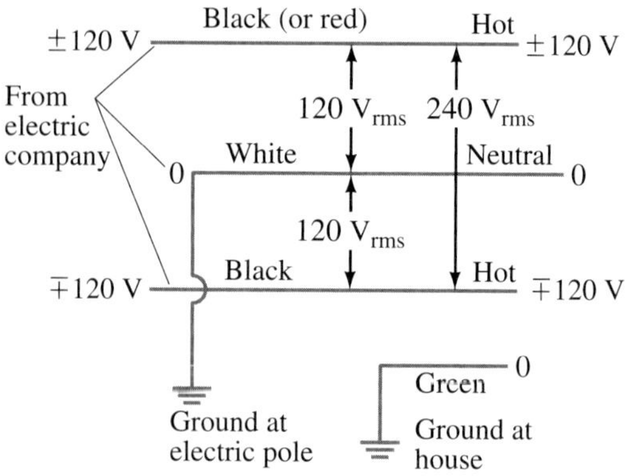

It is current that harms, but it is voltage that drives the current. 30 volts is sometimes said to be the threshhold for danger. But even a 12-V car battery (which can supply large currents) can cause nasty burns and shock.

*Leakage current*

Another danger is *leakage current*, by which we mean a current along an unintended path. Leakage currents are often "capacitively coupled." For example, a wire in a lamp forms a capacitor with the metal case; charges moving in one conductor attract or repel charge in the other, so there is a current. Typical electrical codes limit leakage currents to 1 mA for any device. A 1-mA leakage current is usually harmless. It can be very dangerous, however, to a hospital patient with implanted electrodes connected to ground through the apparatus. This is due to the absence of the protective skin layer and because the current can pass directly through the heart as compared to the usual situation where the current enters at the hands and spreads out through the body. Although 100 mA may be needed to cause heart fibrillation when entering through the hands (very little of it actually passes through the heart), as little as 0.02 mA has been known to cause fibrillation when passing directly to the heart. Thus, a "wired" patient is in considerable danger from leakage current even from as simple an act as touching a lamp.

Finally, don't touch a downed power line (lethal!) or even get near it. A hot power line is at thousands of volts. A huge current can flow along the ground or pavement, from where the high-voltage wire touches it over to the grounding point of the neutral line, enough that the voltage between your two legs could be large. Tip: stand on one foot or run (only one foot touches the ground at a time).

## * 19–8 Ammeters and Voltmeters

PHYSICS APPLIED
*DC meters*

An **ammeter** is used to measure current, and a **voltmeter** measures potential difference or voltage. Measurements of current and voltage are made with meters that are of two types: (1) *analog* meters, which display numerical values by the position of a pointer that can move across a scale (Fig. 19–29a); and (2) *digital* meters, which display the numerical value in numbers (Fig. 19–29b). We now discuss the meters themselves and how they work, then how they are connected to circuits to make measurements. Finally we will discuss how using meters affects the circuit being measured, possibly causing erroneous results—and what to do about it.

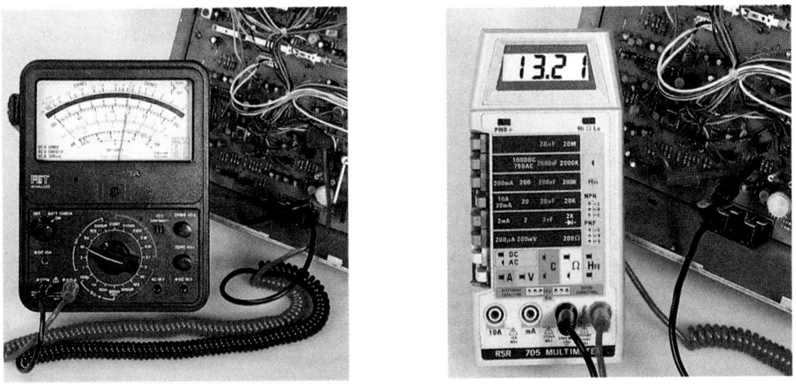

(a) (b)

**FIGURE 19–29** (a) An analog multimeter being used as a voltmeter. (b) An electronic digital meter.

### * Analog Ammeters and Voltmeters

The crucial part of an analog ammeter or voltmeter, in which the reading is by a pointer on a scale (Fig. 19–29a), is a *galvanometer*. The galvanometer works on the principle of the force between a magnetic field and a current-carrying coil of wire, and will be discussed in Chapter 20. For now, we merely need to know that the deflection of the needle of a galvanometer is proportional to the current flowing through it. The *full-scale current sensitivity*, $I_m$, of a galvanometer is the current needed to make the needle deflect full scale.

A galvanometer can be used directly to measure small dc currents. For example, a galvanometer whose sensitivity $I_m$ is 50 $\mu$A can measure currents from about 1 $\mu$A (currents smaller than this would be hard to read on the scale) up to 50 $\mu$A. To measure larger currents, a resistor is placed in parallel with the galvanometer. Thus, an ammeter, represented by the symbol •Ⓐ•, consists of a galvanometer (•Ⓖ•) in parallel with a resistor called the **shunt resistor**, as shown in Fig. 19–30. ("Shunt" is a synonym for "in parallel.") The shunt resistance is $R_{sh}$, and the resistance of the galvanometer coil, through which current passes, is $r$. The value of $R_{sh}$ is chosen according to the full-scale deflection desired; $R_{sh}$ is normally very small—giving an ammeter a very small net resistance—so most of the current passes through $R_{sh}$ and very little ($\lesssim 50\,\mu$A) passes through the galvanometer to deflect the needle.

*Ammeter uses shunt resistor in parallel*

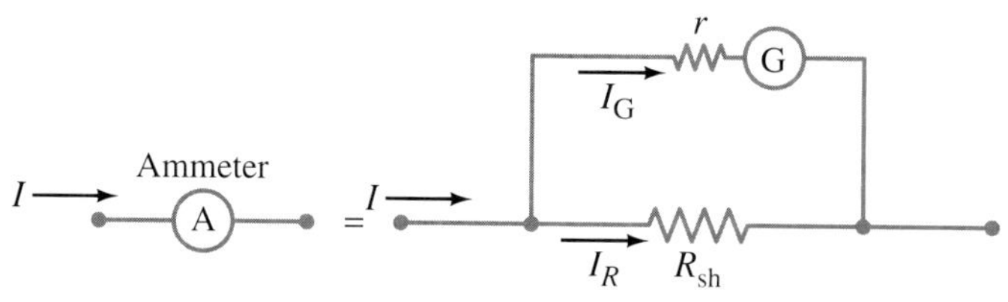


**FIGURE 19–30** An ammeter is a galvanometer in parallel with a (shunt) resistor with low resistance, $R_{sh}$.

**EXAMPLE 19–14** **Ammeter design.** Design an ammeter to read 1.0 A at full scale using a galvanometer with a full-scale sensitivity of 50 $\mu$A and a resistance $r = 30\,\Omega$. Check if the scale is linear.

**APPROACH** Only 50 $\mu$A $(= I_G = 0.000050\text{ A})$ of the 1.0-A current must pass through the galvanometer to give full-scale deflection. The rest of the current $(I_R = 0.999950\text{ A})$ passes through the small shunt resistor, $R_{sh}$, Fig. 19–30. The potential difference across the galvanometer equals that across the shunt resistor (they are in parallel). We apply Ohm's law to find $R_{sh}$.

**SOLUTION** Because $I = I_G + I_R$, when $I = 1.0\text{ A}$ flows into the meter, we want $I_R$ through the shunt resistor to be $I_R = 0.999950\text{ A}$. The potential difference across the shunt is the same as across the galvanometer, so Ohm's law tells us

$$I_R R_{sh} = I_G r;$$

then

$$R_{sh} = \frac{I_G r}{I_R} = \frac{(5.0 \times 10^{-5}\text{ A})(30\,\Omega)}{(0.999950\text{ A})}$$
$$= 1.5 \times 10^{-3}\,\Omega,$$

or 0.0015 Ω. The shunt resistor must thus have a very low resistance and most of the current passes through it.

If the current $I$ into the meter is 0.50 A, say, this will produce a current to the galvanometer equal to

$$I_G = \frac{I_R R_{sh}}{r} = \frac{(0.50\text{ A})(1.5 \times 10^{-3}\,\Omega)}{30\,\Omega}$$
$$= 25\,\mu\text{A},$$

which gives a deflection half of full scale; so the scale is linear.

A voltmeter (•Ⓥ•) also consists of a galvanometer and a resistor. But the resistor $R_{ser}$ is connected in series, Fig. 19–31, and it is usually large, giving a voltmeter a high internal resistance.

*Voltmeter uses series resistor*

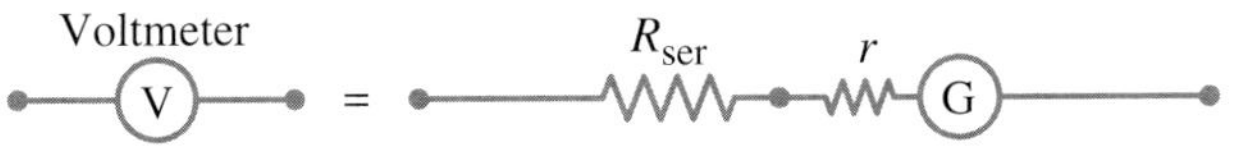


**FIGURE 19–31** A voltmeter is a galvanometer in series with a resistor with high resistance, $R_{ser}$.

**EXERCISE F** Using the same galvanometer as in Example 19–14 with internal resistance $r = 30\,\Omega$ and full-scale current sensitivity of $50\,\mu\text{A}$, use Ohm's law to determine the value of $R_{ser}$ to make a voltmeter that reads from 0 to 15 V.

The meters just described are for direct current. A dc meter can be modified to measure ac (alternating current, Section 18–7) with the addition of diodes (Chapter 29), which allow current to flow in one direction only. An ac meter can be calibrated to read rms or peak values.

*AC meters*

Voltmeters and ammeters can have several series or shunt resistors to offer a choice of range. **Multimeters** can measure voltage, current, and resistance. Sometimes a multimeter is called a VOM (Volt-Ohm-Meter or Volt-Ohm-Milliammeter).

*Multimeters*
*VOM*
*Ohmmeters*

An **ohmmeter** measures resistance, and must contain a battery of known voltage connected in series to a resistor $(R_{ser})$ and to an ammeter (Fig. 19–32). The resistor whose resistance is to be measured completes the circuit. The needle deflection is inversely proportional to the resistance. The scale calibration depends on the value of the series resistor. Because an ohmmeter sends a current through the device whose resistance is to be measured, it should not be used on very delicate devices that could be damaged by the current.

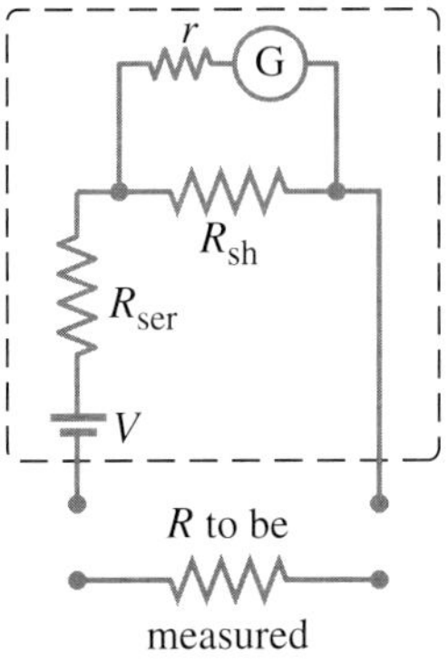


**FIGURE 19–32** An ohmmeter.

The **sensitivity** of a meter is generally specified on the face. It may be given as so many ohms per volt, which indicates how many ohms of resistance there are in the meter per volt of full-scale reading. For example, if the sensitivity is $30{,}000\,\Omega/\text{V}$, this means that on the 10-V scale the meter has a resistance of $300{,}000\,\Omega$, whereas on a 100-V scale the meter resistance is $3\,\text{M}\Omega$. The full-scale current sensitivity, $I_m$, discussed earlier, is just the reciprocal of the sensitivity in $\Omega/\text{V}$.

## * How to Connect Meters

**PHYSICS APPLIED**
*How to use meters correctly*

Suppose you wish to determine the current $I$ in the circuit shown in Fig. 19–33a and the voltage $V$ across the resistor $R_1$. How exactly are ammeters and voltmeters connected to the circuit being measured?

**FIGURE 19–33** Measuring current and voltage.

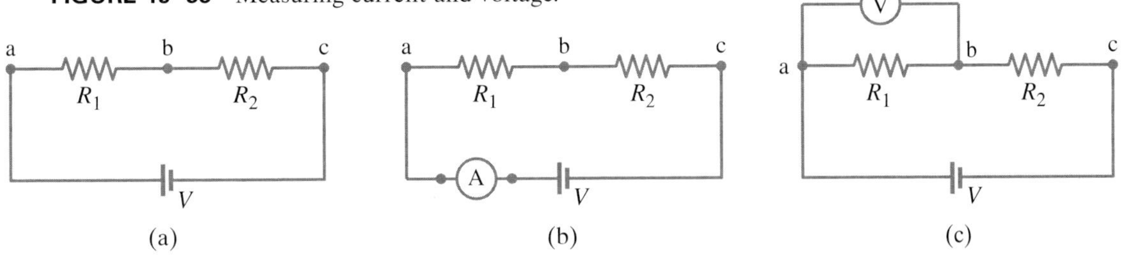


Because an ammeter is used to measure the current flowing in the circuit, it must be inserted directly into the circuit, in series with the other elements, as shown in Fig. 19–33b. The smaller its internal resistance, the less it affects the circuit.

*Ammeter is inserted into the circuit*

A voltmeter, on the other hand, is connected "externally," in parallel with the circuit element across which the voltage is to be measured. It is used to measure the potential difference between two points. Its two wire leads (connecting wires) are connected to the two points, as shown in Fig. 19–33c where the voltage across $R_1$ is being measured. The larger its internal resistance, $(R_{ser} + r)$ in Fig. 19–31, the less it affects the circuit being measured.

*Voltmeter is connected in parallel*

## * Effects of Meter Resistance

PHYSICS APPLIED
*Correcting for meter resistance*

It is important to know the sensitivity of a meter, for in many cases the resistance of the meter can seriously affect your results. Take the following Example.

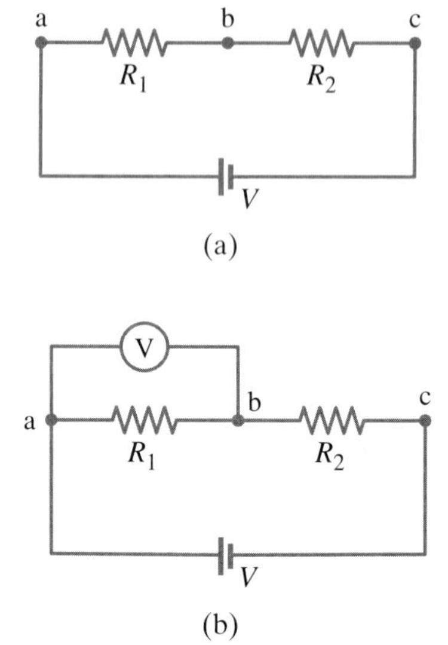


**FIGURE 19–34** Example 19–15.

**EXAMPLE 19–15 Voltage reading versus true voltage.** Suppose you are testing an electronic circuit which has two resistors, $R_1$ and $R_2$, each 15 kΩ, connected in series as shown in Fig. 19–34a. The battery maintains 8.0 V across them and has negligible internal resistance. A voltmeter whose sensitivity is 10,000 Ω/V is put on the 5.0-V scale. What voltage does the meter read when connected across $R_1$, Fig. 19–34b, and what error is caused by the finite resistance of the meter?

**APPROACH** The meter acts as a resistor in parallel with $R_1$. We use parallel and series resistor analyses and Ohm's law to find currents and voltages.

**SOLUTION** On the 5.0-V scale, the voltmeter has an internal resistance of $(5.0\text{ V})(10{,}000\ \Omega/\text{V}) = 50{,}000\ \Omega$. When connected across $R_1$, as in Fig. 19–34b, we have this 50 kΩ in parallel with $R_1 = 15\text{ k}\Omega$. The net resistance $R_{eq}$ of these two is given by

$$\frac{1}{R_{eq}} = \frac{1}{50\text{ k}\Omega} + \frac{1}{15\text{ k}\Omega} = \frac{13}{150\text{ k}\Omega};$$

so $R_{eq} = 11.5\text{ k}\Omega$. This $R_{eq} = 11.5\text{ k}\Omega$ is in series with $R_2 = 15\text{ k}\Omega$, so the total resistance of the circuit is now 26.5 kΩ (instead of the original 30 kΩ). Hence the current from the battery is

$$I = \frac{8.0\text{ V}}{26.5\text{ k}\Omega} = 3.0 \times 10^{-4}\text{ A} = 0.30\text{ mA}.$$

Then the voltage drop across $R_1$, which is the same as that across the voltmeter, is $(3.0 \times 10^{-4}\text{ A})(11.5 \times 10^3\ \Omega) = 3.5\text{ V}$. [The voltage drop across $R_2$ is $(3.0 \times 10^{-4}\text{ A})(15 \times 10^3\ \Omega) = 4.5\text{ V}$, for a total of 8.0 V.] If we assume the meter is precise, it will read 3.5 V. In the original circuit, without the meter, $R_1 = R_2$ so the voltage across $R_1$ is half that of the battery, or 4.0 V. Thus the voltmeter, because of its internal resistance, gives a low reading. In this case it is off by 0.5 V, or more than 10%.

Example 19–15 illustrates how seriously a meter can affect a circuit and give a misleading reading. If the resistance of a voltmeter is much higher than the resistance of the circuit, however, it will have little effect and its readings can be trusted, at least to the manufactured precision of the meter, which for ordinary analog meters is typically 3% to 4% of full-scale deflection. An ammeter also can interfere with a circuit, but the effect is minimal if its resistance is much less than that of the circuit as a whole. For both voltmeters and ammeters, the more sensitive the galvanometer, the less effect it will have. A 50,000-Ω/V meter is far better than a 1000-Ω/V meter.

## * Digital Meters

Digital meters (see Fig. 19–29b) are used in the same way as analog meters: they are inserted directly into the circuit, in series, to measure current (Fig. 19–33b), and connected "outside," in parallel with the circuit, to measure voltage (Fig. 19–33c).

The internal construction of digital meters, however, is different from that of analog meters in that digital meters do not use a galvanometer. The electronic circuitry and digital readout are more sensitive than the galvanometer and its needle that they replace, and have less effect on the circuit to be measured. When we measure dc voltages, the meter's resistance is very high, commonly on the order of 10 to 100 MΩ $(10^7\text{–}10^8\ \Omega)$. This internal resistance doesn't change significantly when different voltage scales are selected (as it does for analog meters). A digital meter with such high resistance will draw off very little current when connected across a circuit element of even 1-MΩ resistance.

The precision of digital meters is exceptional, often one part in $10^4$ (= 0.01%) or better. This precision is not the same as accuracy, however. A precise meter of internal resistance $10^8\ \Omega$ will not give accurate results if used to measure a voltage across a $10^8$-Ω resistor—in which case it is necessary to do a calculation like that in Example 19–15.

A major aspect of this Section has been to show that whenever we make a measurement on a circuit, to some degree we affect that circuit (recall Example 19–15). This lesson is true for other types of measurement as well: whenever we make a measurement on a system, we generally affect that system in some way. On a temperature measurement, for example, the thermometer has a specific heat and can exchange heat with the system, thus altering its temperature (usually just slightly). It can be important to be able to make any needed corrections, as we saw how to do in Example 19–15.

## Summary


A device that transforms another type of energy into electrical energy is called a **source** of **emf**. A battery behaves like a source of emf in series with an **internal resistance**. The emf is the potential difference determined by the chemical reactions in the battery and equals the terminal voltage when no current is drawn. When a current is drawn, the voltage at the battery's terminals is less than its emf by an amount equal to the potential decrease $Ir$ across the internal resistance.

When resistances are connected in **series** (end to end in a single linear path), the equivalent resistance is the sum of the individual resistances:

$$R_{eq} = R_1 + R_2 + \cdots. \tag{19–3}$$

In a series combination, $R_{eq}$ is greater than any component resistance.

When resistors are connected in **parallel**, the reciprocal of the equivalent resistance equals the sum of the reciprocals of the individual resistances:

$$\frac{1}{R_{eq}} = \frac{1}{R_1} + \frac{1}{R_2} + \cdots. \tag{19–4}$$

In a parallel connection, the net resistance is less than any of the individual resistances.

**Kirchhoff's rules** are helpful in determining the currents and voltages in circuits. Kirchhoff's **junction rule** is based on conservation of electric charge and states that the sum of all currents entering any junction equals the sum of all currents leaving that junction. The second, or **loop rule**, is based on conservation of energy and states that the algebraic sum of the changes in potential around any closed path of the circuit must be zero.

When capacitors are connected in **parallel**, the equivalent capacitance is the sum of the individual capacitances:

$$C_{eq} = C_1 + C_2 + \cdots. \tag{19–5}$$

When capacitors are connected in **series**, the reciprocal of the equivalent capacitance equals the sum of the reciprocals of the individual capacitances:

$$\frac{1}{C_{eq}} = \frac{1}{C_1} + \frac{1}{C_2} + \cdots. \tag{19–6}$$

If an ***RC* circuit** containing a resistance $R$ in series with a capacitance $C$ is connected to a dc source of emf, the voltage across the capacitor rises gradually in time characterized by the **time constant**

$$\tau = RC. \tag{19–7}$$

This is the time it takes for the voltage to reach 63% of its maximum value. A capacitor discharging through a resistor is characterized by the same time constant: in a time $\tau = RC$, the voltage across the capacitor drops to 37% of its initial value.

Electric shocks are caused by current passing through the body. To avoid shocks, the body must not become part of a complete circuit by allowing different parts of the body to touch objects at different potentials. Commonly, shocks are caused by one part of the body touching ground and another part touching a high electric potential.

[*An **ammeter** measures current. An analog ammeter consists of a galvanometer and a parallel **shunt resistor** that carries most of the current. An analog **voltmeter** consists of a galvanometer and a series resistor. An ammeter is inserted *into* the circuit whose current is to be measured. A voltmeter is external, being connected in parallel to the element whose voltage is to be measured. Digital meters have greater internal resistance and affect the circuit to be measured less than do analog meters.]


## Questions

1. Explain why birds can sit on power lines safely, whereas leaning a metal ladder up against a power line to fetch a stuck kite is extremely dangerous.
2. Discuss the advantages and disadvantages of Christmas tree lights connected in parallel versus those connected in series.
3. If all you have is a 120-V line, would it be possible to light several 6-V lamps without burning them out? How?
4. Two lightbulbs of resistance $R_1$ and $R_2$ $(R_2 > R_1)$ are connected in series. Which is brighter? What if they are connected in parallel? Explain.

**5.** Household outlets are often double outlets. Are these connected in series or parallel? How do you know?

**6.** With two identical lightbulbs and two identical batteries, how would you arrange the bulbs and batteries in a circuit to get the maximum possible total power out? (Assume the batteries have negligible internal resistance.)

**7.** If two identical resistors are connected in series to a battery, does the battery have to supply more power or less power than when only one of the resistors is connected? Explain.

**8.** You have a single 60-W bulb on in your room. How does the overall resistance of your room's electric circuit change when you turn on an additional 100-W bulb?

**9.** When applying Kirchhoff's loop rule (such as in Fig. 19–35), does the sign (or direction) of a battery's emf depend on the direction of current through the battery? What about the terminal voltage?

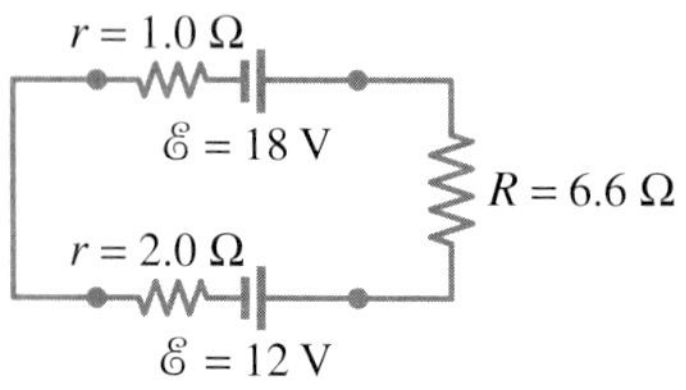


**FIGURE 19–35** Question 9.

**10.** Given the circuit shown in Fig. 19–36, use the words "increases," "decreases," or "stays the same" to complete the following statements:

(*a*) If $R_7$ increases, the potential difference between A and E _____. Assume no resistance in Ⓐ and ℰ.

(*b*) If $R_7$ increases, the potential difference between A and E _____. Assume Ⓐ and ℰ have resistance.

(*c*) If $R_7$ increases, the voltage drop across $R_4$ _____.

(*d*) If $R_2$ decreases, the current through $R_1$ _______.

(*e*) If $R_2$ decreases, the current through $R_6$ _______.

(*f*) If $R_2$ decreases, the current through $R_3$ _______.

(*g*) If $R_5$ increases, the voltage drop across $R_2$ _____.

(*h*) If $R_5$ increases, the voltage drop across $R_4$ _____.

(*i*) If $R_2$, $R_5$, and $R_7$ increase, ℰ $(r = 0)$ _________.

**FIGURE 19–36** Question 10. $R_2$, $R_5$, and $R_7$ are *variable* resistors (you can change their resistance), given the symbol ⏦.

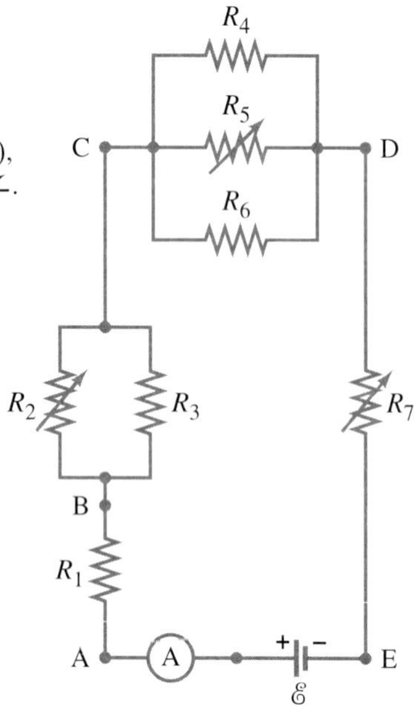


**11.** For what use are batteries connected in series? For what use are they connected in parallel? Does it matter if the batteries are nearly identical or not in either case?

**12.** Can the terminal voltage of a battery ever exceed its emf? Explain.

**13.** Explain in detail how you could measure the internal resistance of a battery.

**14.** Compare and discuss the formulas for resistors and for capacitors when connected in series and in parallel.

**15.** Suppose that three identical capacitors are connected to a battery. Will they store more energy if connected in series or in parallel?

**16.** Why is it more dangerous to turn on an electric appliance when you are standing outside in bare feet than when you are inside wearing shoes with thick soles?

**17.** Figure 19–37 is a diagram of a capacitor (or condenser) *microphone*. The changing air pressure in a sound wave causes one plate of the capacitor $C$ to move back and forth. Explain how a current of the same frequency as the sound wave is produced.

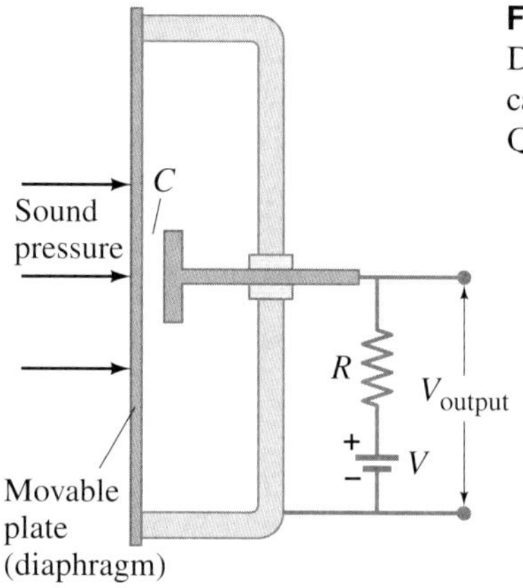


**FIGURE 19–37** Diagram of a capacitor microphone. Question 17.

**18.** Design a circuit in which two different switches of the type shown in Fig. 19–38 can be used to operate the same lightbulb from opposite sides of a room.

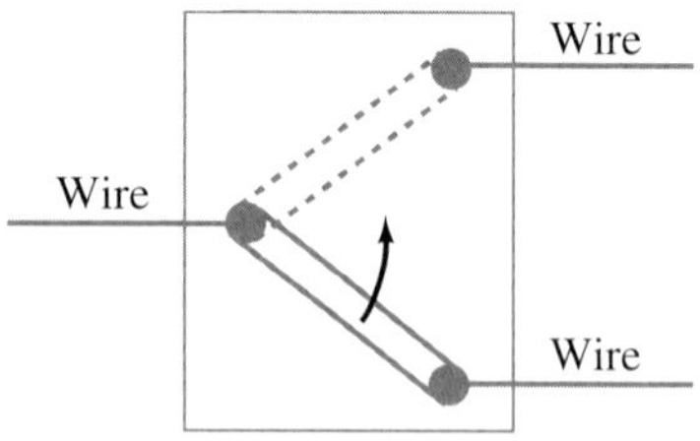


**FIGURE 19–38** Question 18.

**19.** In an *RC* circuit, current flows from the battery until the capacitor is completely charged. Is the total energy supplied by the battery equal to the total energy stored by the capacitor? If not, where does the extra energy go?

* **20.** What is the main difference between an analog voltmeter and an analog ammeter?

* **21.** What would happen if you mistakenly used an ammeter where you needed to use a voltmeter?

* **22.** Explain why an ideal ammeter would have zero resistance and an ideal voltmeter infinite resistance.

* **23.** A voltmeter connected across a resistor always reads *less* than the actual voltage across the resistor when the meter is not present. Explain.

* **24.** A small battery-operated flashlight requires a single 1.5-V battery. The bulb is barely glowing, but when you take the battery out and check it with a voltmeter, it registers 1.5 V. How would you explain this?

## Problems

### 19–1 Emf and Terminal Voltage

1. (I) Calculate the terminal voltage for a battery with an internal resistance of 0.900 Ω and an emf of 8.50 V when the battery is connected in series with (*a*) an 81.0-Ω resistor, and (*b*) an 810-Ω resistor.
2. (I) Four 1.5-V cells are connected in series to a 12-Ω lightbulb. If the resulting current is 0.45 A, what is the internal resistance of each cell, assuming they are identical and neglecting the wires?
3. (II) What is the internal resistance of a 12.0-V car battery whose terminal voltage drops to 8.4 V when the starter draws 75 A? What is the resistance of the starter?
4. (II) A 1.5-V dry cell can be tested by connecting it to a low-resistance ammeter. It should be able to supply at least 22 A. What is the internal resistance of the cell in this case, assuming it is much greater than that of the ammeter?

### 19–2 Resistors in Series and Parallel

In these Problems neglect the internal resistance of a battery unless the Problem refers to it.

5. (I) Four 240-Ω lightbulbs are connected in series. What is the total resistance of the circuit? What is their resistance if they are connected in parallel?
6. (I) Three 45-Ω lightbulbs and three 75-Ω lightbulbs are connected in series. (*a*) What is the total resistance of the circuit? (*b*) What is their resistance if all six are wired in parallel?
7. (I) A 650-Ω and a 2200-Ω resistor are connected in series with a 12-V battery. What is the voltage across the 2200-Ω resistor?
8. (I) Given only one 25-Ω and one 35-Ω resistor, list all possible values of resistance that can be obtained.
9. (I) Suppose that you have a 680-Ω, a 940-Ω, and a 1.20-kΩ resistor. What is (*a*) the maximum, and (*b*) the minimum resistance you can obtain by combining these?
10. (II) Suppose that you have a 6.0-V battery and you wish to apply a voltage of only 4.0 V. Given an unlimited supply of 1.0-Ω resistors, how could you connect them so as to make a "voltage divider" that produces a 4.0-V output for a 6.0-V input?
11. (II) Three 240-Ω resistors can be connected together in four different ways, making combinations of series and/or parallel circuits. What are these four ways, and what is the net resistance in each case?
12. (II) A battery with an emf of 12.0 V shows a terminal voltage of 11.8 V when operating in a circuit with two lightbulbs rated at 3.0 W (at 12.0 V) which are connected in parallel. What is the battery's internal resistance?
13. (II) Eight identical lights are connected in series across a 110-V line. (*a*) What is the voltage across each bulb? (*b*) If the current is 0.50 A, what is the resistance of each bulb, and what is the power dissipated in each?
14. (II) Eight lights are connected in parallel to a 110-V source by two long leads of total resistance 1.6 Ω. If 240 mA flows through each bulb, what is the resistance of each, and what fraction of the total power is wasted in the leads?
15. (II) Eight 7.0-W Christmas tree lights are connected in series to each other and to a 110-V source. What is the resistance of each bulb?
16. (II) A close inspection of an electric circuit reveals that a 480-Ω resistor was inadvertently soldered in the place where a 320-Ω resistor is needed. How can this be fixed without removing anything from the existing circuit?
17. (II) Determine (*a*) the equivalent resistance of the circuit shown in Fig. 19–39, and (*b*) the voltage across each resistor.

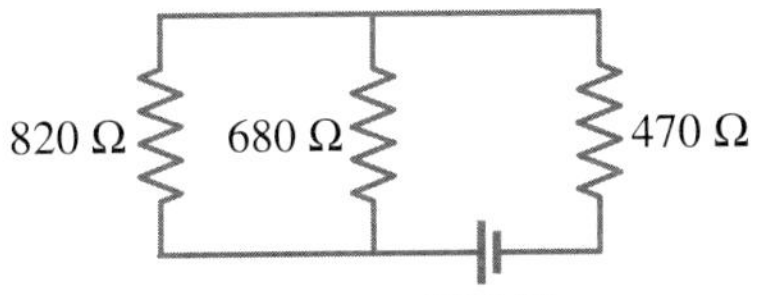


**FIGURE 19–39** Problem 17.

18. (II) A 75-W, 110-V bulb is connected in parallel with a 40-W, 110-V bulb. What is the net resistance?
19. (III) Consider the network of resistors shown in Fig. 19–40. Answer qualitatively: (*a*) What happens to the voltage across each resistor when the switch S is closed? (*b*) What happens to the current through each when the switch is closed? (*c*) What happens to the power output of the battery when the switch is closed? (*d*) Let $R_1 = R_2 = R_3 = R_4 = 125\ \Omega$ and $V = 22.0$ V. Determine the current through each resistor before and after closing the switch. Are your qualitative predictions confirmed?

**FIGURE 19–40** Problem 19.

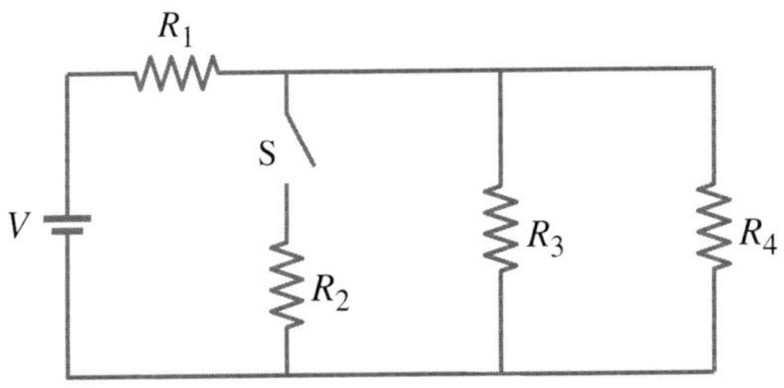

20. (III) What is the net resistance of the circuit connected to the battery in Fig. 19–41? Each resistance has $R = 2.8\ \text{k}\Omega$.

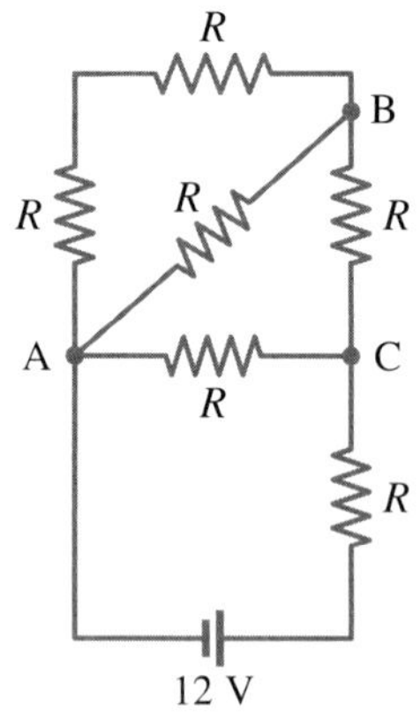


**FIGURE 19–41** Problem 20.

21. (III) Three equal resistors ($R$) are connected to a battery as shown in Fig. 19–42. Qualitatively, what happens to (*a*) the voltage drop across each of these resistors, (*b*) the current flow through each, and (*c*) the terminal voltage of the battery, when the switch S is opened, after having been closed for a long time? (*d*) If the emf of the battery is 15.0 V, what is its terminal voltage when the switch is closed if the internal resistance is $0.50\ \Omega$ and $R = 5.50\ \Omega$? (*e*) What is the terminal voltage when the switch is open?

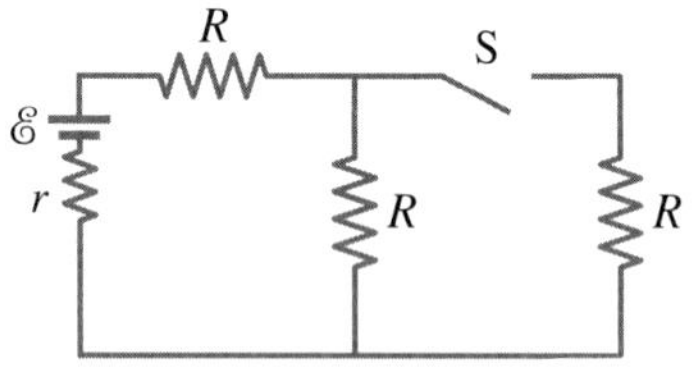


**FIGURE 19–42** Problem 21.

22. (III) A 2.8-kΩ and a 2.1-kΩ resistor are connected in parallel; this combination is connected in series with a 1.8-kΩ resistor. If each resistor is rated at $\frac{1}{2}$ W (maximum without overheating), what is the maximum voltage that can be applied across the whole network?

### 19–3 Kirchhoff's Rules

23. (I) Calculate the current in the circuit of Fig. 19–43 and show that the sum of all the voltage changes around the circuit is zero.

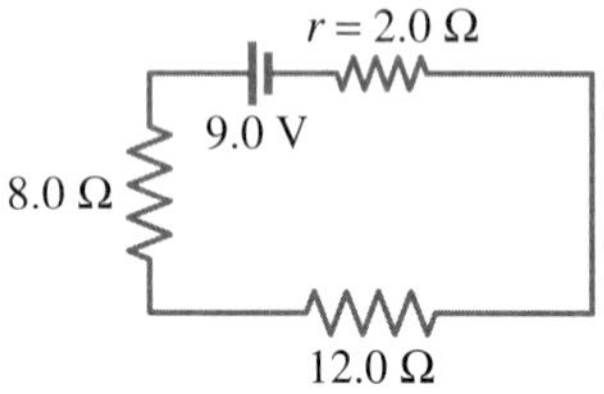


**FIGURE 19–43** Problem 23.

24. (II) Determine the terminal voltage of each battery in Fig. 19–44.

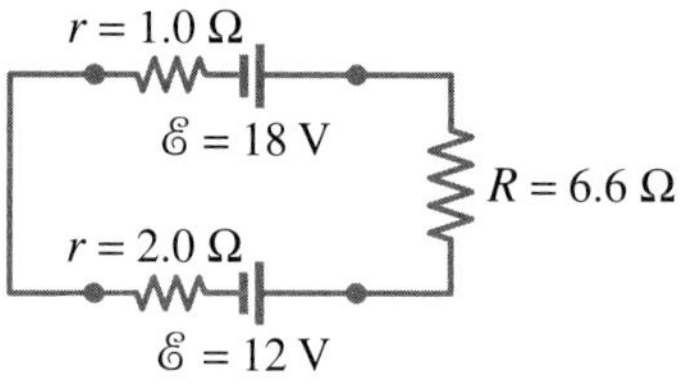


**FIGURE 19–44** Problem 24.

25. (II) (*a*) What is the potential difference between points a and d in Fig. 19–45 (same circuit as Fig. 19–13, Example 19–8), and (*b*) what is the terminal voltage of each battery?

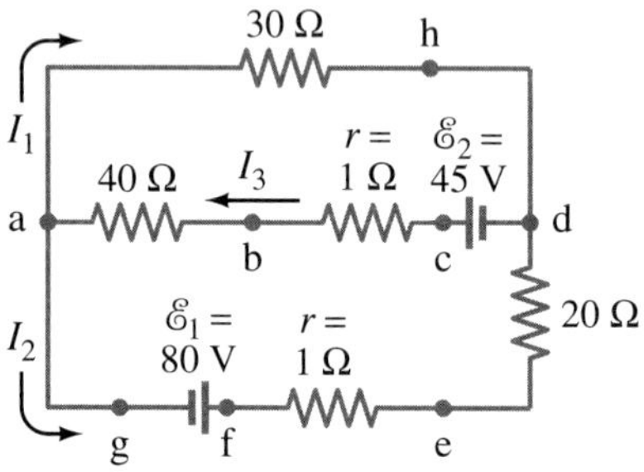


**FIGURE 19–45** Problem 25.

26. (II) For the circuit shown in Fig. 19–46, find the potential difference between points a and b. Each resistor has $R = 75\ \Omega$ and each battery is 1.5 V.

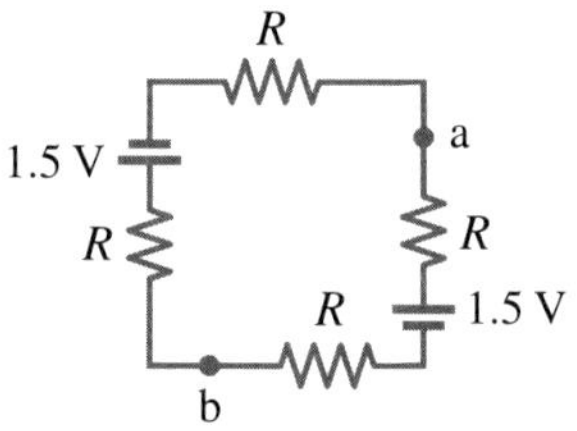


**FIGURE 19–46** Problem 26.

27. (II) Determine the magnitudes and directions of the currents through $R_1$ and $R_2$ in Fig. 19–47.

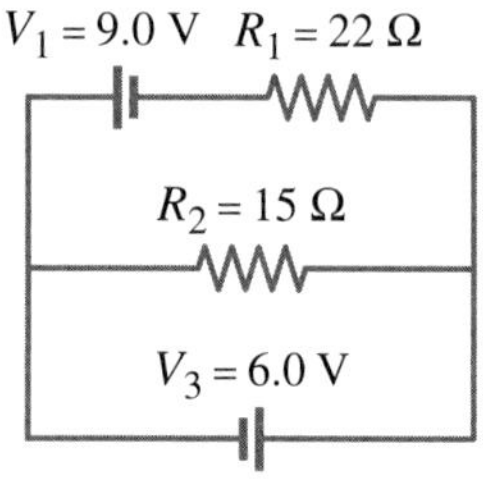


**FIGURE 19–47** Problems 27 and 28.

28. (II) Repeat Problem 27, now assuming that each battery has an internal resistance $r = 1.2\ \Omega$.

29. (II) Determine the magnitudes and directions of the currents in each resistor shown in Fig. 19–48. The batteries have emfs of $\mathscr{E}_1 = 9.0\,\text{V}$ and $\mathscr{E}_2 = 12.0\,\text{V}$ and the resistors have values of $R_1 = 25\,\Omega$, $R_2 = 18\,\Omega$, and $R_3 = 35\,\Omega$.

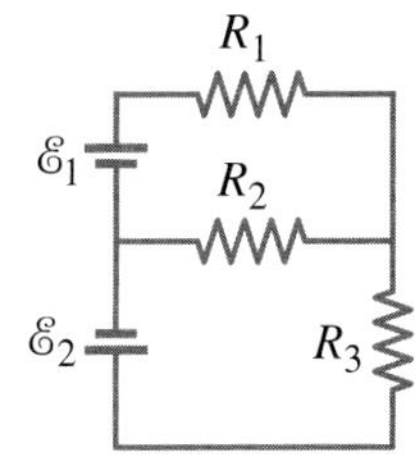


**FIGURE 19–48** Problems 29 and 30.

30. (II) Repeat Problem 29, assuming each battery has internal resistance $r = 1.0\,\Omega$.

31. (II) Calculate the currents in each resistor of Fig. 19–49.

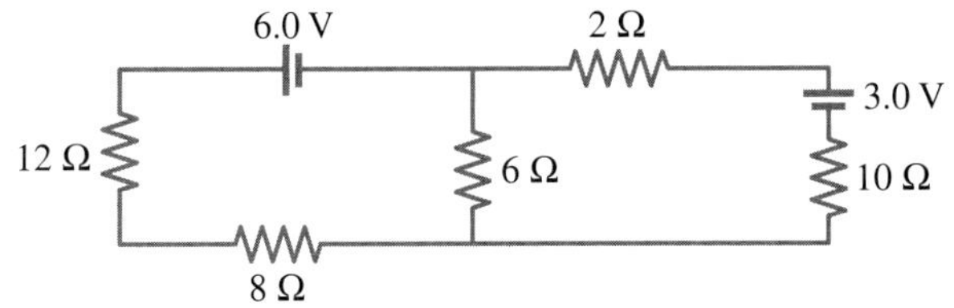


**FIGURE 19–49** Problem 31.

32. (III) (*a*) Determine the currents $I_1$, $I_2$, and $I_3$ in Fig. 19–50. Assume the internal resistance of each battery is $r = 1.0\,\Omega$. (*b*) What is the terminal voltage of the 6.0-V battery?

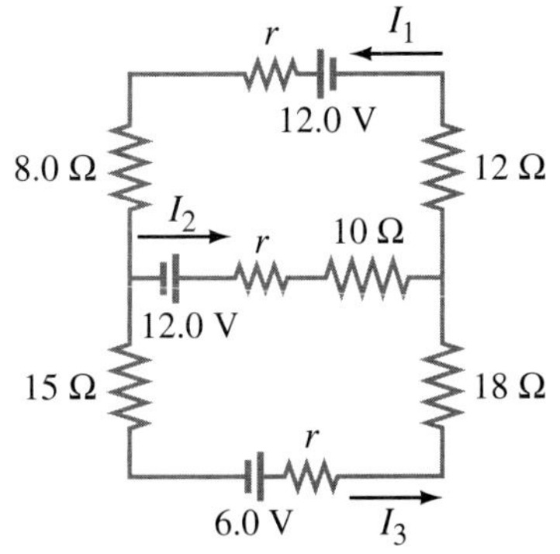


**FIGURE 19–50** Problems 32 and 33.

33. (III) What would the current $I_1$ be in Fig. 19–50 if the 12-Ω resistor is shorted out? Let $r = 1.0\,\Omega$.

## * 19–4 Emfs Combined, Battery Charging

* 34. (II) Suppose two batteries, with unequal emfs of 2.00 V and 3.00 V, are connected as shown in Fig. 19–51. If each internal resistance is $r = 0.100\,\Omega$, and $R = 4.00\,\Omega$, what is the voltage across the resistor $R$?

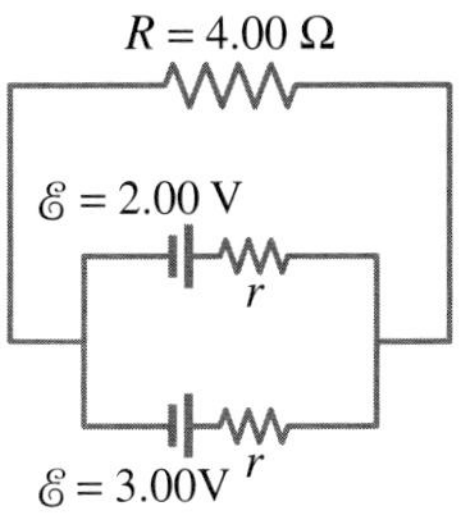


**FIGURE 19–51** Problem 34.

## 19–5 Capacitors in Series and in Parallel

35. (I) (*a*) Six 4.7-μF capacitors are connected in parallel. What is the equivalent capacitance? (*b*) What is their equivalent capacitance if connected in series?

36. (I) You have three capacitors, of capacitance 3200 pF, 7500 pF, and 0.0100 μF. What maximum and minimum capacitance can you form from these? How do you make the connection in each case?

37. (I) A 3.00-μF and a 4.00-μF capacitor are connected in series, and this combination is connected in parallel with a 2.00-μF capacitor (see Fig. 19–52). What is the net capacitance?

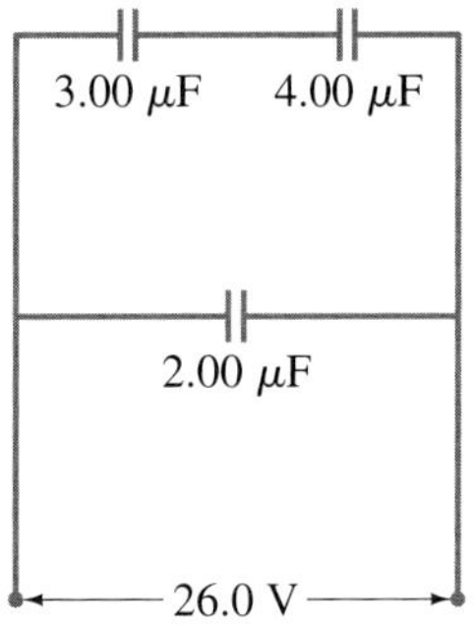


**FIGURE 19–52** Problems 37 and 38.

38. (II) If 26.0 V is applied across the whole network of Fig. 19–52, calculate the voltage across each capacitor.

39. (II) The capacitance of a portion of a circuit is to be reduced from 4800 pF to 2900 pF. What capacitance can be added to the circuit to produce this effect without removing existing circuit elements? Must any existing connections be broken in the process?

40. (II) An electric circuit was accidentally constructed using a 5.0-μF capacitor instead of the required 16-μF value. Without removing the 5.0-μF capacitor, what can a technician add to correct this circuit?

41. (II) Determine the equivalent capacitance of the circuit shown in Fig. 19–53.

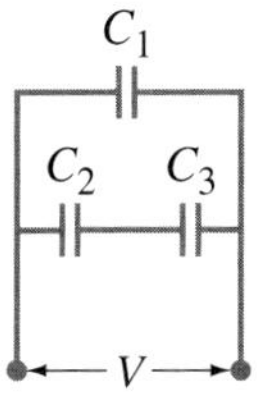


**FIGURE 19–53** Problems 41, 42, 43, and 44.

* 42. (II) In Fig. 19–53, if $C_1 = C_2 = 2C_3 = 22.6\,\mu\text{F}$, how much charge is stored on each capacitor when $V = 45.0\,\text{V}$?

* 43. (II) In Fig. 19–53, suppose $C_1 = C_2 = C_3 = 16.0\,\mu\text{F}$. If the charge on $C_2$ is $Q_2 = 24.0\,\mu\text{C}$, determine the charge on each of the other capacitors, the voltage across each capacitor, and the voltage $V$ across the entire combination.

* 44. (II) In Fig. 19–53, let $V = 78\,\text{V}$ and $C_1 = C_2 = C_3 = 7.2\,\mu\text{F}$. How much energy is stored in the capacitor network?

* 45. (II) A 0.40-μF and a 0.60-μF capacitor are connected in series to a 9.0-V battery. Calculate (*a*) the potential difference across each capacitor, and (*b*) the charge on each. (*c*) Repeat parts (*a*) and (*b*) assuming the two capacitors are in parallel.

46. (II) Three conducting plates, each of area $A$, are connected as shown in Fig. 19–54. ($a$) Are the two capacitors formed connected in series or in parallel? ($b$) Determine $C$ as a function of $d_1$, $d_2$, and $A$. Assume $d_1 + d_2$ is much less than the dimensions of the plates.

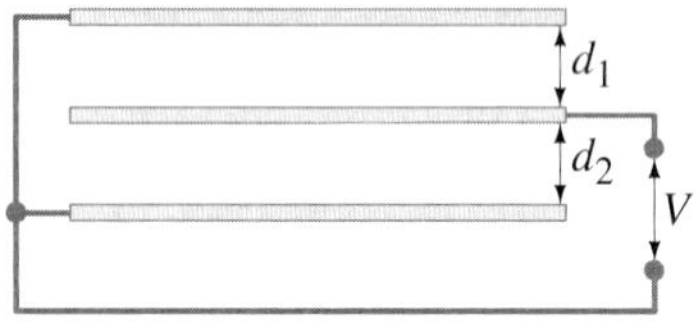


**FIGURE 19–54** Problem 46.

47. (II) A circuit contains a single 250-pF capacitor hooked across a battery. It is desired to store three times as much energy in a combination of two capacitors by adding a single capacitor to this one. How would you hook it up, and what would its value be?

48. (III) A 185-pF capacitor is connected in series with an unknown capacitance, and as a series combination they are connected to a battery with an emf of 25.0 V. If the 185-pF capacitor stores 125 pC of charge on its plates, what is the unknown capacitance?

## 19–6 *RC* Circuits

49. (I) Electrocardiographs are often connected as shown in Fig. 19–55. The leads are said to be capacitively coupled. A time constant of 3.0 s is typical and allows rapid changes in potential to be recorded accurately. If $C = 3.0\,\mu\text{F}$, what value must $R$ have? [*Hint*: consider each leg as a separate circuit.]

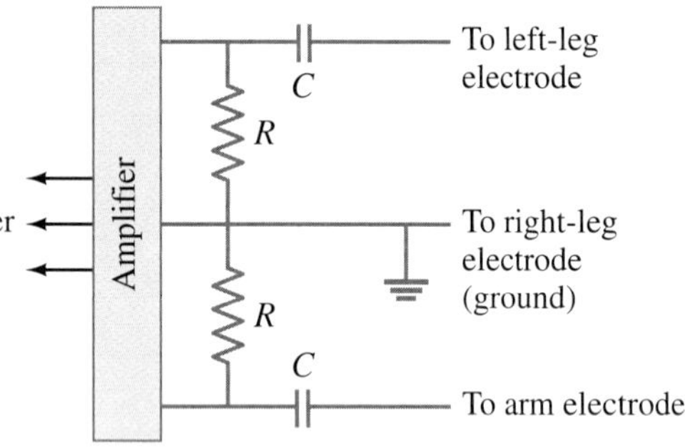


**FIGURE 19–55** Problem 49.

50. (II) In Fig. 19–56 (same as Fig. 19–20a), the total resistance is 15.0 kΩ, and the battery's emf is 24.0 V. If the time constant is measured to be 35.0 μs, calculate ($a$) the total capacitance of the circuit and ($b$) the time it takes for the voltage across the resistor to reach 16.0 V after the switch is closed.

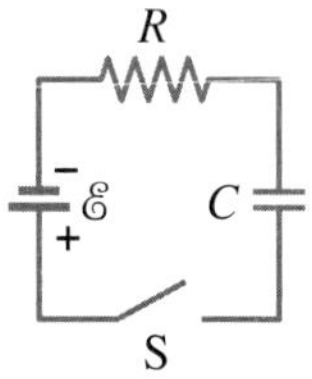


**FIGURE 19–56** Problem 50.

51. (II) The $RC$ circuit of Fig. 19–57 (same as Fig. 19–21a) has $R = 6.7\,\text{k}\Omega$ and $C = 3.0\,\mu\text{F}$. The capacitor is at voltage $V_0$ at $t = 0$, when the switch is closed. How long does it take the capacitor to discharge to 1.0% of its initial voltage?

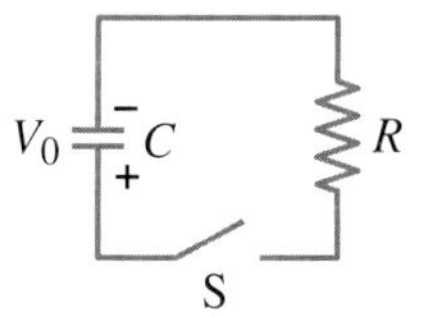


**FIGURE 19–57** Problem 51.

52. (III) Two resistors and two uncharged capacitors are arranged as shown in Fig. 19–58. Then a potential difference of 24 V is applied across the combination as shown. ($a$) What is the potential at point a with switch S open? (Let $V = 0$ at the negative terminal of the source.) ($b$) What is the potential at point b with the switch open? ($c$) When the switch is closed, what is the final potential of point b? ($d$) How much charge flows through the switch S after it is closed?

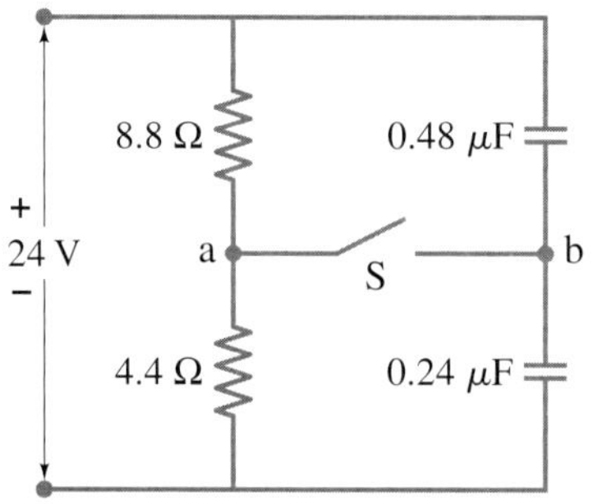


**FIGURE 19–58** Problem 52.

## * 19–8 Ammeters and Voltmeters

* 53. (I) What is the resistance of a voltmeter on the 250-V scale if the meter sensitivity is 30,000 Ω/V?

* 54. (I) An ammeter has a sensitivity of 20,000 Ω/V. What current in the galvanometer produces full-scale deflection?

* 55. (II) A galvanometer has an internal resistance of 30 Ω and deflects full scale for a 50-μA current. Describe how to use this galvanometer to make ($a$) an ammeter to read currents up to 30 A, and ($b$) a voltmeter to give a full-scale deflection of 250 V.

* 56. (II) A galvanometer has a sensitivity of 35 kΩ/V and internal resistance 20.0 Ω. How could you make this into ($a$) an ammeter that reads 2.0 A full scale, or ($b$) a voltmeter reading 1.00 V full scale?

* 57. (II) A milliammeter reads 10 mA full scale. It consists of a 0.20-Ω resistor in parallel with a 33-Ω galvanometer. How can you change this ammeter to a voltmeter giving a full-scale reading of 10 V without taking the ammeter apart? What will be the sensitivity (Ω/V) of your voltmeter?

* 58. (II) A 45-V battery of negligible internal resistance is connected to a 38-kΩ and a 27-kΩ resistor in series. What reading will a voltmeter, of internal resistance 95 kΩ, give when used to measure the voltage across each resistor? What is the percent inaccuracy due to meter resistance for each case?

* 59. (II) An ammeter whose internal resistance is 63 Ω reads 5.25 mA when connected in a circuit containing a battery and two resistors in series whose values are 750 Ω and 480 Ω. What is the actual current when the ammeter is absent?

* 60. (II) A battery with $\mathscr{E} = 12.0\text{ V}$ and internal resistance $r = 1.0\,\Omega$ is connected to two 9.0-kΩ resistors in series. An ammeter of internal resistance 0.50 Ω measures the current, and at the same time a voltmeter with internal resistance 15 kΩ measures the voltage across one of the 9.0-kΩ resistors in the circuit. What do the ammeter and voltmeter read?

* 61. (III) Two 9.4-kΩ resistors are placed in series and connected to a battery. A voltmeter of sensitivity 1000 Ω/V is on the 3.0-V scale and reads 2.0 V when placed across either resistor. What is the emf of the battery? (Ignore its internal resistance.)

* 62. (III) What internal resistance should the voltmeter of Example 19–15 have to be in error by less than 3%?

* 63. (III) When the resistor $R$ in Fig. 19–59 is 35 Ω, the high-resistance voltmeter reads 9.7 V. When $R$ is replaced by a 9.0-Ω resistor, the voltmeter reading drops to 8.1 V. What are the emf and internal resistance of the battery?

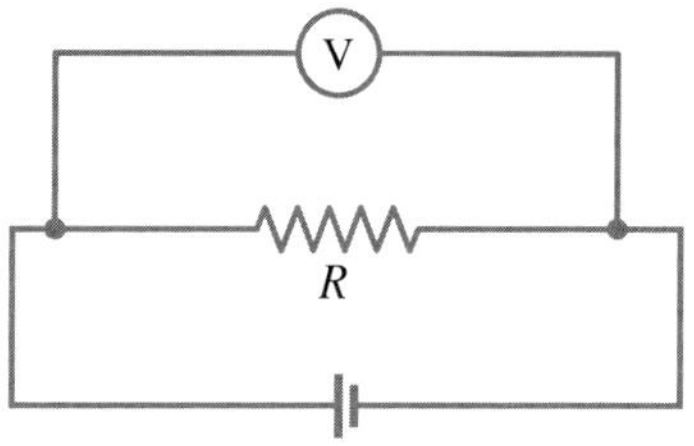


**FIGURE 19–59** Problem 63.

## General Problems

64. Suppose that you wish to apply a 0.25-V potential difference between two points on the human body. The resistance is about 2000 Ω, and you only have a 9.0-V battery. How can you connect up one or more resistors to produce the desired voltage?

65. A **three-way lightbulb** can produce 50 W, 100 W, or 150 W, at 120 V. Such a bulb contains two filaments that can be connected to the 120 V individually or in parallel. (*a*) Describe how the connections to the two filaments are made to give each of the three wattages. (*b*) What must be the resistance of each filament?

66. Suppose you want to run some apparatus that is 95 m from an electric outlet. Each of the wires connecting your apparatus to the 120-V source has a resistance per unit length of 0.0065 Ω/m. If your apparatus draws 3.0 A, what will be the voltage drop across the connecting wires and what voltage will be applied to your apparatus?

67. Electricity can be a hazard in hospitals, particularly to patients who are connected to electrodes, such as an ECG. For example, suppose that the motor of a motorized bed shorts out to the bed frame, and the bed frame's connection to a ground has broken (or was not there in the first place). If a nurse touches the bed and the patient at the same time, she becomes a conductor and a complete circuit can be made through the patient to ground through the ECG apparatus. This is shown schematically in Fig. 19–60. Calculate the current through the patient.

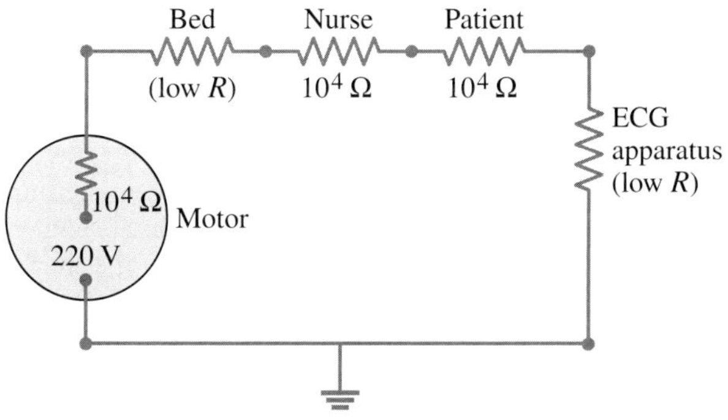


**FIGURE 19–60** Problem 67.

68. How much energy must a 45-V battery expend to charge a 0.40-μF and a 0.60-μF capacitor fully when they are placed (*a*) in parallel, (*b*) in series? (*c*) How much charge flowed from the battery in each case?

69. A heart pacemaker is designed to operate at 72 beats/min using a 7.5-μF capacitor in a simple *RC* circuit. What value of resistance should be used if the pacemaker is to fire (capacitor discharge) when the voltage reaches 63% of maximum?

70. Suppose that a person's body resistance is 950 Ω. (*a*) What current passes through the body when the person accidentally is connected to 110 V? (*b*) If there is an alternative path to ground whose resistance is 45 Ω, what current passes through the person? (*c*) If the voltage source can produce at most 1.5 A, how much current passes through the person in case (*b*)?

71. A **Wheatstone bridge** is a type of "bridge circuit" used to make measurements of resistance. The unknown resistance to be measured, $R_x$, is placed in the circuit with accurately known resistances $R_1$, $R_2$, and $R_3$ (Fig. 19–61). One of these, $R_3$, is a variable resistor which is adjusted so that when the switch is closed momentarily, the ammeter Ⓐ shows zero current flow. (*a*) Determine $R_x$ in terms of $R_1$, $R_2$, and $R_3$. (*b*) If a Wheatstone bridge is "balanced" when $R_1 = 630\,\Omega$, $R_2 = 972\,\Omega$, and $R_3 = 42.6\,\Omega$, what is the value of the unknown resistance?

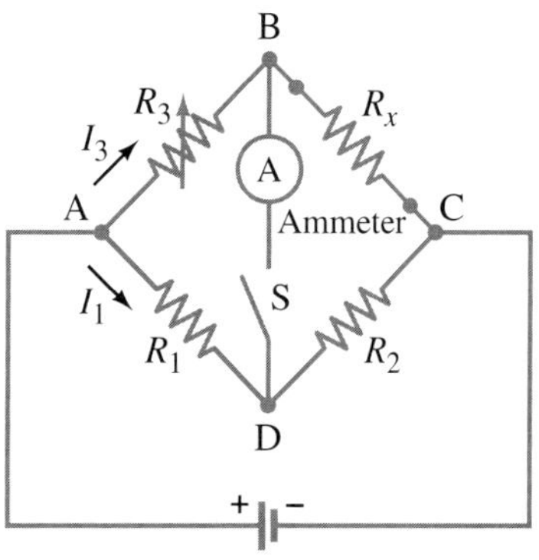


**FIGURE 19–61** Problems 71 and 72. Wheatstone bridge.

72. An unknown length of platinum wire 0.920 mm in diameter is placed as the unknown resistance in a Wheatstone bridge (see Problem 71; Fig. 19–61). Arms 1 and 2 have resistance of 38.0 Ω and 46.0 Ω, respectively. Balance is achieved when $R_3$ is 3.48 Ω. How long is the platinum wire?

73. What are the values of effective capacitance which can be obtained by connecting four identical capacitors, each having a capacitance $C$?

74. The variable capacitance of an old radio tuner consists of four plates connected together placed alternately between four other plates, also connected together (Fig. 19–62). Each plate is separated from its neighbor by 1.5 mm of air. One set of plates can move so that the area of overlap of each plate varies from $2.0\,\text{cm}^2$ to $9.5\,\text{cm}^2$. (*a*) Are these seven capacitors connected in series or in parallel? (*b*) Determine the range of capacitance values.

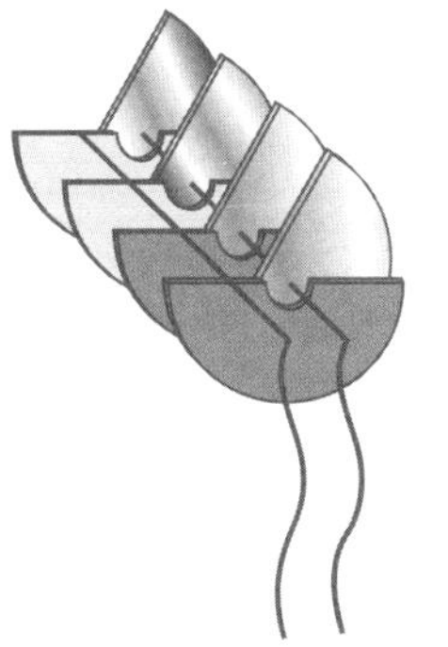

**FIGURE 19–62** Problem 74.

75. A battery produces 40.8 V when 7.40 A is drawn from it and 47.3 V when 2.20 A is drawn. What are the emf and internal resistance of the battery?

76. How many $\frac{1}{2}$-W resistors, each of the same resistance, must be used to produce an equivalent 2.2-kΩ, 3.5-W resistor? What is the resistance of each, and how must they be connected? Do not exceed $P = \frac{1}{2}\,\text{W}$ in each resistor.

77. The current through the 4.0-kΩ resistor in Fig. 19–63 is 3.50 mA. What is the terminal voltage $V_{\text{ba}}$ of the "unknown" battery? (There are two answers. Why?) [*Hint*: use conservation of energy or Kirchhoff's rules.]

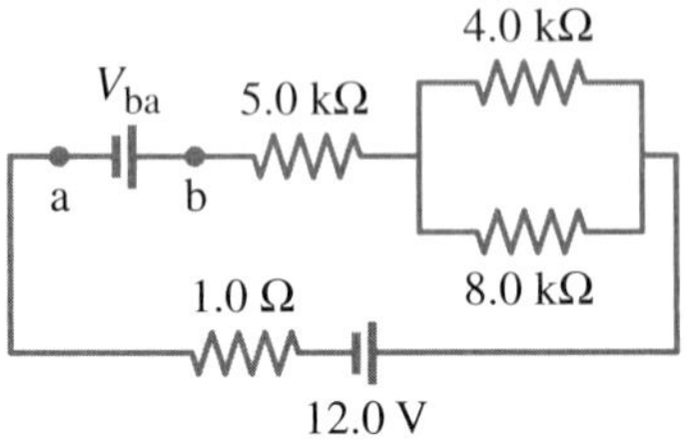


**FIGURE 19–63** Problem 77.

78. An air-filled parallel-plate capacitor has capacitance $C_0$. If two identically sized dielectric slabs of dielectric constants $K_1$ and $K_2$ are inserted as shown in Fig. 19–64, what is the new capacitance? [*Hint*: treat this as two capacitors in combination.]

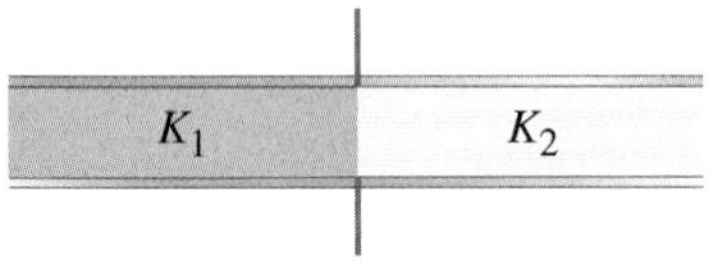


**FIGURE 19–64** Problem 78.

79. For the circuit shown in Fig. 19–65, determine (*a*) the current through the 14-V battery and (*b*) the potential difference between points a and b, $V_{\text{a}} - V_{\text{b}}$.

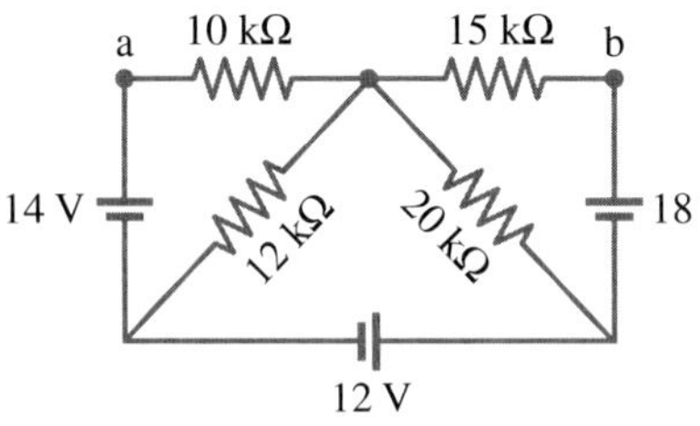


**FIGURE 19–65** Problem 79.

80. A solar cell, 3.0 cm square, has an output of 350 mA at 0.80 V when exposed to full sunlight. A solar panel that delivers close to 1.0 A of current at an emf of 120 V to an external load is needed. How many cells will you need to create the panel? How big a panel will you need, and how should you connect the cells to one another? How can you optimize the output of your solar panel?

81. A power supply has a fixed output voltage of 12.0 V, but you need $V_{\text{T}} = 3.0\,\text{V}$ for an experiment. (*a*) Using the voltage divider shown in Fig. 19–66, what should $R_2$ be if $R_1$ is 10.0 Ω? (*b*) What will the terminal voltage $V_{\text{T}}$ be if you connect a load to the 3.0-V terminal, assuming the load has a resistance of 7.0 Ω?

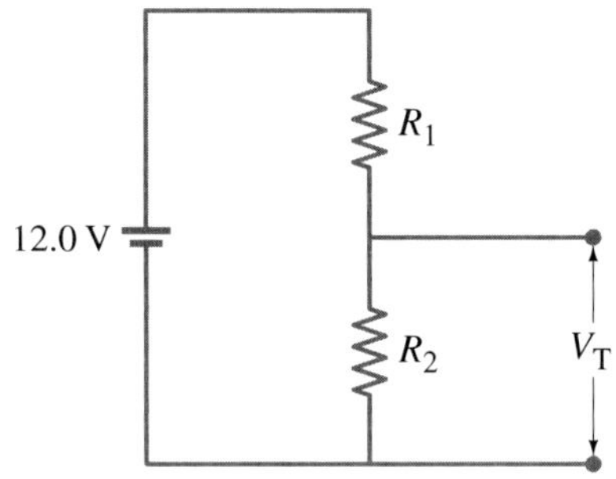


**FIGURE 19–66** Problem 81.

82. The circuit shown in Fig. 19–67 uses a neon-filled tube as in Fig. 19–23a. This neon lamp has a threshold voltage $V_0$ for conduction, because no current flows until the neon gas in the tube is ionized by a sufficiently strong electric field. Once the threshold voltage is exceeded, the lamp has negligible resistance. The capacitor stores electrical energy, which can be released to flash the lamp. Assume that $C = 0.150\,\mu\text{F}$, $R = 2.35 \times 10^6\,\Omega$, $V_0 = 90.0\,\text{V}$ and $\mathscr{E} = 105\,\text{V}$. (*a*) Assuming that the circuit is hooked up to the emf at time $t = 0$, at what time will the light first flash? (*b*) If the value of $R$ is increased, will the time you found in part (*a*) increase or decrease? (*c*) The flashing of the lamp is very brief. Why? (*d*) Explain what happens after the lamp flashes for the first time.

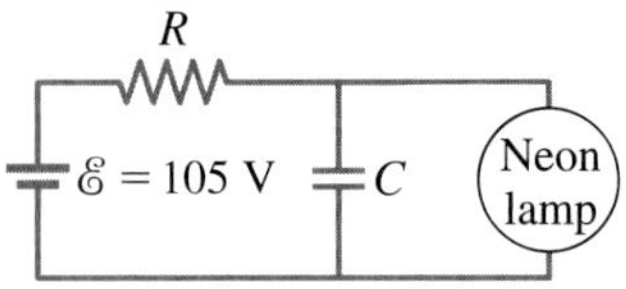


**FIGURE 19–67** Problem 82.

83. The current through the 20-Ω resistor in Fig. 19–68 does not change whether the two switches $S_1$ and $S_2$ are both open or both closed. Use this clue to determine the value of the unknown resistance $R$.

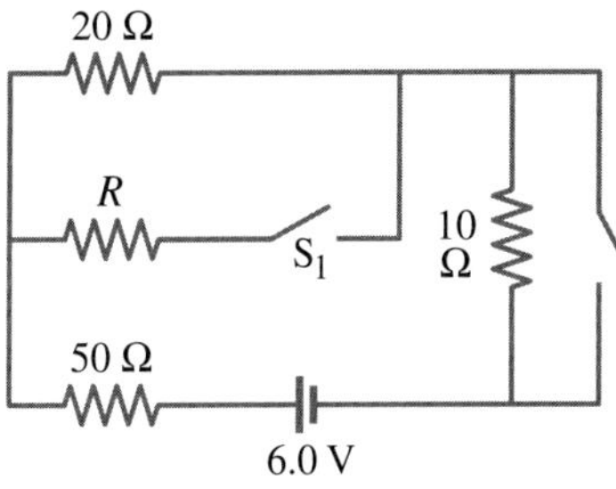


**FIGURE 19–68** Problem 83.

84. In the circuit shown in Fig. 19–69, the 33-Ω resistor dissipates 0.50 W. What is the battery voltage?

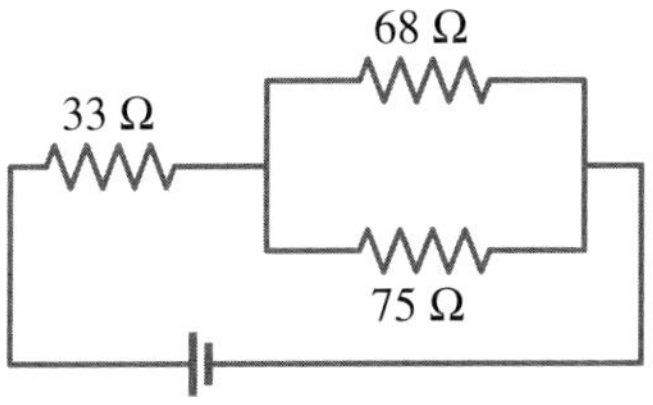


**FIGURE 19–69** Problem 84.

85. (*a*) What is the equivalent resistance of the circuit shown in Fig. 19–70? (*b*) What is the current in the 18-Ω resistor? (*c*) What is the current in the 12-Ω resistor? (*d*) What is the power dissipation in the 4.5-Ω resistor?

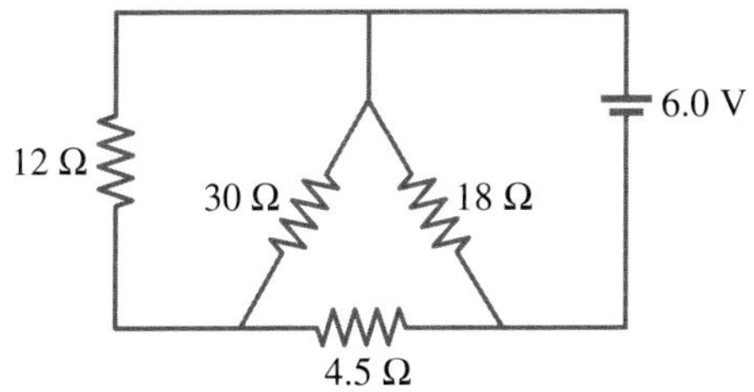


**FIGURE 19–70** Problem 85.

* 86. (*a*) A voltmeter and an ammeter can be connected as shown in Fig. 19–71a to measure a resistance $R$. If $V$ is the voltmeter reading, and $I$ is the ammeter reading, the value of $R$ will not quite be $V/I$ (as in Ohm's law) because some of the current actually goes through the voltmeter. Show that the actual value of $R$ is given by

$$\frac{1}{R} = \frac{I}{V} - \frac{1}{R_V},$$

where $R_V$ is the voltmeter resistance. Note that $R \approx V/I$ if $R_V \gg R$. (*b*) A voltmeter and an ammeter can also be connected as shown in Fig. 19–71b to measure a resistance $R$. Show in this case that

$$R = \frac{V}{I} - R_A,$$

where $V$ and $I$ are the voltmeter and ammeter readings and $R_A$ is the resistance of the ammeter. Note that $R \approx V/I$ if $R_A \ll R$.

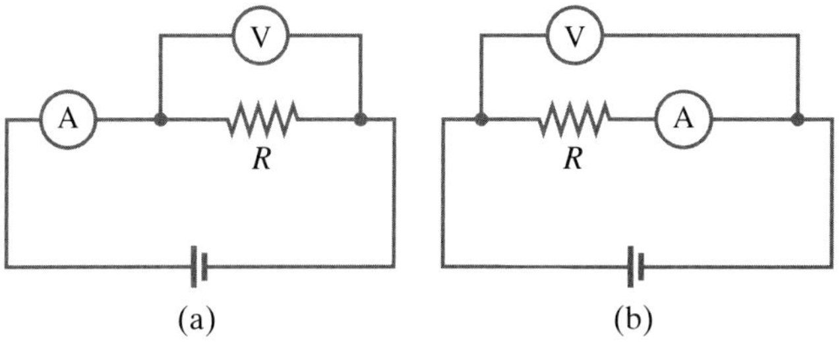


**FIGURE 19–71** Problem 86.

87. A flashlight bulb rated at 2.5 W and 3.0 V is operated by a 9.0-V battery. To light the bulb at its rated voltage and power, a resistor $R$ is connected in series as shown in Fig. 19–72. What value should the resistor have?

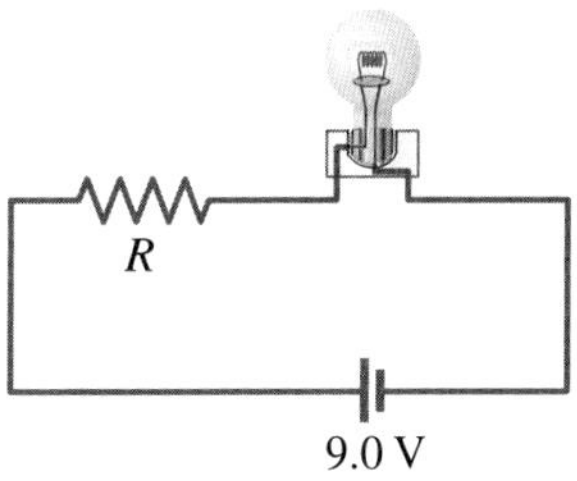


**FIGURE 19–72** Problem 87.

## Answers to Exercises

**A:** (*a*) 1.14 A; (*b*) 11.4 V; (*c*) $P_R = 13.1$ W, $P_r = 0.65$ W.
**B:** Series with $R_1/R_2 = 4.0$.
**C:** $41I_3 - 45 + 21I_2 - 80 = 0$.
**D:** 180 A; this high current through the batteries could cause them to become very hot: the power dissipated in the weak battery would be $P = I^2r = (180\text{ A})^2(0.10\,\Omega) = 3200$ W!
**E:** 12 kΩ.
**F:** The voltmeter will consist of a resistance $R_{ser} = 300$ kΩ in series with the galvanometer.

Magnets produce magnetic fields, but so do electric currents. An electric current flowing in this straight wire produces a magnetic field which causes the tiny pieces of iron (iron "filings") to align in the field. We shall see in this Chapter how magnetic field is defined, and that the magnetic field direction is along the iron filings. The magnetic field lines due to the electric current in this long wire are in the shape of circles around the wire.

We also discuss how magnetic fields exert forces on electric currents and on charged particles, as well as useful applications of the interaction between magnetic fields and electric currents and moving electric charges.

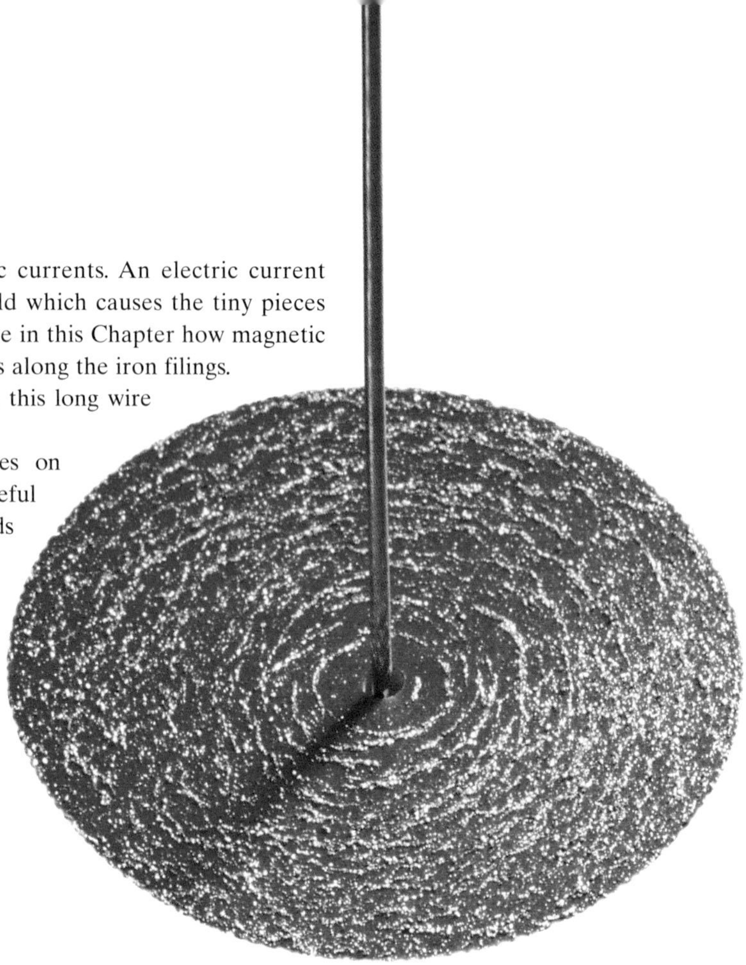

CHAPTER 20

# Magnetism

**FIGURE 20–1** A horseshoe magnet attracts pins.

*Poles of a magnet*

The history of magnetism begins thousands of years ago. In a region of Asia Minor known as Magnesia, rocks were found that could attract each other. These rocks were called "magnets" after their place of discovery.

Not until the nineteenth century, however, was it seen that magnetism and electricity are closely related. A crucial discovery was that electric currents produce magnetic effects (we will say "magnetic fields") like magnets do. All kinds of practical devices depend on magnetism, as we shall see: from compasses to motors, loudspeakers, computer memory, and electric generators.

## 20–1 Magnets and Magnetic Fields

We have all observed a magnet attract paper clips, nails, and other objects made of iron, Fig. 20–1. Any magnet, whether it is in the shape of a bar or a horseshoe, has two ends or faces, called **poles**, which is where the magnetic effect is strongest. If a bar magnet is suspended from a fine thread, it is found that one pole of the magnet will always point toward the north. It is not known for sure when this fact was discovered, but it is known that the Chinese were making use of it as an aid to navigation by the eleventh century and perhaps earlier. This is the principle of a compass. A compass needle is simply a bar magnet which is supported at its center of gravity so that it can rotate freely. The pole of a freely suspended magnet that points toward geographic north is called the **north pole** of the magnet. The other pole points toward the south and is called the **south pole**.

It is a familiar observation that when two magnets are brought near one another, each exerts a force on the other. The force can be either attractive or repulsive and can be felt even when the magnets don't touch. If the north pole of one bar magnet is brought near the north pole of a second magnet, the force is repulsive. Similarly, if two south poles are brought close, the force is repulsive. But when a north pole is brought near a south pole, the force is attractive. These results are shown in Fig. 20–2, and are reminiscent of the forces between electric charges: like poles repel, and unlike poles attract. *But do not confuse magnetic poles with electric charge.* They are very different. One important difference is that a positive or negative electric charge can easily be isolated. But the isolation of a single magnetic pole has never been observed. If a bar magnet is cut in half, you do not obtain isolated north and south poles. Instead, two new magnets are produced, Fig. 20–3, each with north (N) and south (S) poles. If the cutting operation is repeated, more magnets are produced, each with a north and a south pole. Physicists have searched for isolated single magnetic poles (monopoles), but no *magnetic monopole* has ever been observed.

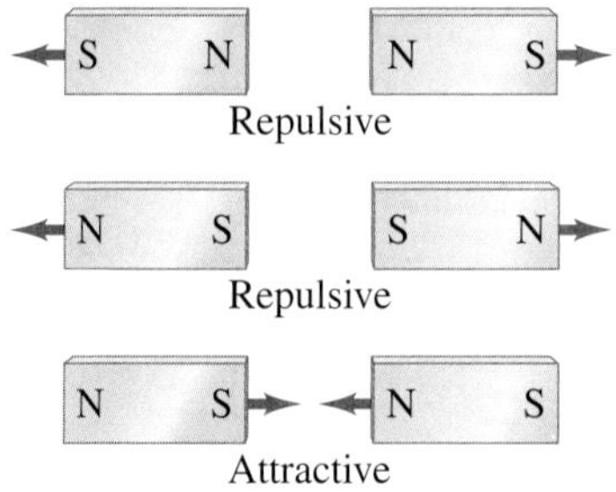


**FIGURE 20–2** Like poles of a magnet repel; unlike poles attract.

**FIGURE 20–3** If you split a magnet, you won't get isolated north and south poles; instead, two new magnets are produced, each with a north and a south pole.

Only iron and a few other materials, such as cobalt, nickel, gadolinium, and some of their oxides and alloys, show strong magnetic effects. They are said to be **ferromagnetic** (from the Latin word *ferrum* for iron). Other materials show some slight magnetic effect, but it is very weak and can be detected only with delicate instruments. We will look in more detail at ferromagnetism in Section 20–12.

**CAUTION**

*Magnets do not attract all metals*

In Chapter 16, we used the concept of an electric field surrounding an electric charge. In the same way, we can imagine a **magnetic field** surrounding a magnet. The force one magnet exerts on another can then be described as the interaction between one magnet and the magnetic field of the other. Just as we drew electric field lines, we can also draw **magnetic field lines**. They can be drawn, as for electric field lines, so that (1) the direction of the magnetic field is tangent to a field line at any point, and (2) the number of lines per unit area is proportional to the strength of the magnetic field.

*Magnetic field lines*

The *direction* of the magnetic field at a given point can be defined as the direction that the north pole of a compass needle would point if placed at that point. (A more precise definition will be given in Section 20–3.) Figure 20–4a shows how thin iron filings (acting like tiny magnets) reveal the magnetic field lines by lining up like the compass needles. The magnetic field determined in this way for the field surrounding a bar magnet is shown in Fig. 20–4b. Notice that because of our definition, the lines always point out from the north pole toward the south pole of a magnet (the north pole of a magnetic compass needle is attracted to the south pole of the magnet).

Magnetic field lines continue inside a magnet, as indicated in Fig. 20–4b. Indeed, given the lack of single magnetic poles, magnetic field lines always form closed loops, unlike electric field lines that begin on positive charges and end on negative charges.

**CAUTION**

*Magnetic field lines form closed loops, unlike electric field lines*

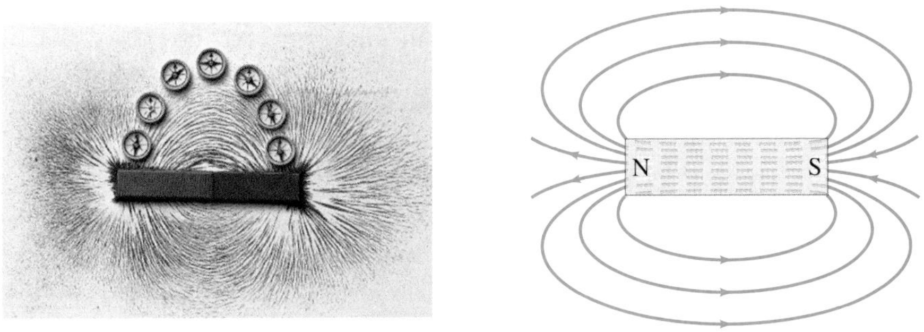


(a) (b)

**FIGURE 20–4** (a) Visualizing magnetic field lines around a bar magnet, using iron filings and compass needles. The red end of the bar magnet is its north pole. The N pole of a nearby compass needle points away from the north pole of the magnet. (b) Magnetic field lines for a bar magnet.

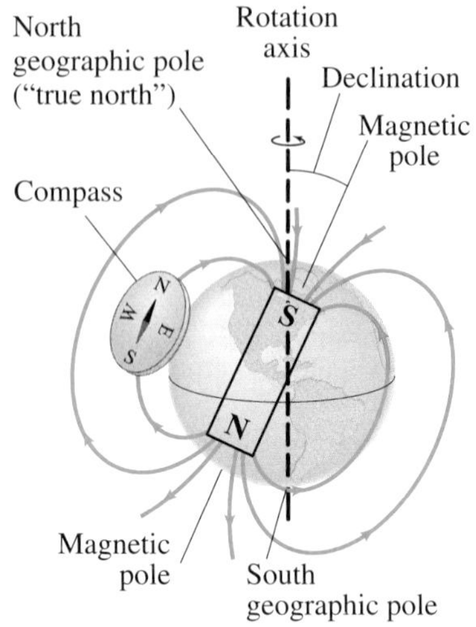


**FIGURE 20–5** The Earth acts like a huge magnet; but its magnetic poles are not at the geographic poles, which are on the Earth's rotation axis.

## Earth's Magnetic Field

The Earth's magnetic field is shown in Fig. 20–5. The pattern of field lines is as if there were an imaginary bar magnet inside the Earth. Since the north pole (N) of a compass needle points north, the Earth's magnetic pole which is in the geographic north is magnetically a south pole, as indicated in Fig. 20–5 by the S on the schematic bar magnet inside the Earth. Remember that the north pole of one magnet is attracted to the south pole of another magnet. Nonetheless, Earth's pole in the north is still often called the "north magnetic pole," or "geomagnetic north," simply because it is in the north. Similarly, the Earth's southern magnetic pole, which is near the geographic south pole, is magnetically a north pole (N). The Earth's magnetic poles do not coincide with the *geographic* poles, which are on the Earth's axis of rotation. The north magnetic pole, for example, is in the Canadian Arctic,† about 900 km from the geographic north pole, or "true north." This difference must be taken into account when you use a compass (Fig. 20–6). The angular difference between magnetic north and true (geographical) north is called the **magnetic declination**. In the U.S. it varies from 0° to about 20°, depending on location.

Notice in Fig. 20–5 that the Earth's magnetic field at most locations is not tangent to the Earth's surface. The angle that the Earth's magnetic field makes with the horizontal at any point is referred to as the **angle of dip**.

**EXERCISE A** Does the Earth's magnetic field have a greater magnitude near the poles or near the equator? Hint: note the field lines in Fig. 20–5.

PHYSICS APPLIED

*Use of a compass*

**FIGURE 20–6** Using a map and compass in the wilderness. First you align the compass case so the needle points away from true north (N) exactly the number of degrees of declination as stated on the map (15° for the place shown on this topographic map of a part of California). Then align the map with true north, as shown, *not* with the compass needle.

**FIGURE 20–7** Magnetic field between two wide poles of a magnet is nearly uniform, except at the edges.

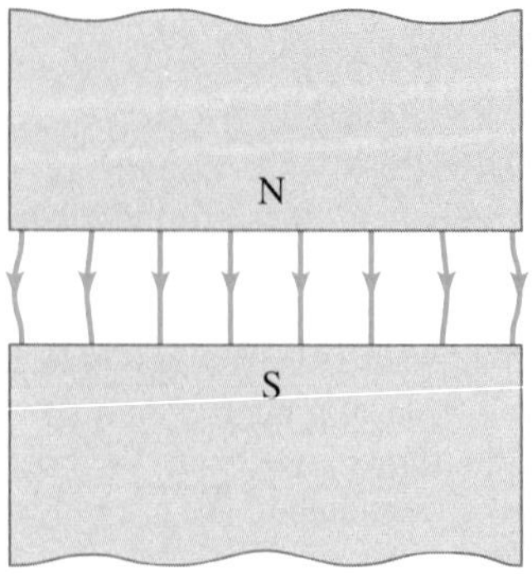


## Uniform Magnetic Field

The simplest magnetic field is one that is uniform—it doesn't change in magnitude or direction from one point to another. A perfectly uniform field over a large area is not easy to produce. But the field between two flat parallel pole pieces of a magnet is nearly uniform if the area of the pole faces is large compared to their separation, as shown in Fig. 20–7. At the edges, the field "fringes" out somewhat: the magnetic field lines are no longer quite parallel and uniform. The parallel evenly spaced field lines in the central region of the gap indicate that the field is uniform at points not too near the edge, much like the electric field between two parallel plates (Fig. 17–1).

†Magnetic north is moving many kilometers a year at present. Magnetism in rocks suggests that the Earth's poles have not only moved significantly over geologic time, but have also reversed direction 400 times over the last 330 million years.

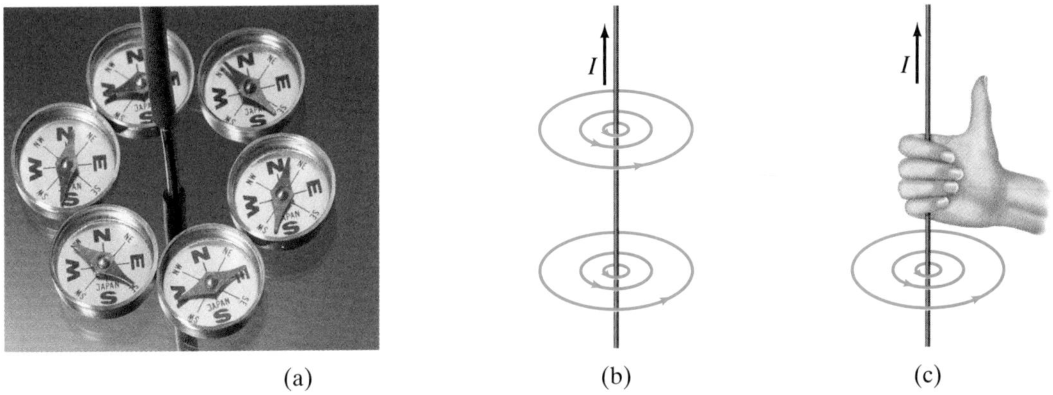


**FIGURE 20–8** (a) Deflection of compass needles near a current-carrying wire, showing the presence and direction of the magnetic field. (b) Magnetic field lines around an electric current in a straight wire. (c) Right-hand rule for remembering the direction of the magnetic field: when the thumb points in the direction of the conventional current, the fingers wrapped around the wire point in the direction of the magnetic field.

## 20–2 Electric Currents Produce Magnetic Fields

During the eighteenth century, many scientists sought to find a connection between electricity and magnetism. A stationary electric charge and a magnet were shown to have no influence on each other. But in 1820, Hans Christian Oersted (1777–1851) found that when a compass needle is placed near an electric wire, the needle deflects as soon as the wire is connected to a battery and the wire carries an electric current. As we have seen, a compass needle is deflected by a magnetic field. So Oersted's experiment showed that **an electric current produces a magnetic field**. He had found a connection between electricity and magnetism.

*Electric currents produce magnetic fields*

A compass needle placed near a straight section of current-carrying wire experiences a force, causing the needle to align tangent to a circle around the wire, Fig. 20–8a. Thus, the magnetic field lines produced by a current in a straight wire are in the form of circles with the wire at their center, Fig. 20–8b. The direction of these lines is indicated by the north pole of the compasses in Fig. 20–8a. There is a simple way to remember the direction of the magnetic field lines in this case. It is called a **right-hand rule**: grasp the wire with your right hand so that your thumb points in the direction of the conventional (positive) current; then your fingers will encircle the wire in the direction of the magnetic field, Fig. 20–8c.

*Right-hand-rule-1: magnetic field direction produced by electric current*

The magnetic field lines due to a circular loop of current-carrying wire can be determined in a similar way using a compass. The result is shown in Fig. 20–9. Again the right-hand rule can be used, as shown in Fig. 20–10. Unlike the uniform field shown in Fig. 20–7, the magnetic fields shown in Figs. 20–8 and 20–9 are *not* uniform—the fields are different in magnitude and direction at different points.

**EXERCISE B** A straight wire carries a current directly toward you. In what direction are the magnetic field lines surrounding the wire?

**FIGURE 20–9** Magnetic field lines due to a circular loop of wire.

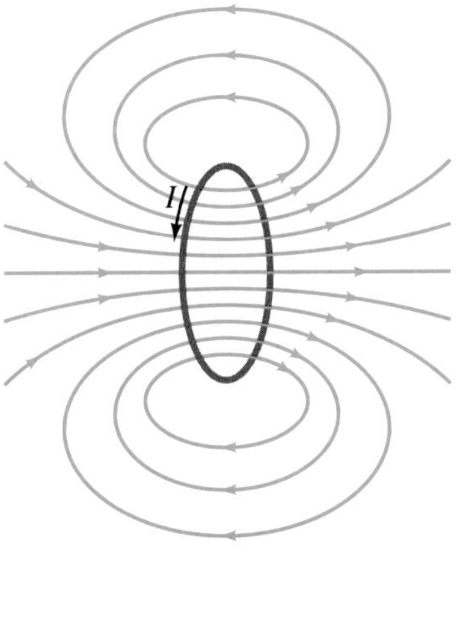


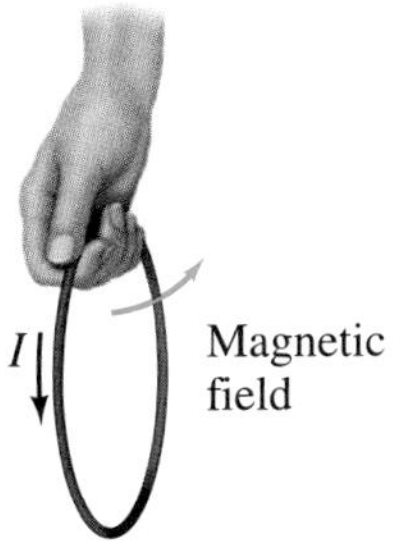


**FIGURE 20–10** Right-hand rule for determining the direction of the magnetic field relative to the current.

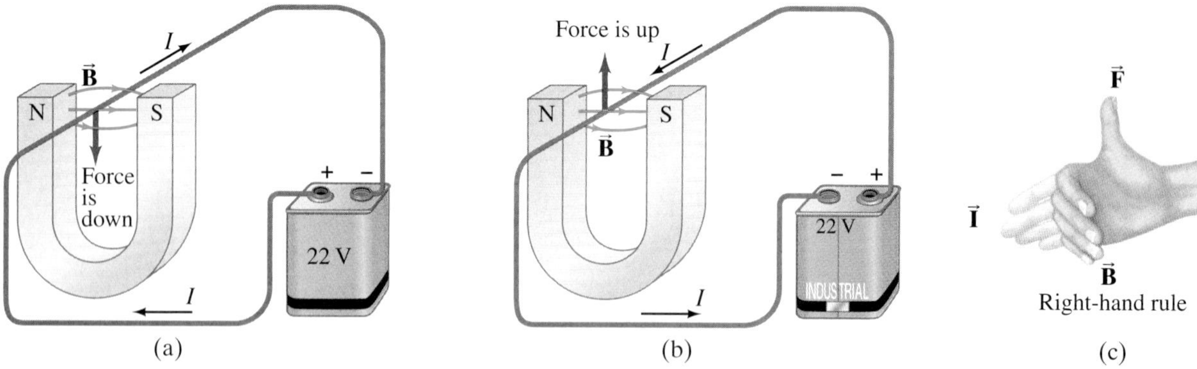


**FIGURE 20–11** (a) Force on a current-carrying wire placed in a magnetic field $\vec{\mathbf{B}}$; (b) same, but current reversed; (c) right-hand rule for setup in (b).

## 20–3 Force on an Electric Current in a Magnetic Field; Definition of $\vec{\mathbf{B}}$

*Magnet exerts a force on an electric current*

In Section 20–2 we saw that an electric current exerts a force on a magnet, such as a compass needle. By Newton's third law, we might expect the reverse to be true as well: we should expect that *a magnet exerts a force on a current-carrying wire*. Experiments indeed confirm this effect, and it too was first observed by Oersted.

Suppose a straight wire is placed in the magnetic field between the poles of a horseshoe magnet as shown in Fig. 20–11. When a current flows in the wire, experiment shows that a force is exerted on the wire. But this force is *not* toward one or the other pole of the magnet. Instead, the force is directed at right angles to the magnetic field direction, downward in Fig. 20–11a. If the current is reversed in direction, the force is in the opposite direction, upward as shown in Fig. 20–11b. Experiments show that *the direction of the force is always perpendicular to the direction of the current and also perpendicular to the direction of the magnetic field*, $\vec{\mathbf{B}}$.

*Right-hand-rule-2: force on current exerted by $\vec{\mathbf{B}}$*

The direction of the force is given by another **right-hand rule**, as illustrated in Fig. 20–11c. Orient your right hand until your outstretched fingers can point in the direction of the conventional current $I$, and when you bend your fingers they point in the direction of the magnetic field lines, $\vec{\mathbf{B}}$. Then your outstretched thumb will point in the direction of the force $\vec{\mathbf{F}}$ on the wire.

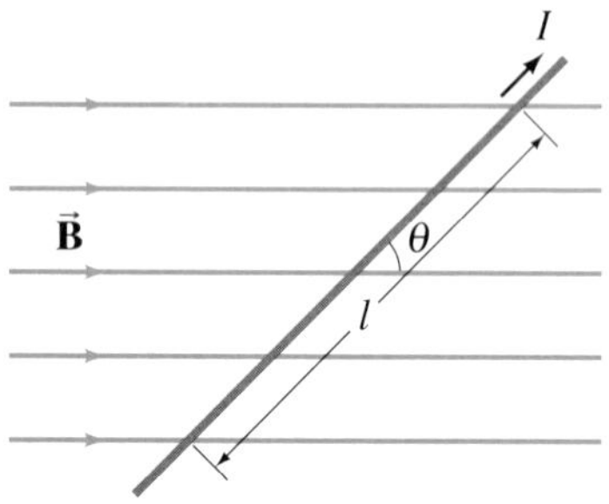


**FIGURE 20–12** Current-carrying wire in a magnetic field. Force on the wire is directed into the page.

This right-hand rule describes the direction of the force. What about the magnitude of the force on the wire? It is found experimentally that the magnitude of the force is directly proportional to the current $I$ in the wire, and to the length $l$ of wire exposed to the magnetic field (assumed uniform). Furthermore, if the magnetic field $B$ is made stronger, the force is found to be proportionally greater. The force also depends on the angle $\theta$ between the current direction and the magnetic field (Fig. 20–12), being proportional to $\sin\theta$. Thus, the force on a wire carrying a current $I$ with length $l$ in a uniform magnetic field $B$ is given by

$$F \propto IlB\sin\theta.$$

When the current is perpendicular to the field lines ($\theta = 90°$), the force is strongest. When the wire is parallel to the magnetic field lines ($\theta = 0°$), there is no force at all.

Up to now we have not defined the magnetic field strength precisely. In fact, the magnetic field $B$ can be conveniently defined in terms of the above proportion so that the proportionality constant is precisely 1. Thus we have

*Force on electric current in a uniform magnetic field*

$$F = IlB\sin\theta. \qquad \textbf{(20–1)}$$

If the direction of the current is perpendicular to the field $\vec{\mathbf{B}}$ ($\theta = 90°$), then the force is

$$F_{max} = IlB. \qquad [\text{current} \perp \vec{\mathbf{B}}] \quad \textbf{(20–2)}$$

*Definition of magnetic field*

If the current is parallel to the field ($\theta = 0°$), the force is zero. The magnitude of $\vec{\mathbf{B}}$ can be defined using Eq. 20–2 as $B = F_{max}/Il$, where $F_{max}$ is the magnitude of the force on a straight length $l$ of wire carrying a current $I$ when the wire is perpendicular to $\vec{\mathbf{B}}$.†

†In our discussion, we have assumed that the magnetic field is uniform. If it is not, then $B$ in Eqs. 20–1 and 20–2 is the average field over the length $l$ of the wire.

The SI unit for magnetic field $B$ is the **tesla** (T). From Eq. 20–1 or 20–2, it is clear that $1\,\mathrm{T} = 1\,\mathrm{N/A \cdot m}$. An older name for the tesla is the "weber per meter squared" $(1\,\mathrm{Wb/m^2} = 1\,\mathrm{T})$. Another unit sometimes used to specify magnetic field is a cgs unit, the **gauss** (G): $1\,\mathrm{G} = 10^{-4}\,\mathrm{T}$. A field given in gauss should always be changed to teslas before using with other SI units. To get a "feel" for these units, we note that the magnetic field of the Earth at its surface is about $\frac{1}{2}$ G or $0.5 \times 10^{-4}\,\mathrm{T}$. On the other hand, strong electromagnets can produce fields on the order of 2 T and superconducting magnets can produce over 10 T.

*Magnetic field units: The tesla and the gauss*

**EXAMPLE 20–1** **Magnetic force on a current-carrying wire.** A wire carrying a 30-A current has a length $l = 12\,\mathrm{cm}$ between the pole faces of a magnet at an angle $\theta = 60°$ (Fig. 20–12). The magnetic field is approximately uniform at 0.90 T. We ignore the field beyond the pole pieces. What is the magnitude of the force on the wire?

**APPROACH** We use Eq. 20–1 to find the force $F$ on the 12-cm length of wire within the uniform field $B$.

**SOLUTION** Using Eq. 20–1 with $l = 12\,\mathrm{cm}$, $I = 30\,\mathrm{A}$, $B = 0.90\,\mathrm{T}$, and $\theta = 60°$ gives

$$\begin{aligned} F &= IlB \sin\theta \\ &= (30\,\mathrm{A})(0.12\,\mathrm{m})(0.90\,\mathrm{T})(0.866) = 2.8\,\mathrm{N}. \end{aligned}$$

**EXERCISE C** A straight power line carries 30 A and is perpendicular to the Earth's magnetic field of $0.50 \times 10^{-4}\,\mathrm{T}$. What magnitude force is exerted on 100 m of this power line?

On a diagram, when we want to represent an electric current or a magnetic field that is pointing out of the page (toward us) or into the page, we use ⊙ or ×, respectively. The ⊙ is meant to resemble the tip of an arrow pointing directly toward the reader, whereas the × or ⊗ resembles the tail of an arrow going away. (See Fig. 20–13.)

**EXAMPLE 20–2** **Measuring a magnetic field.** A rectangular loop of wire hangs vertically as shown in Fig. 20–13. A magnetic field $\vec{\mathbf{B}}$ is directed horizontally, perpendicular to the wire, and points out of the page at all points as represented by the symbol ⊙. The magnetic field $\vec{\mathbf{B}}$ is very nearly uniform along the horizontal portion of wire ab (length $l = 10.0\,\mathrm{cm}$) which is near the center of the gap of a large magnet producing the field. The top portion of the wire loop is free of the field. The loop hangs from a balance which measures a downward force (in addition to the gravitational force) of $F = 3.48 \times 10^{-2}\,\mathrm{N}$ when the wire carries a current $I = 0.245\,\mathrm{A}$. What is the magnitude of the magnetic field $B$?

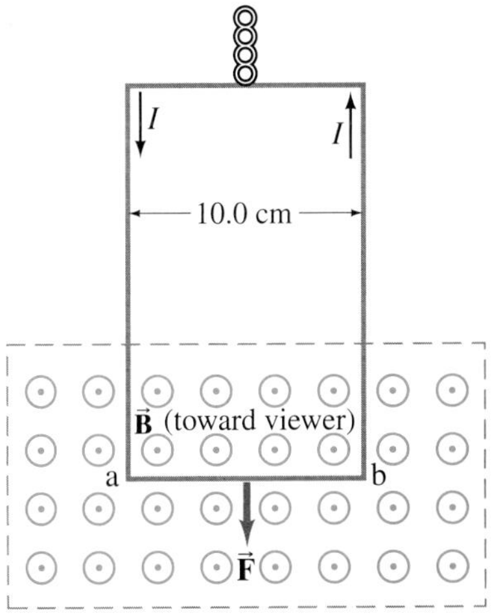

**FIGURE 20–13** Measuring a magnetic field $\vec{\mathbf{B}}$. Example 20–2.

**APPROACH** Three straight sections of the wire loop are in the magnetic field: a horizontal section and two vertical sections. We apply Eq. 20–1 to each section and use the right-hand rule.

**SOLUTION** The magnetic force on the left vertical section of wire points to the left; the force on the vertical section on the right points to the right. These two forces are equal and in opposite directions and so add up to zero. Hence, the net magnetic force on the loop is that on the horizontal section ab, whose length is $l = 0.100\,\mathrm{m}$. The angle $\theta$ between $\vec{\mathbf{B}}$ and the wire is $\theta = 90°$, so $\sin\theta = 1$. Thus Eq. 20–1 gives

$$B = \frac{F}{Il} = \frac{3.48 \times 10^{-2}\,\mathrm{N}}{(0.245\,\mathrm{A})(0.100\,\mathrm{m})} = 1.42\,\mathrm{T}.$$

**NOTE** This technique can be a precise means of determining magnetic field strength.

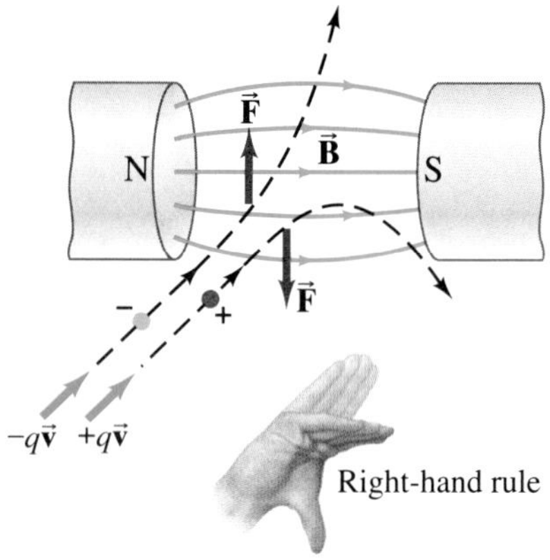


**FIGURE 20–14** Force on charged particles due to a magnetic field is perpendicular to the magnetic field direction.

## 20–4 Force on Electric Charge Moving in a Magnetic Field

We have seen that a current-carrying wire experiences a force when placed in a magnetic field. Since a current in a wire consists of moving electric charges, we might expect that freely moving charged particles (not in a wire) would also experience a force when passing through a magnetic field. Although free electric charges are not as easy to produce in the lab as a current in a wire, it can be done, and experiments do show that moving electric charges experience a force in a magnetic field.

From what we already know we can predict the force on a single electric charge moving in a magnetic field $\vec{\mathbf{B}}$. If $N$ such particles of charge $q$ pass by a given point in time $t$, they constitute a current $I = Nq/t$. We let $t$ be the time for a charge $q$ to travel a distance $l$ in a magnetic field $\vec{\mathbf{B}}$; then $l = vt$ where $v$ is the magnitude of the velocity $\vec{\mathbf{v}}$ of the particle. Thus, the force on these $N$ particles is, by Eq. 20–1, $F = IlB\sin\theta = (Nq/t)(vt)B\sin\theta = NqvB\sin\theta$. The force on *one* of the $N$ particles is then

*Force on moving charge in magnetic field*

$$F = qvB\sin\theta. \qquad \textbf{(20–3)}$$

This equation gives the magnitude of the force exerted by a magnetic field on a particle of charge $q$ moving with velocity $v$ at a point where the magnetic field has magnitude $B$. The angle between $\vec{\mathbf{v}}$ and $\vec{\mathbf{B}}$ is $\theta$. The force is greatest when the particle moves perpendicular to $\vec{\mathbf{B}}$ ($\theta = 90°$):

$$F_{max} = qvB. \qquad [\vec{\mathbf{v}} \perp \vec{\mathbf{B}}] \quad \textbf{(20–4)}$$

The force is *zero* if the particle moves *parallel* to the field lines ($\theta = 0°$). The *direction* of the force is perpendicular to the magnetic field $\vec{\mathbf{B}}$ and to the velocity $\vec{\mathbf{v}}$ of the particle. It is again given by a **right-hand rule**: you orient your right hand so that your outstretched fingers point along the direction of the particle's velocity ($\vec{\mathbf{v}}$), and when you bend your fingers they must point along the direction of $\vec{\mathbf{B}}$. Then your thumb will point in the direction of the force. This is true only for *positively* charged particles, and will be "down" for the situation shown in Fig. 20–14. For negatively charged particles, the force is in exactly the opposite direction, "up" in Fig. 20–14.

*Right-hand-rule-3: force on moving charge exerted by* $\vec{\mathbf{B}}$

**CONCEPTUAL EXAMPLE 20–3** **Negative charge near a magnet.** A negative charge $-Q$ is placed at rest near a magnet. Will the charge begin to move? Will it feel a force? What if the charge were positive, $+Q$?

**RESPONSE** No to all questions. A charge at rest has velocity equal to zero. Magnetic fields exert a force only on moving electric charges (Eq. 20–3).

**EXAMPLE 20–4** **Magnetic force on a proton.** A proton having a speed of $5.0 \times 10^6$ m/s in a magnetic field feels a force of $8.0 \times 10^{-14}$ N toward the west when it moves vertically upward (Fig. 20–15a). When moving horizontally in a northerly direction, it feels zero force (Fig. 20–15b). Determine the magnitude and direction of the magnetic field in this region. (The charge on a proton is $q = +e = 1.6 \times 10^{-19}$ C.)

**FIGURE 20–15** Example 20–4.

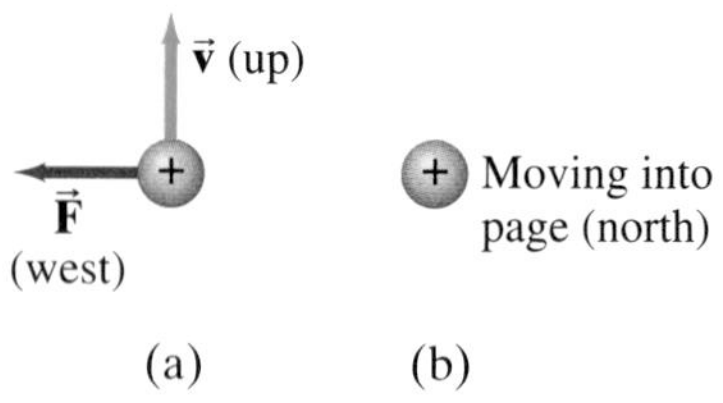


**APPROACH** Since the proton feels no force when moving north, the field must be in a north–south direction. In order to produce a force to the west when the proton moves upward, the right-hand rule tells us that $\vec{\mathbf{B}}$ must point toward the north. (Your thumb points west and the outstretched fingers of your right hand point upward only when your bent fingers point north.) The magnitude of $\vec{\mathbf{B}}$ is found using Eq. 20–3.

**SOLUTION** Equation 20–3 with $\theta = 90°$ gives

$$B = \frac{F}{qv} = \frac{8.0 \times 10^{-14}\,\text{N}}{(1.6 \times 10^{-19}\,\text{C})(5.0 \times 10^6\,\text{m/s})} = 0.10\,\text{T}.$$

**EXERCISE D** Determine the force on the proton of Example 20–4 if it heads horizontally south.

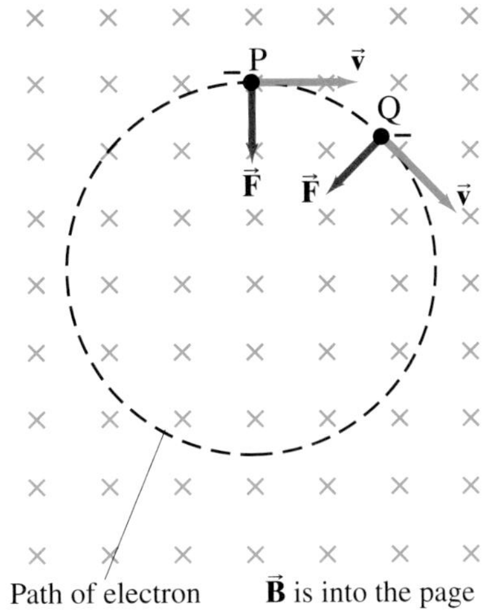


**FIGURE 20–16** Force exerted by a uniform magnetic field on a moving charged particle (in this case, an electron) produces a circular path.

The path of a charged particle moving in a plane perpendicular to a uniform magnetic field is a circle as we shall now show. In Fig. 20–16 the magnetic field is directed *into* the paper, as represented by ×'s. An electron at point P is moving to the right, and the force on it at this point is downward as shown (use the right-hand rule and reverse the direction for negative charge). The electron is thus deflected downward. A moment later, say, when it reaches point Q, the force is still perpendicular to the velocity and is in the direction shown. Because the force is always perpendicular to $\vec{v}$, the magnitude of $\vec{v}$ does not change—the electron moves at constant speed. We saw in Chapter 5 that if the force on a particle is always perpendicular to its velocity $\vec{v}$, the particle moves in a circle and undergoes a centripetal acceleration $a = v^2/r$ (Eq. 5–1). Thus a charged particle moves in a circular path with constant centripetal acceleration (see Example 20–5) in a uniform magnetic field. The electron moves clockwise in Fig. 20–16. A positive particle would feel a force in the opposite direction and would thus move counterclockwise.

**EXAMPLE 20–5 Electron's path in a uniform magnetic field.** An electron travels at $2.0 \times 10^7\,\text{m/s}$ in a plane perpendicular to a uniform 0.010-T magnetic field. Describe its path quantitatively.

**APPROACH** The electron moves at speed $v$ in a curved path and so must have a centripetal acceleration $a = v^2/r$ (Eq. 5–1). We find the radius of curvature using Newton's second law. The force is given by Eq. 20–3 with $\sin\theta = 1$, $F = qvB$.

**SOLUTION** We insert $F$ and $a$ into Newton's second law:

$$\Sigma F = ma$$

$$qvB = \frac{mv^2}{r}.$$

We solve for $r$ and find

$$r = \frac{mv}{qB}.$$

Since $\vec{F}$ is perpendicular to $\vec{v}$, the magnitude of $\vec{v}$ doesn't change. From this equation we see that if $\vec{B} = \text{constant}$, then $r = \text{constant}$, and the curve must be a circle as we claimed above. To get $r$ we put in the numbers:

$$r = \frac{(9.1 \times 10^{-31}\,\text{kg})(2.0 \times 10^7\,\text{m/s})}{(1.6 \times 10^{-19}\,\text{C})(0.010\,\text{T})} = 1.1 \times 10^{-2}\,\text{m} = 1.1\,\text{cm}.$$

## PROBLEM SOLVING Magnetic Fields

Magnetic fields are somewhat analogous to the electric fields of Chapter 16, but there are several important differences to recall:

1. The force experienced by a charged particle moving in a magnetic field is *perpendicular* to the direction of the magnetic field (and to the direction of the velocity of the particle), whereas the force exerted by an electric field is *parallel* to the direction of the field (and unaffected by the velocity of the particle).
2. The *right-hand rule*, in its different forms, is intended to help you determine the directions of magnetic field, and the forces they exert, and/or the directions of electric current or charged particle velocity. The right-hand rules (Table 20–1) are designed to deal with the "perpendicular" nature of these quantities.
3. The equations in this Chapter are generally not printed as vector equations, but involve magnitudes only. Right-hand rules are to be used to find directions of vector quantities.

**TABLE 20–1 Summary of Right-hand Rules (= RHR)**

| Physical Situation | Example | How to Orient Right Hand | Result |
|---|---|---|---|
| **1.** Magnetic field produced by current (RHR-1) | 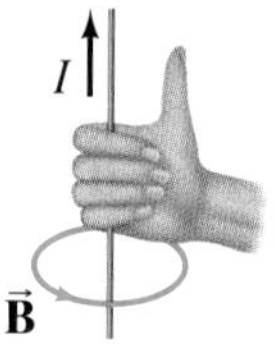  Fig. 20–8c | Wrap fingers around wire with thumb pointing in direction of current $I$ | Fingers point in direction of $\vec{\mathbf{B}}$ |
| **2.** Force on electric current $I$ due to magnetic field (RHR-2) | 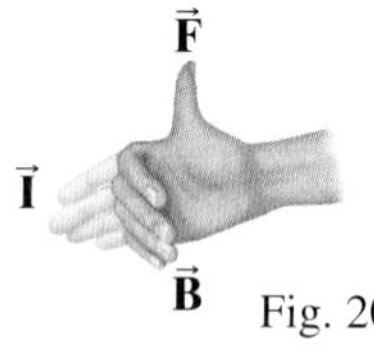  Fig. 20–11c | Fingers point straight along current $I$, then bent along magnetic field $\vec{\mathbf{B}}$ | Thumb points in direction of force |
| **3.** Force on electric charge $+q$ due to magnetic field (RHR-3) | 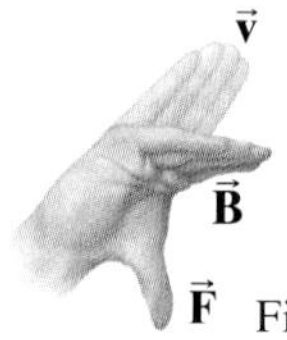  Fig. 20–14 | Fingers point along particle's velocity $\vec{\mathbf{v}}$, then along $\vec{\mathbf{B}}$ | Thumb points in direction of force |

**CONCEPTUAL EXAMPLE 20–6 A helical path.** What is the path of a charged particle in a uniform magnetic field if its velocity is *not* perpendicular to the magnetic field?

**RESPONSE** The velocity vector can be broken down into components parallel and perpendicular to the field. The velocity component parallel to the field lines results in no force, so this component remains constant. The velocity component perpendicular to the field results in circular motion about the field lines. Putting these two motions together produces a helical (spiral) motion around the field lines as shown in Fig. 20–17.

**EXERCISE E** What is the sign of the charge in Fig. 20–17? How would you modify the drawing if the sign were reversed?

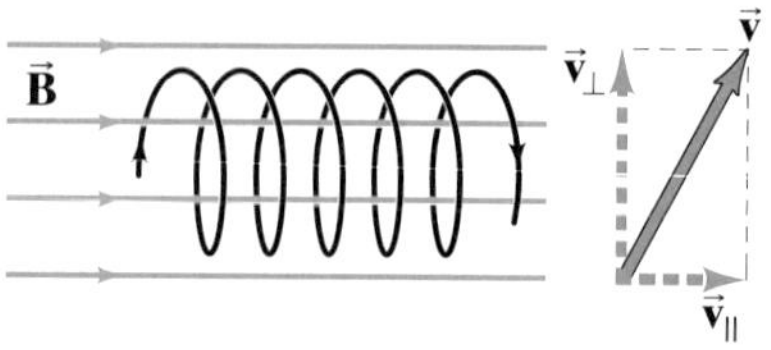

**FIGURE 20–17** Example 20–6.

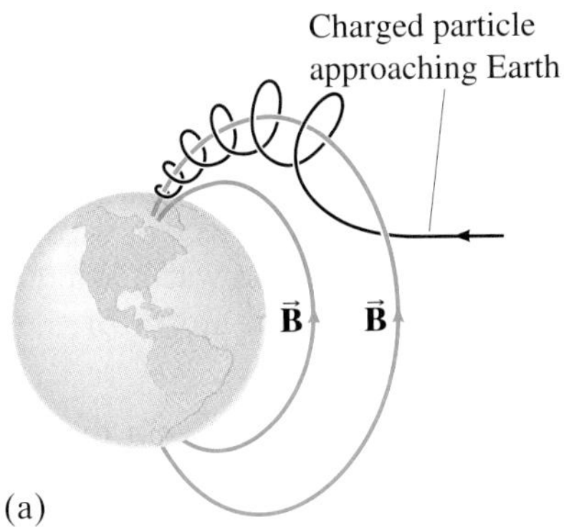

**FIGURE 20–18** (a) Diagram showing a charged particle that approaches the Earth and is "captured" by the magnetic field of the Earth. Such particles follow the field lines toward the poles as shown. (b) Photo of aurora borealis.

## * Aurora Borealis

PHYSICS APPLIED
*The aurora borealis*

Charged ions approach the Earth from the Sun (the "solar wind") and enter the atmosphere mainly near the poles, sometimes causing a phenomenon called the **aurora borealis** or "northern lights" in northern latitudes. To see why, consider Example 20–6 and Fig. 20–18 (see also Fig. 20–17). In Fig. 20–18 we imagine a stream of charged particles approaching the Earth. The velocity component *perpendicular* to the field for each particle becomes a circular orbit around the field lines, whereas the velocity component *parallel* to the field carries the particle along the field lines toward the poles. As a particle approaches the N pole, the magnetic field is stronger and the radius of the helical path becomes smaller.

The high concentration of charged particles ionizes the air, and as the electrons recombine with atoms, light is emitted (Chapter 27) which is the aurora. Auroras are especially spectacular during periods of high sunspot activity when the solar wind brings more charged particles toward Earth.

## * Vector Product

Equation 20–3 can be written in a vector form that incorporates the right-hand rule:

$$\vec{\mathbf{F}} = q\vec{\mathbf{v}} \times \vec{\mathbf{B}} \qquad \textbf{(20–5)}$$

The cross $\times$ implies the right-hand rule: first point your fingers along the velocity vector $\vec{\mathbf{v}}$ so that when you bend them, they point in the direction of the magnetic field $\vec{\mathbf{B}}$. Then your thumb gives the direction of the force $\vec{\mathbf{F}}$. The cross $\times$ also implies the use of $\sin\theta$ for the magnitude of $F$. Equation 20–5 is a vector equation known as the *vector cross product*.

# 20–5 Magnetic Field Due to a Long Straight Wire

We saw in Section 20–2, Fig. 20–8, that the magnetic field surrounding the electric current in a long straight wire is such that the field lines are circles with the wire at the center (Fig. 20–19). You might expect that the field strength at a given point would be greater if the current flowing in the wire were greater; and that the field would be less at points farther from the wire. This is indeed the case. Careful experiments show that the magnetic field $B$ due to the current in a long straight wire is directly proportional to the current $I$ in the wire and inversely proportional to the distance $r$ from the wire:

$$B \propto \frac{I}{r}.$$

This relation is valid as long as $r$, the perpendicular distance to the wire, is much less than the distance to the ends of the wire (i.e., the wire is long).

**FIGURE 20–19** Same as Fig. 20–8b, magnetic field lines around a long straight wire carrying an electric current $I$.

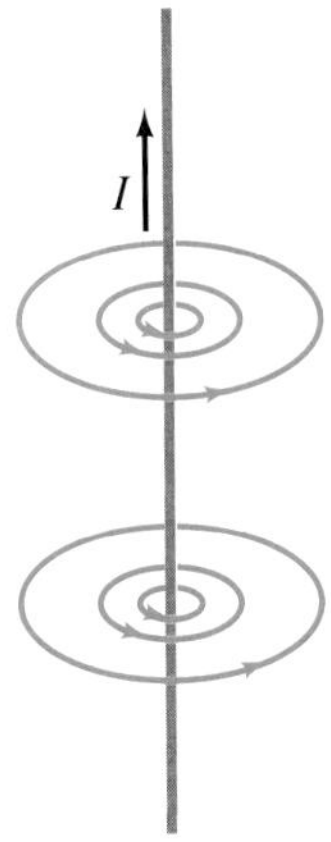

The proportionality constant is written† as $\mu_0/2\pi$; thus,

Magnetic field due to current in straight wire

$$B = \frac{\mu_0}{2\pi}\frac{I}{r}. \qquad \text{[near a long straight wire]} \quad \textbf{(20–6)}$$

The value of the constant $\mu_0$, which is called the **permeability of free space**, is $\mu_0 = 4\pi \times 10^{-7}\,\text{T}\cdot\text{m/A}$.

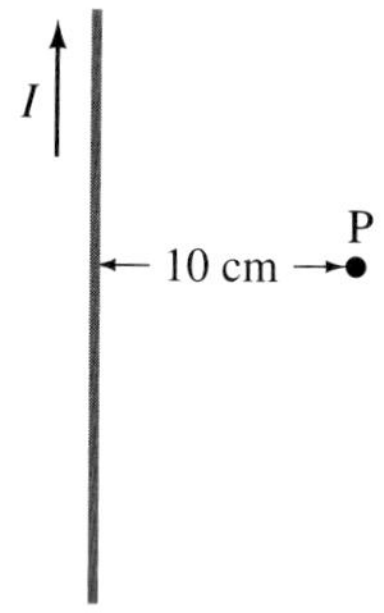


**FIGURE 20–20** Example 20–7.

**CAUTION**
A compass, near a current, may not point north

**EXAMPLE 20–7 Calculation of $\vec{B}$ near a wire.** An electric wire in the wall of a building carries a dc current of 25 A vertically upward. What is the magnetic field due to this current at a point P 10 cm due north of the wire (Fig. 20–20)?

**APPROACH** We assume the wire is much longer than the 10-cm distance to the point P so we can apply Eq. 20–6.

**SOLUTION** According to Eq. 20–6:

$$B = \frac{\mu_0 I}{2\pi r} = \frac{(4\pi \times 10^{-7}\,\text{T}\cdot\text{m/A})(25\,\text{A})}{(2\pi)(0.10\,\text{m})} = 5.0 \times 10^{-5}\,\text{T},$$

or 0.50 G. By the right-hand rule (Fig. 20–8c), the field points to the west (into the page in Fig. 20–20) at this point.

**NOTE** The wire's field has about the same magnitude as Earth's, so a compass would not point north but in a northwesterly direction.

**NOTE** Most electrical wiring in buildings consists of cables with two wires in each cable. Since the two wires carry current in opposite directions, their magnetic fields will cancel to a large extent.

**EXERCISE F** At what distance from the wire in Example 20–7 is its magnetic field 5 times greater than the Earth's?

**FIGURE 20–21** Example 20–8. Wire 1 carrying current $I_1$ out towards us, and wire 2 carrying current $I_2$ into the page, produce magnetic fields whose lines are circles around their respective wires.

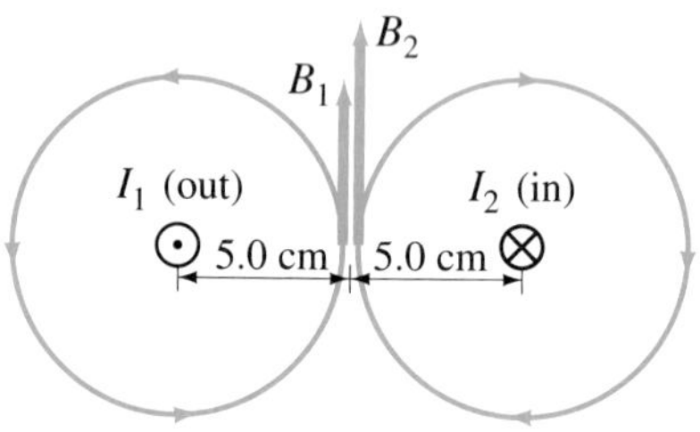


**EXAMPLE 20–8 Magnetic field midway between two currents.** Two parallel straight wires 10.0 cm apart carry currents in opposite directions (Fig. 20–21). Current $I_1 = 5.0\,\text{A}$ is out of the page, and $I_2 = 7.0\,\text{A}$ is into the page. Determine the magnitude and direction of the magnetic field halfway between the two wires.

**APPROACH** The magnitude of the field produced by each wire is calculated from Eq. 20–6. The direction of *each* wire's field is determined with the right-hand rule. The total field is the vector sum of the two fields at the midway point.

**SOLUTION** The magnetic field lines due to current $I_1$ form circles around the wire of $I_1$, and right-hand-rule-1 (Fig. 20–8c) tells us they point counterclockwise around the wire. The field lines due to $I_2$ form circles around the wire of $I_2$ and point clockwise, Fig. 20–21. At the midpoint, both fields point upward as shown, and so add together. The midpoint is 0.050 m from each wire, and from Eq. 20–6 the magnitudes of $B_1$ and $B_2$ are

$$B_1 = \frac{\mu_0 I_1}{2\pi r} = \frac{(4\pi \times 10^{-7}\,\text{T}\cdot\text{m/A})(5.0\,\text{A})}{2\pi(0.050\,\text{m})} = 2.0 \times 10^{-5}\,\text{T};$$

$$B_2 = \frac{\mu_0 I_2}{2\pi r} = \frac{(4\pi \times 10^{-7}\,\text{T}\cdot\text{m/A})(7.0\,\text{A})}{2\pi(0.050\,\text{m})} = 2.8 \times 10^{-5}\,\text{T}.$$

The total field is *up* with a magnitude of

$$B = B_1 + B_2 = 4.8 \times 10^{-5}\,\text{T}.$$

†The constant is chosen in this complicated way so that Ampère's law (Section 20–8), which is considered more fundamental, will have a simple and elegant form.

**CONCEPTUAL EXAMPLE 20–9** **Magnetic field due to four wires.** Figure 20–22 shows four long parallel wires which carry equal currents into or out of the page as shown. In which configuration, (*a*) or (*b*), is the magnetic field greater at the center of the square?

**RESPONSE** It is greater in (*a*). The arrows illustrate the directions of the field produced by each wire; check it out, using the right-hand rule to confirm these results. The net field at the center is the superposition of the four fields, which will point to the left in (*a*) and is zero in (*b*).

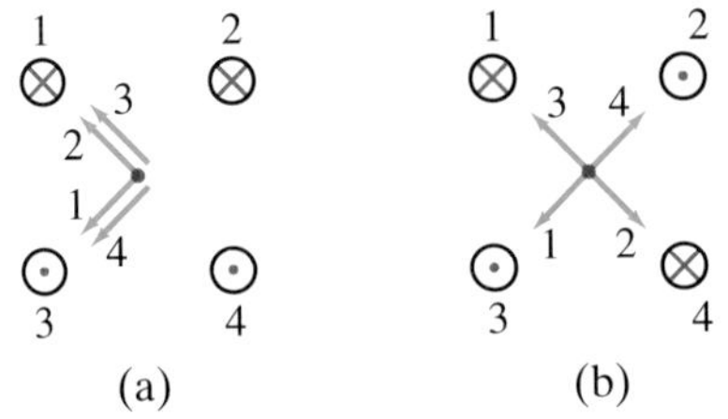


**FIGURE 20–22** Example 20–9.

## 20–6 Force between Two Parallel Wires

We have seen that a wire carrying a current produces a magnetic field (magnitude given by Eq. 20–6 for a long straight wire). Also, a current-carrying wire feels a force when placed in a magnetic field (Section 20–3, Eq. 20–1). Thus, we expect that two current-carrying wires will exert a force on each other.

Consider two long parallel wires separated by a distance *d*, as in Fig. 20–23a. They carry currents $I_1$ and $I_2$, respectively. Each current produces a magnetic field that is "felt" by the other, so each must exert a force on the other. For example, the magnetic field $B_1$ produced by $I_1$ in Fig 20–23 is given by Eq. 20–6, which at the location of wire 2 is

$$B_1 = \frac{\mu_0}{2\pi}\frac{I_1}{d}.$$

See Fig. 20–23b, where the field due *only* to $I_1$ is shown. According to Eq. 20–2, the force $F_2$ exerted by $B_1$ on a length $l_2$ of wire 2, carrying current $I_2$, is

$$F_2 = I_2 B_1 l_2.$$

Note that the force on $I_2$ is due only to the field produced by $I_1$. Of course, $I_2$ also produces a field, but it does not exert a force on itself. We substitute $B_1$ into the formula for $F_2$ and find that the force on a length $l_2$ of wire 2 is

$$F_2 = \frac{\mu_0}{2\pi}\frac{I_1 I_2}{d} l_2. \qquad \textbf{(20–7)}$$

If we use right-hand-rule-1 of Fig. 20–8c, we see that the lines of $B_1$ are as shown in Fig. 20–23b. Then using right-hand-rule-2 of Fig. 20–11c, we see that the force exerted on $I_2$ will be to the left in Fig. 20–23b. That is, $I_1$ exerts an attractive force on $I_2$ (Fig. 20–24a). This is true as long as the currents are in the same direction. If $I_2$ is in the opposite direction, the right-hand rule indicates that the force is in the opposite direction. That is, $I_1$ exerts a repulsive force on $I_2$ (Fig. 20–24b).

Reasoning similar to that above shows that the magnetic field produced by $I_2$ exerts an equal but opposite force on $I_1$. We expect this to be true also from Newton's third law, of course. Thus, as shown in Fig. 20–24, parallel currents in the same directions attract each other, whereas parallel currents in opposite directions repel.

**FIGURE 20–23** (a) Two parallel conductors carrying currents $I_1$ and $I_2$. (b) Magnetic field $\vec{\mathbf{B}}_1$ produced by $I_1$. (Field produced by $I_2$ is not shown.) $\vec{\mathbf{B}}_1$ points into page at position of $I_2$.

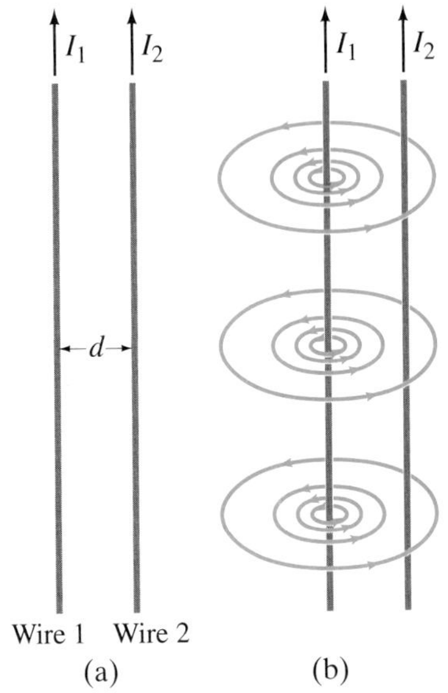


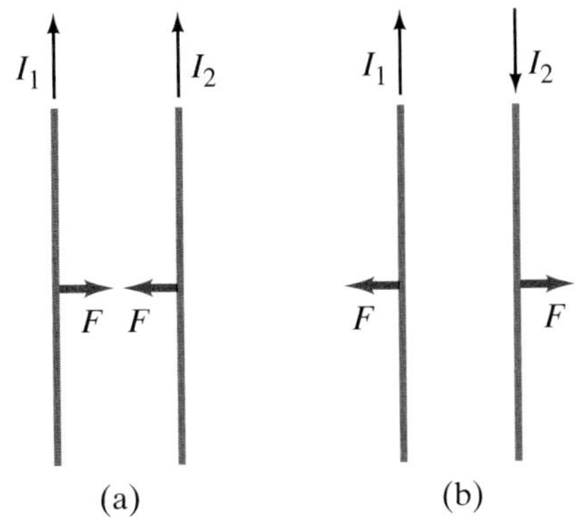


**FIGURE 20–24** (a) Parallel currents in the same direction exert an attractive force on each other. (b) Antiparallel currents (in opposite directions) exert a repulsive force on each other.

**EXAMPLE 20–10** **Force between two current-carrying wires.** The two wires of a 2.0-m-long appliance cord are 3.0 mm apart and carry a current of 8.0 A dc. Calculate the force one wire exerts on the other.

**APPROACH** Each wire is in the magnetic field of the other when the current is on, so we can apply Eq. 20–7. We can write $\mu_0/2\pi = 2.0 \times 10^{-7}\,\mathrm{T\cdot m/A}$.

**SOLUTION** Equation 20–7 gives

$$F = \frac{(2.0 \times 10^{-7}\,\mathrm{T\cdot m/A})(8.0\,\mathrm{A})^2(2.0\,\mathrm{m})}{(3.0 \times 10^{-3}\,\mathrm{m})} = 8.5 \times 10^{-3}\,\mathrm{N}.$$

The currents are in opposite directions (one toward the appliance, the other away from it), so the force would be repulsive and tend to spread the wires apart.

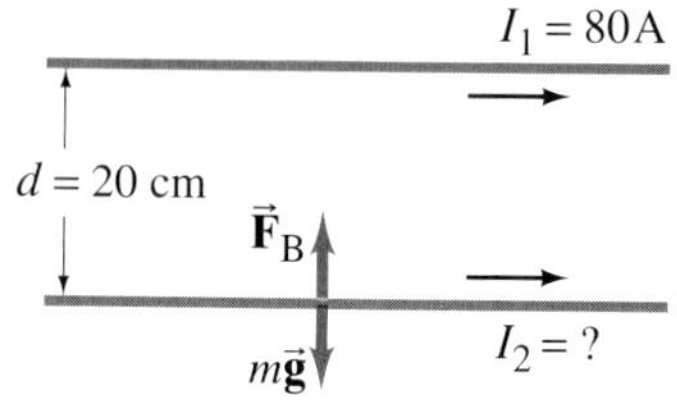


**FIGURE 20–25** Example 20–11.

**EXAMPLE 20–11** **Suspending a current with a current.** A horizontal wire carries a current $I_1 = 80\,\mathrm{A}$ dc. A second parallel wire 20 cm below it (Fig. 20–25) must carry how much current $I_2$ so that it doesn't fall due to gravity? The lower wire has a mass of 0.12 g per meter of length.

**APPROACH** If wire 2 is not to fall under gravity, which acts downward, the magnetic force on it must be upward. This means that the current in the two wires must be in the same direction. We can find the current $I_2$ by equating the magnitudes of the magnetic force and the gravitational force on the wire.

**SOLUTION** The force of gravity on wire 2 is downward. For each 1.0 m of wire length, the gravitational force has magnitude

$$F = mg = (0.12 \times 10^{-3}\,\mathrm{kg/m})(1.0\,\mathrm{m})(9.8\,\mathrm{m/s^2}) = 1.18 \times 10^{-3}\,\mathrm{N}.$$

The magnetic force on wire 2 must be upward, and Eq. 20–7 gives

$$F = \frac{\mu_0}{2\pi}\frac{I_1 I_2}{d}\,l$$

where $d = 0.20\,\mathrm{m}$ and $I_1 = 80\,\mathrm{A}$. We solve this for $I_2$ and set the two force magnitudes equal (letting $l = 1.0\,\mathrm{m}$):

$$I_2 = \frac{2\pi d}{\mu_0 I_1}\left(\frac{F}{l}\right) = \frac{2\pi(0.20\,\mathrm{m})}{(4\pi \times 10^{-7}\,\mathrm{T\cdot m/A})(80\,\mathrm{A})}(1.18 \times 10^{-3}\,\mathrm{N/m}) = 15\,\mathrm{A}.$$

## * Definition of the Ampere and the Coulomb

You may have wondered how the constant $\mu_0$ in Eq. 20–6 could be exactly $4\pi \times 10^{-7}\,\mathrm{T\cdot m/A}$. Here is how it happened. With an older definition of the ampere, $\mu_0$ was measured experimentally to be very close to this value. Today, however, $\mu_0$ is *defined* to be exactly $4\pi \times 10^{-7}\,\mathrm{T\cdot m/A}$. This, of course, could not be done if the ampere were defined independently. The ampere, the unit of current, is now defined in terms of the magnetic field $B$ it produces using the defined value of $\mu_0$.

In particular, we use the force between two parallel current-carrying wires, Eq. 20–7, to define the ampere precisely. If $I_1 = I_2 = 1\,\mathrm{A}$ exactly, and the two wires are exactly 1 m apart, then

$$\frac{F}{l} = \frac{\mu_0}{2\pi}\frac{I_1 I_2}{d} = \frac{(4\pi \times 10^{-7}\,\mathrm{T\cdot m/A})}{(2\pi)}\frac{(1\,\mathrm{A})(1\,\mathrm{A})}{(1\,\mathrm{m})} = 2 \times 10^{-7}\,\mathrm{N/m}.$$

*Definitions of ampere and coloumb*

Thus, *one* **ampere** *is defined as that current flowing in each of two long parallel wires, 1 m apart, which results in a force of exactly $2 \times 10^{-7}\,\mathrm{N/m}$ of length of each wire.*

This is the precise definition of the ampere. The **coulomb** is then defined as being *exactly* one ampere-second: $1\,\mathrm{C} = 1\,\mathrm{A\cdot s}$.

## 20–7 Solenoids and Electromagnets

A long coil of wire consisting of many loops (or turns) of wire is called a **solenoid**. The magnetic field within a solenoid can be fairly large because it is the sum of the fields due to the current in each loop (Fig. 20–26). A solenoid acts like a magnet; one end can be considered the north pole and the other the south pole, depending on the direction of the current in the loops (use the right-hand rule). Since the magnetic field lines leave the north pole of a magnet, the north pole of the solenoid in Fig. 20–26 is on the right. As we will see in the next Section, the magnetic field inside a tightly wrapped solenoid with $N$ turns of wire in a length $l$, each carrying current $I$, is

$$B = \mu_0 I N / l. \qquad \textbf{(20–8)}$$

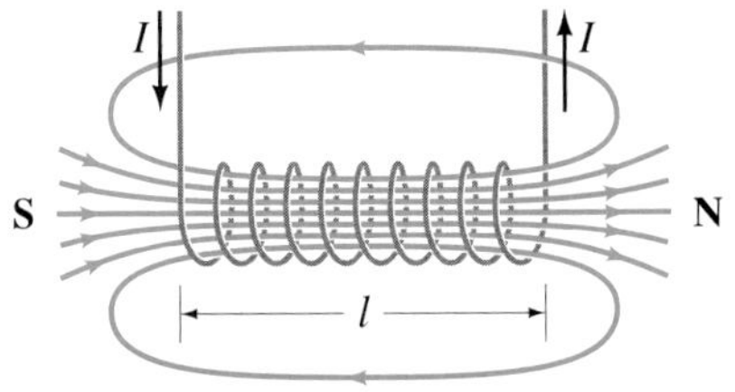


**FIGURE 20–26** Magnetic field of a solenoid. The north pole of this solenoid, thought of as a magnet, is on the right, and the south pole is on the left.

If a piece of iron is placed inside a solenoid, the magnetic field is increased greatly because the iron becomes a magnet. The resulting magnetic field is the sum of that due to the current and that due to the iron, and can be hundreds or thousands of times that due to the current alone (see Section 20–12). Such an iron-core solenoid is an **electromagnet**.

PHYSICS APPLIED
*Electromagnets and solenoids*

Electromagnets have many practical applications, from use in motors and generators to producing large magnetic fields for research. Sometimes an iron core is not present—the magnetic field comes only from the current in the wire coils. For some applications, the current-carrying wires are made of superconducting material kept below the transition temperature (Section 18–9). Very high fields can be produced with superconducting wire without using an iron core. No electric power is needed to maintain large current in the superconducting coils, which means large savings of energy; nor must huge amounts of heat be dissipated.

Another useful device consists of a solenoid into which a rod of iron is partially inserted. This combination is also referred to as a solenoid. One simple use is as a doorbell (Fig. 20–27). When the circuit is closed by pushing the button, the coil effectively becomes a magnet and exerts a force on the iron rod. The rod is pulled into the coil and strikes the bell. A large solenoid is used in the starters of cars; when you engage the starter, you are closing a circuit that not only turns the starter motor, but activates a solenoid that first moves the starter into direct contact with the gears on the engine's flywheel. Solenoids are used as switches in many devices. They have the advantage of moving mechanical parts quickly and accurately.

PHYSICS APPLIED
*Doorbell, car starter*

Modern circuit breakers that protect houses and buildings from overload and fire contain not only a "thermal" part (bimetallic strip as described in Section 18–6, Fig. 18–19) but also a magnetic sensor. If the current is above a certain level, the magnetic field it produces pulls an iron plate that breaks the same contact points as in Fig. 18–19b and c. In more sophisticated circuit breakers, including ground fault circuit interrupters (GFCIs—discussed in Section 21–8), a solenoid is used. The iron rod of Fig. 20–27, instead of striking a bell, strikes one side of a pair of points, opening them and opening the circuit. Magnetic circuit breakers react quickly ($<10$ msec), and for buildings are designed to react to the high currents of shorts (but not shut off for the start-up surges of motors).

PHYSICS APPLIED
*Magnetic circuit breakers*

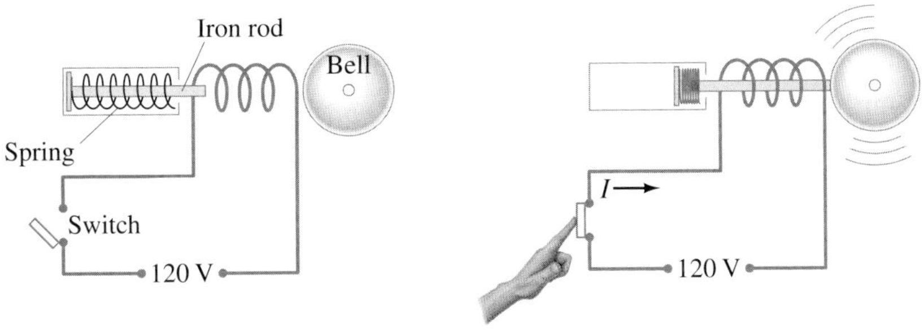


**FIGURE 20–27** Solenoid used as a doorbell.

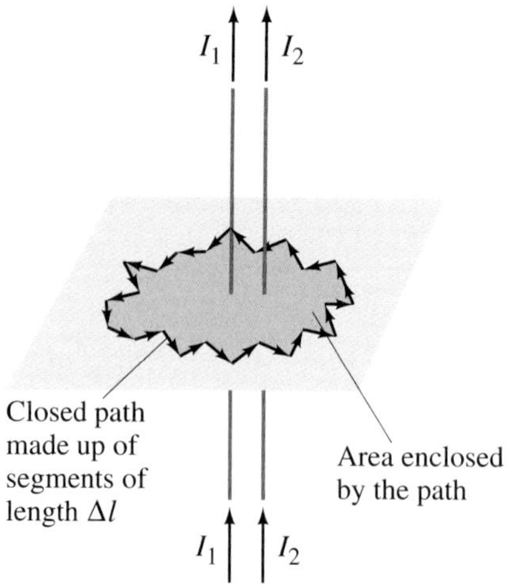


**FIGURE 20–28** Arbitrary path enclosing electric currents, for Ampère's law. The path is broken down into segments of equal length $\Delta l$. The total current enclosed by the path shown is $I_{\text{encl}} = I_1 + I_2$.

## * 20–8 Ampère's Law

In Section 20–5 we saw that Eq. 20–6 gives the relation between the current in a long straight wire and the magnetic field it produces. This equation is valid *only* for a long straight wire. Is there a general relation between a current in a wire of any shape and the magnetic field around it? Yes: the French scientist André Marie Ampère (1775–1836) proposed such a relation shortly after Oersted's discovery. Consider any (arbitrary) closed path around a current, as shown in Fig. 20–28, and imagine this path as being made up of short segments each of length $\Delta l$. We take the product of the length of each segment times the component of magnetic field $\vec{\mathbf{B}}$ parallel to that segment. If we now sum all these terms, the result (said Ampère) will be equal to $\mu_0$ times the net current $I_{\text{encl}}$ that passes through the surface *enclosed* by the path. This is known as **Ampère's law** and can be written

AMPÈRE'S LAW

$$\Sigma B_{\parallel}\,\Delta l = \mu_0 I_{\text{encl}}. \qquad \textbf{(20–9)}$$

The symbol $\Sigma$ means "the sum of" and $B_{\parallel}$ means the component of $\vec{\mathbf{B}}$ parallel to that particular $\Delta l$. The lengths $\Delta l$ are chosen small enough so that $B_{\parallel}$ is essentially constant on each length. The sum must be made over a closed path, and $I_{\text{encl}}$ is the total net current enclosed by the closed path.

### * Field Due to a Straight Wire

We can check Ampère's law by applying it to the simple case of a long straight wire carrying a current $I$. Let us find the magnitude of $B$ at point A, a distance $r$ from the wire in Fig. 20–29. The magnetic field lines are circles with the wire at their center (as in Fig. 20–8). As the path to be used in Eq. 20–9, we choose a convenient one: a circle of radius $r$, because at any point on this path, $\vec{\mathbf{B}}$ will be tangent to this circle. For any short segment of the circle (Fig. 20–29), $\vec{\mathbf{B}}$ will be parallel to that segment, so $B_{\parallel} = B$. Suppose we break the circular path down into 100 segments.[†] Then Ampère's law states that

**FIGURE 20–29** Circular path of radius $r$.

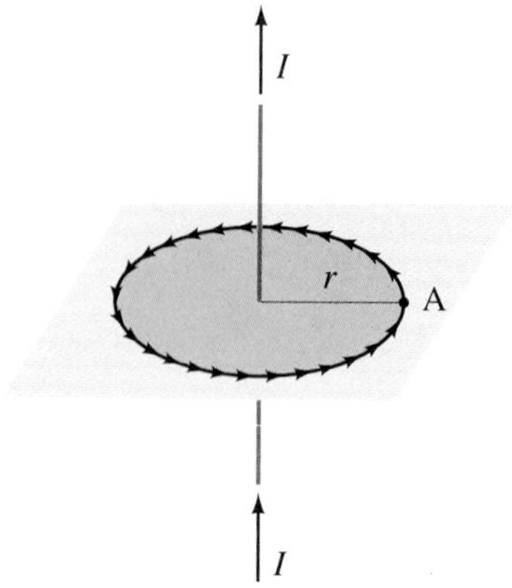


$$(B\,\Delta l)_1 + (B\,\Delta l)_2 + (B\,\Delta l)_3 + \cdots + (B\,\Delta l)_{100} = \mu_0 I.$$

The dots represent all the terms we did not write down. All the segments are the same distance from the wire, so by symmetry we expect $B$ to be the same at each segment. We can then factor out $B$ from the sum:

$$B(\Delta l_1 + \Delta l_2 + \Delta l_3 + \cdots + \Delta l_{100}) = \mu_0 I.$$

The sum of the segment lengths $\Delta l$ is just the circumference of the circle, $2\pi r$.

[†]Actually, Ampère's law is precisely accurate when there is an infinite number of infinitesimally short segments, but that leads into calculus.

Thus we have

$$B(2\pi r) = \mu_0 I,$$

or

$$B = \frac{\mu_0 I}{2\pi r}.$$

*B due to straight wire using Ampère's law*

This is just Eq. 20–6 for the field near a long straight wire, so Ampère's law agrees with experiment in this case.

A great many experiments indicate that Ampère's law is valid in general. However, it can be used to calculate the magnetic field mainly for simple or symmetric situations. Its importance is that it relates the magnetic field to the current in a direct and mathematically elegant way. Ampère's law is thus considered one of the basic laws of electricity and magnetism. It is valid for any situation where the currents and fields are not changing in time.

## * Field Inside a Solenoid

We now use Ampère's law to calculate the magnetic field inside a *solenoid*, a long coil of wire with many loops or turns, Fig. 20–30. Each loop produces a magnetic field as shown in Fig. 20–9, and the total field inside the solenoid will be the sum of the fields due to each current loop as shown in Fig. 20–30a for a few loops. If the loops of the solenoid are many and are closely spaced, the field inside will be essentially parallel to the axis except at the ends, as shown in Fig. 20–30b. Outside the solenoid, the field lines spread out in space, so the magnetic field is much weaker outside the solenoid than inside. For applying Ampère's law, we choose the path abcd shown in Fig. 20–31 far from either end. We consider this path as made up of four straight segments, the sides of the rectangle: ab, bc, cd, da. Then Ampère's law, Eq. 20–9, becomes

$$(B_{\parallel}\,\Delta l)_{ab} + (B_{\parallel}\,\Delta l)_{bc} + (B_{\parallel}\,\Delta l)_{cd} + (B_{\parallel}\,\Delta l)_{da} = \mu_0 I_{encl}.$$

The first term in the sum on the left will be (nearly) zero since the field outside the solenoid is negligible compared to the field inside. Furthermore, $\vec{\mathbf{B}}$ is perpendicular to the segments bc and da, so these terms are zero, too. Thus the left side of our equation above is simply $(B_{\parallel}\,\Delta l)_{cd} = Bl$, where $B$ is the field inside the solenoid, and $l$ is the length cd. We set $Bl$ equal to $\mu_0$ times the current enclosed

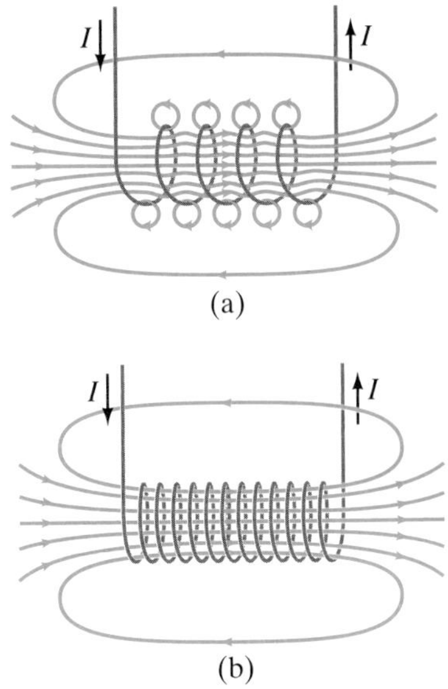


**FIGURE 20–30** (a) Magnetic field due to several loops of a solenoid. (b) For many closely spaced loops, the field is very nearly uniform.

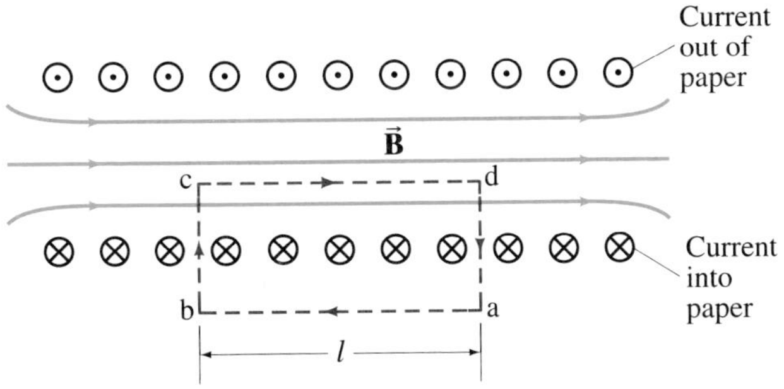


**FIGURE 20–31** Cross-sectional view into a solenoid. The magnetic field inside is straight except at the ends. Red dashed lines indicate the path chosen for use in Ampère's law. ⊙ and ⊗ are electric current direction (in the wire loops) out of the page and into the page.

by our chosen rectangular loop: if a current $I$ flows in the wire of the solenoid, the total current enclosed by our path abcd is $NI$, where $N$ is the number of loops (or turns) our path encircles (five in Fig. 20–31). Thus Ampère's law gives us

$$Bl = \mu_0 NI.$$

*Magnetic field inside a solenoid*

and

$$B = \frac{\mu_0 IN}{l}, \qquad \text{[solenoid]} \quad \textbf{(20–8 } \textit{repeated}\textbf{)}$$

which we quoted in the previous Section. This is the magnetic field magnitude inside a solenoid. $B$ depends only on the number of loops per unit length, $N/l$, and the current $I$. The field does not depend on the position within the solenoid, so $B$ is uniform inside the solenoid. This is strictly true only for an infinite solenoid, but it is a good approximation for real ones for points not close to the ends.

The direction of the magnetic field is found using right-hand-rule-1 (Fig. 20–8c), and is as shown in Fig. 20–31.

# * 20–9 Torque on a Current Loop; Magnetic Moment

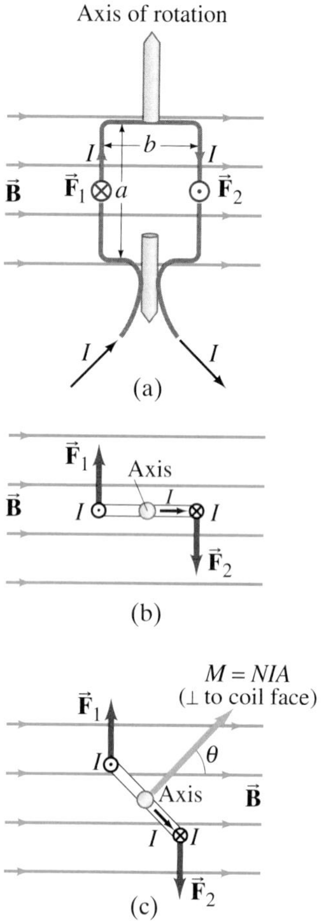


**FIGURE 20–32** Calculating the torque on a current loop in a magnetic field $\vec{\mathbf{B}}$. (a) Loop face parallel to $\vec{\mathbf{B}}$ field lines; (b) top view; (c) loop makes an angle to $\vec{\mathbf{B}}$, reducing the torque since the lever arm is reduced.

When an electric current flows in a closed loop of wire placed in an external magnetic field, as shown in Fig. 20–32, the magnetic force on the current can produce a torque. This is the principle behind a number of important practical devices, including voltmeters, ammeters, and motors. (We discuss these applications in the next Section.) The interaction between a current and a magnetic field is important in other areas as well, including atomic physics.

Current flows through the loop in Fig. 20–32a, whose face we assume is parallel to $\vec{\mathbf{B}}$ and is rectangular. $\vec{\mathbf{B}}$ exerts no force and no torque on the horizontal segments of wire because they are parallel to the field and $\sin\theta = 0$ in Eq. 20–1. But the magnetic field does exert a force on each of the vertical sections of wire as shown, $\vec{\mathbf{F}}_1$ and $\vec{\mathbf{F}}_2$ (see also top view, Fig. 20–32b). By right-hand-rule-2 (Fig. 20–11c) the direction of the force on the upward current on the left is in the opposite direction from the equal magnitude force $\vec{\mathbf{F}}_2$ on the descending current on the right. These forces give rise to a net torque that tends to rotate the coil about its vertical axis.

*Torque on current loop*

Let us calculate the magnitude of this torque. From Eq. 20–2 (current $\perp \vec{\mathbf{B}}$), the force $F = IaB$, where $a$ is the length of the vertical arm of the coil. The lever arm for each force is $b/2$, where $b$ is the width of the coil and the "axis" is at the midpoint. The torques produced by $\vec{\mathbf{F}}_1$ and $\vec{\mathbf{F}}_2$ act in the same direction, so the total torque is the sum of the two torques:

$$\tau = IaB\frac{b}{2} + IaB\frac{b}{2} = IabB = IAB,$$

where $A = ab$ is the area of the coil. If the coil consists of $N$ loops of wire, the current is then $NI$, so the torque becomes

$$\tau = NIAB.$$

If the coil makes an angle $\theta$ with the magnetic field, as shown in Fig. 20–32c, the forces are unchanged, but each lever arm is reduced from $\frac{1}{2}b$ to $\frac{1}{2}b\sin\theta$. Note that the angle $\theta$ is taken to be the angle between $\vec{\mathbf{B}}$ and the perpendicular to the face of the coil, Fig. 20–32c. So the torque becomes

$$\tau = NIAB\sin\theta. \qquad \textbf{(20–10)}$$

This formula, derived here for a rectangular coil, is valid for any shape of flat coil.

*Magnetic dipole moment*

The quantity $NIA$ is called the **magnetic dipole moment** of the coil:

$$M = NIA \qquad \textbf{(20–11)}$$

and is considered a vector perpendicular to the coil.

**EXAMPLE 20–12** **Torque on a coil.** A circular coil of wire has a diameter of 20.0 cm and contains 10 loops. The current in each loop is 3.00 A, and the coil is placed in a 2.00-T external magnetic field. Determine the maximum and minimum torque exerted on the coil by the field.

**APPROACH** Equation 20–10 is valid for any shape of coil, including circular loops. Maximum and minimum torque are determined by the angle $\theta$ the coil makes with the magnetic field.

**SOLUTION** The area of one loop of the coil is

$$A = \pi r^2 = \pi(0.100\,\text{m})^2 = 3.14 \times 10^{-2}\,\text{m}^2.$$

The maximum torque occurs when the coil's face is parallel to the magnetic field, so $\theta = 90°$ in Fig. 20–32c, and $\sin\theta = 1$ in Eq. 20–10:

$$\tau = NIAB\sin\theta = (10)(3.00\,\text{A})(3.14 \times 10^{-2}\,\text{m}^2)(2.00\,\text{T})(1) = 1.88\,\text{N}\cdot\text{m}.$$

The minimum torque occurs if $\sin\theta = 0$, for which $\theta = 0°$, and then $\tau = 0$ from Eq. 20–10.

**NOTE** If the coil is free to turn, it will rotate toward the orientation with $\theta = 0°$.

# * 20–10 Applications: Galvanometers, Motors, Loudspeakers

## * Galvanometer

The basic component of analog meters (those with pointer and dial), including analog ammeters, voltmeters, and ohmmeters, is a galvanometer. We have already seen how these meters are designed (Section 19–8), and now we can examine how the crucial element, a galvanometer, works. As shown in Fig. 20–33, a **galvanometer** consists of a coil of wire (with attached pointer) suspended in the magnetic field of a permanent magnet. When current flows through the loop of wire, the magnetic field exerts a torque on the loop, as given by Eq. 20–10,

$$\tau = NIAB\sin\theta.$$

This torque is opposed by a spring which exerts a torque $\tau_s$ approximately proportional to the angle $\phi$ through which it is turned (Hooke's law). That is,

$$\tau_s = k\phi,$$

where $k$ is the stiffness constant of the spring. The coil and attached pointer rotate to the angle where the torques balance. When the needle is in equilibrium at rest, the torques are equal: $k\phi = NIAB\sin\theta$, or

$$\phi = \frac{NIAB\sin\theta}{k}.$$

The deflection of the pointer, $\phi$, is directly proportional to the current $I$ flowing in the coil, but also depends on the angle $\theta$ the coil makes with $\vec{\mathbf{B}}$. For a useful meter we need $\phi$ to depend only on the current $I$, independent of $\theta$. To solve this problem, magnets with curved pole pieces are used and the galvanometer coil is wrapped around a cylindrical iron core as shown in Fig. 20–34. The iron tends to concentrate the magnetic field lines so that $\vec{\mathbf{B}}$ always points parallel to the face of the coil at the wire outside the core. The force is then always perpendicular to the face of the coil, and the torque will not vary with angle. Thus $\phi$ will be proportional to $I$, as required.

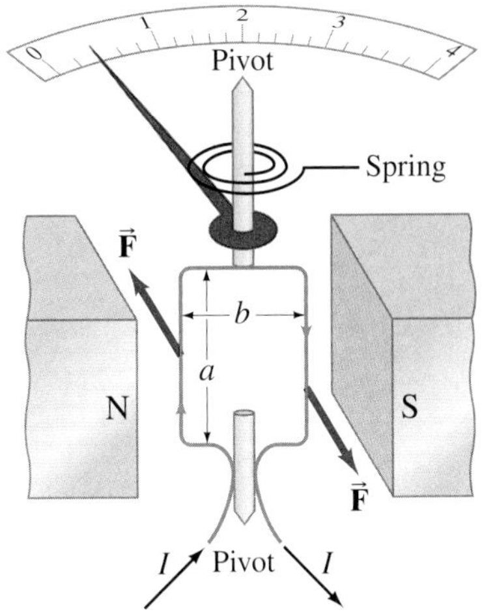


FIGURE 20–33 Galvanometer.

FIGURE 20–34 Galvanometer coil wrapped on an iron core.

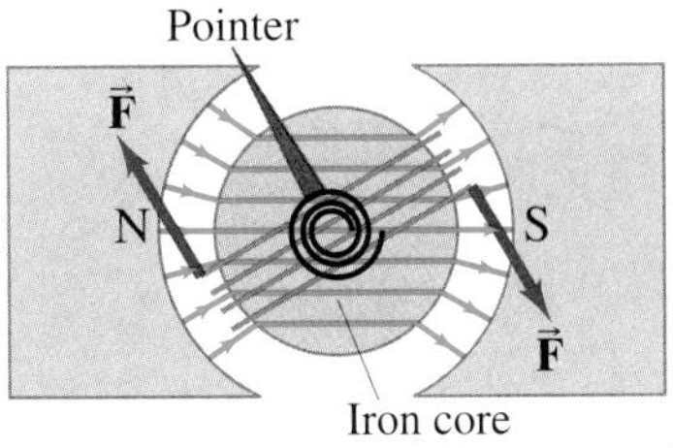


## * Electric Motors

An **electric motor** changes electric energy into (rotational) mechanical energy. A motor works on the same principle as a galvanometer, except that there is no spring so the coil can rotate continuously in one direction. The coil is larger and is mounted on a large cylinder called the **rotor** or **armature**, Fig. 20–35. Actually, there are several coils, although only one is indicated in the Figure. The armature is mounted on a shaft or axle. When the armature is in the position shown in Fig. 20–35, the magnetic field exerts forces on the current in the loop as shown. However, when the coil, which is rotating clockwise in Fig. 20–35, passes beyond the vertical position, the forces would then act to return the coil back to vertical if the current remained the same. But if the current could somehow be reversed at that critical moment, the forces would reverse, and the coil would continue rotating in the same direction. Thus, alternation of the current is necessary if a motor is to turn continuously in one direction. This can be achieved in a **dc motor** with the use of **commutators** and **brushes**: as shown in Fig. 20–36, the brushes are stationary contacts that rub against the conducting commutators mounted on the motor shaft. At every half revolution, each commutator changes its connection over to the other brush. Thus the current in the coil reverses every half revolution as required for continuous rotation.

PHYSICS APPLIED
*DC Motor*

FIGURE 20–35 Diagram of a simple dc motor.

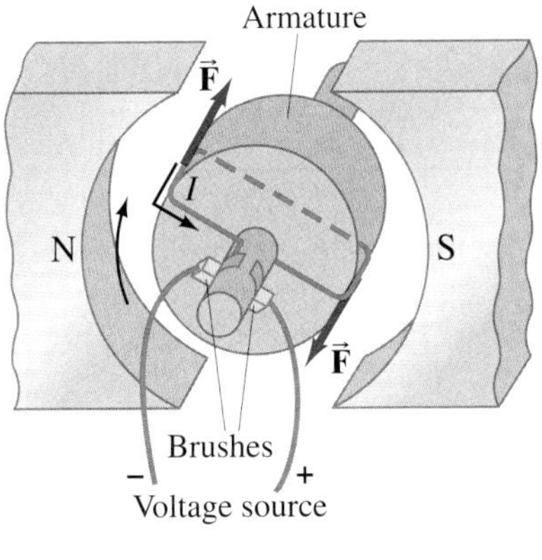


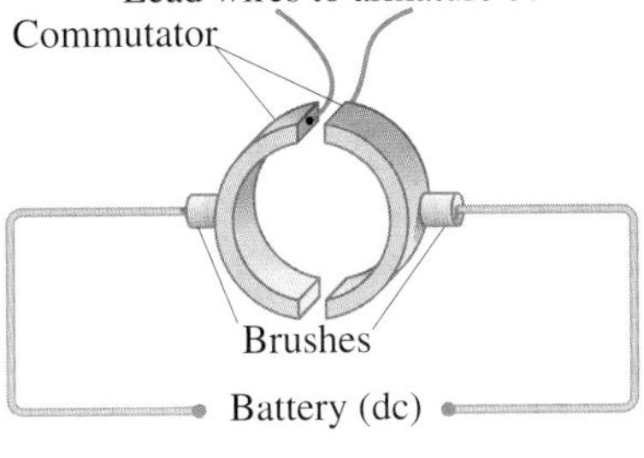


FIGURE 20–36 The commutator-brush arrangement in a dc motor ensures alternation of the current in the armature to keep rotation continuous. The commutators are attached to the motor shaft and turn with it, whereas the brushes remain stationary.

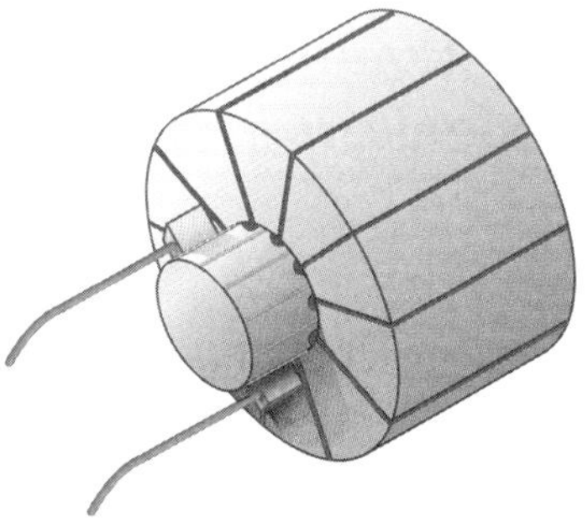

**FIGURE 20–37** Motor with many windings.

Most motors contain several coils, called *windings*, each located in a different place on the armature, Fig. 20–37. Current flows through each coil only during a small part of a revolution, at the time when its orientation results in the maximum torque. In this way, a motor produces a much steadier torque than can be obtained from a single coil.

PHYSICS APPLIED
*AC motor*

An **ac motor**, with ac current as input, can work without commutators since the current itself alternates. Many motors use wire coils to produce the magnetic field (electromagnets) instead of a permanent magnet. Indeed the design of most motors is more complex than described here, but the general principles remain the same.

## * Loudspeakers

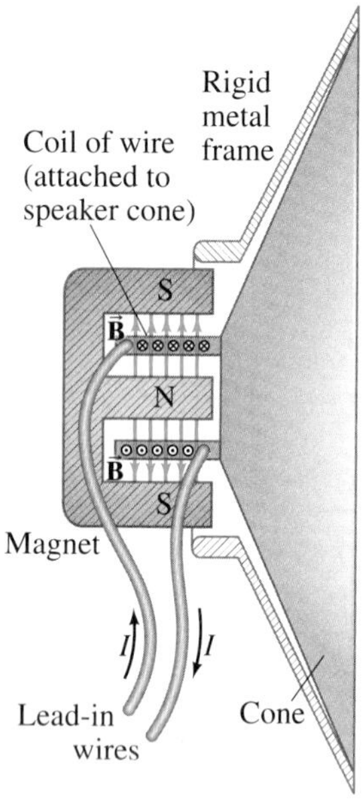


**FIGURE 20–38** Loudspeaker.

A **loudspeaker** also works on the principle that a magnet exerts a force on a current-carrying wire. The electrical output of a stereo or TV set is connected to the wire leads of the speaker. The speaker leads are connected internally to a coil of wire, which is itself attached to the speaker cone, Fig. 20–38. The speaker cone is usually made of stiffened cardboard and is mounted so that it can move back and forth freely. A permanent magnet is mounted directly in line with the coil of wire. When the alternating current of an audio signal flows through the wire coil, which is free to move within the magnet, the coil experiences a force due to the magnetic field of the magnet. As the current alternates at the frequency of the audio signal, the coil and attached speaker cone move back and forth at the same frequency, causing alternate compressions and rarefactions of the adjacent air, and sound waves are produced. A speaker thus changes electrical energy into sound energy, and the frequencies and intensities of the emitted sound waves can be an accurate reproduction of the electrical input.

# * 20–11 Mass Spectrometer

PHYSICS APPLIED
*The mass spectrometer*

**FIGURE 20–39** Bainbridge-type mass spectrometer. The magnetic fields $B$ and $B'$ point out of the paper (indicated by the dots).

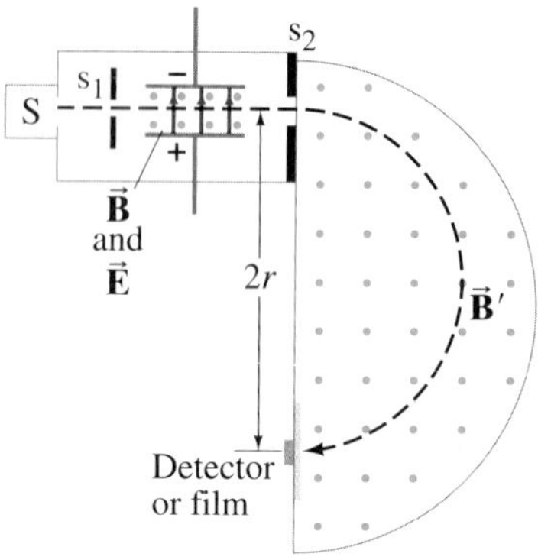


A **mass spectrometer** is a device to measure masses of atoms. It is used today not only in physics but also in chemistry, geology, and medicine, often to identify atoms (and their concentration) in given samples. As shown in Fig. 20–39, ions are produced by heating, or by an electric current, in the source or sample S. They pass through slit $s_1$ and enter a region where there are crossed electric and magnetic fields. Ions follow a straight-line path in this region if the electric force $qE$ (upward on a positive ion) is just balanced by the magnetic force $qvB$ (downward on a positive ion): that is, if $qE = qvB$, or

$$v = \frac{E}{B}.$$

Only those ions whose speed is $v = E/B$ will pass through undeflected and emerge through slit $s_2$. (This arrangement is called a **velocity selector**.) In the semicircular region, after $s_2$, there is only a magnetic field, $B'$, so the ions follow a circular path. The radius of the circular path is found from their mark on film (or detectors) if $B'$ is fixed; if instead $r$ is fixed by the position of a detector, then $B'$ is varied until detection occurs. Newton's second law, $\Sigma F = ma$, applied to an ion moving in a circle under the influence only of the magnetic field $B'$ gives $qvB' = mv^2/r$. Since $v = E/B$, we have

$$m = \frac{qB'r}{v} = \frac{qBB'r}{E}.$$

All the quantities on the right side are known or can be measured, and thus $m$ can be determined.

Historically, the masses of many atoms were measured this way. When a pure substance was used, it was sometimes found that two or more closely spaced marks would appear on the film. For example, neon produced two marks whose radii corresponded to atoms of mass 20 and 22 atomic mass units (u). Impurities were ruled out and it was concluded that there must be two types of neon with different masses. These different forms were called **isotopes**. It was soon found that most elements are mixtures of isotopes, and the difference in mass is due to different numbers of neutrons (discussed in Chapter 30).

*Isotopes*

**EXAMPLE 20–13** **Mass spectrometry.** Carbon atoms of atomic mass 12.0 u are found to be mixed with another, unknown, element. In a mass spectrometer with fixed $B'$, the carbon traverses a path of radius 22.4 cm and the unknown's path has a 26.2-cm radius. What is the unknown element? Assume they have the same charge.

**APPROACH** The carbon and unknown atoms pass through the same electric and magnetic fields. Hence their masses are proportional to the radius of their respective paths (see equation above).

**SOLUTION** We write a ratio for the masses, using the equation at the top of this page:

$$\frac{m_x}{m_C} = \frac{qBB'r_x/E}{qBB'r_C/E} = \frac{26.2\text{ cm}}{22.4\text{ cm}} = 1.17.$$

Thus $m_x = 1.17 \times 12.0\text{ u} = 14.0\text{ u}$. The other element is probably nitrogen (see the periodic table, inside the back cover).

**NOTE** The unknown could also be an isotope such as carbon-14 ($^{14}_{6}C$). See Appendix B. Further physical or chemical analysis would be needed.

## 20–12 Ferromagnetism: Domains and Hysteresis

We saw in Section 20–1 that iron (and a few other materials) can be made into strong magnets. These materials are said to be **ferromagnetic**.

### Sources of Ferromagnetism

Microscopic examination reveals that a magnet is made up of tiny regions known as **domains**, at most about 1 mm in length or width. Each domain behaves like a tiny magnet with a north and a south pole. In an unmagnetized piece of iron, the domains are arranged randomly, Fig. 20–40a. The magnetic effects of the domains cancel each other out, so this piece of iron is not a magnet. In a magnet, the domains are preferentially aligned in one direction as shown in Fig. 20–40b (downward in this case). A magnet can be made from an unmagnetized piece of iron by placing it in a strong magnetic field. (You can make a needle magnetic, for example, by stroking it with one pole of a strong magnet.) The magnetization direction of domains may actually rotate slightly to be more nearly parallel to an external field, or the borders of domains move so domains with magnetic orientation parallel to the external field grow larger (compare Figs. 20–40a and b). This explains how a magnet can pick up unmagnetized pieces of iron like paper clips. The magnet's field causes a slight alignment of the domains in the unmagnetized object, which becomes a temporary magnet with its north pole facing the south pole of the permanent magnet, and vice versa; thus, attraction results. Similarly, elongated iron filings in a magnetic field

*Domains*

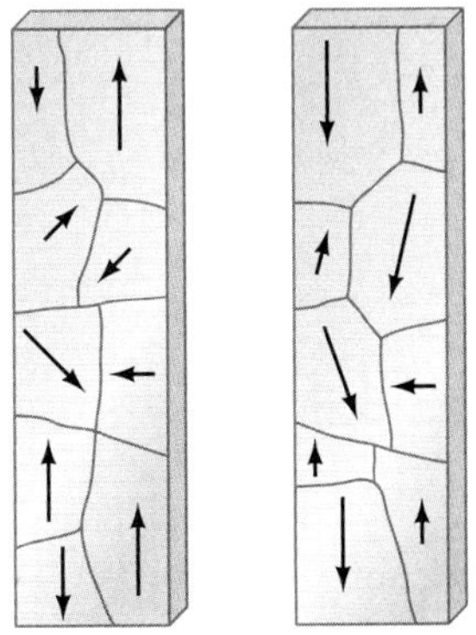


**FIGURE 20–40** (a) An unmagnetized piece of iron is made up of domains that are randomly arranged. Each domain is like a tiny magnet; the arrows represent the magnetization direction, with the arrowhead being the N pole. (b) In a magnet, the domains are preferentially aligned in one direction (down in this case), and may be altered in size by the magnetization process.

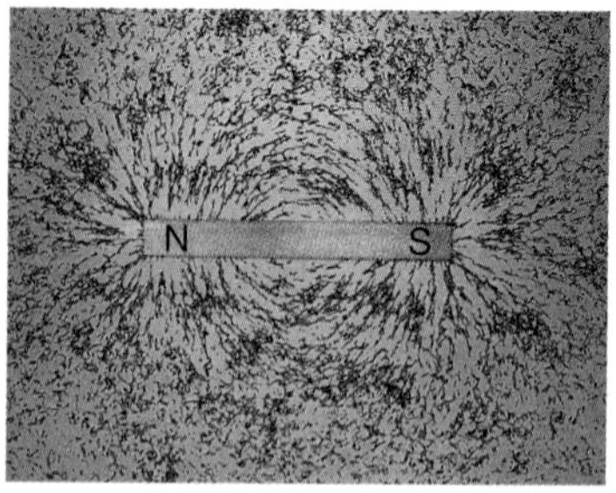


FIGURE 20–41 Iron filings line up along magnetic field lines due to a permanent magnet.

acquire aligned domains and align themselves to reveal the shape of the magnetic field, Fig. 20–41. See also this Chapter's opening photograph p. 554.

An iron magnet can remain magnetized for a long time, and is referred to as a "permanent magnet." But if you drop a magnet on the floor or strike it with a hammer, you can jar the domains into randomness and the magnet loses some or all of its magnetism. Heating a permanent magnet can also cause loss of magnetism, for raising the temperature increases the random thermal motion of atoms, which tends to randomize the domains. Above a certain temperature known as the **Curie temperature** (1043 K for iron), a magnet cannot be made at all.

The striking similarity between the fields produced by a bar magnet and by a loop of electric current or a solenoid (Figs. 20–4b, 20–9, and 20–30) offers a clue that perhaps the magnetic field produced by a current may have something to do with ferromagnetism. According to modern atomic theory, the atoms that make up any material can be roughly visualized as having electrons that orbit around a central nucleus. The electrons are charged, and so constitute an electric current and therefore produce a magnetic field. Electrons themselves produce an additional magnetic field, almost as if they and their electric charge were spinning about their own axes. It is the magnetic field due to electron *spin*[†] that is believed to produce ferromagnetism in most ferromagnetic materials.

**CAUTION**

*$\vec{\mathbf{B}}$ lines form closed loops, $\vec{\mathbf{E}}$ start on + and end on −*

It is believed today that *all* magnetic fields are caused by electric currents. This means that magnetic field lines always form closed loops, unlike electric field lines which begin on positive charges and end on negative charges.

## * Magnetic Permeability

If a piece of iron is placed inside a solenoid to form an electromagnet, the magnetic field increases greatly over that produced by the current in the solenoid coils alone. The total magnetic field $\vec{\mathbf{B}}$ is then the sum of two terms, $\vec{\mathbf{B}} = \vec{\mathbf{B}}_0 + \vec{\mathbf{B}}_M$ where $\vec{\mathbf{B}}_0$ is the field due to the current in the wire and $\vec{\mathbf{B}}_M$ is the additional field due to the iron (or other magnetic material inserted instead). Often $B_M \gg B_0$. The total field can also be written by replacing the constant $\mu_0$ in Eq. 20–8 ($B = \mu_0 NI/l$ for a solenoid) by the **magnetic permeability** $\mu$, which is characteristic of the magnetic material inside the coil. Then $B = \mu NI/l$. For ferromagnetic materials, $\mu$ is much greater than $\mu_0$. For all other materials, its value is very close to $\mu_0$.[‡] The value of $\mu$, however, is not constant for ferromagnetic materials; it depends on the strength of the "external" field $B_0$, as the following experiment shows.

## * Hysteresis

FIGURE 20–42 Iron-core toroid.

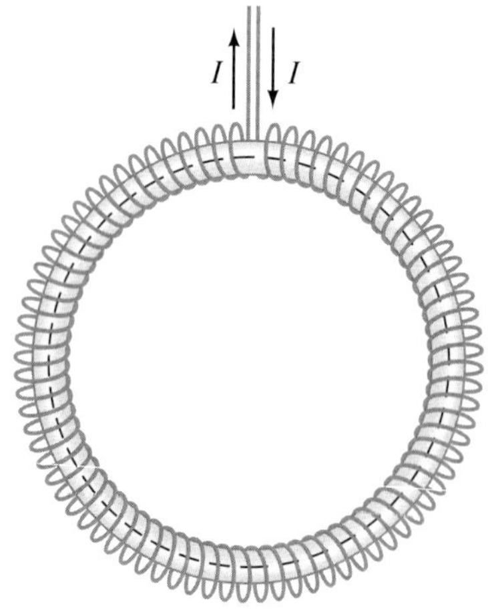


To make measurements on magnetic materials, a toroid is used, which is essentially a long solenoid bent into the shape of a donut (Fig. 20–42), so practically all the lines of $\vec{\mathbf{B}}$ remain within the toroid. Consider a toroid with an iron core that is initially unmagnetized and there is no current in the wire loops. Then the current $I$ is slowly increased. The total magnetic field $B$, which is the sum of the field due to the current alone $(B_0)$ plus the field due to the iron, also increases, but follows the curved line shown in the graph of

[†] The name "spin" comes from the early suggestion that the additional magnetic field arises from the electron "spinning" on its axis (as well as "orbiting" the nucleus) to produce the extra field. However, this view of a spinning electron is oversimplified and not valid (see Chapter 28).

[‡] All materials are slightly magnetic. Nonferromagnetic materials fall into two principal classes: (1) **paramagnetic** materials consist of atoms that have a net magnetic dipole moment which can align slightly with an external field, just as the galvanometer coil in Fig. 20–33 experiences a torque that tends to align it; (2) **diamagnetic** materials have atoms with no net dipole moment, but in the presence of an external field electrons revolving in one direction increase in speed slightly whereas electrons revolving in the opposite direction are reduced in speed; the result is a slight net magnetic effect that opposes the external field.

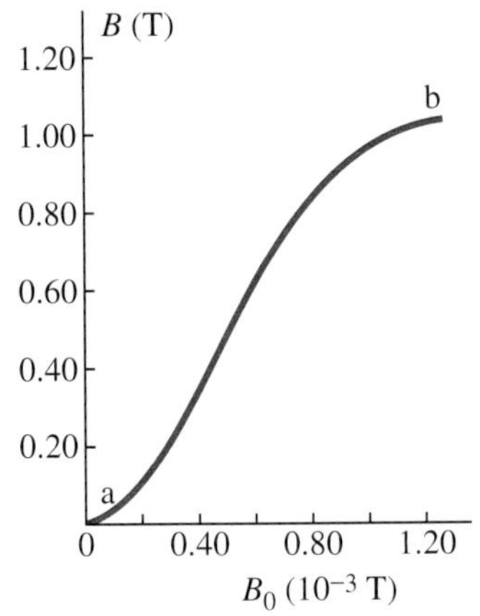


**FIGURE 20–43** Total magnetic field $B$ in an iron-core toroid as a function of the external field $B_0$ ($B_0$ is caused by the current $I$ in the coil).

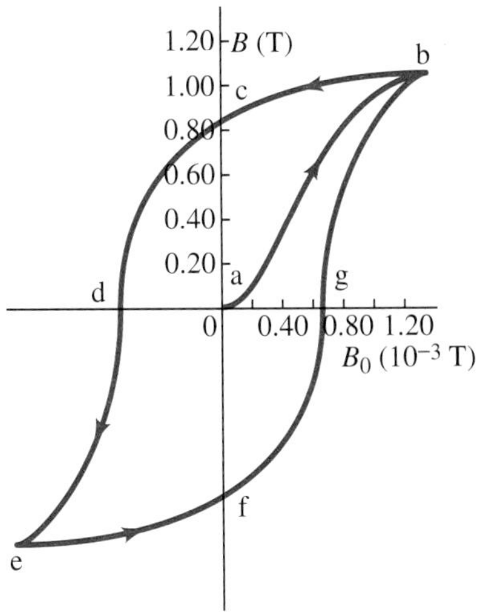


**FIGURE 20–44** Hysteresis curve.

Fig. 20–43. (Note the different scales: $B \gg B_0$.) At the initial point a, the domains are randomly oriented. As $B_0$ increases, the domains become more and more aligned until at point b, nearly all are aligned. The iron is said to be approaching **saturation**. Next, suppose current in the coils is reduced, so the field $B_0$ decreases. If the current (and $B_0$) is reduced to zero, point c in Fig. 20–44, the domains do *not* become completely random. Instead, some permanent magnetism remains in the iron core. If the current is increased in the opposite direction, enough domains can be turned around so the total $B$ becomes zero at point d. As the reverse current is increased further, the iron approaches saturation in the opposite direction, point e. Finally, if the current is again reduced to zero and then increased in the original direction, the total field follows the path efgb, again approaching saturation at point b.

*Hysteresis*

Notice that the field did not pass through the origin (point a) in this cycle. The fact that the curve does not retrace itself on the same path is called **hysteresis**. The curve bcdefgb is called a **hysteresis loop**. In such a cycle, much energy is transformed to thermal energy (friction) due to realigning of the domains. Note that at points c and f, the iron core is magnetized even though there is no current in the coils. These points correspond to a permanent magnet.

# Summary

A magnet has two **poles**, north and south. The north pole is that end which points toward geographic north when the magnet is freely suspended. Like poles of two magnets repel each other, whereas unlike poles attract.

We can imagine that a **magnetic field** surrounds every magnet. The SI unit for magnetic field is the **tesla** (T).

Electric currents produce magnetic fields. For example, the lines of magnetic field due to a current in a straight wire form circles around the wire, and the field exerts a force on magnets (or currents) near it.

A magnetic field exerts a force on an electric current. For a straight wire of length $l$ carrying a current $I$, the force has magnitude

$$F = IlB \sin\theta, \qquad \textbf{(20–1)}$$

where $\theta$ is the angle between the magnetic field $\vec{\mathbf{B}}$ and the current. The direction of the force is perpendicular to the current-carrying wire and to the magnetic field, and is given by a right-hand rule. Equation 20–1 serves as the definition of magnetic field $\vec{\mathbf{B}}$.

Similarly, a magnetic field exerts a force on a charge $q$ moving with velocity $v$ of magnitude

$$F = qvB \sin\theta, \qquad \textbf{(20–3)}$$

where $\theta$ is the angle between $\vec{\mathbf{v}}$ and $\vec{\mathbf{B}}$. The direction of $\vec{\mathbf{F}}$ is perpendicular to $\vec{\mathbf{v}}$ and to $\vec{\mathbf{B}}$ (again a right-hand rule). The path of a charged particle moving perpendicular to a uniform magnetic field is a circle.

The magnitude of the magnetic field produced by a current $I$ in a long straight wire, at a distance $r$ from the wire, is

$$B = \frac{\mu_0}{2\pi}\frac{I}{r}. \qquad \textbf{(20–6)}$$

Two currents exert a force on each other via the magnetic field each produces. Parallel currents in the same direction attract each other; currents in opposite directions repel.

The magnetic field inside a long tightly wound solenoid is

$$B = \mu_0 NI/l, \qquad \textbf{(20–8)}$$

where $N$ is the number of loops in a length $l$ of coil, and $I$ is the current in each loop.

[**Ampère's law** states that around any chosen closed loop path, the sum of each path segment $\Delta l$ times the component of $\vec{\mathbf{B}}$ parallel to the segment equals $\mu_0$ times the current $I$ enclosed by the closed path:

$$\Sigma B_{\parallel}\, \Delta l = \mu_0 I_{\text{encl}}. \qquad \textbf{(20–9)}]$$

[*The torque $\tau$ on $N$ loops of current $I$ in a magnetic field $\vec{\mathbf{B}}$ is

$$\tau = NIAB \sin\theta. \qquad \textbf{(20–10)}$$

The force or torque exerted on a current-carrying wire by a magnetic field is the basis for operation of many devices, such as meters, motors, and loudspeakers.]

[*A **mass spectrometer** uses electric and magnetic fields to determine the masses of atoms.]

Iron and a few other materials that are **ferromagnetic** can be made into strong permanent magnets. Ferromagnetic materials are made up of tiny **domains**—each a tiny magnet—which are preferentially aligned in a permanent magnet.

[*When iron or another ferromagnetic material is placed in a magnetic field $B_0$ due to a current, the iron becomes magnetized. When the current is turned off, the material remains magnetized; when the current is increased in the opposite direction, a graph of the total field $B$ versus $B_0$ is a **hysteresis loop**, and the fact that the curve does not retrace itself is called **hysteresis**.]

# Questions

1. A compass needle is not always balanced parallel to the Earth's surface, but one end may dip downward. Explain.
2. Draw the magnetic field lines around a straight section of wire carrying a current horizontally to the left.
3. In what direction are the magnetic field lines surrounding a straight wire carrying a current that is moving directly away from you?
4. A horseshoe magnet is held vertically with the north pole on the left and south pole on the right. A wire passing between the poles, equidistant from them, carries a current directly away from you. In what direction is the force on the wire?
5. Will a magnet attract any metallic object, or only those made of iron? (Try it and see.) Why is this so?
6. Two iron bars attract each other no matter which ends are placed close together. Are both magnets? Explain.
7. The magnetic field due to current in wires in your home can affect a compass. Discuss the effect in terms of currents, including if they are ac or dc.
8. If a negatively charged particle enters a region of uniform magnetic field which is perpendicular to the particle's velocity, will the kinetic energy of the particle increase, decrease, or stay the same? Explain your answer. (Neglect gravity and assume there is no electric field.)
9. In Fig. 20–45, charged particles move in the vicinity of a current-carrying wire. For each charged particle, the arrow indicates the direction of motion of the particle, and the + or − indicates the sign of the charge. For each of the particles, indicate the direction of the magnetic force due to the magnetic field produced by the wire.

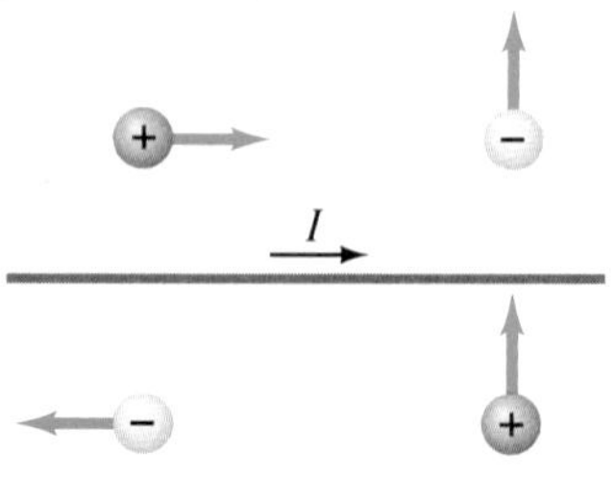

**FIGURE 20–45** Question 9.

10. Three particles, a, b, and c, enter a magnetic field as shown in Fig. 20–46. What can you say about the charge on each particle?

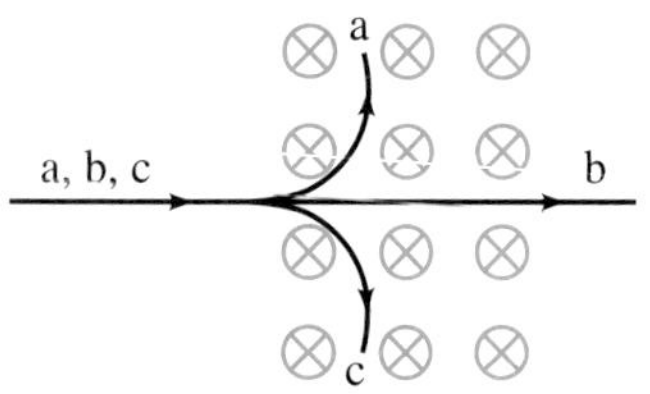

**FIGURE 20–46** Question 10.

11. A positively charged particle in a nonuniform magnetic field follows the trajectory shown in Fig. 20–47. Indicate the direction of the magnetic field everywhere in space, assuming the path is always in the plane of the page, and indicate the relative magnitudes of the field in each region.

**FIGURE 20–47** Question 11.

12. Can an iron rod attract a magnet? Can a magnet attract an iron rod? What must you consider to answer these questions?
13. Explain why a strong magnet held near a CRT television screen (Section 17–10) causes the picture to become distorted. Also, explain why the picture sometimes goes completely black where the field is the strongest. [But don't risk damage to your TV by trying this.]
14. Suppose you have three iron rods, two of which are magnetized but the third is not. How would you determine which two are the magnets without using any additional objects?
15. Can you set a resting electron into motion with a magnetic field? With an electric field? Explain.
16. A charged particle is moving in a circle under the influence of a uniform magnetic field. If an electric field that points in the same direction as the magnetic field is turned on, describe the path the charged particle will take.
17. The force on a particle in a magnetic field is the idea behind *electromagnetic pumping*. It is used to pump metallic fluids (such as sodium) and to pump blood in artificial heart machines. The basic design is shown in Fig. 20–48. An electric field is applied perpendicular to a blood vessel and to a magnetic field. Explain how ions are caused to move. Do positive and negative ions feel a force in the same direction?

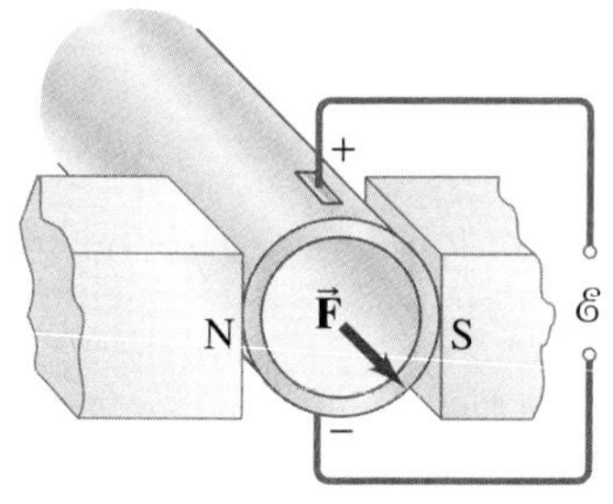

**FIGURE 20–48** Electromagnetic pumping in a blood vessel. Question 17.

18. A beam of electrons is directed toward a horizontal wire carrying a current from left to right (Fig. 20–49). In what direction is the beam deflected?

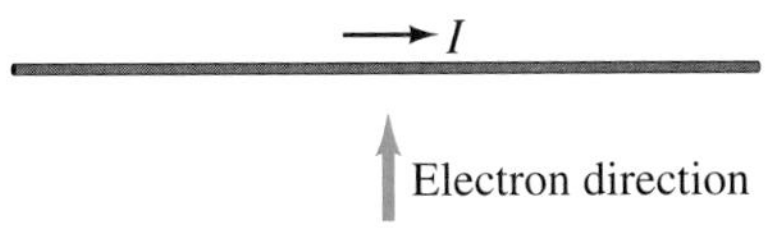


**FIGURE 20–49** Question 18.

19. Describe electric and/or magnetic fields that surround a moving electric charge.
20. A charged particle moves in a straight line through a particular region of space. Could there be a nonzero magnetic field in this region? If so, give two possible situations.
21. If a moving charged particle is deflected sideways in some region of space, can we conclude, for certain, that $\vec{\mathbf{B}} \neq 0$ in that region? Explain.
22. In a particular region of space there is a uniform magnetic field $\vec{\mathbf{B}}$. Outside this region, $B = 0$. Can you inject an electron from outside into the field perpendicularly so that it will move in a closed circular path in the field? What if the electron is injected near the center?
23. How could you tell whether moving electrons in a certain region of space are being deflected by an electric field or by a magnetic field (or by both)?
24. How can you make a compass without using iron or other ferromagnetic material?
25. Two long wires carrying equal currents $I$ are at right angles to each other, but don't quite touch. Describe the magnetic force one exerts on the other.
26. A horizontal current-carrying wire, free to move in Earth's gravitational field, is suspended directly above a second, parallel, current-carrying wire. (*a*) In what direction is the current in the lower wire? (*b*) Can the upper wire be held in stable equilibrium due to the magnetic force of the lower wire? Explain.
27. Why will either pole of a magnet attract an unmagnetized piece of iron?
28. An unmagnetized nail will not attract an unmagnetized paper clip. However, if one end of the nail is in contact with a magnet, the other end *will* attract a paper clip. Explain.
* 29. Two ions have the same mass, but one is singly ionized and the other is doubly ionized. How will their positions on the film of a mass spectrometer (Fig. 20–39) differ?
30. What would be the effect on $B$ inside a long solenoid if (*a*) the diameter of all the loops was doubled, (*b*) the spacing between loops was doubled, or (*c*) the solenoid's length was doubled along with a doubling in the total number of loops?
31. A type of magnetic switch similar to a solenoid is a **relay** (Fig. 20–50). A relay is an electromagnet (the iron rod inside the coil does not move) which, when activated, attracts a piece of iron on a pivot. Design a relay to close an electrical switch. A relay is used when you need to switch on a circuit carrying a very large current but you do not want that large current flowing through the main switch. For example, the starter switch of a car is connected to a relay so that the large current needed for the starter doesn't pass to the dashboard switch.

**FIGURE 20–50** Question 31.

# Problems

## 20–3 Force on Electric Current in Magnetic Field

1. (I) (*a*) What is the magnitude of the force per meter of length on a straight wire carrying an 8.40-A current when perpendicular to a 0.90-T uniform magnetic field? (*b*) What if the angle between the wire and field is 45.0°?
2. (I) Calculate the magnitude of the magnetic force on a 160-m length of straight wire stretched between two towers carrying a 150-A current. The Earth's magnetic field of $5.0 \times 10^{-5}$ T makes an angle of 65° with the wire.
3. (I) How much current is flowing in a wire 4.80 m long if the maximum force on it is 0.750 N when placed in a uniform 0.0800-T field?
4. (II) A 1.5-m length of wire carrying 4.5 A of current is oriented horizontally. At that point on the Earth's surface, the dip angle of the Earth's magnetic field makes an angle of 38° to the wire. Estimate the magnitude of the magnetic force on the wire due to the Earth's magnetic field of $5.5 \times 10^{-5}$ T at this point.
5. (II) The force on a wire carrying 8.75 A is a maximum of 1.28 N when placed between the pole faces of a magnet. If the pole faces are 55.5 cm in diameter, what is the approximate strength of the magnetic field?
6. (II) The magnetic force per meter on a wire is measured to be only 35% of its maximum possible value. Sketch the relationship of the wire and the field if the force had been a maximum, and sketch the relationship as it actually is, calculating the angle between the wire and the magnetic field.
7. (II) The force on a wire is a maximum of $6.50 \times 10^{-2}$ N when placed between the pole faces of a magnet. The current flows horizontally to the right and the magnetic field is vertical. The wire is observed to "jump" toward the observer when the current is turned on. (*a*) What type of magnetic pole is the top pole face? (*b*) If the pole faces have a diameter of 10.0 cm, estimate the current in the wire if the field is 0.16 T. (*c*) If the wire is tipped so that it makes an angle of 10.0° with the horizontal, what force will it now feel?
8. (II) Suppose a straight 1.00-mm-diameter copper wire could just "float" horizontally in air because of the force due to the Earth's magnetic field $\vec{\mathbf{B}}$, which is horizontal, perpendicular to the wire, and of magnitude $5.0 \times 10^{-5}$ T. What current would the wire carry? Does the answer seem feasible? Explain briefly.

## 20–4 Force on Charge Moving in Magnetic Field

9\. (I) Alpha particles of charge $q = +2e$ and mass $m = 6.6 \times 10^{-27}$ kg are emitted from a radioactive source at a speed of $1.6 \times 10^7$ m/s. What magnetic field strength would be required to bend them into a circular path of radius $r = 0.25$ m?

10\. (I) Determine the magnitude and direction of the force on an electron traveling $8.75 \times 10^5$ m/s horizontally to the east in a vertically upward magnetic field of strength 0.75 T.

11\. (I) Find the direction of the force on a negative charge for each diagram shown in Fig. 20–51, where $\vec{\mathbf{v}}$ (green) is the velocity of the charge and $\vec{\mathbf{B}}$ (blue) is the direction of the magnetic field. (⊗ means the vector points inward. ⊙ means it points outward, toward you.)

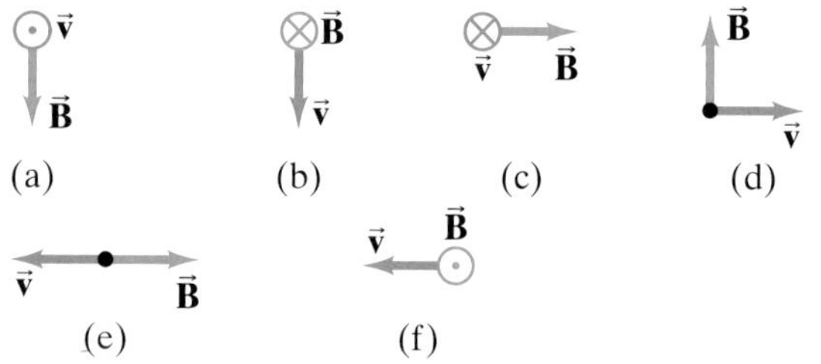


**FIGURE 20–51** Problem 11.

12\. (I) Determine the direction of $\vec{\mathbf{B}}$ for each case in Fig. 20–52, where $\vec{\mathbf{F}}$ represents the maximum magnetic force on a positively charged particle moving with velocity $\vec{\mathbf{v}}$.

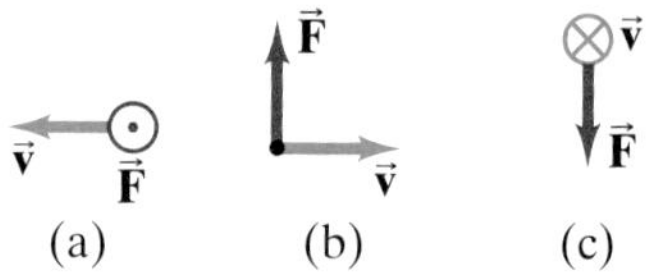


**FIGURE 20–52** Problem 12.

13\. (I) An electron is projected vertically upward with a speed of $1.70 \times 10^6$ m/s into a uniform magnetic field of 0.350 T that is directed horizontally away from the observer. Describe the electron's path in this field.

14\. (II) A 5.0-MeV (kinetic energy) proton enters a 0.20-T field, in a plane perpendicular to the field. What is the radius of its path?

15\. (II) An electron experiences the greatest force as it travels $2.9 \times 10^6$ m/s in a magnetic field when it is moving northward. The force is upward and of magnitude $7.2 \times 10^{-13}$ N. What are the magnitude and direction of the magnetic field?

16\. (II) What is the velocity of a beam of electrons that go undeflected when passing through perpendicular electric and magnetic fields of magnitude $8.8 \times 10^3$ V/m and $3.5 \times 10^{-3}$ T, respectively? What is the radius of the electron orbit if the electric field is turned off?

17\. (II) A doubly charged helium atom whose mass is $6.6 \times 10^{-27}$ kg is accelerated by a voltage of 2100 V. (*a*) What will be its radius of curvature if it moves in a plane perpendicular to a uniform 0.340-T field? (*b*) What is its period of revolution?

18\. (II) A proton (mass $m_p$), a deuteron $(m = 2m_p,\ Q = e)$, and an alpha particle $(m = 4m_p,\ Q = 2e)$ are accelerated by the same potential difference $V$ and then enter a uniform magnetic field $\vec{\mathbf{B}}$, where they move in circular paths perpendicular to $\vec{\mathbf{B}}$. Determine the radius of the paths for the deuteron and alpha particle in terms of that for the proton.

19\. (II) Show that the time $T$ required for a particle of charge $q$ moving with constant speed $v$ to make one circular revolution in a uniform magnetic field $\vec{\mathbf{B}}\ (\perp \vec{\mathbf{v}})$ is

$$T = \frac{2\pi m}{qB}.$$

[*Hint:* see Example 20–5 and Chapter 5.]

20\. (II) A particle of charge $q$ moves in a circular path of radius $r$ in a uniform magnetic field $B$. Show that its momentum is $p = qBr$.

21\. (II) A particle of mass $m$ and charge $q$ moves in a circular path in a magnetic field $B$. Show that its kinetic energy is proportional to $r^2$, the square of the radius of curvature of its path.

22\. (II) Show that the angular momentum of the particle in Problem 21 is $L = qBr^2$ about the center of the circle.

23\. (III) A 3.40-g bullet moves with a speed of 160 m/s perpendicular to the Earth's magnetic field of $5.00 \times 10^{-5}$ T. If the bullet possesses a net charge of $13.5 \times 10^{-9}$ C, by what distance will it be deflected from its path due to the Earth's magnetic field after it has traveled 1.00 km?

24\. (III) Suppose the Earth's magnetic field at the equator has magnitude $0.40 \times 10^{-4}$ T and a northerly direction at all points. Estimate the speed a singly ionized uranium ion $(m = 238\ \text{u},\ q = e)$ would need to circle the Earth 5.0 km above the equator. Can you ignore gravity?

25\. (III) A proton moving with speed $v = 2.0 \times 10^5$ m/s in a field-free region abruptly enters an essentially uniform magnetic field $B = 0.850$ T $(\vec{\mathbf{B}} \perp \vec{\mathbf{v}})$. If the proton enters the magnetic field region at a 45° angle as shown in Fig. 20–53, (*a*) at what angle does it leave, and (*b*) at what distance $x$ does it exit the field?

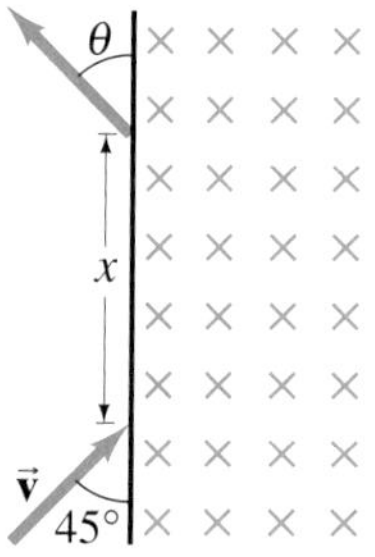


**FIGURE 20–53** Problem 25.

## 20–5 and 20–6 Magnetic Field of Straight Wire, Force Between Two Wires

26\. (I) A jumper cable used to start a stalled vehicle carries a 65-A current. How strong is the magnetic field 6.0 cm away from it? Compare to the Earth's magnetic field.

27\. (I) If an electric wire is allowed to produce a magnetic field no larger than that of the Earth $(0.55 \times 10^{-4}\ \text{T})$ at a distance of 25 cm, what is the maximum current the wire can carry?

28\. (I) In Fig. 20–54, a long straight wire carries current $I$ out of the page toward you. Indicate, with appropriate arrows, the direction of $\vec{\mathbf{B}}$ at each of the points C, D, and E in the plane of the page.

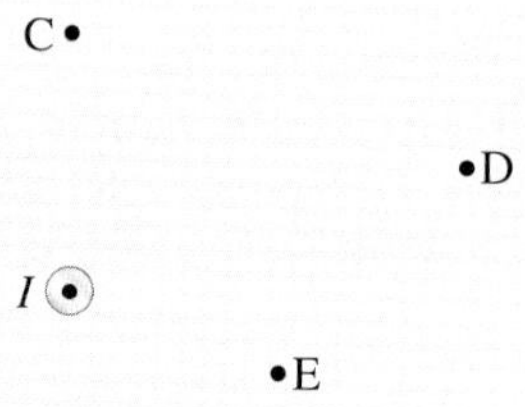


**FIGURE 20–54** Problem 28.

29\. (I) A vertical straight wire carrying an upward 24-A current exerts an attractive force per unit length of $8.8 \times 10^{-4}$ N/m on a second parallel wire 7.0 cm away. What current (magnitude and direction) flows in the second wire?

30\. (I) Determine the magnitude and direction of the force between two parallel wires 35 m long and 6.0 cm apart, each carrying 25 A in the same direction.

31. (II) An experiment on the Earth's magnetic field is being carried out 1.00 m from an electric cable. What is the maximum allowable current in the cable if the experiment is to be accurate to $\pm 1.0\%$?

32. (II) A power line carries a current of 95 A along the tops of 8.5-m-high poles. What is the magnitude of the magnetic field produced by this wire at the ground? How does this compare with the Earth's field of about $\frac{1}{2}$ G?

33. (II) Two long thin parallel wires 13.0 cm apart carry 25-A currents in the same direction. Determine the magnetic field at point P, 12.0 cm from one wire and 5.0 cm from the other (Fig. 20–55).

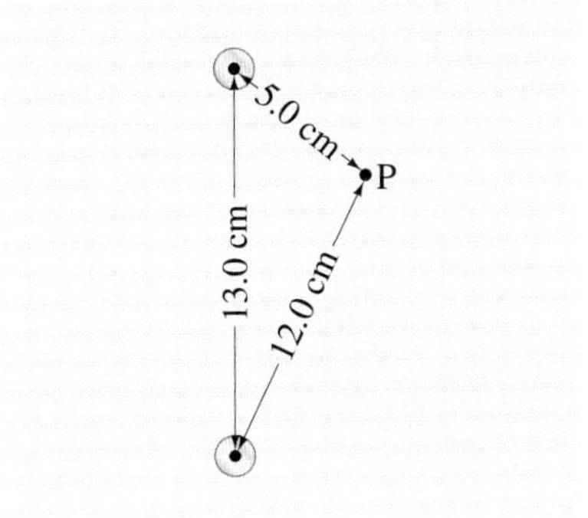


**FIGURE 20–55** Problem 33.

34. (II) A horizontal compass is placed 18 cm due south from a straight vertical wire carrying a 35-A current downward. In what direction does the compass needle point at this location? Assume the horizontal component of the Earth's field at this point is $0.45 \times 10^{-4}$ T and the magnetic declination is 0°.

35. (II) A long horizontal wire carries 22.0 A of current due north. What is the net magnetic field 20.0 cm due west of the wire if the Earth's field there points north but downward, 37° below the horizontal, and has magnitude $5.0 \times 10^{-5}$ T?

36. (II) A straight stream of protons passes a given point in space at a rate of $1.5 \times 10^{9}$ protons/s. What magnetic field do they produce 2.0 m from the beam?

37. (II) Determine the magnetic field midway between two long straight wires 2.0 cm apart in terms of the current $I$ in one when the other carries 15 A. Assume these currents are (*a*) in the same direction, and (*b*) in opposite directions.

38. (II) A long pair of wires conducts 25.0 A of dc current to, and from, an instrument. If the insulated wires are of negligible diameter but are 2.8 mm apart, what is the magnetic field 10.00 cm from their midpoint, in their plane (Fig. 20–56)? Compare to the magnetic field of the Earth.

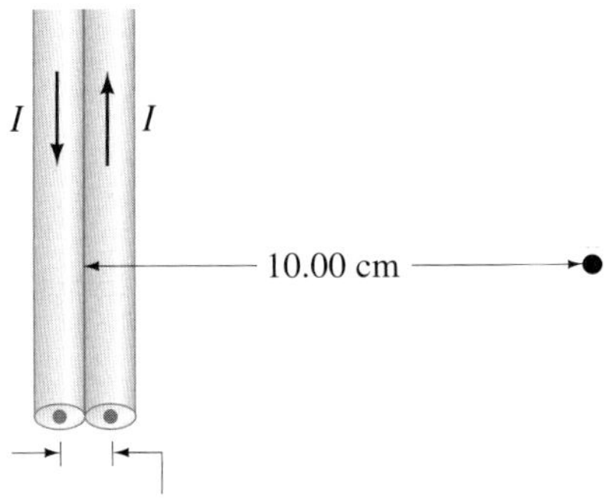


**FIGURE 20–56** Problems 38 and 39.

39. (II) A third wire is placed in the plane of the two wires shown in Fig. 20–56, parallel and just to the right. If it carries 25.0 A upward, what force per meter of length does it exert on each of the other two wires? Assume it is 2.8 mm from the nearest wire, center to center.

40. (II) A compass needle points 23° E of N outdoors. However, when it is placed 12.0 cm to the east of a vertical wire inside a building, it points 55° E of N. What are the magnitude and direction of the current in the wire? The Earth's field there is $0.50 \times 10^{-4}$ T and is horizontal.

41. (II) A rectangular loop of wire lies in the same plane as a straight wire, as shown in Fig. 20–57. There is a current of 2.5 A in both wires. Determine the magnitude and direction of the net force on the loop.

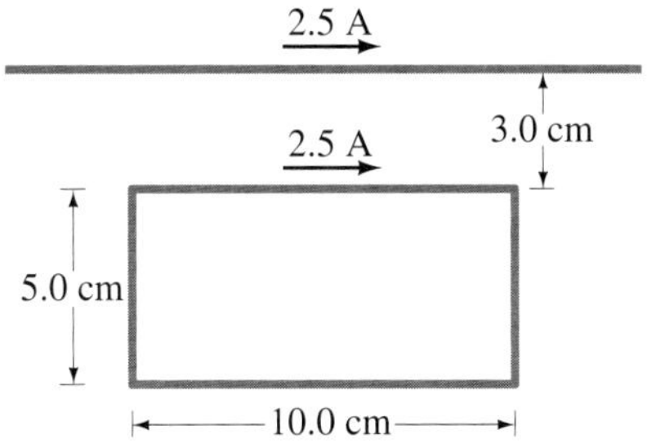


**FIGURE 20–57** Problem 41.

42. (II) A long horizontal wire carries a current of 48 A. A second wire, made of 2.5-mm-diameter copper wire and parallel to the first, is kept in suspension magnetically 15 cm below (Fig. 20–58). (*a*) Determine the magnitude and direction of the current in the lower wire. (*b*) Is the lower wire in stable equilibrium? (*c*) Repeat parts (*a*) and (*b*) if the second wire is suspended 15 cm *above* the first due to the latter's field.

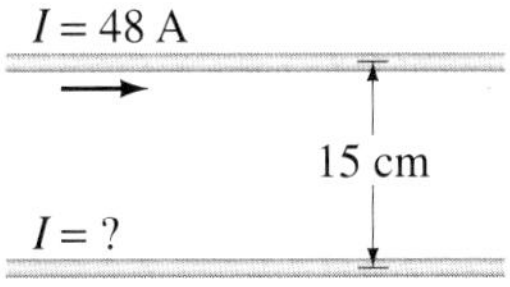


**FIGURE 20–58** Problem 42.

43. (II) Two long wires are oriented so that they are perpendicular to each other. At their closest, they are 20.0 cm apart (Fig. 20–59). What is the magnitude of the magnetic field at a point midway between them if the top one carries a current of 20.0 A and the bottom one carries 5.0 A?

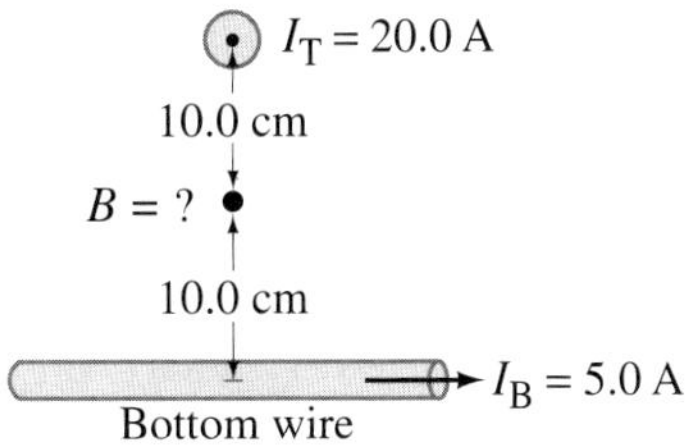


**FIGURE 20–59** Problem 43.

44. (II) Two long straight parallel wires are 15 cm apart. Wire A carries 2.0 A current. Wire B's current is 4.0 A in the same direction. (*a*) Determine the magnetic field magnitude due to wire A at the position of wire B. (*b*) Determine the magnetic field due to wire B at the position of wire A. (*c*) Are these two magnetic fields equal and opposite? Why or why not? (*d*) Determine the force on wire A due to wire B, and the force on wire B due to wire A. Are these two forces equal and opposite? Why or why not?

45. (II) Three long parallel wires are 3.8 cm from one another. (Looking along them, they are at three corners of an equilateral triangle.) The current in each wire is 8.00 A, but its direction in wire M is opposite to that in wires N and P (Fig. 20–60). Determine the magnetic force per unit length on each wire due to the other two.

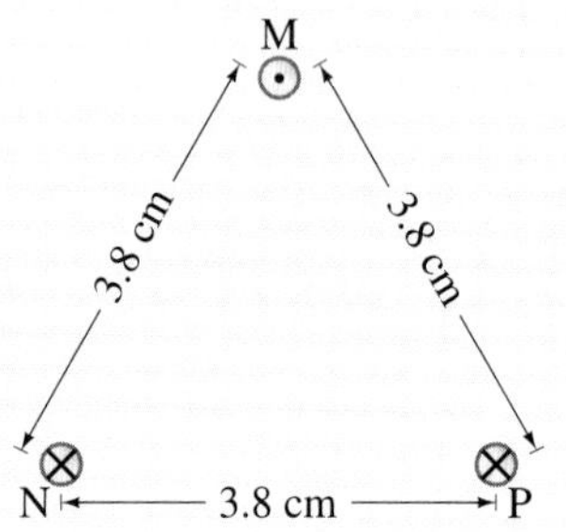


**FIGURE 20–60** Problems 45, 46, and 74.

46. (II) In Fig. 20–60, determine the magnitude and direction of the magnetic field at the midpoint of the side of the triangle between wire M and wire N.

47. (II) Let two long parallel wires, a distance $d$ apart, carry equal currents $I$ in the same direction. One wire is at $x = 0$, the other is at $x = d$, Fig. 20–61. Determine $\vec{\mathbf{B}}$ along the $x$ axis between the wires as a function of $x$.

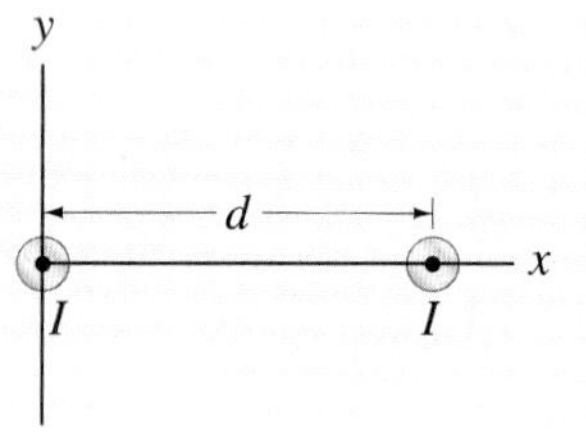


**FIGURE 20–61** Problem 47.

## 20–7 Solenoids and Electromagnets

48. (I) A thin 12-cm-long solenoid has a total of 420 turns of wire and carries a current of 2.0 A. Calculate the field inside near the center.

49. (I) A 30.0-cm long solenoid 1.25 cm in diameter is to produce a field of 0.385 T at its center. How much current should the solenoid carry if it has 975 turns of the wire?

50. (II) A 550-turn solenoid is 15 cm long. The current in it is 33 A. A 3.0-cm-long straight wire cuts through the center of the solenoid, along a diameter. This wire carries a 22-A current downward (and is connected by other wires that don't concern us). What is the force on this wire assuming the solenoid's field points due east?

51. (III) You have 1.0 kg of copper and want to make a practical solenoid that produces the greatest possible magnetic field for a given voltage. Should you make your copper wire long and thin, short and fat, or something else? Consider other variables, such as solenoid diameter, length, and so on.

## * 20–8 Ampère's Law

* 52. (II) A toroid is a solenoid in the shape of a circle (Fig. 20–62). Use Ampère's law along the circular path, shown dashed in Fig. 20–62a, to determine that the magnetic field (*a*) inside the toroid is $B = \mu_0 NI/2\pi R$, where $N$ is the total number of turns, and (*b*) outside the toroid is $B = 0$. (*c*) Is the field inside a toroid uniform like a solenoid's? If not, how does it vary?

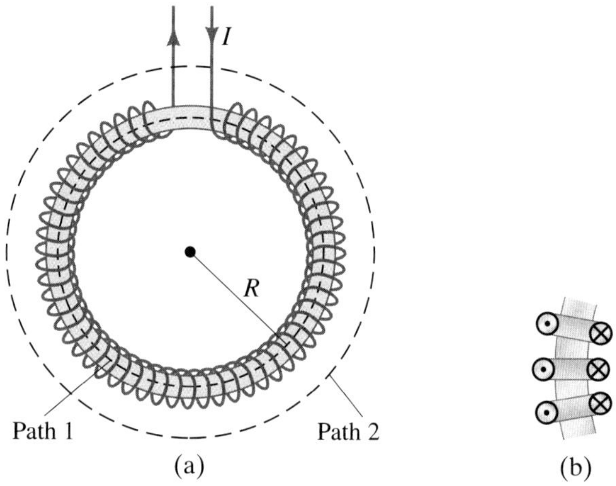


**FIGURE 20–62** Problem 52. (a) A toroid. (b) A section of the toroid showing direction of the current for three loops: ⊙ means current toward you, and ⊗ means current away from you.

* 53. (III) (*a*) Use Ampère's law to show that the magnetic field between the conductors of a *coaxial cable* (Fig. 20–63) is $B = \mu_0 I/2\pi r$ if $r$ is greater than the radius of the inner wire and less than the radius of the outer cylindrical braid. (*b*) Show that $B = 0$ outside the coaxial cable.

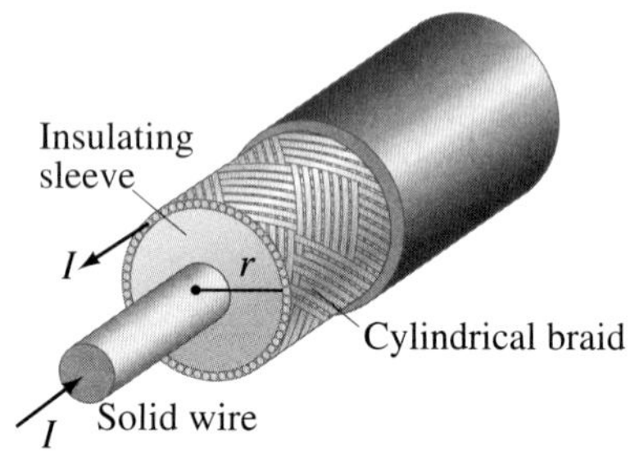


**FIGURE 20–63** Coaxial cable. Problem 53.

## * 20–9 and 20–10 Torque on Current Loop, Applications

* 54. (I) A single square loop of wire 22.0 cm on a side is placed with its face parallel to the magnetic field between the pole pieces of a large magnet. When 6.30 A flows in the coil, the torque on it is 0.325 m·N. What is the magnetic field strength?

* 55. (I) A galvanometer needle deflects full scale for a 53.0-$\mu$A current. What current will give full-scale deflection if the magnetic field weakens to 0.860 of its original value?

* 56. (I) If the restoring spring of a galvanometer weakens by 25% over the years, what current will give full-scale deflection if it originally required 36 $\mu$A?

* 57. (I) If the current to a motor drops by 12%, by what factor does the output torque change?

* 58. (II) Show that the magnetic dipole moment $M$ of an electron orbiting the proton nucleus of a hydrogen atom is related to the orbital angular momentum $L$ of the electron by

$$M = \frac{e}{2m} L.$$

* 59. (II) A circular coil 16.0 cm in diameter and containing nine loops lies flat on the ground. The Earth's magnetic field at this location has magnitude $5.50 \times 10^{-5}$ T and points into the Earth at an angle of 56.0° below a line pointing due north. If a 7.20-A clockwise current passes through the coil, (*a*) determine the torque on the coil, and (*b*) which edge of the coil rises up: north, east, south, or west?

### * 20–11 Mass Spectrometer

* 60. (I) Protons move in a circle of radius 5.10 cm in a 0.566-T magnetic field. What value of electric field could make their paths straight? In what direction must it point?

* 61. (I) In a mass spectrometer, germanium atoms have radii of curvature equal to 21.0, 21.6, 21.9, 22.2, and 22.8 cm. The largest radius corresponds to an atomic mass of 76 u. What are the atomic masses of the other isotopes?

* 62. (II) Suppose the electric field between the electric plates in the mass spectrometer of Fig. 20–39 is $2.48 \times 10^4$ V/m and the magnetic fields $B = B' = 0.68$ T. The source contains carbon isotopes of mass numbers 12, 13, and 14 from a long-dead piece of a tree. (To estimate atomic masses, multiply by $1.67 \times 10^{-27}$ kg.) How far apart are the lines formed by the singly charged ions of each type on the photographic film? What if the ions were doubly charged?

* 63. (II) A mass spectrometer is being used to monitor air pollutants. It is difficult, however, to separate molecules with nearly equal mass such as CO (28.0106 u) and $N_2$ (28.0134 u). How large a radius of curvature must a spectrometer have if these two molecules are to be separated on the film by 0.50 mm?

* 64. (II) One form of mass spectrometer accelerates ions by a voltage $V$ before they enter a magnetic field $B$. The ions are assumed to start from rest. Show that the mass of an ion is $m = qB^2R^2/2V$, where $R$ is the radius of the ions' path in the magnetic field and $q$ is their charge.

### 20–12 Ferromagnetism, Hysteresis

* 65. (I) A long thin solenoid has 430 loops of wire per meter, and a 25-A current flows through the wire. If the permeability of the iron is $3000\mu_0$, what is the total field $B$ inside the solenoid?

* 66. (II) An iron-core solenoid is 38 cm long and 1.8 cm in diameter, and has 640 turns of wire. The magnetic field inside the solenoid is 2.2 T when 48 A flows in the wire. What is the permeability $\mu$ at this high field strength?

## General Problems

67. Protons with momentum $4.8 \times 10^{-16}$ kg·m/s are magnetically steered clockwise in a circular path 2.0 km in diameter at Fermi National Accelerator Laboratory in Illinois. Determine the magnitude and direction of the field in the magnets surrounding the beam pipe.

68. A proton and an electron have the same kinetic energy upon entering a region of constant magnetic field. What is the ratio of the radii of their circular paths?

69. The power cable for an electric trolley (Fig. 20–64) carries a horizontal current of 330 A toward the east. The Earth's magnetic field has a strength $5.0 \times 10^{-5}$ T and makes an angle of dip of 22° at this location. Calculate the magnitude and direction of the magnetic force on a 15-m length of this cable.

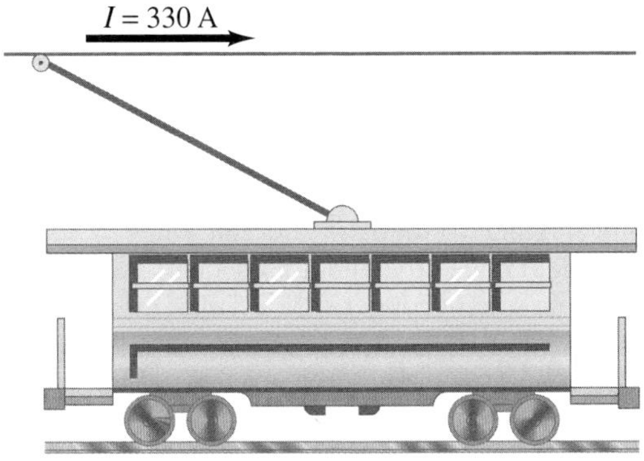


**FIGURE 20–64** Problem 69.

70. Calculate the force on an airplane which has acquired a net charge of 1550 $\mu$C and moves with a speed of 120 m/s perpendicular to the Earth's magnetic field of $5.0 \times 10^{-5}$ T.

71. Near the equator, the Earth's magnetic field points almost horizontally to the north and has magnitude $B = 0.50 \times 10^{-4}$ T. What should be the magnitude and direction for the velocity of an electron if its weight is to be exactly balanced by the magnetic force?

72. A doubly charged helium atom, whose mass is $6.6 \times 10^{-27}$ kg, is accelerated by a voltage of 2400 V. (*a*) What will be its radius of curvature in a uniform 0.240-T field? (*b*) What is its period of revolution?

73. A sort of "projectile launcher" is shown in Fig. 20–65. A large current moves in a closed loop composed of fixed rails, a power supply, and a very light, almost frictionless bar touching the rails. A magnetic field is perpendicular to the plane of the circuit. If the bar has a length $L = 22$ cm, a mass of 1.5 g, and is placed in a field of 1.7 T, what constant current flow is needed to accelerate the bar from rest to 28 m/s in a distance of 1.0 m? In what direction must the magnetic field point?

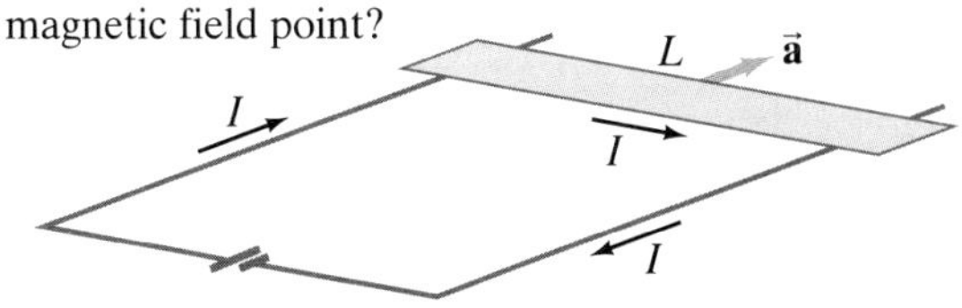


**FIGURE 20–65** Problem 73.

74. In Fig. 20–60 the top wire is 1.00-mm-diameter copper wire and is suspended in air due to the two magnetic forces from the bottom two wires. The current flow through the two bottom wires is 95 A in each. Calculate the required current flow in the suspended wire.

75. Two stiff parallel wires a distance $l$ apart in a horizontal plane act as rails to support a light metal rod of mass $m$ (perpendicular to each rail), Fig. 20–66. A magnetic field $\vec{\mathbf{B}}$, directed vertically upward (outward in the diagram), acts throughout. At $t = 0$, wires connected to the rails are connected to a constant current source and a current $I$ begins to flow through the system. Determine the speed of the rod, which starts from rest at $t = 0$, as a function of time (*a*) assuming no friction between the rod and the rails, and (*b*) if the coefficient of friction is $\mu_k$. (*c*) Does the rod move east or west if the current through it heads north?

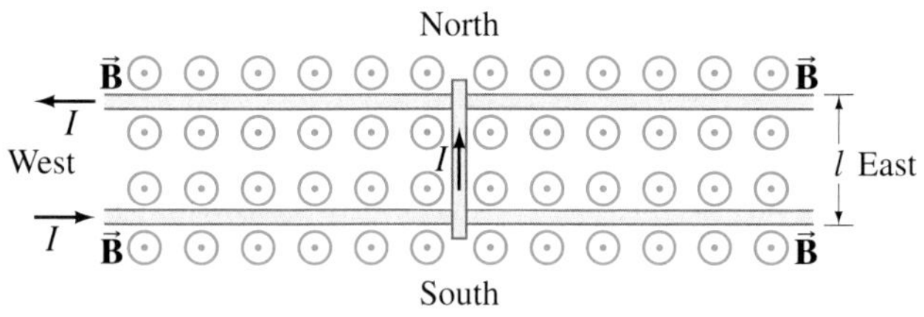


**FIGURE 20–66** Looking down on a rod sliding on rails. Problem 75.

76. Estimate the approximate maximum deflection of the electron beam near the center of a TV screen due to the Earth's $5.0 \times 10^{-5}$ T field. Assume the CRT screen (Section 17–10) is 22 cm from the electron gun, where the electrons are accelerated (*a*) by 2.0 kV, or (*b*) by 30 kV. Note that in color TV sets, the CRT beam must be directed accurately to within less than 1 mm in order to strike the correct phosphor. Because the Earth's field is significant here, mu-metal shields are used to reduce the Earth's field in the CRT.

77. The **cyclotron** (Fig. 20–67) is a device used to accelerate elementary particles such as protons to high speeds. Particles starting at point A with some initial velocity travel in circular orbits in the magnetic field $B$. The particles are accelerated to higher speeds each time they pass through the gap between the metal "dees," where there is an electric field $E$. (There is no electric field inside the hollow metal dees.) The electric field changes direction each half-cycle, owing to an ac voltage $V = V_0 \sin 2\pi f t$, so that the particles are increased in speed at each passage through the gap. (*a*) Show that the frequency $f$ of the voltage must be $f = Bq/2\pi m$, where $q$ is the charge on the particles and $m$ their mass. (*b*) Show that the kinetic energy of the particles increases by $2qV_0$ each revolution, assuming that the gap is small. (*c*) If the radius of the cyclotron is 2.0 m and the magnetic field strength is 0.50 T, what will be the maximum kinetic energy of accelerated protons in MeV?

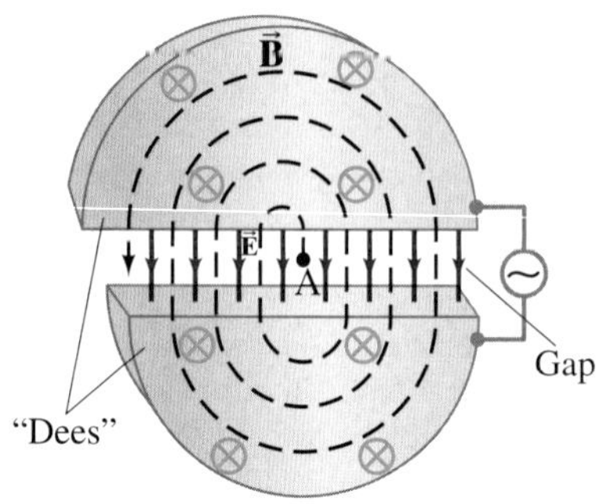


**FIGURE 20–67** A cyclotron. Problem 77.

78. Four very long straight parallel wires, located at the corners of a square of side $l$, carry equal currents $I_0$ perpendicular to the page as shown in Fig. 20–68. Determine the magnitude and direction of $\vec{\mathbf{B}}$ at the center C of the square.

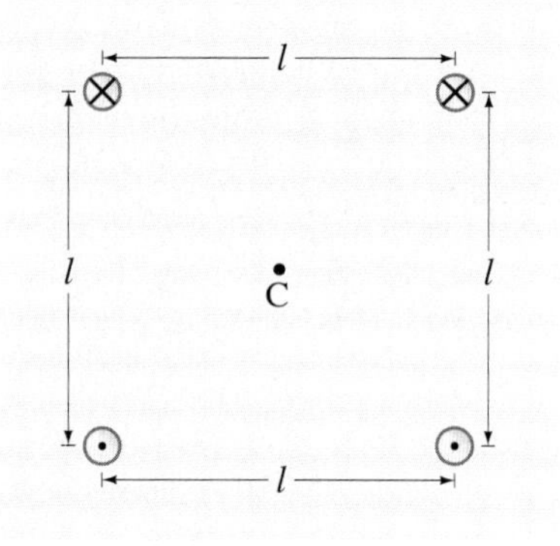


**FIGURE 20–68** Problem 78.

79. Magnetic fields are very useful in particle accelerators for "beam steering"; that is, the magnetic fields can be used to change the beam's direction without altering its speed (Fig. 20–69). Show how this works with a beam of protons. What happens to protons that are not moving with the speed that the magnetic field is designed for? If the field extends over a region 5.0 cm wide and has a magnitude of 0.33 T, by approximately what angle will a beam of protons traveling at $1.0 \times 10^7$ m/s be bent?

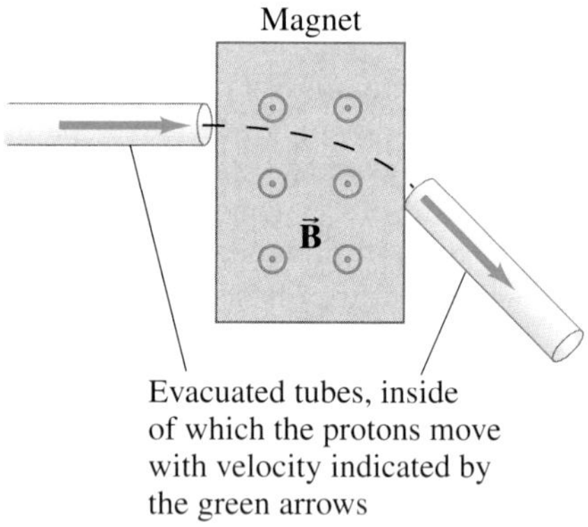


**FIGURE 20–69** Problem 79.

80. The magnetic field $B$ at the center of a circular coil of wire carrying a current $I$ (as in Fig. 20–9) is

$$B = \frac{\mu_0 NI}{2r},$$

where $N$ is the number of loops in the coil and $r$ is its radius. Suppose that an electromagnet uses a coil 1.2 m in diameter made from square copper wire 1.6 mm on a side. The power supply produces 120 V at a maximum power output of 4.0 kW. (*a*) How many turns are needed to run the power supply at maximum power? (*b*) What is the magnetic field strength at the center of the coil? (*c*) If you use a greater number of turns and this same power supply (so the voltage remains at 120 V), will a greater magnetic field strength result? Explain.

81. Near the Earth's poles the magnetic field is about 1 G $(1 \times 10^{-4}\,\mathrm{T})$. Imagine a simple model in which the Earth's field is produced by a single current loop around the equator. Roughly estimate the current this loop would carry. [*Hint:* use the formula given in Problem 80.]

82. You want to get an idea of the magnitude of magnetic fields produced by overhead power lines. You estimate that the two wires are each about 30 m above the ground and are about 3 m apart. The local power company tells you that the lines operate at 10 kV and provide a maximum of 40 MW to the local area. Estimate the maximum magnetic field you might experience walking under these power lines, and compare to the Earth's field. [For an ac current, values are rms, and the magnetic field will be changing.]

83. (*a*) What value of magnetic field would make a beam of electrons, traveling to the right at a speed of $4.8 \times 10^6\,\mathrm{m/s}$, go undeflected through a region where there is a uniform electric field of 10,000 V/m pointing vertically up? (*b*) What is the direction of the magnetic field if it is known to be perpendicular to the electric field? (*c*) What is the frequency of the circular orbit of the electrons if the electric field is turned off?

84. A proton follows a spiral path through a gas in a magnetic field of 0.010 T, perpendicular to the plane of the spiral, as shown in Fig. 20–70. In two successive loops, at points P and Q, the radii are 10.0 mm and 8.5 mm, respectively. Calculate the change in the kinetic energy of the proton as it travels from P to Q.

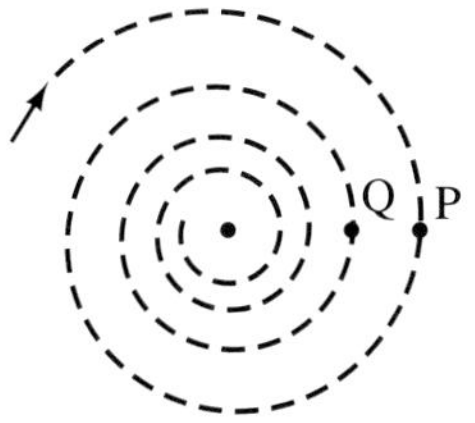


**FIGURE 20–70** Problem 84.

85. A 32-cm-long solenoid, 1.8 cm in diameter, is to produce a 0.30-T magnetic field at its center. If the maximum current is 5.7 A, how many turns must the solenoid have?

86. Two long straight aluminum wires, each of diameter 0.50 mm, carry the same current but in opposite directions. They are suspended by 0.50-m-long strings as shown in Fig. 20–71. If the suspension strings make an angle of 3.0° with the vertical, what is the current in the wires?

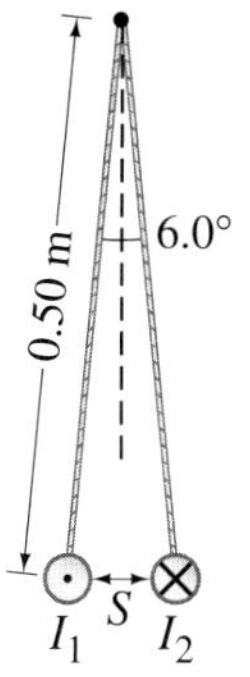


**FIGURE 20–71** Problem 86.

87. An electron enters a uniform magnetic field $B = 0.23\,\mathrm{T}$ at a 45° angle to $\vec{\mathbf{B}}$. Determine the radius $r$ and pitch $p$ (distance between loops) of the electron's helical path assuming its speed is $3.0 \times 10^6\,\mathrm{m/s}$. See Fig. 20–72.

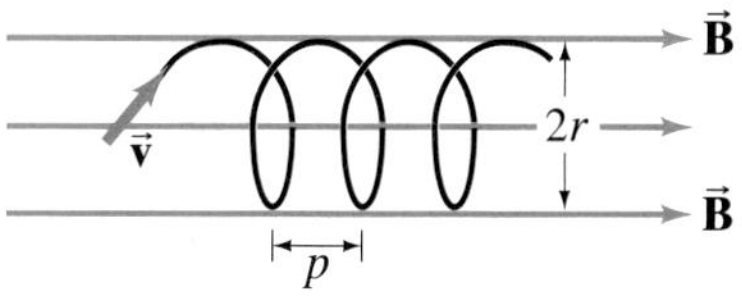


**FIGURE 20–72** Problem 87.

## Answers to Exercises

**A:** Near the poles, where the field lines are closer together.
**B:** Counterclockwise.
**C:** 0.15 N.
**D:** Zero.
**E:** Negative; the direction of the helical path would be reversed.
**F:** 2.0 cm.

One of the great laws of physics is Faraday's law of induction, which says that a changing magnetic flux produces an induced emf. This photo shows a bar magnet moving inside a coil of wire, and the galvanometer registers an induced current. This phenomenon of electromagnetic induction is the basis for many practical devices, from generators to alternators to transformers, tape recording, and computer memory.

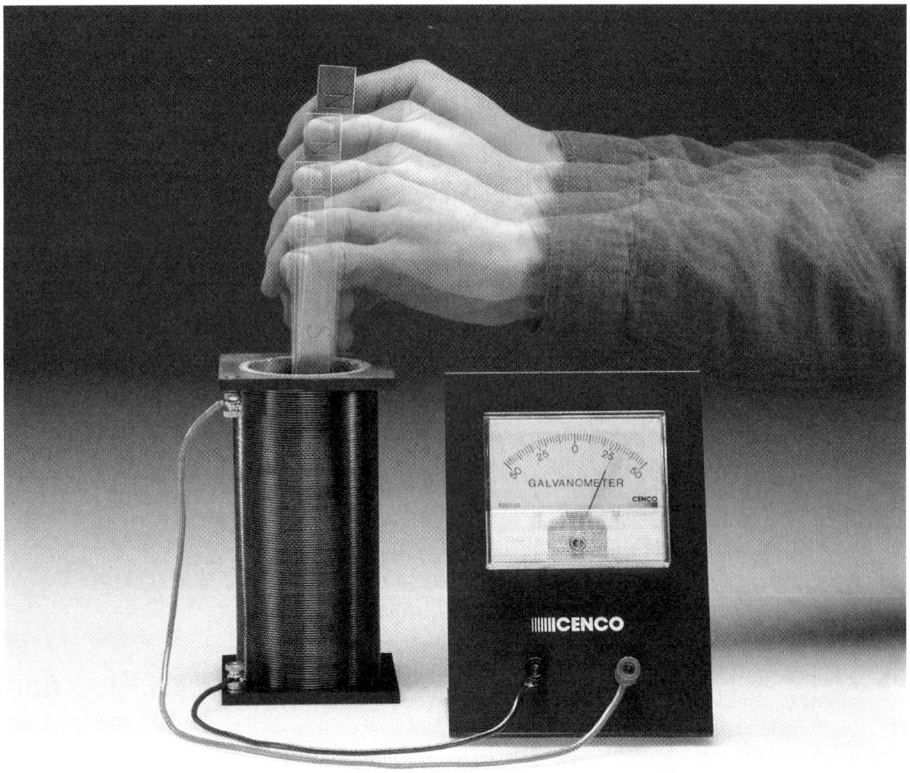


CHAPTER 21

# Electromagnetic Induction and Faraday's Law

In Chapter 20, we discussed two ways in which electricity and magnetism are related: (1) an electric current produces a magnetic field; and (2) a magnetic field exerts a force on an electric current or moving electric charge. These discoveries were made in 1820–1821. Scientists then began to wonder: if electric currents produce a magnetic field, is it possible that a magnetic field can produce an electric current? Ten years later the American Joseph Henry (1797–1878) and the Englishman Michael Faraday (1791–1867) independently found that it was possible. Henry actually made the discovery first. But Faraday published his results earlier and investigated the subject in more detail. We now discuss this phenomenon and some of its world-changing applications such as the electric generator.

## 21–1 Induced EMF

In his attempt to produce an electric current from a magnetic field, Faraday used an apparatus like that shown in Fig. 21–1. A coil of wire, X, was connected to a battery. The current that flowed through X produced a magnetic field that was intensified by the iron core around which the wire was wrapped. Faraday hoped that a strong steady current in X would produce a great enough magnetic

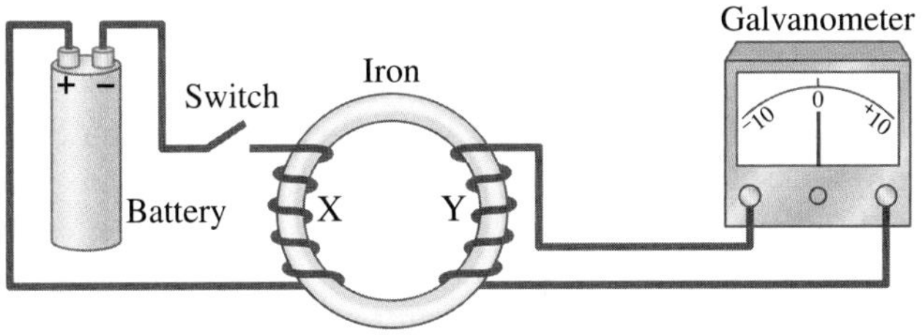


**FIGURE 21–1** Faraday's experiment to induce an emf.

field to produce a current in a second coil Y which shared the same iron core. This second circuit, Y, contained a galvanometer to detect any current but contained no battery. He met no success with constant currents. But the long-sought effect was finally observed when Faraday noticed the galvanometer in circuit Y deflect strongly at the moment he closed the switch in circuit X. And the galvanometer deflected strongly in the opposite direction when he opened the switch in X. A constant current in X produced a constant magnetic field which produced *no* current in Y. Only when the current in X was starting or stopping was a current produced in Y.

Faraday concluded that although a constant magnetic field produces no current in a conductor, a *changing* magnetic field can produce an electric current. Such a current is called an **induced current**. When the magnetic field through coil Y changes, a current occurs in Y as if there were a source of emf in circuit Y. We therefore say that

**CAUTION**

*Changing $\vec{\mathbf{B}}$, not $\vec{\mathbf{B}}$ itself, induces current*

**a changing magnetic field induces an emf.**

*Changing $\vec{\mathbf{B}}$ induces an emf*

Faraday did further experiments on **electromagnetic induction**, as this phenomenon is called. For example, Fig. 21–2 shows that if a magnet is moved quickly into a coil of wire, a current is induced in the wire. If the magnet is quickly removed, a current is induced in the opposite direction ($\vec{\mathbf{B}}$ through the coil decreases). Furthermore, if the magnet is held steady and the coil of wire is moved toward or away from the magnet, again an emf is induced and a current flows. Motion or change is required to induce an emf. It doesn't matter whether the magnet or the coil moves. It is their *relative motion* that counts.

**CAUTION**

*Relative motion—magnet or coil moving induces current*

**FIGURE 21–2** (a) A current is induced when a magnet is moved toward a coil, momentarily increasing the magnetic field through the coil. (b) The induced current is opposite when the magnet is moved away from the coil ($\vec{\mathbf{B}}$ decreases). Note that the galvanometer zero is at the center of the scale and the needle deflects left or right, depending on the direction of the current. In (c), no current is induced if the magnet does not move relative to the coil. It is the relative motion that counts here: the magnet can be held steady and the coil moved, which also induces an emf.

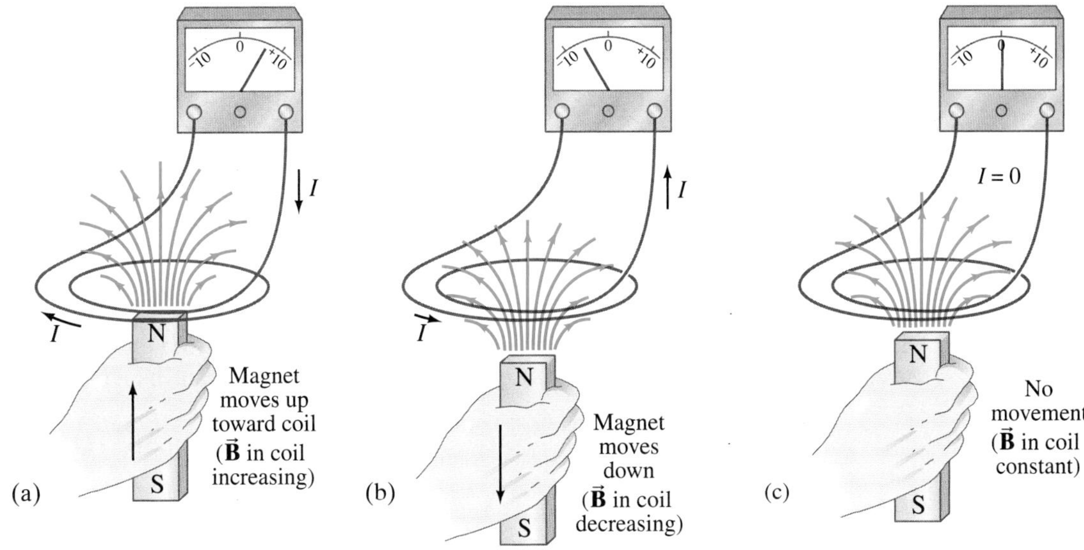

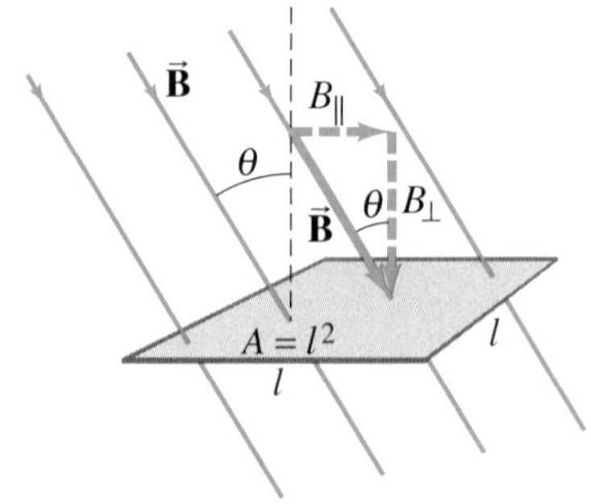


**FIGURE 21–3** Determining the flux through a flat loop of wire. This loop is square, of side $l$ and area $A = l^2$.

**FIGURE 21–4** Magnetic flux $\Phi_B$ is proportional to the number of lines of $\vec{B}$ that pass through the loop.

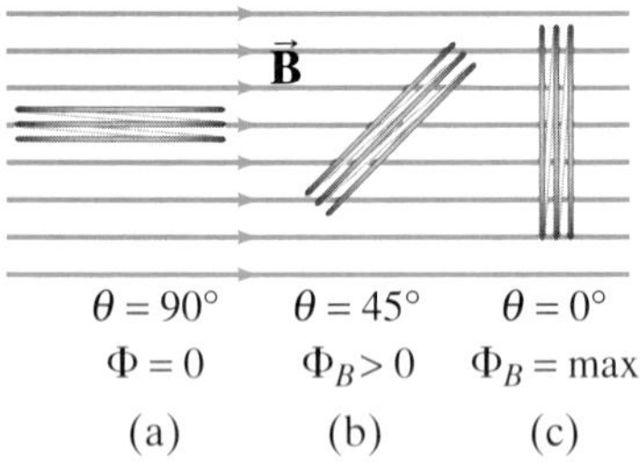


**FIGURE 21–5** Example 21–1.

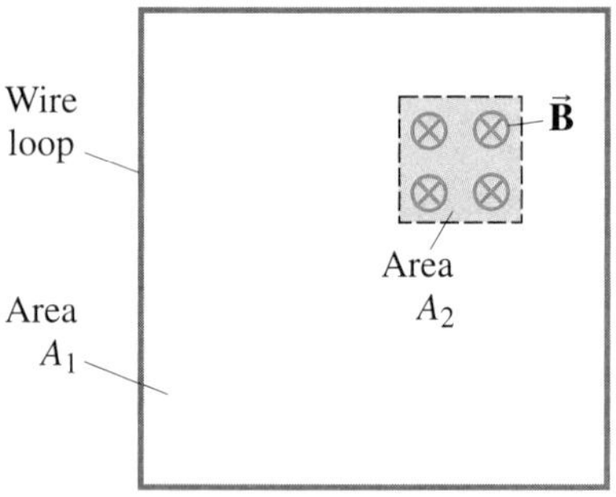


## 21–2 Faraday's Law of Induction; Lenz's Law

Faraday investigated quantitatively what factors influence the magnitude of the emf induced. He found first of all that the more rapidly the magnetic field changes, the greater the induced emf in a loop of wire. But the emf is not simply proportional to the rate of change of the magnetic field, $\vec{B}$; it depends also on the loop's area and angle. That is, the emf is proportional to the rate of change of the **magnetic flux**, $\Phi_B$, through the loop. Magnetic flux for a uniform magnetic field through a loop of area $A$ is defined as

$$\Phi_B = B_{\perp} A = BA\cos\theta. \qquad [B \text{ uniform}] \quad \textbf{(21–1)}$$

Here $B_{\perp}$ is the component of the magnetic field $\vec{B}$ perpendicular to the face of the loop, and $\theta$ is the angle between $\vec{B}$ and a line perpendicular to the face of the loop. These quantities are shown in Fig. 21–3 for a square loop of side $l$ whose area is $A = l^2$. When the face of the loop is parallel to $\vec{B}$, $\theta = 90°$ and $\Phi_B = 0$. When $\vec{B}$ is perpendicular to the loop, $\theta = 0°$, and

$$\Phi_B = BA. \qquad [\text{uniform } \vec{B} \perp \text{loop face}]$$

As we saw in Chapter 20, the lines of $\vec{B}$ (like lines of $\vec{E}$) can be drawn such that the number of lines per unit area is proportional to the field strength. Then the flux $\Phi_B$ can be thought of as being proportional to the *total number of lines passing through the area enclosed by the loop*. This is illustrated in Fig. 21–4, where the loop is viewed from the side (on edge). For $\theta = 90°$, no magnetic field lines pass through the loop and $\Phi_B = 0$, whereas $\Phi_B$ is a maximum when $\theta = 0°$. The unit of magnetic flux is the tesla-meter$^2$; this is called a **weber**: $1\text{ Wb} = 1\text{ T}\cdot\text{m}^2$.

**CONCEPTUAL EXAMPLE 21–1** **Determining flux.** A square loop of wire encloses area $A_1$ as shown in Fig. 21–5. A uniform magnetic field $\vec{B}$ perpendicular to the loop extends over the area $A_2$. What is the magnetic flux through the loop $A_1$?

**RESPONSE** We assume that the magnetic field is zero outside the area $A_2$. The total magnetic flux through area $A_1$ is the flux through area $A_2$, which by Eq. 21–1 for a uniform field is $BA_2$, plus the flux through the remaining area $(= A_1 - A_2)$, which is zero because $B = 0$. So the total flux is $\Phi_B = BA_2 + 0(A_1 - A_2) = BA_2$. It is *not* equal to $BA_1$ because $\vec{B}$ is not uniform over $A_1$.

**EXAMPLE 21–2** **Calculate the flux.** A square loop of wire 10.0 cm on a side is in a 1.25-T magnetic field $B$. What are the maximum and minimum values of flux that can pass through the loop?

**APPROACH** The flux is given by Eq. 21–1. It is a maximum for $\theta = 0°$, which occurs when the plane of the loop is perpendicular to $\vec{B}$. The minimum value occurs when $\theta = 90°$ and the plane of the loop is aligned with $\vec{B}$.

**SOLUTION** From Eq. 21–1, the maximum value is

$$\Phi_B = BA\cos\theta = (1.25\text{ T})(0.100\text{ m})(0.100\text{ m})\cos 0° = 0.0125\text{ Wb}.$$

The minimum value is 0 Wb when $\theta = 90°$ and $\cos 90° = 0$.

**EXERCISE A** Find the flux in Example 21–2 when the perpendicular to the coil makes a 35° angle with $\vec{B}$.

With our definition of flux, Eq. 21–1, we can now write down the results of Faraday's investigations. If the flux through a loop of wire changes by an amount $\Delta\Phi_B$ over a very brief time interval $\Delta t$, the induced emf at this instant is

*FARADAY'S LAW OF INDUCTION*

$$\mathscr{E} = -\frac{\Delta\Phi_B}{\Delta t}. \qquad [1 \text{ loop}] \quad \textbf{(21–2a)}$$

This fundamental result is known as **Faraday's law of induction**, and it is one of the basic laws of electromagnetism.

If the circuit contains $N$ closely wrapped loops, the emfs induced in each loop add together, so

$$\mathscr{E} = -N\frac{\Delta\Phi_B}{\Delta t}. \qquad [N \text{ loops}] \quad \textbf{(21–2b)}$$

*FARADAY'S LAW OF INDUCTION*

The minus sign in Eqs. 21–2 is there to remind us in which direction the induced emf acts. Experiments show that

*Lenz's law*

**a current produced by an induced emf moves in a direction so that its magnetic field opposes the original change in flux.**

This is known as **Lenz's law**. Be aware that we are now discussing two distinct magnetic fields: (1) the changing magnetic field or flux that induces the current, and (2) the magnetic field produced by the induced current (all currents produce a field). The second field opposes the change in the first.

CAUTION
*Distinguish two different magnetic fields*

Let us now apply Lenz's law to the relative motion between a magnet and a coil, Fig. 21–2. The changing flux through the coil induces an emf in the coil, producing a current. This induced current produces its own magnetic field. In Fig. 21–2a the distance between the coil and the magnet decreases. The magnet's magnetic field (and number of field lines) through the coil increases, and therefore the flux increases. The magnetic field of the magnet points upward. To oppose the upward increase, the magnetic field inside the coil produced by the induced current needs to point *downward*. Thus, Lenz's law tells us that the current moves as shown (use the right-hand rule). In Fig. 21–2b, the flux *decreases* (because the magnet is moved away and $B$ decreases), so the induced current in the coil produces an *upward* magnetic field through the coil that is "trying" to maintain the status quo. Thus the current in Fig. 21–2b is in the opposite direction from Fig. 21–2a.

It is important to note that an emf is induced whenever there is a change in *flux* through the coil, and we now consider some more possibilities.

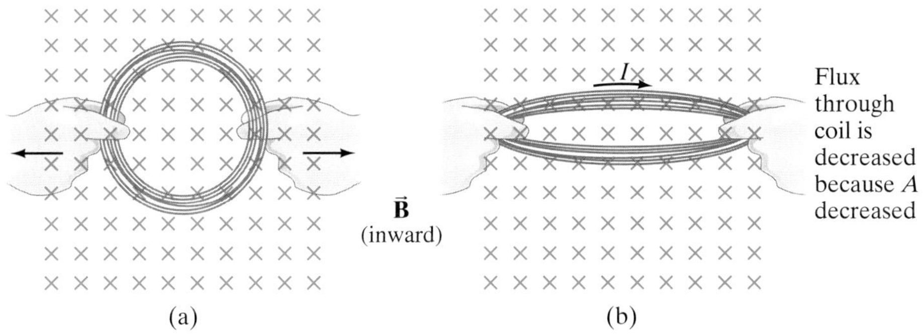


**FIGURE 21–6** A current can be induced by changing the area of the coil, even though $B$ doesn't change. In both this case and that of Fig. 21–7, the *flux* through the coil is reduced as we go from (a) to (b). Here the brief induced current acts in the direction shown so as to try to maintain the original flux ($\Phi = BA$) by producing its own magnetic field into the page. That is, as the area $A$ decreases, the current acts to increase $B$ in the original (inward) direction.

Since magnetic flux $\Phi_B = BA\cos\theta$, we see that an emf can be induced in three ways: (1) by a changing magnetic field $B$; (2) by changing the area $A$ of the loop in the field; or (3) by changing the loop's orientation $\theta$ with respect to the field. Figures 21–1 and 21–2 illustrated case 1. Examples of cases 2 and 3 are illustrated in Figs. 21–6 and 21–7, respectively.

*Three ways to change the magnetic flux: change B, A, or θ*

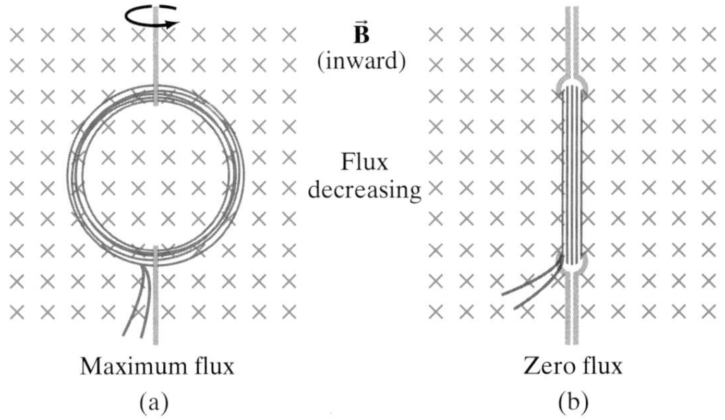


**FIGURE 21–7** A current can be induced by rotating a coil in a magnetic field. The flux through the coil changes from (a) to (b) because $\theta$ (in Eq. 21–1) went from 0° ($\cos\theta = 1$) to 90° ($\cos\theta = 0$).

**FIGURE 21–8** Example 21–3: An induction stove.

CONCEPTUAL EXAMPLE 21–3 **Induction stove.** In an induction stove (Fig. 21–8), an ac current passes around a coil that is the "burner" (a burner that never gets hot). Why will it heat a metal pan but not a glass container?

**RESPONSE** The ac current sets up a changing magnetic field that passes through the pan bottom. This changing magnetic field induces a current in the pan bottom, and since the pan offers resistance, electric energy is transformed to thermal energy which heats the pot and its contents. A glass container offers such high resistance that little current is induced and little energy is transferred $(P = V^2/R)$.

## PROBLEM SOLVING Lenz's Law

Lenz's law is used to determine the direction of the (conventional) electric current induced in a loop due to a change in magnetic flux inside the loop. To produce an induced current you need

(a) a closed conducting loop, and
(b) an external magnetic flux through the loop that is changing in time.

1. Determine whether the magnetic flux ($\Phi = BA\cos\theta$) inside the loop is decreasing, increasing, or unchanged.
2. The magnetic field due to the induced current: (a) points in the same direction as the external field if the flux is decreasing; (b) points in the opposite direction as the external field if the flux is increasing; or (c) is zero if the flux is not changing.
3. Once you know the direction of the induced magnetic field, use right-hand-rule-1 (p. 562) to find the direction of the induced current.
4. Always keep in mind that there are two magnetic fields: (1) an external field whose flux must be changing if it is to induce an electric current, and (2) a magnetic field produced by the induced current.

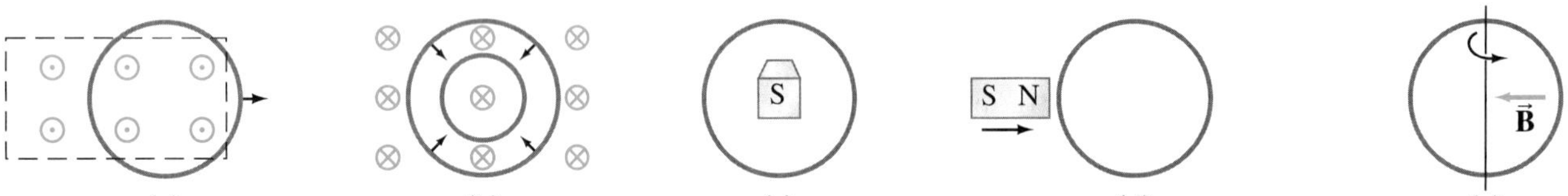


(a) Pulling the loop to the right out of a magnetic field which points out of the page

(b) Shrinking a loop in a magnetic field pointing into the page

(c) N magnetic pole moving toward loop into the page

(d) N magnetic pole moving toward the loop in the plane of the page

(e) Rotating the loop by pulling the left side toward us and pushing the right side in; the magnetic field points from right to left

**FIGURE 21–9** Example 21–4.

CONCEPTUAL EXAMPLE 21–4 **Practice with Lenz's law.** In which direction is the current induced in the loop for each situation in Fig. 21–9?

**CAUTION** *Magnetic field of induced current opposes change in external flux, not necessarily opposing the external field*

**RESPONSE** (*a*) Initially, the magnetic field pointing out of the page passes through the loop. If you pull the loop out of the field, magnetic flux through the loop decreases; so the induced current will be in a direction to maintain the decreasing flux through the loop: the current will be counterclockwise to produce a magnetic field outward (toward the reader).
(*b*) The external field is into the page. The coil area gets smaller, so the flux will decrease; hence the induced current will be clockwise, producing its own field into the page to make up for the flux decrease.
(*c*) Magnetic field lines point out from the N pole of a magnet, so as the magnet moves toward the loop, the magnet's field points into the page and is getting stronger. The current in the loop will be induced in the counterclockwise direction in order to produce a field $\vec{\mathbf{B}}$ *out* of the page.
(*d*) The field is in the plane of the loop, so no magnetic field lines pass through the loop and the flux through the loop is zero throughout the process; hence there is no change in external magnetic flux with time, and there will be no induced emf or current in the loop.
(*e*) Initially there is no flux through the loop. When you start to rotate the loop, the external field through the loop begins increasing to the left. To counteract this change in flux, the loop will have current induced in a counterclockwise direction so as to produce its own field to the right.

**EXAMPLE 21–5 Pulling a coil from a magnetic field.** A square coil of wire with side $l = 5.00\,\text{cm}$ contains 100 loops and is positioned perpendicular to a uniform 0.600-T magnetic field, as shown in Fig. 21–10. It is quickly pulled from the field at constant speed (moving perpendicular to $\vec{\mathbf{B}}$) to a region where $B$ drops abruptly to zero. At $t = 0$, the right edge of the coil is at the edge of the field. It takes 0.100 s for the whole coil to reach the field-free region. The coil's total resistance is 100 Ω. Find (*a*) the rate of change in flux through the coil, and (*b*) the emf and current induced. (*c*) How much energy is dissipated in the coil? (*d*) What was the average force required?

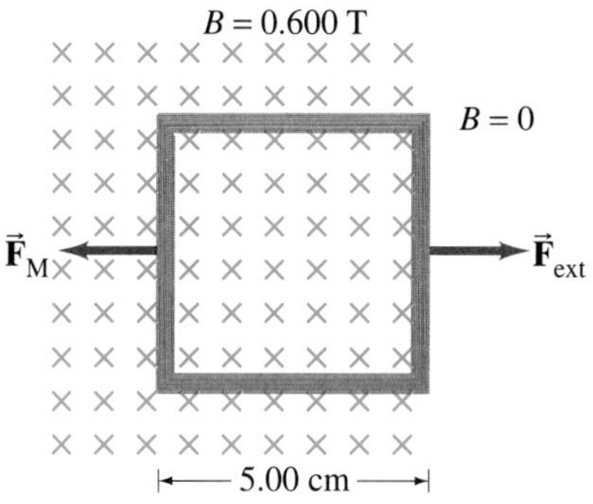


**FIGURE 21–10** Example 21–5. The square coil in a magnetic field $B = 0.600\,\text{T}$ is pulled abruptly to the right to a region where $B = 0$.

**APPROACH** We start by finding how the magnetic flux, $\Phi_B = BA$, changes during the time interval $\Delta t = 0.100\,\text{s}$. Faraday's law then gives the induced emf and Ohm's law gives the current.

**SOLUTION** (*a*) The area of the coil is $A = l^2 = (5.00 \times 10^{-2}\,\text{m})^2 = 2.50 \times 10^{-3}\,\text{m}^2$. The flux is initially $\Phi_B = BA = (0.600\,\text{T})(2.50 \times 10^{-3}\,\text{m}^2) = 1.50 \times 10^{-3}\,\text{Wb}$. After 0.100 s, the flux is zero. The rate of change in flux is constant (because the coil is square), equal to

$$\frac{\Delta\Phi_B}{\Delta t} = \frac{0 - (1.50 \times 10^{-3}\,\text{Wb})}{0.100\,\text{s}} = -1.50 \times 10^{-2}\,\text{Wb/s}.$$

(*b*) The emf induced (Eq. 21–2) in the 100-loop coil during this 0.100-s interval is

$$\mathscr{E} = -N\frac{\Delta\Phi_B}{\Delta t} = -(100)(-1.50 \times 10^{-2}\,\text{Wb/s}) = 1.50\,\text{V}.$$

The current is found by applying Ohm's law to the 100-Ω coil:

$$I = \frac{\mathscr{E}}{R} = \frac{1.50\,\text{V}}{100\,\Omega} = 1.50 \times 10^{-2}\,\text{A} = 15.0\,\text{mA}.$$

By Lenz's law, the current must be clockwise to produce more $\vec{\mathbf{B}}$ into the page and thus oppose the decreasing flux into the page.

(*c*) The total energy dissipated in the coil is the product of the power $(= I^2R)$ and the time:

$$E = Pt = I^2Rt = (1.50 \times 10^{-2}\,\text{A})^2(100\,\Omega)(0.100\,\text{s}) = 2.25 \times 10^{-3}\,\text{J}.$$

(*d*) We can use the result of part (*c*) and apply the work-energy principle: the energy dissipated $E$ is equal to the work $W$ needed to pull the coil out of the field (Chapter 6). Because $W = \bar{F}d$ where $d = 5.00\,\text{cm}$, then

$$\bar{F} = \frac{W}{d} = \frac{2.25 \times 10^{-3}\,\text{J}}{5.00 \times 10^{-2}\,\text{m}} = 0.0450\,\text{N}.$$

***Alternate Solution*** (*d*) We can also calculate the force directly using $F = IlB$, Eq. 20–2 for constant $\vec{\mathbf{B}}$. The force the magnetic field exerts on the top and bottom sections of the square coil of Fig. 21–10 are in opposite directions and cancel each other. The magnetic force $\vec{\mathbf{F}}_M$ exerted on the left vertical section of the square coil acts to the left as shown because the current is up (clockwise). The right side of the loop is in the region where $\vec{\mathbf{B}} = 0$. Hence the external force, to the right, needed to just overcome the magnetic force to the left (on $N = 100$ loops) is

$$F_{\text{ext}} = NIlB = (100)(0.0150\,\text{A})(0.0500\,\text{m})(0.600\,\text{T}) = 0.0450\,\text{N},$$

which is the same answer, confirming our use of energy conservation above.

**EXERCISE B** What is the direction of the induced current in the circular loop due to the current shown in each part of Fig. 21–11?

**FIGURE 21–11** Exercise B.

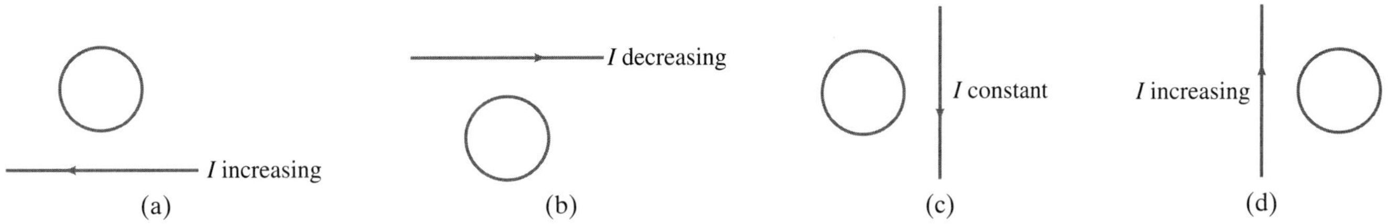

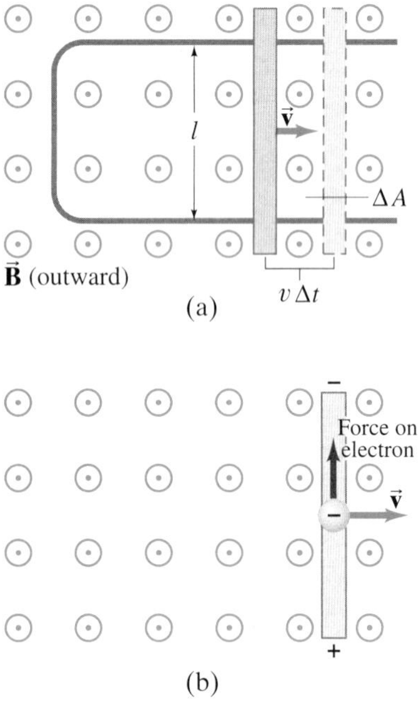


**FIGURE 21–12** (a) A conducting rod is moved to the right on a U-shaped conductor in a uniform magnetic field $\vec{\mathbf{B}}$ that points out of the paper. (b) Upward force on an electron in the metal rod (moving to the right) due to $\vec{\mathbf{B}}$ pointing out of page.

## 21–3 EMF Induced in a Moving Conductor

Another way to induce an emf is shown in Fig. 21–12a, and this situation helps illuminate the nature of the induced emf. Assume that a uniform magnetic field $\vec{\mathbf{B}}$ is perpendicular to the area bounded by the U-shaped conductor and the movable rod resting on it. If the rod is made to move at a speed $v$, it travels a distance $\Delta x = v\,\Delta t$ in a time $\Delta t$. Therefore, the area of the loop increases by an amount $\Delta A = l\,\Delta x = lv\,\Delta t$ in a time $\Delta t$. By Faraday's law there is an induced emf $\mathscr{E}$ whose magnitude is given by

$$\mathscr{E} = \frac{\Delta\Phi_B}{\Delta t} = \frac{B\,\Delta A}{\Delta t} = \frac{Blv\,\Delta t}{\Delta t} = Blv. \qquad \textbf{(21–3)}$$

Equation 21–3 is valid as long as $B$, $l$, and $v$ are mutually perpendicular. (If they are not, we use only the components of each that are mutually perpendicular.) An emf induced on a conductor moving in a magnetic field is sometimes called *motional emf*.

We can also obtain Eq. 21–3 without using Faraday's law. We saw in Chapter 20 that a charged particle moving perpendicular to a magnetic field $B$ with speed $v$ experiences a force $F = qvB$ (Eq. 20–4). When the rod of Fig. 21–12a moves to the right with speed $v$, the electrons in the rod also move with this speed. Therefore, since $\vec{\mathbf{v}} \perp \vec{\mathbf{B}}$, each electron feels a force $F = qvB$, which acts up the page as shown in Fig. 21–12b. If the rod was not in contact with the U-shaped conductor, electrons would collect at the upper end of the rod, leaving the lower end positive (see signs in Fig. 21–12b). There must thus be an induced emf. If the rod does slide on the U-shaped conductor (Fig. 21–12a), the electrons will flow into the U. There will then be a clockwise (conventional) current in the loop. To calculate the emf, we determine the work $W$ needed to move a charge $q$ from one end of the rod to the other against this potential difference: $W = \text{force} \times \text{distance} = (qvB)(l)$. The emf equals the work done per unit charge, so $\mathscr{E} = W/q = qvBl/q = Blv$, the same result as from Faraday's law above, Eq. 21–3.

**EXERCISE C** In what direction will the electrons flow in Fig. 21–12 if the rod moves to the left, decreasing the area of the current loop?

**FIGURE 21–13** Example 21–6.

**EXAMPLE 21–6 Does a moving airplane develop a large emf?** An airplane travels 1000 km/h in a region where the Earth's magnetic field is $5.0 \times 10^{-5}\,\text{T}$ and is nearly vertical (Fig. 21–13). What is the potential difference induced between the wing tips that are 70 m apart?

**APPROACH** We consider the wings to be a 70-m-long conductor moving through the Earth's magnetic field. We use Eq. 21–3 to get the emf.

**SOLUTION** Since $v = 1000\,\text{km/h} = 280\,\text{m/s}$, and $\vec{\mathbf{v}} \perp \vec{\mathbf{B}}$, we have

$$\mathscr{E} = Blv = \left(5.0 \times 10^{-5}\,\text{T}\right)(70\,\text{m})(280\,\text{m/s}) = 1.0\,\text{V}.$$

**NOTE** Not much to worry about.

PHYSICS APPLIED
*Blood flow measurement*

**FIGURE 21–14** Measurement of blood velocity from the induced emf. Example 21–7.

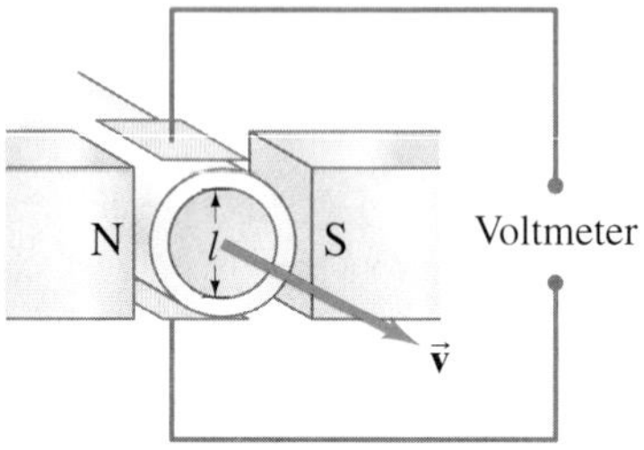


**EXAMPLE 21–7 Electromagnetic blood-flow measurement.** The rate of blood flow in our body's vessels can be measured using the apparatus shown in Fig. 21–14, since blood contains charged ions. Suppose that the blood vessel is 2.0 mm in diameter, the magnetic field is 0.080 T, and the measured emf is 0.10 mV. What is the flow velocity of the blood?

**APPROACH** The magnetic field $\vec{\mathbf{B}}$ points horizontally from left to right (N pole toward S pole). The induced emf acts over the width $l = 2.0\,\text{mm}$ of the blood vessel (Fig. 21–14), perpendicular to $\vec{\mathbf{B}}$ and $\vec{\mathbf{v}}$, just as in Fig. 21–12. We can then use Eq. 21–3 to get $v$.

**SOLUTION** We solve for $v$ in Eq. 21–3:

$$v = \frac{\mathscr{E}}{Bl} = \frac{\left(1.0 \times 10^{-4}\,\text{V}\right)}{(0.080\,\text{T})\left(2.0 \times 10^{-3}\,\text{m}\right)} = 0.63\,\text{m/s}.$$

**NOTE** In actual practice, an alternating current is used to produce an alternating magnetic field. The induced emf is then alternating.

## Additional Example

**EXAMPLE 21–8** **Force on the rod.** To make the rod of Fig. 21–12a move to the right at speed $v$, you need to apply an external force on the rod to the right. (*a*) Explain and determine the magnitude of the required force. (*b*) What external power is needed to move the rod? (Do not confuse this external force on the rod with the upward force on the electrons shown in Fig. 21–12b.)

**APPROACH** When the rod moves to the right, electrons flow upward in the rod according to right-hand-rule-3 (p. 562). So the conventional current is downward in the rod. We can see this also from Lenz's law: the outward magnetic flux through the loop is increasing, so the induced current must oppose the increase. Thus the current is clockwise so as to produce a magnetic field into the page (right-hand-rule-1). The magnetic force on the moving rod is $F = IlB$ for a constant $B$ (Eq. 20–2). Right-hand-rule-2 tells us this magnetic force is to the left, and is thus a "drag force" opposing our effort to move the rod to the right.

**SOLUTION** (*a*) The magnitude of the external force, to the right, needs to balance the magnetic force $F = IlB$. The current $I = \mathscr{E}/R = Blv/R$ (see Eq. 21–3), and the resistance $R$ is that of the whole circuit: the rod and the U-shaped conductor. The force $F$ required to move the rod is thus

$$F = IlB = \left(\frac{Blv}{R}\right)lB = \frac{B^2l^2}{R}v.$$

If $B$, $l$, and $R$ are constant, then a constant speed $v$ is produced by a constant force. (Constant $R$ implies that the parallel rails have negligible resistance.)
(*b*) The external power needed to move the rod for constant $R$ is

$$P_{\text{ext}} = Fv = \frac{B^2l^2v^2}{R}.$$

The power dissipated in the resistance is $P = I^2R$. With $I = \mathscr{E}/R = Blv/R$,

$$P_{\text{R}} = I^2R = \frac{B^2l^2v^2}{R},$$

so the power input equals that dissipated in the resistance at any moment.

## 21–4 Changing Magnetic Flux Produces an Electric Field

We have seen that a changing magnetic flux induces an emf; there also is an induced current. This implies there is an electric field in a wire, causing the electrons to start moving. Indeed, this and other results suggest the important conclusion that

**a changing magnetic field induces an electric field.**

This applies not only to wires and other conductors, but is a general result that applies to any region in space: an electric field will be induced at any point in space where there is a changing magnetic field.

We can get a simple formula for $E$ in terms of $B$ for the case of electrons in a moving conductor, as in Fig. 21–12. The electrons feel a force (upwards in Fig. 21–12b); and if we put ourselves in the reference frame of the conductor, this force accelerating the electrons implies that there is an electric field in the conductor. Electric field is defined as the force per unit charge, $E = F/q$, where here $F = qvB$ (Eq. 20–4). Thus the effective field $E$ in the rod must be

$$E = \frac{F}{q} = \frac{qvB}{q} = vB. \qquad \textbf{(21–4)}$$

## 21–5 Electric Generators

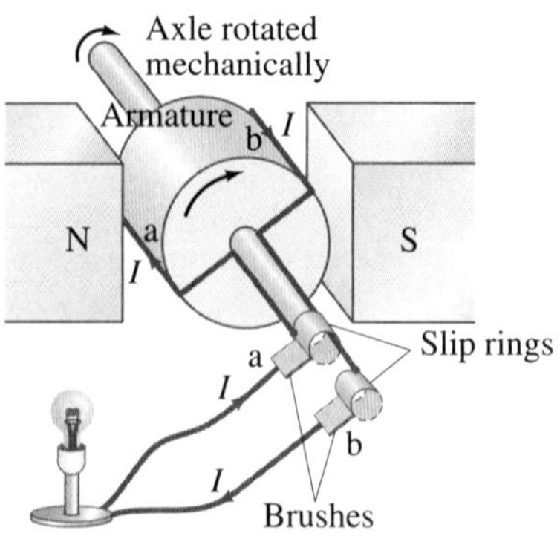


**FIGURE 21–15** An ac generator.

We discussed alternating currents (ac) in Section 18–7. Now we examine how ac is generated, by an **electric generator** or **dynamo**, one of the most important practical results of Faraday's great discovery. A generator transforms mechanical energy into electric energy, just the opposite of what a motor does. A simplified diagram of an **ac generator** is shown in Fig. 21–15. A generator consists of many loops of wire (only one is shown) wound on an *armature* that can rotate in a magnetic field. The axle is turned by some mechanical means (falling water, steam turbine, car motor belt), and an emf is induced in the rotating coil. An electric current is thus the *output* of a generator. Suppose in Fig. 21–15 that the armature is rotating clockwise; then right-hand-rule-3 applied to charged particles in the wire (or Lenz's law) tells us that the (conventional) current in the wire labeled b on the armature is outward; therefore the current is outward at brush b. (Each brush is fixed and presses against a continuous slip ring that rotates with the armature.) After one-half revolution, wire b will be where wire a is now in the drawing, and the current then at brush b will be inward. Thus the current produced is alternating.

The frequency $f$ is 60 Hz for general use in the United States and Canada, whereas 50 Hz is used in many countries. Most of the power generated in the United States is done at steam plants, where the burning of fossil fuels (coal, oil, natural gas) boils water to produce high-pressure steam that turns a turbine connected to the generator axle (Fig. 15–21). At nuclear power plants, the nuclear energy released is used to produce steam to turn turbines. Indeed, a heat engine (Chapter 15) connected to a generator is the principal means of generating electric power. The frequency of 60 Hz or 50 Hz is maintained very precisely by power companies.

**FIGURE 21–16** (a) A dc generator with one set of commutators, and (b) a dc generator with many sets of commutators and windings.

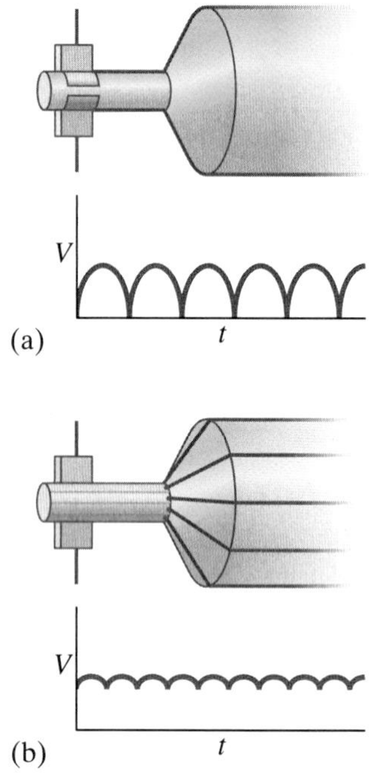


A **dc generator** is much like an ac generator, except the slip rings are replaced by split-ring commutators, Fig. 21–16a, just as in a dc motor. The output of such a generator is as shown and can be smoothed out by placing a capacitor in parallel with the output (Section 19–6). More common is the use of many armature windings, as in Fig. 21–16b, which produces a smoother output.

Automobiles used to use dc generators. Today they mainly use **alternators**, which avoid the problems of wear and electrical arcing (sparks) across the split-ring commutators of dc generators. Alternators differ from generators in that an electromagnet, called the *rotor*, is fed by current from the battery and is made to rotate by a belt from the engine. The magnetic field of the turning rotor passes through a surrounding set of stationary coils called the *stator*, inducing an alternating current in the stator coils, which is the output. This ac output is changed to dc for charging the battery by the use of semiconductor diodes, which allow current flow in one direction only.

### Deriving the Generator Equation

**FIGURE 21–17** The emf is induced in the segments ab and cd, whose velocity components perpendicular to the field $\vec{\mathbf{B}}$ are $v \sin\theta$.

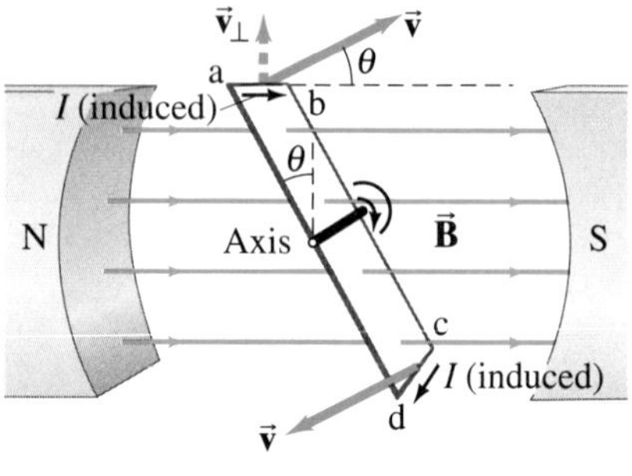


Figure 21–17 shows the wire loop on a generator armature. The loop is being made to rotate clockwise in a uniform magnetic field $\vec{\mathbf{B}}$. The velocity of the two lengths ab and cd at this instant are shown. Although the sections of wire bc and da are moving, the force on electrons in these sections is toward the side of the wire, not along the wire's length. The emf generated is thus due only to the force on charges in the sections ab and cd. From right-hand-rule-3, we see that the direction of the induced current in ab is from a toward b. And in the lower section, it is from c to d; so the flow is continuous in the loop. The magnitude of the emf generated in ab is given by Eq. 21–3, except that we must take the component of the velocity perpendicular to $B$:

$$\mathscr{E} = Blv_\perp,$$

where $l$ is the length of ab. From Fig. 21–17 we can see that $v_\perp = v \sin\theta$, where $\theta$ is the angle the face of the loop makes with the vertical. The emf induced in cd has the same magnitude and is in the same direction. Therefore their emfs add, and the total emf is

$$\mathscr{E} = 2NBlv \sin\theta,$$

where we have multiplied by $N$, the number of loops in the coil.

If the coil is rotating with constant angular velocity $\omega$, then the angle $\theta = \omega t$. We also have from the angular equations (Eq. 8–4) that $v = \omega r = \omega(h/2)$, where $h$ is the length of bc or ad. Thus $\mathscr{E} = 2NB\omega l(h/2)\sin\omega t$, or

$$\mathscr{E} = NB\omega A \sin\omega t, \qquad \textbf{(21–5)}$$

where $A = lh$ is the area of the loop. This equation holds for any shape coil, not just for a rectangle as derived. Thus, the output emf of the generator is sinusoidally alternating (see Fig. 21–18 and Section 18–7). Since $\omega$ is expressed in radians per second, we can write $\omega = 2\pi f$, where $f$ is the frequency.

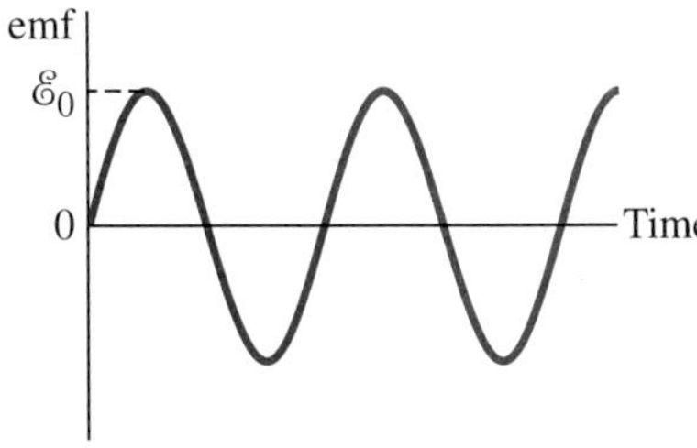


**FIGURE 21–18** An ac generator produces an alternating current. The output emf $\mathscr{E} = \mathscr{E}_0 \sin\omega t$, where $\mathscr{E}_0 = NA\omega B$ (Eq. 21–5).

## * 21–6 Back EMF and Counter Torque; Eddy Currents

### * Back EMF

A motor turns and produces mechanical energy when a current is made to flow in it. From our description in Section 20–10 of a simple dc motor, you might expect that the armature would accelerate indefinitely due to the torque on it. However, as the armature of the motor turns, the magnetic flux through the coil changes and an emf is generated. This induced emf acts to oppose the motion (Lenz's law) and is called the **back emf** or **counter emf**. The greater the speed of the motor, the greater the back emf. A motor normally turns and does work on something, but if there were no load, the motor's speed would increase until the back emf equaled the input voltage. When there is a mechanical load, the speed of the motor may be limited also by the load. The back emf will then be less than the external applied voltage. The greater the mechanical load, the slower the motor rotates and the lower is the back emf ($\mathscr{E} \propto \omega$, Eq. 21–5).

**EXAMPLE 21–9** **Back emf in a motor.** The armature windings of a dc motor have a resistance of 5.0 Ω. The motor is connected to a 120-V line, and when the motor reaches full speed against its normal load, the back emf is 108 V. Calculate ($a$) the current into the motor when it is just starting up, and ($b$) the current when the motor reaches full speed.

**APPROACH** As the motor is just starting up, it is turning very slowly, so there is no induced back emf. The only voltage is the 120-V line. The current is given by Ohm's law with $R = 5.0\,\Omega$. At full speed, we must include as emfs both the 120-V applied emf and the opposing back emf.

**SOLUTION** ($a$) At start up, the current is controlled by the 120 V applied to the coil's 5.0-Ω resistance. By Ohm's law,

$$I = \frac{V}{R} = \frac{120\text{ V}}{5.0\,\Omega} = 24\text{ A}.$$

($b$) When the motor is at full speed, the back emf must be included in the equivalent circuit shown in Fig. 21–19. In this case, Ohm's law (or Kirchhoff's rule) gives

$$120\text{ V} - 108\text{ V} = I(5.0\,\Omega).$$

Therefore

$$I = \frac{12\text{ V}}{5.0\,\Omega} = 2.4\text{ A}.$$

**NOTE** This result shows that the current can be very high when a motor first starts up. This is why the lights in your house may dim when the motor of the refrigerator (or other large motor) starts up. The large initial current causes the voltage at the outlets to drop, since the house wiring has resistance and there is some voltage drop across it when large currents are drawn.

**FIGURE 21–19** Circuit of a motor showing induced back emf. Example 21–9.

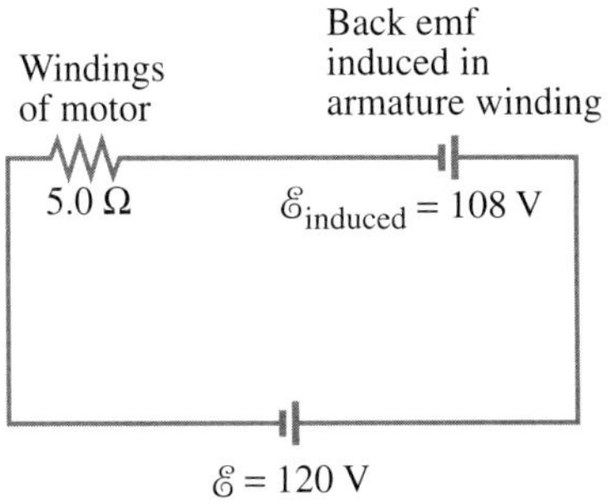


*Effect of back emf on current*

CONCEPTUAL EXAMPLE 21–10 **Motor overload.** When using an appliance such as a blender, electric drill, or sewing machine, if the appliance is overloaded or jammed so that the motor slows appreciably or stops while the power is still connected, the device can burn out and be ruined. Explain why this happens.

PHYSICS APPLIED
*Burning out a motor*

**RESPONSE** The motors are designed to run at a certain speed for a given applied voltage, and the designer must take the expected back emf into account. If the rotation speed is reduced, the back emf will not be as high as expected ($\mathscr{E} \propto \omega$, Eq. 21–5), and the current will increase, and may become large enough that the windings of the motor heat up to the point of ruining the motor.

## * Counter Torque

In a generator, the situation is the reverse of that for a motor. As we saw, the mechanical turning of the armature induces an emf in the loops, which is the output. If the generator is not connected to an external circuit, the emf exists at the terminals but there is no current. In this case, it takes little effort to turn the armature. But if the generator *is* connected to a device that draws current, then a current flows in the coils of the armature. Because this current-carrying coil is in an external magnetic field, there will be a torque exerted on it (as in a motor), and this torque opposes the motion (use right-hand-rule-2 for the force on a wire, in Fig. 21–15 or 21–17). This is called a **counter torque**. The greater the electrical load—that is, the more current that is drawn—the greater will be the counter torque. Hence the external applied torque will have to be greater to keep the generator turning. This makes sense from the conservation of energy principle. More mechanical-energy input is needed to produce more electrical-energy output.

*Counter torque*

## * Eddy Currents

**FIGURE 21–20** Production of eddy currents in a rotating wheel.

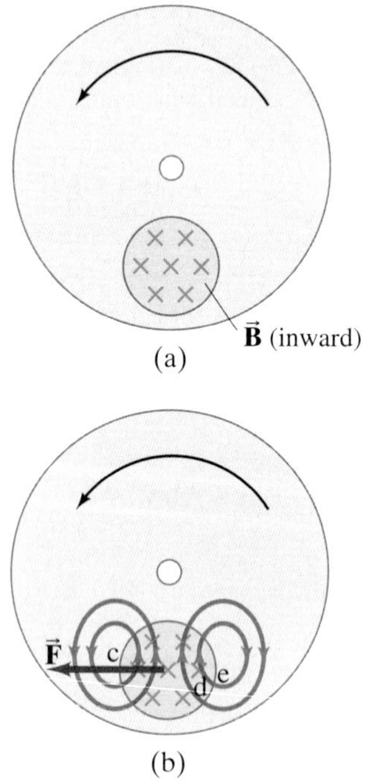


Induced currents are not always confined to well-defined paths such as in wires. Consider, for example, the rotating metal wheel in Fig. 21–20a. An external magnetic field is applied to a limited area of the wheel as shown and points into the paper. The section of wheel in the magnetic field has an emf induced in it because the conductor is moving, carrying electrons with it. The flow of (conventional) current in the wheel is upward in the region of the magnetic field (Fig. 21–20b), and the current follows a downward return path outside that region. Why? According to Lenz's law, the induced currents oppose the change that causes them. Consider the part of the wheel labeled c in Fig. 21–20b, where the magnetic field is zero but is just about to enter a region where $\vec{\mathbf{B}}$ points into the page. To oppose this inward increase in magnetic field, the induced current is counterclockwise to produce a field pointing out of the page (right-hand-rule-1). Similarly, region d is about to move to e, where $\vec{\mathbf{B}}$ is zero; hence the current is clockwise to produce an inward field opposed to this decreasing flux inward. These currents are referred to as **eddy currents**. They can be present in any conductor that is moving across a magnetic field or through which the magnetic flux is changing.

In Fig. 21–20b, the magnetic field exerts a force $\vec{\mathbf{F}}$ on the induced currents it has created, and that force opposes the rotational motion. Eddy currents can be used in this way as a smooth braking device on, say, a rapid-transit car. In order to stop the car, an electromagnet can be turned on that applies its field either to the wheels or to the moving steel rail below. Eddy currents can also be used to dampen (reduce) the oscillation of a vibrating system. Eddy currents, however, can be a problem. For example, eddy currents induced in the armature of a motor or generator produce heat ($P = I\mathscr{E}$) and waste energy. To reduce the eddy currents, the armatures are *laminated*; that is, they are made of very thin sheets of iron that are well insulated from one another. The total path length of the eddy currents is confined to each slab, which increases the total resistance; hence the current is less and there is less wasted energy.

Walk-through metal detectors at airports (Fig. 21–21) detect metal objects using electromagnetic induction and eddy currents. Several coils are situated in the walls of the walk-through at different heights. In a technique called "pulse induction," the coils are given repeated brief pulses of current (on the order of microseconds), hundreds or thousands of times a second. Each pulse in a coil produces a magnetic field for a very brief period of time. When a passenger passes through the walk-through, any metal object being carried will have eddy currents induced in it. The eddy currents persist briefly after each input pulse, and the small magnetic field produced by the persisting eddy current (before the next external pulse) can be detected, setting off an alert or alarm. Stores and libraries use similar systems to prevent theft.

**PHYSICS APPLIED**
*Airport metal detector*

**FIGURE 21–21** Airport metal detector.

## 21–7 Transformers and Transmission of Power

A transformer is a device for increasing or decreasing an ac voltage. Transformers are found everywhere: in TV sets to give the high voltage needed for the picture tube, in converters for plugging in a portable stereo, on utility poles (Fig. 21–22) to reduce the high voltage from the electric company to a usable voltage in houses (120 V or 240 V), and in many other applications. A **transformer** consists of two coils of wire known as the **primary** and **secondary** coils. The two coils can be interwoven (with insulated wire); or they can be linked by an iron core which is laminated to minimize eddy-current losses (Section 21–6), as shown in Fig. 21–23. Transformers are designed so that (nearly) all the magnetic flux produced by the current in the primary coil also passes through the secondary coil, and we assume this is true in what follows. We also assume that energy losses (in resistance and hysteresis) can be ignored—a good approximation for real transformers, which are often better than 99% efficient.

**FIGURE 21–22** Repairing a step-down transformer on a utility pole.

When an ac voltage is applied to the primary coil, the changing magnetic field it produces will induce an ac voltage of the same frequency in the secondary coil. However, the voltage will be different according to the number of loops in each coil. From Faraday's law, the voltage or emf induced in the secondary coil is

$$V_S = N_S \frac{\Delta \Phi_B}{\Delta t},$$

where $N_S$ is the number of turns in the secondary coil, and $\Delta\Phi_B/\Delta t$ is the rate at which the magnetic flux changes.

The input primary voltage, $V_P$, is related to the rate at which the flux changes through it,

$$V_P = N_P \frac{\Delta \Phi_B}{\Delta t},$$

where $N_P$ is the number of turns in the primary coil. We divide these two equations, assuming little or no flux is lost, to find

**FIGURE 21–23** Step-up transformer $(N_P = 4,\ N_S = 12)$.

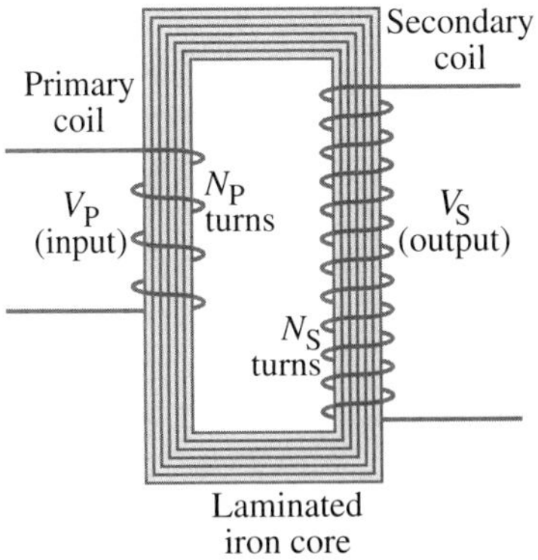


$$\frac{V_S}{V_P} = \frac{N_S}{N_P}. \tag{21–6}$$

*Transformer equation*

This *transformer equation* tells how the secondary (output) voltage is related to the primary (input) voltage; $V_S$ and $V_P$ in Eq. 21–6 can be the rms values (Section 18–7) for both, or peak values for both. DC voltages don't work in a transformer because there would be no changing magnetic flux.

If the secondary coil contains more loops than the primary coil ($N_S > N_P$), we have a **step-up transformer**. The secondary voltage is greater than the primary voltage. For example, if the secondary coil has twice as many turns as the primary coil, then the secondary voltage will be twice that of the primary voltage. If $N_S$ is less than $N_P$, we have a **step-down transformer**.

Although ac voltage can be increased (or decreased) with a transformer, we don't get something for nothing. Energy conservation tells us that the power output can be no greater than the power input. A well-designed transformer can be greater than 99% efficient, so little energy is lost to heat. The power output thus essentially equals the power input. Since power $P = IV$ (Eq. 18–5), we have

$$I_P V_P = I_S V_S,$$

or

*Transformer equation II*

$$\frac{I_S}{I_P} = \frac{N_P}{N_S}. \qquad \textbf{(21–7)}$$

**EXAMPLE 21–11 Portable radio transformer.** A transformer for home use of a portable radio reduces 120-V ac to 9.0-V ac. (Such a device also contains diodes to change the 9.0-V ac to dc, to be like its 9.0-V battery.) The secondary coil contains 30 turns and the radio draws 400 mA. Calculate (*a*) the number of turns in the primary coil, (*b*) the current in the primary, and (*c*) the power transformed.

**APPROACH** We assume the transformer is ideal, with no flux loss, so we can use Eq. 21–6 and then Eq. 21–7.

**SOLUTION** (*a*) This is a step-down transformer, and from Eq. 21–6 we have

$$N_P = N_S \frac{V_P}{V_S} = \frac{(30)(120\text{ V})}{(9.0\text{ V})} = 400 \text{ turns}.$$

(*b*) From Eq. 21–7,

$$I_P = I_S \frac{N_S}{N_P} = (0.40\text{ A})\left(\frac{30}{400}\right) = 0.030\text{ A}.$$

(*c*) The power transformed is

$$P = I_S V_S = (0.40\text{ A})(9.0\text{ V}) = 3.6\text{ W}.$$

**NOTE** The power in the primary coil, $P = (0.030\text{ A})(120\text{ V}) = 3.6\text{ W}$, is the same as the power in the secondary coil. There is 100% efficiency in power transfer for our ideal transformer.

**EXERCISE D** How many turns would you want in the secondary coil of the transformer in Example 21–11 ($N_P = 400$ turns) if it were to reduce the voltage from 120-V ac to 3.0-V ac?

**FIGURE 21–24** A dc voltage turned on and off as shown in (a) produces voltage pulses in the secondary (b). Voltage scales in (a) and (b) are not the same.

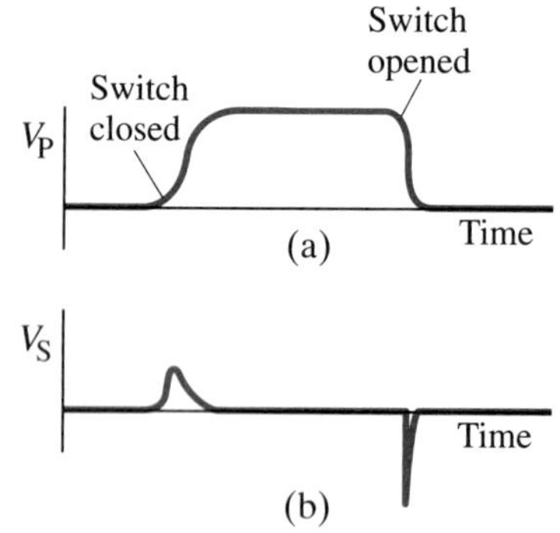


A transformer operates only on ac. A dc current in the primary coil does not produce a changing flux and therefore induces no emf in the secondary. However, if a dc voltage is applied to the primary through a switch, at the instant the switch is opened or closed there will be an induced current in the secondary. For example, if the dc is turned on and off as shown in Fig. 21–24a, the voltage induced in the secondary is as shown in Fig. 21–24b. Notice that the secondary voltage drops to zero when the dc voltage is steady. This is basically how, in the **ignition system** of an automobile, the high voltage is created to produce the spark across the gap of a spark plug that ignites the gas-air mixture. The transformer is referred to simply as an "ignition coil," and transforms the 12 V of the battery (when switched off in the primary) into a spike of as much as 30 kV in the secondary.

PHYSICS APPLIED

*Car ignition system*

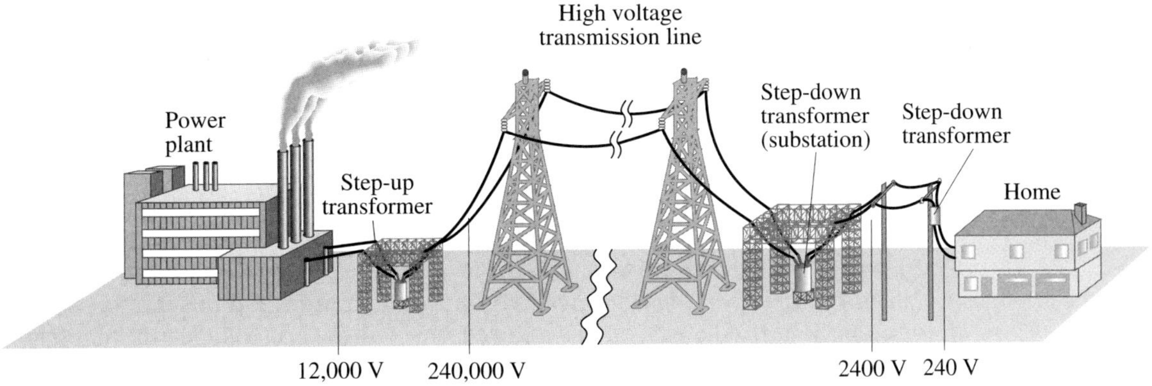


**FIGURE 21–25** The transmission of electric power from power plants to homes makes use of transformers at various stages.

PHYSICS APPLIED
*Transformers help power transmission*

Transformers play an important role in the transmission of electricity. Power plants are often situated some distance from metropolitan areas, so electricity must then be transmitted over long distances (Fig. 21–25). There is always some power loss in the transmission lines, and this loss can be minimized if the power is transmitted at high voltage, using transformers, as the following Example shows.

**EXAMPLE 21–12 Transmission lines.** An average of 120 kW of electric power is sent to a small town from a power plant 10 km away. The transmission lines have a total resistance of 0.40 Ω. Calculate the power loss if the power is transmitted at (*a*) 240 V and (*b*) 24,000 V.

**APPROACH** We cannot use $P = V^2/R$ because if $R$ is the resistance of the transmission lines, we don't know the voltage drop along them; the given voltages are applied across the lines plus the load (the town). But we can determine the current $I$ in the lines $(= P/V)$, and then find the power loss from $P_L = I^2R$, for both cases (*a*) and (*b*).

**SOLUTION** (*a*) If 120 kW is sent at 240 V, the total current will be

$$I = \frac{P}{V} = \frac{1.2 \times 10^5\ \mathrm{W}}{2.4 \times 10^2\ \mathrm{V}} = 500\ \mathrm{A}.$$

The power loss in the lines, $P_L$, is then

$$P_L = I^2R = (500\ \mathrm{A})^2(0.40\ \Omega) = 100\ \mathrm{kW}.$$

Thus, over 80% of all the power would be wasted as heat in the power lines!
(*b*) If 120 kW is sent at 24,000 V, the total current will be

$$I = \frac{P}{V} = \frac{1.2 \times 10^5\ \mathrm{W}}{2.4 \times 10^4\ \mathrm{V}} = 5.0\ \mathrm{A}.$$

The power loss in the lines is then

$$P_L = I^2R = (5.0\ \mathrm{A})^2(0.40\ \Omega) = 10\ \mathrm{W},$$

which is less than $\frac{1}{100}$ of 1%.

**NOTE** We see that the higher voltage results in less current, and thus less power is wasted as heat in the transmission lines. It is for this reason that power is usually transmitted at very high voltages, as high as 700 kV.

The great advantage of ac, and a major reason it is in nearly universal use, is that the voltage can easily be stepped up or down by a transformer. The output voltage of an electric generating plant is stepped up prior to transmission. Upon arrival in a city, it is stepped down in stages at electric substations prior to distribution. The voltage in lines along city streets is typically 2400 V and is stepped down to 240 V or 120 V for home use by transformers (Figs. 21–22 and 21–25).

# 21–8 Applications of Induction: Sound Systems, Computer Memory, Seismograph, GFCI

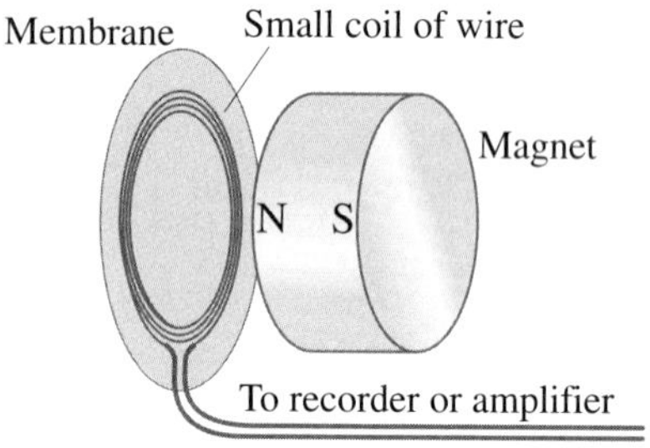


**FIGURE 21–26** Diagram of a microphone that works by induction.

## Microphone

There are various types of *microphones*, and many operate on the principle of induction. In one form, a microphone is just the inverse of a loudspeaker (Section 20–10). A small coil connected to a membrane is suspended close to a small permanent magnet, as shown in Fig. 21–26. The coil moves in the magnetic field when sound waves strike the membrane and this motion induces an emf. The frequency of the induced emf will be just that of the impinging sound waves, and this emf is the "signal" that can be amplified and sent to loudspeakers, or sent to a recorder.

## Read/Write on Tape and Disks

Recording and playback on tape or disks is done by magnetic *heads*. Recording tapes for use in audio and video tape recorders contain a thin layer of magnetic oxide on a thin plastic tape. During recording, the audio and/or video signal voltage is sent to the recording head, which acts as a tiny electromagnet (Fig. 21–27) that magnetizes the tiny section of tape passing over the narrow gap in the head at each instant. In playback, the changing magnetism of the moving tape at the gap causes corresponding changes in the magnetic field within the soft-iron head, which in turn induces an emf in the coil (Faraday's law). This induced emf is the output signal that can be amplified and sent to a loudspeaker (audio) or to the picture tube (video). In audio and video recorders, the signals may be *analog*—they vary continuously in amplitude over time. The variation in degree of magnetization of the tape at any point reflects the variation in amplitude and frequency of the audio or video signal.

PHYSICS APPLIED

*Computers and digital information*

*Digital* information, such as used on computer disks (hard drive or zip drive) or on magnetic computer tape and some types of digital tape recorders, is read and written using heads that are basically the same as just described (Fig. 21–27). The essential difference is in the signals, which are not analog, but are digital, and in particular binary, meaning that only two values are possible for each of the extremely high number of predetermined spaces on the tape or disk. The two possible values are usually referred to as 1 and 0. The signal voltage does not vary continuously but rather takes on only two values, +5 V and 0 V, for example, corresponding to the 1 or 0. Thus, information is carried as a series of "bits," each of which can have only one of two values, 1 or 0.

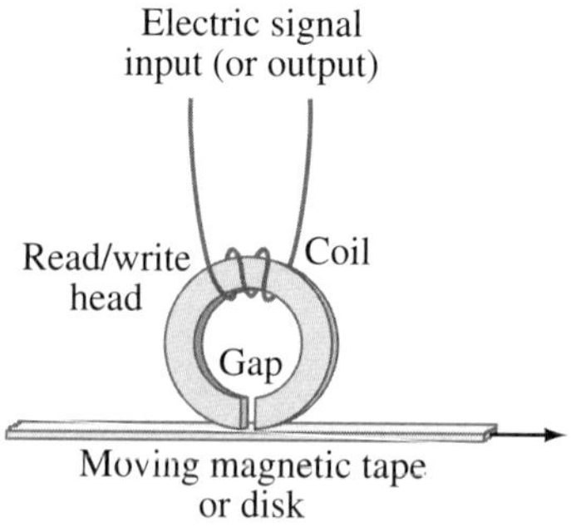


(a)

(b)

**FIGURE 21–27** (a) Read/Write (playback/recording) head for tape or disk. In writing or recording, the electric input signal to the head, which acts as an electromagnet, magnetizes the passing tape or disk. In reading or playback, the changing magnetic field of the passing tape or disk induces a changing magnetic field in the head, which in turn induces in the coil an emf that is the output signal. (b) Photo of a hard drive showing several platters and read/write heads that can quickly move from the edge of the disk to the center.

## Credit Card Swipe

When you swipe your credit card at a store or gas station, the magnetic stripe on the back of the card passes over a read head just as in a tape recorder or computer. The magnetic stripe contains personal information about your account and connects by telephone line for approval if your account is in order.

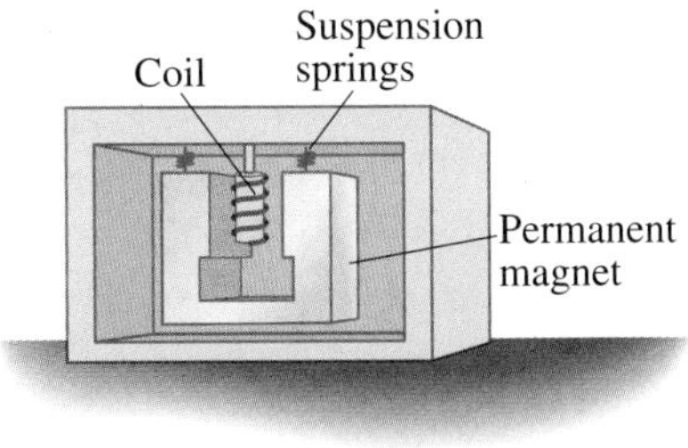


**FIGURE 21–28** One type of seismograph, in which the coil is fixed to the case and moves with the Earth.

## Seismograph

In geophysics, a **seismograph** measures the intensity of earthquake waves using a magnet and a coil of wire. Either the magnet or the coil is fixed to the case, and the other is inertial (suspended by a spring; Fig. 21–28). The relative motion of magnet and coil when the Earth shakes induces an emf output.

## Ground Fault Circuit Interrupter (GFCI)

Fuses and circuit breakers (Sections 18–6 and 20–7) protect buildings from fire, and apparatus from damage, due to undesired high currents. But they do not turn off the current until it is very much greater than that which causes permanent damage to humans or death ($\approx 100\,\mathrm{mA}$). If fast enough, they may protect in case of a short. A *ground fault circuit interrupter* (GFCI) is meant to protect humans; GFCIs can react to currents as small as 5 mA.

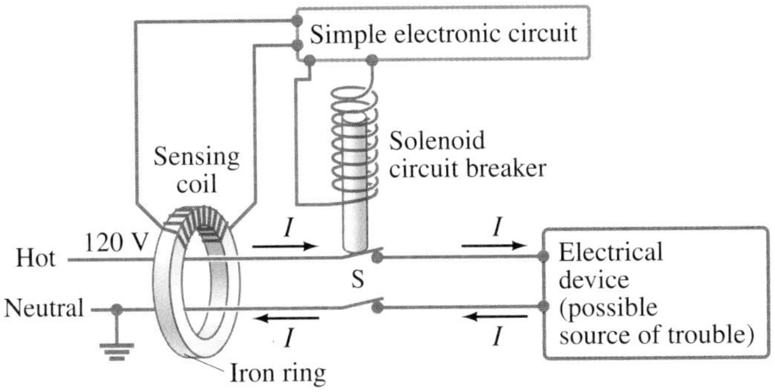


**FIGURE 21–29** A ground fault circuit interrupter (GFCI).

Electromagnetic induction is the physical basis of a GFCI. As shown in Fig. 21–29, the two conductors of a power line leading to an electrical device (red) pass through a small iron ring. Around the ring are many loops of thin wire that serve as a sensing coil. Under normal conditions (no ground fault), the current moving in the hot wire is exactly balanced by the returning current in the neutral wire. If something goes wrong and the hot wire touches the ungrounded metal case of the device or appliance, some of the entering current can pass through a person who touches the case and then to ground (a *ground fault*). Then the return current in the neutral wire will be less than the entering current in the hot wire, so there is a *net current* passing through the GFCI's iron ring. Because the current is ac, it is changing and produces a changing magnetic field in the iron, thus inducing an emf in the sensing coil wrapped around the iron. For example, if a device draws 8.0 A, and there is a ground fault through a person of 100 mA (= 0.1 A), then 7.9 A will appear in the neutral wire. The emf induced in the sensing coil by this 100-mA difference is amplified by a simple transistor circuit and sent to its own solenoid circuit breaker that opens the circuit at the switch S.

If the case of the faulty device is grounded, the current difference is even higher when there is a fault, and the GFCI trips immediately.

GFCIs can sense currents as low as 5 mA and react in 1 msec, saving lives. They can be small enough to fit as a wall outlet (Fig. 21–30), or as a plug-in unit into which you plug a hair dryer or toaster. It is especially important to have GFCIs installed in kitchens, bathrooms, outdoors, and near swimming pools, where people are most in danger of touching ground. GFCIs always have a "test" button (to be sure it works) and a "reset" button (after it goes off).

**FIGURE 21–30** A GFCI wall outlet. GFCIs can be recognized because they have "test" and "reset" buttons.

## * 21–9 Inductance

### * Mutual Inductance

If two coils of wire are near one another, as in Fig. 21–31, a changing current in one will induce an emf in the other. We apply Faraday's law to coil 2: the emf $\mathscr{E}_2$ induced in coil 2 is proportional to the rate of change of flux passing through it. A changing flux in coil 2 is produced by a changing current in coil 1. So $\mathscr{E}_2$ is proportional to the rate of change of the current in coil 1:

*Mutual inductance*

$$\mathscr{E}_2 = -M\frac{\Delta I_1}{\Delta t}, \tag{21–8a}$$

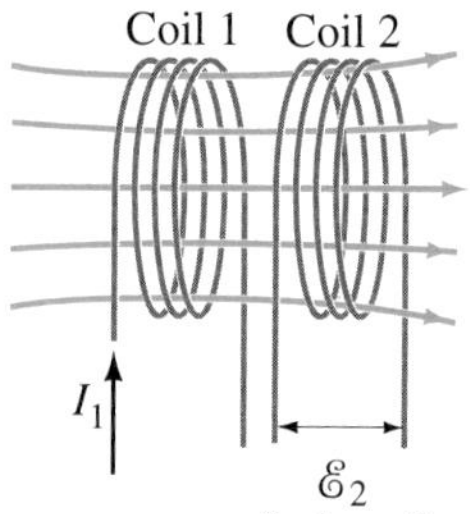


**FIGURE 21–31** A changing current in one coil will induce a current in the second coil.

where we assume the time interval $\Delta t$ is very small, and the constant of proportionality, $M$, is called the **mutual inductance**. (The minus sign is because of Lenz's law.) Mutual inductance has units of $\mathrm{V \cdot s/A} = \Omega \cdot \mathrm{s}$, which is called the **henry** (H), after Joseph Henry: $1\ \mathrm{H} = 1\ \Omega \cdot \mathrm{s}$.

The mutual inductance $M$ is a "constant" in that it does not depend on $I_1$; $M$ depends on "geometric" factors such as the size, shape, number of turns, and relative positions of the two coils, and also on whether iron (or other ferromagnetic material) is present. For example, the farther apart the two coils are in Fig. 21–31, the fewer lines of flux can pass through coil 2, so $M$ will be less. If we consider the inverse situation—a changing current in coil 2 inducing an emf in coil 1—the proportionality constant, $M$, turns out to have the same value,

$$\mathscr{E}_1 = -M\frac{\Delta I_2}{\Delta t}. \tag{21–8b}$$

PHYSICS APPLIED
*Pacemaker*

A transformer is an example of mutual inductance in which the coupling is maximized so that nearly all flux lines pass through both coils. Mutual inductance has other uses as well, including some types of *pacemakers* used to maintain blood flow in heart patients (Section 19–6). Power in an external coil is transmitted via mutual inductance to a second coil in the pacemaker at the heart. This type has the advantage over battery-powered pacemakers in that surgery is not needed to replace a battery when it wears out.

### * Self-Inductance

The concept of inductance applies also to an isolated single coil. When a changing current passes through a coil or solenoid, a changing magnetic flux is produced inside the coil, and this in turn induces an emf. This induced emf opposes the change in flux (Lenz's law); it is much like the back emf generated in a motor. (For example, if the current through the coil is increasing, the increasing magnetic flux induces an emf that opposes the original current and tends to retard its increase.) The induced emf $\mathscr{E}$ is proportional to the rate of change in current (and is in the direction opposed to the change):

*Self-inductance (induced emf for an inductor)*

$$\mathscr{E} = -L\frac{\Delta I}{\Delta t}. \tag{21–9}$$

The constant of proportionality $L$ is called the **self-inductance**, or simply the **inductance** of the coil. It, too, is measured in henrys. The magnitude of $L$ depends on the size and shape of the coil and on the presence of an iron core.

An ac circuit (Section 18–7) always contains some inductance, but often it is quite small unless the circuit contains a coil of many loops or turns. A coil that has significant self-inductance $L$ is called an **inductor**. It is shown on circuit diagrams by the symbol

*Inductors*

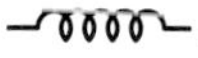. [inductor symbol]

**CONCEPTUAL EXAMPLE 21–13** **Direction of emf in inductor.** Current passes through the coil in Fig. 21–32 from left to right as shown. (*a*) If the current is increasing with time, in which direction is the induced emf? (*b*) If the current is decreasing in time, what then is the direction of the induced emf?

**RESPONSE** (*a*) From Lenz's law we know that the induced emf must oppose the change in magnetic flux. If the current is increasing, so is the magnetic flux. The induced emf acts to oppose the increasing flux, which means it acts like a source of emf that opposes the outside source of emf driving the current. So the induced emf in the coil acts to oppose $I$ in Fig. 21–32a. In other words, the inductor might be thought of as a battery with a positive terminal at point A (tending to block the current entering at A), and negative at point B.
(*b*) If the current is decreasing, then by Lenz's law the induced emf acts to bolster the flux—like a source of emf reinforcing the external emf. The induced emf acts to increase $I$ in Fig. 21–32b, so in this situation you can think of the induced emf as a battery with its negative terminal at point A to attract more (+) current to move to the right.

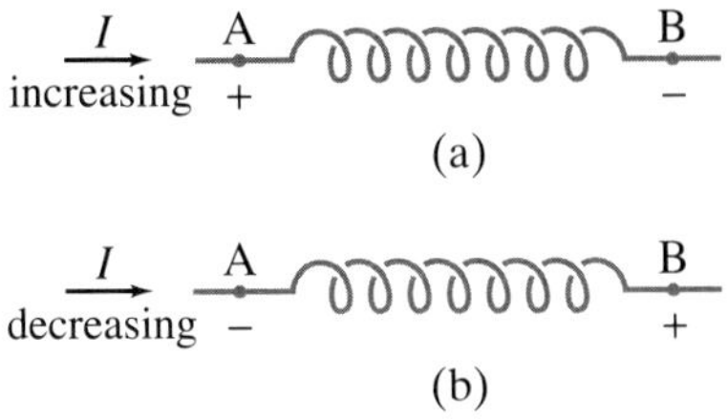


**FIGURE 21–32** Example 21–13. The + and − signs refer to the induced emf due to the changing current, as if points A and B were the terminals of a battery (and the coiled loops were the insides of the battery).

**EXAMPLE 21–14** **Solenoid inductance.** (*a*) Determine a formula for the self-inductance $L$ of a tightly wrapped solenoid (a long coil) of length $l$ and cross-sectional area $A$, that contains $N$ turns (or loops) of wire. (*b*) Calculate the value of $L$ if $N = 100$, $l = 5.0\,\text{cm}$, $A = 0.30\,\text{cm}^2$ and the solenoid is air filled.

**APPROACH** The induced emf in a coil can be determined either from Faraday's law $(\mathscr{E} = -N\,\Delta\Phi_B/\Delta t)$ or the self-inductance $(\mathscr{E} = -L\,\Delta I/\Delta t)$. If we equate these two expressions, we can solve for the inductance $L$ since we know how to calculate the flux $\Phi_B$ for a solenoid using Eq. 20–8.

**SOLUTION** (*a*) We equate Faraday's law (Eq. 21–2b) and Eq. 21–9 for the inductance:

$$\mathscr{E} = -N\frac{\Delta\Phi_B}{\Delta t} = -L\frac{\Delta I}{\Delta t},$$

and solve for $L$:

$$L = N\frac{\Delta\Phi_B}{\Delta I}.$$

We know $\Phi_B = BA$ (Eq. 21–1), and Eq. 20–8 gives us the magnetic field $B$ for a solenoid, $B = \mu_0 NI/l$, so the magnetic flux inside the solenoid is

*Calculating self-inductance of a coil*

$$\Phi_B = \frac{\mu_0 NIA}{l}.$$

Any change in current, $\Delta I$, causes a change in flux

$$\Delta\Phi_B = \frac{\mu_0 N\,\Delta I\,A}{l}.$$

We put this into our equation above for $L$:

$$L = N\frac{\Delta\Phi_B}{\Delta I} = \frac{\mu_0 N^2 A}{l}.$$

(*b*) Using $\mu_0 = 4\pi \times 10^{-7}\,\text{T}\cdot\text{m/A}$, and putting in values given,

$$L = \frac{(4\pi \times 10^{-7}\,\text{T}\cdot\text{m/A})(100)^2(3.0 \times 10^{-5}\,\text{m}^2)}{(5.0 \times 10^{-2}\,\text{m})} = 7.5\,\mu\text{H}.$$

## * 21–10 Energy Stored in a Magnetic Field

In Section 17–9 we saw that the energy stored in a capacitor is equal to $\frac{1}{2}CV^2$. By using a similar argument, it can be shown that the energy $U$ stored in an inductance $L$, carrying a current $I$, is

$$U = \text{energy} = \tfrac{1}{2}LI^2.$$

Just as the energy stored in a capacitor can be considered to reside in the electric field between its plates, so the energy in an inductor can be considered to be stored in its magnetic field.

To write the energy in terms of the magnetic field, we use the result of Example 21–14 that the inductance of a solenoid is $L = \mu_0 N^2 A/l$. Now the magnetic field $B$ in a solenoid is related to the current $I$ (see Eq. 20–8) by $B = \mu_0 NI/l$. Thus, $I = Bl/\mu_0 N$, and

$$U = \text{energy} = \tfrac{1}{2}LI^2 = \frac{1}{2}\left(\frac{\mu_0 N^2 A}{l}\right)\left(\frac{Bl}{\mu_0 N}\right)^2 = \frac{1}{2}\frac{B^2}{\mu_0}Al.$$

We can think of this energy as residing in the volume enclosed by the windings, which is $Al$. Then the energy per unit volume, or **energy density**, is

*Energy density in magnetic field*

$$u = \text{energy density} = \frac{1}{2}\frac{B^2}{\mu_0}. \qquad \textbf{(21–10)}$$

This formula, which was derived for the special case of a solenoid, can be shown to be valid for any region of space where a magnetic field exists. If a ferromagnetic material is present, $\mu_0$ is replaced by $\mu$. This equation is analogous to that for an electric field, $\frac{1}{2}\epsilon_0 E^2$, Section 17–9.

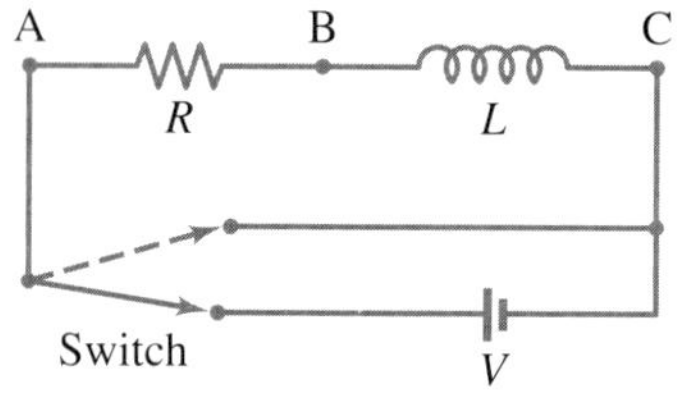


**FIGURE 21–33** *LR* circuit.

**FIGURE 21–34** (a) Growth of current in an *LR* circuit when connected to a battery; (b) decay of current when the *LR* circuit is shorted out (battery is out of the circuit).

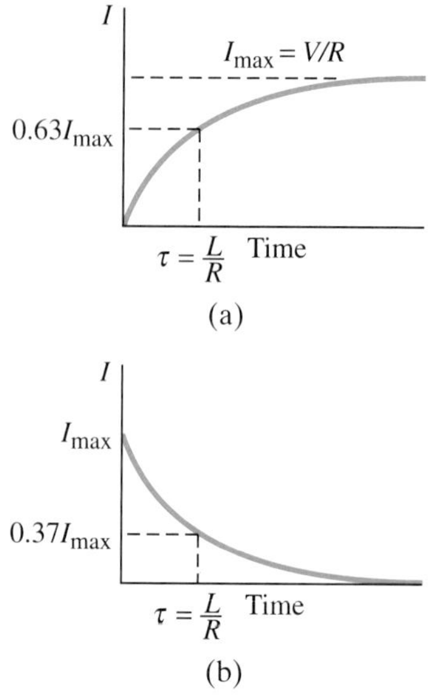


## * 21–11 *LR* Circuit

Any inductor will have some resistance. We represent this situation by drawing the inductance $L$ and the resistance $R$ separately, as in Fig. 21–33. The resistance $R$ could also include a separate resistor connected in series. Now we ask, what happens when a dc source is connected in series to such an $LR$ circuit? At the instant the switch connecting the battery is closed, the current starts to flow. It is opposed by the induced emf in the inductor because of the changing current. However, as soon as current starts to flow, there is a voltage drop across the resistance ($V = IR$). Hence, the voltage drop across the inductance is reduced, and there is then less impedance to the current flow from the inductance. The current thus rises gradually, as shown in Fig. 21–34a, and approaches the steady value $I_{\max} = V/R$ when all the voltage drop is across the resistance. The shape of the curve for $I$ as a function of time is

$$I = \left(\frac{V}{R}\right)\left(1 - e^{-t/\tau}\right), \qquad [LR \text{ circuit with emf}]$$

where $e$ is the number $e = 2.718\cdots$ (see Section 19–6) and $\tau = L/R$ is the **time constant** of the circuit. When $t = \tau$, then $\left(1 - e^{-1}\right) = 0.63$, so $\tau$ is the time required for the current to reach $0.63I_{\max}$.

If the battery is suddenly removed from the circuit (dashed line in Fig. 21–33), the current decreases as shown in Fig. 21–34b. This is an exponential decay curve given by

$$I = I_{\max}e^{-t/\tau}. \qquad [LR \text{ circuit without emf}]$$

The time constant $\tau$ is the time for the current to decrease to 37% of the original value, and again equals $L/R$.

These graphs show that there is always some "reaction time" when an electromagnet, for example, is turned on or off. We also see that an $LR$ circuit has properties similar to an $RC$ circuit (Section 19–6). Unlike the capacitor case, however, the time constant here is *inversely* proportional to $R$.

**EXAMPLE 21–15** **Solenoid time constant.** A solenoid has an inductance of 87.5 mH and a resistance of 0.250 Ω. Find (*a*) the time constant for this circuit, and (*b*) how long it would take for the current to go from zero to 63% of its final (maximum) value when connected to a battery of voltage $V$.

**APPROACH** The time constant is $\tau = L/R$. Then we use the equation for $I$, setting $I = 0.63 I_{max}$ and solving it for $t$.

**SOLUTION** (*a*) By definition, $\tau = L/R = (87.5 \times 10^{-3}\,\mathrm{H})/(0.250\,\Omega) = 0.350\,\mathrm{s}$. (*b*) We saw above that $I = (V/R)(1 - e^{-t/\tau})$. We wish to find $t$ such that $I = (0.63)(V/R)$ where $V/R = I_{max}$. This occurs when $t = \tau = L/R$, so $t = 0.350\,\mathrm{s}$.

## * 21–12 AC Circuits and Reactance

We have previously discussed circuits that contain combinations of resistor, capacitor, and inductor, but only when they are connected to a dc source of emf or to no source (as in the discharge of a capacitor in an $RC$ circuit). Now we discuss these circuit elements when they are connected to a source of alternating voltage that produces an alternating current (ac).

First we examine, one at a time, how a resistor, a capacitor, and an inductor behave when connected to a source of alternating voltage, represented by the symbol

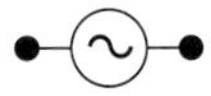 [alternating voltage]

which produces a sinusoidal voltage of frequency $f$. We assume in each case that the emf gives rise to a current

$$I = I_0 \cos 2\pi f t,$$

where $t$ is time and $I_0$ is the peak current. Remember (Section 18–7) that $V_{rms} = V_0/\sqrt{2}$ and $I_{rms} = I_0/\sqrt{2}$ (Eq. 18–8).

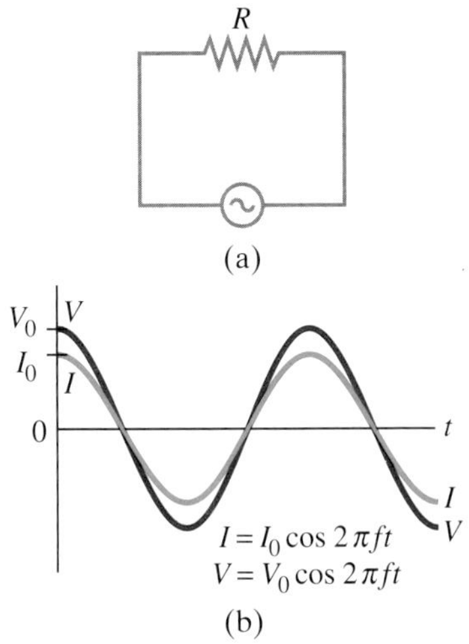


**FIGURE 21–35** (a) Resistor connected to an ac source. (b) Current (blue curve) is in phase with the voltage (red) across a resistor.

*Resistor: current and voltage are in phase*

### * Resistor

When an ac source is connected to a resistor as in Fig. 21–35a, the current increases and decreases with the alternating emf according to Ohm's law, $I = V/R$. Figure 21–35b shows the voltage (red curve) and the current (blue curve). Because the current is zero when the voltage is zero and the current reaches a peak when the voltage does, we say that the current and voltage are **in phase**. Energy is transformed into heat (Section 18–7), at an average rate $\overline{P} = \overline{IV} = I_{rms}^2 R = V_{rms}^2/R$.

### * Inductor

In Fig. 21–36a an inductor of inductance $L$ (symbol –ᥫᥫᥫ–) is connected to the ac source. We ignore any resistance it might have (it is usually small). The voltage applied to the inductor will be equal to the "back" emf generated in the inductor by the changing current as given by Eq. 21–9. This is because the sum of the emfs around any closed circuit must be zero, as Kirchhoff's rule tells us. Thus

$$V - L\frac{\Delta I}{\Delta t} = 0 \qquad \text{or} \qquad V = L\frac{\Delta I}{\Delta t},$$

where $V$ is the sinusoidally varying voltage of the source and $L\,\Delta I/\Delta t$ is the voltage induced in the inductor. According to this equation, $I$ is increasing most rapidly when $V$ has its maximum value, $V = V_0$. And $I$ will be decreasing most rapidly when $V = -V_0$. These two instants correspond to points d and b on the graph of voltage versus time in Fig. 21–36b. By going point by point in this manner, the curve of $I$ versus $t$ as compared to that for $V$ versus $t$ can be constructed, and they are shown by the blue and red lines, respectively, in Fig. 21–36b. Notice that the current reaches its peaks (and troughs) $\frac{1}{4}$ cycle after the voltage does. We say that

**the current lags the voltage by 90° in an inductor.**

Because the current and voltage in an inductor are out of phase by 90°, the product $IV$ (= power) is as often positive as it is negative (Fig. 21–36b). So no energy is transformed in an inductor on the average; and no energy is dissipated as thermal energy.

**FIGURE 21–36** (a) Inductor connected to an ac source. (b) Current (blue curve) lags voltage (red curve) by a quarter cycle or 90°.

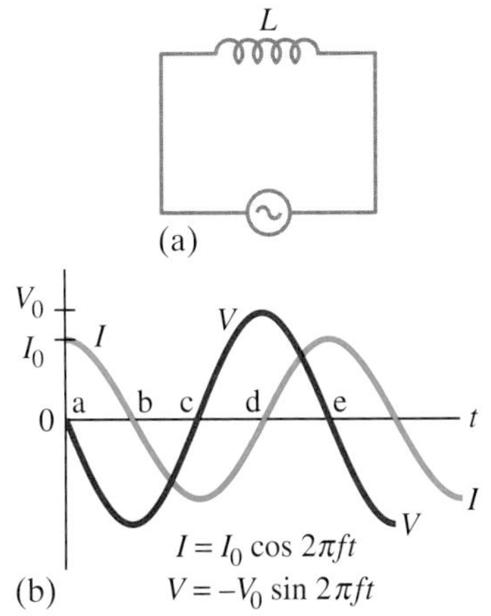


*Inductor: current lags voltage*

Just as a resistor impedes the flow of charge, so too an inductor impedes the flow of charge in an alternating current due to the back emf produced. For a resistor $R$, the current and voltage are related by $V = IR$. We can write a similar relation for an inductor:

$$V = IX_L, \qquad \begin{bmatrix}\text{rms or peak values,}\\ \text{not at any instant}\end{bmatrix} \qquad \textbf{(21–11a)}$$

*Reactance*

where $X_L$ is called the **inductive reactance**. $X_L$ has units of ohms. The quantities $V$ and $I$ in Eq. 21–11a can refer either to rms for both, or to peak values for both (see Section 18–7). Although this equation can relate the peak values, the peak current and voltage are not reached at the same time; so Eq. 21–11a is *not valid at a particular instant*, as is the case for a resistor ($V = IR$). Careful calculation (using calculus), as well as experiment, shows that

*Inductive reactance*

$$X_L = \omega L = 2\pi f L, \qquad \textbf{(21–11b)}$$

where $\omega = 2\pi f$ and $f$ is the frequency of the ac.

**EXAMPLE 21–16 Reactance of a coil.** A coil has a resistance $R = 1.00\,\Omega$ and an inductance of 0.300 H. Determine the current in the coil if (*a*) 120-V dc is applied to it, (*b*) 120-V ac (rms) at 60.0 Hz is applied.

**APPROACH** When the voltage is dc, there is no inductive reactance ($X_L = 2\pi fL = 0$ since $f = 0$), so we apply Ohm's law for the resistance. When the voltage is ac, we calculate the reactance $X_L$ and then use Eq. 21–11a.

**SOLUTION** (*a*) With dc, we have no $X_L$ so we simply apply Ohm's law:

$$I = \frac{V}{R} = \frac{120\text{ V}}{1.00\,\Omega} = 120\text{ A}.$$

(*b*) The inductive reactance is

$$X_L = 2\pi f L = (6.28)(60.0\text{ s}^{-1})(0.300\text{ H}) = 113\,\Omega.$$

In comparison to this, the resistance can be ignored. Thus,

$$I_{\text{rms}} = \frac{V_{\text{rms}}}{X_L} = \frac{120\text{ V}}{113\,\Omega} = 1.06\text{ A}.$$

**NOTE** It might be tempting to say that the total impedance is $113\,\Omega + 1\,\Omega = 114\,\Omega$. This might imply that about 1% of the voltage drop is across the resistor, or about 1 V; and that across the inductance is 119 V. Although the 1 V across the resistor is correct, the other statements are not true because of the alteration in phase in an inductor. This will be discussed in the next Section.

**FIGURE 21–37** (a) Capacitor connected to an ac source. (b) Current leads voltage by a quarter cycle, or 90°.

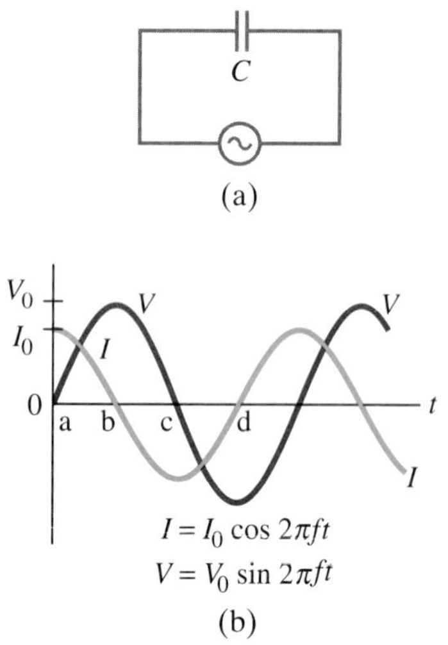


## * Capacitor

When a capacitor is connected to a battery, the capacitor plates quickly acquire equal and opposite charges; but no steady current flows in the circuit. A capacitor prevents the flow of a dc current. But if a capacitor is connected to an alternating source of voltage, as in Fig. 21–37a, an alternating current will flow continuously. This can happen because when the ac voltage is first turned on, charge begins to flow and one plate acquires a negative charge and the other a positive charge. But when the voltage reverses itself, the charges flow in the opposite direction. Thus, for an alternating applied voltage, an ac current is present in the circuit continuously.

The applied voltage must equal the voltage across the capacitor: $V = Q/C$, where $C$ is the capacitance and $Q$ the charge on the plates. Thus the charge $Q$ on the plates follows the voltage. But what about the current $I$? At point a in Fig. 21–37b, when the voltage is zero and starts increasing, the charge on the plates is zero. Thus charge flows readily toward the plates and the current $I$ is large. As the voltage approaches its maximum of $V_0$ (point b), the charge that has accumulated on the plates tends to prevent more charge from flowing, so the current $I$ drops to zero at point b. Thus the current follows the blue curve in Fig. 21–37b.

Like an inductor, the voltage and current are out of phase by 90°. But for a capacitor, the current reaches its peaks $\frac{1}{4}$ cycle before the voltage does, so we say that the

**current leads the voltage by 90° in a capacitor.**

*Capacitor: current leads voltage*

Because the current and voltage are out of phase, the average power dissipated is zero, just as for an inductor. Thus *only a resistance will dissipate energy* as thermal energy in an ac circuit.

*Only R (not C or L) dissipates energy*

A relationship between the applied voltage and the current in a capacitor can be written just as for an inductance:

$$V = IX_C, \qquad \left[\begin{array}{l}\text{rms or peak}\\ \text{values}\end{array}\right] \tag{21–12a}$$

where $X_C$ is the **capacitive reactance** and has units of ohms. $V$ and $I$ can both be rms or both maximum ($V_0$ and $I_0$); $X_C$ depends on both the capacitance $C$ and the frequency $f$:

$$X_C = \frac{1}{\omega C} = \frac{1}{2\pi f C}, \tag{21–12b}$$

*Capacitive reactance*

where $\omega = 2\pi f$. For dc conditions, $f = 0$ and $X_C$ becomes infinite, as it should because a capacitor does not pass dc current.

**EXAMPLE 21–17** **Capacitor reactance.** What is the rms current in the circuit of Fig. 21–37a if $C = 1.0\,\mu\text{F}$ and $V_{\text{rms}} = 120\text{ V}$? Calculate for (*a*) $f = 60\text{ Hz}$, and then for (*b*) $f = 6.0 \times 10^5\text{ Hz}$.

**APPROACH** We find the reactance using Eq. 21–12b, and solve for current in the equivalent form of Ohm's law, Eq. 21–12a.

**SOLUTION** (*a*) $X_C = 1/2\pi f C = 1/(6.28)(60\text{ s}^{-1})(1.0 \times 10^{-6}\text{ F}) = 2.7\text{ k}\Omega$. The rms current is (Eq. 21–12a):

$$I_{\text{rms}} = \frac{V_{\text{rms}}}{X_C} = \frac{120\text{ V}}{2.7 \times 10^3\,\Omega} = 44\text{ mA}.$$

(*b*) For $f = 6.0 \times 10^5\text{ Hz}$, $X_C$ will be $0.27\,\Omega$ and $I_{\text{rms}} = 440\text{ A}$, vastly larger!

**NOTE** The dependence on $f$ is dramatic. For high frequencies, the capacitive reactance is very small.

PHYSICS APPLIED
*Capacitors as filters*

Two common applications of capacitors are illustrated in Fig. 21–38a and b. In Fig. 21–38a, circuit A is said to be capacitively coupled to circuit B. The purpose of the capacitor is to prevent a dc voltage from passing from A to B but allowing an ac signal to pass relatively unimpeded (if $C$ is sufficiently large). In Fig. 21–38b, the

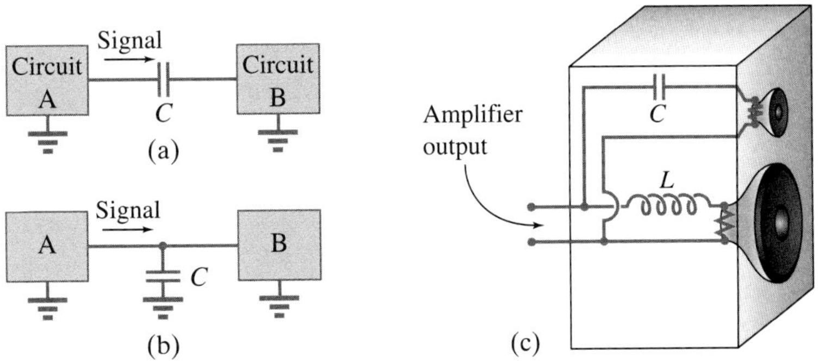


**FIGURE 21–38** (a) (b) Two common uses for a capacitor. (c) Simple loudspeaker cross-over.

capacitor also passes ac but not dc. In this case, a dc voltage can be maintained between circuits A and B, but an ac signal leaving A passes to ground instead of into B. Thus the capacitor in Fig. 21–38b acts like a *filter* when a constant dc voltage is required; any sharp variation in voltage will pass to ground instead of into circuit B.

PHYSICS APPLIED
*Loudspeaker cross-over*

Loudspeakers having separate "woofer" (low-frequency speaker) and "tweeter" (high-frequency speaker) may use a simple "cross-over" that consists of a capacitor in the tweeter circuit to impede low-frequency signals, and an inductor in the woofer circuit to impede high-frequency signals $(X_L = 2\pi f L)$. Hence mainly low-frequency sounds reach and are emitted by the woofer. See Fig. 21–38c.

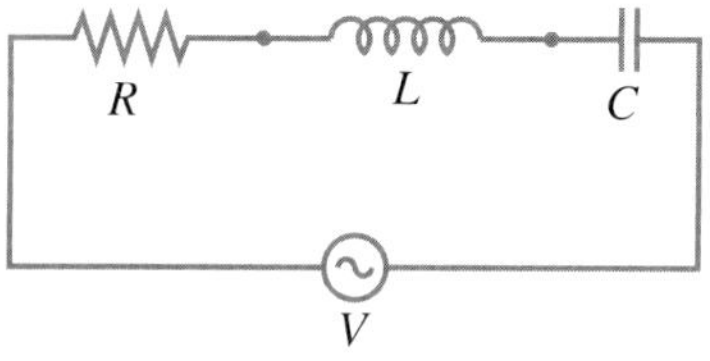


**FIGURE 21–39** An *LRC* circuit.

## * 21–13 *LRC* Series AC Circuit

Let us examine a circuit containing all three elements in series: a resistor $R$, an inductor $L$, and a capacitor $C$, Fig. 21–39. If a given circuit contains only two of these elements, we can still use the results of this Section by setting $R = 0$, $X_L = 0$, or $X_C = 0$, as needed. We let $V_R$, $V_L$, and $V_C$ represent the voltage across each element at a *given instant* in time; and $V_{R0}$, $V_{L0}$, and $V_{C0}$ represent the *maximum* (peak) values of these voltages. The voltage across each of the elements will follow the phase relations we discussed in the previous Section. At any instant the voltage $V$ supplied by the source will be, by Kirchhoff's loop rule,

$$V = V_R + V_L + V_C. \tag{21–13}$$

**CAUTION**

*Peak voltages do not add to yield source voltage*

Because the various voltages are not in phase, they do not reach their peak values at the same time, so the peak voltage of the source $V_0$ will *not* equal $V_{R0} + V_{L0} + V_{C0}$.

### * Phasor Diagrams

Let us now examine an *LRC* circuit in detail. The current at any instant must be the same at all points in the circuit. Thus the currents in each element are in phase with each other, even though the voltages are not. We choose our origin in time ($t = 0$) so that the current $I$ at any time $t$ is

$$I = I_0 \cos 2\pi f t.$$

We analyze an *LRC* circuit using a **phasor diagram**. Arrows (treated like vectors) are drawn in an $xy$ coordinate system to represent each voltage. The length of each arrow represents the magnitude of the peak voltage across each element:

$$V_{R0} = I_0 R, \qquad V_{L0} = I_0 X_L, \qquad \text{and} \qquad V_{C0} = I_0 X_C.$$

$V_{R0}$ is in phase with the current and is initially ($t = 0$) drawn along the positive $x$ axis, as is the current. $V_{L0}$ leads the current by 90°, so it leads $V_{R0}$ by 90° and is initially drawn along the positive $y$ axis. $V_{C0}$ lags the current by 90°, so $V_{C0}$ is drawn initially along the negative $y$ axis. See Fig. 21–40a. If we let the vector diagram rotate counterclockwise at frequency $f$, we get the diagram shown in Fig. 21–40b; after a time, $t$, each arrow has rotated through an angle $2\pi f t$. Then the projections of each arrow on the $x$ axis represent the voltages across each element at the instant $t$ (Fig. 21–40c). For example $I = I_0 \cos 2\pi f t$.

The sum of the projections of the three voltage vectors represents the instantaneous voltage across the whole circuit, $V$. Therefore, the vector sum of these vectors will be the vector that represents the peak source voltage, $V_0$, as shown in Fig. 21–41 where it is seen that $V_0$ makes an angle $\phi$ with $I_0$ and $V_{R0}$. As time passes, $V_0$ rotates with the other vectors, so the instantaneous voltage $V$ (projection of $V_0$ on the $x$ axis) is (see Fig. 21–41)

$$V = V_0 \cos(2\pi f t + \phi).$$

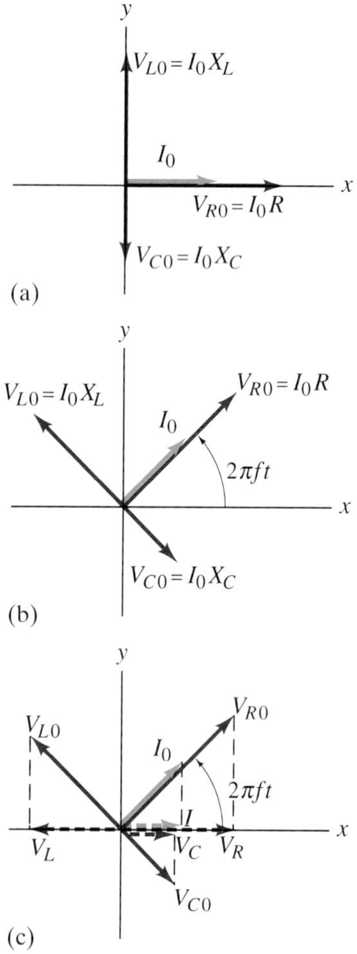


**FIGURE 21–40** Phasor diagram for a series *LRC* circuit.

The voltage $V$ across the whole circuit must, of course, equal the source voltage (Fig. 21–39). Thus the voltage from the source is out of phase with the current by an angle $\phi$.

From this analysis we can now determine the total **impedance** $Z$ of the circuit, which is defined by the relation

*Impedance*

$$V_{rms} = I_{rms} Z, \qquad \text{or} \qquad V_0 = I_0 Z. \tag{21–14}$$

From Fig. 21–41 we see, using the Pythagorean theorem ($V_0$ is the hypotenuse of

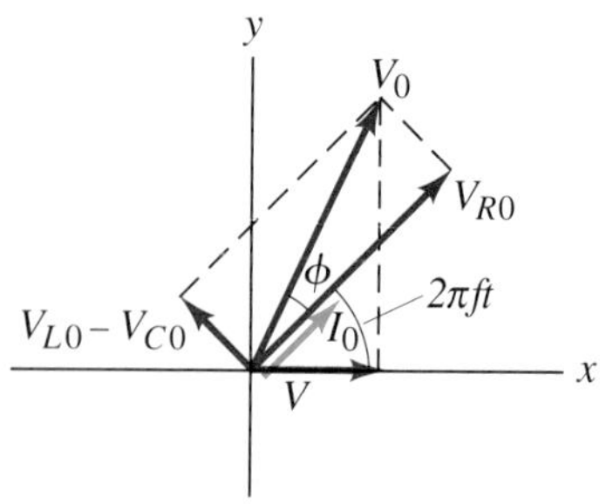


**FIGURE 21–41** Phasor diagram for a series *LRC* circuit showing the sum vector, $V_0$.

a right triangle), that

$$V_0 = \sqrt{V_{R0}^2 + (V_{L0} - V_{C0})^2}$$
$$= I_0\sqrt{R^2 + (X_L - X_C)^2}.$$

Thus, from Eq. 21–14, the total impedance $Z$ is

$$Z = \sqrt{R^2 + (X_L - X_C)^2}. \qquad \textbf{(21–15)}$$

*Total impedance*

Also from Fig. 21–41, we can find the phase angle $\phi$ between voltage and current:

$$\tan\phi = \frac{V_{L0} - V_{C0}}{V_{R0}} = \frac{I_0(X_L - X_C)}{I_0 R} = \frac{X_L - X_C}{R} \qquad \textbf{(21–16a)}$$

and

$$\cos\phi = \frac{V_{R0}}{V_0} = \frac{I_0 R}{I_0 Z} = \frac{R}{Z}. \qquad \textbf{(21–16b)}$$

Figure 21–41 was drawn for the case $X_L > X_C$, and the current lags the source voltage by $\phi$. When the reverse is true, $X_L < X_C$, then $\phi$ in Eqs. 21–16 is less than zero, and the current leads the source voltage.

We saw earlier that power is dissipated only by a resistance; none is dissipated by inductance or capacitance. Therefore, the average power $\overline{P} = I_{\text{rms}}^2 R$. But from Eq. 21–16b, $R = Z\cos\phi$. Therefore

$$\overline{P} = I_{\text{rms}}^2 Z\cos\phi = I_{\text{rms}} V_{\text{rms}} \cos\phi. \qquad \textbf{(21–17)}$$

*Power factor*

The factor $\cos\phi$ is referred to as the *power factor* of the circuit.

**EXAMPLE 21–18** ***LRC* circuit.** Suppose $R = 25.0\,\Omega$, $L = 30.0\,\text{mH}$, and $C = 12.0\,\mu\text{F}$ in Fig. 21–39, and they are connected to a 90.0-V ac (rms) 500-Hz source. Calculate (*a*) the current in the circuit, and (*b*) the voltmeter readings (rms) across each element.

**APPROACH** To obtain the current, we need to determine the impedance (Eq. 21–15 plus Eqs. 21–11b and 21–12b), and then use $I_{\text{rms}} = V_{\text{rms}}/Z$. Voltage drops across each element are found using Ohm's law or equivalent for each element: $V_R = IR$, $V_L = IX_L$, and $V_C = IX_C$.

**SOLUTION** (*a*) First, we find the reactance of the inductor and capacitor at $f = 500\,\text{Hz} = 500\,\text{s}^{-1}$:

$$X_L = 2\pi f L = 94.2\,\Omega, \qquad X_C = \frac{1}{2\pi f C} = 26.5\,\Omega.$$

Then the total impedance is

$$Z = \sqrt{R^2 + (X_L - X_C)^2} = \sqrt{(25.0\,\Omega)^2 + (94.2\,\Omega - 26.5\,\Omega)^2} = 72.2\,\Omega.$$

From the impedance version of Ohm's law, Eq. 21–14,

$$I_{\text{rms}} = \frac{V_{\text{rms}}}{Z} = \frac{90.0\,\text{V}}{72.2\,\Omega} = 1.25\,\text{A}.$$

(*b*) The rms voltage across each element is

$$(V_R)_{\text{rms}} = I_{\text{rms}} R = (1.25\,\text{A})(25.0\,\Omega) = 31.2\,\text{V}$$
$$(V_L)_{\text{rms}} = I_{\text{rms}} X_L = (1.25\,\text{A})(94.2\,\Omega) = 118\,\text{V}$$
$$(V_C)_{\text{rms}} = I_{\text{rms}} X_C = (1.25\,\text{A})(26.5\,\Omega) = 33.1\,\text{V}.$$

**NOTE** These voltages do *not* add up to the source voltage, 90.0 V (rms). Indeed, the rms voltage across the inductance *exceeds* the source voltage. This can happen because the different voltages are out of phase with each other, and at any instant one voltage can be negative, to compensate for a large positive voltage of another. The rms voltages, however, are always positive by definition. Although the rms voltages need not add up to the source voltage, the instantaneous voltages at any time must add up to the source voltage at that instant.

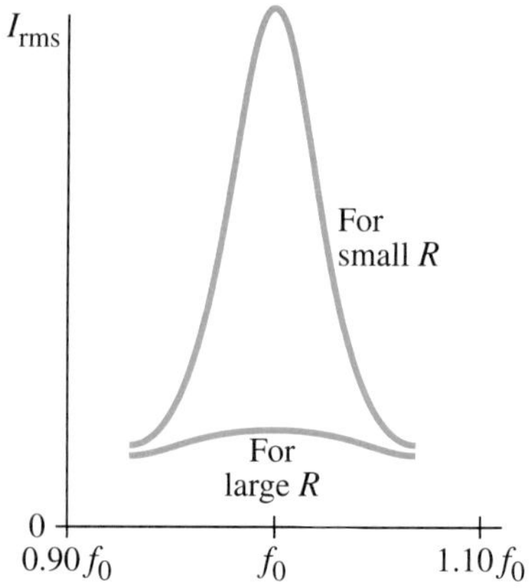


**FIGURE 21–42** Current in an $LRC$ circuit as a function of frequency, showing resonance peak at $f = f_0 = (1/2\pi)\sqrt{1/LC}$.

## * 21–14 Resonance in AC Circuits

The rms current in an $LRC$ series circuit is given by (see Eqs. 21–14, 21–15, 21–11b, and 21–12b):

$$I_{rms} = \frac{V_{rms}}{Z} = \frac{V_{rms}}{\sqrt{R^2 + \left(2\pi f L - \dfrac{1}{2\pi f C}\right)^2}}. \quad \textbf{(21–18)}$$

Because the reactance of inductors and capacitors depends on the frequency $f$ of the source, the current in an $LRC$ circuit depends on frequency. From Eq. 21–18 we see that the current will be maximum at a frequency that satisfies

$$2\pi f L - \frac{1}{2\pi f C} = 0.$$

We solve this for $f$, and call the solution $f_0$:

*Resonant frequency*

$$f_0 = \frac{1}{2\pi}\sqrt{\frac{1}{LC}}. \quad \textbf{(21–19)}$$

When $f = f_0$, the circuit is in resonance, and $f_0$ is the **resonant frequency** of the circuit. At this frequency, $X_C = X_L$, so the impedance is purely resistive. A graph of $I_{rms}$ versus $f$ is shown in Fig. 21–42 for particular values of $R$, $L$, and $C$. For smaller $R$ compared to $X_L$ and $X_C$, the resonance peak will be higher and sharper.

*LC circuit*

When $R$ is very small, we speak of an ***LC* circuit**. The energy in an $LC$ circuit oscillates, at frequency $f_0$, between the inductor and the capacitor, with some being dissipated in $R$ (some resistance is unavoidable). This is called an ***LC* oscillation** or an **electromagnetic oscillation**. Not only does the charge oscillate back and forth, but so does the energy, which oscillates between being stored in the electric field of the capacitor and in the magnetic field of the inductor.

*EM oscillations*

Electric resonance is used in many circuits. Radio and TV sets, for example, use resonant circuits for tuning in a station. Many frequencies reach the circuit from the antenna, but a significant current flows only for frequencies at or near the resonant frequency. Either $L$ or $C$ is variable so that different stations can be tuned in (more on this in Chapter 22).

## Summary

The **magnetic flux** passing through a loop is equal to the product of the area of the loop times the perpendicular component of the magnetic field strength:

$$\Phi_B = B_\perp A = BA\cos\theta. \quad \textbf{(21–1)}$$

If the magnetic flux through a coil of wire changes in time, an emf is induced in the coil. The magnitude of the induced emf equals the time rate of change of the magnetic flux through the loop times the number $N$ of loops in the coil:

$$\mathscr{E} = -N\frac{\Delta\Phi_B}{\Delta t}. \quad \textbf{(21–2b)}$$

This is **Faraday's law of induction**.

The induced emf can produce a current whose magnetic field opposes the original change in flux (**Lenz's law**).

Faraday's law also tells us that a changing magnetic field produces an electric field; and that a straight wire of length $l$ moving with speed $v$ perpendicular to a magnetic field of strength $B$ has an emf induced between its ends equal to

$$\mathscr{E} = Blv. \quad \textbf{(21–3)}$$

An electric **generator** changes mechanical energy into electrical energy. Its operation is based on Faraday's law: a coil of wire is made to rotate uniformly by mechanical means in a magnetic field, and the changing flux through the coil induces a sinusoidal current, which is the output of the generator.

[*A motor, which operates in the reverse of a generator, acts like a generator in that a **back emf**, or **counter emf**, is induced in its rotating coil. Because this back emf opposes the input voltage, it can act to limit the current in a motor coil. Similarly, a generator acts somewhat like a motor in that a **counter torque** acts on its rotating coil.]

A **transformer**, which is a device to change the magnitude of an ac voltage, consists of a primary coil and a secondary coil. The changing flux due to an ac voltage in the primary coil induces an ac voltage in the secondary coil. In a 100% efficient transformer, the ratio of output to input voltages $(V_S/V_P)$ equals the ratio of the number of turns $N_S$ in the secondary to the number $N_P$ in the primary:

$$\frac{V_S}{V_P} = \frac{N_S}{N_P}. \quad \textbf{(21–6)}$$

The ratio of secondary to primary current is in the inverse ratio of turns:

$$\frac{I_S}{I_P} = \frac{N_P}{N_S}. \quad \textbf{(21–7)}$$

Microphones, ground fault circuit interrupters, seismographs, and read/write heads for computer drives and tape recorders are applications of electromagnetic induction.

[*A changing current in a coil of wire will produce a changing magnetic field that induces an emf in a second coil placed nearby. The **mutual inductance**, $M$, is defined by

$$\mathscr{E}_2 = -M\frac{\Delta I_1}{\Delta t}. \qquad \textbf{(21–8)]}$$

[*Within a single coil, the changing $B$ due to a changing current induces an opposing emf, $\mathscr{E}$, so a coil has a **self-inductance** $L$ defined by

$$\mathscr{E} = -L\frac{\Delta I}{\Delta t}. \qquad \textbf{(21–9)]}$$

[*The energy stored in an inductance $L$ carrying current $I$ is given by $U = \frac{1}{2}LI^2$. This energy can be thought of as being stored in the magnetic field of the inductor. The energy density $u$ in any magnetic field $B$ is given by

$$u = \frac{1}{2}\frac{B^2}{\mu_0}. \qquad \textbf{(21–10)]}$$

[*When an inductance $L$ and resistor $R$ are connected in series to a source of emf, $V$, the current rises as

$$I = \frac{V}{R}\left(1 - e^{-t/\tau}\right),$$

where $\tau = L/R$ is the time constant. If the battery is suddenly switched out of the $LR$ circuit, the current drops exponentially, $I = I_{max}e^{-t/\tau}$.]

[*Inductive and capacitive **reactance**, $X$, defined as for resistors, is the proportionality constant between voltage and current (either the rms or peak values). Across an inductor,

$$V = IX_L, \qquad \textbf{(21–11a)}$$

and across a capacitor,

$$V = IX_C. \qquad \textbf{(21–12a)}$$

The reactance of an inductor increases with frequency

$$X_L = 2\pi fL, \qquad \textbf{(21–11b)}$$

whereas the reactance of a capacitor decreases with frequency $f$,

$$X_C = \frac{1}{2\pi fC}. \qquad \textbf{(21–12b)}$$

The current through a resistor is always in phase with the voltage across it, but in an inductor, the current lags the voltage by 90°, and in a capacitor the current leads the voltage by 90°.]

[*In an $LRC$ series circuit, the total **impedance** $Z$ is defined by the equivalent of $V = IR$ for resistance, namely,

$$V_0 = I_0Z \quad \text{or} \quad V_{rms} = I_{rms}Z; \qquad \textbf{(21–14)}$$

$Z$ is given by

$$Z = \sqrt{R^2 + (X_L - X_C)^2}. \qquad \textbf{(21–15a)]}$$

[*An $LRC$ series circuit **resonates** at a frequency given by

$$f_0 = \frac{1}{2\pi}\sqrt{\frac{1}{LC}}. \qquad \textbf{(21–19)}$$

The rms current in the circuit is largest when the applied voltage has a frequency equal to $f_0$.]

## Questions

**1.** What would be the advantage, in Faraday's experiments (Fig. 21–1), of using coils with many turns?

**2.** What is the difference between magnetic flux and magnetic field?

**3.** Suppose you are holding a circular ring of wire and suddenly thrust a magnet, south pole first, away from you toward the center of the circle. Is a current induced in the wire? Is a current induced when the magnet is held steady within the ring? Is a current induced when you withdraw the magnet? In each case, if your answer is yes, specify the direction.

**4.** Two loops of wire are moving in the vicinity of a very long straight wire carrying a steady current as shown in Fig. 21–43. Find the direction of the induced current in each loop.

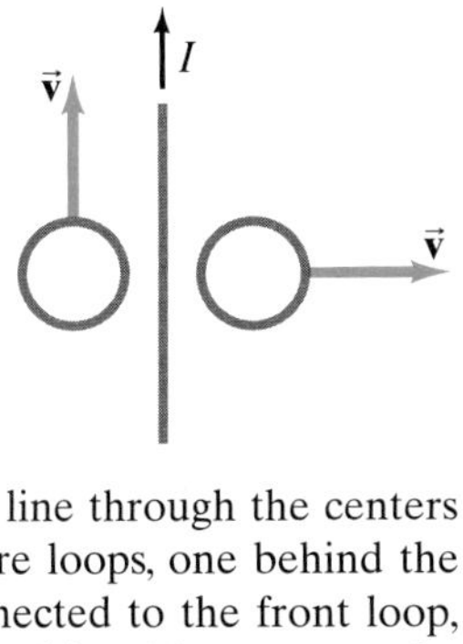


**FIGURE 21–43** Question 4.

**5.** Suppose you are looking along a line through the centers of two circular (but separate) wire loops, one behind the other. A battery is suddenly connected to the front loop, establishing a clockwise current. (*a*) Will a current be induced in the second loop? (*b*) If so, when does this current start? (*c*) When does it stop? (*d*) In what direction is this current? (*e*) Is there a force between the two loops? (*f*) If so, in what direction?

**6.** In Fig. 21–44, determine the direction of the induced current in resistor $R_A$ when (*a*) coil B is moved toward coil A, (*b*) when coil B is moved away from A, (*c*) when the resistance $R_B$ is increased.

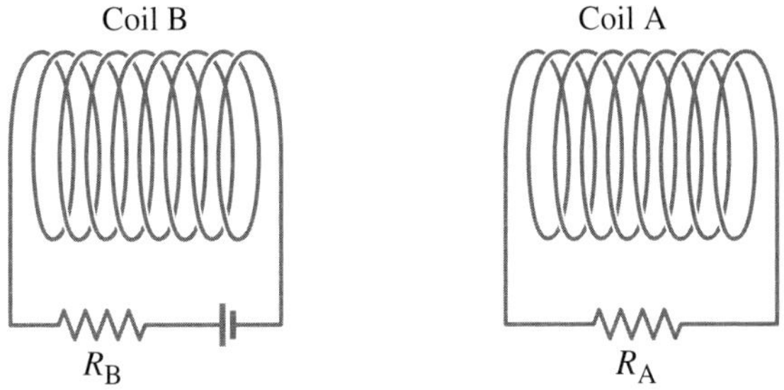


**FIGURE 21–44** Question 6.

**7.** In situations where a small signal must travel over a distance, a "shielded cable" is used in which the signal wire is surrounded by an insulator and then enclosed by a cylindrical conductor carrying the return current. Why is a "shield" necessary?

**8.** What is the advantage of placing the two insulated electric wires carrying ac close together or even twisted about each other?

***9.** Explain why, exactly, the lights may dim briefly when a refrigerator motor starts up. When an electric heater is turned on, the lights may stay dimmed as long as the heater is on. Explain the difference.

* **10.** Use Figs. 21–15 and 21–17 plus the right-hand rules to show why the counter torque in a generator *opposes* the motion.

* **11.** Will an eddy current brake (Fig. 21–20) work on a copper or aluminum wheel, or must the wheel be ferromagnetic? Explain.

* **12.** It has been proposed that eddy currents be used to help sort solid waste for recycling. The waste is first ground into tiny pieces and iron removed with a dc magnet. The waste then is allowed to slide down an incline over permanent magnets. How will this aid in the separation of nonferrous metals (Al, Cu, Pb, brass) from nonmetallic materials?

* **13.** The pivoted metal bar with slots in Fig. 21–45 falls much more quickly through a magnetic field than does a solid bar. Explain.

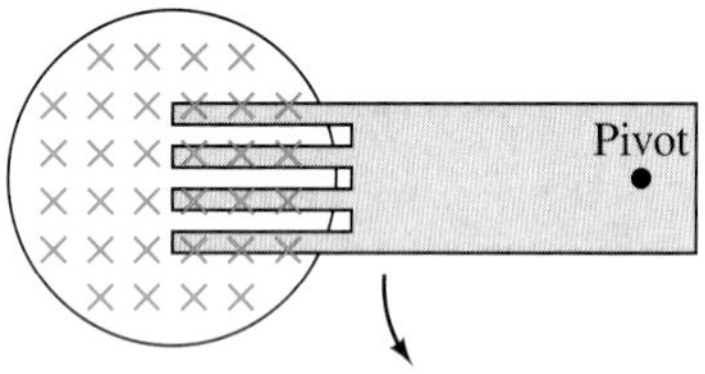


**FIGURE 21–45** Question 13.

* **14.** If an aluminum sheet is held between the poles of a large bar magnet, it requires some force to pull it out of the magnetic field even though the sheet is not ferromagnetic and does not touch the pole faces. Explain.

* **15.** A bar magnet falling inside a vertical metal tube reaches a terminal velocity even if the tube is evacuated so that there is no air resistance. Explain.

* **16.** A metal bar, pivoted at one end, oscillates freely in the absence of a magnetic field; but in a magnetic field, its oscillations are quickly damped out. Explain. (This *magnetic damping* is used in a number of practical devices.)

**17.** An enclosed transformer has four wire leads coming from it. How could you determine the ratio of turns on the two coils without taking the transformer apart? How would you know which wires paired with which?

**18.** The use of higher-voltage lines in homes—say, 600 V or 1200 V—would reduce energy waste. Why are they not used?

**19.** A transformer designed for a 120-V ac input will often "burn out" if connected to a 120-V dc source. Explain. [*Hint*: the resistance of the primary coil is usually very low.]

* **20.** How would you arrange two flat circular coils so that their mutual inductance was (*a*) greatest, (*b*) least (without separating them by a great distance)?

* **21.** Does the emf of the battery in Fig. 21–33 affect the time needed for the *LR* circuit to reach (*a*) a given fraction of its maximum possible current, (*b*) a given value of current? Explain.

* **22.** In an *LRC* circuit, can the rms voltage across (*a*) an inductor, (*b*) a capacitor, be greater than the rms voltage of the ac source? Explain.

* **23.** Describe briefly how the frequency of the source emf affects the impedance of (*a*) a pure resistance, (*b*) a pure capacitance, (*c*) a pure inductance, (*d*) an *LRC* circuit near resonance (*R* small), (*e*) an *LRC* circuit far from resonance (*R* small).

* **24.** Describe how to make the impedance in an *LRC* circuit a minimum.

# Problems

### 21–1 to 21–4 Faraday's Law of Induction

1. (I) The magnetic flux through a coil of wire containing two loops changes from −50 Wb to +38 Wb in 0.42 s. What is the emf induced in the coil?

2. (I) The rectangular loop shown in Fig. 21–46 is pushed into the magnetic field which points inward. In what direction is the induced current?

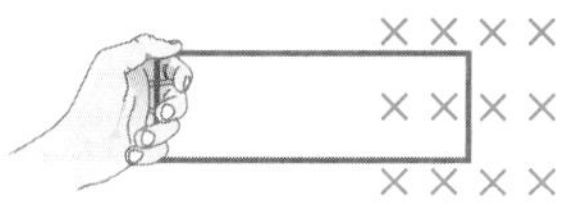

**FIGURE 21–46** Problem 2.

3. (I) The north pole of the magnet in Fig. 21–47 is being inserted into the coil. In which direction is the induced current flowing through the resistor *R*?

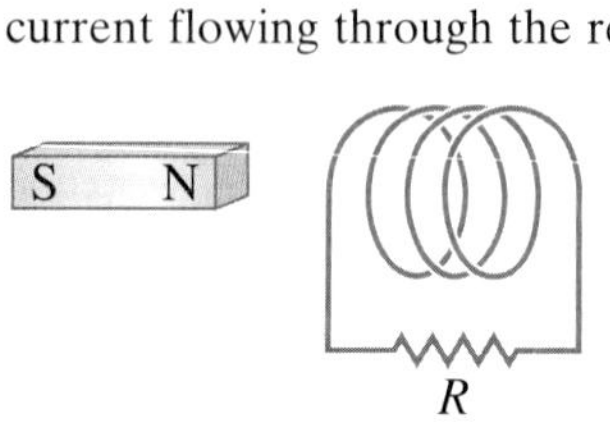


**FIGURE 21–47** Problem 3.

4. (I) A 9.6-cm-diameter circular loop of wire is in a 1.10-T magnetic field. The loop is removed from the field in 0.15 s. What is the average induced emf?

5. (I) A 12.0-cm-diameter loop of wire is initially oriented perpendicular to a 1.5-T magnetic field. The loop is rotated so that its plane is parallel to the field direction in 0.20 s. What is the average induced emf in the loop?

6. (II) A 10.2-cm-diameter wire coil is initially oriented so that its plane is perpendicular to a magnetic field of 0.63 T pointing up. During the course of 0.15 s, the field is changed to one of 0.25 T pointing down. What is the average induced emf in the coil?

7. (II) A 15-cm-diameter circular loop of wire is placed in a 0.50-T magnetic field. (*a*) When the plane of the loop is perpendicular to the field lines, what is the magnetic flux through the loop? (*b*) The plane of the loop is rotated until it makes a 35° angle with the field lines. What is the angle $\theta$ in Eq. 21–1 for this situation? (*c*) What is the magnetic flux through the loop at this angle?

8. (II) (*a*) If the resistance of the resistor in Fig. 21–48 is slowly increased, what is the direction of the current induced in the small circular loop inside the larger loop? (*b*) What would it be if the small loop were placed outside the larger one, to the left?

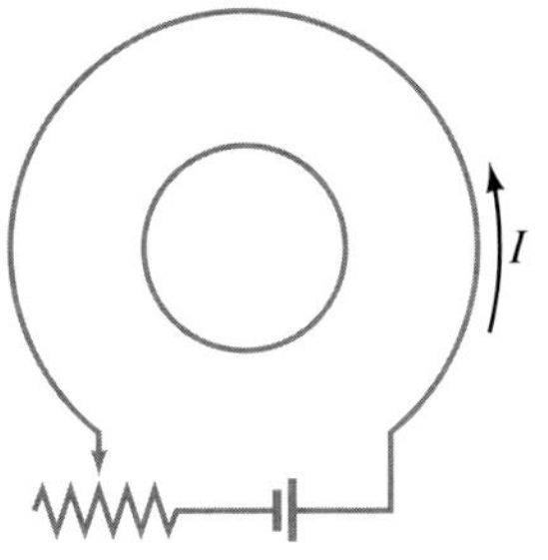


**FIGURE 21–48** Problem 8.

9. (II) What is the direction of the induced current in the circular loop due to the current shown in each part of Fig. 21–49?

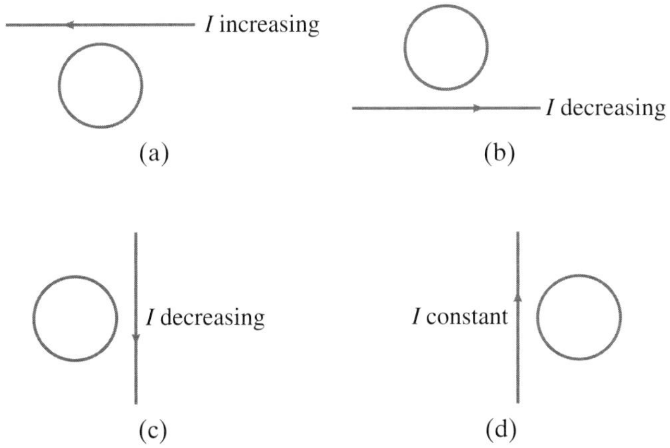


**FIGURE 21–49** Problem 9.

10. (II) If the solenoid in Fig. 21–50 is being pulled away from the loop shown, in what direction is the induced current in the loop?

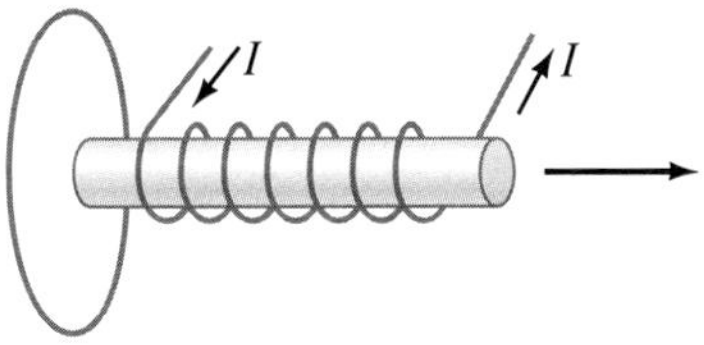


**FIGURE 21–50** Problem 10.

11. (II) The magnetic field perpendicular to a circular wire loop 12.0 cm in diameter is changed from +0.52 T to −0.45 T in 180 ms, where + means the field points away from an observer and − toward the observer. (*a*) Calculate the induced emf. (*b*) In what direction does the induced current flow?

12. (II) The moving rod in Fig. 21–12 is 12.0 cm long and is pulled at a speed of 15.0 cm/s. If the magnetic field is 0.800 T, calculate (*a*) the emf developed, and (*b*) the electric field felt by electrons in the rod.

13. (II) A circular loop in the plane of the paper lies in a 0.75-T magnetic field pointing into the paper. If the loop's diameter changes from 20.0 cm to 6.0 cm in 0.50 s, (*a*) what is the direction of the induced current, (*b*) what is the magnitude of the average induced emf, and (*c*) if the coil resistance is 2.5 Ω, what is the average induced current?

14. (II) The moving rod in Fig. 21–12 is 13.2 cm long and generates an emf of 120 mV while moving in a 0.90-T magnetic field. (*a*) What is its speed? (*b*) What is the electric field in the rod?

15. (II) Part of a single rectangular loop of wire with dimensions shown in Fig. 21–51 is situated inside a region of uniform magnetic field of 0.550 T. The total resistance of the loop is 0.230 Ω. Calculate the force required to pull the loop from the field (to the right) at a constant velocity of 3.40 m/s. Neglect gravity.

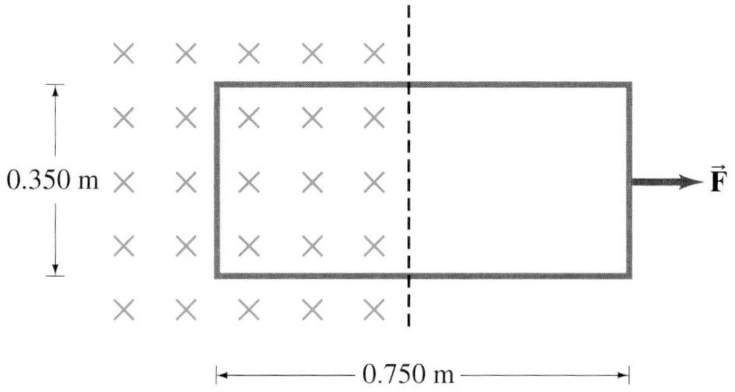


**FIGURE 21–51** Problem 15.

16. (II) A 500-turn solenoid, 25 cm long, has a diameter of 2.5 cm. A 10-turn coil is wound tightly around the center of the solenoid. If the current in the solenoid increases uniformly from 0 to 5.0 A in 0.60 s, what will be the induced emf in the short coil during this time?

17. (II) In Fig. 21–12, the rod moves with a speed of 1.6 m/s, is 30.0 cm long, and has a resistance of 2.5 Ω. The magnetic field is 0.35 T, and the resistance of the U-shaped conductor is 25.0 Ω at a given instant. Calculate (*a*) the induced emf, (*b*) the current in the U-shaped conductor, and (*c*) the external force needed to keep the rod's velocity constant at that instant.

18. (III) A 22.0-cm-diameter coil consists of 20 turns of circular copper wire 2.6 mm in diameter. A uniform magnetic field, perpendicular to the plane of the coil, changes at a rate of $8.65 \times 10^{-3}$ T/s. Determine (*a*) the current in the loop, and (*b*) the rate at which thermal energy is produced.

19. (III) The magnetic field perpendicular to a single 13.2-cm-diameter circular loop of copper wire decreases uniformly from 0.750 T to zero. If the wire is 2.25 mm in diameter, how much charge moves past a point in the coil during this operation?

## 21–5 Generators

20. (I) A simple generator is used to generate a peak output voltage of 24.0 V. The square armature consists of windings that are 6.0 cm on a side and rotates in a field of 0.420 T at a rate of 60.0 rev/s. How many loops of wire should be wound on the square armature?

21. (II) The generator of a car idling at 1100 rpm produces 12.4 V. What will the output be at a rotation speed of 2500 rpm, assuming nothing else changes?

22. (II) Show that the rms output (Section 18–7) of an ac generator is $V_{rms} = NAB\omega/\sqrt{2}$, where $\omega = 2\pi f$.

23. (II) A simple generator has a 320-loop square coil 21.0 cm on a side. How fast must it turn in a 0.650-T field to produce a 120-V peak output?

24. (II) A 450-loop circular armature coil with a diameter of 8.0 cm rotates at 120 rev/s in a uniform magnetic field of strength 0.55 T. (*a*) What is the rms voltage output of the generator? (*b*) What would you do to the rotation frequency in order to double the rms voltage output?

25. (II) A generator rotates at 85 Hz in a magnetic field of 0.030 T. It has 1000 turns and produces an rms voltage of 150 V and an rms current of 70.0 A. (*a*) What is the peak current produced? (*b*) What is the area of each turn of the coil?

### * 21–6 Back EMF and Torque

* 26. (I) A motor has an armature resistance of 3.25 Ω. If it draws 8.20 A when running at full speed and connected to a 120-V line, how large is the back emf?

* 27. (I) The back emf in a motor is 72 V when operating at 1800 rpm. What would be the back emf at 2500 rpm if the magnetic field is unchanged?

* 28. (II) The back emf in a motor is 95 V when the motor is operating at 1000 rpm. How would you change the motor's magnetic field if you wanted to reduce the back emf to 65 V when the motor was running at 2500 rpm?

* 29. (II) What will be the current in the motor of Example 21–9 if the load causes it to run at half speed?

### 21–7 Transformers

[Assume 100% efficiency, unless stated otherwise.]

30. (I) A transformer is designed to change 120 V into 10,000 V, and there are 164 turns in the primary coil. How many turns are in the secondary coil?

31. (I) A transformer has 320 turns in the primary coil and 120 in the secondary coil. What kind of transformer is this, and by what factor does it change the voltage? By what factor does it change the current?

32. (I) A step-up transformer increases 25 V to 120 V. What is the current in the secondary coil as compared to the primary coil?

33. (I) Neon signs require 12 kV for their operation. To operate from a 240-V line, what must be the ratio of secondary to primary turns of the transformer? What would the voltage output be if the transformer were connected backward?

34. (II) A model-train transformer plugs into 120-V ac and draws 0.35 A while supplying 7.5 A to the train. (*a*) What voltage is present across the tracks? (*b*) Is the transformer step-up or step-down?

35. (II) The output voltage of a 95-W transformer is 12 V, and the input current is 22 A. (*a*) Is this a step-up or a step-down transformer? (*b*) By what factor is the voltage multiplied?

36. (II) A transformer has 330 primary turns and 1340 secondary turns. The input voltage is 120 V and the output current is 15.0 A. What are the output voltage and input current?

37. (II) If 30 MW of power at 45 kV (rms) arrives at a town from a generator via 4.0-Ω transmission lines, calculate (*a*) the emf at the generator end of the lines, and (*b*) the fraction of the power generated that is wasted in the lines.

38. (III) 65 kW is to arrive at a town over two 0.100-Ω lines. Estimate how much power is saved if the voltage is stepped up from 120 V to 1200 V and then down again, rather than simply transmitting at 120 V. Assume the transformers are each 99% efficient.

### * 21–9 Inductance

* 39. (I) If the current in a 180-mH coil changes steadily from 25.0 A to 10.0 A in 350 ms, what is the magnitude of the induced emf?

* 40. (I) What is the inductance of a coil if the coil produces an emf of 2.50 V when the current in it changes from −28.0 mA to +31.0 mA in 12.0 ms?

* 41. (I) What is the inductance $L$ of a 0.60-m-long air-filled coil 2.9 cm in diameter containing 10,000 loops?

* 42. (I) How many turns of wire would be required to make a 130-mH inductance out of a 30.0-cm-long air-filled coil with a diameter of 5.2 cm?

* 43. (II) An air-filled cylindrical inductor has 2800 turns, and it is 2.5 cm in diameter and 28.2 cm long. (*a*) What is its inductance? (*b*) How many turns would you need to generate the same inductance if the core were iron-filled instead? Assume the magnetic permeability of iron is about 1200 times that of free space.

* 44. (II) A coil has 2.25-Ω resistance and 440-mH inductance. If the current is 3.00 A and is increasing at a rate of 3.50 A/s, what is the potential difference across the coil at this moment?

* 45. (III) A long thin solenoid of length $l$ and cross-sectional area $A$ contains $N_1$ closely packed turns of wire. Wrapped tightly around it is an insulated coil of $N_2$ turns, Fig. 21–52. Assume all the flux from coil 1 (the solenoid) passes through coil 2, and calculate the mutual inductance.

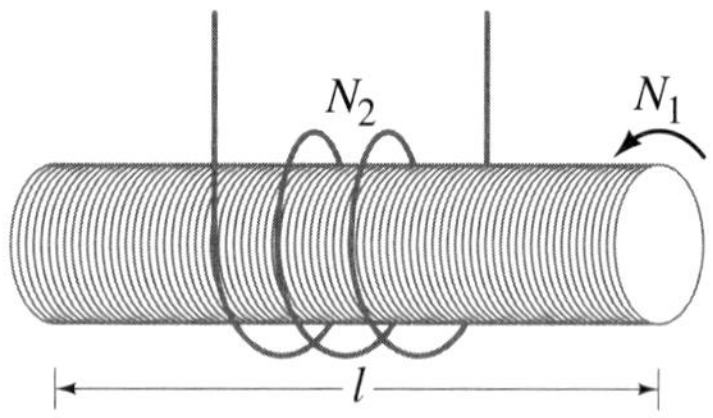


**FIGURE 21–52** Problem 45.

* 46. (III) The wire of a tightly wound solenoid is unwound and used to make another tightly wound solenoid of twice the diameter. By what factor does the inductance change?

### * 21–10 Magnetic Energy Storage

* 47. (I) The magnetic field inside an air-filled solenoid 36 cm long and 2.0 cm in diameter is 0.80 T. Approximately how much energy is stored in this field?

* 48. (II) At a given instant the current through an inductor is 50.0 mA and is increasing at the rate of 115 mA/s. What is the initial energy stored in the inductor if the inductance is known to be 60.0 mH, and how long does it take for the energy to increase by a factor of 10 from the initial value?

* 49. (II) Assuming the Earth's magnetic field averages about $0.50 \times 10^{-4}$ T near the surface of the Earth, estimate the total energy stored in this field in the first 10 km above the Earth's surface.

### * 21–11 *LR* Circuit

* 50. (II) Determine $\Delta I/\Delta t$ at $t = 0$ (when the battery is connected) for the *LR* circuit of Fig. 21–33 and show that if $I$ continued to increase at this rate, it would reach its maximum value in one time constant.

* 51. (III) After how many time constants does the current in Fig. 21–33 reach within (*a*) 10%, (*b*) 1.0%, and (*c*) 0.1% of its maximum value?

* 52. (III) Two tightly wound solenoids have the same length and circular cross-sectional area. But solenoid 1 uses wire that is half as thick as solenoid 2. (*a*) What is the ratio of their inductances? (*b*) What is the ratio of their inductive time constants (assuming no other resistance in the circuits)?

### * 21–12 AC Circuits and Reactance

* 53. (I) What is the reactance of a 7.20-$\mu$F capacitor at a frequency of (*a*) 60.0 Hz, (*b*) 1.00 MHz?

* 54. (I) At what frequency will a 22.0-mH inductor have a reactance of 660 Ω?

* 55. (I) At what frequency will a 2.40-$\mu$F capacitor have a reactance of 6.70 kΩ?

* 56. (II) Plot a graph of the reactance of a 1.0-$\mu$F capacitor as a function of frequency from 10 to 1000 Hz.

* 57. (II) Plot a graph of the reactance of a 1.0-mH inductor as a function of frequency from 100 to 10,000 Hz.

* 58. (II) Calculate the reactance of, and rms current in, a 160-mH radio coil connected to a 240-V (rms) 10.0-kHz ac line. Ignore resistance.

* 59. (II) An inductance coil operates at 240 V and 60.0 Hz. It draws 12.8 A. What is the coil's inductance?

* 60. (II) (*a*) What is the reactance of a well-insulated 0.030-$\mu$F capacitor connected to a 2.0-kV (rms) 720-Hz line? (*b*) What will be the peak value of the current?

### * 21–13 *LRC* Circuits

* 61. (I) A 30-kΩ resistor is in series with a 45-mH inductor and an ac source. Calculate the impedance of the circuit if the source frequency is (*a*) 50 Hz, and (*b*) $3.0 \times 10^4$ Hz.

* 62. (I) A 3.5-kΩ resistor and a 4.0-$\mu$F capacitor are connected in series to an ac source. Calculate the impedance of the circuit if the source frequency is (*a*) 60 Hz, and (*b*) 60,000 Hz.

* 63. (I) For a 120-V rms 60-Hz voltage, an rms current of 70 mA passing through the human body for 1.0 s could be lethal. What must be the impedance of the body for this to occur?

* 64. (II) What is the resistance of a coil if its impedance is 235 Ω and its reactance is 135 Ω?

* 65. (II) What are the total impedance, phase angle, and rms current in an *LRC* circuit connected to a 10.0-kHz, 725-V (rms) source if $L = 22.0$ mH, $R = 8.70$ kΩ, and $C = 6250$ pF?

* 66. (III) A 2.5-kΩ resistor in series with a 420-mH inductor is driven by an ac power supply. At what frequency is the impedance double that of the impedance at 60 Hz?

* 67. (III) (*a*) What is the rms current in an *RL* circuit when a 60.0-Hz 120-V rms ac voltage is applied, where $R = 1.80$ kΩ, and $L = 350$ mH? (*b*) What is the phase angle between voltage and current? (*c*) What are the rms voltage readings across $R$ and $L$?

* 68. (III) (*a*) What is the rms current in an *RC* circuit if $R = 8.80$ kΩ, $C = 1.80\ \mu$F, and the rms applied voltage is 120 V at 60.0 Hz? (*b*) What is the phase angle between voltage and current? (*c*) What are the voltmeter readings across $R$ and $C$?

### * 21–14 Resonance in AC Circuits

* 69. (I) A 3500-pF capacitor is connected to a 55.0-$\mu$H coil of resistance 3.00 Ω. What is the resonant frequency of this circuit?

* 70. (I) The variable capacitor in the tuner of an AM radio has a capacitance of 2800 pF when the radio is tuned to a station at 580 kHz. (*a*) What must be the capacitance for a station at 1600 kHz? (*b*) What is the inductance (assumed constant)?

* 71. (II) An *LRC* circuit has $L = 14.8$ mH and $R = 4.40$ Ω. (*a*) What value must $C$ have to produce resonance at 3600 Hz? (*b*) What will be the maximum current at resonance if the peak external voltage is 150 V?

## General Problems

72. Suppose you are looking at two current loops in the plane of the page as shown in Fig. 21–53. When switch S is thrown in the left-hand coil, (*a*) what is the direction of the induced current in the other loop? (*b*) What is the situation after a "long" time? (*c*) What is the direction of the induced current in the right-hand loop if that loop is quickly pulled horizontally to the right?

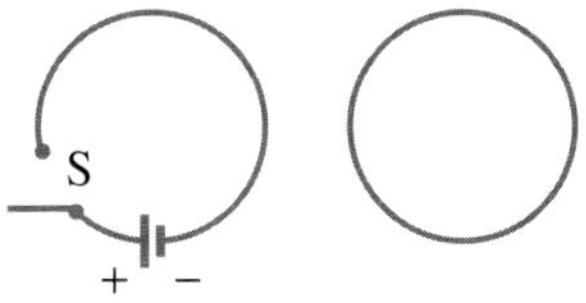


**FIGURE 21–53** Problem 72.

73. A square loop 24.0 cm on a side has a resistance of 5.20 Ω. It is initially in a 0.665-T magnetic field, with its plane perpendicular to $\vec{\mathbf{B}}$, but is removed from the field in 40.0 ms. Calculate the electric energy dissipated in this process.

74. A high-intensity desk lamp is rated at 45 W but requires only 12 V. It contains a transformer that converts 120-V household voltage. (*a*) Is the transformer step-up or step-down? (*b*) What is the current in the secondary coil when the lamp is on? (*c*) What is the current in the primary coil? (*d*) What is the resistance of the bulb when on?

75. Power is generated at 24 kV at a generating plant located 118 km from a town that requires 50 MW of power at 12 kV. Two transmission lines from the plant to the town each have a resistance of 0.10 Ω/km. What should the output voltage of the transformer at the generating plant be for an overall transmission efficiency of 98.5%, assuming a perfect transformer?

76. The primary windings of a transformer which has an 80% efficiency are connected to 110-V ac. The secondary windings are connected across a 2.4-Ω, 75-W lightbulb. (*a*) Calculate the current through the primary windings of the transformer. (*b*) Calculate the ratio of the number of primary windings of the transformer to the number of secondary windings of the transformer.

77. A pair of power transmission lines each have a 0.80-Ω resistance and carry 740 A over 9.0 km. If the rms input voltage is 42 kV, calculate (*a*) the voltage at the other end, (*b*) the power input, (*c*) power loss in the lines, and (*d*) the power output.

78. Two resistanceless rails rest 32 cm apart on a 6.0° ramp. They are joined at the bottom by a 0.60-Ω resistor. At the top a copper bar of mass 0.040 kg (ignore its resistance) is laid across the rails. The whole apparatus is immersed in a vertical 0.55-T field. What is the terminal (steady) velocity of the bar as it slides frictionlessly down the rails?

79. Show that the power loss in transmission lines, $P_L$, is given by $P_L = (P_T)^2 R_L/V^2$, where $P_T$ is the power transmitted to the user, $V$ is the delivered voltage, and $R_L$ is the resistance of the power lines.

80. A coil with 150 turns, a radius of 5.0 cm, and a resistance of 12 Ω surrounds a solenoid with 230 turns/cm and a radius of 4.5 cm; see Fig. 21–54. The current in the solenoid changes at a constant rate from 0 to 2.0 A in 0.10 s. Calculate the magnitude and direction of the induced current in the coil.

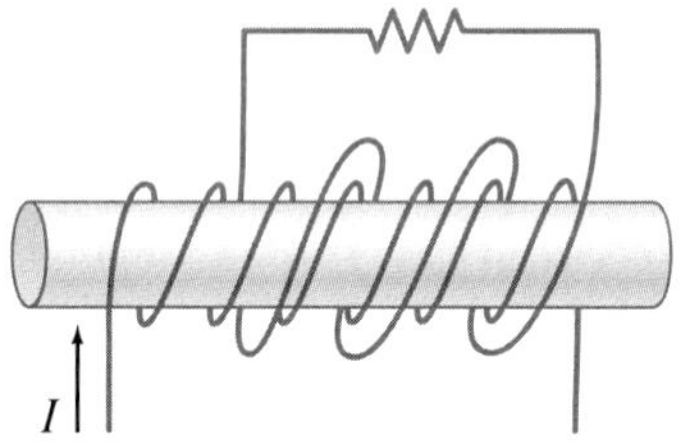


**FIGURE 21–54** Problem 80.

81. A certain electronic device needs to be protected against sudden surges in current. In particular, after the power is turned on the current should rise no more than 7.5 mA in the first 120 μs. The device has resistance 150 Ω and is designed to operate at 55 mA. How would you protect this device?

82. A 25-turn 12.5-cm-diameter coil is placed between the pole pieces of an electromagnet. When the magnet is turned on, the flux through the coil changes, inducing an emf. At what rate (in T/s) must the field produced by the magnet change if the emf is to be 120 V?

* 83. Calculate the peak output voltage of a simple generator whose square armature windings are 6.60 cm on a side; the armature contains 155 loops and rotates in a field of 0.200 T at a rate of 120 rev/s.

* 84. Typical large values for electric and magnetic fields attained in laboratories are about $1.0 \times 10^4$ V/m and 2.0 T. (*a*) Determine the energy density for each field and compare. (*b*) What magnitude electric field would be needed to produce the same energy density as the 2.0-T magnetic field?

* 85. What is the inductance $L$ of the primary of a transformer whose input is 220 V at 60.0 Hz if the current drawn is 5.8 A? Assume no current in the secondary.

* 86. A 130-mH coil whose resistance is 18.5 Ω is connected to a capacitor $C$ and a 1360-Hz source voltage. If the current and voltage are to be in phase, what value must $C$ have?

* 87. An inductance coil draws 2.5-A dc when connected to a 36-V battery. When connected to a 60-Hz 120-V (rms) source, the current drawn is 3.8 A (rms). Determine the inductance and resistance of the coil.

* 88. A 135-mH inductor with 2.0-Ω resistance is connected in series to a 20-μF capacitor and a 60-Hz, 45-V source. Calculate (*a*) the rms current, and (*b*) the phase angle.

* 89. The ***Q* factor** of a resonance circuit can be defined as the ratio of the voltage across the capacitor (or inductor) to the voltage across the resistor, at resonance. The larger the $Q$ factor, the sharper the resonance curve will be and the sharper the tuning. (*a*) Show that the $Q$ factor is given by the equation $Q = (1/R)\sqrt{L/C}$. (*b*) At a resonant frequency $f_0 = 1.0$ MHz, what must be the values of $L$ and $R$ to produce a $Q$ factor of 550? Assume that $C = 0.010\ \mu$F.

## Answers to Exercises

**A:** 0.0102 Wb.

**B:** (*a*) Counterclockwise; (*b*) clockwise; (*c*) zero; (*d*) counterclockwise.

**C:** Counterclockwise.

**D:** 10 turns.

These circular disk antennas, each 25 m in diameter, are pointed to receive radio waves from out in space. Radio waves are electromagnetic (EM) waves that have frequencies from a few hundred Hz to about 100 MHz. These antennas are connected together electronically to achieve better detail, and are a part of the Very Large Array in New Mexico searching the heavens for information about the Cosmos.

Maxwell predicted the existence of EM waves from his famous equations, which are a magnificent summary of electromagnetism.

CHAPTER 22

# Electromagnetic Waves

**FIGURE 22–1** James Clerk Maxwell.

The culmination of electromagnetic theory in the nineteenth century was the prediction, and the experimental verification, that waves of electromagnetic fields could travel through space. This achievement opened a whole new world of communication: first the wireless telegraph, then radio and television, and more recently cell phones and remote-control devices. And it yielded the spectacular prediction that light is an electromagnetic wave.

The theoretical prediction of electromagnetic waves was the work of the Scottish physicist James Clerk Maxwell (1831–1879; Fig. 22–1), who unified, in one magnificent theory, all the phenomena of electricity and magnetism.

## 22–1 Changing Electric Fields Produce Magnetic Fields; Maxwell's Equations

The development of electromagnetic theory in the early part of the nineteenth century by Oersted, Ampère, and others was not actually done in terms of electric and magnetic fields. The idea of the field was introduced somewhat later by Faraday, and was not generally used until Maxwell showed that all electric and magnetic phenomena could be described using only four equations involving electric and magnetic fields. These equations, known as **Maxwell's equations**, are the basic equations for all electromagnetism. They are fundamental in the same sense that Newton's three laws of motion and the law of universal gravitation are for mechanics. In a sense, they are even more fundamental, because they are consistent with the theory of relativity (Chapter 26), whereas Newton's laws are not. Because all of electromagnetism is contained in this set of four equations, Maxwell's equations are considered one of the great triumphs of the human intellect.

Although we will not present Maxwell's equations in mathematical form since they involve calculus, we will summarize them here in words. They are:

*Maxwell's equations*

(1) a generalized form of Coulomb's law known as Gauss's law (Section 16–10) that relates electric field to its source, electric charge;
(2) a similar law for the magnetic field, except that magnetic field lines are always continuous—they do not begin or end (as electric field lines do, on charges);
(3) an electric field is produced by a changing magnetic field (Faraday's law);
(4) a magnetic field is produced by an electric current (Ampère's law), or by a changing electric field.

Law (3) is Faraday's law (see Chapter 21, especially Section 21–4). The first part of law (4), that a magnetic field is produced by an electric current, was discovered by Oersted, and the mathematical relation is given by Ampère's law (Section 20–8). But the second part of law (4) is an entirely new aspect predicted by Maxwell. Maxwell argued that if a changing magnetic field produces an electric field, as given by Faraday's law, then the reverse might be true as well: **a changing electric field will produce a magnetic field**. This was an *hypothesis* by Maxwell, based on the idea of symmetry in nature. Indeed, the size of the effect in most cases is so small that Maxwell recognized it would be difficult to detect it experimentally.

*Changing $\vec{\mathbf{E}}$ produces $\vec{\mathbf{B}}$*

### * Maxwell's Fourth Equation (Ampère's Law Extended)

To back up the idea that a changing electric field might produce a magnetic field, we use an indirect argument that goes something like this. According to Ampère's law (Section 20–8), $\Sigma B_{\parallel}\,\Delta l = \mu_0 I$. That is, divide any closed path you choose into short segments $\Delta l$, multiply each segment by the parallel component of the magnetic field $B$ at that segment, and then sum all these products over the complete closed path. That sum will then equal $\mu_0$ times the total current $I$ that passes through a surface bounded by the path. When we applied Ampère's law to the field around a straight wire (Section 20–8), we imagined the current as passing through the circular area enclosed by our circular loop. That area is the flat surface 1 shown in Fig. 22–2. However, we could just as well use the sack-shaped surface 2 in Fig. 22–2 as the surface for Ampère's law because the same current $I$ passes through it.

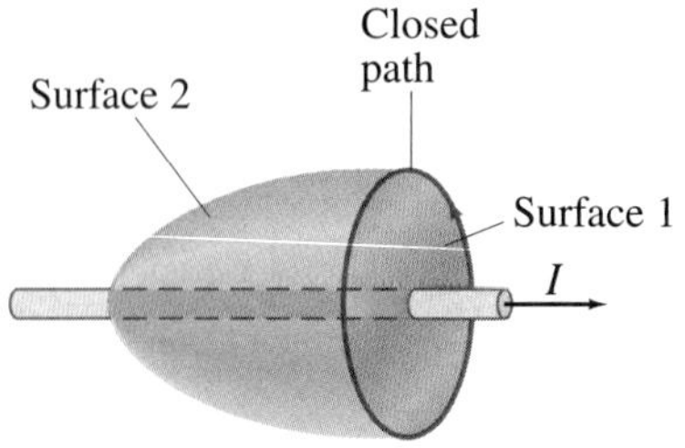


**FIGURE 22–2** Ampère's law applied to two different surfaces bounded by the same closed path.

Now consider the closed path for the situation of Fig. 22–3, where a capacitor is being discharged. Ampère's law works for surface 1 (current $I$ passes through surface 1), but it does not work for surface 2 because no current passes through surface 2. There is a magnetic field around the wire, so the left side of Ampère's law is not zero around the circular closed path; yet no current flows through surface 2, so the right side *is* zero for surface 2. We seem to have a contradiction of Ampère's law. There is a magnetic field present in Fig. 22–3, however, only if charge is flowing to or away from the capacitor plates. The changing charge on the plates means that the electric field between the plates is changing in time. Maxwell resolved the problem of no current through surface 2 in Fig. 22–3 by proposing that the changing electric field between the plates is *equivalent to* an electric current. He called it a **displacement current**, $I_D$. An ordinary current $I$ is then called a "conduction current," and Ampère's law, as generalized by Maxwell, becomes

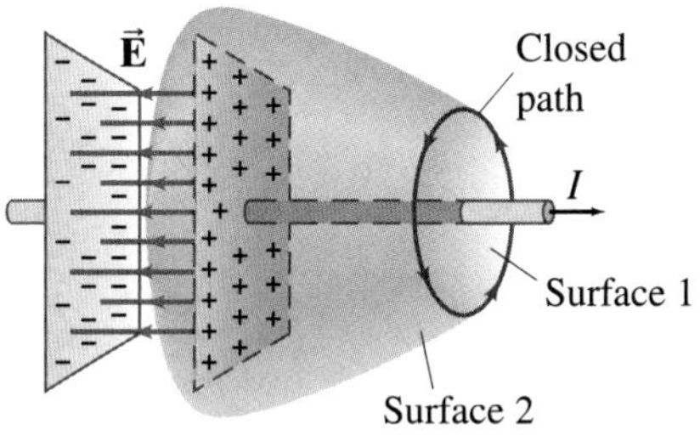


**FIGURE 22–3** A capacitor discharging. No conduction current passes through surface 2. An extra term is needed in Ampère's law.

$$\Sigma B_{\parallel}\,\Delta l = \mu_0(I + I_D).$$

Ampère's law will now apply also for surface 2 in Fig. 22–3, where $I_D$ refers to the changing electric field.

By combining Eq. 17–7 for the charge on a capacitor, $Q = CV$, with Eq. 17–4a, $V = Ed$, and Eq. 17–8, $C = \epsilon_0 A/d$, we can write $Q = CV = (\epsilon_0 A/d)(Ed) = \epsilon_0 AE$. Then the current $I_D$ becomes

$$I_D = \frac{\Delta Q}{\Delta t} = \epsilon_0 \frac{\Delta \Phi_E}{\Delta t},$$

where $\Phi_E = EA$ is the **electric flux**, defined in analogy to magnetic flux (Section 21–2). Then, Ampère's law becomes

*Ampère's law (generalized)*

$$\Sigma B_{\parallel}\,\Delta l = \mu_0 I + \mu_0 \epsilon_0 \frac{\Delta \Phi_E}{\Delta t}. \qquad \textbf{(22–1)}$$

This equation embodies Maxwell's idea that a magnetic field can be caused not only by a normal electric current, but also by a changing electric field or changing electric flux.

## 22–2 Production of Electromagnetic Waves

According to Maxwell, a magnetic field will be produced in empty space if there is a changing electric field. From this, Maxwell derived another startling conclusion. If a changing magnetic field produces an electric field, that electric field is itself changing. This changing electric field will, in turn, produce a magnetic field, which will be changing, and so it too will produce a changing electric field; and so on. When Maxwell worked with his equations, he found that the net result of these interacting changing fields was a *wave* of electric and magnetic fields that can propagate (travel) through space! We now examine, in a simplified way, how such **electromagnetic waves** can be produced.

*How EM waves are produced*

Consider two conducting rods that will serve as an "antenna" (Fig. 22–4a). Suppose that these two rods are connected by a switch to the opposite terminals of a battery. As soon as the switch is closed, the upper rod quickly becomes positively charged and the lower one negatively charged. Electric field lines are formed as indicated by the lines in Fig. 22–4b. While the charges are flowing, a current exists whose direction is indicated by the black arrows. A magnetic field is therefore produced near the antenna. The magnetic field lines encircle the rod-like antenna and therefore, in Fig. 22–4, $\vec{B}$ points into the page (⊗) on the right and out of the page (⊙) on the left. Now we ask, how far out do these electric and magnetic fields extend? In the static case, the fields extend outward indefinitely far. However, when the switch in Fig. 22–4 is closed, the fields quickly appear nearby, but it takes time for them to reach distant points. Both electric and magnetic fields store energy, and this energy cannot be transferred to distant points at infinite speed.

**FIGURE 22–4** Fields produced by charge flowing into conductors. It takes time for the $\vec{E}$ and $\vec{B}$ fields to travel outward to distant points. The fields are shown to the right of the antenna, but they move out in all directions, symmetrically about the (vertical) antenna.

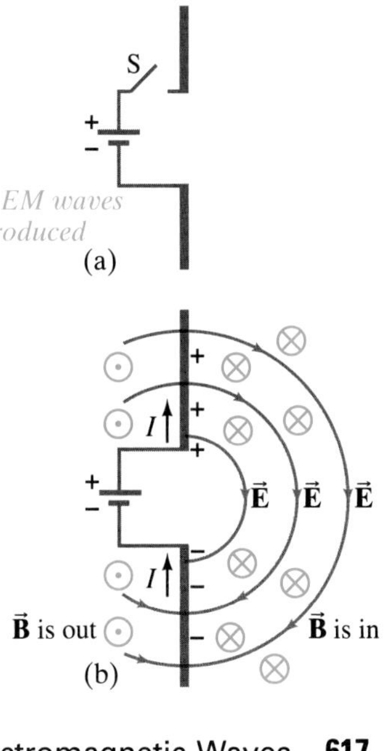

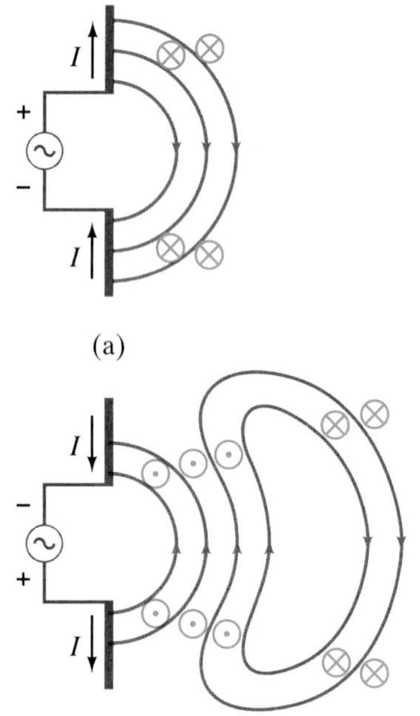


**FIGURE 22–5** Sequence showing electric and magnetic fields that spread outward from oscillating charges on two conductors (the antenna) connected to an ac source (see the text).

Now we look at the situation of Fig. 22–5, where our antenna is connected to an ac generator. In Fig. 22–5a, the connection has just been completed. Charge starts building up, and fields form just as in Fig. 22–4b. The + and − signs in Fig. 22–5a indicate the net charge on each rod. The black arrows indicate the direction of the current. The electric field is represented by red lines in the plane of the page; and the magnetic field, according to the right-hand rule, is into (⊗) or out of (⊙) the page. In Fig. 22–5b, the voltage of the ac generator has reversed in direction; the current is reversed and the new magnetic field is in the opposite direction. Because the new fields have changed direction, the old lines fold back to connect up to some of the new lines and form closed loops as shown.[†] The old fields, however, don't suddenly disappear; they are on their way to distant points. Indeed, because a changing magnetic field produces an electric field, and a changing electric field produces a magnetic field, this combination of changing electric and magnetic fields moving outward is self-supporting, no longer depending on the antenna charges.

The fields not far from the antenna, referred to as the *near field*, become quite complicated, but we are not so interested in them. We are mainly interested in the fields far from the antenna (they are generally what we detect), which we refer to as the **radiation field**. The electric field lines form loops, as shown in Fig. 22–6, and continue moving outward. The magnetic field lines also form closed loops, but are not shown since they are perpendicular to the page. Although the lines are shown only on the right of the source, fields also travel in other directions. The field strengths are greatest in directions perpendicular to the oscillating charges; and they drop to zero along the direction of oscillation—above and below the antenna in Fig. 22–6.

**FIGURE 22–6** (a) The radiation fields (far from the antenna) produced by a sinusoidal signal on the antenna. The red closed loops represent electric field lines. The magnetic field lines, perpendicular to the page and represented by blue ⊗ and ⊙, also form closed loops. (b) Very far from the antenna, the wave fronts (field lines) are essentially flat over a fairly large area, and are referred to as *plane waves*.

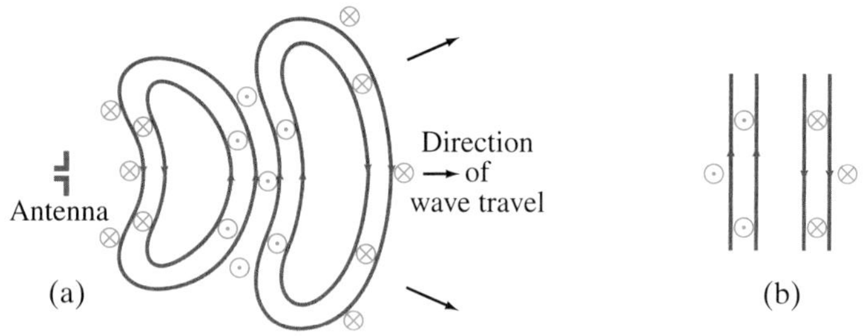


The magnitudes of both $\vec{\mathbf{E}}$ and $\vec{\mathbf{B}}$ in the radiation field are found to decrease with distance as $1/r$. (Compare this to the static electric field given by Coulomb's law where $\vec{\mathbf{E}}$ decreases as $1/r^2$.) The energy carried by the electromagnetic wave is proportional (as for any wave, Chapter 11) to the square of the amplitude, $E^2$ or $B^2$, as will be discussed further in Section 22–7, so the intensity of the wave decreases as $1/r^2$.

$\vec{\mathbf{E}} \perp \vec{\mathbf{B}} \perp \vec{\mathbf{v}}$ *in EM wave*

Several things about the radiation field can be noted from Fig. 22–6. First, *the electric and magnetic fields at any point are perpendicular to each other, and to the direction of wave travel.* Second, we can see that the fields alternate in direction ($\vec{\mathbf{B}}$ is into the page at some points and out of the page at others; $\vec{\mathbf{E}}$ points up at some points and down at others). Thus, the field strengths vary from a maximum in one direction, to zero, to a maximum in the other direction. The electric and magnetic fields are "in phase": that is, they each are zero at the same points and reach their maxima at the same points in space. Finally, very far from the antenna (Fig. 22–6b) the field lines are quite flat over a reasonably large area, and the waves are referred to as **plane waves**.

[†]We are considering waves traveling through empty space. There are no charges for lines of $\vec{\mathbf{E}}$ to start or stop on, so they form closed loops. Magnetic field lines always form closed loops.

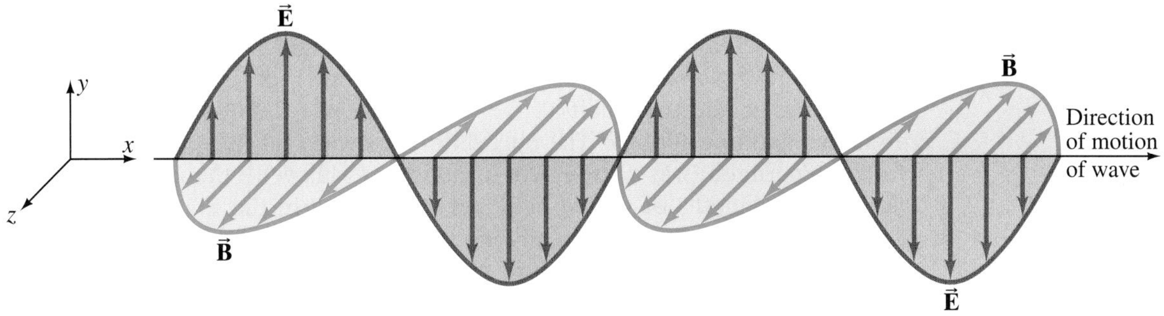


**FIGURE 22–7** Electric and magnetic field strengths in an electromagnetic wave. $\vec{\mathbf{E}}$ and $\vec{\mathbf{B}}$ are at right angles to each other. The entire pattern moves in a direction perpendicular to both $\vec{\mathbf{E}}$ and $\vec{\mathbf{B}}$.

If the source voltage varies sinusoidally, then the electric and magnetic field strengths in the radiation field will also vary sinusoidally. The sinusoidal character of the waves is shown in Fig. 22–7, which displays the field *strengths* as a function of position along the direction of wave travel. Notice that $\vec{\mathbf{B}}$ and $\vec{\mathbf{E}}$ are perpendicular to each other and to the direction of wave travel.

We call these waves electromagnetic (EM) waves. They are *transverse* waves because the amplitude is perpendicular to the direction of wave travel. However, EM waves are always waves of *fields*, not of matter (like waves on water or a rope). Because they are fields, EM waves can propagate in empty space.

As we have seen, EM waves are produced by electric charges that are oscillating, and hence are undergoing acceleration. In fact, we can say in general that

*EM waves are produced by accelerating electric charges*

**accelerating electric charges give rise to electromagnetic waves.**

Maxwell derived a formula for the speed of EM waves:

$$v = c = \frac{E}{B}, \tag{22–2}$$

*c is symbol for speed of light*

where $c$ is the special symbol for the speed of electromagnetic waves in empty space, and $E$ and $B$ are the magnitudes of electric and magnetic fields at the same point in space. More specifically, it was easily shown also that

*Speed of EM waves*

$$c = \frac{1}{\sqrt{\epsilon_0 \mu_0}}. \tag{22–3}$$

When Maxwell put in the values for $\epsilon_0$ and $\mu_0$, he found

$$c = \frac{1}{\sqrt{\epsilon_0 \mu_0}} = \frac{1}{\sqrt{(8.85 \times 10^{-12}\,\mathrm{C^2/N\cdot m^2})(4\pi \times 10^{-7}\,\mathrm{N\cdot s^2/C^2})}}$$
$$= 3.00 \times 10^8\,\mathrm{m/s},$$

which is equal to the measured speed of light in vacuum.

## 22–3 Light as an Electromagnetic Wave and the Electromagnetic Spectrum

Maxwell's prediction that EM waves should exist was startling. Equally remarkable was the speed at which EM waves were predicted to travel—$3.00 \times 10^8\,\mathrm{m/s}$, the same as the measured speed of light.

Light had been shown some 60 years before Maxwell's work to behave like a wave (we'll discuss this in Chapter 24). But nobody knew what kind of wave it was. What is it that is oscillating in a light wave? Maxwell, on the basis of the calculated speed of EM waves, argued that light must be an electromagnetic wave. This idea soon came to be generally accepted by scientists, but not fully until after EM waves were experimentally detected. EM waves were first generated and detected experimentally by Heinrich Hertz (1857–1894) in 1887, eight years after Maxwell's death. Hertz used a spark-gap apparatus in which charge was made to rush back and forth for a short time, generating waves whose frequency was about $10^9$ Hz. He detected them some distance away using a loop of wire in which an emf was produced when a changing magnetic field passed through. These waves were later shown to travel at the speed of light, $3.00 \times 10^8$ m/s, and to exhibit all the characteristics of light such as reflection, refraction, and interference. The only difference was that they were not visible. Hertz's experiment was a strong confirmation of Maxwell's theory.

The wavelengths of visible light were measured in the first decade of the nineteenth century, long before anyone imagined that light was an electromagnetic wave. The wavelengths were found to lie between $4.0 \times 10^{-7}$ m and $7.5 \times 10^{-7}$ m; or 400 nm to 750 nm $(1\text{ nm} = 10^{-9}\text{ m})$. The frequencies of visible light can be found using Eq. 11–12, which we rewrite here:

*Wavelength and frequency related to speed*

$$c = \lambda f, \tag{22–4}$$

where $f$ and $\lambda$ are the frequency and wavelength, respectively, of the wave. Here, $c$ is the speed of light, $3.00 \times 10^8$ m/s; it gets the special symbol $c$ because of its universality for all EM waves in free space. Equation 22–4 tells us that the frequencies of visible light are between $4.0 \times 10^{14}$ Hz and $7.5 \times 10^{14}$ Hz. (Recall that $1\text{ Hz} = 1$ cycle per second $= 1\text{ s}^{-1}$.)

But visible light is only one kind of EM wave. As we have seen, Hertz produced EM waves of much lower frequency, about $10^9$ Hz. These are now called **radio waves**, since frequencies in this range are used to transmit radio and TV signals. Electromagnetic waves, or EM radiation as we sometimes call it, have been produced or detected over a wide range of frequencies. They are usually categorized as shown in Fig. 22–8, which is known as the **electromagnetic spectrum**.

*EM spectrum*

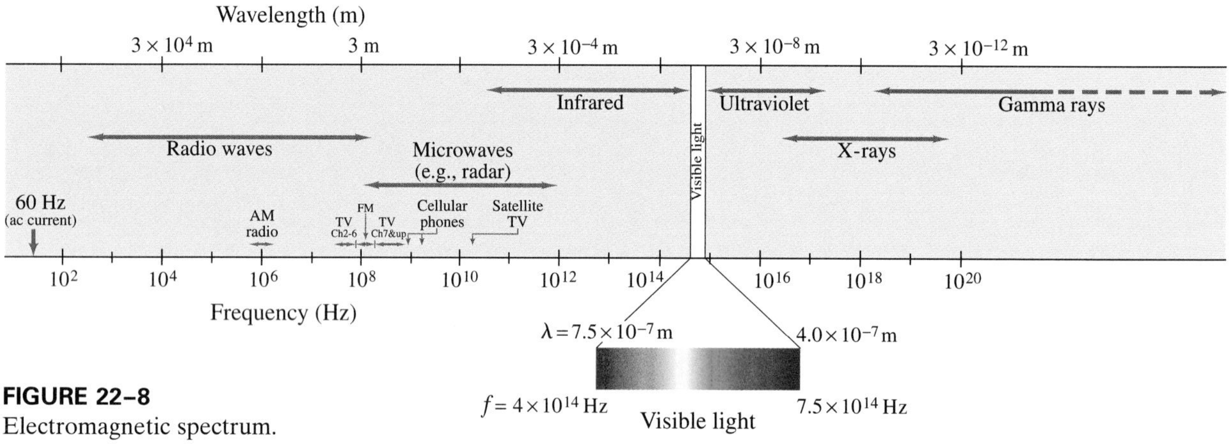


**FIGURE 22–8**
Electromagnetic spectrum.

Radio waves and microwaves can be produced in the laboratory using electronic equipment (Fig. 22–5). Higher-frequency waves are very difficult to produce electronically. These and other types of EM waves are produced in natural processes, as emission from atoms, molecules, and nuclei (more on this later). EM waves can be produced by the acceleration of electrons or other charged particles, such as electrons accelerating in the antenna of Fig. 22–5. Another example is X-rays, which are produced (Chapters 25 and 28) when fast-moving electrons are rapidly decelerated upon striking a metal target. Even the visible light emitted by an ordinary incandescent bulb is due to electrons undergoing acceleration within the hot filament.

We will meet various types of EM waves later. However, it is worth mentioning here that infrared (IR) radiation (EM waves whose frequency is just less than that of visible light) is mainly responsible for the heating effect of the Sun. The Sun emits not only visible light but substantial amounts of IR and UV (ultraviolet) as well. The molecules of our skin tend to "resonate" at infrared frequencies, so it is these that are preferentially absorbed and thus warm us. We humans experience EM waves differently depending on their wavelengths: Our eyes detect wavelengths between about $4 \times 10^{-7}$ m and $7.5 \times 10^{-7}$ m (visible light), whereas our skin detects longer wavelengths (IR). Many EM wavelengths we don't detect directly at all.

Light and other electromagnetic waves travel at a speed of $3 \times 10^8\,\text{m/s}$. Compare this to sound, which travels (see Chapter 12) at a speed of about 300 m/s in air, a million times slower; or to typical freeway speeds of a car, 30 m/s (100 km/h, or 60 mi/h), 10 million times slower than light. EM waves differ from sound waves in another big way: sound waves travel in a medium such as air, and involve motion of air molecules; EM waves do not involve any material—only fields, and they can travel in empty space.

**CAUTION**
*Sound and EM waves are different*

**EXAMPLE 22–1** **Wavelengths of EM waves.** Calculate the wavelength (*a*) of a 60-Hz EM wave, (*b*) of a 93.3-MHz FM radio wave, and (*c*) of a beam of visible red light from a laser at frequency $4.74 \times 10^{14}$ Hz.

**APPROACH** All of these waves are electromagnetic waves, so their speed is $c = 3.00 \times 10^8\,\text{m/s}$. We solve for $\lambda$ in Eq. 22–4: $\lambda = c/f$.

**SOLUTION** (*a*)

$$\lambda = \frac{c}{f} = \frac{3.00 \times 10^8\,\text{m/s}}{60\,\text{s}^{-1}} = 5.0 \times 10^6\,\text{m},$$

or 5000 km. 60 Hz is the frequency of ac current in the United States, and, as we see here, one wavelength stretches all the way across the continental USA.

(*b*)

$$\lambda = \frac{3.00 \times 10^8\,\text{m/s}}{93.3 \times 10^6\,\text{s}^{-1}} = 3.22\,\text{m}.$$

The length of an FM antenna is about half this $(\frac{1}{2}\lambda)$, or $1\frac{1}{2}$ m.

(*c*)

$$\lambda = \frac{3.00 \times 10^8\,\text{m/s}}{4.74 \times 10^{14}\,\text{s}^{-1}} = 6.33 \times 10^{-7}\,\text{m}\ (=633\,\text{nm}).$$

**EXERCISE A** What are the frequencies of (*a*) an 80-m-wavelength radio wave, and (*b*) an X-ray of wavelength $5.5 \times 10^{-11}$ m?

**EXAMPLE 22–2** **ESTIMATE** **Cell phone antenna.** The antenna of a cell phone is often $\frac{1}{4}$ wavelength long. A particular cell phone has an 8.5-cm-long straight rod for its antenna. Estimate the operating frequency of this phone.

**APPROACH** The basic equation relating wave speed, wavelength, and frequency is $c = \lambda f$; the wavelength $\lambda$ equals four times the antenna's length.

**SOLUTION** The antenna is $\frac{1}{4}\lambda$ long, so $\lambda = 4(8.5\,\text{cm}) = 34\,\text{cm} = 0.34\,\text{m}$. Then $f = c/\lambda = (3.0 \times 10^8\,\text{m/s})/(0.34\,\text{m}) = 8.8 \times 10^8\,\text{Hz} = 880\,\text{MHz}$.

**NOTE** Radio antennas are not always straight conductors. The conductor may be a round loop to save space. See Fig. 22–17b.

**EXERCISE B** How long should a $\frac{1}{4}$-$\lambda$ antenna be for an aircraft radio operating at 165 MHz?

Electromagnetic waves can travel along transmission lines as well as in empty space. When a source of emf is connected to a transmission line—be it two parallel wires or a coaxial cable (Fig. 22–9)—the electric field within the wire is not set up immediately at all points along the wires. This is based on the same argument we used in Section 22–2 with reference to Fig. 22–5. Indeed, it can be shown that if the wires are separated by empty space or air, the electrical signal travels along the wires at the speed $c = 3.0 \times 10^8\,\text{m/s}$. For example, when you flip a light switch, the light actually goes on a tiny fraction of a second later. If the wires are in a medium whose electric permittivity is $\epsilon$ and magnetic permeability is $\mu$ (Sections 17–8 and 20–12, respectively), the speed is not given by Eq. 22–3, but by

$$v = \frac{1}{\sqrt{\epsilon\mu}}.$$

**FIGURE 22–9** Coaxial cable.

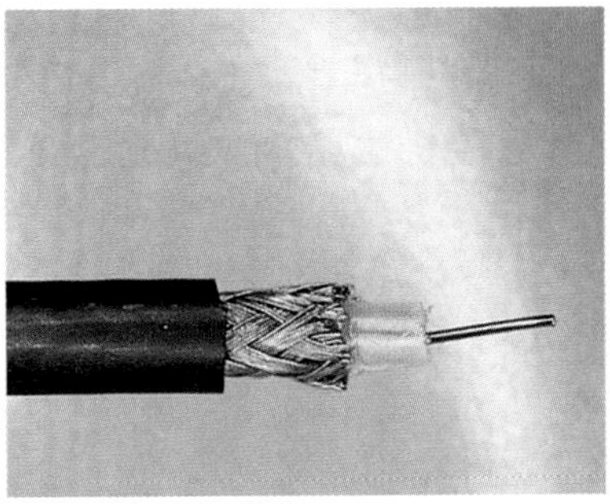

**EXAMPLE 22–3 ESTIMATE** **Voice speed through the wires.** When you speak on the telephone from Los Angeles to a friend in New York some 4000 km away, how long does it take the signal carrying your voice to travel that distance?

**APPROACH** The signal is carried on a telephone wire or in the air via satellite. In either case it is an electromagnetic wave. Electronics as well as the wire or cable slow things down, but as a rough estimate we take the speed to be $c = 3.0 \times 10^8\,\mathrm{m/s}$.

**SOLUTION** Since speed = distance/time, then time = distance/speed = $(4.0 \times 10^6\,\mathrm{m})/(3.0 \times 10^8\,\mathrm{m/s}) = 1.3 \times 10^{-2}\,\mathrm{s}$, or about $\frac{1}{100}$ s.

**NOTE** Such a small amount of time normally goes unnoticed.

**EXERCISE C** If your voice traveled as a sound wave, how long would it take in Example 22–3?

## 22–4 Measuring the Speed of Light

Galileo attempted to measure the speed of light by trying to measure the time required for light to travel a known distance between two hilltops. He stationed an assistant on one hilltop and himself on another, and ordered the assistant to lift the cover from a lamp the instant he saw a flash from Galileo's lamp. Galileo measured the time between the flash of his lamp and when he received the light from his assistant's lamp. The time was so short that Galileo concluded it merely represented human reaction time, and that the speed of light must be extremely high.

The first successful determination that the speed of light is finite was made by the Danish astronomer Ole Roemer (1644–1710). Roemer had noted that the carefully measured orbital period of Io, a moon of Jupiter with an average period of 42.5 h, varied slightly, depending on the relative motion of Earth and Jupiter. When Earth was moving away from Jupiter, the period of Io was slightly longer, and when Earth was moving toward Jupiter, the period was slightly shorter. He attributed this variation in the apparent period to the change in distance between the Earth and Jupiter during one of Io's periods, and the time it took light to travel this distance. Roemer concluded that the speed of light—though great—is finite.

*Michelson measures c*

Since then a number of techniques have been used to measure the speed of light. Among the most important were those carried out by the American Albert A. Michelson (1852–1931). Michelson used the rotating mirror apparatus diagrammed in Fig. 22–10 for a series of high-precision experiments carried out from 1880 to the 1920s. Light from a source was directed at one face of a rotating eight-sided mirror. The reflected light traveled to a stationary mirror a large distance away and back again as shown. If the rotating mirror

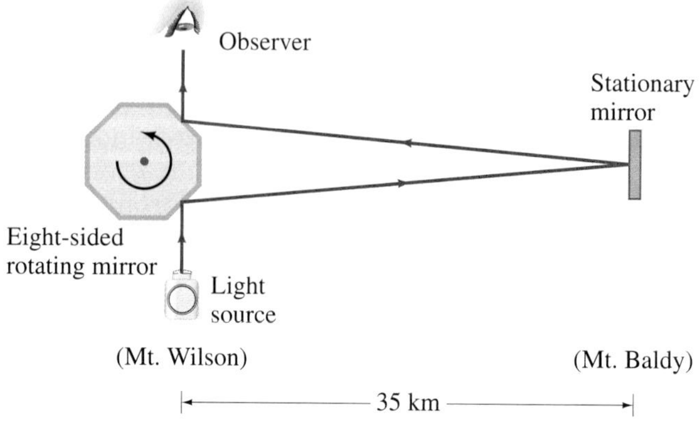


**FIGURE 22–10** Michelson's speed-of-light apparatus (not to scale).

was turning at just the right rate, the returning beam of light would reflect from one face of the mirror into a small telescope through which the observer looked. If the speed of rotation was only slightly different, the beam would be deflected to one side and would not be seen by the observer. From the required speed of the rotating mirror and the known distance to the stationary mirror, the speed of light could be calculated. In the 1920s, Michelson set up the rotating mirror on the top of Mt. Wilson in southern California and the stationary mirror on Mt. Baldy (Mt. San Antonio) 35 km away. He later measured the speed of light in vacuum using a long evacuated tube.

Today the speed of light, $c$, in vacuum is taken as

$$c = 2.99792458 \times 10^8\ \mathrm{m/s},$$

and is defined to be this value. This means that the standard for length, the meter, is no longer defined separately. Instead, as we noted in Section 1–5, the meter is now formally defined as the distance light travels in vacuum in 1/299,792,458 of a second.

We usually round off $c$ to

$$c = 3.00 \times 10^8\ \mathrm{m/s}$$

when extremely precise results are not required. In air, the speed is only slightly less.

## * 22–5 Energy in EM Waves

Electromagnetic waves carry energy from one region of space to another. This energy is associated with the moving electric and magnetic fields. In Section 17–9, we saw that the energy density $u_E\ (\mathrm{J/m^3})$ stored in an electric field $E$ is $u_E = \frac{1}{2}\epsilon_0 E^2$ (Eq. 17–11). The energy density stored in a magnetic field $B$, as we discussed in Section 21–10, is given by $u_B = \frac{1}{2}B^2/\mu_0$ (Eq. 21–10). Thus, the total energy stored per unit volume in a region of space where there is an electromagnetic wave is

$$u = u_E + u_B = \frac{1}{2}\epsilon_0 E^2 + \frac{1}{2}\frac{B^2}{\mu_0}. \qquad \textbf{(22–5)}$$

In this equation, $E$ and $B$ represent the electric and magnetic field strengths of the wave at any instant in a small region of space. We can write Eq. 22–5 in terms of the $E$ field only using Eqs. 22–2 $(B = E/c)$ and 22–3 $(c = 1/\sqrt{\epsilon_0\mu_0})$ to obtain

$$u = \frac{1}{2}\epsilon_0 E^2 + \frac{1}{2}\frac{\epsilon_0\mu_0 E^2}{\mu_0} = \epsilon_0 E^2. \qquad \textbf{(22–6a)}$$

Note here that the energy density associated with the $B$ field equals that due to the $E$ field, and each contributes half to the total energy. We can also write the energy density in terms of the $B$ field only:

$$u = \epsilon_0 E^2 = \epsilon_0 c^2 B^2 = \frac{B^2}{\mu_0}, \qquad \textbf{(22–6b)}$$

or in one term containing both $E$ and $B$,

$$u = \epsilon_0 E^2 = \epsilon_0 EcB = \frac{\epsilon_0 EB}{\sqrt{\epsilon_0\mu_0}} = \sqrt{\frac{\epsilon_0}{\mu_0}}\,EB. \qquad \textbf{(22–6c)}$$

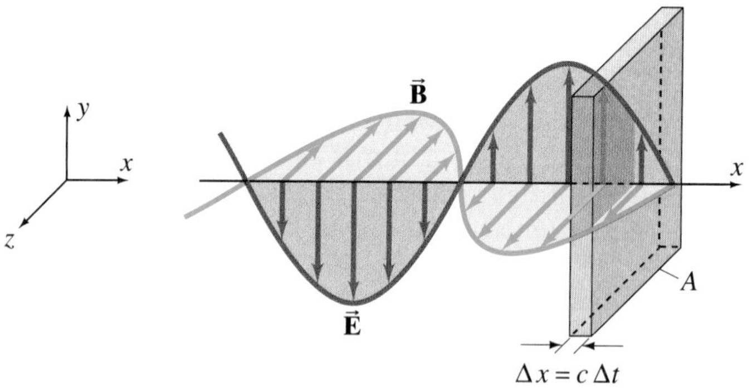


**FIGURE 22–11** Electromagnetic wave carrying energy through area $A$.

The energy a wave transports per unit time per unit area is the **intensity** $I$, as defined in Sections 11–9 and 12–2.† The units of $I$ are $\mathrm{W/m^2}$. The energy passing through an area $A$ in a time $\Delta t$ (see Fig. 22–11) is

$$\Delta U = u\,\Delta V = (u)(A\,\Delta x) = \left(\epsilon_0 E^2\right)(Ac\,\Delta t)$$

because $\Delta x = c\,\Delta t$. Therefore, the magnitude of the intensity (energy per unit area per time $\Delta t$, or power per unit area) is

$$I = \frac{\Delta U}{A\,\Delta t} = \frac{\left(\epsilon_0 E^2\right)(Ac\,\Delta t)}{A\,\Delta t} = \epsilon_0 c E^2.$$

From Eqs. 22–2 and 22–3, this can also be written

*Intensity of EM waves*

$$I = \epsilon_0 c E^2 = \frac{c}{\mu_0} B^2 = \frac{EB}{\mu_0}. \qquad \textbf{(22–7)}$$

The *average intensity* over an extended period of time, if $E$ and $B$ are sinusoidal so that $\overline{E^2} = E_0^2/2$ (just as for electric currents and voltages, Section 18–7), is

*Average intensity*

$$\overline{I} = \frac{1}{2}\epsilon_0 c E_0^2 = \frac{1}{2}\frac{c}{\mu_0} B_0^2 = \frac{E_0 B_0}{2\mu_0}. \qquad \textbf{(22–8)}$$

Here $E_0$ and $B_0$ are the maximum values of $E$ and $B$. We can also write

$$\overline{I} = \frac{E_{\mathrm{rms}} B_{\mathrm{rms}}}{\mu_0},$$

where $E_{\mathrm{rms}}$ and $B_{\mathrm{rms}}$ are the rms values $\left(E_{\mathrm{rms}} = \sqrt{\overline{E^2}},\ B_{\mathrm{rms}} = \sqrt{\overline{B^2}}\right)$.

**EXAMPLE 22–4** ***E* and *B* from the Sun.** Radiation from the Sun reaches the Earth (above the atmosphere) at a rate of about $1350\ \mathrm{J/s\cdot m^2}$ $(= 1350\ \mathrm{W/m^2})$. Assume that this is a single EM wave, and calculate the maximum values of $E$ and $B$.

**APPROACH** We are given the intensity $\overline{I} = 1350\ \mathrm{J/s\cdot m^2}$. We solve Eq. 22–8 $\left(\overline{I} = \frac{1}{2}\epsilon_0 c E_0^2\right)$ for $E_0$ in terms of $\overline{I}$.

**SOLUTION**

$$E_0 = \sqrt{\frac{2\overline{I}}{\epsilon_0 c}} = \sqrt{\frac{2\left(1350\ \mathrm{J/s\cdot m^2}\right)}{\left(8.85 \times 10^{-12}\ \mathrm{C^2/N\cdot m^2}\right)\left(3.00 \times 10^8\ \mathrm{m/s}\right)}}$$
$$= 1.01 \times 10^3\ \mathrm{V/m}.$$

From Eq. 22–2, $B = E/c$, so

$$B_0 = \frac{E_0}{c} = \frac{1.01 \times 10^3\ \mathrm{V/m}}{3.00 \times 10^8\ \mathrm{m/s}} = 3.37 \times 10^{-6}\ \mathrm{T}.$$

**NOTE** Although $B$ has a small numerical value compared to $E$ (because of the way the different units for $E$ and $B$ are defined), $B$ contributes the same energy to the wave as $E$ does, as we saw earlier.

†The intensity $I$ for EM waves is often called the **Poynting vector** and given the symbol $\vec{\mathbf{S}}$. Its direction is that in which the energy is being transported, which is the direction the wave is traveling, and its magnitude is the intensity $(S = I)$.

## * 22–6 Momentum Transfer and Radiation Pressure

If electromagnetic waves carry energy, then we might expect them to also carry linear momentum. When an electromagnetic wave encounters the surface of an object and is absorbed or reflected, a force will be exerted on the surface as a result of the momentum transfer ($F = \Delta p/\Delta t$) just as when a moving object strikes a surface. The force per unit area exerted by the waves is called **radiation pressure**, and its existence was predicted by Maxwell. He showed that if a beam of EM radiation (light, for example) is completely absorbed by an object, then the momentum transferred is

$$\Delta p = \frac{\Delta U}{c}, \qquad \begin{bmatrix}\text{radiation}\\ \text{absorbed}\end{bmatrix} \qquad \textbf{(22–9a)}$$

where $\Delta U$ is the energy absorbed by the object in a time $\Delta t$ and $c$ is the speed of light. If, instead, the radiation is fully reflected (suppose the object is a mirror), then the momentum transferred is twice as great, just as when a ball bounces elastically off a surface:

$$\Delta p = \frac{2\Delta U}{c}. \qquad \begin{bmatrix}\text{radiation}\\ \text{reflected}\end{bmatrix} \qquad \textbf{(22–9b)}$$

If a surface absorbs some of the energy, and reflects some of it, then $\Delta p = a\,\Delta U/c$, where $a$ has a value between 1 and 2.

Using Newton's second law we can calculate the force and the pressure exerted by EM radiation on an object. The force $F$ is given by

$$F = \frac{\Delta p}{\Delta t}.$$

The radiation pressure $P$ (assuming full absorption) is given by (see Eq. 22–9a)

$$P = \frac{F}{A} = \frac{1}{A}\frac{\Delta p}{\Delta t} = \frac{1}{Ac}\frac{\Delta U}{\Delta t}.$$

We discussed in Section 22–5 that the average intensity $\bar{I}$ is defined as energy per unit time per unit area:

$$\bar{I} = \frac{\Delta U}{A\,\Delta t}.$$

Hence the radiation pressure is

$$P = \frac{\bar{I}}{c}. \qquad \textbf{(22–10a)}$$

*Radiation pressure (absorbed)*

If the light is fully reflected, the pressure is twice as great (Eq. 22–9b):

$$P = \frac{2\bar{I}}{c}. \qquad \textbf{(22–10b)}$$

*Radiation pressure (reflected)*

**EXAMPLE 22–5 ESTIMATE Solar pressure.** Radiation from the Sun that reaches the Earth's surface (after passing through the atmosphere) transports energy at a rate of about $1000\,\mathrm{W/m^2}$. Estimate the pressure and force exerted by the Sun on your outstretched hand.

**APPROACH** The radiation is partially reflected and partially absorbed, so let us estimate simply $P = \bar{I}/c$.

**SOLUTION** $$P \approx \frac{\bar{I}}{c} = \frac{1000\,\mathrm{W/m^2}}{3\times10^{8}\,\mathrm{m/s}} \approx 3\times10^{-6}\,\mathrm{N/m^2}.$$

An estimate of the area of your outstretched hand might be about 10 cm by 20 cm, so $A = 0.02\,\mathrm{m^2}$. Then the force is

$$F = PA \approx (3\times10^{-6}\,\mathrm{N/m^2})(0.02\,\mathrm{m^2}) \approx 6\times10^{-8}\,\mathrm{N}.$$

**NOTE** These numbers are tiny. The force of gravity on your hand, for comparison, is maybe a half pound, or with $m = 0.2$ kg, $mg \approx (0.2\,\mathrm{kg})(9.8\,\mathrm{m/s^2}) \approx 2\,\mathrm{N}$. The radiation pressure on your hand is imperceptible compared to gravity.

PHYSICS APPLIED
*Optical tweezers*

Although you cannot directly feel the effects of radiation pressure, the phenomenon is quite dramatic when applied to atoms irradiated by a finely focused laser beam. An atom has a mass on the order of $10^{-27}$ kg, and a laser beam can deliver energy at a rate of $1000\,W/m^2$. This is the same intensity used in Example 22–5, above, but here a radiation pressure of $10^{-6}\,N/m^2$ would be very significant on a molecule whose mass might be $10^{-23}$ to $10^{-26}$ kg. It is possible to move atoms and molecules around by steering them with a laser beam, in a device called "optical tweezers." Optical tweezers have some remarkable applications. They are of great interest to biologists, especially since optical tweezers can manipulate live microorganisms, and components within a cell, without damaging them. Optical tweezers have been used to measure the elastic properties of DNA by pulling each end of the molecule with such a laser "tweezers."

## * 22–7 Radio and Television; Wireless Communication

PHYSICS APPLIED
*"Wireless" transmission*

Electromagnetic waves offer the possibility of transmitting information over long distances. Among the first to realize this and put it into practice was Guglielmo Marconi (1874–1937) who, in the 1890s, invented the radio and developed the wireless telegraph. With it, messages could be sent at the speed of light without the use of wires. The first signals were merely long and short pulses that could be translated into words by a code, such as the "dots" and "dashes" of the Morse code: they were digital wireless, believe it or not. In 1895 Marconi sent wireless signals a kilometer or two. By 1901 he had sent test signals 3000 km across the ocean from Newfoundland, Canada, to Cornwall, England. In 1903 he sent the first practical commercial messages from Cape Cod, Massachusetts, to England: the London *Times* printed news items sent from its New York correspondent. 1903 was also the year of the first powered airplane flight by the Wright brothers. The hallmarks of the modern age—wireless communication and flight—date from the same year.

The next decade saw the development of vacuum tubes. Out of this early work radio and television were born. We now discuss briefly (1) how radio and TV signals are transmitted, and (2) how they are received at home.

*Transmission of radio waves*

The process by which a radio station transmits information (words and music) is outlined in Fig. 22–12. The audio (sound) information is changed into an electrical signal of the same frequencies by, say, a microphone or recording head. This electrical signal is called an audiofrequency (AF) signal, since the frequencies are in the audio range (20 to 20,000 Hz). The signal is amplified electronically and is then mixed with a radio-frequency (RF) signal called its **carrier frequency**, which represents that station. AM radio stations have carrier frequencies from about 530 kHz to 1700 kHz. For example, "710 on your dial" means a station whose carrier frequency is 710 kHz. FM radio stations have much higher carrier frequencies, between 88 MHz and 108 MHz. The carrier frequencies for broadcast TV stations in the United States lie between 54 MHz and 88 MHz, between 174 MHz and 216 MHz, and between 470 MHz and 890 MHz.

*Carrier frequency*

**FIGURE 22–12** Block diagram of a radio transmitter.

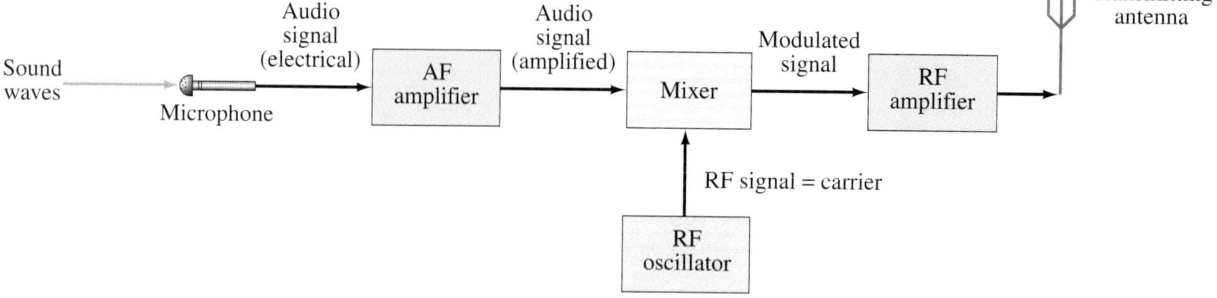

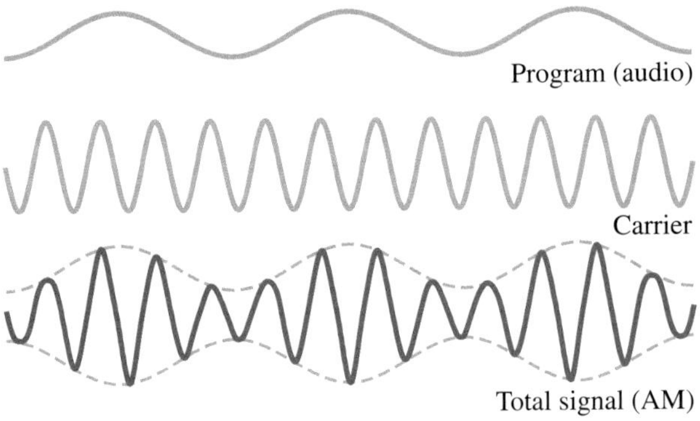


**FIGURE 22–13** In amplitude modulation (AM), the amplitude of the carrier signal is made to vary in proportion to the audio signal's amplitude.

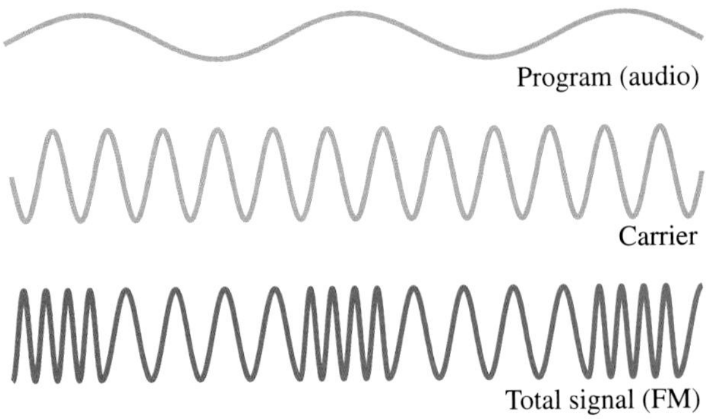


**FIGURE 22–14** In frequency modulation (FM), the frequency of the carrier signal is made to change in proportion to the audio signal's amplitude. This method is used by FM radio and television.

**PHYSICS APPLIED**
*AM and FM*

The mixing of the audio and carrier frequencies is done in two ways. In **amplitude modulation** (AM), the amplitude of the high frequency carrier wave is made to vary in proportion to the amplitude of the audio signal, as shown in Fig. 22–13. It is called "amplitude modulation" because the *amplitude* of the carrier is altered ("modulate" means to change or alter). In **frequency modulation** (FM), the *frequency* of the carrier wave is made to change in proportion to the audio signal's amplitude, as shown in Fig. 22–14. The mixed signal is amplified further and sent to the transmitting antenna, where the complex mixture of frequencies is sent out in the form of EM waves.

A television transmitter works in a similar way, using FM for audio and AM for video; both audio and video signals (see Section 17–10) are mixed with carrier frequencies.

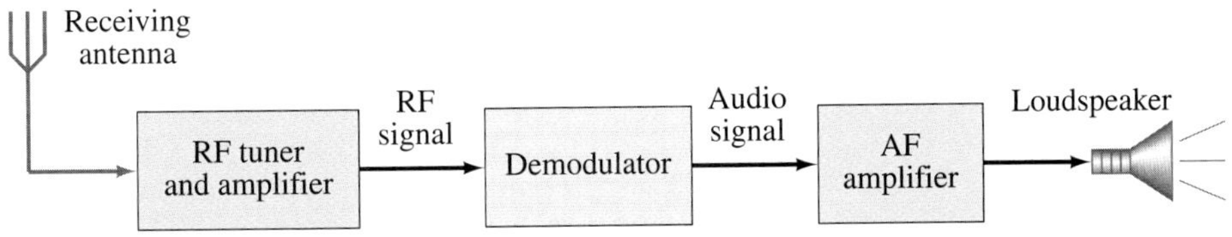


**FIGURE 22–15** Block diagram of a simple radio receiver.

**PHYSICS APPLIED**
*Radio and TV receivers*

Now let us look at the other end of the process, the reception of radio and TV programs at home. A simple radio receiver is diagrammed in Fig. 22–15. The EM waves sent out by all stations are received by the antenna. The signal the antenna detects and sends to the receiver is very small and contains frequencies from many different stations. The receiver selects out a particular RF frequency (actually a narrow range of frequencies) corresponding to a particular station using a resonant $LC$ circuit (Section 21–14). A simple way of tuning a station is shown in Fig. 22–16. A particular station is "tuned-in" by adjusting $C$ and/or $L$ so that the resonant frequency of the circuit equals that of the station's carrier frequency. The signal, containing both audio and carrier frequencies, next goes to the *demodulator*, or *detector* (Fig. 22–15), where "demodulation" takes place—that is, the RF carrier frequency is separated from the audio signal. The audio signal is amplified and sent to a loudspeaker or headphones.

**FIGURE 22–16** Simple tuning stage of a radio.

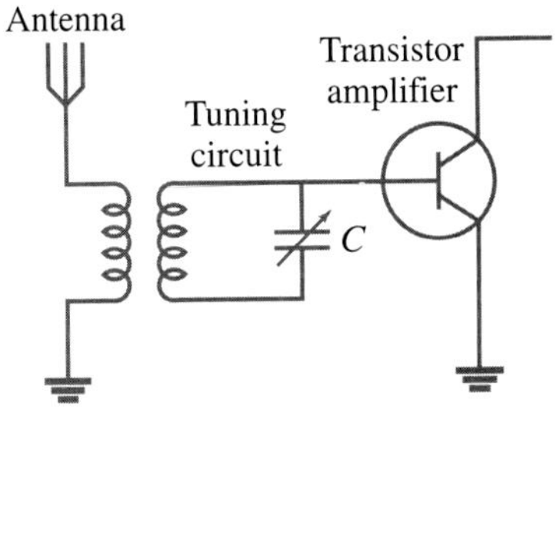


Modern receivers have more stages than those shown. Various means are used to increase the sensitivity and selectivity (ability to detect weak signals and distinguish them from other stations), and to minimize distortion of the original signal.†

†For *FM stereo broadcasting*, two signals are carried by the carrier wave. One signal contains frequencies up to about 15 kHz, which includes most audio frequencies. The other signal includes the same range of frequencies, but 19 kHz is added to it. A stereo receiver subtracts this 19,000-Hz signal and distributes the two signals to the left and right channels. The first signal consists of the sum of left and right channels (L + R), so mono radios detect all the sound. The second signal is the difference between left and right (L − R). Hence the receiver must add and subtract the two signals to get pure left and right signal for each channel.

*Television*

A television receiver does similar things to both the audio and the video signals. The audio signal goes finally to the loudspeaker, and the video signal to the monitor, such as a *cathode ray tube* (CRT) or LCD screen (Sections 17–10 and 24–11).

*Antennas*

One kind of antenna consists of one or more conducting rods; the electric field in the EM waves exerts a force on the electrons in the conductor, causing them to move back and forth at the frequencies of the waves (Fig. 22–17a). A second type of antenna consists of a tubular coil of wire which detects the magnetic field of the wave: the changing $B$ field induces an emf in the coil (Fig. 22–17b). A satellite dish (Fig. 22–18) consists of a parabolic reflector that focuses the EM waves onto a "horn," similar to a concave mirror telescope (Fig. 25–21).

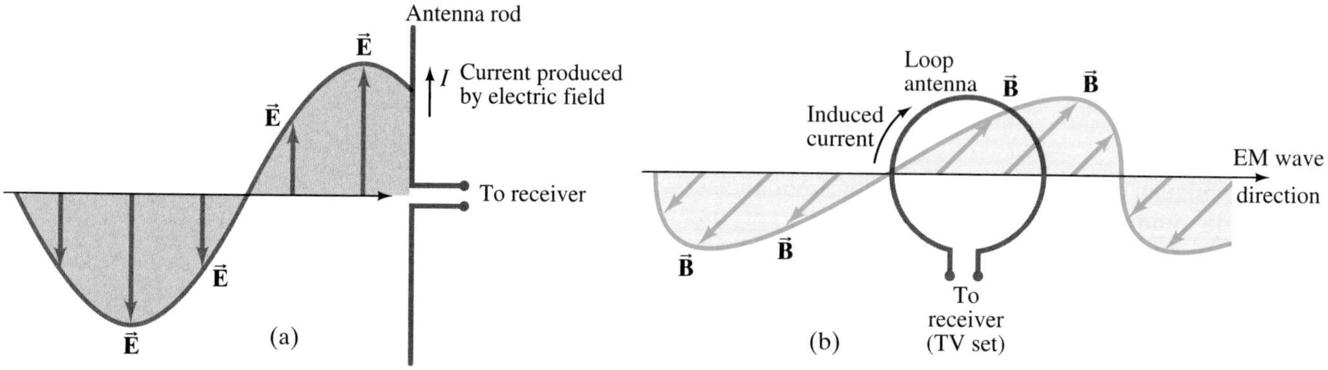


**FIGURE 22–17** Antennas. (a) Electric field of EM wave produces a current in an antenna consisting of straight wire or rods. (b) Changing magnetic field induces an emf and current in a loop antenna.

**FIGURE 22–18** A satellite dish.

**EXAMPLE 22–6** **Tuning a station.** Calculate the transmitting wavelength of an FM radio station that transmits at 100 MHz.

**APPROACH** Radio is transmitted as an EM wave, so the speed is $c = 3.0 \times 10^8\,\mathrm{m/s}$. The wavelength is found from Eq. 22–4, $\lambda = c/f$.

**SOLUTION** The carrier frequency is $f = 100\,\mathrm{MHz} = 1.0 \times 10^8\,\mathrm{s^{-1}}$, so

$$\lambda = \frac{c}{f} = \frac{(3.0 \times 10^8\,\mathrm{m/s})}{(1.0 \times 10^8\,\mathrm{s^{-1}})} = 3.0\,\mathrm{m}.$$

**NOTE** The wavelengths of other FM signals (88 MHz to 108 MHz) are close to the 3.0-m wavelength of this station. FM antennas are typically 1.5 m long, or about a half wavelength. This length is chosen so that the antenna reacts in a resonant fashion and thus is more sensitive to FM frequencies. AM radio antennas would have to be much too long to be either $\frac{1}{2}\lambda$ or $\frac{1}{4}\lambda$.

## Other EM Wave Communications

PHYSICS APPLIED

*Cell phones, radio control, remote control, cable TV, and satellite TV and radio*

The various regions of the radio-wave spectrum are assigned by governmental agencies for various purposes. Besides those mentioned above, there are "bands" assigned for use by ships, airplanes, police, military, amateurs, satellites and space, and radar. Cell phones, for example, are complete radio transmitters and receivers which in the U.S. function on two different bands: 800 MHz and 1900 MHz (=1.9 GHz), whereas in Europe and Asia 900-MHz and 1800-MHz bands are used in the international standard called GSM (Global System for Mobile Communication). Radio-controlled toys (cars, sailboats, robotic animals, etc.) can use various frequencies from 27 MHz to 75 MHz. Automobile remote (keyless) entry may operate around 300 MHz or 400 MHz.

Cable TV channels are carried as electromagnetic waves along a coaxial cable (see Fig. 22–9) rather than being broadcast and received through the "air." The channels are in the same part of the EM spectrum, hundreds of MHz, but some are at frequencies not available for TV broadcast. Digital satellite TV and radio are carried in the microwave portion of the spectrum (12 to 14 GHz and 2.3 GHz, respectively).

## Summary

James Clerk Maxwell synthesized an elegant theory in which all electric and magnetic phenomena could be described using four equations, now called **Maxwell's equations**. They are based on earlier ideas, but Maxwell added one more—that a changing electric field produces a magnetic field.

Maxwell's theory predicted that transverse **electromagnetic (EM) waves** would be produced by accelerating electric charges, and these waves would propagate (move) through space at the speed of light, given by the formula

$$c = \frac{1}{\sqrt{\epsilon_0 \mu_0}}. \qquad \textbf{(22–3)}$$

The oscillating electric and magnetic fields in an EM wave are perpendicular to each other and to the direction of propagation. These waves are waves of fields, not matter, and can propagate in empty space.

The wavelength $\lambda$ and frequency $f$ of EM waves are related to their speed $c$ by

$$c = \lambda f, \qquad \textbf{(22–4)}$$

just as for other waves.

After EM waves were experimentally detected, the idea that light is an EM wave (of very high frequency) became generally accepted. The **electromagnetic spectrum** includes EM waves of a wide variety of wavelengths, from microwaves and radio waves to visible light to X-rays and gamma rays, all of which travel through space at a speed $c = 3.0 \times 10^8\,\mathrm{m/s}$.

[*The average *intensity* $(\mathrm{W/m^2})$ of an EM wave is

$$\bar{I} = \frac{1}{2}\epsilon_0 c E_0^2 = \frac{1}{2}\frac{c}{\mu_0}B_0^2 = \frac{1}{2}\frac{E_0 B_0}{\mu_0}, \qquad \textbf{(22–8)}$$

where $E_0$ and $B_0$ are the peak values of the electric and magnetic fields, respectively, in the wave.]

[*EM waves carry momentum and exert a *radiation pressure* proportional to the intensity $I$ of the wave.]

## Questions

1. The electric field in an EM wave traveling north oscillates in an east–west plane. Describe the direction of the magnetic field vector in this wave.
2. Is sound an electromagnetic wave? If not, what kind of wave is it?
3. Can EM waves travel through a perfect vacuum? Can sound waves?
4. When you flip a light switch on, does the light go on immediately? Explain.
5. Are the wavelengths of radio and television signals longer or shorter than those detectable by the human eye?
6. When you connect two loudspeakers to the output of a stereo amplifier, should you be sure the lead-in wires are equal in length so that there will not be a time lag between speakers? Explain.
7. In the electromagnetic spectrum, what type of EM wave would have a wavelength of $10^3$ km? 1 km? 1 m? 1 cm? 1 mm? 1 $\mu$m?
8. Can radio waves have the same frequencies as sound waves (20 Hz–20,000 Hz)?

*9. Can two radio or TV stations broadcast on the same carrier frequency? Explain.

*10. If a radio transmitter has a vertical antenna, should a receiver's antenna (rod type) be vertical or horizontal to obtain best reception?

*11. The carrier frequencies of FM broadcasts are much higher than for AM broadcasts. On the basis of what you learned about diffraction in Chapter 11, explain why AM signals can be detected more readily than FM signals behind low hills or buildings.

*12. Discuss how cordless telephones make use of EM waves. What about cell phones?

*13. A lost person may signal by flashing a flashlight on and off using Morse code. This is actually a modulated EM wave. Is it AM or FM? What is the frequency of the carrier, approximately?

## Problems

### 22–1 Changing $\vec{E}$ Produces $\vec{B}$

*1. (II) At a given instant, a 1.8-A current flows in the wires connected to a parallel-plate capacitor. What is the rate at which the electric field is changing between the plates if the square plates are 1.60 cm on a side?

*2. (II) A 1200-nF capacitor with circular parallel plates 2.0 cm in diameter is accumulating charge at the rate of 35.0 mC/s at some instant in time. What will be the magnitude of the induced magnetic field 10.0 cm radially outward from the center of the plates? What will be the magnitude of the field after the capacitor is fully charged?

### 22–2 EM Waves

3. (I) If the magnetic field in a traveling EM wave has a peak magnitude of 17.5 nT at a given point, what is the peak magnitude of the electric field?
4. (I) In an EM wave traveling west, the $B$ field oscillates vertically and has a frequency of 80.0 kHz and an rms strength of $6.75 \times 10^{-9}$ T. What are the frequency and rms strength of the electric field, and what is its direction? [*Hint*: see Fig. 22–7.]

### 22–3 and 22–4 EM Spectrum and Speed

5. (I) What is the frequency of a microwave whose wavelength is 1.60 cm?
6. (I) What is the wavelength of a $29.75 \times 10^9$-Hz radar signal?
7. (I) An EM wave has frequency $9.66 \times 10^{14}$ Hz. What is its wavelength, and how would we classify it?
8. (I) An EM wave has a wavelength of 650 nm. What is its frequency, and how would we classify it?
9. (I) How long does it take light to reach us from the Sun, $1.50 \times 10^8$ km away?

10. (I) A widely used "short-wave" radio broadcast band is referred to as the 49-m band. What is the frequency of a 49-m radio signal?

11. (II) Our nearest star (other than the Sun) is 4.2 light-years away. That is, it takes 4.2 years for the light it emits to reach Earth. How far away is it in meters?

12. (II) A light-year is a measure of distance (not time). How many meters does light travel in a year?

13. (II) How long would it take a message sent as radio waves from Earth to reach Mars (*a*) when nearest Earth, (*b*) when farthest from Earth? [*Hint*: see Table 5–2, p. 125.]

14. (II) What is the minimum angular speed at which Michelson's eight-sided mirror would have had to rotate to reflect light into an observer's eye by succeeding mirror faces (Fig. 22–10)?

15. (II) A student wants to scale down Michelson's light-speed experiment to a size that will fit in one room. A six-sided mirror is available, and the stationary mirror can be mounted 12 m from the rotating mirror. If the arrangement is otherwise as shown in Fig. 22–10, at what minimum rate must the mirror rotate?

16. (II) Who will hear the voice of a singer first—a person in the balcony 50.0 m away from the stage (Fig. 22–19), or a person 3000 km away at home whose ear is next to the radio? How much sooner? Assume that the microphone is a few centimeters from the singer and the temperature is 20°C.

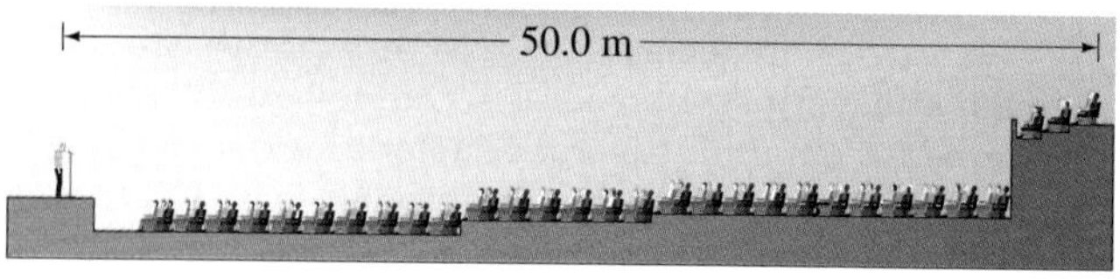


**FIGURE 22–19** Problem 16.

17. (II) Pulsed lasers used in science and medicine produce very short bursts of electromagnetic energy. If the laser light wavelength is 1062 nm (this corresponds to a Neodymium-YAG laser), and the pulse lasts for 32 picoseconds, how many wavelengths are found within the laser pulse? How short would the pulse need to be to fit only one wavelength?

### * 22–5 Energy in EM Waves

* 18. (I) The $\vec{\mathbf{E}}$ field in an EM wave in free space has a peak of 21.8 mV/m. What is the average rate at which this wave carries energy across unit area per unit time?

* 19. (II) The magnetic field in a traveling EM wave has an rms strength of 28.5 nT. How long does it take to deliver 235 J of energy to 1.00 $\text{cm}^2$ of a wall that it hits perpendicularly?

* 20. (II) How much energy is transported across a 1.00-$\text{cm}^2$ area per hour by an EM wave whose $E$ field has an rms strength of 38.6 mV/m?

* 21. (II) A spherically spreading EM wave comes from a 1200-W source. At a distance of 10.0 m, what is the average intensity, and what is the rms value of the electric field?

* 22. (II) A 12.8-mW laser puts out a narrow beam 1.75 mm in diameter. What are the average (rms) values of $E$ and $B$ in the beam?

* 23. (II) Estimate the average power output of the Sun, given that about 1350 $\text{W/m}^2$ reaches the upper atmosphere of the Earth.

* 24. (II) If the amplitude of the $B$ field of an EM wave is $2.5 \times 10^{-7}$ T, (*a*) what is the amplitude of the $E$ field? (*b*) What is the average power per unit area of the EM wave?

* 25. (II) A high-energy pulsed laser emits a 1.0-ns-long pulse of average power $2.8 \times 10^{11}$ W. The beam is $2.2 \times 10^{-3}$ m in radius. Determine (*a*) the energy delivered in each pulse, and (*b*) the rms value of the electric field.

### * 22–6 Radiation Pressure

* 26. (II) Estimate the radiation pressure due to a 100-W bulb at a distance of 8.0 cm from the center of the bulb. Estimate the force exerted on your fingertip if you place it at this point.

### * 22–7 Radio, TV

* 27. (I) What is the range of wavelengths for (*a*) FM radio (88 MHz to 108 MHz) and (*b*) AM radio (535 kHz to 1700 kHz)?

* 28. (I) Estimate the wavelength for 1.9-GHz cell phone reception.

* 29. (I) Compare 940 on the AM dial to 94 on the FM dial. Which has the longer wavelength, and by what factor is it larger?

* 30. (I) What are the wavelengths for two TV channels that broadcast at 54.0 MHz (Channel 2) and 806 MHz (Channel 69)?

* 31. (I) The variable capacitor in the tuner of an AM radio has a capacitance of 2800 pF when the radio is tuned to a station at 550 kHz. What must the capacitance be for a station near the other end of the dial, 1610 kHz?

* 32. (I) The oscillator of a 96.1-MHz FM station has an inductance of 1.8 $\mu$H. What value must the capacitance be?

* 33. (II) A certain FM radio tuning circuit has a fixed capacitor $C = 840$ pF. Tuning is done by a variable inductance. What range of values must the inductance have to tune stations from 88 MHz to 108 MHz?

* 34. (II) An amateur radio operator wishes to build a receiver that can tune a range from 14.0 MHz to 15.0 MHz. A variable capacitor has a minimum capacitance of 82 pF. (*a*) What is the required value of the inductance? (*b*) What is the maximum capacitance used on the variable capacitor?

* 35. (II) A satellite beams microwave radiation with a power of 10 kW toward the Earth's surface, 550 km away. When the beam strikes Earth, its circular diameter is about 1500 m. Find the rms electric field strength of the beam.

* 36. (III) A 1.60-m-long FM antenna is oriented parallel to the electric field of an EM wave. How large must the electric field be to produce a 1.00-mV (rms) voltage between the ends of the antenna? What is the rate of energy transport per square meter?

## General Problems

37. If the Sun were to disappear or somehow radically change its output, how long would it take for us on Earth to learn about it?

38. Light is emitted from an ordinary lightbulb filament in wave-train bursts about $10^{-8}$ s in duration. What is the length in space of such wave trains?

39. (*a*) How long did it take for a message sent from Earth to reach the first astronauts on the Moon? (*b*) How long will it take for a message from Earth to reach the first astronauts who arrive on Mars; assume Mars is at its closest approach to Earth ($78 \times 10^6$ km)?

40. A radio voice signal from the *Apollo* crew on the Moon (Fig. 22–20) was beamed to a listening crowd from a radio speaker. If you were standing 25 m from the loudspeaker, what was the total time lag between when you heard the sound and when the sound left the Moon?

**FIGURE 22–20** Problem 40.

* 41. Cosmic microwave background radiation fills all space with an average energy density of $4 \times 10^{-14}\,\mathrm{J/m^3}$. (*a*) Find the rms value of the electric field associated with this radiation. (*b*) How far from a 10-kW radio transmitter emitting uniformly in all directions would you find a comparable value?

* 42. What are $E_0$ and $B_0$ 2.00 m from a 95-W light source? Assume the bulb emits radiation of a single frequency uniformly in all directions.

* 43. Estimate the rms electric field in the sunlight that hits Mars, knowing that the Earth receives about $1350\,\mathrm{W/m^2}$ and that Mars is 1.52 times farther from the Sun (on average) than is the Earth.

* 44. At a given instant in time, a traveling EM wave is noted to have its maximum magnetic field pointing west and its maximum electric field pointing south. In which direction is the wave traveling? If the rate of energy flow is $560\,\mathrm{W/m^2}$, what are the maximum values for the two fields?

* 45. Estimate how long an AM antenna would have to be if it were (*a*) $\frac{1}{2}\lambda$ or (*b*) $\frac{1}{4}\lambda$. AM radio is roughly 1 MHz (530 kHz to 1.7 MHz).

* 46. How large an emf (rms) will be generated in an antenna that consists of a 380-loop circular coil of wire 2.2 cm in diameter if the EM wave has a frequency of 810 kHz and is transporting energy at an average rate of $1.0 \times 10^{-4}\,\mathrm{W/m^2}$ at the antenna? [*Hint*: you can use Eq. 21–5 for a generator, since it could be applied to an observer moving with the coil so that the magnetic field is oscillating with the frequency $f = \omega/2\pi$.]

* 47. The average intensity of a particular TV station's signal is $1.0 \times 10^{-13}\,\mathrm{W/m^2}$ when it arrives at a 33-cm-diameter satellite TV antenna. (*a*) Calculate the total energy received by the antenna during 6.0 hours of viewing this station's programs. (*b*) What are the amplitudes of the $E$ and $B$ fields of the EM wave?

* 48. 15 km from a radio station's transmitting antenna, the amplitude of the electric field is 0.12 V/m. What is the average power output of the radio station?

* 49. The variable capacitance of a radio tuner consists of six plates connected together placed alternately between six other plates, also connected together (Fig. 22–21). Each plate is separated from its neighbor by 1.1 mm of air. One set of plates can move so that the area of overlap varies from $1.0\,\mathrm{cm^2}$ to $9.0\,\mathrm{cm^2}$. (*a*) Are these capacitors connected in series or in parallel? (*b*) Determine the range of capacitance values. (*c*) What value of inductor is needed if the radio is to tune AM stations from 550 kHz to 1600 kHz?

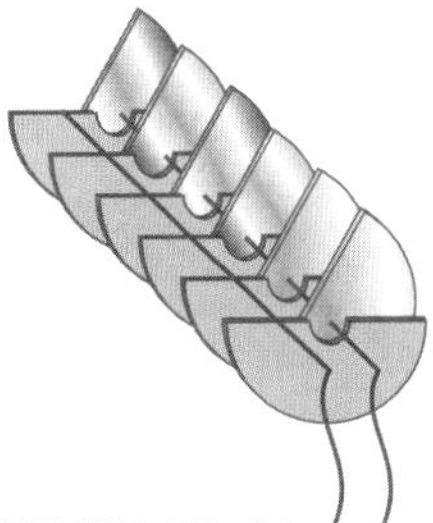

**FIGURE 22–21** Problem 49.

* 50. A radio station is allowed to broadcast at an average power not to exceed 25 kW. If an electric field amplitude of 0.020 V/m is considered to be acceptable for receiving the radio transmission, estimate how many kilometers away you might be able to hear this station.

* 51. A point source emits light energy uniformly in all directions at an average rate $P_0$ with a single frequency $f$. Show that the peak electric field in the wave is given by

$$E_0 = \sqrt{\frac{\mu_0 c P_0}{2\pi r^2}}.$$

* 52. Suppose a 50-kW radio station emits EM waves uniformly in all directions. (*a*) How much energy per second crosses a $1.0\text{-m}^2$ area 100 m from the transmitting antenna? (*b*) What is the rms magnitude of the $\vec{\mathbf{E}}$ field at this point, assuming the station is operating at full power? (*c*) What is the voltage induced in a 1.0-m-long vertical car antenna at this distance?

* 53. Repeat Problem 52 for a distance of 100 km from the station.

* 54. What is the maximum power level of the radio station of Problem 52 so as to avoid electrical breakdown of air at a distance of 1.0 m from the antenna? Assume the antenna is a point source. Air breaks down in an electric field of about $3 \times 10^6$ V/m. [*Hint*: see Problem 51.]

### Answers to Exercises

**A:** (*a*) $3.8 \times 10^6$ Hz; (*b*) $5.5 \times 10^{18}$ Hz.

**B:** 45 cm.

**C:** 3 hours.

Reflection from still water, as from a glass mirror, can be analyzed using the ray model of light.

Is this picture right side up? How can you tell? What are the clues? Ray diagrams, which we will learn to draw in this Chapter, can provide the answer (= upside down).

In this first Chapter on light and optics, we use the ray model of light to understand the formation of images by mirrors, both plane and curved (spherical), as well as by lenses, which are the crucial part of so many optical instruments.

CHAPTER 23

# Light: Geometric Optics

The sense of sight is extremely important to us, for it provides us with a large part of our information about the world. How do we see? What is the something called *light* that enters our eyes and causes the sensation of sight? How does light behave so that we can see everything that we do? We saw in Chapter 22 that light can be considered a form of electromagnetic radiation. We now examine the subject of light in detail in the next three Chapters.

*Light arrives at our eyes (1) from a source, (2) by reflection*

We see an object in one of two ways: (1) the object may be a *source* of light, such as a lightbulb, a flame, or a star, in which case we see the light emitted directly from the source; or, more commonly, (2) we see an object by light *reflected* from it. In the latter case, the light may have originated from the Sun, artificial lights, or a campfire. An understanding of how bodies *emit* light was not achieved until the 1920s, and will be discussed in Chapter 27. How light is *reflected* from objects was understood much earlier, and will be discussed in Section 23–2.

## 23–1 The Ray Model of Light

A great deal of evidence suggests that *light travels in straight lines* under a wide variety of circumstances. For example, a point source of light like the Sun casts distinct shadows, and the beam of a flashlight appears to be a straight line. In fact, we infer the positions of objects in our environment by assuming that light moves from the object to our eyes in straight-line paths. Our orientation to the physical world is based on this assumption.

*Light rays*

This reasonable assumption has led to the **ray model** of light. This model assumes that light travels in straight-line paths called light **rays**. Actually, a ray is an idealization; it is meant to represent an extremely narrow beam of light.

When we see an object, according to the ray model, light reaches our eyes from each point on the object. Although light rays leave each point in many different directions, normally only a small bundle of these rays can enter the pupil of an observer's eye, as shown in Fig. 23–1. If the person's head moves to one side, a different bundle of rays will enter the eye from each point.

We saw in Chapter 22 that light can be considered as an electromagnetic wave. Although the ray model of light does not deal with this aspect of light (we discuss the wave nature of light in Chapter 24), the ray model has been very successful in describing many aspects of light such as reflection, refraction, and the formation of images by mirrors and lenses. Because these explanations involve straight-line rays at various angles, this subject is referred to as **geometric optics**.

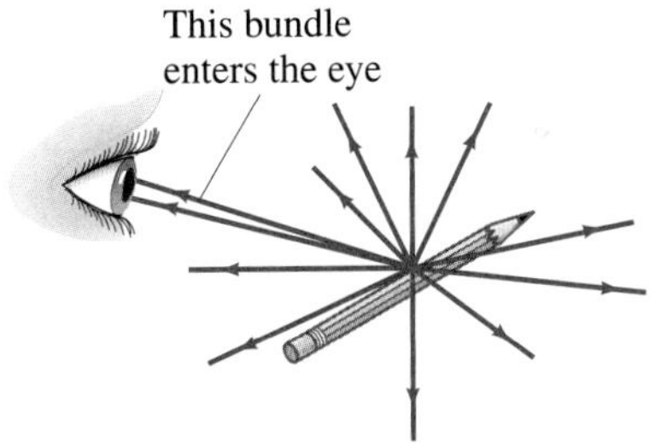


**FIGURE 23–1** Light rays come from each single point on an object. A small bundle of rays leaving one point is shown entering a person's eye.

## 23–2 Reflection; Image Formation by a Plane Mirror

When light strikes the surface of an object, some of the light is reflected. The rest can be absorbed by the object (and transformed to thermal energy) or, if the object is transparent like glass or water, part can be transmitted through. For a very shiny object such as a silvered mirror, over 95% of the light may be reflected.

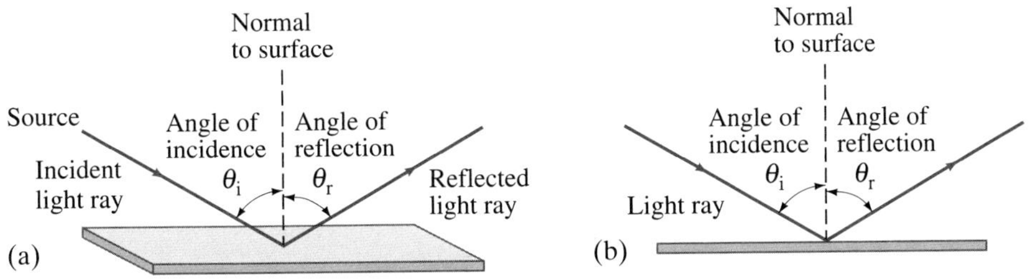


**FIGURE 23–2** Law of reflection: (a) Shows a 3-D view of an incident ray being reflected at the top of a flat surface; (b) shows a side or "end-on" view, which we will usually use because of its clarity.

When a narrow beam of light strikes a flat surface (Fig. 23–2), we define the **angle of incidence, $\theta_i$**, to be the angle an incident ray makes with the normal (perpendicular) to the surface, and the **angle of reflection, $\theta_r$**, to be the angle the reflected ray makes with the normal. It is found that the *incident and reflected rays lie in the same plane with the normal to the surface*, and that

*Angles of incidence and reflection (measure to ⊥ at surface)*

**the angle of reflection equals the angle of incidence, $\theta_r = \theta_i$.**

*Law of reflection*

This is the **law of reflection**, and it is depicted in Fig. 23–2. It was known to the ancient Greeks, and you can confirm it yourself by shining a narrow flashlight beam at a mirror in a darkened room.

When light is incident upon a rough surface, even microscopically rough such as this page, it is reflected in many directions, Fig. 23–3. This is called **diffuse reflection**. The law of reflection still holds, however, at each small section of the surface. Because of diffuse reflection in all directions, an ordinary object can be seen at many different angles by the light reflected from it. When you move your head to the side, different reflected rays reach your eye from each point on the object (such as this page), Fig. 23–4a. Let us compare diffuse reflection to reflection from a mirror, which is known as *specular* reflection. ("Speculum" is Latin for mirror.) When a narrow beam of light shines on a mirror, the light will not reach your eye unless your eye is positioned at just the right place where the law of reflection is satisfied, as shown in Fig. 23–4b. This is what gives rise to the special image-forming properties of mirrors.

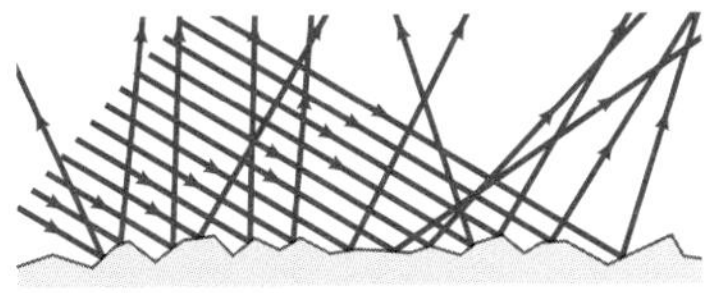

**FIGURE 23–3** Diffuse reflection from a rough surface.

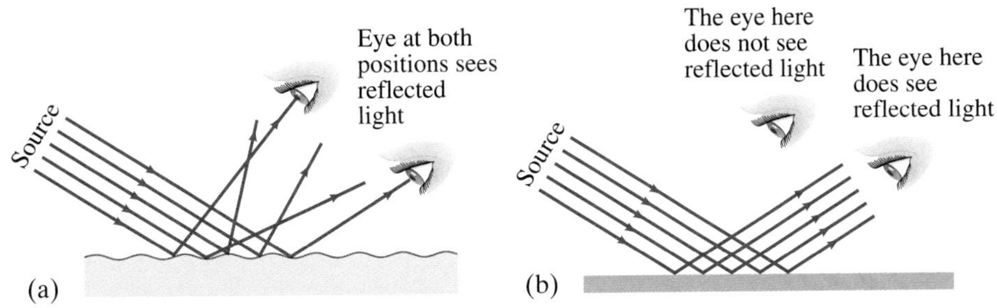


**FIGURE 23–4** A beam of light from a flashlight shines on (a) white paper, and (b) a mirror. In part (a), you can see the white light reflected at various positions because of diffuse reflection. But in part (b), you see the reflected light only when your eye is placed correctly ($\theta_r = \theta_i$); this is known as specular reflection. (Galileo, using similar arguments, showed that the Moon must have a rough surface rather than a highly polished surface like a mirror, as some people thought.)

**FIGURE 23–5** When you look in a mirror, you see an image of yourself and objects around you. You don't see yourself as others see you, because left and right appear reversed in the image.

When you look straight into a mirror, you see what appears to be yourself as well as various objects around and behind you, Fig. 23–5. Your face and the other objects look as if they are in front of you, beyond the mirror; but they aren't. What you see in the mirror is an **image** of the objects, including yourself, that are in front of the mirror.

A "plane" mirror is one with a smooth flat reflecting surface. Figure 23–6 shows how an image is formed by a plane mirror according to the ray model. We are viewing the mirror, on edge, in the diagram of Fig. 23–6, and the rays are shown reflecting from the front surface. (Good mirrors are generally made by putting a highly reflective metallic coating on one surface of a very flat piece of glass.) Rays from two different points on an object (a bottle) are shown in Fig. 23–6: two rays are shown leaving from a point on the top of the bottle, and two more from a point on the bottom. Rays leave each point on the object going in many directions, but only those that enclose the bundle of rays that enter the eye from each of the two points are shown. Each set of diverging rays that enter the eye *appear* to come from a single point (called the image point) behind the mirror, as shown by the dashed lines. That is, our eyes and brain interpret any rays that enter an eye as having traveled straight-line paths. The point from which each bundle of rays seems to come is one point on the image. For each point on the object, there is a corresponding image point.

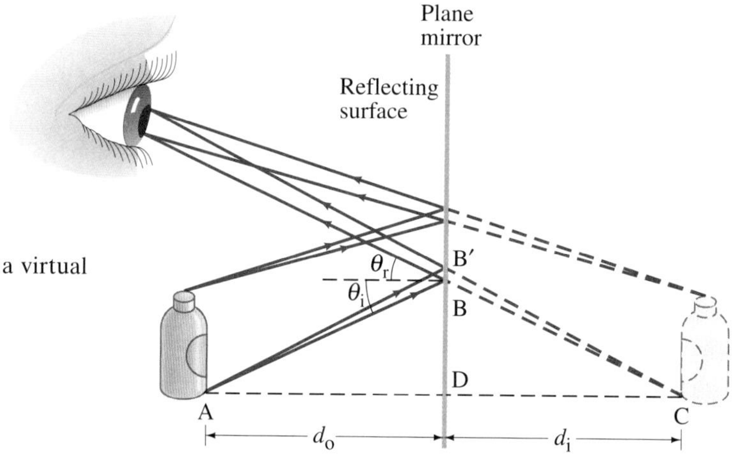


**FIGURE 23–6** Formation of a virtual image by a plane mirror.

Let us concentrate on the two rays that leave point A on the object in Fig. 23–6, and strike the mirror at points B and B′. We use geometry now, for the rays at B. The angles ADB and CDB are right angles; and because of the law of reflection, $\theta_i = \theta_r$ at point B. Therefore, by geometry, angles ABD and CBD are also equal. The two triangles ABD and CBD are thus congruent, and the length AD = CD. That is, the image appears as far behind the mirror as the object is in front. The **image distance**, $d_i$ (distance from mirror to image, Fig. 23–6), equals the **object distance**, $d_o$ (distance from object to mirror). From the geometry, we also see that the height of the image is the same as that of the object.

*Image distance = object distance (plane mirror)*

The light rays do not actually pass through the image location itself in Fig. 23–6. (Note where the red lines are dashed to show they are our projections, not rays.) The image would not appear on paper or film placed at the location of the image. Therefore, it is called a **virtual image**. This is to distinguish it from a **real image** in which the light does pass through the image and which therefore could appear on paper or film placed at the image position. Our eyes can see both real and virtual images, as long as the diverging rays enter our pupils. We will see that curved mirrors and lenses can form real images, as well as virtual. A movie projector lens, for example, produces a real image that is visible on the screen.

*Real and virtual images*

**EXAMPLE 23–1** **How tall must a full-length mirror be?** A woman 1.60 m tall stands in front of a vertical plane mirror. What is the minimum height of the mirror, and how high must its lower edge be above the floor, if she is to be able to see her whole body? (Assume her eyes are 10 cm below the top of her head.)

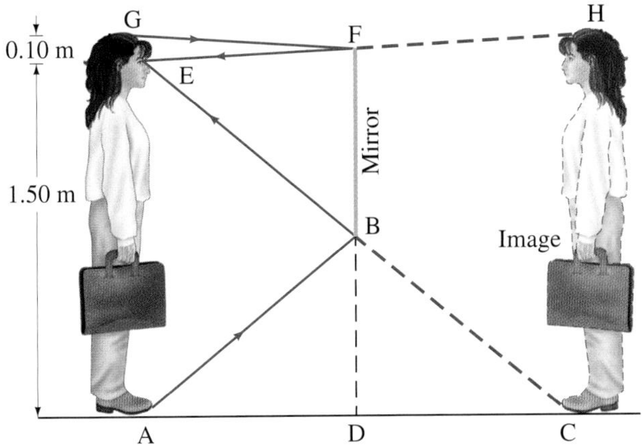


**FIGURE 23–7** Seeing oneself in a mirror. Example 23–1.

**APPROACH** For her to see her whole body, light rays from the top of her head and from the bottom of her foot must reflect from the mirror and enter her eye: see Fig. 23–7. We don't show two rays diverging from each point as we did in Fig. 23–6, where we wanted to find where the image is. Now that we know the image is the same distance behind a plane mirror as the object is in front, we only need to show one ray leaving point G (top of head) and one ray leaving point A (her toe), and then use simple geometry.

**SOLUTION** First consider the ray that leaves her foot at A, reflects at B, and enters the eye at E. The mirror needs to extend no lower than B. Because the angle of reflection equals the angle of incidence, the height BD is half of the height AE. Because $AE = 1.60\text{ m} - 0.10\text{ m} = 1.50\text{ m}$, then $BD = 0.75\text{ m}$. Similarly, if the woman is to see the top of her head, the top edge of the mirror only needs to reach point F, which is 5 cm below the top of her head (half of $GE = 10\text{ cm}$). Thus, $DF = 1.55\text{ m}$, and the mirror need have a vertical height of only $(1.55\text{ m} - 0.75\text{ m}) = 0.80\text{ m}$. And the mirror's bottom edge must be 0.75 m above the floor.

**NOTE** We see that a mirror need be only half as tall as a person for that person to see all of himself or herself.

PHYSICS APPLIED

*How tall a mirror do you need to see a reflection of your entire self?*

**EXERCISE A** Does the result of Example 23–1 depend on the person's distance from the mirror? (Try it and see, it's fun.)

## 23–3 Formation of Images by Spherical Mirrors

Reflecting surfaces do not have to be flat. The most common *curved* mirrors are *spherical*, which means they form a section of a sphere. A spherical mirror is called **convex** if the reflection takes place on the outer surface of the spherical shape so that the center of the mirror surface bulges out toward the viewer (Fig. 23–8a). A mirror is called **concave** if the reflecting surface is on the inner surface of the sphere so that the center of the mirror sinks away from the viewer (like a "cave"), Fig. 23–8b. Concave mirrors are used as shaving or cosmetic mirrors (Fig. 23–9a), and convex mirrors are sometimes used on cars and trucks (rearview mirrors) and in shops (to watch for thieves), because they take in a wide field of view (Fig. 23–9b).

**FIGURE 23–8** Mirrors with convex and concave spherical surfaces. Note that $\theta_r = \theta_i$ for each ray.

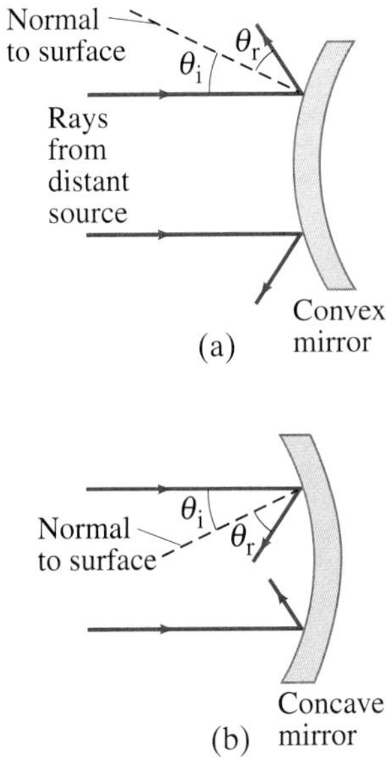


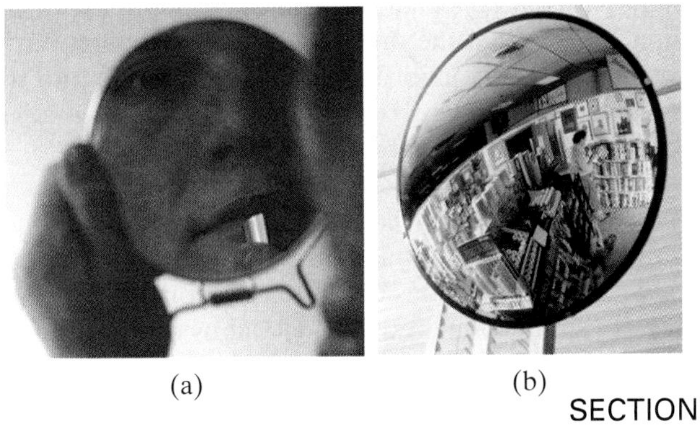


**FIGURE 23–9** (a) A concave cosmetic mirror gives a magnified image. (b) A convex mirror in a store reduces image size and so includes a wide field of view.

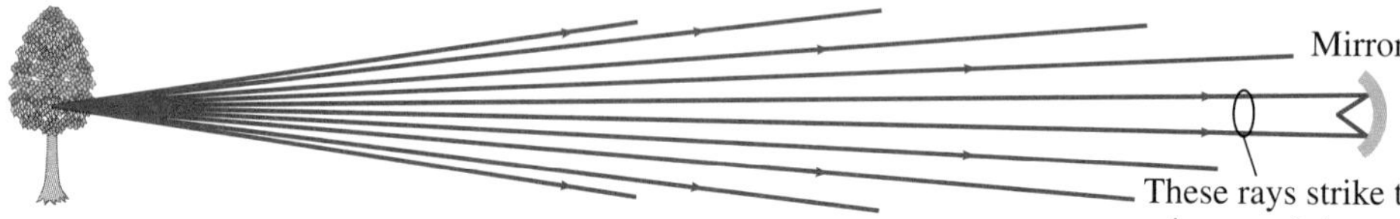


**FIGURE 23–10** If the object's distance is large compared to the size of the mirror (or lens), the rays are nearly parallel. They are parallel for an object at infinity (∞).

## Focal Point and Focal Length

To see how spherical mirrors form images, we first consider an object that is very far from a concave mirror. For a distant object, as shown in Fig. 23–10, the rays from each point on the object that strike the mirror will be nearly parallel. *For an object infinitely far away* (the Sun and stars approach this), *the rays would be precisely parallel.* Now consider such parallel rays falling on a concave mirror as in Fig. 23–11. The law of reflection holds for each of these rays at the point each strikes the mirror. As can be seen, they are not all brought to a single point. In order to form a sharp image, the rays must come to a point. Thus a spherical mirror will not make as sharp an image as a plane mirror will. However, as we show below, if the mirror is small compared to its radius of curvature, so that a reflected ray makes only a *small angle* with the incident ray ($2\theta$ in Fig. 23–12), then the rays will cross each other at very nearly a single point, or **focus**. In the case shown in Fig. 23–12, the rays are parallel to the **principal axis**, which is defined as the straight line perpendicular to the curved surface at its center (line CA in the diagram). The point F, where incident parallel rays come to a focus after reflection, is called the **focal point** of the mirror. The distance between F and the center of the mirror, length FA, is called the **focal length**, $f$, of the mirror. The focal point is also the *image point for an object infinitely far away* along the principal axis. The image of the Sun, for example, would be at F.

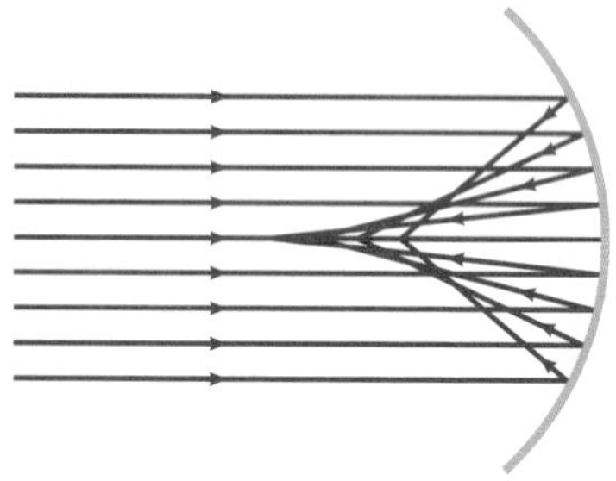

**FIGURE 23–11** Parallel rays striking a concave spherical mirror do not focus at precisely a single point. (This "defect" is referred to as "spherical aberration.")

**FIGURE 23–12** Rays parallel to the principal axis of a concave spherical mirror come to a focus at F, the focal point, as long as the mirror is small in width as compared to its radius of curvature, $r$, so that the rays are "paraxial"—that is, make only small angles with the axis.

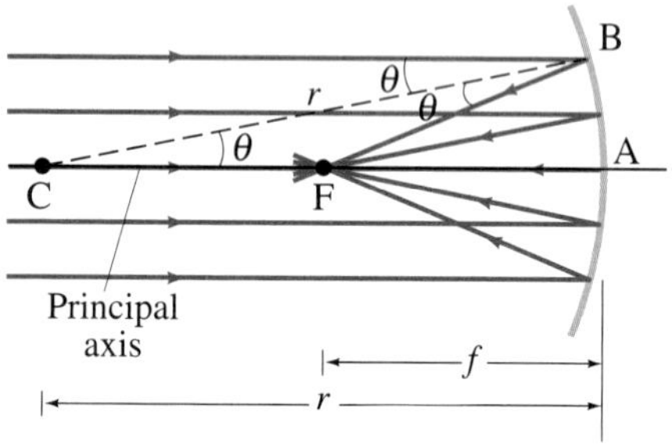


Now we will show, for a mirror whose reflecting surface is small compared to its radius of curvature, that the rays very nearly meet at a common point, F, and we will also calculate the focal length $f$. In this approximation, we consider only rays that make a small angle with the principal axis; such rays are called **paraxial rays**, and their angles are exaggerated in Fig. 23–12 to make the labels clear. First we consider a ray that strikes the mirror at B in Fig. 23–12. The point C is the center of curvature of the mirror (the center of the sphere of which the mirror is a part). So the dashed line CB is equal to $r$, the radius of curvature, and CB is normal to the mirror's surface at B. The incoming ray that hits the mirror at B makes an angle $\theta$ with this normal, and hence the reflected ray, BF, also makes an angle $\theta$ with the normal (law of reflection). Note that angle BCF is also $\theta$ as shown. The triangle CBF is isosceles because two of its angles are equal. Thus we have length CF = BF. We assume the mirror surface is small compared to the mirror's radius of curvature, so the angles are small, and the length FB is nearly equal to length FA. In this approximation, FA = FC. But FA = $f$, the focal length, and CA = 2 × FA = $r$. Thus the focal length is half the radius of curvature:

*Focal length of mirror*

$$f = \frac{r}{2}. \tag{23–1}$$

We assumed only that the angle $\theta$ was small, so this result applies for all other incident paraxial rays. Thus all paraxial rays pass through the same point F.

Since it is only approximately true that the rays come to a perfect focus at F, the more curved the mirror, the worse the approximation (Fig. 23–11) and the more blurred the image. This "defect" of spherical mirrors is called **spherical aberration**; we will discuss it more with regard to lenses in Chapter 25. A *parabolic* reflector, on the other hand, will reflect the rays to a perfect focus. However, because parabolic shapes are much harder to make and thus much more expensive, spherical mirrors are used for most purposes. (Many astronomical telescopes use parabolic reflectors.) We consider here only spherical mirrors and we will assume that they are small compared to their radius of curvature so that the image is sharp and Eq. 23–1 holds.

*Parabolic mirror*

## Image Formation—Ray Diagrams

We saw that for an object at infinity, the image is located at the focal point of a concave spherical mirror, where $f = r/2$. But where does the image lie for an object not at infinity? First consider the object shown as an arrow in Fig. 23–13, which is placed between F and C at point O (O for object). Let us determine where the image will be for a given point O′ at the top of the object. To do this we can draw several rays and make sure these reflect from the mirror such that the angle of reflection equals the angle of incidence. Many rays could be drawn leaving any point on an object, but determining the image position is simplified if we deal with three particularly simple rays. These are the rays labeled 1, 2, and 3 in Fig. 23–13 and we draw them leaving object point O′ as follows:

**RAY DIAGRAM**
*Finding the image position for a curved mirror*

Ray 1 is drawn parallel to the axis; therefore after reflection it must pass along a line through F (as we saw in Fig. 23–12, and drawn here in Fig. 23–13a).

Ray 2 leaves O′ and is made to pass through F; therefore it must reflect so it is parallel to the axis (Fig. 23–13b).

Ray 3 passes through C, the center of curvature; it is along a radius of the spherical surface and is perpendicular to the mirror, so it is reflected back on itself (Fig. 23–13c).

All three rays leave a single point O′ on the object. After reflection from a (small) mirror, the point at which these rays cross is the image point I′. All other rays from the same object point will also pass through this image point. To find the image point for any object point, only these three types of rays need to be drawn. Only two of these rays are needed, but the third serves as a check.

*Image point is where reflected rays intersect*

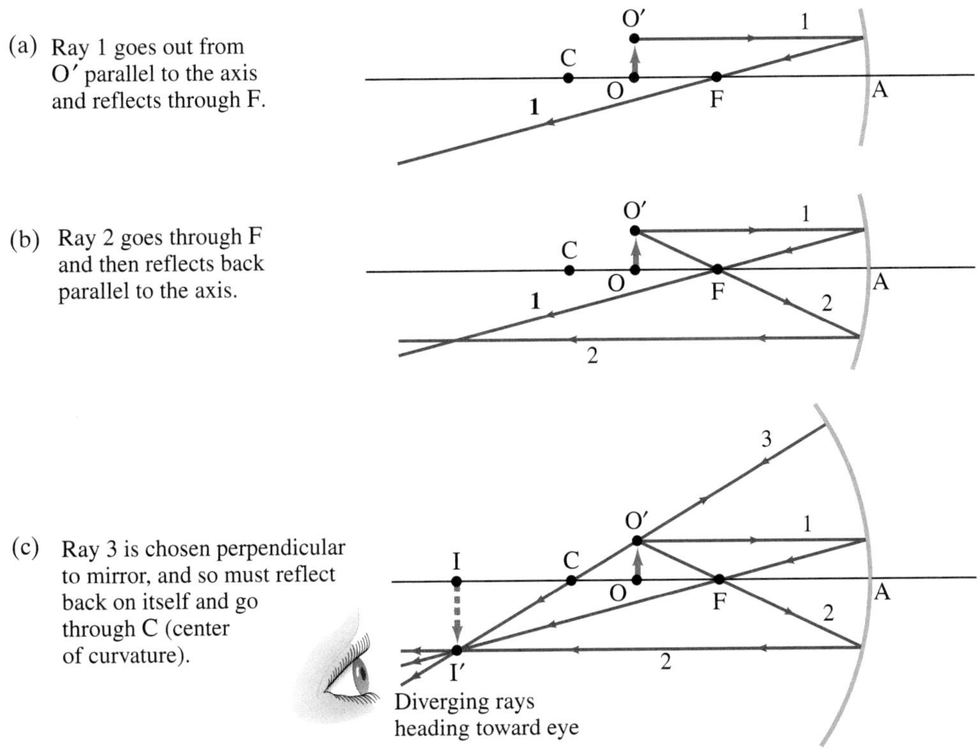


**FIGURE 23–13** Rays leave point O′ on the object (an arrow). Shown are the three most useful rays for determining where the image I′ is formed. [Note that our mirror is not small compared to $f$, so our diagram will not give the precise position of the image.]

We have shown the image point in Fig. 23–13 only for a single point on the object. Other points on the object are imaged nearby, so a complete image of the object is formed, as shown by the dashed arrow in Fig. 23–13c. Because the light actually passes through the image itself, this is a *real image* that will appear on a piece of paper or film placed there. This can be compared to the virtual image formed by a plane mirror (the light does not actually pass through that image, Fig. 23–6).

*Real image*

The image in Fig. 23–13 can be seen by the eye when the eye is placed to the left of the image so that some of the rays diverging from each point on the image (as point I′) can enter the eye as shown in Fig. 23–13c. (See also Figs. 23–1 and 23–6.)

## Mirror Equation and Magnification

Image points can be determined, roughly, by drawing the three rays as just described, Fig. 23–13; but it is difficult to draw small angles for the "paraxial" rays as we assumed. For more accurate results, we now derive an equation that gives the image distance if the object distance and radius of curvature of the mirror are known. To do this, we refer to Fig. 23–14. The **object distance**, $d_o$, is the distance of the object (point O) from the center of the mirror. The **image distance**, $d_i$, is the distance of the image (point I) from the center of the mirror. The height of the object OO′ is called $h_o$ and the height of the image, I′I, is $h_i$. Two rays leaving O′ are

*Distances $d_o$ and $d_i$ are measured from center of mirror*

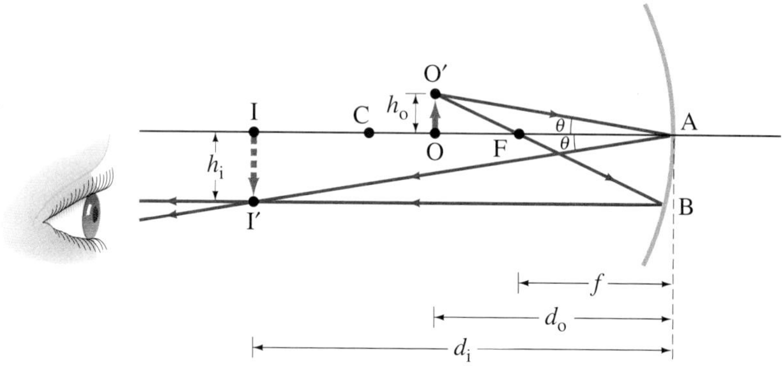


**FIGURE 23–14** Diagram for deriving the mirror equation. For the derivation, we assume the mirror size is small compared to its radius of curvature.

shown: O′FBI′ (same as ray 2 in Fig. 23–13) and O′AI′, which is a fourth type of ray that reflects at the center of the mirror and can also be used to find an image point. The ray O′AI′ obeys the law of reflection, so the two right triangles O′AO and I′AI are similar. Therefore, we have

$$\frac{h_o}{h_i} = \frac{d_o}{d_i}.$$

For the other ray shown, O′FBI′, the triangles O′FO and AFB are also similar because the angles are equal and we use the approximation $AB = h_i$ (mirror small compared to its radius). Furthermore $FA = f$, the focal length of the mirror, so

$$\frac{h_o}{h_i} = \frac{OF}{FA} = \frac{d_o - f}{f}.$$

The left sides of the two preceding expressions are the same, so we can equate the right sides:

$$\frac{d_o}{d_i} = \frac{d_o - f}{f}.$$

We now divide both sides by $d_o$ and rearrange to obtain

*Mirror equation*

$$\frac{1}{d_o} + \frac{1}{d_i} = \frac{1}{f}. \tag{23–2}$$

This is the equation we were seeking. It is called the **mirror equation** and relates the object and image distances to the focal length $f$ (where $f = r/2$).

The **magnification**, $m$, of a mirror is defined as the height of the image divided by the height of the object. From our first set of similar triangles above, or the first equation on this page, we can write:

*Magnification of curved mirror*

$$m = \frac{h_i}{h_o} = -\frac{d_i}{d_o}. \tag{23–3}$$

The minus sign in Eq. 23–3 is inserted as a convention. Indeed, we must be careful about the signs of all quantities in Eqs. 23–2 and 23–3. Sign conventions are chosen so as to give the correct locations and orientations of images, as predicted by ray diagrams. The sign conventions we use are: the image height $h_i$ is positive if the image is upright, and negative if inverted, relative to the object (assuming $h_o$ is taken as positive); $d_i$ or $d_o$ is positive if image or object is in front of the mirror (as in Fig. 23–14); if either image or object is behind the mirror, the corresponding distance is negative (an example can be seen in Fig. 23–16, Example 23–3). Thus the magnification (Eq. 23–3) is positive for an upright image and negative for an inverted image (upside down). We summarize sign conventions more fully after discussing convex mirrors later in this Section.

**CAUTION**
*Sign conventions*

**EXERCISE B** Does the mirror equation, Eq. 23–2, hold for a plane mirror? Explain.

## Concave Mirror Examples

**EXAMPLE 23–2** **Image in a concave mirror.** A 1.50-cm-high diamond ring is placed 20.0 cm from a concave mirror with radius of curvature 30.0 cm. Determine (*a*) the position of the image, and (*b*) its size.

**APPROACH** We determine the focal length from the radius of curvature (Eq. 23–1), $f = r/2 = 15.0\text{ cm}$. The ray diagram is basically like that shown in Fig. 23–13 or Fig. 23–14, since the object is between F and C. The position and size of the image are found from Eqs. 23–2 and 23–3.

**SOLUTION** Referring to Fig. 23–14, we have $CA = r = 30.0\text{ cm}$, $FA = f = 15.0\text{ cm}$, and $OA = d_o = 20.0\text{ cm}$.

(*a*) From Eq. 23–2,

$$\frac{1}{d_i} = \frac{1}{f} - \frac{1}{d_o} = \frac{1}{15.0\text{ cm}} - \frac{1}{20.0\text{ cm}} = 0.0167\text{ cm}^{-1}.$$

So $d_i = 1/(0.0167\text{ cm}^{-1}) = 60.0\text{ cm}$. Because $d_i$ is positive, the image is 60.0 cm in front of the mirror, on the same side as the object.

**CAUTION**
*Remember to take the reciprocal*

(*b*) From Eq. 23–3, the magnification is

$$m = -\frac{d_i}{d_o} = -\frac{60.0\text{ cm}}{20.0\text{ cm}} = -3.00.$$

The image height is 3.0 times the object height, and is

$$h_i = mh_o = (-3.00)(1.5\text{ cm}) = -4.5\text{ cm}.$$

The minus sign reminds us that the image is inverted, as in Fig. 23–14.

**NOTE** When an object is beyond the focal point of a concave mirror, we can see from Fig. 23–13 or 23–14 that the image is always inverted and real.

For a person's eye to see a sharp image, the eye must be at a place where it intercepts diverging rays from points on the image, as is the case for the eye's position in Figs. 23–13 and 23–14. Our eyes are made to see normal objects, which always means the rays are diverging toward the eye as shown in Fig. 23–1. (Or, for very distant objects like stars, the rays become essentially parallel—see Fig. 23–10.) If you placed your eye between points O and I in Fig. 23–14, for example, *converging* rays from the object OO′ would enter your eye and the lens of your eye could not bring them to a focus; you would see a blurry image. We will discuss the eye more in Chapter 25.

If *you* are the object OO′ in Fig. 23–14, situated between F and C, and are trying to see yourself in the mirror, you would see a blur; but the person whose eye is shown in Fig. 23–14 can see you clearly. You can see yourself clearly, but upside down, if you are to the left of C in Fig. 23–14, so $d_o > 2f$. Why? Because then the rays reflected from the image will be *diverging* at your position as shown in Fig. 23–15, and your eye can focus them. You can also see yourself clearly, and right-side up, if you are closer to the mirror than its focal point $(d_o < f)$, as we will see in Example 23–3, Fig. 23–16.

**FIGURE 23–15** You can see a clear inverted image of your face when you are beyond C $(d_o > 2f)$, because the rays that arrive at your eye are diverging. Standard rays 2 and 3 are shown leaving point O on your nose. Ray 2 (and other nearby rays) enters your eye. Notice that rays are diverging as they move to the left of image point I.

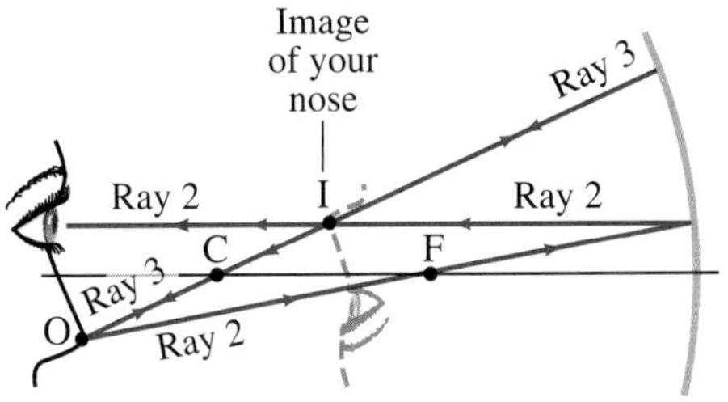

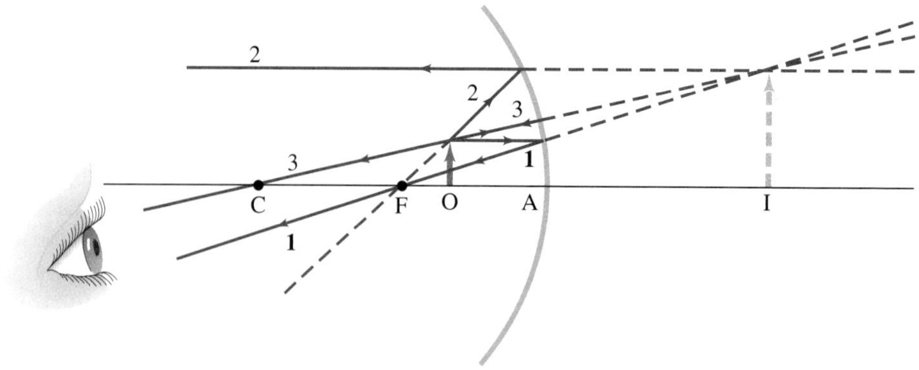


**FIGURE 23–16** Object placed within the focal point F. The image is *behind* the mirror and is *virtual*, Example 23–3. [Note that the vertical scale (height of object = 1.0 cm) is different from the horizontal (OA = 10.0 cm) for ease of drawing, and affects the precision of the drawing.]

**EXAMPLE 23–3 Object closer to concave mirror.** A 1.00-cm-high object is placed 10.0 cm from a concave mirror whose radius of curvature is 30.0 cm. (*a*) Draw a ray diagram to locate (approximately) the position of the image. (*b*) Determine the position of the image and the magnification analytically.

**APPROACH** We draw the ray diagram using the rays of Fig. 23–13. An analytic solution uses Eqs. 23–1, 23–2, and 23–3.

**SOLUTION** (*a*) Since $f = r/2 = 15.0\,\text{cm}$, the object is between the mirror and the focal point. We draw the three rays as described earlier (Fig. 23–13); they are shown leaving the tip of the object in Fig. 23–16. Ray 1 leaves the tip of our object heading toward the mirror parallel to the axis, and reflects through F. Ray 2 cannot head toward F because it would not strike the mirror; so ray 2 must point as if it started at F (dashed line) and heads to the mirror, and then is reflected parallel to the principal axis. Ray 3 is perpendicular to the mirror, as before. The rays reflected from the mirror diverge and so never meet at a point. They appear, however, to be coming from a point behind the mirror. This point locates the image of the tip of the arrow. The image is thus behind the mirror and *virtual*. (Why?)
(*b*) We use Eq. 23–2 to find $d_i$ when $d_o = 10.0\,\text{cm}$:

$$\frac{1}{d_i} = \frac{1}{f} - \frac{1}{d_o} = \frac{1}{15.0\,\text{cm}} - \frac{1}{10.0\,\text{cm}} = \frac{2-3}{30.0\,\text{cm}} = -\frac{1}{30.0\,\text{cm}}.$$

Therefore, $d_i = -30.0\,\text{cm}$. The minus sign means the image is behind the mirror. The magnification is $m = -d_i/d_o = -(-30.0\,\text{cm})/(10.0\,\text{cm}) = +3.00$. So the image is 3.00 times larger than the object. The plus sign indicates that the image is upright (same as object), which is consistent with the ray diagram, Fig. 23–16).

**NOTE** The image distance cannot be obtained accurately by measuring on Fig. 23–16, because our diagram violates the paraxial ray assumption (so as to make all rays clearly visible).]

*Seeing yourself upright and magnified in a concave mirror*

**NOTE** When the object is located inside the focal point of a concave mirror $(d_o < f)$, the image is always upright and vertical. And if the object O in Fig. 23–16 is you, you see yourself clearly, because the reflected rays at O are diverging. Your image is upright and enlarged.

PHYSICS APPLIED
*Magnifying mirror (shaving/cosmetic)*

It is useful to compare Figs. 23–13 and 23–16. We can see that if the object is within the focal point $(d_o < f)$, as in Fig. 23–16, the image is virtual, upright, and magnified. This is how a shaving or cosmetic mirror is used—you must place your head closer to the mirror than the focal point if you are to see yourself right-side up (Fig. 23–9a). If the object is *beyond* the focal point, as in Fig. 23–13, the image is real and inverted (upside down—and hard to use!). Whether the magnification is greater or less than 1.0 in the latter case depends on the position of the object relative to the center of curvature, point C.

## Convex Mirrors

The analysis used for concave mirrors can be applied to **convex** mirrors. Even the mirror equation (Eq. 23–2) holds for a convex mirror, although the quantities involved must be carefully defined. Figure 23–17a shows parallel rays falling on a convex mirror. Again spherical aberration will be present (Fig. 23–11), but we assume the mirror's size is small compared to its radius of curvature. The reflected rays diverge, but seem to come from point F behind the mirror. This is the **focal point**, and its distance from the center of the mirror is the **focal length**, $f$. It is easy to show that again $f = r/2$. We see that an object at infinity produces a virtual image in a convex mirror. Indeed, no matter where the object is placed on the reflecting side of a convex mirror, the image will be virtual and upright, as indicated in Fig. 23–17b. To find the image we draw rays 1 and 3 according to the rules used before on the concave mirror, as shown in Fig. 23–17b. Note that although rays 1 and 3 don't actually pass through points F and C, the line along which each is drawn does (shown dashed).

The mirror equation, Eq. 23–2, holds for convex mirrors but the focal length $f$ must be considered negative, as must the radius of curvature. The proof is left as a Problem. It is also left as a Problem to show that Eq. 23–3 for the magnification is also valid.

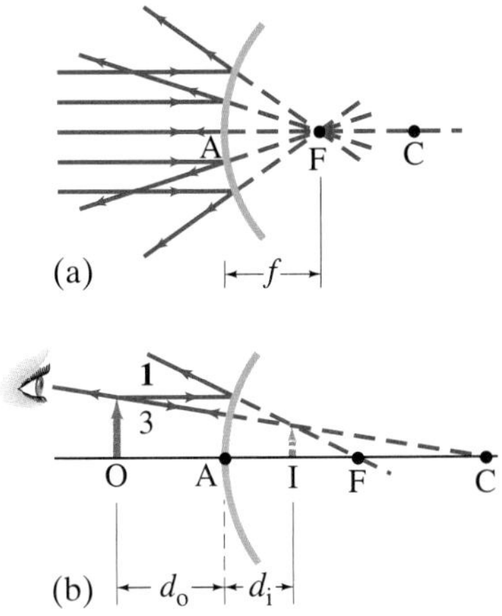


**FIGURE 23–17** Convex mirror: (a) the focal point is at F, behind the mirror; (b) the image I of the object at O is virtual, upright, and smaller than the object. [Not to scale for Example 23–4.]

**PROBLEM SOLVING** Spherical Mirrors

1. Always **draw a ray diagram** even though you are going to make an analytic calculation—the diagram serves as a check, even if not precise. From one point on the object, draw at least two, preferably three, of the easy-to-draw rays using the rules described in Fig. 23–13. The image point is where the reflected rays intersect or appear to intersect.
2. Apply the **mirror equation**, Eq. 23–2, and the **magnification equation**, Eq. 23–3. It is crucially important to follow the sign conventions—next point.
3. **Sign Conventions**
   (a) When the object, image, or focal point is on the reflecting side of the mirror (on the left in our drawings), the corresponding distance is positive. If any of these points is behind the mirror (on the right) the corresponding distance is negative.†
   (b) The image height $h_i$ is positive if the image is upright, and negative if inverted, relative to the object ($h_o$ is always taken as positive).
4. **Check** that the analytical solution is consistent with the ray diagram.

†Object distances are positive for material objects, but can be negative in systems with more than one mirror or lens—see Section 23–9.

**EXAMPLE 23–4** **Convex rearview mirror.** An external rearview car mirror is convex with a radius of curvature of 16.0 m (Fig. 23–18). Determine the location of the image and its magnification for an object 10.0 m from the mirror.

**APPROACH** We follow the steps of the Problem Solving Box explicitly.

**SOLUTION (1) Draw a ray diagram:** The ray diagram will be like Fig. 23–17, but the large object distance $(d_o = 10.0\,\mathrm{m})$ makes a precise drawing difficult. We have a convex mirror, so $r$ is negative by convention.

**(2) Mirror and magnification equations:** The center of curvature of a convex mirror is behind the mirror, as is its focal point, so we set $r = -16.0\,\mathrm{m}$ so that the focal length is $f = r/2 = -8.0\,\mathrm{m}$. The object is in front of the mirror, $d_o = 10.0\,\mathrm{m}$. Solving the mirror equation, Eq. 23–2, for $1/d_i$ gives

$$\frac{1}{d_i} = \frac{1}{f} - \frac{1}{d_o} = \frac{1}{-8.0\,\mathrm{m}} - \frac{1}{10.0\,\mathrm{m}} = \frac{-10.0 - 8.0}{80.0\,\mathrm{m}} = -\frac{18}{80.0\,\mathrm{m}}.$$

Thus $d_i = -80.0\,\mathrm{m}/18 = -4.4\,\mathrm{m}$. Equation 23–3 gives the magnification

$$m = -\frac{d_i}{d_o} = -\frac{(-4.4\,\mathrm{m})}{(10.0\,\mathrm{m})} = +0.44.$$

**(3) Sign conventions:** The image distance is negative, $-4.4\,\mathrm{m}$, so the image is *behind* the mirror. The magnification is $m = +0.44$, so the image is *upright* (same orientation as object) and less than half as tall as the object.

**(4) Check:** Our results are consistent with Fig. 23–17b.

PHYSICS APPLIED

*Convex rearview mirror*

**FIGURE 23–18** Example 23–4.

Convex rearview mirrors on vehicles sometimes come with a warning that objects are closer than they appear in the mirror. The fact that $d_i$ may be smaller than $d_o$ (as in this Example) seems to contradict this observation. The real reason the object seems farther away is that its image in the convex mirror is *smaller*, and we judge distance of ordinary objects such as other cars mostly by their size.

**TABLE 23–1**
**Indices of Refraction†**

| Medium | $n = c/v$ |
|---|---|
| Vacuum | 1.0000 |
| Air (at STP) | 1.0003 |
| Water | 1.33 |
| Ethyl alcohol | 1.36 |
| Glass | |
| Fused quartz | 1.46 |
| Crown glass | 1.52 |
| Light flint | 1.58 |
| Lucite or Plexiglas | 1.51 |
| Sodium chloride | 1.53 |
| Diamond | 2.42 |

† $\lambda = 589$ nm.

## 23–4 Index of Refraction

We saw in Chapter 22 that the speed of light in vacuum is

$$c = 2.99792458 \times 10^8 \text{ m/s},$$

which we usually round off to

$$c = 3.00 \times 10^8 \text{ m/s}$$

when extremely precise results are not required. This speed applies to all electromagnetic waves, including visible light.

In air the speed is only slightly less. In other transparent materials, such as glass and water, the speed is always less than that in vacuum. For example, in water light travels at about $\frac{3}{4}c$. The ratio of the speed of light in vacuum to the speed $v$ in a given material is called the **index of refraction**, $n$, of that material:

*Index of refraction*

$$n = \frac{c}{v}. \qquad \textbf{(23–4)}$$

The index of refraction is never less than 1, and values for various materials are given in Table 23–1. As we shall see later, $n$ varies somewhat with the wavelength of the light—except in vacuum—so a particular wavelength is specified in the Table, that of yellow light with wavelength $\lambda = 589$ nm.

**EXAMPLE 23–5** **Light's speed in diamond.** Calculate the speed of light in diamond.

**APPROACH** We use Eq. 23–4, finding from Table 23–1 that $n = 2.42$ for diamond.

**SOLUTION** The speed of light traveling inside a diamond is

$$v = \frac{c}{n} = \frac{c}{2.42} = 0.413c$$

or

$$v = \frac{3.00 \times 10^8 \text{ m/s}}{2.42} = 1.24 \times 10^8 \text{ m/s}.$$

That light travels more slowly in matter than in vacuum can be explained at the atomic level as being due to the absorption and reemission of light by atoms and molecules of the material.

## 23–5 Refraction: Snell's Law

When light passes from one transparent medium into another with a different index of refraction, part of the incident light is reflected at the boundary. The remainder passes into the new medium. If a ray of light is incident at an angle to the surface (other than perpendicular), the ray changes direction as it enters the new medium. This change in direction, or bending, is called **refraction**.

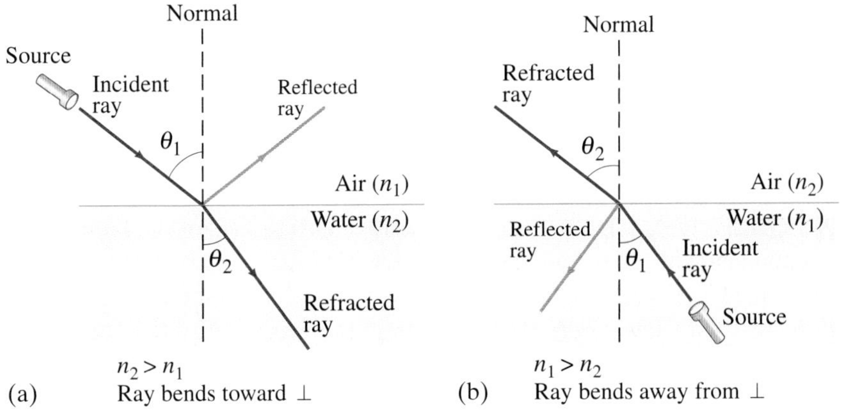


**FIGURE 23–19** Refraction. (a) Light refracted when passing from air ($n_1$) into water ($n_2$): $n_2 > n_1$. (b) Light refracted when passing from water ($n_1$) into air ($n_2$): $n_1 > n_2$.

Figure 23–19a shows a ray passing from air into water. Angle $\theta_1$ is the angle the incident ray makes with the normal (perpendicular) to the surface and is called the **angle of incidence**. Angle $\theta_2$ is the **angle of refraction**, the angle the refracted ray makes with the normal to the surface. Notice that the ray bends toward the normal when entering the water. This is always the case when the ray enters a medium where the speed of light is *less* (and the index of refraction greater, Eq. 23–4). If light travels from one medium into a second where its speed is *greater*, the ray bends away from the normal; this is shown in Fig. 23–19b for a ray traveling from water to air.

*Angle of refraction*

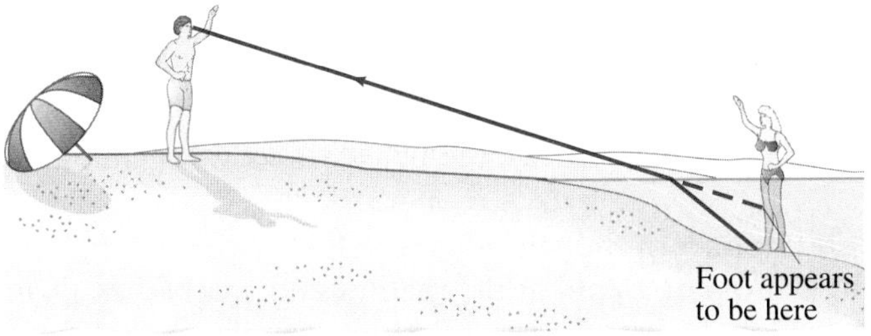


**FIGURE 23–20** Ray diagram showing why a person's legs look shorter when standing in waist-deep water: the path of light traveling from the bather's foot to the observer's eye bends at the water's surface, and our brain interprets the light as having traveled in a straight line, from higher up (dashed line).

**FIGURE 23–21** A pencil in water looks bent even when it isn't.

Refraction is responsible for a number of common optical illusions. For example, a person standing in waist-deep water appears to have shortened legs. As shown in Fig. 23–20, the rays leaving the person's foot are bent at the surface. The observer's brain assumes the rays to have traveled a straight-line path (dashed red line), and so the feet appear to be higher than they really are. Similarly, when you put a pencil in water, it appears to be bent (Fig. 23–21).

**PHYSICS APPLIED**
*Optical illusions*

## Snell's Law

The angle of refraction depends on the speed of light in the two media and on the incident angle. An analytical relation between $\theta_1$ and $\theta_2$ was arrived at experimentally about 1621 by Willebrord Snell (1591–1626). It is known as **Snell's law** and is written:

$$n_1 \sin\theta_1 = n_2 \sin\theta_2. \tag{23–5}$$

*Snell's law (law of refraction)*

$\theta_1$ is the angle of incidence and $\theta_2$ is the angle of refraction; $n_1$ and $n_2$ are the respective indices of refraction in the materials. See Fig. 23–19. The incident and refracted rays lie in the same plane, which also includes the perpendicular to the surface. Snell's law is the basic **law of refraction**. (Snell's law was derived in Section 11–14 where Eq. 11–20 is just a combination of Eqs. 23–5 and 23–4.)

**CAUTION**
*Angles $\theta_1$ and $\theta_2$ are measured from the perpendicular, not from surface*

It is clear from Snell's law that if $n_2 > n_1$, then $\theta_2 < \theta_1$. That is, if light enters a medium where $n$ is greater (and its speed less), then the ray is bent toward the normal. And if $n_2 < n_1$, then $\theta_2 > \theta_1$, so the ray bends away from the normal. This is what we saw in Fig. 23–19.

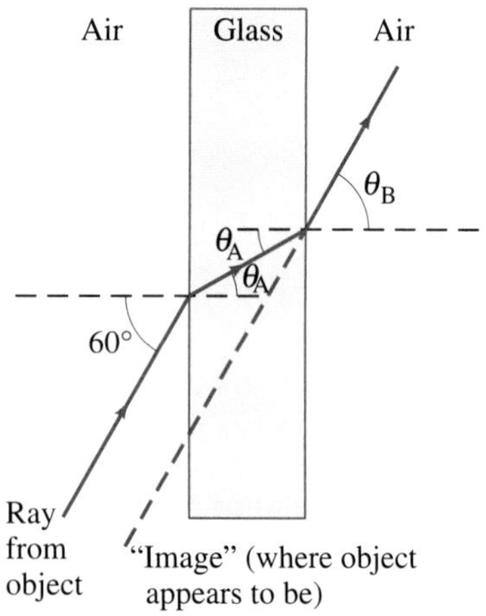


**FIGURE 23–22** Light passing through a piece of glass (Example 23–6).

**EXERCISE C** Light passes from a medium with $n = 1.3$ into a medium with $n = 1.5$. Is the light bent toward or away from the perpendicular to the interface?

**EXAMPLE 23–6** **Refraction through flat glass.** Light traveling in air strikes a flat piece of uniformly thick glass at an incident angle of 60°, as shown in Fig. 23–22. If the index of refraction of the glass is 1.50, (*a*) what is the angle of refraction $\theta_A$ in the glass; (*b*) what is the angle $\theta_B$ at which the ray emerges from the glass?

**APPROACH** We apply Snell's law at the first surface, where the light enters the glass, and again at the second surface where it leaves the glass and enters the air.

**SOLUTION** (*a*) The incident ray is in air, so $n_1 = 1.00$ and $n_2 = 1.50$. Applying Snell's law where the light enters the glass $(\theta_1 = 60°)$ gives

$$\sin\theta_A = \frac{1.00}{1.50}\sin 60° = 0.577,$$

so $\theta_A = 35.2°$.

(*b*) Since the faces of the glass are parallel, the incident angle at the second surface is just $\theta_A$ (simple geometry), so $\sin\theta_A = 0.577$. At this second interface, $n_1 = 1.50$ and $n_2 = 1.00$. Thus the ray re-enters the air at an angle $\theta_B\ (= \theta_2)$ given by

$$\sin\theta_B = \frac{1.50}{1.00}\sin\theta_A = 0.866,$$

and $\theta_B = 60°$. The direction of a light ray is thus unchanged by passing through a flat piece of glass of uniform thickness.

**NOTE** It should be clear that this works for any angle of incidence. The ray is displaced slightly to one side, however. You can observe this by looking through a piece of glass (near its edge) at some object and then moving your head to the side slightly so that you see the object directly. It "jumps."

**FIGURE 23–23** Example 23–7.

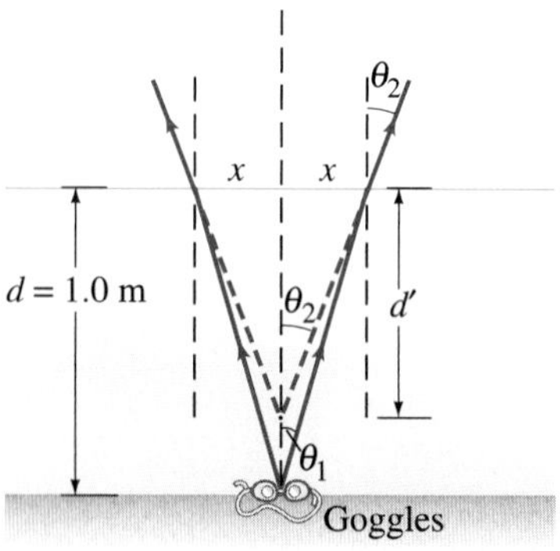


**EXAMPLE 23–7** **Apparent depth of a pool.** A swimmer has dropped her goggles to the bottom of a pool at the shallow end, marked as 1.0 m deep. But the goggles don't look that deep. Why? How deep do the goggles appear to be when you look straight down into the water?

**APPROACH** We draw a ray diagram showing two rays going upward from a point on the goggles at a small angle, and being refracted at the water's (flat) surface. This is shown in Fig. 23–23, and the dashed lines show why the water seems less deep than it actually is. The two rays traveling upward from the goggles are refracted *away* from the normal as they exit the water, and so appear to be diverging from a point above the goggles (dashed lines).

**SOLUTION** To calculate the apparent depth $d'$ (Fig. 23–23), given a real depth $d = 1.0$ m, we use Snell's law with $n_1 = 1.33$ for water and $n_2 = 1$ for air:

$$\sin\theta_2 = n_1\sin\theta_1.$$

We are considering only small angles, so $\sin\theta \approx \tan\theta \approx \theta$, with $\theta$ in radians. So Snell's law becomes

$$\theta_2 \approx n_1\theta_1.$$

From Fig. 23–23, we see that

$$\theta_2 \approx \tan\theta_2 = \frac{x}{d'} \qquad \text{and} \qquad \theta_1 \approx \tan\theta_1 = \frac{x}{d}.$$

Putting these into Snell's law, $\theta_2 \approx n_1\theta_1$, we get

$$\frac{x}{d'} \approx n_1\frac{x}{d}$$

or

$$d' \approx \frac{d}{n_1} = \frac{1.0\text{ m}}{1.33} = 0.75\text{ m}.$$

The pool seems only three-fourths as deep as it actually is.

## 23–6 Total Internal Reflection; Fiber Optics

When light passes from one material into a second material where the index of refraction is less (say, from water into air), the light bends away from the normal, as for rays I and J in Fig. 23–24. At a particular incident angle, the angle of refraction will be 90°, and the refracted ray would skim the surface (ray K) in this case. The incident angle at which this occurs is called the **critical angle**, $\theta_C$. From Snell's law, $\theta_C$ is given by

$$\sin\theta_C = \frac{n_2}{n_1}\sin 90° = \frac{n_2}{n_1}. \qquad \textbf{(23–6)}$$

*Critical angle*

For any incident angle less than $\theta_C$, there will be a refracted ray, although part of the light will also be reflected at the boundary. However, for incident angles greater than $\theta_C$, Snell's law would tell us that $\sin\theta_2$ is greater than 1.00. Yet the sine of an angle can never be greater than 1.00. In this case there is no refracted ray at all, and *all of the light is reflected*, as for ray L in Fig. 23–24. This effect is called **total internal reflection**. But note that total internal reflection can occur only when light strikes a boundary where the medium beyond has a lower index of refraction.

**CAUTION**
*Total internal reflection (occurs only if refractive index is smaller beyond boundary)*

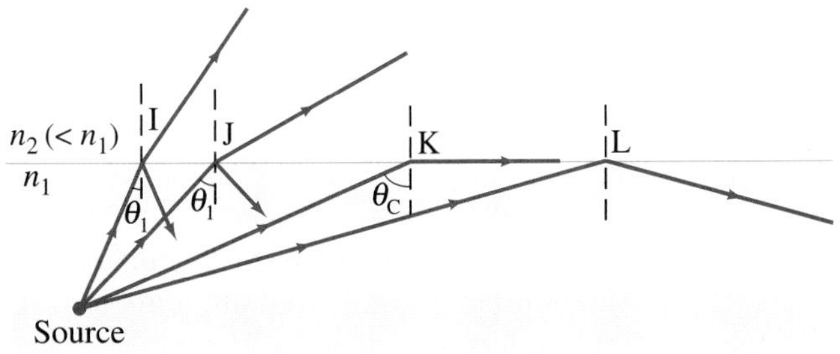


**FIGURE 23–24** Since $n_2 < n_1$, light rays are totally internally reflected if the incident angle $\theta_1 > \theta_C$, as for ray L. If $\theta_1 < \theta_C$, as for rays I and J, only a part of the light is reflected, and the rest is refracted.

**CONCEPTUAL EXAMPLE 23–8** **View up from under water.** Describe what a person would see who looked up at the world from beneath the perfectly smooth surface of a lake or swimming pool.

**RESPONSE** For an air–water interface, the critical angle is given by

$$\sin\theta_C = \frac{1.00}{1.33} = 0.750.$$

Therefore, $\theta_C = 49°$. Thus the person would see the outside world compressed into a circle whose edge makes a 49° angle with the vertical. Beyond this angle, the person would see reflections from the sides and bottom of the lake or pool (Fig. 23–25).

**EXERCISE D** Light traveling in air strikes a glass surface with $n = 1.48$. For what range of angles will total internal reflection occur?

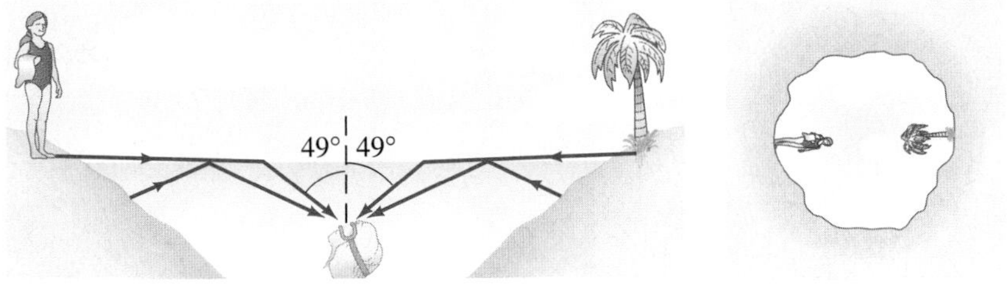


(a) (b)

**FIGURE 23–25** (a) Light rays, and (b) view looking upward from beneath the water (the surface of the water must be very smooth). Example 23–8.

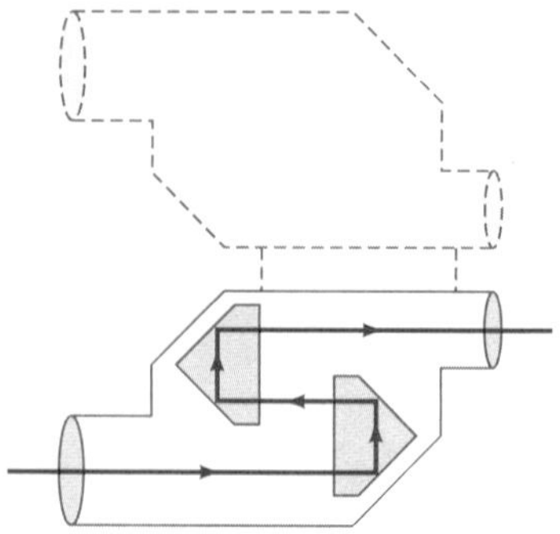

FIGURE 23–26 Total internal reflection of light by prisms in binoculars.

Many optical instruments, such as binoculars, use total internal reflection within a prism to reflect light. The advantage is that very nearly 100% of the light is reflected, whereas even the best mirrors reflect somewhat less than 100%. Thus the image is brighter, especially after several reflections. For glass with $n = 1.50$, $\theta_C = 41.8°$. Therefore, 45° prisms will reflect all the light internally, if oriented as shown in the binoculars of Fig. 23–26.

**EXERCISE E** If 45° plastic lenses were used in binoculars, what minimum index of refraction must the plastic have?

**EXERCISE F** What would happen if the 45° glass prisms of Exercise E were immersed in water?

## Fiber Optics

Total internal reflection is the principle behind **fiber optics**. Glass and plastic fibers as thin as a few micrometers in diameter are common. A bundle of such tiny fibers is called a **light pipe** or cable, and light† can be transmitted along it with almost no loss because of total internal reflection. Figure 23–27 shows how light traveling down a thin fiber makes only glancing collisions with the walls so that total internal reflection occurs. Even if the light pipe is bent into a complicated shape, the critical angle still won't be exceeded, so light is transmitted practically undiminished to the other end. Very small losses do occur, mainly by reflection at the ends and absorption within the fiber.

FIGURE 23–27 Light reflected totally at the interior surface of a glass or transparent plastic fiber.

PHYSICS APPLIED

*Fiber optics in communications*

Important applications of fiber-optic cables are in communications and medicine. They are used in place of wire to carry telephone calls, video signals, and computer data. The signal is a modulated light beam (a light beam whose intensity can be varied) and data is transmitted at a much higher rate and with less loss and less interference than an electrical signal in a copper wire. Fibers have been developed that can support over one hundred separate wavelengths, each modulated to carry up to 10 gigabits ($10^{10}$ bits) of information per second. That amounts to a terabit ($10^{12}$ bits) per second for the full one hundred wavelengths. The sophisticated use of fiber optics to transmit a clear picture is particularly useful in medicine, Fig. 23–28. For example, a patient's lungs can be examined by inserting a light pipe known as a bronchoscope through the mouth and down the bronchial tube. Light is sent down an outer set of fibers to illuminate the lungs. The reflected light returns up a central core set of fibers. Light directly in front of each fiber travels up that fiber. At the opposite end, a viewer sees a series of bright and dark spots, much like a TV screen—that is, a picture of what lies at the opposite end. Lenses are used at each end: at the object end to bring the rays in parallel, and at the viewing end as a telescope. The image may be viewed directly or on a monitor screen or film. The fibers must be optically insulated from one another, usually by a thin coating of material with index of refraction less than that of the fiber. The more fibers there are, and the smaller they are, the more detailed the picture. Such instruments, including bronchoscopes, colonoscopes (for viewing the colon), and endoscopes (stomach or other organs), are extremely useful for examining hard-to-reach places.

PHYSICS APPLIED

*Medicine—bronchoscopes, colonoscopes, endoscopes*

†Fiber optics finds use not only with visible light but also with infrared light, ultraviolet light, and microwaves.

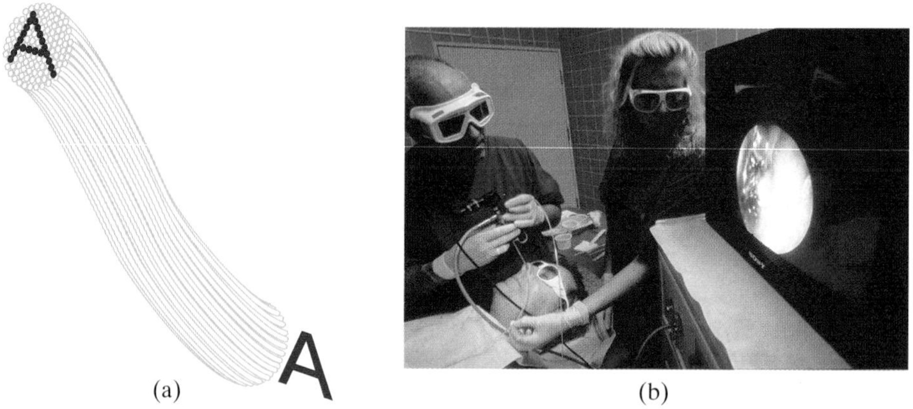


(a) (b)

FIGURE 23–28 (a) How a fiber-optic image is made. (b) Example of a fiber-optic device inserted through the nose, and the image seen.

**FIGURE 23–29** (a) Converging lenses and (b) diverging lenses, shown in cross section. (c) Photo of a converging lens (on the left) and a diverging lens (right). (d) Converging lenses (above), and diverging lenses (below), lying flat, and raised off the paper to form images.

## 23–7 Thin Lenses; Ray Tracing

The most important simple optical device is no doubt the thin lens. The development of optical devices using lenses dates to the sixteenth and seventeenth centuries, although the earliest record of eyeglasses dates from the late thirteenth century. Today we find lenses in eyeglasses, cameras, magnifying glasses, telescopes, binoculars, microscopes, and medical instruments. A thin lens is usually circular, and its two faces are portions of a sphere. (Although cylindrical surfaces are also possible, we will concentrate on spherical.) The two faces can be concave, convex, or plane; several types are shown in Fig. 23–29, in cross section. The importance of lenses is that they form images of objects, as shown in Fig. 23–30.

**FIGURE 23–30** Converging lens (in holder) forms an image (large "F" on screen at right) of a bright object (illuminated "F" at the left).

Consider parallel rays striking the double convex lens shown in cross section in Fig. 23–31a. We assume the lens is made of glass or transparent plastic, so its index of refraction is greater than that of the air outside. The **axis** of a lens is a straight line passing through the center of the lens and perpendicular to its two surfaces (Fig. 23–31). From Snell's law, we can see that each ray in Fig. 23–31a is bent toward the axis when the ray enters the lens and again when it leaves the lens at the back surface. (Note the dashed lines indicating the normals to each surface for the top ray.) If rays parallel to the axis fall on a thin lens, they will be focused to a point called the **focal point**, F. This will not be precisely true for a lens with spherical surfaces. But it will be very nearly true—that is, parallel rays will be focused to a tiny region that is nearly a point—if the diameter of the lens is small compared to the radii of curvature of the two lens surfaces. This criterion is satisfied by a **thin lens**, one that is very thin compared to its diameter, and we consider only thin lenses here.

**FIGURE 23–31** (below) Parallel rays are brought to a focus by a converging thin lens.

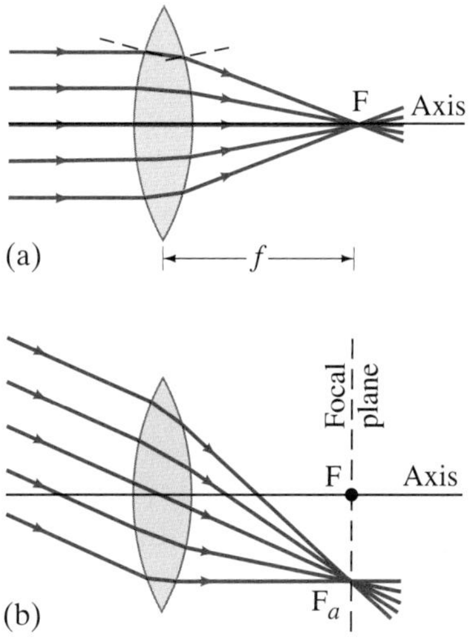

The rays from a point on a distant object are essentially parallel—see Fig. 23–10. Therefore we can say that *the focal point is the image point for an object at infinity on the lens axis*. Thus, the focal point of a lens can be found by locating the point where the Sun's rays (or those of some other distant object) are brought to a sharp image, Fig. 23–32. The distance of the focal point from the center of the lens is called the **focal length**, $f$. A lens can be turned around so that light can pass through it from the opposite side. The focal length is *the same* on both sides, as we shall see later, even if the curvatures of the two lens surfaces are different. If parallel rays fall on a lens at an angle, as in Fig. 23–31b, they focus at a point $F_a$. The plane in which all points such as F and $F_a$ fall is called the **focal plane** of the lens.

*Focal length of lens*

**FIGURE 23–32** Image of the Sun burning a hole, almost, on a piece of paper.

Any lens† that is thicker in the center than at the edges will make parallel rays converge to a point, and is called a **converging lens** (see Fig. 23–29a). Lenses that are thinner in the center than at the edges (Fig. 23–29b) are called **diverging lenses** because they make parallel light diverge, as shown in Fig. 23–33. The focal point, F, of a diverging lens is defined as that point from which refracted rays, originating from parallel incident rays, seem to emerge as shown in Fig. 23–33. And the distance from F to the lens is called the **focal length**, $f$, just as for a converging lens.

Optometrists and ophthalmologists, instead of using the focal length, use the reciprocal of the focal length to specify the strength of eyeglass (or contact) lenses. This is called the **power**, $P$, of a lens:

*Power of lens*

$$P = \frac{1}{f}. \tag{23–7}$$

*Diopters*

The unit for lens power is the **diopter** (D), which is an inverse meter: $1\ \text{D} = 1\ \text{m}^{-1}$. For example, a 20-cm-focal-length lens has a power $P = 1/(0.20\ \text{m}) = 5.0\ \text{D}$. We will mainly use the focal length, but we will refer again to the power of a lens when we discuss eyeglass lenses in Chapter 25.

**FIGURE 23–33** Diverging lens.

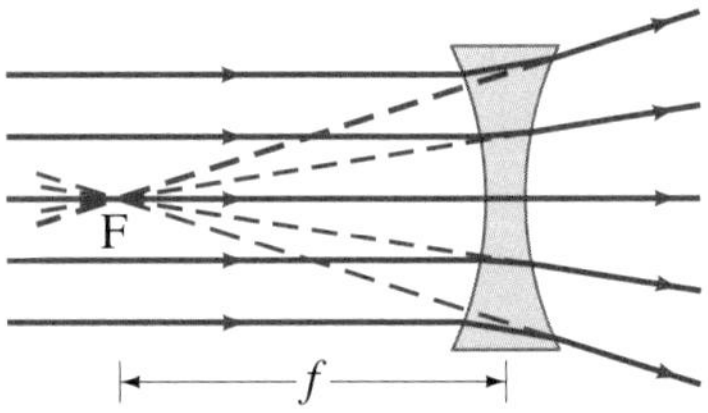


The most important parameter of a lens is its focal length $f$. For a converging lens, $f$ is easily measured by finding the image point for the Sun or other distant objects. Once $f$ is known, the image position can be calculated for any object. To find the image point by drawing rays would be difficult if we had to determine the refractive angles at the front surface of the lens and again at the back surface where the ray exits. We can save ourselves a lot of effort by making use of certain facts we already know, such as that a ray parallel to the axis of the lens passes (after refraction) through the focal point. To determine an image point, we need to consider only the three rays indicated in Fig. 23–34, which uses an arrow (on the left) as the object, and a converging lens forming an image to the right. These rays, emanating from a single point on the object, are drawn as if the lens were infinitely thin, and we show only a single sharp bend at the center line of the lens instead of the refractions at each surface. These three rays are drawn as follows:

**➥ RAY DIAGRAM**

*Finding the image position formed by a thin lens*

Ray 1 is drawn parallel to the axis; therefore it is refracted by the lens so that it passes along a line through the focal point F behind the lens, Fig. 23–34a. (See also Fig. 23–31a.)

Ray 2 is drawn on a line passing through the other focal point F′ (front side of lens in Fig. 23–34) and emerges from the lens parallel to the axis, Fig. 23–34b.

Ray 3 is directed toward the very center of the lens, where the two surfaces are essentially parallel to each other; this ray therefore emerges from the lens at the same angle as it entered; as we saw in Example 23–6, the ray would be displaced slightly to one side, but since we assume the lens is thin, we draw ray 3 straight through as shown, Fig. 23–34c.

The point where these three rays cross is the image point for that object point. Actually, any two of these rays will suffice to locate the image point, but drawing the third ray can serve as a check.

† We are assuming the lens has an index of refraction greater than that of the surrounding material, such as a glass or plastic lens in air, which is the usual situation.

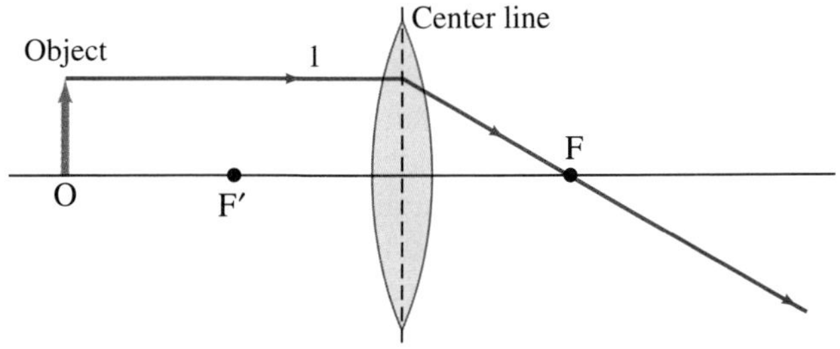


(a) Ray 1 leaves one point on object going parallel to the axis, then refracts through focal point behind.

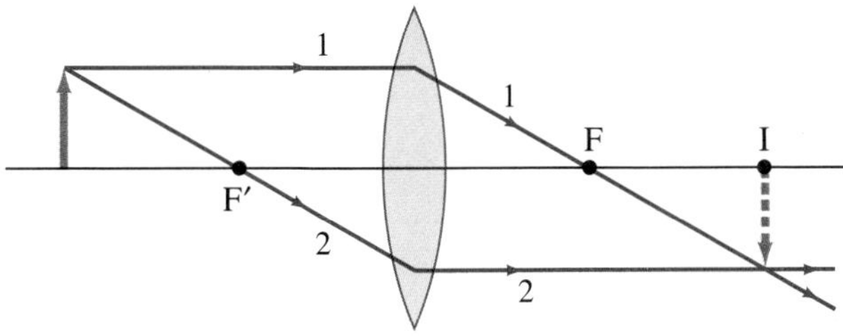


(b) Ray 2 passes through F′ in front of the lens; therefore it is parallel to the axis behind the lens.

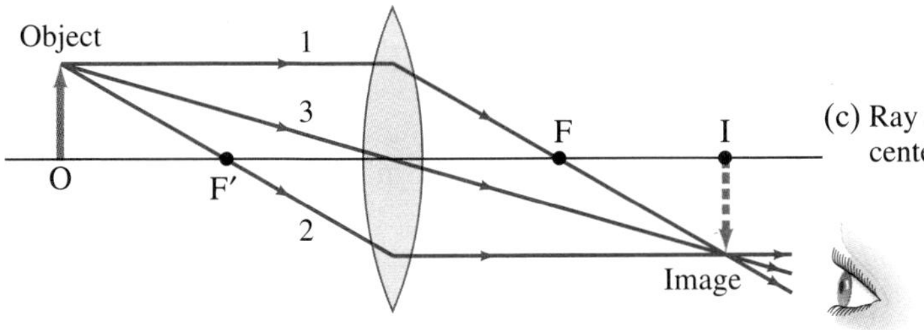


(c) Ray 3 passes straight through the center of the lens (assumed very thin).

**FIGURE 23–34** Finding the image by ray tracing for a converging lens. Rays are shown leaving one point on the object (an arrow). Shown are the three most useful rays, leaving the tip of the object, for determining where the image of that point is formed.

Using these three rays for one object point, we can find the image point for that point of the object (the top of the arrow in Fig. 23–34). The image points for all other points on the object can be found similarly to determine the complete image of the object. Because the rays actually pass through the image for the case shown in Fig. 23–34, it is a **real image** (see page 634). The image could be detected by film, or actually seen on a white surface or screen placed at the position of the image (Fig. 23–35).

*Seeing the image*

The image can also be seen directly by the eye when the eye is placed behind the image, as shown in Fig. 23–34c, so that some of the rays diverging from each point on the image can enter the eye. We can see a sharp image only for rays *diverging* from each point on the image, because we see normal objects when diverging rays from each point enter the eye as shown in Fig. 23–1. Your eye cannot focus rays converging on it; if your eye was positioned between points F and I in Fig. 23–34c, it would not see a clear image. (More about our eyes in Section 25–2.) Figure 23–35 shows an image seen (a) on a screen and (b) directly by the eye (and a camera) placed behind the image.

(a)

(b)

**FIGURE 23–35** (a) A converging lens can form a real image (here of a distant building, upside down) on a screen. (b) That same real image is also directly visible to the eye. [Figure 23–29d shows images (graph paper) seen by the eye made by both diverging and converging lenses.]

## Diverging Lens

By drawing the same three rays emerging from a single object point, we can determine the image position formed by a diverging lens, as shown in Fig. 23–36. Note that ray 1 is drawn parallel to the axis, but does not pass through the focal point F′ behind the lens. Instead it seems to come from the focal point F in front of the lens (dashed line). Ray 2 is directed toward F′ and is refracted parallel to the lens axis by the lens. Ray 3 passes directly through the center of the lens. The three refracted rays seem to emerge from a point on the left of the lens. This is the image point, I. Because the rays do not pass through the image, it is a **virtual image**. Note that the eye does not distinguish between real and virtual images—both are visible.

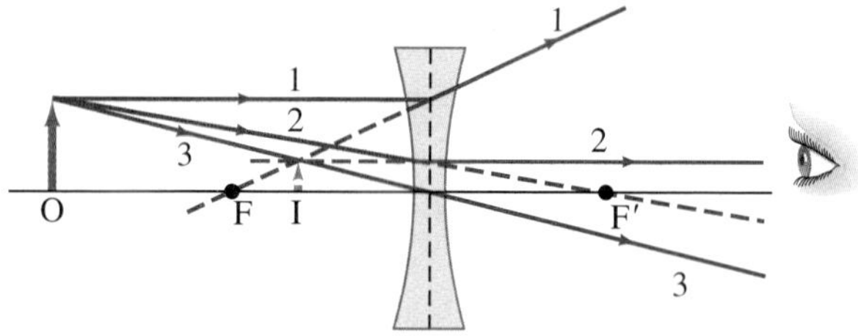


**FIGURE 23–36** Finding the image by ray tracing for a diverging lens.

# 23–8 The Thin Lens Equation; Magnification

We now derive an equation that relates the image distance to the object distance and the focal length of a thin lens. This equation will make the determination of image position quicker and more accurate than doing ray tracing. Let $d_o$ be the object distance, the distance of the object from the center of the lens, and $d_i$ be the image distance, the distance of the image from the center of the lens. And let $h_o$ and $h_i$ refer to the heights of the object and image. Consider the two rays shown in

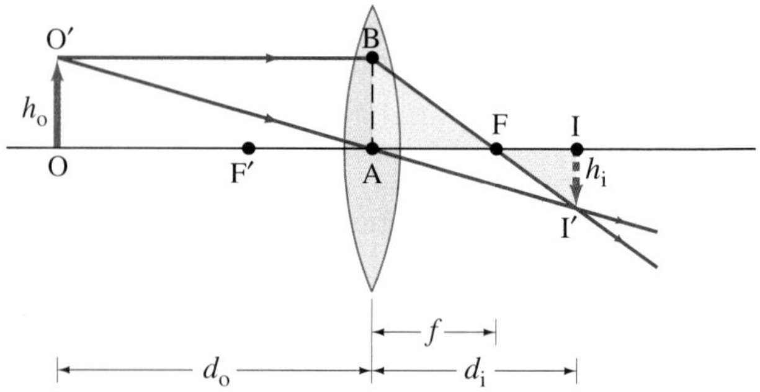


**FIGURE 23–37** Deriving the lens equation for a converging lens.

Fig. 23–37 for a converging lens, assumed to be very thin. The right triangles FI′I and FBA (highlighted in yellow) are similar because angle AFB equals angle IFI′; so

$$\frac{h_i}{h_o} = \frac{d_i - f}{f},$$

since length AB $= h_o$. Triangles OAO′ and IAI′ are similar as well. Therefore,

$$\frac{h_i}{h_o} = \frac{d_i}{d_o}.$$

We equate the right sides of these two equations (the left sides are the same), and divide by $d_i$ to obtain

$$\frac{1}{f} - \frac{1}{d_i} = \frac{1}{d_o}$$

or

THIN LENS EQUATION

$$\frac{1}{d_o} + \frac{1}{d_i} = \frac{1}{f}. \qquad \textbf{(23–8)}$$

This is called the **thin lens equation**. It relates the image distance $d_i$ to the object distance $d_o$ and the focal length $f$. It is the most useful equation in geometric optics. (Interestingly, it is exactly the same as the mirror equation, Eq. 23–2). If the object is at infinity, then $1/d_o = 0$, so $d_i = f$. Thus the focal length is the image distance for an object at infinity, as mentioned earlier.

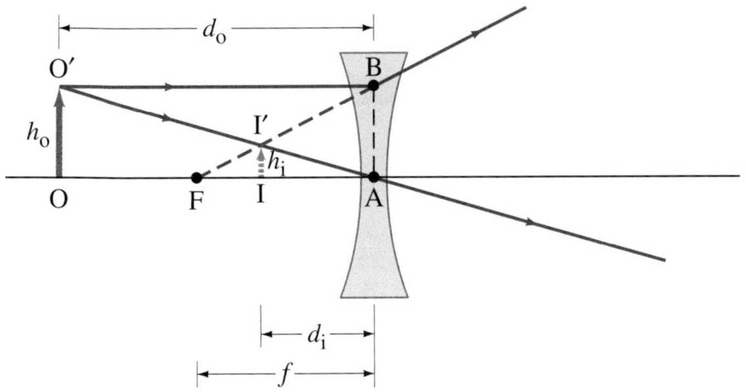


**FIGURE 23–38** Deriving the lens equation for a diverging lens.

We can derive the lens equation for a diverging lens using Fig. 23–38. Triangles IAI′ and OAO′ are similar; and triangles IFI′ and AFB are similar. Thus (noting that length $AB = h_o$)

$$\frac{h_i}{h_o} = \frac{d_i}{d_o} \quad \text{and} \quad \frac{h_i}{h_o} = \frac{f - d_i}{f}.$$

When we equate the right sides of these two equations and simplify, we obtain

$$\frac{1}{d_o} - \frac{1}{d_i} = -\frac{1}{f}.$$

This equation becomes the same as Eq. 23–8 if we make $f$ and $d_i$ negative. That is, we take $f$ to be *negative for a diverging lens*, and $d_i$ negative when the image is on the same side of the lens as the light comes from. Thus Eq. 23–8 will be valid for both converging and diverging lenses, and for *all* situations, if we use the following **sign conventions**:

CAUTION
*Focal length is negative for diverging lens*

PROBLEM SOLVING
*SIGN CONVENTIONS for lenses*

1. The focal length is positive for converging lenses and negative for diverging lenses.
2. The object distance is positive if the object is on the side of the lens from which the light is coming (this is usually the case, although when lenses are used in combination, it might not be so); otherwise, it is negative.
3. The image distance is positive if the image is on the opposite side of the lens from where the light is coming; if it is on the same side, $d_i$ is negative. Equivalently, the image distance is positive for a real image and negative for a virtual image.
4. The height of the image, $h_i$, is positive if the image is upright, and negative if the image is inverted relative to the object. ($h_o$ is always taken as positive.)

The **magnification**, $m$, of a lens is defined as the ratio of the image height to object height, $m = h_i/h_o$. From Figs. 23–37 and 23–38 and the conventions just stated (for which we'll need a minus sign below), we have

$$m = \frac{h_i}{h_o} = -\frac{d_i}{d_o}. \tag{23–9}$$

*Magnification of a lens*

For an upright image the magnification is positive, and for an inverted image the magnification is negative.

From sign convention 1, it follows that the power (Eq. 23–7) of a converging lens, in diopters, is positive, whereas the power of a diverging lens is negative. A converging lens is sometimes referred to as a **positive lens**, and a diverging lens as a **negative lens**.

## PROBLEM SOLVING Thin Lenses

1. Draw a **ray diagram**, as precise as possible, but even a rough one can serve as confirmation of analytic results. Choose one point on the object and draw at least two, preferably three, of the easy-to-draw rays described in Figs. 23–34 and 23–36. The image point is where the rays intersect.
2. For analytic solutions, solve for unknowns in the **thin lens equation** (Eq. 23–8) and the **magnification equation** (Eq. 23–9). The thin lens equation involves reciprocals—don't forget to take the reciprocal.
3. Follow the **sign conventions** above.
4. Check that your analytic answers are **consistent** with your ray diagram.

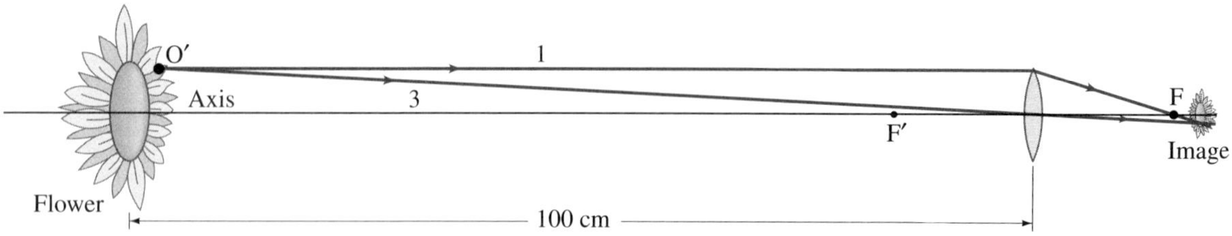


**FIGURE 23–39** Example 23–9. (Not to scale.)

**EXAMPLE 23–9 Image formed by converging lens.** What is (*a*) the position, and (*b*) the size, of the image of a 7.6-cm-high flower placed 1.00 m from a +50.0-mm-focal-length camera lens?

**APPROACH** We follow the steps of the Problem Solving Box explicitly.

**SOLUTION**

**(1) Ray diagram:** Figure 23–39 is an approximate ray diagram, showing only rays 1 and 3 for a single point on the flower. We see that the image ought to be a little behind the focal point F, to the right of the lens.

**(2) Thin lens and magnification equations:** (*a*) We find the image position analytically using the thin lens equation, Eq. 23–8. The camera lens is converging, with $f = +5.00\text{ cm}$, and $d_o = 100\text{ cm}$, and so the thin lens equation gives

$$\frac{1}{d_i} = \frac{1}{f} - \frac{1}{d_o} = \frac{1}{5.00\text{ cm}} - \frac{1}{100\text{ cm}}$$

$$= \frac{20.0 - 1.0}{100\text{ cm}} = \frac{19.0}{100\text{ cm}}.$$

Then

$$d_i = \frac{100\text{ cm}}{19.0} = 5.26\text{ cm},$$

or 52.6 mm behind the lens.

(*b*) The magnification is

$$m = -\frac{d_i}{d_o} = -\frac{5.26\text{ cm}}{100\text{ cm}} = -0.0526,$$

so

$$h_i = mh_o = (-0.0526)(7.6\text{ cm}) = -0.40\text{ cm}.$$

The image is 4.0 mm high.

**(3) Sign conventions:** The image distance $d_i$ came out positive, so the image is behind the lens. The image height is $h_i = -0.40\text{ cm}$; the minus sign means the image is inverted.

**(4) Consistency:** The analytic results of steps (2) and (3) are consistent with the ray diagram, Fig. 23–39: the image is behind the lens and inverted.

**NOTE** Part (*a*) tells us that the image is 2.6 mm farther from the lens than the image for an object at infinity, which equals the focal length, 50.0 mm. Indeed, when focusing a camera lens, the closer the object is to the camera, the farther the lens must be from the film.

**EXERCISE G** If the flower (object) of Example 23–9 is moved farther from the lens, does the image move closer to or farther from the lens? (Don't calculate!)

**EXAMPLE 23–10** **Object close to converging lens.** An object is placed 10 cm from a 15-cm-focal-length converging lens. Determine the image position and size (*a*) analytically, and (*b*) using a ray diagram.

**APPROACH** We first use Eqs. 23–8 and 23–9 to obtain an analytic solution, and then confirm with a ray diagram using the special rays 1, 2, and 3 for a single object point.

**SOLUTION** (*a*) Given $f = 15\text{ cm}$ and $d_o = 10\text{ cm}$, then

$$\frac{1}{d_i} = \frac{1}{15\text{ cm}} - \frac{1}{10\text{ cm}} = -\frac{1}{30\text{ cm}},$$

and $d_i = -30\text{ cm}$. (Remember to take the reciprocal!) Because $d_i$ is negative, the image must be virtual and on the same side of the lens as the object. The magnification

$$m = -\frac{d_i}{d_o} = -\frac{-30\text{ cm}}{10\text{ cm}} = 3.0.$$

The image is three times as large as the object and is upright. This lens is being used as a simple magnifying glass, which we discuss in more detail in Section 25–3.

(*b*) The ray diagram is shown in Fig. 23–40 and confirms the result in part (*a*). We choose point O′ on the top of the object and draw ray 1, which is easy. But ray 2 may take some thought: if we draw it heading toward F′, it is going the wrong way—so we have to draw it as if coming from F′ (and so dashed), striking the lens, and then going out parallel to the lens axis. We project it backward with a dashed line, as we must do also for ray 1, in order to find where they cross. Ray 3 is drawn through the lens center, and it crosses the other two rays at the image point, I′.

**NOTE** From Fig. 23–40 we can see that, whenever an object is placed between a converging lens and its focal point, the image is virtual.

**CAUTION**
*Don't forget to take the reciprocal*

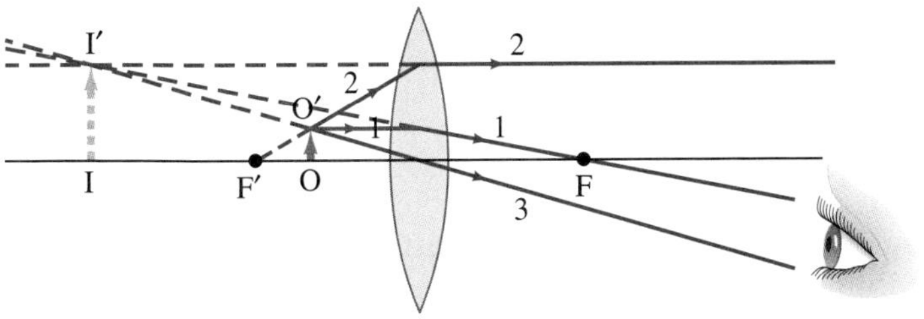


**FIGURE 23–40** An object placed within the focal point of a converging lens produces a virtual image. Example 23–10.

**EXAMPLE 23–11** **Diverging lens.** Where must a small insect be placed if a 25-cm-focal-length diverging lens is to form a virtual image 20 cm in front of the lens?

**APPROACH** The ray diagram is basically that of Fig. 23–38 because our lens here is diverging and our image is in front of the lens within the focal distance. (It would be a valuable exercise to draw the ray diagram to scale, precisely, now.) The insect's distance, $d_o$, can be calculated using the thin lens equation.

**SOLUTION** The lens is diverging, so $f$ is negative: $f = -25\text{ cm}$. The image distance must be negative too because the image is in front of the lens (sign conventions), so $d_i = -20\text{ cm}$. Equation 23–8 gives

$$\frac{1}{d_o} = \frac{1}{f} - \frac{1}{d_i} = -\frac{1}{25\text{ cm}} + \frac{1}{20\text{ cm}} = \frac{-4+5}{100\text{ cm}} = \frac{1}{100\text{ cm}}.$$

So the object must be 100 cm in front of the lens.

**EXERCISE H** An object is placed 12 cm from a lens with 15-cm focal length. Will the image be real or virtual if the lens is (*a*) converging or (*b*) diverging?

**EXERCISE I** Determine the position of the image produced by a 15.0-cm-focal-length converging lens when an object is placed 13.0 cm in front of it.

## * 23–9 Combinations of Lenses

*Multiple lenses: image formed by first lens is object for second lens*

We now consider how to deal with lenses used in combination. When light passes through more than one lens, we find the image formed by the first lens as if it were alone. This image becomes the *object* for the second lens, and we find the image then formed by this second lens, which is the final image if there are only two lenses. The total magnification will be the product of the separate magnifications of each lens, as we shall see. Even if the second lens intercepts the light from the first lens before it forms an image, this technique still works.

**EXAMPLE 23–12** **A two-lens system.** Two converging lenses, A and B, with focal lengths $f_A = 20.0\,\text{cm}$ and $f_B = 25.0\,\text{cm}$, are placed 80.0 cm apart, as shown in Fig. 23–41a. An object is placed 60.0 cm in front of the first lens as shown in Fig. 23–41b. Determine (*a*) the position, and (*b*) the magnification, of the final image formed by the combination of the two lenses.

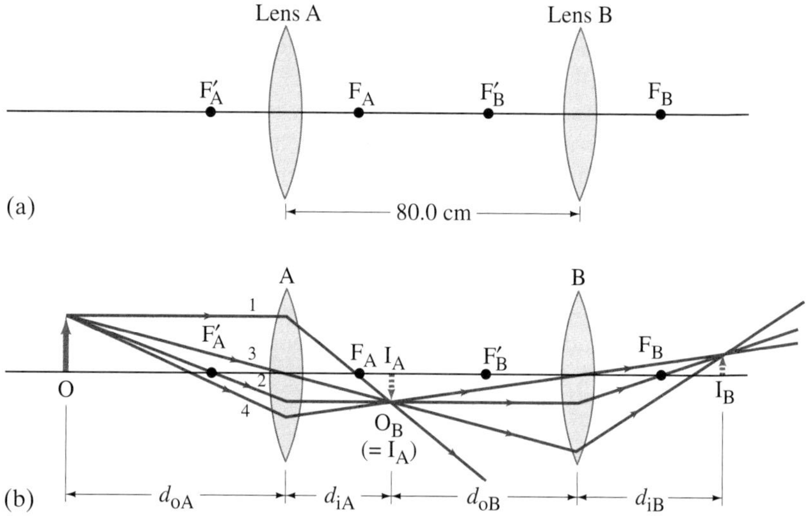


**FIGURE 23–41** Two lenses, A and B, used in combination, Example 23–12. The small numbers refer to the easily drawn rays.

**APPROACH** Starting at the tip of our object O, we draw rays 1, 2, and 3 for the first lens, A, and also a ray 4 which, after passing through lens A, acts as "ray 3" (through the center) for the second lens, B. Ray 2 for lens A exits parallel, and so is ray 1 for lens B. To determine the position of the image $I_A$ formed by lens A, we use Eq. 23–8 with $f_A = 20.0\,\text{cm}$ and $d_{oA} = 60.0\,\text{cm}$. The distance of $I_A$ from lens B is the object distance $d_{oB}$ for lens B. The final image is found using the thin lens equation, this time with all distances relative to lens B. For (*b*) the magnifications are found from Eq. 23–9 for each lens in turn.

**SOLUTION** (*a*) The object is a distance $d_{oA} = +60.0\,\text{cm}$ from the first lens, A, and this lens forms an image whose position can be calculated using the thin lens equation:

$$\frac{1}{d_{iA}} = \frac{1}{f_A} - \frac{1}{d_{oA}} = \frac{1}{20.0\,\text{cm}} - \frac{1}{60.0\,\text{cm}} = \frac{3-1}{60.0\,\text{cm}} = \frac{1}{30.0\,\text{cm}}.$$

**CAUTION**
*Note that object distance for second lens is **not** equal to the image distance for first lens*

So the first image $I_A$ is at $d_{iA} = 30.0\,\text{cm}$ behind the first lens. This image becomes the object for the second lens, B. It is a distance $d_{oB} = 80.0\,\text{cm} - 30.0\,\text{cm} = 50.0\,\text{cm}$ in front of lens B, as shown in Fig. 23–41b. The image formed by lens B, again using the thin lens equation, is at a distance $d_{iB}$ from the lens B:

$$\frac{1}{d_{iB}} = \frac{1}{f_B} - \frac{1}{d_{oB}} = \frac{1}{25.0\,\text{cm}} - \frac{1}{50.0\,\text{cm}} = \frac{2-1}{50.0\,\text{cm}} = \frac{1}{50.0\,\text{cm}}.$$

Hence $d_{iB} = 50.0\,\text{cm}$ behind lens B. This is the final image—see Fig. 23–41b.

(*b*) Lens A has a magnification (Eq. 23–9)

$$m_A = -\frac{d_{iA}}{d_{oA}} = -\frac{30.0\ \text{cm}}{60.0\ \text{cm}} = -0.500.$$

Thus, the first image is inverted and is half as high as the object (again Eq. 23–9):

$$h_{iA} = m_A h_{oA} = -0.500 h_{oA}.$$

Lens B takes this image as object and changes its height by a factor

$$m_B = -\frac{d_{iB}}{d_{oB}} = -\frac{50.0\ \text{cm}}{50.0\ \text{cm}} = -1.000.$$

The second lens reinverts the image (the minus sign) but doesn't change its size. The final image height is (remember $h_{oB}$ is the same as $h_{iA}$)

$$h_{iB} = m_B h_{oB} = m_B h_{iA} = m_B m_A h_{oA} = (m_{total})h_{oA}.$$

*Total magnification is* $m_{total} = m_A m_B$

The total magnification is the product of $m_A$ and $m_B$, which here equals $m_{total} = m_A m_B = (-1.000)(-0.500) = +0.500,$ or half the original height, and the final image is upright.

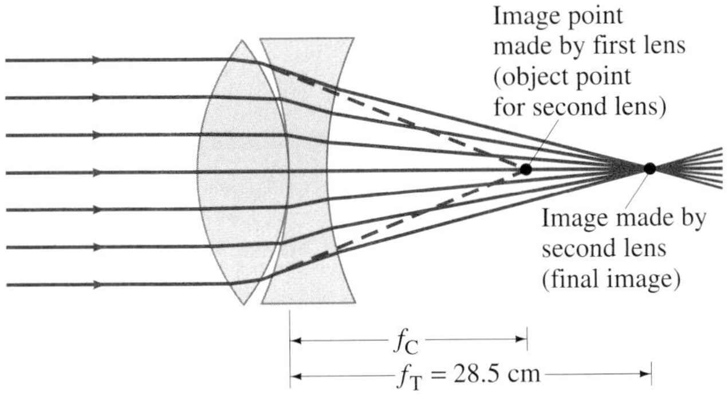


**FIGURE 23–42** Determining the focal length of a diverging lens. Example 23–13.

**EXAMPLE 23–13** **Measuring *f* for a diverging lens.** To measure the focal length of a diverging lens, a converging lens is placed in contact with it, as shown in Fig. 23–42. The Sun's rays are focused by this combination at a point 28.5 cm, behind the lenses as shown. If the converging lens has a focal length $f_C$ of 16.0 cm, what is the focal length $f_D$ of the diverging lens? Assume both lenses are thin and the space between them is negligible.

**APPROACH** The image distance for the first lens equals its focal length (16.0 cm) since the object distance is infinity ($\infty$). The position of this image, even though it is never actually formed, acts as the object for the second (diverging) lens. We apply the thin lens equation to the diverging lens to find where the final image is.

**SOLUTION** Rays from the Sun are focused 28.5 cm behind the combination, so the focal length of the total combination is $f_T = 28.5$ cm. If the diverging lens was absent, the converging lens would form the image at its focal point—that is, at a distance $f_C = 16.0$ cm behind it (dashed lines in Fig. 23–42). When the diverging lens is placed next to the converging lens, we treat the image formed by the first lens as the *object* for the second lens. Since this object lies to the right of the diverging lens, this is a situation where $d_o$ is negative (see the sign conventions, page 651). Thus, for the diverging lens, the object is virtual and $d_o = -16.0$ cm. The diverging lens forms the image of this virtual object at a distance $d_i = 28.5$ cm away (this was given). Thus,

$$\frac{1}{f_D} = \frac{1}{d_o} + \frac{1}{d_i} = \frac{1}{-16.0\ \text{cm}} + \frac{1}{28.5\ \text{cm}} = -0.0274\ \text{cm}^{-1}.$$

We take the reciprocal to find $f_D = -1/(0.0274\ \text{cm}^{-1}) = -36.5$ cm.

**NOTE** If this technique is to work, the converging lens must be "stronger" than the diverging lens—that is, it must have a focal length whose magnitude is less than that of the diverging lens.

## * 23–10 Lensmaker's Equation

A useful equation, known as the **lensmaker's equation**, relates the focal length of a lens to the radii of curvature $R_1$ and $R_2$ of its two surfaces and its index of refraction $n$:

*Lensmaker's equation*

$$\frac{1}{f} = (n-1)\left(\frac{1}{R_1} + \frac{1}{R_2}\right). \qquad \textbf{(23–10)}$$

If both surfaces are convex, $R_1$ and $R_2$ are considered positive.† For a concave surface, the radius must be considered *negative*.

Notice that Eq. 23–10 is symmetrical in $R_1$ and $R_2$. Thus, if a lens is turned around so that light impinges on the other surface, the focal length is the same even if the two lens surfaces are different.

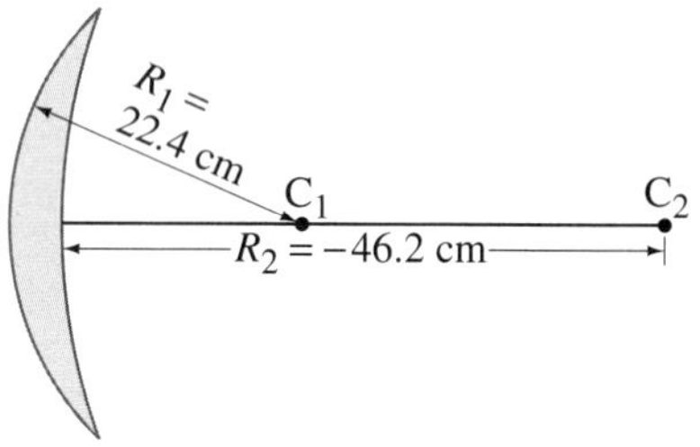

**FIGURE 23–43** Example 23–14.

**EXAMPLE 23–14 Calculating *f* for a converging lens.** A convex meniscus lens (Figs. 23–29a and 23–43) is made from glass with $n = 1.50$. The radius of curvature of the convex surface is 22.4 cm, and that of the concave surface is 46.2 cm. What is the focal length?

**APPROACH** We use the lensmaker's equation, Eq. 23–10, to find $f$.

**SOLUTION** $R_1 = 22.4\text{ cm}$ and $R_2 = -46.2\text{ cm}$ (concave surface). Then

$$\frac{1}{f} = (1.50 - 1.00)\left(\frac{1}{22.4\text{ cm}} - \frac{1}{46.2\text{ cm}}\right) = 0.0115\text{ cm}^{-1}.$$

So

$$f = \frac{1}{0.0115\text{ cm}^{-1}} = 87\text{ cm},$$

and the lens is converging since $f > 0$.

**NOTE** If we turn the lens around so that $R_1 = -46.2\text{ cm}$ and $R_2 = +22.4\text{ cm}$, we get the same result.

†Some books use a different convention—for example, $R_1$ and $R_2$ are considered positive if their centers of curvature are to the right of the lens, in which case a minus sign replaces the + sign in their equivalent of Eq. 23–10.

## Summary

Light appears to travel in straight-line paths, called **rays**, at a speed $v$ that depends on the **index of refraction**, $n$, of the material; that is

$$n = \frac{c}{v}, \qquad \textbf{(23–4)}$$

where $c$ is the speed of light in vacuum.

When light reflects from a flat surface, the *angle of reflection equals the angle of incidence*. This **law of reflection** explains why mirrors can form **images**.

In a **plane mirror**, the image is virtual, upright, the same size as the object, and is as far behind the mirror as the object is in front.

A **spherical mirror** can be concave or convex. A **concave** spherical mirror focuses parallel rays of light (light from a very distant object) to a point called the **focal point**. The distance of this point from the mirror is the **focal length** $f$ of the mirror and

$$f = \frac{r}{2}, \qquad \textbf{(23–1)}$$

where $r$ is the radius of curvature of the mirror.

Parallel rays falling on a **convex mirror** reflect from the mirror as if they diverged from a common point behind the mirror. The distance of this point from the mirror is the focal length and is considered negative for a convex mirror.

For a given object, the approximate position and size of the image formed by a mirror can be found by ray tracing. Algebraically, the relation between image and object distances, $d_i$ and $d_o$, and the focal length $f$, is given by the **mirror equation:**

$$\frac{1}{d_o} + \frac{1}{d_i} = \frac{1}{f}. \qquad \textbf{(23–2)}$$

The ratio of image height $h_i$ to object height $h_o$, which equals the magnification $m$ of a mirror, is

$$m = \frac{h_i}{h_o} = -\frac{d_i}{d_o}. \qquad \textbf{(23–3)}$$

If the rays that converge to form an image actually pass through the image, so the image would appear on film or a screen placed there, the image is said to be a **real image**. If the light rays do not actually pass through the image, the image is a **virtual image**.

When light passes from one transparent medium into another, the rays bend or refract. The **law of refraction** (**Snell's law**) states that

$$n_1 \sin\theta_1 = n_2 \sin\theta_2, \tag{23–5}$$

where $n_1$ and $\theta_1$ are the index of refraction and angle with the normal to the surface for the incident ray, and $n_2$ and $\theta_2$ are for the refracted ray.

When light rays reach the boundary of a material where the index of refraction decreases, the rays will be **totally internally reflected** if the incident angle, $\theta_1$, is such that Snell's law would predict $\sin\theta_2 > 1$. This occurs if $\theta_1$ exceeds the critical angle $\theta_C$ given by

$$\sin\theta_C = \frac{n_2}{n_1}. \tag{23–6}$$

A lens uses refraction to produce a real or virtual image. Parallel rays of light are focused to a point, called the **focal point**, by a **converging** lens. The distance of the focal point from the lens is called the **focal length** $f$ of the lens.

After parallel rays pass through a **diverging** lens, they appear to diverge from a point, its focal point; and the corresponding focal length is considered negative.

The **power** $P$ of a lens, which is $P = 1/f$ (Eq. 23–7), is given in diopters, which are units of inverse meters ($m^{-1}$).

For a given object, the position and size of the image formed by a lens can be found approximately by ray tracing. Algebraically, the relation between image and object distances, $d_i$ and $d_o$, and the focal length $f$, is given by the **thin lens equation**:

$$\frac{1}{d_o} + \frac{1}{d_i} = \frac{1}{f}. \tag{23–8}$$

The ratio of image height to object height, which equals the magnification $m$ for a lens, is

$$m = \frac{h_i}{h_o} = -\frac{d_i}{d_o}. \tag{23–9}$$

When using the various equations of geometrical optics, it is important to remember the **sign conventions** for all quantities involved: carefully review them (pages 641 and 651) when doing Problems.

[* When two (or more) thin lenses are used in combination to produce an image, the thin lens equation can be used for each lens in sequence. The image produced by the first lens acts as the object for the second lens. The **lensmaker's equation** relates the radii of curvature of the lens surfaces and the lens' index of refraction to the focal length of the lens.]

## Questions

1. What would be the appearance of the Moon if it had (*a*) a rough surface; (*b*) a polished mirrorlike surface?
2. Archimedes is said to have burned the whole Roman fleet in the harbor of Syracuse by focusing the rays of the Sun with a huge spherical mirror. Is this reasonable?
3. Although a plane mirror appears to reverse left and right, it doesn't reverse up and down. Explain.
4. If a concave mirror produces a real image, is the image necessarily inverted? Explain.
5. An object is placed along the principal axis of a spherical mirror. The magnification of the object is $-3.0$. Is the image real or virtual, inverted or upright? Is the mirror concave or convex? On which side of the mirror is the image located?
6. Using the rules for the three rays discussed with reference to Fig. 23–13, draw ray 2 for Fig. 23–17b.
7. What is the focal length of a plane mirror? What is the magnification of a plane mirror?
8. When you look at the Moon's reflection from a ripply sea, it appears elongated (Fig. 23–44). Explain.

**FIGURE 23–44** Question 8.

9. What is the angle of refraction when a light ray meets the boundary between two materials perpendicularly?
10. How might you determine the speed of light in a solid, rectangular, transparent object?
11. When you look down into a swimming pool or a lake, are you likely to underestimate or overestimate its depth? Explain. How does the apparent depth vary with the viewing angle? (Use ray diagrams.)
12. Draw a ray diagram to show why a stick looks bent when part of it is under water (Fig. 23–21).
13. Your eye looks into an aquarium and views a fish inside. One ray of light that emerges from the tank is shown in Fig. 23–45, as well as the apparent position of the fish. In the drawing, indicate the approximate position of the actual fish. Briefly justify your answer.

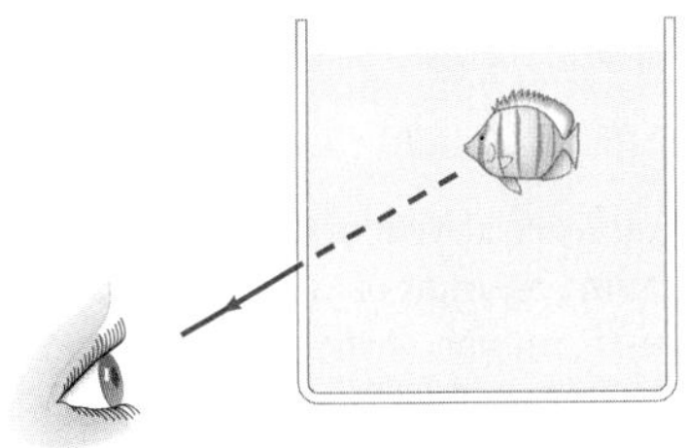

**FIGURE 23–45** Question 13.

14. How can you "see" a round drop of water on a table even though the water is transparent and colorless?
15. When you look up at an object in air from beneath the surface in a swimming pool, does the object appear to be the same size as when you see it directly in air? Explain.
16. How can a spherical mirror have a negative object distance?

**17.** Light rays from stars (including our Sun) always bend toward the vertical direction as they pass through the Earth's atmosphere. (*a*) Why does this make sense? (*b*) What can you conclude about the apparent positions of stars as viewed from Earth?

**18.** Where must the film be placed if a camera lens is to make a sharp image of an object very far away?

**19.** What type of mirror is shown in Fig. 23–46? Explain.

**FIGURE 23–46** Question 19.

**20.** A photographer moves closer to his subject and then refocuses. Does the camera lens move farther from or closer to the film? Explain.

**21.** Can a diverging lens form a real image under any circumstances? Explain.

**22.** Use ray diagrams to show that a real image formed by a thin lens is always inverted, whereas a virtual image is always upright if the object is real.

**23.** Light rays are said to be "reversible." Is this consistent with the thin lens equation? Explain.

**24.** Can real images be projected on a screen? Can virtual images? Can either be photographed? Discuss carefully.

**25.** A thin converging lens is moved closer to a nearby object. Does the real image formed change (*a*) in position, (*b*) in size? If yes, describe how.

**26.** A lens is made of a material with an index of refraction $n = 1.30$. In air, it is a converging lens. Will it still be a converging lens if placed in water? Explain, using a ray diagram.

**27.** A dog with its tail in the air stands facing a converging lens. If the nose and the tail are each focused on a screen in turn, which will have the greater magnification?

**28.** A cat with its tail in the air stands facing a converging lens. Under what circumstances (if any) would the image of the nose be virtual and the image of the tail be real? Where would the image of the rest of the cat be?

* **29.** Why, in Example 23–13, must the converging lens have a shorter focal length than the diverging lens if the latter's focal length is to be determined by combining them?

* **30.** Explain how you could have a virtual object.

* **31.** An unsymmetrical lens (say, planoconvex) forms an image of a nearby object. Does the image point change if the lens is turned around?

* **32.** The thicker a double convex lens is in the center as compared to its edges, the shorter its focal length for a given lens diameter. Explain.

* **33.** Consider two converging lenses separated by some distance. An object is placed so that the image from the first lens lies exactly at the focal point of the second lens. Will this combination produce an image? If so, where? If not, why not?

## Problems

### 23–2 Reflection; Plane Mirrors

1. (I) Suppose that you want to take a photograph of yourself as you look at your image in a flat mirror 2.5 m away. For what distance should the camera lens be focused?

2. (I) When you look at yourself in a 60-cm-tall plane mirror, you see the same amount of your body whether you are close to the mirror or far away. (Try it and see.) Use ray diagrams to show why this should be true.

3. (II) Two mirrors meet at a 135° angle, Fig. 23–47. If light rays strike one mirror at 40° as shown, at what angle $\phi$ do they leave the second mirror?

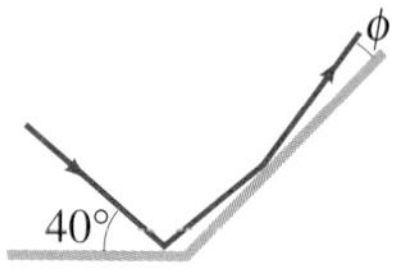


**FIGURE 23–47** Problem 3.

4. (II) A person whose eyes are 1.68 m above the floor stands 2.20 m in front of a vertical plane mirror whose bottom edge is 43 cm above the floor, Fig. 23–48. What is the horizontal distance $x$ to the base of the wall supporting the mirror of the nearest point on the floor that can be seen reflected in the mirror?

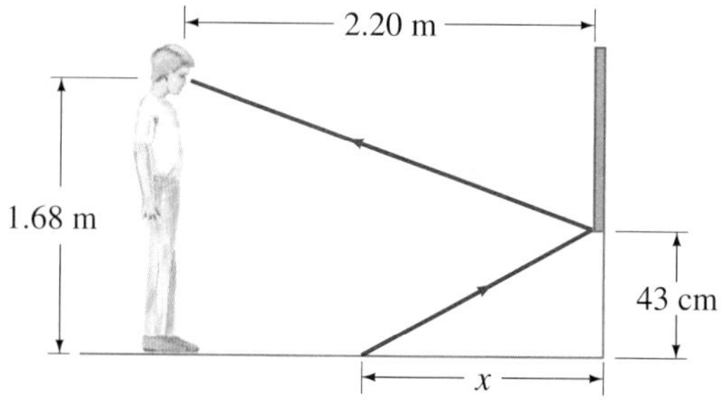


**FIGURE 23–48** Problem 4.

5. (II) Suppose you are 90 cm from a plane mirror. What area of the mirror is used to reflect the rays entering one eye from a point on the tip of your nose if your pupil diameter is 5.5 mm?

6. (III) Show that if two plane mirrors meet at an angle $\phi$, a single ray reflected successively from both mirrors is deflected through an angle of $2\phi$ independent of the incident angle. Assume $\phi < 90°$ and that only two reflections, one from each mirror, take place.

## 23–3 Spherical Mirrors

7. (I) A solar cooker, really a concave mirror pointed at the Sun, focuses the Sun's rays 18.0 cm in front of the mirror. What is the radius of the spherical surface from which the mirror was made?

8. (I) How far from a concave mirror (radius 23.0 cm) must an object be placed if its image is to be at infinity?

9. (II) If you look at yourself in a shiny Christmas tree ball with a diameter of 9.0 cm when your face is 30.0 cm away from it, where is your image? Is it real or virtual? Is it upright or inverted?

10. (II) A mirror at an amusement park shows an upright image of any person who stands 1.4 m in front of it. If the image is three times the person's height, what is the radius of curvature?

11. (II) A dentist wants a small mirror that, when 2.20 cm from a tooth, will produce a 4.5× upright image. What kind of mirror must be used and what must its radius of curvature be?

12. (II) Some rearview mirrors produce images of cars behind you that are smaller than they would be if the mirror were flat. Are the mirrors concave or convex? What is a mirror's radius of curvature if cars 20.0 m away appear 0.33× their normal size?

13. (II) A luminous object 3.0 mm high is placed 20.0 cm from a convex mirror of radius of curvature 20.0 cm. (*a*) Show by ray tracing that the image is virtual, and estimate the image distance. (*b*) Show that the (negative) image distance can be computed from Eq. 23–2 using a focal length of −10.0 cm. (*c*) Compute the image size, using Eq. 23–3.

14. (II) You are standing 3.0 m from a convex security mirror in a store. You estimate the height of your image to be half of your actual height. Estimate the radius of curvature of the mirror.

15. (II) (*a*) Where should an object be placed in front of a concave mirror so that it produces an image at the same location as the object? (*b*) Is the image real or virtual? (*c*) Is the image inverted or upright? (*d*) What is the magnification of the image?

16. (II) The image of a distant tree is virtual and very small when viewed in a curved mirror. The image appears to be 18.0 cm behind the mirror. What kind of mirror is it, and what is its radius of curvature?

17. (II) Use two different techniques, (*a*) a ray diagram, and (*b*) the mirror equation, to show that the magnitude of the magnification of a concave mirror is less than 1 if the object is beyond the center of curvature $C$ ($d_o > r$), and is greater than 1 if the object is within $C$ ($d_o < r$).

18. (II) Show, using a ray diagram, that the magnification $m$ of a convex mirror is $m = -d_i/d_o$, just as for a concave mirror. [*Hint*: consider a ray from the top of the object that reflects at the center of the mirror.]

19. (II) Use ray diagrams to show that the mirror equation, Eq. 23–2, is valid for a convex mirror as long as $f$ is considered negative.

20. (II) The magnification of a convex mirror is +0.65× for objects 2.2 m from the mirror. What is the focal length of this mirror?

21. (III) A 4.5-cm-tall object is placed 28 cm in front of a spherical mirror. It is desired to produce a virtual image that is upright and 3.5 cm tall. (*a*) What type of mirror should be used? (*b*) Where is the image located? (*c*) What is the focal length of the mirror? (*d*) What is the radius of curvature of the mirror?

22. (III) A shaving/makeup mirror is designed to magnify your face by a factor of 1.33 when your face is placed 20.0 cm in front of it. (*a*) What type of mirror is it? (*b*) Describe the type of image that it makes of your face. (*c*) Calculate the required radius of curvature for the mirror.

## 23–4 Index of Refraction

23. (I) What is the speed of light in (*a*) crown glass, (*b*) Lucite, and (*c*) ethyl alcohol?

24. (I) The speed of light in ice is $2.29 \times 10^8$ m/s. What is the index of refraction of ice?

25. (II) The speed of light in a certain substance is 89% of its value in water. What is the index of refraction of this substance?

## 23–5 Refraction: Snell's Law

26. (I) A flashlight beam strikes the surface of a pane of glass ($n = 1.58$) at a 63° angle to the normal. What is the angle of refraction?

27. (I) A diver shines a flashlight upward from beneath the water at a 42.5° angle to the vertical. At what angle does the light leave the water?

28. (I) A light beam coming from an underwater spotlight exits the water at an angle of 66.0° to the vertical. At what angle of incidence does it hit the air–water interface from below the surface?

29. (I) Rays of the Sun are seen to make a 31.0° angle to the vertical beneath the water. At what angle above the horizon is the Sun?

30. (II) An aquarium filled with water has flat glass sides whose index of refraction is 1.52. A beam of light from outside the aquarium strikes the glass at a 43.5° angle to the perpendicular (Fig. 23–49). What is the angle of this light ray when it enters (*a*) the glass, and then (*b*) the water? (*c*) What would be the refracted angle if the ray entered the water directly?

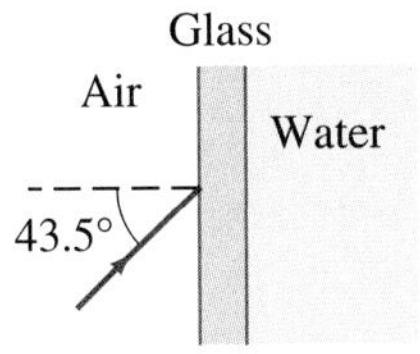


**FIGURE 23–49** Problem 30.

31. (II) In searching the bottom of a pool at night, a watchman shines a narrow beam of light from his flashlight, 1.3 m above the water level, onto the surface of the water at a point 2.7 m from the edge of the pool (Fig. 23–50). Where does the spot of light hit the bottom of the pool, measured from the wall beneath his foot, if the pool is 2.1 m deep?

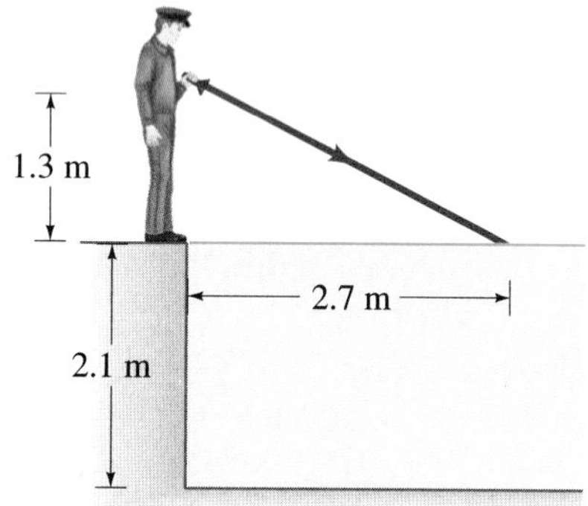


**FIGURE 23–50** Problem 31.

32. (II) Light is incident on an equilateral glass prism at a 45.0° angle to one face, Fig. 23–51. Calculate the angle at which light emerges from the opposite face. Assume that $n = 1.58$.

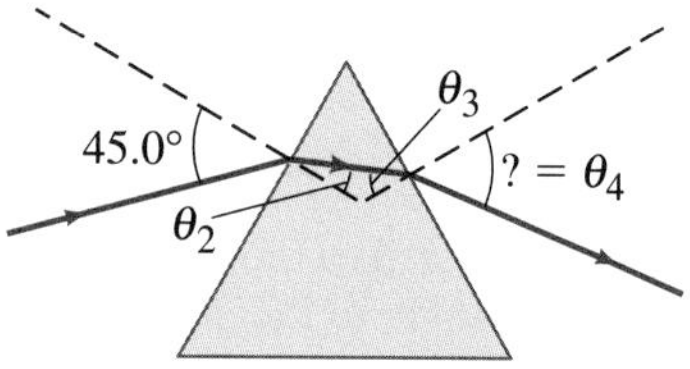


**FIGURE 23–51** Problems 32 and 40.

33. (II) A beam of light in air strikes a slab of glass ($n = 1.52$) and is partially reflected and partially refracted. Find the angle of incidence if the angle of reflection is twice the angle of refraction.

34. (III) Prove in general that for a light beam incident on a uniform layer of transparent material, as in Fig. 23–22, the direction of the emerging beam is parallel to the incident beam, independent of the incident angle $\theta$. Assume air on both sides of the glass.

35. (III) A light ray is incident on a flat piece of glass with index of refraction $n$ as in Fig. 23–22. Show that if the incident angle $\theta$ is small, the emerging ray is displaced a distance $d = t\theta(n - 1)/n$ from the incident ray, where $t$ is the thickness of the glass and $\theta$ is in radians. [*Hint*: for small $\theta$, $\sin\theta \approx \tan\theta \approx \theta$ in radians.]

## 23–6 Total Internal Reflection

36. (I) What is the critical angle for the interface between water and Lucite? To be totally internally reflected, the light must start in which material?

37. (I) The critical angle for a certain liquid–air surface is 47.7°. What is the index of refraction of the liquid?

38. (II) A beam of light is emitted in a pool of water from a depth of 62.0 cm. Where must it strike the air–water interface, relative to the spot directly above it, in order that the light does *not* exit the water?

39. (II) A beam of light is emitted 8.0 cm beneath the surface of a liquid and strikes the surface 7.0 cm from the point directly above the source. If total internal reflection occurs, what can you say about the index of refraction of the liquid?

40. (III) Suppose a ray strikes the left face of the prism in Fig. 23–51 at 45.0° as shown, but is totally internally reflected at the opposite side. If the prism apex angle (at the top) is $\phi = 75.0°$, what can you say about the index of refraction of the prism?

41. (III) A beam of light enters the end of an optic fiber as shown in Fig. 23–52. Show that we can guarantee total internal reflection at the side surface of the material (at point a), if the index of refraction is greater than about 1.42. In other words, regardless of the angle $\alpha$, the light beam reflects back into the material at point a.

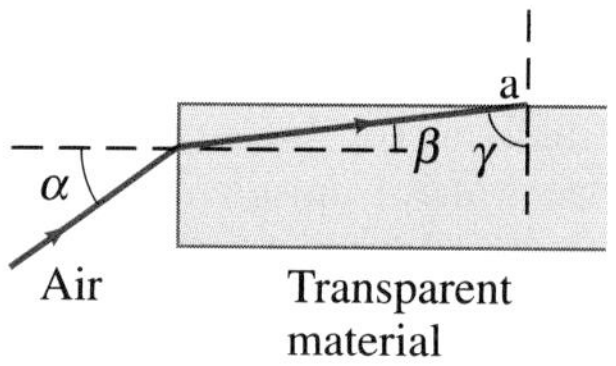


**FIGURE 23–52** Problem 41.

42. (III) (*a*) What is the minimum index of refraction for a glass or plastic prism to be used in binoculars (Fig. 23–26) so that total internal reflection occurs at 45°? (*b*) Will binoculars work if its prisms (assume $n = 1.50$) are immersed in water? (*c*) What minimum $n$ is needed if the prisms are immersed in water?

## 23–7 and 23–8 Thin Lenses

43. (I) A sharp image is located 78.0 mm behind a 65.0-mm-focal-length converging lens. Find the object distance (*a*) using a ray diagram, (*b*) by calculation.

44. (I) Sunlight is observed to focus at a point 18.5 cm behind a lens. (*a*) What kind of lens is it? (*b*) What is its power in diopters?

45. (I) A certain lens focuses light from an object 2.75 m away as an image 48.3 cm on the other side of the lens. What type of lens is it and what is its focal length? Is the image real or virtual?

46. (I) (*a*) What is the power of a 20.5-cm-focal-length lens? (*b*) What is the focal length of a −6.25-diopter lens? (*c*) Are these lenses converging or diverging?

47. (II) A stamp collector uses a converging lens with focal length 24 cm to view a stamp 18 cm in front of the lens. (*a*) Where is the image located? (*b*) What is the magnification?

48. (II) A −5.5-D lens is held 14.0 cm from an object 4.0 mm high. What are the position, type, and height of the image?

49. (II) An 80-mm-focal-length lens is used to focus an image on the film of a camera. The maximum distance allowed between the lens and the film plane is 120 mm. (*a*) How far ahead of the film should the lens be if the object to be photographed is 10.0 m away? (*b*) 3.0 m away? (*c*) 1.0 m away? (*d*) What is the closest object this lens could photograph sharply?

50. (II) It is desired to magnify reading material by a factor of 2.5× when a book is placed 8.0 cm behind a lens. (*a*) Draw a ray diagram and describe the type of image this would be. (*b*) What type of lens is needed? (*c*) What is the power of the lens in diopters?

51. (II) An object is located 1.5 m from an 8.0-D lens. By how much does the image move if the object is moved (*a*) 1.0 m closer to the lens, and (*b*) 1.0 m farther from the lens?

52. (II) How far from a converging lens with a focal length of 25 cm should an object be placed to produce a real image which is the same size as the object?

53. (II) (*a*) How far from a 50.0-mm-focal-length lens must an object be placed if its image is to be magnified 2.00× and be real? (*b*) What if the image is to be virtual and magnified 2.00×?

54. (II) Repeat Problem 53 for a −50.0-mm-focal-length lens. [*Hint*: consider objects real or virtual (formed by some other piece of optics).]

55. (II) (*a*) A 2.00-cm-high insect is 1.20 m from a 135-mm-focal-length lens. Where is the image, how high is it, and what type is it? (*b*) What if $f = -135$ mm?

56. (III) How far apart are an object and an image formed by a 75-cm-focal-length converging lens if the image is 2.5× larger than the object and is real?

57. (III) A bright object and a viewing screen are separated by a distance of 66.0 cm. At what location(s) between the object and the screen should a lens of focal length 12.5 cm be placed in order to produce a crisp image on the screen? [*Hint*: first draw a diagram.]

## * 23–9 Lens Combinations

* 58. (II) Two 28.0-cm-focal-length converging lenses are placed 16.5 cm apart. An object is placed 36.0 cm in front of one lens. Where will the final image formed by the second lens be located? What is the total magnification?

* 59. (II) A diverging lens with $f = -31.5$ cm is placed 14.0 cm behind a converging lens with $f = 20.0$ cm. Where will an object at infinity be focused?

* 60. (II) A 31.0-cm-focal-length converging lens is 21.0 cm behind a diverging lens. Parallel light strikes the diverging lens. After passing through the converging lens, the light is again parallel. What is the focal length of the diverging lens? [*Hint*: first draw a ray diagram.]

* 61. (II) The two converging lenses of Example 23–12 are now placed only 20.0 cm apart. The object is still 60.0 cm in front of the first lens as in Fig. 23–41. In this case, determine (*a*) the position of the final image, and (*b*) the overall magnification. (*c*) Sketch the ray diagram for this system.

* 62. (II) Two converging lenses are placed 30.0 cm apart. The focal length of the lens on the right is 20.0 cm, and the focal length of the lens on the left is 15.0 cm. An object is placed to the left of the 15.0-cm-focal-length lens. A final image from both lenses is inverted and located halfway between the two lenses. How far to the left of the 15.0-cm-focal-length lens is the original object?

* 63. (II) A diverging lens with a focal length of −14 cm is placed 12 cm to the right of a converging lens with a focal length of 18 cm. An object is placed 33 cm to the left of the converging lens. (*a*) Where will the final image be located? (*b*) Where will the image be if the diverging lens is 38 cm from the converging lens?

* 64. (II) Two lenses, one converging with focal length 20.0 cm and one diverging with focal length −10.0 cm, are placed 25.0 cm apart. An object is placed 60.0 cm in front of the converging lens. Determine (*a*) the position and (*b*) the magnification of the final image formed. (*c*) Sketch a ray diagram for this system.

* 65. (III) A diverging lens is placed next to a converging lens of focal length $f_C$, as in Fig. 23–42. If $f_T$ represents the focal length of the combination, show that the focal length of the diverging lens, $f_D$, is given by

$$\frac{1}{f_D} = \frac{1}{f_T} - \frac{1}{f_C}.$$

## * 23–10 Lensmaker's Equation

* 66. (I) A double concave lens has surface radii of 34.2 cm and 23.8 cm. What is the focal length if $n = 1.52$?

* 67. (I) Both surfaces of a double convex lens have radii of 31.0 cm. If the focal length is 28.9 cm, what is the index of refraction of the lens material?

* 68. (II) A planoconcave lens ($n = 1.50$) has a focal length of −23.4 cm. What is the radius of the concave surface?

* 69. (II) A Lucite planoconcave lens (see Fig. 23–29b) has one flat surface and the other has $R = -18.4$ cm. What is the focal length?

* 70. (II) A symmetric double convex lens with a focal length of 25.0 cm is to be made from glass with an index of refraction of 1.52. What should be the radius of curvature for each surface?

* 71. (II) A prescription for a corrective lens calls for +1.50 D. The lensmaker grinds the lens from a "blank" with $n = 1.56$ and a preformed convex front surface of radius of curvature of 40.0 cm. What should be the radius of curvature of the other surface?

## General Problems

72. Two plane mirrors face each other 2.0 m apart as in Fig. 23–53. You stand 1.5 m away from one of these mirrors and look into it. You will see multiple images of yourself. (*a*) How far away from you are the first three images in the mirror in front of you? (*b*) Are these first three images facing toward you or away from you?

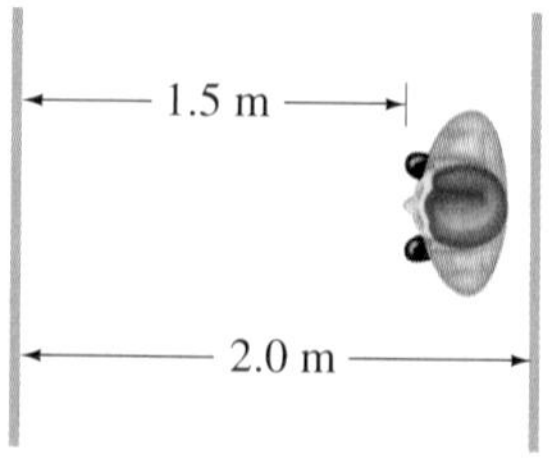


**FIGURE 23–53** Problem 72.

73. We wish to determine the depth of a swimming pool filled with water. We measure the width ($x = 5.50$ m) and then note that the bottom edge of the pool is just visible at an angle of 14.0° above the horizontal as shown in Fig. 23–54. Calculate the depth of the pool.

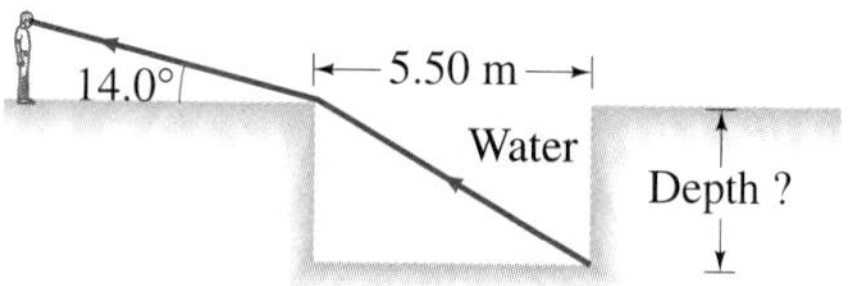


**FIGURE 23–54** Problem 73.

74. The critical angle of a certain piece of plastic in air is $\theta_C = 37.3°$. What is the critical angle of the same plastic if it is immersed in water?

75. (*a*) A plane mirror can be considered a limiting case of a spherical mirror. Specify what this limit is. (*b*) Determine an equation that relates the image and object distances in this limit of a plane mirror. (*c*) Determine the magnification of a plane mirror in this same limit. (*d*) Are your results in parts (*b*) and (*c*) consistent with the discussion of Section 23–2 on plane mirrors?

76. Stand up two plane mirrors so they form a 90° angle as in Fig. 23–55. When you look into this double mirror, you see yourself as others see you, instead of reversed as in a single mirror. Make a careful ray diagram to show how this occurs.

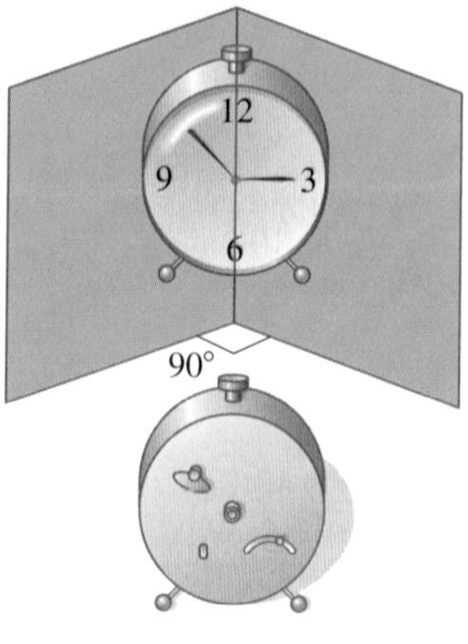


**FIGURE 23–55** Problem 76.

77. Show analytically that a diverging lens can never form a real image of a real object. Can you describe a situation in which a diverging lens can form a real image?

78. Each student in a physics lab is assigned to find the location where a bright object may be placed in order that a concave mirror with radius of curvature $r = 40$ cm will produce an image three times the size of the object. Two students complete the assignment at different times using identical equipment, but when they compare notes later, they discover that their answers for the object distance are not the same. Explain why they do not necessarily need to repeat the lab, and justify your response with a calculation.

79. If the apex angle of a prism is $\phi = 72°$ (see Fig. 23–56), what is the minimum incident angle for a ray if it is to emerge from the opposite side (i.e., not be totally internally reflected), given $n = 1.50$?

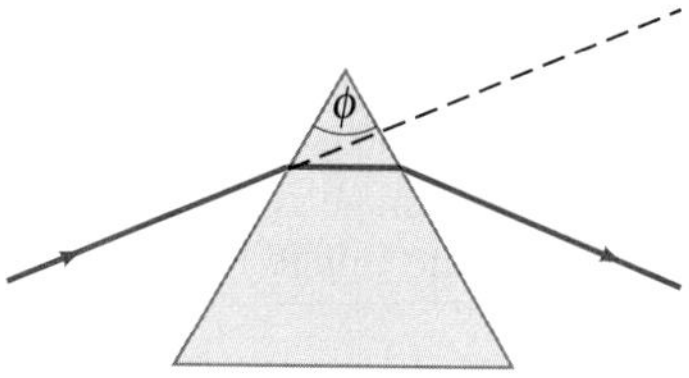


**FIGURE 23–56** Problem 79.

80. The end faces of a cylindrical glass rod ($n = 1.54$) are perpendicular to the sides. Show that a light ray entering an end face at any angle will be totally internally reflected inside the rod when the ray strikes the sides. Assume the rod is in air. What if it were in water?

* 81. A lighted candle is placed 33 cm in front of a converging lens of focal length $f_1 = 15$ cm, which in turn is 55 cm in front of another converging lens of focal length $f_2 = 12$ cm (see Fig. 23–57). (*a*) Draw a ray diagram and estimate the location and the relative size of the final image. (*b*) Calculate the position and relative size of the final image.

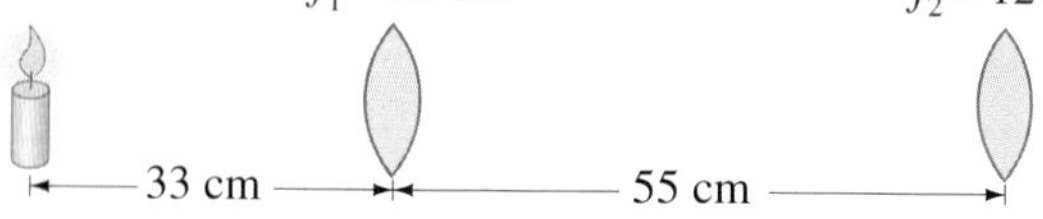


**FIGURE 23–57** Problem 81.

82. A bright object is placed on one side of a converging lens of focal length $f$, and a white screen for viewing the image is on the opposite side. The distance $d_T = d_i + d_o$ between the object and the screen is kept fixed, but the lens can be moved. (*a*) Show that if $d_T > 4f$, there will be two positions where the lens can be placed and a sharp image will be produced on the screen. (*b*) If $d_T < 4f$, show that there will be no lens position where a sharp image is formed. (*c*) Determine a formula for the distance between the two lens positions in part (*a*), and the ratio of the image sizes.

83. In a slide or movie projector, the film acts as the object whose image is projected on a screen (Fig. 23–58). If a 105-mm-focal-length lens is to project an image on a screen 8.00 m away, how far from the lens should the slide be? If the slide is 36 mm wide, how wide will the picture be on the screen?

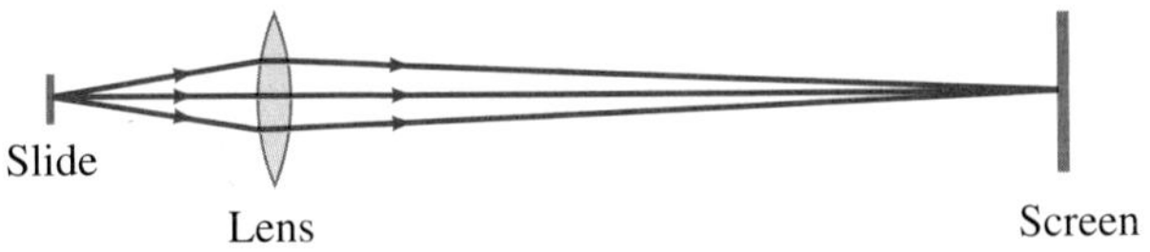


**FIGURE 23–58** Problem 83.

84. A 35-mm slide (picture size is actually 24 by 36 mm) is to be projected on a screen 1.80 m by 2.70 m placed 7.50 m from the projector. What focal-length lens should be used if the image is to cover the screen?

85. Show analytically that the image formed by a converging lens is real and inverted if the object is beyond the focal point ($d_o > f$), and is virtual and upright if the object is within the focal point ($d_o < f$). Describe the image if the object is itself an image, formed by another lens, so its position is beyond the lens, for which $-d_o > f$, and for which $0 < -d_o < f$.

86. A movie star catches a reporter shooting pictures of her at home. She claims the reporter was trespassing. To prove her point, she gives as evidence the film she seized. Her 1.75-m height is 8.25 mm high on the film, and the focal length of the camera lens was 210 mm. How far away from the subject was the reporter standing?

87. How large is the image of the Sun on film used in a camera with (*a*) a 28-mm-focal-length lens, (*b*) a 50-mm-focal-length lens, and (*c*) a 135-mm-focal-length lens? (*d*) If the 50-mm lens is considered normal for this camera, what relative magnification does each of the other two lenses provide? The Sun has diameter $1.4 \times 10^6$ km, and it is $1.5 \times 10^8$ km away.

88. (*a*) An object 34.5 cm in front of a certain lens is imaged 8.20 cm in front of that lens (on the same side as the object). What type of lens is this, and what is its focal length? Is the image real or virtual? (*b*) If the image were located, instead, 41.5 cm in front of the lens, what type of lens would it be and what focal length would it have?

89. When an object is placed 60.0 cm from a certain converging lens, it forms a real image. When the object is moved to 40.0 cm from the lens, the image moves 10.0 cm farther from the lens. Find the focal length of this lens.

90. A small object is 25.0 cm from a diverging lens as shown in Fig. 23–59. A converging lens with a focal length of 12.0 cm is 30.0 cm to the right of the diverging lens. The two-lens system forms a real inverted image 17.0 cm to the right of the converging lens. What is the focal length of the diverging lens?

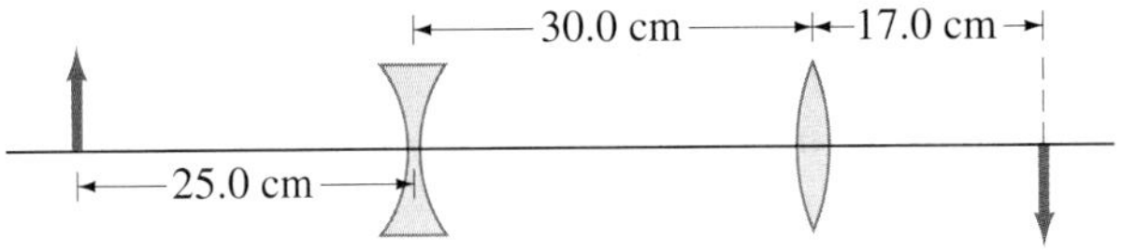


**FIGURE 23–59** Problem 90.

91. An object is placed 15 cm from a certain mirror. The image is half the size of the object, inverted, and real. How far is the image from the mirror, and what is the radius of curvature of the mirror?

92. (*a*) Show that the lens equation can be written in the *Newtonian form*

$$xx' = f^2,$$

where $x$ is the distance of the object from the focal point on the front side of the lens, and $x'$ is the distance of the image to the focal point on the other side of the lens. Calculate the location of an image if the object is placed 45.0 cm in front of a convex lens with a focal length $f$ of 32.0 cm using (*b*) the standard form of the thin lens equation, and (*c*) the Newtonian form, stated above.

* 93. A converging lens with focal length of 10.0 cm is placed in contact with a diverging lens with a focal length of −20.0 cm. What is the focal length of the combination, and is the combination converging or diverging?

* 94. (*a*) Show that if two thin lenses of focal lengths $f_1$ and $f_2$ are placed in contact with each other, the focal length of the combination is given by $f_T = f_1 f_2/(f_1 + f_2)$. (*b*) Show that the power $P$ of the combination of two lenses is the sum of their separate powers, $P = P_1 + P_2$.

## Answers to Exercises

**A:** No.
**B:** Yes; for a plane mirror, $r = \infty$, so $f = \infty$; then Eq. 23–2 gives $1/d_o + 1/d_i = 0$, or $d_i = -d_o$.
**C:** Toward.
**D:** None.
**E:** 1.414.
**F:** No total internal reflection, $\theta_C > 45°$.
**G:** Closer to it.
**H:** (*a*) Virtual; (*b*) virtual.
**I:** −97.5 cm (that is, 97.5 cm in front of lens).

The beautiful colors from the surface of this soap bubble can be nicely explained by the wave theory of light. A soap bubble is a very thin spherical film filled with air; light reflected from the outer and inner surfaces of this thin film of soapy water interferes constructively to produce the bright colors. Which color we see at any point depends on the thickness of the soapy water film at that point and also on the viewing angle.

We cover fundamental aspects of the wave nature of light, including interference and diffraction, thin-film interference, and polarization. We also cover many applications, from spectrometry to LCD monitor screens.

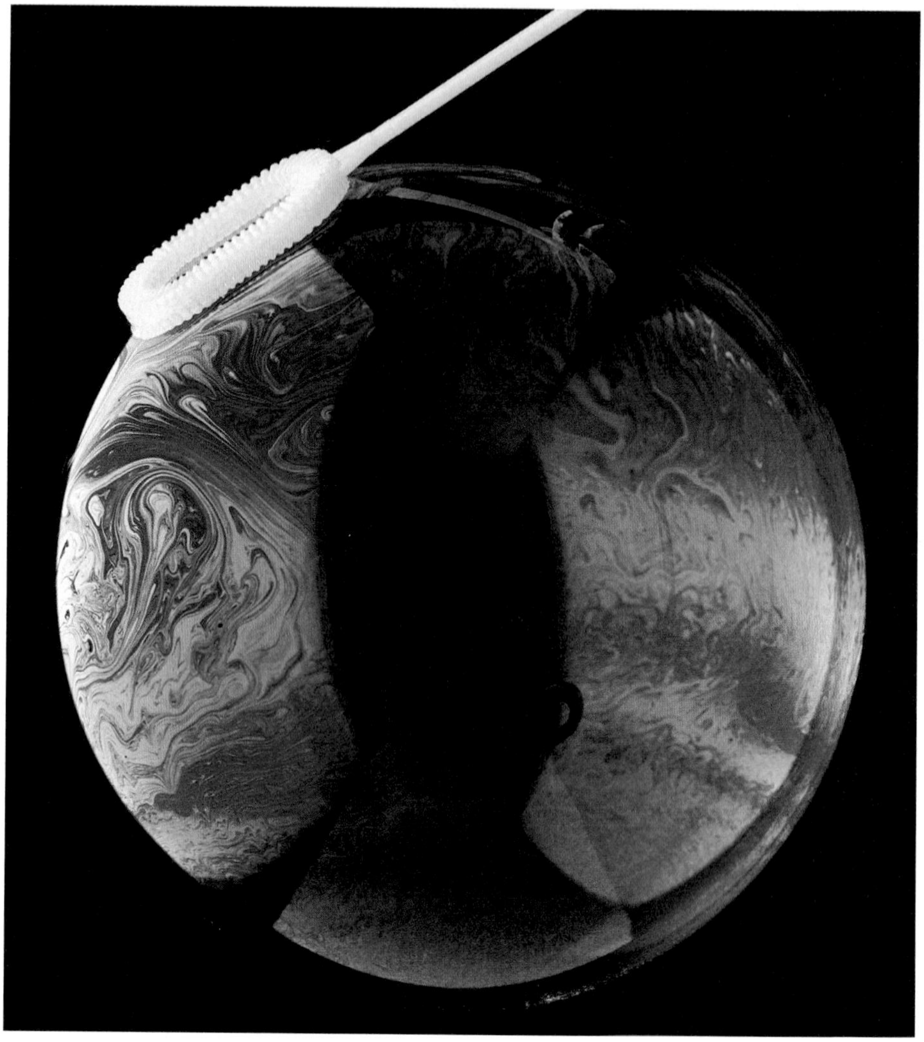

CHAPTER 24

# The Wave Nature of Light

That light carries energy is obvious to anyone who has focused the Sun's rays with a magnifying glass on a piece of paper and burned a hole in it. But how does light travel, and in what form is this energy carried? In our discussion of waves in Chapter 11, we noted that energy can be carried from place to place in basically two ways: by particles or by waves. In the first case, material objects or particles can carry energy, such as an avalanche or rushing water. In the second case, water waves and sound waves, for example, can carry energy over long distances even though the oscillating particles of the medium do not travel these distances. In view of this, what can we say about the nature of light: does light travel as a stream of particles away from its source, or does light travel in the form of waves that spread outward from the source?

Historically, this question has turned out to be a difficult one. For one thing, light does not reveal itself in any obvious way as being made up of tiny particles; nor do we see tiny light waves passing by as we do water waves. The evidence seemed to favor first one side and then the other until about 1830, when most physicists had accepted the wave theory. By the end of the nineteenth century, light was considered to be an *electromagnetic wave* (Chapter 22). In the early twentieth century, light was shown to have a particle nature as well, as we shall discuss in Chapter 27. Nonetheless, the wave theory of light remains valid and has proved very successful. We now investigate the evidence for the wave theory and how it has been used to explain a wide range of phenomena.

## 24–1 Waves Versus Particles; Huygens' Principle and Diffraction

The Dutch scientist Christian Huygens (1629–1695), a contemporary of Newton, proposed a wave theory of light that had much merit. Still useful today is a technique Huygens developed for predicting the future position of a wave front when an earlier position is known. By a wave front, we mean all the points along a two- or three-dimensional wave that form a wave crest—what we simply call a "wave" as seen on the ocean. Wave fronts are perpendicular to rays as we discussed in Chapter 11 (Fig. 11–34). **Huygens' principle** can be stated as follows: *Every point on a wave front can be considered as a source of tiny wavelets that spread out in the forward direction at the speed of the wave itself. The new wave front is the envelope of all the wavelets*—that is, *the tangent to all of them.*

*Huygens' principle*

As a simple example of the use of Huygens' principle, consider the wave front AB in Fig. 24–1, which is traveling away from a source S. We assume the medium is *isotropic*—that is, the speed $v$ of the waves is the same in all directions. To find the wave front a short time $t$ after it is at AB, tiny circles are drawn with radius $r = vt$. The centers of these tiny circles are blue dots on the original wave front AB, and the circles represent Huygens' (imaginary) wavelets. The tangent to all these wavelets, the curved line CD, is the new position of the wave front.

Huygens' principle is particularly useful for analyzing what happens when waves impinge on an obstacle and the wave fronts are partially interrupted. Huygens' principle predicts that waves bend in behind an obstacle, as shown in Fig. 24–2. This is just what water waves do, as we saw in Chapter 11 (Figs. 11–44 and 11–45). The bending of waves behind obstacles into the "shadow region" is known as **diffraction**. Since diffraction occurs for waves, but not for particles, it can serve as one means for distinguishing the nature of light.

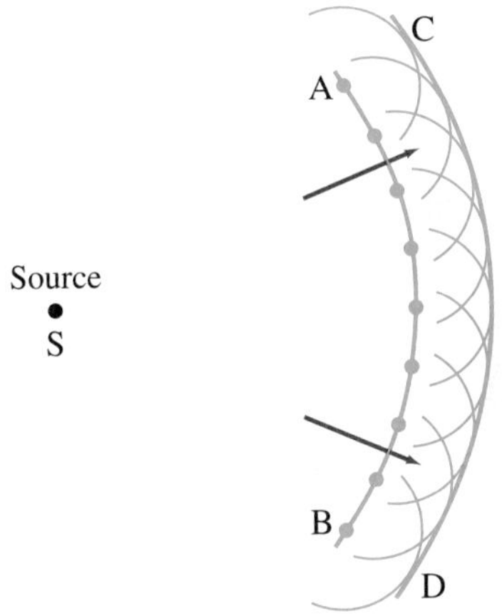


**FIGURE 24–1** Huygens' principle, used to determine wave front CD when wave front AB is given.

**FIGURE 24–2** Huygens' principle is consistent with diffraction (a) around the edge of an obstacle, (b) through a large hole, (c) through a small hole whose size is on the order of the wavelength of the wave.

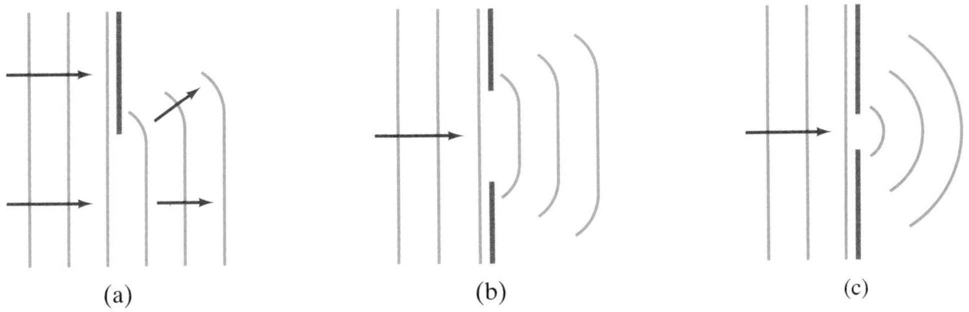

Does light exhibit diffraction? In the mid-seventeenth century, the Jesuit priest Francesco Grimaldi (1618–1663) had observed that when sunlight entered a darkened room through a tiny hole in a screen, the spot on the opposite wall was larger than would be expected from geometric rays. He also observed that the border of the image was not clear but was surrounded by colored fringes. Grimaldi attributed this to the diffraction of light.

The wave model of light nicely accounts for diffraction. But the ray model (Chapter 23) cannot account for diffraction, and it is important to be aware of such limitations to the ray model. Geometric optics using rays is successful in a wide range of situations only because normal openings and obstacles are much larger than the wavelength of the light, and so relatively little diffraction or bending occurs.

## * 24–2 Huygens' Principle and the Law of Refraction

The laws of reflection and refraction were well known in Newton's time. The law of reflection could not distinguish between the two theories we just discussed: waves versus particles. For when waves reflect from an obstacle, the angle of incidence equals the angle of reflection (Fig. 11–35). The same is true of particles—think of a tennis ball without spin striking a flat surface.

The law of refraction is another matter. Consider a ray of light entering a medium where it is bent toward the normal, as when traveling from air into water. As shown in Fig. 24–3, this bending can be constructed using Huygens' principle if we

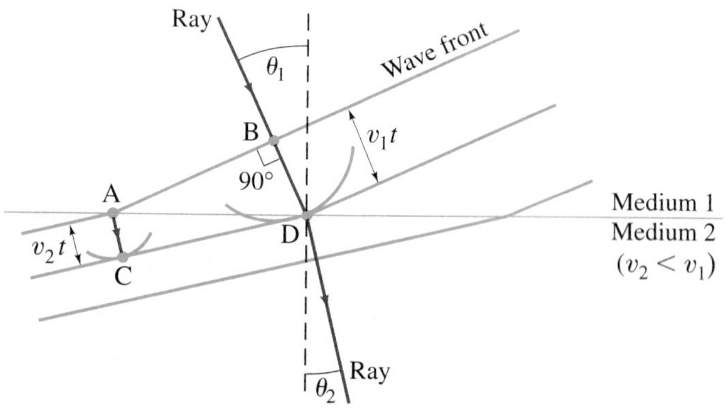


**FIGURE 24–3** Refraction explained, using Huygens' principle. Wave fronts are perpendicular to the rays.

assume the speed of light is less in the second medium $(v_2 < v_1)$. In time *t*, point B on wave front AB (perpendicular to the incoming ray) travels a distance $v_1 t$ to reach point D. Point A on the wave front, traveling in the second medium, goes a distance $v_2 t$ to reach point C, and $v_2 t < v_1 t$. Huygens' principle is applied to points A and B to obtain the curved wavelets shown at C and D. The wave front is tangent to these two wavelets, so the new wave front is the line CD. Hence the rays, which are perpendicular to the wave fronts, bend toward the normal if $v_2 < v_1$, as drawn. (This is basically the same discussion we used around Fig. 11–43).

Newton favored a particle theory of light which predicted the opposite result, that the speed of light would be greater in the second medium $(v_2 > v_1)$. Thus the wave theory predicts that the speed of light in water, for example, is less than in air; and Newton's particle theory predicts the reverse. An experiment to actually measure the speed of light in water was performed in 1850 by the French physicist Jean Foucault, and it confirmed the wave-theory prediction. By then, however, the wave theory was already fully accepted, as we shall see in the next Section.

Snell's law of refraction follows directly from Huygens' principle, given that the speed of light $v$ in any medium is related to the speed in a vacuum, $c$, and the index of refraction, $n$, by Eq. 23–4: that is, $v = c/n$. From the Huygens' construction of Fig. 24–3, angle ADC is equal to $\theta_2$ and angle BAD is equal to $\theta_1$. Then for the two triangles that have the common side AD, we have

$$\sin\theta_1 = \frac{v_1 t}{\mathrm{AD}}, \qquad \sin\theta_2 = \frac{v_2 t}{\mathrm{AD}}.$$

We divide these two equations and obtain

$$\frac{\sin\theta_1}{\sin\theta_2} = \frac{v_1}{v_2}.$$

Then, since $v_1 = c/n_1$ and $v_2 = c/n_2$,

$$n_1 \sin\theta_1 = n_2 \sin\theta_2,$$

which is Snell's law of refraction, Eq. 23–5. (The law of reflection can be derived from Huygens' principle in a similar way.)

*Wavelength depends on n*

When a light wave travels from one medium to another, its frequency does not change, but its wavelength does. This can be seen from Fig. 24–3, where each of the blue lines representing a wave front corresponds to a crest (peak) of the wave. Then

$$\frac{\lambda_2}{\lambda_1} = \frac{v_2 t}{v_1 t} = \frac{v_2}{v_1} = \frac{n_1}{n_2},$$

where, in the last step, we used Eq. 23–4, $v = c/n$. If medium 1 is a vacuum (or air), so $n_1 = 1$, $v_1 = c$, and we call $\lambda_1$ simply $\lambda$, then the wavelength in another medium of index of refraction $n\,(= n_2)$ will be

$$\lambda_n = \frac{\lambda}{n}. \qquad \textbf{(24–1)}$$

This result is consistent with the frequency $f$ being unchanged no matter what medium the wave is traveling in, since $c = f\lambda$.

**PHYSICS APPLIED**
*Highway mirages*

Wave fronts can be used to explain how mirages are produced by refraction of light. For example, on a hot day motorists sometimes see a mirage of water on the highway ahead of them, with distant vehicles seemingly reflected in it (Fig. 24–4a). On a hot day, there can be a layer of very hot air next to the roadway (made hot by the Sun beating on the road). Hot air is less dense than cooler air, so the index of refraction is slightly lower in the hot air. In Fig. 24–4b, we see a diagram of light coming from one point on a distant car (on the right) heading left toward the observer. Wave fronts and two rays are shown. Ray A heads directly at the observer and follows a straight-line path, and represents the normal view of the distant car. Ray B is a ray initially directed slightly downward, but it bends slightly as it moves through layers of air of different index of refraction. The wave fronts, shown in blue in Fig. 24–4b, move slightly faster in the layers of air nearer the ground (as in Fig. 24–3, and also the soldier analogy in Fig. 11–43). Thus ray B is bent as shown, and seems to the observer to be coming from below (dashed line) as if reflected off the road. Hence the mirage.

**FIGURE 24–4** (a) A highway mirage. (b) Drawing (greatly exaggerated) showing wave fronts and rays to explain highway mirages. Note how sections of the wave fronts near the ground move faster and so are farther apart.

(a)

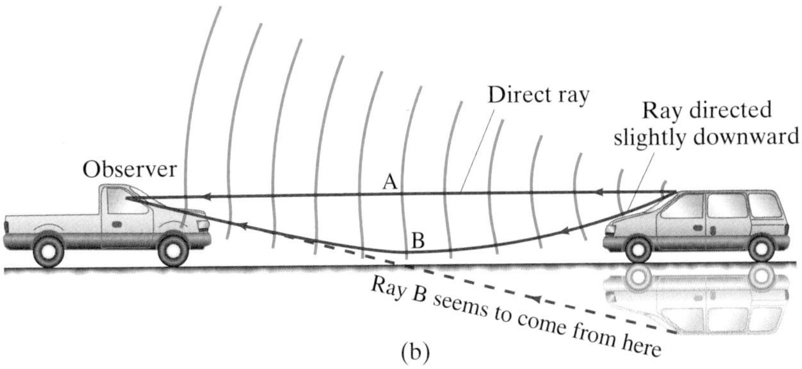


(b)

## 24–3 Interference—Young's Double-Slit Experiment

In 1801, the Englishman Thomas Young (1773–1829) obtained convincing evidence for the wave nature of light and was even able to measure wavelengths for visible light. Figure 24–5a shows a schematic diagram of Young's famous double-slit experiment. Light from a single source (Young used the Sun) falls on a screen containing two closely spaced slits $S_1$ and $S_2$. If light consists of tiny particles, we might expect to see two bright lines on a screen placed behind the slits as in (b). But instead a series of bright lines are seen, as in (c). Young was able to explain this result as a **wave-interference** phenomenon. To see this, imagine plane waves of light of a single wavelength—called **monochromatic**, meaning "one color"—falling on the two slits as shown in Fig. 24–6. Because of diffraction, the waves leaving the two small slits spread out as shown. This is equivalent to the interference pattern produced when two rocks are thrown into a lake (Fig. 11–37), or when sound from two loudspeakers interferes (Fig. 12–16). Recall Section 11–12 on wave interference.

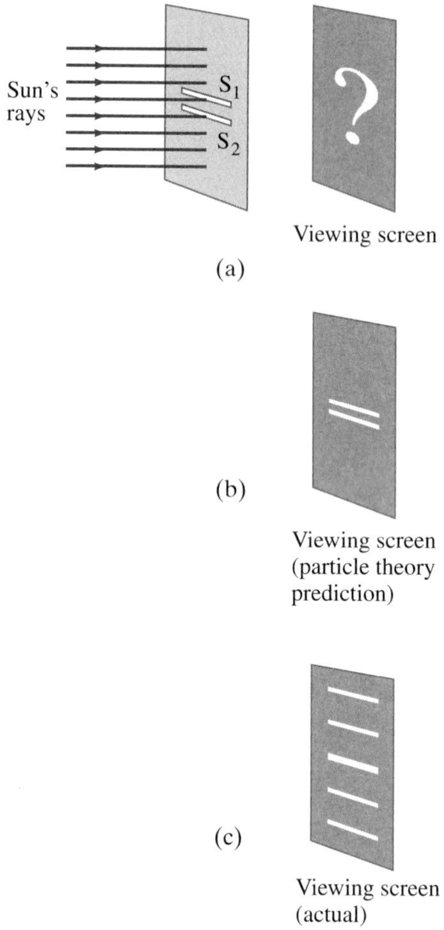


**FIGURE 24–5** (a) Young's double-slit experiment. (b) If light consists of particles, we would expect to see two bright lines on the screen behind the slits. (c) In fact, many lines are observed.

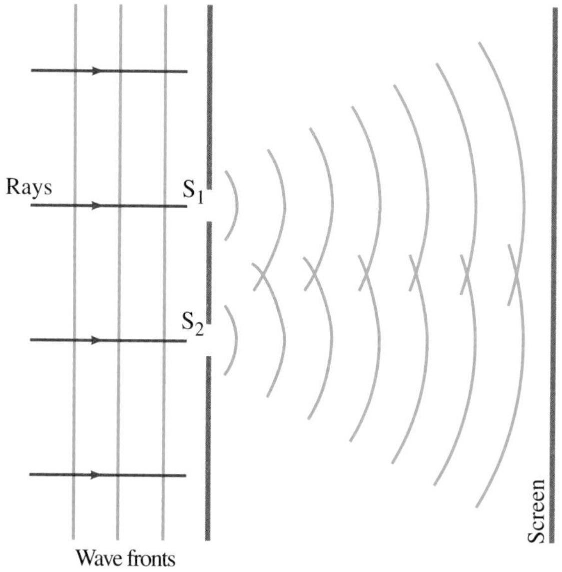


**FIGURE 24–6** If light is a wave, light passing through one of two slits should interfere with light passing through the other slit.

To see how an interference pattern is produced on the screen, we make use of Fig. 24–7. Waves of wavelength $\lambda$ are shown entering the slits $S_1$ and $S_2$, which are a distance $d$ apart. The waves spread out in all directions after passing through the slits, but they are shown only for three different angles $\theta$. In Fig. 24–7a, the waves reaching the center of the screen are shown ($\theta = 0°$). The waves from the two slits travel the same distance, so they are in phase: a crest of one wave arrives at the same time as a crest of the other wave. Hence the amplitudes of the two waves add to form a larger amplitude as shown in Fig. 24–8a. This is **constructive interference**, and there is a bright area at the center of the screen. Constructive interference also occurs when the paths of the two rays differ by one wavelength (or any whole number of wavelengths), as shown in Fig. 24–7b; also here there will be brightness on the screen. But if one ray travels an extra distance of one-half wavelength (or $\frac{3}{2}\lambda$, $\frac{5}{2}\lambda$, and so on), the two waves are exactly out of phase when they reach the screen: the crests of one wave arrive at the same time as the troughs of the other wave, and so they add to produce zero amplitude (Fig. 24–8b). This is **destructive interference**, and the screen is dark, Fig. 24–7c. Thus, there will be a series of bright and dark lines (or **fringes**) on the viewing screen.

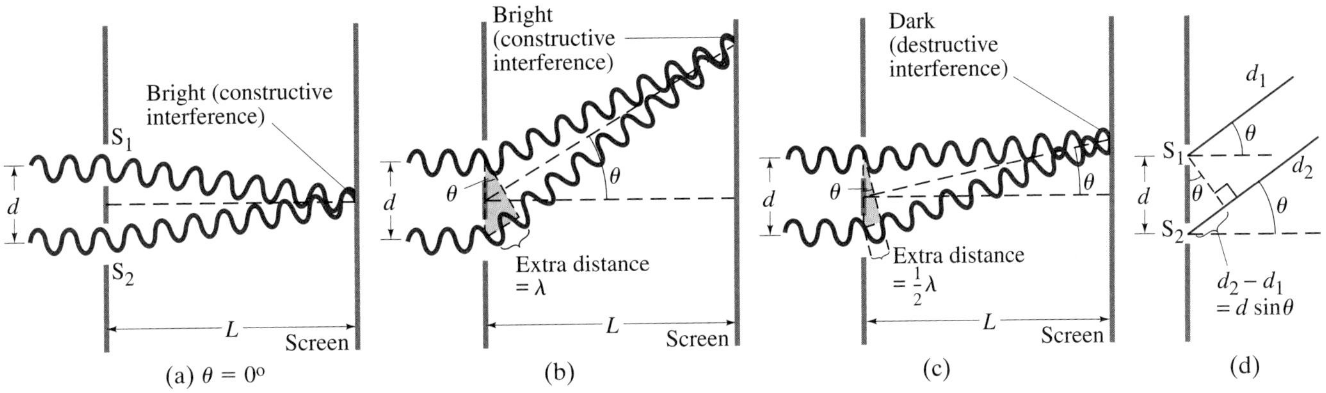


**FIGURE 24–7** How the wave theory explains the pattern of lines seen in the double-slit experiment. (a) At the center of the screen the waves from each slit travel the same distance and are in phase. (b) At this angle $\theta$, the lower wave travels an extra distance of one whole wavelength, and the waves are in phase; note from the shaded triangle that the path difference equals $d \sin\theta$. (c) For this angle $\theta$, the lower wave travels an extra distance equal to one-half wavelength, so the two waves arrive at the screen fully out of phase. (d) A more detailed diagram showing the geometry for parts (b) and (c).

To determine exactly where the bright lines fall, first note that Fig. 24–7 is somewhat exaggerated; in real situations, the distance $d$ between the slits is very small compared to the distance $L$ to the screen. The rays from each slit for each case will therefore be essentially parallel, and $\theta$ is the angle they make with the horizontal as shown in Fig. 24–7d. From the shaded right triangles shown in Figs. 24–7b and c, we can see that the extra distance traveled by the lower ray is $d \sin\theta$ (seen more clearly in Fig. 24–7d). **Constructive interference** will occur, and a bright fringe will appear on the screen, when the *path difference*, $d \sin\theta$, equals a whole number of wavelengths:

$$d \sin\theta = m\lambda, \qquad m = 0, 1, 2, \cdots. \qquad \begin{bmatrix}\text{constructive}\\ \text{interference}\\ \text{(bright)}\end{bmatrix} \qquad \textbf{(24–2a)}$$

The value of $m$ is called the **order** of the interference fringe. The first order ($m = 1$), for example, is the first fringe on each side of the central fringe (which is at $\theta = 0, m = 0$). Destructive interference occurs when the path difference $d \sin\theta$ is $\frac{1}{2}\lambda$, $\frac{3}{2}\lambda$, and so on:

$$d \sin\theta = \left(m + \tfrac{1}{2}\right)\lambda, \qquad m = 0, 1, 2, \cdots. \qquad \begin{bmatrix}\text{destructive}\\ \text{interference}\\ \text{(dark)}\end{bmatrix} \qquad \textbf{(24–2b)}$$

The bright fringes are peaks or maxima of light intensity, the dark fringes are minima. The intensity of the bright fringes is greatest for the central fringe ($m = 0$) and decreases for higher orders, as shown in Fig. 24–9. How much the intensity decreases with increasing order depends on the width of the two slits.

**FIGURE 24–8** Two traveling waves are shown undergoing (a) constructive interference, (b) destructive interference. (See also Section 11–12.)

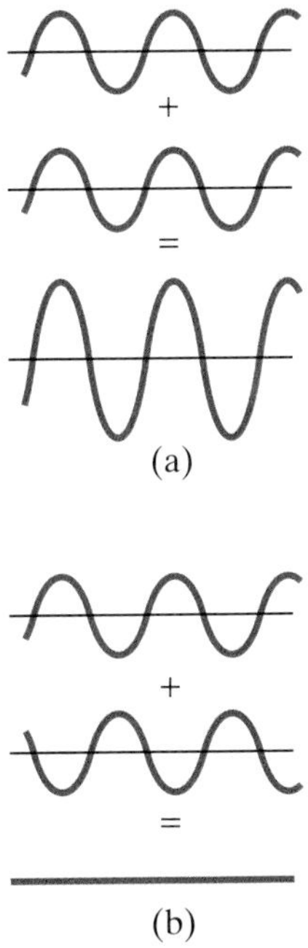


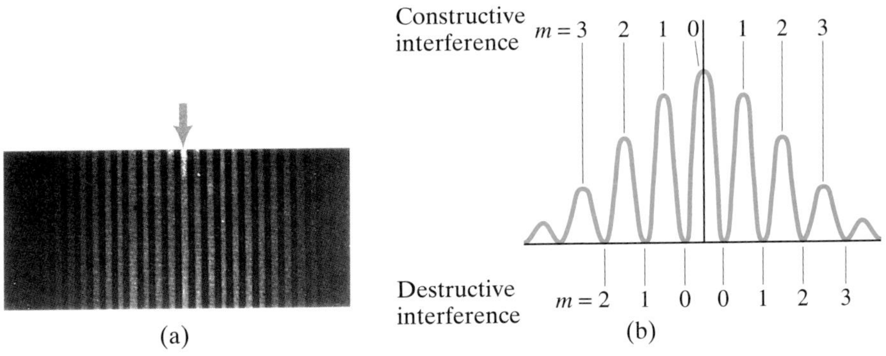


**FIGURE 24–9** (a) Interference fringes produced by a double-slit experiment and detected by photographic film placed on the viewing screen. The arrow marks the central fringe. (b) Graph of the intensity of light in the interference pattern. Also shown are values of $m$ for Eq. 24–2a (constructive interference) and Eq. 24–2b (destructive interference).

**EXAMPLE 24–1 Line spacing for double-slit interference.** A screen containing two slits 0.100 mm apart is 1.20 m from the viewing screen. Light of wavelength $\lambda = 500\text{ nm}$ falls on the slits from a distant source. Approximately how far apart will adjacent bright interference fringes be on the screen?

**APPROACH** The angular position of bright (constructive interference) fringes is found using Eq. 24–2a. The distance between the first two fringes (say) can be found using right triangles as shown in Fig. 24–10.

**SOLUTION** Given $d = 0.100\text{ mm} = 1.00 \times 10^{-4}\text{ m}$, $\lambda = 500 \times 10^{-9}\text{ m}$, and $L = 1.20\text{ m}$, the first-order fringe $(m = 1)$ occurs at an angle $\theta$ given by

$$\sin\theta_1 = \frac{m\lambda}{d} = \frac{(1)(500 \times 10^{-9}\text{ m})}{1.00 \times 10^{-4}\text{ m}} = 5.00 \times 10^{-3}.$$

**CAUTION**
*Use the approximation $\theta \approx \tan\theta$ or $\theta \approx \sin\theta$ only if $\theta$ is small and in radians*

This is a very small angle, so we can take $\sin\theta \approx \theta$, with $\theta$ in radians. The first-order fringe will occur a distance $x_1$ above the center of the screen (see Fig. 24–10), given by $x_1/L = \tan\theta_1 \approx \theta_1$, so

$$x_1 \approx L\theta_1 = (1.20\text{ m})(5.00 \times 10^{-3}) = 6.00\text{ mm}.$$

The second-order fringe $(m = 2)$ will occur at

$$x_2 \approx L\theta_2 = L\frac{2\lambda}{d} = 12.0\text{ mm}$$

above the center, and so on. Thus the lower order fringes are 6.00 mm apart.

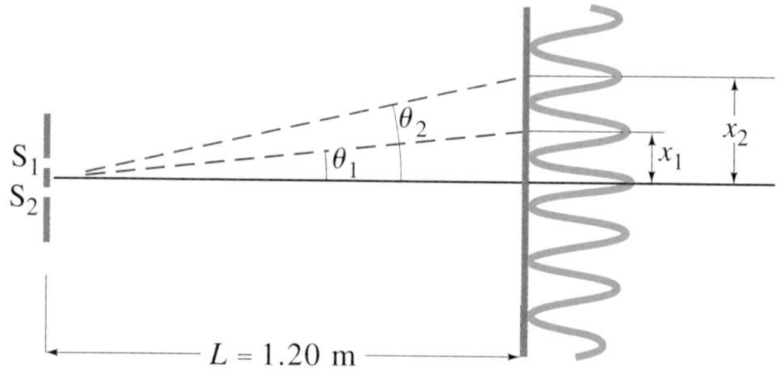


**FIGURE 24–10** Examples 24–1 and 24–2. For small angles, the interference fringes occur at distance $x = \theta L$ above the center fringe $(m = 0)$; $\theta_1$ and $x_1$ are for the first-order fringe $(m = 1)$, $\theta_2$ and $x_2$ are for $m = 2$.

**CONCEPTUAL EXAMPLE 24–2 Changing the wavelength.** (*a*) What happens to the interference pattern shown in Fig. 24–10, Example 24–1, if the incident light (500 nm) is replaced by light of wavelength 700 nm? (*b*) What happens instead if the wavelength stays at 500 nm but the slits are moved farther apart?

**RESPONSE** (*a*) When $\lambda$ increases in Eq. 24–2a but $d$ stays the same, then the angle $\theta$ for bright fringes increases and the interference pattern spreads out. (*b*) Increasing the slit spacing $d$ reduces $\theta$ for each order, so the lines are closer together.

*Wavelength (or frequency) determines color*

From Eqs. 24–2 we can see that, except for the zeroth-order fringe at the center, the position of the fringes depends on wavelength. Consequently, when white light falls on the two slits, as Young found in his experiments, the central fringe is white, but the first- (and higher-) order fringes contain a spectrum of colors like a rainbow; $\theta$ was found to be smallest for violet light and largest for red (Fig. 24–11). By measuring the position of these fringes, Young was the first to determine the wavelengths of visible light (using Eqs. 24–2). In doing so, he showed that what distinguishes different colors physically is their wavelength (or frequency), an idea put forward earlier by Grimaldi in 1665.

**FIGURE 24–11** First-order fringes are a full spectrum, like a rainbow. Also Example 24–3.

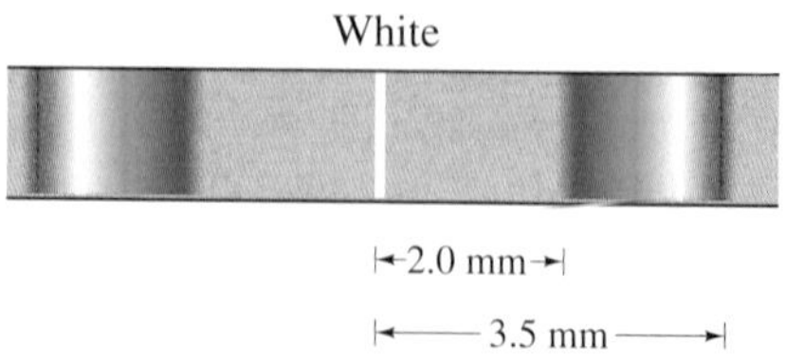


**EXAMPLE 24–3 Wavelengths from double-slit interference.** White light passes through two slits 0.50 mm apart, and an interference pattern is observed on a screen 2.5 m away. The first-order fringe resembles a rainbow with violet and red light at opposite ends. The violet light falls about 2.0 mm and the red 3.5 mm from the center of the central white fringe (Fig. 24–11). Estimate the wavelengths for the violet and red light.

**APPROACH** We find the angles for violet and red light from the distances given and the diagram of Fig. 24–10. Then we use Eq. 24–2a to obtain the wavelengths. Because 3.5 mm is much less than 2.5 m, we can use the small-angle approximation.

**SOLUTION** We use Eq. 24–2a with $m = 1$ and $\sin\theta \approx \tan\theta \approx \theta$. Then for violet light, $x = 2.0\,\text{mm}$, so (see also Fig. 24–10)

$$\lambda = \frac{d\sin\theta}{m} \approx \frac{d\theta}{m} \approx \frac{d}{m}\frac{x}{L} = \left(\frac{5.0\times10^{-4}\,\text{m}}{1}\right)\left(\frac{2.0\times10^{-3}\,\text{m}}{2.5\,\text{m}}\right) = 4.0\times10^{-7}\,\text{m},$$

or 400 nm. For red light, $x = 3.5\,\text{mm}$, so

$$\lambda = \frac{d}{m}\frac{x}{L} = \left(\frac{5.0\times10^{-4}\,\text{m}}{1}\right)\left(\frac{3.5\times10^{-3}\,\text{m}}{2.5\,\text{m}}\right) = 7.0\times10^{-7}\,\text{m} = 700\,\text{nm}.$$

**EXERCISE A** For the setup in Example 24–3, how far from the central white fringe is the first-order fringe for green light $\lambda = 500\,\text{nm}$?

## Coherent Light

*Coherent and incoherent sources*

*Interference patterns occur only if sources are coherent*

The two slits in Fig. 24–7 act as if they were two sources of radiation. They are called **coherent sources** because the waves leaving them have the same wavelength and frequency, and bear the same phase relationship to each other at all times. This happens because the waves come from a single source to the left of the two slits in Fig. 24–7. An interference pattern is observed only when the sources are coherent. If two tiny lightbulbs replaced the two slits, an interference pattern would not be seen. The light emitted by one lightbulb would have a random phase with respect to the second bulb, and the screen would be more or less uniformly illuminated. Two such sources, whose output waves bear no fixed phase relationship to each other, are called **incoherent sources**.

# 24–4 The Visible Spectrum and Dispersion

The two most obvious properties of light are readily describable in terms of the wave theory of light: intensity (or brightness) and color. The **intensity** of light is the energy it carries per unit area per unit time, and is related to the square of the amplitude of the wave, just as for any wave (see Section 11–10, or Eqs. 22–7 and 22–8). The **color** of the light is related to the frequency $f$ or wavelength $\lambda$ of the light. (Recall $\lambda f = c = 3.0\times10^8\,\text{m/s}$, Eq. 22–4.) Visible light—that to which our eyes are sensitive—consists of frequencies from $4\times10^{14}\,\text{Hz}$ to $7.5\times10^{14}\,\text{Hz}$, corresponding to wavelengths in air of about 400 nm to 750 nm.† This is known as the **visible spectrum**, and within it lie the different colors from violet to red, as shown in Fig. 24–12. Light with wavelength shorter than 400 nm is called **ultraviolet** (UV), and light with wavelength longer than 750 nm is called **infrared** (IR).‡ Although human eyes are not sensitive to UV or IR, some types of photographic film and other detectors do respond to them.

†Sometimes the angstrom (Å) unit is used when referring to light: $1\,\text{Å} = 1\times10^{-10}\,\text{m}$. Visible light has wavelengths in air of 4000 Å to 7500 Å.

‡The complete electromagnetic spectrum is illustrated in Fig. 22–8.

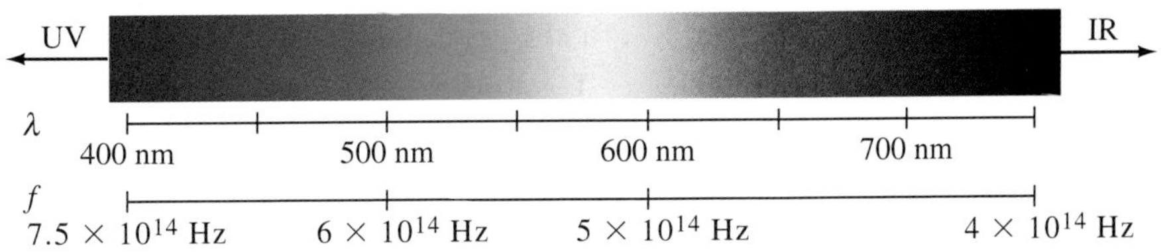


**FIGURE 24–12** The spectrum of visible light, showing the range of frequencies and wavelengths (in air) for the various colors.

FIGURE 24–13 White light passing through a prism is broken down into its constituent colors.

[The wavelengths of visible light are measured in air to be 400 nm to 750 nm, and this range is what we usually quote. But, as we shall see in Chapter 25, the interior of the eye is filled with a fluid with index of refraction $n \approx 1.4$, so the wavelengths where they actually reach our retinas are smaller by this factor, Eq. 24–1.]

A prism separates white light into a rainbow of colors, as shown in Fig. 24–13. This happens because the index of refraction of a material depends on the wavelength, as shown for several materials in Fig. 24–14. White light is a mixture of all visible wavelengths, and when incident on a prism, as in Fig. 24–15, the different wavelengths are bent to varying degrees. Because the index of refraction is greater for the shorter wavelengths, violet light is bent the most and red the least. This spreading of white light into the full spectrum is called **dispersion**.

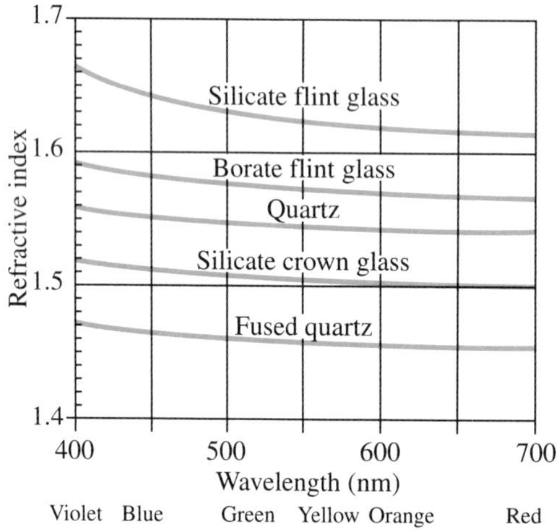


FIGURE 24–14 Index of refraction as a function of wavelength for various transparent solids.

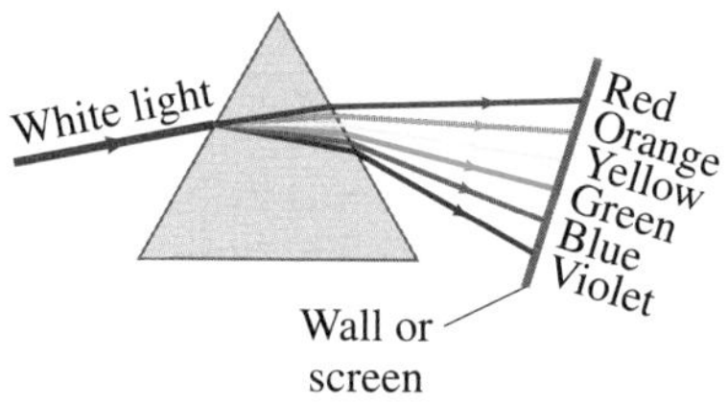


FIGURE 24–15 White light dispersed by a prism into the visible spectrum.

PHYSICS APPLIED

*Rainbows*

Rainbows are a spectacular example of dispersion—by drops of water. You can see rainbows when you look at falling water droplets with the Sun behind you. Figure 24–16 shows how red and violet rays are bent by spherical water droplets and are reflected off the back surface. Red is bent the least and so reaches the observer's eyes from droplets higher in the sky, as shown in the diagram. Thus the top of the rainbow is red.

FIGURE 24–16 (a) Ray diagram explaining how a rainbow (b) is formed.

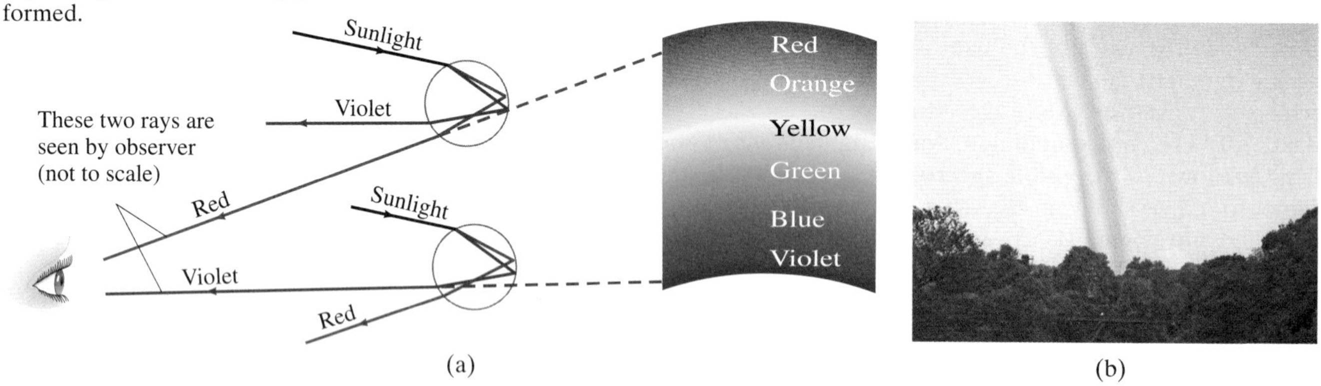


FIGURE 24–17 Diamond.

Diamonds achieve their brilliance (Fig. 24–17) from a combination of dispersion and total internal reflection. Because diamonds have a very high index of refraction of about 2.4, the critical angle for total internal reflection is only 25°. The light dispersed into a spectrum inside the diamond therefore strikes many of the internal surfaces before it strikes one at less than 25° and emerges. After many such reflections, the light has traveled far enough that the colors have become sufficiently separated to be seen individually and brilliantly by the eye after leaving the crystal.

The visible spectrum, Fig. 24–12, does not show all the colors seen in nature. For example, there is no brown in Fig. 24–12. Many of the colors we see are a mixture of wavelengths. For practical purposes, most natural colors can be reproduced using three primary colors. They are red, green, and blue for direct source viewing such as TV and computer monitors. For inks used in printing, the primary colors are cyan (the color of the margin notes in this book), yellow, and magenta (the color we use for light rays in diagrams).

## 24–5 Diffraction by a Single Slit or Disk

Young's double-slit experiment put the wave theory of light on a firm footing. But full acceptance came only with studies on diffraction (Section 24–1) more than a decade later, in the 1810s and 1820s.

We have already discussed diffraction briefly with regard to water waves (Section 11–15) as well as for light (Section 24–1), and we have seen that it refers to the spreading or bending of waves around edges. Let's look in more detail.

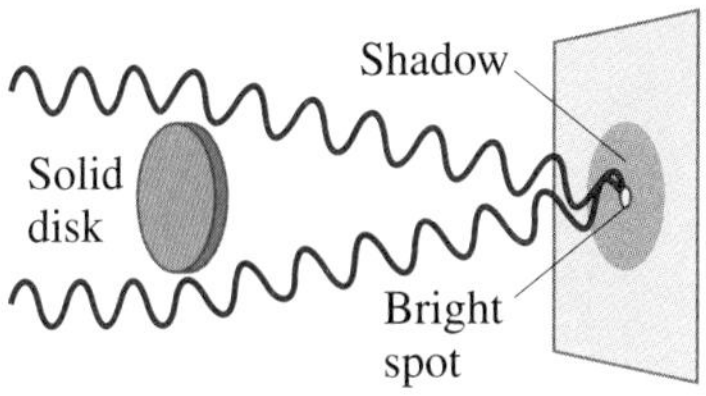


**FIGURE 24–18** If light is a wave, a bright spot will appear at the center of the shadow of a solid disk illuminated by a point source of monochromatic light.

*The (un)expected diffraction spot*

In 1819 Augustin Fresnel (1788–1827) presented to the French Academy a wave theory of light that predicted and explained interference and diffraction effects. Almost immediately Siméon Poisson (1781–1840) pointed out a counterintuitive inference: according to Fresnel's wave theory, if light from a point source were to fall on a solid disk, part of the incident light would be diffracted around the edges and would constructively interfere at the center of the shadow (Fig. 24–18). That prediction seemed very unlikely. But when the experiment was actually carried out by Francois Arago, the bright spot was seen at the very center of the shadow (Fig. 24–19a). This was strong evidence for the wave theory.

Figure 24–19a is a photograph of the shadow cast by a coin using a (nearly) point source of light, a laser in this case. The bright spot is clearly present at the center. Notice also the bright and dark fringes beyond the shadow. These resemble the interference fringes of a double slit. Indeed, they are due to interference of waves diffracted around the disk, and the whole is referred to as a **diffraction pattern**. A diffraction pattern exists around any sharp object illuminated by a point source, as shown in Figs. 24–19b and c. We are not always aware of them because most sources of light in everyday life are not points, so light from different parts of the source washes out the pattern.

**FIGURE 24–19** Diffraction pattern of (a) a circular disk (a coin), (b) scissors, (c) a single slit, each illuminated by a (nearly) point source of monochromatic light.

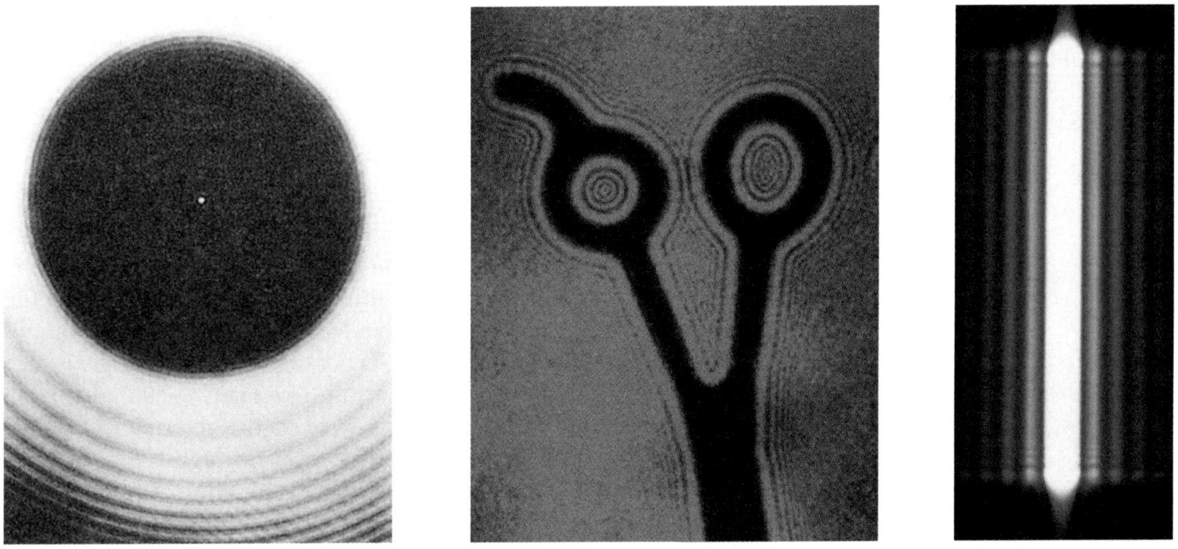

(a) (b) (c)

To see how a diffraction pattern arises, we will analyze the important case of monochromatic light passing through a narrow slit. We will assume that parallel rays (plane waves) of light fall on the slit of width $D$, and pass through to a viewing screen very far away.† As we know from studying water waves and from Huygens' principle, the waves passing through the slit spread out in all directions. We will now examine how the waves passing through different parts of the slit interfere with each other.

Parallel rays of monochromatic light pass through the narrow slit as shown in Fig. 24–20a. The light falls on a screen which is assumed to be very far away, so the rays heading for any point are very nearly parallel before they meet at the screen. First we consider rays that pass straight through as in Fig. 24–20a. They are all in phase, so there will be a central bright spot on the screen. In Fig. 24–20b, we consider rays moving at an angle $\theta$ such that the ray from the top of the slit travels exactly one wavelength farther than the ray from the bottom edge to reach the screen. The ray passing through the very center of the slit will travel one-half wavelength farther than the ray at the bottom of the slit. These two rays will be exactly out of phase with one another and so will destructively interfere when they overlap at the screen. Similarly, a ray slightly above the bottom one will cancel a ray that is the same distance above the central one. Indeed, each ray passing through the lower half of the

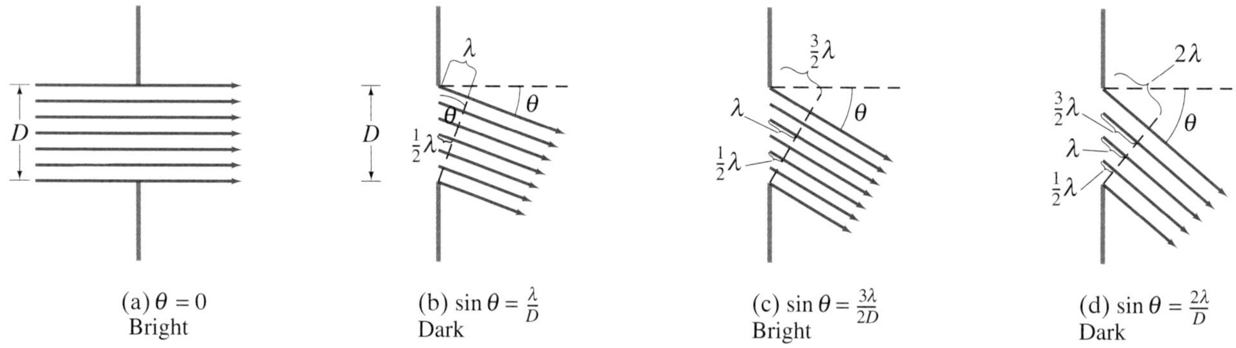


**FIGURE 24–20** Analysis of diffraction pattern formed by light passing through a narrow slit.

slit will cancel with a corresponding ray passing through the upper half. Thus, all the rays destructively interfere in pairs, and so the light intensity will be zero on the viewing screen at this angle. The angle $\theta$ at which this takes place can be seen from Fig. 24–20b to occur when $\lambda = D\sin\theta$, so

*Diffraction equation (angular half width of central spot)*

$$\sin\theta = \frac{\lambda}{D}. \qquad \text{[first minimum]} \quad \textbf{(24–3a)}$$

The light intensity is a maximum at $\theta = 0°$ and decreases to a minimum (intensity = zero) at the angle $\theta$ given by Eq. 24–3a.

Now consider a larger angle $\theta$ such that the top ray travels $\frac{3}{2}\lambda$ farther than the bottom ray, as in Fig. 24–20c. In this case, the rays from the bottom third of the slit will cancel in pairs with those in the middle third because they will be $\lambda/2$ out of phase. However, light from the top third of the slit will still reach the screen, so there will be a bright spot centered near $\sin\theta \approx 3\lambda/2D$, but it will not be nearly as bright as the central spot at $\theta = 0°$. For an even larger angle $\theta$ such that the top ray travels $2\lambda$ farther than the bottom ray, Fig. 24–20d, rays from the bottom quarter of the slit will cancel with those in the quarter just above it because the path lengths differ by $\lambda/2$. And the rays through the quarter of the slit just above center will cancel with those through the top quarter. At this angle there will again be a minimum of zero intensity in the diffraction

†If the viewing screen is not far away, lenses can be used to make the rays parallel.

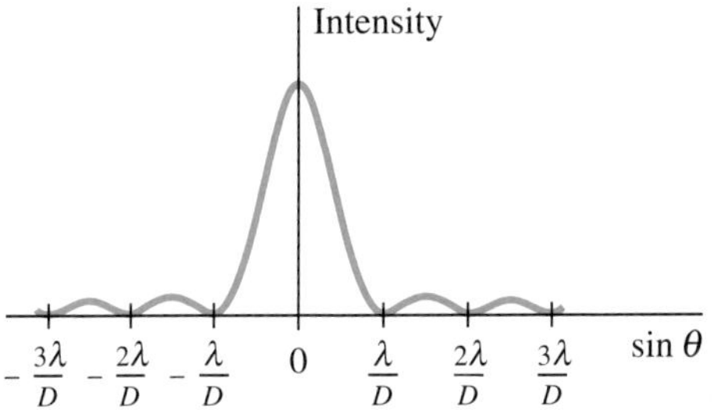


**FIGURE 24–21** Intensity in the diffraction pattern of a single slit as a function of $\sin\theta$. Note that the central maximum is not only much higher than the maxima to each side, but it is also twice as wide ($2\lambda/D$ wide) as any of the others (only $\lambda/D$ wide each).

pattern. A plot of the intensity as a function of angle is shown in Fig. 24–21. This corresponds well with the photo of Fig. 24–19c. Notice that minima (zero intensity) occur at

$$D\sin\theta = m\lambda, \qquad m = 1, 2, 3, \cdots, \qquad \text{[minima]} \quad \textbf{(24–3b)}$$

*Single-slit diffraction minima*

but *not* at $m = 0$ where there is the strongest maximum. Between the minima, smaller intensity maxima occur at approximately (not exactly) $m \approx \frac{3}{2}, \frac{5}{2}, \cdots$.

Note that the *minima* for a diffraction pattern, Eq. 24–3b, satisfy a criterion that looks very similar to that for the *maxima* (bright spots) for double-slit interference, Eq. 24–2a. Also note that $D$ is a single slit width, whereas $d$ in Eq. 24–2 is the distance between two slits.

**CAUTION**
*Don't confuse Eqs. 24–2 for interference with Eqs. 24–3 for diffraction; note the differences*

**EXAMPLE 24–4** **Single-slit diffraction maximum.** Light of wavelength 750 nm passes through a slit $1.0 \times 10^{-3}$ mm wide. How wide is the central maximum (*a*) in degrees, and (*b*) in centimeters, on a screen 20 cm away?

**APPROACH** The width of the central maximum goes from the first minimum on one side to the first minimum on the other side. We use Eq. 24–3a to find the angular position of the first single-slit diffraction minimum.

**SOLUTION** (*a*) The first minimum occurs at

$$\sin\theta = \frac{\lambda}{D} = \frac{7.5 \times 10^{-7}\,\text{m}}{1 \times 10^{-6}\,\text{m}} = 0.75.$$

So $\theta = 49°$. This is the angle between the center and the first minimum, Fig. 24–22. The angle subtended by the whole central maximum, between the minima above and below the center, is twice this, or 98°.

(*b*) The width of the central maximum is $2x$, where $\tan\theta = x/20\,\text{cm}$. So $2x = 2(20\,\text{cm})(\tan 49°) = 46\,\text{cm}$.

**NOTE** A large width of the screen will be illuminated, but it will not normally be very bright since the amount of light that passes through such a small slit will be small and it is spread over a large area. Note also that we *cannot* use the small-angle approximation here ($\theta \approx \sin\theta \approx \tan\theta$) because $\theta$ is large.

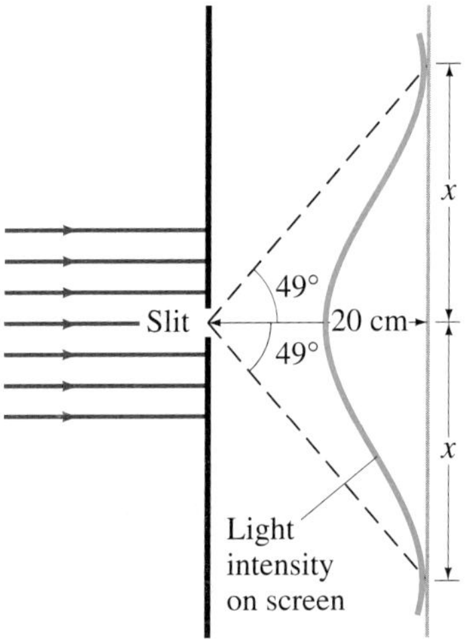


**FIGURE 24–22** Example 24–4.

**EXERCISE B** In Example 24–4, red light ($\lambda = 750$ nm) was used. If instead yellow light ($\lambda = 550$ nm) had been used, would the central maximum be wider or narrower?

**CONCEPTUAL EXAMPLE 24–5** **Diffraction spreads.** Light shines through a rectangular hole that is narrower in the vertical direction than the horizontal, Fig. 24–23. (*a*) Would you expect the diffraction pattern to be more spread out in the vertical direction or in the horizontal direction? (*b*) Should a rectangular loudspeaker horn at a stadium be high and narrow, or wide and flat?

**FIGURE 24–23** Example 24–5.

**RESPONSE** (*a*) From Eq. 24–3a we can see that if we make the slit (width $D$) narrower, the pattern spreads out more. This is consistent with our study of waves in Chapter 11. The diffraction through the rectangular hole will be wider vertically, since the opening is smaller in that direction.

(*b*) For a loudspeaker, the sound pattern desired is one spread out horizontally, so the horn should be tall and narrow (rotate Fig. 24–23 by 90°).

## 24–6 Diffraction Grating

A large number of equally spaced parallel slits is called a **diffraction grating**, although the term "interference grating" might be as appropriate. Gratings can be made by precision machining of very fine parallel lines on a glass plate. The untouched spaces between the lines serve as the slits. Photographic transparencies of an original grating serve as inexpensive gratings. Gratings containing 10,000 lines per centimeter are common, and are very useful for precise measurements of wavelengths. A diffraction grating containing slits is called a **transmission grating**. Another type of diffraction grating is the **reflection grating**, made by ruling fine lines on a metallic or glass surface from which light is reflected and analyzed. The analysis is basically the same as for a transmission grating, which we now discuss.

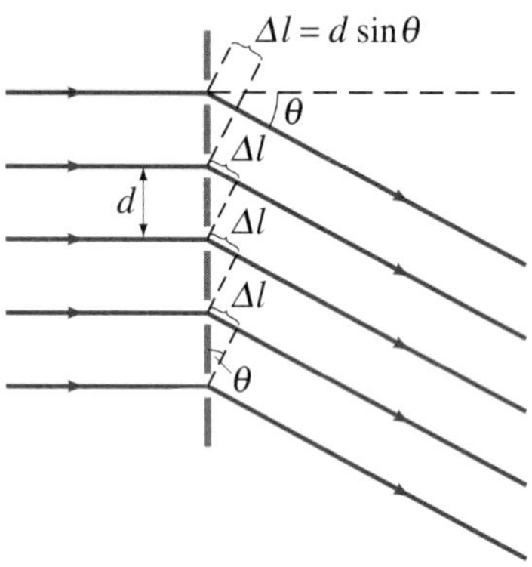


**FIGURE 24–24** Diffraction grating.

The analysis of a diffraction grating is much like that of Young's double-slit experiment. We assume parallel rays of light are incident on the grating as shown in Fig. 24–24. We also assume that the slits are narrow enough so that diffraction by each of them spreads light over a very wide angle on a distant screen beyond the grating, and interference can occur with light from all the other slits. Light rays that pass through each slit without deviation ($\theta = 0°$) interfere constructively to produce a bright line at the center of the screen. Constructive interference also occurs at an angle $\theta$ such that rays from adjacent slits travel an extra distance of $\Delta l = m\lambda$, where $m$ is an integer. If $d$ is the distance between slits, then we see from Fig. 24–24 that $\Delta l = d \sin\theta$, and

*Diffraction grating maxima (m = order)*

$$\sin\theta = \frac{m\lambda}{d}, \qquad m = 0, 1, 2, \cdots \qquad \text{[principal maxima]} \quad \textbf{(24–4)}$$

is the criterion to have a brightness maximum. This is the same equation as for the double-slit situation, and again $m$ is called the order of the pattern.

**CAUTION**

*Diffraction grating is analyzed using interference formulas, not diffraction formulas*

*Why more slits yield sharper peaks*

There is an important difference between a double-slit and a multiple-slit pattern. The bright maxima are much *sharper* and *narrower* for a grating. Why? Suppose that the angle $\theta$ is increased just slightly beyond that required for a maximum. In the case of only two slits, the two waves will be only slightly out of phase, so nearly full constructive interference occurs. This means the maxima are wide (see Fig. 24–10). For a grating, the waves from two adjacent slits will also not be significantly out of phase. But waves from one slit and those from a second one a few hundred slits away may be exactly out of phase; all or nearly all the light can cancel in pairs in this way. For example, suppose the angle $\theta$ is very slightly different from its first-order maximum, so that the extra path length for a pair of adjacent slits is not exactly $\lambda$ but rather $1.0010\lambda$. The wave through one slit and another one 500 slits below will have a path difference of $1\lambda + (500)(0.001\lambda) = 1.5000\lambda$, or $1\frac{1}{2}$ wavelengths, so the two will cancel. A pair of slits, one below each of these, will also cancel. That is, the light from slit 1 cancels with that from slit 501; light from slit 2 cancels with that from slit 502, and so on. Thus even for a tiny angle† corresponding to an extra path length of $\frac{1}{1000}\lambda$, there is much destructive interference, and so the maxima are very narrow. The more lines there are in a grating, the sharper will be the peaks (see Fig. 24–25). Because a grating produces much sharper (and brighter) lines than two slits alone can, it is a far more precise device for measuring wavelengths.

**FIGURE 24–25** Intensity as a function of viewing angle $\theta$ (or position on the screen) for (a) two slits, (b) six slits. For a diffraction grating, the number of slits is very large ($\approx 10^4$) and the peaks are narrower still.

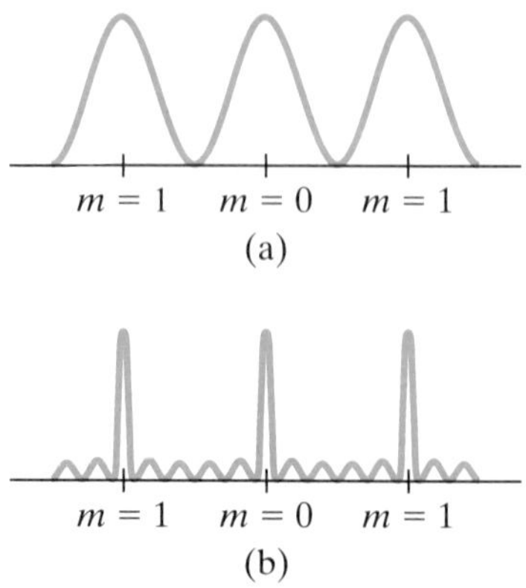


Suppose the light striking a diffraction grating is not monochromatic, but consists of two or more distinct wavelengths. Then for all orders other than $m = 0$, each wavelength will produce a maximum at a different angle (Fig. 24–26a), just as for a double slit. If white light strikes a grating, the central ($m = 0$) maximum will be a sharp white peak. But for all other orders, there

†Depending on the total number of slits, there may or may not be complete cancellation for such an angle, so there will be very tiny peaks between the main maxima (see Fig. 24–25b), but they are usually much too small to be seen.

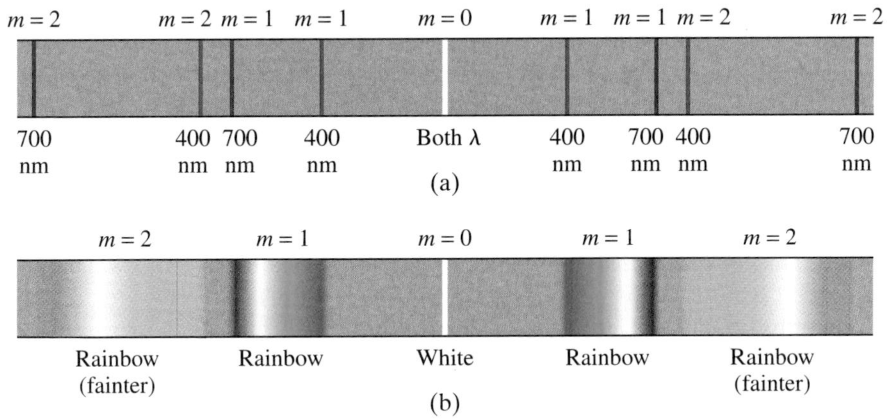


**FIGURE 24–26** Spectra produced by a grating: (a) two wavelengths, 400 nm and 700 nm; (b) white light. The second order will normally be dimmer than the first order. (Higher orders are not shown.) If grating spacing is small enough, the second and higher orders will be missing.

will be a distinct spectrum of colors spread out over a certain angular width, Fig. 24–26b. Because a diffraction grating spreads out light into its component wavelengths, the resulting pattern is called a **spectrum**.

**EXAMPLE 24–6** **Diffraction grating: lines.** Determine the angular positions of the first- and second-order maxima for light of wavelength 400 nm and 700 nm incident on a grating containing 10,000 lines/cm.

**APPROACH** First we find the distance $d$ between grating lines: if the grating has $N$ lines in 1 m, then the distance between lines must be $d = 1/N$ meters. Then we use Eq. 24–4 to find the angles for the two wavelengths for $m = 1$ and 2.

**SOLUTION** The grating contains $1.00 \times 10^4$ lines/cm $= 1.00 \times 10^6$ lines/m, which means the distance between lines is $d = (1/1.00 \times 10^6)\,\text{m} = 1.00 \times 10^{-6}\,\text{m} = 1.00\,\mu\text{m}$. In first order ($m = 1$), the angles are

$$\sin\theta_{400} = \frac{m\lambda}{d} = \frac{(1)(4.00 \times 10^{-7}\,\text{m})}{1.00 \times 10^{-6}\,\text{m}} = 0.400$$

$$\sin\theta_{700} = \frac{(1)(7.00 \times 10^{-7}\,\text{m})}{1.00 \times 10^{-6}\,\text{m}} = 0.700$$

so $\theta_{400} = 23.6^\circ$ and $\theta_{700} = 44.4^\circ$. In second order,

$$\sin\theta_{400} = \frac{2\lambda}{d} = \frac{(2)(4.00 \times 10^{-7}\,\text{m})}{1.00 \times 10^{-6}\,\text{m}} = 0.800$$

$$\sin\theta_{700} = \frac{(2)(7.00 \times 10^{-7}\,\text{m})}{1.00 \times 10^{-6}\,\text{m}} = 1.40$$

so $\theta_{400} = 53.1^\circ$. But the second order does not exist for $\lambda = 700\,\text{nm}$ because $\sin\theta$ cannot exceed 1. No higher orders will appear.

**EXAMPLE 24–7** **Spectra overlap.** White light containing wavelengths from 400 nm to 750 nm strikes a grating containing 4000 lines/cm. Show that the blue at $\lambda = 450\,\text{nm}$ of the third-order spectrum overlaps the red at 700 nm of the second order.

**APPROACH** We use Eq. 24–4 to calculate the angular positions of the $m = 3$ blue maximum and the $m = 2$ red one.

**SOLUTION** The grating spacing is $d = (1/4000)\,\text{cm} = 2.50 \times 10^{-6}\,\text{m}$. The blue of the third order occurs at an angle $\theta$ given by

$$\sin\theta = \frac{m\lambda}{d} = \frac{(3)(4.50 \times 10^{-7}\,\text{m})}{(2.50 \times 10^{-6}\,\text{m})} = 0.540.$$

Red in second order occurs at

$$\sin\theta = \frac{(2)(7.00 \times 10^{-7}\,\text{m})}{(2.50 \times 10^{-6}\,\text{m})} = 0.560,$$

which is a greater angle; so the second order overlaps into the beginning of the third-order spectrum.

**EXERCISE C** How many lines per cm are in a grating that produces the first-order maximum of 633-nm light at 18°?

**EXERCISE D** You are shown the spectra produced by red light shining through two different gratings. The lines in spectrum A are farther apart than those in spectrum B. Which grating has more lines/cm?

## * 24–7 The Spectrometer and Spectroscopy

A **spectrometer** or **spectroscope**, Fig. 24–27, is a device to measure wavelengths accurately using a diffraction grating (or a prism) to separate different wavelengths of light. Light from a source passes through a narrow slit S in the "collimator." The slit is at the focal point of the lens L, so parallel light falls on the grating. The movable telescope can bring the rays to a focus.

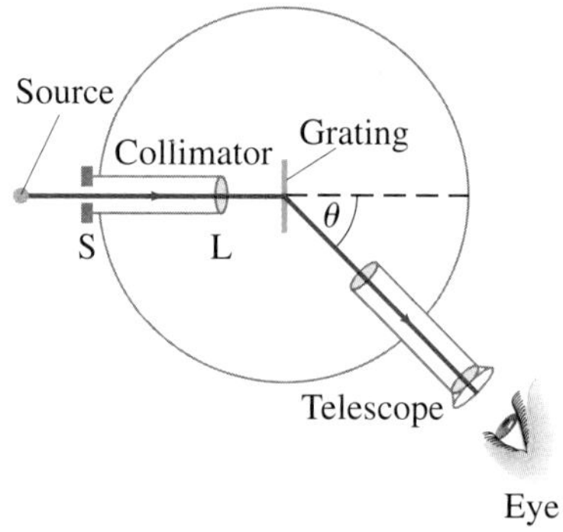


**FIGURE 24–27** Spectrometer or spectroscope.

Nothing will be seen in the viewing telescope unless it is positioned at an angle $\theta$ that corresponds to a diffraction peak (first order is usually used) of a wavelength emitted by the source. The angle $\theta$ can be measured to very high accuracy, so the wavelength of a line can be determined to high accuracy using Eq. 24–4:

$$\lambda = \frac{d}{m}\sin\theta,$$

where $m$ is an integer representing the order, and $d$ is the distance between grating lines. The line you see in a spectrometer corresponding to each wavelength is actually an image of the slit S. The narrower the slit, the narrower—but dimmer—the line is, and the more precisely we can measure its angular position. If the light contains a continuous range of wavelengths, then a continuous spectrum is seen in the spectroscope.

In many spectrometers, a reflection grating is used, and sometimes a prism. A prism works because of dispersion (Section 24–4), bending light of different wavelengths into different angles. (A prism is not a linear device and must be calibrated.)

An important use of a spectrometer is for the identification of atoms or molecules. When a gas is heated or an electric current is passed through it, the gas emits a characteristic **line spectrum**. That is, only certain discrete wavelengths of light are emitted, and these are different for different elements and compounds.[†] Figure 24–28 shows the line spectra for a number of elements in the gas state. Line spectra occur only for gases at high temperatures and low pressure and density. The light from heated solids, such as a lightbulb filament, and even from a dense gaseous object such as the Sun, produces a **continuous spectrum** including a wide range of wavelengths.

*Line spectra*

Figure 24–28 also shows the Sun's "continuous spectrum," which contains a number of *dark* lines (only the most prominent are shown), called **absorption lines**. Atoms and molecules can absorb light at the same wavelengths at which they emit light. The Sun's absorption lines are due to absorption by atoms and molecules in the cooler outer atmosphere of the Sun, as well as by atoms and molecules in the Earth's atmosphere. A careful analysis of all these thousands of

[†]Why atoms and molecules emit line spectra was a great mystery for many years and played a central role in the development of modern quantum theory, as we shall see in Chapter 27.

**FIGURE 24–28** Line spectra for the gases indicated, and spectrum from the Sun showing absorption lines.

lines reveals that at least two-thirds of all elements are present in the Sun's atmosphere. The presence of elements in the atmosphere of other planets, in interstellar space, and in stars is also determined by spectroscopy.

Spectroscopy is useful for determining the presence of certain types of molecules in laboratory specimens where chemical analysis would be difficult. For example, biological DNA and different types of protein absorb light in particular regions of the spectrum (such as in the UV). The material to be examined, which is often in solution, is placed in a monochromatic light beam whose wavelength is selected by placement angle of a diffraction grating or prism. The amount of absorption, as compared to a standard solution without the specimen, can reveal not only the presence of a particular type of molecule, but also its concentration.

PHYSICS APPLIED
*Chemical and biochemical analysis by spectroscopy*

Light emission and absorption also occur outside the visible part of the spectrum, such as in the UV and IR regions. Glass absorbs light in these regions, so reflection gratings and mirrors (in place of lenses) are used. Special types of film or detectors are used for detection.

## 24–8 Interference by Thin Films

Interference of light gives rise to many everyday phenomena such as the bright colors reflected from soap bubbles and from thin oil films on water, Fig. 24–29. In these and other cases, the colors are a result of constructive interference between light reflected from the two surfaces of the thin film. The effect is present only if the thickness of the film is on the order of the wavelength of the light. If the film thickness is greater than a few wavelengths, the effect gets washed out.

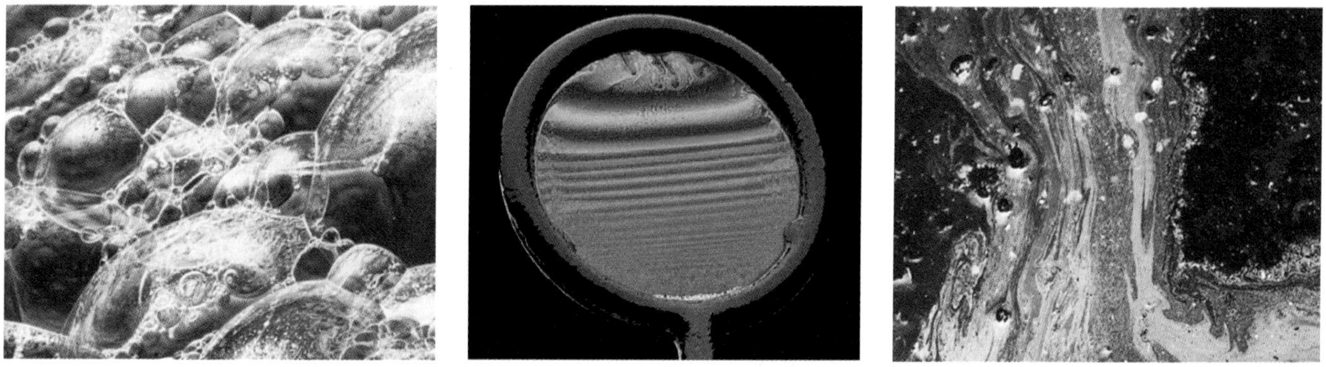

(a) (b) (c)

**FIGURE 24–29** Thin-film interference patterns seen in (a) soap bubbles, (b) a thin film of soapy water, and (c) a thin layer of oil on the water of a street puddle.

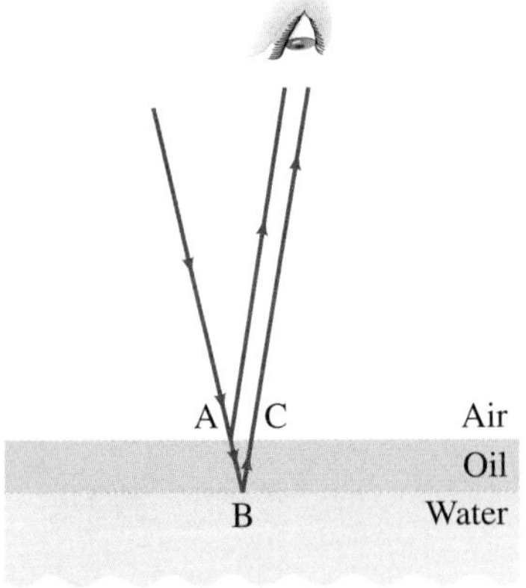


**FIGURE 24–30** Light reflected from the upper and lower surfaces of a thin film of oil lying on water. This analysis assumes the light strikes the surface nearly perpendicularly, but is shown here at an angle so we can display each ray.

To see how this **thin-film interference** happens, consider a smooth surface of water on top of which is a thin uniform layer of another substance, say an oil whose index of refraction is less than that of water (we'll see why we assume this in a moment); see Fig. 24–30. Assume for the moment that the incident light is of a single wavelength. Part of the incident light is reflected at A on the top surface, and part of the light transmitted is reflected at B on the lower surface. The part reflected at the lower surface must travel the extra distance ABC. If this *path difference* ABC equals one or a whole number of wavelengths in the film $(\lambda_n)$, the two waves will reach the eye in phase and interfere constructively. Hence the region AC on the surface film will appear bright. But if ABC equals $\frac{1}{2}\lambda_n$, $\frac{3}{2}\lambda_n$, and so on, the two waves will be exactly out of phase and destructive interference occurs: the area AC on the film will be dark. The wavelength $\lambda_n$ is *the wavelength in the film*: $\lambda_n = \lambda/n$, where $n$ is the index of refraction in the film and $\lambda$ is the wavelength in vacuum. See Eq. 24–1.

When white light falls on such a film, the path difference ABC will equal $\lambda_n$ (or $m\lambda_n$, with $m$ = an integer) for only one wavelength at a given viewing angle. The color corresponding to $\lambda$ ($\lambda$ in air) will be seen as very bright. For light viewed at a slightly different angle, the path difference ABC will be longer or shorter and a different color will undergo constructive interference. Thus, for an extended (nonpoint) source emitting white light, a series of bright colors will be seen next to one another. Variations in thickness of the film will also alter the path difference ABC and therefore affect the color of light that is most strongly reflected.

When a curved glass surface is placed in contact with a flat glass surface, Fig. 24–31, a series of concentric rings is seen when illuminated from above by

**FIGURE 24–31** Newton's rings.

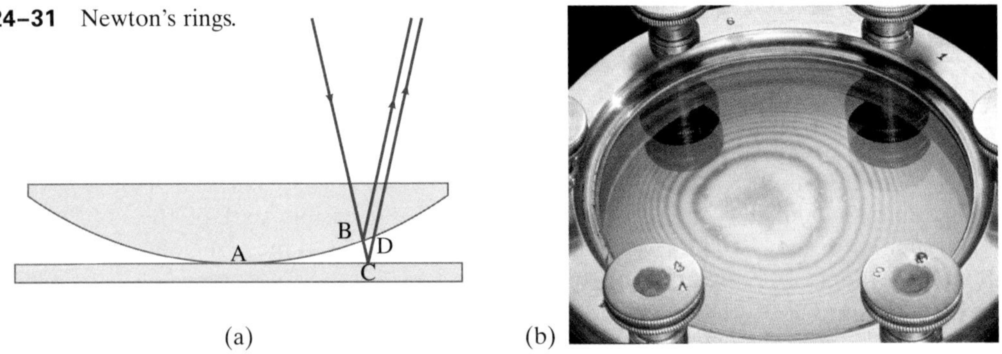


Newton's rings

monochromatic light. These are called **Newton's rings**† and they are due to interference between rays reflected by the top and bottom surfaces of the very thin *air gap* between the two pieces of glass. Because this gap (which is equivalent to a thin film) increases in width from the central contact point out to the edges, the extra path length for the lower ray (equal to BCD) varies; where it equals $0, \frac{1}{2}\lambda, \lambda, \frac{3}{2}\lambda, 2\lambda$, and so on, it corresponds to constructive and destructive interference; and this gives rise to the series of bright and dark lines seen in Fig. 24–31b.

The point of contact of the two glass surfaces (A in Fig. 24–31a) is dark in Fig. 24–31b. Since the path difference is zero here, our previous analysis would suggest that the rays reflected from each surface are in phase and so this central point ought to be bright. But it is dark, which tells us something else is happening here: the two rays must be completely out of phase. This can happen only because one of the waves, upon reflection, flips over—a crest becomes a trough—see Fig. 24–32. We say the wave has undergone a phase change of 180°, or of half a wave cycle. Indeed, this and other experiments reveal that, at normal incidence, *a beam of light reflected by a material with index of refraction greater than that of the material in which it is traveling, changes phase by 180° or $\frac{1}{2}$ cycle*; see Fig. 24–32. This phase change acts just like a path difference of $\frac{1}{2}\lambda$. If the index of refraction is less than that of the material in which the light is traveling, no phase change occurs.

**FIGURE 24–32** (a) Reflected ray changes phase by 180° or $\frac{1}{2}$ cycle if $n_2 > n_1$, but (b) does not if $n_2 < n_1$.

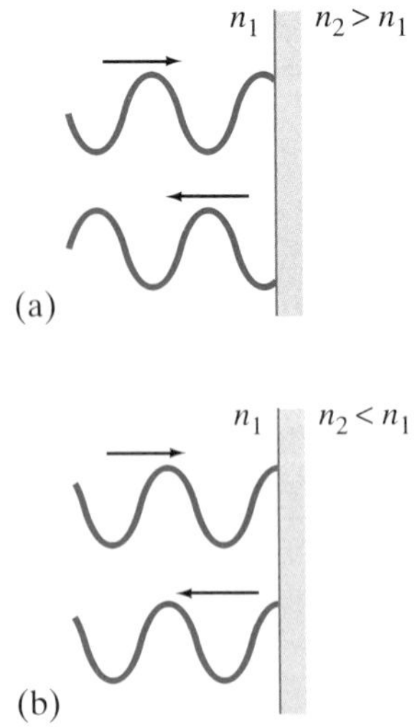


†Although Newton gave an elaborate description of them, they had been first observed and described by his contemporary, Robert Hooke.

Thus the ray reflected by the curved surface above the air gap in Fig. 24–31a undergoes no change in phase. The ray reflected at the lower surface, where the beam in air strikes the glass, undergoes a $\frac{1}{2}$-cycle phase change, equivalent to a $\frac{1}{2}\lambda$ path difference. Thus the two rays reflected at the point of contact A of the two glass surfaces (where the air gap approaches zero thickness) will be a half cycle (or 180°) out of phase, and a dark spot occurs. Other dark bands will occur when the path difference BCD in Fig. 24–31a is equal to an integral number of wavelengths. Bright bands will occur when the path difference is $\frac{1}{2}\lambda$, $\frac{3}{2}\lambda$, and so on, because the phase change at one surface effectively adds a path difference of $\frac{1}{2}\lambda\left(=\frac{1}{2}\text{ cycle}\right)$.

Returning for a moment to Fig. 24–30, the light reflecting at both interfaces, air–oil and oil–water, underwent a phase change of 180° equivalent to a path difference of $\frac{1}{2}\lambda$, since we assumed $n_{\text{water}} > n_{\text{oil}} > n_{\text{air}}$; since the phase changes were equal, they didn't affect our analysis.

**FIGURE 24–33** (a) Light rays reflected from the upper and lower surfaces of a thin wedge of air interfere to produce bright and dark bands. (b) Pattern observed when glass plates are optically flat; (c) pattern when plates are not so flat. See Example 24–8.

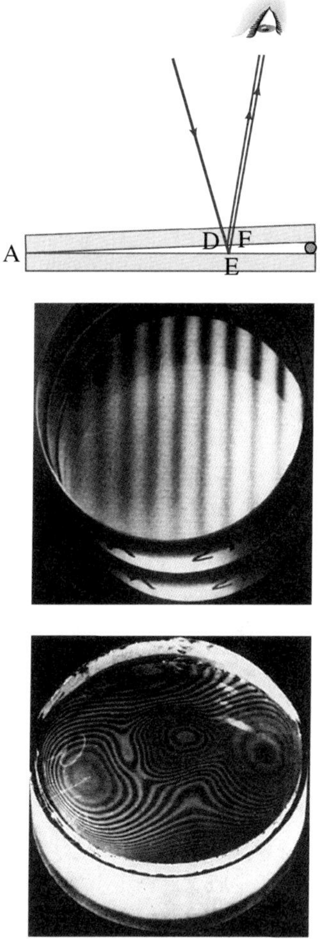

(a) (b) (c)

**EXAMPLE 24–8** **Thin film of air, wedge-shaped.** A very fine wire $7.35 \times 10^{-3}$ mm in diameter is placed between two flat glass plates as in Fig. 24–33a. Light whose wavelength in air is 600 nm falls (and is viewed) perpendicular to the plates, and a series of bright and dark bands is seen, Fig. 24–33b. How many light and dark bands will there be in this case? Will the area next to the wire be bright or dark?

**APPROACH** We need to consider two effects: (1) path differences for rays reflecting from the two close surfaces (thin wedge of air between the two glass plates), and (2) the $\frac{1}{2}$-cycle phase change at the lower surface (point E in Fig. 24–33a), where rays in air can enter glass. Because of the phase change at the lower surface, there will be a dark band when the path difference is 0, $\lambda$, $2\lambda$, $3\lambda$, and so on. Since the light rays are perpendicular to the plates, the extra path length equals $2t$, where $t$ is the thickness of the air gap at any point.

**SOLUTION** Dark bands will occur where

$$2t = m\lambda, \qquad m = 0, 1, 2, \cdots.$$

Bright bands occur when $2t = \left(m + \frac{1}{2}\right)\lambda$, where $m$ is an integer. At the position of the wire, $t = 7.35 \times 10^{-6}$ m. At this point there will be $2t/\lambda = (2)\left(7.35 \times 10^{-6}\text{ m}\right)/\left(6.00 \times 10^{-7}\text{ m}\right) = 24.5$ wavelengths. This is a "half integer," so the area next to the wire will be bright. There will be a total of 25 dark lines along the plates, corresponding to path lengths of $0\lambda$, $1\lambda$, $2\lambda$, $3\lambda$, $\cdots$, $24\lambda$, including the one at the point of contact A $(m = 0)$. Between them, there will be 24 bright lines plus the one at the end, or 25.

**NOTE** The bright and dark bands will be straight only if the glass plates are extremely flat. If they are not, the pattern is uneven, as in Fig. 24–33c. Thus we see a very precise way of testing a glass surface for flatness. Spherical lens surfaces can be tested for precision by placing the lens on a flat glass surface and observing Newton's rings (Fig. 24–31b) for perfect circularity.

PHYSICS APPLIED
*Testing glass for flatness*

If the wedge between the two glass plates of Example 24–8 is filled with some transparent substance other than air—say, water—the pattern shifts because the wavelength of the light changes. In a material where the index of refraction is $n$, the wavelength is $\lambda_n = \lambda/n$, where $\lambda$ is the wavelength in vacuum (see Eq. 24–1). For instance, if the thin wedge of Example 24–8 were filled with water, then $\lambda_n = 600\text{ nm}/1.33 = 450\text{ nm}$; instead of 25 dark lines, there would be 33.

When white light (rather than monochromatic light) is incident on the thin wedge of air in Figs. 24–31a or 24–33a, a colorful series of fringes is seen. This is because constructive interference occurs for different wavelengths in the reflected light at different thicknesses along the wedge.

A soap bubble is a thin spherical shell (or film) with air inside. The variations in thickness of a soap bubble film gives rise to bright colors reflected from the soap bubble. (There is air on both sides of the bubble film.) Similar variations in film thickness produce the bright colors seen reflecting from a thin layer of oil or gasoline on a puddle or lake (Fig. 24–29). Which wavelengths appear brightest also depends on the viewing angle.

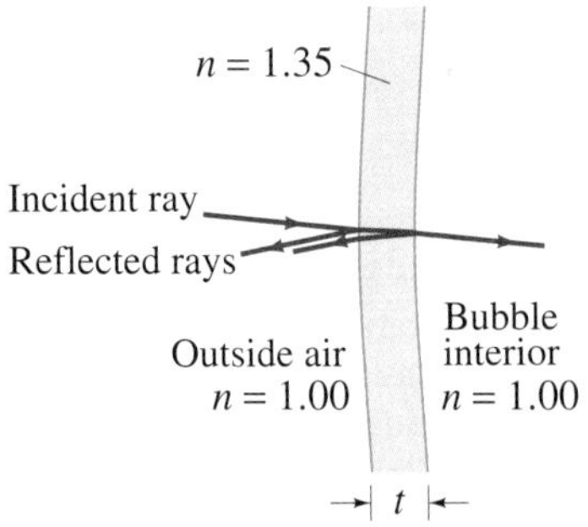


**FIGURE 24–34** Example 24–9. The incident and reflected rays are assumed to be perpendicular to the bubble's surface. They are shown at a slight angle so we can distinguish them.

**EXAMPLE 24–9 Thickness of soap bubble skin.** A soap bubble appears green ($\lambda = 540\,\text{nm}$) at the point on its front surface nearest the viewer. What is the smallest thickness the soap bubble film could have? Assume $n = 1.35$.

**APPROACH** Assume the light is reflected perpendicularly from the point on a spherical surface nearest the viewer, Fig. 24–34. The light rays also reflect from the inner surface of the soap bubble film as shown. The path difference of these two reflected rays is $2t$, where $t$ is the thickness of the soap film. Light reflected from the first (outer) surface undergoes a 180° phase change (index of refraction of soap is greater than that of air), whereas reflection at the second (inner) surface does not. To determine the thickness $t$ for an interference maximum, we must use the wavelength of light in the soap ($n = 1.35$).

**CAUTION**
*A formula is not enough: you must also check for phase changes at surfaces*

**SOLUTION** The 180° phase change at only one surface is equivalent to a $\frac{1}{2}\lambda$ path difference. Therefore, green light is bright when the minimum path difference equals $\frac{1}{2}\lambda_n$. Thus, $2t = \lambda/2n$, so

$$t = \frac{\lambda}{4n} = \frac{(540\,\text{nm})}{(4)(1.35)} = 100\,\text{nm}.$$

This is the smallest thickness.

**NOTE** The front surface would also appear green if $2t = 3\lambda/2n$, and, in general, if $2t = (2m + 1)\lambda/2n$, where $m$ is an integer. Note that green is seen in air, so $\lambda = 540\,\text{nm}$ (not $\lambda/n$).

**PHYSICS APPLIED**
*Lens coatings*

An important application of thin-film interference is in the coating of glass to make it "nonreflecting," particularly for lenses. A glass surface reflects about 4% of the light incident upon it. Good-quality cameras, microscopes, and other optical devices may contain six to ten thin lenses. Reflection from all these surfaces can reduce the light level considerably, and multiple reflections produce a background haze that reduces the quality of the image. By reducing reflection, transmission is increased. A very thin coating on the lens surfaces can reduce reflections considerably: the thickness of the film is chosen so that light (at least for one wavelength) reflecting from the front and rear surfaces of the film destructively interferes. The amount of reflection at a boundary depends on the difference in index of refraction between the two materials. Ideally, the coating material should have an index of refraction which is the geometric mean ($= \sqrt{n_1 n_2}$) of those for air and glass, so that the amount of reflection at each surface is about equal. Then destructive interference can occur nearly completely for one particular wavelength depending on the thickness of the coating. Nearby wavelengths will at least partially destructively interfere, but a single coating cannot eliminate reflections for all wavelengths. Nonetheless, a single coating can reduce total reflection from 4% to 1% of the incident light. Often the coating is designed to eliminate the center of the reflected spectrum (around 550 nm). The extremes of the spectrum—red and violet—will not be reduced as much. Since a mixture of red and violet produces purple, the light seen reflected from such coated lenses is purple (Fig. 24–35). Lenses containing two or three separate coatings can more effectively reduce a wider range of reflecting wavelengths.

**FIGURE 24–35** A coated lens. Note color of light reflected from the front lens surface.

## PROBLEM SOLVING Interference

1. **Interference effects** depend on the simultaneous arrival of two or more waves at the same point in space.
2. **Constructive interference** occurs when the waves arrive in phase with each other: a crest of one wave arrives at the same time as a crest of the other wave. The amplitudes of the waves then add to form a larger amplitude. Constructive interference also occurs when the path difference is exactly one full wavelength or any integer multiple of a full wavelength: $1\lambda, 2\lambda, 3\lambda, \cdots$.
3. **Destructive interference** occurs when a crest of one wave arrives at the same time as a trough of the other wave. The amplitudes add, but they are of opposite sign, so the total amplitude is reduced to zero if the two amplitudes are equal. Destructive interference occurs whenever the phase difference is half a wave cycle, or the path difference is a half-integral number of wavelengths. Thus, the total amplitude will be zero if two identical waves arrive one-half wavelength out of phase, or $\left(m + \frac{1}{2}\right)\lambda$ out of phase, where $m$ is an integer.
4. For thin-film interference, an extra half-wavelength **phase shift** occurs when light **reflects** from an optically more dense medium (going from a medium of lesser toward greater index of refraction).

**EXAMPLE 24–10 Nonreflective coating.** What is the thickness of an optical coating of $MgF_2$ whose index of refraction is $n = 1.38$ and is designed to eliminate reflected light at wavelengths (in air) around 550 nm when incident normally on glass for which $n = 1.50$?

**APPROACH** We explicitly follow the procedure outlined in the Problem Solving Box above.

**SOLUTION**

**(1) Interference effects:** Consider two rays reflected from the front and rear surfaces of the coating on the lens as shown in Fig. 24–36. The rays are drawn not quite perpendicular to the lens so we can see each of them. These two reflected rays will interfere with each other.

**(2) Constructive interference:** We want to eliminate reflected light, so we do not consider constructive interference.

**(3) Destructive interference:** To eliminate reflection, we want reflected rays 1 and 2 to be $\frac{1}{2}$ cycle out of phase with each other so that they destructively interfere. The phase difference is due to the path difference $2t$ traveled by ray 2, as well as any phase change in either ray due to reflection.

**(4) Reflection phase shift:** Rays 1 and 2 *both* undergo a change of phase by $\frac{1}{2}$ cycle when they reflect from the coating's front and rear surfaces, respectively (at both surfaces the index of refraction increases). Thus there is no net change in phase due to the reflections. The net phase difference will be due to the extra path $2t$ taken by ray 2 in the coating, where $n = 1.38$. We want $2t$ to equal $\frac{1}{2}\lambda_n$ so that destructive interference occurs, where $\lambda_n = \lambda/n$ is the wavelength in the coating. With $2t = \lambda_n/2 = \lambda/2n$, then

$$t = \frac{\lambda_n}{4} = \frac{\lambda}{4n} = \frac{(550\,\text{nm})}{(4)(1.38)} = 99.6\,\text{nm}.$$

**NOTE** We could have set $2t = \left(m + \frac{1}{2}\right)\lambda_n$, where $m$ is an integer. The smallest thickness ($m = 0$) is usually chosen because destructive interference will occur over the widest angle.

**NOTE** Complete destructive interference occurs only for the given wavelength of visible light. Longer and shorter wavelengths will have only partial cancellation.

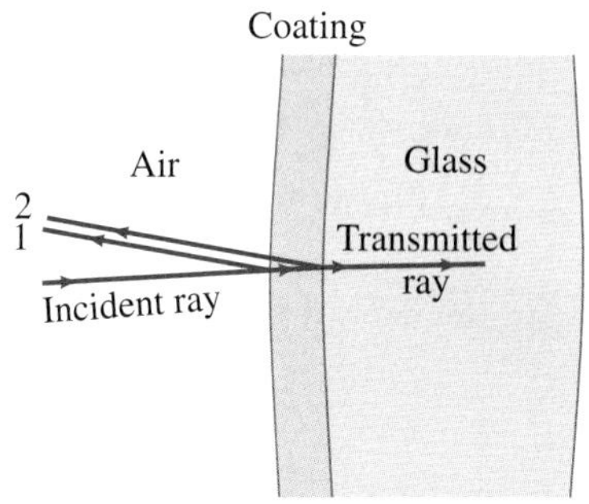


**FIGURE 24–36** Example 24–10. Incident ray of light is partially reflected at the front surface of a lens coating (ray 1) and again partially reflected at the rear surface of the coating (ray 2), with most of the energy passing as the transmitted ray into the glass.

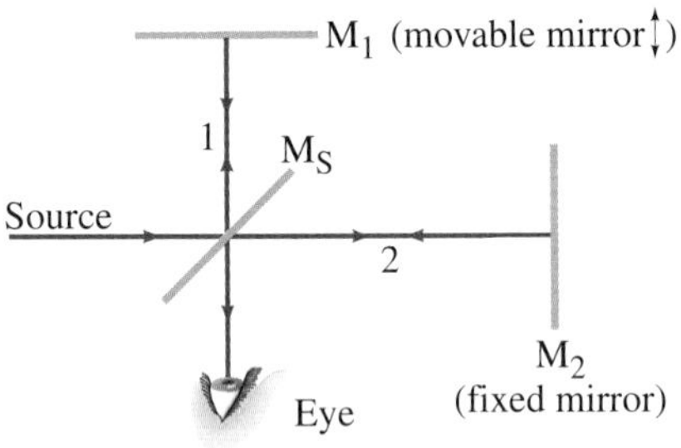


**FIGURE 24–37** Michelson interferometer.

## * 24–9 Michelson Interferometer

A useful instrument involving wave interference is the **Michelson interferometer** (Fig. 24–37),† invented by the American Albert A. Michelson (Section 22–4). Monochromatic light from a single point on an extended source is shown striking a half-silvered mirror $M_S$. This **beam splitter** mirror $M_S$ has a thin layer of silver that reflects only half the light that hits it, so that half of the beam passes through to a fixed mirror $M_2$, where it is reflected back. The other half is reflected by $M_S$ up to a mirror $M_1$ that is movable (by a fine-thread screw), where it is also reflected back. Upon its return, part of beam 1 passes through $M_S$ and reaches the eye; and part of beam 2, on its return, is reflected by $M_S$ into the eye. If the two path lengths are identical, the two coherent beams entering the eye constructively interfere and brightness will be seen. If the movable mirror is moved a distance $\lambda/4$, one beam will travel an extra distance equal to $\lambda/2$ (because it travels back and forth over the distance $\lambda/4$). In this case, the two beams will destructively interfere and darkness will be seen. As $M_1$ is moved farther, brightness will recur (when the path difference is $\lambda$), then darkness, and so on.

Very precise length measurements can be made with an interferometer. The motion of mirror $M_1$ by only $\frac{1}{4}\lambda$ produces a clear difference between brightness and darkness. For $\lambda = 400\,\text{nm}$, this means a precision of 100 nm, or $10^{-4}$ mm! If mirror $M_1$ is tilted very slightly, the bright or dark spots are seen instead as a series of bright and dark lines or "fringes." By counting the number of fringes, or fractions thereof, extremely precise length measurements can be made.

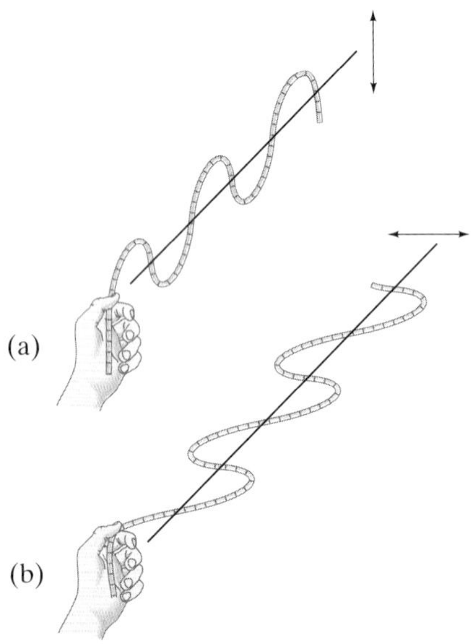


**FIGURE 24–38** Transverse waves on a rope polarized (a) in a vertical plane and (b) in a horizontal plane.

## 24–10 Polarization

An important and useful property of light is that it can be *polarized*. To see what this means, let us examine waves traveling on a rope. A rope can be set into oscillation in a vertical plane as in Fig. 24–38a, or in a horizontal plane as in Fig. 24–38b. In either case, the wave is said to be **linearly polarized** or **plane-polarized**—that is, the oscillations are in a plane.

If we now place an obstacle containing a vertical slit in the path of the wave, Fig. 24–39, a vertically polarized wave passes through the vertical slit, but a horizontally polarized wave will not. If a horizontal slit were used, the vertically polarized wave would be stopped. If both types of slit were used, both types of wave would be stopped by one slit or the other. Note that polarization can exist *only* for *transverse waves*, and not for longitudinal waves such as sound. The latter oscillate only along the direction of motion, and neither orientation of slit would stop them.

**FIGURE 24–39** Vertically polarized wave passes through a vertical slit, but a horizontally polarized wave will not.

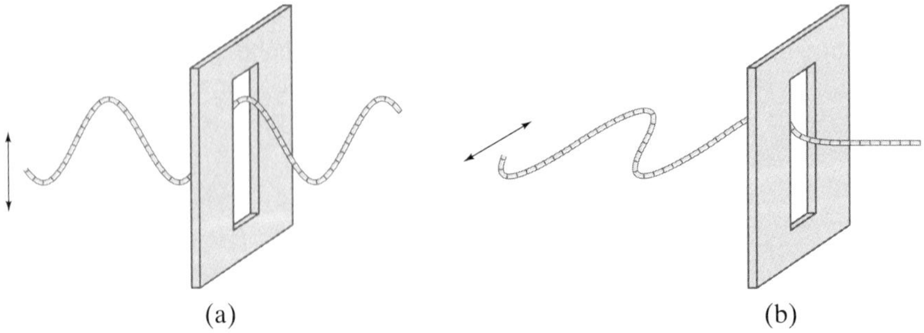


**FIGURE 24–40** Oscillation of the electric field vectors in unpolarized light. The light is traveling into or out of the page.

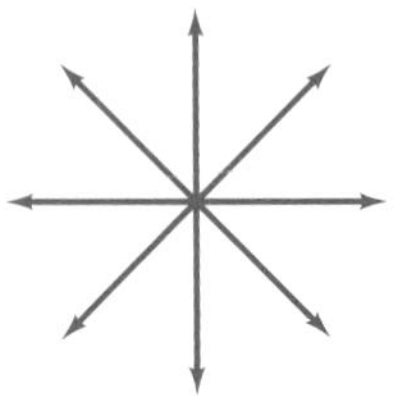

Maxwell's theory of light as electromagnetic (EM) waves predicted that light can be polarized since an EM wave is a transverse wave. The direction of polarization in a plane-polarized EM wave is taken as the direction of the electric field vector $\vec{\mathbf{E}}$.

Light is not necessarily polarized. It can also be **unpolarized**, which means that the source has oscillations in many planes at once, as shown in Fig. 24–40. An ordinary incandescent lightbulb emits unpolarized light, as does the Sun.

†There are other types of interferometer, but Michelson's is the best known.

## Polaroids

Plane-polarized light can be obtained from unpolarized light using certain crystals such as tourmaline. Or, more commonly today, we can use a **Polaroid sheet**. (Polaroid materials were invented in 1929 by Edwin Land.) A Polaroid sheet consists of complicated long molecules arranged parallel to one another. Such a Polaroid acts like a series of parallel slits to allow one orientation of polarization to pass through nearly undiminished. This direction is called the *transmission axis* of the Polaroid. A perpendicular polarization is absorbed almost completely by the Polaroid.

[Absorption by a Polaroid can be explained at the molecular level. An electric field $\vec{\mathbf{E}}$ that oscillates parallel to the long molecules can set electrons into motion along the molecules, thus doing work on them and transferring energy. Hence, if $\vec{\mathbf{E}}$ is parallel to the molecules, it gets absorbed. An electric field $\vec{\mathbf{E}}$ perpendicular to the long molecules does not have this possibility of doing work and transferring its energy, and so passes through freely. When we speak of the *transmission axis* of a Polaroid, we mean the direction for which $\vec{\mathbf{E}}$ is passed, so a Polaroid axis is *perpendicular* to the long molecules. If we want to think of there being slits between the parallel molecules in the sense of Fig. 24–39, then Fig. 24–39 would apply for the $\vec{\mathbf{B}}$ field in the EM wave, not the $\vec{\mathbf{E}}$ field.]

If a beam of plane-polarized light strikes a Polaroid whose transmission axis is at an angle $\theta$ to the incident polarization direction, the beam will emerge plane-polarized parallel to the Polaroid transmission axis, and the amplitude of $E$ will be reduced to $E\cos\theta$, Fig. 24–41. Thus, a Polaroid passes only that component of polarization (the electric field vector, $\vec{\mathbf{E}}$) that is parallel to its transmission axis. Because the intensity of a light beam is proportional to the square of the amplitude (Sections 11–10 and 22–5), we see that the intensity of a plane-polarized beam transmitted by a polarizer is

$$I = I_0 \cos^2\theta, \qquad \textbf{(24–5)}$$

*Intensity of plane polarized wave reduced by polarizer*

where $I_0$ is the incoming intensity and $\theta$ is the angle between the polarizer transmission axis and the plane of polarization of the incoming wave.†

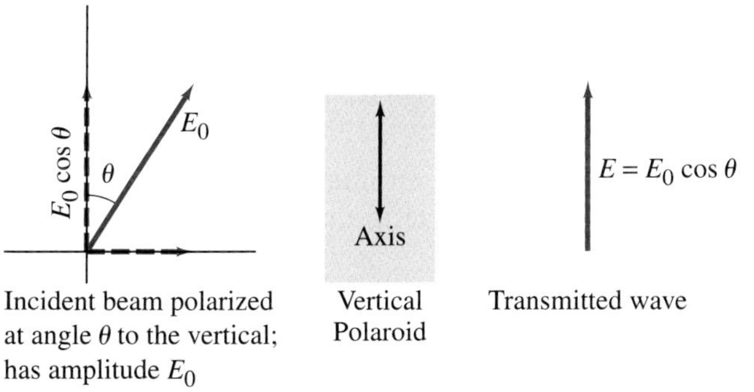


**FIGURE 24–41** Vertical Polaroid transmits only the vertical component of a wave (electric field) incident upon it.

A Polaroid can be used as a **polarizer** to produce plane-polarized light from unpolarized light, since only the component of light parallel to the axis is transmitted. A Polaroid can also be used as an **analyzer** to determine (1) if light is polarized and (2) the plane of polarization. A Polaroid acting as an analyzer will pass the same amount of light independent of the orientation of its axis if the light is unpolarized; try rotating one lens of a pair of Polaroid sunglasses while looking through it at a lightbulb. If the light is polarized, however, when you rotate the Polaroid the transmitted light will be a maximum when the plane of polarization is parallel to the Polaroid's axis, and a minimum when perpendicular to it. If you do this while looking at the sky, preferably at right angles to the Sun's direction, you will see that skylight is polarized. (Direct sunlight is unpolarized, but don't look directly at the Sun, even through a polarizer, for damage to the eye may occur.) If the light transmitted by an analyzer Polaroid falls to zero at one orientation, then the light is 100% plane-polarized. If it merely reaches a minimum, the light is *partially polarized*.

†Equation 24–5 is often referred to as **Malus' law**, after Etienne Malus, a contemporary of Fresnel.

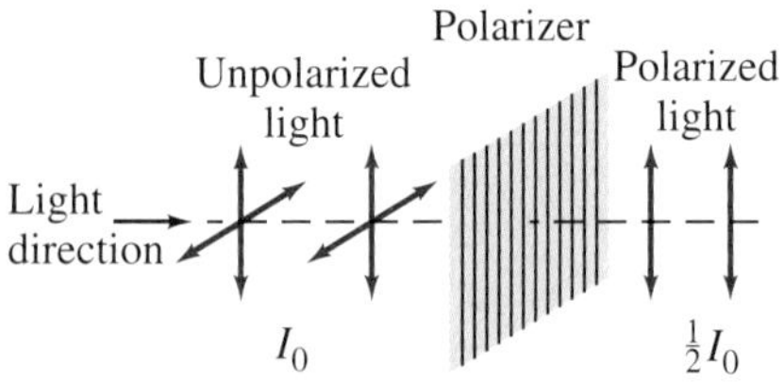


**FIGURE 24–42** Unpolarized light has equal intensity vertical and horizontal components. After passing through a polarizer, one of these components is eliminated. The intensity of the light is reduced to half.

Unpolarized light consists of light with random directions of polarization. Each of these polarization directions can be resolved into components along two mutually perpendicular directions. On average, an unpolarized beam can be thought of as two plane-polarized beams of equal magnitude perpendicular to one another. When unpolarized light passes through a polarizer, one component is eliminated. So the intensity of the light passing through is reduced by half since half the light is eliminated: $I = \frac{1}{2} I_0$ (Fig. 24–42).

When two Polaroids are *crossed*—that is, their polarizing axes are perpendicular to one another—unpolarized light can be entirely stopped. As shown in Fig. 24–43, unpolarized light is made plane-polarized by the first Polaroid (the polarizer).

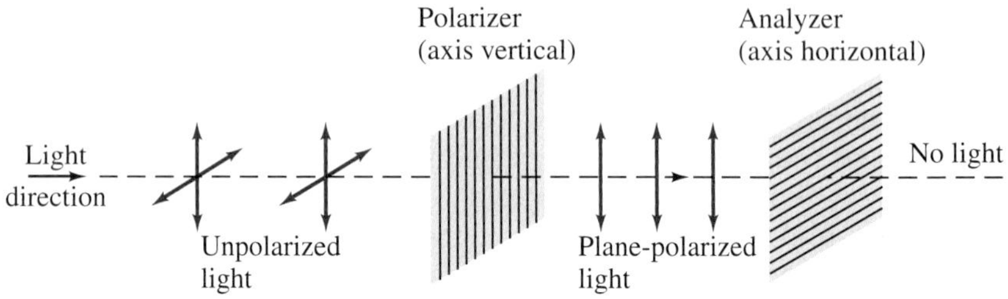


**FIGURE 24–43** Crossed Polaroids completely eliminate light.

The second Polaroid, the analyzer, then eliminates this component since its transmission axis is perpendicular to the first. You can try this with Polaroid sunglasses (Fig. 24–44). Note that Polaroid sunglasses eliminate 50% of unpolarized light because of their polarizing property; they absorb even more because they are colored.

**FIGURE 24–44** Crossed Polaroids. When the two polarized sunglass lenses overlap, with axes perpendicular, almost no light passes through.

**EXAMPLE 24–11** **Two Polaroids at 60°.** Unpolarized light passes through two Polaroids; the axis of one is vertical and that of the other is at 60° to the vertical. Describe the orientation and intensity of the transmitted light.

**APPROACH** Half of the unpolarized light is absorbed by the first Polaroid, and emerges plane polarized. When that light passes through the second Polaroid, the intensity is further reduced according to Eq. 24–5, and the plane of polarization becomes along the axis of the second Polaroid.

**SOLUTION** The first Polaroid eliminates half the light, so the intensity is reduced by half: $I_1 = \frac{1}{2} I_0$. The light reaching the second polarizer is vertically polarized and so is reduced in intensity (Eq. 24–5) to

$$I_2 = I_1(\cos 60°)^2 = \tfrac{1}{4} I_1 .$$

Thus, $I_2 = \frac{1}{8} I_0$. The transmitted light has an intensity one-eighth that of the original and is plane-polarized at a 60° angle to the vertical.

**CONCEPTUAL EXAMPLE 24–12** **Three Polaroids.** We saw in Fig. 24–43 that when unpolarized light falls on two crossed Polaroids (axes at 90°), no light passes through. What happens if a third Polaroid, with axis at 45° to each of the other two, is placed between them (Fig. 24–45a)?

**FIGURE 24–45** Example 24–12.

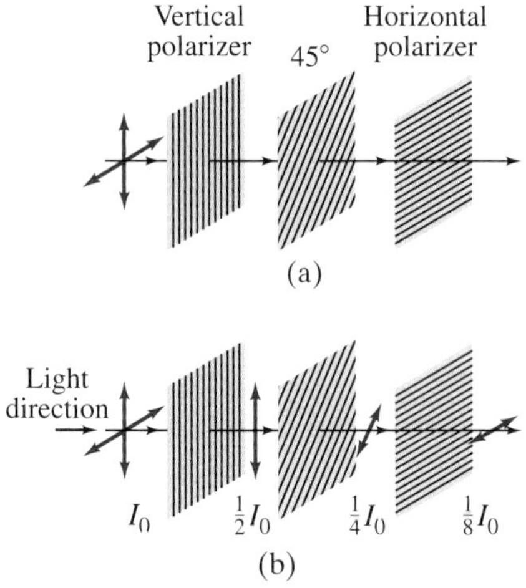


**RESPONSE** We start just as in Example 24–11 and recall again that light emerging from each Polaroid is polarized parallel to that Polaroid's axis. Thus the angle in Eq. 24–5 is that between the transmission axes of each pair of Polaroids taken in turn. The first Polaroid changes the unpolarized light to plane-polarized and reduces the intensity from $I_0$ to $I_1 = \frac{1}{2} I_0$. The second polarizer further reduces the intensity by $(\cos 45°)^2$, Eq. 24–5:

$$I_2 = I_1(\cos 45°)^2 = \tfrac{1}{2} I_1 = \tfrac{1}{4} I_0 .$$

The light leaving the second polarizer is plane polarized at 45° (Fig. 24–45b) relative to the third polarizer, so the third one reduces the intensity to

$$I_3 = I_2(\cos 45°)^2 = \tfrac{1}{2} I_2 ,$$

or $I_3 = \frac{1}{8} I_0$. Thus $\frac{1}{8}$ of the original intensity gets transmitted.

**NOTE** If we don't insert the 45° Polaroid, zero intensity results (Fig. 24–43).

**EXERCISE E** How much light would pass through if the 45° Polarizer in Example 24–12 was placed not between the other two polarizers but (a) before the vertical (first) polarizer, or (b) after the horizontal polarizer?

## Polarization by Reflection

Another means of producing polarized light from unpolarized light is by reflection. When light strikes a nonmetallic surface at any angle other than perpendicular, the reflected beam is polarized preferentially in the plane parallel to the surface, Fig. 24–46. In other words, the component with polarization in the plane perpendicular to the surface is preferentially transmitted or absorbed. You can check this by rotating Polaroid sunglasses while looking through them at a flat surface of a lake or road. Since most outdoor surfaces are horizontal, Polaroid sunglasses are made with their axes vertical to eliminate the more strongly reflected horizontal component, and thus reduce glare. People who go fishing wear Polaroids to eliminate reflected glare from the surface of a lake or stream and thus see beneath the water more clearly (Fig. 24–47).

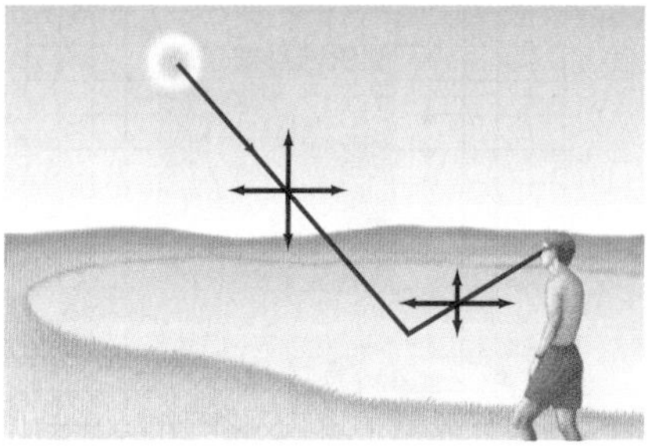

**FIGURE 24–46** Light reflected from a nonmetallic surface, such as the smooth surface of water in a lake, is partially polarized parallel to the surface.

**FIGURE 24–47** Photographs of a river, (a) allowing all light into the camera lens, and (b) using a polarizer. The polarizer is adjusted to absorb most of the (polarized) light reflected from the water's surface, allowing the dimmer light from the bottom of the river, and any fish lying there, to be seen more readily.

The amount of polarization in the reflected beam depends on the angle, varying from no polarization at normal incidence to 100% polarization at an angle known as the **polarizing angle**, $\theta_p$.[†] This angle is related to the index of refraction of the two materials on either side of the boundary by the equation

$$\tan\theta_p = \frac{n_2}{n_1}, \qquad \textbf{(24–6a)}$$

where $n_1$ is the index of refraction of the material in which the beam is traveling, and $n_2$ is that of the medium beyond the reflecting boundary. If the beam is traveling in air, $n_1 = 1$, and Eq. 24–6a becomes

$$\tan\theta_p = n. \qquad \textbf{(24–6b)}$$

The polarizing angle $\theta_p$ is also called **Brewster's angle**, and Eqs. 24–6 *Brewster's law*, after the Scottish physicist David Brewster (1781–1868), who worked it out experimentally in 1812. Equations 24–6 can be derived from the electromagnetic wave theory of light. It is interesting that at Brewster's angle, the reflected ray and the transmitted (refracted) ray make a 90° angle to each other; that is, $\theta_p + \theta_r = 90°$, where $\theta_r$ is the refraction angle (Fig. 24–48). This can be seen by substituting Eq. 24–6a, $n_2 = n_1 \tan\theta_p = n_1 \sin\theta_p / \cos\theta_p$, into Snell's law, $n_1 \sin\theta_p = n_2 \sin\theta_r$, and get $\cos\theta_p = \sin\theta_r$ which can only hold if $\theta_p = 90° - \theta_r$.

**FIGURE 24–48** At $\theta_p$ the reflected light is plane-polarized parallel to the surface, and $\theta_p + \theta_r = 90°$, where $\theta_r$ is the refraction angle. (The large dots represent vibrations perpendicular to the page.)

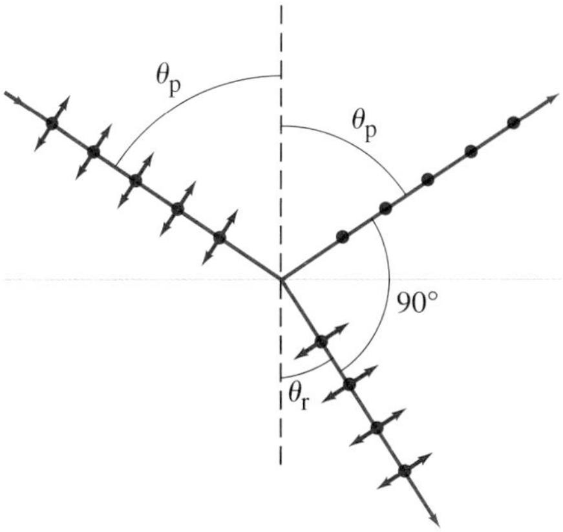


**EXAMPLE 24–13** **Polarizing angle.** (*a*) At what incident angle is sunlight reflected from a lake plane-polarized? (*b*) What is the refraction angle?

**APPROACH** The polarizing angle at the surface is Brewster's angle, Eq. 24–6b. We find the angle of refraction from Snell's law.

**SOLUTION** (*a*) We use Eq. 24–6b with $n = 1.33$, so $\tan\theta_p = 1.33$ giving $\theta_p = 53.1°$.
(*b*) From Snell's law, $\sin\theta_r = \sin\theta_p / n = \sin 53.1° / 1.33 = 0.601$ giving $\theta_r = 36.9°$.

**NOTE** $\theta_p + \theta_r = 53.1° + 36.9° = 90.0°$, as expected.

[†]Only a fraction of the incident light is reflected at the surface of a transparent medium. Although this reflected light is 100% polarized (if $\theta = \theta_p$), the remainder of the light, which is transmitted into the new medium, is only partially polarized.

# * 24–11 Liquid Crystal Displays (LCD)

FIGURE 24–49 Example of an image made up of many small squares or *pixels* (picture elements). This one has rather poor resolution.

A wonderful use of polarization is in a **liquid crystal display** (LCD). LCDs are used as the display in hand-held calculators, digital wrist watches, cell phones, and in beautiful color flat-panel computer and television screens.

A liquid crystal display is made up of many tiny rectangles called **pixels**, or "picture elements." The picture you see depends on which pixels are dark or light and of what color, as suggested in Fig. 24–49 for a simple black and white picture.

Liquid crystals are organic materials that at room temperature exist in a phase that is neither fully solid nor fully liquid. They are sort of gooey, and their molecules display a randomness of position characteristic of liquids, as we discussed in Section 13–1 and Fig. 13–2. They also show some of the orderliness of a solid crystal (Fig. 13–2a), but only in one dimension. The liquid crystals we find useful are made up of relatively rigid rod-like molecules that interact weakly with each other and tend to align parallel to each other, as shown in Fig. 24–50.

FIGURE 24–50 Liquid crystal molecules tend to align in one dimension (parallel to each other) but have random positions (left-right, up-down).

In a simple LCD, each pixel (picture element) contains a liquid crystal sandwiched between two glass plates whose inner surfaces have been brushed to form nanometer-wide parallel scratches. The rod-like liquid crystal molecules in contact with the scratches tend to line up along the scratches. The two plates typically have their scratches at 90° to each other, and the weak forces between the rod-like molecules tend to keep them nearly aligned with their nearest neighbors, resulting in the twisted pattern shown in Fig. 24–51a.

The outer surfaces of the glass plates each have a thin film polarizer, they too oriented at 90° to each other. Unpolarized light incident from the left becomes plane-polarized and the liquid crystal molecules keep this polarization aligned with their rod-like shape. That is, the plane of polarization of the light rotates with the molecules as the light passes through the liquid crystal. The light emerges with its plane of polarization rotated by 90°, and passes through the second polarizer readily. A tiny LCD pixel in this situation will appear bright.

Now suppose a voltage is applied to transparent electrodes on each glass plate of the pixel. The rod-like molecules are polar (or can acquire an internal separation of charge due to the applied electric field). The applied voltage tends to align the molecules and they no longer follow the twisted pattern shown in Fig. 24–51a, with the end molecules always lying in a plane parallel to the glass plates. Now the applied electric field tends to align the molecules flat, left to right (perpendicular to the glass plates), and they don't affect the light polarization significantly. The entering plane-polarized light no longer has its plane of polarization rotated as it passes through, and no light can exit through the second (horizontal) polarizer. With the voltage on, the pixel appears dark.†

†In some displays, the polarizers are parallel to each other (the scratches remain at 90° to maintain the twist). Then voltage off results in black (no light), and voltage on results in bright light.

FIGURE 24–51 (a) "Twisted" form of liquid crystal. Light polarization plane is rotated 90°. Only one line of molecules is shown. (b) Molecules disoriented by electric field. Plane of polarization is not changed, so light does not pass through the horizontal polarizer. (The transparent electrodes are not shown.)

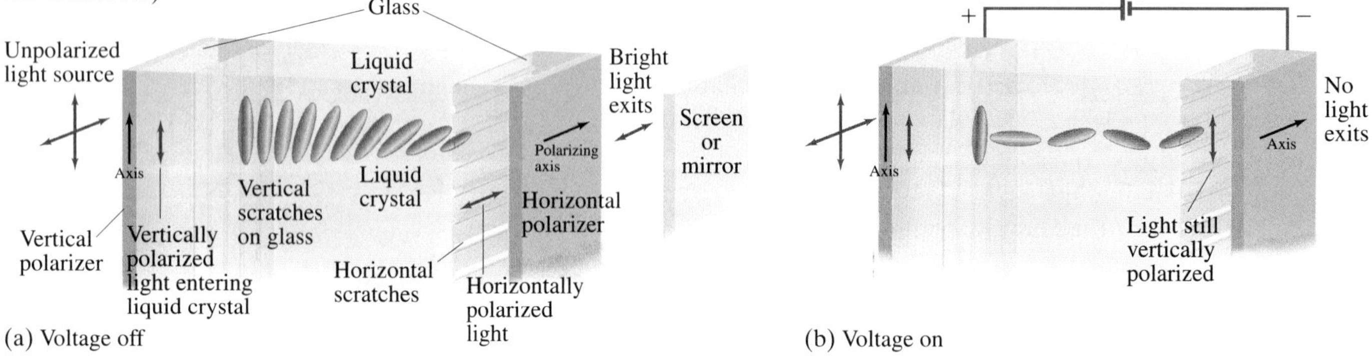

The simple display screens of watches and calculators use ambient light as the source (you can't see the display in the dark), and a mirror behind the LCD to reflect the light back. There are only a few pixels, corresponding to the elongated segments needed to form the numbers from 0 to 9 (and letters in some displays), as seen in Fig. 24–52. Any pixels to which a voltage is applied appear dark and form part of a number. With no voltage, pixels pass light through the polarizers to the mirror and back out, which forms a bright background to the dark numbers on the display.

Color television and computer LCDs are more sophisticated. A color pixel consists of three cells, or subpixels, each covered with a red, green, or blue filter. Varying brightnesses of these three primary colors can yield almost any natural color. A good-quality screen consists of a million or more pixels, much like the surface of a color CRT monitor (Fig. 17–20). Behind this array of pixels is a light source, often thin fluorescent tubes the diameter of a straw. The light passes through the pixels, or not, depending on the voltage applied to each subpixel, as in Fig. 24–51a and b. See Fig. 24–53.

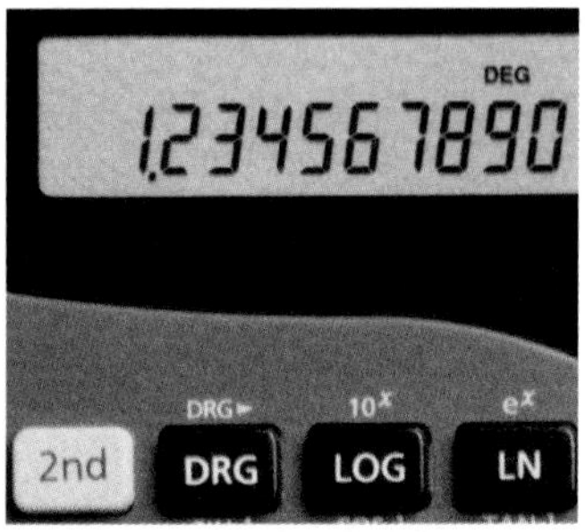


**FIGURE 24–52** Calculator LCD display. The black segments or pixels have a voltage applied to them. Note that the 8 uses all seven segments (pixels), whereas other numbers use fewer.

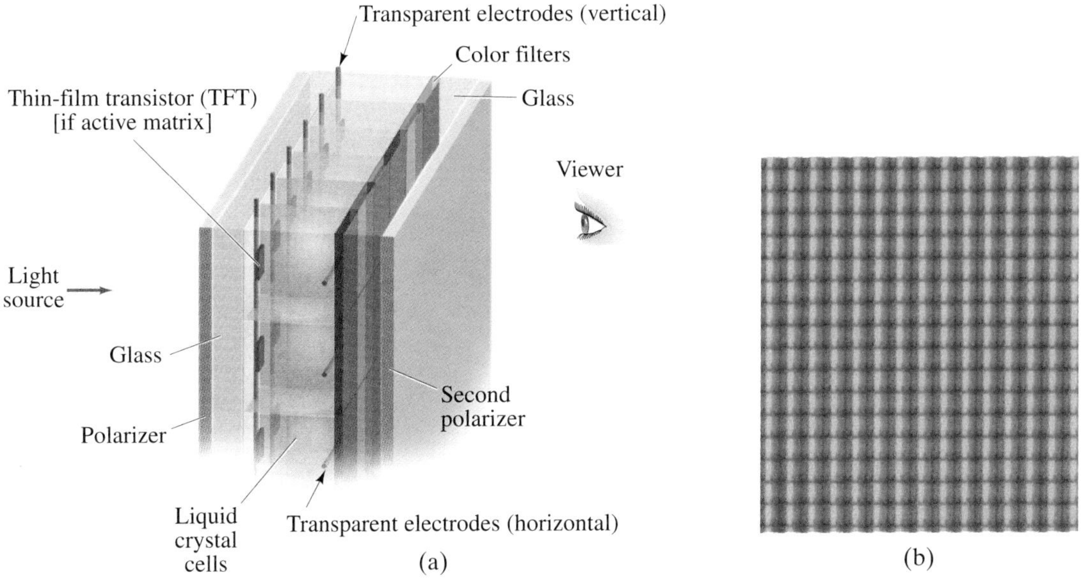


**FIGURE 24–53** Basic layer construction for an LCD computer or television screen. Every pixel contains three cells (subpixels), each with a red, green, or blue filter. An active matrix display has thin-film transistors and is more complex.

In a *passive matrix* LCD, a set of vertical and a set of horizontal electrodes carry electric signals to the pixels: two wires, one from each set, "intersect" at each subpixel, and careful electronic timing (called "addressing") turns the voltage there on or off. The signals can affect nearby subpixels, reducing the contrast and quality of the picture. Better pictures are obtained with an *active matrix* LCD which has a *thin-film transistor* (TFT) at each subpixel to accurately control its brightness.

To obtain a range of gray scale or range of color brightness, each subpixel cannot simply go on or off as in Fig. 24–51. Several techniques can be used depending on the construction of the LCD. If the voltage applied in Fig. 24–51b is small enough, the disorientation of the molecules may be small, allowing some rotation of the polarization vector and thus some light can pass through, the actual amount depending on the voltage. Alternatively, each subpixel can be pulsed—the length of time it is *on* affects the perceived brightness. The effect of stronger or weaker brightness can instead be provided by the number of nearby subpixels of the same color that are turned on or off; this type lets the eye "average" over many pixels, but reduces the sharpness or resolution of the picture.

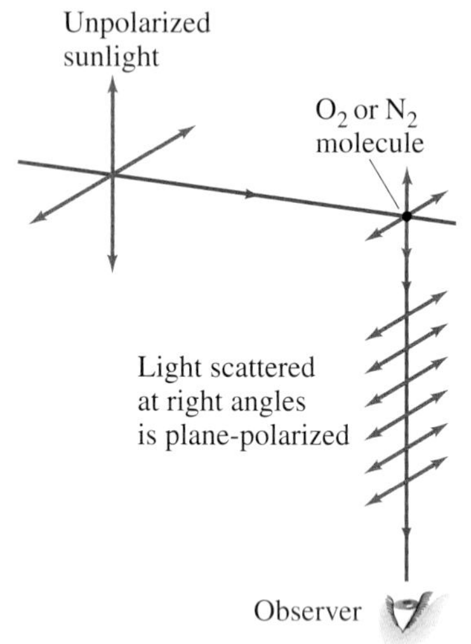


**FIGURE 24–54** Unpolarized sunlight scattered by molecules of the air. An observer at right angles sees plane-polarized light, since the component of oscillation along the line of sight emits no light along that line.

## * 24–12 Scattering of Light by the Atmosphere

Sunsets are red, the sky is blue, and skylight is polarized (at least partially). These phenomena can be explained on the basis of the *scattering* of light by the molecules of the atmosphere. In Fig. 24–54 we see unpolarized light from the Sun impinging on a molecule of the Earth's atmosphere. The electric field of the EM wave sets the electric charges within the molecule into motion, and the molecule absorbs some of the incident radiation. But it quickly reemits this light since the charges are oscillating. As discussed in Section 22–2, oscillating electric charges produce EM waves. The intensity is strongest along a line perpendicular to the oscillation, and drops to zero along the line of oscillation (Section 22–2). In Fig. 24–54 the motion of the charges is resolved into two components. An observer at right angles to the direction of the sunlight, as shown, will see plane-polarized light because no light is emitted along the line of the other component of the oscillation. (When viewing along the line of an oscillation, you don't see that oscillation, and hence see no waves made by it.) At other viewing angles, both components will be present; one will be stronger, however, so the light appears partially polarized. Thus, the process of scattering explains the polarization of skylight.

PHYSICS APPLIED
*Why the sky is blue*
*Why sunsets are red*

Scattering of light by the Earth's atmosphere depends on $\lambda$. For particles much smaller than the wavelength of light (such as molecules of air), the particles will be less of an obstruction to long wavelengths than to short ones. The scattering decreases, in fact, as $1/\lambda^4$. Blue and violet light are thus scattered much more than red and orange, which is why the sky looks blue. At sunset, the Sun's rays pass through a maximum length of atmosphere. Much of the blue has been taken out by scattering. The light that reaches the surface of the Earth, and reflects off clouds and haze, is thus lacking in blue. That is why sunsets appear reddish.

The dependence of scattering on $1/\lambda^4$ is valid only if the scattering objects are much smaller than the wavelength of the light. This is valid for oxygen and nitrogen molecules whose diameters are about 0.2 nm. Clouds, however, contain water droplets or crystals that are much larger than $\lambda$. They scatter all frequencies of light nearly uniformly. Hence clouds appear white (or gray, if shadowed).

*Why clouds are white*

## Summary

The wave theory of light is strongly supported by the observations that light exhibits **interference** and **diffraction**. Wave theory also explains the refraction of light and the fact that light travels more slowly in transparent solids and liquids than it does in air.

An aid to predicting wave behavior is **Huygens' principle**, which states that every point on a wave front can be considered as a source of tiny wavelets that spread out in the forward direction at the speed of the wave itself. The new wave front is the envelope (the common tangent) of all the wavelets.

The wavelength of light in a medium with index of refraction $n$ is

$$\lambda_n = \frac{\lambda}{n}, \qquad \textbf{(24–1)}$$

where $\lambda$ is the wavelength in vacuum; the frequency is not changed.

Young's double-slit experiment clearly demonstrated the interference of light. The observed bright spots of the interference pattern were explained as constructive interference between the beams coming through the two slits, where the beams differ in path length by an integral number of wavelengths. The dark areas in between are due to destructive interference when the path lengths differ by $\frac{1}{2}\lambda$, $\frac{3}{2}\lambda$, and so on. The angles $\theta$ at which **constructive interference** occurs are given by

$$\sin\theta = m\frac{\lambda}{d}, \qquad \textbf{(24–2a)}$$

where $\lambda$ is the wavelength of the light, $d$ is the separation of the slits, and $m$ is an integer $(0, 1, 2, \cdots)$. **Destructive interference** occurs at angles $\theta$ given by

$$\sin\theta = \left(m + \tfrac{1}{2}\right)\frac{\lambda}{d}, \qquad \textbf{(24–2b)}$$

where $m$ is an integer $(0, 1, 2, \cdots)$.

Two sources of light are perfectly **coherent** if the waves leaving them are of the same single frequency and maintain the same phase relationship at all times. If the light waves from the two sources have a random phase with respect to each other over time (as for two incandescent lightbulbs) the two sources are **incoherent**.

The frequency or wavelength of light determines its color. The **visible spectrum** extends from about 400 nm (violet) to about 750 nm (red).

Glass prisms break down white light into its constituent colors because the index of refraction varies with wavelength, a phenomenon known as **dispersion**.

The formula $\sin\theta = m\lambda/d$ for constructive interference also holds for a **diffraction grating**, which consists of many parallel slits or lines, separated from each other by a distance $d$. The peaks of constructive interference are much brighter and sharper for a diffraction grating than for the simple two-slit apparatus.

A diffraction grating (or a prism) is used in a **spectroscope** to separate different colors or to observe **line spectra**; for a given order $m$, $\theta$ depends on $\lambda$. Precise determination of wavelength can be done with a spectroscope by careful measurement of $\theta$.

**Diffraction** refers to the fact that light, like other waves, bends around objects it passes, and spreads out after passing through narrow slits. This bending gives rise to a **diffraction pattern** due to interference between rays of light that travel different distances.

Light passing through a very narrow slit of width $D$ (on the order of the wavelength $\lambda$) will produce a pattern with a bright central maximum of half-width $\theta$ given by

$$\sin\theta = \frac{\lambda}{D}, \qquad \textbf{(24–3a)}$$

flanked by fainter lines to either side.

Light reflected from the front and rear surfaces of a thin film of transparent material can interfere. A phase change of $180°$ $(\frac{1}{2}\lambda)$ occurs when the light reflects at a surface where the index of refraction increases. Such **thin-film interference** has many practical applications, such as lens coatings and Newton's rings.

In **unpolarized light**, the electric field vectors oscillate in all transverse directions. If the electric vector oscillates only in one plane, the light is said to be **plane-polarized**. Light can also be partially polarized.

When an unpolarized light beam passes through a **Polaroid** sheet, the emerging beam is plane-polarized. When a light beam is polarized and passes through a Polaroid, the intensity varies as the Polaroid is rotated. Thus a Polaroid can act as a **polarizer** or as an **analyzer**.

The intensity of a plane-polarized light beam incident on a Polaroid is reduced by the factor

$$I = I_0\cos^2\theta, \qquad \textbf{(24–5)}$$

where $\theta$ is the angle between the axis of the Polaroid and the initial plane of polarization.

Light can also be partially or fully **polarized by reflection**. If light traveling in air is reflected from a medium of index of refraction $n$, the reflected beam will be *completely* plane-polarized if the incident angle $\theta_p$ is given by

$$\tan\theta_p = n. \qquad \textbf{(24–6b)}$$

The fact that light can be polarized shows that it must be a transverse wave.

## Questions

1. Does Huygens' principle apply to sound waves? To water waves? Explain.
2. What is the evidence that light is energy?
3. Why is light sometimes described as rays and sometimes as waves?
4. We can hear sounds around corners, but we cannot see around corners; yet both sound and light are waves. Explain the difference.
5. If Young's double-slit experiment were submerged in water, how would the fringe pattern be changed?
6. Monochromatic red light is incident on a double slit, and the interference pattern is viewed on a screen some distance away. Explain how the fringe pattern would change if the red light source is replaced by a blue light source.
7. Two rays of light from the same source destructively interfere if their path lengths differ by how much?
8. Why was the observation of the double-slit interference pattern more convincing evidence for the wave theory of light than the observation of diffraction?
9. Compare a double-slit experiment for sound waves to that for light waves. Discuss the similarities and differences.
10. Why doesn't the light from the two headlights of a distant car produce an interference pattern?
11. Suppose white light falls on the two slits of Fig. 24–7, but one slit is covered by a red filter (700 nm) and the other by a blue filter (450 nm). Describe the pattern on the screen.
12. When white light passes through a flat piece of window glass, it is not broken down into colors as it is by a prism. Explain.
13. For both converging and diverging lenses, discuss how the focal length for red light differs from that for violet light.
14. A ray of light is refracted through three different materials (Fig. 24–55). Rank the materials according to their index of refraction, least to greatest.

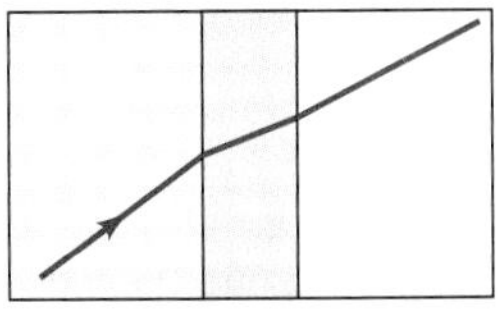

**FIGURE 24–55** Question 14.

15. Hold one hand close to your eye and focus on a distant light source through a narrow slit between two fingers. (Adjust your fingers to obtain the best pattern.) Describe the pattern that you see.
16. What happens to the diffraction pattern of a single slit if the whole apparatus is immersed in (*a*) water, (*b*) a vacuum, instead of in air.
17. For diffraction by a single slit, what is the effect of increasing (*a*) the slit width, and (*b*) the wavelength?
18. What is the difference in the interference patterns formed (*a*) by two slits $10^{-4}$ cm apart, (*b*) by a diffraction grating containing $10^4$ lines/cm?
19. For a diffraction grating, what is the advantage of (*a*) many slits, (*b*) closely spaced slits?
20. White light strikes (*a*) a diffraction grating, and (*b*) a prism. A rainbow appears on a wall just below the direction of the horizontal incident beam in each case. What is the color of the top of the rainbow in each case? Explain.
21. For light consisting of wavelengths between 400 nm and 700 nm, incident normally on a diffraction grating, for what orders (if any) would there be overlap in the observed spectrum? Does your answer depend on the slit spacing?
22. Why are interference fringes noticeable only for a *thin* film like a soap bubble and not for a thick piece of glass, say?

23. When a compact disk (CD) is held at an angle in white light, the reflected light is a full spectrum (Fig. 24–56). Explain. What would you expect to see if monochromatic light was used?

**FIGURE 24–56** Question 23.

24. Why are Newton's rings (Fig. 24–31) closer together farther from the center?

25. Some coated lenses appear greenish yellow when seen by reflected light. What wavelengths do you suppose the coating is designed to transmit completely?

26. A drop of oil on a pond appears bright at its edges, where its thickness is much less than the wavelengths of visible light. What can you say about the index of refraction of the oil?

27. What does polarization tell us about the nature of light?

28. Explain the advantage of polarized sunglasses over normal tinted sunglasses.

29. How can you tell if a pair of sunglasses is polarizing or not?

30. Two polarized sheets rotated at an angle of 90° with respect to each other will not let any light through. Three polarized sheets, each rotated at an angle of 45° with respect to each other, will let some light through. What will happen to unpolarized light if you align four polarized sheets, each rotated at an angle of 30° with respect to the one in front of it?

* 31. What would be the color of the sky if the Earth had no atmosphere?

* 32. If the Earth's atmosphere were 50 times denser than it is, would sunlight still be white, or would it be some other color?

## Problems

### 24–3 Double-Slit Interference

1. (I) Monochromatic light falling on two slits 0.016 mm apart produces the fifth-order fringe at an 8.8° angle. What is the wavelength of the light used?

2. (I) The third-order fringe of 610 nm light is observed at an angle of 18° when the light falls on two narrow slits. How far apart are the slits?

3. (II) Monochromatic light falls on two very narrow slits 0.048 mm apart. Successive fringes on a screen 5.00 m away are 6.5 cm apart near the center of the pattern. Determine the wavelength and frequency of the light.

4. (II) A parallel beam of light from a He-Ne laser, with a wavelength 656 nm, falls on two very narrow slits 0.060 mm apart. How far apart are the fringes in the center of the pattern on a screen 3.6 m away?

5. (II) Light of wavelength 680 nm falls on two slits and produces an interference pattern in which the fourth-order fringe is 38 mm from the central fringe on a screen 2.0 m away. What is the separation of the two slits?

6. (II) If 720-nm and 660-nm light passes through two slits 0.58 mm apart, how far apart are the second-order fringes for these two wavelengths on a screen 1.0 m away?

7. (II) In a double-slit experiment, it is found that blue light of wavelength 460 nm gives a second-order maximum at a certain location on the screen. What wavelength of visible light would have a minimum at the same location?

8. (II) Water waves having parallel crests 2.5 cm apart pass through two openings 5.0 cm apart in a board. At a point 2.0 m beyond the board, at what angle relative to the "straight-through" direction would there be little or no wave action?

9. (II) Suppose a thin piece of glass is placed in front of the lower slit in Fig. 24–7 so that the two waves enter the slits 180° out of phase (Fig. 24–57). Describe in detail the interference pattern on the screen.

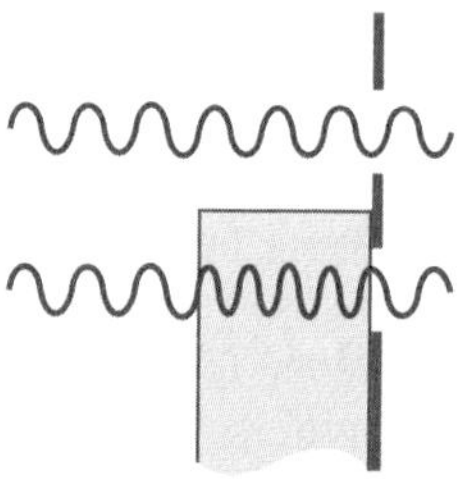

**FIGURE 24–57** Problem 9.

10. (II) In a double-slit experiment, the third-order maximum for light of wavelength 500 nm is located 12 mm from the central bright spot on a screen 1.6 m from the slits. Light of wavelength 650 nm is then projected through the same slits. How far from the central bright spot will the second-order maximum of this light be located?

11. (II) Two narrow slits separated by 1.0 mm are illuminated by 544 nm light. Find the distance between adjacent bright fringes on a screen 5.0 m from the slits.

12. (III) Light of wavelength 480 nm in air falls on two slits $6.00 \times 10^{-2}$ mm apart. The slits are immersed in water, as is a viewing screen 40.0 cm away. How far apart are the fringes on the screen?

13. (III) A very thin sheet of plastic ($n = 1.60$) covers one slit of a double-slit apparatus illuminated by 640-nm light. The center point on the screen, instead of being a maximum, is dark. What is the (minimum) thickness of the plastic?

### 24–4 Dispersion

14. (I) By what percent, approximately, does the speed of red light (700 nm) exceed that of violet light (400 nm) in silicate flint glass? (See Fig. 24–14.)

15. (II) A light beam strikes a piece of glass at a 60.00° incident angle. The beam contains two wavelengths, 450.0 nm and 700.0 nm, for which the index of refraction of the glass is 1.4820 and 1.4742, respectively. What is the angle between the two refracted beams?

16. (III) A parallel beam of light containing two wavelengths, $\lambda_1 = 450\text{ nm}$ and $\lambda_2 = 650\text{ nm}$, enters the silicate flint glass of an equilateral prism as shown in Fig. 24–58. At what angle does each beam leave the prism (give angle with normal to the face)?

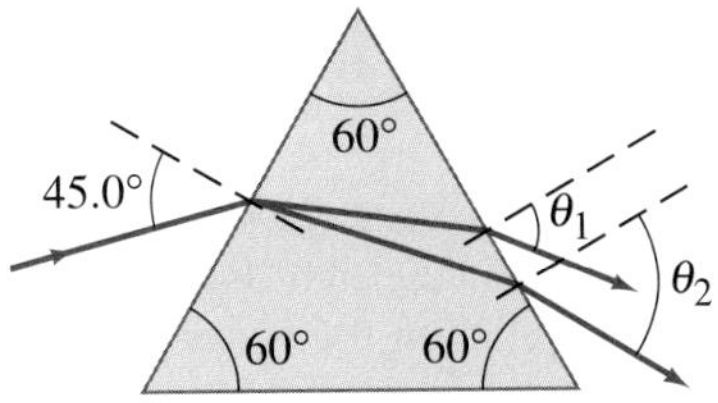


**FIGURE 24–58** Problems 16 and 87.

## 24–5 Single-Slit Diffraction

17. (I) If 580-nm light falls on a slit 0.0440 mm wide, what is the full angular width of the central diffraction peak?

18. (I) Monochromatic light falls on a slit that is $2.60 \times 10^{-3}$ mm wide. If the angle between the first dark fringes on either side of the central maximum is 35.0° (dark fringe to dark fringe), what is the wavelength of the light used?

19. (II) Light of wavelength 520 nm falls on a slit that is $3.20 \times 10^{-3}$ mm wide. Estimate how far the first brightish diffraction fringe is from the strong central maximum if the screen is 10.0 m away.

20. (II) A single slit 1.0 mm wide is illuminated by 450-nm light. What is the width of the central maximum (in cm) in the diffraction pattern on a screen 5.0 m away?

21. (II) Monochromatic light of wavelength 653 nm falls on a slit. If the angle between the first bright fringes on either side of the central maximum is 32°, estimate the slit width.

22. (II) How wide is the central diffraction peak on a screen 2.30 m behind a 0.0348-mm-wide slit illuminated by 589-nm light?

23. (II) When blue light of wavelength 440 nm falls on a single slit, the first dark bands on either side of center are separated by 55.0°. Determine the width of the slit.

24. (II) When violet light of wavelength 415 nm falls on a single slit, it creates a central diffraction peak that is 9.20 cm wide on a screen that is 2.55 m away. How wide is the slit?

25. (II) If a slit diffracts 650-nm light so that the diffraction maximum is 4.0 cm wide on a screen 1.50 m away, what will be the width of the diffraction maximum for light of wavelength 420 nm?

26. (II) For a given wavelength $\lambda$, what is the maximum slit width for which there will be no diffraction minima?

## 24–6 and 24–7 Gratings

27. (I) At what angle will 560-nm light produce a second-order maximum when falling on a grating whose slits are $1.45 \times 10^{-3}$ cm apart?

28. (I) A 3500-line/cm grating produces a third-order fringe at a 28.0° angle. What wavelength of light is being used?

29. (II) How many lines per centimeter does a grating have if the third-order occurs at an 18.0° angle for 630-nm light?

30. (II) A grating has 8300 lines/cm. How many complete spectral orders can be seen (400 nm to 700 nm) when it is illuminated by white light?

31. (II) The first-order line of 589-nm light falling on a diffraction grating is observed at a 15.5° angle. How far apart are the slits? At what angle will the third order be observed?

32. (II) A diffraction grating has $6.0 \times 10^5$ lines/m. Find the angular spread in the second-order spectrum between red light of wavelength $7.0 \times 10^{-7}$ m and blue light of wavelength $4.5 \times 10^{-7}$ m.

33. (II) Light falling normally on a 9700-line/cm grating is revealed to contain three lines in the first-order spectrum at angles of 31.2°, 36.4°, and 47.5°. What wavelengths are these?

34. (II) What is the highest spectral order that can be seen if a grating with 6000 lines per cm is illuminated with 633-nm laser light? Assume normal incidence.

35. (II) Two (and only two) full spectral orders can be seen on either side of the central maximum when white light is sent through a diffraction grating. What is the maximum number of lines per cm for the grating?

36. (II) White light containing wavelengths from 410 nm to 750 nm falls on a grating with 8500 lines/cm. How wide is the first-order spectrum on a screen 2.30 m away?

37. (II) A He-Ne gas laser which produces monochromatic light of a known wavelength $\lambda = 6.328 \times 10^{-7}$ m is used to calibrate a reflection grating in a spectroscope. The first-order diffraction line is found at an angle of 21.5° to the incident beam. How many lines per meter are there on the grating?

38. (II) Two first-order spectrum lines are measured by a 9500-line/cm spectroscope at angles, on each side of center, of +26°38′, +41°08′ and −26°48′, −41°19′. What are the wavelengths?

## 24–8 Thin-Film Interference

39. (I) If a soap bubble is 120 nm thick, what wavelength is most strongly reflected at the center of the outer surface when illuminated normally by white light? Assume that $n = 1.34$.

40. (I) How far apart are the dark fringes in Example 24–8 if the glass plates are each 26.5 cm long?

41. (II) What is the smallest thickness of a soap film ($n = 1.42$) that would appear black if illuminated with 480-nm light? Assume there is air on both sides of the soap film.

42. (II) A lens appears greenish yellow ($\lambda = 570\text{ nm}$ is strongest) when white light reflects from it. What minimum thickness of coating ($n = 1.25$) do you think is used on such a glass ($n = 1.52$) lens, and why?

43. (II) A total of 31 bright and 31 dark Newton's rings (not counting the dark spot at the center) are observed when 550-nm light falls normally on a planoconvex lens resting on a flat glass surface (Fig. 24–31). How much thicker is the center than the edges?

44. (II) A fine metal foil separates one end of two pieces of optically flat glass, as in Fig. 24–33. When light of wavelength 670 nm is incident normally, 28 dark lines are observed (with one at each end). How thick is the foil?

45. (II) How thick (minimum) should the air layer be between two flat glass surfaces if the glass is to appear bright when 450-nm light is incident normally? What if the glass is to appear dark?

46. (II) A piece of material, suspected of being a stolen diamond ($n = 2.42$), is submerged in oil of refractive index 1.43 and illuminated by unpolarized light. It is found that the reflected light is completely polarized at an angle of 59°. Is it diamond?

47. (III) A thin film of alcohol ($n = 1.36$) lies on a flat glass plate ($n = 1.51$). When monochromatic light, whose wavelength can be changed, is incident normally, the reflected light is a minimum for $\lambda = 512\text{ nm}$ and a maximum for $\lambda = 640\text{ nm}$. What is the minimum thickness of the film?

48. (III) When a Newton's ring apparatus (Fig. 24–31) is immersed in a liquid, the diameter of the eighth dark ring decreases from 2.92 cm to 2.48 cm. What is the refractive index of the liquid?

### * 24–9 Michelson Interferometer

* 49. (II) What is the wavelength of the light entering an interferometer if 644 bright fringes are counted when the movable mirror moves 0.225 mm?

* 50. (II) A micrometer is connected to the movable mirror of an interferometer. When the micrometer is tightened down on a thin metal foil, the net number of bright fringes that move, compared to the empty micrometer, is 272. What is the thickness of the foil? The wavelength of light used is 589 nm.

* 51. (II) How far must the mirror $M_1$ in a Michelson interferometer be moved if 850 fringes of 589-nm light are to pass by a reference line?

* 52. (III) One of the beams of an interferometer (Fig. 24–59) passes through a small glass container containing a cavity 1.30 cm deep. When a gas is allowed to slowly fill the container, a total of 236 dark fringes are counted to move past a reference line. The light used has a wavelength of 610 nm. Calculate the index of refraction of the gas, assuming that the interferometer is in vacuum.

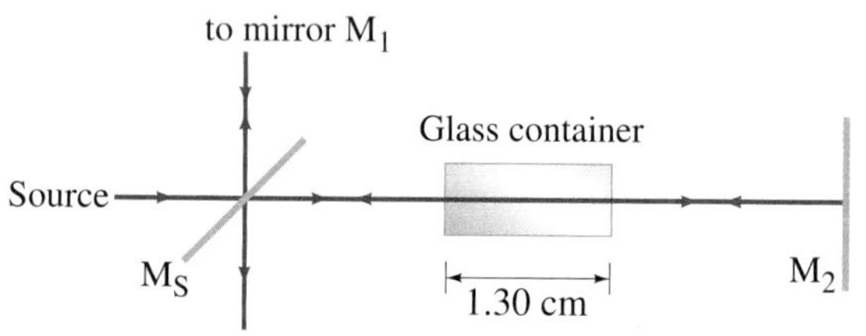


**FIGURE 24–59** Problem 52.

### 24–10 Polarization

53. (I) Two polarizers are oriented at 65° to one another. Unpolarized light falls on them. What fraction of the light intensity is transmitted?

54. (I) What is Brewster's angle for an air–glass ($n = 1.52$) surface?

55. (II) What is Brewster's angle for a diamond submerged in water if the light is hitting the diamond ($n = 2.42$) while traveling in the water?

56. (II) Two Polaroids are aligned so that the light passing through them is a maximum. At what angle should one of them be placed so that the intensity is subsequently reduced by half?

57. (II) At what angle should the axes of two Polaroids be placed so as to reduce the intensity of the incident unpolarized light to (*a*) $\frac{1}{3}$, (*b*) $\frac{1}{10}$?

58. (II) Two polarizers are oriented at 40° to each other and plane-polarized light is incident on them. If only 15% of the light gets through both of them, what was the initial polarization direction of the incident light?

59. (II) Two polarizers are oriented at 38.0° to one another. Light polarized at a 19.0° angle to each polarizer passes through both. What percent reduction in intensity takes place?

60. (II) What would Brewster's angle be for reflections off the surface of water for light coming from beneath the surface? Compare to the angle for total internal reflection, and to Brewster's angle from above the surface.

61. (II) Unpolarized light passes through five successive Polaroid sheets, each of whose axis makes a 45° angle with the previous one. What is the intensity of the transmitted beam?

## General Problems

62. Light of wavelength $5.0 \times 10^{-7}$ m passes through two parallel slits and falls on a screen 4.0 m away. Adjacent bright bands of the interference pattern are 2.0 cm apart. (*a*) Find the distance between the slits. (*b*) The same two slits are next illuminated by light of a different wavelength, and the fifth-order minimum for this light occurs at the same point on the screen as the fourth-order minimum for the previous light. What is the wavelength of the second source of light?

63. Television and radio waves reflecting from mountains or airplanes can interfere with the direct signal from the station. (*a*) What kind of interference will occur when 75-MHz television signals arrive at a receiver directly from a distant station, and are reflected from a nearby airplane 118 m directly above the receiver? Assume $\frac{1}{2}\lambda$ change in phase of the signal upon reflection. (*b*) What kind of interference will occur if the plane is 22 m closer to the receiver?

64. Red light from three separate sources passes through a diffraction grating with $3.00 \times 10^5$ lines/m. The wavelengths of the three lines are $6.56 \times 10^{-7}$ m (hydrogen), $6.50 \times 10^{-7}$ m (neon), and $6.97 \times 10^{-7}$ m (argon). Calculate the angles for the first-order diffraction lines of each of these sources.

65. Light of wavelength 590 nm passes through two narrow slits 0.60 mm apart. The screen is 1.70 m away. A second source of unknown wavelength produces its second-order fringe 1.33 mm closer to the central maximum than the 590-nm light. What is the wavelength of the unknown light?

66. A radio station operating at 102.1 MHz broadcasts from two identical antennae at the same elevation but separated by an 8.0-m horizontal distance *d*, Fig. 24–60. A maximum signal is found along the midline, perpendicular to *d* at its midpoint and extending horizontally in both directions. If the midline is taken as 0°, at what other angle(s) $\theta$ is a maximum signal detected? A minimum signal? Assume all measurements are made much farther than 8.0 m from the antenna towers.

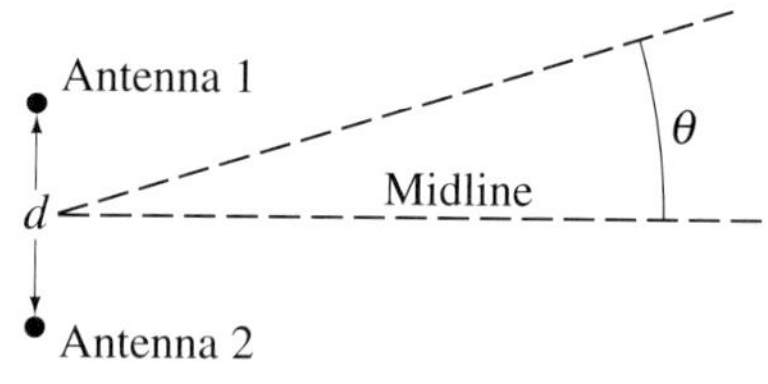


**FIGURE 24–60** Problem 66.

67. A teacher stands well back from an outside doorway 0.88 m wide, and blows a whistle of frequency 750 Hz. Ignoring reflections, estimate at what angle(s) it is *not* possible to hear the whistle clearly on the playground outside the doorway.

68. If parallel light falls on a single slit of width $D$ at a 30° angle to the normal, describe the diffraction pattern.

69. The wings of a certain beetle have a series of parallel lines across them. When normally incident 460-nm light is reflected from the wing, the wing appears bright when viewed at an angle of 51°. How far apart are the lines?

70. How many lines per centimeter must a grating have if there is to be no second-order spectrum for any visible wavelength?

71. Show that the second- and third-order spectra of white light produced by a diffraction grating always overlap. What wavelengths overlap exactly?

72. When yellow sodium light, $\lambda = 589$ nm, falls on a diffraction grating, its first-order peak on a screen 60.0 cm away falls 3.32 cm from the central peak. Another source produces a line 3.71 cm from the central peak. What is the wavelength of the new source? How many lines/cm are on the grating?

73. Light is incident on a diffraction grating with 8600 lines/cm, and the pattern is viewed on a screen 2.5 m from the grating. The incident light beam consists of two wavelengths, $\lambda_1 = 4.6 \times 10^{-7}$ m and $\lambda_2 = 6.8 \times 10^{-7}$ m. Calculate the linear distance between the first-order bright fringes of these two wavelengths on the screen.

74. What is the index of refraction of a clear material if a minimum of 150 nm thickness of it, when laid on glass, is needed to reduce reflection to nearly zero when light of 600 nm is incident normally upon it? Do you have a choice for an answer?

75. Monochromatic light of variable wavelength is incident normally on a thin sheet of plastic film in air. The reflected light is a minimum only for $\lambda = 512$ nm and $\lambda = 640$ nm in the visible spectrum. What is the thickness of the film ($n = 1.58$)? [*Hint*: assume successive values of $m$.]

76. Compare the minimum thickness needed for an anti-reflective coating ($n = 1.38$) applied to a glass lens in order to eliminate (*a*) blue (450 nm), or (*b*) red (700 nm) reflections for light at normal incidence.

77. What is the minimum (non-zero) thickness for the air layer between two flat glass surfaces if the glass is to appear dark when 640-nm light is incident normally? What if the glass is to appear bright?

78. Suppose you viewed the light *transmitted* through a thin film layered on a flat piece of glass. Draw a diagram, similar to Fig. 24–30 or 24–36, and describe the conditions required for maxima and minima. Consider all possible values of index of refraction. Discuss the relative size of the minima compared to the maxima and to zero.

79. At what angle above the horizon is the Sun when light reflecting off a smooth lake is polarized most strongly?

80. At what angle should the axes of two Polaroids be placed so as to reduce the intensity of the incident unpolarized light by an additional factor (after the first Polaroid cuts it in half) of (*a*) 4, (*b*) 10, (*c*) 100?

81. Unpolarized light falls on two polarizer sheets whose transmission axes are at right angles. A third polarizer is placed between the first two so that its axis makes a 62° angle with the axis of the first polarizer. (*a*) What fraction of the incident light intensity is transmitted? (*b*) What if the third polarizer is in front of the other two?

82. Four polarizers are placed in succession with their axes vertical, at 30° to the vertical, at 60° to the vertical, and at 90° to the vertical. (*a*) Calculate what fraction of the incident unpolarized light is transmitted by the four polarizers. (*b*) Can the transmitted light be *decreased* by removing one of the polarizers? If so, which one? (*c*) Can the transmitted light intensity be extinguished by removing polarizers? If so, which one(s)?

83. A laser beam passes through a slit of width 1.0 cm and is pointed at the Moon, which is approximately 380,000 km from the Earth. Assume the laser emits waves of wavelength 630 nm (the red light of a He-Ne laser). Estimate the width of the beam when it reaches the Moon.

84. A series of polarizers are each placed at a 10° interval from the previous polarizer. Unpolarized light is incident on this series of polarizers. How many polarizers does the light have to go through before it is $\frac{1}{4}$ of its original intensity?

85. A thin film of soap ($n = 1.34$) coats a piece of flat glass ($n = 1.52$). How thick is the film if it reflects 643-nm red light most strongly when illuminated normally by white light?

86. Consider two antennas radiating 6.0-MHz radio waves in phase with each other. They are located at points $S_1$ and $S_2$, separated by a distance $d = 175$ m, Fig. 24–61. What are the first three points on the $y$ axis where the signals from the two sources will be out of phase (crests of one meet troughs of the other)?

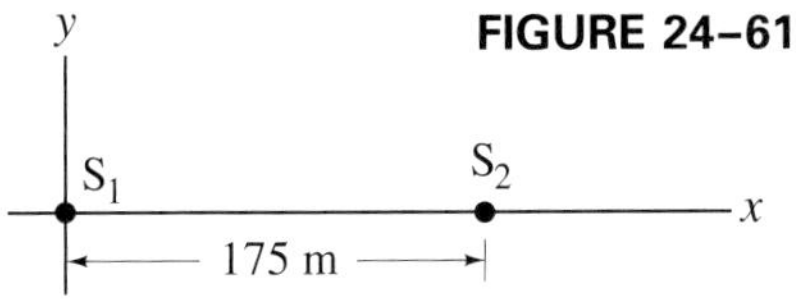


**FIGURE 24–61** Problem 86.

87. A parallel beam of light containing two wavelengths, 420 nm and 650 nm, enters a silicate flint glass equilateral prism (Fig. 24–58). (*a*) What is the angle between the two beams leaving the prism? (*b*) Repeat part (*a*) for a diffraction grating with 6200 lines/cm.

* 88. A Lucite planoconvex lens has one flat surface and one with $R = 18.4$ cm. It is used to view an object, located 66.0 cm away from the lens, which is a mixture of red and yellow. The index of refraction of the Lucite is 1.5106 for red light and 1.5226 for yellow light. What are the locations of the red and yellow images formed by the lens? [*Hint*: see Section 23–10.]

## Answers to Exercises

**A:** 2.5 mm.

**B:** Narrower.

**C:** 4900 lines/cm.

**D:** A.

**E:** Zero for both (*a*) and (*b*), because the two successive polarizers at 90° cancel all light. The 45° Polaroid must be inserted *between* the other two if transmission is to occur.

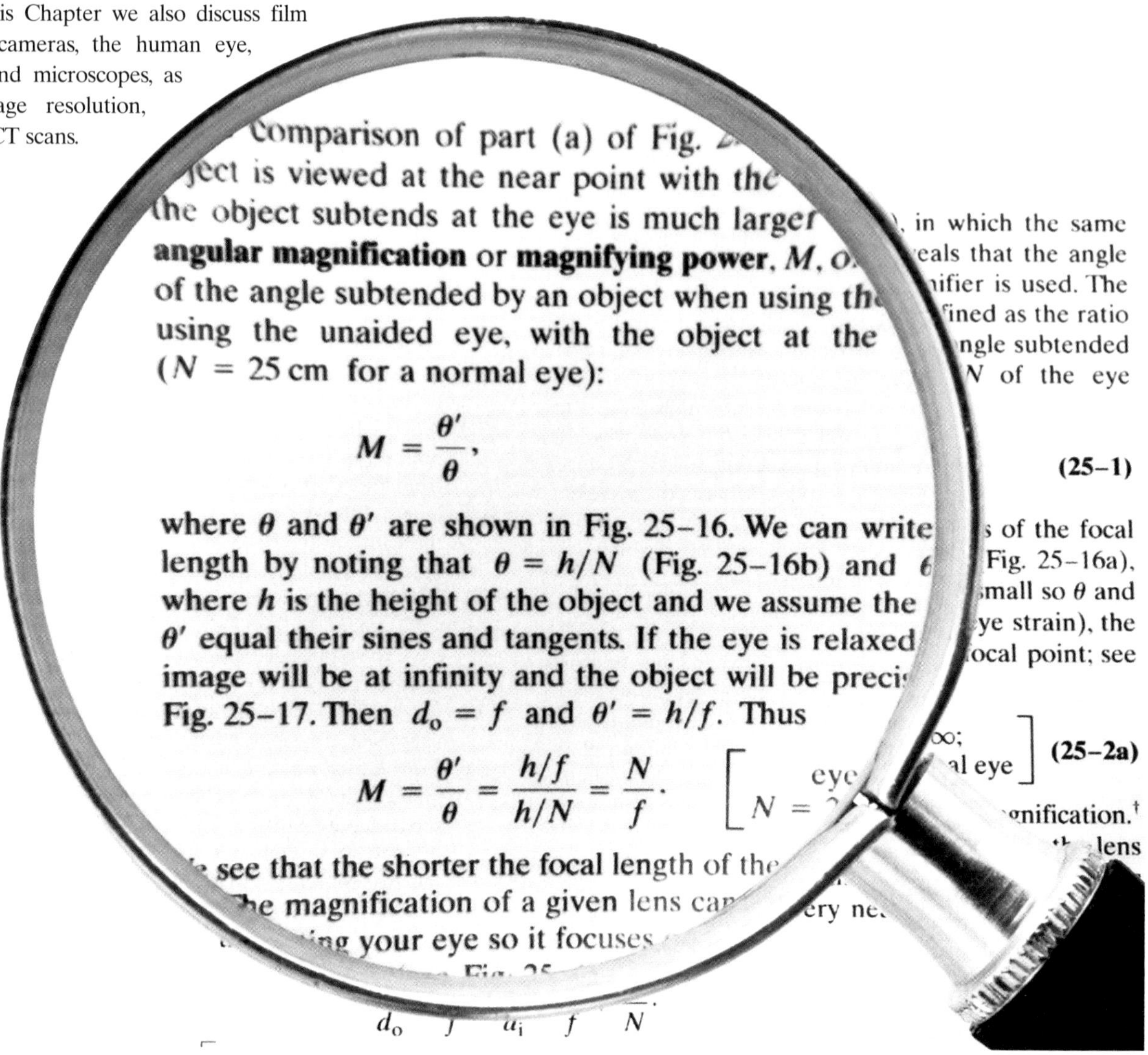


Of the many optical devices we discuss in this Chapter, the magnifying glass is the simplest. Here it is magnifying page 705 of this Chapter, which describes how the magnifying glass works according to the ray model. In this Chapter we also discuss film and digital cameras, the human eye, telescopes, and microscopes, as well as image resolution, X-rays, and CT scans.

CHAPTER 25

# Optical Instruments

In our discussion of the behavior of light in the two previous Chapters, we also described a few instruments such as the spectrometer and the Michelson interferometer. In this Chapter, we will discuss some other, more common, instruments, most of which use lenses, such as the camera, telescope, microscope, and the human eye. To describe their operation, we will use ray diagrams. However, we will see that understanding some aspects of their operation will require the wave nature of light.

## 25–1 Cameras, Film and Digital

PHYSICS APPLIED
*The camera*

The basic elements of a **camera** are a lens, a light-tight box, a shutter to let light pass through the lens only briefly, and in a traditional camera a piece of film (Fig. 25–1), or in a digital camera an electronic sensor. When the shutter is opened, light from external objects in the field of view is focused by the lens as an image on the film or sensor. Film contains light-sensitive chemicals that change when light strikes them. In the development process, chemical reactions cause the changed areas to turn opaque, so the image is recorded on the film.† You can see the image yourself if you remove the back of a conventional camera and view through a piece of tissue paper (on which an image can form) placed where the film should be with the shutter open.

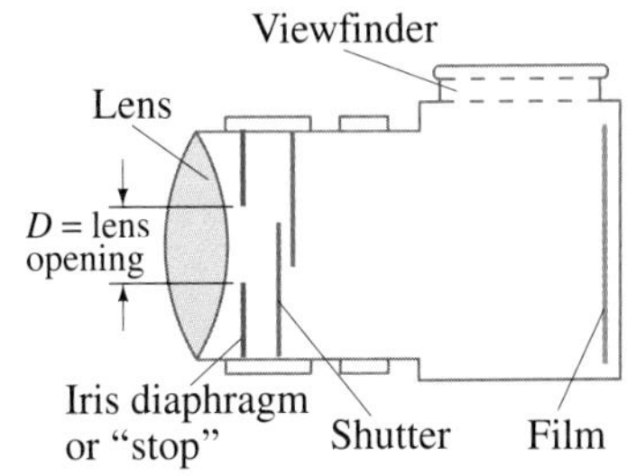


**FIGURE 25–1** A simple camera.

### Digital Cameras, CCD Sensors

PHYSICS APPLIED
*Digital cameras*

In a **digital camera**, the film is replaced by a semiconductor sensor known as a **charge-coupled device (CCD)**. A CCD sensor is made up of millions of tiny pixels ("picture elements")—see Fig. 24–49. A 3-MP (3-megapixel) sensor‡ would contain about 1500 pixels vertically by 2000 pixels horizontally over an area of perhaps $9\text{ mm} \times 12\text{ mm}$. Light reaching any pixel liberates electrons from the semiconductor. The more intense the light, the more charge accumulates during the brief exposure time. Conducting electrodes carry each pixel's charge (serially in time, row by row—hence the name "charge-coupled") to a central processor that stores the relative brightness of pixels, and allows reformation of the image later on a computer screen or printer.

A CCD is fully reusable. Once the pixel charges are transferred to memory, a new picture can be taken.

Color is achieved by red, green, and blue filters over alternating pixels as shown in Fig. 25–2, similar to a color CRT or LCD screen. The sensor type shown in Fig. 25–2 contains twice as many green pixels as red or blue (green is claimed to have a stronger influence on the sensation of sharpness). The computer-analyzed color at each pixel is that pixel's intensity averaged with the intensities of the nearest-neighbor colors.

To reduce the amount of memory for each picture, compression programs can average over pixels, but with a consequent loss of sharpness, or "resolution."

**FIGURE 25–2** Portion of a typical CCD sensor. A square group of four pixels $\substack{\mathrm{RG}\\ \mathrm{GB}}$ is sometimes called a "color pixel."

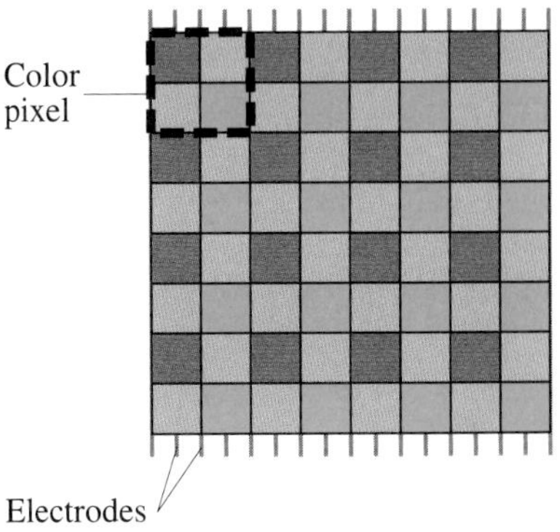


### * Digital Artifacts

Digital cameras can produce image artifacts (errors in the image not present in the original, resulting from the imaging process). One example using the "mosaic" pixels of Fig. 25–2 is described in Fig. 25–3. Another technology uses a semitransparent silicon semiconductor layer system, exploiting the fact that different wavelengths of light penetrate silicon to different depths: each pixel is a sandwich of partly transparent layers, one for each color. The top layer can absorb blue light, allowing green and red light to pass through. The second layer absorbs green and the bottom layer detects the red. All three colors are detected by each pixel, resulting in better color resolution and fewer artifacts.

†This is called a *negative*, because the black areas correspond to bright objects and vice versa. The same process occurs during printing to produce a black-and-white "positive" picture from the negative. Color film has three emulsion layers (or dyes) corresponding to the three primary colors.

‡Each different color of pixel in a CCD is counted as a separate pixel. In contrast, in an LCD screen (Section 24–11), a group of three subpixels is counted as one pixel, a more conservative count.

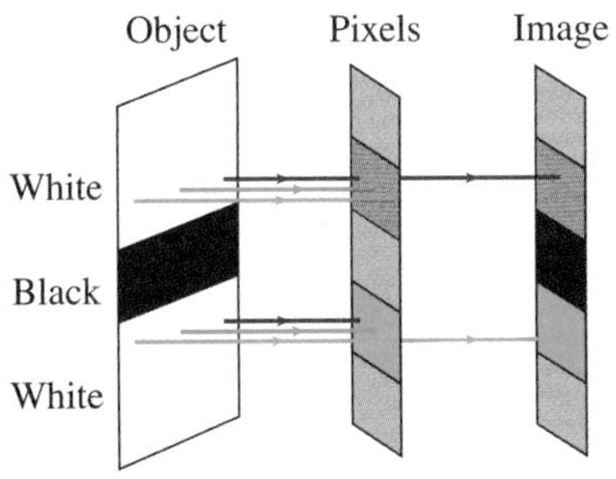


**FIGURE 25–3** Suppose we take a picture that includes a thin black line (our object) on a white background. The image of this black line has a colored halo (red above, blue below) due to the mosaic arrangement of color filter pixels, as shown by the colors transmitted. Computer averaging can minimize color problems such as this (the green at top and bottom of image can be averaged with nearby pixels to give white or nearly so) but the image is consequently "softened" or blurred. The layered color pixel described in the text would avoid this artifact.

## Camera Adjustments

There are three main adjustments on good-quality cameras: shutter speed, $f$-stop, and focusing. Although most cameras today make these adjustments automatically, it is valuable to understand these adjustments to use a camera effectively. For special or top-quality work, a manual camera is indispensable (Fig. 25–4).

**Shutter speed** This refers to how long the shutter is open and the film exposed. It may vary from a second or more ("time exposures") to $\frac{1}{1000}$ s or less. To avoid blurring from camera movement, speeds faster than $\frac{1}{100}$ s are normally used. If the object is moving, faster shutter speeds are needed to "stop" the action. A shutter can open and close "behind the lens," as in Fig. 25–1, or be a "focal plane" shutter which is a moveable curtain just in front of the film.

*Digital camera shutter*

Digital cameras have "electronic shutters," which are the brief sampling times for collecting pixel charges; they may also have a mechanical shutter which is normally open so you can view the shot on the built-in LCD screen, but closes just before the shot is taken, opens briefly to shoot, and reopens afterward. Digital still cameras that take short movies must have a fast "sampling" time and a fast "clearing" (of the charge) time so as to take pictures of at least 12 or 15 frames per second.

**FIGURE 25–4** On this camera, the $f$-stops and the focusing ring are on the camera lens. Shutter speeds are selected on the small wheel on top of the camera body.

*$f$-stop*

**$f$-stop** The amount of light reaching the film must be carefully controlled to avoid **underexposure** (too little light so the picture is dark and only the brightest objects show up) or **overexposure** (too much light, so that all bright objects look the same, with a consequent lack of contrast and a "washed-out" appearance). To control the exposure, a "stop" or iris diaphragm, whose opening is of variable diameter, is placed behind the lens (Fig. 25–1). The size of the opening is varied to compensate for bright or dark lighting conditions, the sensitivity of the film[†] used, and for different shutter speeds. The size of the opening is specified by the **$f$-number** or **$f$-stop**, defined as

$$f\text{-stop} = \frac{f}{D},$$

where $f$ is the focal length of the lens and $D$ is the diameter of the lens opening (Fig. 25–1). For example, when a 50-mm-focal-length lens has an opening $D = 25\,\text{mm}$, we say it is set at $f/2$. When this lens is set at $f/8$, the opening is only $6\frac{1}{4}$ mm $(50/6\frac{1}{4} = 8)$. For faster shutter speeds, or low light conditions, a greater lens opening must be used to get a proper exposure. This corresponds to a smaller $f$-stop number. The smaller the $f$-stop number, the larger the opening and the more light passes through the lens to the film. The smallest $f$-number of a lens (largest opening) is referred to as the *speed* of the lens. It is common to find $f/2.0$ lenses today, and some even faster. The advantage of a fast lens is that it allows pictures to be taken under poor lighting conditions. Good quality lenses consist of several elements to reduce the defects present in simple thin lenses (Section 25–6). Standard $f$-stop markings on good lenses are 1.0, 1.4, 2.0, 2.8, 4.0, 5.6, 8, 11, 16, 22, and 32 (Fig. 25–4). Each of these stops corresponds to a diameter reduction by a factor of about $\sqrt{2} = 1.4$. Because the amount of light reaching the film is proportional to the *area* of the opening, and therefore proportional to the diameter squared, each standard $f$-stop corresponds to a factor of 2 in light intensity reaching the film.

*Focusing*

**Focusing** Focusing is the operation of placing the lens at the correct position relative to the film for the sharpest image. The image distance is smallest for objects at infinity (the symbol $\infty$ is used for infinity) and is equal to the focal length. For closer objects, the image distance is greater than the focal length, as can be seen from the lens equation, $1/f = 1/d_o + 1/d_i$ (Eq. 23–8). To focus on nearby objects, the lens must therefore be moved away from the film, and this is usually done on a manual camera by turning a ring on the lens.

[†] Different films have different sensitivities to light, referred to as the "film speed" and specified as an "ASA number" or "ISO number." A "faster" film is more sensitive and needs less light to produce a good image. Faster films are grainier so offer less sharpness (resolution) when enlarged. Digital cameras may have a "gain" or "ISO" adjustment for sensitivity. Adjusting a CCD to be "faster" for low light conditions results in "noise," the digital equivalent of graininess.

(a)

(b)

**FIGURE 25–5** Photos taken with a camera (a) focused on a nearby object with distant object blurry, and (b) focused on a more distant object with nearby object blurry.

If the lens is focused on a nearby object, a sharp image of it will be formed, but the image of distant objects may be blurry (Fig. 25–5). The rays from a point on the distant object will be out of focus—they will form a circle on the film as shown (exaggerated) in Fig. 25–6. The distant object will thus produce an image consisting of overlapping circles and will be blurred. These circles are called **circles of confusion**. To include near and distant objects in the same photo, you can try setting the lens focus at an intermediate position. For a given distance setting, there is a range of distances over which the circles of confusion will be small enough that the images will be reasonably sharp. This is called the **depth of field**. The depth of field varies with the lens opening. If the lens opening is smaller, only rays through the central part of the lens are accepted, and these form smaller circles of confusion for a given object distance. Hence, at smaller lens openings, a greater range of object distances will fit within the circle of confusion criterion, so the depth of field is greater. For 35-mm cameras, the depth of field is based on a maximum circle of confusion diameter of 0.03 mm.

*Depth of field*

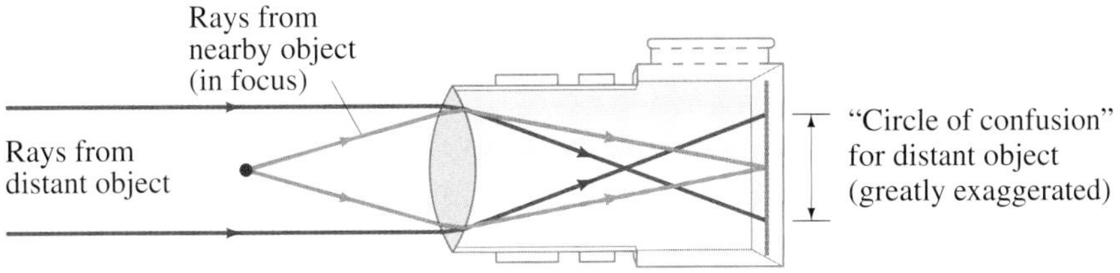


**FIGURE 25–6** When the lens is positioned to focus on a nearby object, points on a distant object produce circles and are therefore blurred. (The effect is shown greatly exaggerated.)

**EXAMPLE 25–1** **Camera focus.** How far must a 50.0-mm-focal-length camera lens be moved from its infinity setting to sharply focus an object 3.00 m away?

**APPROACH** For an object at infinity, the image is at the focal point, by definition as discussed in Section 23–7. For an object distance of 3.00 m, we use the thin lens equation, Eq. 23–8, to find the image distance (distance of lens to film or sensor).

**SOLUTION** When focused at infinity, the lens is 50.0 mm from the film. When focused at $d_o = 3.00\text{ m}$, the image distance is given by the lens equation,

$$\frac{1}{d_i} = \frac{1}{f} - \frac{1}{d_o} = \frac{1}{50.0\text{ mm}} - \frac{1}{3000\text{ mm}} = \frac{3000 - 50}{(3000)(50.0)\text{ mm}} = \frac{2950}{150{,}000\text{ mm}}.$$

We solve for $d_i$ and find $d_i = 50.8\text{ mm}$, so the lens needs to move 0.8 mm away from the film or digital sensor.

**EXERCISE A** If the lens of Example 25–1 is 50.4 mm from the film or sensor, what is the object distance for sharp focus?

**CONCEPTUAL EXAMPLE 25–2** **Shutter speed.** To improve the depth of field, you "stop down" your camera lens by two $f$-stops from $f/4$ to $f/8$. What should you do to the shutter speed to maintain the same exposure?

**RESPONSE** The amount of light admitted by the lens is proportional to the area of the lens opening. Reducing the lens opening by two $f$-stops reduces the diameter by a factor of 2, and the area by a factor of 4. To maintain the same exposure, the shutter must be open four times as long. If the shutter speed had been $\frac{1}{500}$ s, you would have to increase it to $\frac{1}{125}$ s.

## Picture Sharpness

The sharpness of a picture depends not only on accurate focusing, but also on the graininess of the film, or the number of pixels for a digital camera. Fine-grained films are "slower," meaning they require longer exposures for a given light level.

The quality of the lens strongly affects the image quality, and we discuss lens resolution and diffraction effects in Sections 25–6 and 25–7. The sharpness, or *resolution*, of a lens is often given as so many lines per millimeter, measured by photographing a standard set of parallel lines on fine-grain film. The minimum spacing of distinguishable lines gives the resolution; 50 lines/mm is reasonable, 100 lines/mm is very good.

*Pixels and resolution*

**EXAMPLE 25–3** **Pixels and resolution.** A high-quality 6-MP (6-megapixel) digital camera offers a maximum resolution of $2000 \times 3000$ pixels on a 16-mm $\times$ 24-mm CCD sensor. How sharp should the lens be to make use of this resolution?

**APPROACH** We find the number of pixels per millimeter and require the lens to be at least that good.

**SOLUTION** We can either take the image height (2000 pixels in 16 mm) or the width (3000 pixels in 24 mm):

$$\frac{3000\text{ pixels}}{24\text{ mm}} = 125\text{ pixels/mm}.$$

We would want the lens to be able to resolve at least 125 lines/mm as well. If it can't, we could use fewer pixels and less memory.

**NOTE** Increasing lens resolution is a tougher problem today than is squeezing more pixels on a CCD.

*When is a photo sharp?*

**EXAMPLE 25–4** **Blown-up photograph.** An enlarged photograph looks sharp at normal viewing distances if the dots or lines are resolved to about 10 dots/mm. Would an $8 \times 10$-inch enlargement of a photo taken by the camera in Example 25–3 seem sharp? To what maximum size could you enlarge this $2000 \times 3000$-pixel image?

**APPROACH** We assume the image is $2000 \times 3000$ pixels on a $16 \times 24$-mm CCD as in Example 25–3, or 125 pixels per mm. We make an enlarged photo $8 \times 10$ inches $= 20\text{ cm} \times 25\text{ cm}$.

**SOLUTION** The short side of the CCD is $16\text{ mm} = 1.6\text{ cm}$ long, and that side of the photograph is 8 inches or 20 cm. Thus the enlargement is by a factor of $20\text{ cm}/1.6\text{ cm} = 12.5\times$ (or $25\text{ cm}/2.4\text{ cm} \approx 10\times$). To fill the $8 \times 10$-inch paper, we assume the enlargement is $12.5\times$. The pixels are thus enlarged $12.5\times$; the pixel count of 125 per mm on the CCD becomes 10 per mm on the print, so an $8 \times 10$-inch print is just about the maximum possible size for a sharp photograph. If you feel 7 dots per mm is good enough, you can enlarge to maybe $11 \times 14$ inches.

## Telephotos and Wide-angles

Camera lenses are categorized into normal, telephoto, and wide angle, according to focal length and film size. A **normal lens** covers the film with a field of view that corresponds approximately to that of normal vision. A normal lens for 35-mm film has a focal length in the vicinity of 50 mm.† **Telephoto lenses** act like telescopes to magnify images. They have longer focal lengths than a normal lens: as we saw in Chapter 23 (Eq. 23–9), the height of the image for a given object distance is proportional to the image distance, and the image distance will be greater for a lens with longer focal length. For distant objects, the image height is very nearly proportional to the focal length. Thus a 200-mm telephoto lens for use with a 35-mm camera gives a 4× magnification over the normal 50-mm lens. A **wide-angle lens** has a shorter focal length than normal: a wider field of view is included, and objects appear smaller. A **zoom lens** is one whose focal length can be changed so that you seem to zoom up to, or away from, the subject as you change the focal length.

*Telephoto and wide-angle lenses*

Digital cameras may have an "optical zoom" meaning the lens can change focal length and maintain resolution. But an "electronic" or "digital zoom" just enlarges the dots (pixels) with loss of sharpness.

Different types of viewing systems are common in cameras today. In many cameras, you view through a small window just above the lens as in Fig. 25–1. In a **single-lens reflex** camera (SLR), you actually view through the lens with the use of prisms and mirrors (Fig. 25–7). A mirror hangs at a 45° angle behind the lens and flips up out of the way just before the shutter opens. SLRs have the great advantage that you can see almost exactly what you will get on film. This is also true of the LCD display on a digital camera if it is carefully constructed.

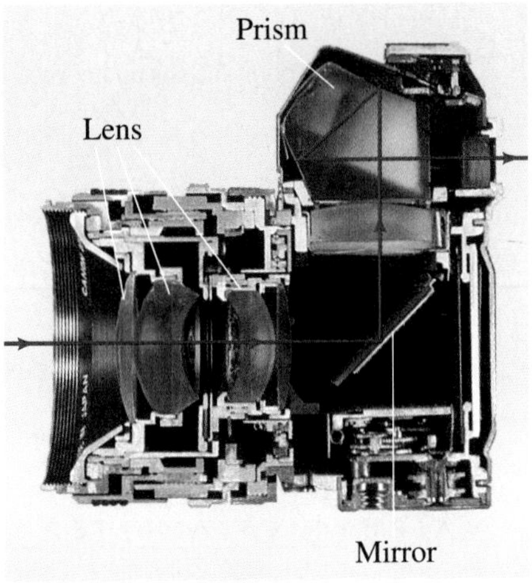


**FIGURE 25–7** Single-lens reflex (SLR) camera, showing how the image is viewed through the lens with the help of a movable mirror and prism.

## 25–2 The Human Eye; Corrective Lenses

PHYSICS APPLIED
*The eye*

The human eye resembles a camera in its basic structure (Fig. 25–8), but is far more sophisticated. The interior of the eye is filled with a transparent gel-like substance called the *vitreous humor* with index of refraction $n = 1.337$. Light enters this enclosed volume through the cornea and lens. Between the cornea and lens is a watery fluid, the aqueous humor (*aqua* is "water" in Latin) with $n = 1.336$. A diaphragm, called the **iris** (the colored part of your eye) adjusts automatically to control the amount of light entering the eye, similar to a camera. The hole in the iris through which light passes (the **pupil**) is black because no light is reflected from it (it's a hole), and very little light is reflected back out from the interior of the eye. The **retina**, which plays the role of the film or sensor in a camera, is on the curved rear surface of the eye. The retina consists of a complex array of nerves and receptors known as *rods* and *cones* which act to change light energy into electrical signals that travel along the nerves. The reconstruction of the image from all these tiny receptors is done mainly in the brain, although some analysis may also be done in the complex interconnected nerve network at the retina itself. At the center of the retina is a small area called the **fovea**, about 0.25 mm in diameter, where the cones are very closely packed and the sharpest image and best color discrimination are found.

*Anatomy of the eye*

**FIGURE 25–8** Diagram of a human eye.

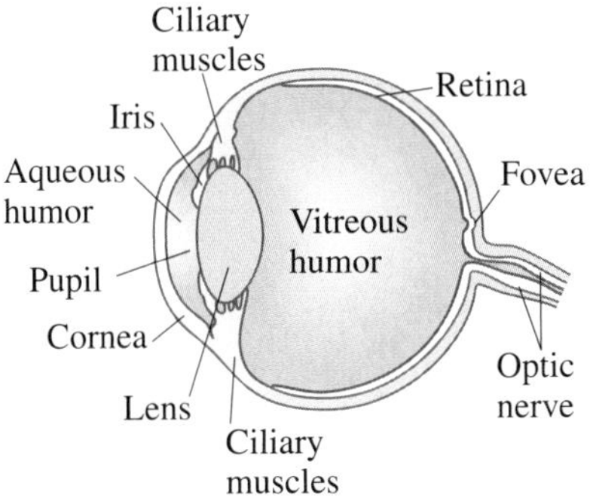


Unlike a camera, the eye contains no shutter. The equivalent operation is carried out by the nervous system, which analyzes the signals to form images at the rate of about 30 per second. This can be compared to motion picture or television cameras, which operate by taking a series of still pictures at a rate of 24 (movies) or 30 (U.S. television) per second. Their rapid projection on the screen gives the appearance of motion.

The lens of the eye ($n = 1.386$ to 1.406) does little of the bending of the light rays. Most of the refraction is done at the front surface of the **cornea** ($n = 1.376$) at its interface with air ($n = 1.0$). The lens acts as a fine adjustment for focusing at different distances. This is accomplished by the ciliary muscles (Fig. 25–8), which change the curvature of the lens so that its focal length is changed.

*Focusing the eye*

† A "35-mm camera" uses film that is 35 mm wide; that 35 mm is not to be confused with a focal length.

To focus on a distant object, the ciliary muscles of the eye are relaxed and the lens is thin, as shown in Fig. 25–9a, and parallel rays focus at the focal point (on the retina). To focus on a nearby object, the muscles contract, causing the center of the lens to thicken, Fig. 25–9b, thus shortening the focal length so that images of nearby objects can be focused on the retina, behind the new focal point. This focusing adjustment is called **accommodation**.

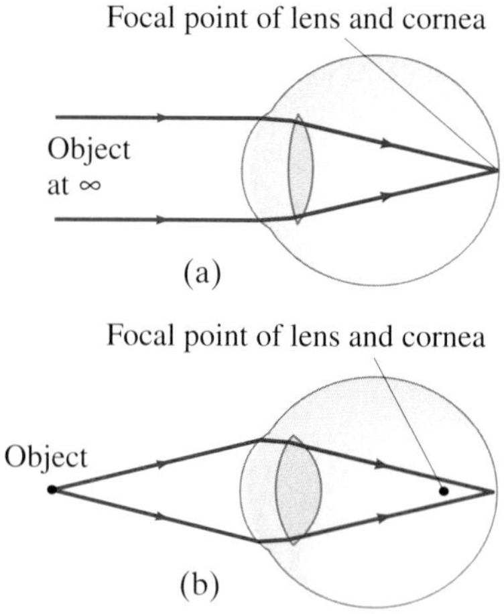


**FIGURE 25–9** Accommodation by a normal eye: (a) lens relaxed, focused at infinity; (b) lens thickened, focused on a nearby object.

The closest distance at which the eye can focus clearly is called the **near point** of the eye. For young adults it is typically 25 cm, although younger children can often focus on objects as close as 10 cm. As people grow older, the ability to accommodate is reduced and the near point increases. A given person's **far point** is the farthest distance at which an object can be seen clearly. For some purposes it is useful to speak of a **normal eye** (a sort of average over the population), defined as an eye having a near point of 25 cm and a far point of infinity. To check your own near point, place this book close to your eye and slowly move it away until the type is sharp.

PHYSICS APPLIED

*Corrective lenses*

The "normal" eye is sort of an ideal. Many people have eyes that do not accommodate within the "normal" range of 25 cm to infinity, or have some other defect. Two common defects are nearsightedness and farsightedness. Both can be corrected to a large extent with lenses—either eyeglasses or contact lenses.

*Nearsightedness*

In **nearsightedness**, or *myopia*, the eye can focus only on nearby objects. The far point is not infinity but some shorter distance, so distant objects are not seen clearly. It is usually caused by an eyeball that is too long, although sometimes it is the curvature of the cornea that is too great. In either case, images of distant objects are focused in front of the retina. A diverging lens, because it causes parallel rays to diverge, allows the rays to be focused at the retina (Fig. 25–10a) and thus corrects this defect.

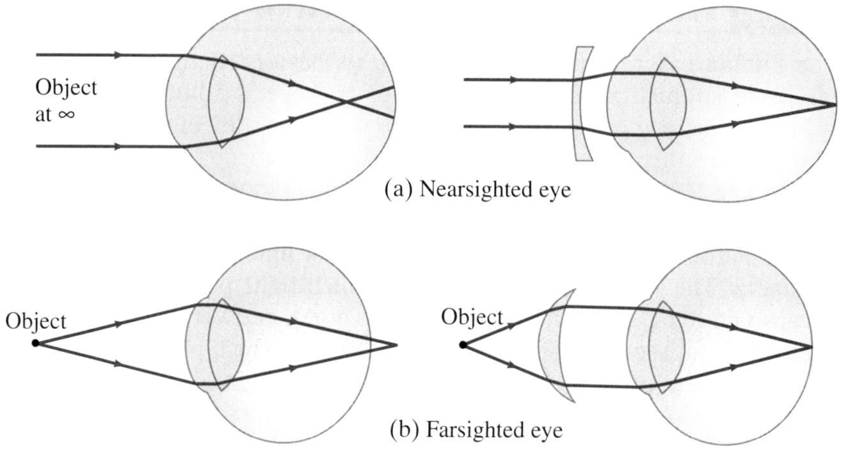


**FIGURE 25–10** Correcting eye defects with lenses: (a) a nearsighted eye, which cannot focus clearly on distant objects, can be corrected by use of a diverging lens; (b) a farsighted eye, which cannot focus clearly on nearby objects, can be corrected by use of a converging lens.

*Farsightedness*

In **farsightedness**, or *hyperopia*, the eye cannot focus on nearby objects. Although distant objects are usually seen clearly, the near point is somewhat greater than the "normal" 25 cm, which makes reading difficult. This defect is caused by an eyeball that is too short or (less often) by a cornea that is not sufficiently curved. It is corrected by a converging lens, Fig. 25–10b. Similar to hyperopia is *presbyopia*, which refers to the lessening ability of the eye to accommodate as one ages, and the near point moves out. Converging lenses also compensate for this.

*Astigmatism*

**Astigmatism** is usually caused by an out-of-round cornea or lens so that point objects are focused as short lines, which blurs the image. It is as if the cornea were spherical with a cylindrical section superimposed. As shown in Fig. 25–11, a cylindrical lens focuses a point into a line parallel to its axis. An astigmatic eye may focus rays in one plane, such as the vertical plane, at a shorter distance than it does for rays in a horizontal plane. Astigmatism is corrected with the use of a compensating cylindrical lens. Lenses for eyes that are nearsighted or farsighted as well as astigmatic are ground with superimposed spherical and cylindrical surfaces, so that the radius of curvature of the correcting lens is different in different planes.

**FIGURE 25–11** A cylindrical lens forms a line image of a point object because it is converging in one plane only.

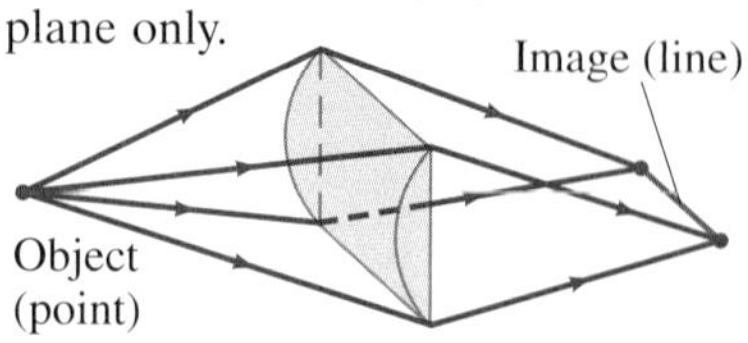

**EXAMPLE 25–5** **Farsighted eye.** Sue is farsighted with a near point of 100 cm. Reading glasses must have what lens power so that she can read a newspaper at a distance of 25 cm? Assume the lens is very close to the eye.

**APPROACH** When the object is placed 25 cm from the lens, we want the image to be 100 cm away on the *same* side of the lens (so the eye can focus it), and so the image is virtual, Fig. 25–12, and $d_i = -100\text{ cm}$ will be negative. We use the thin lens equation (Eq. 23–8) to determine the needed focal length. Optometrists' prescriptions specify the power ($P = 1/f$, Eq. 23–7) given in diopters $\left(1\text{ D} = 1\text{ m}^{-1}\right)$.

**SOLUTION** Given that $d_o = 25\text{ cm}$ and $d_i = -100\text{ cm}$, the thin lens equation gives

$$\frac{1}{f} = \frac{1}{d_o} + \frac{1}{d_i} = \frac{1}{25\text{ cm}} + \frac{1}{-100\text{ cm}} = \frac{4-1}{100\text{ cm}} = \frac{1}{33\text{ cm}}.$$

So $f = 33\text{ cm} = 0.33\text{ m}$. The power $P$ of the lens is $P = 1/f = +3.0\text{ D}$. The plus sign indicates that it is a converging lens.

**NOTE** We chose the image position to be where the eye can actually focus. The lens needs to put the image there, given the desired placement of the object (newspaper).

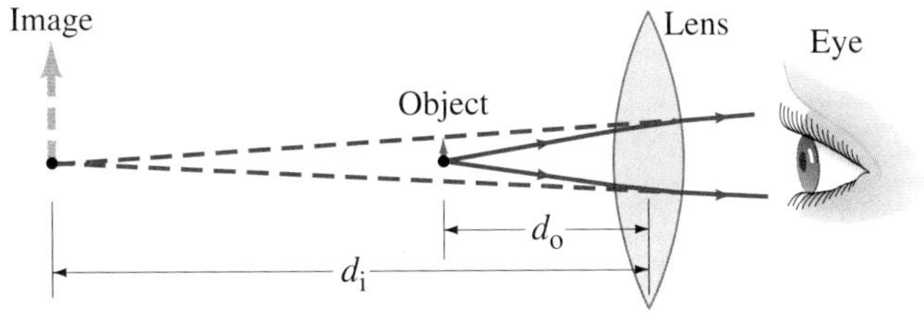


**FIGURE 25–12** Lens of reading glasses (Example 25–5).

**EXAMPLE 25–6** **Nearsighted eye.** A nearsighted eye has near and far points of 12 cm and 17 cm, respectively. (*a*) What lens power is needed for this person to see distant objects clearly, and (*b*) what then will be the near point? Assume that the lens is 2.0 cm from the eye (typical for eyeglasses).

**APPROACH** For a distant object $(d_o = \infty)$, the lens must put the image at the far point of the eye as shown in Fig. 25–13a, 17 cm in front of the eye. We can use the thin lens equation to find the focal length of the lens, and from this its lens power. The new near point (as shown in Fig. 25–13b) can be calculated for the lens by again using the thin lens equation.

**SOLUTION** (*a*) For an object at infinity $(d_o = \infty)$, the image must be in front of the lens 17 cm from the eye or $(17\text{ cm} - 2\text{ cm}) = 15\text{ cm}$ from the lens; hence $d_i = -15\text{ cm}$. We use the thin lens equation to solve for the focal length of the needed lens:

$$\frac{1}{f} = \frac{1}{d_o} + \frac{1}{d_i} = \frac{1}{\infty} + \frac{1}{-15\text{ cm}} = -\frac{1}{15\text{ cm}}.$$

So $f = -15\text{ cm} = -0.15\text{ m}$ or $P = 1/f = -6.7\text{ D}$. The minus sign indicates that it must be a diverging lens for the myopic eye.

(*b*) The near point when glasses are worn is where an object is placed $(d_o)$ so that the lens forms an image at the "near point of the naked eye," namely 12 cm from the eye. That image point is $(12\text{ cm} - 2\text{ cm}) = 10\text{ cm}$ in front of the lens, so $d_i = -0.10\text{ m}$ and the thin lens equation gives

$$\frac{1}{d_o} = \frac{1}{f} - \frac{1}{d_i} = -\frac{1}{0.15\text{ m}} + \frac{1}{0.10\text{ m}} = \frac{-2+3}{0.30\text{ m}} = \frac{1}{0.30\text{ m}}.$$

So $d_o = 30\text{ cm}$, which means the near point when the person is wearing glasses is 30 cm in front of the lens, or 32 cm from the eye.

**FIGURE 25–13** Example 25–6.

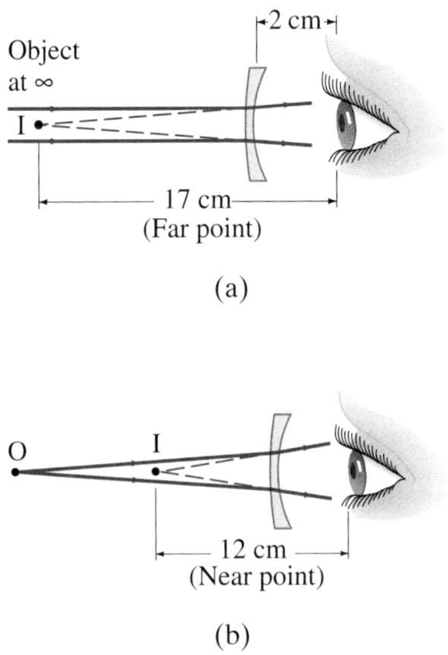


*Contact lenses*

Suppose contact lenses are used to correct the eye in Example 25–6. Since contacts are placed directly on the cornea, we would not subtract out the 2.0 cm for the image distances. That is, for distant objects $d_i = f = -17\text{ cm}$, so $P = 1/f = -5.9\text{ D}$. The new near point would be 41 cm. Thus we see that a contact lens and an eyeglass lens will require slightly different powers, or focal lengths, for the same eye because of their different placements relative to the eye. We also see that glasses in this case give a better near point than contacts.

**EXERCISE B** What power contact lens is needed for an eye to see distant objects if its far point is 25 cm?

### Underwater Vision

PHYSICS APPLIED
*Underwater vision*

When your eyes are under water, distant underwater objects look blurry because at the water–cornea interface, the difference in indices of refraction is very small: $n = 1.33$ for water, 1.376 for the cornea. Hence light rays are bent very little and are focused far behind the retina, Fig. 25–14a. If you wear goggles or a face mask, you restore an air–cornea interface ($n = 1.0$ and 1.376, respectively) and the rays can be focused, Fig. 25–14b.

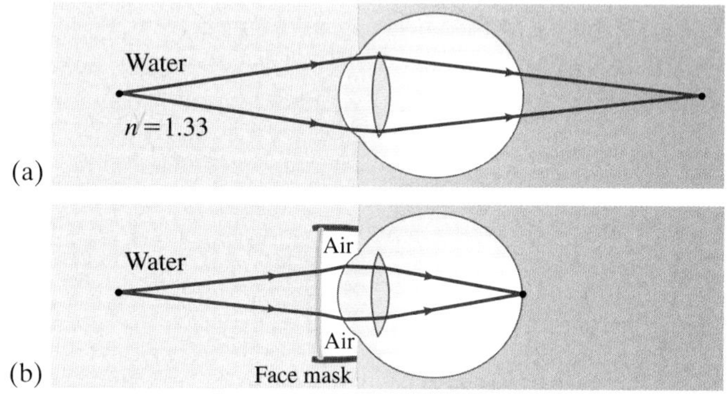


**FIGURE 25–14** (a) Under water, we see a blurry image because light rays are bent much less than in air. (b) If we wear goggles, we again have an air–cornea interface and can see clearly.

## 25–3 Magnifying Glass

Much of the remainder of this Chapter will deal with optical devices that are used to produce magnified images of objects. We first discuss the **simple magnifier**, or **magnifying glass**, which is simply a converging lens (see Chapter-opening photo).

How large an object appears, and how much detail we can see on it, depends on the size of the image it makes on the retina. This, in turn, depends on the angle subtended by the object at the eye. For example, a penny held 30 cm from the eye looks twice as tall as one held 60 cm away because the angle it subtends is twice as great (Fig. 25–15). When we want to examine detail on an object, we bring it up close to our eyes so that it subtends a greater angle. However, our eyes can accommodate only up to a point (the near point), and we will assume a standard distance of $N = 25$ cm as the near point in what follows.

A magnifying glass allows us to place the object closer to our eye so that it subtends a greater angle. As shown in Fig. 25–16a, the object is placed at the focal point or just within it. Then the converging lens produces a virtual image, which must be at least 25 cm from the eye if the eye is to focus on it. If the eye is relaxed, the image will be at infinity, and in this case the object is exactly at the focal point. (You make this slight adjustment yourself when you "focus" on the object by moving the magnifying glass.)

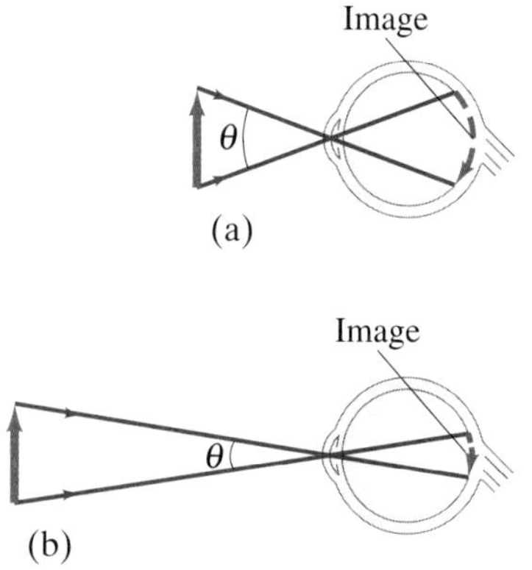


**FIGURE 25–15** When the same object is viewed at a shorter distance, the image on the retina is greater, so the object appears larger and more detail can be seen. The angle $\theta$ that the object subtends in (a) is greater than in (b). *Note*: This is not a normal ray diagram because we are showing only one ray from each point.

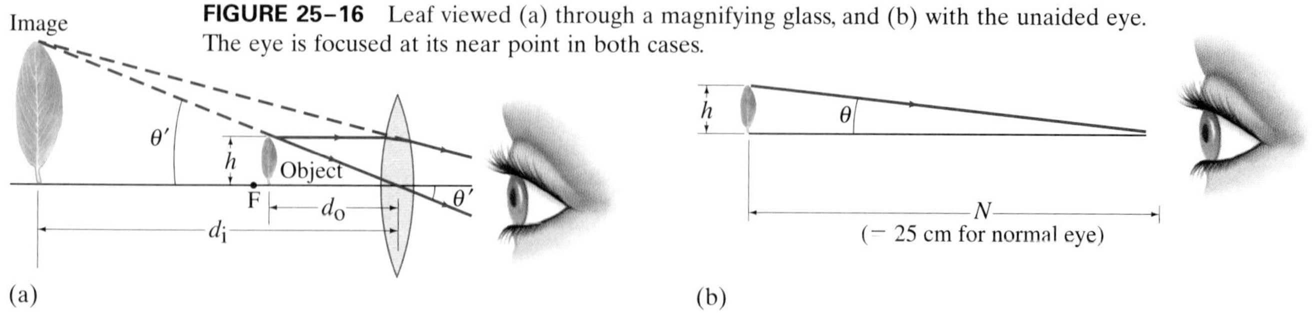


**FIGURE 25–16** Leaf viewed (a) through a magnifying glass, and (b) with the unaided eye. The eye is focused at its near point in both cases.

A comparison of part (a) of Fig. 25–16 with part (b), in which the same object is viewed at the near point with the unaided eye, reveals that the angle the object subtends at the eye is much larger when the magnifier is used. The **angular magnification** or **magnifying power**, $M$, of the lens is defined as the ratio of the angle subtended by an object when using the lens, to the angle subtended using the unaided eye, with the object at the near point $N$ of the eye ($N = 25\text{ cm}$ for a normal eye):

$$M = \frac{\theta'}{\theta}, \qquad \textbf{(25–1)}$$

where $\theta$ and $\theta'$ are shown in Fig. 25–16. We can write $M$ in terms of the focal length by noting that $\theta = h/N$ (Fig. 25–16b) and $\theta' = h/d_o$ (Fig. 25–16a), where $h$ is the height of the object and we assume the angles are small so $\theta$ and $\theta'$ equal their sines and tangents. If the eye is relaxed (for least eye strain), the image will be at infinity and the object will be precisely at the focal point; see Fig. 25–17. Then $d_o = f$ and $\theta' = h/f$. Thus

*Small angles assumed, so $\sin\theta \approx \tan\theta \approx \theta$ (in radians)*

$$M = \frac{\theta'}{\theta} = \frac{h/f}{h/N} = \frac{N}{f}. \qquad \left[\begin{array}{c}\text{eye focused at } \infty; \\ N = 25\text{ cm for normal eye}\end{array}\right] \qquad \textbf{(25–2a)}$$

*Magnification of a simple magnifier*

We see that the shorter the focal length of the lens, the greater the magnification.†

The magnification of a given lens can be increased a bit by moving the lens and adjusting your eye so it focuses on the image at the eye's near point. In this case, $d_i = -N$ (see Fig. 25–16a) if your eye is very near the magnifier. Then the object distance $d_o$ is given by

$$\frac{1}{d_o} = \frac{1}{f} - \frac{1}{d_i} = \frac{1}{f} + \frac{1}{N}.$$

We see from this equation that $d_o = fN/(f + N) < f$, as shown in Fig. 25–16a, since $N/(f + N)$ must be less than 1. With $\theta' = h/d_o$ the magnification is

$$M = \frac{\theta'}{\theta} = \frac{h/d_o}{h/N} = \frac{N}{d_o} = N\left(\frac{1}{f} + \frac{1}{N}\right)$$

or

$$M = \frac{N}{f} + 1. \qquad \left[\begin{array}{c}\text{eye focused at near point, } N; \\ N = 25\text{ cm for normal eye}\end{array}\right] \qquad \textbf{(25–2b)}$$

We see that the magnification is slightly greater when the eye is focused at its near point, rather than relaxed.

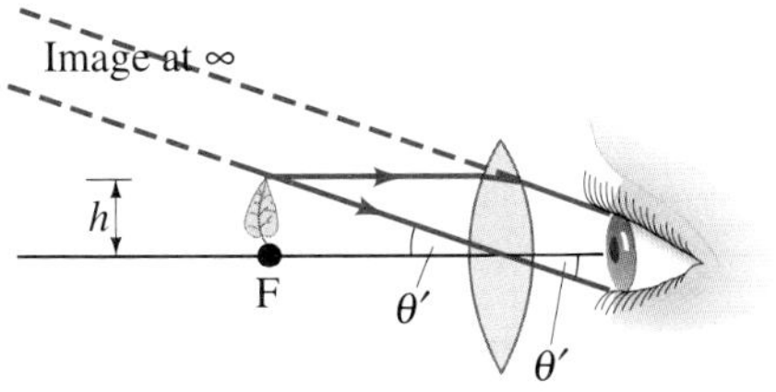


**FIGURE 25–17** With the eye relaxed, the object is placed at the focal point, and the image is at infinity. Compare to Fig. 25–16a where the image is at the eye's near point.

**EXAMPLE 25–7 ESTIMATE A jeweler's "loupe."** An 8-cm-focal-length converging lens is used as a "jeweler's loupe," which is a magnifying glass. Estimate (*a*) the magnification when the eye is relaxed, and (*b*) the magnification if the eye is focused at its near point $N = 25\text{ cm}$.

**APPROACH** The magnification when the eye is relaxed is given by Eq. 25–2a. When the eye is focused at its near point, we use Eq. 25–2b and we assume the lens is near the eye.

**SOLUTION** (*a*) With the relaxed eye focused at infinity,

$$M = \frac{N}{f} = \frac{25\text{ cm}}{8\text{ cm}} \approx 3\times.$$

(*b*) The magnification when the eye is focused at its near point ($N = 25\text{ cm}$), and the lens is near the eye, is

$$M = 1 + \frac{N}{f} = 1 + \frac{25}{8} \approx 4\times.$$

†Simple single-lens magnifiers are limited to about 2 or 3× because of distortion due to spherical aberration (Section 25–6).

## 25–4 Telescopes

A telescope is used to magnify objects that are very far away. In most cases, the object can be considered to be at infinity.

Galileo, although he did not invent it,[†] developed the telescope into a usable and important instrument. He was the first to examine the heavens with the telescope (Fig. 25–18), and he made world-shaking discoveries: the moons of Jupiter, the phases of Venus, sunspots, the structure of the Moon's surface, that the Milky Way is made up of a huge number of individual stars, and others.

Several types of **astronomical telescope** exist. The common **refracting** type, sometimes called **Keplerian**, contains two converging lenses located at opposite ends of a long tube, as illustrated in Fig. 25–19. The lens closest to the object is called the **objective lens** (focal length $f_o$) and forms a real image $I_1$ of the distant object in the plane of its focal point $F_o$ (or near it if the object is not at infinity). Although this image, $I_1$, is smaller than the original object, it subtends a greater angle and is very close to the second lens, called the **eyepiece** (focal length $f_e$), which acts as a magnifier. That is, the eyepiece magnifies the image produced by the objective lens to produce a second, greatly magnified image, $I_2$, which is virtual and inverted. If the viewing eye is relaxed, the eyepiece is adjusted so the image $I_2$ is at infinity. Then the real image $I_1$ is at the focal point $F_e'$ of the eyepiece, and the distance between the lenses is $f_o + f_e$ for an object at infinity.

(a)

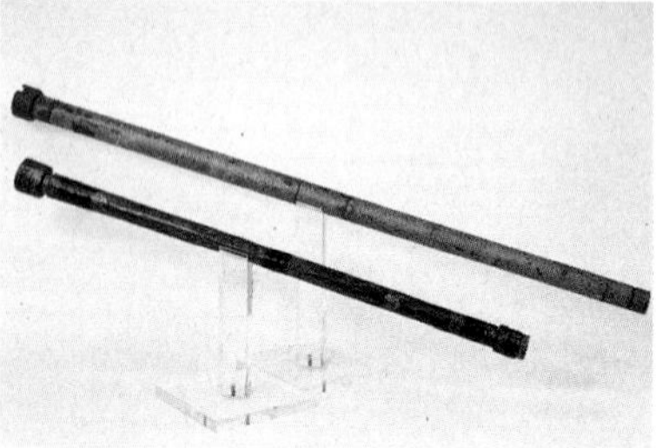

(b)

**FIGURE 25–18** (a) Objective lens (mounted now in an ivory frame) from the telescope with which Galileo made his world-shaking discoveries, including the moons of Jupiter. (b) Later telescopes made by Galileo.

To find the total magnification of this telescope, we note that the angle an object subtends as viewed by the unaided eye is just the angle $\theta$ subtended at the telescope objective. From Fig. 25–19 we can see that $\theta \approx h/f_o$, where $h$ is the height of the image $I_1$ and we assume $\theta$ is small so that $\tan\theta \approx \theta$. Note, too, that the thickest of the three rays drawn in Fig. 25–19 is parallel to the axis before it strikes the eyepiece and therefore is refracted through the eyepiece focal point $F_e$ on the far side. Thus, $\theta' \approx h/f_e$ and the total magnifying power (angular magnification) of this telescope is

*Telescope magnification*

$$M = \frac{\theta'}{\theta} = \frac{(h/f_e)}{(h/f_o)} = -\frac{f_o}{f_e}, \qquad \textbf{(25–3)}$$

where we have inserted a minus sign to indicate that the image is inverted. To achieve a large magnification, the objective lens should have a long focal length and the eyepiece a short focal length.

[†]Galileo built his first telescope in 1609 after having heard of such an instrument existing in Holland. The first telescopes magnified only three to four times, but Galileo soon made a 30-power instrument. The first Dutch telescope seems to date from about 1604, but there is a reference suggesting it may have been copied from an Italian telescope built as early as 1590. Kepler (see Chapter 5) gave a ray description (in 1611) of the Keplerian telescope, which is named for him because he first described it, although he did not build it.

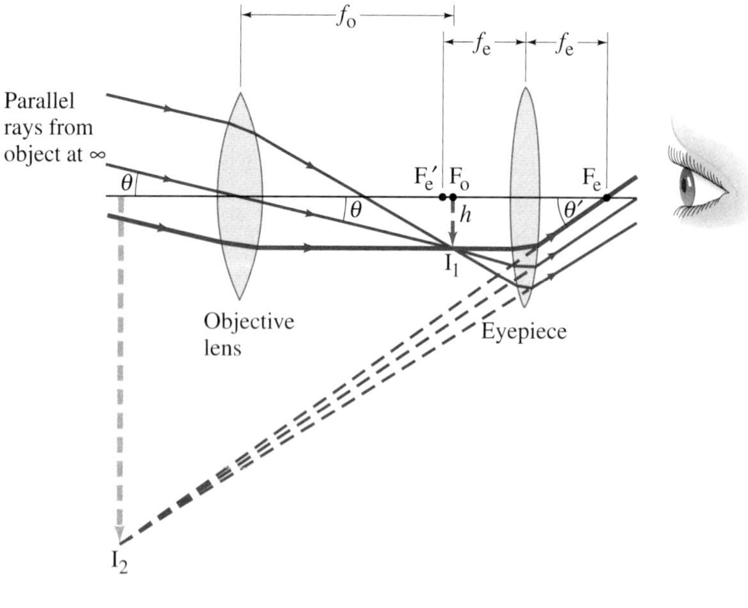


**FIGURE 25–19** Astronomical telescope (refracting). Parallel light from one point on a distant object ($d_o = \infty$) is brought to a focus by the objective lens in its focal plane. This image ($I_1$) is magnified by the eyepiece to form the final image $I_2$. Only two of the rays shown entering the objective are standard rays (2 and 3) as described in Fig. 23–34.

**EXAMPLE 25–8** **Telescope magnification.** The largest optical refracting telescope in the world is located at the Yerkes Observatory in Wisconsin, Fig. 25–20. It is referred to as a "40-inch" telescope, meaning that the diameter of the objective is 40 in., or 102 cm. The objective lens has a focal length of 19 m, and the eyepiece has a focal length of 10 cm. (*a*) Calculate the total magnifying power of this telescope. (*b*) Estimate the length of the telescope.

**APPROACH** Equation 25–3 gives the magnification. The length of the telescope is the distance between the two lenses.

**SOLUTION** (*a*) From Eq. 25–3 we find

$$M = -\frac{f_o}{f_e} = -\frac{19\text{ m}}{0.10\text{ m}} = -190\times.$$

(*b*) For a relaxed eye, the image $I_1$ is at the focal point of both the eyepiece and the objective lenses. The distance between the two lenses is thus $f_o + f_e \approx 19$ m, which is essentially the length of the telescope.

**FIGURE 25–20** This large refracting telescope was built in 1897 and is housed at Yerkes Observatory in Wisconsin. The objective lens is 102 cm (40 inches) in diameter, and the telescope tube is about 19 m long. Example 25–8.

**EXERCISE C** A 40× telescope has a 1.2-cm focal length eyepiece. What is the focal length of the objective lens?

For an astronomical telescope to produce bright images of distant stars, the objective lens must be large to allow in as much light as possible. Indeed, the diameter of the objective lens (and hence its "light-gathering power") is an important parameter for an astronomical telescope, which is why the largest ones are specified by giving the objective diameter (such as the 10-meter Keck telescope in Hawaii). The construction and grinding of large lenses is very difficult. Therefore, the largest telescopes are **reflecting telescopes** which use a curved mirror as the objective, Fig. 25–21. A mirror has only one surface to be ground and can be supported along its entire surface† (a large lens, supported at its edges, would sag under its own weight). Often, the eyepiece lens or mirror (see Fig. 25–21) is removed so that the real image formed by the objective mirror can be recorded directly on film or on a CCD digital sensor (Section 25–1).

*Reflecting telescopes*

†Another advantage of mirrors is that they exhibit no chromatic aberration because the light doesn't pass through them; and they can be ground in a parabolic shape to correct for spherical aberration (Section 25–6). The reflecting telescope was first proposed by Newton.

**FIGURE 25–21** A concave mirror can be used as the objective of an astronomical telescope. Either (a) a lens or (b) a mirror can be used as the eyepiece. Arrangement (a) is called the Newtonian focus, and (b) the Cassegrainian focus. Other arrangements are also possible. (c) The 200-inch (mirror diameter) Hale telescope on Palomar Mountain in California. (d) The 10-meter Keck telescope on Mauna Kea, Hawaii. The Keck combines thirty-six 1.8-meter six-sided mirrors into the equivalent of a very large single reflector, 10 m in diameter.

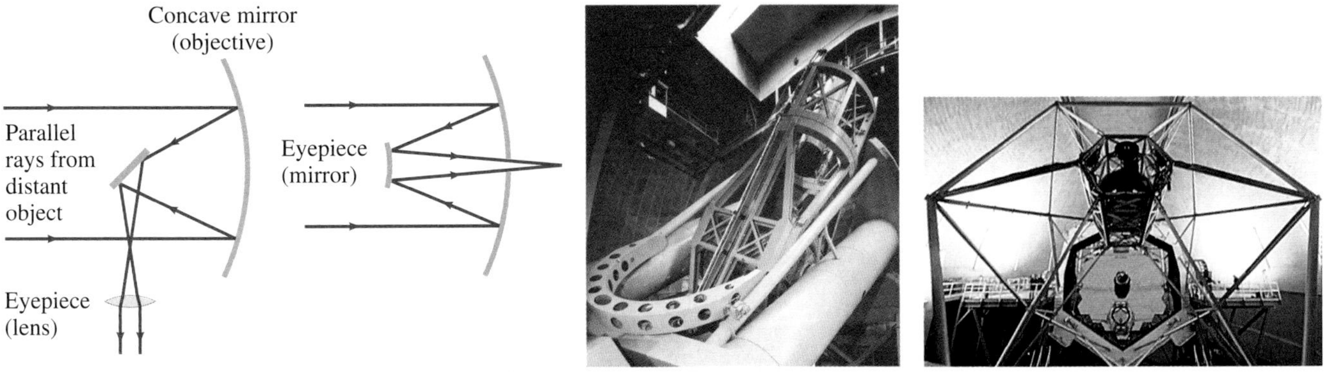


(a) (b) (c) (d)

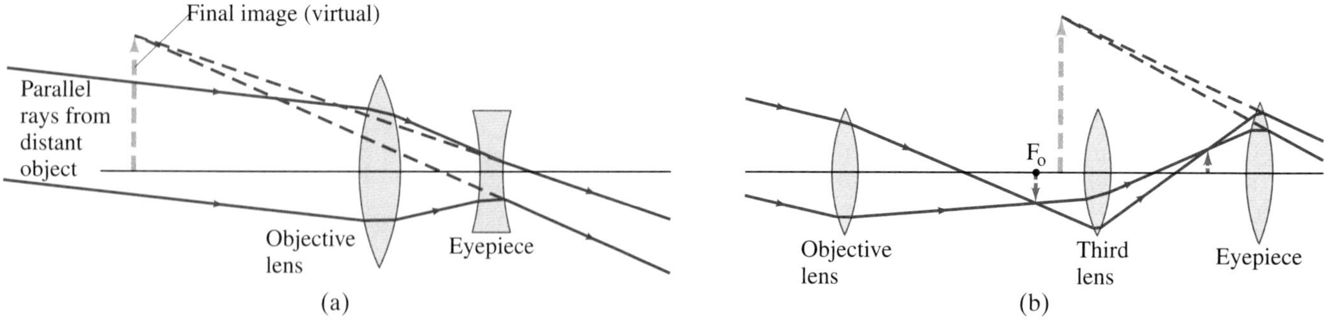


**FIGURE 25–22** Terrestrial telescopes that produce an upright image: (a) Galilean; (b) spyglass, or field-lens, type.

A **terrestrial telescope**, for viewing objects on Earth, must provide an upright image—seeing normal objects upside down would be difficult (much less important for viewing stars). Two designs are shown in Fig. 25–22. The **Galilean** type, which Galileo used for his great astronomical discoveries, has a diverging lens as eyepiece which intercepts the converging rays from the objective lens before they reach a focus, and acts to form a virtual upright image, Fig. 25–22a. This design is often used in opera glasses. The tube is reasonably short, but the field of view is small. The second type, shown in Fig. 25–22b, is often called a **spyglass** and makes use of a third convex lens that acts to make the image upright as shown. A spyglass must be quite long. The most practical design today is the **prism binocular** which was shown in Fig. 23–26. The objective and eyepiece are converging lenses. The prisms reflect the rays by total internal reflection and shorten the physical size of the device, and they also act to produce an upright image. One prism reinverts the image in the vertical plane, the other in the horizontal plane.

## * 25–5 Compound Microscope

PHYSICS APPLIED
*Microscopes*

The compound **microscope**, like the telescope, has both objective and eyepiece (or ocular) lenses, Fig. 25–23. The design is different from that for a telescope because a microscope is used to view objects that are very close, so the object distance is very small. The object is placed just beyond the objective's focal point as shown in Fig. 25–23a. The image $I_1$ formed by the objective lens is real, quite far from the lens, and much enlarged. This image is magnified by the eyepiece into a very large virtual image, $I_2$, which is seen by the eye and is inverted.

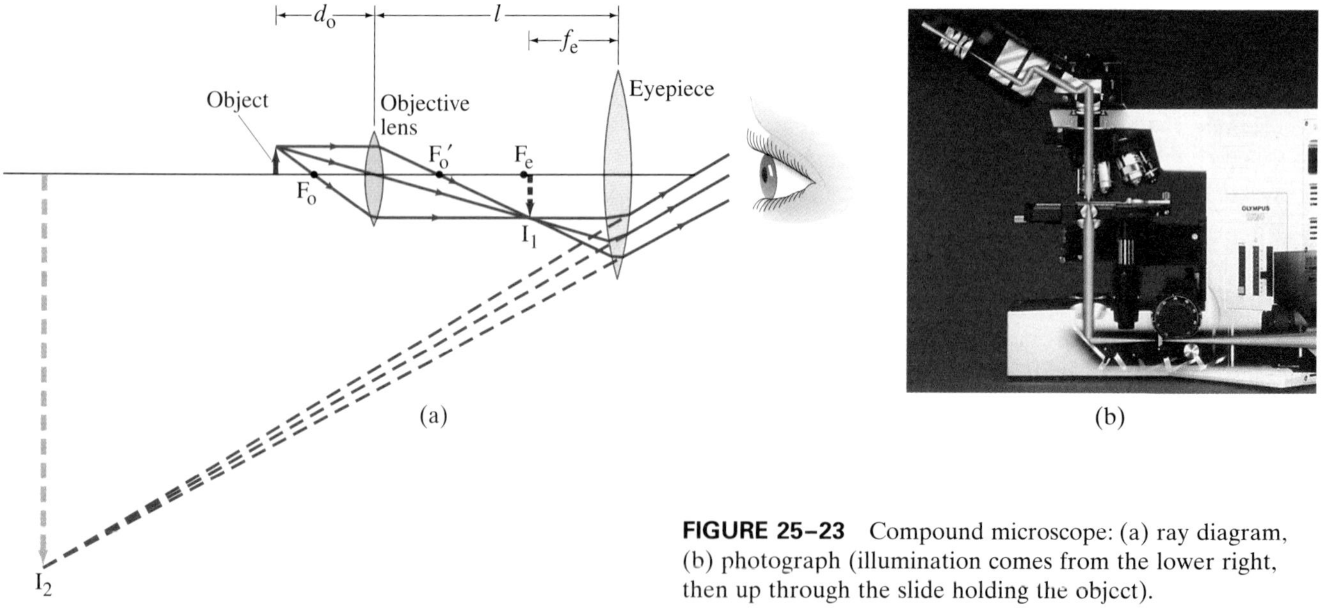


**FIGURE 25–23** Compound microscope: (a) ray diagram, (b) photograph (illumination comes from the lower right, then up through the slide holding the object).

The overall magnification of a microscope is the product of the magnifications produced by the two lenses. The image $I_1$ formed by the objective lens is a factor $m_o$ greater than the object itself. From Fig. 25–23a and Eq. 23–9 for the magnification of a simple lens, we have

$$m_o = \frac{h_i}{h_o} = \frac{d_i}{d_o} = \frac{l - f_e}{d_o}, \tag{25–4}$$

where $d_o$ and $d_i$ are the object and image distances for the objective lens, $l$ is the distance between the lenses (equal to the length of the barrel), and we ignored the minus sign in Eq. 23–9 which only tells us that the image is inverted. We set $d_i = l - f_e$, which is true only if the eye is relaxed, so that the image $I_1$ is at the eyepiece focal point $F_e$. The eyepiece acts like a simple magnifier. If we assume that the eye is relaxed, the eyepiece angular magnification $M_e$ is (from Eq. 25–2a)

$$M_e = \frac{N}{f_e}, \tag{25–5}$$

where the near point $N = 25\text{ cm}$ for the normal eye. Since the eyepiece enlarges the image formed by the objective, the overall angular magnification $M$ is the product of the lateral magnification of the objective lens, $m_o$, times the angular magnification, $M_e$, of the eyepiece lens (Eqs. 25–4 and 25–5):

Magnification of microscope

$$M = M_e m_o = \left(\frac{N}{f_e}\right)\left(\frac{l - f_e}{d_o}\right) \tag{25–6a}$$

$$\approx \frac{Nl}{f_e f_o}. \qquad [f_o \text{ and } f_e \ll l] \tag{25–6b}$$

The approximation, Eq. 25–6b, is accurate when $f_e$ and $f_o$ are small compared to $l$, so $l - f_e \approx l$ and $d_o \approx f_o$ (Fig. 25–23a). This is a good approximation for large magnifications, which are obtained when $f_o$ and $f_e$ are very small (they are in the denominator of Eq. 25–6b). To make lenses of very short focal length, which can be done best for the objective, compound lenses involving several elements must be used to avoid serious aberrations, as discussed in the next Section.

**EXAMPLE 25–9** **Microscope.** A compound microscope consists of a 10× eyepiece and a 50× objective 17.0 cm apart. Determine (*a*) the overall magnification, (*b*) the focal length of each lens, and (*c*) the position of the object when the final image is in focus with the eye relaxed. Assume a normal eye, so $N = 25\text{ cm}$.

**APPROACH** The overall magnification is the product of the eyepiece magnification and the objective magnification. The focal length of the eyepiece is found from Eq. 25–2a or 25–5 for the magnification of a simple magnifier. For the objective lens, it is easier to next find $d_o$ (part *c*) using Eq. 25–4 before we find $f_o$.

**SOLUTION** (*a*) The overall magnification is $(10\times)(50\times) = 500\times$.
(*b*) The eyepiece focal length is (Eq. 25–5) $f_e = N/M_e = 25\text{ cm}/10 = 2.5\text{ cm}$. Next we solve Eq. 25–4 for $d_o$, and find

$$d_o = \frac{l - f_e}{m_o} = \frac{(17.0\text{ cm} - 2.5\text{ cm})}{50} = 0.29\text{ cm}.$$

Then, from the thin lens equation for the objective with $d_i = l - f_e = 14.5\text{ cm}$ (see Fig. 25–23a),

$$\frac{1}{f_o} = \frac{1}{d_o} + \frac{1}{d_i} = \frac{1}{0.29\text{ cm}} + \frac{1}{14.5\text{ cm}} = 3.52\text{ cm}^{-1};$$

so $f_o = 1/(3.52\text{ cm}^{-1}) = 0.28\text{ cm}$.
(*c*) We just calculated $d_o = 0.29\text{ cm}$, which is very close to $f_o$.

## * 25–6 Aberrations of Lenses and Mirrors

In Chapter 23, we developed a theory of image formation by a thin lens. We found, for example, that all rays from each point on an object are brought to a single point as the image point. This, and other results, were based on approximations such as that all rays make small angles with one another and we can use $\sin\theta \approx \theta$. Because of these approximations, we expect deviations from the simple theory, and these are referred to as **lens aberrations**. There are several types of aberration; we will briefly discuss each of them separately, but all may be present at one time.

*Spherical aberration*

Consider an object at any point (even at infinity) on the axis of a lens. Rays from this point that pass through the outer regions of the lens are brought to a focus at a different point from those that pass through the center of the lens. This is called **spherical aberration,** and is shown exaggerated in Fig. 25–24.

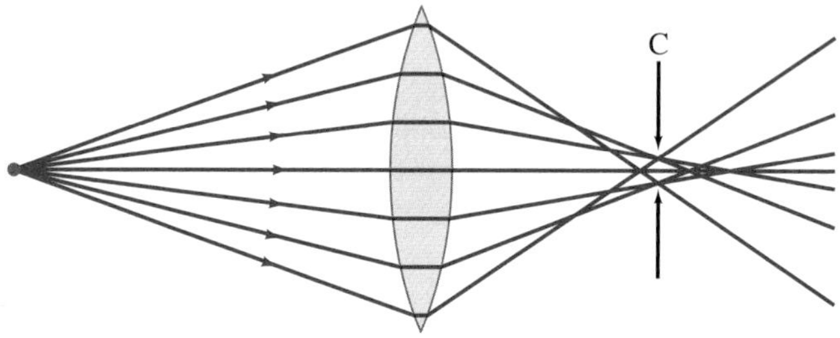


**FIGURE 25–24** Spherical aberration (exaggerated). Circle of least confusion is at C.

Consequently, the image seen on a piece of film (for example) will not be a point but a tiny circular patch of light. If the film is placed at the point C, as indicated, the circle will have its smallest diameter, which is referred to as the **circle of least confusion**. Spherical aberration is present whenever spherical surfaces are used. It can be corrected by using nonspherical lens surfaces, but to grind such lenses is difficult and expensive. It can be minimized with spherical surfaces by choosing the curvatures so that equal amounts of bending occur at each lens surface; a lens can be designed like this for only one particular object distance. Spherical aberration is usually corrected (by which we mean reduced greatly) by the use of several lenses in combination, and by using only the central part of lenses.

*Off-axis aberrations*

For object points off the lens axis, additional aberrations occur. Rays passing through the different parts of the lens cause spreading of the image that is noncircular. There are two effects: **coma** (because the image of a point is comet-shaped rather than a circle) and **off-axis astigmatism.**† Furthermore, the image points for objects off the axis but at the same distance from the lens do not fall on a flat plane but on a curved surface—that is, the focal plane is not flat. (We expect this because the points on a flat plane, such as the film in a camera, are not equidistant from the lens.) This aberration is known as **curvature of field** and is a problem in cameras and other devices where the film is placed in a flat plane. In the eye, however, the retina is curved, which compensates for this effect.

Another aberration, known as **distortion**, is a result of variation of magnification at different distances from the lens axis. Thus a straight-line object some distance from the axis may form a curved image. A square grid of lines may be distorted to produce "barrel distortion," or "pincushion distortion," Fig. 25–25. The latter is common in extreme wide-angle lenses.

All the above aberrations occur for monochromatic light and hence are referred to as *monochromatic aberrations*. Normal light is not monochromatic, and there will also be **chromatic aberration**. This aberration arises because of dispersion—the variation of index of refraction of transparent materials with wavelength (Section 24–4). For example, blue light is bent more than red light

†Although the effect is the same as for astigmatism in the eye (Section 25–2), the cause is different. Off-axis astigmatism is no problem in the eye because objects are clearly seen only at the fovea, on the lens axis.

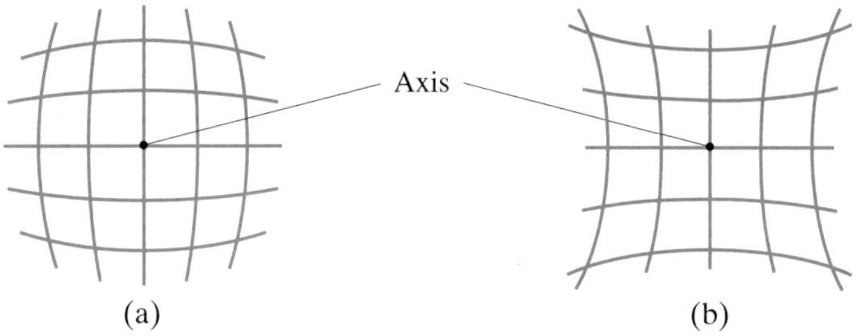


**FIGURE 25–25** Distortion: lenses may image a square grid of perpendicular lines to produce (a) barrel distortion or (b) pincushion distortion. These distortions can be seen in the photograph of Fig. 23–29d.

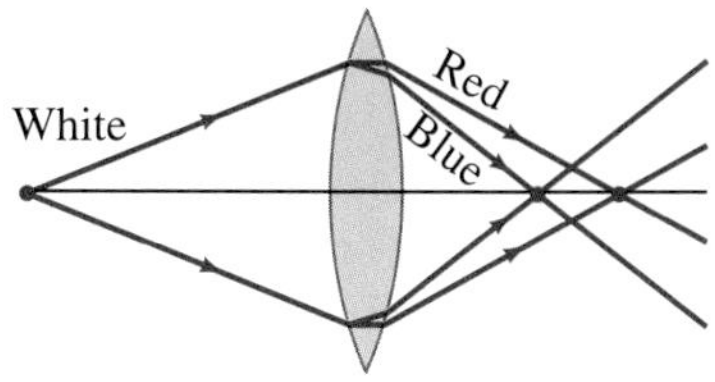


**FIGURE 25–26** Chromatic aberration. Different colors are focused at different points.

**FIGURE 25–27** Achromatic doublet.

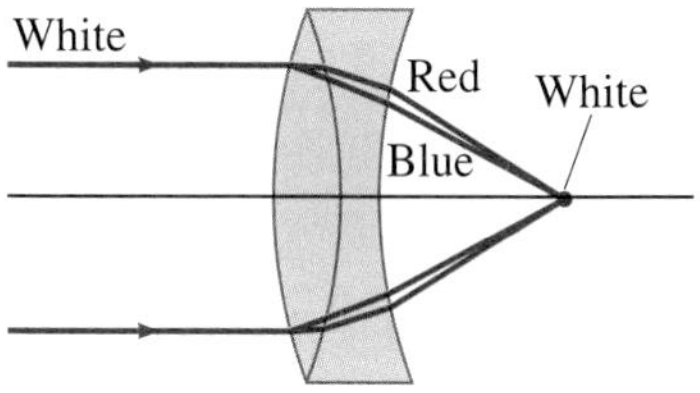


by glass. So if white light is incident on a lens, the different colors are focused at different points, Fig. 25–26, and there will be colored fringes in the image. Chromatic aberration can be eliminated for any two colors (and reduced greatly for all others) by the use of two lenses made of different materials with different indices of refraction and dispersion. Normally one lens is converging and the other diverging, and they are often cemented together (Fig. 25–27). Such a lens combination is called an **achromatic doublet** (or "color-corrected" lens).

It is not possible to fully correct all aberrations. Combining two or more lenses together can reduce them. High-quality lenses used in cameras, microscopes, and other devices are **compound lenses** consisting of many simple lenses (referred to as **elements**). A typical high-quality camera lens may contain six to eight (or more) elements. For simplicity we will usually indicate lenses in diagrams as if they were simple lenses.

The human eye is also subject to aberrations, but they are minimal. Spherical aberration, for example, is minimized because (1) the cornea is less curved at the edges than at the center, and (2) the lens is less dense at the edges than at the center. Both effects cause rays at the outer edges to be bent less strongly, and thus help to reduce spherical aberration. Chromatic aberration is partially compensated for because the lens absorbs the shorter wavelengths appreciably and the retina is less sensitive to the blue and violet wavelengths. This is just the region of the spectrum where dispersion—and thus chromatic aberration—is greatest (Fig. 24–14).

Spherical mirrors (Section 23–3) also suffer aberrations including spherical aberration (see Fig. 23–11). Mirrors can be ground in a parabolic shape to correct for spherical aberration, but they are much harder to make and therefore very expensive. Spherical mirrors do not, however, exhibit chromatic aberration because the light does not pass through them (no refraction, no dispersion).

## 25–7 Limits of Resolution; Circular Apertures

The ability of a lens to produce distinct images of two point objects very close together is called the **resolution** of the lens. The closer the two images can be and still be seen as distinct (rather than overlapping blobs), the higher the resolution. The resolution of a camera lens, for example, is often specified as so many lines per millimeter, as mentioned in Section 25–1.

Two principal factors limit the resolution of a lens. The first is lens aberrations. As we saw, because of spherical and other aberrations, a point object is not a point on the image but a tiny blob. Careful design of compound lenses can reduce aberrations significantly, but they cannot be eliminated entirely. The second factor that limits resolution is *diffraction*, which cannot be corrected for optically because it is a natural result of the wave nature of light. We discuss it now.

In Section 24–5 we saw that because light travels as a wave, light from a point source passing through a slit is spread out into a diffraction pattern (Figs. 24–19 and 24–21). A lens, because it has edges, acts like a slit. When a lens forms the image of a point object, the image is actually a tiny diffraction pattern. Thus *an image would be blurred even if aberrations were absent.*

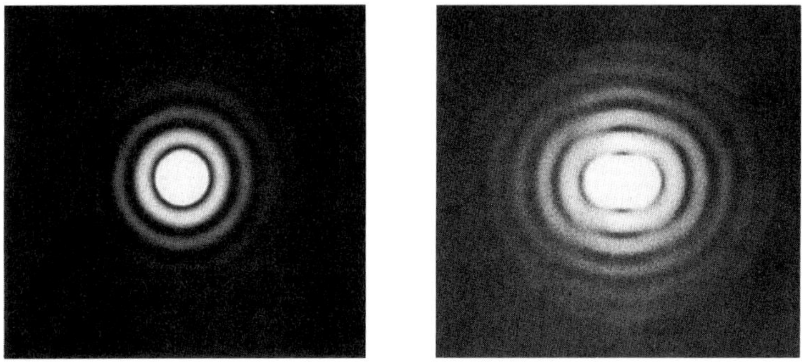


**FIGURE 25–28** Photographs of images (greatly magnified) formed by a lens, showing the diffraction pattern of an image for: (a) a single point object; (b) two point objects whose images are barely resolved.

In the analysis that follows, we assume that the lens is free of aberrations, so we can concentrate on diffraction effects and how much they limit the resolution of a lens. In Fig. 24–21 we saw that the diffraction pattern produced by light passing through a rectangular slit has a central maximum in which most of the light falls. This central peak falls to a minimum on either side of its center at an angle $\theta$ given by

$$\sin\theta = \frac{\lambda}{D}$$

(this is Eq. 24–3a), where $D$ is the slit width and $\lambda$ the wavelength of light used. $\theta$ is the angular half-width of the central maximum, and for small angles can be written

$$\theta \approx \sin\theta = \frac{\lambda}{D}.$$

There are also low-intensity fringes beyond. For a lens, or any circular hole, the image of a point object will consist of a *circular* central peak (called the *diffraction spot* or *Airy disk*) surrounded by faint circular fringes, as shown in Fig. 25–28a. The central maximum has an angular half width given by

*Smaller angle means better resolution*

$$\theta = \frac{1.22\lambda}{D},$$

where $D$ is the diameter of the circular opening.

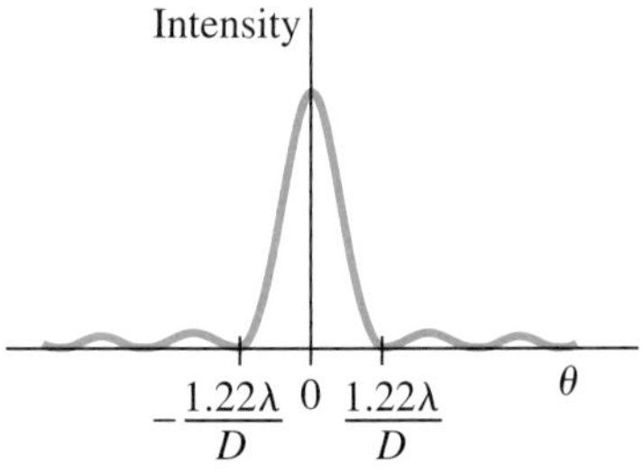


**FIGURE 25–29** Intensity of light across the diffraction pattern of a circular hole.

This formula differs from that for a slit (Eq. 24–3) by the factor 1.22. This factor appears because the width of a circular hole is not uniform (like a rectangular slit) but varies from its diameter $D$ to zero. A mathematical analysis shows that the "average" width is $D/1.22$. Hence we get the equation above rather than Eq. 24–3. The intensity of light in the diffraction pattern of light from a point source passing through a circular opening is shown in Fig. 25–29. The image for a non-point source is a superposition of such patterns. For most purposes we need consider only the central spot, since the concentric rings are so much dimmer.

If two point objects are very close, the diffraction patterns of their images will overlap as shown in Fig. 25–28b. As the objects are moved closer, a separation is reached where you can't tell if there are two overlapping images or a single image. The separation at which this happens may be judged differently by different observers. However, a generally accepted criterion is that proposed by Lord Rayleigh (1842–1919). This **Rayleigh criterion** states that *two images are just resolvable when the center of the diffraction disk of one image is directly over the first minimum in the diffraction pattern of the other*. This is shown in Fig. 25–30. Since the first minimum is at an angle $\theta = 1.22\lambda/D$ from the central maximum, Fig. 25–30 shows that two objects can be considered *just resolvable* if they are separated by at least the angle $\theta$ given by

*Rayleigh criterion (resolution limit)*

$$\theta = \frac{1.22\lambda}{D}. \qquad [\theta \text{ in radians}] \quad \textbf{(25–7)}$$

This is the limit on resolution set by the wave nature of light due to diffraction. A smaller angle means better resolution: you can make out closer objects. We see from Eq. 25–7 that using a shorter wavelength $\lambda$ can increase resolution.

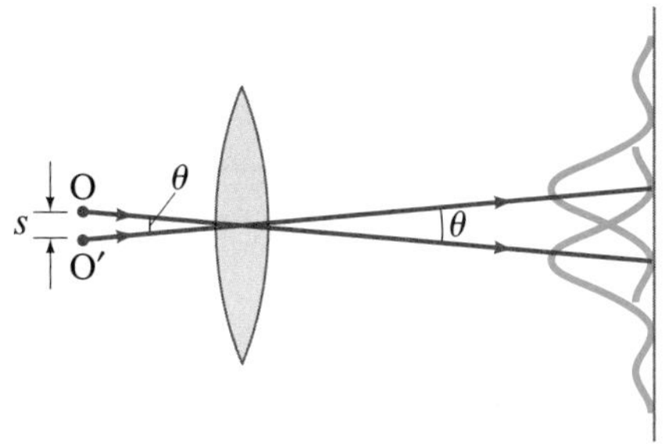


**FIGURE 25–30** The *Rayleigh criterion.* Two images are just resolvable when the center of the diffraction peak of one is directly over the first minimum in the diffraction pattern of the other. The two point objects O and O′ subtend an angle $\theta$ at the lens; only one ray (it passes through the center of the lens) is drawn for each object, to indicate the center of the diffraction pattern of its image.

**EXAMPLE 25–10** **Hubble Space Telescope.** The Hubble Space Telescope (HST) is a reflecting telescope that was placed in orbit above the Earth's atmosphere, so its resolution would not be limited by turbulence in the atmosphere (Fig. 25–31). Its objective diameter is 2.4 m. For visible light, say $\lambda = 550\,\text{nm}$, estimate the improvement in resolution the Hubble offers over Earth-bound telescopes, which are limited in resolution by movement of the Earth's atmosphere to about half an arc second. (Each degree is divided into 60 minutes each containing 60 seconds, so $1^\circ = 3600$ arc seconds.)

**APPROACH** Angular resolution for the Hubble is given (in radians) by Eq. 25–7. The resolution for Earth telescopes is given, and we first convert it to radians so we can compare.

**SOLUTION** Earth-bound telescopes are limited to an angular resolution of

$$\theta = \tfrac{1}{2}\left(\frac{1}{3600}\right)^{\circ}\left(\frac{2\pi\text{ rad}}{360^\circ}\right) = 2.4 \times 10^{-6}\,\text{rad}.$$

The Hubble, on the other hand, is limited by diffraction (Eq. 25–7) which for $\lambda = 550\,\text{nm}$ is

$$\theta = \frac{1.22\lambda}{D} = \frac{1.22(550 \times 10^{-9}\,\text{m})}{2.4\,\text{m}} = 2.8 \times 10^{-7}\,\text{rad},$$

thus giving almost ten times better resolution $(2.4 \times 10^{-6}\,\text{rad}/2.8 \times 10^{-7}\,\text{rad} \approx 9\times)$.

**NOTE** The Hubble can also observe radiation in the near ultraviolet (wavelengths as small as 115 nm) and infrared (wavelengths as long as 1 mm), which are ranges of the spectrum blocked by the atmosphere. The sensor is a CCD, as in a camera (see Section 25–1), with a pixel count of 16 MP.

**FIGURE 25–31** Hubble Space Telescope, with Earth in the background. The flat orange panels are solar cells that collect energy from the Sun.

**EXAMPLE 25–11** **ESTIMATE** **Eye resolution.** You are in an airplane at an altitude of 10,000 m. If you look down at the ground, estimate the minimum separation $s$ between objects that you could distinguish. Consider only diffraction, and assume your pupil is about 3.0 mm in diameter and $\lambda = 550\,\text{nm}$.

PHYSICS APPLIED
*How well the eye can see*

**APPROACH** We use the Rayleigh criterion, Eq. 25–7, to estimate $\theta$. The separation $s$ of objects equals their distance away, $L = 10^4\,\text{m}$, times $\theta$ (in radians) as $\theta$ is small, so $s = L\theta$.

**SOLUTION** In Eq. 25–7, we set $D = 3.0\,\text{mm}$ for the opening of the eye:

$$s = L\theta = L\frac{1.22\lambda}{D}$$

$$= \frac{(10^4\,\text{m})(1.22)(550 \times 10^{-9}\,\text{m})}{3.0 \times 10^{-3}\,\text{m}} = 2.2\,\text{m}.$$

**EXERCISE D** Someone claims a spy satellite camera can see 3-cm-high newspaper headlines from an altitude of 100 km. If diffraction were the only limitation ($\lambda = 550\,\text{nm}$), use Eq. 25–7 to determine what diameter lens the camera would have.

## 25–8 Resolution of Telescopes and Microscopes; the λ Limit

You might think that a microscope or telescope could be designed to produce any desired magnification, depending on the choice of focal lengths and quality of the lenses. But this is not possible, because of diffraction. An increase in magnification above a certain point merely results in magnification of the diffraction patterns. This can be highly misleading since we might think we are seeing details of an object when we are really seeing details of the diffraction pattern. To examine this problem, we apply the Rayleigh criterion: two objects (or two nearby points on one object) are just resolvable if they are separated by an angle $\theta$ (Fig. 25–30) given by Eq. 25–7:

$$\theta = \frac{1.22\lambda}{D}.$$

This formula is valid for either a microscope or a telescope, where $D$ is the diameter of the objective lens. For a telescope, the resolution is specified by stating $\theta$ as given by this equation.†

For a microscope, it is more convenient to specify the actual distance, $s$, between two points that are just barely resolvable: see Fig. 25–30. Since objects are normally placed near the focal point of the microscope objective, the angle subtended by two objects is $\theta = s/f$, or $s = f\theta$. If we combine this with Eq. 25–7, we obtain for the **resolving power (RP)** of a microscope

*Resolving power*

$$\text{RP} = s = f\theta = \frac{1.22\lambda f}{D}, \qquad \textbf{(25–8)}$$

where $f$ is the objective lens' focal length (not frequency). This distance $s$ is called the resolving power of the lens because it is the minimum separation of two object points that can just be resolved, assuming the highest quality lens since this limit is imposed by the wave nature of light. A smaller RP means better resolution, better detail.

**FIGURE 25–32** The 300-meter radiotelescope in Arecibo, Puerto Rico, uses radio waves (Fig. 22–8) instead of visible light.

**EXAMPLE 25–12 Telescope resolution (radio wave vs. visible light).** What is the theoretical minimum angular separation of two stars that can just be resolved by (*a*) the 200-inch telescope on Palomar Mountain (Fig. 25–21c); and (*b*) the Arecibo radiotelescope (Fig. 25–32), whose diameter is 300 m and whose radius of curvature is also 300 m. Assume $\lambda = 550\,\text{nm}$ for the visible-light telescope in part (*a*), and $\lambda = 4\,\text{cm}$ (the shortest wavelength at which the radiotelescope has been operated) in part (*b*).

**APPROACH** We apply the Rayleigh criterion (Eq. 25–7) for each telescope.

**SOLUTION** (*a*) Since $D = 200\,\text{in.} = 5.1\,\text{m}$, we have from Eq. 25–7 that

$$\theta = \frac{1.22\lambda}{D} = \frac{(1.22)(5.50 \times 10^{-7}\,\text{m})}{(5.1\,\text{m})} = 1.3 \times 10^{-7}\,\text{rad},$$

or $0.75 \times 10^{-5}$ deg. (Note that this is equivalent to resolving two points less than 1 cm apart from a distance of 100 km!)

(*b*) For radio waves with $\lambda = 0.04\,\text{m}$, the resolution is

$$\theta = \frac{(1.22)(0.04\,\text{m})}{(300\,\text{m})} = 1.6 \times 10^{-4}\,\text{rad}.$$

The resolution is less because the wavelength is so much larger, but the larger objective is a plus.

† Earth-bound telescopes with large-diameter objectives are usually limited not by diffraction but by other effects such as turbulence in the atmosphere. The resolution of a high-quality microscope, on the other hand, normally *is* limited by diffraction; microscope objectives are complex compound lenses containing many elements of small diameter (since $f$ is small), thus reducing aberrations.

**NOTE** In both cases, we determined the limit set by diffraction. The resolution for a visible-light Earth-bound telescope is not this good because of aberrations and, more importantly, turbulence in the atmosphere. In fact, large-diameter objectives are not justified by increased resolution, but by their greater light-gathering ability—they allow more light in, so fainter objects can be seen. Radiotelescopes are not hindered by atmospheric turbulence, and the resolution found in (*b*) is a good estimate.

Diffraction sets an ultimate limit on the detail that can be seen on any object. In Eq. 25–8 for resolving power, the focal length of a lens cannot practically be made less than (approximately) the radius of the lens, and even that is very difficult (see the lensmaker's equation, Eq. 23–10). In this best case, Eq. 25–8 gives, with $f \approx D/2$,

$$\mathrm{RP} \approx \frac{\lambda}{2}. \qquad \textbf{(25–9)}$$

Thus we can say, to within a factor of 2 or so, that

**it is not possible to resolve detail of objects smaller than the wavelength of the radiation being used.**

*Resolution limited to $\lambda$*

This is an important and useful rule of thumb.

Compound lenses in microscopes are now designed so well that the actual limit on resolution is often set by diffraction—that is, by the wavelength of the light used. To obtain greater detail, one must use radiation of shorter wavelength. The use of UV radiation can increase the resolution by a factor of perhaps 2. Far more important, however, was the discovery in the early twentieth century that electrons have wave properties (Chapter 27) and that their wavelengths can be very small. The wave nature of electrons is utilized in the electron microscope (Section 27–9), which can magnify 100 to 1000 times more than a visible-light microscope because of the much shorter wavelengths. X-rays, too, have very short wavelengths and are often used to study objects in great detail (Section 25–11).

## 25–9 Resolution of the Human Eye and Useful Magnification

The resolution of the human eye is limited by several factors, all of roughly the same order of magnitude. The resolution is best at the fovea, where the cone spacing is smallest, about $3\,\mu\mathrm{m}$ (= 3000 nm). The diameter of the pupil varies from about 0.1 cm to about 0.8 cm. So for $\lambda = 550\,\mathrm{nm}$ (where the eye's sensitivity is greatest), the diffraction limit is about $\theta \approx 1.22\lambda/D \approx 8 \times 10^{-5}\,\mathrm{rad}$ to $6 \times 10^{-4}\,\mathrm{rad}$. The eye is about 2 cm long, giving a resolving power (Eq. 25–8) of $s \approx (2 \times 10^{-2}\,\mathrm{m})(8 \times 10^{-5}\,\mathrm{rad}) \approx 2\,\mu\mathrm{m}$ at best, to about $15\,\mu\mathrm{m}$ at worst (pupil small). Spherical and chromatic aberration also limit the resolution to about $10\,\mu\mathrm{m}$. The net result is that the eye can resolve objects whose angular separation is about

$$5 \times 10^{-4}\,\mathrm{rad}$$

*Best eye resolution*

at best. This corresponds to objects separated by 1 cm at a distance of about 20 m.

The typical near point of a human eye is about 25 cm. At this distance, the eye can just resolve objects that are $(25\,\mathrm{cm})(5 \times 10^{-4}\,\mathrm{rad}) \approx 10^{-4}\,\mathrm{m} = \frac{1}{10}\,\mathrm{mm}$ apart. Since the best light microscopes can resolve objects no smaller than about 200 nm at best (Eq. 25–9 for violet light, $\lambda = 400\,\mathrm{nm}$), the useful magnification [= (resolution by naked eye)/(resolution by microscope)] is limited to about

$$\frac{10^{-4}\,\mathrm{m}}{200 \times 10^{-9}\,\mathrm{m}} \approx 500\times.$$

*Maximum useful microscope magnification*

In practice, magnifications of about 1000× are often used to minimize eyestrain. Any greater magnification would simply make visible the diffraction pattern produced by the microscope objective.

## * 25–10 Specialty Microscopes and Contrast

All the resolving power a microscope can attain will be useless if the object to be seen cannot be distinguished from the background. The difference in brightness between the image of an object and the image of the surroundings is called **contrast**. Achieving high contrast is an important problem in microscopy and other forms of imaging. The problem arises in biology, for example, because cells consist largely of water and are almost uniformly transparent to light. We now briefly discuss two special types of microscope that can increase contrast: the interference and phase-contrast microscopes.

PHYSICS APPLIED
*Interference microscope*

An **interference microscope** makes use of the wave properties of light in a direct way to increase contrast in a transparent object. Consider a transparent object—say, a bacterium in water (Fig. 25–33). Light enters uniformly from the left and is coherent (in phase) at all points such as a and b. If the object is as transparent as the water, the beam leaving at d will be as bright as that at c. There will be no contrast and the object will not be seen. However, if the object's refractive index is slightly different from that of the surrounding medium, the wavelength within the object will be altered as shown. Hence light waves at points c and d will differ in phase, if not in amplitude. The interference microscope changes this difference in phase into a difference of amplitude which our eyes can detect. Light that passes through the sample is superimposed onto a reference beam that does not pass through the object, so that they interfere. One way of doing this is shown in Fig. 25–34. Light from a source is split into two equal beams by a half-silvered mirror, $MS_1$. One beam passes through the object, and the second (comparison beam) passes through an identical system without the object. The two meet again and are superposed by the half-silvered mirror $MS_2$ before entering the eyepiece and the eye. The path length (and amplitude) of the comparison beam is adjustable so that the background can be dark; that is, full destructive interference occurs. Light passing through the object (beam bd in Fig. 25–33) will also interfere with the comparison beam. But because of its different phase, the interference will not be completely destructive. Thus it will appear brighter than the background. Where the object varies in thickness, the phase difference between beams ac and bd in Fig. 25–33 will be different, thus affecting the amount of interference. Hence *variation in the thickness of the object will appear as variations in brightness in the image.*

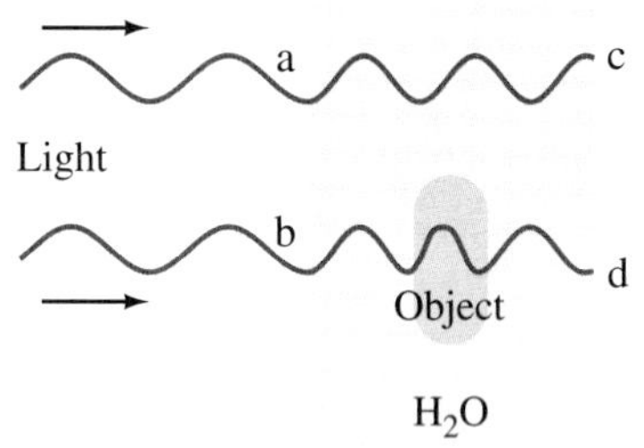


**FIGURE 25–33** Object—say, a bacterium—in a water solution.

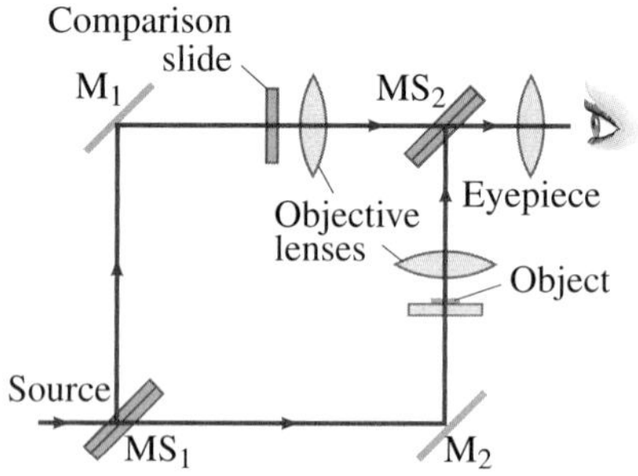


**FIGURE 25–34** Diagram of an interference microscope.

PHYSICS APPLIED
*Phase-contrast microscope*

A **phase-contrast microscope** also makes use of interference and differences in phase to produce a high-contrast image. Contrast is achieved by a circular glass *phase plate* that has a groove (or a raised portion) in the shape of a ring, positioned so undeviated source rays pass through it, but rays deviated by the object do not pass through this ring. Because the rays deviated by the object travel through a different thickness of glass than the undeviated source rays, the two can be out of phase and can interfere destructively at the object image plane. Thus the image of the object can contrast sharply with the background. Phase-contrast microscope images tend to have "halos" around them (as a result of diffraction from the phase-plate opening), so care must be taken in the interpretation of images.

## * 25–11 X-Rays and X-Ray Diffraction

In 1895, W. C. Roentgen (1845–1923) discovered that when electrons were accelerated by a high voltage in a vacuum tube and allowed to strike a glass or metal surface inside the tube, fluorescent minerals some distance away would glow, and photographic film would become exposed. Roentgen attributed these effects to a new type of radiation (different from cathode rays). They were given the name **X-rays** after the algebraic symbol $x$, meaning an unknown quantity. He soon found that X-rays penetrated through some materials better than through others, and within a few weeks he presented the first X-ray photograph (of his wife's hand). The production of X-rays today is usually done in a tube (Fig. 25–35) similar to Roentgen's, using voltages of typically 30 kV to 150 kV.

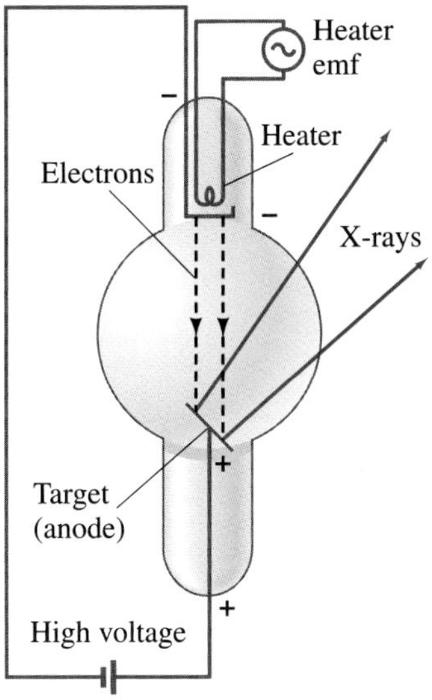


**FIGURE 25–35** X-ray tube. Electrons emitted by a heated filament in a vacuum tube are accelerated by a high voltage. When they strike the surface of the anode, the "target," X-rays are emitted.

Investigations into the nature of X-rays indicated they were not charged particles (such as electrons) since they could not be deflected by electric or magnetic fields. It was suggested that they might be a form of invisible light. However, they showed no diffraction or interference effects using ordinary gratings. Indeed, if their wavelengths were much smaller than the typical grating spacing of $10^{-6}$ m $(= 10^{3}$ nm$)$, no effects would be expected. Around 1912, Max von Laue (1879–1960) suggested that if the atoms in a crystal were arranged in a regular array (see Fig. 13–2a), such a crystal might serve as a diffraction grating for very short wavelengths on the order of the spacing between atoms, estimated to be about $10^{-10}$ m $(= 10^{-1}$ nm$)$. Experiments soon showed that X-rays scattered from a crystal did indeed show the peaks and valleys of a diffraction pattern (Fig. 25–36). Thus it was shown, in a single blow, that X-rays have a wave nature and that atoms are arranged in a regular way in crystals. Today, X-rays are recognized as electromagnetic radiation with wavelengths in the range of about $10^{-2}$ nm to 10 nm, the range readily produced in an X-ray tube.

**FIGURE 25–36** This X-ray diffraction pattern is one of the first observed by Max von Laue in 1912 when he aimed a beam of X-rays at a zinc sulfide crystal. The diffraction pattern was detected directly on a photographic plate.

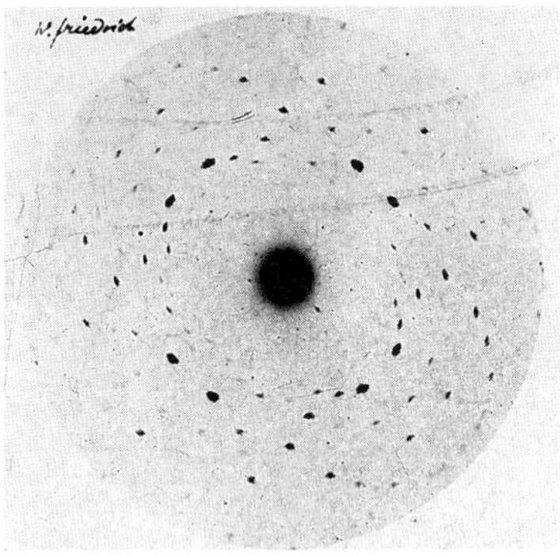

We saw in Sections 25–7 and 25–8 that light of shorter wavelength provides greater resolution when we are examining an object microscopically. Since X-rays have much shorter wavelengths than visible light, they should in principle offer much greater resolution. However, there seems to be no effective material to use as lenses for the very short wavelengths of X-rays. Instead, the clever but complicated technique of **X-ray diffraction** (or **crystallography**) has proved very effective for examining the microscopic world of atoms and molecules. In a simple crystal such as NaCl, the atoms are arranged in an orderly cubical fashion, Fig. 25–37, with atoms spaced a distance $d$ apart. Suppose that a beam of X-rays is incident on the crystal at an angle $\phi$ to the surface, and that the two rays shown are reflected from two subsequent planes of atoms as shown. The two rays will constructively interfere if the extra distance ray I travels is a whole number of wavelengths farther than the distance ray II travels. This extra distance is $2d \sin\phi$. Therefore, constructive interference will occur when

$$m\lambda = 2d\sin\phi, \qquad m = 1, 2, 3, \cdots, \tag{25–10}$$

where $m$ can be any integer. (Notice that $\phi$ is *not* the angle with respect to the normal to the surface.) This is called the **Bragg equation** after W. L. Bragg (1890–1971), who derived it and who, together with his father W. H. Bragg (1862–1942), developed the theory and technique of X-ray diffraction by crystals in 1912–1913. If the X-ray wavelength is known and the angle $\phi$ is measured, the distance $d$ between atoms can be obtained. This is the basis for X-ray crystallography.

*Bragg equation*

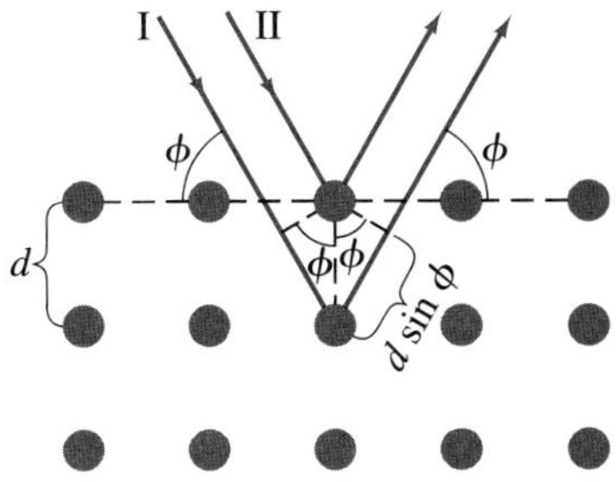


**FIGURE 25–37** X-ray diffraction by a crystal.

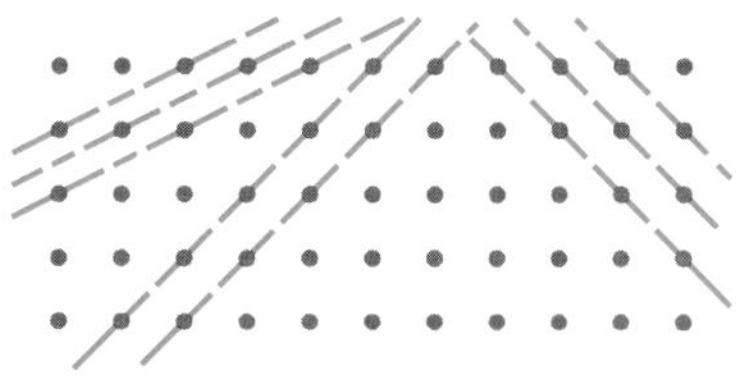

FIGURE 25–38 X-rays can be diffracted from many possible planes within a crystal.

Actual X-ray diffraction patterns are quite complicated. First of all, a crystal is a three-dimensional object, and X-rays can be diffracted from different planes at different angles within the crystal, as shown in Fig. 25–38. Although the analysis is complex, a great deal can be learned about any substance that can be put in crystalline form. If the substance is not a single crystal but a mixture of many tiny crystals—as in a metal or a powder—then instead of a series of spots, as in Fig. 25–36, a series of circles is obtained, Fig. 25–39, each corresponding to diffraction of a certain order $m$ from a particular set of parallel planes.

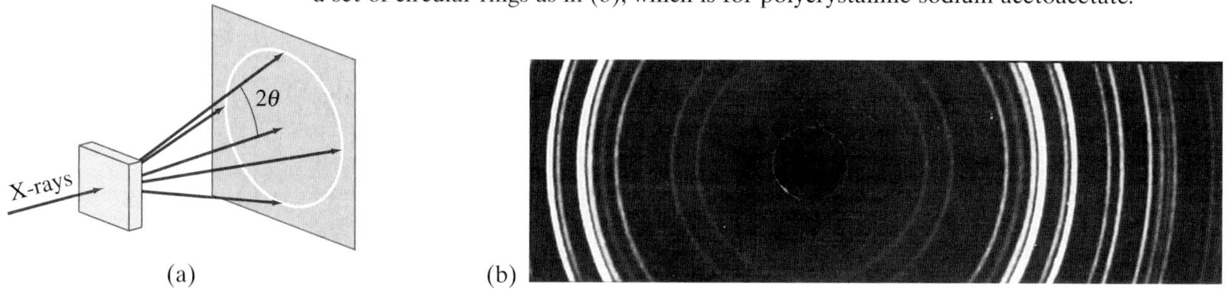


FIGURE 25–39 (a) Diffraction of X-rays from a polycrystalline substance produces a set of circular rings as in (b), which is for polycrystalline sodium acetoacetate.

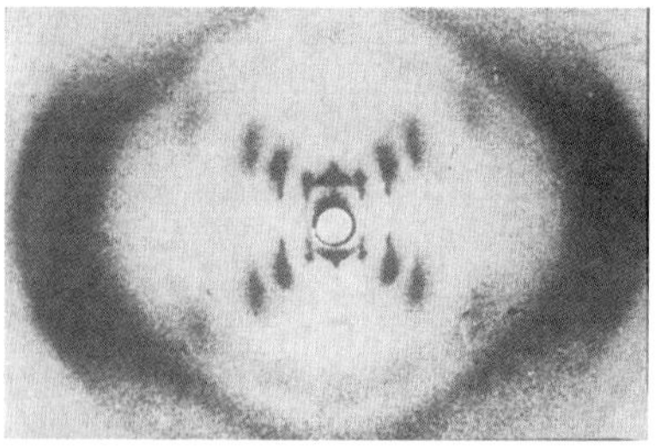

FIGURE 25–40 X-ray diffraction photo of DNA molecules taken by Rosalind Franklin in the early 1950s. The cross of spots suggested that DNA is a helix.

X-ray diffraction has been very useful in determining the structure of biologically important molecules, such as the double helix structure of DNA, worked out by James Watson and Francis Crick in 1953. See Fig. 25–40, and for models of the double helix, Figs. 16–44a and 16–45. Around 1960, the first detailed structure of a protein molecule, myoglobin, was elucidated with the aid of X-ray diffraction. Soon the structure of an important constituent of blood, hemoglobin, was worked out, and since then the structures of a great many molecules have been determined with the help of X-rays.

## * 25–12 X-Ray Imaging and Computed Tomography (CT Scan)

### * Normal X-ray Image

PHYSICS APPLIED
*Normal X-ray image*

For a conventional medical or dental X-ray photograph, the X-rays emerging from the tube (Fig. 25–35) pass through the body and are detected on photographic film or a fluorescent screen, Fig. 25–41. The rays travel in very nearly straight lines through the body with minimal deviation since at X-ray wavelengths there is little diffraction or refraction. There is absorption (and scattering), however; and the difference in absorption by different structures in the body is what gives rise to the image produced by the transmitted rays. The less the absorption, the greater the transmission and the darker the film. The image is, in a sense, a "shadow" of what the rays have passed through. The X-ray image is *not* produced by focusing rays with lenses as for the instruments discussed earlier in this Chapter.

CAUTION
*X-ray images are a sort of shadow; no lenses are involved*

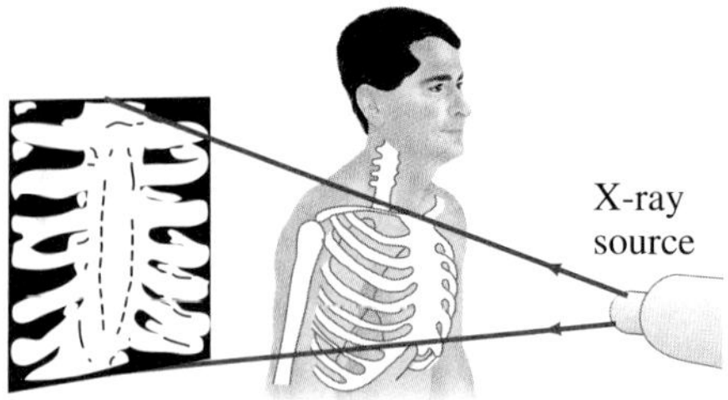


FIGURE 25–41 Conventional X-ray imaging, which is essentially shadowing.

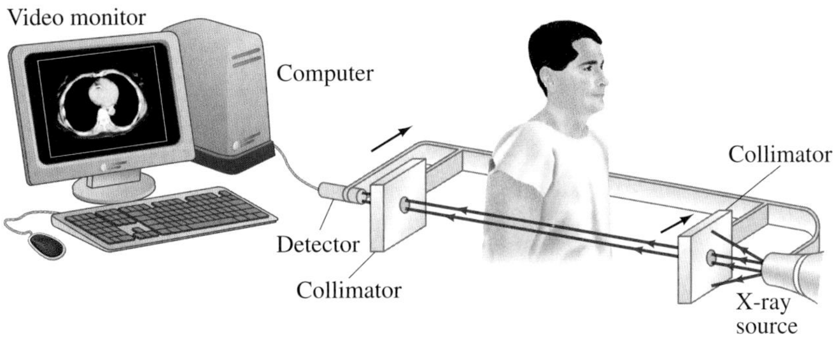


**FIGURE 25–42** Tomographic imaging: the X-ray source and detector move together across the body, the transmitted intensity being measured at a large number of points. Then the source–detector assembly is rotated slightly (say, 1°) and another scan is made. This process is repeated for perhaps 180°. The computer reconstructs the image of the slice and it is presented on a TV monitor.

## * Tomography Images (CT)

In conventional X-ray images, the entire thickness of the body is projected onto the film; structures overlap and in many cases are difficult to distinguish. In the 1970s, a revolutionary new X-ray technique was developed called **computed tomography** (CT), which produces an image of a *slice* through the body. (The word **tomography** comes from the Greek: *tomos* = slice, *graph* = picture.) Structures and lesions previously impossible to visualize can now be seen with remarkable clarity. The principle behind CT is shown in Fig. 25–42: a thin collimated beam of X-rays (to "collimate" means to "make straight") passes through the body to a detector that measures the transmitted intensity. Measurements are made at a large number of points as the source and detector are moved past the body together. The apparatus is then rotated slightly about the body axis and again scanned; this is repeated at (perhaps) 1° intervals for 180°. The intensity of the transmitted beam for the many points of each scan, and for each angle, are sent to a computer that reconstructs the image of the slice. Note that the imaged slice is perpendicular to the long axis of the body. For this reason, CT is sometimes called **computerized axial tomography** (CAT), although the abbreviation CAT, as in CAT scan, can also be read as **computer-assisted tomography**.

PHYSICS APPLIED
*Computed tomography images*

*CAT scans*

The use of a single detector as in Fig. 25–42 would require a few minutes for the many scans needed to form a complete image. Much faster scanners use a fan beam, Fig. 25–43a, in which beams passing through the entire cross section of the body are detected simultaneously by many detectors. The source and detectors are then rotated about the patient, and an image requires only a few seconds. Even faster, and therefore useful for heart scans, are fixed source machines wherein an electron beam is directed (by magnetic fields) to tungsten targets surrounding the patient, creating the X-rays. See Fig. 25–43b.

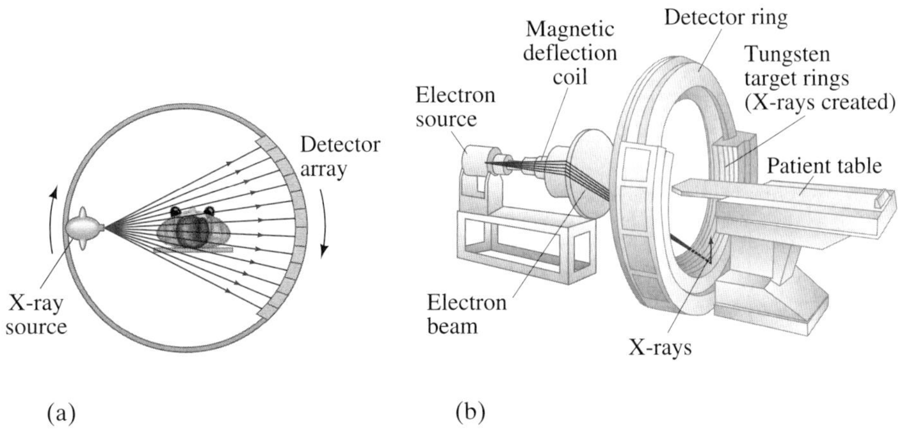


**FIGURE 25–43** (a) Fan-beam scanner. Rays transmitted through the entire body are measured simultaneously at each angle. The source and detector rotate to take measurements at different angles. In another type of fan-beam scanner, there are detectors around the entire 360° of the circle which remain fixed as the source moves. (b) In another type, a beam of electrons from the source is directed by magnetic fields at tungsten targets surrounding the patient.

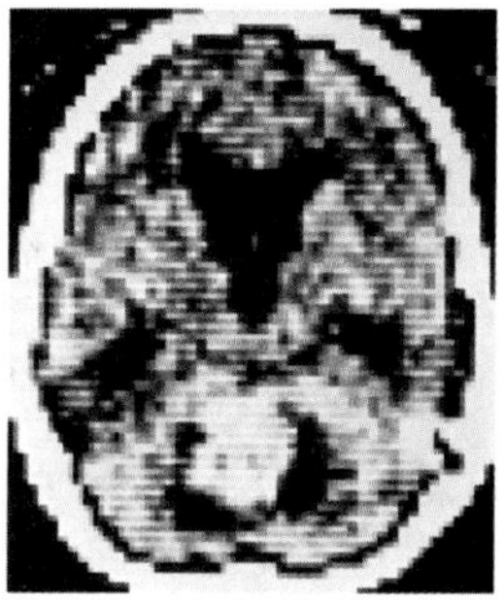

(a)

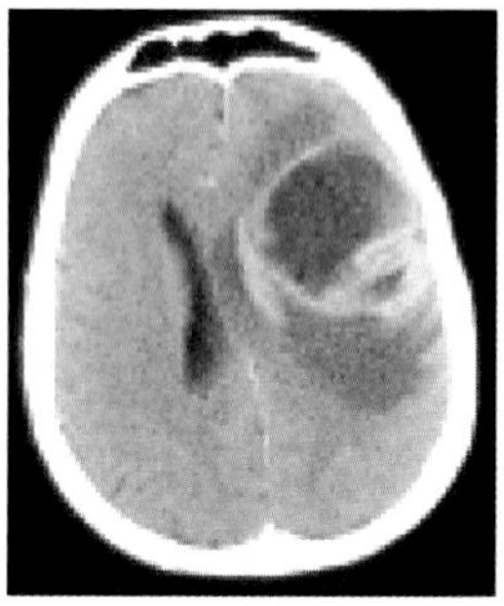

(b)

FIGURE 25–44 Two CT images, with different resolutions, each showing a cross section of a brain. Photo (a) is of low resolution; photo (b), of higher resolution, shows a brain tumor (dark area on the right).

## * Image Formation

But how is the image formed? We can think of the slice to be imaged as being divided into many tiny picture elements (or pixels), which could be squares. (See, for example, Fig. 24–49.) For CT, the width of each pixel is chosen according to the width of the detectors and/or the width of the X-ray beams, and this determines the resolution of the image, which might be 1 mm. An X-ray detector measures the intensity of the transmitted beam. Subtracting this value from the intensity of the beam at the source, yields the total absorption (called a "projection") along that beam line. Complicated mathematical techniques are used to analyze all the absorption projections for the huge number of beam scans measured (see the next subsection), obtaining the absorption at each pixel and assigning each a "grayness value" according to how much radiation was absorbed. The image is made up of tiny spots (pixels) of varying shades of gray. Often the amount of absorption is color-coded. The colors in the resulting "false-color" image have nothing to do, however, with the actual color of the object.

Figure 25–44 illustrates what actual CT images look like. It is generally agreed that CT scanning has revolutionized some areas of medicine by providing much less invasive, and/or more accurate, diagnosis.

Computed tomography can also be applied to ultrasound imaging (Section 12–9) and to emissions from radioisotopes and nuclear magnetic resonance (Sections 31–8 and 31–9).

## * Tomographic Image Reconstruction

How can the "grayness" of each pixel be determined even though all we can measure is the total absorption along each beam line in the slice? It can be done only by using the many beam scans made at a great many different angles. Suppose the image is to be an array of $100 \times 100$ elements for a total of $10^4$ pixels. If we have 100 detectors and measure the absorption projections at 100 different angles, then we get $10^4$ pieces of information. From this information, an image can be reconstructed, but not precisely. If more angles are measured, the reconstruction of the image can be done more accurately.

*Image reconstruction*

To suggest how mathematical reconstruction is done, we consider a very simple case using the "iterative" technique ("to iterate" is from the Latin "to repeat"). Suppose our sample slice is divided into the simple $2 \times 2$ pixels as shown in Fig. 25–45. The number in each pixel represents the amount of absorption by the material in that area (say, in tenths of a percent): that is, 4 represents twice as much absorption as 2. But we cannot directly measure these values—they are the unknowns we want to solve for. All we can measure are the projections—the total absorption along each beam line—and these are shown in the diagram as the sum of the absorptions for the pixels along each line at four different angles. These projections (given at the tip of each arrow) are what we can measure, and we now want to work back from them to see how close we can get to the true absorption value for each pixel. We start our analysis with each pixel being assigned a zero value, Fig. 25–46a. In the iterative technique, we use the projections to estimate the absorption value in each square, and repeat for each angle. The angle 1 projections are 7 and 13. We divide each of these equally between their two squares: each square in the left column gets $3\frac{1}{2}$ (half of 7), and each square in the right column gets $6\frac{1}{2}$ (half of 13); see Fig. 25–46b. Next we use

FIGURE 25–45 A simple $2 \times 2$ image showing true absorption values and measured projections.

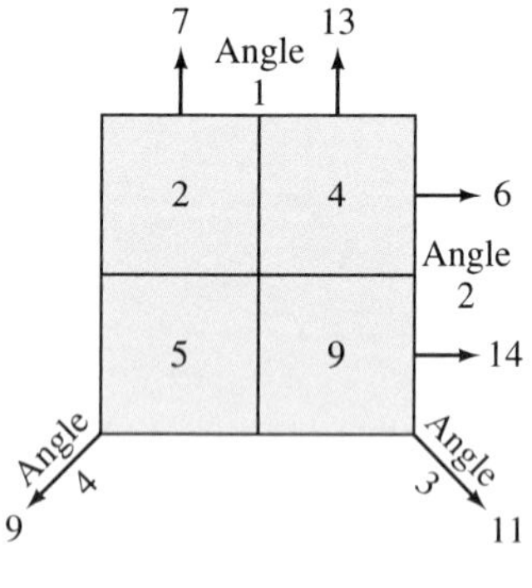


FIGURE 25–46 Reconstructing the image using projections in an iterative procedure.

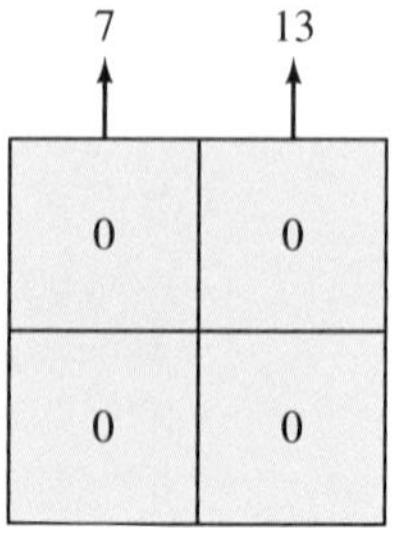


(a)

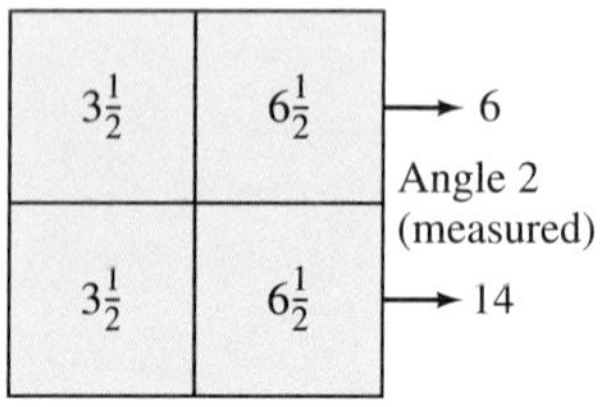


(b)

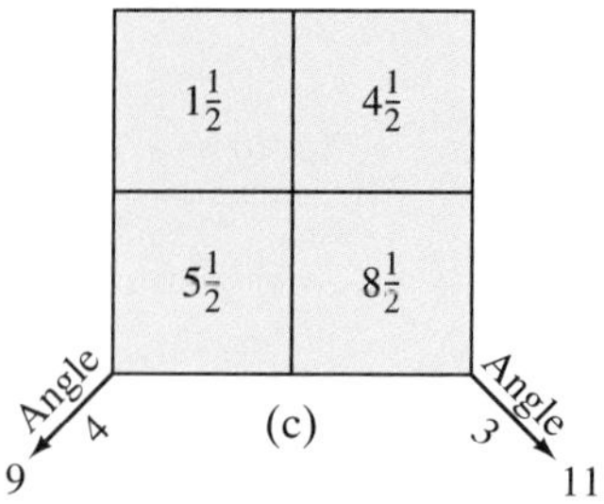


(c)

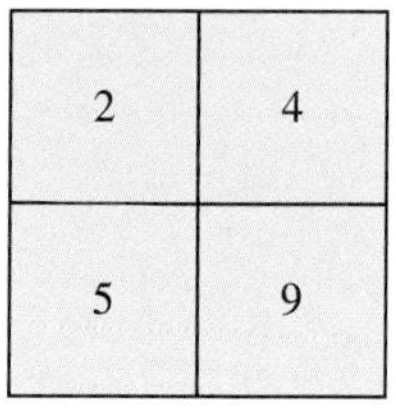


(d)

the projections at angle 2. We calculate the difference between the measured projections at angle 2 (6 and 14) and the projections based on the previous estimate (top row: $3\frac{1}{2} + 6\frac{1}{2} = 10$; same for bottom row). Then we distribute this difference equally to the squares in that row. For the top row, we have

$$3\tfrac{1}{2} + \frac{6 - 10}{2} = 1\tfrac{1}{2} \quad \text{and} \quad 6\tfrac{1}{2} + \frac{6 - 10}{2} = 4\tfrac{1}{2};$$

and for the bottom row,

$$3\tfrac{1}{2} + \frac{14 - 10}{2} = 5\tfrac{1}{2} \quad \text{and} \quad 6\tfrac{1}{2} + \frac{14 - 10}{2} = 8\tfrac{1}{2}.$$

These values are inserted as shown in Fig. 25–46c. Next, the projection at angle 3 gives

$$\text{(upper left)}\ 1\tfrac{1}{2} + \frac{11 - 10}{2} = 2 \quad \text{and} \quad \text{(lower right)}\ 8\tfrac{1}{2} + \frac{11 - 10}{2} = 9;$$

and that for angle 4 gives

$$\text{(lower left)}\ 5\tfrac{1}{2} + \frac{9 - 10}{2} = 5 \quad \text{and} \quad \text{(upper right)}\ 4\tfrac{1}{2} + \frac{9 - 10}{2} = 4.$$

The result, shown in Fig. 25–46d, corresponds exactly to the true values. (In real situations, the true values are not known, which is why these computer techniques are required.) To obtain these numbers exactly, we used six pieces of information (two each at angles 1 and 2, one each at angles 3 and 4). For the much larger number of pixels used for actual images, exact values are generally not attained. Many iterations may be needed, and the calculation is considered sufficiently precise when the difference between calculated and measured projections is sufficiently small. The above example illustrates the "convergence" of the process: the first iteration (b to c in Fig. 25–46) changed the values by 2, the last iteration (c to d) by only $\frac{1}{2}$.

## Summary

A **camera** lens forms an image on film, or on a charge-coupled device in a digital camera, by allowing light in through a shutter. The lens is focused by moving it relative to the film, and its ***f*-stop** (or lens opening) must be adjusted for the brightness of the scene and the chosen shutter speed. The $f$-stop is defined as the ratio of the focal length to the diameter of the lens opening.

The human **eye** also adjusts for the available light—by opening and closing the iris. It focuses not by moving the lens, but by adjusting the shape of the lens to vary its focal length. The image is formed on the retina, which contains an array of receptors known as rods and cones.

Diverging eye-glass or contact lenses are used to correct the defect of a nearsighted eye, which cannot focus well on distant objects. Converging lenses are used to correct for defects in which the eye cannot focus on close objects.

A **simple magnifier** is a converging lens that forms a virtual image of an object placed at (or within) the focal point. The **angular magnification**, when viewed by a relaxed normal eye, is

$$M = \frac{N}{f}, \qquad \textbf{(25–2a)}$$

where $f$ is the focal length of the lens and $N$ is the near point of the eye (25 cm for a "normal" eye).

An **astronomical telescope** consists of an **objective lens** or mirror, and an **eyepiece** that magnifies the real image formed by the objective. The **magnification** is equal to the ratio of the objective and eyepiece focal lengths, and the image is inverted:

$$M = -\frac{f_o}{f_e}. \qquad \textbf{(25–3)}$$

[*A compound **microscope** also uses objective and eyepiece lenses, and the final image is inverted. The total magnification is the product of the magnifications of the two lenses and is approximately

$$M \approx \frac{Nl}{f_e f_o}, \qquad \textbf{(25–6b)}$$

where $l$ is the distance between the lenses, $N$ is the near point of the eye, and $f_o$ and $f_e$ are the focal lengths of objective and eyepiece, respectively.]

Microscopes, telescopes, and other optical instruments are limited in the formation of sharp images by **lens aberrations**. These include **spherical aberration**, in which rays passing through the edge of a lens are not focused at the same point as those that pass near the center; and **chromatic aberration**, in which different colors are focused at different points. Compound lenses, consisting of several elements, can largely correct for aberrations.

The wave nature of light also limits the sharpness, or **resolution**, of images. Because of diffraction, it is *not possible to discern details smaller than the wavelength* of the radiation being used. This limits the useful magnification of a light microscope to about 500×.

[***X-rays** are a form of electromagnetic radiation of very short wavelength. They are produced when high-speed electrons, accelerated by high voltage in an evacuated tube, strike a glass or metal target.]

[***Computed tomography** (CT or CAT scans) uses many narrow X-ray beams through a section of the body to construct an image of that section.]

## Questions

1. Why is the depth of field greater, and the image sharper, when a camera lens is "stopped down" to a larger $f$-number? Ignore diffraction.
2. Describe how diffraction affects the statement of Question 1. [*Hint*: see Eq. 24–3 or 25–7.]
3. Why must a camera lens be moved farther from the film to focus on a closer object?
4. Why are bifocals needed mainly by older persons and not generally by younger people?
5. Will a nearsighted person who wears corrective lenses in her glasses be able to see clearly underwater when wearing those glasses? Use a diagram to show why or why not.
6. You can tell whether a person is nearsighted or farsighted by looking at the width of the face through their glasses. If the person's face appears narrower through the glasses (Fig. 25–47), is the person farsighted or nearsighted?

**FIGURE 25–47** Question 6.

7. In attempting to discern distant details, people will sometimes squint. Why does this help?
8. Is the image formed on the retina of the human eye upright or inverted? Discuss the implications of this for our perception of objects.
9. The human eye is much like a camera—yet, when a camera shutter is left open and the camera is moved, the image will be blurred; but when you move your head with your eyes open, you still see clearly. Explain.
10. Reading glasses use converging lenses. A simple magnifier is also a converging lens. Are reading glasses therefore magnifiers? Discuss the similarities and differences between converging lenses as used for these two different purposes.

* 11. Inexpensive microscopes for children's use usually produce images that are colored at the edges. Why?

* 12. Spherical aberration in a thin lens is minimized if rays are bent equally by the two surfaces. If a planoconvex lens is used to form a real image of an object at infinity, which surface should face the object? Use ray diagrams to show why.

* 13. Which aberrations present in a simple lens are not present (or are greatly reduced) in the human eye?

* 14. Explain why chromatic aberration occurs for thin lenses but not for mirrors.

15. By what factor can you improve resolution, other things being equal, if you use blue light ($\lambda = 450\,\text{nm}$) rather than red (700 nm)?
16. Give at least two advantages for the use of large reflecting mirrors in astronomical telescopes.
17. Which color of visible light would give the best resolution in a microscope? Explain.
18. Atoms have diameters of about $10^{-8}$ cm. Can visible light be used to "see" an atom? Explain.

## Problems

### 25–1 Camera

1. (I) A 55-mm-focal-length lens has $f$-stops ranging from $f/1.4$ to $f/22$. What is the corresponding range of lens diaphragm diameters?
2. (I) A television camera lens has a 14-cm focal length and a lens diameter of 6.0 cm. What is its $f$-number?
3. (I) A light meter reports that a camera setting of $\frac{1}{250}$ s at $f/5.6$ will give a correct exposure. But the photographer wishes to use $f/11$ to increase the depth of field. What should the shutter speed be?
4. (I) A properly exposed photograph is taken at $f/16$ and $\frac{1}{60}$ s. What lens opening would be required if the shutter speed were $\frac{1}{1000}$ s?
5. (II) If an $f = 135$-mm telephoto lens is designed to cover object distances from 1.2 m to $\infty$, over what distance must the lens move relative to the plane of the film?
6. (II) A 200-mm-focal-length lens can be adjusted so that it is 200.0 mm to 206.0 mm from the film. For what range of object distances can it be adjusted?
7. (II) A nature photographer wishes to photograph a 28-m-tall tree from a distance of 58 m. What focal-length lens should be used if the image is to fill the 24-mm height of the film?
8. (II) A "pinhole" camera uses a tiny pinhole instead of a lens. Show, using ray diagrams, how reasonably sharp images can be formed using such a pinhole camera. In particular, consider two point objects 2.0 cm apart that are 1.0 m from a 1.0-mm-diameter pinhole. Show that on a piece of film 7.0 cm behind the pinhole the two objects produce two separate circles that do not overlap.
9. (III) Suppose that a correct exposure is $\frac{1}{250}$ s at $f/11$. Under the same conditions, what exposure time would be needed for a pinhole camera (Problem 8) if the pinhole diameter is 1.0 mm and the film is 7.0 cm from the hole?

### 25–2 Eye and Corrective Lenses

10. (I) A human eyeball is about 2.0 cm long, and the pupil has a maximum diameter of about 8.0 mm. What is the "speed" of this lens?

11. (I) If the nearsighted person in Example 25–6 wore contact lenses corrected for the far point ($= \infty$), show that the near point would be 41 cm. (Would glasses be better in this case?)

12. (II) Reading glasses of what power are needed for a person whose near point is 115 cm, so that he can read a computer screen at 55 cm? Assume a lens–eye distance of 1.8 cm.

13. (II) A person has a far point of 14 cm. What power glasses would correct this vision if the glasses were placed 2.0 cm from the eye? What power contact lenses, placed on the eye, would the person need?

14. (II) A person struggles to read by holding a book at arm's length, a distance of 45 cm away (= near point). What power of reading glasses should be prescribed for him, assuming they will be placed 2.0 cm from the eye and he wants to read at the normal near point of 25 cm?

15. (II) A person's left eye is corrected by a −3.50-diopter lens, 2.0 cm from the eye. (*a*) Is this person's left eye near- or farsighted? (*b*) What is this eye's far point without glasses?

16. (II) A person's right eye can see objects clearly only if they are between 25 cm and 75 cm away. (*a*) What power of contact lens is required so that objects far away are sharp? (*b*) What will be the near point with the lens in place?

17. (II) About how much longer is the nearsighted eye in Example 25–6 than the 2.0 cm of a normal eye?

18. (II) One lens of a nearsighted person's eyeglasses has a focal length of −22.0 cm, and the lens is 1.8 cm from the eye. If the person switches to contact lenses that are placed directly on the eye, what should be the focal length of the corresponding contact lens?

19. (II) What is the focal length of the eye–lens system when viewing an object (*a*) at infinity, and (*b*) 33 cm from the eye? Assume that the lens–retina distance is 2.0 cm.

20. (III) A nearsighted person has near and far points of 10.0 and 20.0 cm, respectively. If she puts on contact lenses with power $P = -4.00\,\text{D}$, what are her new near and far points?

## 25–3 Magnifying Glass

21. (I) What is the magnification of a lens used with a relaxed eye if its focal length is 12 cm?

22. (I) What is the focal length of a magnifying glass of 3.5× magnification for a relaxed normal eye?

23. (I) A magnifier is rated at 2.5× for a normal eye focusing on an image at the near point. (*a*) What is its focal length? (*b*) What is its focal length if the 2.5× refers to a relaxed eye?

24. (II) Sherlock Holmes is using a 9.00-cm-focal-length lens as his magnifying glass. To obtain maximum magnification, where must the object be placed (assume a normal eye), and what will be the magnification?

25. (II) A 3.30-mm-wide beetle is viewed with a 9.50-cm-focal-length lens. A normal eye views the image at its near point. Calculate (*a*) the angular magnification, (*b*) the width of the image, and (*c*) the object distance from the lens.

26. (II) A small insect is placed 5.55 cm from a +6.00-cm-focal-length lens. Calculate (*a*) the position of the image, and (*b*) the angular magnification.

27. (II) A magnifying glass with a focal length of 8.5 cm is used to read print placed at a distance of 7.5 cm. Calculate (*a*) the position of the image; (*b*) the angular magnification.

28. (III) A magnifying glass is rated at 3.0× for a normal eye that is relaxed. What would be the magnification of this lens for a relaxed eye whose near point is (*a*) 55 cm, and (*b*) 16 cm? Explain the differences.

## 25–4 Telescopes

29. (I) What is the magnification of an astronomical telescope whose objective lens has a focal length of 76 cm and whose eyepiece has a focal length of 2.8 cm? What is the overall length of the telescope when adjusted for a relaxed eye?

30. (I) The overall magnification of an astronomical telescope is desired to be 25×. If an objective of 78-cm focal length is used, what must be the focal length of the eyepiece? What is the overall length of the telescope when adjusted for use by the relaxed eye?

31. (I) An 8.0× binocular has 2.8-cm-focal-length eyepieces. What is the focal length of the objective lenses?

32. (II) An astronomical telescope has an objective with focal length 85 cm and a +35-D eyepiece. What is the total magnification?

33. (II) An astronomical telescope has its two lenses spaced 75.2 cm apart. If the objective lens has a focal length of 74.5 cm, what is the magnification of this telescope? Assume a relaxed eye.

34. (II) A Galilean telescope adjusted for a relaxed eye is 32.8 cm long. If the objective lens has a focal length of 36.0 cm, what is the magnification?

35. (II) What is the magnifying power of an astronomical telescope using a reflecting mirror whose radius of curvature is 6.0 m and an eyepiece whose focal length is 3.2 cm?

36. (II) The Moon's image appears to be magnified 120× by a reflecting astronomical telescope with an eyepiece having a focal length of 3.2 cm. What are the focal length and radius of curvature of the main (objective) mirror?

37. (II) A 170× astronomical telescope is adjusted for a relaxed eye when the two lenses are 1.25 m apart. What is the focal length of each lens?

38. (III) A reflecting telescope (Fig. 25–21b) has a radius of curvature of 3.0 m for its objective mirror and a radius of curvature of −1.50 m for its eyepiece mirror. If the distance between the two mirrors is 0.90 m, how far in front of the eyepiece should you place the photographic film to record the image of a star?

## * 25–5 Microscope

* 39. (I) A microscope uses an eyepiece with a focal length of 1.40 cm. Using a normal eye with a final image at infinity, the tube length is 17.5 cm and the focal length of the objective lens is 0.65 cm. What is the magnification of the microscope?

* 40. (I) A 620× microscope uses a 0.40-cm-focal-length objective lens. If the tube length is 17.5 cm, what is the focal length of the eyepiece? Assume a normal eye and that the final image is at infinity.

* 41. (I) A 17-cm-long microscope has an eyepiece with a focal length of 2.5 cm and an objective with a focal length of 0.28 cm. What is the approximate magnification?

* 42. (II) A microscope has a 12.0× eyepiece and a 59.0× objective lens 20.0 cm apart. Calculate (*a*) the total magnification, (*b*) the focal length of each lens, and (*c*) where the object must be for a normal relaxed eye to see it in focus.

* 43. (II) A microscope has a 1.8-cm-focal-length eyepiece and a 0.80-cm objective lens. Assuming a relaxed normal eye, calculate (*a*) the position of the object if the distance between the lenses is 16.0 cm, and (*b*) the total magnification.

* 44. (II) Repeat Problem 43 assuming that the final image is located 25 cm from the eyepiece (near point of a normal eye).

* 45. (III) The eyepiece of a compound microscope has a focal length of 2.70 cm, and the objective lens has $f = 0.740$ cm. If an object is placed 0.790 cm from the objective lens, calculate (*a*) the distance between the lenses when the microscope is adjusted for a relaxed eye, and (*b*) the total magnification.

### * 25–6 Aberrations

* 46. (II) An achromatic lens is made of two very thin lenses, placed in contact, that have focal lengths of $f_1 = -28$ cm and $f_2 = +23$ cm. (*a*) Is the combination converging or diverging? (*b*) What is the net focal length?

* 47. (III) Let's examine spherical aberration in a particular situation. A planoconvex lens of index of refraction 1.50 and radius of curvature $R = 12.0$ cm is shown in Fig. 25–48. Consider an incoming ray parallel to the principal axis and a height $h$ above it as shown. Determine the distance $d$, from the flat face of the lens, to where this ray crosses the principal axis if (*a*) $h = 1.0$ cm, and (*b*) $h = 6.0$ cm. (*c*) How far apart are these "focal points"? (*d*) What is the radius of the "circle of least confusion" produced by the $h = 6.0$-cm ray at the "focal point" for $h = 1.0$ cm?

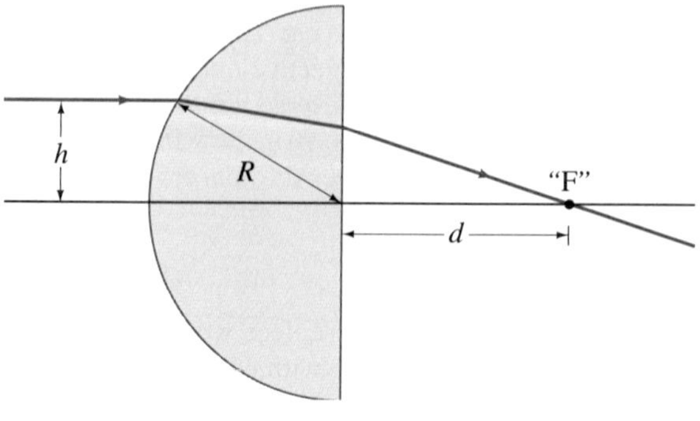


**FIGURE 25–48** Problem 47.

### 25–7 to 25–9 Resolution

48. (I) What is the angular resolution limit (degrees) set by diffraction for the 100-in. (254-cm mirror diameter) Mt. Wilson telescope ($\lambda = 550$ nm)?

49. (II) Suppose that you wish to construct a telescope that can resolve features 7.0 km across on the Moon, 384,000 km away. You have a 2.0-m-focal-length objective lens whose diameter is 11.0 cm. What focal-length eyepiece is needed if your eye can resolve objects 0.10 mm apart at a distance of 25 cm? What is the resolution limit (radians) set by the size of the objective lens (that is, by diffraction)? Use $\lambda = 550$ nm.

50. (II) The normal lens on a 35-mm camera has a focal length of 50.0 mm. Its aperture diameter varies from a maximum of 25 mm ($f/2$) to a minimum of 3.0 mm ($f/16$). Determine the resolution limit set by diffraction for $f/2$ and $f/16$. Specify as the number of lines per millimeter resolved on the film. Take $\lambda = 550$ nm.

51. (II) Two stars 15 light-years away are barely resolved by a 55-cm (mirror diameter) telescope. How far apart are the stars? Assume $\lambda = 550$ nm and that the resolution is limited by diffraction.

52. (II) (*a*) How far away can a human eye distinguish two car headlights 2.0 m apart? Consider only diffraction effects and assume an eye pupil diameter of 5.0 mm and a wavelength of 550 nm. (*b*) What is the minimum angular separation an eye could resolve when viewing two stars, considering only diffraction effects? In reality, it is about 1′ of arc. Why is it not equal to your answer in (*b*)?

53. (II) The Earth and Moon are separated by about $400 \times 10^6$ m. When Mars is $8 \times 10^{10}$ m from Earth, could a person standing on Mars resolve the Earth and its Moon as two separate objects without a telescope? Assume a pupil diameter of 5 mm and $\lambda = 550$ nm.

### * 25–11 X-rays

* 54. (II) X-rays of wavelength 0.133 nm fall on a crystal whose atoms, lying in planes, are spaced 0.280 nm apart. At what angle $\phi$ (relative to the surface, Fig. 25–37) must the X-rays be directed if the first diffraction maximum is to be observed?

* 55. (II) X-rays of wavelength 0.0973 nm are directed at an unknown crystal. The second diffraction maximum is recorded when the X-rays are directed at an angle of 23.4° relative to the crystal surface. What is the spacing between crystal planes?

* 56. (II) First-order Bragg diffraction is observed at 25.2° related to the crystal surface, with spacing between atoms of 0.24 nm. (*a*) At what angle will second order be observed? (*b*) What is the wavelength of the X-rays?

### * 25–12 Computed Tomography

* 57. (II) (*a*) Suppose for a conventional X-ray image that the X-ray beam consists of parallel rays. What would be the magnification of the image? (*b*) Suppose, instead, the X-rays come from a point source (as in Fig. 25–41) that is 15 cm in front of a human body 25 cm thick, and the film is pressed against the person's back. Determine and discuss the range of magnifications that results.

## General Problems

58. Sam purchases +3.50-diopter eyeglasses which correct his faulty vision to put his near point at 25 cm. (Assume he wears the lenses 2.0 cm from his eyes.) (*a*) Calculate the focal length of Sam's glasses. (*b*) Calculate Sam's near point without glasses. (*c*) Pam, who has normal eyes with near point at 25 cm, puts on Sam's glasses. Calculate Pam's near point with Sam's glasses on.

59. As early morning passed toward midday, and the sunlight got more intense, a photographer noted that, if she kept her shutter speed constant, she had to change the $f$-number from $f/5.6$ to $f/22$. By what factor had the sunlight intensity increased during that time?

60. Show that for objects very far away (assume infinity), the magnification of a camera lens is proportional to its focal length.

61. For a camera equipped with a 50-mm-focal-length lens, what is the object distance if the image height equals the object height? How far is the object from the film?

62. A woman can see clearly with her right eye only when objects are between 45 cm and 155 cm away. Prescription bifocals should have what powers so that she can see distant objects clearly (upper part) and be able to read a book 25 cm away (lower part) with her right eye? Assume that the glasses will be 2.0 cm from the eye.

63. A child has a near point of 15 cm. What is the maximum magnification the child can obtain using an 8.0-cm-focal-length magnifier? What magnification can a normal eye obtain with the same lens? Which person sees more detail?

64. What is the magnifying power of a +4.0-D lens used as a magnifier? Assume a relaxed normal eye.

65. A physicist lost in the mountains tries to make a telescope using the lenses from his reading glasses. They have powers of +2.0 D and +4.5 D, respectively. (*a*) What maximum magnification telescope is possible? (*b*) Which lens should be used as the eyepiece?

66. A 50-year-old man uses +2.5-diopter lenses to read a newspaper 25 cm away. Ten years later, he must hold the paper 35 cm away to see clearly with the same lenses. What power lenses does he need now in order to hold the paper 25 cm away? (Distances are measured from the lens.)

67. Spy planes fly at extremely high altitudes (25 km) to avoid interception. Their cameras are reportedly able to discern features as small as 5 cm. What must be the minimum aperture of the camera lens to afford this resolution? (Use $\lambda = 550$ nm.)

68. When shooting pictures at very short distances, exposure times must be increased because of the increased distance of the lens from the film for a focused image. (*a*) Show that when the object is so close to the camera that the image height equals the object height, the exposure time must be four times longer (or 2 $f$-stops) than when the object is a long distance away (say, $\infty$), given the same illumination and $f$-stop. (*b*) Show that if $d_o$ is at least four or five times the focal length $f$ of the lens, the exposure time is increased by less than half an $f$-stop relative to the same object being a great distance away.

69. The objective lens and the eyepiece of a telescope are spaced 85 cm apart. If the eyepiece is +23 diopters, what is the total magnification of the telescope?

70. The Hubble Space Telescope, with an objective diameter of 2.4 m, is viewing the Moon. Estimate the minimum distance between two objects on the Moon that the Hubble can distinguish. Consider diffraction of light of wavelength 550 nm. Assume the Hubble is near the Earth.

71. Two converging lenses, one with $f = 4.0$ cm and the other with $f = 44$ cm, are made into a telescope. (*a*) What are the length and magnification? Which lens should be the eyepiece? (*b*) Assume these lenses are now combined to make a microscope; if the magnification needs to be 25×, how long would the microscope be?

72. An astronomical telescope has a magnification of 8.0. If the two lenses are 28 cm apart, determine the focal length of each lens.

73. You want to design a spy satellite to photograph license plate numbers. Assuming it is necessary to resolve points separated by 5 cm with 550-nm light, and that the satellite orbits at a height of 130 km, what minimum lens aperture (diameter) is required?

* 74. A Lucite planoconvex lens (Fig. 23–29a) has one flat surface and the other has $R = 18.4$ cm. This lens is used to view an object, located 66.0 cm away from the lens, which is a mixture of red and yellow. The index of refraction of the glass is 1.5106 for red light and 1.5226 for yellow light. What are the locations of the red and yellow images formed by the lens?

## Answers to Exercises

**A:** 6.3 m.
**B:** $P = -4.0$ D.
**C:** 48 cm.
**D:** 2 m.

An early science fantasy book (1940), called *Mr Tompkins in Wonderland* by physicist George Gamow, imagined a world in which the speed of light was only 10 m/s (20 mi/h). Mr Tompkins had studied relativity and when he began "speeding" on a bicycle, he "expected that he would be immediately shortened, and was very happy about it as his increasing figure had lately caused him some anxiety. To his great surprise, however, nothing happened to him or to his cycle. On the other hand, the picture around him completely changed. The streets grew shorter, the windows of the shops began to look like narrow slits, and the policeman on the corner became the thinnest man he had ever seen. 'By Jove!' exclaimed Mr Tompkins excitedly, 'I see the trick now. This is where the word *relativity* comes in.' "

Relativity does indeed predict that objects moving relative to us at high speed, close to the speed of light $c$, are shortened in length. We don't notice it as Mr Tompkins did, because $c = 3 \times 10^8\,\mathrm{m/s}$ is incredibly fast. We will study length contraction, time dilation, simultaneity non-agreement, and how energy and mass are equivalent $(E = mc^2)$.

CHAPTER 26

# The Special Theory of Relativity

Physics at the end of the nineteenth century looked back on a period of great progress. The theories developed over the preceding three centuries had been very successful in explaining a wide range of natural phenomena. Newtonian mechanics beautifully explained the motion of objects on Earth and in the heavens. Furthermore, it formed the basis for successful treatments of fluids, wave motion, and sound. Kinetic theory explained the behavior of gases and other materials. Maxwell's theory of electromagnetism not only brought together and explained electric and magnetic phenomena, but it predicted the existence of electromagnetic waves that would behave in every way just like light—so light came to be thought of as an electromagnetic wave.

Indeed, it seemed that the natural world, as seen through the eyes of physicists, was very well explained. A few puzzles remained, but it was felt that these would soon be explained using already known principles.

It did not turn out so simply. Instead, these puzzles were to be solved only by the introduction, in the early part of the twentieth century, of two revolutionary new theories that changed our whole conception of nature: the *theory of relativity* and *quantum theory*.

Physics as it was known at the end of the nineteenth century (what we've covered up to now in this book) is referred to as **classical physics**. The new physics that grew out of the great revolution at the turn of the twentieth century is now called **modern physics**. In this Chapter, we present the special theory of relativity, which was first proposed by Albert Einstein (1879–1955; Fig. 26–1) in 1905. In Chapter 27, we introduce the equally momentous quantum theory.

*Classical vs. modern physics*

**FIGURE 26–1** Albert Einstein (1879–1955), one of the great minds of the twentieth century, was the creator of the special and general theories of relativity.

## 26–1 Galilean–Newtonian Relativity

Einstein's special theory of relativity deals with how we observe events, particularly how objects and events are observed from different frames of reference.†
This subject had, of course, already been explored by Galileo and Newton.

The special theory of relativity deals with events that are observed and measured from so-called **inertial reference frames** which (as discussed in Chapter 4) are reference frames in which Newton's first law is valid: if an object experiences no net force, the object either remains at rest or continues in motion with constant speed in a straight line. It is easiest to analyze events when they are observed and measured from inertial frames. The Earth, though not quite an inertial frame (it rotates), is close enough that for most purposes we can consider it an inertial frame. Rotating or otherwise accelerating frames of reference are noninertial frames‡, and won't concern us in this Chapter (they are dealt with in Einstein's general theory of relativity—Section 33–4).

*Inertial reference frame*

† A reference frame is a set of coordinate axes fixed to some body such as the Earth, a train, or the Moon. See Section 2–1.

‡ On a rotating platform (say a merry-go-round), for example, an object at rest starts moving outward even though no body exerts a force on it. This is therefore not an inertial frame. See Appendix C, Fig. C–1.

A reference frame that moves with constant velocity with respect to an inertial frame is itself also an inertial frame, since Newton's laws hold in it as well. When we say that we observe or make measurements from a certain reference frame, it means that we are at rest in that reference frame.

*Relativity principle: the laws of physics are the same in all inertial reference frames*

Both Galileo and Newton were aware of what we now call the **relativity principle** applied to mechanics: that *the basic laws of physics are the same in all inertial reference frames*. You may have recognized its validity in everyday life. For example, objects move in the same way in a smoothly moving (constant-velocity) train or airplane as they do on Earth. (This assumes no vibrations or rocking which would make the reference frame noninertial.) When you walk, drink a cup of soup, play pool, or drop a pencil on the floor while traveling in a train, airplane, or ship moving at constant velocity, the bodies move just as they do when you are at rest on Earth. Suppose you are in a car traveling rapidly at constant velocity. If you release a coin from above your head inside the car, how will it fall? It falls straight downward with respect to the car, and hits the floor directly below the point of release, Fig. 26–2a. (If you drop the coin out the car's window, this won't happen because the moving air drags the coin backward relative to the car.) This is just how objects fall on the Earth—straight down—and thus our experiment in the moving car is in accord with the relativity principle.

**FIGURE 26–2** A coin is dropped by a person in a moving car. The upper views show the moment of the coin's release, the lower views are a short time later. (a) In the reference frame of the car, the coin falls straight down (and the tree moves to the left). (b) In a reference frame fixed on the Earth, the coin follows a curved (parabolic) path.

**CAUTION**

*Laws are the same, but paths may be different in different reference frames*

Note in this example, however, that to an observer on the Earth, the coin follows a curved path, Fig. 26–2b. The actual path followed by the coin is different as viewed from different frames of reference. This does not violate the relativity principle because this principle states that the *laws* of physics are the same in all inertial frames. The same law of gravity, and the same laws of motion, apply in both reference frames. And the acceleration of the coin is the same in both reference frames. The difference in Figs. 26–2a and b is that in the Earth's frame of reference, the coin has an initial velocity (equal to that of the car). The laws of physics therefore predict it will follow a parabolic path like any projectile (Chapter 3). In the car's reference frame, there is no initial velocity, and the laws of physics predict that the coin will fall straight down. The laws are the same in both reference frames, although the specific paths are different.

Galilean–Newtonian relativity involves certain unprovable assumptions that make sense from everyday experience. It is assumed that the lengths of objects are the same in one reference frame as in another, and that time passes at the same rate in different reference frames. In classical mechanics, then, space and time intervals are considered to be **absolute**: their measurement does not change from one reference frame to another. The mass of an object, as well as all forces, are assumed to be unchanged by a change in inertial reference frame.

The position of an object, however, is different when specified in different reference frames, and so is velocity. For example, a person may walk inside a bus toward the front with a speed of 2 m/s. But if the bus moves 10 m/s with respect to the Earth, the person is then moving with a speed of 12 m/s with respect to the Earth. The acceleration of a body, however, is the same in any inertial reference frame according to classical mechanics. This is because the change in velocity, and the time interval, will be the same. For example, the person in the bus may accelerate from 0 to 2 m/s in 1.0 seconds, so $a = 2\,\text{m/s}^2$ in the reference frame of the bus. With respect to the Earth, the acceleration is

**CAUTION**

*Position and velocity are different in different reference frames, but length is the same (classical)*

$$\frac{(12\,\text{m/s} - 10\,\text{m/s})}{1.0\,\text{s}} = 2\,\text{m/s}^2,$$

which is the same.

Since neither $F$, $m$, nor $a$ changes from one inertial frame to another, then Newton's second law, $F = ma$, does not change. Thus Newton's second law satisfies the relativity principle. It is easily shown that the other laws of mechanics also satisfy the relativity principle.

That the laws of mechanics are the same in all inertial reference frames implies that no one inertial frame is special in any sense. We express this important conclusion by saying that **all inertial reference frames are equivalent** for the description of mechanical phenomena. No one inertial reference frame is any better than another. A reference frame fixed to a car or an aircraft traveling at constant velocity is as good as one fixed on the Earth. When you travel smoothly at constant velocity in a car or airplane, it is just as valid to say you are at rest and the Earth is moving as it is to say the reverse. There is no experiment you can do to tell which frame is "really" at rest and which is moving. Thus, there is no way to single out one particular reference frame as being at absolute rest.

*All inertial reference frames are equally valid*

A complication arose, however, in the last half of the nineteenth century. Maxwell's comprehensive and successful theory of electromagnetism (Chapter 22) predicted that light is an electromagnetic wave. Maxwell's equations gave the velocity of light $c$ as $3.00 \times 10^8\,\text{m/s}$; and this is just what is measured, within experimental error. The question then arose: in what reference frame does light have precisely the value predicted by Maxwell's theory? For it was assumed that light would have a different speed in different frames of reference. For example, if observers were traveling on a rocket ship at a speed of $1.0 \times 10^8\,\text{m/s}$ away from a source of light, we might expect them to measure the speed of the light reaching them to be

$$(3.0 \times 10^8\,\text{m/s}) - (1.0 \times 10^8\,\text{m/s}) = 2.0 \times 10^8\,\text{m/s}.$$

But Maxwell's equations have no provision for relative velocity. They predicted the speed of light to be $c = 3.0 \times 10^8\,\text{m/s}$. This seemed to imply there must be some special reference frame where $c$ would have this value.

We discussed in Chapters 11 and 12 that waves can travel on water and along ropes or strings, and sound waves travel in air and other materials. Nineteenth-century physicists viewed the material world in terms of the laws of mechanics, so it was natural for them to assume that light too must travel in some *medium*. They called this transparent medium the **ether** and assumed it permeated all space.[†] It was therefore assumed that the velocity of light given by Maxwell's equations must be with respect to the ether.

*The "ether"*

At first it appeared that Maxwell's equations did *not* satisfy the relativity principle. They were simplest in the frame where $c = 3.00 \times 10^8\,\mathrm{m/s}$; that is, in a reference frame at rest in the ether. In any other reference frame, extra terms would have to be added to take into account the relative velocity. Thus, although most of the laws of physics obeyed the relativity principle, the laws of electricity and magnetism apparently did not. (Einstein's second postulate—see next Section—resolved this problem: Maxwell's equations do satisfy relativity.)

Scientists soon set out to determine the speed of the Earth relative to this absolute frame, whatever it might be. A number of clever experiments were designed. The most direct were performed by A. A. Michelson and E. W. Morley in the 1880s. They measured the difference in the speed of light in different directions using Michelson's interferometer (Section 24–9). They expected to find a difference depending on the orientation of their apparatus with respect to the ether. For just as a boat has different speeds relative to the land when it moves upstream, downstream, or across the stream, so too light would be expected to have different speeds depending on the velocity of the ether past the Earth.

*The Michelson–Morley experiment*

Strange as it may seem, they detected no difference at all. This was a great puzzle. A number of explanations were put forth over a period of years, but they led to contradictions or were otherwise not generally accepted. This **null result** was one of the great puzzles at the end of the nineteenth century.

*The null result*

Then in 1905, Albert Einstein proposed a radical new theory that reconciled these many problems in a simple way. But at the same time, as we shall see, it completely changed our ideas of space and time.

## 26–2 Postulates of the Special Theory of Relativity

The problems that existed at the start of the twentieth century with regard to electromagnetic theory and Newtonian mechanics were beautifully resolved by Einstein's introduction of the theory of relativity in 1905. Unaware of the Michelson–Morley null result, Einstein was motivated by certain questions regarding electromagnetic theory and light waves. For example, he asked himself: "What would I see if I rode a light beam?" The answer was that instead of a traveling electromagnetic wave, he would see alternating electric and magnetic fields at rest whose magnitude changed in space, but did not change in time. Such fields, he realized, had never been detected and indeed were not consistent with Maxwell's electromagnetic theory. He argued, therefore, that it was unreasonable to think that the speed of light relative to any observer could be reduced to zero, or in fact reduced at all. This idea became the second postulate of his theory of relativity.

[†]The medium for light waves could not be air, since light travels from the Sun to Earth through nearly empty space. Therefore, another medium was postulated, the ether. The ether was not only transparent but, because of difficulty in detecting it, was assumed to have zero density.

In his famous 1905 paper, Einstein proposed doing away completely with the idea of the ether and the accompanying assumption of an absolute reference frame at rest. This proposal was embodied in two postulates. The first postulate was an extension of the Galilean–Newtonian relativity principle to include not only the laws of mechanics but also those of the rest of physics, including electricity and magnetism:

> ***First postulate*[†] (*the relativity principle*): The laws of physics have the same form in all inertial reference frames.**

*The first postulate of special relativity*

The second postulate is consistent with the first:

> ***Second postulate* (*constancy of the speed of light*): Light propagates through empty space with a definite speed *c* independent of the speed of the source or observer.**

*The second postulate of special relativity*

These two postulates form the foundation of Einstein's **special theory of relativity**. It is called "special" to distinguish it from his later "general theory of relativity," which deals with noninertial (accelerating) reference frames (Chapter 33). The special theory, which is what we discuss here, deals only with inertial frames.

The second postulate may seem hard to accept, for it seems to violate common sense. First of all, we have to think of light traveling through empty space. Giving up the ether is not too hard, however, since it had never been detected. But the second postulate also tells us that the speed of light in vacuum is always the same, $3.00 \times 10^8\,\mathrm{m/s}$, no matter what the speed of the observer or the source. Thus, a person traveling toward or away from a source of light will measure the same speed for that light as someone at rest with respect to the source. This conflicts with our everyday experience: we would expect to have to add in the velocity of the observer. On the other hand, perhaps we can't expect our everyday experience to be helpful when dealing with the high velocity of light. Furthermore, the null result of the Michelson–Morley experiment is fully consistent with the second postulate.[‡]

Einstein's proposal has a certain beauty. By doing away with the idea of an absolute reference frame, it was possible to reconcile classical mechanics with Maxwell's electromagnetic theory. The speed of light predicted by Maxwell's equations *is* the speed of light in vacuum in *any* reference frame.

Einstein's theory required us to give up commonsense notions of space and time, and in the following Sections we will examine some strange but interesting consequences of special relativity. Our arguments for the most part will be simple ones. We will use a technique that Einstein himself did: we will imagine very simple experimental situations in which little mathematics is needed. In this way, we can see many of the consequences of relativity theory without getting involved in detailed calculations. Einstein called these "thought" experiments.

*"Thought experiment"*

## 26–3 Simultaneity

An important consequence of the theory of relativity is that we can no longer regard time as an absolute quantity. No one doubts that time flows onward and never turns back. But the time interval between two events, and even whether or not two events are simultaneous, depends on the observer's reference frame. By an "event," which we use a lot here, we mean something that happens at a particular place and at a particular time.

*Event defined*

[†]The first postulate can also be stated as: *There is no experiment you can do in an inertial reference frame to tell if you are at rest or moving uniformly at constant velocity.*

[‡]The Michelson–Morley experiment can also be considered as evidence for the first postulate, since it was intended to measure the motion of the Earth relative to an absolute reference frame. Its failure to do so implies the absence of any such preferred frame.

Two events are said to occur simultaneously if they occur at exactly the same time. But how do we know if two events occur precisely at the same time? If they occur at the same point in space—such as two apples falling on your head at the same time—it is easy. But if the two events occur at widely separated places, it is more difficult to know whether the events are simultaneous since we have to take into account the time it takes for the light from them to reach us. Because light travels at finite speed, a person who sees two events must calculate back to find out when they actually occurred. For example, if two events are *observed* to occur at the same time, but one actually took place farther from the observer than the other, then the more distant one must have occurred earlier, and the two events were not simultaneous.

We now imagine a simple thought experiment. Assume an observer, called O, is located exactly halfway between points A and B where two events occur, Fig. 26–3. Suppose the two events are lightning that strikes the points A and B, as shown. For brief events like lightning, only short pulses of light will travel outward from A and B and reach O. Observer O "sees" the events when the pulses of light reach point O. If the two pulses reach O at the same time, then the two events had to be simultaneous. This is because the two light pulses travel at the same speed (postulate 2), and since the distance OA equals OB, the time for the light to travel from A to O and B to O must be the same. Observer O can then definitely state that the two events occurred simultaneously. On the other hand, if O sees the light from one event before that from the other, then the former event occurred first.

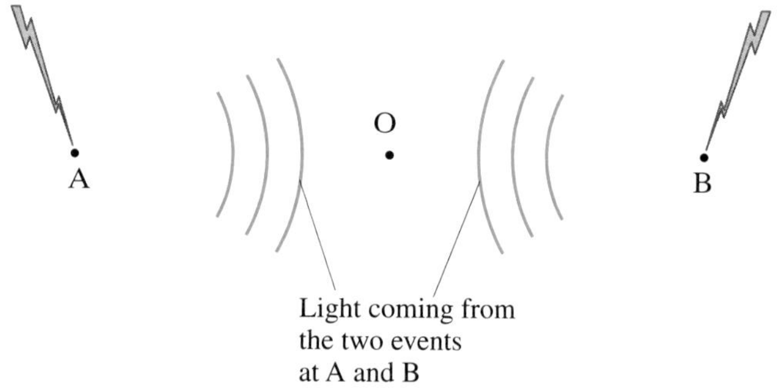


**FIGURE 26–3** A moment after lightning strikes at points A and B, the pulses of light are traveling toward the observer O, but O "sees" the lightning only when the light reaches O.

The question we really want to examine is this: if two events are simultaneous to an observer in one reference frame, are they also simultaneous to another observer moving with respect to the first? Let us call the observers $O_1$ and $O_2$ and assume they are fixed in reference frames 1 and 2 that move with speed $v$ relative to one another. These two reference frames can be thought of as trains (Fig. 26–4). $O_2$ says that $O_1$ is moving to the right with speed $v$, as in Fig. 26–4a; and $O_1$ says $O_2$ is moving to the left with speed $v$, as in Fig. 26–4b. Both viewpoints are legitimate according to the relativity principle. [There is no third point of view which will tell us which one is "really" moving.]

**FIGURE 26–4** Observers $O_1$ and $O_2$, on two different trains (two different reference frames), are moving with relative speed $v$. $O_2$ says that $O_1$ is moving to the right (a); $O_1$ says that $O_2$ is moving to the left (b). Both viewpoints are legitimate—it all depends on your reference frame.

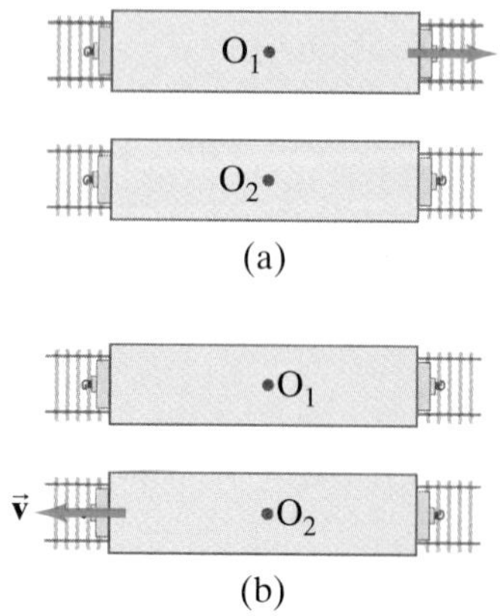

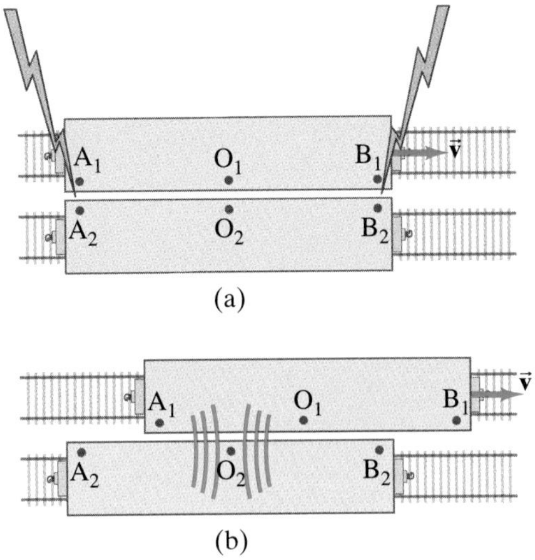


**FIGURE 26–5** Thought experiment on simultaneity. To observer $O_2$, the reference frame of $O_1$ is moving to the right. In (a), one lightning bolt strikes the two reference frames at $A_1$ and $A_2$, and a second lightning bolt strikes at $B_1$ and $B_2$. (b) A moment later, the light from the two events reaches $O_2$ at the same time, so according to observer $O_2$, the two bolts of lightning strike simultaneously. But in $O_1$'s reference frame, the light from $B_1$ has already reached $O_1$, whereas the light from $A_1$ has not yet reached $O_1$. So in $O_1$'s reference frame, the event at $B_1$ must have preceded the event at $A_1$. Simultaneity in time is not absolute.

Now suppose that observers $O_1$ and $O_2$ observe and measure two lightning strikes. The lightning bolts mark both trains where they strike: at $A_1$ and $B_1$ on $O_1$'s train, and at $A_2$ and $B_2$ on $O_2$'s train, Fig. 26–5a. For simplicity, we assume that $O_1$ is exactly halfway between $A_1$ and $B_1$, and that $O_2$ is halfway between $A_2$ and $B_2$. Let us first put ourselves in $O_2$'s reference frame, so we observe $O_1$ moving to the right with speed $v$. Let us also assume that the two events occur *simultaneously* in $O_2$'s frame, and just at the instant when $O_1$ and $O_2$ are opposite each other, Fig. 26–5a. A short time later, Fig. 26–5b, the light from $A_2$ and $B_2$ reaches $O_2$ at the same time (we assumed this). Since $O_2$ knows (or measures) the distances $O_2A_2$ and $O_2B_2$ as equal, $O_2$ knows the two events are simultaneous in the $O_2$ reference frame.

But what does observer $O_1$ observe and measure? From our ($O_2$) reference frame, we can predict what $O_1$ will observe. We see that $O_1$ moves to the right during the time the light is traveling to $O_1$ from $A_1$ and $B_1$. As shown in Fig. 26–5b, we can see from our $O_2$ reference frame that the light from $B_1$ has already passed $O_1$, whereas the light from $A_1$ has not yet reached $O_1$. That is, $O_1$ observes the light coming from $B_1$ before observing the light coming from $A_1$. Given (1) that light travels at the same speed $c$ in any direction and in any reference frame, and (2) that the distance $O_1A_1$ equals $O_1B_1$, then observer $O_1$ can only conclude that the event at $B_1$ occurred before the event at $A_1$. The two events are not simultaneous for $O_1$, even though they are for $O_2$.

*Simultaneity is relative*

We thus find that two events which take place at different locations and are simultaneous to one observer, are actually not simultaneous to a second observer who moves relative to the first.

It may be tempting to ask: "Which observer is right, $O_1$ or $O_2$?" The answer, according to relativity, is that they are *both* right. There is no "best" reference frame we can choose to determine which observer is right. Both frames are equally good. We can only conclude that *simultaneity is not an absolute concept*, but is relative. We are not aware of it in everyday life, however, because the effect is noticeable only when the relative speed of the two reference frames is very large (near $c$), or the distances involved are very large.

**EXERCISE A** Examine the experiment of Fig. 26–5 from $O_1$'s reference frame. In this case, $O_1$ will be at rest and will see event $B_1$ occur before $A_1$. Will $O_1$ recognize that $O_2$, who is moving with speed $v$ to the left, will see the two events as simultaneous? (*Hint*: draw a diagram equivalent to Fig. 26–5.)

## 26–4 Time Dilation and the Twin Paradox

The fact that two events simultaneous to one observer may not be simultaneous to a second observer suggests that time itself is not absolute. Could it be that time passes differently in one reference frame than in another? This is, indeed, just what Einstein's theory of relativity predicts, as the following thought experiment shows.

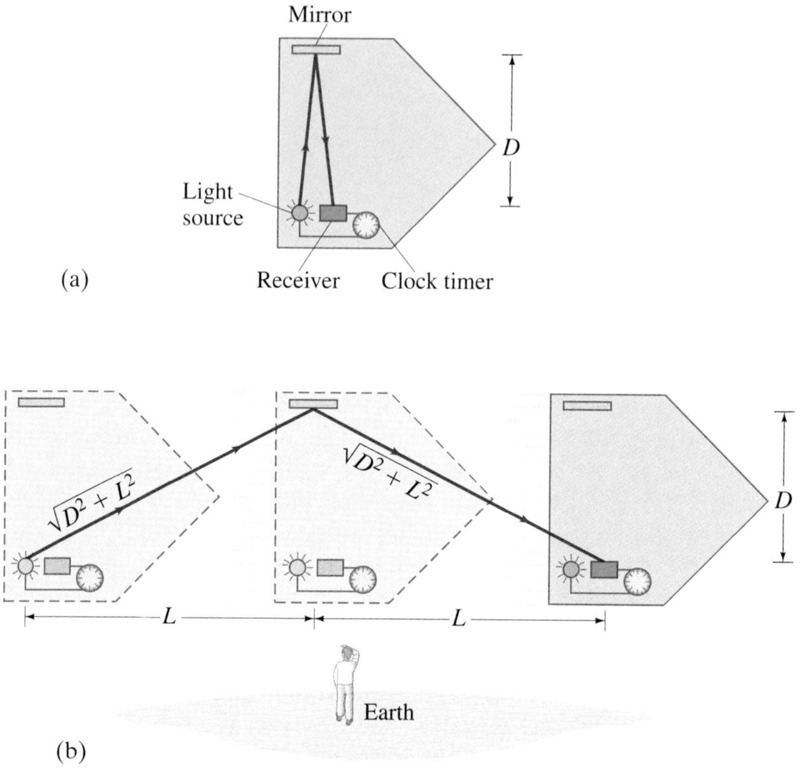


**FIGURE 26–6** Time dilation can be shown by a thought experiment: the time it takes for light to travel across a spaceship and back is longer for the observer on Earth (b) than for the observer on the spaceship (a).

Figure 26–6 shows a spaceship traveling past Earth at high speed. The point of view of an observer on the spaceship is shown in part (a), and that of an observer on Earth in part (b). Both observers have accurate clocks. The person on the spaceship (a) flashes a light and measures the time it takes the light to travel across the spaceship and return after reflecting from a mirror. In the reference frame of the spaceship, the light travels a distance $2D$ at speed $c$; so the time required to go across and back, which we call $\Delta t_0$, is

*Time interval measured by observer on spaceship*

$$\Delta t_0 = \frac{2D}{c}.$$

The observer on Earth, Fig. 26–6b, observes the same process. But to this observer, the spaceship is moving. So the light travels the diagonal path shown going across the spaceship, reflecting off the mirror, and returning to the sender. Although the light travels at the same speed to this observer (the second postulate), it travels a greater distance. Hence the time required, as measured by the observer on Earth, will be *greater* than that measured by the observer on the spaceship.

The time interval, $\Delta t$, observed by the observer on Earth can be calculated as follows. In the time $\Delta t$, the spaceship travels a distance $2L = v\,\Delta t$ where $v$ is the speed of the spaceship (Fig. 26–6b). Thus, the light travels a total distance on its diagonal path (Pythagorean theorem) of $2\sqrt{D^2 + L^2}$, where $L = v\,\Delta t/2$, and therefore

$$c = \frac{2\sqrt{D^2 + L^2}}{\Delta t} = \frac{2\sqrt{D^2 + v^2(\Delta t)^2/4}}{\Delta t}.$$

We square both sides,

$$c^2 = \frac{4D^2}{(\Delta t)^2} + v^2,$$

and solve for $\Delta t$, to find

$$(\Delta t)^2 = \frac{4D^2}{c^2 - v^2}$$

$$\Delta t = \frac{2D}{c\sqrt{1 - v^2/c^2}}.$$

We combine this equation with the formula on page 734, $\Delta t_0 = 2D/c$:

$$\Delta t = \frac{\Delta t_0}{\sqrt{1 - v^2/c^2}}. \qquad \textbf{(26–1a)}$$

*Time dilation formula*

Since $\sqrt{1 - v^2/c^2}$ is always less than 1, we see that $\Delta t > \Delta t_0$. That is, the time interval between the two events (the sending of the light, and its reception on the spaceship) is *greater* for the observer on Earth than for the observer on the spaceship. This is a general result of the theory of relativity, and is known as **time dilation**. Stated simply, the time dilation effect says that

*Time dilation: moving clocks run slow*

> **clocks moving relative to an observer are measured by that observer to run more slowly (as compared to clocks at rest).**

However, we should not think that the clocks are somehow at fault. Time is actually measured to pass more slowly in any moving reference frame as compared to your own. This remarkable result is an inevitable outcome of the two postulates of the theory of relativity.

The factor $1/\sqrt{1 - v^2/c^2}$ occurs so often in relativity that we often give it the shorthand symbol $\gamma$, and write Eq. 26–1a as

$$\Delta t = \gamma\,\Delta t_0 \qquad \textbf{(26–1b)}$$

*Time dilation*

where

$$\gamma = \frac{1}{\sqrt{1 - v^2/c^2}}. \qquad \textbf{(26–2)}$$

*$\gamma$ defined*

Note that $\gamma$ is never less than one. At normal speeds, $\gamma = 1$ to a few decimal places; in general, $\gamma \geq 1$.

The concept of time dilation may be hard to accept, for it contradicts our experience. We can see from Eq. 26–1 that the time dilation effect is indeed negligible unless $v$ is reasonably close to $c$. If $v$ is much less than $c$, then the term $v^2/c^2$ is much smaller than the 1 in the denominator of Eq. 26–1a, and then $\Delta t \approx \Delta t_0$ (see Example 26–2). The speeds we experience in everyday life are much smaller than $c$, so it is little wonder we don't ordinarily notice time dilation. Experiments have tested the time dilation effect, and have confirmed Einstein's predictions. In 1971, for example, extremely precise atomic clocks were flown around the world in jet planes. The speed of the planes $(10^3\ \text{km/h})$ was much less than $c$, so the clocks had to be accurate to nanoseconds $(10^{-9}\ \text{s})$ in order to detect any time dilation. They were this accurate, and they confirmed Eq. 26–1 to within experimental error. Time dilation had been confirmed decades earlier, however, by observation on "elementary particles" which have very small masses (typically $10^{-30}$ to $10^{-27}$ kg) and so require little energy to be accelerated to speeds close to the speed of light, $c$. Many of these elementary particles are not stable and decay after a time into lighter particles. One example is the muon, whose mean lifetime is $2.2\ \mu\text{s}$ when at rest. Careful experiments showed that when a muon is traveling at high speeds, its lifetime is measured to be longer than when it is at rest, just as predicted by the time dilation formula.

*Why we don't usually notice time dilation*

*Experimental confirmation*

**EXAMPLE 26–1 Lifetime of a moving muon.** (*a*) What will be the mean lifetime of a muon as measured in the laboratory if it is traveling at $v = 0.60c = 1.80 \times 10^8\,\text{m/s}$ with respect to the laboratory? Its mean lifetime at rest is $2.20\,\mu\text{s} = 2.20 \times 10^{-6}\,\text{s}$. (*b*) How far does a muon travel in the laboratory, on average, before decaying?

**APPROACH** If an observer were to move along with the muon (the muon would be at rest to this observer), the muon would have a mean life of $2.2 \times 10^{-6}\,\text{s}$. To an observer in the lab, the muon lives longer because of time dilation. We find the mean lifetime using Eq. 26–1a and the average distance from $d = v\,\Delta t$.

**SOLUTION** (*a*) From Eq. 26–1a with $v = 0.60c$, we have

$$\Delta t = \frac{\Delta t_0}{\sqrt{1-\frac{v^2}{c^2}}} = \frac{2.20 \times 10^{-6}\,\text{s}}{\sqrt{1-\frac{0.36c^2}{c^2}}} = \frac{2.20 \times 10^{-6}\,\text{s}}{\sqrt{0.64}} = 2.8 \times 10^{-6}\,\text{s}.$$

(*b*) Relativity predicts that a muon would travel an average distance $d = v\,\Delta t = (0.60)(3.0 \times 10^8\,\text{m/s})(2.8 \times 10^{-6}\,\text{s}) = 500\,\text{m}$, and this is the distance that is measured experimentally in the laboratory.

**NOTE** At a speed of $1.8 \times 10^8\,\text{m/s}$, classical physics would tell us that with a mean life of $2.2\,\mu\text{s}$, an average muon would travel $d = vt = (1.8 \times 10^8\,\text{m/s})(2.2 \times 10^{-6}\,\text{s}) = 400\,\text{m}$. This is shorter than the distance measured.

**EXERCISE B** What is the muon's mean life in Example 26–1 if $v$ is (*a*) $0.10c$, (*b*) $0.90c$?

*The proper time $\Delta t_0$ is in a reference frame where the two events occur at the same point in space*

We need to clarify how to use Eq. 26–1, and the meaning of $\Delta t$ and $\Delta t_0$. The equation is true only when $\Delta t_0$ represents the time interval between the two events in a reference frame where the two events occur at *the same point in space* (as in Fig. 26–6a where the two events are the light flash being sent and being received). This time interval, $\Delta t_0$, is called the **proper time**. Then $\Delta t$ in Eq. 26–1 represents the time interval between the two events as measured in a reference frame moving with speed $v$ with respect to the first. In Example 26–1 above, $\Delta t_0$ (and not $\Delta t$) was set equal to $2.2 \times 10^{-6}\,\text{s}$ because it is only in the rest frame of the muon that the two events ("birth" and "decay") occur at the same point in space. The proper time $\Delta t_0$ is the shortest time between the events any observer can measure. In any other moving reference frame, the time $\Delta t$ is greater.

**EXAMPLE 26–2 Time dilation at 100 km/h.** Let's check time dilation for everyday speeds. A car traveling 100 km/h covers a certain distance in 10.00 s according to the driver's watch. What does an observer at rest on Earth measure for the time interval?

**APPROACH** The car's speed relative to Earth is $100\,\text{km/h} = (1.00 \times 10^5\,\text{m})/(3600\,\text{s}) = 27.8\,\text{m/s}$. The driver is at rest in the reference frame of the car, so we set $\Delta t_0 = 10.00\,\text{s}$ in the time dilation formula.

**SOLUTION** We use Eq. 26–1a:

$$\Delta t = \frac{\Delta t_0}{\sqrt{1-\frac{v^2}{c^2}}} = \frac{10.00\,\text{s}}{\sqrt{1-\left(\frac{27.8\,\text{m/s}}{3.00 \times 10^8\,\text{m/s}}\right)^2}} = \frac{10.00\,\text{s}}{\sqrt{1-(8.59 \times 10^{-15})}}.$$

If you put these numbers into a calculator, you will obtain $\Delta t = 10.00\,\text{s}$, since the denominator differs from 1 by such a tiny amount. Indeed, the time measured by an observer on Earth would show no difference from that measured by the driver, even with the best instruments. A computer that could calculate to a large number of decimal places would show $\Delta t$ is greater than $\Delta t_0$ by about $4 \times 10^{-14}\,\text{s}$.

**NOTE** We can estimate the difference using the binomial expansion (Appendix A),

$$(1 \pm x)^n \approx 1 \pm nx. \qquad \text{[for } x \ll 1]$$

In our time dilation formula, we have the factor $\gamma = (1 - v^2/c^2)^{-\frac{1}{2}}$. Thus

$$\begin{aligned}
\Delta t &= \gamma\, \Delta t_0 \\
&= \Delta t_0 \left(1 - \frac{v^2}{c^2}\right)^{-\frac{1}{2}} \\
&\approx \Delta t_0 \left(1 + \frac{1}{2}\frac{v^2}{c^2}\right) \\
&\approx 10.00\,\text{s}\left[1 + \frac{1}{2}\left(\frac{27.8\,\text{m/s}}{3.00 \times 10^8\,\text{m/s}}\right)^2\right] \\
&\approx 10.00\,\text{s} + 4 \times 10^{-14}\,\text{s}.
\end{aligned}$$

So the difference between $\Delta t$ and $\Delta t_0$ is predicted to be $4 \times 10^{-14}$ s, an extremely small amount.

**PROBLEM SOLVING**
*Use of the binomial expansion*

**EXERCISE C** A certain atomic clock keeps perfect time on Earth. If the clock is taken on a spaceship traveling at a speed $v = 0.60c$, does this clock now run slow according to the people (*a*) on the spaceship, (*b*) on Earth?

## Space Travel?

Time dilation has aroused interesting speculation about space travel. According to classical (Newtonian) physics, to reach a star 100 light-years away would not be possible for ordinary mortals (1 light-year is the distance light can travel in $1\text{ year} = 3.0 \times 10^8\,\text{m/s} \times 3.16 \times 10^7\,\text{s} = 9.5 \times 10^{15}\,\text{m}$). Even if a spaceship could travel at close to the speed of light, it would take over 100 years to reach such a star. But time dilation tells us that the time involved would be less for an astronaut. In a spaceship traveling at $v = 0.999c$, the time for such a trip would be only about

$$\begin{aligned}
\Delta t_0 &= \Delta t\sqrt{1 - v^2/c^2} \\
&= (100\,\text{yr})\sqrt{1 - (0.999)^2} \\
&= 4.5\,\text{yr}.
\end{aligned}$$

Thus time dilation allows such a trip, but the enormous practical problems of achieving such speeds may not be possible to overcome, certainly not in the near future.

In this example, 100 years would pass on Earth, whereas only 4.5 years would pass for the astronaut on the trip. Is it just the clocks that would slow down for the astronaut? No. All processes, including aging and other life processes, run more slowly for the astronaut according to the Earth observer. But to the astronaut, time would pass in a normal way. The astronaut would experience 4.5 years of normal sleeping, eating, reading, and so on. And people on Earth would experience 100 years of ordinary activity.

## Twin Paradox

Twin paradox

Not long after Einstein proposed the special theory of relativity, an apparent paradox was pointed out. According to this **twin paradox**, suppose one of a pair of 20-year-old twins takes off in a spaceship traveling at very high speed to a distant star and back again, while the other twin remains on Earth. According to the Earth twin, the astronaut twin will age less. Whereas 20 years might pass for the Earth twin, perhaps only 1 year (depending on the spacecraft's speed) would pass for the traveler. Thus, when the traveler returns, the earthbound twin could expect to be 40 years old whereas the traveling twin would be only 21.

This is the viewpoint of the twin on the Earth. But what about the traveling twin? If all inertial reference frames are equally good, won't the traveling twin make all the claims the Earth twin does, only in reverse? Can't the astronaut twin claim that since the Earth is moving away at high speed, time passes more slowly on Earth and the twin on Earth will age less? This is the opposite of what the Earth twin predicts. They cannot both be right, for after all the spacecraft returns to Earth and a direct comparison of ages and clocks can be made.

There is, however, no contradiction here. The consequences of the special theory of relativity—in this case, time dilation—can be applied only by observers in an inertial reference frame. The Earth is such a frame (or nearly so), whereas the spacecraft is not. The spacecraft accelerates at the start and end of its trip and when it turns around at the far point of its journey. During the acceleration, the twin on the spacecraft is not in an inertial frame. In between, the astronaut twin may be in an inertial frame (and is justified in saying the Earth twin's clocks run slow), but it is not always the same frame. So she cannot predict their relative ages when she returns to Earth. The Earth twin stays in the same inertial frame, and we can thus trust her predictions based on special relativity. Thus, there is no paradox. The prediction of the Earth twin that the traveling twin ages less is the proper one.

## * Additional Example—Using $\gamma$

**EXAMPLE 26–3** **$\gamma$ for various speeds.** Determine the value of $\gamma$ for a speed $v$ equal to (*a*) 0, (*b*) $0.010c$, (*c*) $0.10c$, (*d*) $0.50c$, (*e*) $0.90c$, (*f*) $0.990c$.

**APPROACH** We simply plug into Eq. 26–2.

**SOLUTION** (*a*) For $v = 0, \gamma = 1/1 = 1$ exactly.
(*b*) For $v = 0.010c = 3.0 \times 10^6\,\mathrm{m/s}$ (a pretty high speed):

$$\gamma = \frac{1}{\sqrt{1 - \left(\dfrac{0.010c}{c}\right)^2}}$$

$$= \frac{1}{\sqrt{1 - (0.010)^2}} = \frac{1}{\sqrt{0.99990}} = 1.00005.$$

Unless $v$ is given to more significant figures, $\gamma = 1.0$ here. We see that $\gamma$ is never less than 1.0 and will only exceed 1.0 significantly at higher speeds.
(*c*) For a speed 10 times higher, $v = 0.10c$, we get

$$\gamma = \frac{1}{\sqrt{1 - (0.10)^2}} = \frac{1}{\sqrt{0.99}} = 1.005.$$

(*d*) At a speed half the speed of light

$$\gamma = \frac{1}{\sqrt{1 - (0.50)^2}} = 1.15.$$

(*e*) At $v = 0.90c$ we get $\gamma = 2.3$.
(*f*) At $v = 0.990c$ we get $\gamma = 7.1$.

Table 26–1 is a handy summary of these results.

**TABLE 26–1 Values of $\gamma$**

| $v$ | $\gamma$ |
|---|---|
| 0 | 1.000 |
| 0.01$c$ | 1.000 |
| 0.10$c$ | 1.005 |
| 0.50$c$ | 1.15 |
| 0.90$c$ | 2.3 |
| 0.99$c$ | 7.1 |

## * Global Positioning System (GPS)

PHYSICS APPLIED
*Global positioning system (GPS)*

Airplanes, cars, boats, and hikers use **global positioning system (GPS)** receivers to tell them quite accurately where they are, at a given moment. The 24 global positioning system satellites send out precise time signals using atomic clocks. Your receiver compares the times received from at least four satellites, all of whose times are carefully synchronized to within 1 part in $10^{13}$. By comparing the time differences with the known satellite positions and the fixed speed of light, the receiver can determine how far it is from each satellite and thus where it is on the Earth. It can do this to a typical accuracy of 15 m, if it has been constructed to make corrections such as the one below due to special relativity.

CONCEPTUAL EXAMPLE 26–4 **A relativity correction to GPS.** GPS satellites move at about $4\,\mathrm{km/s} = 4000\,\mathrm{m/s}$. Show that a good GPS receiver needs to correct for time dilation if it is to produce results consistent with atomic clocks accurate to 1 part in $10^{13}$.

**RESPONSE** Let us calculate the magnitude of the time dilation effect by inserting $v = 4000\,\mathrm{m/s}$ into Eq. 26–1a:

$$\begin{aligned}\Delta t &= \frac{1}{\sqrt{1-\dfrac{v^2}{c^2}}}\,\Delta t_0 \\ &= \frac{1}{\sqrt{1-\left(\dfrac{4\times10^3\,\mathrm{m/s}}{3\times10^8\,\mathrm{m/s}}\right)^2}}\,\Delta t_0 \\ &= \frac{1}{\sqrt{1-1.8\times10^{-10}}}\,\Delta t_0.\end{aligned}$$

We use the binomial expansion: $(1 \pm x)^n \approx 1 \pm nx$ for $x \ll 1$ (see Appendix A) which here is $(1-x)^{-\frac{1}{2}} \approx 1 + \frac{1}{2}x$. That is

$$\Delta t = \left(1 + \tfrac{1}{2}(1.8\times10^{-10})\right)\Delta t_0 = (1 + 9\times10^{-11})\,\Delta t_0.$$

The time "error" divided by the time interval is

$$\frac{(\Delta t - \Delta t_0)}{\Delta t_0} = 1 + 9\times10^{-11} - 1 = 9\times10^{-11} \approx 1\times10^{-10}.$$

Time dilation, if not accounted for, would introduce an error of about 1 part in $10^{10}$, which is 1000 times greater than the precision of the atomic clocks. Not correcting for time dilation means a receiver could give much poorer position accuracy.

**NOTE** GPS devices must make other corrections as well, including effects associated with General Relativity.

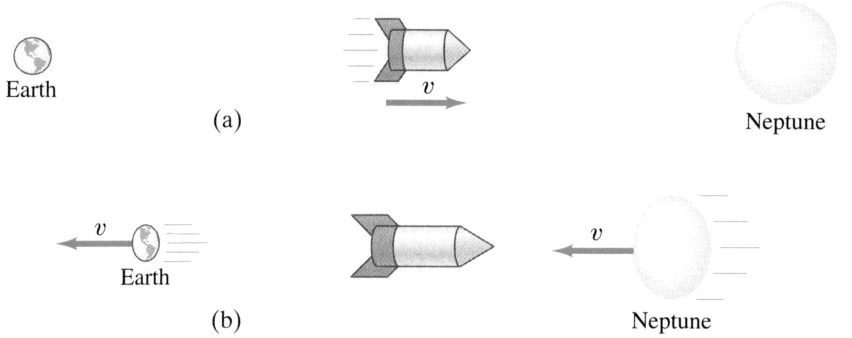


**FIGURE 26–7** (a) A spaceship traveling at very high speed from Earth to the planet Neptune, as seen from Earth's frame of reference. (b) According to an observer on the spaceship, Earth and Neptune are moving at the very high speed $v$: Earth leaves the spaceship, and a time $\Delta t_0$ later Neptune arrives at the spaceship.

## 26–5 Length Contraction

Not only time intervals are different in different reference frames. Space intervals—lengths and distances—are different as well, according to the special theory of relativity, and we illustrate this with a thought experiment.

Observers on Earth watch a spacecraft traveling at speed $v$ from Earth to, say, Neptune, Fig. 26–7a. The distance between the planets, as measured by the Earth observers, is $L_0$. The time required for the trip, measured from Earth, is

$$\Delta t = \frac{L_0}{v}. \qquad \text{[Earth observer]}$$

In Fig. 26–7b we see the point of view of observers on the spacecraft. In this frame of reference, the spaceship is at rest; Earth and Neptune move† with speed $v$. The time between departure of Earth and arrival of Neptune (observed from the spacecraft) is the "proper time," since the two events occur at the same point in space (i.e., on the spacecraft). Therefore the time interval is less for the spacecraft observers than for the Earth observers. That is, because of time dilation (Eq. 26–1), the time for the trip as viewed by the spacecraft is

$$\begin{aligned} \Delta t_0 &= \Delta t \sqrt{1 - v^2/c^2} \\ &= \Delta t/\gamma. \end{aligned} \qquad \text{[spacecraft observer]}$$

Because the spacecraft observers measure the same speed but less time between these two events, they also measure the distance as less. If we let $L$ be the distance between the planets as viewed by the spacecraft observers, then $L = v\,\Delta t_0$, which we can rewrite as $L = v\,\Delta t_0 = v\,\Delta t\sqrt{1 - v^2/c^2} = L_0\sqrt{1 - v^2/c^2}$. Thus we have the important result that

*Length contraction formula*

$$L = L_0\sqrt{1 - v^2/c^2} \qquad \textbf{(26–3a)}$$

or, using $\gamma$ (Eq. 26–2),

$$L = \frac{L_0}{\gamma}. \qquad \textbf{(26–3b)}$$

This is a general result of the special theory of relativity and applies to lengths of objects as well as to distance between objects. The result can be stated most simply in words as:

*Length contraction: moving objects are shorter (in the direction of motion)*

**the length of an object is measured to be shorter when it is moving relative to the observer than when it is at rest.**

**CAUTION**

*Proper length is measured in reference frame where the two positions are at rest*

This is called **length contraction**. The length $L_0$ in Eq. 26–3 is called the **proper length**. It is the length of the object (or distance between two points whose positions are measured at the same time) as determined by *observers at rest* with respect to it. Equation 26–3 gives the length $L$ that will be measured by observers when the object travels past them at speed $v$.

†We assume $v$ is much greater than the relative speed of Neptune and Earth, so the latter can be ignored.

It is important to note that length contraction occurs *only along the direction of motion*. For example, the moving spaceship in Fig. 26–7a is shortened in length, but its height is the same as when it is at rest.

Length contraction, like time dilation, is not noticeable in everyday life because the factor $\sqrt{1 - v^2/c^2}$ in Eq. 26–3 differs from 1.00 significantly only when $v$ is very large.

**EXAMPLE 26–5** **Painting's contraction.** A rectangular painting measures 1.00 m tall and 1.50 m wide. It is hung on the side wall of a spaceship which is moving past the Earth at a speed of $0.90c$. See Fig. 26–8a. (*a*) What are the dimensions of the picture according to the captain of the spaceship? (*b*) What are the dimensions as seen by an observer on the Earth?

**APPROACH** We apply the length contraction formula, Eq. 26–3, to the dimension parallel to the motion; $v$ is the speed of the painting relative to the observer.

**SOLUTION** (*a*) The painting is at rest ($v = 0$) on the spaceship so it (as well as everything else in the spaceship) looks perfectly normal to everyone on the spaceship. The captain sees a 1.00-m by 1.50-m painting.

(*b*) Only the dimension in the direction of motion is shortened, so the height is unchanged at 1.00 m, Fig. 26–8b. The length, however, is contracted to

$$L = L_0\sqrt{1 - \frac{v^2}{c^2}}$$

$$= (1.50\text{ m})\sqrt{1 - (0.90)^2} = 0.65\text{ m}.$$

So the picture has dimensions 1.00 m × 0.65 m.

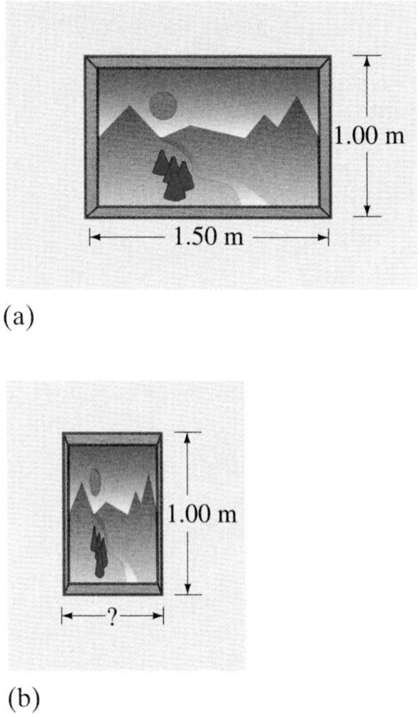


**FIGURE 26–8** Example 26–5.

**EXAMPLE 26–6** **A fantasy supertrain.** A very fast train with a proper length of 500 m is passing through a 200-m-long tunnel. The train's speed is so great that the train fits completely within the tunnel as seen by an observer at rest on the Earth (on the mountain above the tunnel); that is, the engine is just about to emerge from one end of the tunnel as the last car disappears into the other end. What is the train's speed?

**APPROACH** Since the train just fits inside the tunnel, its length measured by the person on the ground is 200 m. The length contraction formula, Eq. 26–3, can thus be used to solve for $v$.

**SOLUTION** Substituting $L = 200\text{ m}$ and $L_0 = 500\text{ m}$ into Eq. 26–3 gives

$$200\text{ m} = 500\text{ m}\sqrt{1 - \frac{v^2}{c^2}};$$

dividing both sides by 500 m and squaring, we get

$$(0.40)^2 = 1 - \frac{v^2}{c^2}$$

or

$$\frac{v}{c} = \sqrt{1 - (0.40)^2}$$

$$v = 0.92c.$$

**NOTE** No real train could go this fast. But it is fun to think about.

**NOTE** An observer on the *train* would *not* see the two ends of the train inside the tunnel at the same time; simultaneity is relative.

**EXERCISE D** At what spaceship speed would the painting of Example 26–5 look contracted by only 10 cm (to $L = 1.40$ m) according to Earth observers?

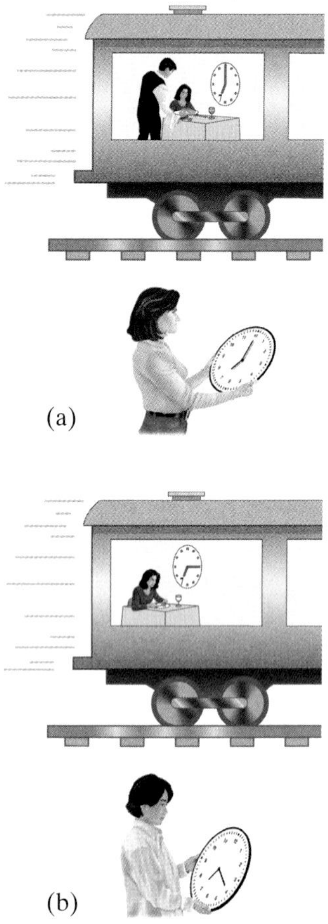


**FIGURE 26–9** According to an accurate clock on a fast-moving train, a person (a) begins dinner at 7:00 and (b) finishes at 7:15. At the beginning of the meal, observers on Earth set their watches to correspond with the clock on the train. These observers measure the eating time as 20 minutes.

## * 26–6 Four-Dimensional Space–Time

Let us imagine a person is on a train moving at a very high speed, say $0.65c$, Fig. 26–9. This person begins a meal at 7:00 and finishes at 7:15, according to a clock on the train. The two events, beginning and ending the meal, take place at the same point on the train. So the proper time between these two events is 15 min. To observers on Earth, the meal will take longer—20 min according to Eq. 26–1. Let us assume that the meal was served on a 20-cm-diameter plate. To observers on the Earth, the plate is only 15 cm wide (length contraction). Thus, to observers on the Earth, the meal looks smaller but lasts longer.

In a sense the two effects, time dilation and length contraction, balance each other. When viewed from the Earth, what an object seems to lose in size it gains in length of time it lasts. Space, or length, is exchanged for time.

Considerations like this led to the idea of **four-dimensional space–time**: space takes up three dimensions and time is a fourth dimension. Space and time are intimately connected. Just as when we squeeze a balloon we make one dimension larger and another smaller, so when we examine objects and events from different reference frames, a certain amount of space is exchanged for time, or vice versa.

Although the idea of four dimensions may seem strange, it refers to the idea that any object or event is specified by four quantities—three to describe where in space, and one to describe when in time. The really unusual aspect of four-dimensional space–time is that space and time can intermix: a little of one can be exchanged for a little of the other when the reference frame is changed.

It is difficult for most of us to understand the idea of four-dimensional space–time. Somehow we feel, just as physicists did before the advent of relativity, that space and time are completely separate entities. Yet we have found in our thought experiments that they are not completely separate. And think about Galileo and Newton. Before Galileo, the vertical direction, that in which objects fall, was considered to be distinctly different from the two horizontal dimensions. Galileo showed that the vertical dimension differs only in that it happens to be the direction in which gravity acts. Otherwise, all three dimensions are equivalent, a viewpoint we all accept today. Now we are asked to accept one more dimension, time, which we had previously thought of as being somehow different. This is not to say that there is no distinction between space and time. What relativity has shown is that space and time determinations are not independent of one another.

## 26–7 Relativistic Momentum and Mass

So far in this Chapter, we have seen that two basic mechanical quantities, length and time intervals, need modification because they are relative—their value depends on the reference frame from which they are measured. We might expect that other physical quantities might need some modification according to the theory of relativity, such as momentum, energy, and mass.

The analysis of collisions between two particles shows that if we want to preserve the law of conservation of momentum in relativity, we must redefine momentum as

*Relativistic momentum*

$$p = \frac{m_0 v}{\sqrt{1 - v^2/c^2}} = \gamma m_0 v. \qquad \textbf{(26–4)}$$

Here $\gamma$ is shorthand for $1/\sqrt{1 - v^2/c^2}$ as before (Eq. 26–2). For speeds much less than the speed of light, Eq. 26–4 gives the classical momentum, $p = m_0 v$.

We have written $m_0$ rather than $m$ because Eq. 26–4 suggests to some physicists a relativistic interpretation of mass. Namely, that an object at rest has a **rest mass** $m_0$, but that its mass can increase with speed according to the formula

$$m_{\text{rel}} = \frac{m_0}{\sqrt{1 - v^2/c^2}} = \gamma m_0, \qquad \textbf{(26–5)}$$

*Mass increase formula*

where $m_{\text{rel}}$ is called the **relativistic mass**. But be careful *not* to think a mass acquires more particles or more molecules as its speed becomes very large. It doesn't. In fact, many physicists believe an object has only one mass (its rest mass), and that it is only the momentum that increases with speed, a relativistic effect that everyone agrees to. [We use subscripts on $m$ ($m_0$ and $m_{\text{rel}}$) to avoid any misunderstanding. If you see $m$ without a subscript, you can feel pretty confident that it means rest mass.]

Relativistic momentum has been tested many times on tiny elementary particles (such as muons), and it has been found to increase in accord with Eq. 26–4.

**EXAMPLE 26–7** **Momentum of moving electron.** Compare the momentum of an electron when it has a speed of (*a*) $4.00 \times 10^7\,\text{m/s}$ in the CRT of a television set, and (*b*) $0.98c$ in an accelerator used for cancer therapy.

**APPROACH** We use Eq. 26–4 for the momentum of a moving electron.

**SOLUTION** (*a*) At $v = 4.00 \times 10^7\,\text{m/s}$, the electron's momentum is

$$p = \frac{m_0 v}{\sqrt{1 - \dfrac{v^2}{c^2}}} = \frac{m_0 v}{\sqrt{1 - \dfrac{(4.00 \times 10^7\,\text{m/s})^2}{(3.00 \times 10^8\,\text{m/s})^2}}} = 1.01 m_0 v.$$

The factor $\gamma = 1/\sqrt{1 - v^2/c^2} \approx 1.01$, so the momentum is only about 1% greater than the classical value. (If we put in the rest mass of an electron, $m_0 = 9.11 \times 10^{-31}\,\text{kg}$, the momentum is $p = 1.01 m_0 v = 3.68 \times 10^{-23}\,\text{kg}\cdot\text{m/s}$.)

(*b*) With $v = 0.98c$, the momentum is

$$p = \frac{m_0 v}{\sqrt{1 - \dfrac{v^2}{c^2}}} = \frac{m_0 v}{\sqrt{1 - \dfrac{(0.98c)^2}{c^2}}} = \frac{m_0 v}{\sqrt{1 - (0.98)^2}} = 5.0 m_0 v.$$

An electron traveling at 98% the speed of light has $\gamma = 5.0$ and a momentum 5.0 times its classical value.

## 26–8 The Ultimate Speed

A basic result of the special theory of relativity is that the speed of an object cannot equal or exceed the speed of light. That the speed of light is a natural speed limit in the universe can be seen from any of Eqs. 26–1, 26–3, or 26–4. It is perhaps easiest to see from Eq. 26–4: as an object is accelerated to greater and greater speeds, its momentum becomes larger and larger. Indeed, if $v$ were to equal $c$, the denominator in this equation would be zero (in the other equations too), and the momentum would become infinite. To accelerate an object up to $v = c$ would thus require infinite energy, and so is not possible.

## 26–9 $E = mc^2$; Mass and Energy

If momentum needs to be modified to fit with relativity as we just saw in Eq. 26–4, then we might expect energy too would need to be rethought. Indeed, Einstein not only developed a new formula for kinetic energy, but also found a new relation between mass and energy, and the startling idea that mass is a form of energy.†

We can start with the work–energy principle (Chapter 6) and assume it is still valid in relativity. That is, the net work done on a particle is equal to its change in kinetic energy (KE). Using this principle, Einstein showed that at high speeds the formula $\text{KE} = \frac{1}{2}mv^2$ is not correct. Instead, Einstein showed that the kinetic energy of a particle of rest mass $m_0$ traveling at speed $v$ is given by

*Relativistic kinetic energy*

$$\text{KE} = \frac{m_0c^2}{\sqrt{1 - v^2/c^2}} - m_0c^2. \qquad \textbf{(26–6a)}$$

In terms of $\gamma = 1/\sqrt{1 - v^2/c^2}$ we can rewrite Eq. 26–6a as

$$\text{KE} = \gamma m_0c^2 - m_0c^2 = (\gamma - 1)m_0c^2. \qquad \textbf{(26–6b)}$$

Equations 26–6 require some interpretation. The first term increases with the speed $v$ of the particle. The second term, $m_0c^2$, is constant; it is called the **rest energy** $E_0$ of the particle, and represents a form of energy that a particle has even when at rest. Note that if a particle is at rest $(v = 0)$ the first term in Eq. 26–6a becomes $m_0c^2$, so $\text{KE} = 0$ as it should.

We can rearrange Eq. 26–6b to get

$$\gamma m_0c^2 = m_0c^2 + \text{KE}.$$

We call $\gamma m_0c^2$ the *total energy* $E$ of the particle (assuming no potential energy), because it equals the rest energy plus the kinetic energy:

*Total energy (defined)*

$$E = m_0c^2 + \text{KE}. \qquad \textbf{(26–7a)}$$

The total energy can also be written, using Eqs. 26–6, as

$$E = \gamma m_0c^2 = \frac{m_0c^2}{\sqrt{1 - v^2/c^2}}. \qquad \textbf{(26–7b)}$$

For a particle at rest in a given reference frame, KE is zero in Eqs. 26–7, so the total energy is its rest energy $E_0$:

*MASS RELATED TO ENERGY*

$$E_0 = m_0c^2. \qquad \textbf{(26–8)}$$

Here we have Einstein's famous formula, usually written simply as $E = mc^2$. This formula mathematically relates the concepts of energy and mass. But if this idea is to have any meaning from a practical point of view, then mass ought to be convertible to other forms of energy and vice versa. Einstein suggested that this might be possible, and indeed changes of mass to other forms of energy, and vice versa, have been experimentally confirmed countless times. The interconversion of mass and energy is most easily detected in nuclear and elementary particle physics. For example, the neutral pion $(\pi^0)$ of rest mass $2.4 \times 10^{-28}$ kg is observed to decay into pure electromagnetic radiation (photons). The $\pi^0$ completely disappears in the process. The amount of electromagnetic energy produced is found to be exactly equal to that predicted by Einstein's formula, $E = mc^2$. The reverse process is also commonly observed in the laboratory: electromagnetic radiation under certain conditions can be converted into material particles such as electrons (see Section 27–6 on pair production).

*Mass and energy interchangeable*

†The concept of mass being a form of energy emerges nicely from the concept of relativistic mass, Eq. 26–5. When work is done on an object, its kinetic energy increases. The object's speed cannot increase indefinitely because it cannot exceed $c$; but the object's relativistic mass increases. That is, the work done on an object not only increases its speed but also contributes to increasing its *mass*.

On a larger scale, the energy produced in nuclear power plants is a result of the loss in rest mass of the uranium fuel as it undergoes the process called fission (Chapter 31). Even the radiant energy we receive from the Sun is an example of $E = mc^2$; the Sun's mass is continually decreasing as it radiates electromagnetic energy outward.

The relation $E = mc^2$ is now believed to apply to all processes, although the changes are often too small to measure. That is, when the energy of a system changes by an amount $\Delta E$, the mass of the system changes by an amount $\Delta m$ given by

$$\Delta E = (\Delta m)(c^2). \qquad \textbf{(26–9)}$$

In a nuclear reaction where an energy $E$ is released (or required to make it go), the masses of the reactants and the products will be different by $\Delta m = \Delta E/c^2$. Even when water is heated on a stove, the mass of the water is assumed to increase very slightly.

**EXAMPLE 26–8** **Pion's KE.** A $\pi^0$ meson $(m_0 = 2.40 \times 10^{-28}\,\text{kg})$ travels at a speed $v = 0.80c = 2.4 \times 10^8\,\text{m/s}$. What is its kinetic energy? Compare to a classical calculation.

**APPROACH** Relativistically, kinetic energy is given by Eqs. 26–6. Classically, $\text{KE} = \frac{1}{2}m_0v^2$.

**SOLUTION** The kinetic energy of our $\pi^0$ meson at speed $v = 0.80c$ is (Eq. 26–6a):

$$\begin{aligned}\text{KE} &= m_0c^2\left(\frac{1}{\sqrt{1 - v^2/c^2}} - 1\right)\\ &= (2.40 \times 10^{-28}\,\text{kg})(3.0 \times 10^8\,\text{m/s})^2\left(\frac{1}{(1 - 0.64)^{\frac{1}{2}}} - 1\right)\\ &= 1.4 \times 10^{-11}\,\text{J}.\end{aligned}$$

➡ PROBLEM SOLVING

*Relativistic KE*

Notice that the units of $m_0c^2$ are $\text{kg}\cdot\text{m}^2/\text{s}^2$, which is the joule. A classical calculation would give $\text{KE} = \frac{1}{2}m_0v^2 = \frac{1}{2}(2.4 \times 10^{-28}\,\text{kg})(2.4 \times 10^8\,\text{m/s})^2 = 6.9 \times 10^{-12}\,\text{J}$, about half as much, but this is not a correct result.

**NOTE** Do not try to calculate the relativistic kinetic energy by using the classical equation with a relativistic mass instead of the rest mass (here $m_{\text{rel}} = m_0/\sqrt{1 - v^2/c^2} = 4.0 \times 10^{-28}\,\text{kg}$). This would give $\text{KE} = \frac{1}{2}mv^2 = \frac{1}{2}(4.0 \times 10^{-28}\,\text{kg})(2.4 \times 10^8\,\text{m/s})^2 = 1.2 \times 10^{-11}\,\text{J}$, which is incorrect.

**EXAMPLE 26–9** **Energy from nuclear decay.** The energy required or released in nuclear reactions and decays comes from a change in mass between the initial and final particles. In one type of radioactive decay (Chapter 30), an atom of uranium $(m = 232.03714\,\text{u})$ decays to an atom of thorium $(m = 228.02873\,\text{u})$ plus an atom of helium $(m = 4.00260\,\text{u})$ where the masses given are in atomic mass units $(1\,\text{u} = 1.6605 \times 10^{-27}\,\text{kg})$. Calculate the energy released in this decay.

**APPROACH** The initial mass minus the total final mass gives the mass loss in atomic mass units (u); we convert that to kg, and multiply by $c^2$ to find the energy released, $\Delta E = \Delta m\, c^2$.

**SOLUTION** The initial mass is 232.03714 u, and after the decay the mass is $228.02873\,\text{u} + 4.00260\,\text{u} = 232.03133\,\text{u}$, so there is a decrease in mass of 0.00581 u. This mass, which equals $(0.00581\,\text{u})(1.66 \times 10^{-27}\,\text{kg}) = 9.64 \times 10^{-30}\,\text{kg}$, is changed into energy. By $\Delta E = \Delta m\, c^2$, we have

*Energy released in nuclear process*

$$\Delta E = (9.64 \times 10^{-30}\,\text{kg})(3.0 \times 10^8\,\text{m/s})^2 = 8.68 \times 10^{-13}\,\text{J}.$$

Since $1\,\text{MeV} = 1.60 \times 10^{-13}\,\text{J}$, the energy released is 5.4 MeV.

**EXAMPLE 26–10** **Mass change in a chemical reaction.** When two moles of hydrogen and one mole of oxygen react to form two moles of water, the energy released is 484 kJ. How much does the mass decrease in this reaction?

**APPROACH** We use Einstein's great concept of the interchangeability of mass and energy $(E = mc^2)$.

**SOLUTION** Using Eq. 26–9 we have for the change in mass $\Delta m$:

$$\Delta m = \frac{\Delta E}{c^2} = \frac{(-484 \times 10^3\,\text{J})}{(3.00 \times 10^8\,\text{m/s})^2} = -5.38 \times 10^{-12}\,\text{kg}.$$

The initial mass of the system is $0.002\,\text{kg} + 0.016\,\text{kg} = 0.018\,\text{kg}$. Thus the change in mass is relatively very tiny and can normally be neglected. [Conservation of mass is usually a reasonable principle to apply to chemical reactions.]

*Units: eV/c for p, eV/c² for m*

In the tiny world of atoms and nuclei, it is common to quote energies in eV (electron volts) or multiples such as MeV $(10^6\,\text{eV})$. Momentum (see Eq. 26–4) can be quoted in units of eV/$c$ (or MeV/$c$). And mass can be quoted (from $E = mc^2$) in units of eV/$c^2$ (or MeV/$c^2$). Note the use of $c$ to keep the units correct. The rest masses of the electron and the proton are readily shown to be 0.511 MeV/$c^2$ and 938 MeV/$c^2$, respectively. See also the Table inside the front cover.

**EXAMPLE 26–11** **A 1-TeV proton.** The Tevatron accelerator at Fermilab in Illinois can accelerate protons to a kinetic energy of 1.0 TeV $(10^{12}\,\text{eV})$. What is the speed of such a proton?

**APPROACH** We solve the kinetic energy formula, Eq. 26–6a, for $v$.

**SOLUTION** The rest energy of a proton is $E_0 = 938\,\text{MeV}$ or $9.38 \times 10^8\,\text{eV}$. Compared to the KE of $10^{12}$ eV, the rest energy can be neglected, so we simplify Eq. 26–6a to

$$\text{KE} \approx \frac{m_0c^2}{\sqrt{1 - v^2/c^2}}.$$

We solve this for $v$ in the following steps:

$$\sqrt{1 - \frac{v^2}{c^2}} = \frac{m_0c^2}{\text{KE}};$$

$$1 - \frac{v^2}{c^2} = \left(\frac{m_0c^2}{\text{KE}}\right)^2;$$

$$\frac{v^2}{c^2} = 1 - \left(\frac{m_0c^2}{\text{KE}}\right)^2 = 1 - \left(\frac{9.38 \times 10^8\,\text{eV}}{1.0 \times 10^{12}\,\text{eV}}\right)^2;$$

$$v = \sqrt{1 - (9.38 \times 10^{-4})^2}\,c = 0.99999956c.$$

So the proton is traveling at a speed very nearly equal to $c$.

At low speeds, $v \ll c$, the relativistic formula for KE reduces to the classical one, as we show by using the binomial expansion, $(1 \pm x)^n = 1 \pm nx + n(n-1)x^2/2! + \cdots$. With $n = -\frac{1}{2}$, we expand the square root in Eq. 26–6a

$$\text{KE} = m_0c^2\left(\frac{1}{\sqrt{1 - v^2/c^2}} - 1\right)$$

so that

$$\text{KE} \approx m_0c^2\left(1 + \frac{1}{2}\frac{v^2}{c^2} + \cdots - 1\right)$$
$$\approx \tfrac{1}{2}m_0v^2.$$

The dots in the first expression represent very small terms in the expansion which we neglect since we assumed that $v \ll c$. Thus at low speeds, the relativistic form for kinetic energy reduces to the classical form, $\text{KE} = \frac{1}{2}mv^2$. This makes relativity a viable theory in that it can predict accurate results at low speed as well as at high. Indeed, the other equations of special relativity also reduce to their classical equivalents at ordinary speeds: length contraction, time dilation, and modifications to momentum as well as kinetic energy, all disappear for $v \ll c$ since $\sqrt{1 - v^2/c^2} \approx 1$.

A useful relation between the total energy $E$ of a particle and its momentum $p$ can also be derived. The momentum of a particle of rest mass $m_0$ and speed $v$ is given by Eq. 26–4:

$$p = \frac{m_0 v}{\sqrt{1 - v^2/c^2}} = \gamma m_0 v.$$

*Relativistic momentum*

The total energy is (Eq. 26–7b)

$$E = \gamma m_0 c^2 = \frac{m_0 c^2}{\sqrt{1 - v^2/c^2}}.$$

We square this equation (and add a term "$v^2 - v^2$" which is zero, but will help us):

$$E^2 = \frac{m_0^2 c^2 (v^2 - v^2 + c^2)}{1 - v^2/c^2}$$

$$= p^2c^2 + \frac{m_0^2 c^4 (1 - v^2/c^2)}{1 - v^2/c^2}$$

or

$$E^2 = p^2c^2 + m_0^2 c^4. \qquad \textbf{(26–10)}$$

*Energy related to momentum*

Thus, the total energy can be written in terms of the momentum $p$, or in terms of the kinetic energy (Eq. 26–7a), where we have assumed there is no potential energy.

## * When Do We Use Relativistic Formulas?

From a practical point of view, we do not have much opportunity in our daily lives to use the mathematics of relativity. For example, the $\gamma$ factor, $\gamma = 1/\sqrt{1 - v^2/c^2}$, which appears in many relativistic formulas, has a value of 1.005 when $v = 0.10c$. Thus, for speeds even as high as $0.10c = 3.0 \times 10^7\,\text{m/s}$, the factor $\sqrt{1 - v^2/c^2}$ in relativistic formulas gives a numerical correction of less than 1%. For speeds less than $0.10c$, or unless mass and energy are interchanged, we don't usually need to use the more complicated relativistic formulas, and can use the simpler classical formulas.

If you are given a particle's rest mass $m_0$ and its kinetic energy KE, you can do a quick calculation to determine if you need to use relativistic formulas or if classical ones are good enough. You simply compute the ratio $\text{KE}/m_0c^2$ because (Eq. 26–6b)

$$\frac{\text{KE}}{m_0 c^2} = \gamma - 1 = \frac{1}{\sqrt{1 - v^2/c^2}} - 1.$$

If this ratio comes out to be less than, say, 0.01, then $\gamma \leq 1.01$ and relativistic equations will correct the classical ones by about 1%. If your expected precision is no better than 1%, classical formulas are good enough. But if your precision is 1 part in 1000 (0.1%) then you would want to use relativistic formulas. If your expected precision is only 10%, you need relativity if $(\text{KE}/m_0c^2) \gtrsim 0.1$.

**EXERCISE E** For 1% accuracy, does an electron with $\text{KE} = 100\,\text{eV}$ need to be treated relativistically? [*Hint*: the rest mass of an electron is 0.511 MeV.]

## 26–10 Relativistic Addition of Velocities

Consider a rocket ship that travels away from the Earth with speed $v$, and assume that this rocket has fired off a second rocket that travels at speed $u'$ with respect to the first (Fig. 26–10). We might expect that the speed $u$ of rocket 2 with respect to Earth is $u = v + u'$, which in the case shown in Fig. 26–10 is $u = 0.60c + 0.60c = 1.20c$. But, as discussed in Section 26–8, no object can travel faster than the speed of light in any reference frame. Indeed, Einstein showed that since length and time are different in different reference frames, the old addition-of-velocities formula is no longer valid. Instead, the correct formula is

**CAUTION**

*Relative velocities do not add simply, as in classical ($v \ll c$) mechanics*

*Relativistic addition of velocities formula ($\vec{\mathbf{u}}$ and $\vec{\mathbf{v}}$ along same line)*

$$u = \frac{v + u'}{1 + vu'/c^2} \qquad \left[\begin{array}{l}\vec{\mathbf{u}} \text{ and } \vec{\mathbf{v}} \text{ along}\\ \text{the same direction}\end{array}\right] \qquad \textbf{(26–11)}$$

for motion along a straight line. We derive this formula in Appendix E. If $u'$ is in the opposite direction from $v$, then $u'$ must have a minus sign in the above equation so $u = (v - u')/(1 - vu'/c^2)$.

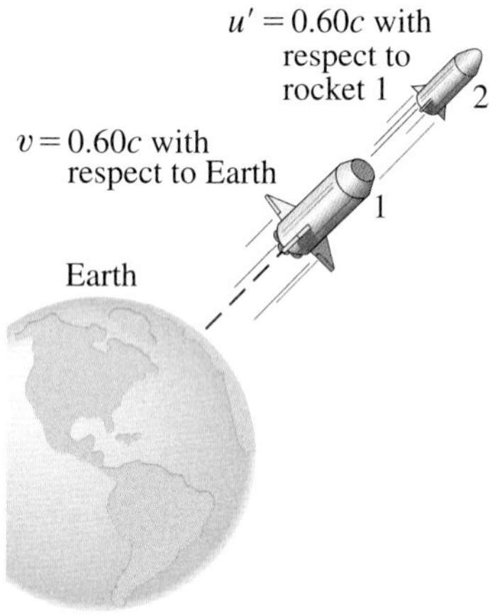


**FIGURE 26–10** Rocket 2 is fired from rocket 1 with speed $u' = 0.60c$. What is the speed of rocket 2 with respect to the Earth?

**EXAMPLE 26–12 Relative velocity, relativistically.** Calculate the speed of rocket 2 in Fig. 26–10 with respect to Earth.

**APPROACH** We add the speed of rocket 2 relative to rocket 1, to the speed of rocket 1 relative to Earth, using the relativistic Eq. 26–11 because the speeds are high and they are along the same line.

**SOLUTION** Rocket 2 moves with speed $u' = 0.60c$ with respect to rocket 1. Rocket 1 has speed $v = 0.60c$ with respect to Earth. The speed of rocket 2 with respect to Earth is (Eq. 26–11)

$$u = \frac{0.60c + 0.60c}{1 + \dfrac{(0.60c)(0.60c)}{c^2}} = \frac{1.20c}{1.36} = 0.88c.$$

**NOTE** The speed of rocket 2 relative to Earth is found to be less than $c$, as it must be.

We can see that Eq. 26–11 reduces to the classical form for velocities small compared to the speed of light since $1 + vu'/c^2 \approx 1$ for $v$ and $u' \ll c$. Thus, $u \approx v + u'$, as in classical physics (Chapter 3).

Let us test our formula in one more case, that of the speed of light. Suppose that rocket 1 in Fig. 26–10 sends out a beam of light so that $u' = c$. Equation 26–11 tells us that the speed of this light with respect to Earth is

$$u = \frac{0.60c + c}{1 + \dfrac{(0.60c)(c)}{c^2}} = \frac{1.60c}{1.60} = c,$$

which is fully consistent with the second postulate of relativity.

**EXERCISE F** Use Eq. 26–11 to calculate the speed of rocket 2 in Fig. 26–10 relative to Earth if it was shot from rocket 1 at a speed $u' = 3000\,\text{km/s} = 0.010c$. Assume rocket 1 had a speed $v = 6000\,\text{km/s} = 0.020c$.

## 26–11 The Impact of Special Relativity

A great many experiments have been performed to test the predictions of the special theory of relativity. Within experimental error, no contradictions have been found. Scientists have therefore accepted relativity as an accurate description of nature.

At speeds much less than the speed of light, the relativistic formulas reduce to the old classical ones, as we have discussed. We would, of course, hope—or rather, insist—that this be true since Newtonian mechanics works so well for objects moving with speeds $v \ll c$. This insistence that a more general theory (such as relativity) give the same results as a more restricted theory (such as classical mechanics which works for $v \ll c$) is called the **correspondence principle**. The two theories must correspond where their realms of validity overlap. Relativity thus does not contradict classical mechanics. Rather, it is a more general theory, of which classical mechanics is now considered to be a limiting case.

*Correspondence principle*

The importance of relativity is not simply that it gives more accurate results, especially at very high speeds. Much more than that, it has changed the way we view the world. The concepts of space and time are now seen to be relative, and intertwined with one another, whereas before they were considered absolute and separate. Even our concepts of matter and energy have changed: either can be converted to the other. The impact of relativity extends far beyond physics. It has influenced the other sciences, and even the world of art and literature; it has, indeed, entered the general culture.

From a practical point of view, we do not have much opportunity in our daily lives to use the mathematics of relativity. For example, the $\gamma$ factor $1/\sqrt{1 - v^2/c^2}$, which appears in relativistic formulas, has a value of only 1.005 even for a speed as high as $0.10c = 3.0 \times 10^7\,\mathrm{m/s}$, giving a correction of less than 1%. For speeds less than $0.10c$, or unless mass and energy are interchanged, we don't usually need to use the more complicated relativistic formulas, and can use the simpler classical formulas.

The special theory of relativity we have studied in this Chapter deals with inertial (nonaccelerating) reference frames. In Chapter 33 we will discuss briefly the more complicated "general theory of relativity" which can deal with noninertial reference frames.

## Summary

An **inertial reference frame** is one in which Newton's law of inertia holds. Inertial reference frames can move at constant velocity relative to one another; accelerating reference frames are **noninertial**.

The **special theory of relativity** is based on two principles: the **relativity principle**, which states that the laws of physics are the same in all inertial reference frames, and the principle of the **constancy of the speed of light**, which states that the speed of light in empty space has the same value in all inertial reference frames.

One consequence of relativity theory is that two events that are simultaneous in one reference frame may not be simultaneous in another. Other effects are **time dilation**: moving clocks are measured to run slow; and **length contraction**: the length of a moving object is measured to be shorter (in its direction of motion) than when it is at rest. Quantitatively,

$$\Delta t = \frac{\Delta t_0}{\sqrt{1 - v^2/c^2}} = \gamma\,\Delta t_0 \qquad \textbf{(26–1)}$$

$$L = L_0\sqrt{1 - v^2/c^2} = \frac{L_0}{\gamma} \qquad \textbf{(26–3)}$$

where $L$ and $\Delta t$ are the length and time interval of objects (or events) observed as they move by at the speed $v$; $L_0$ and $\Delta t_0$ are the **proper length** and **proper time**—that is, the same quantities as measured in the rest frame of the objects or events. The quantity $\gamma$ is shorthand for

$$\gamma = \frac{1}{\sqrt{1 - v^2/c^2}}. \qquad \textbf{(26–2)}$$

The theory of relativity has changed our notions of space and time, and of momentum, energy, and mass. Space and time are seen to be intimately connected, with time being the fourth dimension in addition to the three dimensions of space.

The **momentum** of an object is given by

$$p = \gamma m_0 v = \frac{m_0 v}{\sqrt{1 - v^2/c^2}}. \qquad \textbf{(26–4)}$$

This formula can be interpreted as a **mass increase**, where the relativistic mass is

$$m_{\mathrm{rel}} = \gamma m_0 = \frac{m_0}{\sqrt{1 - v^2/c^2}}, \qquad \textbf{(26–5)}$$

and $m_0$ is the **rest mass** of the object $(v = 0)$.

Mass and energy are interconvertible. The equation

$$E_0 = m_0c^2 \tag{26–8}$$

tells how much energy $E_0$ is needed to create a mass $m_0$, or vice versa. Said another way, $E_0 = m_0c^2$ is the amount of energy an object has because of its mass $m_0$. The law of conservation of energy must include mass as a form of energy.

The kinetic energy KE of an object moving at speed $v$ is given by

$$\text{KE} = \frac{m_0c^2}{\sqrt{1 - v^2/c^2}} - m_0c^2 = (\gamma - 1)m_0c^2 \tag{26–6}$$

where $m_0$ is the rest mass of the object. The total energy $E$, if there is no potential energy, is

$$E = \text{KE} + m_0c^2 = \gamma m_0c^2. \tag{26–7}$$

The momentum $p$ of an object is related to its total energy $E$ (assuming no potential energy) by

$$E^2 = p^2c^2 + m_0^2c^4. \tag{26–10}$$

Velocity addition also must be done in a special way. All these relativistic effects are significant only at high speeds, close to the speed of light, which itself is the ultimate speed in the universe.

# Questions

1. You are in a windowless car in an exceptionally smooth train moving at constant velocity. Is there any physical experiment you can do in the train car to determine whether you are moving? Explain.
2. You might have had the experience of being at a red light when, out of the corner of your eye, you see the car beside you creep forward. Instinctively you stomp on the brake pedal, thinking that you are rolling backward. What does this say about absolute and relative motion?
3. A worker stands on top of a moving railroad car, and throws a heavy ball straight up (from his point of view). Ignoring air resistance, will the ball land on the car or behind it?
4. Does the Earth really go around the Sun? Or is it also valid to say that the Sun goes around the Earth? Discuss in view of the first principle of relativity (that there is no best reference frame). Explain.
5. If you were on a spaceship traveling at $0.5c$ away from a star, at what speed would the starlight pass you?
6. The time dilation effect is sometimes expressed as "moving clocks run slowly." Actually, this effect has nothing to do with motion affecting the functioning of clocks. What then does it deal with?
7. Does time dilation mean that time actually passes more slowly in moving reference frames or that it only *seems* to pass more slowly?
8. A young-looking woman astronaut has just arrived home from a long trip. She rushes up to an old gray-haired man and in the ensuing conversation refers to him as her son. How might this be possible?
9. If you were traveling away from Earth at speed $0.5c$, would you notice a change in your heartbeat? Would your mass, height, or waistline change? What would observers on Earth using telescopes say about you?
10. Do time dilation and length contraction occur at ordinary speeds, say 90 km/h?
11. Suppose the speed of light were infinite. What would happen to the relativistic predictions of length contraction and time dilation?
12. Discuss how our everyday lives would be different if the speed of light were only 25 m/s.
13. Explain how the length contraction and time dilation formulas might be used to indicate that $c$ is the limiting speed in the universe.
14. The drawing at the start of this Chapter shows the street as seen by Mr Tompkins, for whom the speed of light is $c = 20$ mi/h. What does Mr Tompkins look like to the people standing on the street (Fig. 26–11)? Explain.

**FIGURE 26–11** Question 14. Mr Tompkins as seen by people on the sidewalk. See also Chapter-opening photograph.

15. An electron is limited to travel at speeds less than $c$. Does this put an upper limit on the momentum of an electron? If so, what is this upper limit? If not, explain.
16. Can a particle of nonzero rest mass attain the speed of light?
17. Does the equation $E = mc^2$ conflict with the conservation of energy principle? Explain.
18. If mass is a form of energy, does this mean that a spring has more mass when compressed than when relaxed?
19. It is not correct to say that "matter can neither be created nor destroyed." What must we say instead?
20. Is our intuitive notion that velocities simply add, as we did in Section 3–8, completely wrong?

## Problems

### 26–4 and 26–5 Time Dilation, Length Contraction

1. (I) A spaceship passes you at a speed of $0.750c$. You measure its length to be 28.2 m. How long would it be when at rest?

2. (I) A certain type of elementary particle travels at a speed of $2.70 \times 10^8$ m/s. At this speed, the average lifetime is measured to be $4.76 \times 10^{-6}$ s. What is the particle's lifetime at rest?

3. (I) Lengths and time intervals depend on the factor

$$\sqrt{1 - v^2/c^2}$$

according to the theory of relativity (Eqs. 26–1 and 26–3). Evaluate this factor for speeds of: (*a*) $v = 20{,}000$ m/s (typical speed of a satellite); (*b*) $v = 0.020c$; (*c*) $v = 0.200c$; (*d*) $v = 0.95c$; (*e*) $v = 0.98c$; (*f*) $v = 0.999c$.

4. (II) If you were to travel to a star 125 light-years from Earth at a speed of $2.50 \times 10^8$ m/s, what would you measure this distance to be?

5. (II) What is the speed of a pion if its average lifetime is measured to be $4.10 \times 10^{-8}$ s? At rest, its average lifetime is $2.60 \times 10^{-8}$ s.

6. (II) In an Earth reference frame, a star is 82 light-years away. How fast would you have to travel so that to you the distance would be only 35 light-years?

7. (II) Suppose you decide to travel to a star 85 light-years away at a speed that tells you the distance is only 25 light-years. How many years would it take you to make the trip?

8. (II) At what speed $v$ will the length of a 1.00-m stick look 10.0% shorter (90.0 cm)?

9. (II) Escape velocity from the Earth is 40,000 km/h. What would be the percent decrease in length of a 95.2-m-long spacecraft traveling at that speed?

10. (II) At what speed do the relativistic formulas for (*a*) length and (*b*) time intervals differ from classical values by 1.00%? (This is a reasonable way to estimate when to do relativistic calculations rather than classical.)

11. (II) Suppose a news report stated that starship *Enterprise* had just returned from a 5-year voyage while traveling at $0.84c$. (*a*) If the report meant 5.0 years of *Earth time*, how much time elapsed on the ship? (*b*) If the report meant 5.0 years of *ship time*, how much time passed on Earth?

12. (II) A certain star is 10.6 light-years away. How long would it take a spacecraft traveling $0.960c$ to reach that star from Earth, as measured by observers: (*a*) on Earth, (*b*) on the spacecraft? (*c*) What is the distance traveled according to observers on the spacecraft? (*d*) What will the spacecraft occupants compute their speed to be from the results of (*b*) and (*c*)?

13. (II) A friend speeds by you in her "Ferrari" spacecraft at a speed of $0.660c$. It is measured in your frame to be 4.80 m long and 1.25 m high. (*a*) What will be its length and height at rest? (*b*) How many seconds would you say elapsed on your friend's watch when 20.0 s passed on yours? (*c*) How fast did you appear to be traveling according to your friend? (*d*) How many seconds would she say elapsed on your watch when she saw 20.0 s pass on hers?

14. (III) How fast must an average pion be moving to travel 15 m before it decays? The average lifetime, at rest, is $2.6 \times 10^{-8}$ s.

### 26–7 Relativistic Momentum

15. (I) What is the momentum of a proton traveling at $v = 0.85c$?

16. (I) At what speed will an object's relativistic mass be twice its rest mass?

17. (II) A particle of rest mass $m_0$ travels at a speed $v = 0.20c$. At what speed will its momentum be doubled?

18. (II) (*a*) A particle travels at $v = 0.10c$. By what percentage will a calculation of its momentum be wrong if you use the classical formula? (*b*) Repeat for $v = 0.50c$.

19. (II) What is the percent change in momentum of a proton that accelerates (*a*) from $0.45c$ to $0.90c$, (*b*) from $0.90c$ to $0.98c$?

### 26–9 $E = mc^2$

20. (I) A certain chemical reaction requires $4.82 \times 10^4$ J of energy input for it to go. What is the increase in mass of the products over the reactants?

21. (I) When a uranium nucleus at rest breaks apart in the process known as fission in a nuclear reactor, the resulting fragments have a total kinetic energy of about 200 MeV. How much mass was lost in the process?

22. (I) Calculate the rest energy of an electron in joules and in MeV $(1\text{ MeV} = 1.60 \times 10^{-13}\text{ J})$.

23. (I) Calculate the rest mass of a proton in MeV/$c^2$.

24. (I) The total annual energy consumption in the United States is about $8 \times 10^{19}$ J. How much mass would have to be converted to energy to fuel this need?

25. (II) How much energy can be obtained from conversion of 1.0 gram of mass? How much mass could this energy raise to a height of 0.25 km above the Earth's surface?

26. (II) What is the speed of a particle when its kinetic energy equals its rest energy?

27. (II) At what speed will an object's kinetic energy be 25% of its rest energy?

28. (II) (*a*) How much work is required to accelerate a proton from rest up to a speed of $0.997c$? (*b*) What would be the momentum of this proton?

29. (II) Calculate the kinetic energy and momentum of a proton traveling $2.60 \times 10^8$ m/s.

30. (II) What is the momentum of a 750-MeV proton (that is, its kinetic energy is 750 MeV)?

31. (II) What is the speed of a proton accelerated by a potential difference of 105 MV?

32. (II) What is the speed of an electron whose kinetic energy is 1.00 MeV?

33. (II) What is the speed of an electron just before it hits a television screen after being accelerated from rest by the 25,000 V of the picture tube?

34. (II) Two identical particles of rest mass $m_0$ approach each other at equal and opposite speeds, $v$. The collision is completely inelastic and results in a single particle at rest. What is the rest mass of the new particle? How much energy was lost in the collision? How much kinetic energy is lost in this collision?

35. (II) Calculate the speed of a proton $(m_0 = 1.67 \times 10^{-27}\,\mathrm{kg})$ whose kinetic energy is exactly half (*a*) its total energy, (*b*) its rest energy.

36. (II) What is the speed and the momentum of an electron $(m = 9.11 \times 10^{-31}\,\mathrm{kg})$ whose kinetic energy equals its rest energy?

37. (II) Suppose a spacecraft of mass 27,000 kg is accelerated to $0.21c$. (*a*) How much kinetic energy would it have? (*b*) If you used the classical formula for kinetic energy, by what percentage would you be in error?

38. (II) Calculate the kinetic energy and momentum of a proton $(m_0 = 1.67 \times 10^{-27}\,\mathrm{kg})$ traveling $7.35 \times 10^7\,\mathrm{m/s}$. By what percentages would your calculations have been in error if you had used classical formulas?

39. (II) The americium nucleus, ${}^{241}_{95}\mathrm{Am}$, decays to a neptunium nucleus, ${}^{237}_{93}\mathrm{Np}$, by emitting an alpha particle of mass 4.00260 u and kinetic energy 5.5 MeV. Estimate the mass of the neptunium nucleus, ignoring its recoil, given that the americium mass is 241.05682 u.

40. (II) An electron $(m_0 = 9.11 \times 10^{-31}\,\mathrm{kg})$ is accelerated from rest to speed $v$ by a conservative force. In this process, its potential energy decreases by $6.60 \times 10^{-14}\,\mathrm{J}$. Determine the electron's speed, $v$.

41. (II) Make a graph of the kinetic energy versus momentum for (*a*) a particle of nonzero rest mass, and (*b*) a particle with zero rest mass.

42. (II) What magnetic field intensity is needed to keep 998-GeV protons revolving in a circle of radius 1.0 km (at, say, the Fermilab synchrotron)? Use the relativistic mass. The proton's rest mass is $0.938\,\mathrm{GeV}/c^2$. $(1\,\mathrm{GeV} = 10^9\,\mathrm{eV}.)$ [*Hint*: in relativity, it is still true that $mv^2/r = qvB$ in a magnetic field.]

### 26–10 Relativistic Addition of Velocities

43. (I) A person on a rocket traveling at $0.50c$ (with respect to the Earth) observes a meteor come from behind and pass her at a speed she measures as $0.50c$. How fast is the meteor moving with respect to the Earth?

44. (II) Two spaceships leave Earth in opposite directions, each with a speed of $0.50c$ with respect to Earth. (*a*) What is the velocity of spaceship 1 relative to spaceship 2? (*b*) What is the velocity of spaceship 2 relative to spaceship 1?

45. (II) A spaceship leaves Earth traveling at $0.71c$. A second spaceship leaves the first at a speed of $0.87c$ with respect to the first. Calculate the speed of the second ship with respect to Earth if it is fired (*a*) in the same direction the first spaceship is already moving, (*b*) directly backward toward Earth.

46. (II) An observer on Earth sees an alien vessel approach at a speed of $0.60c$. The *Enterprise* comes to the rescue (Fig. 26–12), overtaking the aliens while moving directly toward Earth at a speed of $0.90c$ relative to Earth. What is the relative speed of one vessel as seen by the other?

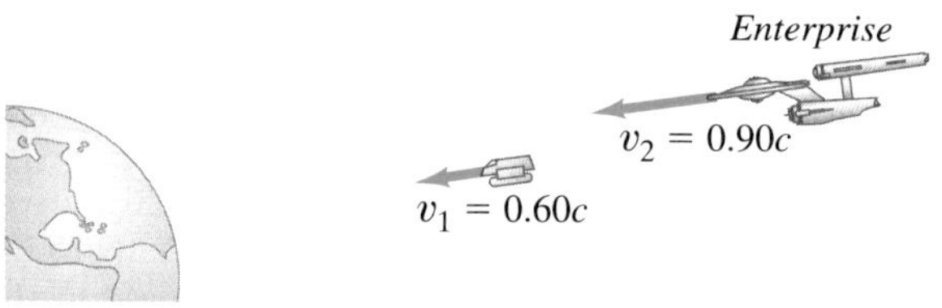


**FIGURE 26–12** Problem 46.

47. (II) A spaceship in distress sends out two escape pods in opposite directions. One travels at a speed $v_1 = -0.60c$ in one direction, and the other travels at a speed $v_2 = +0.70c$ in the other direction, as observed from the spaceship. What speed does the first escape pod measure for the second escape pod?

48. (II) Rocket A passes Earth at a speed of $0.75c$. At the same time, rocket B passes Earth moving $0.95c$ relative to Earth in the same direction. How fast is B moving relative to A when it passes A?

## General Problems

49. The nearest star to Earth is Proxima Centauri, 4.3 light-years away. (*a*) At what constant velocity must a spacecraft travel from Earth if it is to reach the star in 4.0 years, as measured by travelers on the spacecraft? (*b*) How long does the trip take according to Earth observers?

50. As a rule of thumb, anything traveling faster than about $0.1c$ is called *relativistic*—i.e., for which the correction using special relativity is a significant effect. Determine the speed of an electron in a hydrogen atom (radius $0.5 \times 10^{-10}\,\mathrm{m}$) and state if it is relativistic. (Treat the electron as though it were in a circular orbit around the proton.)

51. (*a*) What is the speed $v$ of an electron whose kinetic energy is 14,000 times its rest energy? You can state the difference, $c - v$. Such speeds are reached in the Stanford Linear Accelerator, SLAC. (*b*) If the electrons travel in the lab through a tube 3.0 km long (as at SLAC), how long is this tube in the electrons' reference frame? [*Hint*: use the binomial expansion.]

52. How many grams of matter would have to be totally destroyed to run a 100-W lightbulb for 1 year?

53. What minimum amount of electromagnetic energy is needed to produce an electron and a positron together? A positron is a particle with the same rest mass as an electron, but has the opposite charge. (Note that electric charge is conserved in this process. See Section 27–6.)

54. An electron $(m = 9.11 \times 10^{-31}\,\text{kg})$ enters a uniform magnetic field $B = 1.8\,\text{T}$, and moves perpendicular to the field lines with a speed $v = 0.92c$. What is the radius of curvature of its path? See hint for Problem 42.

55. A negative muon traveling at 33% the speed of light collides head on with a positive muon traveling at 50% the speed of light. The two muons (each of rest mass $105.7\,\text{MeV}/c^2$) annihilate, and produce how much electromagnetic energy?

56. A free neutron can decay into a proton, an electron, and a neutrino. Assume the neutrino's rest mass is zero, and the other masses can be found in the Table inside the front cover. Determine the total kinetic energy shared among the three particles when a neutron decays at rest.

57. The Sun radiates energy at a rate of about $4 \times 10^{26}\,\text{W}$. (*a*) At what rate is the Sun's mass decreasing? (*b*) How long does it take for the Sun to lose a mass equal to that of Earth? (*c*) Estimate how long the Sun could last if it radiated constantly at this rate.

58. An unknown particle is measured to have a negative charge and a speed of $2.24 \times 10^8\,\text{m/s}$. Its momentum is determined to be $3.07 \times 10^{-22}\,\text{kg}\cdot\text{m/s}$. Identify the particle by finding its rest mass.

59. How much energy would be required to break a helium nucleus into its constituents, two protons and two neutrons? The rest masses of a proton (including an electron), a neutron, and helium are, respectively, 1.00783 u, 1.00867 u, and 4.00260 u. (This energy difference is called the *total binding energy* of the $^4_2\text{He}$ nucleus.)

60. What is the percentage increase in the (relativistic) mass of a car traveling 110 km/h as compared to at rest? [*Hint*: use the binomial expansion.]

61. Two protons, each having a speed of $0.935c$ in the laboratory, are moving toward each other. Determine (*a*) the momentum of each proton in the laboratory, (*b*) the total momentum of the two protons in the laboratory, and (*c*) the momentum of one proton as seen by the other proton.

62. Show analytically that a particle with momentum $p$ and energy $E$ has a speed given by

$$v = \frac{pc^2}{E} = \frac{pc}{\sqrt{m_0^2c^2 + p^2}}.$$

63. The fictional starship *Enterprise* obtains its power by combining matter and antimatter, achieving complete conversion of mass into energy. If the mass of the *Enterprise* is approximately $5 \times 10^9\,\text{kg}$, how much mass must be converted into kinetic energy to accelerate it from rest to one-tenth the speed of light?

64. An electron is accelerated so that its kinetic energy is greater than its rest energy $m_0c^2$ by a factor of (*a*) 5.00, (*b*) 999. What is the speed of the electron in each case?

65. A farm boy studying physics believes that he can fit a 15.0-m-long pole into a 12.0-m-long barn if he runs fast enough (carrying the pole). Can he do it? Explain in detail. How does this fit with the idea that when he is running the barn looks even shorter to him than 12.0 m?

66. When two moles of hydrogen and one mole of oxygen react to form two moles of water, the energy released is 484 kJ. How much does the mass of the elements decrease in this reaction? What % of the total original mass of the system does this mass change represent?

67. In a nuclear reaction two identical particles are created, traveling in opposite directions. If the speed of each particle is $0.75c$, relative to the laboratory frame of reference, what is one particle's speed relative to the other particle?

68. An astronaut on a spaceship traveling at $0.75c$ relative to Earth measures his ship to be 25 m long. On the ship, he eats his lunch in 23 min. (*a*) What length is the spaceship according to observers on Earth? (*b*) How long does the astronaut's lunch take to eat according to observers on Earth?

69. You are traveling in a spaceship at a speed of $0.85c$ away from Earth. You send a laser beam toward the Earth traveling at velocity $c$ relative to you. What do observers on the Earth measure for the speed of the laser beam?

70. A spaceship and its occupants have a total mass of 150,000 kg. The occupants would like to travel to a star that is 25 light-years away at a speed of $0.60c$. To accelerate, the engine of the spaceship changes mass directly to energy. How much mass will be converted to energy to accelerate the spaceship to this speed? Assume the acceleration is rapid, so the speed for the entire trip can be taken to be $0.60c$, and ignore decrease in total mass for the calculation. How long will the trip take according to the astronauts on board?

71. Suppose a 12,500-kg spaceship left Earth at a speed of $0.99c$. What is the spaceship's kinetic energy? Compare with the total U.S. annual energy consumption (about $10^{20}\,\text{J}$).

72. A 42,000-kg spaceship is to travel to the vicinity of a star 6.0 light-years from Earth. Passengers on the ship want the (one-way) trip to take no more than 1.0 year. How much work must be done on the spaceship to bring it to the speed necessary for this trip?

73. A 1.68-kg mass oscillates on the end of a spring whose spring stiffness constant is $k = 48.7\,\text{N/m}$. If this system is in a spaceship moving past Earth at $0.900c$, what is its period of oscillation according to (*a*) observers on the ship, and (*b*) observers on Earth?

74. A pi meson of rest mass $m_\pi$ decays at rest into a muon (rest mass $m_\mu$) and a neutrino of negligible or zero rest mass. Show that the kinetic energy of the muon is $\text{KE}_\mu = (m_\pi - m_\mu)^2c^2/2m_\pi$.

## Answers to Exercises

**A:** Yes.
**B:** (*a*) 2.21 $\mu$s; (*b*) 5.0 $\mu$s.
**C:** (*a*) No; (*b*) yes.
**D:** $0.36c$.
**E:** No.
**F:** $0.030c$, same as classical, to an accuracy of better than 0.1%.

Electron microscopes produce images using electrons which have wave properties just as light does. Since the wavelength of electrons can be much smaller than that of visible light, much greater resolution and magnification can be obtained. A scanning electron microscope can produce images with a three-dimensional quality, as for these *Giardia* cells inside a human small intestine. Magnification is about 2000×. *Giardia* is on the minds of backpackers (and others) because it has become too common in untreated water, even in the high mountains, and causes an unpleasant intestinal infection not easy to get rid of.

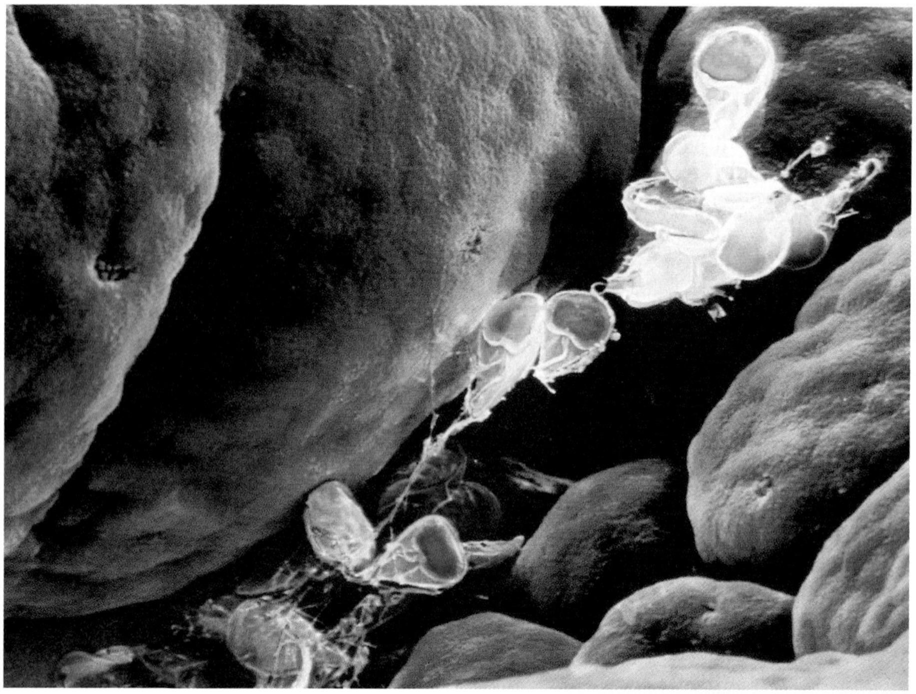

CHAPTER 27

# Early Quantum Theory and Models of the Atom

The second aspect of the revolution that shook the world of physics in the early part of the twentieth century (the first was Einstein's theory of relativity) was the quantum theory. Unlike the special theory of relativity, the revolution of quantum theory required almost three decades to unfold, and many scientists contributed to its development. It began in 1900 with Planck's quantum hypothesis, and culminated in the mid-1920s with the theory of quantum mechanics of Schrödinger and Heisenberg which has been so effective in explaining the structure of matter. The discovery of the electron in the 1890s, with which we begin this Chapter, might be said to mark the beginning of modern physics, and is a sort of precursor to the quantum theory.

## 27–1 Discovery and Properties of the Electron

Toward the end of the nineteenth century, studies were being done on the discharge of electricity through rarefied gases. One apparatus, diagrammed in Fig. 27–1, consisted of a glass tube fitted with electrodes and evacuated so only a small amount of gas remained inside. When a very high voltage was applied to the electrodes, a dark space seemed to extend outward from the cathode (negative electrode) toward the opposite end of the tube; and that far end of the tube would glow. If one or more screens containing a small hole were inserted as shown, the glow was restricted to a tiny spot on the end of the tube. It seemed as though something being emitted by the cathode traveled across to the opposite end of the tube. These "somethings" were named **cathode rays**.

**FIGURE 27–1** Discharge tube. In some models, one of the screens is the anode (positive plate).

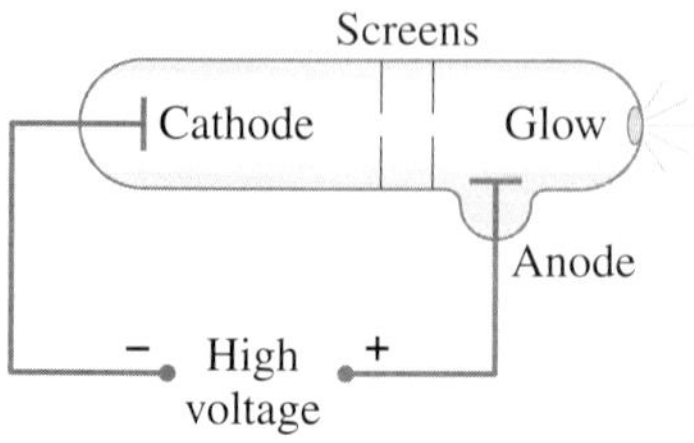


There was much discussion at the time about what these rays might be. Some scientists thought they might resemble light. But the observation that the bright spot at the end of the tube could be deflected to one side by an electric or magnetic field suggested that cathode rays could be charged particles; and the direction of the deflection was consistent with a negative charge. Furthermore, if the tube contained certain types of rarefied gas, the path of the cathode rays was made visible by a slight glow.

Estimates of the charge $e$ of the (assumed) cathode-ray particles, as well as of their charge-to-mass ratio $e/m$, had been made by 1897. But in that year, J. J. Thomson (1856–1940) was able to measure $e/m$ directly, using the apparatus shown in Fig. 27–2. Cathode rays are accelerated by a high voltage and then pass between a pair of parallel plates built into the tube. The voltage applied to the plates produces an electric field, and a pair of coils produces a magnetic field.

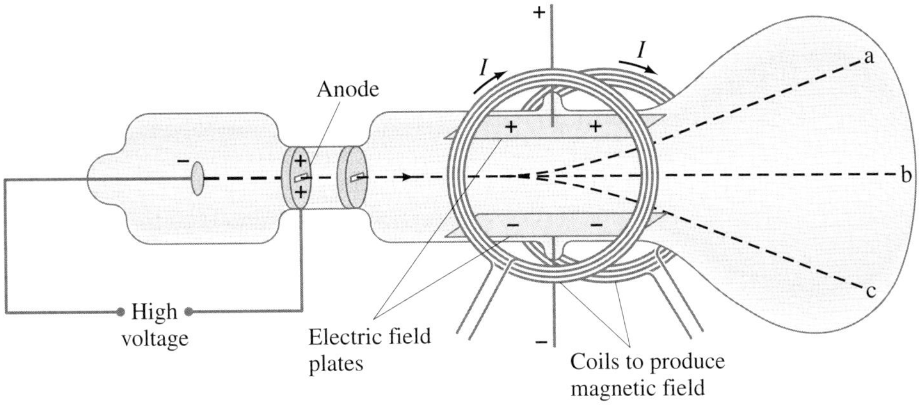


**FIGURE 27–2** Cathode rays deflected by electric and magnetic fields.

When only the electric field is present, say with the upper plate positive, the cathode rays are deflected upward as in path a in Fig. 27–2. If only a magnetic field exists, say inward, the rays are deflected downward along path c. These observations are just what is expected for a negatively charged particle. The magnitude of force on the rays due to the magnetic field is $F_{mag} = evB$, where $e$ is the charge and $v$ is the velocity of the cathode rays (Eq. 20–4). In the absence of an electric field, the rays are bent into a curved path, and applying Newton's second law $F = ma$ to a cathode ray gives

$$evB = m\frac{v^2}{r},$$

and thus

$$\frac{e}{m} = \frac{v}{Br}.$$

The radius of curvature $r$ can be measured and so can $B$. The velocity $v$ can be found by applying an electric field in addition to the magnetic field. The electric field $E$ is adjusted so that the cathode rays are undeflected and follow path b in Fig. 27–2. In this situation the upward force due to the electric field, $F_{el} = eE$, is balanced by the downward force due to the magnetic field, $F_{mag} = evB$. We equate the two forces, $eE = evB$, and find

$$v = \frac{E}{B}.$$

Combining this with the above equation we have

$$\frac{e}{m} = \frac{E}{B^2 r}. \quad \textbf{(27–1)}$$

*e/m measured*

The quantities on the right side can all be measured, and although $e$ and $m$ could not be determined separately, the ratio $e/m$ could be determined. The accepted value today is $e/m = 1.76 \times 10^{11}$ C/kg. Cathode rays soon came to be called **electrons**.

*"Discovery" of the electron*

The "discovery" of the electron, like many others in science, is not quite so obvious as discovering gold or oil. Should the discovery of the electron be credited to the person who first saw a glow in the tube? Or to the person who first called them cathode rays? Perhaps neither one, for they had no conception of the electron as we know it today. In fact, the credit for the discovery is generally given to Thomson, but not because he was the first to see the glow in the tube.

Rather it is because he believed that this phenomenon was due to tiny negatively charged particles and made careful measurements on them. Furthermore he argued that these particles were constituents of atoms, and not ions or atoms themselves as many thought, and he developed an electron theory of matter. His view is close to what we accept today, and this is why Thomson is credited with the "discovery." Note, however, that neither he nor anyone else ever actually saw an electron itself. We discuss this briefly, for it illustrates the fact that discovery in science is not always a clear-cut matter. In fact some philosophers of science think the word "discovery" is often not appropriate, such as in this case.

Thomson believed that an electron was not an atom, but rather a constituent, or part, of an atom. Convincing evidence for this came soon with the determination of the charge and the mass of the cathode rays. Thomson's student J. S. Townsend made the first direct (but rough) measurements of $e$ in 1897. But it was the more refined **oil-drop experiment** of Robert A. Millikan (1868–1953) that yielded a precise value for the charge on the electron and showed that charge comes in discrete amounts. In this experiment, tiny droplets of mineral oil carrying an electric charge were allowed to fall under gravity between two parallel plates, Fig. 27–3. The electric field $E$ between the plates was adjusted until the drop was suspended in midair. The downward pull of gravity on a drop of mass $m_{\mathrm{dr}}$ was $m_{\mathrm{dr}}g$, and was just balanced by the upward force due to the electric field. Thus $qE = m_{\mathrm{dr}}g$ so the charge $q$ on a droplet was $q = m_{\mathrm{dr}}g/E$. The mass of the droplet was determined by measuring its terminal velocity in the absence of the electric field. Often the droplet was charged negatively, but sometimes it was positive, suggesting that the droplet had acquired or lost electrons (by friction, leaving the atomizer). Millikan's painstaking observations and analysis presented convincing evidence that any charge was an integral multiple of a smallest charge, $e$, that was ascribed to the electron, and that the value of $e$ was $1.6 \times 10^{-19}\,\mathrm{C}$. (Today's value of $e$, as mentioned in Chapter 16, is $e = 1.602 \times 10^{-19}\,\mathrm{C}$.) This value of $e$, combined with the measurement of $e/m$, gives the mass of the electron to be $(1.6 \times 10^{-19}\,\mathrm{C})/(1.76 \times 10^{11}\,\mathrm{C/kg}) = 9.1 \times 10^{-31}\,\mathrm{kg}$. This mass is less than a thousandth the mass of the smallest atom, and thus confirmed the idea that the electron is only a part of an atom. The accepted value today for the mass of the electron is $m_{\mathrm{e}} = 9.11 \times 10^{-31}\,\mathrm{kg}$. The experimental results that any charge seems to be an integral multiple of $e$ means that electric charge is *quantized* (exists only in discrete amounts), as we discussed in Chapter 16.

*Millikan oil-drop experiment*

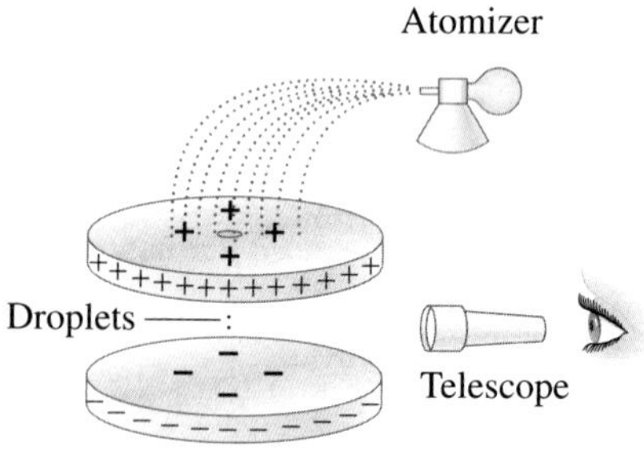


**FIGURE 27–3** Millikan's oil-drop experiment.

## 27–2 Planck's Quantum Hypothesis; Blackbody Radiation

### Blackbody Radiation

One of the observations that was unexplained at the end of the nineteenth century was the spectrum of light emitted by hot objects. We saw in Section 14–8 that all objects emit radiation whose total intensity is proportional to the fourth power of the Kelvin (absolute) temperature $(T^4)$. At normal temperatures ($\approx$300 K), we are not aware of this electromagnetic radiation because of its low intensity. At higher temperatures, there is sufficient infrared radiation that we can feel heat if we are close to the object. At still higher temperatures (on the order of 1000 K), objects actually glow, such as a red-hot electric stove burner or the element in a toaster. At temperatures above 2000 K, objects glow with a yellow or whitish color, such as white-hot iron and the filament of a lightbulb. The light emitted is of a continuous range of wavelengths or frequencies, and the spectrum is a plot of intensity vs. wavelength or frequency. As the temperature increases, the electromagnetic radiation emitted by objects not only increases in total intensity but is strongest at higher and higher frequencies.

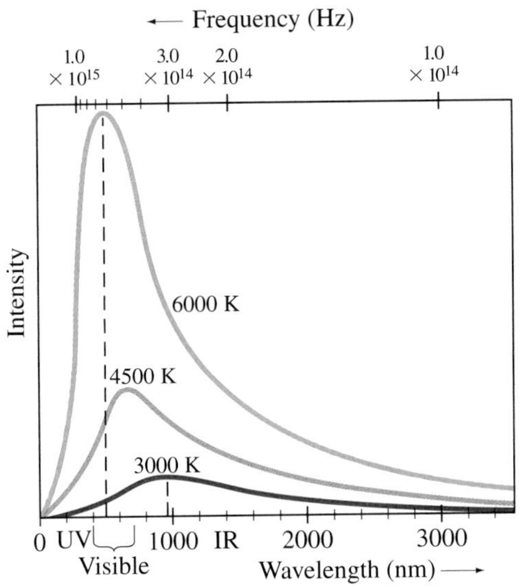


**FIGURE 27–4** Measured spectra of wavelengths and frequencies emitted by a blackbody at three different temperatures.

The spectrum of light emitted by a hot dense object is shown in Fig. 27–4 for an idealized **blackbody**. A blackbody is a body that would absorb all the radiation falling on it (and so would appear black under reflection when illuminated from outside). The radiation such a blackbody would emit when hot and luminous, called **blackbody radiation** (though not necessarily black in color), is the easiest to deal with, and the radiation approximates that from many real objects. The 6000-K curve in Fig. 27–4, corresponding to the temperature of the surface of the Sun, peaks in the visible part of the spectrum. For lower temperatures, the total radiation drops considerably and the peak occurs at longer wavelengths (or lower frequencies). Hence the blue end of the visible spectrum (and the UV) is relatively weaker at lower temperatures. (This is why objects glow with a red color at around 1000 K.) It is found experimentally that the wavelength at the peak of the spectrum, $\lambda_P$, is related to the Kelvin temperature $T$ by

*Blackbody radiation*

$$\lambda_P T = 2.90 \times 10^{-3}\,\mathrm{m \cdot K}. \qquad \textbf{(27–2)}$$

This is known as **Wien's law**.

**EXAMPLE 27–1** **The Sun's surface temperature.** Estimate the temperature of the surface of our Sun, given that the Sun emits light whose peak intensity occurs in the visible spectrum at around 500 nm.

**APPROACH** We assume the Sun acts as a blackbody, and use $\lambda_P = 500\,\mathrm{nm}$ in Wien's law (Eq. 27–2).

**SOLUTION** Wien's law gives

$$T = \frac{2.90 \times 10^{-3}\,\mathrm{m \cdot K}}{\lambda_P} = \frac{2.90 \times 10^{-3}\,\mathrm{m \cdot K}}{500 \times 10^{-9}\,\mathrm{m}} \approx 6000\,\mathrm{K}.$$

**EXAMPLE 27–2** **Star color.** Suppose a star has a surface temperature of 32,500 K. What color would this star appear?

**APPROACH** We assume the star emits radiation as a blackbody, and solve for $\lambda_P$ in Wien's law, Eq. 27–2.

**SOLUTION** From Wien's law we have

$$\lambda_P = \frac{2.90 \times 10^{-3}\,\mathrm{m \cdot K}}{T} = \frac{2.90 \times 10^{-3}\,\mathrm{m \cdot K}}{3.25 \times 10^{4}\,\mathrm{K}} = 89.2\,\mathrm{nm}.$$

The peak is in the UV range of the spectrum, and will be way to the left in Fig. 27–4. In the visible region, the curve will be descending, so the shortest visible wavelengths will be strongest. Hence the star will appear bluish (or blue-white).

**NOTE** This example helps us to understand why stars have different colors (reddish for the coolest stars, orangish, yellow, white, bluish for "hotter" stars.)

**EXERCISE A** What is the color of an object at 4000 K?

## Planck's Quantum Hypothesis

In the year 1900, Max Planck (1858–1947) proposed a theory that was able to reproduce the graphs of Fig. 27–4. His theory, still accepted today, made a new and radical assumption: that the energy of the oscillations of atoms within molecules cannot have just any value; instead each has energy which is a multiple of a minimum value related to the frequency of oscillation by

$$E = hf.$$

Here $h$ is a new constant, now called **Planck's constant**, whose value was estimated by Planck by fitting his formula for the blackbody radiation curve to experiment. The value accepted today is

$$h = 6.626 \times 10^{-34}\,\mathrm{J \cdot s}.$$

Planck's assumption suggests that the energy of any molecular vibration could be only some whole number multiple of $hf$:

*Planck's quantum hypothesis*

$$E = nhf, \qquad n = 1, 2, 3, \cdots, \tag{27–3}$$

where $n$ is called a **quantum number** ("quantum" means "discrete amount" as opposed to "continuous"). This idea is often called **Planck's quantum hypothesis**, although little attention was brought to this point at the time. In fact, it appears that Planck considered it more as a mathematical device to get the "right answer" rather than as a discovery comparable to those of Newton. Planck himself continued to seek a classical explanation for the introduction of $h$. The recognition that this was an important and radical innovation did not come until later, after about 1905 when others, particularly Einstein, entered the field.

The quantum hypothesis, Eq. 27–3, states that the energy of an oscillator can be $E = hf$, or $2hf$, or $3hf$, and so on, but there cannot be vibrations with energies between these values. That is, energy would not be a continuous quantity as had been believed for centuries; rather it is **quantized**—it exists only in discrete amounts. The smallest amount of energy possible ($hf$) is called the **quantum of energy**. Recall from Chapter 11 that the energy of an oscillation is proportional to the amplitude squared. Thus another way of expressing the quantum hypothesis is that not just any amplitude of vibration is possible. The possible values for the amplitude are related to the frequency $f$.

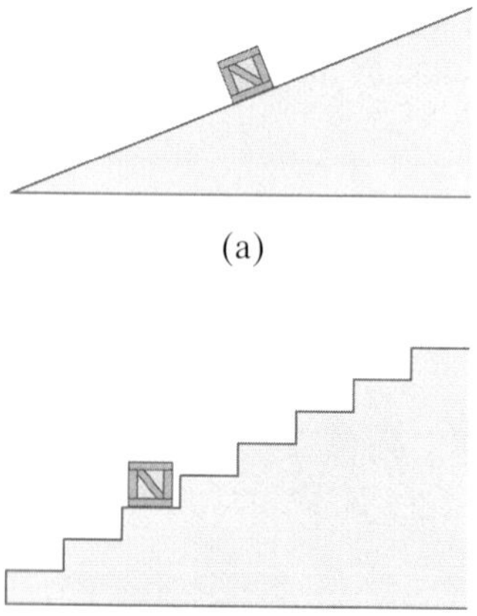
(a)

(b)

**FIGURE 27–5** Ramp versus stair analogy. (a) On a ramp, a box can have continuous values of potential energy. (b) But on stairs, the box can have only discrete (quantized) values of energy.

A simple analogy may help. A stringed instrument such as a violin or guitar can be played over a continuous range of frequencies by moving your finger along the string. A flute or piano, on the other hand, is "quantized" in the sense that only certain frequencies (notes) can be played. Or compare a ramp, on which a box can be placed at any height, to a flight of stairs on which the box can have only certain discrete amounts of potential energy, as shown in Fig. 27–5.

# 27–3 Photon Theory of Light and the Photoelectric Effect

In 1905, the same year that he introduced the special theory of relativity, Einstein made a bold extension of the quantum idea by proposing a new theory of light. Planck's work had suggested that the vibrational energy of molecules in a radiating object is quantized with energy $E = nhf$, where $n$ is an integer and $f$ is the frequency of molecular vibration. Einstein argued that when light is emitted by a molecular oscillator, the molecule's vibrational energy of $nhf$ must decrease by an amount $hf$ (or by $2hf$, etc.) to another integer times $hf$, such as $(n-1)hf$. Then to conserve energy, the light ought to be emitted in packets, or *quanta*, each with an energy

*Photon energy*

$$E = hf, \tag{27–4}$$

where $f$ is here the frequency of the emitted light.

Again $h$ is Planck's constant. Since all light ultimately comes from a radiating source, this suggests that perhaps *light is transmitted as tiny particles*, or **photons**, as they are now called, in addition to the waves predicted by Maxwell's electromagnetic theory. The photon theory of light was also a radical departure from classical ideas. Einstein proposed a test of the quantum theory of light: quantitative measurements on the photoelectric effect.

*Photons*

When light shines on a metal surface, electrons are found to be emitted from the surface. This effect is called the **photoelectric effect** and it occurs in many materials, but is most easily observed with metals. It can be observed using the apparatus shown in Fig. 27–6. A metal plate P and a smaller electrode C are placed inside an evacuated glass tube, called a **photocell**. The two electrodes are connected to an ammeter and a source of emf, as shown. When the photocell is in the dark, the ammeter reads zero. But when light of sufficiently high frequency illuminates the plate, the ammeter indicates a current flowing in the circuit. We explain completion of the circuit by imagining that electrons, ejected by the impinging radiation, flow across the tube from the plate to the "collector" C as indicated in Fig. 27–6.

*Photoelectric effect*

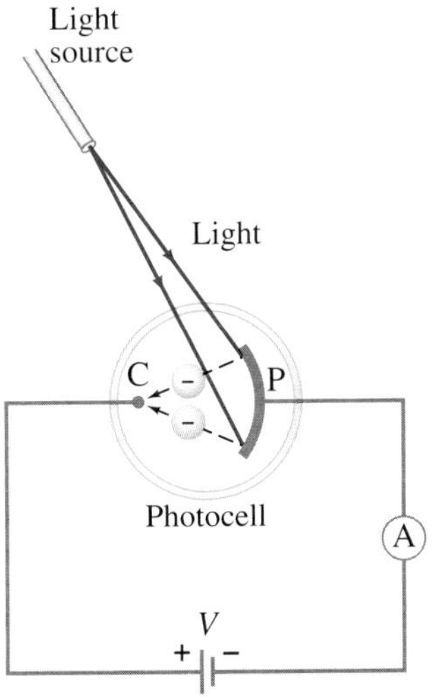


**FIGURE 27–6** The photoelectric effect.

That electrons should be emitted when light shines on a metal is consistent with the electromagnetic (EM) wave theory of light: the electric field of an EM wave could exert a force on electrons in the metal and eject some of them. Einstein pointed out, however, that the wave theory and the photon theory of light give very different predictions on the details of the photoelectric effect. For example, one thing that can be measured with the apparatus of Fig. 27–6 is the maximum kinetic energy ($\text{KE}_{\text{max}}$) of the emitted electrons. This can be done by using a variable voltage source and reversing the terminals so that electrode C is negative and P is positive. The electrons emitted from P will be repelled by the negative electrode, but if this reverse voltage is small enough, the fastest electrons will still reach C and there will be a current in the circuit. If the reversed voltage is increased, a point is reached where the current reaches zero—no electrons have sufficient kinetic energy to reach C. This is called the *stopping potential*, or *stopping voltage*, $V_0$, and from its measurement, $\text{KE}_{\text{max}}$ can be determined using conservation of energy (loss of KE = gain in PE):

$$\text{KE}_{\text{max}} = eV_0 .$$

Now let us examine the details of the photoelectric effect from the point of view of the wave theory versus Einstein's particle theory.

First the wave theory, assuming monochromatic light. The two important properties of a light wave are its intensity and its frequency (or wavelength). When these two quantities are varied, the wave theory makes the following predictions:

*Wave theory predictions*

1. If the light intensity is increased, the number of electrons ejected and their maximum kinetic energy should be increased because the higher intensity means a greater electric field amplitude, and the greater electric field should eject electrons with higher speed.
2. The frequency of the light should not affect the kinetic energy of the ejected electrons. Only the intensity should affect $\text{KE}_{\text{max}}$.

The photon theory makes completely different predictions. First we note that in a monochromatic beam, all photons have the same energy $(= hf)$. Increasing the intensity of the light beam means increasing the number of photons in the beam, but does not affect the energy of each photon as long as the frequency is not changed. According to Einstein's theory, an electron is ejected from the metal by a collision with a single photon. In the process, all the photon energy is transferred to the electron and the photon ceases to exist. Since electrons are held in the metal by attractive forces, some minimum energy $W_0$ is required just to get an electron out through the surface. $W_0$ is called the **work function**, and is a few electron volts $\left(1\text{ eV} = 1.6 \times 10^{-19}\text{ J}\right)$ for most metals. If the frequency $f$ of the incoming light is so low that $hf$ is less than $W_0$, then the photons will not have enough energy to eject any electrons at all. If $hf > W_0$, then electrons will be ejected and energy will be conserved in the process. That is, the input energy (of the photon), $hf$, will equal the outgoing kinetic energy KE of the electron plus the energy required to get it out of the metal, $W$:

*One photon collides with one electron, ejecting it*

$$hf = \text{KE} + W. \qquad \textbf{(27–5a)}$$

The least tightly held electrons will be emitted with the most kinetic energy $\left(\text{KE}_{\text{max}}\right)$, in which case $W$ in this equation becomes the work function $W_0$, and KE becomes $\text{KE}_{\text{max}}$:

$$hf = \text{KE}_{\text{max}} + W_0. \qquad \text{[least bound electrons]} \qquad \textbf{(27–5b)}$$

Many electrons will require more energy than the bare minimum $\left(W_0\right)$ to get out of the metal, and thus the kinetic energy of such electrons will be less than the maximum.

From these considerations, the photon theory makes the following predictions:

*Photon theory predictions*

1. An increase in intensity of the light beam means more photons are incident, so more electrons will be ejected; but since the energy of each photon is not changed, the maximum kinetic energy of electrons is not changed by an increase in intensity.
2. If the frequency of the light is increased, the maximum kinetic energy of the electrons increases linearly, according to Eq. 27–5b. That is,

$$\text{KE}_{\text{max}} = hf - W_0.$$

This relationship is plotted in Fig. 27–7.

3. If the frequency $f$ is less than the "cutoff" frequency $f_0$, where $hf_0 = W_0$, no electrons will be ejected, no matter how great the intensity of the light.

**FIGURE 27–7** Photoelectric effect: the maximum kinetic energy of ejected electrons increases linearly with the frequency of incident light. No electrons are emitted if $f < f_0$.

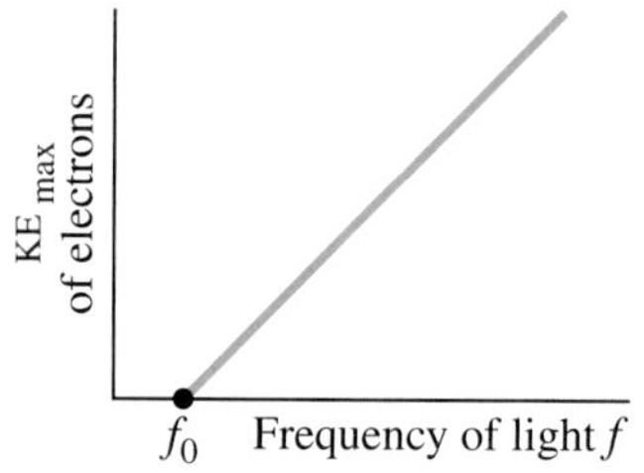


These predictions of the photon theory are clearly very different from the predictions of the wave theory. In 1913–1914, careful experiments were carried out by R. A. Millikan. The results were fully in agreement with Einstein's photon theory.

One other aspect of the photoelectric effect also confirmed the photon theory. If extremely low light intensity is used, the wave theory predicts a time delay before electron emission so that an electron can absorb enough energy to exceed the work function. The photon theory predicts no such delay—it only takes one photon (if its frequency is high enough) to eject an electron—and experiments showed no delay. This too confirmed Einstein's photon theory.

**EXAMPLE 27–3** **Photon energy.** Calculate the energy of a photon of blue light, $\lambda = 450\,\text{nm}$ in air (or vacuum).

**APPROACH** The photon has energy $E = hf$ (Eq. 27–4) where $f = c/\lambda$ (Eq. 22–4).

**SOLUTION** Since $f = c/\lambda$, we have

$$E = hf = \frac{hc}{\lambda} = \frac{(6.63 \times 10^{-34}\,\text{J}\cdot\text{s})(3.0 \times 10^{8}\,\text{m/s})}{(4.5 \times 10^{-7}\,\text{m})} = 4.4 \times 10^{-19}\,\text{J},$$

or $(4.4 \times 10^{-19}\,\text{J})/(1.60 \times 10^{-19}\,\text{J/eV}) = 2.8\,\text{eV}$. (See definition of eV in Section 17–4, $1\,\text{eV} = 1.60 \times 10^{-19}\,\text{J}$.)

**EXERCISE B** A beam contains infrared light of a single wavelength, 1000 nm, and monochromatic UV at 100 nm, both of the same intensity. Are there more 100-nm photons or more 1000-nm photons?

**EXAMPLE 27–4** **Photoelectron speed and energy.** What is the kinetic energy and the speed of an electron ejected from a sodium surface whose work function is $W_0 = 2.28\,\text{eV}$ when illuminated by light of wavelength (*a*) 410 nm, (*b*) 550 nm?

**APPROACH** We first find the energy of the photons ($E = hf = hc/\lambda$). If the energy is greater than $W_0$, then electrons will be ejected with varying amounts of KE, with a maximum of $\text{KE}_{\text{max}} = hf - W_0$.

**SOLUTION** (*a*) For $\lambda = 410\,\text{nm}$,

$$hf = \frac{hc}{\lambda} = 4.85 \times 10^{-19}\,\text{J} \qquad \text{or} \qquad 3.03\,\text{eV}.$$

The maximum kinetic energy an electron can have is given by Eq. 27–5b, $\text{KE}_{\text{max}} = 3.03\,\text{eV} - 2.28\,\text{eV} = 0.75\,\text{eV}$, or $(0.75\,\text{eV})(1.60 \times 10^{-19}\,\text{J/eV}) = 1.2 \times 10^{-19}\,\text{J}$. Since $\text{KE} = \frac{1}{2}mv^2$ where $m = 9.1 \times 10^{-31}\,\text{kg}$,

$$v_{\text{max}} = \sqrt{\frac{2\text{KE}}{m}} = 5.1 \times 10^{5}\,\text{m/s}.$$

Most ejected electrons will have less KE and less speed than these maximum values.

(*b*) For $\lambda = 550\,\text{nm}$, $hf = hc/\lambda = 3.61 \times 10^{-19}\,\text{J} = 2.26\,\text{eV}$. Since this photon energy is less than the work function, no electrons are ejected.

**NOTE** In (*a*) we used the nonrelativistic equation for kinetic energy. If $v$ had turned out to be more than about $0.1c$, our calculation would have been inaccurate by more than a percent or so, and we would probably prefer to redo it using the relativistic form (Eq. 26–6).

**EXERCISE C** Determine the lowest frequency and the longest wavelength needed to emit electrons from sodium.

It is easy to show (see Problem 28) just by converting units that the energy of a photon in electron volts, when given the wavelength $\lambda$ in nm, is

$$E\,(\text{eV}) = \frac{1.240 \times 10^{3}\,\text{eV}\cdot\text{nm}}{\lambda\,(\text{nm})}. \qquad \text{[photon energy in eV]}$$

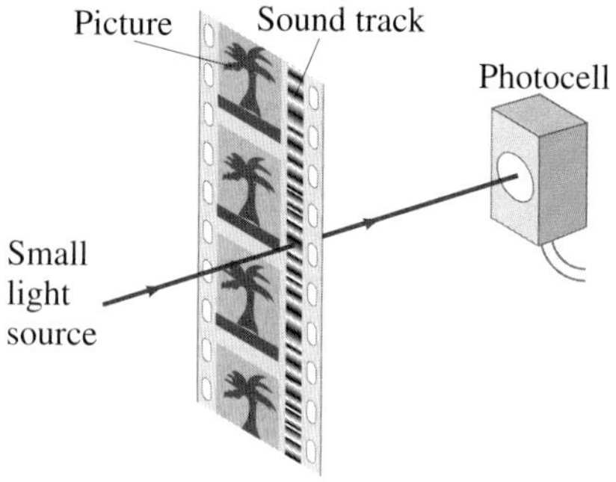


**FIGURE 27–8** Optical sound track on movie film. In the projector, light from a small source (different from that for the picture) passes through the sound track on the moving film. The light and dark areas on the sound track vary the intensity of the transmitted light which reaches the photocell, whose current output is then a replica of the original sound. This output is amplified and sent to the loudspeakers. High-quality projectors can show movies containing several parallel sound tracks to go to different speakers around the theater.

### Applications of the Photoelectric Effect

The photoelectric effect, besides playing an important historical role in confirming the photon theory of light, also has many practical applications. Burglar alarms and automatic door openers often make use of the photocell circuit of Fig. 27–6. When a person interrupts the beam of light, the sudden drop in current in the circuit activates a switch—often a solenoid—which operates a bell or opens the door. UV or IR light is sometimes used in burglar alarms because of its invisibility. Many smoke detectors use the photoelectric effect to detect tiny amounts of smoke that interrupt the flow of light and so alter the electric current. Photographic light meters use this circuit as well. Photocells are used in many other devices, such as absorption spectrophotometers, to measure light intensity. One type of film sound track is a variably shaded narrow section at the side of the film. Light passing through the film is thus "modulated," and the output electrical signal of the photocell detector follows the frequencies on the sound track. See Fig. 27–8. For many applications today, the vacuum-tube photocell of Fig. 27–6 has been replaced by a semiconductor device known as a **photodiode** (Section 29–8). In these semiconductors, the absorption of a photon liberates a bound electron, which changes the conductivity of the material, so the current through a photodiode is altered.

## 27–4 Energy, Mass, and Momentum of a Photon

We have just seen (Eq. 27–4) that the total energy of a single photon is given by $E = hf$. Because a photon always travels at the speed of light, it is truly a relativistic particle. Thus we must use relativistic formulas for dealing with its mass, energy, and momentum. The momentum of any particle of rest mass $m_0$ is given by $p = m_0 v/\sqrt{1 - v^2/c^2}$. Since $v = c$ for a photon, the denominator is zero. To avoid having an infinite momentum, we conclude that the photon's rest mass must be zero: $m_0 = 0$. This makes sense too because a photon can never be at rest (it goes at the speed of light). A photon's kinetic energy is its total energy:

$$\text{KE} = E = hf. \qquad \text{[photon]}$$

The momentum of a photon can be obtained from the relativistic formula (Eq. 26–10) $E^2 = p^2c^2 + m_0^2c^4$ where we set $m_0 = 0$ so $E^2 = p^2c^2$ or

**CAUTION** Momentum of photon is not $mv$

$$p = \frac{E}{c}. \qquad \text{[photon]}$$

Since $E = hf$ for a photon, its momentum is related to its wavelength by

$$p = \frac{E}{c} = \frac{hf}{c} = \frac{h}{\lambda}. \qquad \textbf{(27–6)}$$

**EXAMPLE 27–5 ESTIMATE** **Photons from a lightbulb.** Estimate how many visible light photons a 100-W lightbulb emits per second. Assume the bulb has a typical efficiency of about 3% (that is, 97% of the energy goes to heat).

**APPROACH** Let's assume an average wavelength in the middle of the visible spectrum, $\lambda \approx 500$ nm. The energy of each photon is $E = hf = hc/\lambda$. Only 3% of the 100-W power is emitted as light, or $3\text{ W} = 3\text{ J/s}$. The number of photons emitted per second equals the light output of 3 J per second divided by the energy of each photon.

**SOLUTION** The energy emitted in one second ($= 3$ J) is $E = Nhf$ where $N$ is the number of photons emitted per second and $f = c/\lambda$. Hence

$$N = \frac{E}{hf} = \frac{E\lambda}{hc} = \frac{(3\text{ J})(500 \times 10^{-9}\text{ m})}{(6.63 \times 10^{-34}\text{ J}\cdot\text{s})(3.0 \times 10^{8}\text{ m/s})} \approx 8 \times 10^{18}$$

per second, or almost $10^{19}$ photons emitted per second, an enormous number.

**EXAMPLE 27–6** **Photon momentum and force.** Suppose the $10^{19}$ photons emitted per second from the 100-W lightbulb in Example 27–5 were all focused onto a piece of black paper and absorbed. (*a*) Calculate the momentum of one photon and (*b*) estimate the force all these photons could exert on the paper.

**APPROACH** Each photon's momentum is obtained from Eq. 27–6, $p = h/\lambda$. Next, each absorbed photon's momentum changes from $p = h/\lambda$ to zero. We use Newton's second law, $F = \Delta p/\Delta t$, to get the force.

**SOLUTION** (*a*) Each photon has a momentum

$$p = \frac{h}{\lambda} = \frac{6.63 \times 10^{-34}\,\mathrm{J \cdot s}}{500 \times 10^{-9}\,\mathrm{m}} = 1.3 \times 10^{-27}\,\mathrm{kg \cdot m/s}.$$

(*b*) Using Newton's second law for $N = 10^{19}$ photons (Example 27–5) whose momentum changes from $h/\lambda$ to 0, we obtain

$$F = \frac{\Delta p}{\Delta t} = \frac{Nh/\lambda - 0}{1\,\mathrm{s}} = N\frac{h}{\lambda} \approx \left(10^{19}\,\mathrm{s}^{-1}\right)\left(10^{-27}\,\mathrm{kg \cdot m/s}\right) \approx 10^{-8}\,\mathrm{N}.$$

This is a pretty tiny force, but we can see that a very strong light source could exert a measurable force, and near the Sun or a star the force due to photons in electromagnetic radiation could be considerable.

**EXAMPLE 27–7** **Photosynthesis.** In *photosynthesis*, pigments such as chlorophyll in plants capture the energy of sunlight to change $CO_2$ to useful carbohydrate. About nine photons are needed to transform one molecule of $CO_2$ to carbohydrate and $O_2$. Assuming light of wavelength $\lambda = 670\,\mathrm{nm}$ (chlorophyll absorbs most strongly in the range 650 nm to 700 nm), how efficient is the photosynthetic process? The reverse chemical reaction releases an energy of 4.9 eV/molecule of $CO_2$.

PHYSICS APPLIED
*Photosynthesis*

**APPROACH** The efficiency is the minimum energy required (4.9 eV) divided by the actual energy absorbed, nine times the energy ($hf$) of one photon.

**SOLUTION** The energy of nine photons, each of energy $hf = hc/\lambda$ is $(9)(6.63 \times 10^{-34}\,\mathrm{J \cdot s})(3.0 \times 10^{8}\,\mathrm{m/s})/(6.7 \times 10^{-7}\,\mathrm{m}) = 2.7 \times 10^{-18}\,\mathrm{J}$ or 17 eV. Thus the process is $(4.9\,\mathrm{eV}/17\,\mathrm{eV}) = 29\%$ efficient.

## * 27–5 Compton Effect

Besides the photoelectric effect, a number of other experiments were carried out in the early twentieth century which also supported the photon theory. One of these was the **Compton effect** (1923) named after its discoverer, A. H. Compton (1892–1962). Compton scattered short-wavelength light (actually X-rays) from various materials. He found that the scattered light had a slightly longer wavelength than did the incident light, and therefore a slightly lower frequency indicating a loss of energy. He explained this result on the basis of the photon theory as incident photons colliding with electrons of the material, Fig. 27–9. Using Eq. 27–6 for momentum of a photon, Compton applied the laws of conservation of momentum and energy to the collision of Fig. 27–9 and derived the following equation for the wavelength of the scattered photons:

$$\lambda' = \lambda + \frac{h}{m_0 c}(1 - \cos\phi), \qquad \textbf{(27–7)}$$

where $m_0$ is the rest mass of the electron. (The quantity $h/m_0 c$, which has the dimensions of length, is called the **Compton wavelength** of the electron.) We see that the predicted wavelength of scattered photons depends on the angle $\phi$ at which they are detected. Compton's measurements of 1923 were consistent with this formula. The wave theory of light predicts no such shift: an incoming EM wave of frequency $f$ should set electrons into oscillation at frequency $f$; and such oscillating electrons would reemit EM waves of this same frequency $f$ (Section 22–2), which would not change with angle ($\phi$). Hence the Compton effect adds to the firm experimental foundation for the photon theory of light.

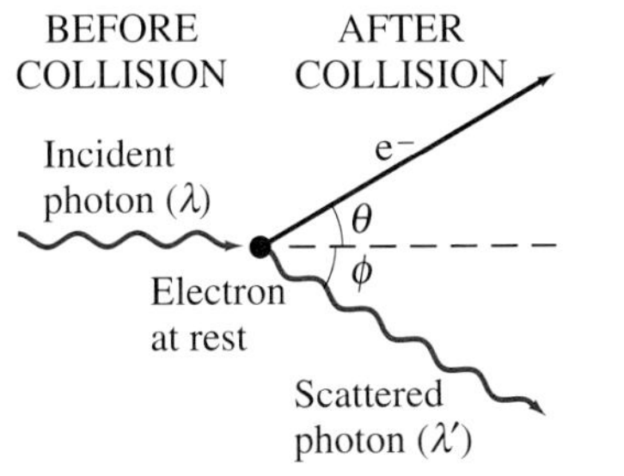


**FIGURE 27–9** The Compton effect. A single photon of wavelength $\lambda$ strikes an electron in some material, knocking it out of its atom. The scattered photon has less energy (since some is given to the electron) and hence has a longer wavelength $\lambda'$. Experiments found scattered X-rays of just the wavelengths predicted by conservation of energy and momentum using the photon model.

**EXERCISE D** When a photon scatters off an electron by the Compton effect, which of the following increase: its energy, frequency, wavelength?

**EXAMPLE 27–8 X-ray scattering.** X-rays of wavelength 0.140 nm are scattered from a very thin slice of carbon. What will be the wavelengths of X-rays scattered at (*a*) 0°, (*b*) 90°, (*c*) 180°?

**APPROACH** This is an example of the Compton effect, and we use Eq. 27–7 to find the wavelengths.

**SOLUTION** (*a*) For $\phi = 0°$, $\cos\phi = 1$ and $1 - \cos\phi = 0$. Then Eq. 27–7 gives $\lambda' = \lambda = 0.140\,\text{nm}$. This makes sense since for $\phi = 0°$, there really isn't any collision as the photon goes straight through without interacting.
(*b*) For $\phi = 90°$, $\cos\phi = 0$, and $1 - \cos\phi = 1$. So

$$\lambda' = \lambda + \frac{h}{m_0 c} = 0.140\,\text{nm} + \frac{6.63 \times 10^{-34}\,\text{J}\cdot\text{s}}{(9.11 \times 10^{-31}\,\text{kg})(3.00 \times 10^{8}\,\text{m/s})}$$
$$= 0.140\,\text{nm} + 2.4 \times 10^{-12}\,\text{m} = 0.142\,\text{nm};$$

that is, the wavelength is longer by one Compton wavelength (= 0.0024 nm for an electron).
(*c*) For $\phi = 180°$, which means the photon is scattered backward, returning in the direction from which it came (a direct "head-on" collision), $\cos\phi = -1$, and $1 - \cos\phi = 2$. So

$$\lambda' = \lambda + 2\frac{h}{m_0 c} = 0.140\,\text{nm} + 2(0.0024\,\text{nm}) = 0.145\,\text{nm}.$$

**NOTE** The maximum shift in wavelength occurs for backward scattering, and it is twice the Compton wavelength.

PHYSICS APPLIED
*Measuring bone density*

The Compton effect has been used to diagnose bone disease such as osteoporosis. Gamma rays, which are photons of even shorter wavelength than X-rays, coming from a radioactive source are scattered off bone material. The total intensity of the scattered radiation is proportional to the density of electrons, which is in turn proportional to the bone density. Changes in the density of bone can indicate the onset of osteoporosis.

## 27–6 Photon Interactions; Pair Production

When a photon passes through matter, it interacts with the atoms and electrons. There are four important types of interactions that a photon can undergo:

*Photon interactions*

1. The *photoelectric effect*: a photon may knock an electron out of an atom and in the process itself disappear.
2. The photon may knock an atomic electron to a higher energy state in the atom if its energy is not sufficient to knock the electron out altogether. In this process the photon also disappears, and all its energy is given to the atom. Such an atom is then said to be in an *excited state*, and we shall discuss it more later.
3. The photon can be scattered from an electron (or a nucleus) and in the process lose some energy; this is the *Compton effect* (Section 27–5). But notice that the photon is not slowed down. It still travels with speed *c*, but its frequency will be lower because it has lost some energy.
4. *Pair production*: A photon can actually create matter, such as the production of an electron and a positron, Fig. 27–10. (A positron has the same mass as an electron, but the opposite charge, $+e$.)

**FIGURE 27–10** Pair production: a photon disappears and produces an electron and a positron.

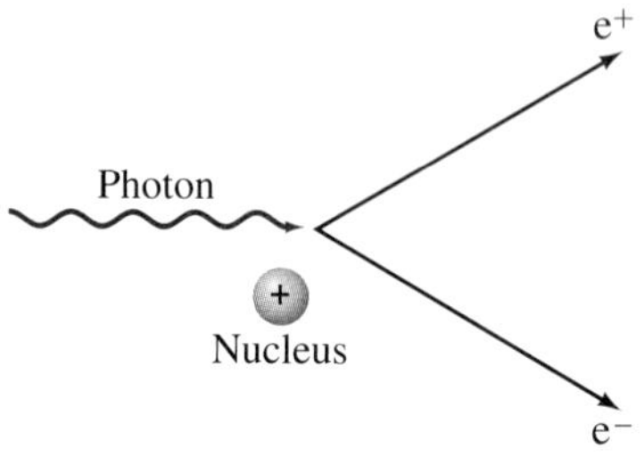


In process 4, **pair production**, the photon disappears in the process of creating the electron–positron pair. This is an example of rest mass being created from pure energy, and it occurs in accord with Einstein's equation $E = mc^2$.

Notice that a photon cannot create an electron alone since electric charge would not then be conserved. The inverse of pair production also occurs: if an electron collides with a positron, the two **annihilate** each other and their energy, including their mass, appears as electromagnetic energy of photons. Because of this process, positrons usually do not last long in nature.

Electron–positron annihilation is the basis for the type of medical imaging known as PET, as discussed in Section 31–8.

**EXAMPLE 27–9** **Pair production.** (*a*) What is the minimum energy of a photon that can produce an electron–positron pair? (*b*) What is this photon's wavelength?

**APPROACH** The minimum photon energy $E$ equals the rest energy $\left(m_0c^2\right)$ of the two particles created, via Einstein's famous equation $E = m_0c^2$ (Eq. 26–8). There is no energy left over, so the particles produced will have zero KE. The wavelength is $\lambda = c/f$ where $E = hf$ for the original photon.

**SOLUTION** (*a*) Because $E = m_0c^2$, and the mass created is equal to two electron rest masses, the photon must have energy

$$E = 2\left(9.11 \times 10^{-31}\,\text{kg}\right)\left(3.0 \times 10^{8}\,\text{m/s}\right)^2 = 1.64 \times 10^{-13}\,\text{J} = 1.02\,\text{MeV}$$

*Minimum energy to produce $e^+e^-$ pair is 1.02 MeV*

$\left(1\,\text{MeV} = 10^{6}\,\text{eV} = 1.60 \times 10^{-13}\,\text{J}\right)$. A photon with less energy cannot undergo pair production.

(*b*) Since $E = hf = hc/\lambda$, the wavelength of a 1.02-MeV photon is

$$\lambda = \frac{hc}{E} = \frac{\left(6.63 \times 10^{-34}\,\text{J}\cdot\text{s}\right)\left(3.0 \times 10^{8}\,\text{m/s}\right)}{\left(1.64 \times 10^{-13}\,\text{J}\right)} = 1.2 \times 10^{-12}\,\text{m},$$

which is 0.0012 nm. Such photons are in the gamma-ray (or very short X-ray) region of the electromagnetic spectrum (Fig. 22–8).

**NOTE** Photons of higher energy (shorter wavelength) can also create an electron–positron pair, with the excess energy becoming kinetic energy of the particles.

Pair production cannot occur in empty space, for momentum could not be conserved. In Example 27–9, for instance, energy is conserved, but only enough energy was provided to create the electron–positron pair at rest and thus with no momentum to carry away the initial momentum of the photon. Indeed, it can be shown that at any energy, an additional massive object, such as an atomic nucleus, must take part in the interaction to carry off some of the momentum.

## 27–7 Wave–Particle Duality; the Principle of Complementarity

The photoelectric effect, the Compton effect, and other experiments have placed the particle theory of light on a firm experimental basis. But what about the classic experiments of Young and others (Chapter 24) on interference and diffraction which showed that the wave theory of light also rests on a firm experimental basis?

*Wave–particle duality*

We seem to be in a dilemma. Some experiments indicate that light behaves like a wave; others indicate that it behaves like a stream of particles. These two theories seem to be incompatible, but both have been shown to have validity. Physicists finally came to the conclusion that this duality of light must be accepted as a fact of life. It is referred to as the **wave–particle duality**. Apparently, light is a more complex phenomenon than just a simple wave or a simple beam of particles.

**FIGURE 27–11** Niels Bohr (right), walking with Enrico Fermi along the Appian Way outside Rome. This photo shows one important way physics is done.

**CAUTION**

*Not correct to say light is a wave and/or a particle. Light can* **act** *like a wave or like a particle*

To clarify the situation, the great Danish physicist Niels Bohr (1885–1962, Fig. 27–11) proposed his famous **principle of complementarity**. It states that to understand an experiment, sometimes we find an explanation using wave theory and sometimes using particle theory. Yet we must be aware of both the wave and particle aspects of light if we are to have a full understanding of light. Therefore these two aspects of light complement one another.

It is not easy to "visualize" this duality. We cannot readily picture a combination of wave and particle. Instead, we must recognize that the two aspects of light are different "faces" that light shows to experimenters.

Part of the difficulty stems from how we think. Visual pictures (or models) in our minds are based on what we see in the everyday world. We apply the concepts of waves and particles to light because in the macroscopic world we see that energy is transferred from place to place by these two methods. We cannot see directly whether light is a wave or particle—so we do indirect experiments. To explain the experiments, we apply the models of waves or of particles to the nature of light. But these are abstractions of the human mind. When we try to conceive of what light really "is," we insist on a visual picture. Yet there is no reason why light should conform to these models (or visual images) taken from the macroscopic world. The "true" nature of light—if that means anything—is not possible to visualize. The best we can do is recognize that our knowledge is limited to the indirect experiments, and that in terms of everyday language and images, light reveals both wave and particle properties.

It is worth noting that Einstein's equation $E = hf$ itself links the particle and wave properties of a light beam. In this equation, $E$ refers to the energy of a particle; and on the other side of the equation, we have the frequency $f$ of the corresponding wave.

## 27–8 Wave Nature of Matter

In 1923, Louis de Broglie (1892–1987) extended the idea of the wave–particle duality. He much appreciated the symmetry in nature, and argued that if light sometimes behaves like a wave and sometimes like a particle, then perhaps those things in nature thought to be particles—such as electrons and other material objects—might also have wave properties. De Broglie proposed that the wavelength of a material particle would be related to its momentum in the same way as for a photon, Eq. 27–6, $p = h/\lambda$. That is, for a particle having linear momentum $p = mv$, the wavelength $\lambda$ is given by

*de Broglie wavelength*

$$\lambda = \frac{h}{p}, \qquad \textbf{(27–8)}$$

and is valid classically ($p = m_0 v$ for $v \ll c$) and relativistically $\left(p = \gamma m_0 v = m_0 v/\sqrt{1 - v^2/c^2}\right)$. This is sometimes called the **de Broglie wavelength** of a particle.

**EXAMPLE 27–10** **Wavelength of a ball.** Calculate the de Broglie wavelength of a 0.20-kg ball moving with a speed of 15 m/s.

**APPROACH** We simply use Eq. 27–8.

**SOLUTION** $$\lambda = \frac{h}{p} = \frac{h}{mv} = \frac{(6.6 \times 10^{-34}\,\mathrm{J\cdot s})}{(0.20\,\mathrm{kg})(15\,\mathrm{m/s})} = 2.2 \times 10^{-34}\,\mathrm{m}.$$

The wavelength of Example 27–10 is an unimaginably small wavelength. Even if the speed were extremely small, say $10^{-4}$ m/s, the wavelength would be about $10^{-29}$ m. Indeed, the wavelength of any ordinary object is much too small to be measured and detected. The problem is that the properties of waves, such as interference and diffraction, are significant only when the size of objects or slits is not much larger than the wavelength. And there are no known objects or slits to diffract waves only $10^{-30}$ m long, so the wave properties of ordinary objects go undetected.

But tiny elementary particles, such as electrons, are another matter. Since the mass $m$ appears in the denominator of Eq. 27–8, a very small mass should have a much larger wavelength.

**EXAMPLE 27–11** **Wavelength of an electron.** Determine the wavelength of an electron that has been accelerated through a potential difference of 100 V.

**APPROACH** If the kinetic energy is much less than the rest energy, we can use classical $\text{KE} = \frac{1}{2}mv^2$ (see end of Section 26–9). For an electron, $m_0c^2 = 0.511\,\text{MeV}$. We then apply conservation of energy: the KE acquired by the electron equals its loss in PE. After solving for $v$, we use Eq. 27–8 to find the de Broglie wavelength.

**SOLUTION** The gain in kinetic energy will equal the loss in potential energy $(\Delta\text{PE} = eV - 0)$: $\text{KE} = eV$, so $\text{KE} = 100\,\text{eV}$. The ratio $\text{KE}/m_0c^2 = 100\,\text{eV}/(0.511 \times 10^6\,\text{eV}) \approx 10^{-4}$, so relativity is not needed. Thus

$$\frac{1}{2}mv^2 = eV$$

and

$$v = \sqrt{\frac{2\,eV}{m}} = \sqrt{\frac{(2)(1.6 \times 10^{-19}\,\text{C})(100\,\text{V})}{(9.1 \times 10^{-31}\,\text{kg})}} = 5.9 \times 10^6\,\text{m/s}.$$

Then

$$\lambda = \frac{h}{mv} = \frac{(6.63 \times 10^{-34}\,\text{J}\cdot\text{s})}{(9.1 \times 10^{-31}\,\text{kg})(5.9 \times 10^6\,\text{m/s})} = 1.2 \times 10^{-10}\,\text{m},$$

or 0.12 nm.

**EXERCISE E** As a particle travels faster, does its de Broglie wavelength decrease, increase, or remain the same?

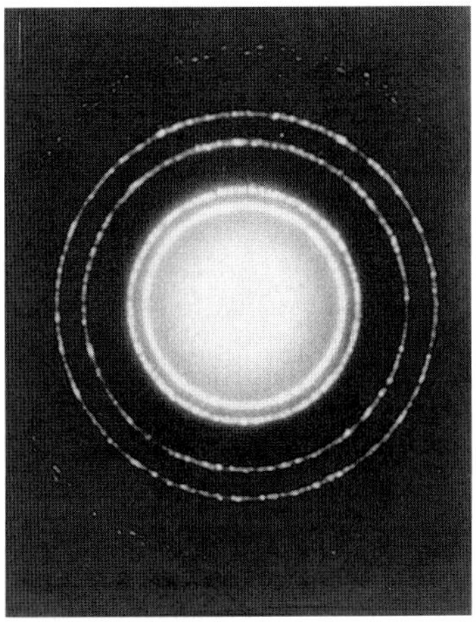

**FIGURE 27–12** Diffraction pattern of electrons scattered from aluminum foil, as recorded on film.

From Example 27–11, we see that electrons can have wavelengths on the order of $10^{-10}$ m, and even smaller. Although small, this wavelength can be detected: the spacing of atoms in a crystal is on the order of $10^{-10}$ m and the orderly array of atoms in a crystal could be used as a type of diffraction grating, as was done earlier for X-rays (see Section 25–11). C. J. Davisson and L. H. Germer performed the crucial experiment; they scattered electrons from the surface of a metal crystal and, in early 1927, observed that the electrons were scattered into a pattern of regular peaks. When they interpreted these peaks as a diffraction pattern, the wavelength of the diffracted electron wave was found to be just that predicted by de Broglie, Eq. 27–8. In the same year, G. P. Thomson (son of J. J. Thomson) used a different experimental arrangement and also detected diffraction of electrons. (See Fig. 27–12. Compare it to X-ray diffraction, Section 25–11.) Later experiments showed that protons, neutrons, and other particles also have wave properties.

Thus the wave–particle duality applies to material objects as well as to light. The principle of complementarity applies to matter as well. That is, we must be aware of both the particle and wave aspects in order to have an understanding of matter, including electrons. But again we must recognize that a visual picture of a "wave–particle" is not possible.

*Wave–particle duality and complementarity apply to matter as well as light*

## What Is an Electron?

We might ask ourselves: "What is an electron?" The early experiments of J. J. Thomson (Section 27–1) indicated a glow in a tube, and that glow moved when a magnetic field was applied. The results of these and other experiments were best interpreted as being caused by tiny negatively charged particles which we now call electrons. No one, however, has actually seen an electron directly. The drawings we sometimes make of electrons as tiny spheres with a negative charge on them are merely convenient pictures (now recognized to be inaccurate). Again we must rely on experimental results, some of which are best interpreted using the particle model and others using the wave model. These models are mere pictures that we use to extrapolate from the macroscopic world to the tiny microscopic world of the atom. And there is no reason to expect that these models somehow reflect the reality of an electron. We thus use a wave or a particle model (whichever works best in a situation) so that we can talk about what is happening. But we should not be led to believe that an electron *is* a wave or a particle. Instead we could say that an electron is the set of its properties that we can measure. Bertrand Russell said it well when he wrote that an electron is "a logical construction."

# * 27–9 Electron Microscopes

PHYSICS APPLIED
*Electron microscope*

The idea that electrons have wave properties led to the development of the **electron microscope**, which can produce images of much greater magnification than does a light microscope. Figures 27–13 and 27–14 are diagrams of two types, developed around the middle of the twentieth century: the **transmission electron microscope**, which produces a two-dimensional image, and the **scanning electron microscope** (SEM), which produces images with a three-dimensional quality. In both types, the objective and eyepiece lenses are actually magnetic fields that exert forces on the electrons to bring them to a focus. The fields are produced by carefully designed current-carrying coils of wire. Photographs using each type are shown in Fig. 27–15.

**FIGURE 27–13** Transmission electron microscope. The magnetic-field coils are designed to be "magnetic lenses," which bend the electron paths and bring them to a focus, as shown.

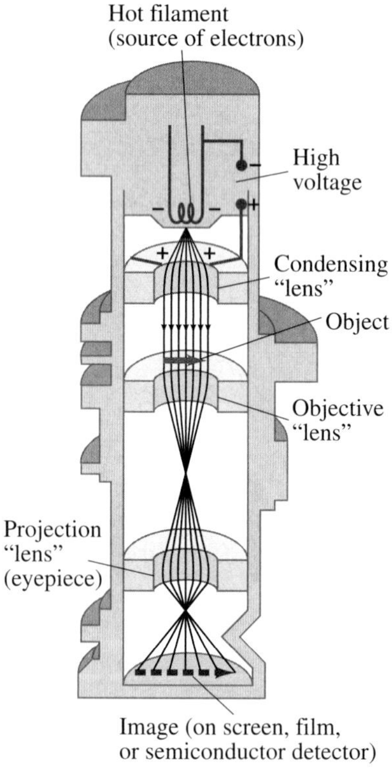


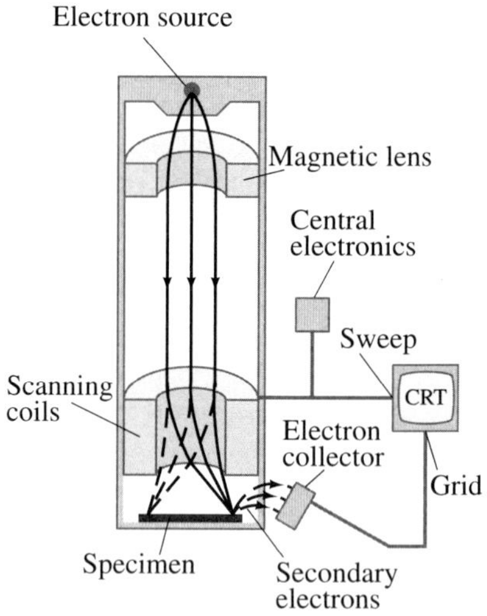


**FIGURE 27–14** Scanning electron microscope. Scanning coils move an electron beam back and forth across the specimen. Secondary electrons produced when the beam strikes the specimen are collected and modulate the intensity of the beam in the CRT to produce a picture.

As discussed in Sections 25–7 and 25–8, the maximum resolution of details on an object is about the size of the wavelength of the radiation used to view it. Electrons accelerated by voltages on the order of $10^5$ V have wavelengths on the order of 0.004 nm. The maximum resolution obtainable would be on this order, but in practice, aberrations in the magnetic lenses limit the resolution in transmission electron microscopes to at best about 0.1 to 0.5 nm. This is still $10^3$ times finer than that attainable with a visible-light microscope, and corresponds to a useful magnification of about a million. Such magnifications are difficult to attain, and more common magnifications are $10^4$ to $10^5$. The maximum resolution attainable with a scanning electron microscope is somewhat less, typically 5 to 10 nm although new high-resolution SEMs approach 1 nm.

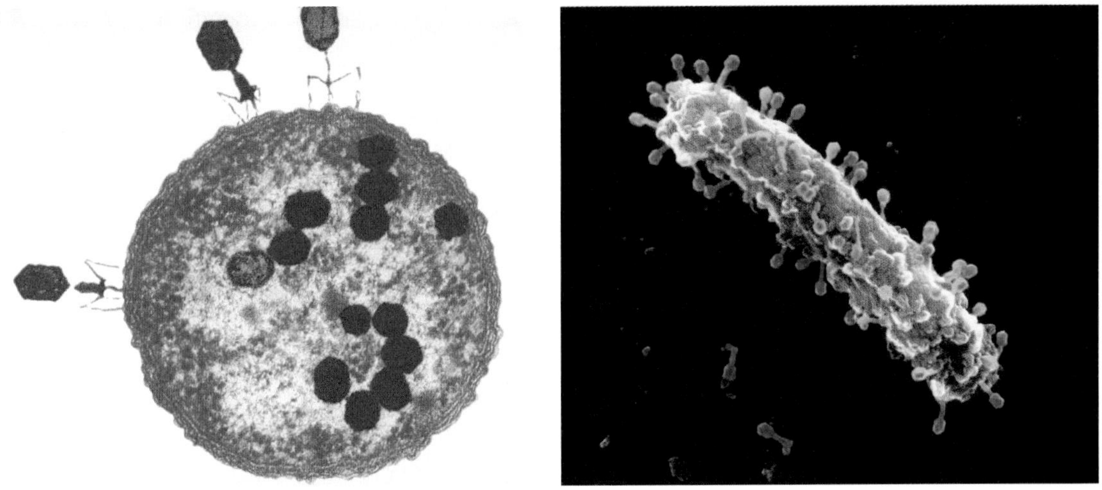


**FIGURE 27–15** Electron micrographs (in false color) of viruses attacking a cell of the bacterium *Escherichia coli*: (a) transmission electron micrograph ($\approx 50{,}000\times$); (b) scanning electron micrograph ($\approx 35{,}000\times$).

The **scanning tunneling electron microscope** (STM), developed in the 1980s, contains a tiny probe, whose tip may be only two or three atoms wide, that is moved across the specimen to be examined in a series of linear passes, like those made by the electron beam in a TV tube (CRT, Section 17–10). The tip, as it scans, remains very close to the surface of the specimen, about 1 nm above it, Fig. 27–16. A small voltage applied between the probe and the surface causes electrons to leave the surface and pass through the vacuum to the probe, by a process known as *tunneling* (discussed in Section 30–12). This "tunneling" current is very sensitive to the gap width, so a feedback mechanism can be used to raise and lower the probe to maintain a constant electron current. The probe's vertical motion, following the surface of the specimen, is then plotted as a function of position, producing a three-dimensional image of the surface. Surface features as fine as the size of an atom can be resolved: a resolution better than 0.1 nm laterally and 0.01 nm or better vertically. This kind of resolution has given a great impetus to the study of the surface structure of materials. The "topographic" image of a surface actually represents the distribution of electron charge.

The **atomic force microscope** (AFM), developed in the 1980s, is in many ways similar to an STM, but can be used on a wider range of sample materials. Instead of detecting an electric current, the AFM measures the force between a cantilevered tip and the sample, a force which depends strongly on the tip-sample separation at each point. The tip is moved as for the STM.

PHYSICS APPLIED
*STM and AFM*

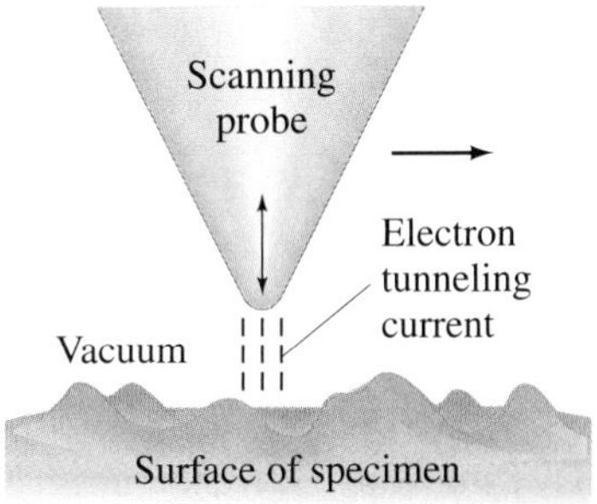


**FIGURE 27–16** Probe tip of scanning tunneling electron microscope moves up and down to maintain constant tunneling current. A plot of the probe's motion produces an image of the surface.

## 27–10 Early Models of the Atom

The idea that matter is made up of atoms was accepted by most scientists by 1900. With the discovery of the electron in the 1890s, scientists began to think of the atom itself as having a structure with electrons as part of that structure. We now introduce our modern approach to the atom and the quantum theory with which it is intertwined.†

†Some readers may say: "Tell us the facts as we know them today, and don't bother us with the historical background and its outmoded theories." Such an approach would ignore the creative aspect of science and thus give a false impression of how science develops. Moreover, it is not really possible to understand today's view of the atom without insight into the concepts that led to it.

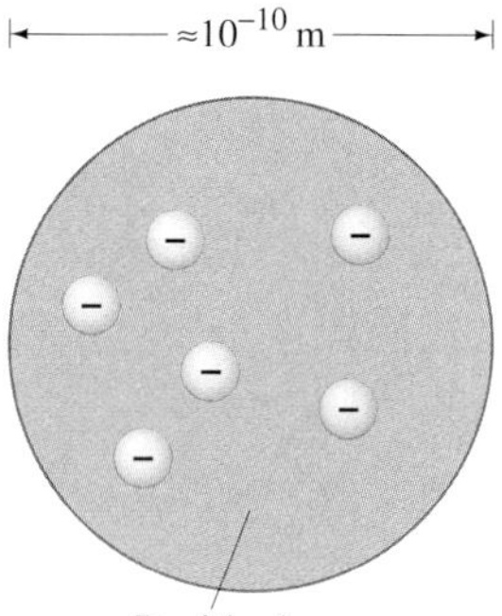


**FIGURE 27–17** Plum-pudding model of the atom.

A typical model of the atom in the 1890s visualized the atom as a homogeneous sphere of positive charge inside of which there were tiny negatively charged electrons, a little like plums in a pudding, Fig. 27–17.

Around 1911, Ernest Rutherford (1871–1937) and his colleagues performed experiments whose results contradicted the plum-pudding model of the atom. In these experiments a beam of positively charged "alpha ($\alpha$) particles" was directed at a thin sheet of metal foil such as gold, Fig. 27–18a. (These newly discovered $\alpha$ particles were emitted by certain radioactive materials and were soon shown to be doubly ionized helium atoms—that is, having a charge of $+2e$.) It was expected from the plum-pudding model that the alpha particles would not be deflected significantly because electrons are so much lighter than alpha particles, and the alpha particles should not have encountered any massive concentration of positive charge to strongly repel them. The experimental results completely contradicted these predictions. It was found that most of the alpha particles passed through the foil unaffected, as if the foil were mostly empty space. And of those deflected, a few were deflected at very large angles—some even backward, nearly in the direction from which they had come. This could happen, Rutherford reasoned, only if the positively charged alpha particles were being repelled by a massive positive charge concentrated in a very small region of space (see Fig. 27–18b). He hypothesized that the atom must

*Rutherford's planetary model*

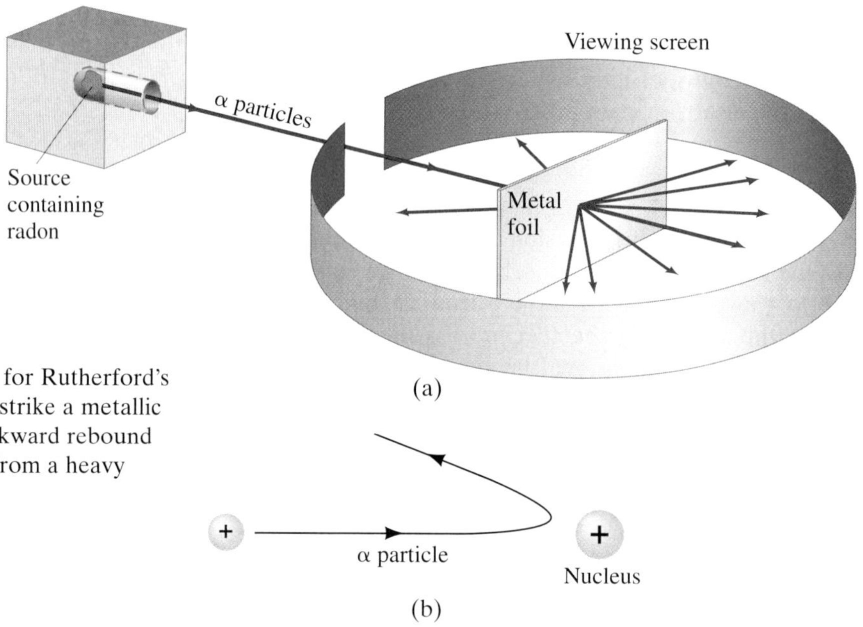


**FIGURE 27–18** (a) Experimental setup for Rutherford's experiment: $\alpha$ particles emitted by radon strike a metallic foil and some rebound backward; (b) backward rebound of $\alpha$ particles explained as the repulsion from a heavy positively charged nucleus.

consist of a tiny but massive positively charged nucleus, containing over 99.9% of the mass of the atom, surrounded by electrons some distance away. The electrons would be moving in orbits about the nucleus—much as the planets move around the Sun—because if they were at rest, they would fall into the nucleus due to electrical attraction, Fig. 27–19. Rutherford's experiments suggested that the nucleus must have a radius of about $10^{-15}$ to $10^{-14}$ m. From kinetic theory, and especially Einstein's analysis of Brownian motion (see Section 13–1), the radius of atoms was estimated to be about $10^{-10}$ m. Thus the electrons would seem to be at a distance from the nucleus of about 10,000 to 100,000 times the radius of the nucleus itself. (If the nucleus were the size of a baseball, the atom would have the diameter of a big city several kilometers across.) So an atom would be mostly empty space.

Rutherford's "planetary" model of the atom (also called the "nuclear model of the atom") was a major step toward how we view the atom today. It was not, however, a complete model and presented some major problems, as we shall see.

**FIGURE 27–19** Rutherford's model of the atom, in which electrons orbit a tiny positive nucleus (not to scale). The atom is visualized as mostly empty space.

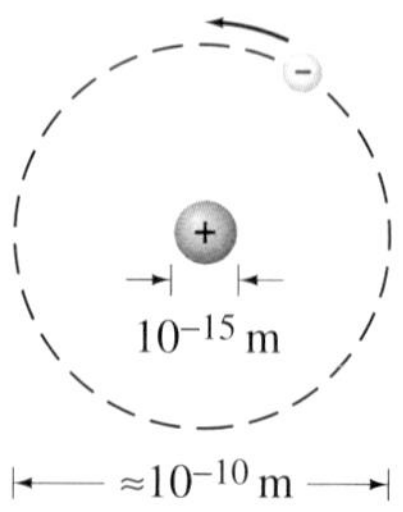

## 27–11 Atomic Spectra: Key to the Structure of the Atom

Earlier in this Chapter we saw that heated solids (as well as liquids and dense gases) emit light with a continuous spectrum of wavelengths. This radiation is assumed to be due to oscillations of atoms and molecules, which are largely governed by the interaction of each atom or molecule with its neighbors.

Rarefied gases can also be excited to emit light. This is done by intense heating, or more commonly by applying a high voltage to a "discharge tube" containing the gas at low pressure, Fig. 27–20. The radiation from excited gases had been observed early in the nineteenth century, and it was found that the spectrum was not continuous, but *discrete*. Since excited gases emit light of only certain wavelengths, when this light is analyzed through the slit of a spectroscope or spectrometer, a **line spectrum** is seen rather than a continuous spectrum. The line spectra emitted by a number of elements in the visible region are shown here in Fig. 27–21, and also in Chapter 24, Fig. 24–28. The **emission spectrum** is characteristic of the material and can serve as a type of "fingerprint" for identification of the gas.

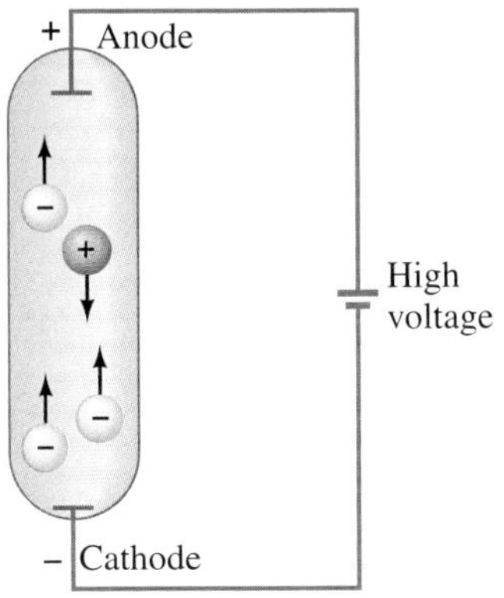

(a)

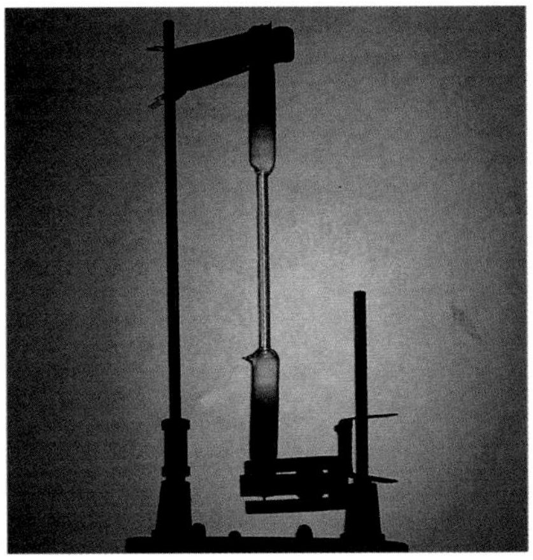
(b)

**FIGURE 27–20** Gas-discharge tube: (a) diagram; (b) photo of an actual discharge tube for hydrogen.

We also saw (Chapter 24) that if a continuous spectrum passes through a rarefied gas, dark lines are observed in the emerging spectrum, at wavelengths corresponding to lines normally emitted by the gas. This is called an **absorption spectrum** (Fig. 27–21c), and it became clear that gases can absorb light at the same frequencies at which they emit. Using film sensitive to ultraviolet and to infrared light, it was found that gases emit and absorb discrete frequencies in these regions as well as in the visible.

**FIGURE 27–21** Emission spectra of the gases (a) atomic hydrogen, (b) helium, and (c) the *solar absorption* spectrum.

(a)

(b)

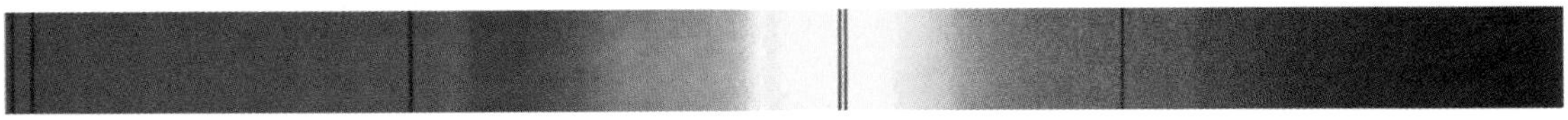
(c)

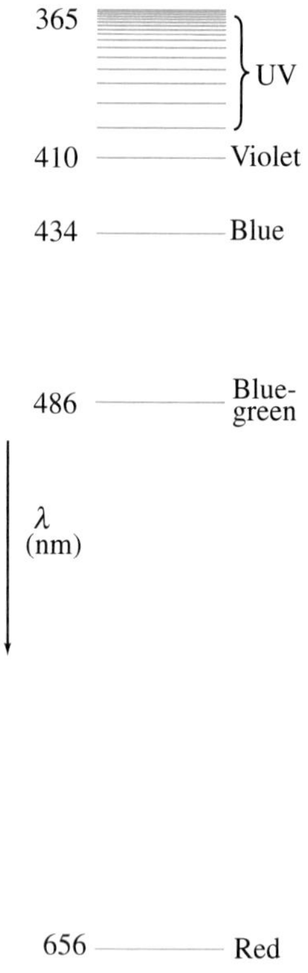


**FIGURE 27–22** Balmer series of lines for hydrogen.

In low density gases, the atoms are far apart on the average and hence the light emitted or absorbed is assumed to be by *individual atoms* rather than through interactions between atoms, as in a solid, liquid, or dense gas. Thus the line spectra serve as a key to the structure of the atom: any theory of atomic structure must be able to explain why atoms emit light only of discrete wavelengths, and it should be able to predict what these wavelengths are.

Hydrogen is the simplest atom—it has only one electron orbiting its nucleus. It also has the simplest spectrum. The spectrum of most atoms shows little apparent regularity. But the spacing between lines in the hydrogen spectrum decreases in a regular way, Fig. 27–22. Indeed, in 1885, J. J. Balmer (1825–1898) showed that the four lines in the visible portion of the hydrogen spectrum (with measured wavelengths 656 nm, 486 nm, 434 nm, and 410 nm) have wavelengths that fit the formula

$$\frac{1}{\lambda} = R\left(\frac{1}{2^2} - \frac{1}{n^2}\right), \qquad n = 3, 4, \cdots. \tag{27–9}$$

Here $n$ takes on the values 3, 4, 5, 6 for the four visible lines, and $R$, called the **Rydberg constant**, has the value $R = 1.0974 \times 10^7\,\mathrm{m}^{-1}$. Later it was found that this **Balmer series** of lines extended into the UV region, ending at $\lambda = 365$ nm, as shown in Fig. 27–22. Balmer's formula, Eq. 27–9, also worked for these lines with higher integer values of $n$. The lines near 365 nm became too close together to distinguish, but the limit of the series at 365 nm corresponds to $n = \infty$ (so $1/n^2 = 0$ in Eq. 27–9).

Later experiments on hydrogen showed that there were similar series of lines in the UV and IR regions, and each series had a pattern just like the Balmer series, but at different wavelengths, Fig. 27–23. Each of these series was found to fit a formula with the same form as Eq. 27–9 but with the $1/2^2$ replaced by $1/1^2$, $1/3^2$, $1/4^2$, and so on. For example, the so-called **Lyman series** contains lines with wavelengths from 91 nm to 122 nm (in the UV region) and fits the formula

$$\frac{1}{\lambda} = R\left(\frac{1}{1^2} - \frac{1}{n^2}\right), \qquad n = 2, 3, \cdots.$$

And the wavelengths of the **Paschen series** (in the IR region) fit

$$\frac{1}{\lambda} = R\left(\frac{1}{3^2} - \frac{1}{n^2}\right), \qquad n = 4, 5, \cdots.$$

The Rutherford model was unable to explain why atoms emit line spectra. It had other difficulties as well. According to the Rutherford model, electrons orbit the nucleus, and since their paths are curved the electrons are accelerating. Hence they should give off light like any other accelerating electric charge (Chapter 22). Since light carries off energy and energy is conserved, the electron's own energy must decrease to compensate. Hence electrons would be

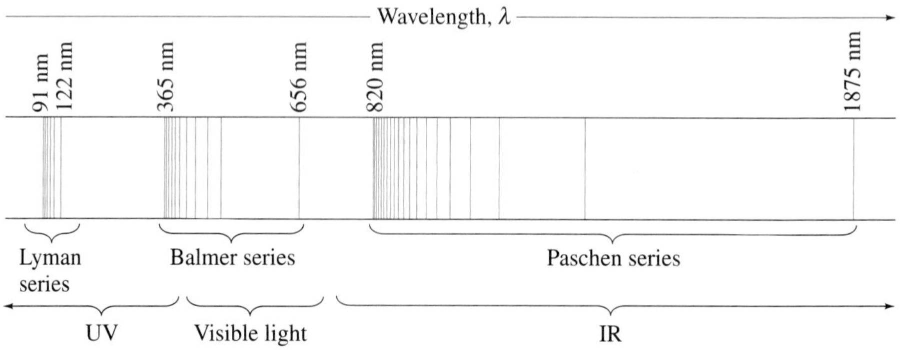


**FIGURE 27–23** Line spectrum of atomic hydrogen. Each series fits the formula $\frac{1}{\lambda} = R\left(\frac{1}{n'^2} - \frac{1}{n^2}\right)$ where $n' = 1$ for the Lyman series, $n' = 2$ for the Balmer series, $n' = 3$ for the Paschen series, and so on; $n$ can take on all integer values from $n = n' + 1$ up to infinity. The only lines in the visible region of the electromagnetic spectrum are part of the Balmer series.

expected to spiral into the nucleus. As they spiraled inward, their frequency would increase in a short time and so too would the frequency of the light emitted. Thus the two main difficulties of the Rutherford model are these: (1) it predicts that light of a continuous range of frequencies will be emitted, whereas experiment shows line spectra; (2) it predicts that atoms are unstable—electrons would quickly spiral into the nucleus—but we know that atoms in general are stable, because there is stable matter all around us.

Clearly Rutherford's model was not sufficient. Some sort of modification was needed, and Niels Bohr provided it in a model that included the quantum hypothesis. Although the Bohr model has been superceded, it did provide a crucial stepping stone to our present understanding. And some aspects of the Bohr model are still useful today, so we examine it in detail in the next Section.

## 27–12 The Bohr Model

Bohr had studied in Rutherford's laboratory for several months in 1912 and was convinced that Rutherford's planetary model of the atom had validity. But in order to make it work, he felt that the newly developing quantum theory would somehow have to be incorporated in it. The work of Planck and Einstein had shown that in heated solids, the energy of oscillating electric charges must change discontinuously—from one discrete energy state to another, with the emission of a quantum of light. Perhaps, Bohr argued, the electrons in an atom also cannot lose energy continuously, but must do so in quantum "jumps." In working out his model during the next year, Bohr postulated that electrons move about the nucleus in circular orbits, but that only certain orbits are allowed. He further postulated that an electron in each orbit would have a definite energy and would move in the orbit *without radiating energy* (even though this violated classical ideas since accelerating electric charges are supposed to emit EM waves; see Chapter 22). He thus called the possible orbits **stationary states**. Light is emitted, he hypothesized, only when an electron jumps from a higher (upper) stationary state to another of lower energy. When such a jump occurs, a single photon of light is emitted whose energy, by energy conservation, is given by

*Stationary state*

$$hf = E_u - E_l, \tag{27–10}$$

where $E_u$ refers to the energy of the upper state and $E_l$ the energy of the lower state. See Fig. 27–24.

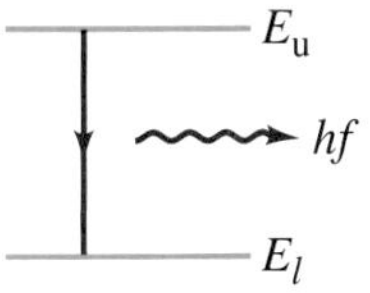


**FIGURE 27–24** An atom emits a photon (energy = $hf$) when its energy changes from $E_u$ to a lower energy $E_l$.

Bohr set out to determine what energies these orbits would have in the simplest atom, hydrogen; then the spectrum of light emitted could be predicted from Eq. 27–10. In the Balmer formula he had the key he was looking for. Bohr quickly found that his theory would be in accord with the Balmer formula if he assumed that the electron's angular momentum $L$ is quantized and equal to an integer $n$ times $h/2\pi$. As we saw in Chapter 8 angular momentum is given by $L = I\omega$, where $I$ is the moment of inertia and $\omega$ is the angular velocity. For a single particle of mass $m$ moving in a circle of radius $r$ with speed $v$, $I = mr^2$ and $\omega = v/r$; hence, $L = I\omega = (mr^2)(v/r) = mvr$. Bohr's **quantum condition** is

$$L = mvr_n = n\frac{h}{2\pi}, \qquad n = 1, 2, 3, \cdots, \tag{27–11}$$

*Angular momentum quantized*

where $n$ is an integer and $r_n$ is the radius of the $n^{\text{th}}$ possible orbit. The allowed orbits are numbered $1, 2, 3, \cdots$, according to the value of $n$, which is called the **principal quantum number** of the orbit.

*Quantum number, n*

Equation 27–11 did not have a firm theoretical foundation. Bohr had searched for some "quantum condition," and such tries as $E = hf$ (where $E$ represents the energy of the electron in an orbit) did not give results in accord with experiment. Bohr's reason for using Eq. 27–11 was simply that it worked; and we now look at how. In particular, let us determine what the Bohr theory predicts for the measurable wavelengths of emitted light.

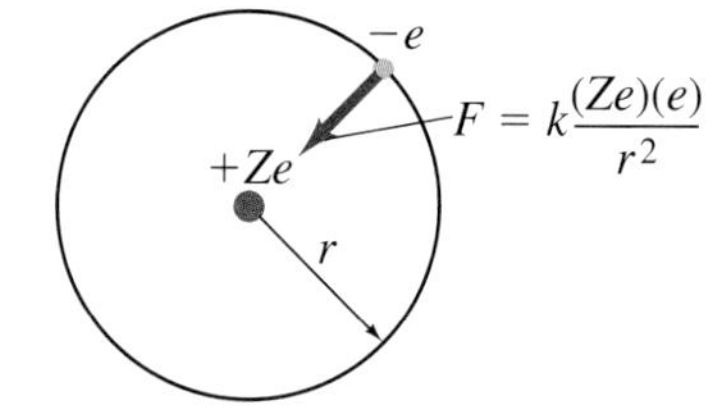


**FIGURE 27–25** Electric force (Coulomb's law) keeps the negative electron in orbit around the positively charged nucleus.

An electron in a circular orbit of radius $r$ (Fig. 27–25) would have a centripetal acceleration $v^2/r$ produced by the electrical force of attraction between the negative electron and the positive nucleus. This force is given by Coulomb's law,

$$F = k\frac{(Ze)(e)}{r^2},$$

where $k = 1/4\pi\epsilon_0 = 9.00 \times 10^9\,\mathrm{N \cdot m^2/C^2}$. The charge on the electron is $q_1 = -e$, and that on the nucleus is $q_2 = +Ze$, where $Z$ is the number of positive charges[†] (i.e., protons). For the hydrogen atom, $Z = +1$.

In Newton's second law, $F = ma$, we substitute Coulomb's law for $F$ and $a = v^2/r_n$ for a particular allowed orbit of radius $r_n$, and obtain

$$F = ma$$
$$k\frac{Ze^2}{r_n^2} = \frac{mv^2}{r_n}.$$

We solve this for $r_n$,

$$r_n = \frac{kZe^2}{mv^2},$$

and then substitute for $v$ from Eq. 27–11 (which says $v = nh/2\pi m r_n$):

$$r_n = \frac{kZe^2 4\pi^2 m r_n^2}{n^2h^2}.$$

We solve for $r_n$ (it appears on both sides, so we cancel one of them) and find

$$r_n = \frac{n^2h^2}{4\pi^2 mkZe^2} = \frac{n^2}{Z}r_1 \qquad \textbf{(27–12)}$$

where

$$r_1 = \frac{h^2}{4\pi^2 mke^2}.$$

Equation 27–12 gives the radii of each possible orbit. The smallest orbit is for $n = 1$, and for hydrogen ($Z = 1$) has the value

$$r_1 = \frac{(1)^2(6.626 \times 10^{-34}\,\mathrm{J \cdot s})^2}{4(3.14)^2(9.11 \times 10^{-31}\,\mathrm{kg})(9.00 \times 10^9\,\mathrm{N \cdot m^2/C^2})(1.602 \times 10^{-19}\,\mathrm{C})^2}$$

*Bohr radius*

$$r_1 = 0.529 \times 10^{-10}\,\mathrm{m}. \qquad \textbf{(27–13)}$$

The radius of the smallest orbit in hydrogen, $r_1$, is sometimes called the **Bohr radius**. From Eq. 27–12, we see that the radii of the larger orbits[‡] increase as $n^2$, so

$$r_2 = 4r_1 = 2.12 \times 10^{-10}\,\mathrm{m},$$
$$r_3 = 9r_1 = 4.76 \times 10^{-10}\,\mathrm{m},$$
$$\vdots$$
$$r_n = n^2 r_1, \qquad n = 1, 2, 3, \cdots.$$

**FIGURE 27–26** Possible orbits in the Bohr model of hydrogen; $r_1 = 0.529 \times 10^{-10}\,\mathrm{m}$.

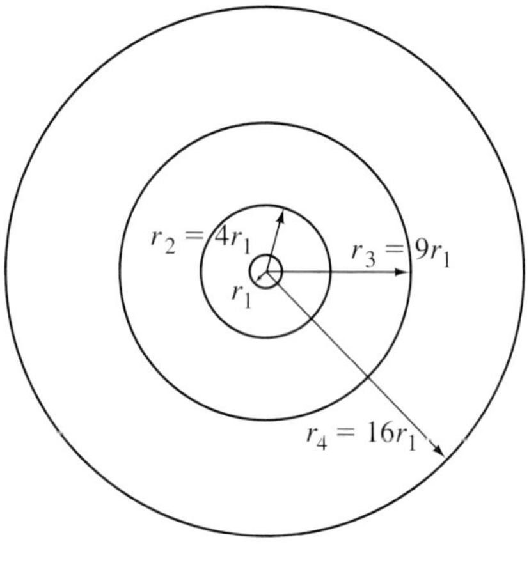


The first four orbits are shown in Fig. 27–26. Notice that, according to Bohr's model, an electron can exist only in the orbits given by Eq. 27–12. There are no allowable orbits in between.

For an atom with $Z \neq 1$, we can write the orbital radii, $r_n$, using Eq. 27–12:

$$r_n = \frac{n^2}{Z}(0.529 \times 10^{-10}\,\mathrm{m}), \qquad n = 1, 2, 3, \cdots. \qquad \textbf{(27–14)}$$

In each of its possible orbits, the electron in a Bohr model atom would have

[†]We include $Z$ in our derivation so that we can treat other single-electron ("hydrogenlike") atoms such as the ions $He^+$ ($Z = 2$) and $Li^{2+}$ ($Z = 3$). Helium in the neutral state has two electrons; if one electron is missing, the remaining $He^+$ ion consists of one electron revolving around a nucleus of charge $+2e$. Similarly, doubly ionized lithium, $Li^{2+}$, also has a single electron, and in this case $Z = 3$.

[‡]Be careful not to believe that these well-defined orbits actually exist. Today electrons are better thought of as forming "clouds," as discussed in Chapter 28.

a definite energy, as the following calculation shows. The total energy equals the sum of the kinetic and potential energies. The potential energy of the electron is given by $\text{PE} = qV = -eV$, where $V$ is the potential due to a point charge $+Ze$ as given by Eq. 17–5: $V = kQ/r = kZe/r$. So

$$\text{PE} = -eV = -k\frac{Ze^2}{r}.$$

The total energy $E_n$ for an electron in the $n^{\text{th}}$ orbit of radius $r_n$ is the sum of the kinetic and potential energies:

$$E_n = \frac{1}{2}mv^2 - \frac{kZe^2}{r_n}.$$

When we substitute $v$ from Eq. 27–11 and $r_n$ from Eq. 27–12 into this equation, we obtain

$$E_n = -\frac{2\pi^2 Z^2 e^4 mk^2}{h^2}\frac{1}{n^2} \qquad n = 1, 2, 3, \cdots. \qquad \textbf{(27–15a)}$$

*Energy levels*

If we evaluate the constant term in Eq. 27–15a and convert it to electron volts, as is customary in atomic physics, we obtain

$$E_n = -(13.6\,\text{eV})\frac{Z^2}{n^2}, \qquad n = 1, 2, 3, \cdots. \qquad \textbf{(27–15b)}$$

The lowest energy level $(n = 1)$ for hydrogen $(Z = 1)$ is

$$E_1 = -13.6\,\text{eV}.$$

*Ground state of hydrogen*

Since $n^2$ appears in the denominator of Eq. 27–15b, the energies of the larger orbits in hydrogen $(Z = 1)$ are given by

$$E_n = \frac{-13.6\,\text{eV}}{n^2}.$$

For example,

$$E_2 = \frac{-13.6\,\text{eV}}{4} = -3.40\,\text{eV},$$

$$E_3 = \frac{-13.6\,\text{eV}}{9} = -1.51\,\text{eV}.$$

*Excited states (first two)*

We see that not only are the orbit radii quantized, but from Eqs. 27–15, so is the energy. The quantum number $n$ that labels the orbit radii also labels the energy levels. The lowest **energy level** or **energy state** has energy $E_1$, and is called the **ground state**. The higher states, $E_2$, $E_3$, and so on, are called **excited states**.

Notice that although the energy for the larger orbits has a smaller numerical value, all the energies are less than zero. Thus, $-3.4\,\text{eV}$ is a greater energy than $-13.6\,\text{eV}$. Hence the orbit closest to the nucleus $(r_1)$ has the lowest total energy. The reason the energies have negative values has to do with the way we defined the zero for potential energy. For two point charges, $\text{PE} = kq_1q_2/r$ corresponds to zero PE when the two charges are infinitely far apart as discussed in Section 17–5. Thus, an electron that can just barely be free from the atom by reaching $r = \infty$ (or, at least, far from the nucleus) with zero KE will have $E = \text{KE} + \text{PE} = 0 + 0 = 0$, corresponding to $n = \infty$ in Eqs. 27–15. If an electron is free and has some kinetic energy, then $E > 0$. To remove an electron that is part of an atom requires an energy input (otherwise atoms would not be stable). Since $E \geq 0$ for a free electron, then it makes sense that an electron bound to an atom must have $E < 0$. That is, energy must be added to bring the electron's total energy up, from a negative value to at least zero in order to free it.

The minimum energy required to remove an electron from the ground state of an atom is called the **binding energy** or **ionization energy**. The ionization energy for hydrogen has been measured to be 13.6 eV, and this corresponds precisely to removing an electron from the lowest state, $E_1 = -13.6\,\text{eV}$, up to $E = 0$ where it can be free.

*Binding energy (ionization energy)*

It is useful to show the various possible energy values as horizontal lines on an energy-level diagram. This is shown for hydrogen in Fig. 27–27.† The electron in a hydrogen atom can be in any one of these levels according to Bohr theory. But it could never be in between, say at $-9.0\,\text{eV}$. At room temperature, nearly all H atoms will be in the ground state ($n = 1$). At higher temperatures, or during an electric discharge when there are many collisions between free electrons and atoms, many atoms can be in excited states ($n > 1$). Once in an excited state, an atom's electron can jump down to a lower state, and give off a photon in the process. This is, according to the Bohr model, the origin of the emission spectra of excited gases.

*Line spectra emission explained*

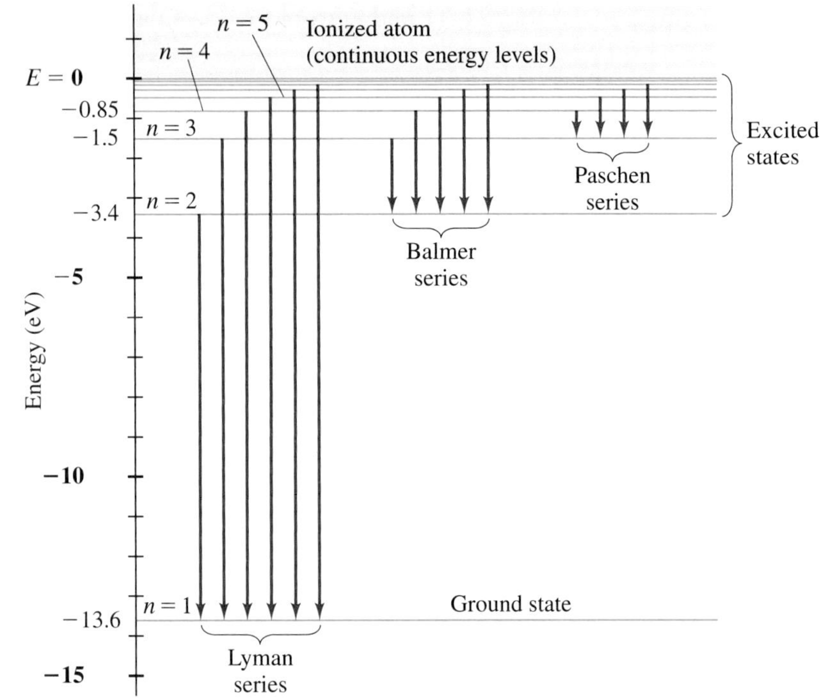


**FIGURE 27–27** Energy-level diagram for the hydrogen atom, showing origin of spectral lines for the Lyman, Balmer, and Paschen series (Fig. 27–23). Each vertical arrow represents an atomic transition that gives rise to the photons of one spectral line (a single wavelength or frequency).

The vertical arrows in Fig. 27–27 represent the transitions or jumps that correspond to the various observed spectral lines. For example, an electron jumping from the level $n = 3$ to $n = 2$ would give rise to the 656-nm line in the Balmer series, and the jump from $n = 4$ to $n = 2$ would give rise to the 486-nm line (see Fig. 27–22). We can predict wavelengths of the spectral lines emitted by combining Eq. 27–10 with Eq. 27–15. Since $hf = hc/\lambda$, we have from Eq. 27–10

$$\frac{1}{\lambda} = \frac{hf}{hc} = \frac{1}{hc}(E_n - E_{n'}),$$

where $n$ refers to the upper state and $n'$ to the lower state. Then using Eq. 27–15,

$$\frac{1}{\lambda} = \frac{2\pi^2 Z^2 e^4 mk^2}{h^3 c}\left(\frac{1}{n'^2} - \frac{1}{n^2}\right). \tag{27–16}$$

This theoretical formula has the same form as the experimental Balmer formula, Eq. 27–9, with $n' = 2$. Thus we see that the Balmer series of lines corresponds to transitions or "jumps" that bring the electron down to the second energy level. Similarly, $n' = 1$ corresponds to the Lyman series and $n' = 3$ to the Paschen series (see Fig. 27–27).

†Note that above $E = 0$, an electron is free and can have any energy ($E$ is not quantized). Thus there is a continuum of energy states above $E = 0$, as indicated in the energy-level diagram of Fig. 27–27.

When the constant in Eq. 27–16 is evaluated with $Z = 1$, it is found to have the measured value of the Rydberg constant, $R = 1.0974 \times 10^7\,\text{m}^{-1}$ in Eq. 27–9, in accord with experiment (see Problem 53).

The great success of Bohr's model is that it gives an explanation for why atoms emit line spectra, and accurately predicts the wavelengths of emitted light for hydrogen. The Bohr model also explains absorption spectra: photons of just the right wavelength can knock an electron from one energy level to a higher one. To conserve energy, only photons that have just the right energy will be absorbed. This explains why a continuous spectrum of light entering a gas will emerge with dark (absorption) lines at frequencies that correspond to emission lines (Fig. 27–21c).

*Absorption lines explained*

The Bohr theory also ensures the stability of atoms. It establishes stability by decree: the ground state is the lowest state for an electron and there is no lower energy level to which it can go and emit more energy. Finally, as we saw above, the Bohr theory accurately predicts the ionization energy of 13.6 eV for hydrogen. However, the Bohr model was not so successful for other atoms, and has been superseded as we shall discuss in the next Chapter. We discuss the Bohr model because it *was* an important start and because we still use the concept of stationary states, the ground state, and transitions between states. Also, the terminology used in the Bohr model is still used by chemists and spectroscopists.

**EXAMPLE 27–12 Wavelength of a Lyman line.** Use Fig. 27–27 to determine the wavelength of the first Lyman line, the transition from $n = 2$ to $n = 1$. In what region of the electromagnetic spectrum does this lie?

**APPROACH** We use Eq. 27–10, $hf = E_u - E_l$, with the energies obtained from Fig. 27–27 to find the energy and the wavelength of the transition. The region of the electromagnetic spectrum is found using the EM spectrum in Fig. 22–8.

**SOLUTION** In this case, $hf = E_2 - E_1 = \{-3.4\,\text{eV} - (-13.6\,\text{eV})\} = 10.2\,\text{eV} = (10.2\,\text{eV})(1.60 \times 10^{-19}\,\text{J/eV}) = 1.63 \times 10^{-18}\,\text{J}$. Since $\lambda = c/f$, we have

$$\lambda = \frac{c}{f} = \frac{hc}{E_2 - E_1} = \frac{(6.63 \times 10^{-34}\,\text{J}\cdot\text{s})(3.00 \times 10^8\,\text{m/s})}{1.63 \times 10^{-18}\,\text{J}} = 1.22 \times 10^{-7}\,\text{m},$$

or 122 nm, which is in the UV region of the EM spectrum, Fig. 22–8. See also Fig. 27–23.

**NOTE** An alternate approach would be to use Eq. 27–16 to find $\lambda$, and it gives the same result.

**EXAMPLE 27–13 Wavelength of a Balmer line.** Determine the wavelength of light emitted when a hydrogen atom makes a transition from the $n = 6$ to the $n = 2$ energy level according to the Bohr model.

**APPROACH** We can use Eq. 27–16 or its equivalent, Eq. 27–9, with $R = 1.097 \times 10^7\,\text{m}^{-1}$.

**SOLUTION** We find

$$\frac{1}{\lambda} = (1.097 \times 10^7\,\text{m}^{-1})\left(\frac{1}{4} - \frac{1}{36}\right) = 2.44 \times 10^6\,\text{m}^{-1}.$$

So $\lambda = 1/(2.44 \times 10^6\,\text{m}^{-1}) = 4.10 \times 10^{-7}\,\text{m}$ or 410 nm. This is the fourth line in the Balmer series, Fig. 27–22, and is violet in color.

**EXAMPLE 27–14** **Absorption wavelength.** Use Figure 27–27 to determine the maximum wavelength that hydrogen in its ground state can absorb. What would be the next smaller wavelength that would work?

**APPROACH** Maximum wavelength corresponds to minimum energy, and this would be the jump from the ground state up to the first excited state (Fig. 27–27). The next smaller wavelength occurs for the jump from the ground state to the second excited state. In each case, the energy difference can be used to find the wavelength.

**SOLUTION** The energy needed to jump from the ground state to the first excited state is $13.6\,\text{eV} - 3.4\,\text{eV} = 10.2\,\text{eV}$; the required wavelength, as we saw in Example 27–12, is 122 nm. The energy to jump from the ground state to the second excited state is $13.6\,\text{eV} - 1.5\,\text{eV} = 12.1\,\text{eV}$, which corresponds to a wavelength

$$\lambda = \frac{c}{f} = \frac{hc}{hf} = \frac{hc}{E_3 - E_1}$$

$$= \frac{(6.63 \times 10^{-34}\,\text{J}\cdot\text{s})(3.00 \times 10^8\,\text{m/s})}{(12.1\,\text{eV})(1.60 \times 10^{-19}\,\text{J/eV})} = 103\,\text{nm}.$$

## Additional Examples

**EXAMPLE 27–15** **Ionization energy.** (*a*) Use the Bohr model to determine the ionization energy of the $He^+$ ion, which has a single electron. (*b*) Also calculate the maximum wavelength a photon can have to cause ionization.

**APPROACH** We want to determine the minimum energy required to lift the electron from its ground state and to barely reach the free state at $E = 0$. The ground state energy of $He^+$ is given by Eq. 27–15b with $n = 1$ and $Z = 2$.

**SOLUTION** (*a*) Since all the symbols in Eq. 27–15b are the same as for the calculation for hydrogen, except that $Z$ is 2 instead of 1, we see that $E_1$ will be $Z^2 = 2^2 = 4$ times the $E_1$ for hydrogen. That is,

$$E_1 = 4(-13.6\,\text{eV}) = -54.4\,\text{eV}.$$

Thus, to ionize the $He^+$ ion should require 54.4 eV, and this value agrees with experiment.

(*b*) The maximum wavelength photon that can cause ionization will have energy $hf = 54.4\,\text{eV}$ and wavelength

$$\lambda = \frac{c}{f} = \frac{hc}{hf} = \frac{(6.63 \times 10^{-34}\,\text{J}\cdot\text{s})(3.00 \times 10^8\,\text{m/s})}{(54.4\,\text{eV})(1.60 \times 10^{-19}\,\text{J/eV})} = 22.8\,\text{nm}.$$

If $\lambda > 22.8\,\text{nm}$, ionization can not occur.

**NOTE** If the atom absorbed a photon of greater energy (wavelength shorter than 22.8 nm), the atom could still be ionized and the freed electron would have kinetic energy of its own.

In this last Example, we saw that $E_1$ for the $He^+$ ion is four times more negative than that for hydrogen. Indeed, the energy-level diagram for $He^+$ looks just like that for hydrogen, Fig. 27–27, except that the numerical values for each energy level are four times larger. Note, however, that we are talking here about the $He^+$ *ion*. Normal (neutral) helium has two electrons and its energy level diagram is entirely different.

**CONCEPTUAL EXAMPLE 27–16** **Hydrogen at 20°C.** Estimate the average kinetic energy of whole hydrogen atoms (not just the electrons) at room temperature, and use the result to explain why nearly all H atoms are in the ground state at room temperature, and hence emit no light.

**RESPONSE** According to kinetic theory (Chapter 13), the average KE of atoms or molecules in a gas is given by Eq. 13–8:

$$\overline{\text{KE}} = \tfrac{3}{2}kT,$$

where $k = 1.38 \times 10^{-23}\,\text{J/K}$ is Boltzmann's constant, and $T$ is the kelvin (absolute) temperature. Room temperature is about $T = 300\,\text{K}$, so

$$\overline{\text{KE}} = \tfrac{3}{2}(1.38 \times 10^{-23}\,\text{J/K})(300\,\text{K}) = 6.2 \times 10^{-21}\,\text{J},$$

or, in electron volts:

$$\overline{\text{KE}} = \frac{6.2 \times 10^{-21}\,\text{J}}{1.6 \times 10^{-19}\,\text{J/eV}} = 0.04\,\text{eV}.$$

The average KE of an atom as a whole is thus very small compared to the energy between the ground state and the next higher energy state $(13.6\,\text{eV} - 3.4\,\text{eV} = 10.2\,\text{eV})$. Any atoms in excited states quickly fall to the ground state and emit light. Once in the ground state, collisions with other atoms can transfer energy of only 0.04 eV on the average. A small fraction of atoms can have much more energy (see Section 13–11 on the distribution of molecular speeds), but even a KE that is 10 times the average is not nearly enough to excite atoms above the ground state. Thus, at room temperature, nearly all atoms are in the ground state. Atoms can be excited to upper states by very high temperatures, or by passing a current of high energy electrons through the gas, as in a discharge tube (Fig. 27–20).

## Correspondence Principle

We should note that Bohr made some radical assumptions that were at variance with classical ideas. He assumed that electrons in fixed orbits do not radiate light even though they are accelerating (moving in a circle), and he assumed that angular momentum is quantized. Furthermore, he was not able to say how an electron moved when it made a transition from one energy level to another. On the other hand, there is no real reason to expect that in the tiny world of the atom electrons would behave as ordinary-sized objects do. Nonetheless, he felt that where quantum theory overlaps with the macroscopic world, it should predict classical results. This is the **correspondence principle**, already mentioned in regard to relativity (Section 26–11). This principle does work for Bohr's theory of the hydrogen atom. The orbit sizes and energies are quite different for $n = 1$ and $n = 2$, say. But orbits with $n = 100{,}000{,}000$ and 100,000,001 would be very close in size and energy (see Fig. 27–27). Indeed, jumps between such large orbits, which would approach macroscopic sizes, would be imperceptible. Such orbits would thus appear to be continuously spaced, which is what we expect in the everyday world.

*Correspondence principle*

Finally, it must be emphasized that the well-defined orbits of the Bohr model do not actually exist. The Bohr model is only a model, not reality. The idea of electron orbits was rejected a few years later, and today electrons are thought of (Chapter 28) as forming "probability clouds."

## 27–13 de Broglie's Hypothesis Applied to Atoms

Bohr's theory was largely of an *ad hoc* nature. Assumptions were made so that theory would agree with experiment. But Bohr could give no reason why the orbits were quantized, nor why there should be a stable ground state. Finally, ten years later, a reason was proposed by Louis de Broglie. We saw in Section 27–8 that in 1923, de Broglie proposed that material particles, such as electrons, have a wave nature; and that this hypothesis was confirmed by experiment several years later.

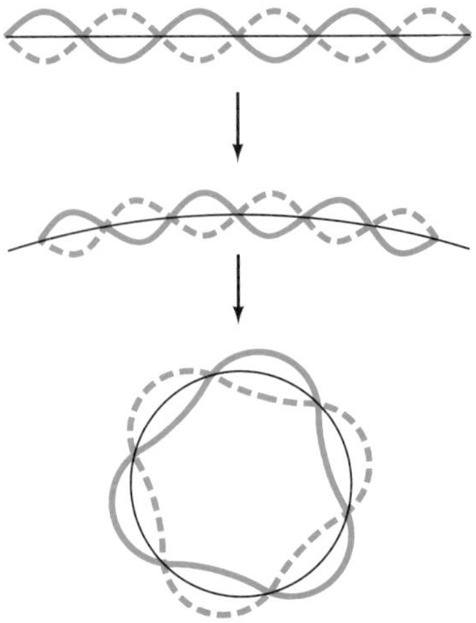

FIGURE 27–28 An ordinary standing wave compared to a circular standing wave.

One of de Broglie's original arguments in favor of the wave nature of electrons was that it provided an explanation for Bohr's theory of the hydrogen atom. According to de Broglie, a particle of mass $m$ moving with a nonrelativistic speed $v$ would have a wavelength (Eq. 27–8) of

$$\lambda = \frac{h}{mv}.$$

Each electron orbit in an atom, he proposed, is actually a standing wave. As we saw in Chapter 11, when a violin or guitar string is plucked, a vast number of wavelengths are excited. But only certain ones—those that have nodes at the ends—are sustained. These are the *resonant* modes of the string. Waves with other wavelengths interfere with themselves upon reflection and their amplitudes quickly drop to zero. With electrons moving in circles, according to Bohr's theory, de Broglie argued that the electron wave was a *circular* standing wave that closes on itself, Fig. 27–28. If the wavelength of a wave does not close on itself, as in Fig. 27–29, destructive interference takes place as the wave travels around the loop, and the wave quickly dies out. Thus, the only waves that persist are those for which the circumference of the circular orbit contains a whole number of wavelengths, Fig. 27–30. The circumference of a Bohr orbit of radius $r_n$ is $2\pi r_n$, so we have

FIGURE 27–29 When a wave does not close (and hence interferes destructively with itself), it rapidly dies out.

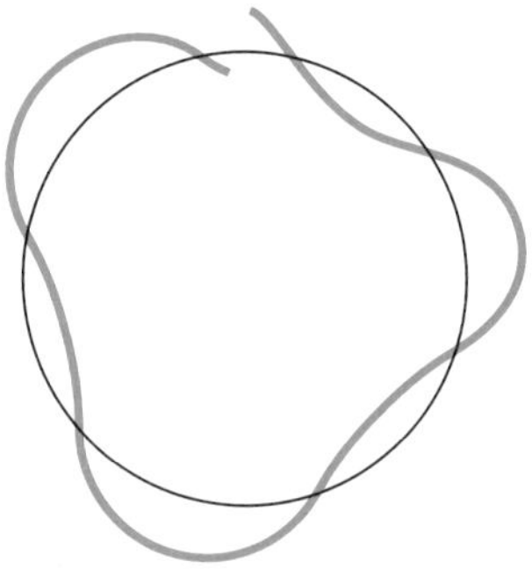

$$2\pi r_n = n\lambda, \qquad n = 1, 2, 3, \cdots.$$

When we substitute $\lambda = h/mv$, we get $2\pi r_n = nh/mv$, or

$$mvr_n = \frac{nh}{2\pi}.$$

*Quantized orbits are a result of wave nature*

This is just the *quantum condition* proposed by Bohr on an *ad hoc* basis, Eq. 27–11. It is from this equation that the discrete orbits and energy levels were derived. Thus we have a first explanation for the quantized orbits and energy states in the Bohr model: they are due to the wave nature of the electron, and only

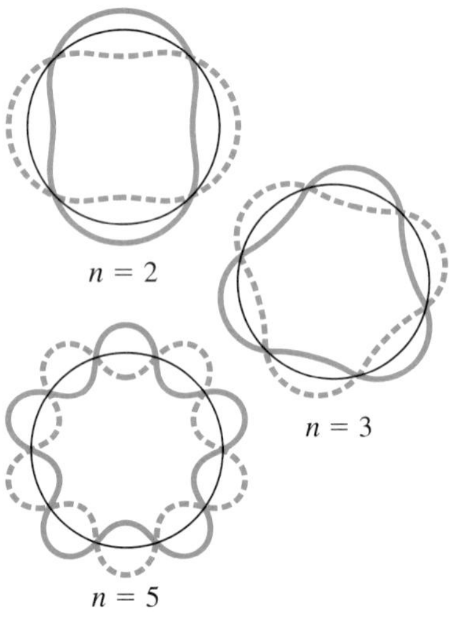


FIGURE 27–30 Standing circular waves for two, three, and five wavelengths on the circumference; $n$, the number of wavelengths, is also the quantum number.

resonant "standing" waves can persist.† This implies that the *wave–particle duality* is at the root of atomic structure.

In viewing the circular electron waves of Fig. 27–30, the electron is not to be thought of as following the oscillating wave pattern. In the Bohr model of hydrogen, the electron moves in a circle. The circular wave, on the other hand, represents the *amplitude* of the electron "matter wave," and in Fig. 27–30 the wave amplitude is shown superimposed on the circular path of the particle orbit for convenience.

Bohr's theory worked well for hydrogen and for one-electron ions. But it did not prove successful for multi-electron atoms. Bohr theory could not predict line spectra even for the next simplest atom, helium. It could not explain why some emission lines are brighter than others, nor why some lines are split into two or more closely spaced lines ("fine structure"). A new theory was needed and was indeed developed in the 1920s. This new and radical theory is called *quantum mechanics*. It finally solved the problem of atomic structure, but it gives us a very different view of the atom: the idea of electrons in well-defined orbits was replaced with the idea of electron "clouds." This new theory of quantum mechanics has given us a wholly different view of the basic mechanisms underlying physical processes.

†We note, however, that Eq. 27–11 is no longer considered valid, as discussed in the next Chapter.

## Summary

Quantum theory has its origins in **Planck's quantum hypothesis** that molecular oscillations are **quantized**: their energy $E$ can only be integer ($n$) multiples of $hf$, where $h$ is Planck's constant and $f$ is the natural frequency of oscillation:

$$E = nhf. \qquad \textbf{(27–3)}$$

This hypothesis explained the spectrum of radiation emitted by a **blackbody** at high temperature.

Einstein proposed that for some experiments, light could be pictured as being emitted and absorbed as **quanta** (particles), which we now call **photons**, each with energy

$$E = hf \qquad \textbf{(27–4)}$$

and momentum

$$p = \frac{E}{c} = \frac{hf}{c} = \frac{h}{\lambda}. \qquad \textbf{(27–6)}$$

He proposed the photoelectric effect as a test for the photon theory of light. In the **photoelectric effect**, the photon theory says that each incident photon can strike an electron in a material and eject it if it has sufficient energy. The maximum energy of ejected electrons is then linearly related to the frequency of the incident light.

The photon theory is also supported by the **Compton effect** and the observation of electron–positron **pair production**.

The **wave–particle duality** refers to the idea that light and matter (such as electrons) have both wave and particle properties. The wavelength of an object is given by

$$\lambda = \frac{h}{p}, \qquad \textbf{(27–8)}$$

where $p$ is the momentum of the object ($p = mv$ for a particle of mass $m$ and speed $v$).

The **principle of complementarity** states that we must be aware of both the particle and wave properties of light and of matter for a complete understanding of them.

Early models of the atom include the plum-pudding model, and Rutherford's planetary (or nuclear) model of an atom which consists of a tiny but massive positively charged nucleus surrounded (at a relatively great distance) by electrons.

To explain the **line spectra** emitted by atoms, as well as the stability of atoms, **Bohr theory** postulated that: (1) electrons bound in an atom can only occupy orbits for which the angular momentum is quantized, which results in discrete values for the radius and energy; (2) an electron in such a **stationary state** emits no radiation; (3) if an electron jumps to a lower state, it emits a photon whose energy equals the difference in energy between the two states; (4) the angular momentum $L$ of atomic electrons is quantized by the rule

$$L = \frac{nh}{2\pi}, \qquad \textbf{(27–11)}$$

where $n$ is an integer called the **quantum number**. The $n = 1$ state is the **ground state**, which in hydrogen has an energy $E_1 = -13.6\,\text{eV}$. Higher values of $n$ correspond to **excited states**, and their energies are

$$E_n = -(13.6\,\text{eV})\frac{Z^2}{n^2}. \qquad \textbf{(27–15b)}$$

Atoms are excited to these higher states by collisions with other atoms or electrons, or by absorption of a photon of just the right frequency.

De Broglie's hypothesis that electrons (and other matter) have a wavelength $\lambda = h/mv$ gave an explanation for Bohr's quantized orbits by bringing in the wave–particle duality: the orbits correspond to circular standing waves in which the circumference of the orbit equals a whole number of wavelengths.

# Questions

1. What can be said about the relative temperatures of whitish-yellow, reddish, and bluish stars? Explain.
2. If energy is radiated by all objects, why can we not see them in the dark? (See also Section 14–8.)
3. Does a lightbulb at a temperature of 2500 K produce as white a light as the Sun at 6000 K? Explain.
4. Darkrooms for developing black-and-white film were sometimes lit by a red bulb. Why red? Would such a bulb work in a darkroom for developing color photographs?
5. If the threshold wavelength in the photoelectric effect increases when the emitting metal is changed to a different metal, what can you say about the work functions of the two metals?
6. Explain why the existence of a cutoff frequency in the photoelectric effect more strongly favors a particle theory rather than a wave theory of light.
7. UV light causes sunburn, whereas visible light does not. Suggest a reason.
8. If an X-ray photon is scattered by an electron, does its wavelength change? If so, does it increase or decrease?
9. In both the photoelectric effect and in the Compton effect, a photon collides with an electron causing the electron to fly off. What then, is the difference between the two processes?
10. Consider a point source of light. How would the intensity of light vary with distance from the source according to (*a*) wave theory, (*b*) particle (photon) theory? Would this help to distinguish the two theories?
11. Explain how the photoelectric circuit of Fig. 27–6 could be used in (*a*) a burglar alarm, (*b*) a smoke detector, (*c*) a photographic light meter.
12. Why do we say that light has wave properties? Why do we say that light has particle properties?
13. Why do we say that electrons have wave properties? Why do we say that electrons have particle properties?
14. What is the difference between a photon and an electron? Be specific: make a list.
15. If an electron and a proton travel at the same speed, which has the shorter wavelength? Explain.
16. In Rutherford's planetary model of the atom, what keeps the electrons from flying off into space?
17. How can you tell if there is oxygen near the surface of the Sun?
18. When a wide spectrum of light passes through hydrogen gas at room temperature, absorption lines are observed that correspond only to the Lyman series. Why don't we observe the other series?
19. Explain how the closely spaced energy levels for hydrogen near the top of Fig. 27–27 correspond to the closely spaced spectral lines at the top of Fig. 27–22.
20. Is it possible for the de Broglie wavelength of a "particle" to be greater than the dimensions of the particle? To be smaller? Is there any direct connection?
21. In a helium atom, which contains two electrons, do you think that on average the electrons are closer to the nucleus or farther away than in a hydrogen atom? Why?
22. How can the spectrum of hydrogen contain so many lines when hydrogen contains only one electron?
23. The Lyman series is brighter than the Balmer series, because this series of transitions ends up in the most common state for hydrogen, the ground state. Why then was the Balmer series discovered first?
24. Use conservation of momentum to explain why photons emitted by hydrogen atoms have slightly less energy than that predicted by Eq. 27–10.
25. The work functions for sodium and cesium are 2.28 eV and 2.14 eV, respectively. For incident photons of a given frequency, which metal will give a higher maximum kinetic energy for the electrons?
26. (*a*) Does a beam of infrared photons always have less energy than a beam of ultraviolet photons? Explain. (*b*) Does a single infrared photon always have less energy than a single ultraviolet photon?
27. Light of 450-nm wavelength strikes a metal surface, and a stream of electrons emerges from the metal. If light of the same intensity but of wavelength 400 nm strikes the surface, are more electrons emitted? Does the energy of the emitted electrons change? Explain.
28. Suppose we obtain an emission spectrum for hydrogen at very high temperature (when some of the atoms are in excited states), and an absorption spectrum at room temperature, when all atoms are in the ground state. Will the two spectra contain identical lines?

# Problems

## 27–1 Discovery of the Electron

1. (I) What is the value of $e/m$ for a particle that moves in a circle of radius 7.0 mm in a 0.86-T magnetic field if a perpendicular 320-V/m electric field will make the path straight?
2. (II) (*a*) What is the velocity of a beam of electrons that go undeflected when passing through crossed (perpendicular) electric and magnetic fields of magnitude $1.88 \times 10^4$ V/m and $2.90 \times 10^{-3}$ T, respectively? (*b*) What is the radius of the electron orbit if the electric field is turned off?
3. (II) An oil drop whose mass is determined to be $2.8 \times 10^{-15}$ kg is held at rest between two large plates separated by 1.0 cm when the potential difference between them is 340 V. How many excess electrons does this drop have?

## 27–2 Planck's Quantum Hypothesis

4. (I) How hot is a metal being welded if it radiates most strongly at 440 nm?
5. (I) Estimate the peak wavelength for radiation from (*a*) ice at 0°C, (*b*) a floodlamp at 3500 K, (*c*) helium at 4 K, (*d*) for the universe at $T = 2.725$ K, assuming blackbody emission. In what region of the EM spectrum is each?
6. (I) (*a*) What is the temperature if the peak of a blackbody spectrum is at 18.0 nm? (*b*) What is the wavelength at the peak of a blackbody spectrum if the body is at a temperature of 2000 K?

7. (I) An HCl molecule vibrates with a natural frequency of $8.1 \times 10^{13}$ Hz. What is the difference in energy (in joules and electron volts) between possible values of the oscillation energy?

8. (II) The steps of a flight of stairs are 20.0 cm high (vertically). If a 68.0-kg person stands with both feet on the same step, what is the gravitational potential energy of this person, relative to the ground, on (*a*) the first step, (*b*) the second step, (*c*) the third step, (*d*) the $n^{\text{th}}$ step? (*e*) What is the change in energy as the person descends from step 6 to step 2?

9. (II) Estimate the peak wavelength of light issuing from the pupil of the human eye (which approximates a blackbody) assuming normal body temperature.

## 27–3 and 27–4 Photons and the Photoelectric Effect

10. (I) What is the energy of photons (joules) emitted by an 88.5-MHz FM radio station?

11. (I) What is the energy range (in joules and eV) of photons in the visible spectrum, of wavelength 400 nm to 750 nm?

12. (I) A typical gamma ray emitted from a nucleus during radioactive decay may have an energy of 300 keV. What is its wavelength? Would we expect significant diffraction of this type of light when it passes through an everyday opening, like a door?

13. (I) About 0.1 eV is required to break a "hydrogen bond" in a protein molecule. Calculate the minimum frequency and maximum wavelength of a photon that can accomplish this.

14. (I) Calculate the momentum of a photon of yellow light of wavelength $6.00 \times 10^{-7}$ m.

15. (I) What is the momentum of a $\lambda = 0.010$ nm X-ray photon?

16. (II) The human eye can respond to as little as $10^{-18}$ J of light energy. For a wavelength at the peak of visual sensitivity, 550 nm, how many photons lead to an observable flash?

17. (II) What minimum frequency of light is needed to eject electrons from a metal whose work function is $4.3 \times 10^{-19}$ J?

18. (II) What is the longest wavelength of light that will emit electrons from a metal whose work function is 3.10 eV?

19. (II) The work functions for sodium, cesium, copper, and iron are 2.3, 2.1, 4.7, and 4.5 eV, respectively. Which of these metals will not emit electrons when visible light shines on it?

20. (II) In a photoelectric-effect experiment it is observed that no current flows unless the wavelength is less than 570 nm. (*a*) What is the work function of this material? (*b*) What is the stopping voltage required if light of wavelength 400 nm is used?

21. (II) What is the maximum kinetic energy of electrons ejected from barium $(W_0 = 2.48\,\text{eV})$ when illuminated by white light, $\lambda = 400$ to 750 nm?

22. (II) Barium has a work function of 2.48 eV. What is the maximum kinetic energy of electrons if the metal is illuminated by UV light of wavelength 365 nm? What is their speed?

23. (II) When UV light of wavelength 285 nm falls on a metal surface, the maximum kinetic energy of emitted electrons is 1.40 eV. What is the work function of the metal?

24. (II) The threshold wavelength for emission of electrons from a given surface is 350 nm. What will be the maximum kinetic energy of ejected electrons when the wavelength is changed to (*a*) 280 nm, (*b*) 360 nm?

25. (II) A certain type of film is sensitive only to light whose wavelength is less than 660 nm. What is the energy (eV and kcal/mol) needed for the chemical reaction to occur which causes the film to change?

26. (II) When 230-nm light falls on a metal, the current through a photoelectric circuit (Fig. 27–6) is brought to zero at a stopping voltage of 1.64 V. What is the work function of the metal?

27. (II) In a photoelectric experiment using a clean sodium surface, the maximum energy of the emitted photons was measured for a number of different incident frequencies, with the following results.

| Frequency ($10^{14}$ Hz) | Energy (eV) |
|---|---|
| 11.8 | 2.60 |
| 10.6 | 2.11 |
| 9.9 | 1.81 |
| 9.1 | 1.47 |
| 8.2 | 1.10 |
| 6.9 | 0.57 |

Plot the graph of these results and find: (*a*) Planck's constant; (*b*) the cutoff frequency of sodium; (*c*) the work function.

28. (II). Show that the energy $E$ (in electron volts) of a photon whose wavelength is $\lambda$ (nm) is given by

$$E = \frac{1.240 \times 10^3\,\text{eV}\cdot\text{nm}}{\lambda\,(\text{nm})}.$$

## * 27–4 Compton Effect

* 29. (II) The quantity $h/m_0c$, which has the dimensions of length, is called the *Compton wavelength*. Determine the Compton wavelength for (*a*) an electron, (*b*) a proton. (*c*) Show that if a photon has wavelength equal to the Compton wavelength of a particle, the photon's energy is equal to the rest energy of the particle.

* 30. (II) X-rays of wavelength $\lambda = 0.120$ nm are scattered from carbon. What is the Compton wavelength shift for photons detected at angles (relative to the incident beam) of (*a*) 45°, (*b*) 90°, (*c*) 180°?

* 31. (III) In the Compton effect, a 0.100-nm photon strikes a free electron in a head-on collision and knocks it into the forward direction. The rebounding photon recoils directly backward. Use conservation of (relativistic) energy and momentum to determine (*a*) the kinetic energy of the electron, and (*b*) the wavelength of the recoiling photon. (*Note*: use Eq. 27–6, but not Eq. 27–7.)

## 27–6 Pair Production

32. (I) How much total kinetic energy will an electron–positron pair have if produced by a 3.84-MeV photon?

33. (II) What is the longest wavelength photon that could produce a proton–antiproton pair? (Each has a mass of $1.67 \times 10^{-27}$ kg.)

34. (II) What is the minimum photon energy needed to produce a $\mu^+ - \mu^-$ pair? The mass of each $\mu$ (muon) is 207 times the mass of the electron. What is the wavelength of such a photon?

35. (II) An electron and a positron, each moving at $1.0 \times 10^5$ m/s, collide head on, disappear, and produce two photons, each with the same energy and momentum moving in opposite directions. What is the energy and momentum of each photon?

36. (II) A gamma-ray photon produces an electron–positron pair, each with a kinetic energy of 245 keV. What was the energy and wavelength of the photon?

## 27–8 Wave Nature of Matter

37. (I) Calculate the wavelength of a 0.23-kg ball traveling at 0.10 m/s.

38. (I) What is the wavelength of a neutron ($m = 1.67 \times 10^{-27}$ kg) traveling at $6.5 \times 10^4$ m/s?

39. (I) Through how many volts of potential difference must an electron be accelerated to achieve a wavelength of 0.24 nm?

40. (II) Calculate the ratio of the kinetic energy of an electron to that of a proton if their wavelengths are equal. Assume that the speeds are nonrelativistic.

41. (II) An electron has a de Broglie wavelength $\lambda = 5.0 \times 10^{-10}$ m. (*a*) What is its momentum? (*b*) What is its speed? (*c*) What voltage was needed to accelerate it to this speed?

42. (II) What is the wavelength of an electron of energy (*a*) 10 eV, (*b*) 100 eV, (*c*) 1.0 keV?

43. (II) Show that if an electron and a proton have the same nonrelativistic kinetic energy, the proton has the shorter wavelength.

44. (II) Calculate the de Broglie wavelength of an electron in your TV picture tube if it is accelerated by 30,000 V. Is it relativistic? How does its wavelength compare to the size of the "neck" of the tube, typically 5 cm? Do we have to worry about diffraction problems blurring our picture on the screen?

45. (III) A Ferrari with a mass of 1400 kg approaches a freeway underpass that is 10 m across. At what speed must the car be moving, in order for it to have a wavelength such that it might somehow "diffract" after passing through this "single slit"? How do these conditions compare to normal freeway speeds of 30 m/s?

## * 27–9 Electron Microscope

* 46. (II) What voltage is needed to produce electron wavelengths of 0.20 nm? (Assume that the electrons are nonrelativistic.)

* 47. (II) Electrons are accelerated by 2450 V in an electron microscope. What is the maximum possible resolution?

## 27–12 Bohr Model

48. (I) For the three hydrogen transitions indicated below, with $n$ being the initial state and $n'$ being the final state, is the transition an absorption or an emission? Which is higher, the initial state energy or the final state energy of the atom? Finally, which of these transitions involves the largest energy photon? (*a*) $n = 1,\ \ n' = 3$ (*b*) $n = 6,\ \ n' = 2$ (*c*) $n = 4,\ \ n' = 5$.

49. (I) How much energy is needed to ionize a hydrogen atom in the $n = 2$ state?

50. (I) The third longest wavelength in the Paschen series in hydrogen (Fig. 27–27) corresponds to what transition?

51. (I) Calculate the ionization energy of doubly ionized lithium, $Li^{2+}$, which has $Z = 3$.

52. (I) (*a*) Determine the wavelength of the second Balmer line ($n = 4$ to $n = 2$ transition) using Fig. 27–27. Determine likewise (*b*) the wavelength of the second Lyman line and (*c*) the wavelength of the third Balmer line.

53. (I) Evaluate the Rydberg constant $R$ using Bohr theory (compare Eqs. 27–9 and 27–16) and show that its value is $R = 1.0974 \times 10^7\ \text{m}^{-1}$.

54. (II) What is the longest wavelength light capable of ionizing a hydrogen atom in the ground state?

55. (II) What wavelength photon would be required to ionize a hydrogen atom in the ground state and give the ejected electron a kinetic energy of 10.0 eV?

56. (II) In the Sun, an ionized helium ($He^+$) atom makes a transition from the $n = 6$ state to the $n = 2$ state, emitting a photon. Can that photon be absorbed by hydrogen atoms present in the Sun? If so, between what energy states will the hydrogen atom jump?

57. (II) Construct the energy-level diagram for the $He^+$ ion (see Fig. 27–27).

58. (II) Construct the energy-level diagram for doubly ionized lithium, $Li^{2+}$.

59. (II) What is the potential energy and the kinetic energy of an electron in the ground state of the hydrogen atom?

60. (II) An excited hydrogen atom could, in principle, have a radius of 1.00 mm. What would be the value of $n$ for a Bohr orbit of this size? What would its energy be?

61. (II) Is the use of nonrelativistic formulas justified in the Bohr atom? To check, calculate the electron's velocity, $v$, in terms of $c$, for the ground state of hydrogen, and then calculate $\sqrt{1 - v^2/c^2}$.

62. (III) Suppose an electron was bound to a proton, as in the hydrogen atom, but by the gravitational force rather than by the electric force. What would be the radius, and energy, of the first Bohr orbit?

## 27–13 de Broglie's Hypothesis Applied to Atoms

63. (III) Suppose a particle of mass $m$ is confined to a one-dimensional box of width $L$. According to quantum theory, the particle's wave (with $\lambda = h/mv$) is a standing wave with nodes at the edges of the box. (*a*) Show the possible modes of vibration on a diagram. (*b*) Show that the kinetic energy of the particle has quantized energies given by $\text{KE} = n^2h^2/8mL^2$, where $n$ is an integer. (*c*) Calculate the ground-state energy ($n = 1$) for an electron confined to a box of width $0.50 \times 10^{-10}$ m. (*d*) What is the ground-state energy, and speed, of a baseball ($m = 140$ g) in a box 0.50 m wide? (*e*) An electron confined to a box has a ground-state energy of 22 eV. What is the width of the box?

# General Problems

64. The Big Bang theory states that the beginning of the universe was accompanied by a huge burst of photons. Those photons are still present today and make up the so-called cosmic microwave background radiation. The universe radiates like a blackbody with a temperature of about 2.7 K. Calculate the peak wavelength of this radiation.

65. At low temperatures, nearly all the atoms in hydrogen gas will be in the ground state. What minimum frequency photon is needed if the photoelectric effect is to be observed?

66. A beam of 85-eV electrons is scattered from a crystal, as in X-ray diffraction, and a first-order peak is observed at $\theta = 38°$. What is the spacing between planes in the diffracting crystal? (See Section 25–11.)

67. A microwave oven produces electromagnetic radiation at $\lambda = 12.2$ cm and produces a power of 760 W. Calculate the number of microwave photons produced by the microwave oven each second.

68. Sunlight reaching the Earth's surface has an intensity of about $1000\,\mathrm{W/m^2}$. Estimate how many photons per square meter per second this represents. Take the average wavelength to be 550 nm.

69. A beam of red laser light $(\lambda = 633\,\mathrm{nm})$ hits a black wall and is fully absorbed. If this light exerts a total force $F = 5.5\,\mathrm{nN}$ on the wall, how many photons per second are hitting the wall?

70. If a 100-W lightbulb emits 3.0% of the input energy as visible light (average wavelength 550 nm) uniformly in all directions, estimate how many photons per second of visible light will strike the pupil (4.0 mm diameter) of the eye of an observer 1.0 km away.

71. An electron and a positron collide head on, annihilate, and create two 0.90-MeV photons traveling in opposite directions. What were the initial kinetic energies of electron and positron?

72. By what potential difference must (*a*) a proton $\left(m = 1.67 \times 10^{-27}\,\mathrm{kg}\right)$, and (*b*) an electron $\left(m = 9.11 \times 10^{-31}\,\mathrm{kg}\right)$, be accelerated to have a wavelength $\lambda = 5.0 \times 10^{-12}\,\mathrm{m}$?

73. In some of Rutherford's experiments (Fig. 27–18) the $\alpha$ particles $\left(\text{mass} = 6.64 \times 10^{-27}\,\mathrm{kg}\right)$ had a kinetic energy of 4.8 MeV. How close could they get to a gold nucleus (charge $= +79e$)? Ignore the recoil motion of the nucleus.

74. By what fraction does the mass of an H atom decrease when it makes an $n = 3$ to $n = 1$ transition?

75. Calculate the ratio of the gravitational to electric force for the electron in a hydrogen atom. Can the gravitational force be safely ignored?

76. Electrons accelerated by a potential difference of 12.3 V pass through a gas of hydrogen atoms at room temperature. What wavelengths of light will be emitted?

77. In a particular photoelectric experiment, a stopping potential of 2.10 V is measured when ultraviolet light of wavelength 290 nm is incident on the metal. Using the same setup, what will the new stopping potential be if blue light of wavelength 440 nm is used, instead?

78. In an X-ray tube (see Fig. 25–35 and discussion in Section 25–11), the high voltage between filament and target is $V$. After being accelerated through this voltage, an electron strikes the target where it is decelerated (by positively charged nuclei) and in the process one or more X-ray photons are emitted. (*a*) Show that the photon of shortest wavelength will have

$$\lambda_0 = \frac{hc}{eV}.$$

(*b*) What is the shortest wavelength of X-ray emitted when accelerated electrons strike the face of a 30-kV television picture tube?

79. The intensity of the Sun's light in the vicinity of the Earth is about $1000\,\mathrm{W/m^2}$. Imagine a spacecraft with a mirrored square sail of dimension 1.0 km. Estimate how much thrust (in newtons) this craft will experience due to collisions with the Sun's photons. [*Hint*: assume the photons bounce off the sail with no change in the magnitude of their momentum.]

80. Light of wavelength 300 nm strikes a metal whose work function is 2.2 eV. What is the shortest de Broglie wavelength for the electrons that are produced as photoelectrons?

81. Photons of energy 6.0 eV are incident on a metal. It is found that current flows from the metal until a stopping potential of 4.0 V is applied. If the wavelength of the incident photons is doubled, what is the maximum kinetic energy of the ejected electrons? What would happen if the wavelength of the incident photons was tripled?

82. Visible light incident on a diffraction grating with slit spacing of 0.010 mm has the first maximum at an angle of 3.5° from the central peak. If electrons could be diffracted by the same grating, what electron velocity would produce the same diffraction pattern as the visible light?

83. (*a*) Suppose an unknown element has an absorption spectrum with lines at 2.5, 4.7, and 5.1 eV above its ground state and an ionization energy of 11.5 eV. Draw an energy level diagram for this element. (*b*) If a 5.1-eV photon is absorbed by an atom of this substance, in which state was the atom before absorbing the photon? What will be the energies of the photons that can subsequently be emitted by this atom?

84. Light of wavelength 424 nm falls on a metal which has a work function of 2.28 eV. (*a*) How much voltage should be applied to bring the current to zero? (*b*) What is the maximum speed of the emitted electrons? (*c*) What is the de Broglie wavelength of these electrons?

85. An electron accelerated from rest by a 96-V potential difference is injected into a $3.67 \times 10^{-4}\,\mathrm{T}$ magnetic field where it travels in an 18-cm-diameter circle. Calculate $e/m$ from this information.

86. Estimate the number of photons emitted by the Sun in a year. (Take the average wavelength to be 550 nm and the intensity of sunlight reaching the Earth (outer atmosphere) as $1350\,\mathrm{W/m^2}$.)

87. Apply Bohr's assumptions to the Earth–Moon system to calculate the allowed energies and radii of motion. Given the known distance between the Earth and Moon, is the quantization of the energy and radius apparent?

## Answers to Exercises

**A:** $\lambda_{\mathrm{P}} = 725\,\mathrm{nm}$, so red.
**B:** More 1000-nm photons (lower frequency).
**C:** $5.50 \times 10^{14}\,\mathrm{Hz}$, 545 nm.
**D:** Only $\lambda$.
**E:** Decrease.

A neon tube is a thin glass tube filled with neon (or other) gas that glows with a particular color when a current at high voltage passes through it. Gas atoms, excited to upper energy levels, jump down to lower energy levels and emit light (photons) whose wavelengths (color) are characteristic of the type of gas.

In this Chapter we study what quantum mechanics tells us about atoms and energy levels, and the effect of the exclusion principle.

CHAPTER 28

# Quantum Mechanics of Atoms

Bohr's model of the atom gave us a first (though rough) picture of what an atom is like. It proposed explanations for why there is emission and absorption of light by atoms at only certain wavelengths. The wavelengths of the line spectra and the ionization energy for hydrogen (and one-electron ions) are in excellent agreement with experiment. But the Bohr theory had important limitations. It was not able to predict line spectra for more complex atoms—not even for the neutral helium atom, which has only two electrons. Nor could it explain why emission lines, when viewed with great precision, consist of two or more very closely spaced lines (referred to as *fine structure*). The Bohr theory also did not explain why some spectral lines were brighter than others. And it could not explain the bonding of atoms in molecules or in solids and liquids.

From a theoretical point of view, too, the Bohr theory was not satisfactory: it was a strange mixture of classical and quantum ideas. Moreover, the wave–particle duality was not really resolved.

We mention these limitations of the Bohr theory not to disparage it—for it was a landmark in the history of science. Rather, we mention them to show why, in the early 1920s, it became increasingly evident that a new, more comprehensive

**FIGURE 28–1** Erwin Schrödinger with Lise Meitner (see Chapter 31).

**FIGURE 28–2** Werner Heisenberg (center) on Lake Como with Wolfgang Pauli (right) and Enrico Fermi (left).

theory was needed. It was not long in coming. Less than two years after de Broglie gave us his matter–wave hypothesis, Erwin Schrödinger (1887–1961; Fig. 28–1) and Werner Heisenberg (1901–1976; Fig. 28–2) independently developed a new comprehensive theory.

## 28–1 Quantum Mechanics—A New Theory

The new theory, called **quantum mechanics**, has been extremely successful. It unifies the wave–particle duality into a single consistent theory and has successfully dealt with the spectra emitted by complex atoms, even the fine details. It explains the relative brightness of spectral lines and how atoms form molecules. It is also a much more general theory that covers all quantum phenomena from blackbody radiation to atoms and molecules. It has explained a wide range of natural phenomena and from its predictions many new practical devices have become possible. Indeed, it has been so successful that it is accepted today by nearly all physicists as the fundamental theory underlying physical processes.

Quantum mechanics deals mainly with the microscopic world of atoms and light. But this new theory, when it is applied to macroscopic phenomena, must be able to produce the old classical laws. This, the **correspondence principle** (already mentioned in Section 27–12), is satisfied fully by quantum mechanics.

*Correspondence principle*

This doesn't mean we throw away classical theories such as Newton's laws. In the everyday world, the latter are far easier to apply and they give sufficiently accurate descriptions. But when we deal with high speeds, close to the speed of light, we must use the theory of relativity; and when we deal with the tiny world of the atom, we use quantum mechanics.

Although we won't go into the detailed mathematics of quantum mechanics, we will discuss the main ideas and how they involve the wave and particle properties of matter to explain atomic structure and other applications.

## 28–2 The Wave Function and Its Interpretation; the Double-Slit Experiment

The important properties of any wave are its wavelength, frequency, and amplitude. For an electromagnetic wave, the frequency (or wavelength) determines whether the light is in the visible spectrum or not, and if so, what color it is. We also have seen that the frequency is a measure of the energy of the corresponding photon ($E = hf$). The amplitude or displacement of an electromagnetic wave at any point is the strength of the electric (or magnetic) field at that point, and is related to the intensity of the wave (the brightness of the light).

For material particles such as electrons, quantum mechanics relates the wavelength to momentum according to de Broglie's formula, $\lambda = h/p$, Eq. 27–8. But what corresponds to the *amplitude* or *displacement* of a matter wave? The amplitude of an electromagnetic wave is represented by the electric and magnetic fields, $E$ and $B$. In quantum mechanics, this role is played by the **wave function**, which is given the symbol $\Psi$ (the Greek capital letter psi, pronounced "sigh"). Thus $\Psi$ represents the wave displacement as a function of time and position, of a new kind of field which we might call a "matter" field or a matter wave.

*Wave function*

To understand how to interpret the wave function $\Psi$, we make an analogy with light using the wave–particle duality.

We saw in Chapter 11 that the intensity $I$ of any wave is proportional to the square of the amplitude. This holds true for light waves as well, as we saw in Chapter 22; that is,

$$I \propto E^2,$$

where $E$ is the electric field strength. From the *particle* point of view, the intensity of a light beam (of given frequency) is proportional to the number of photons, $N$, that pass through a given area per unit time. The more photons there are, the greater the intensity. Thus

$$I \propto E^2 \propto N.$$

This proportion can be turned around so that we have

$$N \propto E^2.$$

That is, the number of photons (striking a page of this book, say) is proportional to the square of the electric-field strength.

If the light beam is very weak, only a few photons will be involved. Indeed, it is possible to "build up" a photograph in a camera using very weak light so the effect of individual photons can be seen. If we are dealing with only one photon, the relationship above $(N \propto E^2)$ can be interpreted in a slightly different way. At any point the square of the electric field strength, $E^2$, is a measure of the *probability* that a photon will be at that location. At points where $E^2$ is large, there is a high probability the photon will be there; where $E^2$ is small, the probability is low.

We can interpret matter waves in the same way, as was first suggested by Max Born (1882–1970) in 1927. The wave function $\Psi$ may vary in magnitude from point to point in space and time. If $\Psi$ describes a collection of many electrons, then $\Psi^2$ at any point will be proportional to the number of electrons expected to be found at that point. When dealing with small numbers of electrons we can't make very exact predictions, so $\Psi^2$ takes on the character of a probability. If $\Psi$, which depends on time and position, represents a single electron (say, in an atom), then $\Psi^2$ is interpreted as follows: $\Psi^2$ *at a certain point in space and time represents the probability of finding the electron at the given position and time.*

*Probability* $\propto \Psi^2$

## Double-Slit Interference Experiment for Electrons

To understand this better, we take as a thought experiment the familiar double-slit experiment, and consider it both for light and for electrons.

Consider two slits whose size and separation are on the order of the wavelength of whatever we direct at them, either light or electrons, Fig. 28–3. We know very well what would happen in this case for light, since this is just Young's double-slit experiment (Section 24–3): an interference pattern would be seen on the screen behind. If light were replaced by electrons with wavelength comparable to the slit size, they too would produce an interference pattern (recall Fig. 27–12). In the case of light, the pattern would be visible to the eye or could be recorded on film. For electrons, a fluorescent screen could be used (it glows where an electron strikes).

**FIGURE 28–3** Parallel beam, of light or electrons, falls on two slits whose sizes are comparable to the wavelength. An interference pattern is observed.

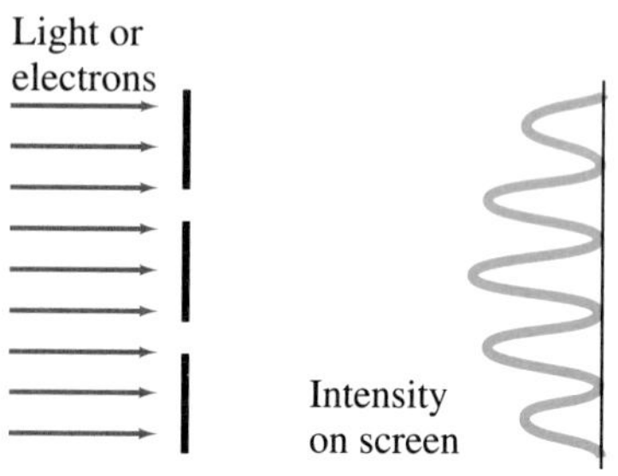

If we reduced the flow of electrons (or photons) so they passed through the slits one at a time, we would see a flash each time one struck the screen. At first, the flashes would seem random. Indeed, there is no way to predict just where any one electron would hit the screen. If we let the experiment run for a long time, and kept track of where each electron hit the screen, we would soon see a pattern emerging—the interference pattern predicted by the wave theory; see Fig. 28–4. Thus, although we could not predict where a given electron would strike the screen, we could predict probabilities. (The same can be said for photons.) The probability, as mentioned before, is proportional to $\Psi^2$. Where $\Psi^2$ is zero, we would get a minimum in the interference pattern. And where $\Psi^2$ is a maximum, we would get a peak in the interference pattern.

The interference pattern would thus occur even when electrons (or photons) passed through the slits one at a time. So the interference pattern could not arise from the interaction of one electron with another. It is as if an electron passed through both slits at the same time, interfering with itself. This is possible because an electron is not precisely a particle. It is as much a wave as it is a particle, and a wave could travel through both slits at once. But what would happen if we covered one of the slits so we knew that the electron passed through the other one, and a little later we covered the second slit so the electron had to have passed through the first? The result would be that no interference pattern would be seen. We would see, instead, two bright areas (or diffraction patterns) on the screen behind the slits. This confirms our idea that if both slits are open, the screen shows an interference pattern as if each electron passed through both slits, like a wave. Yet each electron would make a tiny spot on the screen as if it were a particle.

The main point of this discussion is this: if we treat electrons (and other particles) as if they were waves, then $\Psi$ represents the wave amplitude. If we treat them as particles, then we must treat them on a *probabilistic* basis. The square of the wave function, $\Psi^2$, gives the probability of finding a given electron at a given point. We cannot predict—or even follow—the path of a single electron precisely through space and time.

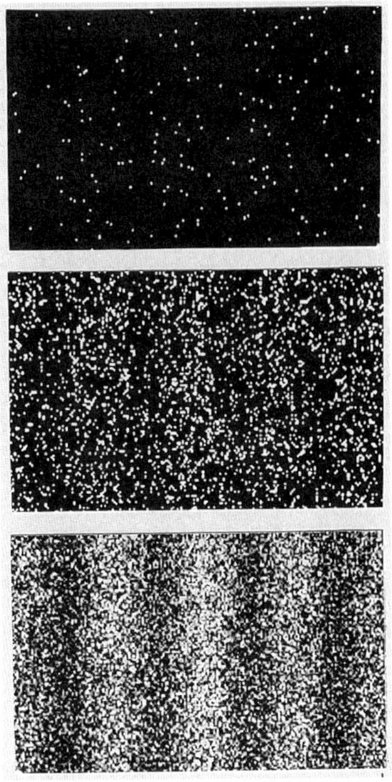

**FIGURE 28–4** Young's double-slit experiment done with electrons—note that the pattern is not evident with only a few electrons (top photo), but with more and more electrons (second and third photos), the familiar double-slit interference pattern (Chapter 24) is seen.

## 28–3 The Heisenberg Uncertainty Principle

Whenever a measurement is made, some uncertainty is always involved. For example, you cannot make an absolutely exact measurement of the length of a table. Even with a measuring stick that has markings 1 mm apart, there will be an inaccuracy of perhaps $\frac{1}{2}$ mm or so. More precise instruments will produce more precise measurements. But there is always some uncertainty involved in a measurement, no matter how good the measuring device. We expect that by using more precise instruments, the uncertainty in a measurement can be made indefinitely small.

But according to quantum mechanics, there is actually a limit to the accuracy of certain measurements. This limit is not a restriction on how well instruments can be made; rather, it is inherent in nature. It is the result of two factors: the wave–particle duality, and the unavoidable interaction between the thing observed and the observing instrument. Let us look at this in more detail.

To make a measurement on an object without disturbing it, at least a little, is not possible. Consider trying to locate a Ping-pong ball in a completely dark room. You grope about trying to find its position; and just when you touch it with your finger, it bounces away. Whenever we measure the position of an object, whether it's a ball or an electron, we always touch it with something else that gives us the information about its position. To locate a lost Ping-pong ball in a dark room, you could probe about with your hand or a stick; or you could shine a light and detect the light reflecting off the ball. When you search with your hand or a stick, you find the ball's position when you touch it. But when you touch the ball you unavoidably bump it, and give it some momentum.

Thus you won't know its *future* position. The same would be true, but to a much lesser extent, if you observe the Ping-pong ball using light. In order to "see" the ball, at least one photon must scatter from it, and the reflected photon must enter your eye or some other detector. When a photon strikes an ordinary-sized object, it does not appreciably alter the motion or position of the object. But when a photon strikes a very tiny object like an electron, it can transfer momentum to the object and thus greatly change the object's motion and position in an unpredictable way. The mere act of measuring the position of an object at one time makes our knowledge of its future position imprecise.

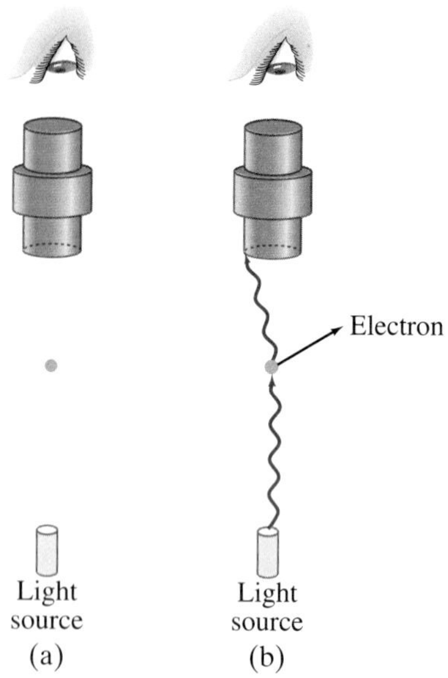


**FIGURE 28–5** Thought experiment for observing an electron with a powerful light microscope. At least one photon must scatter from the electron (transferring some momentum to it) and enter the microscope.

Now let us see where the wave–particle duality comes in. Imagine a thought experiment in which we are trying to measure the position of an object, say an electron, with photons, Fig. 28–5. (The arguments would be similar if we were using, instead, an electron microscope.) As we saw in Chapter 25, objects can be seen to an accuracy at best of about the wavelength of the radiation used. If we want an accurate position measurement, we must use a short wavelength. But a short wavelength corresponds to high frequency and large momentum ($p = h/\lambda$); and the more momentum the photons have, the more momentum they can give the object when they strike it. If we use photons of longer wavelength, and correspondingly smaller momentum, the object's motion when struck by the photons will not be affected as much. But the longer wavelength means lower resolution, so the object's position will be less accurately known. Thus the act of observing produces an uncertainty in both the *position* and the *momentum* of the electron. This is the essence of the *uncertainty principle* first enunciated by Heisenberg in 1927.

Quantitatively, we can make an approximate calculation of the magnitude of this effect. If we use light of wavelength $\lambda$, the position can be measured at best to an accuracy of about $\lambda$. That is, the uncertainty in the position measurement, $\Delta x$, is approximately

$$\Delta x \approx \lambda.$$

Suppose that the object can be detected by a single photon. The photon has a momentum $p_x = h/\lambda$. When the photon strikes our object, it will give some or all of this momentum to the object, Fig. 28–5. Therefore, the final $x$ momentum of our object will be uncertain in the amount

$$\Delta p_x \approx \frac{h}{\lambda}$$

since we can't tell beforehand how much momentum will be transferred. The product of these uncertainties is

$$(\Delta x)(\Delta p_x) \approx h.$$

The uncertainties could be worse than this, depending on the apparatus and the number of photons needed for detection. A more careful mathematical calculation shows the product of the uncertainties as, at best, about

*UNCERTAINTY PRINCIPLE ($\Delta x$ and $\Delta p$)*

$$(\Delta x)(\Delta p_x) \gtrsim \frac{h}{2\pi}. \qquad \textbf{(28–1)}$$

This is a mathematical statement of the **Heisenberg uncertainty principle**, or, as it is sometimes called, the **indeterminancy principle**. It tells us that we cannot measure both the position *and* momentum of an object precisely at the same time. The more accurately we try to measure the position, so that $\Delta x$ is small, the greater will be the uncertainty in momentum, $\Delta p_x$. If we try to measure the momentum very precisely, then the uncertainty in the position becomes large.

The uncertainty principle does not forbid individual precise measurements, however. For example, in principle we could measure the position of an object exactly. But then its momentum would be completely unknown. Thus, although we might know the position of the object exactly at one instant, we could have no idea at all where it would be a moment later. The uncertainties expressed here are inherent in nature, and reflect the best precision theoretically attainable even with the best instruments.

**CAUTION**
*Uncertainties not due to instrument deficiency, but inherent in nature (wave–particle)*

Another useful form of the uncertainty principle relates energy and time, and we examine this as follows. The object to be detected has an uncertainty in position $\Delta x \approx \lambda$. The photon that detects it travels with speed $c$, and it takes a time $\Delta t \approx \Delta x/c \approx \lambda/c$ to pass through the distance of uncertainty. Hence, the measured time when our object is at a given position is uncertain by about

$$\Delta t \approx \frac{\lambda}{c}.$$

Since the photon can transfer some or all of its energy $(= hf = hc/\lambda)$ to our object, the uncertainty in energy of our object as a result is

$$\Delta E \approx \frac{hc}{\lambda}.$$

The product of these two uncertainties is

$$(\Delta E)(\Delta t) \approx h.$$

A more careful calculation gives

$$(\Delta E)(\Delta t) \gtrsim \frac{h}{2\pi}. \qquad \textbf{(28–2)}$$

*UNCERTAINTY PRINCIPLE ($\Delta E$ and $\Delta t$)*

This form of the uncertainty principle tells us that the energy of an object can be uncertain (or can be interpreted as briefly nonconserved) by an amount $\Delta E$ for a time $\Delta t \approx h/(2\pi\,\Delta E)$.

The quantity $(h/2\pi)$ appears so often in quantum mechanics that for convenience it is given the symbol $\hbar$ ("h-bar"). That is,

$$\hbar = \frac{h}{2\pi} = \frac{6.626 \times 10^{-34}\,\mathrm{J\cdot s}}{2\pi} = 1.055 \times 10^{-34}\,\mathrm{J\cdot s}.$$

By using this notation, Eqs. 28–1 and 28–2 for the uncertainty principle can be written

$$(\Delta x)(\Delta p_x) \gtrsim \hbar \qquad \text{and} \qquad (\Delta E)(\Delta t) \gtrsim \hbar.$$

We have been discussing the position and velocity of an electron as if it were a particle. But it isn't simply a particle. Indeed, we have the uncertainty principle because an electron—and matter in general—has wave as well as particle properties. What the uncertainty principle really tells us is that if we insist on thinking of the electron as a particle, then there are certain limitations on this simplified view—namely, that the position and velocity cannot both be known precisely at the same time; and even that the electron does not *have* a precise position and momentum at the same time (because it is not simply a particle). Similarly, the energy can be uncertain in the amount $\Delta E$ for a time $\Delta t \approx \hbar/\Delta E$.

Because Planck's constant, $h$, is so small, the uncertainties expressed in the uncertainty principle are usually negligible on the macroscopic level. But at the level of atomic sizes, the uncertainties are significant. Because we consider ordinary objects to be made up of atoms containing nuclei and electrons, the uncertainty principle is relevant to our understanding of all of nature. The uncertainty principle expresses, perhaps most clearly, the probabilistic nature of quantum mechanics. It thus is often used as a basis for philosophic discussion.

**EXAMPLE 28–1 Position uncertainty of electron.** An electron moves in a straight line with a constant speed $v = 1.10 \times 10^6\,\text{m/s}$ which has been measured to a precision of 0.10%. What is the maximum precision with which its position could be simultaneously measured?

**APPROACH** The momentum is $p = mv$, and the uncertainty in $p$ is $\Delta p = 0.0010p$. The uncertainty principle (Eq. 28–1) gives us the lowest $\Delta x$ using the equals sign.

**SOLUTION** The momentum of the electron is

$$p = mv = \left(9.11 \times 10^{-31}\,\text{kg}\right)\cdot\left(1.10 \times 10^{6}\,\text{m/s}\right) = 1.00 \times 10^{-24}\,\text{kg}\cdot\text{m/s}.$$

The uncertainty in the momentum is 0.10% of this, or $\Delta p = 1.0 \times 10^{-27}\,\text{kg}\cdot\text{m/s}$. From the uncertainty principle, the best simultaneous position measurement will have an uncertainty of

$$\Delta x \approx \frac{\hbar}{\Delta p} = \frac{1.06 \times 10^{-34}\,\text{J}\cdot\text{s}}{1.0 \times 10^{-27}\,\text{kg}\cdot\text{m/s}} = 1.1 \times 10^{-7}\,\text{m},$$

or 110 nm.

**NOTE** This is about 1000 times the diameter of an atom.

**EXERCISE A** An electron's position is measured with an accuracy of $0.50 \times 10^{-10}\,\text{m}$. Find the minimum uncertainty in its momentum and velocity.

**EXAMPLE 28–2 Position uncertainty of a baseball.** What is the uncertainty in position, imposed by the uncertainty principle, on a 150-g baseball thrown at $(93 \pm 2)\,\text{mph} = (42 \pm 1)\,\text{m/s}$?

**APPROACH** The uncertainty in the speed is $\Delta v = 1\,\text{m/s}$. We multiply $\Delta v$ by $m$ to get $\Delta p$ and then use the uncertainty principle, solving for $\Delta x$.

**SOLUTION** The uncertainty in the momentum is

$$\Delta p = m\,\Delta v = (0.150\,\text{kg})(1\,\text{m/s}) = 0.15\,\text{kg}\cdot\text{m/s}.$$

Hence the uncertainty in a position measurement could be as small as

$$\Delta x = \frac{\hbar}{\Delta p} = \frac{1.06 \times 10^{-34}\,\text{J}\cdot\text{s}}{0.15\,\text{kg}\cdot\text{m/s}} = 7 \times 10^{-34}\,\text{m}.$$

**NOTE** This distance is far smaller than any we could imagine observing or measuring. It is trillions of trillions of times smaller than an atom. Indeed, the uncertainty principle sets no relevant limit on measurement for macroscopic objects.

## * 28–4 Philosophic Implications; Probability versus Determinism

The classical Newtonian view of the world is a deterministic one (see Section 5–9). One of its basic ideas is that once the position and velocity of an object are known at a particular time, its future position can be predicted if the forces on it are known. For example, if a stone is thrown a number of times with the same initial velocity and angle, and the forces on it remain the same, the path of the projectile will always be the same. If the forces are known (gravity and air resistance, if any), the stone's path can be precisely predicted. This mechanistic view implies that the future unfolding of the universe, assumed to be made up of particulate bodies, is completely determined.

This classical deterministic view of the physical world has been radically altered by quantum mechanics. As we saw in the analysis of the double-slit experiment (Section 28–2), electrons all released in the same way will not all end up in the same place. According to quantum mechanics, certain probabilities exist that an electron will arrive at different points. This is very different from the classical view, in which the path of a particle is precisely predictable from the initial position and velocity and the forces exerted on it. According to quantum mechanics, the position and velocity of an object cannot even be known accurately at the same time. This is expressed in the uncertainty principle, and arises because basic entities, such as electrons, are not considered simply as particles: they have wave properties as well. Quantum mechanics allows us to calculate only the probability[†] that, say, an electron (when thought of as a particle) will be observed at various places. Quantum mechanics says there is some inherent unpredictability in nature. This is very different from the deterministic view of classical mechanics.

Because matter is considered to be made up of atoms, even ordinary-sized objects are expected to be governed by probability, rather than by strict determinism. For example, quantum mechanics predicts a finite (but negligibly small) probability that when you throw a stone, its path might suddenly curve upward instead of following the downward-curved parabola of normal projectile motion. Quantum mechanics predicts with extremely high probability that ordinary objects will behave just as the classical laws of physics predict. But these predictions are considered of very high probability, not absolute certainties. The reason that macroscopic objects behave in accordance with classical laws with such high probability is due to the large number of molecules involved: when large numbers of objects are present in a statistical situation, deviations from the average (or most probable) approach zero. It is the average configuration of vast numbers of molecules that follows the so-called fixed laws of classical physics with such high probability, and gives rise to an apparent "determinism." Deviations from classical laws are observed when small numbers of molecules are dealt with. We can say, then, that although there are no precise deterministic laws in quantum mechanics, there are statistical laws based on probability.

It is important to note that there is a difference between the probability imposed by quantum mechanics and that used in the nineteenth century to understand thermodynamics and the behavior of gases in terms of molecules (Chapters 13 and 15). In thermodynamics, probability is used because there are far too many particles to keep track of. But the molecules are still assumed to move and interact in a deterministic way following Newton's laws. Probability in quantum mechanics is quite different; it is seen as *inherent* in nature, and not as a limitation on our abilities to calculate or to measure.

The view presented here is the generally accepted one and is called the **Copenhagen interpretation** of quantum mechanics in honor of Niels Bohr's home, since it was largely developed there through discussions between Bohr and other prominent physicists.

*Copenhagen interpretation*

Because electrons are not simply particles, they cannot be thought of as following particular paths in space and time. This suggests that a description of matter in space and time may not be completely correct. This deep and far-reaching conclusion has been a lively topic of discussion among philosophers. Perhaps the most important and influential philosopher of quantum mechanics was Bohr. He argued that a space–time description of actual atoms and electrons is not possible. Yet a description of experiments on atoms or electrons must be given in terms of space and time and other concepts familiar to ordinary experience, such as waves and particles. We must not let our *descriptions* of experiments lead us into believing that atoms or electrons themselves actually move in space and time as classical particles.

[†]Note that these probabilities can be calculated precisely, just like exact predictions of probabilities at dice or playing cards, but unlike predictions of probabilities at sporting events or for natural or man-made disasters, which are only estimates.

## 28–5 Quantum-Mechanical View of Atoms

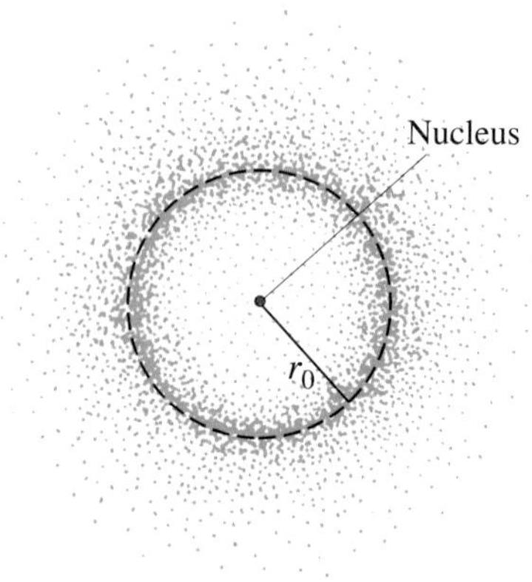


**FIGURE 28–6** Electron cloud or "probability distribution" for the ground state of the hydrogen atom. The dashed circle represents the Bohr radius. (This is a 2-dimensional slice through the atom that includes the nucleus.)

At the beginning of this Chapter, we discussed the limitations of the Bohr theory of atomic structure. Now we examine the quantum-mechanical theory of atoms, which is far more complete than the old Bohr theory. Although the Bohr model has been discarded as an accurate description of nature, nonetheless, quantum mechanics reaffirms certain aspects of the older theory, such as that electrons in an atom exist only in discrete states of definite energy, and that a photon of light is emitted (or absorbed) when an electron makes a transition from one state to another. But quantum mechanics is a much deeper theory, and has provided us with a very different view of the atom. According to quantum mechanics, electrons do not exist in well-defined circular orbits as in the Bohr theory. Rather, the electron (because of its wave nature) might be thought of as spread out in space as a "cloud." The size and shape of the electron cloud can be calculated for a given state of an atom. For the ground state in the hydrogen atom, the electron cloud is spherically symmetric, as shown in Fig. 28–6. The electron cloud roughly indicates the "size" of an atom. But just as a cloud may not have a distinct border, atoms do not have a precise boundary or a well-defined size. Not all electron clouds have a spherical shape, as we shall see later in this Chapter.

*Probability distributions*

The electron cloud can be interpreted from either the particle or the wave viewpoint. Remember that by a particle we mean something that is localized in space—it has a definite position at any given instant. By contrast, a wave is spread out in space. The electron cloud, spread out in space as in Fig. 28–6, is a result of the wave nature of electrons. Electron clouds can also be interpreted as **probability distributions** for a particle. If you were to measure the position of an electron in a hydrogen atom 500 different times, the majority of the results would show the electron at points where the probability is high (dark area in Fig. 28–6). Only occasionally would the electron be found where the probability is low.

## 28–6 Quantum Mechanics of the Hydrogen Atom; Quantum Numbers

We now look more closely at what quantum mechanics tells us about the hydrogen atom. Much of what we say here also applies to more complex atoms, which are discussed in the next Section.

Quantum mechanics is a much more sophisticated and successful theory than Bohr's. Yet in a few details they agree. Quantum mechanics predicts the same basic energy levels (Fig. 27–27) for the hydrogen atom as does the Bohr theory. That is,

$$E_n = -\frac{13.6\text{ eV}}{n^2}, \qquad n = 1, 2, 3, \cdots,$$

where $n$ is an integer. In the simple Bohr theory, there was only one quantum number, $n$. In quantum mechanics, it turns out that four different quantum numbers are needed to specify each state in the atom:

*Principal quantum number, n*

**(1)** The *quantum number, n*, from the Bohr theory is found also in quantum mechanics and is called the **principal quantum number**. It can have any integer value from 1 to $\infty$. The total energy of a state in the hydrogen atom depends on $n$, as we saw above.

*Orbital quantum number, l*
$0 \leq l \leq n - 1$

**(2)** The **orbital quantum number**, $l$, is related to the magnitude of the angular momentum of the electron; $l$ can take on integer values from 0 to $(n - 1)$. For the ground state, $n = 1$, $l$ can only be zero.† For $n = 3$, $l$ can be 0, 1, or 2.

†Contrast this with the Bohr theory, which assigned $l = 1$ to the ground state (Eq. 27–11).

The actual magnitude of the angular momentum $L$ is related to the quantum number $l$ by

$$L = \sqrt{l(l+1)}\,\hbar \tag{28–3}$$

(where again $\hbar = h/2\pi$). The value of $l$ has almost no effect on the total energy in the hydrogen atom; only $n$ does to any appreciable extent (but see *fine structure* below). In atoms with two or more electrons, the energy does depend on $l$ as well as $n$, as we shall see.

**(3)** The **magnetic quantum number**, $m_l$, is related to the *direction* of the electron's angular momentum, and it can take on integer values ranging from $-l$ to $+l$. For example, if $l = 2$, then $m_l$ can be $-2, -1, 0, +1$, or $+2$. Since angular momentum is a vector, it is not surprising that both its magnitude and its direction would be quantized. For $l = 2$, the five different directions allowed can be represented by the diagram of Fig. 28–7. This limitation on the direction of $\vec{\mathbf{L}}$ is often called **space quantization**. In quantum mechanics, the direction of the angular momentum is usually specified by giving its component along the $z$ axis (this choice is arbitrary). Then $L_z$ is related to $m_l$ by the equation

$$L_z = m_l \hbar.$$

The values of $L_x$ and $L_y$ are not definite, however. The name for $m_l$ derives not from theory (which relates it to $L_z$), but from experiment. It was found that when a gas-discharge tube was placed in a magnetic field, the spectral lines were split into several very closely spaced lines. This splitting, known as the **Zeeman effect**, implies that the energy levels must be split (Fig. 28–8), and thus that the energy of a state depends not only on $n$ but also on $m_l$ when a magnetic field is applied—hence the name "magnetic quantum number."

*Magnetic quantum number,* $m_l$
$-l \le m_l < l$

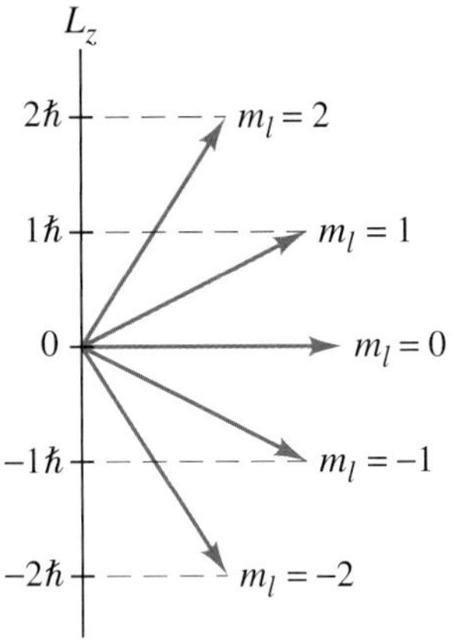


**FIGURE 28–7** Quantization of angular momentum direction for $l = 2$.

**(4)** Finally, there is the **spin quantum number**, $m_s$, which for an electron can have only two values, $m_s = +\frac{1}{2}$ and $m_s = -\frac{1}{2}$. The existence of this quantum number did not come out of Schrödinger's original theory, as did $n$, $l$, and $m_l$. Instead, a subsequent modification by P. A. M. Dirac (1902–1984) explained its presence as a relativistic effect. The first hint that $m_s$ was needed, however, came from experiment. A careful study of the spectral lines of hydrogen showed that each actually consisted of two (or more) very closely spaced lines even in the absence of an external magnetic field. It was at first hypothesized that this tiny splitting of energy levels, called **fine structure**, was due to angular momentum associated with a spinning of the electron. That is, the electron might spin on its axis as well as orbit the nucleus, just as the Earth spins on its axis as it orbits the Sun. The interaction between the tiny current of the spinning electron could then interact with the magnetic field due to the orbiting charge and cause the small observed splitting of energy levels. (The energy thus depends slightly on $m_l$ and $m_s$.) Today we consider this picture of a spinning electron as not legitimate. We cannot even view an electron as a localized object, much less a spinning one. What is important is that the electron can have two different states due to some intrinsic property that behaves like an angular momentum, and we still call this property "spin." The two possible values of $m_s$ ($+\frac{1}{2}$ and $-\frac{1}{2}$) are often said to be "spin up" and "spin down," referring to the two possible directions of the spin angular momentum.

*Spin quantum number,* $m_s$
$m_s = +\frac{1}{2}$ *or* $-\frac{1}{2}$

**FIGURE 28–8** When a magnetic field is applied, an $n = 3$, $l = 2$ energy level is split into five separate levels, corresponding to the five values of $m_l$ (2, 1, 0, −1, −2). An $n = 2$, $l = 1$ level is split into three levels ($m_l = 1, 0, -1$). Transitions can occur between levels (not all transitions are shown), with photons of several slightly different frequencies being given off (the Zeeman effect).

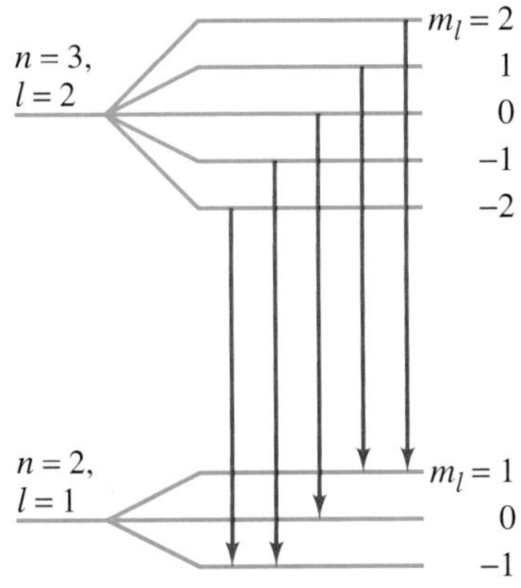


The possible values of the four quantum numbers for an electron in the hydrogen atom are summarized in Table 28–1.

**TABLE 28–1 Quantum Numbers for an Electron**

| Name | Symbol | Possible Values |
|---|---|---|
| Principal | $n$ | $1, 2, 3, \cdots, \infty.$ |
| Orbital | $l$ | For a given $n$: $l$ can be $0, 1, 2, \cdots, n-1$. |
| Magnetic | $m_l$ | For given $n$ and $l$: $m_l$ can be $l, l-1, \cdots, 0, \cdots, -l$. |
| Spin | $m_s$ | For each set of $n$, $l$, and $m_l$: $m_s$ can be $+\frac{1}{2}$ or $-\frac{1}{2}$. |

**CONCEPTUAL EXAMPLE 28–3** **Possible states for $n = 3$.** How many different states are possible for an electron whose principal quantum number is $n = 3$?

**RESPONSE** For $n = 3$, $l$ can have the values $l = 2, 1, 0$. For $l = 2$, $m_l$ can be 2, 1, 0, −1, −2, which is five different possibilities. For each of these, $m_s$ can be either up or down ($+\frac{1}{2}$ or $-\frac{1}{2}$); so for $l = 2$, there are $2 \times 5 = 10$ states. For $l = 1$, $m_l$ can be 1, 0, −1, and since $m_s$ can be $+\frac{1}{2}$ or $-\frac{1}{2}$ for each of these, we have 6 more possible states. Finally, for $l = 0$, $m_l$ can only be 0, and there are only 2 states corresponding to $m_s = +\frac{1}{2}$ and $-\frac{1}{2}$. The total number of states is $10 + 6 + 2 = 18$, as detailed in the following Table:

| $n$ | $l$ | $m_l$ | $m_s$ | $n$ | $l$ | $m_l$ | $m_s$ |
|---|---|---|---|---|---|---|---|
| 3 | 2 | 2 | $\frac{1}{2}$ | 3 | 1 | 1 | $\frac{1}{2}$ |
| 3 | 2 | 2 | $-\frac{1}{2}$ | 3 | 1 | 1 | $-\frac{1}{2}$ |
| 3 | 2 | 1 | $\frac{1}{2}$ | 3 | 1 | 0 | $\frac{1}{2}$ |
| 3 | 2 | 1 | $-\frac{1}{2}$ | 3 | 1 | 0 | $-\frac{1}{2}$ |
| 3 | 2 | 0 | $\frac{1}{2}$ | 3 | 1 | −1 | $\frac{1}{2}$ |
| 3 | 2 | 0 | $-\frac{1}{2}$ | 3 | 1 | −1 | $-\frac{1}{2}$ |
| 3 | 2 | −1 | $\frac{1}{2}$ | 3 | 0 | 0 | $\frac{1}{2}$ |
| 3 | 2 | −1 | $-\frac{1}{2}$ | 3 | 0 | 0 | $-\frac{1}{2}$ |
| 3 | 2 | −2 | $\frac{1}{2}$ | | | | |
| 3 | 2 | −2 | $-\frac{1}{2}$ | | | | |

**EXERCISE B** An electron has $n = 4$, $l = 2$. Which of the following values of $m_l$ are possible: 4, 3, 2, 1, 0, −1, −2, −3, −4?

**EXAMPLE 28–4** ***E* and *L* for $n = 3$.** Determine (*a*) the energy and (*b*) the orbital angular momentum for an electron in each of the hydrogen atom states of Example 28–3.

**APPROACH** (*a*) The energy of a state depends only on $n$, except for the very small corrections mentioned above, which we will ignore. Energy is calculated as in the Bohr theory, $E_n = -13.6\,\text{eV}/n^2$. For angular momentum we use Eq. 28–3.

**SOLUTION** Since $n = 3$ for all these states, they all have the same energy,

$$E_3 = -\frac{13.6\,\text{eV}}{(3)^2} = -1.51\,\text{eV}.$$

(*b*) For $l = 0$, Eq. 28–3 gives

$$L = \sqrt{l(l+1)}\,\hbar = 0.$$

For $l = 1$,

$$L = \sqrt{1(1+1)}\,\hbar = \sqrt{2}\,\hbar = 1.49 \times 10^{-34}\,\text{J}\cdot\text{s}.$$

For $l = 2$, $L = \sqrt{2(2+1)}\,\hbar = \sqrt{6}\,\hbar$.

**NOTE** Atomic angular momenta are generally given as a multiple of $\hbar$ ($\sqrt{2}\,\hbar$ or $\sqrt{6}\,\hbar$ in this case), rather than in SI units.

**EXERCISE C** What are the energy and angular momentum of the electron in a hydrogen atom with $n = 6$, $l = 4$?

Although $l$ and $m_l$ do not significantly affect the energy levels in hydrogen, they do affect the electron probability distribution in space. For $n = 1$, $l$ and $m_l$ can only be zero and the electron distribution is as shown in Fig. 28–6.

For $n = 2$, $l$ can be 0 or 1. The distribution for $n = 2$, $l = 0$ is shown in Fig. 28–9a, and it is seen to differ from that for the ground state (Fig. 28–6), although it is still spherically symmetric. For $n = 2$, $l = 1$, the distributions are not spherically symmetric as shown in Figs. 28–9b (for $m_l = 0$) and 28–9c (for $m_l = +1$ or $-1$).

Although the spatial distributions of the electron can be calculated for the various states, it is difficult to measure them experimentally. Most of the experimental information about the atom has come from a careful examination of the emission spectra under various conditions.

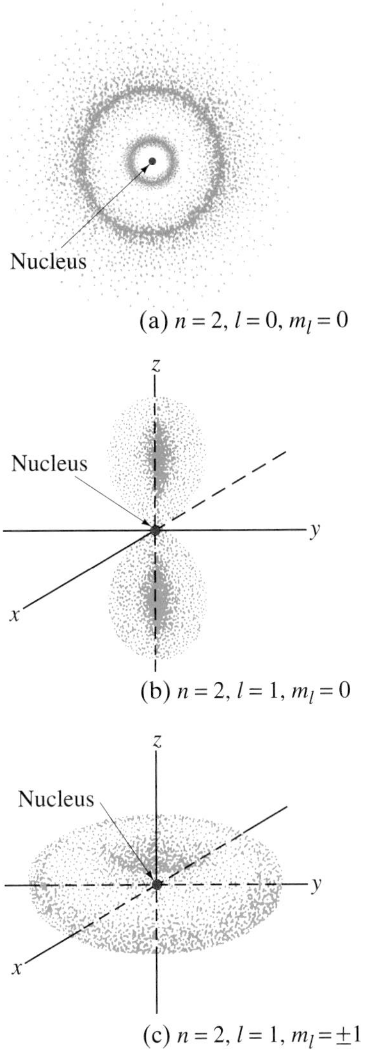


**FIGURE 28–9** Electron cloud, or probability distribution, for $n = 2$ states in hydrogen.

### * Selection Rules: Allowed and Forbidden Transitions

Another prediction of quantum mechanics is that when a photon is emitted or absorbed, transitions can occur only between states with values of $l$ that differ by exactly one unit:

$$\Delta l = \pm 1.$$

According to this **selection rule**, an electron in an $l = 2$ state can jump only to a state with $l = 1$ or $l = 3$. It cannot jump to a state with $l = 2$ or $l = 0$. A transition such as $l = 2$ to $l = 0$ is called a **forbidden transition**. Actually, such a transition is not absolutely forbidden and can occur, but only with very low probability compared to **allowed transitions**—those that satisfy the selection rule $\Delta l = \pm 1$. Since the orbital angular momentum of an H atom must change by one unit when it emits a photon, conservation of angular momentum tells us that the photon must carry off angular momentum. Indeed, experimental evidence of many sorts shows that the photon can be assigned a spin angular momentum of $1\hbar$.

## 28–7 Complex Atoms; the Exclusion Principle

We have discussed the hydrogen atom in detail because it is the simplest to deal with. Now we briefly discuss more complex atoms, those that contain more than one electron, and whose energy levels can be determined experimentally from an analysis of the emission spectra. The energy levels are *not* the same as in the H atom, since the electrons interact with each other as well as with the nucleus. Each electron in a complex atom still occupies a particular state characterized by the same quantum numbers $n$, $l$, $m_l$, and $m_s$. For atoms with more than one electron, the energy levels depend on both $n$ and $l$.

The number of electrons in a neutral atom is called its **atomic number**, $Z$; $Z$ is also the number of positive charges (protons) in the nucleus, and determines what kind of atom it is. That is, $Z$ determines most of the properties that distinguish one atom from another.

Quantum mechanics in the years after 1925 proved successful also in dealing with complex atoms. The mathematics becomes very difficult, however, since in multi-electron atoms, each electron is not only attracted to the nucleus but is repelled by the other electrons.

To understand the possible arrangements of electrons in an atom, a new principle was needed. It was introduced by Wolfgang Pauli (1900–1958; Fig. 28–2) and is called the **Pauli exclusion principle**. It states:

*Pauli exclusion principle*

**No two electrons in an atom can occupy the same quantum state.**

Thus, no two electrons in an atom can have exactly the same set of the quantum numbers $n$, $l$, $m_l$, and $m_s$. The Pauli exclusion principle† forms the basis not only for understanding complex atoms, but also for understanding molecules and bonding, and other phenomena as well.

†The exclusion principle applies to identical particles whose spin quantum number is a half-integer ($\frac{1}{2}$, $\frac{3}{2}$, and so on), including electrons, protons, and neutrons; such particles are called **fermions** (after Enrico Fermi who derived a statistical theory describing them). The exclusion principle does not apply to particles with integer spin (0, 1, 2, and so on), such as the photon and $\pi$ meson, all of which are referred to as **bosons** (after Satyendranath Bose, who derived a statistical theory for them).

**Helium, $Z = 2$**

| $n$ | $l$ | $m_l$ | $m_s$ |
|---|---|---|---|
| 1 | 0 | 0 | $\frac{1}{2}$ |
| 1 | 0 | 0 | $-\frac{1}{2}$ |

**Lithium, $Z = 3$**

| $n$ | $l$ | $m_l$ | $m_s$ |
|---|---|---|---|
| 1 | 0 | 0 | $\frac{1}{2}$ |
| 1 | 0 | 0 | $-\frac{1}{2}$ |
| 2 | 0 | 0 | $\frac{1}{2}$ |

**Sodium, $Z = 11$**

| $n$ | $l$ | $m_l$ | $m_s$ |
|---|---|---|---|
| 1 | 0 | 0 | $\frac{1}{2}$ |
| 1 | 0 | 0 | $-\frac{1}{2}$ |
| 2 | 0 | 0 | $\frac{1}{2}$ |
| 2 | 0 | 0 | $-\frac{1}{2}$ |
| 2 | 1 | 1 | $\frac{1}{2}$ |
| 2 | 1 | 1 | $-\frac{1}{2}$ |
| 2 | 1 | 0 | $\frac{1}{2}$ |
| 2 | 1 | 0 | $-\frac{1}{2}$ |
| 2 | 1 | $-1$ | $\frac{1}{2}$ |
| 2 | 1 | $-1$ | $-\frac{1}{2}$ |
| 3 | 0 | 0 | $\frac{1}{2}$ |

Let us now look at the structure of some of the simpler atoms when they are in the ground state. After hydrogen, the next simplest atom is *helium* with two electrons. Both electrons can have $n = 1$, since one can have spin up $\left(m_s = +\frac{1}{2}\right)$ and the other spin down $\left(m_s = -\frac{1}{2}\right)$, thus satisfying the exclusion principle. Since $n = 1$, then $l$ and $m_l$ must be zero (Table 28–1). Thus the two electrons have the quantum numbers indicated in the Table in the margin.

Lithium has three electrons, two of which can have $n = 1$. But the third cannot have $n = 1$ without violating the exclusion principle. Hence the third electron must have $n = 2$. It happens that the $n = 2$, $l = 0$ level has a lower energy than $n = 2$, $l = 1$, so the electrons in the ground state have the quantum numbers indicated in the Table in the margin. The quantum numbers of the third electron could also be, say, $(n, l, m_l, m_s) = \left(3, 1, -1, \frac{1}{2}\right)$. But the atom in this case would be in an excited state since it would have greater energy. It would not be long before it jumped to the ground state with the emission of a photon. At room temperature, unless extra energy is supplied (as in a discharge tube), the vast majority of atoms are in the ground state.

We can continue in this way to describe the quantum numbers of each electron in the ground state of larger and larger atoms. The quantum numbers for sodium, with its eleven electrons, are shown in the Table in the margin.

Figure 28–10 shows a simple energy level diagram where occupied states are shown as up or down arrows $\left(m_s = +\frac{1}{2} \text{ or } -\frac{1}{2}\right)$, and possible empty states are shown as a small circle.

The ground-state configuration for all atoms is given in the **periodic table**, which is displayed inside the back cover of this book, and discussed in the next Section.

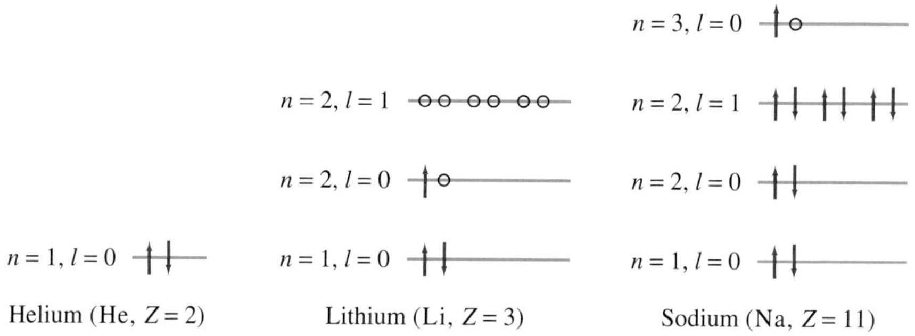


**FIGURE 28–10** Energy level diagram showing occupied states (arrows) and unoccupied states (○) for He, Li, and Na. Note that we have shown the $n = 2$, $l = 1$ level of Li even though it is empty.

## 28–8 The Periodic Table of Elements

**TABLE 28–2 Value of $l$**

| Value of $l$ | Letter Symbol | Maximum Number of Electrons in Subshell |
|---|---|---|
| 0 | $s$ | 2 |
| 1 | $p$ | 6 |
| 2 | $d$ | 10 |
| 3 | $f$ | 14 |
| 4 | $g$ | 18 |
| 5 | $h$ | 22 |
| ⋮ | ⋮ | ⋮ |

More than a century ago, Dmitri Mendeleev (1834–1907) arranged the (then) known elements into what we now call the **periodic table** of the elements. The atoms were arranged according to increasing mass, but also so that elements with similar chemical properties would fall in the same column. Today's version is shown inside the back cover of this book. Each square contains the atomic number $Z$, the symbol for the element, and the atomic mass (in atomic mass units). Finally, the lower left corner shows the configuration of the ground state of the atom. This requires some explanation. Electrons with the same value of $n$ are referred to as being in the same **shell**. Electrons with $n = 1$ are in one shell (the K shell), those with $n = 2$ are in a second shell (the L shell), those with $n = 3$ are in the third (M) shell, and so on. Electrons with the same values of $n$ and $l$ are referred to as being in the same **subshell**. Letters are often used to specify the value of $l$ as shown in Table 28–2. That is, $l = 0$ is the $s$ subshell; $l = 1$ is the $p$ subshell; $l = 2$ is the $d$ subshell; beginning with $l = 3$, the letters follow the alphabet, $f$, $g$, $h$, $i$, and so on. (The first letters $s$, $p$, $d$, and $f$ were originally abbreviations of "sharp," "principal," "diffuse," and "fundamental," experimental terms referring to the spectra.)

The Pauli exclusion principle limits the number of electrons possible in each shell and subshell. For any value of $l$, there are $2l + 1$ possible $m_l$ values ($m_l$ can be any integer from 1 to $l$, from $-1$ to $-l$, or zero), and two possible $m_s$ values. There can be, therefore, at most $2(2l + 1)$ electrons in any $l$ subshell. For example, for $l = 2$, five $m_l$ values are possible (2, 1, 0, −1, −2), and for each of these, $m_s$ can be $+\frac{1}{2}$ or $-\frac{1}{2}$ for a total of $2(5) = 10$ states. Table 28–2 lists the maximum number of electrons that can occupy each subshell.

Since the energy levels depend almost entirely on the values of $n$ and $l$, it is customary to specify the electron configuration simply by giving the $n$ value and the appropriate letter for $l$, with the number of electrons in each subshell given as a superscript. The ground-state configuration of sodium, for example, is written as $1s^2 2s^2 2p^6 3s^1$. This is simplified in the periodic table by specifying the configuration only of the outermost electrons and any other nonfilled subshells (see Table 28–3 here, and the periodic table inside the back cover).

**TABLE 28–3 Electron Configuration of Some Elements**

| Z (Number of Electrons) | Element† | Ground State Configuration (outer electrons) |
|---|---|---|
| 1 | H | $1s^1$ |
| 2 | He | $1s^2$ |
| 3 | Li | $2s^1$ |
| 4 | Be | $2s^2$ |
| 5 | B | $2s^2 2p^1$ |
| 6 | C | $2s^2 2p^2$ |
| 7 | N | $2s^2 2p^3$ |
| 8 | O | $2s^2 2p^4$ |
| 9 | F | $2s^2 2p^5$ |
| 10 | Ne | $2s^2 2p^6$ |
| 11 | Na | $3s^1$ |
| 12 | Mg | $3s^2$ |
| 13 | Al | $3s^2 3p^1$ |
| 14 | Si | $3s^2 3p^2$ |
| 15 | P | $3s^2 3p^3$ |
| 16 | S | $3s^2 3p^4$ |
| 17 | Cl | $3s^2 3p^5$ |
| 18 | Ar | $3s^2 3p^6$ |
| 19 | K | $4s^1$ |
| 20 | Ca | $4s^2$ |
| 21 | Sc | $3d^1 4s^2$ |
| 22 | Ti | $3d^2 4s^2$ |
| 23 | V | $3d^3 4s^2$ |
| 24 | Cr | $3d^5 4s^1$ |
| 25 | Mn | $3d^5 4s^2$ |
| 26 | Fe | $3d^6 4s^2$ |

† Names of elements can be found in Appendix B.

**CONCEPTUAL EXAMPLE 28–5** **Electron configurations.** Which of the following electron configurations are possible, and which are not: (*a*) $1s^2 2s^2 2p^6 3s^3$; (*b*) $1s^2 2s^2 2p^6 3s^2 3p^5 4s^2$; (*c*) $1s^2 2s^2 2p^6 2d^1$?

**RESPONSE** (*a*) This is not allowed, because too many electrons (3) are shown in the $s$ subshell of the M ($n = 3$) shell. The $s$ subshell has $m_l = 0$, with two slots only, for "spin up" and "spin down" electrons.
(*b*) This is allowed, but it is an excited state. One of the electrons from the $3p$ subshell has jumped up to the $4s$ subshell. Since there are 19 electrons, the element is potassium.
(*c*) This is not allowed, because there is no $d$ ($l = 2$) subshell in the $n = 2$ shell (Table 28–1). The outermost electron will have to be (at least) in the $n = 3$ shell.

**EXERCISE D** Write the complete ground-state configuration for gallium, with its 31 electrons.

The grouping of atoms in the periodic table is according to increasing atomic number, $Z$. There is also a strong regularity according to chemical properties. Although this is treated in chemistry textbooks, we discuss it here briefly because it is a result of quantum mechanics. See the periodic table on the inside back cover.

All the noble gases (in column VIII of the periodic table) have completely filled shells or subshells. That is, their outermost subshell is completely full, and the electron distribution is spherically symmetric. With such full spherical symmetry, other electrons are not attracted nor are electrons readily lost (ionization energy is high). This is why the noble gases are nonreactive (more on this when we discuss molecules and bonding in Chapter 29). Column VII contains the **halogens**, which lack one electron from a filled shell. Because of the shapes of the orbits (see Section 29–1), an additional electron can be accepted from another atom, and hence these elements are quite reactive. They have a valence of −1, meaning that when an extra electron is acquired, the resulting ion has a net charge of $-1e$. Column I of the periodic table contains the **alkali metals**, all of which have a single outer $s$ electron. This electron spends most of its time outside the inner closed shells and subshells which shield it from most of the nuclear charge. Indeed, it is relatively far from the nucleus and is attracted to it by a net charge of only about $+1e$, because of the shielding effect of the other electrons. Hence this outer electron is easily removed and can spend much of its time around another atom, forming a molecule. This is why the alkali metals are highly reactive and have a valence of +1. The other columns of the periodic table can be treated similarly.

The presence of the **transition elements** in the center of the table, as well as the lanthanides (rare earths) and actinides below, is a result of incomplete inner shells. For the lowest $Z$ elements, the subshells are filled in a simple order: first $1s$, then $2s$, followed by $2p$, $3s$, and $3p$. You might expect that $3d$ ($n = 3$, $l = 2$) would be filled next, but it isn't. Instead, the $4s$ level actually has a slightly lower energy than the $3d$ (due to electrons interacting with each other), so it fills first (K and Ca). Only then does the $3d$ shell start to fill up, beginning with Sc, as can be seen in Table 28–3. (The $4s$ and $3d$ levels are close, so some elements have only one $4s$ electron, such as Cr.) Most of the chemical properties of these transition elements are governed by the relatively loosely held $4s$ electrons, and hence they usually have valences of $+1$ or $+2$. A similar effect is responsible for the *lanthanides* and *actinides*, which are shown at the bottom of the periodic table for convenience. All have very similar chemical properties, which are determined by their two outer $6s$ or $7s$ electrons, whereas the different numbers of electrons in the unfilled inner shells have little effect.

**CAUTION** *Subshells are not always filled in "order"*

## * 28–9 X-Ray Spectra and Atomic Number

The line spectra of atoms in the visible, UV, and IR regions of the EM spectrum are mainly due to transitions between states of the outer electrons. Much of the charge of the nucleus is shielded from these electrons by the negative charge on the inner electrons. But the innermost electrons in the $n = 1$ shell "see" the full charge of the nucleus. Since the energy of a level is proportional to $Z^2$ (see Eq. 27–15), for an atom with $Z = 50$, we would expect wavelengths about $50^2 = 2500$ times shorter than those found in the Lyman series of hydrogen (around 100 nm), or $10^{-2}$ to $10^{-1}$ nm. Such short wavelengths lie in the X-ray region of the spectrum.

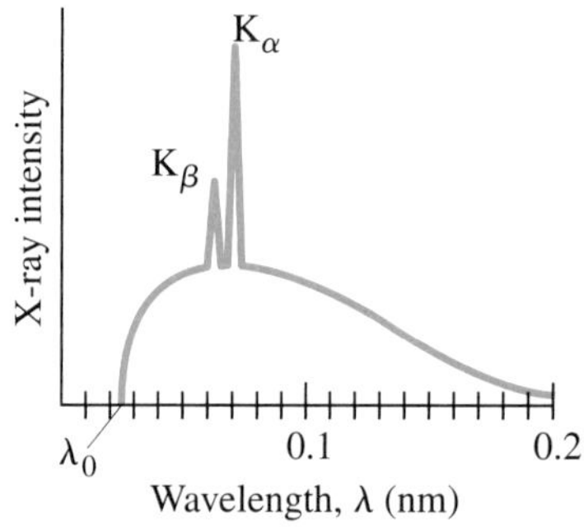


**FIGURE 28–11** Spectrum of X-rays emitted from a molybdenum target in an X-ray tube operated at 50 kV.

X-rays are produced when electrons accelerated by a high voltage strike the metal target inside the X-ray tube (Section 25–11). If we look at the spectrum of wavelengths emitted by an X-ray tube, we see that the spectrum consists of two parts: a continuous spectrum with a cutoff at some $\lambda_0$ which depends only on the voltage across the tube, and a series of peaks superimposed. A typical example is shown in Fig. 28–11. The smooth curve and the cutoff wavelength $\lambda_0$ move to the left as the voltage across the tube increases. The sharp lines or peaks (labeled $K_\alpha$ and $K_\beta$ in Fig. 28–11), however, remain at the same wavelength when the voltage is changed, although they are located at different wavelengths when different target materials are used. This observation suggests that the peaks are characteristic of the material used. Indeed, we can explain them by imagining that the electrons accelerated by the high voltage of the tube can reach sufficient energies that when they collide with the atoms of the target, they can knock out one of the very tightly held inner electrons. Then we explain these **characteristic X-rays** (the peaks in Fig. 28–11) as photons emitted when an electron in an upper state drops down to fill the vacated lower state. The K lines result from transitions *into* the K shell ($n = 1$). The $K_\alpha$ line consists of photons emitted in a transition that originates from the $n = 2$ (L) shell and drops to the $n = 1$ (K) shell, whereas the $K_\beta$ line reflects a transition from the $n = 3$ (M) shell down to the K shell. An L line is due to a transition into the L shell, and so on.

*Characteristic X-rays*

Measurement of the characteristic X-ray spectra has allowed a determination of the inner energy levels of atoms. It has also allowed the determination of $Z$ values for many atoms, since (as we have seen) the wavelength of the shortest X-rays emitted will be inversely proportional to $Z^2$. Actually, for an electron jumping from, say, the $n = 2$ to the $n = 1$ level, the wavelength is inversely proportional to $(Z - 1)^2$ because the nucleus is shielded by the one electron that still remains in the 1$s$ level. In 1914, H. G. J. Moseley (1887–1915) found that a plot of $\sqrt{1/\lambda}$ versus $Z$ produced a straight line, Fig. 28–12. The $Z$ values of a number of elements were determined by fitting them to such a **Moseley plot**. The work of Moseley put the concept of atomic number on a firm experimental basis.

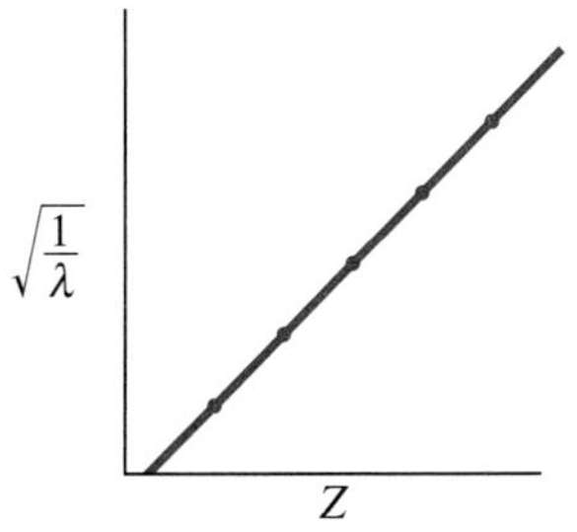


**FIGURE 28–12** Plot of $\sqrt{1/\lambda}$ vs. $Z$ for $K_\alpha$ X-ray lines.

**EXAMPLE 28–6 X-ray wavelength.** Estimate the wavelength for an $n = 2$ to $n = 1$ transition in molybdenum ($Z = 42$). What is the energy of such a photon?

**APPROACH** We use the Bohr formula, Eq. 27–16 for $1/\lambda$, with $Z^2$ replaced by $(Z - 1)^2 = (41)^2$.

**SOLUTION** Equation 27–16 gives

$$\frac{1}{\lambda} = \left(\frac{2\pi^2 e^4 m k^2}{h^3 c}\right)(Z - 1)^2\left(\frac{1}{n'^2} - \frac{1}{n^2}\right)$$

where $n = 2$ and $n' = 1$. We substitute in values:

$$\frac{1}{\lambda} = (1.097 \times 10^7\,\text{m}^{-1})(41)^2\left(\frac{1}{1} - \frac{1}{4}\right)$$
$$= 1.38 \times 10^{10}\,\text{m}^{-1}.$$

So $\lambda = 0.072\,\text{nm}$. This is close to the measured value (Fig. 28–11) of 0.071 nm. Each of these photons would have energy (in eV) of:

$$E = hf = \frac{hc}{\lambda} = \frac{(6.63 \times 10^{-34}\,\text{J}\cdot\text{s})(3.00 \times 10^8\,\text{m/s})}{(7.2 \times 10^{-11}\,\text{m})(1.60 \times 10^{-19}\,\text{J/eV})} = 17\,\text{keV}.$$

The denominator includes the conversion factor from joules to eV.

**EXAMPLE 28–7 Determining atomic number.** High-energy photons are used to bombard an unknown material. The strongest peak is found for X-rays emitted with an energy of 66 keV. Guess what the material is.

**APPROACH** The highest intensity X-rays are generally for the $K_\alpha$ line (see Fig. 28–11) which occurs when photons knock out K shell electrons (the innermost orbit, $n = 1$) and their place is taken by electrons from the L shell ($n = 2$). We use the Bohr model, and assume the electrons "see" a nuclear charge of $Z - 1$ (screened by one electron) instead of $Z = 1$.

**SOLUTION** The hydrogen transition $n = 2$ to $n = 1$ would yield about 10.2 eV (see Fig. 27–27 or Example 27–12). Energy $E$ is proportional to $Z^2$ (Eq. 27–15), or rather $(Z - 1)^2$ because the nucleus is shielded by the one electron in a 1$s$ state (see above), so we can use ratios:

$$\frac{(Z - 1)^2}{1^2} = \frac{66 \times 10^3\,\text{eV}}{10.2\,\text{eV}} = 6.5 \times 10^3,$$

so $Z - 1 = \sqrt{6500} = 81$, and $Z = 82$, which makes it lead.

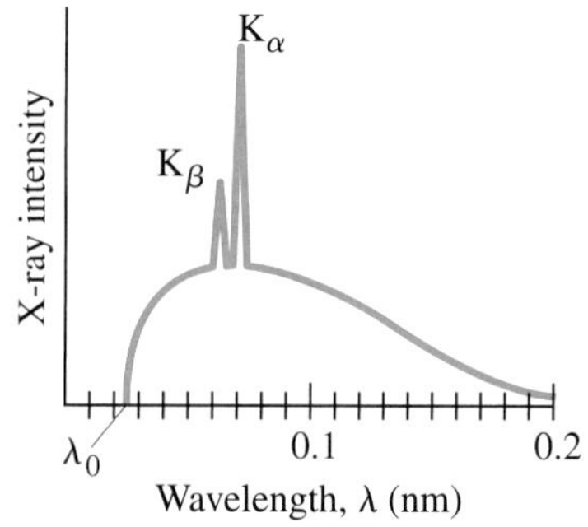


**FIGURE 28–11** (repeated) Spectrum of X-rays emitted from a molybdenum target in an X-ray tube operated at 50 kV.

**FIGURE 28–13** Bremsstrahlung photon produced by an electron decelerated by interaction with a target atom.

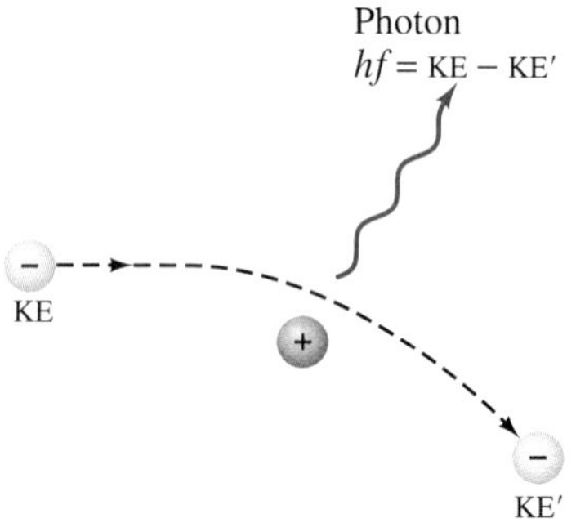


Now we briefly analyze the continuous part of an X-ray spectrum (Fig. 28–11) based on the photon theory of light. When electrons strike the target, they collide with atoms of the material and give up most of their energy as heat (about 99%, so X-ray tubes must be cooled). Electrons can also give up energy by emitting a photon of light: an electron decelerated by interaction with atoms of the target (Fig. 28–13) emits radiation because of its deceleration (Chapter 22), and in this case it is called **bremsstrahlung** (German for "braking radiation"). Because energy is conserved, the energy of the emitted photon, $hf$, must equal the loss of kinetic energy of the electron, $\Delta\text{KE} = \text{KE} - \text{KE}'$, so

$$hf = \Delta\text{KE}.$$

An electron may lose all or a part of its energy in such a collision. The continuous X-ray spectrum (Fig. 28–11) is explained as being due to such bremsstrahlung collisions in which varying amounts of energy are lost by the electrons. The shortest-wavelength X-ray (the highest frequency) must be due to an electron that gives up *all* its kinetic energy to produce one photon in a single collision. Since the initial kinetic energy of an electron is equal to the energy given it by the accelerating voltage, $V$, then $\text{KE} = eV$. In a single collision in which the electron is brought to rest ($\text{KE}' = 0$), then $\Delta\text{KE} = eV$ and

$$hf_0 = eV.$$

We set $f_0 = c/\lambda_0$ where $\lambda_0$ is the cutoff wavelength (Fig. 28–11) and find

$$\lambda_0 = \frac{hc}{eV}. \qquad \textbf{(28–4)}$$

This prediction for $\lambda_0$ corresponds precisely with that observed experimentally. This result is further evidence that X-rays are a form of electromagnetic radiation (light) and that the photon theory of light is valid.

**EXAMPLE 28–8** **Cutoff wavelength.** What is the shortest-wavelength X-ray photon emitted in an X-ray tube subjected to 50 kV?

**APPROACH** The electrons striking the target will have a KE of 50 keV. The shortest-wavelength photons are due to collisions in which all of the electron's KE is given to the photon so $\text{KE} = eV = hf_0$.

**SOLUTION** From Eq. 28–4,

$$\lambda_0 = \frac{hc}{eV} = \frac{(6.63 \times 10^{-34}\,\text{J}\cdot\text{s})(3.0 \times 10^{8}\,\text{m/s})}{(1.6 \times 10^{-19}\,\text{C})(5.0 \times 10^{4}\,\text{V})} = 2.5 \times 10^{-11}\,\text{m},$$

or 0.025 nm.

**NOTE** This result agrees well with experiment, Fig. 28–11.

## * 28–10 Fluorescence and Phosphorescence

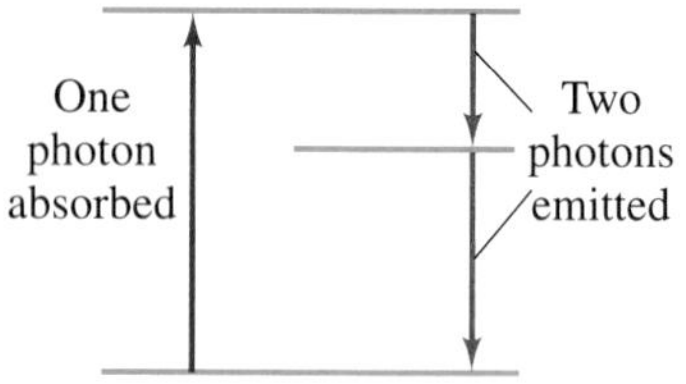


**FIGURE 28–14** Fluorescence.

PHYSICS APPLIED
*Fluorescence analysis and fluorescent lightbulbs*

When an atom is excited from one energy state to a higher one by the absorption of a photon, it may return to the lower level in a series of two (or more) jumps if there is an energy level in between (Fig. 28–14). The photons emitted will consequently have lower energy and frequency than the absorbed photon. When the absorbed photon is in the UV and the emitted photons are in the visible region of the spectrum, this phenomenon is called **fluorescence** (Fig. 28–15).

The wavelength for which fluorescence will occur depends on the energy levels of the particular atoms. Because the frequencies are different for different substances, and because many substances fluoresce readily, fluorescence is a powerful tool for identification of compounds. It is also used for assaying—determining how much of a substance is present—and for following substances along a natural metabolic pathway in plants or animals. For detection of a given compound, the stimulating light must be monochromatic, and solvents or other materials present must not fluoresce in the same region of the spectrum. Sometimes the direct observation of fluorescent light being emitted is sufficient to detect a compound. In other cases, spectrometers are used to measure the wavelengths and intensities of the emitted light.

**Fluorescent lightbulbs** work in a two-step process. The applied voltage accelerates electrons that strike atoms of the gas in the tube and cause them to be excited. When the excited atoms jump down to their normal levels, they emit UV photons which strike a fluorescent coating on the inside of the tube. The light we see is a result of this material fluorescing in response to the UV light striking it.

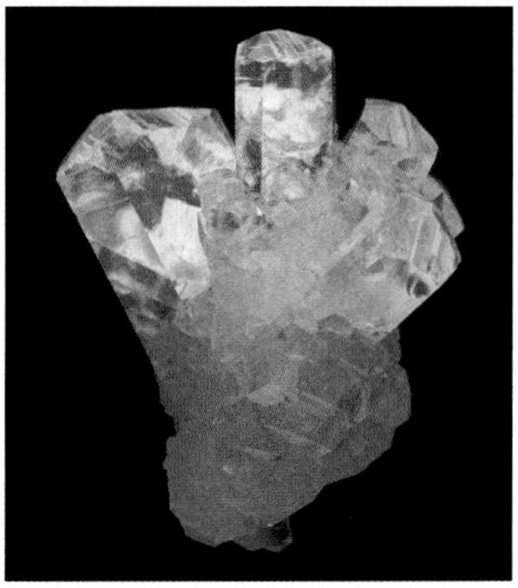

**FIGURE 28–15** When UV light illuminates these rocks, they fluoresce in the visible region of the spectrum.

Materials such as those used for luminous watch dials are said to be **phosphorescent**. When an atom is raised to a normal excited state, it drops back down within about $10^{-8}$ s. In phosphorescent substances, atoms can be excited by photon absorption to energy levels called **metastable**, which are states that last much longer—even a few seconds or longer. In a collection of such atoms, many of the atoms will descend to the lower state fairly soon, but many will remain in the excited state for over an hour. Hence light will be emitted even after long periods. When you put your watch dial close to a bright lamp, it excites many atoms to metastable states, and you can see the glow a long time after.

## * 28–11 Lasers

A **laser** is a device that can produce a very narrow intense beam of monochromatic coherent light. (By *coherent*, we mean that across any cross section of the beam, all parts have the same phase.) The emitted beam is a nearly perfect plane wave. An ordinary light source, on the other hand, emits light in all directions (so the intensity decreases rapidly with distance), and the emitted light is incoherent (the different parts of the beam are not in phase with each other). The excited atoms that emit the light in an ordinary lightbulb act independently, so each photon emitted can be considered as a short wave train, typically 30 cm long and lasting $10^{-8}$ s. These wave trains bear no phase relation to one another. Just the opposite is true of lasers.

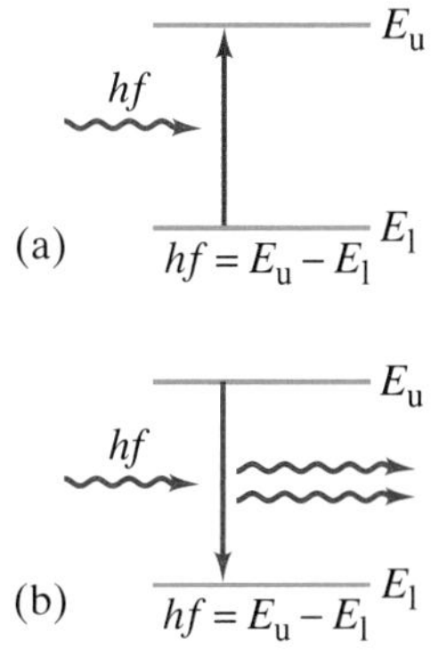


**FIGURE 28–16** (a) Absorption of a photon. (b) Stimulated emission. $E_u$ and $E_l$ refer to "upper" and "lower" energy states.

The action of a laser is based on quantum theory. We have seen that a photon can be absorbed by an atom if (and only if) its energy $hf$ corresponds to the energy difference between an occupied energy level of the atom and an available excited state, Fig. 28–16a. If the atom is already in the excited state, it may jump spontaneously (i.e., no stimulus) to the lower state with the emission of a photon. However, if a photon with this same energy strikes the excited atom, it can stimulate the atom to make the transition sooner to the lower state, Fig. 28–16b. This phenomenon is called **stimulated emission**: not only do we still have the original photon, but also a second one of the same frequency as a result of the atom's transition. These two photons are exactly *in phase*, and they are moving in the same direction. This is how coherent light is produced in a laser. Hence the name **laser**, which is an acronym for ***l**ight **a**mplification by **s**timulated **e**mission of **r**adiation*.

*Stimulated emission*

Normally, most atoms are in the lower state, so the majority of incident photons will be absorbed. To obtain the coherent light from stimulated emission, two conditions must be satisfied. First, the atoms must be excited to the higher state so that an **inverted population** is produced, one in which more atoms are in the upper state than in the lower one (Fig. 28–17). Then *emission* of photons will dominate over absorption. And second, the higher state must be a **metastable state**—a state in which the electrons remain longer than usual[†] so that the transition to the lower state occurs by stimulated emission rather than spontaneously.

**FIGURE 28–17** Two energy levels for a collection of atoms. Each dot represents the energy state of one atom. (a) A normal situation; (b) an inverted population.

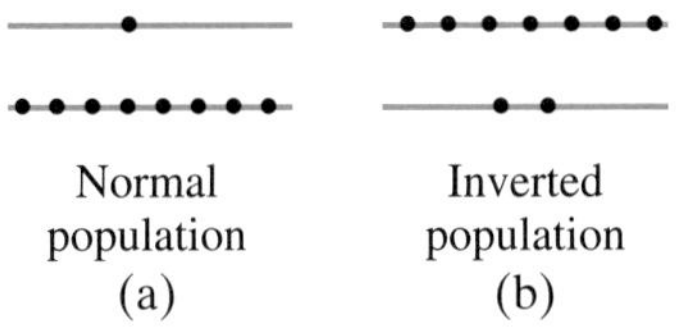


[†] An excited atom may land in such a state and can jump to a lower state only by a so-called forbidden transition (discussed in Section 28–6), which is why its lifetime is longer than normal.

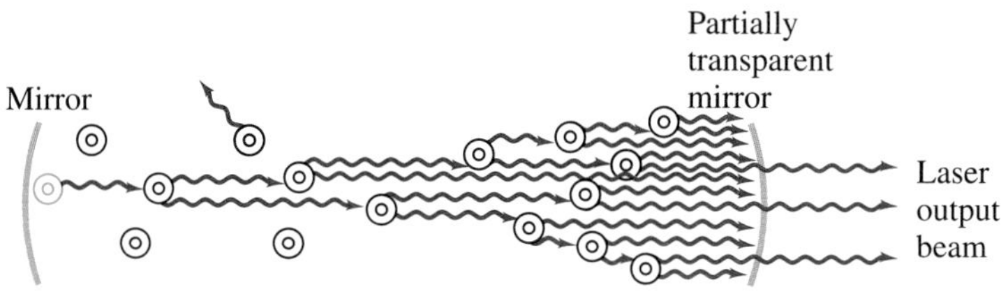


**FIGURE 28–18** Laser diagram, showing excited atoms stimulated to emit light.

Figure 28–18 is a schematic diagram of a laser: the "lasing" material is placed in a long narrow tube at the ends of which are two mirrors, one of which is partially transparent (transmitting perhaps 1 or 2%). Some of the excited atoms drop down fairly soon after being excited. One of these is the blue atom shown on the far left in Fig. 28–18. If the emitted photon strikes another atom in the excited state, it stimulates this atom to emit a photon of the *same* frequency, moving in the *same* direction, and *in phase* with it. These two photons then move on to strike other atoms causing more stimulated emission. As the process continues, the number of photons multiplies. When the photons strike the end mirrors, most are reflected back, and as they move in the opposite direction, they continue to stimulate more atoms to emit photons. As the photons move back and forth between the mirrors, a small percentage passes through the partially transparent mirror at one end. These photons make up the narrow† coherent external laser beam.

In a well-designed laser, the spreading of the beam is limited only by diffraction, so the angular spread is $\approx \lambda / D$ (see Eq. 24–3 or 25–7) where $D$ is the diameter of the end mirror. The diffraction spreading can be incredibly small. The light energy, instead of spreading out in space as it does for an ordinary light source, is directed in a pencil-thin beam.

## * Creating an Inverted Population

*Ruby laser*

The excitation of the atoms in a laser can be done in several ways to produce the necessary inverted population. In a ruby laser, the lasing material is a ruby rod consisting of $Al_2O_3$ with a small percentage of aluminum (Al) atoms replaced by chromium (Cr) atoms. The Cr atoms are the ones involved in lasing. In a process called **optical pumping**, the atoms are excited by strong flashes of light of wavelength 550 nm, which corresponds to a photon energy of 2.2 eV. As shown in Fig. 28–19, the atoms are excited from state $E_0$ to state $E_2$. The atoms quickly decay either back to $E_0$ or to the intermediate state $E_1$, which is metastable with a lifetime of about $3 \times 10^{-3}$ s (compared to $10^{-8}$ s for ordinary levels). With strong pumping action, more atoms can be found in the $E_1$ state than are in the $E_0$ state. Thus we have the inverted population needed for lasing. As soon as a few atoms in the $E_1$ state jump down to $E_0$, they emit photons that produce stimulated emission of the other atoms, and the lasing action begins. A ruby laser thus emits a beam whose photons have energy 1.8 eV and a wavelength of 694.3 nm (or "ruby-red" light).

†Inside the tube, some spontaneously emitted photons will be emitted at an angle to the axis, and these will merely go out the side of the tube and not affect the narrowness of the main beam.

**FIGURE 28–19** Energy levels of chromium in a ruby crystal. Photons of energy 2.2 eV "pump" atoms from $E_0$ to $E_2$, which then decay to metastable state $E_1$. Lasing action occurs by stimulated emission of photons in transition from $E_1$ to $E_0$.

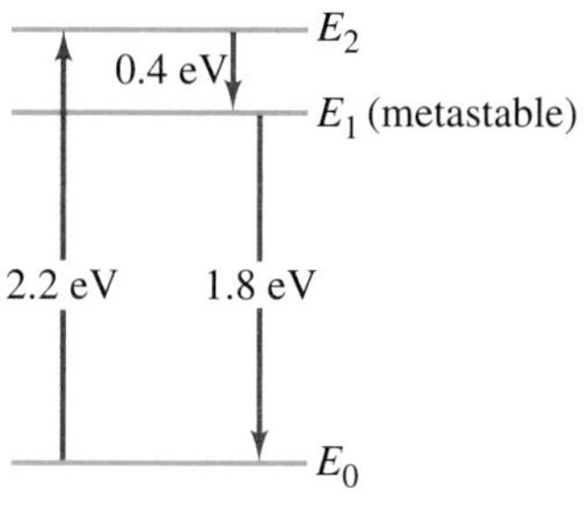

In a helium–neon (He–Ne) laser, the lasing material is a gas, a mixture of about 85% He and 15% Ne. The atoms are excited by applying a high voltage to the tube so that an electric discharge takes place within the gas. In the process, some of the He atoms are raised to the metastable state $E_1$ shown in Fig. 28–20, which corresponds to a jump of 20.61 eV, almost exactly equal to an excited state in neon, 20.66 eV. The He atoms do not quickly return to the ground state by spontaneous emission, but instead often give their excess energy to a Ne atom when they collide—see Fig. 28–20. In such a collision, the He drops to the ground state and the Ne atom is excited to the state $E_3'$ (the prime refers to neon states). The slight difference in energy (0.05 eV) is supplied by the kinetic energy of the moving atoms. In this manner, the $E_3'$ state in Ne—which is metastable—becomes more populated than the $E_2'$ level. This inverted population between $E_3'$ and $E_2'$ is what is needed for lasing.

*He–Ne laser*

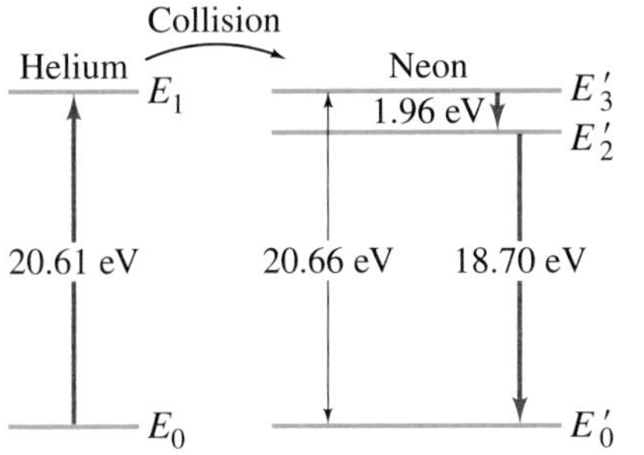


**FIGURE 28–20** Energy levels for He and Ne. He is excited in the electric discharge to the $E_1$ state. This energy is transferred to the $E_3'$ level of the Ne by collision. $E_3'$ is metastable and decays to $E_2'$ by stimulated emission.

Other types of laser include: chemical lasers, in which the energy input comes from the chemical reaction of highly reactive gases; dye lasers, whose frequency is tunable; $CO_2$ gas lasers, capable of high power output in the infrared; rare-earth solid-state lasers such as the high-power Nd:YAG laser; and the semiconductor diode laser, also called *pn* junction laser, in which the transitions occur between the bottom of the conduction band and the upper part of the valence band (Section 29–6). CD and DVD players (see below) use semiconductor lasers.

*Other lasers: chemical*
*dye*
*$CO_2$*
*semiconductor*
*(pn junction)*

The excitation of the atoms in a laser can be done continuously or in pulses. In a **pulsed laser**, the atoms are excited by periodic inputs of energy. In a **continuous laser**, the energy input is continuous: as atoms are stimulated to jump down to the lower level, they are soon excited back up to the upper level so the output is a continuous laser beam. No laser is a source of energy. Energy must be put in, and the laser converts a part of it into an intense narrow beam output.

**CAUTION**
*Laser* not *an energy source*

## * Applications

The unique feature of light from a laser, that it is a coherent narrow beam, has found many applications. Lasers are a useful surgical tool. The narrow intense beam can be used to destroy tissue in a localized area, or to break up gallstones and kidney stones. Because of the heat produced, a laser beam can be used to "weld" broken tissue, such as a detached retina. The laser beam can be carried by an optical fiber (Section 23–6) to the surgical point, sometimes as an additional fiber-optic path on an endoscope, Fig. 28–21 (see also Section 23–6). An example is the removal of plaque clogging human arteries. Tiny organelles within a living cell have been destroyed using lasers by researchers studying how the absence of that organelle affects the behavior of the cell. Laser beams are used to destroy cancerous and precancerous cells; and the heat seals off capillaries and lymph vessels, thus "cauterizing" the wound to prevent spread of the disease.

**PHYSICS APPLIED**
*Medical and other uses of lasers*

**FIGURE 28–21** Laser being used in eye surgery.

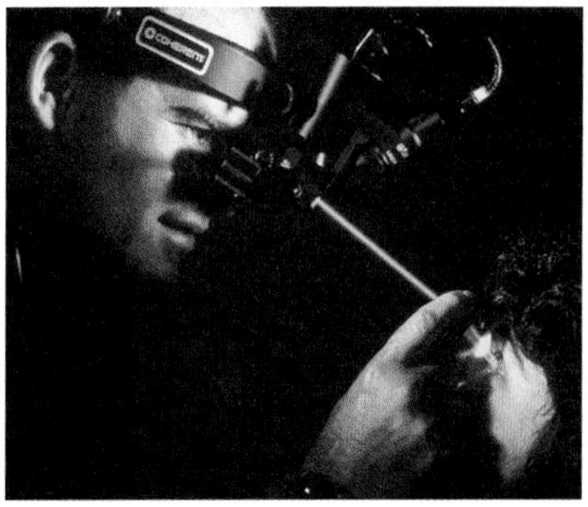

The intense heat produced in a small area by a laser beam is used for welding and machining metals and for drilling tiny holes in hard materials. Because a laser beam is coherent, monochromatic, narrow, and essentially parallel, lenses can be used to focus the light into even smaller areas. The precise straightness of a laser beam is also useful to surveyors for lining up equipment accurately, especially in inaccessible places.

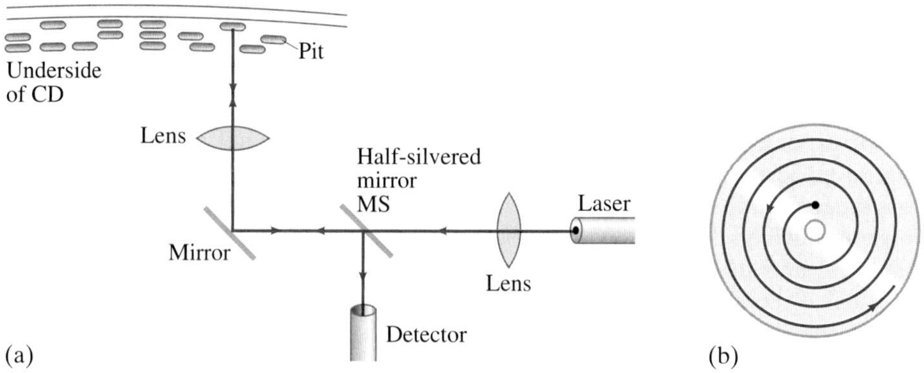


**FIGURE 28–22** (a) Reading a CD (or DVD). The fine beam of a laser, focused even more finely with lenses, is directed at the undersurface of a rotating compact disk. The beam is reflected back from the areas between pits but reflects much less from pits. The reflected light is detected as shown, reflected by a half-reflecting mirror MS. The strong and weak reflections correspond to the 0s and 1s of the binary code representing the audio or video signal. (b) A laser follows the CD track which starts near the center and spirals outward.

PHYSICS APPLIED
*DVD and CD players, bar codes*

In everyday life, lasers are used as bar-code readers (at store checkout stands) and in compact disc (CD) and digital video disc (DVD) players. The laser beam reflects off the stripes and spaces of a bar code, and off the tiny pits of a CD or DVD as shown in Fig. 28–22a. The recorded information on a CD or DVD is a series of pits and spaces representing 0s and 1s (or "off" and "on") of a digitized code that is decoded electronically before being sent to the audio or video system. The laser of a CD player starts reading at the inside of the disc which rotates at about 500 rpm at the start. As the disc rotates, the laser follows the spiral track (Fig. 28–22b), and as it moves outward the disc must slow down because each successive circumference ($C = 2\pi r$) is slightly longer as $r$ increases; at the outer edge, the disc is rotating about 200 rpm. A 1-hour CD has a track roughly 5 km long; the track width is about 1600 nm ($= 1.6\,\mu$m) and the distance between pits is about 800 nm. DVDs contain much more information. They are based on more recent technology and can use a thinner track ($0.7\,\mu$m) and shorter pit length (400 nm, these numbers being for a standard DVD). New versions use a "blue" laser with a shorter wavelength (405 nm) and narrower beam, allowing a narrower track ($0.3\,\mu$m) that can store much more data for high definition. DVDs can also have two layers, one below the other. When the laser focuses on the second layer, the light passes through the semitransparent surface layer. The second layer may start reading at the outer edge instead of inside. DVDs can also have a single or double layer on *both* surfaces of the disc.

## * 28–12 Holography

PHYSICS APPLIED
*Holography*

One of the most interesting applications of laser light is the production of three-dimensional images called **holograms** (see Fig. 28–23.) In an ordinary photograph, the film simply records the intensity of light reaching it at each point. When the photograph or transparency is viewed, light reflecting from it or passing through it gives us a two-dimensional picture. In holography, the images are formed by interference, without lenses. When a laser hologram is made on film, a broadened laser beam is split into two parts by a half-silvered mirror, Fig. 28–23a. One part goes directly to the film; the rest passes to the object to be photographed, from which it is reflected to the film. Light from every point on the object reaches each point on the film, and the interference of the two beams allows the film to record both the intensity and relative phase of the light at each point. It is crucial that the light be coherent—that is, in phase at all points—which is why a laser is used. After the film is developed, it is placed

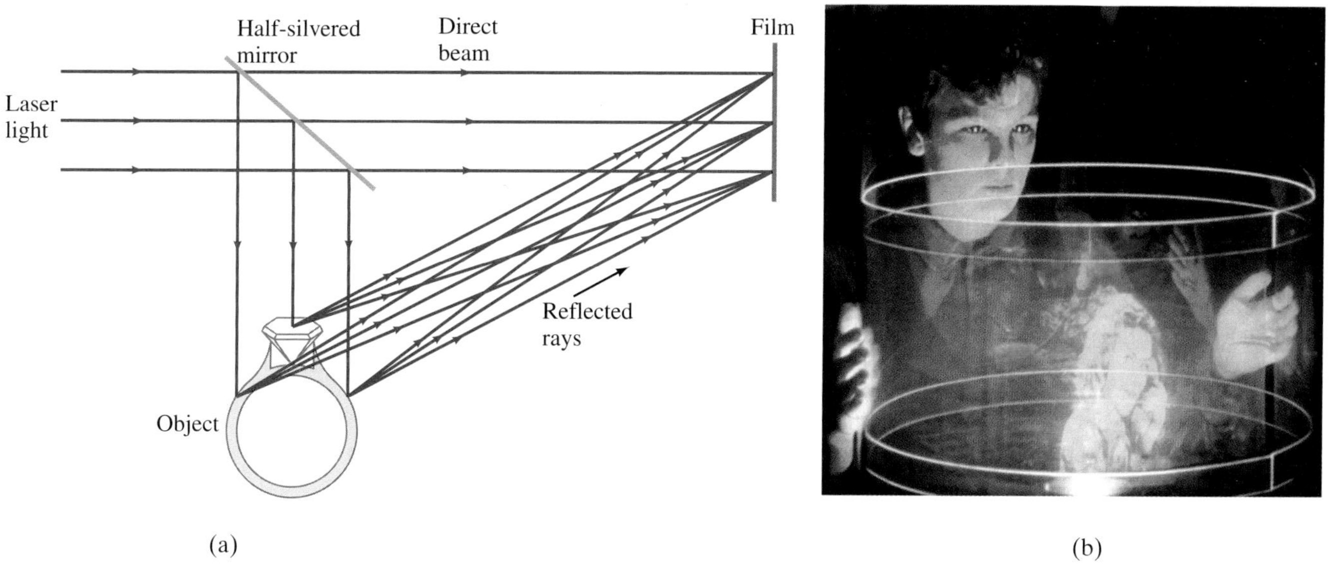


**FIGURE 28–23** (a) Making a hologram. Light reflected from various points on the object interferes (at the film) with light from the direct beam. (b) A boy is looking at a hologram of two women talking on telephones.

again in a laser beam and a three-dimensional image of the object is created. You can walk around such an image and see it from different sides as if it were the original object (Fig. 28–23b). Yet, if you try to touch it with your hand, there will be nothing material there.

*White-light holograms*

**Volume** or **white-light holograms** do not require a laser to see the image, but can be viewed with ordinary white light (preferably a nearly point source, such as the Sun or a clear bulb with a small bright filament). Such holograms must be made, however, with a laser. They are made not on thin film, but on a *thick* emulsion. The interference pattern in the film emulsion can be thought of as an array of bands or ribbons where constructive interference occurred. This array, and the reconstruction of the image, can be compared to Bragg scattering of X-rays from the atoms in a crystal (see Section 25–11). White light can reconstruct the image because the Bragg condition ($m\lambda = 2d\sin\theta$) selects out the appropriate single wavelength. If the hologram is originally produced by lasers emitting the three additive primary colors (red, green, and blue), the three-dimensional image can be seen in full color when viewed with white light.

## Summary

In 1925, Schrödinger and Heisenberg separately worked out a new theory, **quantum mechanics**, which is now considered to be the basic theory at the atomic level. It is a statistical theory rather than a deterministic one.

An important aspect of quantum mechanics is the Heisenberg **uncertainty principle**. It results from the wave–particle duality and the unavoidable interaction between an observed object and the observer.

One form of the uncertainty principle states that the position $x$ and momentum $p_x$ of an object cannot both be measured precisely at the same time. The products of the uncertainties, $(\Delta x)(\Delta p_x)$, can be no less than $\hbar\,(= h/2\pi)$:

$$(\Delta p_x)(\Delta x) \gtrsim \hbar. \qquad \textbf{(28–1)}$$

Another form of the uncertainty principle states that the energy can be uncertain by an amount $\Delta E$ for a time $\Delta t$, where

$$(\Delta E)(\Delta t) \gtrsim \hbar. \qquad \textbf{(28–2)}$$

According to quantum mechanics, the state of an electron in an atom is specified by four **quantum numbers**: $n$, $l$, $m_l$, and $m_s$:

**(1)** $n$, the **principal quantum number**, can take on any integer value $(1, 2, 3, \cdots)$ and corresponds to the quantum number of the old Bohr theory;

**(2)** $l$, the **orbital quantum number**, can take on values from 0 up to $n - 1$;

**(3)** $m_l$, the **magnetic quantum number**, can take on integer values from $-l$ to $+l$;

**(4)** $m_s$, the **spin quantum number**, can be $+\frac{1}{2}$ or $-\frac{1}{2}$.

The energy levels in the hydrogen atom depend on $n$, whereas in other atoms they depend on $n$ and $l$.

When an external magnetic field is applied, the spectral lines are split (the **Zeeman effect**), indicating that the energy depends also on $m_l$ in this case.

Even in the absence of a magnetic field, precise measurements of spectral lines show a tiny splitting of the lines called **fine structure**, whose explanation is that the energy depends very slightly on $m_l$ and $m_s$.

[*Transitions between states that obey the **selection rule** $\Delta l = \pm 1$ are far more probable than other so-called "forbidden" transitions.]

The arrangement of electrons in multi-electron atoms is governed by the **Pauli exclusion principle**, which states that no two electrons can occupy the same quantum state—that is, they cannot have the same set of quantum numbers $n, l, m_l$, and $m_s$.

As a result, electrons in multi-electron atoms are grouped into **shells** (according to the value of $n$) and **subshells** (according to $l$).

Electron configurations are specified using the numerical values of $n$, and using letters for $l$: $s, p, d, f$, etc., for $l = 0, 1, 2, 3$, and so on, plus a superscript for the number of electrons in that subshell. Thus, the ground state of hydrogen is $1s^1$, whereas that for oxygen is $1s^2 2s^2 2p^4$.

The **periodic table** arranges the elements in horizontal rows according to increasing atomic number (number of electrons in the neutral atom). The shell structure gives rise to a periodicity in the properties of the elements, so that each vertical column can contain elements with similar chemical properties.

X-rays, which are a form of electromagnetic radiation of very short wavelength, are produced when high-speed electrons strike a target. The spectrum of X-rays so produced consists of two parts, a continuous spectrum produced when the electrons are decelerated by atoms of the target, and peaks representing photons emitted by atoms of the target after being excited by collision with the high-speed electrons. Measurement of these peaks allows determination of inner energy levels of atoms and determination of $Z$.

[***Fluorescence** occurs when absorbed UV photons are followed by emission of visible light, due to the special arrangement of energy levels of the material. **Phosphorescent** materials have **metastable** states (long-lived) that emit light seconds or minutes after absorption of light.]

[***Lasers** produce a narrow beam of monochromatic coherent light (light waves *in phase*). **Holograms** are images with a 3-dimensional quality, formed by interference of laser light.]

# Questions

1. Compare a matter wave $\Psi$ to (*a*) a wave on a string, (*b*) an EM wave. Discuss similarities and differences.
2. Explain why Bohr's theory of the atom is not compatible with quantum mechanics, particularly the uncertainty principle.
3. Explain why it is that the more massive an object is, the easier it becomes to predict its future position.
4. In view of the uncertainty principle, why does a baseball seem to have a well-defined position and speed whereas an electron does not?
5. Would it ever be possible to balance a very sharp needle precisely on its point? Explain.
6. A cold thermometer is placed in a hot bowl of soup. Will the temperature reading of the thermometer be the same as the temperature of the hot soup before the measurement was made? Explain.
7. Does the uncertainty principle set a limit to how well you can make any single measurement of position?
8. If you knew the position of an object precisely, with no uncertainty, how well would you know its momentum?
9. When you check the pressure in a tire, doesn't some air inevitably escape? Is it possible to avoid this escape of air altogether? What is the relation to the uncertainty principle?
10. It has been said that the ground-state energy in the hydrogen atom can be precisely known but the excited states have some uncertainty in their values (an "energy width"). Is this consistent with the uncertainty principle in its energy form? Explain.
11. Which model of the hydrogen atom, the Bohr model or the quantum-mechanical model, predicts that the electron spends more time near the nucleus?
12. The size of atoms varies by only a factor of three or so, from largest to smallest, yet the number of electrons varies from one to over 100. Explain.
13. Excited hydrogen and excited helium atoms both radiate light as they jump down to the $n = 1$, $l = 0$, $m_l = 0$ state. Yet the two elements have very different emission spectra. Why?
14. How would the periodic table look if there were no electron spin but otherwise quantum mechanics were valid? Consider the first 20 elements or so.
15. Which of the following electron configurations are not allowed: (*a*) $1s^2 2s^2 2p^4 3s^2 4p^2$; (*b*) $1s^2 2s^2 2p^8 3s^1$; (*c*) $1s^2 2s^2 2p^6 3s^2 3p^5 4s^2 4d^5 4f^1$? If not allowed, explain why.
16. Give the complete electron configuration for a uranium atom (careful scrutiny across the periodic table on the inside back cover will provide useful hints).
17. In what column of the periodic table would you expect to find the atom with each of the following configurations: (*a*) $1s^2 2s^2 2p^6 3s^2$; (*b*) $1s^2 2s^2 2p^6 3s^2 3p^6$; (*c*) $1s^2 2s^2 2p^6 3s^2 3p^6 4s^1$; (*d*) $1s^2 2s^2 2p^5$?
18. Why do chlorine and iodine exhibit similar properties?
19. Explain why potassium and sodium exhibit similar properties.
20. The ionization energy for neon ($Z = 10$) is 21.6 eV, and that for sodium ($Z = 11$) is 5.1 eV. Explain the large difference.

* 21. Why does the cutoff wavelength in Fig. 28–11 imply a photon nature for light?

* 22. Why do we not expect perfect agreement between measured values of X-ray line wavelengths and those calculated using Bohr theory, as in Example 28–6?

* 23. How would you figure out which lines in an X-ray spectrum correspond to $K_\alpha$, $K_\beta$, L etc., transitions?

24. Why do we expect electron transitions deep within an atom to produce shorter wavelengths than transitions by outer electrons?

* 25. Compare spontaneous emission to stimulated emission.

* 26. How does laser light differ from ordinary light? How is it the same?

* 27. Explain how a 0.0005-W laser beam, photographed at a distance, can seem much stronger than a 1000-W street lamp at the same distance.

* 28. Does the intensity of light from a laser fall off as the inverse square of the distance? Explain.

## Problems

### 28–2 Wave Function, Double-Slit

1. (II) The neutrons in a parallel beam, each having kinetic energy $\frac{1}{40}$ eV, are directed through two slits 0.50 mm apart. How far apart will the interference peaks be on a screen 1.0 m away? [*Hint*: first find the wavelength of the neutron.]

2. (II) Bullets of mass 3.0 g are fired in parallel paths with speeds of 220 m/s through a hole 3.0 mm in diameter. How far from the hole must you be to detect a 1.0-cm-diameter spread in the beam of bullets?

### 28–3 Uncertainty Principle

3. (I) A proton is traveling with a speed of $(6.560 \pm 0.012) \times 10^5$ m/s. With what maximum accuracy can its position be ascertained? [*Hint*: $\Delta p = m\,\Delta v$.]

4. (I) If an electron's position can be measured to an accuracy of $2.0 \times 10^{-8}$ m, how accurately can its speed be known?

5. (I) An electron remains in an excited state of an atom for typically $10^{-8}$ s. What is the minimum uncertainty in the energy of the state (in eV)?

6. (I) The $Z^0$ boson, discovered in 1985, is the mediator of the weak nuclear force, and it typically decays very quickly. Its average rest energy is 91.19 GeV, but its short lifetime shows up as an intrinsic width of 2.5 GeV (rest energy uncertainty). What is the lifetime of this particle?

7. (II) What is the uncertainty in the mass of a muon $(m = 105.7\ \text{MeV}/c^2)$, specified in eV/$c^2$, given its lifetime of 2.20 $\mu$s? [*Hint*: $\Delta E \approx \hbar/\Delta t$.]

8. (II) A free neutron $(m = 1.67 \times 10^{-27}\ \text{kg})$ has a mean life of 900 s. What is the uncertainty in its mass (in kg)?

9. (II) An electron and a 140-g baseball are each traveling 150 m/s measured to an accuracy of 0.055%. Calculate and compare the uncertainty in position of each.

10. (III) Estimate the lowest possible energy of a neutron contained in a typical nucleus of radius $1.0 \times 10^{-15}$ m. [*Hint*: a particle can have an energy at least as large as its uncertainty.]

11. (III) Use the uncertainty principle to show that if an electron were present in the nucleus $(r \approx 10^{-15} m)$, its kinetic energy (use relativity) would be hundreds of MeV. (Since such electron energies are not observed, we conclude that electrons are not present in the nucleus.) [*Hint*: a particle can have an energy at least as large as its uncertainty.]

12. (III) How accurately can the position of a 3.00-keV electron be measured assuming its energy is known to 1.00%?

### 28–6 to 28–8 Quantum Numbers, Exclusion Principle

13. (I) For $n = 6$, what values can $l$ have?

14. (I) For $n = 5$, $l = 3$, what are the possible values of $m_l$ and $m_s$?

15. (I) How many electrons can be in the $n = 6$, $l = 3$ subshell?

16. (I) How many different states are possible for an electron whose principal quantum number is $n = 4$? Write down the quantum numbers for each state.

17. (I) List the quantum numbers for each electron in the ground state of (*a*) carbon $(Z = 6)$, (*b*) magnesium $(Z = 12)$.

18. (I) List the quantum numbers for each electron in the ground state of nitrogen $(Z = 7)$.

19. (I) Suppose a certain hydrogen atom has $l = 4$. What are the possible values for $n$, $m_l$, and $m_s$?

20. (I) Calculate the magnitude of the angular momentum of an electron in the $n = 4$, $l = 3$ state of hydrogen.

21. (II) If a hydrogen atom has $m_l = -3$, what are the possible values of $n$, $l$, and $m_s$?

22. (II) Show that there can be 18 electrons in a "g" subshell.

23. (II) What is the full electron configuration in the ground state for elements with $Z$ equal to (*a*) 27, (*b*) 36, (*c*) 38? [*Hint*: see the periodic table inside the back cover.]

24. (II) What is the full electron configuration for (*a*) selenium (Se), (*b*) gold (Au), (*c*) radium (Ra)? [*Hint*: see the periodic table inside the back cover.]

25. (II) A hydrogen atom is in the 6*s* state. Determine (*a*) the principal quantum number, (*b*) the energy of the state, (*c*) the orbital angular momentum and its quantum number $l$, and (*d*) the possible values for the magnetic quantum number.

26. (II) Estimate the binding energy of the third electron in lithium using the Bohr theory. [*Hint*: this electron has $n = 2$ and "sees" a net charge of approximately $+1e$.] The measured value is 5.36 eV.

27. (II) Show that the total angular momentum is zero for a filled subshell.

* 28. (II) For each of the following atomic transitions, state whether the transition is *allowed* or *forbidden*, and if forbidden, what rule is being violated: (*a*) $4p \rightarrow 3p$; (*b*) $2p \rightarrow 1s$; (*c*) $3d \rightarrow 2d$; (*d*) $4d \rightarrow 3s$; (*e*) $4s \rightarrow 2p$.

* 29. (II) An excited H atom is in a $6d$ state. (*a*) Name all the states $(n, l)$ to which the atom is "allowed" to jump with the emission of a photon. (*b*) How many different wavelengths are there (ignoring fine structure)?

### * 28–9 X-Rays

* 30. (I) What are the shortest-wavelength X-rays emitted by electrons striking the face of a 33.5-kV TV picture tube? What are the longest wavelengths?

* 31. (I) If the shortest-wavelength bremsstrahlung X-rays emitted from an X-ray tube have $\lambda = 0.030\,\text{nm}$, what is the voltage across the tube?

* 32. (I) Show that the cutoff wavelength $\lambda_0$ is given by

$$\lambda_0 = \frac{1240\,\text{nm}}{V},$$

where $V$ is the X-ray tube voltage in volts.

* 33. (II) Use the result of Example 28–6 to estimate the X-ray wavelength emitted when a Co $(Z = 27)$ atom jumps from $n = 2$ to $n = 1$.

* 34. (II) Estimate the wavelength for an $n = 2$ to $n = 1$ transition in iron $(Z = 26)$.

* 35. (II) Use the Bohr theory to estimate the wavelength for an $n = 3$ to $n = 1$ transition in molybdenum $(Z = 42)$. The measured value is 0.063 nm. Why do we not expect perfect agreement?

* 36. (II) A mixture of iron and an unknown material is bombarded with electrons. The wavelength of the $K_\alpha$ lines are 194 pm for iron and 229 pm for the unknown. What is the unknown material?

### * 28–11 Lasers

* 37. (II) A laser used to weld detached retinas puts out 28-ms-long pulses of 640-nm light which average 0.68-W output during a pulse. How much energy can be deposited per pulse and how many photons does each pulse contain? [*Hint*: see Example 27–5.]

* 38. (II) A low-power laser used in a physics lab might have a power of 0.50 mW and a beam diameter of 3.0 mm. Calculate (*a*) the average light intensity of the laser beam, and (*b*) compare it to the intensity of a lightbulb producing 40-W light viewed from 2.0 m.

* 39. (II) Estimate the angular spread of a laser beam due to diffraction if the beam emerges through a 3.0-mm-diameter mirror. Assume that $\lambda = 694\,\text{nm}$. What would be the diameter of this beam if it struck (*a*) a satellite 300 km above the Earth, or (*b*) the Moon? [*Hint*: see Section 25–7.]

* 40. (II) What is the wavelength of the He–Ne laser?

## General Problems

41. Use the uncertainty principle to estimate the position uncertainty for the electron in the ground state of the hydrogen atom. [*Hint*: determine the momentum using the Bohr model of Section 27–12 and assume the momentum can be anywhere between this value and zero.] How does this result compare to the Bohr radius?

42. An electron in the $n = 2$ state of hydrogen remains there on average about $10^{-8}\,\text{s}$ before jumping to the $n = 1$ state. (*a*) Estimate the uncertainty in the energy of the $n = 2$ state. (*b*) What fraction of the transition energy is this? (*c*) What is the wavelength, and width (in nm), of this line in the spectrum of hydrogen?

43. What are the largest and smallest possible values for the angular momentum $L$ of an electron in the $n = 5$ shell?

44. Estimate (*a*) the quantum number $l$ for the orbital angular momentum of the Earth about the Sun, and (*b*) the number of possible orientations for the plane of Earth's orbit.

45. A 12-g bullet leaves a rifle at a speed of 180 m/s. (*a*) What is the wavelength of this bullet? (*b*) If the position of the bullet is known to an accuracy of 0.60 cm (radius of the barrel), what is the minimum uncertainty in its momentum?

46. Using the Bohr formula for the radius of an electron orbit, estimate the average distance from the nucleus for an electron in the innermost $(n = 1)$ orbit of a uranium atom $(Z = 92)$. Approximately how much energy would be required to remove this innermost electron?

47. An X-ray tube operates at 95 kV with a current of 25 mA and nearly all the electron energy goes into heat. If the specific heat of the 0.085-kg plate is $0.11\,\text{kcal/kg}\cdot\text{C}^\circ$, what will be the temperature rise per minute if no cooling water is used?

48. The ionization (binding) energy of the outermost electron in boron is 8.26 eV. (*a*) Use the Bohr model to estimate the "effective charge," $Z_{\text{eff}}$, seen by this electron. (*b*) Estimate the average orbital radius.

49. Use the Bohr theory (especially Eq. 27–16) to show that the Moseley plot (Fig. 28–12) can be written

$$\sqrt{\frac{1}{\lambda}} = a(Z - b),$$

where $b \approx 1$, and evaluate $a$.

50. (*a*) Show that the number of different states for a given value of $l$ is equal to $2(2l + 1)$. (*b*) What is this number for $l = 0, 1, 2, 3, 4, 5$, and 6?

51. Show that the number of different electron states possible for a given value of $n$ is $2n^2$. (See Problem 50.)

52. A beam of electrons with kinetic energy 45 keV is shot through two narrow slits in a barrier. The slits are a distance $2.0 \times 10^{-6}\,\text{m}$ apart. If a screen is placed 35.0 cm behind the barrier, calculate the spacing between the "bright" fringes of the interference pattern produced on the screen.

53. The angular momentum in the hydrogen atom is given both by the Bohr model and by quantum mechanics. Compare the results for $n = 2$.

54. An 1100-kg car is traveling with a speed of $(22 \pm 0.22)$ m/s. With what maximum accuracy can its position be determined?

55. An atomic spectrum contains a line with a wavelength centered at 488 nm. Careful measurements show the line is really spread out between 487 and 489 nm. Estimate the lifetime of the excited state that produced this line.

56. Protons are accelerated from rest across 550 V. They are then directed at two slits 0.70 mm apart. How far apart will the interference peaks be on a screen 28 m away?

57. An electron and a proton, each initially at rest, are accelerated across the same voltage. Assuming that the uncertainty in their position is given by their de Broglie wavelength, find the ratio of the uncertainty in their momentum.

58. If the principal quantum number $n$ were limited to the range from 1 to 6, how many elements would we find in nature?

59. If your de Broglie wavelength were 0.50 m, how fast would you be moving if your mass is 75.0 kg? Would you notice diffraction effects as you walk through a doorway? Approximately how long would it take you to walk through the doorway?

60. Suppose that the spectrum of an unknown element shows a series of lines with one out of every four matching a line from the Lyman series of hydrogen. Assuming that the unknown element is an ion with $Z$ protons and one electron, determine $Z$ and the element in question.

* 61. Photons of wavelength 0.154 nm are emitted from the surface of a certain metal when it is bombarded with high energy radiation. If this photon wavelength corresponds to the $K_\alpha$ line, what is the element?

* 62. Show that the diffractive spread of a laser beam, $\approx \lambda/D$ as described in Section 28–11, is precisely what you might expect from the uncertainty principle. [*Hint*: since the beam's width is constrained by the dimension of the aperture $D$, the component of the light's momentum perpendicular to the laser axis is uncertain.]

## Answers to Exercises

**A:** $2.1 \times 10^{-24}\,\text{kg}\cdot\text{m/s}$, $2.3 \times 10^{6}\,\text{m/s}$.

**B:** 2, 1, 0, −1, −2.

**C:** −0.38 eV, $\sqrt{20}\,\hbar$.

**D:** $1s^2 2s^2 2p^6 3s^2 3p^6 3d^{10} 4s^2 4p^1$.

A Pentium 4 chip is one of the leading processors used in computers today. The 2004 model contains 125 million transistors, plus diodes and other semiconductor electronic elements, all on a chip only about 1 cm on a side. Before discussing semiconductors and their applications, we study how quantum theory describes bonding of atoms to form molecules, and how it explains molecular behavior. We then examine how atoms and molecules form solids, with emphasis on metals and semiconductors, and their use in electronics.

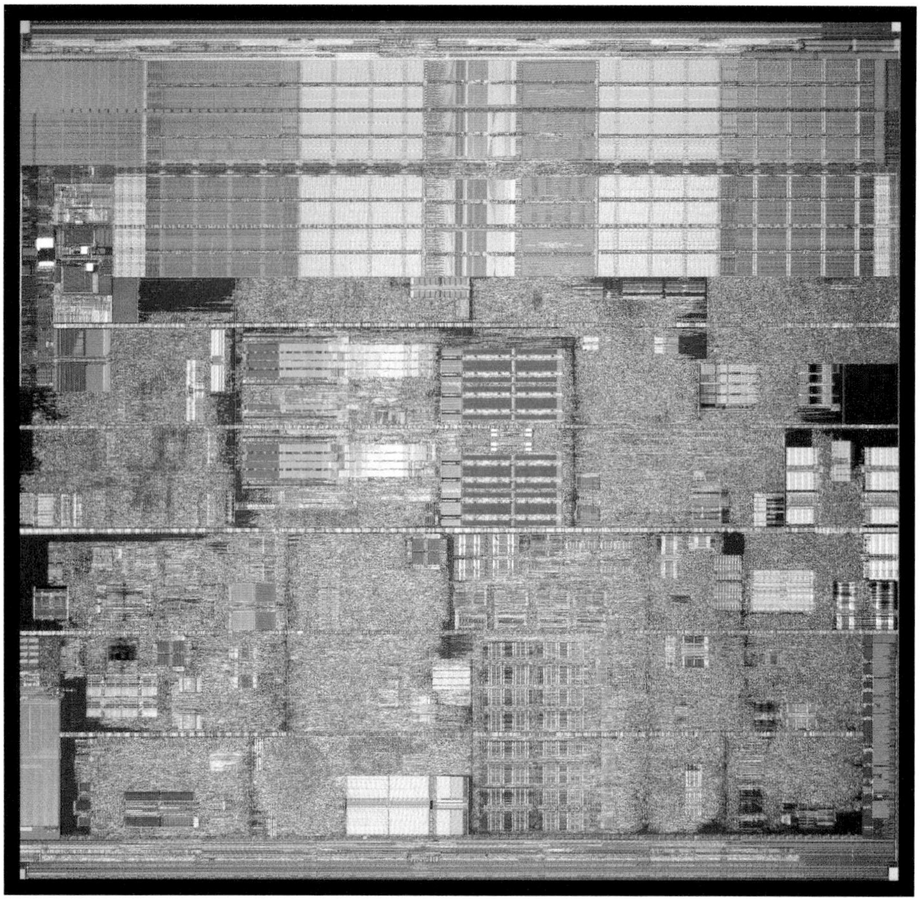

CHAPTER 29

# Molecules and Solids

Since its development in the 1920s, quantum mechanics has had a profound influence on our lives, both intellectually and technologically. Even the way we view the world has changed, as we saw in Chapter 28. Now we discuss how quantum mechanics has given us an understanding of the structure of molecules and matter in bulk, as well as a number of important applications including semiconductor devices and applications to biology.

## *29–1 Bonding in Molecules

One of the great successes of quantum mechanics was to give scientists, at last, an understanding of the nature of chemical bonds. Since it is based in physics, and because this understanding is so important in many fields, we discuss it here.

By a molecule, we mean a group of two or more atoms that are strongly held together so as to function as a single unit. When atoms make such an attachment, we say that a chemical **bond** has been formed. There are two main types of strong chemical bond: covalent and ionic. Many bonds are actually intermediate between these two types.

## Covalent Bonds

To understand how **covalent bonds** are formed, we take the simplest case, the bond that holds two hydrogen atoms together to form the hydrogen molecule, $H_2$. The mechanism is basically the same for other covalent bonds. As two H atoms approach each other, the electron clouds begin to overlap, and the electrons from each atom can "orbit" both nuclei. (This is sometimes called "sharing" electrons.) If both electrons are in the ground state ($n = 1$) of their respective atoms, there are two possibilities: their spins (Chapter 28) can be parallel (both up or both down), in which case the total spin is $S = \frac{1}{2} + \frac{1}{2} = 1$; or their spins can be opposite ($m_s = +\frac{1}{2}$ for one, $m_s = -\frac{1}{2}$ for the other), so that the total spin $S = 0$. We shall now see that a bond is formed only for the $S = 0$ state, when the spins are opposite.

*Covalent bond*

First we consider the $S = 1$ state, for which the spins are the same. The two electrons cannot both be in the lowest energy state and be attached to the same atom, for then they would have identical quantum numbers in violation of the exclusion principle. The exclusion principle tells us that since no two electrons can occupy the same quantum state, if two electrons have the same quantum numbers, they must be different in some other way—namely, by being in different places in space (for example, attached to different atoms). When the two atoms approach each other, the electrons will stay away from each other as shown by the probability distribution of Fig. 29–1. The positively charged nuclei then repel each other, and no bond is formed.

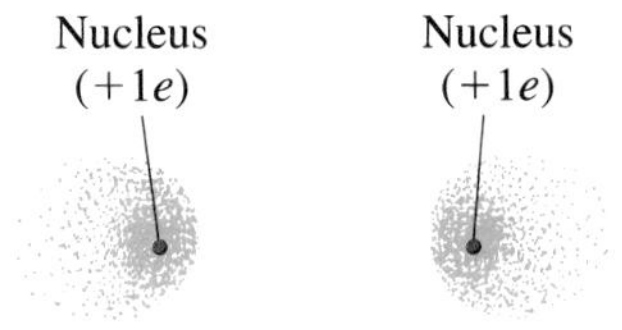


**FIGURE 29–1** Electron probability distribution (electron cloud) for two H atoms when their spins are the same $\left(S = \frac{1}{2} + \frac{1}{2} = 1\right)$.

For the $S = 0$ state, on the other hand, the spins are opposite and the two electrons are consequently in different quantum states ($m_s$ is different, $+\frac{1}{2}$ for one, $-\frac{1}{2}$ for the other). Hence they can come close together. In this case, the probability distribution looks like Fig. 29–2: the electrons can spend much of their time between the two nuclei. The two positively charged nuclei are attracted to the negatively charged electron cloud between them, and this is the attraction that holds the two atoms together to form a molecule. This is a *covalent bond*.

**FIGURE 29–2** Electron probability distribution (cloud) around two H atoms when their spins are opposite ($S = 0$). In this case, a bond is formed because the positive nuclei are attracted to the concentration of negative charge between them. This is a hydrogen molecule, $H_2$.

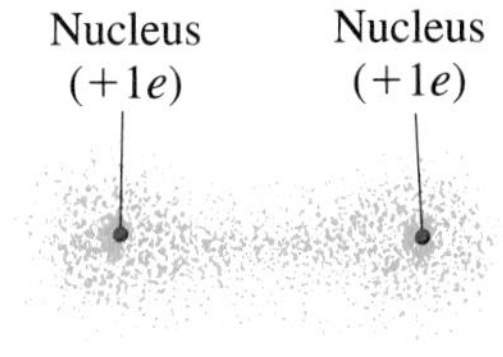


The probability distributions of Figs. 29–1 and 29–2 can perhaps be better understood on the basis of waves. What the exclusion principle requires is that when the spins are the same, there is destructive interference of the electron wave functions in the region between the two atoms. But when the spins are opposite, constructive interference occurs in the region between the two atoms, resulting in a large amount of negative charge there. Thus a covalent bond can be said to be the result of constructive interference of the electron wave functions in the space between the two atoms, and of the electrostatic attraction of the two positive nuclei for the negative charge concentration between them.

Why a bond is formed can also be understood from the energy point of view. When the two H atoms approach close to one another, if the spins of their electrons are opposite, the electrons can occupy the same space, as discussed above. This means that each electron can now move about in the space of two atoms instead of in the volume of only one. Because each electron now occupies more space, it is less well localized. Because each electron has a larger "orbit," its wavelength $\lambda$ can be longer, so its momentum $p = h/\lambda$ (Eq. 27–8) can be less. With less momentum, each electron has less energy when the two atoms combine than when they are separate. That is, the molecule has less energy than the two separate atoms, and so is more stable. An energy input is required to break the $H_2$ molecule into two separate H atoms, so the $H_2$ molecule is a stable entity. This is what we mean by a *bond*. The energy required to break a bond is called the **bond energy**, the **binding energy**, or the **dissociation energy**. For the hydrogen molecule, $H_2$, the bond energy is 4.5 eV.

*Energy explanation of bond*

*Bond energy*

## Ionic Bonds

*Ionic bond*

An **ionic bond** is, in a sense, a special case of the covalent bond. Instead of the electrons being shared equally, they are shared unequally. For example, in sodium chloride (NaCl), the outer electron of the sodium spends nearly all its time around the chlorine (Fig. 29–3). The chlorine atom acquires a net negative charge as a result of the extra electron, whereas the sodium atom is left with a net positive charge. The electrostatic attraction between these two charged atoms holds them together. The resulting bond is called an *ionic bond* because it is created by the attraction between the two ions ($Na^+$ and $Cl^-$). But to understand the ionic bond, we must understand why the extra electron from the sodium spends so much of its time around the chlorine. After all, the chlorine is neutral; why should it attract another electron?

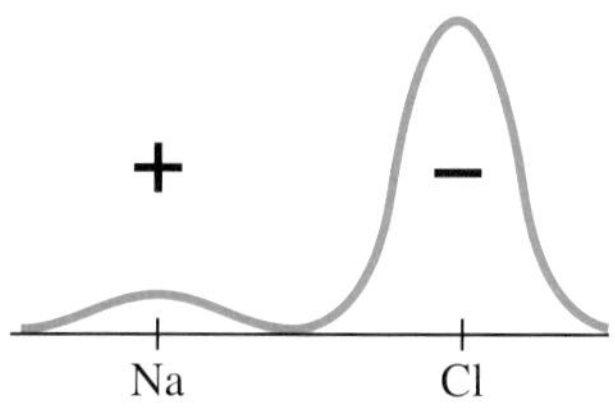


**FIGURE 29–3** Probability distribution for the last electron of Na in NaCl.

The answer lies in the probability distributions of the two neutral atoms. Sodium contains 11 electrons, 10 of which are in spherically symmetric closed shells (Fig. 29–4). The last electron spends most of its time beyond these closed shells. Because the closed shells have a total charge of $-10e$ and the nucleus has charge $+11e$, the outermost electron in sodium "feels" a net attraction due to $+1e$. It is not held very strongly. On the other hand, 12 of chlorine's 17 electrons form closed shells, or subshells (corresponding to $1s^2 2s^2 2p^6 3s^2$). These 12 form a spherically symmetric shield around the nucleus. The other five electrons are in $3p$ states whose probability distributions are not spherically symmetric and have a form similar to those for the $2p$ states in hydrogen shown in Fig. 28–9b and c. Four of these $3p$ electrons can have "doughnut-shaped" distributions symmetric about the $z$ axis, as shown in Fig. 29–5. The fifth can have a "barbell-shaped" distribution (as for $m_l = 0$ in Fig. 28–9b), which in Fig. 29–5 is shown only in dashed outline because it is half empty. That is, the exclusion principle allows one more electron to be in this state (it will have spin opposite to that of the electron already there). If an extra electron—say from a Na atom—happens to be in the vicinity, it can be in this state, say at point $x$ in Fig. 29–5. It could experience an attraction due to as much as $+5e$ because the $+17e$ of the nucleus is partly shielded at this point by the 12 inner electrons. Thus, the outer electron of a sodium atom will be more strongly attracted by the $+5e$ of the chlorine atom than by the $+1e$ of its own atom. This, combined with the strong attraction between the two ions when the extra electron stays with the $Cl^-$, produces the charge distribution of Fig. 29–3, and hence the ionic bond.

**FIGURE 29–4** In a neutral sodium atom, the 10 inner electrons shield the nucleus, so the single outer electron is attracted by a net charge of $+1e$.

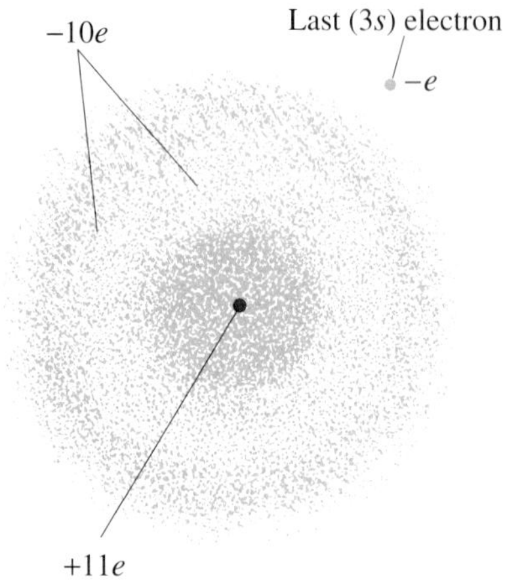


**FIGURE 29–5** Neutral chlorine atom. The $+17e$ of the nucleus is shielded by the 12 electrons in the inner shells and subshells. Four of the five $3p$ electrons are shown in doughnut-shaped clouds, and the fifth is in the (dashed-line) cloud concentrated about the $z$ axis (vertical). An extra electron at $x$ will be attracted by a net charge that can be as much as $+5e$.

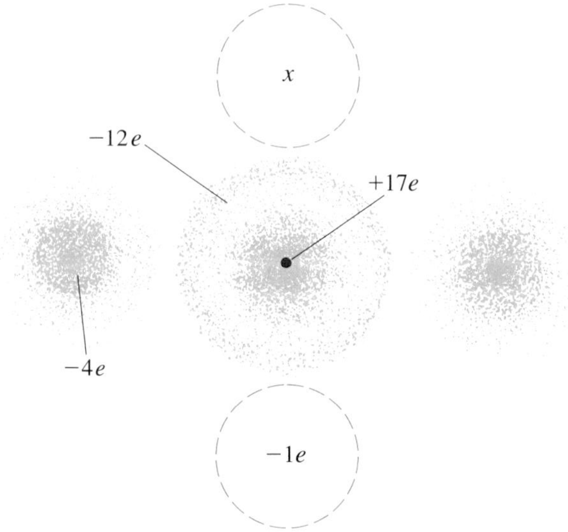

## Partial Ionic Character of Covalent Bonds

A pure covalent bond in which the electrons are shared equally occurs mainly in symmetrical molecules such as $H_2$, $O_2$, and $Cl_2$. When the atoms involved are different from each other, it is usual to find that the shared electrons are more likely to be in the vicinity of one atom than the other. The extreme case is an ionic bond; in intermediate cases the covalent bond is said to have a *partial ionic character*. The molecules themselves are **polar**—that is, one part (or parts) of the molecule has a net positive charge and other parts a net negative charge. An example is the water molecule, $H_2O$ (Fig. 29–6). The shared electrons are more likely to be found around the oxygen atom than around the two hydrogens.

*Polar molecules*

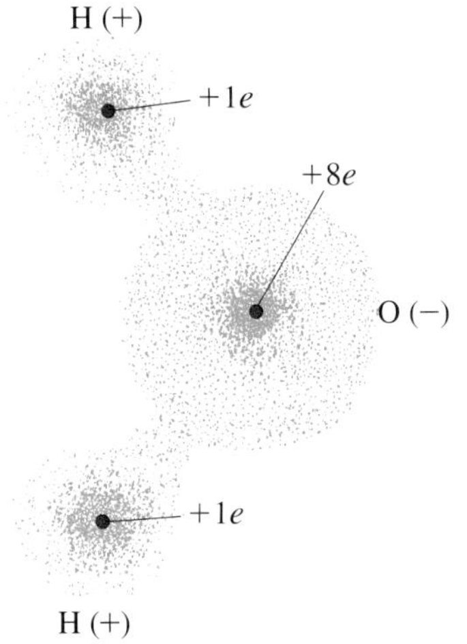


**FIGURE 29–6** The water molecule $H_2O$ is polar.

The reason is similar to that discussed above in connection with ionic bonds. Oxygen has eight electrons $(1s^2 2s^2 2p^4)$, of which four form a spherically symmetric core and the other four could have, for example, a doughnut-shaped distribution. The barbell-shaped distribution on the $z$ axis (like that shown dashed in Fig. 29–5) could be empty, so electrons from hydrogen atoms can be attracted by a net charge of $+4e$. They are also attracted by the H nuclei, so they partly orbit the H atoms as well as the O atom. The net effect is that there is a net positive charge on each H atom (less than $+1e$), because the electrons spend only part of their time there. And, there is a net negative charge on the O atom.

**FIGURE 29–7** Potential energy as a function of separation for two point charges of (a) like sign and (b) opposite sign.

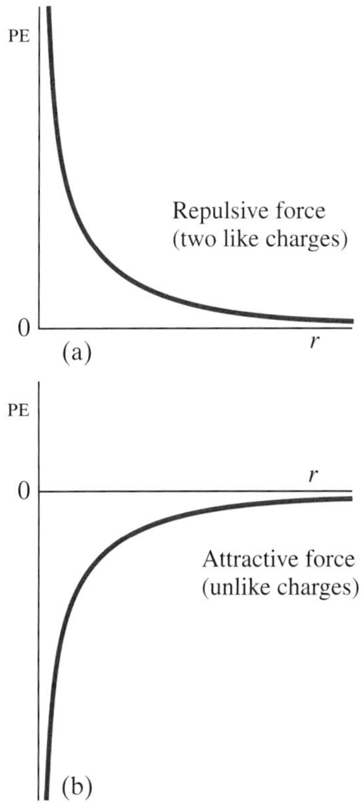


# * 29–2 Potential-Energy Diagrams for Molecules

It is useful to analyze the interaction between two objects—say, between two atoms or molecules—with the use of a potential-energy diagram, a plot of the potential energy versus the separation distance.

For the simple case of two point charges, $q_1$ and $q_2$, the PE is given by (we combine Eqs. 17–2 and 17–5)

$$\text{PE} = \frac{1}{4\pi\epsilon_0}\frac{q_1 q_2}{r},$$

where $r$ is the distance between the charges, and the constant $(1/4\pi\epsilon_0)$ is equal to $9.0 \times 10^9\,\text{N}\cdot\text{m}^2/\text{C}^2$. If the two charges have the same sign, the PE is positive for all values of $r$, and a graph of PE versus $r$ in this case is shown in Fig. 29–7a. The force is repulsive (the charges have the *same* sign) and the curve rises as $r$ decreases; this makes sense since work is done to bring the charges together, thereby increasing their potential energy. If, on the other hand, the two charges are of the *opposite* sign, the PE is negative because the product $q_1 q_2$ is negative. The force is attractive in this case, and the graph of PE versus $r$ looks like Fig. 29–7b. The PE becomes more *negative* as $r$ decreases.

Now let us look at the potential-energy diagram for the formation of a covalent bond, such as for the hydrogen molecule, $H_2$. The potential energy of one H atom in the presence of the other is plotted in Fig. 29–8. Starting at large $r$, the PE decreases as the atoms approach, because the electrons concentrate between the two nuclei (Fig. 29–2), so attraction occurs. However, at very short distances, the electrons would be "squeezed out"—there is no room for them between the two nuclei. Without the electrons between them, each nucleus would feel a repulsive force due to the other, so the curve rises as $r$ decreases further. There is an optimum separation of the atoms, $r_0$ in Fig. 29–8, at which the energy is lowest. This is the point of greatest stability for the hydrogen molecule, and $r_0$ is the average separation of atoms in the $H_2$ molecule. The depth of this "well" is the *binding energy*,† as shown. This is how much energy must be put into the system to separate the two atoms to infinity, where the $PE = 0$. For the $H_2$ molecule, the binding energy is about 4.5 eV and $r_0 = 0.074$ nm.

*Binding energy*

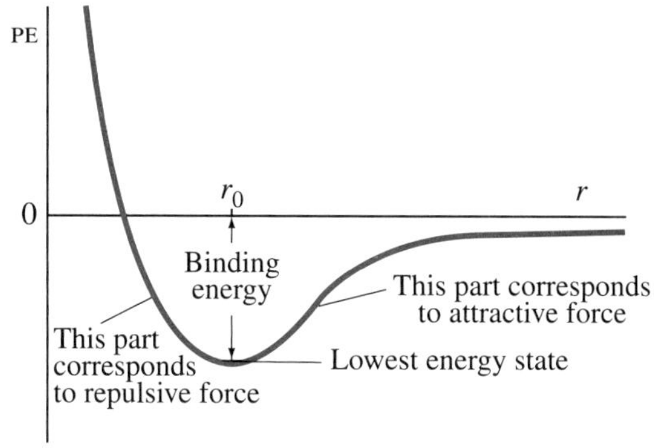


**FIGURE 29–8** Potential-energy diagram for $H_2$ molecule; $r$ is the separation of the two H atoms. The binding energy (the energy difference between $PE = 0$ and the lowest energy state near the bottom of the well) is 4.5 eV, and $r_0 = 0.074$ nm.

For many bonds, the potential-energy curve has the shape shown in Fig. 29–9. There is still an optimum distance $r_0$ at which the molecule is stable. But when the atoms approach from a large distance, the force is initially repulsive rather than attractive. The atoms thus do not interact spontaneously. Instead, some additional energy must be injected into the system to get it over the "hump" (or barrier) in the potential-energy diagram. This required energy is called the **activation energy**.

*Activation energy*

The curve of Fig. 29–9 is much more common than that of Fig. 29–8. The activation energy often reflects a need to break other bonds, before the one under discussion can be made. For example, to make water from $O_2$ and $H_2$, the $H_2$ and $O_2$ molecules must first be broken into H and O atoms by an input of energy; this is what the activation energy represents. Then the H and O atoms

†The binding energy corresponds not quite to the bottom of the PE curve, but to the lowest energy state, slightly above it, as shown in Fig. 29–8.

**FIGURE 29–9** Potential-energy diagram for a bond requiring an activation energy.

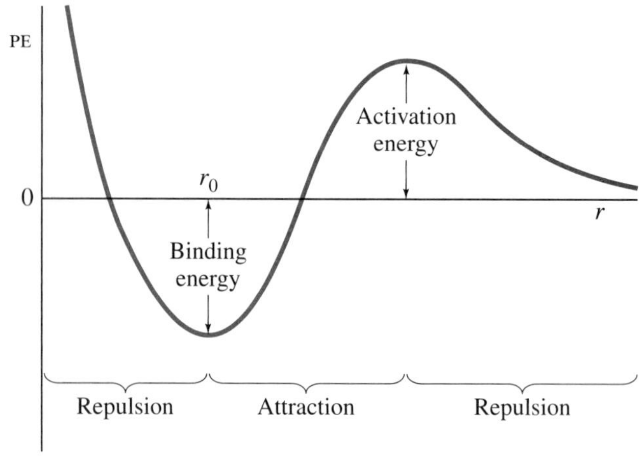

can combine to form $H_2O$ with the release of a great deal more energy than was put in initially. The initial activation energy can be provided by applying an electric spark to a mixture of $H_2$ and $O_2$, breaking a few of these molecules into H and O atoms. The resulting explosive release of energy when these atoms combine to form $H_2O$ quickly provides the activation energy needed for further reactions, so additional $H_2$ and $O_2$ molecules are broken up and recombined to form $H_2O$.

The potential-energy diagrams for ionic bonds can have similar shapes. In NaCl, for example, the $Na^+$ and $Cl^-$ ions attract each other at distances a bit larger than some $r_0$, but at shorter distances the overlapping of inner electron shells gives rise to repulsion. The two atoms thus are most stable at some intermediate separation, $r_0$, and there often is an activation energy.

PHYSICS APPLIED

*ATP and energy in the cell*

Sometimes the potential energy of a bond looks like that of Fig. 29–10. In this case, the energy of the bonded molecule, at a separation $r_0$, is greater than when there is no bond $(r = \infty)$. That is, an energy *input* is required to make the bond (hence the binding energy is negative), and there is energy release when the bond is broken. Such a bond is stable only because there is the barrier of the activation energy. This type of bond is important in living cells, for it is in such bonds that energy can be stored efficiently in certain molecules, particularly ATP (adenosine triphosphate). The bond that connects the last phosphate group (designated Ⓟ in Fig. 29–10) to the rest of the molecule (ADP, meaning adenosine diphosphate, since it contains only two phosphates) has PE of the shape shown in Fig. 29–10. Energy is stored in this bond. When the bond is broken (ATP $\rightarrow$ ADP + Ⓟ), energy is released and this energy can be used to make other chemical reactions "go."

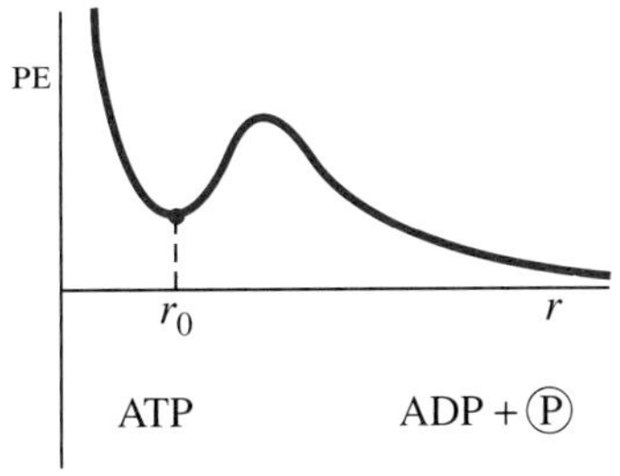


**FIGURE 29–10** Potential-energy diagram for the formation of ATP from ADP and phosphate (Ⓟ).

*Enzymes act to lower activation energy*

In living cells, many chemical reactions have activation energies that are often on the order of several eV. Such energy barriers are not easy to overcome in the cell. This is where enzymes come in. They act as *catalysts*, which means they act to lower the activation energy so that reactions can occur that otherwise would not. Enzymes act by distorting the bonding electron clouds, so that the initial bonds are easily broken.

## * 29–3 Weak (van der Waals) Bonds

Once a bond between two atoms or ions is made, energy must normally be supplied to break the bond and separate the atoms. As mentioned in Section 29–1, this energy is called the *bond energy* or *binding energy*. The binding energy for covalent and ionic bonds is typically 2 to 5 eV. These bonds, which hold atoms together to *form* molecules, are often called **strong bonds** to distinguish them from so-called "weak bonds." The term **weak bond**, as we use it here, refers to an attachment *between* molecules due to simple electrostatic attraction—such as *between* polar molecules (and not *within* a polar molecule, which is a strong bond). The strength of the attachment is much less than for the strong bonds. Binding energies are typically in the range 0.04 to 0.3 eV—hence their name "weak bonds."

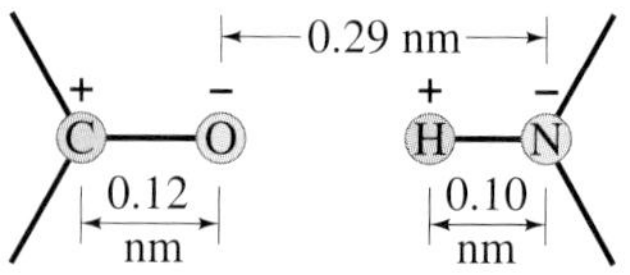


**FIGURE 29–11** The $C^+$—$O^-$ and $H^+$—$N^-$ dipoles attract each other. (These dipoles may be part of, for example, cytosine and guanine molecules. See Fig. 29–12.) The + and − charges typically have magnitudes of a fraction of $e$.

Weak bonds are generally the result of attraction between dipoles. (Two equal point charges $Q$, of opposite sign, separated by a distance $l$, are called an **electric dipole**, as we saw in Chapter 17.) For example, Fig. 29–11 shows two molecules, which have permanent dipole moments, attracting one another. Besides such **dipole–dipole bonds**, there can also be **dipole–induced dipole bonds**, in which a polar molecule with a permanent dipole moment can induce a dipole moment in an otherwise electrically balanced (nonpolar) molecule, just as a single charge can induce a separation of charge in a nearby object (see Fig. 16–7). There can even be an attraction between two nonpolar molecules, because their electrons are moving about: at any instant there may be a transient separation of charge, creating a weak attraction. All these weak bonds are referred to as **van der Waals bonds**, and the forces involved **van der Waals forces**. The potential energy has the general shape shown in Fig. 29–8, with the attractive van der Waals PE varying as $1/r^6$.

When one of the atoms in a dipole–dipole bond is hydrogen, as in Fig. 29–11, it is called a **hydrogen bond**. A hydrogen bond is generally the strongest of the weak bonds, because the hydrogen atom is the smallest atom and can be approached more closely. Hydrogen bonds also have a partial "covalent" character: that is, electrons between the two dipoles may be shared to a small extent, making a stronger, more lasting bond.

PHYSICS APPLIED

*DNA*

Weak bonds are important in liquids and solids when strong bonds are absent (see Section 29–5). They are also very important for understanding the activities of cells, such as the double helix shape of DNA (Fig. 29–12), and DNA replication (see Section 16–11). The average kinetic energy of molecules in a living cell at normal temperatures ($T \approx 300\,\text{K}$) is around $\frac{3}{2}kT \approx 0.04\,\text{eV}$, about the magnitude of weak bonds. This means that a weak bond can readily be broken just by a molecular collision. Hence weak bonds are not very permanent—they are,

**FIGURE 29–12** (a) Section of a DNA double helix. The red dots represent hydrogen bonds between the two strands. (b) "Close-up" view: cytosine (C) and guanine (G) molecules on separate strands of a DNA double helix are held together by the hydrogen bonds (red dots) involving an $H^+$ on one molecule attracted to an $N^-$ or $C^+$—$O^-$ of a molecule on the adjacent chain. See also Section 16–11 and Figs. 16–44 and 16–45.

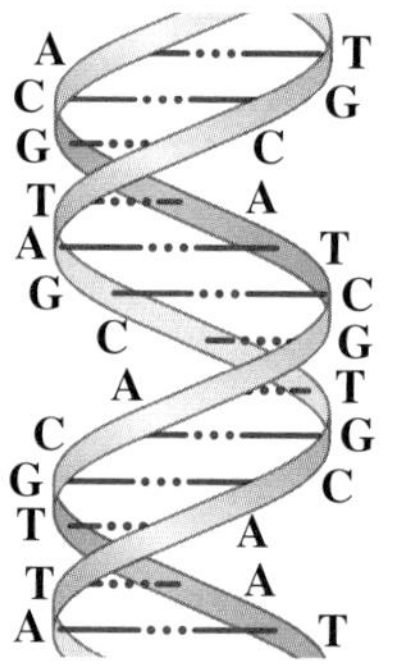

(a)

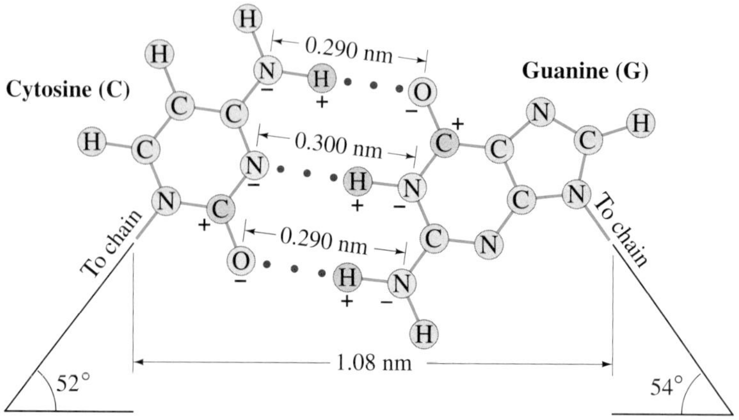


(b)

instead, brief attachments. This helps them play particular roles in the cell. On the other hand, strong bonds—those that hold molecules together—are almost never broken simply by molecular collision. Thus they are relatively permanent. They can be broken by chemical action (the making of even stronger bonds), and this usually happens in the cell with the aid of an enzyme, which is a protein molecule.

**EXAMPLE 29–1** **Nucleotide energy.** Calculate the potential energy between the C=O dipole of thymine and the H—N dipole of adenine, assuming that the two dipoles are lined up as shown in Fig. 29–11. Dipole moment measurements (see Table 17–2) give

$$q_H = -q_N = 0.19e = 3.0 \times 10^{-20}\,\text{C},$$

and

$$q_C = -q_O = 0.41e = 6.6 \times 10^{-20}\,\text{C}.$$

**APPROACH** We want to find the potential energy of the two charges in one dipole due to the two charges in the other, since this will be equal to the work needed to pull them infinitely far apart. The potential energy PE of a charge $q_1$ in the presence of a charge $q_2$ is

$$\text{PE} = k\,\frac{q_1 q_2}{r_{12}}$$

where $k = 9.0 \times 10^9\,\text{N}\cdot\text{m}^2/\text{C}^2$ (see Eqs. 17–2 and 17–5).

**SOLUTION** The potential energy (we use the symbol $U$) will consist of four terms:

$$U = U_{CH} + U_{CN} + U_{OH} + U_{ON},$$

where $U_{CH}$ means the potential energy of C in the presence of H, and similarly for the other terms. We do not have terms corresponding to C and O, or N and H, because the two dipoles are assumed to be stable entities. Then

$$U = k\,\frac{q_C q_H}{r_{CH}} + k\,\frac{q_C q_N}{r_{CN}} + k\,\frac{q_O q_H}{r_{OH}} + k\,\frac{q_O q_N}{r_{ON}}.$$

Using the distances shown in Fig. 29–11, we get:

$$U = (9.0 \times 10^9\,\text{N}\cdot\text{m}^2/\text{C}^2)\left(\frac{(6.6)(3.0)}{0.31} + \frac{(6.6)(-3.0)}{0.41} + \frac{(-6.6)(3.0)}{0.19} + \frac{(-6.6)(-3.0)}{0.29}\right)\frac{(10^{-20}\,\text{C})^2}{(10^{-9}\,\text{m})}$$

$$= -1.83 \times 10^{-20}\,\text{J}$$

$$= -\frac{(1.83 \times 10^{-20}\,\text{J})}{(1.60 \times 10^{-19}\,\text{J/eV})} = -0.11\,\text{eV}.$$

The PE is negative, meaning 0.11 eV of work (or energy input) is required to separate the molecules. That is, the binding energy of this "weak" or hydrogen bond is 0.11 eV. This is only an estimate, of course, since other charges in the vicinity would have an influence too.

## Protein Synthesis

Weak bonds, especially hydrogen bonds, are crucial to the process of protein synthesis. Proteins serve as structural parts of the cell and as enzymes to catalyze chemical reactions needed for the growth and survival of the organism. A protein molecule consists of one or more chains of small molecules known as *amino acids*.

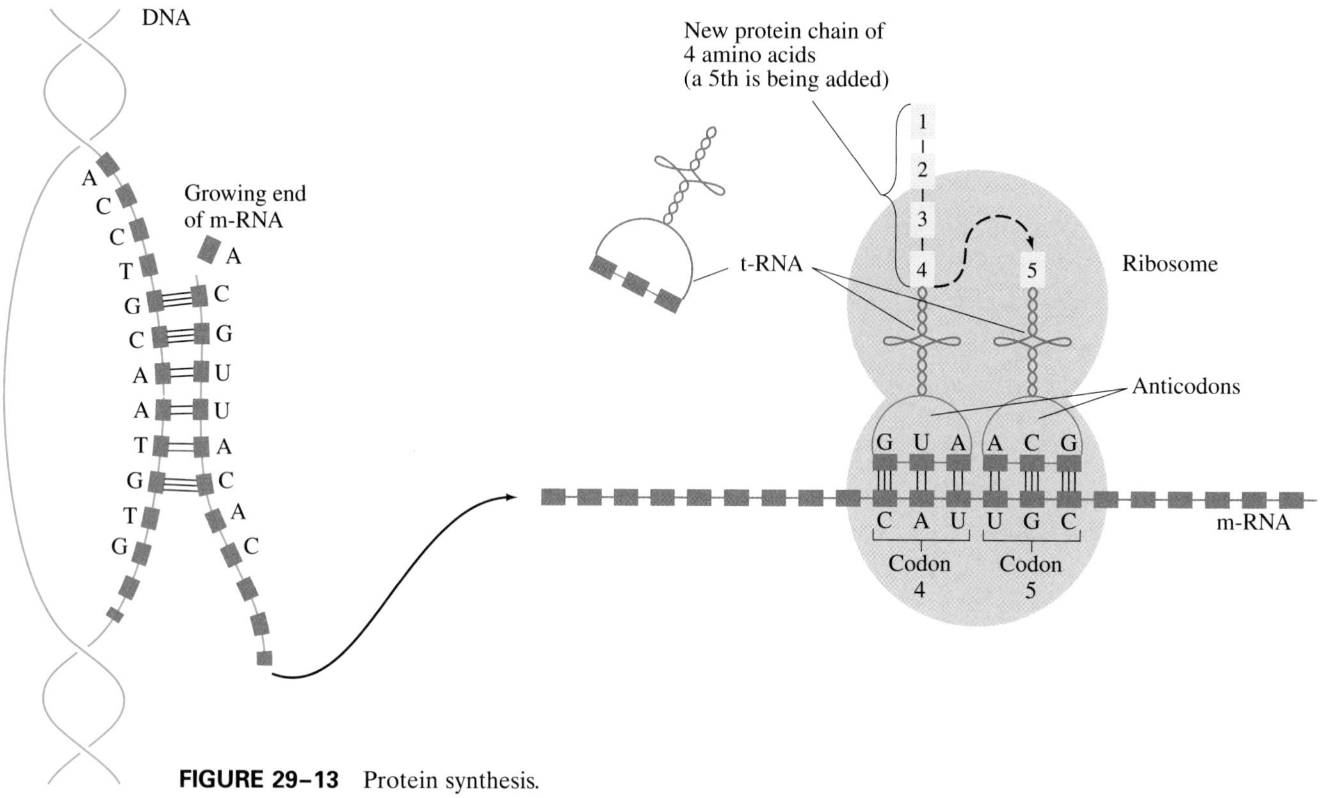


**FIGURE 29–13** Protein synthesis.

PHYSICS APPLIED
*Protein synthesis*

The standard model for how amino acids are connected together in the correct order to form a protein molecule is shown schematically in Fig. 29–13. It begins at the DNA double helix, for each gene on a chromosome contains the information for producing one protein. The ordering of the four bases, A, C, G, and T, provides the "code," the "genetic code," for the order of amino acids in the protein. First, the DNA double helix unwinds and a new molecule called *messenger*-RNA (m-RNA) is synthesized using one strand of the DNA as a "template." m-RNA is a chain molecule containing four different bases, like those of DNA except that thymine (T) is replaced by the similar uracil molecule (U). In Fig. 29–13, a C has just been added to the growing m-RNA chain in much the same way that DNA replicates (Fig. 16–45); and an A, attracted and held close to the T on the DNA chain by the electrostatic force, will soon be attached to the C by an enzyme. The order of the bases, and thus the genetic information, is preserved in the m-RNA. The m-RNA is buffeted about in the cell (remember kinetic theory) until it gets close to a tiny organelle known as a *ribosome*, to which it can become attached by electrostatic attraction, Fig. 29–13. Also held by the electrostatic force to the ribosome are one or two *transfer*-RNA (t-RNA) molecules. These t-RNA molecules "translate" the genetic code of nucleotide bases into amino acids in the following way. There is a different t-RNA molecule for each combination of three bases. At one end of the t-RNA molecule is the "anticodon," a set of three nucleotide bases. If all three bases of the anticodon match (in the sense of G to C and A to U) the three bases of the "codon" on the m-RNA at its attachment to the ribosome, the anticodon is attracted electrostatically to the m-RNA codon and is held there briefly. On the other end of a t-RNA molecule is the appropriate amino acid. The ribosome has two particular attachment sites which hold two t-RNA molecules while enzymes link their two amino acids together to lengthen the amino acid chain (yellow in Fig. 29–13). As each amino acid is connected by an enzyme (4 are already connected in Fig. 29–13, a fifth is about to be connected), the old t-RNA molecule is removed—perhaps by a random collision with some molecule in the cellular fluid. A new one soon becomes attracted as the ribosome moves along the m-RNA.

This process of protein synthesis is often presented as if it occurred in clockwork fashion—as if each molecule knew its role and went to its assigned place. But this is not the case. The forces of attraction between the electric charges of the molecules are rather weak and become significant only when the molecules can come close together and several weak bonds can be made. Indeed, if the shapes are not just right, there is almost no electrostatic attraction, which is why there are few mistakes. The fact that weak bonds are weak is very important. If they were strong, collisions with other molecules would not allow a t-RNA molecule to be released from the ribosome, or the m-RNA to be released from the DNA. If they were not temporary encounters, metabolism would grind to a halt.

*Protein shape*

As each amino acid is added to the next, the protein molecule grows in length until it is complete. Even as it is being made, this chain is being buffeted about in the cellular sea—we might think of a wiggling worm. But a protein molecule has electrically charged polar groups along its length. And as it takes on various shapes, the electric forces of attraction between different parts of the molecule will eventually lead to a particular configuration that is quite stable. Each type of protein has its own special shape, depending on the location of charged atoms. In the last analysis, the final shape depends on the order of the amino acids.

## * 29–4 Molecular Spectra

When atoms combine to form molecules, the probability distributions of the outer electrons overlap and this interaction alters the energy levels. Nonetheless, molecules can undergo transitions between electron energy levels just as atoms do. For example, the $H_2$ molecule can absorb a photon of just the right frequency to excite one of its ground-state electrons to an excited state. The excited electron can then return to the ground state, emitting a photon. The energy of photons emitted by molecules is of the same order of magnitude as for atoms, typically 1 to 10 eV.

Additional energy levels become possible for molecules (but not for atoms) because the molecule as a whole can rotate, and the atoms of the molecule can vibrate relative to each other. The energy levels for both rotational and vibrational levels are quantized, and are generally spaced much more closely ($10^{-3}$ to $10^{-1}$ eV) than the electronic levels. Each atomic energy level thus becomes a set of closely spaced levels corresponding to the vibrational and rotational motions, Fig. 29–14. Transitions from one level to another appear as many very closely spaced lines. In fact, the lines are not always distinguishable, and these spectra are called **band spectra**. Each type of molecule has its own characteristic spectrum, which can be used for identification and for determination of structure. We now look in more detail at rotational and vibrational states in molecules.

**FIGURE 29–14** (a) The individual energy levels of an isolated atom become (b) bands of closely spaced levels in molecules, as well as in solids and liquids.

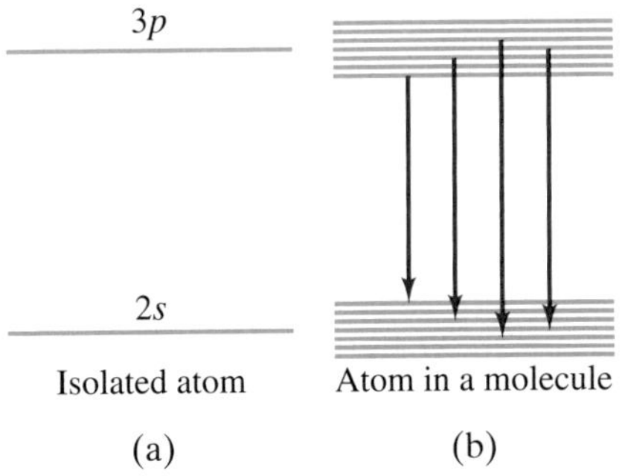

## * Rotational Energy Levels in Molecules

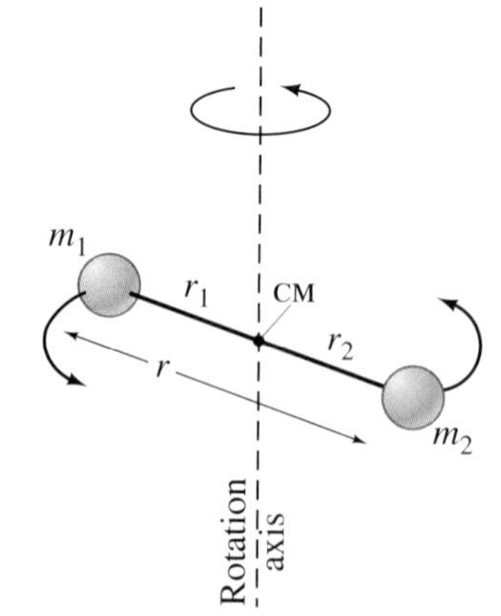


FIGURE 29–15 Diatomic molecule rotating about a vertical axis.

We consider only diatomic molecules, although the analysis can be extended to polyatomic molecules. When a diatomic molecule rotates about its center of mass as shown in Fig. 29–15, its kinetic energy of rotation (see Section 8–7) is

$$E_{\text{rot}} = \frac{1}{2} I\omega^2 = \frac{(I\omega)^2}{2I},$$

where $I\omega$ is the angular momentum (Section 8–8). Quantum mechanics predicts quantization of angular momentum just as in atoms (see Eq. 28–3):

$$I\omega = \sqrt{L(L+1)}\,\hbar, \qquad L = 0, 1, 2, \cdots,$$

where $L$ is an integer called the **rotational angular momentum quantum number**. Thus the rotational energy is quantized:

$$E_{\text{rot}} = \frac{(I\omega)^2}{2I} = L(L+1)\frac{\hbar^2}{2I}, \qquad L = 0, 1, 2, \cdots. \qquad \textbf{(29–1)}$$

Transitions between rotational energy levels are subject to the *selection rule* (as in Section 28–6):

*Selection rule (rotational levels)*

$$\Delta L = \pm 1.$$

The energy of a photon emitted or absorbed for a transition between rotational states with angular momentum quantum number $L$ and $L - 1$ will be

$$\Delta E_{\text{rot}} = E_L - E_{L-1} = \frac{\hbar^2}{2I}L(L+1) - \frac{\hbar^2}{2I}(L-1)(L)$$

$$= \frac{\hbar^2}{I}L. \qquad \left[\begin{array}{l}L \text{ is for upper}\\ \text{energy state}\end{array}\right] \qquad \textbf{(29–2)}$$

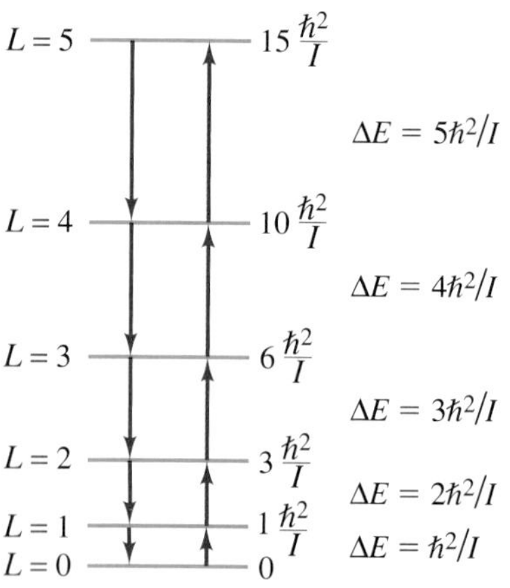


FIGURE 29–16 Rotational energy levels and allowed transitions (emission and absorption) for a diatomic molecule. Upward-pointing arrows represent absorption of a photon, and downward arrows represent emission of a photon.

We see that the transition energy increases directly with $L$. Figure 29–16 shows some of the allowed rotational energy levels and transitions. Measured absorption lines fall in the microwave or far-infrared regions of the spectrum, and their frequencies are generally 2, 3, 4, ··· times higher than the lowest one, as predicted by Eq. 29–2.

**EXAMPLE 29–2** **Rotational transition.** A rotational transition $L = 1$ to $L = 0$ for the molecule CO has a measured absorption wavelength $\lambda_1 = 2.60$ mm (microwave region). Use this to calculate (*a*) the moment of inertia of the CO molecule, and (*b*) the CO bond length, $r$.

**APPROACH** The absorption wavelength is used to find the energy of the absorbed photon, and we can then calculate the moment of inertia, $I$, from Eq. 29–2. The moment of inertia is related to the CO separation (bond length $r$).

**SOLUTION** (*a*) The photon energy, $E = hf = hc/\lambda$, equals the rotational energy level difference, $\Delta E_{\text{rot}}$. From Eq. 29–2, we can write

$$\frac{\hbar^2}{I}L = \Delta E_{\text{rot}} = hf = \frac{hc}{\lambda_1}.$$

With $L = 1$ (the upper state) in this case, we solve for $I$:

$$I = \frac{\hbar^2 L}{hc}\lambda_1 = \frac{h\lambda_1}{4\pi^2 c} = \frac{(6.63 \times 10^{-34}\,\text{J}\cdot\text{s})(2.60 \times 10^{-3}\,\text{m})}{4\pi^2(3.00 \times 10^8\,\text{m/s})}$$

$$= 1.46 \times 10^{-46}\,\text{kg}\cdot\text{m}^2.$$

(*b*) The molecule rotates about its center of mass (CM) as shown in Fig. 29–15. Let $m_1$ be the mass of the C atom, $m_1 = 12$ u, and let $m_2$ be the mass of the O, $m_2 = 16$ u. The distance of the CM from the C atom, which is $r_1$ in Fig. 29–15, is given by the CM formula, Eq. 7–9:

$$r_1 = \frac{0 + m_2 r}{m_1 + m_2} = \frac{16}{12 + 16}r = 0.57r.$$

The O atom is a distance $r_2 = r - r_1 = 0.43r$ from the CM. The moment of inertia of the CO molecule about its CM is then (see Example 8–10)

$$I = m_1 r_1^2 + m_2 r_2^2$$
$$= [(12\,\text{u})(0.57r)^2 + (16\,\text{u})(0.43r)^2][1.66 \times 10^{-27}\,\text{kg/u}]$$
$$= (1.14 \times 10^{-26}\,\text{kg})r^2.$$

We solve for $r$ and use the result of part ($a$) for $I$:

$$r = \sqrt{\frac{1.46 \times 10^{-46}\,\text{kg}\cdot\text{m}^2}{1.14 \times 10^{-26}\,\text{kg}}} = 1.13 \times 10^{-10}\,\text{m} = 0.113\,\text{nm}.$$

**EXERCISE A** What are the wavelengths of the next three rotational transitions for CO?

## * Vibrational Energy Levels in Molecules

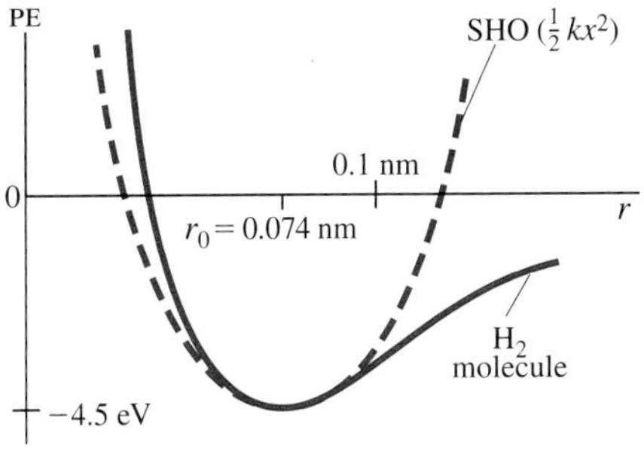


**FIGURE 29–17** Potential energy for the $H_2$ molecule and for a simple harmonic oscillator (PE $= \frac{1}{2}kx^2$, with $|x| = |r - r_0|$).

The potential energy of the two atoms in a typical diatomic molecule has the shape shown in Fig. 29–8 or 29–9, and Fig. 29–17 again shows the PE for the $H_2$ molecule (solid curve). This PE curve, at least in the vicinity of the equilibrium separation $r_0$, closely resembles the potential energy of a harmonic oscillator, PE $= \frac{1}{2}kx^2$, which is shown superimposed in dashed lines. Thus, for small displacements from $r_0$, each atom experiences a restoring force approximately proportional to the displacement, and the molecule vibrates as a simple harmonic oscillator (SHO)—see Chapter 11. According to quantum mechanics, the possible energy levels are quantized according to

$$E_{\text{vib}} = \left(\nu + \tfrac{1}{2}\right)hf, \qquad \nu = 0, 1, 2, \cdots, \tag{29–3}$$

where $f$ is the classical frequency (see Chapter 11—$f$ depends on the mass of the atoms and on the bond strength or "stiffness") and $\nu$ is an integer called the **vibrational quantum number**. The lowest energy state ($\nu = 0$) is not zero (as for rotation), but has $E = \frac{1}{2}hf$. This is called the **zero-point energy**. Higher states have energy $\frac{3}{2}hf$, $\frac{5}{2}hf$, and so on, as shown in Fig. 29–18. Transitions are subject to the *selection rule*:

*Selection rule (vibrational energy)*

$$\Delta\nu = \pm 1,$$

so allowed transitions occur only between adjacent states, and all give off photons of energy

$$\Delta E_{\text{vib}} = hf. \tag{29–4}$$

This is very close to experimental values for small $\nu$, but for higher energies, the PE curve (Fig. 29–17) begins to deviate from a perfect SHO curve, and this then affects the wavelengths and frequencies of the transitions. Typical transition energies are on the order of $10^{-1}$ eV, about 10 times larger than for rotational transitions, with wavelengths in the infrared region of the spectrum ($\approx 10^{-5}$ m).

**FIGURE 29–18** Allowed vibrational energies for a diatomic molecule, where $f$ is the fundamental frequency of vibration (see Chapter 11). The energy levels are equally spaced. Transitions are allowed only between adjacent levels ($\Delta\nu = \pm 1$).

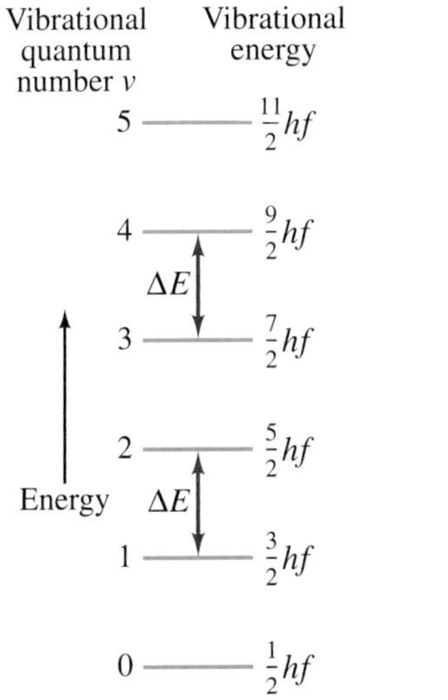


**EXAMPLE 29–3 Vibrational energy levels in hydrogen.** Hydrogen molecule vibrations emit infrared radiation of wavelength around 2300 nm. ($a$) What is the separation in energy between adjacent vibrational levels? ($b$) What is the lowest vibrational energy state?

**APPROACH** The energy separation between adjacent vibrational levels is (Eq. 29–4) $\Delta E_{\text{vib}} = hf = hc/\lambda$. The lowest energy (Eq. 29–3) has $\nu = 0$.

**SOLUTION**

($a$) $$\Delta E_{\text{vib}} = hf = \frac{hc}{\lambda} = \frac{(6.63 \times 10^{-34}\,\text{J}\cdot\text{s})(3.00 \times 10^8\,\text{m/s})}{(2300 \times 10^{-9}\,\text{m})(1.60 \times 10^{-19}\,\text{J/eV})} = 0.54\,\text{eV},$$

where the denominator includes the conversion factor from joules to eV.
($b$) The lowest vibrational energy has $\nu = 0$ in Eq. 29–3:

$$E_{\text{vib}} = \left(\nu + \tfrac{1}{2}\right)hf = \tfrac{1}{2}hf = 0.27\,\text{eV}.$$

**EXERCISE B** What is the energy of the first vibrational state above the ground state in the hydrogen molecule?

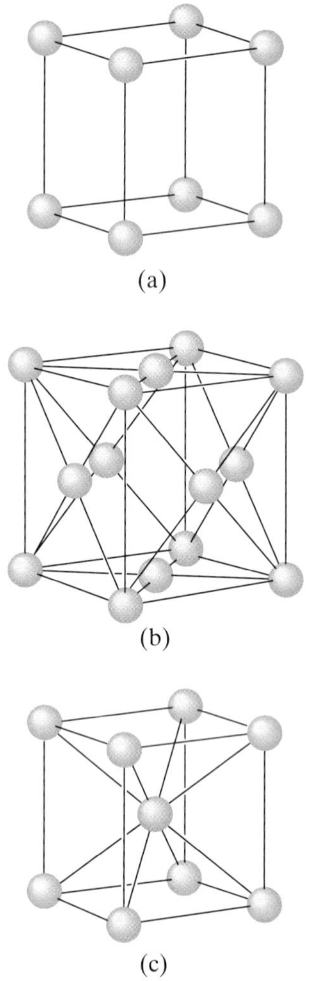


**FIGURE 29–19** Arrangement of atoms in (a) a simple cubic crystal, (b) face-centered cubic crystal (note the atom at the center of each face), and (c) body-centered cubic crystal. Each diagram shows the relationship of the bonds. Each of these "cells" is repeated in three dimensions to the edges of the macroscopic crystal.

**FIGURE 29–20** Diagram of an NaCl crystal, showing the "packing" of atoms.

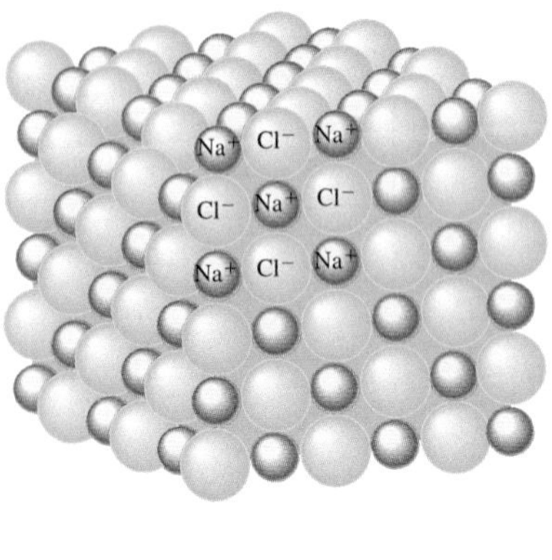


## * 29–5 Bonding in Solids

Quantum mechanics has been a great tool for understanding the structure of solids. This active field of research today is called **solid-state physics**, or **condensed-matter physics** so as to include liquids as well. The rest of this Chapter is devoted to this subject, and we begin with a brief look at the structure of solids and the bonds that hold them together.

Although some solid materials are *amorphous* in structure (such as glass), in that the atoms and molecules show no long-range order, we are interested here in the large class of *crystalline* substances whose atoms, ions, or molecules are generally accepted to form an orderly array in a geometric arrangement known as a **lattice**. Figure 29–19 shows three of the possible arrangements of atoms in a crystal: simple cubic, face-centered cubic, and body-centered cubic. The NaCl crystal lattice is face-centered cubic, with one $Na^+$ ion or one $Cl^-$ ion at each lattice point (see Fig. 29–20).

The molecules of a solid are held together in a number of ways. The most common are by *covalent* bonding (as between the carbon atoms of the diamond crystal) and by *ionic* bonding (as in a NaCl crystal). Often the bonds are partially covalent and partially ionic. Our discussion of these bonds earlier in this Chapter for molecules applies equally well here to solids.

Let us look for a moment at the NaCl crystal of Fig. 29–20. Each $Na^+$ ion feels an attractive Coulomb potential due to each of the six "nearest neighbor" $Cl^-$ ions surrounding it. Note that one $Na^+$ does not "belong" exclusively to one $Cl^-$, so we must not think of ionic solids as consisting of individual molecules. Each $Na^+$ also feels a repulsive Coulomb potential due to other $Na^+$ ions, although this is weaker since the $Na^+$ ions are farther away.

A different type of bond, not discussed in Section 29–1, occurs in metals. Metal atoms have relatively loosely held outer electrons. **Metallic bond** theories propose that in a metallic solid, these outer electrons roam rather freely among all the metal atoms which, without their outer electrons, act like positive ions. The electrostatic attraction between the metal ions and this negative electron "gas" is believed to be, at least in part, responsible for holding the solid together. The binding energy of metal bonds is typically 1 to 3 eV, somewhat weaker than ionic or covalent bonds (5 to 10 eV in solids). The "free electrons" are responsible for the high electrical and thermal conductivity of metals. This theory also nicely accounts for the shininess of smooth metal surfaces: the free electrons can vibrate at any frequency, so when light of a range of frequencies falls on a metal, the electrons can vibrate in response and reemit light of those same frequencies. Hence, the reflected light will consist largely of the same frequencies as the incident light. Compare this to nonmetallic materials that have a distinct color—the atomic electrons exist only in certain energy states, and when white light falls on them, the atoms absorb at certain frequencies, and reflect other frequencies which make up the color we see.

Here is a brief comparison of important strong bonds:

- ionic: an electron is stolen from one atom by another
- covalent: electrons are shared by atoms within a single molecule
- metallic: electrons are shared by all atoms in the metal

The atoms or molecules of some materials, such as the noble gases, can form only **weak bonds** with each other. As we saw in Section 29–3, weak bonds have very low binding energies and would not be expected to hold atoms together as a liquid or solid at room temperature. The noble gases condense only at very low temperatures, where the atomic (thermal) kinetic energy is small and the weak attraction can then hold the atoms together.

# * 29–6 Band Theory of Solids

We saw in Section 29–1 that when two hydrogen atoms approach each other, the wave functions overlap, and the two 1*s* states (one for each atom) divide into two states of different energy. (As we saw, only one of these states, $S = 0$, has low enough energy to give a bound $H_2$ molecule.) Figure 29–21a shows this situation for 1*s* and 2*s* states for two atoms: as the two atoms get closer (toward the left on the graph), the 1*s* and 2*s* states split into two levels. If six atoms come together, as in Fig. 29-21b, each of the states splits into six levels. If a large number of atoms come together to form a solid, then each of the original atomic levels becomes a **band** as shown in Fig. 29–21c. The energy levels are so close together in each band that they seem essentially continuous. This is why the spectrum of heated solids (Section 27–2) appears continuous.

*Energy bands*

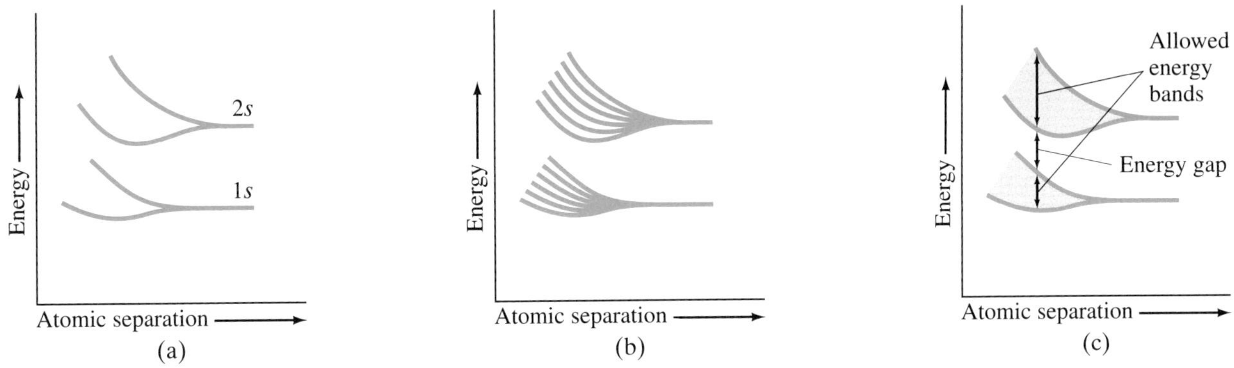


**FIGURE 29–21** The splitting of 1*s* and 2*s* atomic energy levels as (a) two atoms approach each other (the atomic separation decreases toward the left on the graph); (b) the same for six atoms, and (c) for many atoms when they come together to form a solid.

*Conductors*

The crucial aspect of a good **conductor** is that the highest energy band containing electrons is only partially filled. Consider sodium, for example, whose energy bands are shown in Fig. 29–22. The 1*s*, 2*s*, and 2*p* bands are full (just as in a Na atom) and don't concern us. The 3*s* band, however, is only half full. To see why, recall that the exclusion principle stipulates that in an atom, only two electrons can be in the 3*s* state, one with spin up and one with spin down. These two states have slightly different energy. For a solid consisting of $N$ atoms, the 3*s* band will contain $2N$ possible energy states. A sodium atom has a single 3*s* electron, so in a sample of sodium metal containing $N$ atoms, there are $N$ electrons in the 3*s* band, and $N$ unoccupied states. When a potential difference is applied across the metal, electrons can respond by accelerating and increasing their energy, since there are plenty of unoccupied states of slightly higher energy available. Hence, a current flows readily and sodium is a good conductor. The characteristic of all good conductors is that the highest energy band is only partially filled, or two bands overlap so that unoccupied states are available. An example of the latter is magnesium, which has two 3*s* electrons, so its 3*s* band is filled. But the unfilled 3*p* band overlaps the 3*s* band in energy, so there are lots of available states for the electrons to move into. Thus magnesium, too, is a good conductor.

**FIGURE 29–22** Energy bands for sodium.

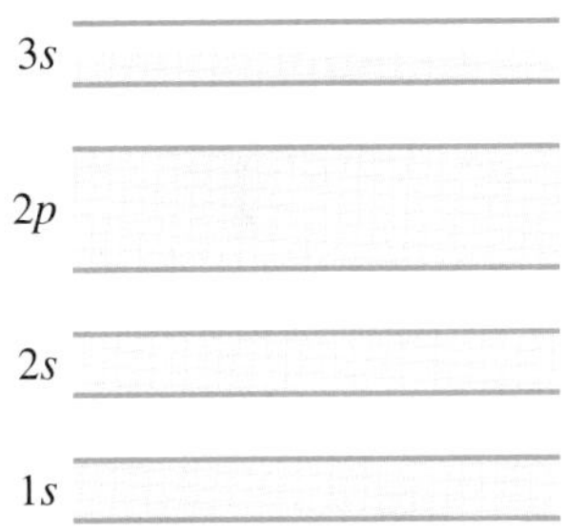


*Insulators*

*Valence and conduction bands*

*Energy gap*

In a material that is a good **insulator**, on the other hand, the highest band containing electrons, called the **valence band**, is completely filled. The next highest energy band, called the **conduction band**, is separated from the valence band by a "forbidden" **energy gap** (or **band gap**), $E_g$, of typically 5 to 10 eV. So at room temperature (300 K), where thermal energies (that is, average kinetic energy—see Chapter 13) are on the order of $\frac{3}{2}kT \approx 0.04$ eV, almost no electrons can acquire the 5 eV needed to reach the conduction band. When a potential difference is applied across the material, no available states are accessible to the electrons, and no current flows. Hence, the material is a good insulator.

FIGURE 29–23 Energy bands for (a) a conductor, (b) an insulator, which has a large energy gap $E_g$, and (c) a semiconductor, which has a small energy gap $E_g$. Shading represents occupied states. Pale shading in (c) represents electrons that can pass from the top of the valence band to the bottom of the conduction band due to thermal agitation at room temperature (exaggerated).

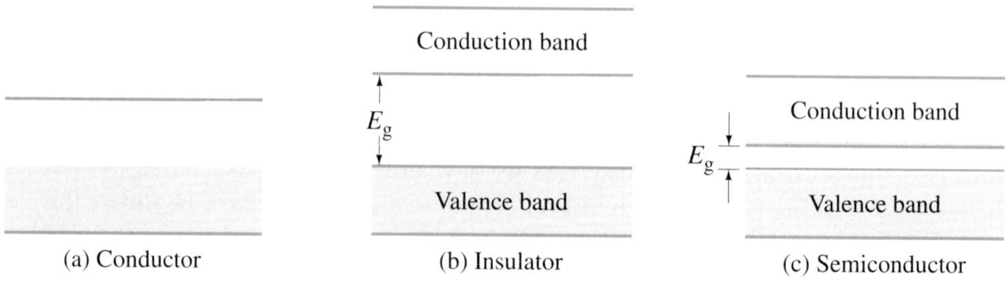


*Semiconductors (pure)*

Figure 29–23 compares the relevant energy bands (a) for conductors, (b) for insulators, and also (c) for the important class of materials known as **semiconductors**. The bands for a pure (or **intrinsic**) semiconductor, such as silicon or germanium, are like those for an insulator, except that the unfilled conduction band is separated from the filled valence band by a much smaller energy gap, $E_g$, typically on the order of 1 eV. At room temperature, a few electrons can acquire enough thermal energy to reach the conduction band, and so a very small current may flow when a voltage is applied. At higher temperatures, more electrons have enough energy to jump the gap. Often this effect can more than offset the effects of more frequent collisions due to increased disorder at higher temperature, so the resistivity of semiconductors can *decrease* with increasing temperature (see Table 18–1). But this is not the whole story of semiconductor conduction. When a potential difference is applied to a semiconductor, the few electrons in the conduction band move toward the positive electrode. Electrons in the valence band try to do the same thing, and a few can because there are a small number of unoccupied states which were left empty by the electrons reaching the conduction band. Such unfilled electron states are called **holes**. Each electron in the valence band that fills a hole in this way as it moves toward the positive electrode leaves behind its own hole, so the holes migrate toward the negative electrode. As the electrons tend to accumulate at one side of the material, the holes tend to accumulate on the opposite side. We will look at this phenomenon in more detail in the next Section.

*Holes (in a semiconductor)*

**EXAMPLE 29–4 Calculating the energy gap.** It is found that the conductivity of a certain semiconductor increases when light of wavelength 345 nm or shorter strikes it, suggesting that electrons are being promoted from the valence band to the conduction band. What is the energy gap, $E_g$, for this semiconductor?

**APPROACH** The longest wavelength (lowest energy) photon to cause an increase in conductivity has $\lambda = 345$ nm, and its energy $(= hf)$ equals the energy gap.

**SOLUTION** The gap energy equals the energy of a $\lambda = 345$-nm photon:

$$E_g = hf = \frac{hc}{\lambda} = \frac{(6.63 \times 10^{-34}\,\mathrm{J\cdot s})(3.00 \times 10^{8}\,\mathrm{m/s})}{(345 \times 10^{-9}\,\mathrm{m})(1.60 \times 10^{-19}\,\mathrm{J/eV})} = 3.6\,\mathrm{eV}.$$

**CONCEPTUAL EXAMPLE 29–5 Which is transparent?** The energy gap for silicon is 1.14 eV at room temperature, whereas that of zinc sulfide (ZnS) is 3.6 eV. Which one of these is opaque to visible light, and which is transparent?

**RESPONSE** Visible light photons span energies from roughly 1.8 eV to 3.2 eV ($E = hf = hc/\lambda$ where $\lambda = 400$ nm to 700 nm and 1 eV $= 1.6 \times 10^{-19}$ J.) Light is absorbed by the electrons in a material. Silicon's energy gap is small enough to absorb these photons, thus bumping electrons well up into the conduction band, so silicon is opaque. On the other hand, zinc sulfide's energy gap is too large to absorb visible photons, so the light can pass through the material; it can be transparent.

# * 29–7 Semiconductors and Doping

Nearly all electronic devices today use semiconductors. The most common are silicon (Si) and germanium (Ge). An atom of silicon or germanium has four outer electrons that act to hold the atoms in the regular lattice structure of the crystal, shown schematically in Fig. 29–24a. Germanium and silicon acquire properties useful for electronics only when a tiny amount of impurity is introduced into the crystal structure (perhaps 1 part in $10^6$ or $10^7$). This is called **doping** the semiconductor. Two kinds of doped semiconductor can be made, depending on the type of impurity used. If the impurity is an element whose atoms have five outer electrons, such as arsenic, we have the situation shown in Fig. 29–24b, with the arsenic atoms holding positions in the crystal lattice where normally silicon atoms would be. Only four of arsenic's electrons fit into the bonding structure. The fifth does not fit in and can move relatively freely, somewhat like the electrons in a conductor. Because of this small number of extra electrons, a doped semiconductor becomes slightly conducting. The density of conduction electrons in an intrinsic (undoped) semiconductor at room temperature is very low, usually less than 1 per $10^9$ atoms. With an impurity concentration of 1 in $10^6$ or $10^7$ when doped, the conductivity will be much higher and it can be controlled with great precision. An arsenic-doped silicon crystal is called an ***n*-type semiconductor** because *negative* charges (electrons) carry the electric current.

*Doped semiconductors*

*n-type*

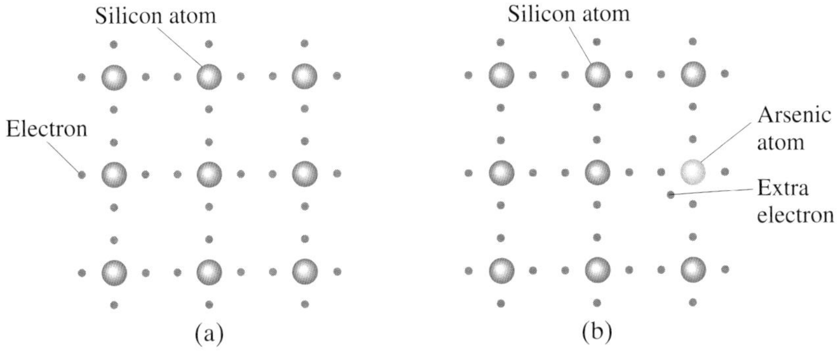


**FIGURE 29–24** Two-dimensional representation of a silicon crystal. (a) Four (outer) electrons surround each silicon atom. (b) Silicon crystal doped with a small percentage of arsenic atoms: the extra electron doesn't fit into the crystal lattice and so is free to move about. This is an *n*-type semiconductor.

In a ***p*-type semiconductor**, a small percentage of semiconductor atoms are replaced by atoms with three outer electrons—such as gallium. As shown in Fig. 29–25a, there is a "hole" in the lattice structure near a gallium atom since it has only three outer electrons. Electrons from nearby silicon atoms can jump into this hole and fill it. But this leaves a hole where that electron had previously been, Fig. 29–25b. The vast majority of atoms are silicon, so holes are almost always next to a silicon atom. Since silicon atoms require four outer electrons to be neutral, this means that there is a net positive charge at the hole. Whenever an electron moves to fill a hole, the positive hole is then at the previous position of that electron. Another electron can then fill this hole, and the hole thus moves to a new location; and so on. This type of semiconductor is called *p-type* because it is the positive holes that seem to carry the electric current. Note, however, that both *p-type* and *n-type* semiconductors have *no net charge* on them.

*p-type*

**CAUTION**

*p-type semiconductors act as though + charges move—but electrons actually do the moving*

*Holes are positive*

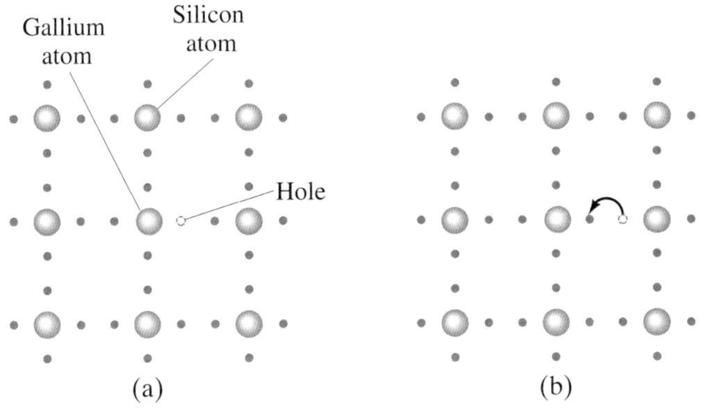


**FIGURE 29–25** A *p*-type semiconductor, gallium-doped silicon. (a) Gallium has only three outer electrons, so there is an empty spot, or *hole* in the structure. (b) Electrons from silicon atoms can jump into the hole and fill it. As a result, the hole moves to a new location (to the right in this figure), to where the electron used to be.

According to the band theory (Section 29–6), in a doped semiconductor the impurity provides additional energy states between the bands as shown in Fig. 29–26. In an $n$-type semiconductor, the impurity energy level lies just below the conduction band, Fig. 29–26a. Electrons in this energy level need only about 0.05 eV in Si (even less in Ge) to reach the conduction band; this is on the order of the thermal energy, $\frac{3}{2}kT$ (= 0.04 eV at 300 K), so transitions occur readily at room temperature. This energy level can thus supply electrons to the conduction band, so it is called a **donor** level. In $p$-type semiconductors, the impurity energy level is just above the valence band (Fig. 29–26b). It is called an **acceptor** level because electrons from the valence band can easily jump into it. Positive holes are left behind in the valence band, and as other electrons move into these holes, the holes move about as discussed earlier.

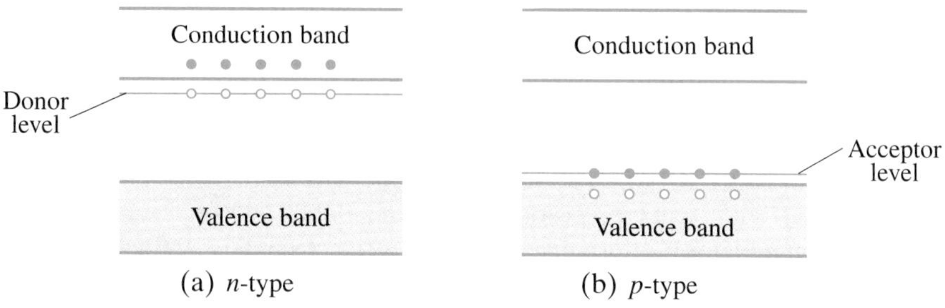


**FIGURE 29–26** Impurity energy levels in doped semiconductors.

## * 29–8 Semiconductor Diodes

Semiconductor diodes and transistors are essential components of modern electronic devices. The miniaturization achieved today allows many thousands of diodes, transistors, resistors, and so on, to be placed on a single *chip* less than a millimeter on a side. We now discuss, briefly and qualitatively, the operation of diodes and transistors.

pn *junction diode*

When an $n$-type semiconductor is joined to a $p$-type, a ***pn* junction diode** is formed. Separately, the two semiconductors are electrically neutral. When joined, a few electrons near the junction diffuse from the $n$-type into the $p$-type semiconductor, where they fill a few of the holes. The $n$-type is left with a positive charge, and the $p$-type acquires a net negative charge. Thus a potential difference is established, with the $n$ side positive relative to the $p$ side, and this prevents further diffusion of electrons.

If a battery is connected to a diode with the positive terminal to the $p$ side and the negative terminal to the $n$ side as in Fig. 29–27a, the externally applied voltage opposes the internal potential difference and the diode is said to be **forward biased**. If the voltage is great enough (about 0.3 V for Ge, 0.6 V for Si at room temperature), a current will flow. The positive holes in the $p$-type semiconductor are repelled by the positive terminal of the battery, and the electrons in the $n$-type are repelled by the negative terminal of the battery. The holes and electrons meet at the junction, and the electrons cross over and fill the holes. A current is flowing. Meanwhile, the positive terminal of the battery is continually pulling electrons off the $p$ end, forming new holes, and electrons are being supplied by the negative terminal at the $n$ end. Consequently, a large current flows through the diode.

When the diode is **reverse biased**, as in Fig. 29–27b, the holes in the $p$ end are attracted to the battery's negative terminal and the electrons in the $n$ end are attracted to the positive terminal. The current carriers do not meet near the junction and, ideally, no current flows.

A graph of current versus voltage for a typical diode is shown in Fig. 29–28. As can be seen, a real diode does allow a small amount of reverse current to flow.† For most practical purposes, this is negligible.

**FIGURE 29–27** Schematic diagram showing how a semiconductor diode operates. Current flows when the voltage is connected in forward bias, as in (a), but not when connected in reverse bias, as in (b).

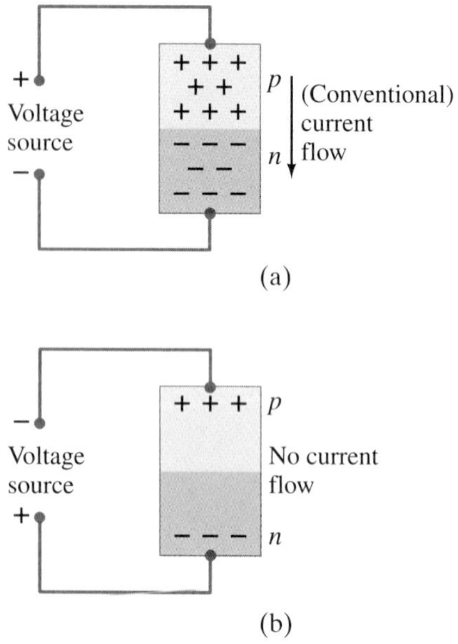


†At room temperature it is a few $\mu$A in Ge, and a few pA in Si. The reverse current increases rapidly with temperature, however, and may render a diode ineffective above 200°C.

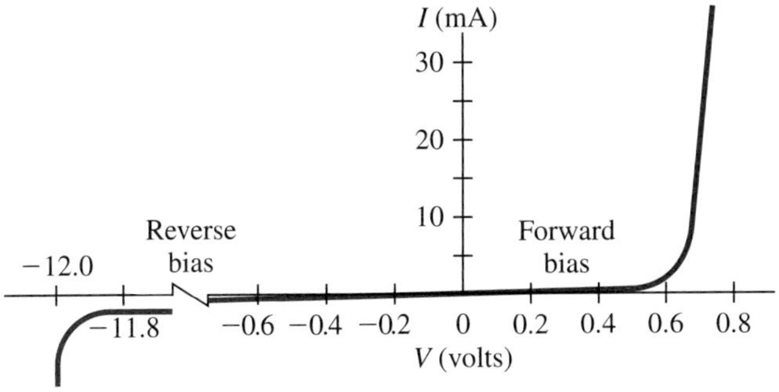


**FIGURE 29–28** Current through a diode as a function of applied voltage.

**EXAMPLE 29–6** **A diode.** The diode whose current–voltage characteristics are shown in Fig. 29–28 is connected in series with a 4.0-V battery and a resistor. If a current of 15 mA is to pass through the diode, what resistance must the resistor have?

**APPROACH** We use Fig. 29–28, where we see that the voltage drop across the diode is about 0.7 V when the current is 15 mA. Then we use simple circuit analysis and Ohm's law (Chapters 18 and 19).

**SOLUTION** The voltage drop across the resistor is $4.0\text{ V} - 0.7\text{ V} = 3.3\text{ V}$, so $R = V/I = (3.3\text{ V})/(1.5 \times 10^{-2}\text{ A}) = 220\ \Omega$.

The symbol for a diode is

[diode]

where the arrow represents the direction conventional (+) current flows readily.

Since a *pn* junction diode allows current to flow only in one direction (as long as the voltage is not too high), it can serve as a **rectifier**—to change ac into dc. A simple rectifier circuit is shown in Fig. 29–29a. The ac source applies a voltage across the diode alternately positive and negative. Only during half of each cycle will a current pass through the diode; only then is there a current through the resistor $R$. Hence, a graph of the voltage $V_{ab}$ across $R$ as a function of time looks like the output voltage shown in Fig. 29–29b. This **half-wave rectification** is not exactly dc, but it is unidirectional. More useful is a **full-wave rectifier** circuit, which uses two diodes (or sometimes four) as shown in Fig. 29–30a. At any given instant, either one diode or the other will conduct current to the right. Therefore, the output across the load resistor $R$ will be as shown in Fig. 29–30b. Actually this is the voltage if the capacitor $C$ were not in the circuit. The capacitor tends to store charge and, if the time constant $RC$ is sufficiently long, helps to smooth out the current as shown in Fig. 29–30c. (The variation in output shown in Fig. 29–30c is called *ripple voltage*.)

Rectifier circuits are important because most line voltage in buildings is ac, and most electronic devices require a dc voltage for their operation. Hence, diodes are found in nearly all electronic devices including radio and TV sets, calculators, and computers.

**FIGURE 29–29** (a) A simple (half-wave) rectifier circuit using a semiconductor diode. (b) AC source input voltage, and output voltage across $R$, as functions of time.

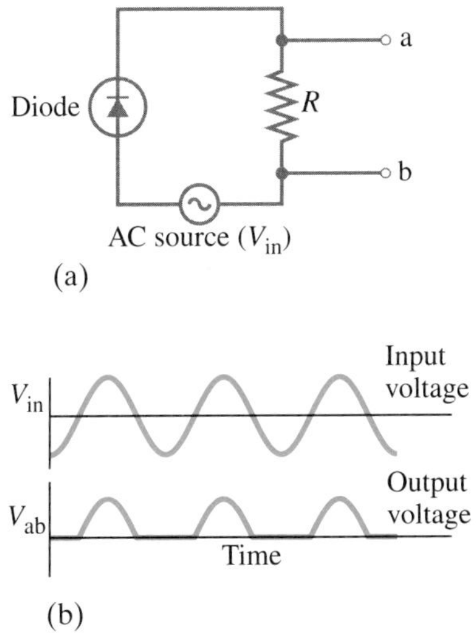


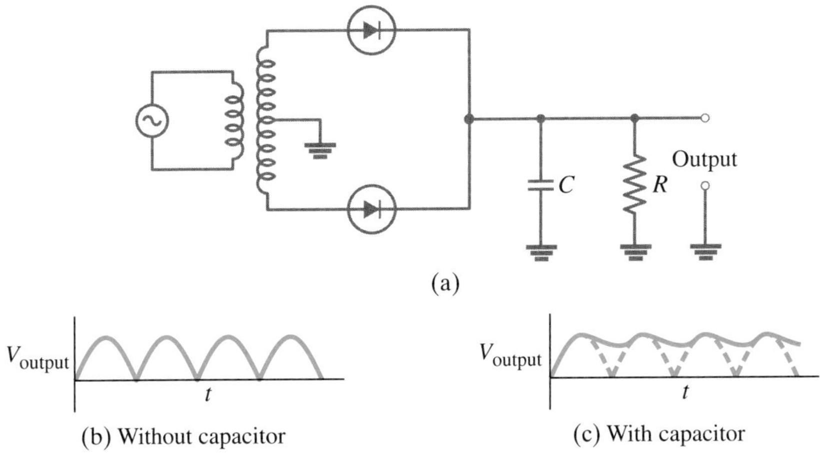


**FIGURE 29–30** (a) Full-wave-rectifier circuit (including a transformer so the magnitude of the voltage can be changed). (b) Output voltage in the absence of capacitor $C$. (c) Output voltage with the capacitor in the circuit.

PHYSICS APPLIED

*LED*

Another useful device is a **light-emitting diode** (LED), invented in the 1960s. When a *pn* junction is forward biased, a current begins to flow. Electrons cross from the *n* region into the *p* region and combine with holes, and a photon can be emitted with an energy approximately equal to the band gap, $E_g$ (see Figs. 29–23c and 29–26). Often the energy, and hence the wavelength, is in the red region of the visible spectrum, producing the familiar LED displays on VCRs, CD players, car instrument panels, digital clocks, and so on. Infrared (i.e., nonvisible) LEDs are used in remote controls for TV, DVDs, and stereos. New types of LEDs emit other colors, and LED "bulbs" are beginning to replace other types of lighting in applications such as flashlights, traffic signals, car brake lights, and outdoor signs, billboards, and theater displays. LED bulbs, sometimes called **solid-state** lighting, are costly, but they offer advantages: they are long-lived, efficient, and rugged. LED traffic lights, for example, last 5 to 10 times longer than traditional incandescent bulbs, and use only 20% of the energy for the same light output. As car brake lights, they light up a fraction of a second sooner, allowing a driver an extra 5 or 6 meters (15–20 ft) more stopping distance at highway speeds.

*Solar cells and photodiodes*

**Solar cells** and **photodiodes** (Section 27–3) are *pn* junctions used in the reverse way. Photons are absorbed, creating electron–hole pairs if the photon energy is greater than the band gap energy, $E_g$. The created electrons and holes produce a current that, when connected to an external circuit, becomes a source of emf and power. *Particle detectors* (Section 30–13) operate similarly.

A diode is called a **nonlinear device** because the current is not proportional to the voltage. That is, a graph of current versus voltage (Fig. 29–28) is not a straight line, as it is for a resistor (which ideally *is* linear). Transistors are also *nonlinear* devices.

## * 29–9 Transistors and Integrated Circuits

*Transistors*

A simple **junction transistor** consists of a crystal of one type of doped semiconductor sandwiched between two crystals of the opposite type. Both *npn* and *pnp* transistors are made, and they are shown schematically in Fig. 29–31a. The three semiconductors are given the names *collector, base,* and *emitter*. The symbols for *npn* and *pnp* transistors are shown in Fig. 29–31b. The arrow is always placed on the emitter and indicates the direction of (conventional) current flow in normal operation.

The operation of a transistor can be analyzed qualitatively—very briefly—as follows. Consider an *npn* transistor connected as shown in Fig. 29–32. A voltage $V_{CE}$ is maintained between the collector and emitter by the battery $\mathscr{E}_C$. The voltage applied to the base is called the *base bias voltage*, $V_{BE}$. If $V_{BE}$ is positive, conduction electrons in the emitter are attracted into the base. Since the base region is very thin (perhaps 1 $\mu$m), most of these electrons flow right across into the collector, which is maintained at a positive voltage. A large current, $I_C$, flows between collector and emitter and a much smaller current, $I_B$,

**FIGURE 29–31** (a) Schematic diagram of *npn* and *pnp* transistors. (b) Symbols for *npn* and *pnp* transistors.

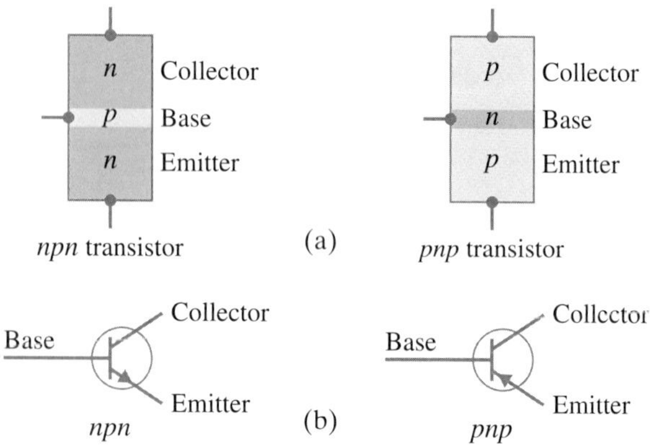


**FIGURE 29–32** An *npn* transistor used as an amplifier.

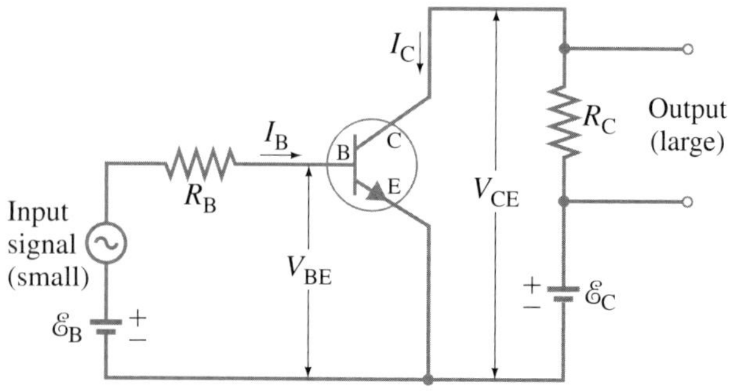

through the base. A small variation in the base voltage due to an input signal causes a large change in the collector current and therefore a large change in the voltage drop across the output resistor $R_C$. Hence a transistor can *amplify* a small signal into a larger one.

*Amplifiers*

Transistors are the basic elements in modern electronic **amplifiers** of all sorts. In **digital circuits**, where "off" and "on" (or zero and one) are basic, transistors can act like a "gate" or switch. That is, they let current pass ("on") or they block it ("off").

*Digital circuits and gates*

A *pnp* transistor operates like an *npn*, except that holes move instead of electrons. The collector voltage is negative, and so is the base voltage in normal operation.

Transistors were a great advance in miniaturization of electronic circuits. Although individual transistors are very small compared to the once used vacuum tubes, they are huge compared to **integrated circuits** or **chips** (see photo at start of this Chapter). Tiny amounts of impurities can be placed at particular locations within a single silicon crystal. These can be arranged to form diodes, transistors, and resistors (undoped semiconductors). Capacitors and inductors can also be formed, although they are often connected separately. A tiny chip, a few mm on a side, may contain millions of transistors and other circuit elements. Integrated circuits are the heart of computers, television, calculators, cameras, and the electronic instruments that control aircraft, space vehicles, and automobiles. The "miniaturization" produced by integrated circuits not only allows extremely complicated circuits to be placed in a small space, but also has allowed a great increase in the speed of operation of, say, computers, because the distances the electronic signals travel are so tiny.

## *Summary

Quantum mechanics explains the bonding together of atoms to form **molecules**. In a **covalent bond**, the electron clouds of two or more atoms overlap because of constructive interference between the electron waves. The positive nuclei are attracted to this concentration of negative charge between them, forming the bond.

An **ionic bond** is an extreme case of a covalent bond in which one or more electrons from one atom spend much more time around the other atom than around their own. The atoms then act as oppositely charged ions that attract each other, forming the bond.

These **strong bonds** hold molecules together, and also hold atoms and molecules together in solids. Also important are **weak bonds** (or **van der Waals bonds**), which are generally dipole attractions between molecules.

When atoms combine to form molecules, the energy levels of the outer electrons are altered because they now interact with each other. Additional energy levels also become possible because the atoms can vibrate with respect to each other, and the molecule as a whole can rotate. The energy levels for both vibrational and rotational motion are quantized, and are very close together (typically, $10^{-1}$ eV to $10^{-3}$ eV apart). Each atomic energy level thus becomes a set of closely spaced levels corresponding to the vibrational and rotational motions. Transitions from one level to another appear as many very closely spaced lines. The resulting spectra are called **band spectra**.

The quantized rotational energy levels are given by

$$E_{\text{rot}} = L(L+1)\frac{\hbar^2}{2I}, \qquad L = 0, 1, 2, \cdots, \qquad \textbf{(29–1)}$$

where $I$ is the moment of inertia of the molecule.

The energy levels for vibrational motion are given by

$$E_{\text{vib}} = \left(\nu + \tfrac{1}{2}\right)hf, \qquad \nu = 0, 1, 2, \cdots, \qquad \textbf{(29–3)}$$

where $f$ is the classical natural frequency of vibration for the molecule. Transitions between energy levels are subject to the selection rules $\Delta L = \pm 1$ and $\Delta\nu = \pm 1$.

Some **solids** are bound together by covalent and ionic bonds, just as molecules are. In metals, the electrostatic force between free electrons and positive ions helps form the **metallic bond**.

In a crystalline solid, the possible energy states for electrons are arranged in **bands**. Within each band the levels are very close together, but between the bands there may be forbidden **energy gaps**. Good conductors are characterized by the highest occupied band (the **conduction band**) being only partially full, so there are many accessible states available to electrons to move about and accelerate when a voltage is applied. In a good insulator, the highest occupied energy band (the **valence band**) is completely full, and there is a large energy gap (5 to 10 eV) to the next highest band, the *conduction band*. At room temperature, molecular kinetic energy (thermal energy) available due to collisions is only about 0.04 eV, so almost no electrons can jump from the valence to the conduction band. In a **semiconductor**, the gap between valence and conduction bands is much smaller, on the order of 1 eV, so a few electrons can make the transition from the essentially full valence band to the nearly empty conduction band.

In a **doped** semiconductor, a small percentage of impurity atoms with five or three valence electrons replace a few of the normal silicon atoms with their four valence electrons. A five-electron impurity produces an ***n*-type** semiconductor with negative electrons as carriers of current. A three-electron impurity produces a ***p*-type** semiconductor in which positive **holes** carry the current. The energy level of impurity atoms lies slightly below the conduction band in an *n*-type semiconductor, and acts as a **donor** from which electrons readily pass into the conduction band. The energy level of impurity atoms in a *p*-type semiconductor lies slightly above the valence band and acts as an **acceptor** level, since electrons from the valence band easily reach it, leaving holes behind to act as charge carriers.

A semiconductor **diode** consists of a ***pn* junction** and allows current to flow in one direction only; it can be used as a **rectifier** to change ac to dc. Common **transistors** consist of three semiconductor sections, either as ***pnp*** or ***npn***. Transistors can amplify electrical signals and find many other uses. An integrated circuit consists of a tiny semiconductor crystal or **chip** on which many transistors, diodes, resistors, and other circuit elements have been constructed using careful placement of impurities.

## Questions

*1. What type of bond would you expect for (*a*) the $N_2$ molecule, (*b*) the HCl molecule, (*c*) Fe atoms in a solid?

*2. Describe how the molecule $CaCl_2$ could be formed.

*3. Does the $H_2$ molecule have a permanent dipole moment? Does $O_2$? Does $H_2O$? Explain.

*4. Although the molecule $H_3$ is not stable, the ion $H_3^+$ is. Explain, using the Pauli exclusion principle.

*5. The energy of a molecule can be divided into four categories. What are they?

*6. Would you expect the molecule $H_2^+$ to be stable? If so, where would the single electron spend most of its time?

*7. Explain why the carbon atom $(Z = 6)$ usually forms four bonds with hydrogen-like atoms.

*8. If conduction electrons are free to roam about in a metal, why don't they leave the metal entirely?

*9. Explain why the resistivity of metals increases with temperature whereas the resistivity of semiconductors may decrease with increasing temperature.

*10. Figure 29–33 shows a "bridge-type" full-wave rectifier. Explain how the current is rectified and how current flows during each half cycle.

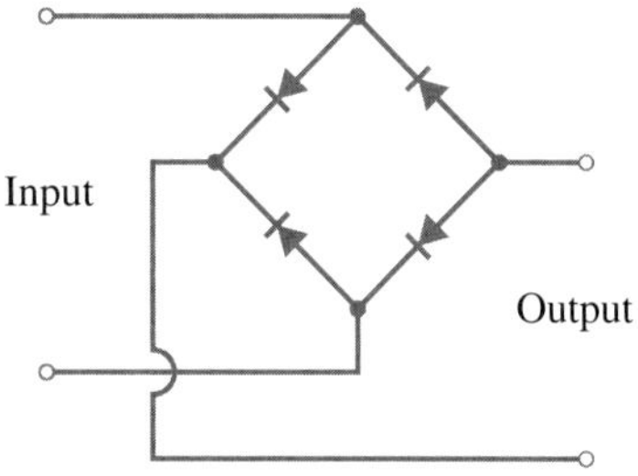


**FIGURE 29–33** Question 10.

*11. Compare the resistance of a *pn* junction diode connected in forward bias to its resistance when connected in reverse bias.

*12. Explain how a transistor could be used as a switch.

*13. What is the main difference between *n*-type and *p*-type semiconductors?

*14. Describe how a *pnp* transistor can operate as an amplifier.

*15. In a transistor, the base–emitter junction and the base–collector junction are essentially diodes. Are these junctions reverse-biased or forward-biased in the application shown in Fig. 29–32?

*16. A transistor can amplify an electronic signal, meaning it can increase the power of an input signal. Where does it get the energy to increase the power?

*17. A silicon semiconductor is doped with phosphorus. Will these atoms be donors or acceptors? What type of semiconductor will this be?

*18. Do diodes and transistors obey Ohm's law? Explain.

*19. Can a diode be used to amplify a signal? Explain.

## Problems

### *29–1 to 29–3 Molecular Bonds

*1. (I) Estimate the binding energy of a KCl molecule by calculating the electrostatic potential energy when the $K^+$ and $Cl^-$ ions are at their stable separation of 0.28 nm. Assume each has a charge of magnitude 1.0*e*.

*2. (II) The measured binding energy of KCl is 4.43 eV. From the result of Problem 1, estimate the contribution to the binding energy of the repelling electron clouds at the equilibrium distance $r_0 = 0.28$ nm.

*3. (II) Estimate the binding energy of the $H_2$ molecule, assuming the two H nuclei are 0.074 nm apart and the two electrons spend 33% of their time midway between them.

*4. (II) Binding energies are often measured experimentally in kcal per mole, and then the binding energy in eV per molecule is calculated from that result. What is the conversion factor in going from kcal per mole to eV per molecule? What is the binding energy of KCl (= 4.43 eV) in kcal per mole?

*5. (III) (*a*) Apply reasoning similar to that in the text for the $S = 0$ and $S = 1$ states in the formation of the $H_2$ molecule to show why the molecule $He_2$ is *not* formed. (*b*) Explain why the $He_2^+$ molecular ion *could* form. (Experiment shows it has a binding energy of 3.1 eV at $r_0 = 0.11$ nm.)

### *29–4 Molecular Spectra

*6. (I) Show that the quantity $\hbar^2/I$ has units of energy.

*7. (II) The so-called "characteristic rotational energy," $\hbar^2/2I$, for $N_2$ is $2.48 \times 10^{-4}$ eV. Calculate the $N_2$ bond length.

*8. (II) (*a*) Calculate the characteristic rotational energy, $\hbar^2/2I$, for the $O_2$ molecule whose bond length is 0.121 nm. (*b*) What are the energy and wavelength of photons emitted in a $L = 2$ to $L = 1$ transition?

*9. (II) The equilibrium separation of H atoms in the $H_2$ molecule is 0.074 nm (Fig. 29–8). Calculate the energies and wavelengths of photons for the rotational transitions (*a*) $L = 1$ to $L = 0$, (*b*) $L = 2$ to $L = 1$, and (*c*) $L = 3$ to $L = 2$.

* 10. (II) Calculate the bond length for the NaCl molecule given that three successive wavelengths for rotational transitions are 23.1 mm, 11.6 mm, and 7.71 mm.

* 11. (III) (*a*) Use the curve of Fig. 29–17 to estimate the stiffness constant $k$ for the $H_2$ molecule. (Recall that $\text{PE} = \frac{1}{2}kx^2$.) (*b*) Then estimate the fundamental wavelength for vibrational transitions using the classical formula (Chapter 11), but use only $\frac{1}{2}$ the mass of an H atom (because both H atoms move).

## * 29–5 Bonding in Solids

* 12. (II) The spacing between "nearest neighbor" Na and Cl ions in a NaCl crystal is 0.24 nm. What is the spacing between two nearest neighbor Na ions?

* 13. (II) Common salt, NaCl, has a density of 2.165 $g/cm^3$. The molecular weight of NaCl is 58.44. Estimate the distance between nearest neighbor Na and Cl ions. [*Hint*: *each* ion can be considered to have one "cube" or "cell" of side $s$ (our unknown) extending out from it.]

* 14. (II) Repeat Problem 13 for KCl whose density is 1.99 $g/cm^3$.

## * 29–6 Band Theory of Solids

* 15. (I) Explain on the basis of energy bands why the sodium chloride crystal is a good insulator. [*Hint*: consider the shells of $Na^+$ and $Cl^-$ ions.]

* 16. (I) A semiconductor, bombarded with light of slowly increased frequency, begins to conduct when the wavelength of light is 640 nm. Estimate the size of the energy gap $E_g$.

* 17. (II) Calculate the longest-wavelength photon that can cause an electron in silicon $(E_g = 1.1\text{ eV})$ to jump from the valence band to the conduction band.

* 18. (II) The energy gap between valence and conduction bands in germanium is 0.72 eV. What range of wavelengths can a photon have to excite an electron from the top of the valence band into the conduction band?

* 19. (II) The energy gap $E_g$ in germanium is 0.72 eV. When used as a photon detector, roughly how many electrons can be made to jump from the valence to the conduction band by the passage of a 760-keV photon that loses all its energy in this fashion?

* 20. (III) We saw that there are $2N$ possible electron states in the $3s$ band of Na, where $N$ is the total number of atoms. How many possible electron states are there in the (*a*) $2s$ band, (*b*) $2p$ band, and (*c*) $3p$ band? (*d*) State a general formula for the total number of possible states in any given electron band.

## * 29–7 Semiconductors and Doping

* 21. (III) Suppose that a silicon semiconductor is doped with phosphorus so that one silicon atom in $10^6$ is replaced by a phosphorus atom. Assuming that the "extra" electron in every phosphorus atom is donated to the conduction band, by what factor is the density of conduction electrons increased? The density of silicon is 2330 $kg/m^3$, and the density of conduction electrons in pure silicon is about $10^{16}\,m^{-3}$ at room temperature.

## * 29–8 Diodes

* 22. (I) At what wavelength will an LED radiate if made from a material with an energy gap $E_g = 1.4$ eV?

* 23. (I) If an LED emits light of wavelength $\lambda = 650$ nm, what is the energy gap (in eV) between valence and conduction bands?

* 24. (II) A silicon diode, whose current–voltage characteristics are given in Fig. 29–28, is connected in series with a battery and a 960-Ω resistor. What battery voltage is needed to produce a 12-mA current?

* 25. (II) Suppose that the diode of Fig. 29–28 is connected in series to a 100-Ω resistor and a 2.0-V battery. What current flows in the circuit? [*Hint*: draw a line on Fig. 29–28 representing the current in the resistor as a function of the voltage across the diode. The intersection of this line with the characteristic curve will give the answer.]

* 26. (II) Sketch the resistance as a function of current, for $V > 0$, for the diode shown in Fig. 29–28.

* 27. (II) An ac voltage of 120 V rms is to be rectified. Estimate very roughly the average current in the output resistor $R$ (25 kΩ) for (*a*) a half-wave rectifier (Fig. 29–29), and (*b*) a full-wave rectifier (Fig. 29–30) without capacitor.

* 28. (III) A silicon diode passes significant current only if the forward-bias voltage exceeds about 0.6 V. Make a rough estimate of the average current in the output resistor $R$ of (*a*) a half-wave rectifier (Fig. 29–29), and (*b*) a full-wave rectifier (Fig. 29–30) without a capacitor. Assume that $R = 150\,\Omega$ in each case and that the ac voltage is 12.0 V rms in each case.

* 29. (III) A 120-V rms 60-Hz voltage is to be rectified with a full-wave rectifier (Fig. 29–30), where $R = 21\text{ k}\Omega$, and $C = 25\,\mu F$. (*a*) Make a rough estimate of the average current. (*b*) What happens if $C = 0.10\,\mu F$? [*Hint*: see Section 19–6.]

## * 29–9 Transistors

* 30. (II) From Fig. 29–32, write an equation for the relationship between the base current $(I_B)$, the collector current $(I_C)$, and the emitter current ($I_E$, not labeled in the figure).

# General Problems

* 31. Estimate the binding energy of the $H_2$ molecule by calculating the difference in kinetic energy of the electrons between when they are in separate atoms and when they are in the molecule, using the uncertainty principle. Take $\Delta x$ for the electrons in the separated atoms to be the radius of the first Bohr orbit, 0.053 nm, and for the molecule take $\Delta x$ to be the separation of the nuclei, 0.074 nm. [*Hint:* let $p \approx \Delta p_x$.]

* 32. The average translational kinetic energy of an atom or molecule is about $\overline{\text{KE}} = \frac{3}{2}kT$ (Eq. 13–8), where $k = 1.38 \times 10^{-23}$ J/K is Boltzmann's constant. At what temperature $T$ will $\overline{\text{KE}}$ be on the order of the bond energy (and hence the bond likely to be broken by thermal motion) for (*a*) a covalent bond of binding energy 4.5 eV (say $H_2$), and (*b*) a "weak" hydrogen bond of binding energy 0.15 eV?

* 33. In the ionic salt KF, the separation distance between ions is about 0.27 nm. (*a*) Estimate the electrostatic potential energy between the ions assuming them to be point charges (magnitude 1*e*). (*b*) It is known that F releases 4.07 eV of energy when it "grabs" an electron, and 4.34 eV is required to ionize K. Find the binding energy of KF relative to free K and F atoms, neglecting the energy of repulsion.

* 34. Consider a monoatomic solid with a weakly bound cubic lattice, with each atom connected to six neighbors, each bond having a binding energy of $3.9 \times 10^{-3}$ eV. When this solid melts, its latent heat of fusion goes directly into breaking the bonds between the atoms. Estimate the latent heat of fusion for this solid, in J/kg. [*Hint*: show that in a simple cubic lattice (Fig. 29–34), there are *three* times as many bonds as there are atoms, when the number of atoms is large.]

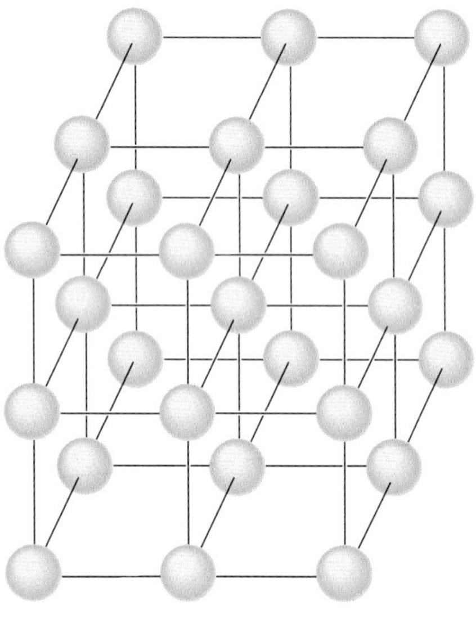

**FIGURE 29–34** Problem 34.

* 35. For $O_2$ with a bond length of 0.121 nm, what is the moment of inertia about the center of mass?

* 36. A diatomic molecule is found to have an activation energy of 1.4 eV. When the molecule is disassociated, 1.6 eV of energy is released. Draw a potential energy curve for this molecule.

* 37. When EM radiation is incident on diamond, it is found that light with wavelengths shorter than 226 nm will cause the diamond to conduct. What is the energy gap between the valence band and the conduction band for diamond?

* 38. A TV remote control emits IR light. If the detector on the TV set is *not* to react to visible light, could it make use of silicon as a "window" with its energy gap $E_g = 1.14$ eV? What is the shortest-wavelength light that can strike silicon without causing electrons to jump from the valence band to the conduction band?

* 39. For an arsenic donor atom in a doped silicon semiconductor, assume that the "extra" electron moves in a Bohr orbit about the arsenic ion. For this electron in the ground state, take into account the dielectric constant $K = 12$ of the Si lattice (which represents the weakening of the Coulomb force due to all the other atoms or ions in the lattice), and estimate (*a*) the binding energy, and (*b*) the orbit radius for this extra electron. [*Hint*: substitute $\epsilon = K\epsilon_0$ in Coulomb's law; see Section 17–8.]

* 40. Most of the Sun's radiation has wavelengths shorter than 1000 nm. For a solar cell to absorb all this, what energy gap ought the material have?

* 41. For a certain semiconductor, the longest wavelength radiation that can be absorbed is 1.92 mm. What is the energy gap in this semiconductor?

* 42. Green and blue LEDs became available many years after red LEDs were first developed. Approximately what energy gaps would you expect to find in green (525 nm) and in blue (465 nm) LEDs?

* 43. A zener diode voltage regulator is shown in Fig. 29–35. Suppose that $R = 1.80$ kΩ and that the diode breaks down at a reverse voltage of 130 V. (The current increases rapidly at this point, as shown on the far left of Fig. 29–28 at a voltage of −12 V on that diagram.) The diode is rated at a maximum current of 120 mA. (*a*) If $R_{load} = 15.0$ kΩ, over what range of supply voltages will the circuit maintain the output voltage at 130 V? (*b*) If the supply voltage is 200 V, over what range of load resistance will the voltage be regulated?

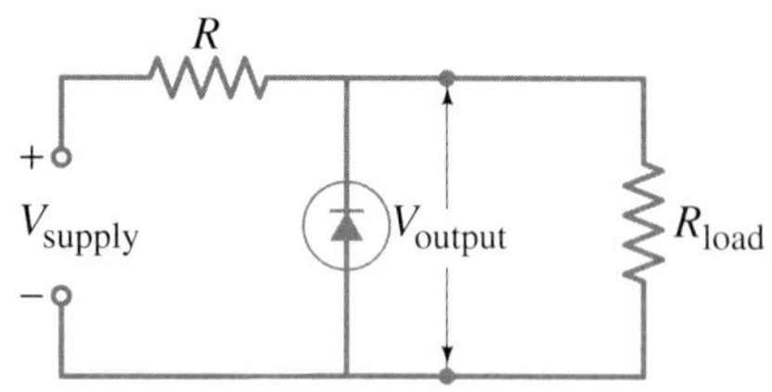


**FIGURE 29–35** Problem 43.

## Answers to Exercises

**A:** 1.30 mm, 0.87 mm, 0.65 mm.

**B:** 0.81 eV.

This archeologist has unearthed the remains of a sea-turtle within an ancient man-made stone circle. Carbon dating of the remains can tell her when humans inhabited the site.

In this Chapter we begin our discussion of nuclear physics including the properties of nuclei, the various forms of radioactivity, and how radioactive decay can be used in a variety of fields to determine the age of old objects, from bones and trees to rocks and other mineral substances, and obtain information on the history of the Earth.

CHAPTER 30

# Nuclear Physics and Radioactivity

In the early part of the twentieth century, Rutherford's experiments led to the idea that at the center of an atom there is a tiny but massive nucleus. At the same time that the quantum theory was being developed and scientists were attempting to understand the structure of the atom and its electrons, investigations into the nucleus itself had also begun. In this Chapter and the next, we take a brief look at *nuclear physics*.

## 30–1 Structure and Properties of the Nucleus

An important question for physicists was whether the nucleus had a structure, and what that structure might be. It turns out that the nucleus is a complicated entity and is not fully understood even today. However, by the early 1930s, a model of the nucleus had been developed that is still useful. According to this model, a nucleus is considered to be an aggregate of two types of particles: protons and neutrons. (These "particles" also have wave properties, but for ease of visualization and language, we often refer to them simply as "particles.") A **proton** is the nucleus of the simplest atom, hydrogen. It has a positive charge ($= +e = +1.60 \times 10^{-19}$ C, the same magnitude as for the electron) and a mass

*Proton*

$$m_{\mathrm{p}} = 1.67262 \times 10^{-27}\ \mathrm{kg}.$$

The **neutron**, whose existence was ascertained in 1932 by the English physicist James Chadwick (1891–1974), is electrically neutral ($q = 0$), as its name implies. Its mass is very slightly larger than that of the proton:

*Neutron*

$$m_{\mathrm{n}} = 1.67493 \times 10^{-27}\ \mathrm{kg}.$$

*Nucleons*

These two constituents of a nucleus, neutrons and protons, are referred to collectively as **nucleons**.

*Z and A*

Although the hydrogen nucleus consists of a single proton alone, the nuclei of all other elements consist of both neutrons and protons. The different nuclei are often referred to as **nuclides**. The number of protons in a nucleus (or nuclide) is called the **atomic number** and is designated by the symbol $Z$. The total number of nucleons, neutrons plus protons, is designated by the symbol $A$ and is called the **atomic mass number**, or sometimes simply **mass number**. This name is used since the mass of a nucleus is very closely $A$ times the mass of one nucleon. A nuclide with 7 protons and 8 neutrons thus has $Z = 7$ and $A = 15$. The **neutron number** $N$ is $N = A - Z$.

To specify a given nuclide, we need give only $A$ and $Z$. A special symbol is commonly used which takes the form

$${}^{A}_{Z}\mathrm{X},$$

where X is the chemical symbol for the element (see Appendix B, and the periodic table inside the back cover), $A$ is the atomic mass number, and $Z$ is the atomic number. For example, ${}^{15}_{7}\mathrm{N}$ means a nitrogen nucleus containing 7 protons and 8 neutrons for a total of 15 nucleons. In a neutral atom, the number of electrons orbiting the nucleus is equal to the atomic number $Z$ (since the charge on an electron has the same magnitude but opposite sign to that of a proton). The main properties of an atom, and how it interacts with other atoms, are largely determined by the number of electrons. Hence $Z$ determines what kind of atom it is: carbon, oxygen, gold, or whatever. It is redundant to specify both the symbol of a nucleus and its atomic number $Z$ as described above. If the nucleus is nitrogen, for example, we know immediately that $Z = 7$. The subscript $Z$ is thus sometimes dropped and ${}^{15}_{7}\mathrm{N}$ is then written simply ${}^{15}\mathrm{N}$; in words we say "nitrogen fifteen."

*Isotopes*

For a particular type of atom (say, carbon), nuclei are found to contain different numbers of neutrons, although they all have the same number of protons. For example, carbon nuclei always have 6 protons, but they may have 5, 6, 7, 8, 9, or 10 neutrons. Nuclei that contain the same number of protons but different numbers of neutrons are called **isotopes**. Thus, ${}^{11}_{6}\mathrm{C}$, ${}^{12}_{6}\mathrm{C}$, ${}^{13}_{6}\mathrm{C}$, ${}^{14}_{6}\mathrm{C}$, ${}^{15}_{6}\mathrm{C}$, and ${}^{16}_{6}\mathrm{C}$ are all isotopes of carbon. The isotopes of a given element are not all equally common. For example, 98.9% of naturally occurring carbon (on Earth) is the isotope ${}^{12}_{6}\mathrm{C}$, and about 1.1% is ${}^{13}_{6}\mathrm{C}$. These percentages are referred to as the **natural abundances**.† Many isotopes that do not occur naturally can be produced in the laboratory by means of nuclear reactions (more on this later). Indeed, all elements beyond uranium ($Z > 92$) do not occur naturally on Earth and are only produced artificially, as are many nuclides with $Z \leq 92$.

The approximate size of nuclei was determined originally by Rutherford from the scattering of charged particles by thin metal foils. We cannot speak about a definite size for nuclei because of the wave–particle duality: their spatial extent must remain somewhat fuzzy. Nonetheless a rough "size" can be measured by scattering high-speed electrons off nuclei. It is found that nuclei have a roughly spherical

†The mass value for each element as given in the periodic table (inside back cover) is an average weighted according to the natural abundances of its isotopes.

shape with a radius that increases with $A$ according to the approximate formula

$$r \approx \left(1.2 \times 10^{-15}\,\mathrm{m}\right)\left(A^{\frac{1}{3}}\right). \tag{30-1}$$

*Nuclear radii*

Since the volume of a sphere is $V = \frac{4}{3}\pi r^3$, we see that the volume of a nucleus is approximately proportional to the number of nucleons, $V \propto A$. This is what we would expect if nucleons were like impenetrable billiard balls: if you double the number of balls, you double the total volume. Hence, all nuclei have nearly the same density, and it is enormous (see Example 30–2).

The metric abbreviation for $10^{-15}$ m is the fermi (after Enrico Fermi) or the femtometer, fm (Table 1–4 or inside the front cover). Thus $1.2 \times 10^{-15}\,\mathrm{m} = 1.2\,\mathrm{fm}$ or 1.2 fermis.

**EXAMPLE 30–1 ESTIMATE Nuclear sizes.** Estimate the diameter of the following nuclei: (*a*) ${}^{1}_{1}\mathrm{H}$, (*b*) ${}^{40}_{20}\mathrm{Ca}$, (*c*) ${}^{208}_{82}\mathrm{Pb}$, (*d*) ${}^{235}_{92}\mathrm{U}$.

**APPROACH** The radius $r$ of a nucleus is related to its number of nucleons $A$ by Eq. 30–1. The diameter $d = 2r$.

**SOLUTION** (*a*) For hydrogen, $A = 1$, Eq. 30–1 gives

$$d = \text{diameter} = 2r \approx 2\left(1.2 \times 10^{-15}\,\mathrm{m}\right)\left(A^{\frac{1}{3}}\right) = 2.4 \times 10^{-15}\,\mathrm{m}$$

since $A^{\frac{1}{3}} = 1^{\frac{1}{3}} = 1$.

(*b*) For calcium $d = 2r \approx \left(2.4 \times 10^{-15}\,\mathrm{m}\right)(40)^{\frac{1}{3}} = 8.2 \times 10^{-15}\,\mathrm{m}$.

(*c*) For lead $d \approx \left(2.4 \times 10^{-15}\,\mathrm{m}\right)(208)^{\frac{1}{3}} = 14 \times 10^{-15}\,\mathrm{m}$.

(*d*) For uranium $d \approx \left(2.4 \times 10^{-15}\,\mathrm{m}\right)(235)^{\frac{1}{3}} = 15 \times 10^{-15}\,\mathrm{m}$.

The range of nuclear diameters is only from 2.4 fm to 15 fm.

**NOTE** Because nuclear radii vary as $A^{\frac{1}{3}}$, the largest nuclei have a radius only about 6 times that of the smallest.

**EXAMPLE 30–2 ESTIMATE Nuclear and atomic densities.** Compare the density of nuclear matter to the density of normal solids.

**APPROACH** The density of normal liquids and solids is on the order of $10^3$ to $10^4\,\mathrm{kg/m^3}$ (see Table 10–1), and because the atoms are close packed, atoms have about this density too. We therefore compare the density (mass per volume) of a nucleus to that of its atom as a whole.

**SOLUTION** The mass of a proton is greater than the mass of an electron by a factor

$$\frac{1.7 \times 10^{-27}\,\mathrm{kg}}{9.1 \times 10^{-31}\,\mathrm{kg}} \approx 2 \times 10^3.$$

Thus, over 99.9% of the mass of an atom is in the nucleus, and for our estimate we can say the mass of the atom equals the mass of the nucleus, $m_{\mathrm{nucl}}/m_{\mathrm{atom}} = 1$. Atoms have a radius of about $10^{-10}$ m (Chapter 27) and nuclei on the order of $10^{-15}$ m (Eq. 30–1). Thus the ratio of nuclear density to atomic density is about

$$\frac{\rho_{\mathrm{nucl}}}{\rho_{\mathrm{atom}}} = \frac{\left(m_{\mathrm{nucl}}/V_{\mathrm{nucl}}\right)}{\left(m_{\mathrm{atom}}/V_{\mathrm{atom}}\right)} = \left(\frac{m_{\mathrm{nucl}}}{m_{\mathrm{atom}}}\right)\frac{\frac{4}{3}\pi r^3_{\mathrm{atom}}}{\frac{4}{3}\pi r^3_{\mathrm{nucl}}} \approx (1)\frac{\left(10^{-10}\right)^3}{\left(10^{-15}\right)^3} = 10^{15}.$$

The nucleus is $10^{15}$ times more dense than ordinary matter.

The masses of nuclei can be determined from the radius of curvature of fast-moving nuclei (as ions) in a known magnetic field using a mass spectrometer, as discussed in Section 20–11. Indeed the existence of different isotopes of the same element (different number of neutrons) was discovered using this device. Nuclear masses can be specified in **unified atomic mass units** (u). On this scale, a neutral ${}^{12}_{6}\mathrm{C}$ atom is given the precise value 12.000000 u. A neutron then has a measured mass of 1.008665 u, a proton 1.007276 u, and a neutral hydrogen atom ${}^{1}_{1}\mathrm{H}$ (proton plus electron) 1.007825 u. The masses of many nuclides are given in Appendix B. It should be noted that the masses in this Table, as is customary, are for the *neutral atom* (including electrons), and not for a bare nucleus.

**CAUTION**
*Masses are for neutral atom (nucleus plus electrons)*

Masses are often specified using the electron-volt energy unit. This can be done because mass and energy are related, and the precise relationship is given by Einstein's equation $E = mc^2$ (Chapter 26). Since the mass of a proton is $1.67262 \times 10^{-27}$ kg, or 1.007276 u, then

$$1.0000\text{ u} = \left(\frac{1.0000\text{ u}}{1.007276\text{ u}}\right)(1.67262 \times 10^{-27}\text{ kg}) = 1.66054 \times 10^{-27}\text{ kg};$$

this is equivalent to an energy (see Table inside front cover) in MeV ($= 10^6$ eV) of

$$E = mc^2 = \frac{(1.66054 \times 10^{-27}\text{ kg})(2.9979 \times 10^8\text{ m/s})^2}{(1.6022 \times 10^{-19}\text{ J/eV})} = 931.5\text{ MeV}.$$

Thus

*Atomic mass unit and MeV*

$$1\text{ u} = 1.6605 \times 10^{-27}\text{ kg} = 931.5\text{ MeV}/c^2.$$

The rest masses of some of the basic particles are given in Table 30–1.

**TABLE 30–1**
**Rest Masses in Kilograms, Unified Atomic Mass Units, and MeV/$c^2$**

| | Mass | | |
|---|---|---|---|
| **Object** | **kg** | **u** | **MeV/$c^2$** |
| Electron | $9.1094 \times 10^{-31}$ | 0.00054858 | 0.51100 |
| Proton | $1.67262 \times 10^{-27}$ | 1.007276 | 938.27 |
| ${}^{1}_{1}$H atom | $1.67353 \times 10^{-27}$ | 1.007825 | 938.78 |
| Neutron | $1.67493 \times 10^{-27}$ | 1.008665 | 939.57 |

Just as an electron has intrinsic spin and angular momentum quantum numbers, so too do nuclei and their constituents, the proton and neutron. Both the proton and the neutron are spin $\frac{1}{2}$ particles. A nucleus, made up of protons and neutrons, has a **nuclear spin** quantum number, $I$, that can be either integer or half integer, depending on whether it is made up of an even or an odd number of nucleons.

## 30–2 Binding Energy and Nuclear Forces

### Binding Energies

The total mass of a stable nucleus is always less than the sum of the masses of its separate protons and neutrons, as the following Example shows.

**EXAMPLE 30–3** **${}^{4}_{2}$He mass compared to its constituents.** Compare the mass of a ${}^{4}_{2}$He atom to the total mass of its constituent particles.

**PROBLEM SOLVING** *Keep track of electron masses*

**APPROACH** The ${}^{4}_{2}$He nucleus contains 2 protons and 2 neutrons. Tables normally give the masses of neutral atoms—that is, nucleus plus its $Z$ electrons—since this is how masses are measured. We must therefore be sure to balance out the electrons when we compare masses. Thus we use the mass of ${}^{1}_{1}$H rather than that of a proton alone. We look up the mass of the ${}^{4}_{2}$He atom in Appendix B (it includes the mass of 2 electrons), as well as the mass for the 2 neutrons and 2 hydrogen atoms ($=$ 2 protons $+$ 2 electrons).

**SOLUTION** The mass of a neutral ${}^{4}_{2}$He atom, from Appendix B, is 4.002603 u. The mass of two neutrons and two H atoms (2 protons including the 2 electrons) is

$$2m_{\text{n}} = 2(1.008665\text{ u}) = 2.017330\text{ u}$$
$$2m({}^{1}_{1}\text{H}) = 2(1.007825\text{ u}) = \underline{2.015650\text{ u}}$$
$$\text{sum} = 4.032980\text{ u}.$$

Thus the mass of $^4_2$He is measured to be $4.032980\,\text{u} - 4.002603\,\text{u} = 0.030377\,\text{u}$ less than the masses of its constituents. Where has this lost mass gone?

It has, in fact, gone into energy of another kind (such as radiation, or kinetic energy, for example). The mass (or energy) difference in the case of $^4_2$He, given in energy units, is $(0.030377\,\text{u})(931.5\,\text{MeV/u}) = 28.30\,\text{MeV}$. This difference is referred to as the **total binding energy** of the nucleus. The total binding energy represents the amount of energy that must be put into a nucleus in order to break it apart into its constituents. If the mass of, say, a $^4_2$He nucleus were exactly equal to the mass of two neutrons plus two protons, the nucleus could fall apart without any input of energy. To be stable, the mass of a nucleus *must* be less than that of its constituent nucleons, so that energy input *is* needed to break it apart. Note that the binding energy is not something a nucleus has—it is energy it "lacks" relative to the total mass of its separate constituents.

*Binding energy*

[We saw in Chapter 27 that the binding energy of the one electron in the hydrogen atom is 13.6 eV; so the mass of a $^1_1$H atom is less than that of a single proton plus a single electron by $13.6\,\text{eV}/c^2$. Compared to the total mass of the atom $(939\,\text{MeV}/c^2)$, this is incredibly small, 1 part in $10^8$. Also, the binding energies of nuclei are on the order of MeV, so the eV binding energies of electrons can be ignored.]

**EXERCISE A** Determine how much less the mass of the $^7_3$Li nucleus is compared to that of its constituents.

The **binding energy per nucleon** is defined as the total binding energy of a nucleus divided by $A$, the total number of nucleons. We calculated above that the binding energy of $^4_2$He is 28.3 MeV, so its binding energy per nucleon is $28.3\,\text{MeV}/4 = 7.1\,\text{MeV}$. Figure 30–1 shows the binding energy per nucleon as a function of $A$ for stable nuclei. The curve rises as $A$ increases and reaches a plateau at about 8.7 MeV per nucleon above $A \approx 40$. Beyond $A \approx 80$, the curve decreases slowly, indicating that larger nuclei are held together a little less tightly than those in the middle of the periodic table. We will see later that these characteristics allow the release of nuclear energy in the processes of fission and fusion.

*Binding energy per nucleon*

**FIGURE 30–1** Binding energy per nucleon for the more stable nuclides as a function of mass number $A$.

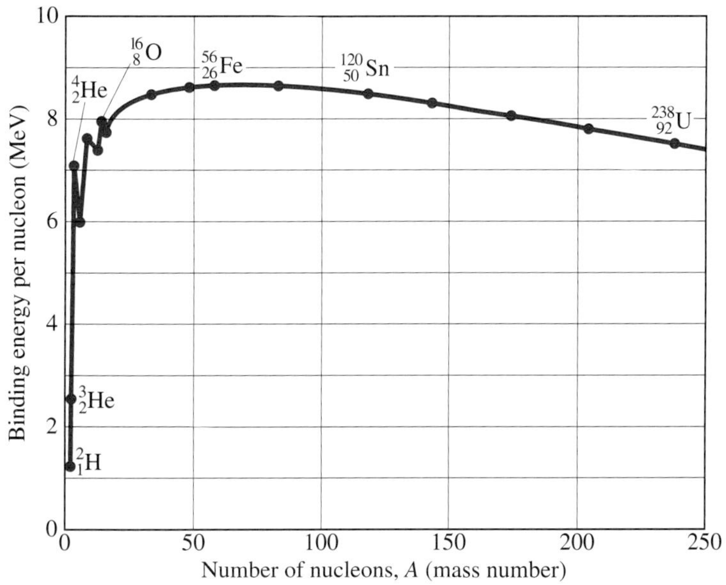

**EXAMPLE 30–4** **Binding energy for iron.** Calculate the total binding energy and the binding energy per nucleon for $^{56}_{26}\text{Fe}$, the most common stable isotope of iron.

**APPROACH** We subtract the mass of a $^{56}_{26}\text{Fe}$ atom from the total mass of 26 hydrogen atoms and 30 neutrons, all found in Appendix B. Then we convert mass units to energy units; finally we divide by $A = 56$, the total number of nucleons.

**SOLUTION** $^{56}_{26}\text{Fe}$ has 26 protons and 30 neutrons whose separate masses are

$$\begin{aligned} 26m(^1_1\text{H}) &= (26)(1.007825\,\text{u}) = 26.20345\,\text{u (includes 26 electrons)} \\ 30m_\text{n} &= (30)(1.008665\,\text{u}) = \underline{30.25995\,\text{u}} \\ \text{sum} &= 56.46340\,\text{u}. \\ \text{Subtract mass of } ^{56}_{26}\text{Fe:} &= \underline{-55.93494\,\text{u}}\ \text{(Appendix B)} \\ \Delta m &= 0.52846\,\text{u}. \end{aligned}$$

The total binding energy is thus

$$(0.52846\,\text{u})(931.5\,\text{MeV/u}) = 492.26\,\text{MeV}$$

and the binding energy per nucleon is

$$\frac{492.26\,\text{MeV}}{56\text{ nucleons}} = 8.79\,\text{MeV}.$$

**NOTE** The binding energy per nucleon graph (Fig. 30–1) peaks just about here, for iron, so the iron nucleus (and its neighbors) is the most stable of nuclei.

**EXERCISE B** Determine the binding energy per nucleon for $^{16}_{8}\text{O}$.

**EXAMPLE 30–5** **Binding energy of last neutron.** What is the binding energy of the last neutron in $^{13}_{6}\text{C}$?

**APPROACH** We subtract the mass of $^{13}_{6}\text{C}$ from the masses of the atom with one less neutron, $^{12}_{6}\text{C}$, and a free neutron.

**SOLUTION** Obtaining the masses from Appendix B, we have

$$\begin{aligned} \text{Mass } ^{12}_{6}\text{C} &= 12.000000\,\text{u} \\ \text{Mass } ^{1}_{0}\text{n} &= \underline{1.008665\,\text{u}} \\ \text{Total} &= 13.008665\,\text{u}. \\ \text{Subtract mass of } ^{13}_{6}\text{C:} &\quad \underline{-13.003355\,\text{u}} \\ \Delta m &= 0.005310\,\text{u} \end{aligned}$$

which in energy is $(931.5\,\text{MeV/u})(0.005310\,\text{u}) = 4.95\,\text{MeV}$. That is, it would require 4.95 MeV input of energy to remove one neutron from $^{13}_{6}\text{C}$.

## Nuclear Forces

We can analyze nuclei not only from the point of view of energy, but also from the point of view of the forces that hold them together. We would not expect a collection of protons and neutrons to come together spontaneously, since protons are all positively charged and thus exert repulsive electric forces on each other. Indeed, the question arises as to how a nucleus stays together at all in view of the fact that the electric force between protons would tend to break it apart. Since stable nuclei *do* stay together, it is clear that another force must be acting. Because this new force is stronger than the electric force (which, in turn, is much stronger than gravity at the nuclear level), it is called the **strong nuclear force**. The strong nuclear force is an attractive force that acts between all nucleons—protons and neutrons alike. Thus protons attract each other via the strong nuclear force at the same time they repel each other via the electric force. Neutrons, since they are electrically neutral, only attract other neutrons or protons via the strong nuclear force.

*Strong nuclear force*

The strong nuclear force turns out to be far more complicated than the gravitational and electromagnetic forces. One important aspect of the strong nuclear force is that it is a **short-range** force: it acts only over a very short distance. It is very strong between two nucleons if they are less than about $10^{-15}$ m apart, but it is essentially zero if they are separated by a distance greater than this. Compare this to electric and gravitational forces, which decrease as $1/r^2$ but continue acting over any distances and are therefore called **long-range** forces.

*Long- and short-range forces*

The strong nuclear force has some strange quirks. For example, if a nuclide contains too many or too few neutrons relative to the number of protons, the binding of the nucleons is reduced; nuclides that are too unbalanced in this regard are unstable. As shown in Fig. 30–2, stable nuclei tend to have the same number of protons as neutrons ($N = Z$) up to about $A = 30$ or 40. Beyond this, stable nuclei contain more neutrons than protons. This makes sense since, as $Z$ increases, the electrical repulsion increases, so a greater number of neutrons—which exert only the attractive nuclear force—are required to maintain stability. For very large $Z$, no number of neutrons can overcome the greatly increased electric repulsion. Indeed, there are no completely stable nuclides above $Z = 82$.

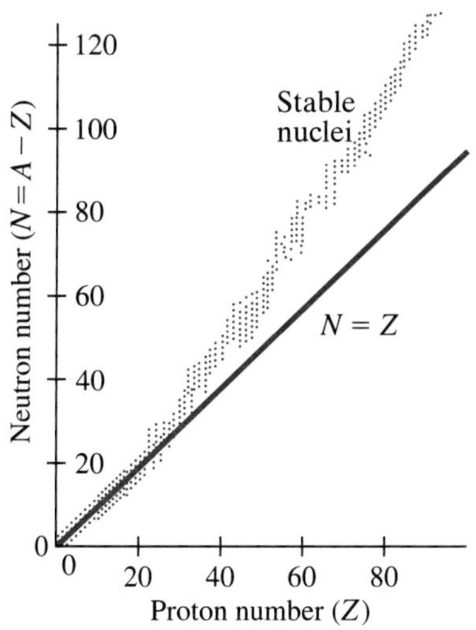


**FIGURE 30–2** Number of neutrons versus number of protons for stable nuclides, which are represented by dots. The straight line represents $N = Z$.

What we mean by a *stable nucleus* is one that stays together indefinitely. What then is an *unstable nucleus*? It is one that comes apart; and this results in radioactive decay. Before we discuss the important subject of radioactivity (next Section), we note that there is a second type of nuclear force that is much weaker than the strong nuclear force. It is called the **weak nuclear force**, and we are aware of its existence only because it shows itself in certain types of radioactive decay. These two nuclear forces, the strong and the weak, together with the gravitational and electromagnetic forces, comprise the four known types of force in nature.

*Weak force*

## 30–3 Radioactivity

Nuclear physics had its beginnings in 1896. In that year, Henri Becquerel (1852–1908) made an important discovery: in his studies of phosphorescence, he found that a certain mineral (which happened to contain uranium) would darken a photographic plate even when the plate was wrapped to exclude light. It was clear that the mineral emitted some new kind of radiation that, unlike X-rays, occurred without any external stimulus. This new phenomenon eventually came to be called **radioactivity**.

*Discovery of radioactivity*

Soon after Becquerel's discovery, Marie Curie (1867–1934) and her husband, Pierre Curie (1859–1906), isolated two previously unknown elements that were very highly radioactive (Fig. 30–3). These were named polonium and radium.

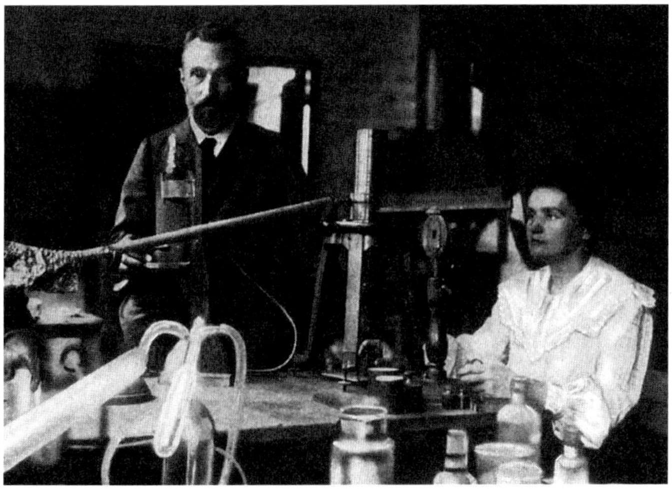

**FIGURE 30–3** Marie and Pierre Curie in their laboratory (about 1906) where radium was discovered.

Other radioactive elements were soon discovered as well. The radioactivity was found in every case to be unaffected by the strongest physical and chemical treatments, including strong heating or cooling and the action of strong chemical reagents. It was clear that the source of radioactivity must be deep within the atom, that it must emanate from the nucleus. And it became apparent that radioactivity is the result of the *disintegration* or *decay* of an unstable nucleus. Certain isotopes are not stable, and they decay with the emission of some type of radiation or "rays."

Many unstable isotopes occur in nature, and such radioactivity is called "natural radioactivity." Other unstable isotopes can be produced in the laboratory by nuclear reactions (Section 31–1); these are said to be produced "artificially" and to have "artificial radioactivity."

Rutherford and others began studying the nature of the rays emitted in radioactivity about 1898. They found that the rays could be classified into three distinct types according to their penetrating power. One type of radiation could barely penetrate a piece of paper. The second type could pass through as much as 3 mm of aluminum. The third was extremely penetrating: it could pass through several centimeters of lead and still be detected on the other side. They named these three types of radiation alpha ($\alpha$), beta ($\beta$), and gamma ($\gamma$), respectively, after the first three letters of the Greek alphabet.

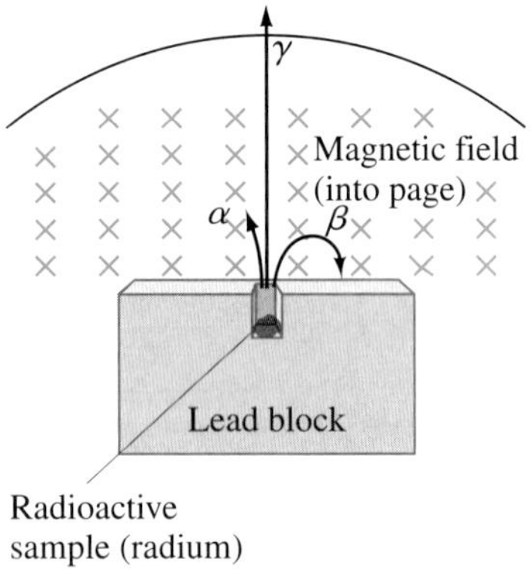


**FIGURE 30–4** Alpha and beta rays are bent in opposite directions by a magnetic field, whereas gamma rays are not bent at all.

Each type of ray was found to have a different charge and hence is bent differently in a magnetic field, Fig. 30–4; $\alpha$ rays are positively charged, $\beta$ rays are negatively charged, and $\gamma$ rays are neutral. It was soon found that all three types of radiation consisted of familiar kinds of particles. Gamma rays are very high-energy photons whose energy is even higher than that of X-rays. Beta rays are electrons, identical to those that orbit the nucleus, but they are created within the nucleus itself. Alpha rays (or $\alpha$ particles) are simply the nuclei of helium atoms, ${}^{4}_{2}\text{He}$; that is, an $\alpha$ ray consists of two protons and two neutrons bound together.

We now discuss each of these three types of radioactivity, or decay, in more detail.

## 30–4 Alpha Decay

**FIGURE 30–5** Radioactive decay of radium to radon with emission of an alpha particle.

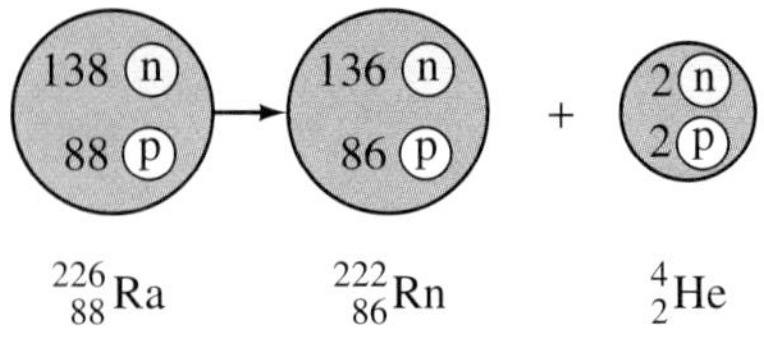


When a nucleus emits an $\alpha$ particle (${}^{4}_{2}\text{He}$), it is clear that the remaining nucleus will be different from the original: it has lost two protons and two neutrons. Radium 226 (${}^{226}_{88}\text{Ra}$), for example, is an $\alpha$ emitter. It decays to a nucleus with $Z = 88 - 2 = 86$ and $A = 226 - 4 = 222$. The nucleus with $Z = 86$ is radon (Rn)—see Appendix B or the periodic table. Thus the radium decays to radon with the emission of an $\alpha$ particle. This is written

*$\alpha$ decay*

$$ {}^{226}_{88}\text{Ra} \rightarrow {}^{222}_{86}\text{Rn} + {}^{4}_{2}\text{He}. $$

See Fig. 30–5.

*Daughter nucleus*
*Parent nucleus*
*Transmutation*

It is clear that when $\alpha$ decay occurs, a new element is formed. The **daughter** nucleus (${}^{222}_{86}\text{Rn}$ in this case) is different from the **parent** nucleus (${}^{226}_{88}\text{Ra}$ in this case). This changing of one element into another is called **transmutation**.

Alpha decay can be written

$$ {}^{A}_{Z}\text{N} \rightarrow {}^{A-4}_{Z-2}\text{N}' + {}^{4}_{2}\text{He} \qquad [\alpha \text{ decay}] $$

where $N$ is the parent, $N'$ the daughter, and $Z$ and $A$ are the atomic number and atomic mass number, respectively, of the parent.

Alpha decay occurs because the strong nuclear force is unable to hold very large nuclei together. Because the nuclear force is a short-range force, it acts only between neighboring nucleons. But the electric force acts all the way across a large nucleus. For very large nuclei, the large $Z$ means the repulsive electric force becomes so large (Coulomb's law) that the strong nuclear force is unable to hold the nucleus together.

*Why the strong nuclear force cannot hold a nucleus together*

We can express the instability in terms of energy (or mass): the mass of the parent nucleus is greater than the mass of the daughter nucleus plus the mass of the $\alpha$ particle. The mass difference appears as kinetic energy, which is carried away by the $\alpha$ particle and the recoiling daughter nucleus. The total energy released is called the **disintegration energy**, $Q$, or the ***Q*-value** of the decay. From conservation of energy,

$$M_{\mathrm{P}}c^2 = M_{\mathrm{D}}c^2 + m_\alpha c^2 + Q,$$

where $Q = \mathrm{KE}$ and $M_{\mathrm{P}}$, $M_{\mathrm{D}}$, and $m_\alpha$ are the masses of the parent, daughter, and $\alpha$ particle, respectively. Thus

$$Q = M_{\mathrm{P}}c^2 - (M_{\mathrm{D}} + m_\alpha)c^2. \qquad \textbf{(30–2)}$$

*Q-value*

If the parent had *less* mass than the daughter plus the $\alpha$ particle (so $Q < 0$), the decay could not occur spontaneously, for the conservation of energy law would be violated.

**EXAMPLE 30–6** **Uranium decay energy release.** Calculate the disintegration energy when $^{232}_{92}\mathrm{U}$ (mass = 232.037146 u) decays to $^{228}_{90}\mathrm{Th}$ (228.028731 u) with the emission of an $\alpha$ particle. (As always, masses are for neutral atoms.)

**APPROACH** We use conservation of energy as expressed in Eq. 30–2. $^{232}_{92}\mathrm{U}$ is the parent, $^{228}_{90}\mathrm{Th}$ is the daughter.

**SOLUTION** Since the mass of the $^{4}_{2}\mathrm{He}$ is 4.002603 u (Appendix B), the total mass in the final state is

$$228.028731\ \mathrm{u} + 4.002603\ \mathrm{u} = 232.031334\ \mathrm{u}.$$

The mass lost when the $^{232}_{92}\mathrm{U}$ decays is

$$232.037146\ \mathrm{u} - 232.031334\ \mathrm{u} = 0.005812\ \mathrm{u}.$$

Since $1\ \mathrm{u} = 931.5\ \mathrm{MeV}$, the energy $Q$ released is

$$\begin{aligned} Q &= (0.005812\ \mathrm{u})(931.5\ \mathrm{MeV/u}) \\ &\approx 5.4\ \mathrm{MeV}, \end{aligned}$$

and this energy appears as kinetic energy of the $\alpha$ particle and the daughter nucleus.

**NOTE** Using conservation of momentum, it can be shown that the $\alpha$ particle emitted by a $^{232}_{92}\mathrm{U}$ nucleus at rest has a kinetic energy of about 5.3 MeV. Thus, the daughter nucleus—which recoils in the opposite direction from the emitted $\alpha$ particle—has about 0.1 MeV of kinetic energy. See the next Example and/or Problem 65.

## Additional Example

**EXAMPLE 30–7** **KE of the $\alpha$ in $^{232}_{92}U$ decay.** For the $^{232}_{92}U$ decay of Example 30–6, how much of the 5.4-MeV disintegration energy will be carried off by the $\alpha$ particle?

**APPROACH** In any reaction, momentum must be conserved as well as energy.

**SOLUTION** Before disintegation, the nucleus can be assumed to be at rest, so the total momentum was zero. After disintegration, the total vector momentum must still be zero so the magnitude of the $\alpha$ particle's momentum must equal the magnitude of the daughter's momentum (Fig. 30–6):

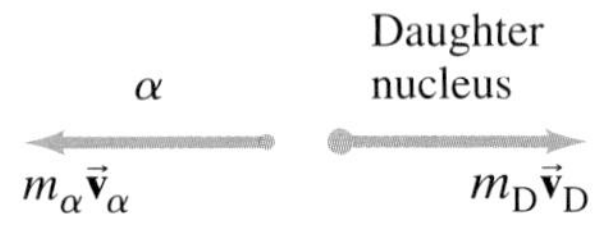


**FIGURE 30–6** Momentum conservation in Example 30–7.

$$m_\alpha v_\alpha = m_D v_D.$$

Thus $v_\alpha = m_D v_D / m_\alpha$ and the $\alpha$'s kinetic energy is

$$\text{KE}_\alpha = \tfrac{1}{2} m_\alpha v_\alpha^2 = \tfrac{1}{2} m_\alpha \left( \frac{m_D v_D}{m_\alpha} \right)^2 = \tfrac{1}{2} m_D v_D^2 \left( \frac{m_D}{m_\alpha} \right) = \left( \frac{m_D}{m_\alpha} \right) \text{KE}_D$$

$$= \left( \frac{228.028731\ \text{u}}{4.002603\ \text{u}} \right) \text{KE}_D = 57\text{KE}_D.$$

The total disintegration energy is $Q = \text{KE}_\alpha + \text{KE}_D = 57\text{KE}_D + \text{KE}_D = 58\text{KE}_D$. Hence

$$\text{KE}_\alpha = \frac{57}{58} Q = 5.3\ \text{MeV}.$$

The lighter $\alpha$ particle carries off (57/58) or 98% of the total KE.

## Why $\alpha$ particles?

Why, you may wonder, do nuclei emit this combination of four nucleons called an $\alpha$ particle? Why not just four separate nucleons, or even one? The answer is that the $\alpha$ particle is very strongly bound, so that its mass is significantly less than that of four separate nucleons. As we saw in Example 30–3, two protons and two neutrons separately have a total mass of about 4.032980 u (electrons included). The total mass of $^{228}_{90}Th$ plus four separate nucleons is 232.061711 u, which is greater than the mass of the parent (232.037146). Such a decay could not occur because it would violate the conservation of energy. Similarly, it is almost always true that the emission of a single nucleon is energetically not possible.

## Smoke Detectors—An Application

PHYSICS APPLIED
*Smoke detector*

One widespread application of nuclear physics is present in nearly every home in the form of an ordinary **smoke detector**. The most common type of detector contains about 0.2 mg of the radioactive americium isotope, $^{241}_{95}Am$, in the form of $AmO_2$. The radiation continually ionizes the nitrogen and oxygen molecules in the air space between two oppositely charged plates. The resulting conductivity allows a small steady current. If smoke enters, the radiation is absorbed by the smoke particles rather than by the air molecules, thus reducing the current. The current drop is detected by the device's electronics and sets off the alarm. The radiation dose that escapes from an intact americium smoke detector is much less than the natural radioactive background, and so can be considered relatively harmless. There is no question that smoke detectors save lives and reduce property damage.

## 30–5 Beta Decay

### $\beta^-$ Decay

Transmutation of elements also occurs when a nucleus decays by $\beta$ decay—that is, with the emission of an electron or $\beta^-$ particle. The nucleus $^{14}_{6}C$, for example, emits an electron when it decays:

$$^{14}_{6}C \rightarrow {}^{14}_{7}N + e^- + \text{a neutrino},$$

where $e^-$ is the symbol for the electron. (The symbol $_{-1}^{0}e$ is sometimes used for the electron whose charge corresponds to $Z = -1$ and, since it is not a nucleon and has very small mass, then $A = 0$.) The particle known as the neutrino, whose charge $q = 0$ and whose rest mass is very small or zero, was not initially detected and was only later hypothesized to exist, as we shall discuss later in this Section. No nucleons are lost when an electron is emitted, and the total number of nucleons, $A$, is the same in the daughter nucleus as in the parent. But because an electron has been emitted from the nucleus itself, the charge on the daughter nucleus is $+1e$ greater than that on the parent. The parent nucleus in the decay written above had $Z = +6$, so from charge conservation the nucleus remaining behind must have a charge of $+7e$. So the daughter nucleus has $Z = 7$, which is nitrogen.

It must be carefully noted that the electron emitted in $\beta$ decay is *not* an orbital electron. Instead, the electron is created *within the nucleus itself.* What happens is that one of the neutrons changes to a proton and in the process (to conserve charge) emits an electron. Indeed, free neutrons actually do decay in this fashion:

**CAUTION**
*$\beta$-decay $e^-$ comes from nucleus (not an orbital electron)*

$$n \rightarrow p + e^- + \text{a neutrino}.$$

Because of their origin in the nucleus, the electrons emitted in $\beta$ decay are often referred to as "$\beta$ particles," rather than as electrons, to remind us of their origin. They are, nonetheless, indistinguishable from orbital electrons.

**EXAMPLE 30–8 Energy release in $^{14}_{6}C$ decay.** How much energy is released when $^{14}_{6}C$ decays to $^{14}_{7}N$ by $\beta$ emission?

**APPROACH** We find the mass difference before and after decay, $\Delta m$. The energy released is $E = (\Delta m)c^2$. The masses given in Appendix B are those of the neutral atom, and we have to keep track of the electrons involved. Assume the parent nucleus has six orbiting electrons so it is neutral; its mass is 14.003242 u. The daughter in this decay, $^{14}_{7}N$, is not neutral since it has the same six orbital electrons circling it but the nucleus has a charge of $+7e$. However, the mass of this daughter with its six electrons, plus the mass of the emitted electron (which makes a total of seven electrons), is just the mass of a neutral nitrogen atom.

**CAUTION**
*Be careful with atomic and electron masses in $\beta$ decay*

**SOLUTION** The total mass in the final state is

$$(\text{mass of } ^{14}_{7}N \text{ nucleus} + 6 \text{ electrons}) + (\text{mass of 1 electron}),$$

and this is equal to

$$\text{mass of neutral } ^{14}_{7}N \text{ (includes 7 electrons)},$$

which, from Appendix B is a mass of 14.003074 u. So the mass difference is $14.003242\,\text{u} - 14.003074\,\text{u} = 0.000168\,\text{u}$, which is equivalent to an energy change $\Delta m\, c^2 = (0.000168\,\text{u})(931.5\,\text{MeV/u}) = 0.156\,\text{MeV}$ or 156 keV.

**NOTE** The neutrino doesn't contribute to either the mass or charge balance since it has $q = 0$ and $m \approx 0$.

According to Example 30–8, we would expect the emitted electron to have a kinetic energy of 156 keV. (The daughter nucleus, because its mass is very much larger than that of the electron, recoils with very low velocity and hence gets very little of the kinetic energy.) Indeed, very careful measurements indicate that a few emitted $\beta$ particles do have kinetic energy close to this calculated value. But the vast majority of emitted electrons have somewhat less energy. In fact, the energy of the emitted electron can be anywhere from zero up to the maximum value as calculated above. This range of electron kinetic energy was found for any $\beta$ decay. It was as if the law of conservation of energy was being violated, and indeed Bohr actually considered this possibility. Careful experiments indicated that linear momentum and angular momentum also did not seem to be conserved. Physicists were troubled at the prospect of having to give up these laws, which had worked so well in all previous situations. In 1930, Wolfgang Pauli proposed an alternate solution: perhaps a new particle that was very difficult to detect was emitted during $\beta$ decay in addition to the electron. This hypothesized particle could be carrying off the energy, momentum, and angular momentum required to maintain the conservation laws. This new particle was named the **neutrino**—meaning "little neutral one"—by the great Italian physicist Enrico Fermi (1901–1954; Fig. 30–7), who in 1934 worked out a detailed theory of $\beta$ decay. (It was Fermi who, in this theory, postulated the existence of the fourth force in nature which we call the *weak nuclear force*.) The electron neutrino has zero charge, spin of $\frac{1}{2}\hbar$, and was long thought to have zero rest mass, although today it seems possible it does have a very tiny rest mass ($< 0.6\,\mathrm{eV}/c^2$). If its rest mass is zero, it is much like a photon in that it is neutral and travels at the speed of light. But the neutrino is far more difficult to detect. In 1956, complex experiments produced further evidence for the existence of the neutrino; but by then, most physicists had already accepted its existence.

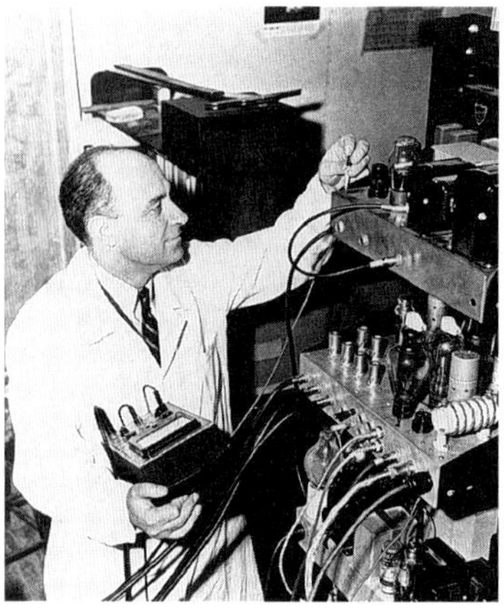

**FIGURE 30–7** Enrico Fermi. Fermi contributed significantly to both theoretical and experimental physics, a feat almost unique in modern times.

The symbol for the neutrino is the Greek letter nu ($\nu$). The correct way of writing the decay of ${}^{14}_{6}\mathrm{C}$ is then

*$\beta^-$ decay*

$$ {}^{14}_{6}\mathrm{C} \rightarrow {}^{14}_{7}\mathrm{N} + \mathrm{e}^- + \bar{\nu}. $$

The bar ($^-$) over the neutrino symbol is to indicate that it is an "antineutrino." (Why this is called an antineutrino rather than simply a neutrino need not concern us now; it is discussed in Chapter 32.)

## $\beta^+$ Decay

Many isotopes decay by electron emission. They are always isotopes that have too many neutrons compared to the number of protons. That is, they are isotopes that lie above the stable isotopes plotted in Fig. 30–2. But what about unstable isotopes that have too few neutrons compared to their number of protons—those that fall below the stable isotopes of Fig. 30–2? These, it turns out, decay by emitting a **positron** instead of an electron. A positron (sometimes called an $\mathrm{e}^+$ or $\beta^+$ particle) has the same mass as the electron, but it has a positive charge of $+1e$. Because it is so like an electron, except for its charge, the positron is called the **antiparticle**† to the electron. An example of a $\beta^+$ decay is that of ${}^{19}_{10}\mathrm{Ne}$:

*Positron ($\beta^+$) decay*

$$ {}^{19}_{10}\mathrm{Ne} \rightarrow {}^{19}_{9}\mathrm{F} + \mathrm{e}^+ + \nu, $$

where $\mathrm{e}^+$ (or ${}^{0}_{1}\mathrm{e}$) stands for a positron. Note that the $\nu$ emitted here is a neutrino, whereas that emitted in $\beta^-$ decay is called an antineutrino. Thus an antielectron (= positron) is emitted with a neutrino, whereas an antineutrino is emitted with an electron; this gives a certain balance as discussed in Chapter 32.

†Discussed in Chapter 32. Briefly, an antiparticle has the same mass as its corresponding particle, but opposite charge.

We can write $\beta^-$ and $\beta^+$ decay, in general, as follows:

$$^A_Z\text{N} \rightarrow {}^{A}_{Z+1}\text{N}' + \text{e}^- + \bar{\nu} \qquad [\beta^- \text{ decay}]$$

$$^A_Z\text{N} \rightarrow {}^{A}_{Z-1}\text{N}' + \text{e}^+ + \nu, \qquad [\beta^+ \text{ decay}]$$

where N is the parent nucleus and N′ is the daughter.

### Electron Capture

Besides $\beta^-$ and $\beta^+$ emission, there is a third related process. This is **electron capture** (abbreviated EC in Appendix B) and occurs when a nucleus absorbs one of its orbiting electrons. An example is $^7_4\text{Be}$, which as a result becomes $^7_3\text{Li}$. The process is written

$$^7_4\text{Be} + \text{e}^- \rightarrow {}^7_3\text{Li} + \nu,$$

*Electron capture*

or, in general,

$$^A_Z\text{N} + \text{e}^- \rightarrow {}^{A}_{Z-1}\text{N}' + \nu. \qquad [\text{electron capture}]$$

Usually it is an electron in the innermost (K) shell that is captured, in which case it is called "K-capture." The electron disappears in the process, and a proton in the nucleus becomes a neutron; a neutrino is emitted as a result. This process is inferred experimentally by detection of emitted X-rays (due to other electrons jumping down to fill the empty state) of just the proper energy.

*K-capture*

In $\beta$ decay, it is the weak nuclear force that plays the crucial role. The neutrino is unique in that it interacts with matter only via the weak force, which is why it is so hard to detect.

## 30–6 Gamma Decay

Gamma rays are photons having very high energy. They have their origin in the decay of a nucleus, much like emission of photons by excited atoms. Like an atom, a nucleus itself can be in an excited state. When it jumps down to a lower energy state, or to the ground state, it emits a photon which we call a $\gamma$ ray. The possible energy levels of a nucleus are much farther apart than those of an atom: on the order of keV or MeV, as compared to a few eV for electrons in an atom. Hence, the emitted photons have energies that can range from a few keV to several MeV. For a given decay, the $\gamma$ ray always has the same energy. Since a $\gamma$ ray carries no charge, there is no change in the element as a result of a $\gamma$ decay.

How does a nucleus get into an excited state? It may occur because of a violent collision with another particle. More commonly, the nucleus remaining after a previous radioactive decay may be in an excited state. A typical example is shown in the energy-level diagram of Fig. 30–8. $^{12}_5\text{B}$ can decay by $\beta$ decay directly to the ground state of $^{12}_6\text{C}$; or it can go by $\beta$ decay to an excited state of $^{12}_6\text{C}$, which then decays by emission of a 4.4-MeV $\gamma$ ray to the ground state.

**FIGURE 30–8** Energy-level diagram showing how $^{12}_5\text{B}$ can decay to the ground state of $^{12}_6\text{C}$ by $\beta$ decay (total energy released = 13.4 MeV), or can instead $\beta$ decay to an excited state of $^{12}_6\text{C}$ (indicated by *), which subsequently decays to its ground state by emitting a 4.4-MeV $\gamma$ ray.

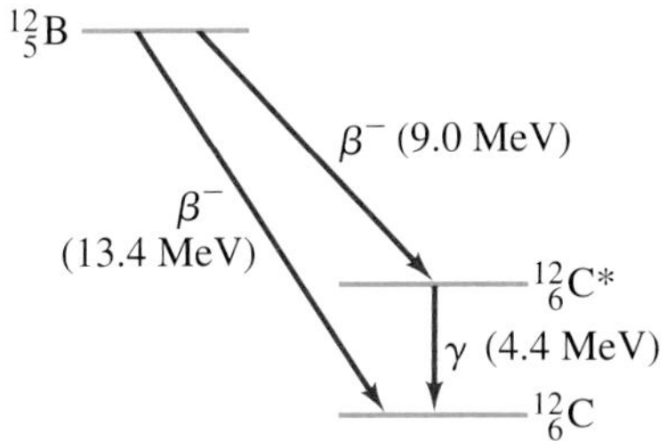


We can write $\gamma$ decay as

$$^A_Z\text{N}^* \rightarrow {}^A_Z\text{N} + \gamma, \qquad [\gamma \text{ decay}]$$

where the asterisk means "excited state" of that nucleus.

### * Isomers; Internal Conversion

In some cases, a nucleus may remain in an excited state for some time before it emits a $\gamma$ ray. The nucleus is then said to be in a **metastable state** and is called an **isomer**.

An excited nucleus can sometimes return to the ground state by another process known as **internal conversion** with no $\gamma$ ray emitted. In this process, the excited nucleus interacts with one of the orbital electrons and ejects this electron from the atom with the same kinetic energy (minus the binding energy of the electron) that an emitted $\gamma$ ray would have had.

*Internal conversion*

What, you may wonder, is the difference between a $\gamma$ ray and an X-ray? They both are electromagnetic radiation (photons) and, though $\gamma$ rays usually have higher energy than X-rays, their range of energies overlap to some extent. The difference is not intrinsic. We use the term X-ray if the photon is produced by an electron–atom interaction, and $\gamma$ ray if the photon is produced in a nuclear process.

**TABLE 30–2 The Three Types of Radioactive Decay**

*α decay:*

$^{A}_{Z}\text{N} \rightarrow {}^{A-4}_{Z-2}\text{N}' + {}^{4}_{2}\text{He}$

*β decay:*

$^{A}_{Z}\text{N} \rightarrow {}^{A}_{Z+1}\text{N}' + e^- + \bar{\nu}$

$^{A}_{Z}\text{N} \rightarrow {}^{A}_{Z-1}\text{N}' + e^+ + \nu$

$^{A}_{Z}\text{N} + \text{e}^- \rightarrow {}^{A}_{Z-1}\text{N}' + \nu$ [EC]†

*γ decay:*

$^{A}_{Z}\text{N}^* \rightarrow {}^{A}_{Z}\text{N} + \gamma$

† Electron capture.

* Indicates the excited state of a nucleus.

## 30–7 Conservation of Nucleon Number and Other Conservation Laws

In all three types of radioactive decay, the classical conservation laws hold. Energy, linear momentum, angular momentum, and electric charge are all conserved. These quantities are the same before the decay as after. But a new conservation law is also revealed, the **law of conservation of nucleon number**. According to this law, the total number of nucleons ($A$) remains constant in any process, although one type can change into the other type (protons into neutrons or vice versa). This law holds in all three types of decay. Table 30–2 gives a summary of $\alpha$, $\beta$, and $\gamma$ decay.

## 30–8 Half-Life and Rate of Decay

A macroscopic sample of any radioactive isotope consists of a vast number of radioactive nuclei. These nuclei do not all decay at one time. Rather, they decay one by one over a period of time. This is a random process: we can not predict exactly when a given nucleus will decay. But we can determine, on a probabilistic basis, approximately how many nuclei in a sample will decay over a given time period, by assuming that each nucleus has the same probability of decaying in each second that it exists.

The number of decays $\Delta N$ that occur in a very short time interval $\Delta t$ is then proportional to $\Delta t$ and to the total number $N$ of radioactive nuclei present:

$$\Delta N = -\lambda N \, \Delta t \tag{30–3a}$$

where the minus sign means $N$ is decreasing. We rewrite this to get the rate of decay, and drop the minus sign

$$\frac{\Delta N}{\Delta t} = \lambda N. \tag{30–3b}$$

In these equations, $\lambda$ is a constant of proportionality called the **decay constant**, which is different for different isotopes. The greater $\lambda$ is, the greater the rate of decay ($\Delta N/\Delta t$) and the more "radioactive" that isotope is said to be. The number of decays that occur in the short time interval $\Delta t$ is designated $\Delta N$ because each decay that occurs corresponds to a decrease by one in the number $N$ of nuclei present. That is, radioactive decay is a "one-shot" process, Fig. 30–9. Once a particular parent nucleus decays into its daughter, it cannot do it again.

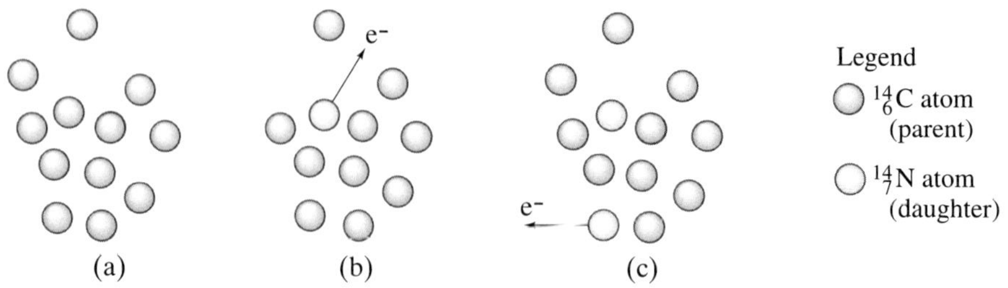


**FIGURE 30–9** Radioactive nuclei decay one by one. Hence, the number of parent nuclei in a sample is continually decreasing. When a $^{14}_{6}$C nucleus emits the electron, the nucleus becomes a $^{14}_{7}$N nucleus.

## Exponential Decay

Equation 30–3a or b can be solved for $N$ (using calculus) and the result is

$$N = N_0 e^{-\lambda t}, \qquad \textbf{(30–4)}$$

*Radioactive decay law*

where $N_0$ is the number of nuclei present at time $t = 0$, and $N$ is the number remaining after a time $t$. The symbol $e$ is the natural exponential (encountered earlier in Sections 19–6 and 21–11) whose value is $e = 2.718\cdots$. Thus the number of parent nuclei in a sample decreases exponentially in time, as shown in Fig. 30–10a for ${}^{14}_{6}C$ decay. Equation 30–4 is called the **radioactive decay law**.

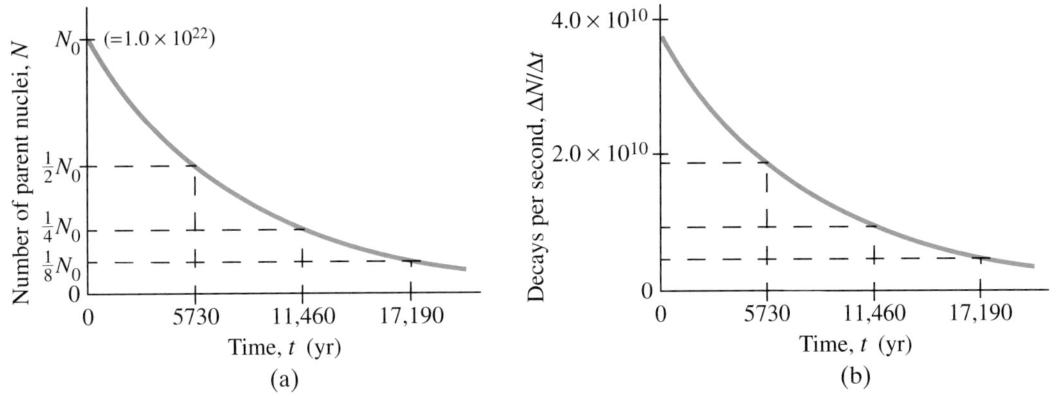


**FIGURE 30–10** (a) The number $N$ of parent nuclei in a given sample of ${}^{14}_{6}C$ decreases exponentially. (b) The number of decays per second also decreases exponentially. The half-life of ${}^{14}_{6}C$ is 5730 yr, which means that the number of parent nuclei, $N$, and the rate of decay, $\Delta N/\Delta t$, decreases by half every 5730 yr.

The number of decays per second, $\Delta N/\Delta t$, is called the **activity** (or rate of decay) of the sample. Since $\Delta N/\Delta t$ is proportional to $N$ (see Eq. 30–3b), it, too, decreases exponentially in time at the same rate (Fig. 30–10b). The activity at time $t$ is given by

$$\frac{\Delta N}{\Delta t} = \left(\frac{\Delta N}{\Delta t}\right)_0 e^{-\lambda t}, \qquad \textbf{(30–5)}$$

*Activity*

where $(\Delta N/\Delta t)_0$ is the activity at $t = 0$.

## Half-Life

The rate of decay of any isotope is often specified by giving its "half-life" rather than the decay constant $\lambda$. The **half-life** of an isotope is defined as the time it takes for half the original amount of parent isotope in a given sample to decay. For example, the half-life of ${}^{14}_{6}C$ is about 5730 years. If at some time a piece of petrified wood contains, say, $1.00 \times 10^{22}$ nuclei of ${}^{14}_{6}C$, then 5730 years later it will contain only $0.50 \times 10^{22}$ of these nuclei. After another 5730 years it will contain $0.25 \times 10^{22}$ nuclei, and so on. This is shown in Fig. 30–10a. Since the rate of decay $\Delta N/\Delta t$ is proportional to $N$, it, too, decreases by a factor of 2 every half-life (Fig. 30–10b).

The half-lives of known radioactive isotopes vary from as short as $10^{-22}$ s to about $10^{28}$ s (about $10^{21}$ yr). The half-lives of many isotopes are given in Appendix B. It should be clear that the half-life (which we designate $T_{\frac{1}{2}}$) bears an inverse relationship to the decay constant. The longer the half-life of an isotope, the more slowly it decays, and hence $\lambda$ is smaller. Conversely, very active isotopes (large $\lambda$) have very short half-lives. The precise relationship between half-life and decay constant is

$$T_{\frac{1}{2}} = \frac{\ln 2}{\lambda} = \frac{0.693}{\lambda}. \qquad \textbf{(30–6)}$$

*Half-life*

We derive this in the next (optional) subsection.

## * Deriving the Half-life Formula; Mean Life

We can derive Eq. 30–6 starting from Eq. 30–4 by setting $N = N_0/2$ at $t = T_{\frac{1}{2}}$:

$$\frac{N_0}{2} = N_0 e^{-\lambda T_{\frac{1}{2}}}$$

so

$$e^{\lambda T_{\frac{1}{2}}} = 2.$$

We take natural logs of both sides ("ln" and "$e$" are inverse operations, meaning $\ln(e^x) = x$) and find

$$\ln\left(e^{\lambda T_{\frac{1}{2}}}\right) = \ln 2,$$

so

$$\lambda T_{\frac{1}{2}} = \ln 2 = 0.693$$

and

$$T_{\frac{1}{2}} = \frac{\ln 2}{\lambda} = \frac{0.693}{\lambda},$$

which is Eq. 30–6.

You may find the *mean life* of an isotope quoted. The mean life $\tau$ is defined as $\tau = 1/\lambda$, so that Eq. 30–4 can written $N = N_0 e^{-t/\tau}$ just as for $RC$ and $LR$ circuits (Chapters 19 and 21) where $\tau$ is called the time constant. Then (see also Eq. 30–6)

$$\tau = \frac{1}{\lambda} = \frac{T_{\frac{1}{2}}}{0.693};$$

the mean life and half-life differ significantly in numerical value, so confusing them can cause serious error (and has).

# 30–9 Calculations Involving Decay Rates and Half-Life

Let us now consider Examples of what we can determine about a sample of radioactive material if we know the half-life.

**EXAMPLE 30–9** **Sample activity.** The isotope $^{14}_{6}C$ has a half-life of 5730 yr. If at some time a sample contains $1.00 \times 10^{22}$ carbon-14 nuclei, what is the activity of the sample?

**APPROACH** We first use the half-life to find the decay constant (Eq. 30–6), and use that to find the activity, Eq. 30–3b. The number of seconds in a year is $(60)(60)(24)(365\frac{1}{4}) = 3.156 \times 10^7$ s.

**SOLUTION** The decay constant $\lambda$ from Eq. 30–6 is

$$\lambda = \frac{0.693}{T_{\frac{1}{2}}} = \frac{0.693}{(5730\,\text{yr})(3.156 \times 10^7\,\text{s/yr})} = 3.83 \times 10^{-12}\,\text{s}^{-1}.$$

From Eq. 30–3b, the magnitude of the activity or rate of decay is

$$\frac{\Delta N}{\Delta t} = \lambda N = \left(3.83 \times 10^{-12}\,\text{s}^{-1}\right)\left(1.00 \times 10^{22}\right)$$
$$= 3.83 \times 10^{10}\,\text{decays/s}.$$

Notice that the graph of Fig. 30–10b starts at this value, corresponding to the original value of $N = 1.0 \times 10^{22}$ nuclei in Fig. 30–10a.

**NOTE** The unit "decays/s" is often written simply as $\text{s}^{-1}$ since "decays" is not a unit but refers only to the number. This simple unit of activity is called the becquerel: 1 Bq = 1 decay/s, as discussed in Chapter 31.

**EXERCISE C** Determine the decay constant for radium $(T_{\frac{1}{2}} = 1600\,\text{yr})$.

**CONCEPTUAL EXAMPLE 30–10** **Safety: activity versus half-life.** One might think that a short half-life material is safer than a long half-life material because it will not last as long. Is this an accurate representation of the situation?

**RESPONSE** No. A shorter half-life means the activity is higher and thus more "radioactive" and dangerous. On the other hand, a shorter half-life means the material will all decay to a low level sooner. For the same sample size $N$, a short half-life material is more radioactive but for a shorter time.

**EXERCISE D** The isotope $^{60}_{27}Co$, used for radiation treatments in hospitals, has a half-life of about 5.3 years. If a hospital buys a $^{60}_{27}Co$ sample, will it all be gone in 10.6 years (two half-lives)?

## Additional Example

**EXAMPLE 30–11** **A sample of radioactive $^{13}_{7}N$.** A laboratory has 1.49 $\mu$g of pure $^{13}_{7}N$, which has a half-life of 10.0 min (600 s). (*a*) How many nuclei are present initially? (*b*) What is the activity initially? (*c*) What is the activity after 1.00 h? (*d*) After approximately how long will the activity drop to less than one per second $(1\ s^{-1})$?

**APPROACH** We use the definition of the mole and Avogadro's number (Sections 13–7 and 13–9) to find the number of nuclei. For (*b*) we get $\lambda$ from the given half-life and use Eq. 30–3b for the activity. For (*c*) and (*d*) we use Eq. 30–5, and/or make a Table of the times.

**SOLUTION** (*a*) The atomic mass is 13.0, so 13.0 g will contain $6.02 \times 10^{23}$ nuclei (Avogadro's number). Since we have only $1.49 \times 10^{-6}$ g, the number of nuclei $N_0$ that we have initially is given by the ratio

$$\frac{N_0}{6.02 \times 10^{23}} = \frac{1.49 \times 10^{-6}\ \text{g}}{13.0\ \text{g}},$$

so $N_0 = 6.90 \times 10^{16}$ nuclei.

(*b*) From Eq. 30–6, $\lambda = (0.693)/(600\ \text{s}) = 1.16 \times 10^{-3}\ \text{s}^{-1}$. Then, at $t = 0$ (Eq. 30–3b),

$$\left(\frac{\Delta N}{\Delta t}\right)_0 = \lambda N_0 = \left(1.16 \times 10^{-3}\ \text{s}^{-1}\right)\left(6.90 \times 10^{16}\right) = 8.00 \times 10^{13}\ \text{decays/s}.$$

(*c*)The half-life is 10.0 min, so the decay rate decreases by half every 10.0 min. We can make the Table of activity (in the margin) after given periods of time. After 1.0 h, the activity is $1.25 \times 10^{12}$ decays/s.

| Time (min) | Activity (decays/s) |
|---|---|
| 0 | $8.00 \times 10^{13}$ |
| 10 | $4.00 \times 10^{13}$ |
| 20 | $2.00 \times 10^{13}$ |
| 30 | $1.00 \times 10^{13}$ |
| 40 | $0.500 \times 10^{13}$ |
| 50 | $0.250 \times 10^{13}$ |
| 60 | $0.125 \times 10^{13}$ |

***Easy Alternate Solution*** **(*c*)** 60 minutes is 6 half-lives, so the activity will decrease to $\left(\frac{1}{2}\right)\left(\frac{1}{2}\right)\left(\frac{1}{2}\right)\left(\frac{1}{2}\right)\left(\frac{1}{2}\right)\left(\frac{1}{2}\right) = \left(\frac{1}{2}\right)^6 = \frac{1}{64}$ of its original value, or $\left(8.00 \times 10^{13}\right)/(64) = 1.25 \times 10^{12}$ per second.

***General Alternate Solution*** **(*c*)** The general way to find the activity, which works even when the time is not a perfect multiple of $T_{\frac{1}{2}}$, is to use Eq. 30–5. We set $t = 60.0$ min $= 3600$ s:

$$\frac{\Delta N}{\Delta t} = \left(\frac{\Delta N}{\Delta t}\right)_0 e^{-\lambda t} = \left(8.00 \times 10^{13}\ \text{s}^{-1}\right)e^{-\left(1.16\times10^{-3}\ \text{s}^{-1}\right)(3600\ \text{s})} = 1.23 \times 10^{12}\ \text{s}^{-1}.$$

**NOTE** The slight discrepancy in results arises because we kept only three significant figures.

(*d*) We want to determine the time $t$ when $\Delta N/\Delta t = 1.00\ \text{s}^{-1}$. From Eq. 30–5, we have

$$e^{-\lambda t} = \frac{(\Delta N/\Delta t)}{(\Delta N/\Delta t)_0} = \frac{1.00\ \text{s}^{-1}}{8.00 \times 10^{13}\ \text{s}^{-1}} = 1.25 \times 10^{-14}.$$

We take the natural log (ln) of both sides (remember $\ln e^{-\lambda t} = -\lambda t$) and divide by $\lambda$ to find

$$t = -\frac{\ln\left(1.25 \times 10^{-14}\right)}{\lambda} = 2.76 \times 10^4\ \text{s} = 7.67\ \text{h}.$$

## 30–10 Decay Series

It is often the case that one radioactive isotope decays to another isotope that is also radioactive. Sometimes this daughter decays to yet a third isotope which also is radioactive. Such successive decays are said to form a **decay series**. An important example is illustrated in Fig. 30–11. As can be seen, ${}^{238}_{92}\text{U}$ decays by $\alpha$ emission to ${}^{234}_{90}\text{Th}$, which in turn decays by $\beta$ decay to ${}^{234}_{91}\text{Pa}$. The series continues as shown, with several possible branches near the bottom, ending at the stable lead isotope, ${}^{206}_{82}\text{Pb}$. The two last decays can be

$$ {}^{206}_{81}\text{Tl} \rightarrow {}^{206}_{82}\text{Pb} + e^- + \bar{\nu}, $$

or

$$ {}^{210}_{84}\text{Po} \rightarrow {}^{206}_{82}\text{Pb} + \alpha. $$

Other radioactive series also exist.

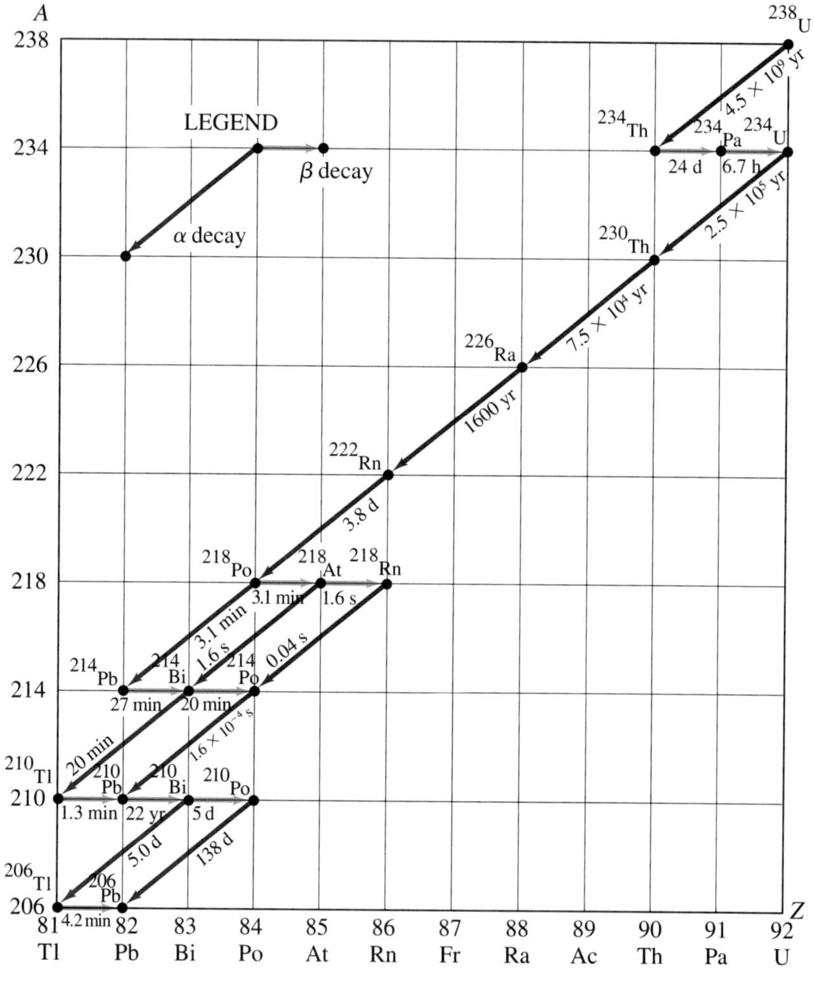


**FIGURE 30–11** Decay series beginning with ${}^{238}_{92}\text{U}$. Nuclei in the series are specified by a dot representing $A$ and $Z$ values. Half-lives are given in seconds (s), minutes (min), hours (h), days (d), or years (yr). Note that a horizontal arrow represents $\beta$ decay ($A$ does not change), whereas a diagonal line represents $\alpha$ decay ($A$ changes by 4, $Z$ changes by 2).

Because of such decay series, certain radioactive elements are found in nature that otherwise would not be. For when the solar system acquired its present form about 5 billion years ago, it is believed that nearly all nuclides were formed (by the fusion process, Sections 31–3 and 33–2). Many isotopes with short half-lives decayed quickly and no longer are detected in nature today. But long-lived isotopes, such as ${}^{238}_{92}\text{U}$ with a half-life of $4.5 \times 10^9$ yr, still do exist in nature today. Indeed, about half of the original ${}^{238}_{92}\text{U}$ still remains (assuming that the origin of the solar system was about $5 \times 10^9$ yr ago). We might expect, however, that radium (${}^{226}_{88}\text{Ra}$), with a half-life of 1600 yr, would long since have disappeared from the Earth. Indeed, the original ${}^{226}_{88}\text{Ra}$ nuclei must by now have all decayed. However, because ${}^{238}_{92}\text{U}$ decays (in several steps) to ${}^{226}_{88}\text{Ra}$, the supply of $^{226}_{88}Ra$ is continually replenished, which is why it is still found on Earth today. The same can be said for many other radioactive nuclides.

CONCEPTUAL EXAMPLE 30–12 **Decay chain.** The decay chain starting with $^{234}_{92}U$ in Fig. 30–11 has four successive nuclides with half-lives of 250,000 yr, 75,000 yr, 1600 yr, and a little under 4 days. Each decay in the chain has an alpha particle of a characteristic energy, and so we can monitor the radioactive decay rate of each nuclide. Given a sample that was pure $^{234}_{92}U$ a million years ago, which alpha decay would you expect to have the highest activity rate in the sample?

**RESPONSE** The first instinct is to say that the process with the shortest half-life would show the highest activity. Surprisingly, however, the activity rates in this sample are all the same! The reason is that in each case the decay of the parent acts as a bottleneck to the decay of the daughter. Compared to the 1600-yr half-life of $^{226}_{88}Ra$, for example, its daughter $^{222}_{86}Rn$ decays almost immediately, but it cannot decay until it is made. (This is like an automobile assembly line: if worker A takes 20 minutes to do a task and then worker B takes only 1 minute to do the next task, worker B still does only one car every 20 minutes).

## 30–11 Radioactive Dating

Radioactive decay has many interesting applications. One is the technique of *radioactive dating* by which the age of ancient materials can be determined.

PHYSICS APPLIED
*Carbon-14 dating*

The age of any object made from once-living matter, such as wood, can be determined using the natural radioactivity of $^{14}_{6}C$. All living plants absorb carbon dioxide ($CO_2$) from the air and use it to synthesize organic molecules. The vast majority of these carbon atoms are $^{12}_{6}C$, but a small fraction, about $1.3 \times 10^{-12}$, is the radioactive isotope $^{14}_{6}C$. The ratio of $^{14}_{6}C$ to $^{12}_{6}C$ in the atmosphere has remained roughly constant over many thousands of years, in spite of the fact that $^{14}_{6}C$ decays with a half-life of about 5730 yr. This is because energetic nuclei in the cosmic radiation, which impinges on the Earth from outer-space, strike nuclei of atoms in the atmosphere and break those nuclei into pieces, releasing free neutrons. Those neutrons can collide with nitrogen nuclei in the atmosphere to produce the following nuclear transformation: $n + ^{14}_{7}N \rightarrow ^{14}_{6}C + p$. That is, a neutron strikes and is absorbed by a $^{14}_{7}N$ nucleus, and a proton is knocked out in the process. The remaining nucleus is $^{14}_{6}C$. This continual production of $^{14}_{6}C$ in the atmosphere roughly balances the loss of $^{14}_{6}C$ by radioactive decay. As long as a plant or tree is alive, it continually uses the carbon from carbon dioxide in the air to build new tissue and to replace old. Animals eat plants, so they too are continually receiving a fresh supply of carbon for their tissues.

*$^{14}C$ formation in atmosphere*

Organisms cannot distinguish† $^{14}_{6}C$ from $^{12}_{6}C$, and since the ratio of $^{14}_{6}C$ to $^{12}_{6}C$ in the atmosphere remains nearly constant, the ratio of the two isotopes within the living organism remains nearly constant as well. When an organism dies, carbon dioxide is no longer absorbed and utilized. Because the $^{14}_{6}C$ decays radioactively, the ratio of $^{14}_{6}C$ to $^{12}_{6}C$ in a dead organism decreases over time. Since the half-life of $^{14}_{6}C$ is about 5730 yr, the $^{14}_{6}C/^{12}_{6}C$ ratio decreases by half every 5730 yr. If, for example, the $^{14}_{6}C/^{12}_{6}C$ ratio of an ancient wooden tool is half of what it is in living trees, then the object must have been made from a tree that was felled about 5730 years ago. Actually, corrections must be made for the fact that the $^{14}_{6}C/^{12}_{6}C$ ratio in the atmosphere has not remained precisely constant over time. The determination of what this ratio has been over the centuries has required techniques such as comparing the expected ratio to the actual ratio for objects whose age is known, such as very old trees whose annual rings can be counted reasonably accurately.

†Organisms operate almost exclusively via chemical reactions—which involve only the outer orbital electrons of the atom; extra neutrons in the nucleus have essentially no effect.

## Additional Example

PHYSICS APPLIED
*Archeological dating*

**EXAMPLE 30–13** **An ancient animal.** The mass of carbon in an animal bone fragment found in an archeological site is 200 g. If the bone registers an activity of 16 decays/s, what is its age?

**APPROACH** First we determine how many ${}^{14}_{6}C$ atoms there were in our 200-g sample when the animal was alive, given the known fraction of ${}^{14}_{6}C$, $1.3 \times 10^{-12}$. Then we use Eq. 30–3b to find the activity back then, and Eq. 30–5 to find out how long ago that was by solving for the time $t$.

**SOLUTION** The 200 g of carbon is nearly all ${}^{12}_{6}C$; 12.0 g of ${}^{12}_{6}C$ contains $6.02 \times 10^{23}$ atoms, so 200 g contains

$$\left(\frac{6.02 \times 10^{23}\text{ atoms}}{12\text{ g}}\right)(200\text{ g}) = 1.00 \times 10^{25}\text{ atoms}.$$

When the animal was alive, the ratio of ${}^{14}_{6}C$ to ${}^{12}_{6}C$ in the bone was $1.3 \times 10^{-12}$. The number of ${}^{14}_{6}C$ nuclei at that time was

$$N_0 = (1.00 \times 10^{25}\text{ atoms})(1.3 \times 10^{-12}) = 1.3 \times 10^{13}\text{ atoms}.$$

From Eq. 30–3b the magnitude of the activity when the animal was alive $(t = 0)$ was

$$\left(\frac{\Delta N}{\Delta t}\right)_0 = \lambda N_0,$$

where $\lambda = 3.83 \times 10^{-12}\text{ s}^{-1}$ as we calculated in Example 30–9. So the original activity was

$$\left(\frac{\Delta N}{\Delta t}\right)_0 = \lambda N_0 = (3.83 \times 10^{-12}\text{ s}^{-1})(1.3 \times 10^{13}) = 50\text{ s}^{-1}.$$

From Eq. 30–5

$$\frac{\Delta N}{\Delta t} = \left(\frac{\Delta N}{\Delta t}\right)_0 e^{-\lambda t}$$

where $\Delta N/\Delta t$ is given as $16\text{ s}^{-1}$. Then

$$16\text{ s}^{-1} = (50\text{ s}^{-1})e^{-\lambda t}$$

or

$$e^{\lambda t} = \frac{50}{16}.$$

We take natural logs of both sides to obtain

$$t = \frac{1}{\lambda}\ln\left(\frac{50}{16}\right) = \frac{1}{3.83 \times 10^{-12}\text{ s}^{-1}}\ln\left(\frac{50}{16}\right)$$
$$= 2.98 \times 10^{11}\text{ s} = 9400\text{ yr},$$

which is the time elapsed since the death of the animal.

## Geological Time Scale Dating

PHYSICS APPLIED
*Geological dating*

Carbon dating is useful only for determining the age of objects less than about 60,000 years old. The amount of ${}^{14}_{6}C$ remaining in objects older than that is usually too small to measure accurately, although new techniques are allowing detection of even smaller amounts of ${}^{14}_{6}C$, pushing the time frame further back. On the other hand, radioactive isotopes with longer half-lives can be used in certain circumstances to obtain the age of older objects. For example, the decay of ${}^{238}_{92}U$, because of its long half-life of $4.5 \times 10^9$ years, is useful in determining the ages of rocks on a geologic time scale. When molten material on Earth long ago solidified into rock as the temperature dropped, different compounds solidified according to the melting points, and thus different compounds separated to some extent.

Uranium present in a material became fixed in position and the daughter nuclei that result from the decay of uranium were also fixed in that position. Thus, by measuring the amount of $^{238}_{92}\text{U}$ remaining in the material relative to the amount of daughter nuclei, the time when the rock solidified can be determined.

Radioactive dating methods using $^{238}_{92}\text{U}$ and other isotopes have shown the age of the oldest Earth rocks to be about $4 \times 10^9$ yr. The age of rocks in which the oldest fossilized organisms are embedded indicates that life appeared more than 3.5 billion years ago. The earliest fossilized remains of mammals are found in rocks 200 million years old, and the first humanlike creatures seem to have appeared about 2 million years ago. Radioactive dating has been indispensable for the reconstruction of Earth's history.

PHYSICS APPLIED
*Oldest Earth rocks and earliest life*

## * 30–12 Stability and Tunneling

We have seen that radioactive decay occurs only when the mass of the parent nucleus is greater than the sum of the masses of the daughter nucleus and all particles emitted. For example, $^{238}_{92}\text{U}$ can decay to $^{234}_{90}\text{Th}$ because the mass of $^{238}_{92}\text{U}$ is greater than the mass of the $^{234}_{90}\text{Th}$ plus the mass of the $\alpha$ particle. Since systems tend to go in the direction that reduces their internal or potential energy (a ball rolls downhill, a positive charge moves toward a negative charge), you may wonder why an unstable nucleus doesn't fall apart immediately. In other words, why do $^{238}_{92}\text{U}$ nuclei $\left(T_{\frac{1}{2}} = 4.5 \times 10^9\,\text{yr}\right)$ and other isotopes have such long half-lives? Why don't parent nuclei all decay at once?

The answer has to do with quantum theory and the nature of the forces involved. One way to view the situation is with the aid of a potential-energy diagram, as in Fig. 30–12. Let us consider the particular case of the decay $^{238}_{92}\text{U} \rightarrow {}^{234}_{90}\text{Th} + {}^{4}_{2}\text{He}$. The blue line represents the potential energy, including rest mass, where we imagine the $\alpha$ particle as a separate entity within the $^{238}_{92}\text{U}$ nucleus. The region labeled A in Fig. 30–12 represents the PE of the $\alpha$ particle when it is held within the uranium nucleus by the nuclear force ($R_0$ is the nuclear radius). Region C represents the PE when the $\alpha$ particle is free of the nucleus. The downward-curving PE (proportional to $1/r$) represents the electrical (Coulomb's law) repulsion between the positively charged $\alpha$ and the $^{234}_{90}\text{Th}$ nucleus. To get to region C, the $\alpha$ particle has to get by the "Coulomb" barrier shown. Since the PE just beyond $r = R_0$ (region B) is greater than the energy of the alpha particle (dashed line), the $\alpha$ particle could not escape the nucleus if it were governed by classical physics. It could escape only if there were an input of energy equal to the height of the barrier. Nuclei decay spontaneously, however, without any input of energy. How, then, does the $\alpha$ particle get from region A to region C? It actually passes through the barrier in a process known as **tunneling**. Classically, this could not happen, because an $\alpha$ particle in region B (within the barrier) would be violating the conservation-of-energy principle.† The uncertainty principle, however, tells us that energy conservation can be violated by an amount $\Delta E$ for a length of time $\Delta t$ given by

$$(\Delta E)(\Delta t) \approx \frac{h}{2\pi}.$$

We saw in Section 28–3 that this is a result of the wave–particle duality. Thus quantum mechanics allows conservation of energy to be violated for brief periods that may be long enough for an $\alpha$ particle to "tunnel" through the barrier. $\Delta E$ would represent the energy difference between the average barrier height and the particle's energy, and $\Delta t$ the time to pass through the barrier. The higher and wider the barrier, the less time the $\alpha$ particle has to escape and the less likely it is to do so. It is therefore the height and width of this barrier that controls the rate of decay and half-life of an isotope.

**FIGURE 30–12** Potential energy for alpha particle and nucleus, showing the "Coulomb barrier" through which the $\alpha$ particle must tunnel to escape. The $Q$-value of the reaction is also shown.

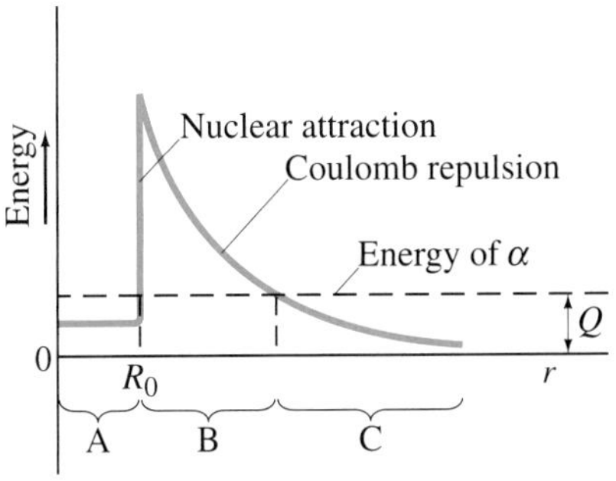


*Tunneling*

†The total energy $E$ (dashed line in Fig. 30–12) would be less than the PE; because $\text{KE} = \frac{1}{2}mv^2 > 0$, then $E = \text{KE} + \text{PE}$ could not be less than the PE classically.

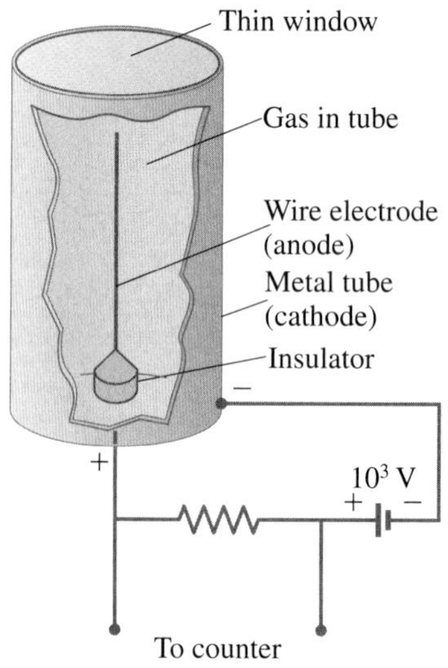


**FIGURE 30–13** Diagram of a Geiger counter.

## 30–13 Detection of Radiation

Individual particles such as electrons, protons, $\alpha$ particles, neutrons, and $\gamma$ rays are not detected directly by our senses. Consequently, a variety of instruments have been developed to detect them.

One of the most common is the **Geiger counter**. As shown in Fig. 30–13, it consists of a cylindrical metal tube filled with a certain type of gas. A long wire runs down the center and is kept at a high positive voltage $(\approx 10^3\,\text{V})$ with respect to the outer cylinder. The voltage is just slightly less than that required to ionize the gas atoms. When a charged particle enters through the thin "window" at one end of the tube, it ionizes a few atoms of the gas. The freed electrons are attracted toward the positive wire, and as they are accelerated they strike and ionize additional atoms. An "avalanche" of electrons is quickly produced, and when it reaches the wire anode, it produces a voltage pulse. The pulse, after being amplified, can be sent to an electronic counter, which counts how many particles have been detected. Or the pulses can be sent to a loudspeaker and each detection of a particle is heard as a "click." Only a fraction of the radiation emitted by a sample is detected by any detector.

*Scintillators*

A **scintillation counter** makes use of a solid, liquid, or gas known as a **scintillator** or **phosphor**. The atoms of a scintillator are easily excited when struck by an incoming particle and emit visible light when they return to their ground states. Typical scintillators are crystals of NaI and certain plastics. One face of a solid scintillator is cemented to a photomultiplier tube, and the whole is wrapped with opaque material to keep it light tight or is placed within a light-tight container. The **photomultiplier** (PM) **tube** converts the energy of the scintillator-emitted photon(s) into an electric signal. A PM tube is a vacuum tube containing several electrodes (typically 8 to 14), called *dynodes*, which are maintained at successively higher voltages as shown in Fig. 30–14. At its top surface is a photoelectric surface, called the *photocathode*, whose work function (Section 27–3) is low enough that an electron is easily released when struck by a photon from the scintillator. Such an electron is accelerated toward the first dynode. When it strikes the first dynode, the electron has acquired sufficient kinetic energy so that it can eject two to five more electrons. These, in turn, are accelerated to the second dynode, and a multiplication process begins. The number of electrons striking the last dynode may be $10^6$ or more. Thus the passage of a particle through the scintillator results in an electric signal at the

*PM tube*

**FIGURE 30–14** Scintillation counter with a photomultiplier tube.

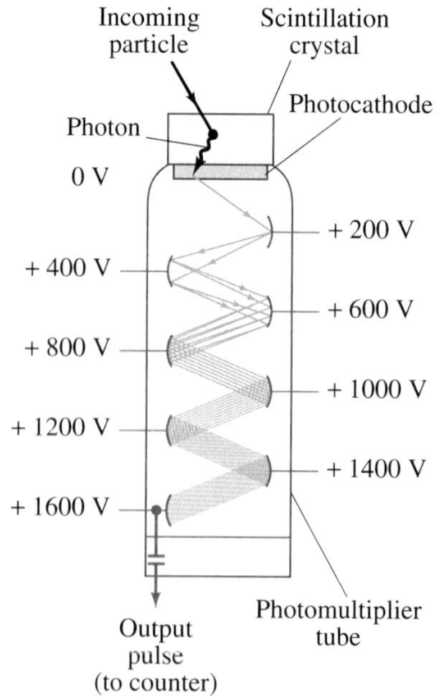

output of the PM tube that can be sent to an electronic counter just as for a Geiger tube. Solid scintillators are much more dense than the gas of a Geiger counter, and so are much more efficient detectors—especially for $\gamma$ rays, which interact less with matter than do $\beta$ rays. Scintillators that can measure the total energy deposited are much used today and are called **calorimeters**.

*Calorimeter*

In tracer work (Section 31–7), **liquid scintillators** are often used. Radioactive samples taken at different times or from different parts of an organism are placed directly in small bottles containing the liquid scintillator. This is particularly convenient for detection of $\beta$ rays from ${}^{3}_{1}H$ and ${}^{14}_{6}C$, which have very low energies and have difficulty passing through the outer covering of a crystal scintillator or Geiger tube. A PM tube is still used to produce the electric signal.

*Semiconductor detector (pn junction)*

A **semiconductor detector** consists of a reverse-biased *pn* junction diode (Section 29–8). A particle passing through the junction can excite electrons into the conduction band, leaving holes in the valence band. The freed charges produce a short electrical pulse that can be counted just as for Geiger and scintillation counters. Silicon wafer semiconductors have their surface etched into tiny pixels, thus providing detailed particle position information.

Hospital workers and others who work around radiation carry *film badges* which detect the accumulation of radiation. The film inside is periodically replaced and developed, the darkness being related to total exposure (see Section 31–5).

The devices discussed so far are used for counting the number of particles (or decays of a radioactive isotope). Other devices allow the track of charged particles to be *seen*. The simplest is the **photographic emulsion**, which can be small and portable, used now particularly for cosmic-ray studies from balloons. A charged particle passing through a layer of photographic emulsion ionizes the atoms along its path. These points undergo a chemical change, and when the emulsion is developed the particle's path is revealed. (One type of neutrino, $\tau$, was indirectly discovered using an emulsion at Fermilab; see Chapter 32.)

*Emulsions*

*Cloud chamber*

In a **cloud chamber**, a gas is cooled to a temperature slightly below its usual condensation point ("supercooled"), and gas molecules condense on any ionized molecules present. Ions produced when a charged particle passes through serve as centers on which tiny droplets form (Fig. 30–15). Light scatters more from these droplets than from the gas background, so a photo of the cloud chamber at the right moment shows the track of the particle. An important instrument in the early days of nuclear physics, it is little used today.

*Bubble chamber*

The **bubble chamber**, invented in 1952 by D. A. Glaser (1926–   ), makes use of a superheated liquid kept close to its normal boiling point. The bubbles characteristic of boiling form around ions produced by the passage of a charged particle. A photograph of the interior of the chamber reveals paths of particles that recently passed through. Because the bubble chamber uses a liquid, often liquid hydrogen, it is a much more efficient device than a cloud chamber for observing the tracks of charged particles and their interactions with the nuclei of the liquid. A magnetic field is usually applied across the chamber and the momentum of the moving particles can be determined from the radius of curvature of their paths.

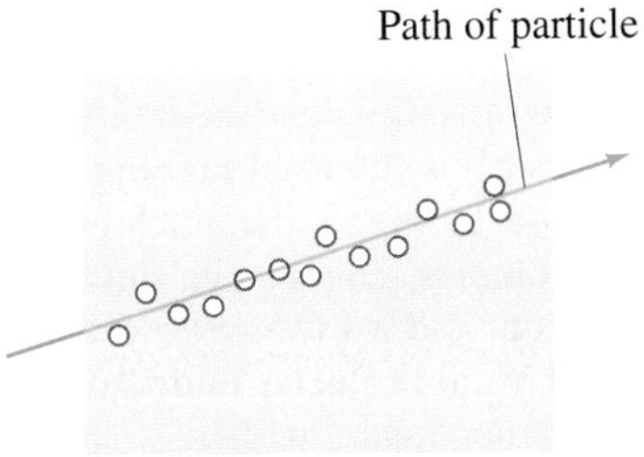


**FIGURE 30–15** In a cloud or bubble chamber, droplets or bubbles are formed around ions produced by the passage of a charged particle.

**FIGURE 30–16** Wire-drift chamber inside the Collider Detector at Fermilab (CDF). The photo at the start of Chapter 32 (page 889) was done with this detector.

*Wire drift chamber*

A **wire drift chamber** consists of a set of closely spaced fine wires immersed in a gas (Fig. 30–16). Many wires are grounded, and the others between are kept at very high voltage. A charged particle passing through produces ions in the gas. Freed electrons drift toward the nearest high voltage wires, creating an "avalanche," and producing an electric pulse or signal at that wire. The positions of the particles are determined electronically by the position of the wire and by the time it takes the pulses to reach "readout" electronics at the ends of the wires. The paths of the particles are reconstructed electronically by computers which can "draw" a picture of the tracks, as shown in the photo at the start of Chapter 32.

## Summary

**Nuclear physics** is the study of atomic nuclei. Nuclei contain **protons** and **neutrons**, which are collectively known as **nucleons**. The total number of nucleons, $A$, is the nucleus's **atomic mass number**. The number of protons, $Z$, is the **atomic number**. The number of neutrons equals $A - Z$. **Isotopes** are nuclei with the same $Z$, but with different numbers of neutrons. For an element X, an isotope of given $Z$ and $A$ is represented by

$$ {}^{A}_{Z}\mathrm{X}. $$

The nuclear radius is approximately proportional to $A^{\frac{1}{3}}$, indicating that all nuclei have about the same density. Nuclear masses are specified in **unified atomic mass units** (u), where the mass of ${}^{12}_{6}\mathrm{C}$ (including its 6 electrons) is defined as exactly 12.000000 u, or in terms of their energy equivalent (because $E = mc^2$), where

$$ 1\,\mathrm{u} = 931.5\,\mathrm{MeV}/c^2 = 1.66 \times 10^{-27}\,\mathrm{kg}. $$

The mass of a stable nucleus is less than the sum of the masses of its constituent nucleons. The difference in mass (times $c^2$) is the **total binding energy**. It represents the energy needed to break the nucleus into its constituent nucleons. The **binding energy per nucleon** averages about 8 MeV per nucleon, and is lowest for low mass and high mass nuclei.

Unstable nuclei undergo **radioactive decay**; they change into other nuclei with the emission of an $\alpha$, $\beta$, or $\gamma$ particle.

An $\alpha$ particle is a $^4_2$He nucleus; a $\beta$ particle is an electron or positron; and a $\gamma$ ray is a high-energy photon. In $\beta$ decay, a **neutrino** is also emitted. The transformation of the parent into the daughter nucleus is called **transmutation** of the elements. Radioactive decay occurs spontaneously only when the rest mass of the products is less than the mass of the parent nucleus. The loss in mass appears as kinetic energy of the products.

Nuclei are held together by the **strong nuclear force**. The **weak nuclear force** makes itself apparent in $\beta$ decay. These two forces, plus the gravitational and electromagnetic forces, are the four known types of force.

Electric charge, linear and angular momentum, mass–energy, and **nucleon number** are **conserved** in all decays.

Radioactive decay is a statistical process. For a given type of radioactive nucleus, the number of nuclei that decay ($\Delta N$) in a time $\Delta t$ is proportional to the number $N$ of parent nuclei present:

$$\Delta N = -\lambda N\,\Delta t; \qquad \textbf{(30–3a)}$$

the minus sign means $N$ *decreases* in time.

The proportionality constant $\lambda$ is called the **decay constant** and is characteristic of the given nucleus. The number $N$ of nuclei remaining after a time $t$ decreases exponentially

$$N = N_0 e^{-\lambda t}, \qquad \textbf{(30–4)}$$

as does the **activity**, $\Delta N/\Delta t$:

$$\frac{\Delta N}{\Delta t} = \left(\frac{\Delta N}{\Delta t}\right)_0 e^{-\lambda t}. \qquad \textbf{(30–5)}$$

The **half-life**, $T_{\frac{1}{2}}$, is the time required for half the nuclei of a radioactive sample to decay. It is related to the decay constant by

$$T_{\frac{1}{2}} = \frac{0.693}{\lambda}. \qquad \textbf{(30–6)}$$

Radioactive decay can be used to determine the age of certain objects.

[*Alpha decay occurs via a purely quantum mechanical process called **tunneling** through a barrier.]

[*Particle **detectors** include **Geiger counters**, **scintillators** with attached **photomultiplier tubes**, and **semiconductor detectors**. Detectors that can image particle tracks include photographic **emulsions, bubble chambers**, and today **wire drift chambers**.]

## Questions

1. What do different isotopes of a given element have in common? How are they different?
2. What are the elements represented by the X in the following: (*a*) $^{232}_{92}$X; (*b*) $^{18}_{7}$X; (*c*) $^{1}_{1}$X; (*d*) $^{82}_{38}$X; (*e*) $^{247}_{97}$X?
3. How many protons and how many neutrons do each of the isotopes in Question 2 have?
4. Identify the element that has 88 nucleons and 50 neutrons.
5. Why are the atomic masses of many elements (see the periodic table) not close to whole numbers?
6. How do we know there is such a thing as the strong nuclear force?
7. What are the similarities and the differences between the strong nuclear force and the electric force?
8. What is the experimental evidence in favor of radioactivity being a nuclear process?
9. The isotope $^{64}_{29}$Cu is unusual in that it can decay by $\gamma$, $\beta^-$, and $\beta^+$ emission. What is the resulting nuclide for each case?
10. A $^{238}_{92}$U nucleus decays to a nucleus containing how many neutrons?
11. Describe, in as many ways as you can, the difference between $\alpha$, $\beta$, and $\gamma$ rays.
12. What element is formed by the radioactive decay of (*a*) $^{24}_{11}$Na ($\beta^-$); (*b*) $^{22}_{11}$Na ($\beta^+$); (*c*) $^{210}_{84}$Po ($\alpha$)? [*Hint*: see Appendix B.]
13. What element is formed by the decay of (*a*) $^{32}_{15}$P ($\beta^-$); (*b*) $^{35}_{16}$S ($\beta^-$); (*c*) $^{211}_{83}$Bi ($\alpha$)? [*Hint*: see Appendix B.]
14. Fill in the missing particle or nucleus:
    (*a*) $^{45}_{20}\text{Ca} \rightarrow ? + e^- + \bar{\nu}$
    (*b*) $^{58}_{29}\text{Cu} \rightarrow ? + \gamma$
    (*c*) $^{46}_{24}\text{Cr} \rightarrow {}^{46}_{23}\text{V} + ?$
    (*d*) $^{234}_{94}\text{Pu} \rightarrow ? + \alpha$
    (*e*) $^{239}_{93}\text{Np} \rightarrow {}^{239}_{94}\text{Pu} + ?$
15. Immediately after a $^{238}_{92}$U nucleus decays to $^{234}_{90}$Th + $^4_2$He, the daughter thorium nucleus still has 92 electrons circling it. Since thorium normally holds only 90 electrons, what do you suppose happens to the two extra ones?
16. When a nucleus undergoes either $\beta^-$ or $\beta^+$ decay, what happens to the energy levels of the atomic electrons? What is likely to happen to these electrons following the decay?
17. The alpha particles from a given alpha-emitting nuclide are generally monoenergetic; that is, they all have the same kinetic energy. But the beta particles from a beta-emitting nuclide have a spectrum of energies. Explain the difference between these two cases.
18. Do isotopes that undergo electron capture generally lie above or below the line of stability in Fig. 30–2?
19. Can hydrogen or deuterium emit an $\alpha$ particle? Explain.
20. Why are many artificially produced radioactive isotopes rare in nature?
21. An isotope has a half-life of one month. After two months, will a given sample of this isotope have completely decayed? If not, how much remains?
22. Why are none of the elements with $Z > 92$ stable?
23. A proton strikes a $^6_3$Li nucleus. As a result, an $\alpha$ particle and another particle are released. What is the other particle?
24. Can $^{14}_{6}$C dating be used to measure the age of stone walls and tablets of ancient civilizations? Explain.
25. In both internal conversion and $\beta$ decay, an electron is emitted. How could you determine which decay process occurred?

## Problems

### 30–1 Nuclear Properties

1. (I) A pi meson has a mass of 139 MeV/$c^2$. What is this in atomic mass units?

2. (I) What is the approximate radius of an alpha particle ($^4_2$He)?

3. (II) What is the rest mass of a bare $\alpha$ particle in MeV/$c^2$?

4. (II) (*a*) What is the approximate radius of a $^{64}_{29}$Cu nucleus? (*b*) Approximately what is the value of $A$ for a nucleus whose radius is $3.9 \times 10^{-15}$ m?

5. (II) (*a*) Show that the density of nuclear matter is essentially the same for all nuclei. (*b*) What would be the radius of the Earth if it had its actual mass but had the density of nuclei? (*c*) What would be the radius of a $^{238}_{92}$U nucleus if it had the density of the Earth?

6. (II) (*a*) What is the fraction of the hydrogen atom's mass that is in the nucleus? (*b*) What is the fraction of the hydrogen atom's volume that is occupied by the nucleus?

7. (II) Approximately how many nucleons are there in a 1.0-kg object? Does it matter what the object is made of? Why or why not?

8. (III) How much energy must an $\alpha$ particle have to just "touch" the surface of a $^{238}_{92}$U nucleus?

### 30–2 Binding Energy

9. (I) Estimate the total binding energy for $^{40}_{20}$Ca, using Fig. 30–1.

10. (I) Use Fig. 30–1 to estimate the total binding energy of (*a*) $^{238}_{92}$U, and (*b*) $^{84}_{36}$Kr.

11. (II) Use Appendix B to calculate the binding energy of $^2_1$H (deuterium).

12. (II) Calculate the binding energy per nucleon for a $^{14}_7$N nucleus.

13. (II) Determine the binding energy of the last neutron in a $^{40}_{19}$K nucleus.

14. (II) Calculate the total binding energy, and the binding energy per nucleon, for (*a*) $^6_3$Li, (*b*) $^{208}_{82}$Pb. Use Appendix B.

15. (II) Compare the average binding energy of a nucleon in $^{23}_{11}$Na to that in $^{24}_{11}$Na.

16. (III) How much energy is required to remove (*a*) a proton, (*b*) a neutron, from $^{16}_8$O? Explain the difference in your answers.

17. (III) (*a*) Show that the nucleus $^8_4$Be (mass = 8.005305 u) is unstable and will decay into two $\alpha$ particles. (*b*) Is $^{12}_6$C stable against decay into three $\alpha$ particles? Show why or why not.

### 30–3 to 30–7 Radioactive Decay

18. (I) How much energy is released when tritium, $^3_1$H, decays by $\beta^-$ emission?

19. (I) What is the maximum kinetic energy of an electron emitted in the $\beta$ decay of a free neutron?

20. (I) Show that the decay $^{11}_6\text{C} \rightarrow {}^{10}_5\text{B} + \text{p}$ is not possible because energy would not be conserved.

21. (II) $^{22}_{11}$Na is radioactive. (*a*) Is it a $\beta^-$ or $\beta^+$ emitter? (*b*) Write down the decay reaction, and estimate the maximum kinetic energy of the emitted $\beta$.

22. (II) Give the result of a calculation that shows whether or not the following decays are possible:

    (*a*) $^{236}_{92}\text{U} \rightarrow {}^{235}_{92}\text{U} + \text{n}$;

    (*b*) $^{16}_8\text{O} \rightarrow {}^{15}_8\text{O} + \text{n}$;

    (*c*) $^{23}_{11}\text{Na} \rightarrow {}^{22}_{11}\text{Na} + \text{n}$.

23. (II) A $^{238}_{92}$U nucleus emits an $\alpha$ particle with kinetic energy = 4.20 MeV. (*a*) What is the daughter nucleus, and (*b*) what is the approximate atomic mass (in u) of the daughter atom? Ignore recoil of the daughter nucleus.

24. (II) When $^{23}_{10}$Ne (mass = 22.9945 u) decays to $^{23}_{11}$Na (mass = 22.9898 u), what is the maximum kinetic energy of the emitted electron? What is its minimum energy? What is the energy of the neutrino in each case? Ignore recoil of the daughter nucleus.

25. (II) A nucleus of mass 238 u, initially at rest, emits an $\alpha$ particle with a KE of 5.0 MeV. What is the KE of the recoiling daughter nucleus?

26. (II) What is the maximum KE of the emitted $\beta$ particle during the decay of $^{60}_{27}$Co?

27. (II) The nuclide $^{32}_{15}$P decays by emitting an electron whose maximum kinetic energy can be 1.71 MeV. (*a*) What is the daughter nucleus? (*b*) Calculate the daughter's atomic mass (in u).

28. (II) The isotope $^{218}_{84}$Po can decay by either $\alpha$ or $\beta^-$ emission. What is the energy release in each case? The mass of $^{218}_{84}$Po is 218.008965 u.

29. (II) How much energy is released in electron capture by beryllium: $^7_4\text{Be} + {}^{0}_{-1}\text{e} \rightarrow {}^7_3\text{Li} + \nu$?

30. (II) A photon with a wavelength of $1.00 \times 10^{-13}$ m is ejected from an atom. Calculate its energy and explain why it is a $\gamma$ ray from the nucleus or a photon from the atom.

31. (II) Determine the maximum kinetic energy of $\beta^+$ particles released when $^{11}_6$C decays to $^{11}_5$B. What is the maximum energy the neutrino can have? What is its minimum energy?

32. (II) How much recoil energy does a $^{40}_{19}$K nucleus get when it emits a 1.46-MeV gamma ray?

33. (III) What is the energy of the $\alpha$ particle emitted in the decay $^{210}_{84}\text{Po} \rightarrow {}^{206}_{82}\text{Pb} + \alpha$? Take into account the recoil of the daughter nucleus.

34. (III) The $\alpha$ particle emitted when $^{238}_{92}$U decays has 4.20 MeV of kinetic energy. Calculate the recoil kinetic energy of the daughter nucleus and the $Q$-value of the decay.

35. (III) Show that when a nucleus decays by $\beta^+$ decay, the total energy released is equal to

$$(M_\text{P} - M_\text{D} - 2m_\text{e})c^2,$$

where $M_\text{P}$ and $M_\text{D}$ are the masses of the parent and daughter atoms (neutral), and $m_\text{e}$ is the mass of an electron or positron.

### 30–8 to 30–11 Half-Life, Decay Rates, Decay Series, Dating

36. (I) A radioactive material produces 1280 decays per minute at one time, and 4.6 h later produces 320 decays per minute. What is its half-life?

37. (I) (*a*) What is the decay constant of $^{238}_{92}U$ whose half-life is $4.5 \times 10^9$ yr? (*b*) The decay constant of a given nucleus is $8.2 \times 10^{-5}\,s^{-1}$. What is its half-life?

38. (I) What is the activity of a sample of $^{14}_{6}C$ that contains $3.1 \times 10^{20}$ nuclei?

39. (I) What fraction of a sample of $^{68}_{32}Ge$, whose half-life is about 9 months, will remain after 3.0 yr?

40. (I) What fraction of a sample is left after exactly 6 half-lives?

41. (II) How many nuclei of $^{238}_{92}U$ remain in a rock if the activity registers 640 decays per second?

42. (II) In a series of decays, the nuclide $^{235}_{92}U$ becomes $^{207}_{82}Pb$. How many $\alpha$ and $\beta^-$ particles are emitted in this series?

43. (II) The iodine isotope $^{131}_{53}I$ is used in hospitals for diagnosis of thyroid function. If 682 $\mu$g are ingested by a patient, determine the activity (*a*) immediately, (*b*) 1.0 h later when the thyroid is being tested, and (*c*) 6 months later. Use Appendix B.

44. (II) $^{124}_{55}Cs$ has a half-life of 30.8 s. (*a*) If we have 8.8 $\mu$g initially, how many Cs nuclei are present? (*b*) How many are present 2.0 min later? (*c*) What is the activity at this time? (*d*) After how much time will the activity drop to less than about 1 per second?

45. (II) Calculate the mass of a sample of pure $^{40}_{19}K$ with an initial decay rate of $2.0 \times 10^5\,s^{-1}$. The half-life of $^{40}_{19}K$ is $1.28 \times 10^9$ yr.

46. (II) Calculate the activity of a pure 9.7-$\mu$g sample of $^{32}_{15}P$ $\left(T_{\frac{1}{2}} = 1.23 \times 10^6\,s\right)$.

47. (II) The activity of a sample of $^{35}_{16}S$ $\left(T_{\frac{1}{2}} = 7.55 \times 10^6\,s\right)$ is $2.65 \times 10^5$ decays per second. What is the mass of the sample?

48. (II) A sample of $^{233}_{92}U$ $\left(T_{\frac{1}{2}} = 1.59 \times 10^5\,yr\right)$ contains $7.50 \times 10^{19}$ nuclei. (*a*) What is the decay constant? (*b*) Approximately how many disintegrations will occur per minute?

49. (II) The activity of a sample drops by a factor of 10 in 8.6 minutes. What is its half-life?

50. (II) A 285-g sample of pure carbon contains 1.3 parts in $10^{12}$ (atoms) of $^{14}_{6}C$. How many disintegrations occur per second?

51. (II) A sample of $^{40}_{19}K$ is decaying at a rate of $6.70 \times 10^2$ decays/s. What is the mass of the sample?

52. (II) The rubidium isotope $^{87}_{37}Rb$, a $\beta$ emitter with a half-life of $4.75 \times 10^{10}$ yr, is used to determine the age of rocks and fossils. Rocks containing fossils of ancient animals contain a ratio of $^{87}_{38}Sr$ to $^{87}_{37}Rb$ of 0.0160. Assuming that there was no $^{87}_{38}Sr$ present when the rocks were formed, estimate the age of these fossils. [*Hint*: use Eq. 30–3.]

53. (II) Use Fig. 30–11 and calculate the relative decay rates for $\alpha$ decay of $^{218}_{84}Po$ and $^{214}_{84}Po$.

54. (II) $^{7}_{4}Be$ decays with a half-life of about 53 d. It is produced in the upper atmosphere, and filters down onto the Earth's surface. If a plant leaf is detected to have 450 decays/s of $^{7}_{4}Be$, (*a*) how long do we have to wait for the decay rate to drop to 15 per second? (*b*) Estimate the initial mass of $^{7}_{4}Be$ on the leaf.

55. (II) Two of the naturally occurring radioactive decay sequences start with $^{232}_{90}Th$, and $^{235}_{92}U$. The first five decays of these two sequences are:

$$\alpha, \beta, \beta, \alpha, \alpha$$

and

$$\alpha, \beta, \alpha, \beta, \alpha.$$

Determine the resulting intermediate daughter nuclei in each case.

56. (II) An ancient wooden club is found that contains 290 g of carbon and has an activity of 8.0 decays per second. Determine its age assuming that in living trees the ratio of $^{14}C/^{12}C$ atoms is about $1.3 \times 10^{-12}$.

57. (III) At $t = 0$, a pure sample of radioactive nuclei contains $N_0$ nuclei whose decay constant is $\lambda$. Determine a formula for the number of daughter nuclei, $N_D$, as a function of time; assume the daughter is stable and that $N_D = 0$ at $t = 0$.

## General Problems

58. Which radioactive isotope of lead is being produced in a reaction where the measured activity of a sample drops to 1.050% of its original activity in 4.00 h?

59. An old wooden tool is found to contain only 6.0% of $^{14}_{6}C$ that a sample of fresh wood would. How old is the tool?

60. A neutron star consists of neutrons at approximately nuclear density. Estimate, for a 10-km-diameter neutron star, (*a*) its mass number, (*b*) its mass (kg), and (*c*) the acceleration of gravity at its surface.

61. The $^{3}_{1}H$ isotope of hydrogen, which is called *tritium* (because it contains three nucleons), has a half-life of 12.33 yr. It can be used to measure the age of objects up to about 100 yr. It is produced in the upper atmosphere by cosmic rays and brought to Earth by rain. As an application, determine approximately the age of a bottle of wine whose $^{3}_{1}H$ radiation is about $\frac{1}{10}$ that present in new wine.

62. Some elementary particle theories (Section 32–11) suggest that the proton may be unstable, with a half-life $\geq 10^{32}$ yr. How long would you expect to wait for one proton in your body to decay (consider that your body is all water)?

63. How long must you wait (in half-lives) for a radioactive sample to drop to 1.00% of its original activity?

64. If the potassium isotope $^{40}_{19}K$ gives 60 decays/s in a liter of milk, estimate how much $^{40}_{19}K$ and regular $^{39}_{19}K$ are in a liter of milk. Use Appendix B.

65. (*a*) In $\alpha$ decay of, say, a $^{226}_{88}Ra$ nucleus, show that the nucleus carries away a fraction $1/(1 + \frac{1}{4}A_D)$ of the total energy available, where $A_D$ is the mass number of the daughter nucleus. [*Hint*: use conservation of momentum as well as conservation of energy.] (*b*) Approximately what percentage of the energy available is thus carried off by the $\alpha$ particle in the case cited?

66. Strontium-90 is produced as a nuclear fission product of uranium in both reactors and atomic bombs. Look at its location in the periodic table to see what other elements it might be similar to chemically, and tell why you think it might be dangerous to ingest. It has too many neutrons, and it decays with a half-life of about 29 yr. How long will we have to wait for the amount of $^{90}_{38}Sr$ on the Earth's surface to reach 1% of its current level, assuming no new material is scattered about? Write down the decay reaction, including the daughter nucleus. The daughter is radioactive: write down its decay.

67. The nuclide $^{191}_{76}Os$ decays with $\beta^-$ energy of 0.14 MeV accompanied by $\gamma$ rays of energy 0.042 MeV and 0.129 MeV. (*a*) What is the daughter nucleus? (*b*) Draw an energy-level diagram showing the ground states of the parent and daughter and excited states of the daughter. To which of the daughter states does $\beta^-$ decay of $^{191}_{76}Os$ occur?

68. Determine the activities of (*a*) 1.0 g of $^{131}_{53}I$ ($T_{\frac{1}{2}} = 8.02$ days) and (*b*) 1.0 g of $^{238}_{92}U$ ($T_{\frac{1}{2}} = 4.47 \times 10^9$ yr).

69. Estimate the total binding energy for copper and then estimate the energy, in joules, needed to break a 3.0-g copper penny into its constituent nucleons. [*Hint*: use Fig. 30–1.]

70. Instead of giving atomic masses for nuclides as in Appendix B, some Tables give the *mass excess*, $\Delta$, defined as $\Delta = M - A$, where $A$ is the atomic number and $M$ is the mass in u. Determine the mass excess, in u and in MeV/$c^2$, for: (*a*) $^4_2He$; (*b*) $^{12}_6C$; (*c*) $^{107}_{47}Ag$; (*d*) $^{235}_{92}U$. (*e*) From a glance at Appendix B, can you make a generalization about the sign of $\Delta$ as a function of $Z$ or $A$?

71. (*a*) A 92-gram sample of natural carbon contains the usual fraction of $^{14}_6C$. Estimate how long it will take before there is only one $^{14}_6C$ nucleus left. (*b*) How does the answer in (*a*) change if the sample is 280 grams? What does this tell you about the limits of carbon dating?

72. If the mass of the proton were just a little closer to the mass of the neutron, the following reaction would be possible even at low collision energies:

$$e^- + p \rightarrow n + \nu.$$

Why would this situation be catastrophic? By what percentage would the proton's mass have to be increased to make this reaction possible?

73. What is the ratio of the kinetic energies for an alpha particle and a beta particle if both make tracks with the same radius of curvature in a magnetic field, oriented perpendicular to the paths of the particles?

74. A 1.00-g sample of natural samarium emits $\alpha$ particles at a rate of $120\ s^{-1}$ due to the presence of $^{147}_{62}Sm$. The natural abundance of $^{147}_{62}Sm$ is 15%. Calculate the half-life for this decay process.

75. Almost all of naturally occurring uranium is $^{238}_{92}U$ with a half-life of $4.468 \times 10^9$ yr. Most of the rest of natural uranium is $^{235}_{92}U$ with a half-life of $7.038 \times 10^8$ yr. Today a sample contains 0.72% $^{235}_{92}U$. (*a*) What was this percentage 1.0 billion years ago? (*b*) What percentage of the sample would be $^{235}_{92}U$ in 100 million years?

76. A typical banana contains 400 mg of potassium, of which a small fraction is the radioactive isotope $^{40}_{19}K$ (see Appendix B). Estimate the activity of an average banana due to $^{40}_{19}K$.

77. The practical limit for carbon-14 dating is about 60,000 years. If a bone contains 1.0 kg of carbon, and the animal died 60,000 years ago, what is the activity today?

78. Decay series, such as that shown in Fig. 30–11, can be classified into four families, depending on whether the mass numbers have the form $4n$, $4n + 1$, $4n + 2$, or $4n + 3$, where $n$ is an integer. Justify this statement and show that for a nuclide in any family, all its daughters will be in the same family.

## Answers to Exercises

**A:** 0.0421 u.

**B:** 7.98 MeV/nucleon.

**C:** $1.37 \times 10^{-11}\ s^{-1}$.

**D:** No: $(\frac{1}{2})(\frac{1}{2}) = \frac{1}{4}$ will be left.

Technicians are looking at an MRI image of sections through a patient's body. MRI is one of several powerful types of medical imaging based on physics used by doctors to diagnose illnesses.

This Chapter opens with basic and important physics topics of nuclear reactions, nuclear fission, and nuclear fusion, and how we obtain nuclear energy. Then we examine the health aspects of radiation—dosimetry, therapy, and imaging: MRI, PET, and SPET.

CHAPTER 31

# Nuclear Energy; Effects and Uses of Radiation

We continue our study of nuclear physics in this Chapter. We begin with a discussion of nuclear reactions, after which we examine the important large energy-releasing processes of fission and fusion. The remainder of the Chapter deals with the effects of nuclear radiation when it passes through matter, particularly biological matter, and how radiation is used medically for therapy and diagnosis, including recently developed imaging techniques.

## 31–1 Nuclear Reactions and the Transmutation of Elements

When a nucleus undergoes $\alpha$ or $\beta$ decay, the daughter nucleus is that of a different element from the parent. The transformation of one element into another, called **transmutation**, also occurs by means of nuclear reactions. A **nuclear reaction** is said to occur when a given nucleus is struck by another nucleus, or by a simpler particle such as a $\gamma$ ray or neutron, so that an interaction takes place. Ernest Rutherford was the first to report seeing a nuclear reaction. In 1919 he observed that some of the $\alpha$ particles passing through nitrogen gas were absorbed and protons emitted. He concluded that nitrogen nuclei had been transformed into oxygen nuclei via the reaction

$$^{4}_{2}\text{He} + ^{14}_{7}\text{N} \rightarrow ^{17}_{8}\text{O} + ^{1}_{1}\text{H},$$

where $^{4}_{2}\text{He}$ is an $\alpha$ particle, and $^{1}_{1}\text{H}$ is a proton.

Since then, a great many nuclear reactions have been observed. Indeed, many of the radioactive isotopes used in the laboratory are made by means of nuclear reactions. Nuclear reactions can be made to occur in the laboratory, but they also occur regularly in nature. In Chapter 30 we saw an example: ${}^{14}_{6}C$ is continually being made in the atmosphere via the reaction† $n + {}^{14}_{7}N \rightarrow {}^{14}_{6}C + p$.

**EXERCISE A** Determine the resulting nucleus in the reaction $n + {}^{137}_{56}Ba \rightarrow ? + \gamma$.

In any nuclear reaction, both electric charge and nucleon number are conserved. These conservation laws are often useful, as the following Example shows.

**CONCEPTUAL EXAMPLE 31–1** **Deuterium reaction.** A neutron is observed to strike an ${}^{16}_{8}O$ nucleus, and a deuteron is given off. (A **deuteron**, or **deuterium**, is the isotope of hydrogen containing one proton and one neutron, ${}^{2}_{1}H$; it is sometimes given the symbol d or D.) What is the nucleus that results?

*Deuterium*

**RESPONSE** We have the reaction $n + {}^{16}_{8}O \rightarrow ? + {}^{2}_{1}H$. The total number of nucleons initially is $1 + 16 = 17$, and the total charge is $0 + 8 = 8$. The same totals apply after the reaction. Hence the product nucleus must have $Z = 7$ and $A = 15$. From the periodic table, we find that it is nitrogen that has $Z = 7$, so the nucleus produced is ${}^{15}_{7}N$.

Energy and momentum are also conserved in nuclear reactions, and can be used to determine whether a given reaction can occur or not. For example, if the total mass of the products is less than the total mass of the initial particles, this decrease in mass (recall $\Delta E = \Delta m\, c^2$) is converted to kinetic energy of the outgoing particles. But if the total mass of the products is greater than the total mass of the initial reactants, the reaction requires energy. The reaction will then not occur unless the bombarding particle has sufficient kinetic energy. Consider a nuclear reaction of the general form

$$a + X \rightarrow Y + b,$$

where a is a projectile particle (or small nucleus) that strikes nucleus X, producing nucleus Y and particle b (typically, p, n, $\alpha$, $\gamma$). We define the **reaction energy**, or ***Q*-value**, in terms of the masses involved, as

*Q-value*

$$Q = \left(M_a + M_X - M_b - M_Y\right)c^2. \qquad \textbf{(31–1)}$$

These are all rest masses; $M = 0$ for a $\gamma$ ray. Since energy is conserved, $Q$ is equal to the change in kinetic energy (final minus initial):

*Energy conservation*

$$Q = \text{KE}_b + \text{KE}_Y - \text{KE}_a - \text{KE}_X. \qquad \textbf{(31–2)}$$

In many reactions, $\text{KE}_X = 0$ since X is the target nucleus at rest (or nearly so) struck by an incoming particle a. For $Q > 0$, the reaction is said to be *exothermic* or *exoergic*; energy is released in the reaction, so the total KE is greater after the reaction than before. If $Q$ is negative ($Q < 0$), the reaction is said to be *endothermic* or *endoergic*. In this case the final total KE is less than the initial KE, and an energy input is required to make the reaction happen. The energy input comes from the kinetic energy of the initial colliding particles (a and X).

**EXAMPLE 31–2** **A slow-neutron reaction.** The nuclear reaction

$$n + {}^{10}_{5}B \rightarrow {}^{7}_{3}Li + {}^{4}_{2}He$$

is observed to occur even when very slow-moving neutrons (mass $M_n = 1.0087$ u) strike a boron atom at rest. For a particular reaction in which $\text{KE}_n \approx 0$, the outgoing helium $M_{He} = 4.0026$ u) is observed to have a speed of $9.30 \times 10^6$ m/s. Determine (*a*) the kinetic energy of the lithium $\left(M_{Li} = 7.0160\text{ u}\right)$, and (*b*) the $Q$-value of the reaction.

†Nuclear reactions are sometimes written in a shortened form: for example, the reaction

$$n + {}^{14}_{7}N \rightarrow {}^{14}_{6}C + p$$

is written

$${}^{14}_{7}N\ (n, p)\ {}^{14}_{6}C.$$

The symbols outside the parentheses on the left and right represent the initial and final nuclei, respectively. The symbols inside the parentheses represent the bombarding particle (first) and the emitted small particle (second).

**APPROACH** Since the neutron and boron are both essentially at rest, the total momentum before the reaction is zero; momentum is conserved and so must be zero afterward as well. Thus,

$$M_{\mathrm{Li}} v_{\mathrm{Li}} = M_{\mathrm{He}} v_{\mathrm{He}}.$$

We solve this for $v_{\mathrm{Li}}$ and substitute it into the equation for kinetic energy.

**SOLUTION** (*a*) We can use classical KE with little error, rather than relativistic formulas, because $v_{\mathrm{He}} = 9.30 \times 10^6\,\mathrm{m/s}$ is not close to the speed of light $c$, and $v_{\mathrm{Li}}$ will be even less since $M_{\mathrm{Li}} > M_{\mathrm{He}}$. Thus we can write:

$$\mathrm{KE}_{\mathrm{Li}} = \frac{1}{2} M_{\mathrm{Li}} v_{\mathrm{Li}}^2 = \frac{1}{2} M_{\mathrm{Li}} \left(\frac{M_{\mathrm{He}} v_{\mathrm{He}}}{M_{\mathrm{Li}}}\right)^2 = \frac{M_{\mathrm{He}}^2 v_{\mathrm{He}}^2}{2M_{\mathrm{Li}}}.$$

We put in numbers, changing the mass in u to kg and recall that $1.60 \times 10^{-13}\,\mathrm{J} = 1\,\mathrm{MeV}$:

$$\mathrm{KE}_{\mathrm{Li}} = \frac{(4.0026\,\mathrm{u})^2(1.66 \times 10^{-27}\,\mathrm{kg/u})^2(9.30 \times 10^6\,\mathrm{m/s})^2}{2(7.0160\,\mathrm{u})(1.66 \times 10^{-27}\,\mathrm{kg/u})}$$

$$= 1.64 \times 10^{-13}\,\mathrm{J} = 1.02\,\mathrm{MeV}.$$

(*b*) We are given the data $\mathrm{KE}_{\mathrm{a}} = \mathrm{KE}_{\mathrm{X}} = 0$ in Eq. 31–2, so $Q = \mathrm{KE}_{\mathrm{Li}} + \mathrm{KE}_{\mathrm{He}}$, where

$$\mathrm{KE}_{\mathrm{He}} = \tfrac{1}{2} M_{\mathrm{He}} v_{\mathrm{He}}^2 = \tfrac{1}{2}(4.0026\,\mathrm{u})(1.66 \times 10^{-27}\,\mathrm{kg/u})(9.30 \times 10^6\,\mathrm{m/s})^2$$

$$= 2.87 \times 10^{-13}\,\mathrm{J} = 1.80\,\mathrm{MeV}.$$

Hence, $Q = 1.02\,\mathrm{MeV} + 1.80\,\mathrm{MeV} = 2.82\,\mathrm{MeV}$.

**EXAMPLE 31–3** **Will the reaction "go"?** Can the reaction $\mathrm{p} + {}^{13}_{6}\mathrm{C} \rightarrow {}^{13}_{7}\mathrm{N} + \mathrm{n}$ occur when ${}^{13}_{6}\mathrm{C}$ is bombarded by 2.0-MeV protons?

**APPROACH** The reaction will "go" if the reaction is exothermic ($Q > 0$) and even if $Q < 0$ if the input momentum and kinetic energy are sufficient. First we calculate $Q$ from the difference between final and initial masses using Eq. 31–1, and looking up the masses in Appendix B.

**SOLUTION** The total masses before and after the reaction are:

| Before | | After | |
|---|---|---|---|
| $M({}^{13}_{6}\mathrm{C}) =$ | 13.003355 | $M({}^{13}_{7}\mathrm{N}) =$ | 13.005739 |
| $M({}^{1}_{1}\mathrm{H}) =$ | 1.007825 | $M(\mathrm{n}) =$ | 1.008665 |
| | 14.011180 | | 14.014404 |

(We must use the mass of the ${}^{1}_{1}\mathrm{H}$ atom rather than that of the bare proton because the masses of ${}^{13}_{6}\mathrm{C}$ and ${}^{13}_{7}\mathrm{N}$ include the electrons, and we must include an equal number of electron masses on each side of the equation since none are created or destroyed.) The products have an excess mass of

$$(14.014404 - 14.011180)\mathrm{u} = 0.003224\,\mathrm{u} \times 931.5\,\mathrm{MeV/u} = 3.00\,\mathrm{MeV}.$$

Thus $Q = -3.00\,\mathrm{MeV}$, and the reaction is endothermic. This reaction requires energy, and the 2.0 MeV protons do not have enough to make it go.

*Threshold energy*

**NOTE** The proton in Example 31–3 would have to have somewhat more than 3.00 MeV of KE to make this reaction go; 3.00 MeV would be enough to conserve energy, but a proton of this energy would produce the ${}^{13}_{7}\mathrm{N}$ and n with no KE and hence no momentum. Since an incident 3.0-MeV proton has momentum, conservation of momentum would be violated. A calculation using conservation of energy *and* of momentum, as we did in Examples 30–7 and 31–2, shows that the minimum proton energy, called the **threshold energy**, is 3.23 MeV in this case.

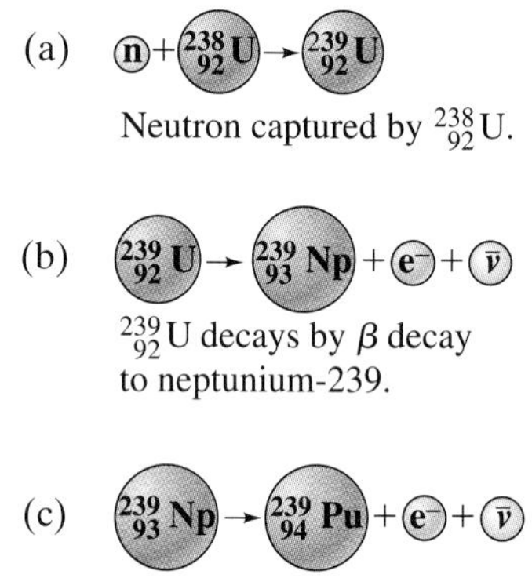


(a) Neutron captured by $^{238}_{92}U$.

(b) $^{239}_{92}U$ decays by $\beta$ decay to neptunium-239.

(c) $^{239}_{93}Np$ itself decays by $\beta$ decay to produce plutonium-239.

**FIGURE 31–1** Neptunium and plutonium are produced in this series of reactions, after bombardment of $^{238}_{92}U$ by neutrons.

The artificial transmutation of elements took a great leap forward in the 1930s when Enrico Fermi realized that neutrons would be the most effective projectiles for causing nuclear reactions and in particular for producing new elements. Because neutrons have no net electric charge, they are not repelled by positively charged nuclei as are protons or alpha particles. Hence the probability of a neutron reaching the nucleus and causing a reaction is much greater than for charged projectiles,[†] particularly at low energies. Between 1934 and 1936, Fermi and his co-workers in Rome produced many previously unknown isotopes by bombarding different elements with neutrons. Fermi realized that if the heaviest known element, uranium, is bombarded with neutrons, it might be possible to produce new elements with atomic numbers greater than that of uranium. After several years of hard work, it was suspected that two new elements had been produced, neptunium ($Z = 93$) and plutonium ($Z = 94$). The full confirmation that such "transuranic" elements could be produced came several years later at the University of California, Berkeley. The reactions are shown in Fig. 31–1.

It was soon shown that what Fermi had actually observed when he bombarded uranium was an even stranger process—one that was destined to play an extraordinary role in the world at large. We discuss it in Section 31–2.

## 31–2 Nuclear Fission; Nuclear Reactors

In 1938, the German scientists Otto Hahn and Fritz Strassmann made an amazing discovery. Following up on Fermi's work, they found that uranium bombarded by neutrons sometimes produced smaller nuclei that were roughly half the size of the original uranium nucleus. Lise Meitner and Otto Frisch, two refugees from Nazi Germany working in Scandinavia, quickly realized what had happened: the uranium nucleus, after absorbing a neutron, actually had split into two roughly equal pieces. This was startling, for until then the known nuclear reactions involved knocking out only a tiny fragment (for example, n, p, or $\alpha$) from a nucleus.

**FIGURE 31–2** Fission of a $^{235}_{92}U$ nucleus after capture of a neutron, according to the liquid-drop model.

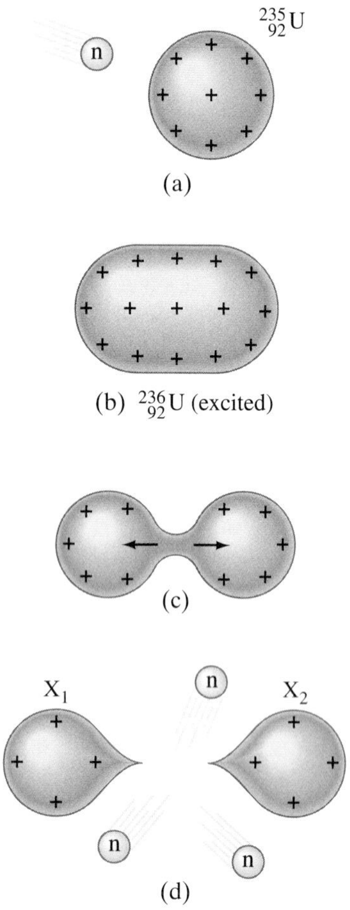


### Nuclear Fission and Chain Reactions

This new phenomenon was named **nuclear fission** because of its resemblance to biological fission (cell division). It occurs much more readily for $^{235}_{92}U$ than for the more common $^{238}_{92}U$. The process can be visualized by imagining the uranium nucleus to be like a liquid drop. According to this **liquid-drop model**, the neutron absorbed by the $^{235}_{92}U$ nucleus gives the nucleus extra internal energy (like heating a drop of water). This intermediate state, or **compound nucleus**, is $^{236}_{92}U$ (because of the absorbed neutron). The extra energy of this nucleus—it is in an excited state—appears as increased motion of the individual nucleons, which causes the nucleus to take on abnormal elongated shapes, Figure 31–2. When the nucleus elongates (in this model) into the shape shown in Fig. 31–2c, the attraction of the two ends via the short-range nuclear force is greatly weakened by the increased separation distance, and the electric repulsive force becomes dominant. So the nucleus splits in two (Fig. 31–2d). The two resulting nuclei, $X_1$ and $X_2$, are called **fission fragments**, and in the process a number of neutrons (typically two or three) are also given off. The reaction can be written

$$n + {}^{235}_{92}U \rightarrow {}^{236}_{92}U \rightarrow X_1 + X_2 + \text{neutrons}. \qquad \textbf{(31–3)}$$

The compound nucleus, $^{236}_{92}U$, exists for less than $10^{-12}$ s, so the process occurs very quickly. The two fission fragments more often split the original uranium mass as about 40%–60% rather than precisely half and half. A typical fission reaction is

$$n + {}^{235}_{92}U \rightarrow {}^{141}_{56}Ba + {}^{92}_{36}Kr + 3n, \qquad \textbf{(31–4)}$$

although many others also occur.

[†]That is, positively charged particles. Electrons rarely cause nuclear reactions because they do not interact via the strong nuclear force.

**CONCEPTUAL EXAMPLE 31–4** **Counting nucleons.** Identify the element X in the fission reaction $n + {}^{235}_{92}U \rightarrow {}^{A}_{Z}X + {}^{93}_{38}Sr + 2n$.

**RESPONSE** The number of nucleons is conserved (Section 30–7). The uranium nucleus with 235 nucleons plus the incoming neutron make $235 + 1 = 236$ nucleons. So there must be 236 nucleons after the reaction. The Sr has 93 nucleons, and the two neutrons make 95 nucleons, so X has $A = 236 - 95 = 141$. Electric charge is also conserved: before the reaction, the total charge is $92e$. After the reaction the total charge is $(Z + 38)e$ and must equal $92e$. Thus $Z = 92 - 38 = 54$. The element with $Z = 54$ (see Appendix B or the periodic table) is xenon, so the isotope is ${}^{141}_{54}Xe$.

**EXERCISE B** In the fission reaction $n + {}^{235}_{92}U \rightarrow {}^{137}_{53}I + {}^{96}_{39}Y +$ neutrons, how many neutrons are produced?

Figure 31–3 shows the distribution of fission fragments according to mass. Note that only rarely (about 1 in $10^4$) does a fission result in equal mass fragments (small arrow in Fig. 31–3).

A tremendous amount of energy is released in a fission reaction because the mass of ${}^{235}_{92}U$ is considerably greater than the total mass of the fission fragments plus neutrons. This can be seen from the binding-energy-per-nucleon curve of Fig. 30–1; the binding energy per nucleon for uranium is about 7.6 MeV/nucleon, but for fission fragments that have intermediate mass (in the center portion of the graph, $A \approx 100$), the average binding energy per nucleon is about 8.5 MeV/nucleon. Since the fission fragments are more tightly bound, they have less mass. The difference in mass, or energy, between the original uranium nucleus and the fission fragments is about $8.5 - 7.6 = 0.9$ MeV per nucleon. Since there are 236 nucleons involved in each fission, the total energy released per fission is

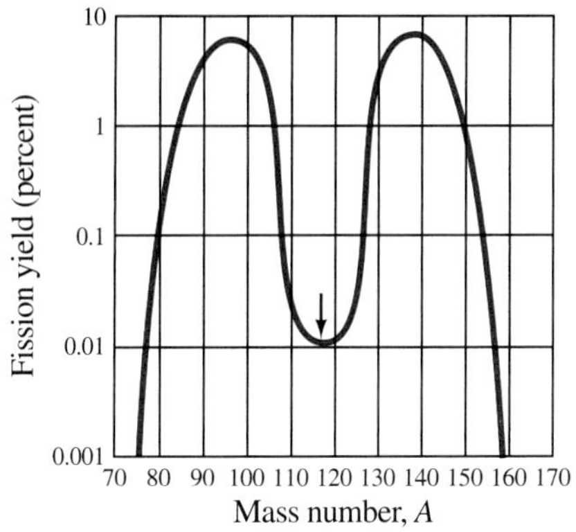


**FIGURE 31–3** Mass distribution of fission fragments from ${}^{235}_{92}U + n$. The small arrow indicates equal mass fragments $(\frac{1}{2} \times (236 - 2) = 117)$. Note that the vertical scale is logarithmic.

*Energy released per fission*

$$(0.9\ \text{MeV/nucleon})(236\ \text{nucleons}) \approx 200\ \text{MeV}. \quad \textbf{(31–5)}$$

This is an enormous amount of energy for one single nuclear event. At a practical level, the energy from one fission is, of course, tiny. But if many such fissions could occur in a short time, an enormous amount of energy at the macroscopic level would be available. A number of physicists, including Fermi, recognized that the neutrons released in each fission (Eqs. 31–3 and 4) could be used to create a **chain reaction**. That is, one neutron initially causes one fission of a uranium nucleus; the two or three neutrons released can go on to cause additional fissions, so the process multiplies as shown schematically in Fig. 31–4. If a **self-sustaining chain reaction** was actually possible in practice, the enormous energy available in fission could be released on a larger scale.

*Chain reaction*

**FIGURE 31–4** Chain reaction.

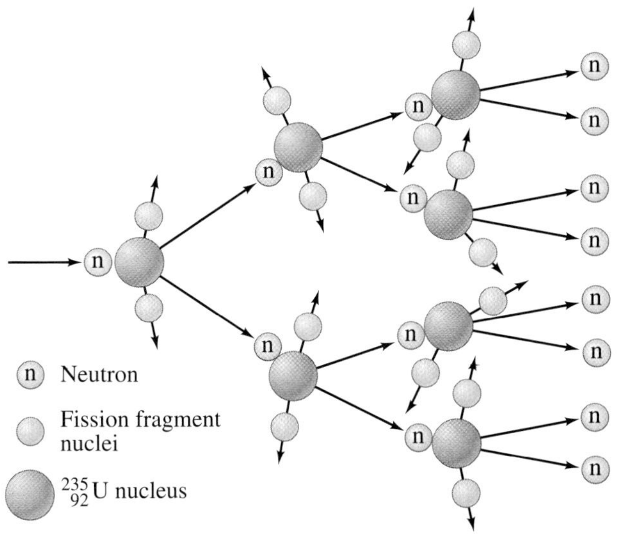

**FIGURE 31–5** Color painting of the first nuclear reactor, built by Fermi under the grandstand of Stagg Field at the University of Chicago. (There are no photographs of the original reactor because of military secrecy.) Natural uranium was used with graphite as moderator. On December 2, 1942, Fermi slowly withdrew the cadmium control rods and the reactor went critical. This first self-sustaining chain reaction was announced to Washington, by telephone, by Arthur Compton who witnessed the event and reported: "The Italian navigator has just landed in the new world." Gary Sheahan, "Birth of the Atomic Age," Chicago (Illinois); 1957. Chicago Historical Society, ICHi-33305.

Fermi and his co-workers (at the University of Chicago) showed it was possible by constructing the first **nuclear reactor** in 1942 (Fig. 31–5).

## Nuclear Reactors

Several problems have to be overcome to make any nuclear reactor function. First, the probability that a $^{235}_{92}\text{U}$ nucleus will absorb a neutron is large only for slow neutrons, but the neutrons emitted during a fission, and which are needed to sustain a chain reaction, are moving very fast. A substance known as a **moderator** must be used to slow down the neutrons. The most effective moderator will consist of atoms whose mass is as close as possible to that of the neutrons. (To see why this is true, recall from Chapter 7 that a billiard ball striking an equal mass ball at rest can itself be stopped in one collision; but a billiard ball striking a heavy object bounces off with nearly unchanged speed.) The best moderator would thus contain $^1_1\text{H}$ atoms. Unfortunately, $^1_1\text{H}$ tends to absorb neutrons. But the isotope of hydrogen called *deuterium*, $^2_1\text{H}$, does not absorb many neutrons and is thus an almost ideal moderator. Either $^1_1\text{H}$ or $^2_1\text{H}$ can be used in the form of water. In the latter case, it is **heavy water**, in which the hydrogen atoms have been replaced by deuterium. Another common moderator is *graphite*, which consists of $^{12}_{6}\text{C}$ atoms.

*Moderator*

A second problem is that the neutrons produced in one fission may be absorbed and produce other nuclear reactions with other nuclei in the reactor, rather than produce further fissions. In a "light-water" reactor, the $^1_1\text{H}$ nuclei absorb neutrons, as does $^{238}_{92}\text{U}$ to form $^{239}_{92}\text{U}$ in the reaction $\text{n} + {}^{238}_{92}\text{U} \rightarrow {}^{239}_{92}\text{U} + \gamma$. Naturally occurring uranium† contains 99.3% $^{238}_{92}\text{U}$ and only 0.7% fissionable $^{235}_{92}\text{U}$. To increase the probability of fission of $^{235}_{92}\text{U}$ nuclei, natural uranium can be **enriched** to increase the percentage of $^{235}_{92}\text{U}$ using processes such as diffusion or centrifugation. Enrichment is not usually necessary for reactors using heavy water as moderator since heavy water doesn't absorb neutrons.

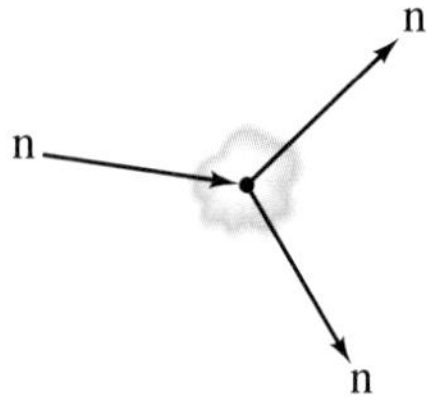


(a)

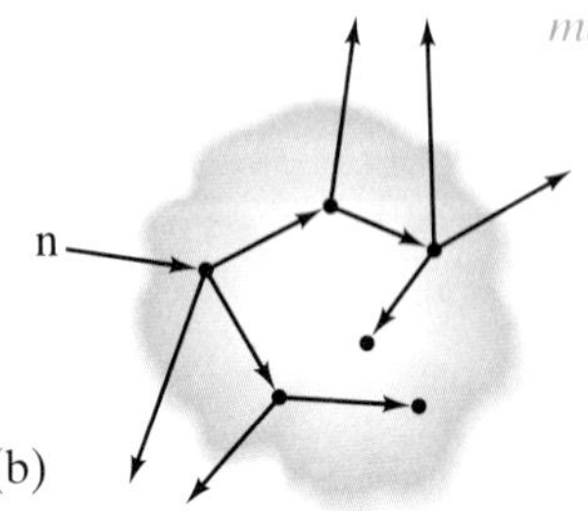


(b)

**FIGURE 31–6** If the amount of uranium exceeds the critical mass, as in (b), a sustained chain reaction is possible. If the mass is less than critical, as in (a), most neutrons escape before additional fissions occur, and the chain reaction is not sustained.

The third problem is that some neutrons will escape through the surface of the reactor core before they can cause further fissions (Fig. 31–6). Thus the mass of fuel must be sufficiently large for a self-sustaining chain reaction to take place. The minimum mass of uranium needed is called the **critical mass**. The value of the critical mass depends on the moderator, the fuel ($^{239}_{94}\text{Pu}$ may be used instead of $^{235}_{92}\text{U}$), and how much the fuel is enriched, if at all. Typical values are on the order of a few kilograms (that is, not grams nor thousands of kilograms).

*Critical mass*

To have a self-sustaining chain reaction, on average at least one neutron produced in each fission must go on to produce another fission. The average number of neutrons per fission that do go on to produce further fissions is

†$^{238}_{92}\text{U}$ will fission, but only with fast neutrons ($^{238}_{92}\text{U}$ is more stable than $^{235}_{92}\text{U}$). The probability of absorbing a fast neutron and producing a fission is too low to produce a self-sustaining chain reaction.

called the **multiplication factor**, $f$. For a self-sustaining chain reaction, we must have $f \geq 1$. If $f < 1$, the reactor is "subcritical." If $f > 1$, it is "supercritical" (and could become dangerously explosive). Reactors are equipped with movable **control rods** (good neutron absorbers like cadmium or boron), whose function is to absorb neutrons and maintain the reactor at just† barely "critical," $f = 1$.

*Critical reaction*

*Types of nuclear reactor*

Nuclear reactors have been built for use in research and to produce electric power. Fission produces many neutrons and a "research reactor" is basically an intense source of neutrons. These neutrons can be used as projectiles in nuclear reactions to produce nuclides not found in nature, including isotopes used as tracers and for therapy. A "power reactor" is used to produce electric power. The energy released in the fission process appears as heat, which is used to boil water and produce steam to drive a turbine connected to an electric generator (Fig. 31–7). The **core** of a nuclear reactor consists of the fuel and a moderator (water in most U.S. commercial reactors). The fuel is usually uranium enriched so that it contains 2 to 4 percent ${}^{235}_{92}U$. Water at high pressure or other liquid (such as liquid sodium) is allowed to flow through the core. The thermal energy it absorbs is used to produce steam in the heat exchanger, so the fissionable fuel acts as the heat input for a heat engine (Chapter 15).

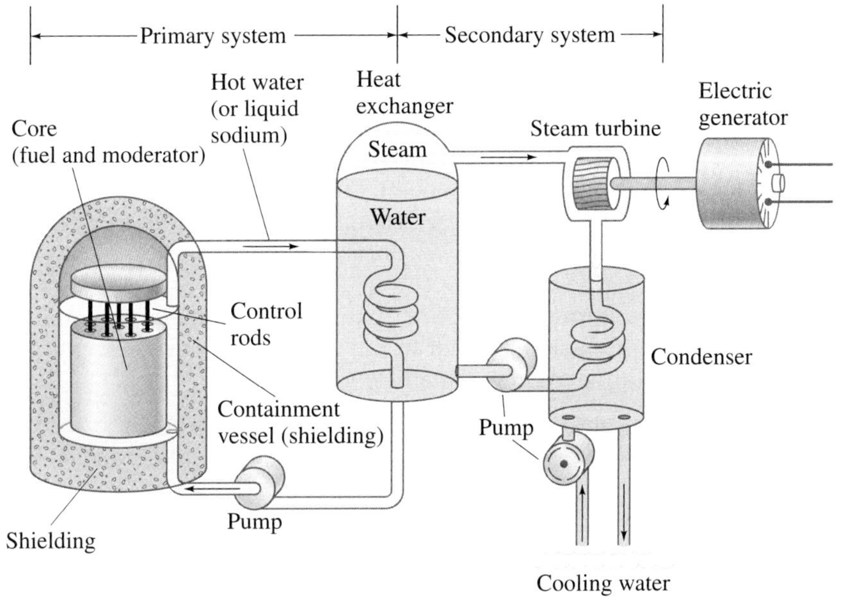


**FIGURE 31–7** A nuclear reactor. The heat generated by the fission process in the fuel rods is carried off by hot water or liquid sodium and is used to boil water to steam in the heat exchanger. The steam drives a turbine to generate electricity and is then cooled in the condenser.

There are problems associated with nuclear power plants. Besides the usual thermal pollution associated with any heat engine (Section 15–12), there is the serious problem of disposal of the radioactive fission fragments produced in the reactor, plus radioactive nuclides produced by neutrons interacting with the structural parts of the reactor. Fission fragments, like their uranium or plutonium parents, have about 50% more neutrons than protons. Nuclei with atomic number in the typical range for fission fragments ($Z \approx 30$ to 60) are stable only if they have more nearly equal numbers of protons and neutrons (see Fig. 30–2). Hence the highly neutron-rich fission fragments are very unstable and decay radioactively. The accidental release of highly radioactive fission fragments into the atmosphere poses a serious threat to human health (Section 31–4), as does possible leakage of the radioactive wastes when they are disposed of.

†The release of neutrons and subsequent fissions occur so quickly that manipulation of the control rods to maintain $f = 1$ would not be possible if it weren't for the small percentage ($\approx 1\%$) of so-called **delayed neutrons**. They come from the decay of neutron-rich fission fragments (or their daughters) having lifetimes on the order of seconds—sufficient to allow enough reaction time to operate the control rods and maintain $f = 1$.

*Delayed neutrons*

The accidents at Three Mile Island, Pennsylvania (1979), and at Chernobyl, Russia (1986), have illustrated some of the dangers and have shown that nuclear plants must be constructed, maintained, and operated with great care and precision (Fig. 31–8). Finally, the lifetime of nuclear power plants is limited to 30-some years, due to buildup of radioactivity and the fact that the structural materials themselves are weakened by the intense conditions inside. "Decommissioning" of a power plant could take a number of forms, but the cost of any method of decommissioning a large plant is very great.

**FIGURE 31–8** Devastation around Chernobyl in Russia, after the nuclear power plant disaster in 1986.

So-called **breeder reactors** were proposed as a solution to the problem of limited supplies of fissionable uranium. A breeder reactor is one in which some of the neutrons produced in the fission of $^{235}_{92}U$ are absorbed by $^{238}_{92}U$, and $^{239}_{94}Pu$ is produced via the set of reactions shown in Fig. 31–1. $^{239}_{94}Pu$ is fissionable with slow neutrons, so after separation it can be used as a fuel in a nuclear reactor. Thus a breeder reactor "breeds" new fuel† $\left(^{239}_{94}Pu\right)$ from otherwise useless $^{238}_{92}U$. Since natural uranium is 99.3 percent $^{238}_{92}U$, this means that the supply of fissionable fuel could be increased by more than a factor of 100. But breeder reactors have the same problems as other reactors, plus other serious problems. Not only is plutonium considered to be a serious health hazard in itself (radioactive with a half-life of 24,000 years), but plutonium produced in a reactor can readily be used in a bomb, increasing the danger of nuclear proliferation and theft of fuel by terrorists to produce a bomb.

Nuclear power presents risks. Other large-scale energy-conversion methods, such as conventional oil and coal-burning steam plants, also present health and environmental hazards; some of them were discussed in Section 15–12, including air pollution, oil spills, and the release of $CO_2$ gas which can trap heat as in a greenhouse to raise the Earth's temperature. The solution to the world's needs for energy is not only technological, but economic and political as well. A major factor surely is to "conserve"—to not waste energy and use as little as possible. "Reduce, reuse, recycle."

**EXAMPLE 31–5** **Uranium fuel amount.** Estimate the minimum amount of $^{235}_{92}U$ that needs to undergo fission in order to run a 1000-MW power reactor per year of continuous operation. Assume an efficiency (Chapter 15) of about 33%.

**APPROACH** At 33% efficiency, we need $3 \times 1000\,\text{MW} = 3000 \times 10^6\,\text{J/s}$ input. Each fission releases about 200 MeV (Eq. 31–5), so we divide the energy for a year by 200 MeV to get the number of fissions needed per year. Then we multiply by the mass of one uranium atom.

**SOLUTION** For 1000 MW output, the total power generation needs to be 3000 MW, of which 2000 MW is dumped as "waste" heat. Thus the total energy release in 1 yr ($3 \times 10^7$ s) from fission needs to be about

$$(3 \times 10^9\,\text{J/s})(3 \times 10^7\,\text{s}) \approx 10^{17}\,\text{J}.$$

If each fission releases 200 MeV of energy, the number of fissions required is

$$\frac{(10^{17}\,\text{J})}{(2 \times 10^8\,\text{eV/fission})(1.6 \times 10^{-19}\,\text{J/eV})} \approx 3 \times 10^{27}\ \text{fissions}.$$

The mass of a single uranium atom is about $(235\,\text{u})(1.66 \times 10^{-27}\,\text{kg/u}) \approx 4 \times 10^{-25}\,\text{kg}$, so the total uranium mass needed is

$$(4 \times 10^{-25}\,\text{kg/fission})(3 \times 10^{27}\ \text{fissions}) \approx 1000\,\text{kg},$$

or about a ton.

**NOTE** Since $^{235}_{92}U$ makes up only 0.7% of natural uranium, the yearly requirement for uranium is on the order of a hundred tons. This is orders of magnitude less than coal, both in mass and volume (coal releases $2.8 \times 10^7\,\text{J/kg}$).

† A breeder reactor does *not* produce more fuel than it uses.

**EXERCISE C** A nuclear-powered submarine needs 6000 kW input power. How many ${}^{235}_{92}U$ fissions is this per second?

## Atom Bomb

The first use of fission, however, was not to produce electric power. Instead, it was first used as a fission bomb (the "atomic bomb"). In early 1940, with Europe already at war, Germany's leader, Adolf Hitler, banned the sale of uranium from the Czech mines he had recently taken over. Research into the fission process suddenly was enshrouded in secrecy. Physicists in the United States were alarmed. A group of them approached Einstein—a man whose name was a household word—to send a letter to President Franklin Roosevelt about the possibilities of using nuclear fission for a bomb far more powerful than any previously known, and inform him that Germany might already have begun development of such a bomb. Roosevelt responded by authorizing the program known as the Manhattan Project, to see if a bomb could be built. Work began in earnest after Fermi's demonstration in 1942 that a sustained chain reaction was possible. A new secret laboratory was developed on an isolated mesa in New Mexico known as Los Alamos. Under the direction of J. Robert Oppenheimer (1904–1967; Fig. 31–9), it became the home of famous scientists from all over Europe and the United States.

**FIGURE 31–9** J. Robert Oppenheimer, on the left, with General Leslie Groves, who was the administrative head of Los Alamos during World War II. The photograph was taken at the Trinity site in the New Mexico desert, where the first atomic bomb was exploded.

To build a bomb that was subcritical during transport but that could be made supercritical (to produce a chain reaction) at just the right moment, two pieces of uranium were used, each less than the critical mass but together greater than the critical mass. The two masses, kept separate until the moment of detonation, were then forced together quickly by a kind of gun, and a chain reaction of explosive proportions occurred. An alternate bomb detonated conventional explosives (TNT) surrounding a plutonium sphere to compress it by implosion to double its density, making it more than critical and causing a nuclear explosion. The first fission bomb was tested in the New Mexico desert in July 1945. It was successful. In early August, a fission bomb using uranium was dropped on Hiroshima and a second, using plutonium, was dropped on Nagasaki (Fig. 31–10), both in Japan. World War II ended shortly thereafter.

**FIGURE 31–10** Photo taken a month after the bomb was dropped on Nagasaki. The shacks were constructed afterwards from debris in the ruins.

Besides its great destructive power, a fission bomb produces many highly radioactive fission fragments, as does a nuclear reactor. When a fission bomb explodes, these radioactive isotopes are released into the atmosphere and are known as *radioactive fallout.*

Testing of nuclear bombs in the atmosphere after World War II was a cause of concern, for the movement of air masses spread the fallout all over the globe. Radioactive fallout eventually settles to the Earth, particularly in rainfall, and is absorbed by plants and grasses and enters the food chain. This is a far more serious problem than the same radioactivity on the exterior of our bodies, since $\alpha$ and $\beta$ particles are largely absorbed by clothing and the outer (dead) layer of skin. But once inside our bodies via food, the isotopes are in direct contact with living cells. One particularly dangerous radioactive isotope is ${}^{90}_{38}Sr$, which is chemically much like calcium and becomes concentrated in bone, where it causes bone cancer and destruction of bone marrow. The 1963 treaty signed by over 100 nations that bans nuclear weapons testing in the atmosphere was motivated because of the hazards of fallout.

# 31–3 Nuclear Fusion

The mass of every stable nucleus is less than the sum of the masses of its constituent protons and neutrons. For example, the mass of the helium isotope ${}^{4}_{2}He$ is less than the mass of two protons plus the mass of two neutrons, as we saw in Example 30–3. Thus, if two protons and two neutrons were to come together to form a helium nucleus, there would be a loss of mass. This mass loss is manifested in the release of a large amount of energy.

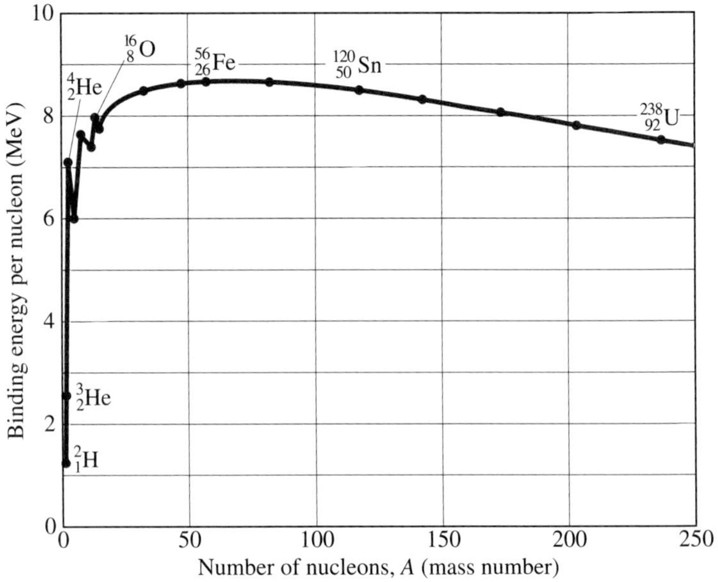


**FIGURE 31–11** Average binding energy per nucleon as a function of mass number $A$ for stable nuclei. Same as Fig. 30–1.

## Nuclear Fusion; Stars

The process of building up nuclei by bringing together individual protons and neutrons, or building larger nuclei by combining small nuclei, is called **nuclear fusion**. A glance at Fig. 31–11 (same as Fig. 30–1) shows why small nuclei can combine to form larger ones with the release of energy: it is because the binding energy per nucleon is smaller for light nuclei than it is for those of increasing mass (up to about $A \approx 60$). It is believed that many of the elements in the universe were originally formed through the process of fusion (see Chapter 33), and that fusion is today continually taking place within the stars, including our Sun, producing the prodigious amounts of radiant energy they emit.

**EXAMPLE 31–6** **Fusion energy release.** One of the simplest fusion reactions involves the production of deuterium, $^{2}_{1}H$, from a neutron and a proton: $^{1}_{1}H + n \rightarrow ^{2}_{1}H + \gamma$. How much energy is released in this reaction?

**APPROACH** The energy released equals the difference in mass (times $c^2$) between the initial and final masses.

**SOLUTION** From Appendix B, the initial rest mass is

$$1.007825\,\text{u} + 1.008665\,\text{u} = 2.016490\,\text{u},$$

and after the reaction the mass is that of the $^{2}_{1}H$, namely 2.014102 u. The mass difference is

$$2.016490\,\text{u} - 2.014102\,\text{u} = 0.002388\,\text{u},$$

so the energy released is

$$(\Delta m)c^2 = (0.002388\,\text{u})(931.5\,\text{MeV/u}) = 2.22\,\text{MeV},$$

and it is carried off by the $^{2}_{1}H$ nucleus and the $\gamma$ ray.

The energy output of our Sun is believed to be due principally to the following sequence of fusion reactions:

*Fusion reactions in the Sun (proton–proton cycle)*

$$^{1}_{1}H + ^{1}_{1}H \rightarrow ^{2}_{1}H + e^{+} + \nu \qquad (0.42\,\text{MeV}) \qquad \textbf{(31–6a)}$$

$$^{1}_{1}H + ^{2}_{1}H \rightarrow ^{3}_{2}He + \gamma \qquad (5.49\,\text{MeV}) \qquad \textbf{(31–6b)}$$

$$^{3}_{2}He + ^{3}_{2}He \rightarrow ^{4}_{2}He + ^{1}_{1}H + ^{1}_{1}H \qquad (12.86\,\text{MeV}) \qquad \textbf{(31–6c)}$$

where the energy released ($Q$-value) for each reaction is given in parentheses.

The net effect of this sequence, which is called the **proton–proton cycle**, is for four protons to combine to form one ${}^4_2\mathrm{He}$ nucleus plus two positrons, two neutrinos, and two gamma rays:

$$4\,{}^1_1\mathrm{H} \rightarrow {}^4_2\mathrm{He} + 2\mathrm{e}^+ + 2\nu + 2\gamma. \qquad \textbf{(31–7)}$$

Note that it takes two of each of the first two reactions (Eqs. 31–6a and b) to produce the two ${}^3_2\mathrm{He}$ for the third reaction. So the total energy release for the net reaction, Eq. 31–7, is $(2 \times 0.42\,\mathrm{MeV} + 2 \times 5.49\,\mathrm{MeV} + 12.86\,\mathrm{MeV}) = 24.7\,\mathrm{MeV}$. However, each of the two $\mathrm{e}^+$ (Eq. 31–6a) quickly annihilates with an electron to produce $2m_\mathrm{e}c^2 = 1.02\,\mathrm{MeV}$; so the total energy released is $(24.7\,\mathrm{MeV} + 2 \times 1.02\,\mathrm{MeV}) = 26.7\,\mathrm{MeV}$. The first reaction, the formation of deuterium from two protons (Eq. 31–6a), has a very low probability, and the infrequency of that reaction serves to limit the rate at which the Sun produces energy.

**EXAMPLE 31–7 ESTIMATE** **Estimating fusion energy.** Estimate the energy released if the following reaction occurred: ${}^2_1\mathrm{H} + {}^2_1\mathrm{H} \rightarrow {}^4_2\mathrm{He}$.

**APPROACH** We use Fig. 31–11.

**SOLUTION** We see in Fig. 31–11 that each ${}^2_1\mathrm{H}$ has a binding energy of about $1\frac{1}{4}\,\mathrm{MeV/nucleon}$, which for 2 nuclei of mass 2 is $4 \times \left(1\frac{1}{4}\right) \approx 5\,\mathrm{MeV}$. The ${}^4_2\mathrm{He}$ has a binding energy per nucleon of about 7 MeV for a total of $4 \times 7\,\mathrm{MeV} = 28\,\mathrm{MeV}$. Hence the energy release is $28\,\mathrm{MeV} - 5\,\mathrm{MeV} = 23\,\mathrm{MeV}$.

In stars hotter than the Sun, it is more likely that the energy output comes principally from the **carbon** (or **CNO**) **cycle**, which comprises the following sequence of reactions:

$$
\begin{aligned}
{}^{12}_6\mathrm{C} + {}^1_1\mathrm{H} &\rightarrow {}^{13}_7\mathrm{N} + \gamma \\
{}^{13}_7\mathrm{N} &\rightarrow {}^{13}_6\mathrm{C} + \mathrm{e}^+ + \nu \\
{}^{13}_6\mathrm{C} + {}^1_1\mathrm{H} &\rightarrow {}^{14}_7\mathrm{N} + \gamma \\
{}^{14}_7\mathrm{N} + {}^1_1\mathrm{H} &\rightarrow {}^{15}_8\mathrm{O} + \gamma \\
{}^{15}_8\mathrm{O} &\rightarrow {}^{15}_7\mathrm{N} + \mathrm{e}^+ + \nu \\
{}^{15}_7\mathrm{N} + {}^1_1\mathrm{H} &\rightarrow {}^{12}_6\mathrm{C} + {}^4_2\mathrm{He}.
\end{aligned}
$$

*Carbon cycle (some stars)*

It is easy to see (see Problem 35) that no carbon is consumed in this cycle (see first and last equations) and that the net effect is the same as the proton–proton cycle, Eq. 31–7 (plus 1 extra $\gamma$). The theory of the proton–proton cycle and of the carbon cycle as the source of energy for the Sun and stars was first worked out by Hans Bethe (1906–    ) in 1939.

**CONCEPTUAL EXAMPLE 31–8** **Stellar fusion.** What is the heaviest element likely to be produced in fusion processes in stars?

**RESPONSE** Fusion is possible if the final products have more binding energy (less mass) than the reactants, for then there is net release of energy. Since the binding energy curve in Fig. 31–11 (or Fig. 30–1) peaks near $A \approx 56$ to 58 which corresponds to iron or nickel, it would not be energetically favorable to produce elements heavier than that. Nevertheless, in the center of massive stars or in supernova explosions, there is enough initial kinetic energy available to drive endothermic reactions that produce heavier elements, as well.

## Possible Fusion Reactors

*Fusion reactor*

The possibility of utilizing the energy released in fusion to make a power reactor is very attractive. The fusion reactions most likely to succeed in a reactor involve the isotopes of hydrogen, ${}^2_1\text{H}$ (deuterium) and ${}^3_1\text{H}$ (tritium), and are as follows, with the energy released given in parentheses:

*Fusion reactions for possible reactor*

$$ {}^2_1\text{H} + {}^2_1\text{H} \rightarrow {}^3_1\text{H} + {}^1_1\text{H} \qquad (4.03\,\text{MeV}) \qquad \textbf{(31–8a)} $$

$$ {}^2_1\text{H} + {}^2_1\text{H} \rightarrow {}^3_2\text{He} + \text{n} \qquad (3.27\,\text{MeV}) \qquad \textbf{(31–8b)} $$

$$ {}^2_1\text{H} + {}^3_1\text{H} \rightarrow {}^4_2\text{He} + \text{n}. \qquad (17.59\,\text{MeV}) \qquad \textbf{(31–8c)} $$

Comparing these energy yields with that for the fission of ${}^{235}_{92}\text{U}$, we can see that the energy released in fusion reactions can be greater for a given mass of fuel than in fission. Furthermore, as fuel, a fusion reactor could use deuterium, which is very plentiful in the water of the oceans (the natural abundance of ${}^2_1\text{H}$ is 0.0115% on average, or about 1 g of deuterium per 80 L of water). The simple proton–proton reaction of Eq. 31–6a, which could use a much more plentiful source of fuel, ${}^1_1\text{H}$, has such a small probability of occurring that it cannot be considered a possibility on Earth.

Although a useful fusion reactor has not yet been achieved, considerable progress has been made in overcoming the inherent difficulties. The problems are associated with the fact that all nuclei have a positive charge and repel each other. However, if they can be brought close enough together so that the short-range attractive nuclear force can come into play, the latter can pull the nuclei together and fusion will occur. For the nuclei to get close enough together, they must have large kinetic energy to overcome the electric repulsion. High kinetic energies are easily attainable with particle accelerators (Chapter 32), but the number of particles involved is too small. To produce realistic amounts of energy, we must deal with matter in bulk, for which high kinetic energy means higher temperatures. Indeed, very high temperatures are required for fusion to occur, and fusion devices are often referred to as **thermonuclear devices**. The Sun and other stars are very hot, many millions of degrees, so the nuclei are moving fast enough for fusion to take place, and the energy released keeps the temperature high so that further fusion reactions can occur. The Sun and the stars represent huge self-sustaining thermonuclear reactors that stay together because of their great gravitational mass; but on Earth, containment of the fast-moving nuclei at the high temperatures and densities required has proven difficult.

It was realized after World War II that the temperature produced within a fission (or "atomic") bomb was close to $10^8$ K. This suggested that a fission bomb could be used to ignite a fusion bomb (popularly known as a thermonuclear or hydrogen bomb) to release the vast energy of fusion. The uncontrollable release of fusion energy in an H-bomb (in 1952) was relatively easy to obtain. But to realize usable energy from fusion at a slow and controlled rate turned out to be a serious challenge.

**EXAMPLE 31–9 ESTIMATE Temperature needed for d–t fusion.** Estimate the temperature required for deuterium–tritium fusion (d–t) to occur.

**APPROACH** We assume the nuclei approach head-on, each with kinetic energy KE, and that the nuclear force comes into play when the distance between their centers equals the sum of their nuclear radii. The electrostatic potential energy (Section 17–5) of the two particles at this distance must equal the total kinetic energy of the two particles when far apart. The average kinetic energy is related to Kelvin temperature by Eq. 13–8.

**SOLUTION** The radii of the two nuclei ($A_1 = 2$ and $A_2 = 3$) are given by Eq. 30–1: $r_d \approx 1.5\,\text{fm}$, $r_t \approx 1.7\,\text{fm}$, so $r_d + r_t = 3.2 \times 10^{-15}\,\text{m}$. We equate the kinetic energy of the two initial particles to the potential energy when very close:

$$2\text{KE} \approx \frac{1}{4\pi\epsilon_0}\frac{e^2}{(r_d + r_t)}$$

$$\approx \left(9.0 \times 10^9\,\frac{\text{N}\cdot\text{m}^2}{\text{C}^2}\right)\frac{(1.6 \times 10^{-19}\,\text{C})^2}{(3.2 \times 10^{-15}\,\text{m})(1.6 \times 10^{-19}\,\text{J/eV})} \approx 0.45\,\text{MeV}.$$

Thus, $\text{KE} \approx 0.22\,\text{MeV}$, and if we ask that the average kinetic energy be this high, then from Eq. 13–8, $\frac{3}{2}kT = \overline{\text{KE}}$, we have

$$T = \frac{2\overline{\text{KE}}}{3k} = \frac{2(0.22\,\text{MeV})(1.6 \times 10^{-13}\,\text{J/MeV})}{3(1.38 \times 10^{-23}\,\text{J/K})} \approx 2 \times 10^9\,\text{K}.$$

**NOTE** More careful calculations show that the temperature required for fusion is actually about an order of magnitude less than this rough estimate, partly because it is not necessary that the *average* kinetic energy be 0.22 MeV—a small percentage with this much energy (particles in the high-energy tail of the Maxwell distribution, Fig. 13–18) would be sufficient. Reasonable estimates for a usable fusion reactor are in the range $T \gtrsim 2$ to $4 \times 10^8\,\text{K}$.

It is not only a high temperature that is required for a fusion reactor. There must also be a high density of nuclei to ensure a sufficiently high collision rate. A real difficulty with controlled fusion is to contain nuclei long enough and at a high enough density for sufficient reactions to occur that a usable amount of energy is obtained. At the temperatures needed for fusion, the atoms are ionized, and the resulting collection of nuclei and electrons is referred to as a **plasma**. Ordinary materials vaporize at a few thousand degrees at best, and hence cannot be used to contain a high-temperature plasma. Two major containment techniques are *magnetic confinement* and *inertial confinement*.

In **magnetic confinement**, magnetic fields are used to try to contain the hot plasma. One possibility is a torus-shaped design, Fig. 31–12, originally called a **tokamak**.

The second method for containing the fuel for fusion is **inertial confinement**: a small pellet of deuterium and tritium is struck simultaneously from several directions by very intense laser beams (Fig. 31–13). The intense influx of energy heats and ionizes the pellet into a plasma, compressing it and heating it to temperatures at which fusion occurs. The confinement time is on the order of $10^{-11}$ to $10^{-9}$ s, during which time the ions do not move appreciably because of their own inertia, fusion takes place, and the pellet explodes.

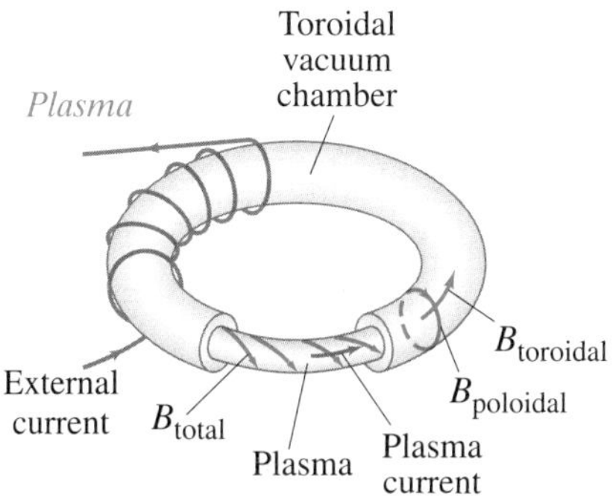


**FIGURE 31–12** Tokamak configuration, showing the total $\vec{\mathbf{B}}$ field due to external current plus current in the plasma itself.

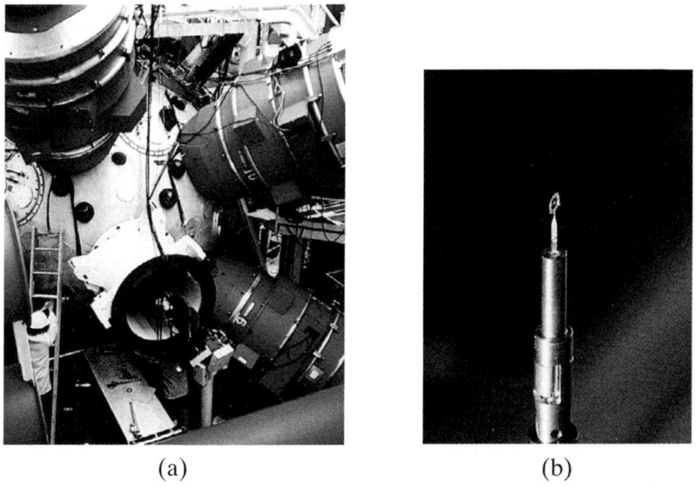


**FIGURE 31–13** (a) Target chamber (5 m in diameter) of the NOVA laser at Lawrence Livermore Laboratory, into which 10 laser beams converge on a target. (b) A 1-mm-diameter DT (deuterium–tritium) target, on its support, at the center of the target chamber.

## 31–4 Passage of Radiation Through Matter; Radiation Damage

When we speak of *radiation*, we include $\alpha$, $\beta$, $\gamma$, and X-rays, as well as protons, neutrons, and other particles such as pions (see Chapter 32). Because charged particles can ionize the atoms or molecules of any material they pass through, they are referred to as **ionizing radiation**. And because radiation produces ionization, it can cause considerable damage to materials, particularly to biological tissue.

Charged particles, such as $\alpha$ and $\beta$ rays and protons, cause ionization because of electric forces. That is, when they pass through a material, they can attract or repel electrons strongly enough to remove them from the atoms of the material. Since the $\alpha$ and $\beta$ rays emitted by radioactive substances have energies on the order of 1 MeV ($10^4$ to $10^7$ eV), whereas ionization of atoms and molecules requires on the order of 10 eV, it is clear that a single $\alpha$ or $\beta$ particle can cause thousands of ionizations.

Neutral particles also give rise to ionization when they pass through materials. For example, X-ray and $\gamma$-ray photons can ionize atoms by knocking out electrons by means of the photoelectric and Compton effects (Chapter 27). Furthermore, if a $\gamma$ ray has sufficient energy (greater than 1.02 MeV), it can undergo pair production: an electron and a positron are produced (Section 27–6). The charged particles produced in all of these processes can themselves go on to produce further ionization. Neutrons, on the other hand, interact with matter mainly by collisions with nuclei, with which they interact strongly. Often the nucleus is broken apart by such a collision, altering the molecule of which it was a part. And the fragments produced can in turn cause ionization.

Radiation passing through matter can do considerable damage. Metals and other structural materials become brittle and their strength can be weakened if the radiation is very intense, as in nuclear reactor power plants and for space vehicles that must pass through areas of intense cosmic radiation.

PHYSICS APPLIED
*Biological damage*

The radiation damage produced in biological organisms is due primarily to ionization produced in cells. Several related processes can occur. Ions or radicals are produced that are highly reactive and take part in chemical reactions that interfere with the normal operation of the cell. All forms of radiation can ionize atoms by knocking out electrons. If these are bonding electrons, the molecule may break apart, or its structure may be altered so that it does not perform its normal function or may perform a harmful function. In the case of proteins, the loss of one molecule is not serious if there are other copies of it in the cell and additional copies can be made from the gene that codes for it. However, large doses of radiation may damage so many molecules that new copies cannot be made quickly enough, and the cell dies. Damage to the DNA is more serious, since a cell may have only one copy. Each alteration in the DNA can affect a gene and alter the molecule it codes for, so that needed proteins or other materials may not be made at all. Again the cell may die. The death of a single cell is not normally a problem, since the body can replace it with a new one. (There are exceptions, such as neurons, which are *not* replaceable, so their loss is serious.) But if many cells die, the organism may not be able to recover. On the other hand, a cell may survive but be defective. It may go on dividing and produce many more defective cells, to the detriment of the whole organism. Thus radiation can cause cancer—the rapid uncontrolled production of cells.

Radiation damage to biological organisms is often separated into categories. *Somatic damage* refers to any part of the body except the reproductive organs. Somatic damage affects that particular organism, causing cancer and, at high doses, radiation sickness (characterized by nausea, fatigue, loss of body hair, and other symptoms) or even death. *Genetic damage* refers to damage to reproductive cells, causing mutations, the majority of which are harmful and are transmitted to future generations. The possible damage done by the medical use of X-rays and other radiation must be balanced against the medical benefits and prolongation of life as a result of their diagnostic use.

## 31–5 Measurement of Radiation—Dosimetry

Although the passage of ionizing radiation through the human body can cause considerable damage, radiation can also be used to treat certain diseases, particularly cancer, often by using very narrow beams directed at a cancerous tumor in order to destroy it (Section 31–6). It is therefore important to be able to quantify the amount, or **dose**, of radiation. This is the subject of **dosimetry**.

The strength of a source can be specified at a given time by stating the **source activity**, or how many disintegrations occur per second. The traditional unit is the **curie** (Ci), defined as

*Source activity*

$$1\ \text{Ci} = 3.70 \times 10^{10}\ \text{disintegrations per second.}$$

*The curie (unit)*

(This figure comes from the original definition as the activity of exactly one gram of radium.) Although the curie is still in common use, the SI unit for source activity is the **becquerel** (Bq), defined as

$$1\ \text{Bq} = 1\ \text{disintegration/s.}$$

*The becquerel (unit)*

Commercial suppliers of **radionuclides** (radioactive nuclides) specify the activity at a given time. Since the activity decreases over time, more so for short-lived isotopes, it is important to take this into account.

The source activity $(\Delta N/\Delta t)$ is related to the number of radioactive nuclei present, $N$, and to the half-life, $T_{\frac{1}{2}}$, by (see Section 30–8):

$$\frac{\Delta N}{\Delta t} = \lambda N = \frac{0.693}{T_{\frac{1}{2}}} N.$$

**EXAMPLE 31–10 Radioactivity taken up by cells.** In a certain experiment, $0.016\,\mu\text{Ci}$ of $^{32}_{15}\text{P}$ is injected into a medium containing a culture of bacteria. After 1.0 h the cells are washed and a detector that is 70% efficient (counts 70% of emitted $\beta$ rays) records 720 counts per minute from all the cells. What percentage of the original $^{32}_{15}\text{P}$ was taken up by the cells?

**APPROACH** The half-life of $^{32}_{15}\text{P}$ is about 14 days (Appendix B), so we can ignore any loss of activity over 1 hour. From the given activity, we find how many $\beta$ rays are emitted. We can compare 70% of this to the $(720/\text{min})/(60\ \text{s/min}) = 12$ per second detected.

**SOLUTION** The total number of disintegrations per second originally was $(0.016 \times 10^{-6})(3.7 \times 10^{10}) = 590.$ The counter could be expected to count 70% of this, or 410 per second. Since it counted $720/60 = 12$ per second, then $12/410 = 0.029$ or 2.9% was incorporated into the cells.

Another type of measurement is the exposure or **absorbed dose**—that is, the effect the radiation has on the absorbing material. The earliest unit of dosage was the **roentgen** (R), defined in terms of the amount of ionization produced by the radiation ($1.6 \times 10^{12}$ ion pairs per gram of dry air at standard conditions). Today, 1 R is defined as the amount of X or $\gamma$ radiation that deposits $0.878 \times 10^{-2}$ J of energy per kilogram of air. The roentgen was largely superseded by another unit of absorbed dose applicable to any type of radiation, the **rad**: *1 rad is that amount of radiation which deposits energy at a rate of $1.00 \times 10^{-2}$ J/kg in any absorbing material.* (This is quite close to the roentgen for X- and $\gamma$ rays.) The proper SI unit for absorbed dose is the **gray** (Gy):

*Absorbed dose*

*The rad (unit)*

$$1\ \text{Gy} = 1\ \text{J/kg} = 100\ \text{rad.} \qquad \textbf{(31–9)}$$

*The gray (unit)*

The absorbed dose depends not only on the strength of a given radiation beam (number of particles per second) and the energy per particle, but also on the type of material that is absorbing the radiation. Bone, for example, absorbs more of the radiation normally used than does flesh, so the same beam passing through a human body deposits a greater dose (in rads or grays) in bone than in flesh.

The gray and the rad are physical units of dose—the energy deposited per unit mass of material. They are, however, not the most meaningful units for measuring the biological damage produced by radiation because equal doses of different types of radiation cause differing amounts of damage. For example, 1 rad of $\alpha$ radiation does 10 to 20 times the amount of damage as 1 rad of $\beta$ or $\gamma$ rays. This difference arises largely because $\alpha$ rays (and other heavy particles such as protons and neutrons) move much more slowly than $\beta$ and $\gamma$ rays of equal energy due to their greater mass. Hence, ionizing collisions occur closer together, so more irreparable damage can be done. The **relative biological effectiveness** (RBE) or **quality factor** (QF) of a given type of radiation is defined as the number of rads of X or $\gamma$ radiation that produces the same biological damage as 1 rad of the given radiation. Table 31–1 gives the QF for several types of radiation. The numbers are approximate since they depend somewhat on the energy of the particles and on the type of damage that is used as the criterion.

*RBE or QF*

*Effective dose*

The **effective dose** can be given as the product of the dose in rads and the QF, and this unit is known as the **rem** (which stands for *rad equivalent man*):

*The rem (unit)*

$$\text{effective dose (in rem)} = \text{dose (in rad)} \times \text{QF}. \qquad \textbf{(31–10a)}$$

This unit is being replaced by the SI unit for "effective dose," the **sievert** (Sv):

*The sievert (unit)*

$$\text{effective dose (Sv)} = \text{dose (Gy)} \times \text{QF}. \qquad \textbf{(31–10b)}$$

By these definitions, 1 rem (or 1 Sv) of any type of radiation does approximately the same amount of biological damage. For example, 50 rem of fast neutrons does the same damage as 50 rem of $\gamma$ rays. But note that 50 rem of fast neutrons is only 5 rads, whereas 50 rem of $\gamma$ rays is 50 rads.

*Natural radioactivity*

*Radon*

We are constantly exposed to low-level radiation from natural sources: cosmic rays, natural radioactivity in rocks and soil, and naturally occurring radioactive isotopes in our food, such as $^{40}_{19}\text{K}$. Radon, $^{222}_{86}\text{Rn}$, is of considerable concern today. It is the product of radium decay and is an intermediate in the decay series from uranium (see Fig. 30–11). Most intermediates remain in the rocks where formed, but radon is a gas that can escape from rock (and from building material like concrete) to enter the atmosphere we breathe. Although radon is inert chemically (it is a noble gas), it is not inert physically—it decays by alpha emission, and its products, also radioactive, are *not* chemically inert and can attach to the interior of the lung.

**TABLE 31–1 Quality Factor (QF) of Different Kinds of Radiation**

| Type | QF |
|---|---|
| X- and $\gamma$ rays | 1 |
| $\beta$ (electrons) | $\approx 1$ |
| Fast protons | 1 |
| Slow neutrons | $\approx 3$ |
| Fast neutrons | Up to 10 |
| $\alpha$ particles and heavy ions | Up to 20 |

The natural radioactive background averages about 0.30 rem (300 mrem) per year per person in the U.S., although there are large variations. From medical X-rays, the average person receives about 50 to 60 mrem per year, giving an average total dose of about 360 mrem (3.6 mSv) per person. Government regulators suggest an upper limit of allowed radiation for an individual in the general populace at about 100 mrem (1 mSv) per year, exclusive of natural sources. It is not known if low doses of radiation increase the chances of cancer or genetic defects, so the attitude today is to play safe and keep the radiation dose as low as possible.

The upper limit for people who work around radiation—in hospitals, in power plants, in research—has been set higher, a maximum of 5 rem (50 mSv) whole-body dose in any one year, and significantly less averaged over more years (below 2 rem/yr averaged over 5 years). To monitor exposure, those people who work around radiation generally carry some type of dosimeter, one common type being a **radiation film badge** which is a piece of film wrapped in light-tight material. The passage of ionizing radiation through the film changes it so that the film is darkened upon development, and so indicates the received dose. Newer types include the *thermoluminescent dosimeter* (TLD). Dosimeters and badges do not protect the worker, but high levels detected suggest reassignment or modified work practices to reduce radiation exposure to acceptable levels.

*Film badges and dosimeters*

Large doses of radiation can cause unpleasant symptoms such as nausea, fatigue, and loss of body hair. Such effects are sometimes referred to as **radiation sickness**. Large doses can be fatal, although the time span of the

*Radiation sickness*

dose is important. A short dose of 1000 rem (10 Sv) is nearly always fatal. A 400-rem (4-Sv) dose in a short period of time is fatal in 50% of the cases. However, the body possesses remarkable repair processes, so that a 400-rem dose spread over several weeks is not usually fatal. It will, nonetheless, cause considerable damage to the body.

The effects of low doses over a long time are difficult to determine and are not well known as yet.

CONCEPTUAL EXAMPLE 31–11 **Limiting the dose.** A worker in an environment with a radioactive source is warned that she is accumulating a dose too quickly and will have to lower her exposure by a factor of ten to continue working for the rest of the year. If the worker is able to work farther away from the source, how much farther away is necessary?

**RESPONSE** If the energy is radiated uniformly in all directions, then the intensity (dose/area) should decrease as the distance squared, just as it does for sound and light. If she can work four times farther away, the exposure lowers by a factor of sixteen, enough to make her safe.

EXAMPLE 31–12 **Whole-body dose.** What whole-body dose is received by a 70-kg laboratory worker exposed to a 40-mCi $^{60}_{27}\mathrm{Co}$ source, assuming the person's body has cross-sectional area 1.5 $\mathrm{m}^2$ and is normally about 4.0 m from the source for 4.0 h per day? $^{60}_{27}\mathrm{Co}$ emits $\gamma$ rays of energy 1.33 MeV and 1.17 MeV in quick succession. Approximately 50% of the $\gamma$ rays interact in the body and deposit all their energy. (The rest pass through.)

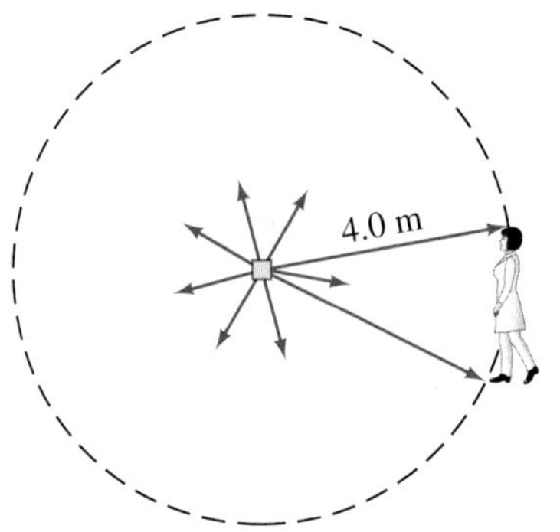


**FIGURE 31–14** Radiation spreads out in all directions. A person 4.0 m away intercepts only a fraction: her cross-sectional area divided by the area of a sphere of radius 4.0 m. Example 31–12.

**APPROACH** Of the given energy emitted, only a fraction passes through the worker, equal to *her* area divided by the total area over a full sphere of radius 4.0 m (Fig. 31–14).

**SOLUTION** The total $\gamma$-ray energy per decay is $(1.33 + 1.17)\,\mathrm{MeV} = 2.50\,\mathrm{MeV}$, so the total energy emitted by the source per second is

$$(0.040\,\mathrm{Ci})(3.7 \times 10^{10}\,\mathrm{decays/Ci\cdot s})(2.50\,\mathrm{MeV}) = 3.7 \times 10^{9}\,\mathrm{MeV/s}.$$

The proportion of this intercepted by the body is its 1.5-$\mathrm{m}^2$ area divided by the area of a sphere of radius 4.0 m (Fig. 31–14):

$$\frac{1.5\,\mathrm{m}^2}{4\pi r^2} = \frac{1.5\,\mathrm{m}^2}{4\pi(4.0\,\mathrm{m})^2} = 7.5 \times 10^{-3}.$$

So the rate energy is deposited in the body (remembering that only 50% of the $\gamma$ rays interact in the body) is

$$\begin{aligned} E &= \left(\tfrac{1}{2}\right)(7.5 \times 10^{-3})(3.7 \times 10^{9}\,\mathrm{MeV/s})(1.6 \times 10^{-13}\,\mathrm{J/MeV}) \\ &= 2.2 \times 10^{-6}\,\mathrm{J/s}. \end{aligned}$$

Since $1\,\mathrm{Gy} = 1\,\mathrm{J/kg}$, the whole-body dose rate for this 70-kg person is $(2.2 \times 10^{-6}\,\mathrm{J/s})/(70\,\mathrm{kg}) = 3.1 \times 10^{-8}\,\mathrm{Gy/s}$. In the space of 4.0 h, this amounts to a dose of

$$(4.0\,\mathrm{h})(3600\,\mathrm{s/h})(3.1 \times 10^{-8}\,\mathrm{Gy/s}) = 4.5 \times 10^{-4}\,\mathrm{Gy}.$$

Since QF $\approx$ 1 for gammas, the effective dose (Eq. 31–10b) is 450 $\mu$Sv or (see Eq. 31–9):

$$(100\,\mathrm{rad/Gy})(4.5 \times 10^{-4}\,\mathrm{Gy})(1) = 45\,\mathrm{mrem} = 0.45\,\mathrm{mSv}.$$

**NOTE** This 45-mrem effective dose is almost 50% of the normal allowed dose for a whole year (100 mrem/yr), or 1% of the maximum one year allowance for radiation workers. This worker should not receive such a dose every day and should seek ways to reduce it (shield the source, vary the work, work farther away, etc.).

## *31–6 Radiation Therapy

Radiation can be very useful (not just a danger)

The applications of radioactivity and radiation to human beings and other organisms is a vast field that has filled many books. In the medical field there are two basic aspects: (1) **radiation therapy**—the treatment of disease (mainly cancer)—which we discuss in this Section; and (2) the *diagnosis* of disease, which we discuss in the following Sections of this Chapter.

PHYSICS APPLIED
Radiation therapy

Radiation can cause cancer. It can also be used to treat it. Rapidly growing cancer cells are especially susceptible to destruction by radiation. Nonetheless, large doses are needed to kill the cancer cells, and some of the surrounding normal cells are inevitably killed as well. It is for this reason that cancer patients receiving radiation therapy often suffer side effects characteristic of radiation sickness. To minimize the destruction of normal cells, a narrow beam of $\gamma$ or X-rays is often used when a cancerous tumor is well localized. The beam is directed at the tumor, and the source (or body) is rotated so that the beam passes through various parts of the body to keep the dose at any one place as low as possible—except at the tumor and its immediate surroundings, where the beam passes at all times (Fig. 31–15). The radiation may be from a radioactive source such as ${}^{60}_{27}\mathrm{Co}$, or it may be from an X-ray machine that produces photons in the range 200 keV to 5 MeV. Protons, neutrons, electrons, and pions, which are produced in particle accelerators (Section 32–1), are also being used in cancer therapy.

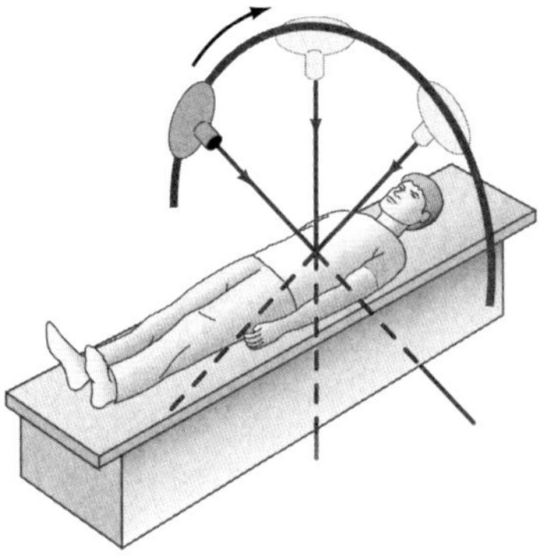

**FIGURE 31–15** Radiation source rotates so that the beam always passes through the diseased tissue, but minimizing the dose in the rest of the body.

In some cases, a tiny radioactive source may be inserted directly inside a tumor, which will eventually kill the majority of the cells. A similar technique is used to treat cancer of the thyroid with the radioactive isotope ${}^{131}_{53}\mathrm{I}$. The thyroid gland concentrates iodine present in the bloodstream, particularly in any area where abnormal growth is taking place. Its intense radioactivity can destroy the defective cells.

Although radiation can increase the lifespan of many patients, it is not always completely effective. It may not be possible to kill all the cancer cells, so a recurrence of the disease is possible. Many cases, especially when the cancerous cells are not well localized in one area, are difficult to treat without damaging healthy organs.

Another application of radiation is for sterilizing bandages, surgical equipment, and even packaged foods, since bacteria and viruses can be killed or deactivated by large doses of radiation.

## *31–7 Tracers and Imaging in Research and Medicine

PHYSICS APPLIED
Tracers in medicine and biology

Radioactive isotopes are commonly used in biological and medical research as **tracers**. A given compound is artificially synthesized using a radioactive isotope such as ${}^{14}_{6}\mathrm{C}$ or ${}^{3}_{1}\mathrm{H}$. Such "tagged" molecules can then be traced as they move through an organism or as they undergo chemical reactions. The presence of these tagged molecules (or parts of them, if they undergo chemical change) can be detected by a Geiger or scintillation counter, which detects emitted radiation (see Section 30–13). How food molecules are digested, and to what parts of the body they are diverted, can be traced in this way. Radioactive tracers have been used to determine how amino acids and other essential compounds are synthesized by organisms. The permeability of cell walls to various molecules and ions can he determined using radioactive isotopes: the tagged molecule or ion is injected into the extracellular fluid, and the radioactivity present inside and outside the cells is measured as a function of time.

In a technique known as **autoradiography**, the position of the radioactive isotopes is detected on film. For example, the distribution of carbohydrates produced in the leaves of plants from absorbed $CO_2$ can be observed by keeping the plant in an atmosphere where the carbon atom in the $CO_2$ is ${}^{14}_{6}C$. After a time, a leaf is placed firmly on a photographic plate and the emitted radiation darkens the film most strongly where the isotope is most strongly concentrated (Fig. 31–16a). Autoradiography using labeled nucleotides (components of DNA) has revealed much about the details of DNA replication (Fig. 31–16b).

For medical diagnosis, the radionuclide commonly used today is ${}^{99m}_{43}Tc$, a long-lived excited state of technetium-99 (the "m" in the symbol stands for "metastable" state). It is formed when ${}^{99}_{42}Mo$ decays. The great usefulness of ${}^{99m}_{43}Tc$ derives from its convenient half-life of 6 h (short, but not too short) and the fact that it can combine with a large variety of compounds. The compound to be labeled with the radionuclide is so chosen because it concentrates in the organ or region of the anatomy to be studied. Detectors outside the body then record, or image, the distribution of the radioactively labeled compound. The detection can be done by a single detector (Fig. 31–17) which is moved across the body, measuring the intensity of radioactivity at a large number of points. The image represents the relative intensity of radioactivity at each point. The relative radioactivity is a diagnostic tool. For example, high or low radioactivity may represent overactivity or underactivity of an organ or part of an organ, or in another case may represent a lesion or tumor. More complex *gamma cameras* make use of many detectors which simultaneously record the radioactivity at many points. The measured intensities can be displayed on a TV or computer monitor, and allow "dynamic" studies (that is, images that change in time) to be performed.

(a)

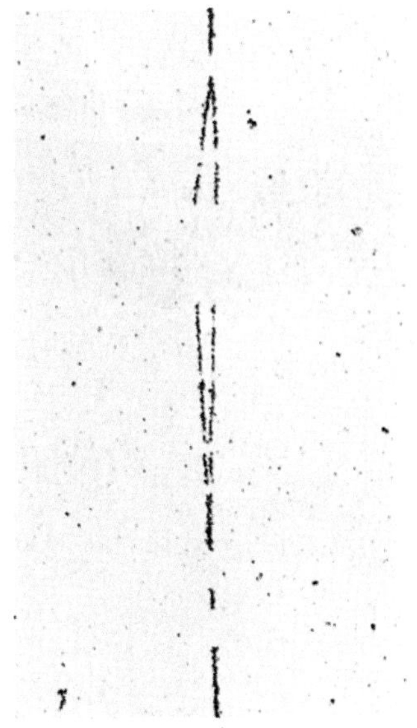
(b)

**FIGURE 31–16** (a) Autoradiograph of a mature leaf of the squash plant *Cucurbita melopepo* exposed for 30 s to ${}^{14}CO_2$. The photosynthetic (green) tissue has become radioactive; the nonphotosynthetic tissue of the veins is free of ${}^{14}C$ and therefore does not blacken the X-ray sheet. This technique is very useful in following patterns of nutrient transport in plants. (b) An autoradiograph of a fiber of chromosomal DNA isolated from the mustard plant *Arabidopsis thaliana*. The dashed arrays of film grains show the Y-shaped growing point of replicating DNA.

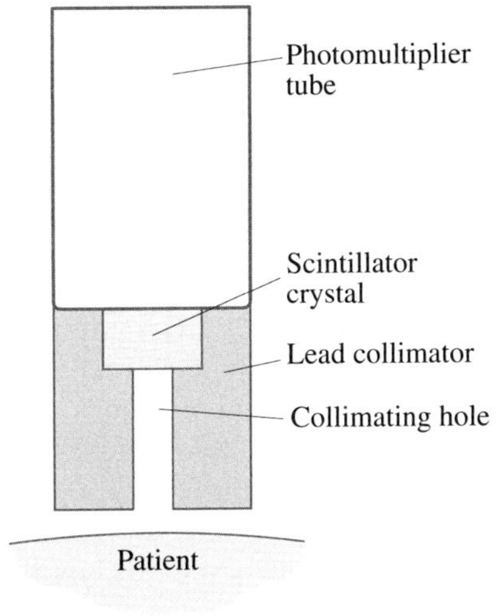


**FIGURE 31–17** Collimated gamma-ray detector for scanning (moving) over a patient. The collimator is necessary to select $\gamma$ rays that come in a straight line from the patient. Without the collimator, $\gamma$ rays from all parts of the body could strike the scintillator, producing a very poor image.

## *31–8 Emission Tomography

PHYSICS APPLIED
*Medical imaging*

The images formed using the standard techniques of nuclear medicine, as briefly discussed in the previous Section, are produced from radioactive tracer sources within the *volume* of the body. It is also possible to image the radioactive emissions in a single plane or slice through the body using the computed tomography techniques discussed in Section 25–12. A basic gamma camera is moved around the patient to measure the radioactive intensity from the tracer at many points and angles; the data are processed in much the same way as for X-ray CT scans (Section 25–12). This technique is referred to as **single photon emission tomography** (SPET).†

*SPET*

† Also known as SPECT, "single photon emission computed tomography."

*PET* Another important technique is **positron emission tomography** (PET), which makes use of positron emitters such as $^{11}_{6}C$, $^{13}_{7}N$, $^{15}_{8}O$, and $^{18}_{9}F$ whose half-lives are short. These isotopes are incorporated into molecules that, when inhaled or injected, accumulate in the organ or region of the body to be studied. When such a nuclide $\beta$ decays, the emitted positron travels at most a few millimeters before it collides with a normal electron. In this collision, the positron and electron are annihilated, producing two $\gamma$ rays $\left(e^{+} + e^{-} \rightarrow 2\gamma\right)$, each having an energy of 511 keV $\left(= m_e c^2\right)$. The two $\gamma$ rays fly off in opposite directions $(180° \pm 0.25°)$ since they must have almost exactly equal and opposite momentum to conserve momentum (the momenta of the initial $e^+$ and $e^-$ are essentially zero compared to the momenta afterwards of the $\gamma$ rays). Because the photons travel along the same line in opposite directions, their detection in coincidence by rings of detectors surrounding the patient (Fig. 31–18) readily establishes the line along which the emission took place. If the difference in time of arrival of the two photons could be determined accurately, the actual position of the emitting nuclide along that line could be calculated. Present-day electronics can measure times to at best $\pm 300$ ps, so at the $\gamma$ ray's speed $\left(c = 3 \times 10^8\,\text{m/s}\right)$, the actual position could be determined to an accuracy on the order of about $d = vt \approx \left(3 \times 10^8\,\text{m/s}\right)\left(300 \times 10^{-12}\,\text{s}\right) \approx 10\,\text{cm}$, which is not very useful. Although there may be future potential for time-of-flight measurements to determine position, today computed tomography techniques are used instead, similar to those for X-ray CT, which can reconstruct PET images with a resolution on the order of 3–5 mm. One big advantage of PET is that no collimators are needed (as for detection of a single photon—see Fig. 31–17). Thus, fewer photons are "wasted" and lower doses can be administered to the patient with PET.

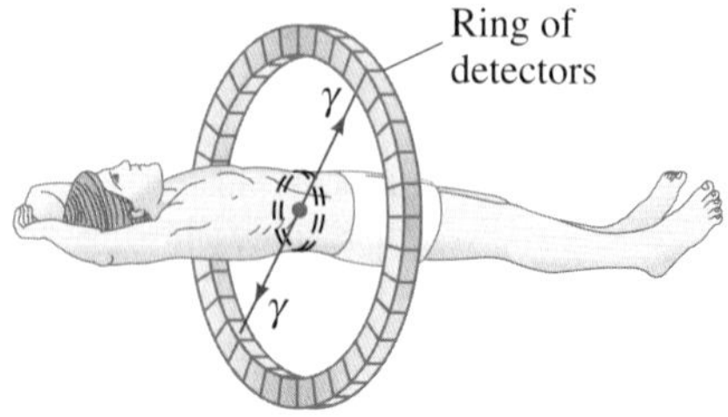


**FIGURE 31–18** Positron emission tomography (PET) uses a ring of detectors, typically scintillators with photomultiplier tubes (Section 30–13), to detect the two annihilation $\gamma$ rays $\left(e^{+} + e^{-} \rightarrow 2\gamma\right)$ emitted at 180° to each other.

Both PET and SPET systems can give images that relate to biochemistry, metabolism, and function. This is to be compared to X-ray CT scans (Section 25–12), whose images reflect shape and structure—that is, the anatomy of the imaged region.

## 31–9 Nuclear Magnetic Resonance (NMR) and Magnetic Resonance Imaging (MRI)

*NMR* *Nuclear magnetic resonance* (NMR) is a phenomenon that soon after its discovery in 1946 became a powerful research tool in a variety of fields from physics to chemistry and biochemistry. It is also an important medical imaging technique. We first briefly discuss the phenomenon, and then look at its applications.

We saw in Chapter 28 (Section 28–6) that when atoms are placed in a magnetic field, atomic energy levels split into several closely spaced levels (see Fig. 28–8). Nuclei, too, exhibit these magnetic properties. We will examine only the simplest, the hydrogen (H) nucleus, since it is the one most used, even for medical imaging. The $^{1}_{1}H$ nucleus consists of a single proton. Its spin angular momentum (and its magnetic moment), like that of the electron, can take on only two values when placed in a magnetic field: we call these "spin up" (parallel to the field) and "spin down" (antiparallel to the field), as suggested in Fig. 31–19. When a magnetic field is present, the energy of the nucleus splits into two levels as shown in Fig. 31–20, with the spin up (parallel to field) having the lower energy. (This is like the Zeeman effect for atomic levels, Fig. 28–8.)

**FIGURE 31–19** Schematic picture of a proton represented in a magnetic field $\vec{\mathbf{B}}$ (pointing upward) with its two possible states of spin, up and down.

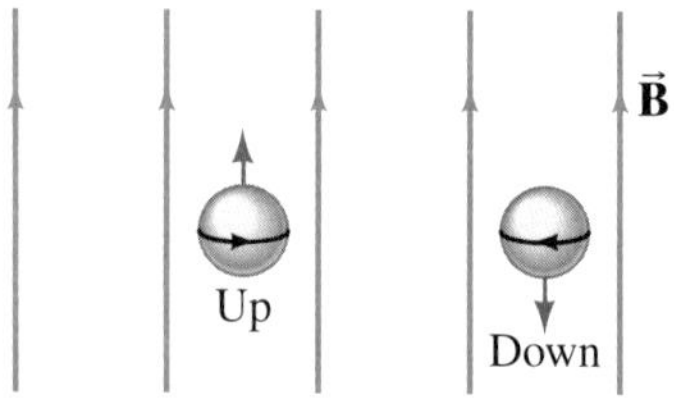


**FIGURE 31–20** Energy $E_0$ in the absence of a magnetic field splits into two levels in the presence of a magnetic field.

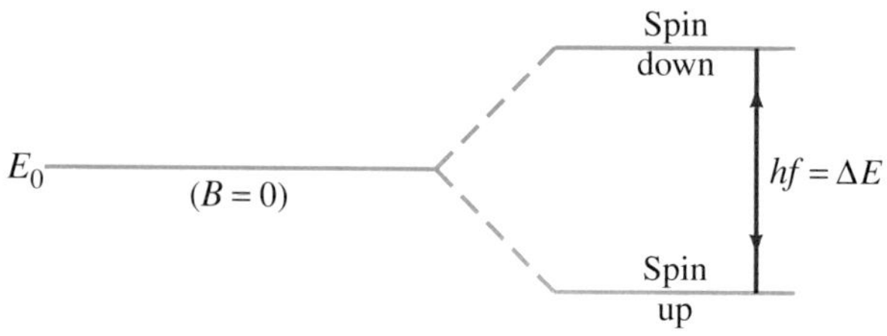

The difference in energy, $\Delta E$, between these two levels is proportional to the total magnetic field, $B_T$, at the nucleus:

$$\Delta E = kB_T,$$

where $k$ is a proportionality constant that is different for different nuclides.

In a standard **nuclear magnetic resonance** (NMR) setup, the sample to be examined is placed in a static magnetic field. A radiofrequency (RF) pulse of electromagnetic radiation (that is, photons) is applied to the sample. If the frequency, $f$, of this pulse corresponds precisely to the energy difference between the two energy levels (Fig. 31–20), so that

$$hf = \Delta E = kB_T, \qquad \textbf{(31–11)}$$

then the photons of the RF beam will be absorbed, exciting many of the nuclei from the lower state to the upper state. This is a resonance phenomenon, whose photons can be detected, since there is significant absorption only if $f$ is very near $f = kB_T/h$. Hence the name "nuclear magnetic resonance." For free $^1_1H$ nuclei, the frequency is 42.58 MHz for a magnetic field $B_T = 1.0\,T$. If the H atoms are bound in a molecule the total magnetic field $B_T$ at the H nuclei will be the sum of the external applied field $(B_{ext})$ plus the local magnetic field $(B_{local})$ due to electrons and nuclei of neighboring atoms. Since $f$ is proportional to $B_T$, the value of $f$ for a given external field will be slightly different for the bound H atoms than for free atoms:

$$hf = k(B_{ext} + B_{local}).$$

This small change in frequency can be measured, and is called the "chemical shift." A great deal has been learned about the structure of molecules and bonds using such NMR measurements.

PHYSICS APPLIED
*NMR imaging (MRI)*

For producing medically useful NMR images—now commonly called MRI, or **magnetic resonance imaging**—the element most used is hydrogen since it is the commonest element in the human body and gives the strongest NMR signals. The experimental apparatus is shown in Fig. 31–21. The large coils set up the static magnetic field, and the RF coils produce the RF pulse of electromagnetic waves (photons) that cause the nuclei to jump from the lower state to the upper one (Fig. 31–20). These same coils (or another coil) can detect the absorption of energy or the emitted radiation (also of frequency $f = \Delta E/h$, Eq. 31–11) when the nuclei jump back down to the lower state.

**FIGURE 31–21** Typical NMR imaging setup: (a) diagram; (b) photograph.

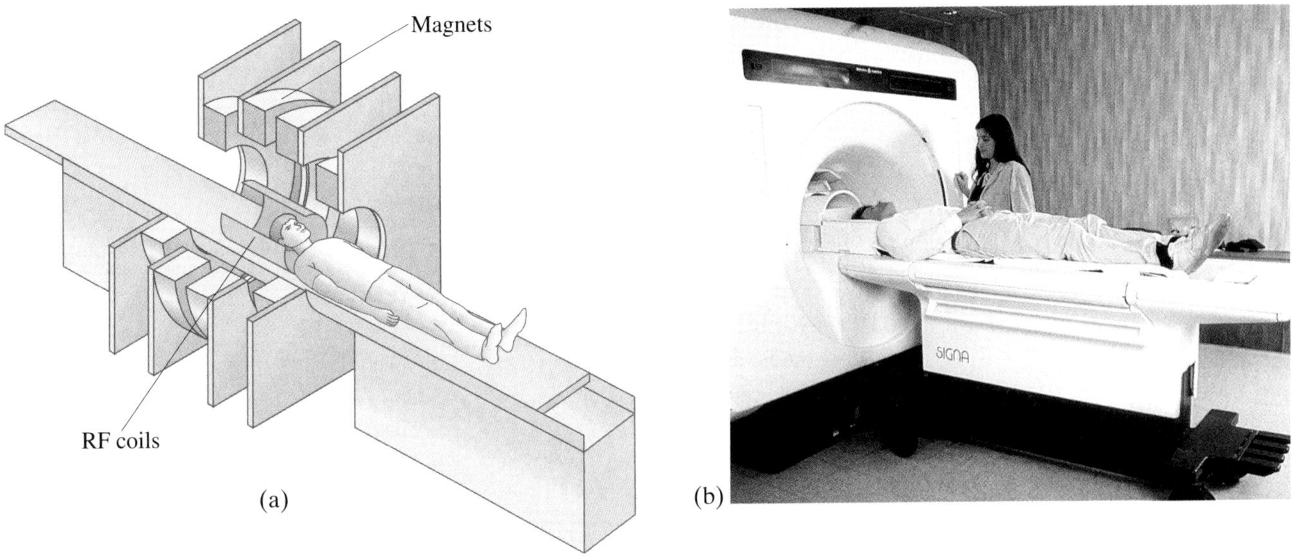

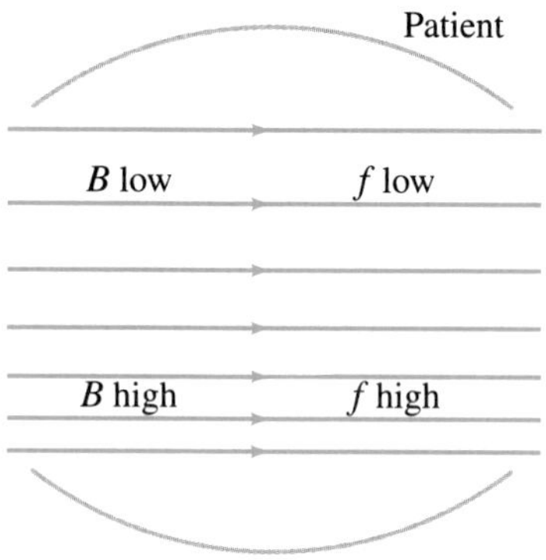


**FIGURE 31–22** A static field that is stronger at the bottom than at the top. The frequency of absorbed or emitted radiation is proportional to $B$ in NMR.

**FIGURE 31–23** False-color NMR image (MRI) of a vertical section through the head showing structures in the normal brain.

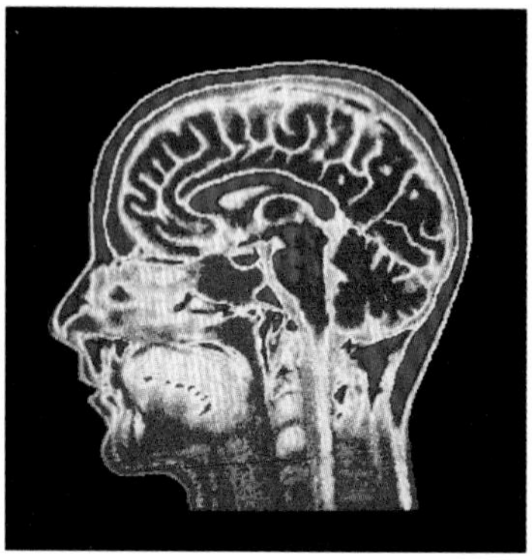

The formation of a two-dimensional or three-dimensional image can be done using techniques similar to those for computed tomography (Section 25–12). The simplest thing to measure for creating an image is the intensity of absorbed and/or reemitted radiation from many different points of the body, and this would be a measure of the density of H atoms at each point. But how do we determine from what part of the body a given photon comes? One technique is to give the static magnetic field a gradient; that is, instead of applying a uniform magnetic field, $B_T$, the field is made to vary with position across the width of the sample (or patient). Since the frequency absorbed by the H nuclei is proportional to $B_T$ (Eq. 31–11), only one plane within the body will have the proper value of $B_T$ to absorb photons of a particular frequency $f$. By varying $f$, absorption by different planes can be measured. Alternately, if the field gradient is applied *after* the RF pulse, the frequency of the emitted photons will be a measure of where they were emitted. See Fig. 31–22. If a magnetic field gradient in one direction is applied during excitation (absorption of photons) and photons of a single frequency are transmitted, only H nuclei in one thin slice will be excited. By applying a gradient in a different direction, perpendicular to the first, during reemission, the frequency $f$ of the reemitted radiation will represent depth in that slice. Other ways of varying the magnetic field throughout the volume of the body can be used in order to correlate NMR frequency with position.

A reconstructed image based on the density of H atoms (that is, the intensity of absorbed or emitted radiation) is not very interesting. More useful are images based on the rate at which the nuclei decay back to the ground state, and such images can produce resolution of 1 mm or better. This NMR technique (sometimes called **spin-echo**) produces images of great diagnostic value, both in the delineation of structure (anatomy) and in the study of metabolic processes. An NMR image is shown in Fig. 31–23.

NMR imaging is considered to be noninvasive. We can calculate the energy of the photons involved: as mentioned above, in a 1.0-T magnetic field, $f = 42.58\,\text{MHz}$ for ${}^1_1\text{H}$. This corresponds to an energy of $hf = (6.6 \times 10^{-34}\,\text{J}\cdot\text{s})(43 \times 10^6\,\text{Hz}) \approx 3 \times 10^{-26}\,\text{J}$ or about $10^{-7}\,\text{eV}$. Since molecular bonds are on the order of 1 eV, it is clear that the RF photons can cause little cellular disruption. This should be compared to X- or $\gamma$ rays, whose energies are $10^4$ to $10^6$ eV and thus can cause significant damage. The static magnetic fields, though often large ($\approx$0.1 to 1 T), are believed to be harmless (except for people wearing heart pacemakers).

Table 31–2 lists the recently developed techniques we have discussed for imaging the interior of the body, along with the optimum resolution attainable today. Of course, resolution is only one factor that must be considered; it must be remembered that the different imaging techniques provide different types of information, useful for different types of diagnosis.

**TABLE 31–2 Medical Imaging Techniques**

| Technique | Where Discussed in This Book | Resolution |
|---|---|---|
| Conventional X-ray | Section 25–12 | $\frac{1}{2}$ mm |
| CT scan, X-ray | Section 25–12 | $\frac{1}{2}$ mm |
| Nuclear medicine (tracers) | Section 31–7 | 1 cm |
| SPET (single photon emission) | Section 31–8 | 1 cm |
| PET (positron emission) | Section 31–8 | 3–5 mm |
| NMR | Section 31–9 | $\frac{1}{2}$–1 mm |
| Ultrasound | Section 12–9 | 2 mm |

# Summary


A **nuclear reaction** occurs when two nuclei collide and two or more other nuclei (or particles) are produced. In this process, as in radioactivity, **transmutation** (change) of elements occurs.

The **reaction energy** or **$Q$-value** of a reaction $a + X \rightarrow Y + b$ is

$$Q = (M_a + M_X - M_b - M_Y)c^2 \quad (31\text{–}1)$$

$$= K_b + K_Y - K_a - K_X. \quad (31\text{–}2)$$

In **fission** a heavy nucleus such as uranium splits into two intermediate-sized nuclei after being struck by a neutron. $^{235}_{92}U$ is fissionable by slow neutrons, whereas some fissionable nuclei require fast neutrons. Much energy is released in fission because the binding energy per nucleon is lower for heavy nuclei than it is for intermediate-sized nuclei, so the mass of a heavy nucleus is greater than the total mass of its fission products. The fission process releases neutrons, so that a **chain reaction** is possible. The **critical mass** is the minimum mass of fuel needed to sustain a chain reaction. In a **nuclear reactor** or nuclear bomb, a **moderator** is needed to slow down the released neutrons.

The **fusion** process, in which small nuclei combine to form larger ones, also releases energy. The energy from our Sun is believed to originate in the fusion reactions known as the **proton–proton cycle** in which four protons fuse to form a $^4_2He$ nucleus producing over 25 MeV of energy. A useful fusion reactor for power generation has not yet proved possible because of the difficulty in containing the fuel (e.g., deuterium) long enough at the high temperature required.

Radiation can cause damage to materials, including biological tissue. Quantifying amounts of radiation is the subject of **dosimetry**. The **curie** (Ci) and the **becquerel** (Bq) are units that measure the **source activity** or rate of decay of a sample: $1\ \text{Ci} = 3.70 \times 10^{10}$ disintegrations per second, whereas $1\ \text{Bq} = 1$ disintegration/s. The **absorbed dose**, often specified in **rads**, measures the amount of energy deposited per unit mass of absorbing material: 1 rad is the amount of radiation that deposits energy at the rate of $10^{-2}$ J/kg of material. The SI unit of absorbed dose is the **gray**: $1\ \text{Gy} = 1\ \text{J/kg} = 100\ \text{rad}$. The **effective dose** is often specified by the **rem** = rad × QF, where QF is the "quality factor" of a given type of radiation; 1 rem of any type of radiation does approximately the same amount of biological damage. The average dose received per person per year in the United States is about 0.36 rem. The SI unit for effective dose is the **sievert**: $1\ \text{Sv} = 10^2$ rem.

[*Nuclear radiation is used in medicine as therapy and for imaging of biological processes, as well as several types of tomographic **imaging** of the human body: PET, SPET, and MRI; the latter makes use of **nuclear magnetic resonance** (NMR).]


# Questions

(NOTE: Masses are found in Appendix B.)

**1.** Fill in the missing particles or nuclei:
(*a*) $n + {}^{137}_{56}Ba \rightarrow ? + \gamma$; (*b*) $n + {}^{137}_{56}Ba \rightarrow {}^{137}_{55}Cs + ?$;
(*c*) $d + {}^2_1H \rightarrow {}^4_2He + ?$; (*d*) $\alpha + {}^{197}_{79}Au \rightarrow ? + d$
where d stands for deuterium.

**2.** The isotope $^{32}_{15}P$ is produced by the reaction: $n + ? \rightarrow {}^{32}_{15}P + p$. What must be the target nucleus?

**3.** When $^{22}_{11}Na$ is bombarded by deuterons ($^2_1H$), an $\alpha$ particle is emitted. What is the resulting nuclide?

**4.** Why are neutrons such good projectiles for producing nuclear reactions?

**5.** A proton strikes a $^{20}_{10}Ne$ nucleus, and an $\alpha$ particle is observed to emerge. What is the residual nucleus? Write down the reaction equation.

**6.** Are fission fragments $\beta^+$ or $\beta^-$ emitters? Explain.

**7.** If $^{235}_{92}U$ released only 1.5 neutrons per fission on the average, would a chain reaction be possible? If so, what would be different?

**8.** $^{238}_{92}U$ releases an average of 2.5 neutrons per fission compared to 2.9 for $^{239}_{94}Pu$. Pure samples of which of these two nuclei do you think would have the smaller critical mass? Explain.

**9.** The energy from nuclear fission appears in the form of thermal energy—but the thermal energy of what?

**10.** Why can't uranium be enriched by chemical means?

**11.** How can a neutron, with practically no kinetic energy, excite a nucleus to the extent shown in Fig. 31–2?

**12.** Why would a porous block of uranium be more likely to explode if kept under water rather than in air?

**13.** A reactor that uses highly enriched uranium can use ordinary water (instead of heavy water) as a moderator and still have a self-sustaining chain reaction. Explain.

**14.** Why must the fission process release neutrons if it is to be useful?

**15.** Discuss the relative merits and disadvantages, including pollution and safety, of power generation by fossil fuels, nuclear fission, and nuclear fusion.

**16.** What is the reason for the "secondary system" in a nuclear reactor, Fig. 31–7? That is, why is the water heated by the fuel in a nuclear reactor not used directly to drive the turbines?

**17.** Why are neutrons released in a fission reaction?

**18.** Why do gamma particles penetrate matter more easily than beta particles do?

**19.** A higher temperature is required for deuterium–deuterium ignition than for deuterium–tritium. Explain.

**20.** Light energy emitted by the Sun and stars comes from the fusion process. What conditions in the interior of stars make this possible?

**21.** How do stars, and our Sun, maintain confinement of the plasma for fusion?

**22.** What is the basic difference between fission and fusion?

**23.** People who work around metals that emit alpha particles are trained that there is little danger from proximity or even touching the material, but that they must take extreme precautions against ingesting it. Hence, there are strong rules against eating and drinking while working, and against machining the metal. Why?

24. Why is the recommended maximum radiation dose higher for women beyond the child-bearing age than for younger women?

25. Radiation is sometimes used to sterilize medical supplies and even food. Explain how it works.

26. What is the difference between absorbed dose and effective dose? What are the SI units for each?

* 27. How might radioactive tracers be used to find a leak in a pipe?

# Problems

(NOTE: Masses are found in Appendix B.)

## 31–1 Nuclear Reactions, Transmutation

1. (I) Natural aluminum is all $^{27}_{13}$Al. If it absorbs a neutron, what does it become? Does it decay by $\beta^+$ or $\beta^-$? What will be the product nucleus?

2. (I) Determine whether the reaction $^2_1\text{H} + ^2_1\text{H} \rightarrow ^3_2\text{He} + \text{n}$ requires a threshold energy.

3. (I) Is the reaction $\text{n} + ^{238}_{92}\text{U} \rightarrow ^{239}_{92}\text{U} + \gamma$ possible with slow neutrons? Explain.

4. (II) Does the reaction $\text{p} + ^7_3\text{Li} \rightarrow ^4_2\text{He} + \alpha$ require energy, or does it release energy? How much energy?

5. (II) Calculate the energy released (or energy input required) for the reaction $\alpha + ^9_4\text{Be} \rightarrow ^{12}_6\text{C} + \text{n}$.

6. (II) (*a*) Can the reaction $\text{n} + ^{24}_{12}\text{Mg} \rightarrow ^{23}_{11}\text{Na} + \text{d}$ occur if the bombarding particles have 10.00 MeV of kinetic energy? (d stands for deuterium, $^2_1$H.) (*b*) If so, how much energy is released?

7. (II) (*a*) Can the reaction $\text{p} + ^7_3\text{Li} \rightarrow ^4_2\text{He} + \alpha$ occur if the incident proton has kinetic energy = 2500 keV? (*b*) If so, what is the total kinetic energy of the products?

8. (II) In the reaction $\alpha + ^{14}_7\text{N} \rightarrow ^{17}_8\text{O} + \text{p}$, the incident $\alpha$ particles have 7.68 MeV of kinetic energy. (*a*) Can this reaction occur? (*b*) If so, what is the total kinetic energy of the products? The mass of $^{17}_8$O is 16.999131 u.

9. (II) Calculate the $Q$-value for the "capture" reaction $\alpha + ^{16}_8\text{O} \rightarrow ^{20}_{10}\text{Ne} + \gamma$.

10. (II) Calculate the total kinetic energy of the products of the reaction $\text{d} + ^{13}_6\text{C} \rightarrow ^{14}_7\text{N} + \text{n}$ if the incoming deuteron (d) has KE = 36.3 MeV.

11. (II) Radioactive $^{14}_6$C is produced in the atmosphere when a neutron is absorbed by $^{14}_7$N. Write the reaction and find its $Q$-value.

12. (II) An example of a "stripping" nuclear reaction is $\text{d} + ^6_3\text{Li} \rightarrow \text{X} + \text{p}$. (*a*) What is X, the resulting nucleus? (*b*) Why is it called a "stripping" reaction? (*c*) What is the $Q$-value of this reaction? Is the reaction endothermic or exothermic?

13. (II) An example of a "pick-up" nuclear reaction is $^3_2\text{He} + ^{12}_6\text{C} \rightarrow \text{X} + \alpha$. (*a*) Why is it called a "pickup" reaction? (*b*) What is the resulting nucleus? (*c*) What is the $Q$-value of this reaction? Is the reaction endothermic or exothermic?

14. (II) (*a*) Complete the following nuclear reaction, $\text{p} + ? \rightarrow ^{32}_{16}\text{S} + \gamma$. (*b*) What is the $Q$-value?

15. (II) The reaction $\text{p} + ^{18}_8\text{O} \rightarrow ^{18}_9\text{F} + \text{n}$ requires an input of energy equal to 2.453 MeV. What is the mass of $^{18}_9$F?

## 31–2 Nuclear Fission

16. (I) Calculate the energy released in the fission reaction $\text{n} + ^{235}_{92}\text{U} \rightarrow ^{88}_{38}\text{Sr} + ^{136}_{54}\text{Xe} + 12\text{n}$. Use Appendix B, and assume the initial kinetic energy of the neutron is very small.

17. (I) What is the energy released in the fission reaction of Eq. 31–4? (The masses of $^{141}_{56}$Ba and $^{92}_{36}$Kr are 140.914411 u and 91.926156 u, respectively.)

18. (I) How many fissions take place per second in a 200-MW reactor? Assume 200 MeV is released per fission.

19. (II) The energy produced by a fission reactor is about 200 MeV per fission. What fraction of the rest mass of a $^{235}_{92}$U nucleus is this?

20. (II) Consider the fission reaction $^{235}_{92}\text{U} + \text{n} \rightarrow ^{133}_{51}\text{Sb} + ^{98}_{41}\text{Nb} + ?\text{n}$. (*a*) How many neutrons are produced in this reaction? (*b*) Calculate the energy release. The atomic masses for Sb and Nb isotopes are 132.915250 u and 97.910328 u, respectively.

21. (II) How much mass of $^{235}_{92}$U is required to produce the same amount of energy as burning 1.0 kg of coal (about $3 \times 10^7$ J)?

22. (II) Suppose that the electric average power consumption, day and night, in a typical house is 950 W. What initial mass of $^{235}_{92}$U would have to undergo fission to supply the electrical needs of such a house for a year? (Assume 200 MeV is released per fission, as well as 100% efficiency.)

23. (II) What initial mass of $^{235}_{92}$U is required to operate a 650-MW reactor for 1 yr? Assume 40% efficiency.

24. (III) Assuming a fission of $^{236}_{92}$U into two roughly equal fragments, estimate the electric potential energy just as the fragments separate from each other. Assume that the fragments are spherical (see Eq. 30–1) and compare your calculation to the nuclear fission energy released, about 200 MeV.

## 31–3 Nuclear Fusion

25. (I) What is the average kinetic energy of protons at the center of a star where the temperature is $10^7$ K? [*Hint*: use Eq. 13–8.]

26. (II) Show that the energy released in the fusion reaction $^2_1\text{H} + ^3_1\text{H} \rightarrow ^4_2\text{He} + \text{n}$ is 17.59 MeV.

27. (II) Show that the energy released when two deuterium nuclei fuse to form $^3_2$He with the release of a neutron is 3.27 MeV.

28. (II) Verify the $Q$-value stated for each of the reactions of Eqs. 31–6. [*Hint*: be careful with electrons.]

29. (II) Calculate the energy release per gram of fuel for the reactions of Eqs. 31–8a, b, and c. Compare to the energy release per gram of uranium in fission.

30. (II) How much energy is released when $^{238}_{92}$U absorbs a slow neutron (KE $\approx$ 0) and becomes $^{239}_{92}$U?

31. (II) If a typical house requires 950 W of electric power on average, what minimum amount of deuterium fuel would have to be used in a year to supply these electrical needs? Assume the reaction of Eq. 31–8b.

32. (II) Show that the energies carried off by the $^4_2$He nucleus and the neutron for the reaction of Eq. 31–8c are about 3.5 MeV and 14 MeV, respectively. Are these fixed values, independent of the plasma temperature?

33. (II) Suppose a fusion reactor ran on "d–d" reactions, Eqs. 31–8a and b. Estimate how much water, for fuel, would be needed per hour to run a 1000-MW reactor, assuming 30% efficiency.

34. (III) How much energy (J) is contained in 1.00 kg of water if its natural deuterium is used in the fusion reaction of Eq. 31–8a? Compare to the energy obtained from the burning of 1.0 kg of gasoline, about $5 \times 10^7$ J.

35. (III) The energy output of massive stars is believed to be due to the *carbon cycle* (see text). (*a*) Show that no carbon is consumed in this cycle and that the net effect is the same as for the proton–proton cycle. (*b*) What is the total energy release? (*c*) Determine the energy output for each reaction and decay. (*d*) Why does the carbon cycle require a higher temperature ($\approx 2 \times 10^7$ K) than the proton–proton cycle ($\approx 1.5 \times 10^7$ K)?

36. (III) (*a*) Compare the energy needed for the first reaction of the carbon cycle to that for a deuterium–tritium reaction (Example 31–9). (*b*) If a deuterium–tritium reaction requires $T \approx 3 \times 10^8$ K, estimate the temperature needed for the first carbon-cycle reaction.

### 31–5 Dosimetry

37. (I) A dose of 4.0 Sv of $\gamma$ rays in a short period would be lethal to about half the people subjected to it. How many grays is this?

38. (I) Fifty rads of $\alpha$-particle radiation is equivalent to how many rads of X-rays in terms of biological damage?

39. (I) How many rads of slow neutrons will do as much biological damage as 75 rads of fast neutrons?

40. (I) How much energy is deposited in the body of a 65-kg adult exposed to a 2.0-Gy dose?

41. (II) A 0.025-$\mu$Ci sample of $^{32}_{15}$P is injected into an animal for tracer studies. If a Geiger counter intercepts 25% of the emitted $\beta$ particles, what will be the counting rate, assumed 85% efficient?

42. (II) A cancer patient is undergoing radiation therapy in which protons with an energy of 1.2 MeV are incident on a 0.25-kg tumor. (*a*) If the patient receives an effective dose of 1.0 rem, what is the absorbed dose? (*b*) How many protons are absorbed by the tumor? Assume QF $\approx$ 1.

43. (II) A 1.0-mCi source of $^{32}_{15}$P (in $NaHPO_4$), a $\beta$ emitter, is implanted in a tumor where it is to administer 36 Gy. The half-life of $^{32}_{15}$P is 14.3 days, and 1 mCi delivers about 10 mGy/min. Approximately how long should the source remain implanted?

44. (II) About 35 eV is required to produce one ion pair in air. Show that this is consistent with the two definitions of the roentgen given in the text.

45. (II) $^{57}_{27}$Co emits 122-keV $\gamma$ rays. If a 70-kg person swallowed 1.85 $\mu$Ci of $^{57}_{27}$Co, what would be the dose rate (Gy/day) averaged over the whole body? Assume that 50% of the $\gamma$-ray energy is deposited in the body. [*Hint*: determine the rate of energy deposited in the body and use the definition of the gray.]

46. (II) What is the mass of a 1.00-$\mu$Ci $^{14}_{6}$C source?

47. (II) Huge amounts of radioactive $^{131}_{53}$I were released in the accident at Chernobyl in 1986. Chemically, iodine goes to the human thyroid. (Doctors can use it for diagnosis and treatment of thyroid problems.) In a normal thyroid, $^{131}_{53}$I absorption can cause damage to the thyroid. (*a*) Write down the reaction for the decay of $^{131}_{53}$I. (*b*) Its half-life is 8.0 d; how long would it take for ingested $^{131}_{53}$I to become 10% of the initial value? (*c*) Absorbing 1 mCi of $^{131}_{53}$I can be harmful; what mass of iodine is this?

48. (III) Assume a liter of milk typically has an activity of 2000 pCi due to $^{40}_{19}$K. If a person drinks two glasses (0.5 L) per day, estimate the total effective dose (in Sv and in rem) received in a year. As a crude model, assume the milk stays in the stomach 12 hr and is then released. Assume also that very roughly 10% of the 1.5 MeV released per decay is absorbed by the body. Compare your result to the normal allowed dose of 100 mrem per year. Make your estimate for (*a*) a 50-kg adult, and (*b*) a 5-kg baby.

49. (III) Radon gas, $^{222}_{86}$Rn, is considered a serious health hazard (see discussion in text). It decays by $\alpha$-emission. (*a*) What is the daughter nucleus? (*b*) Is the daughter nucleus stable or radioactive? If the latter, how does it decay, and what is its half-life? (*c*) Is the daughter nucleus also a noble gas, or is it chemically reacting? (*d*) Suppose 1.0 ng of $^{222}_{86}$Rn seeps into a basement. What will be its activity? If the basement is then sealed, what will be the activity 1 month later? [*Hint*: see Fig. 30–11.]

### 31–9 NMR

50. (II) Calculate the wavelength of photons needed to produce NMR transitions in free protons in a 1.000-T field. In what region of the spectrum does it lie?

## General Problems

51. J. Chadwick discovered the neutron by bombarding $^9_4$Be with the popular projectile of the day, alpha particles. (*a*) If one of the reaction products was the then unknown neutron, what was the other product? (*b*) What is the *Q*-value of this reaction?

52. Fusion temperatures are often given in keV. Determine the conversion factor from kelvins to keV using, as is common in this field, $\overline{\text{KE}} = kT$ without the factor $\frac{3}{2}$.

53. One means of enriching uranium is by diffusion of the gas $UF_6$. Calculate the ratio of the speeds of molecules of this gas containing $^{235}_{92}$U and $^{238}_{92}$U, on which this process depends.

54. (*a*) What mass of $^{235}_{92}$U was actually fissioned in the first atomic bomb, whose energy was the equivalent of about 20 kilotons of TNT (1 kiloton of TNT releases $5 \times 10^{12}$ J)? (*b*) What was the actual mass transformed to energy?

55. In a certain town the average yearly background radiation consists of 21 mrad of X-rays and $\gamma$ rays plus 3.0 mrad of particles having a QF of 10. How many rem will a person receive per year on the average?

56. Deuterium makes up 0.0115% of natural hydrogen on average. Make a rough estimate of the total deuterium in the Earth's oceans and estimate the total energy released if all of it were used in fusion reactors.

57. A shielded $\gamma$-ray source yields a dose rate of 0.052 rad/h at a distance of 1.0 m for an average-sized person. If workers are allowed a maximum dose of 5.0 rem in 1 year, how close to the source may they operate, assuming a 40-h work week? Assume that the intensity of radiation falls off as the square of the distance. (It actually falls off more rapidly than $1/r^2$ because of absorption in the air, so your answer will give a better-than-permissible value.)

58. Radon gas, ${}^{222}_{86}\text{Rn}$, is formed by $\alpha$ decay. (*a*) Write the decay equation. (*b*) Ignoring the kinetic energy of the daughter nucleus (it's so massive), estimate the kinetic energy of the $\alpha$ particle produced. (*c*) Estimate the momentum of the alpha and of the daughter nucleus. (*d*) Estimate the kinetic energy of the daughter, and show that your approximation in (*b*) was valid.

59. Consider a system of nuclear power plants that produce 3400 MW. (*a*) What total mass of ${}^{235}_{92}\text{U}$ fuel would be required to operate these plants for 1 yr, assuming that 200 MeV is released per fission? (*b*) Typically 6% of the ${}^{235}_{92}\text{U}$ nuclei that fission produce ${}^{90}_{38}\text{Sr}$, a $\beta^-$ emitter with a half-life of 29 yr. What is the total radioactivity of the ${}^{90}_{38}\text{Sr}$, in curies, produced in 1 yr? (Neglect the fact that some of it decays during the 1-yr period.)

60. In the net reaction, Eq. 31–7, for the proton–proton cycle in the Sun, the neutrinos escape from the Sun with energy of about 0.5 MeV. The remaining energy, 26.2 MeV, is available within the Sun. Use this value to calculate the "heat of combustion" per kilogram of hydrogen fuel and compare it to the heat of combustion of coal, about $3 \times 10^7$ J/kg.

61. Energy reaches Earth from the Sun at a rate of about 1400 W/m$^2$. Calculate (*a*) the total power output of the Sun, and (*b*) the number of protons consumed per second in the reaction of Eq. 31–7, assuming that this is the source of all the Sun's energy. (*c*) Assuming that the Sun's mass of $2.0 \times 10^{30}$ kg was originally all protons and that all could be involved in nuclear reactions in the Sun's core, how long would you expect the Sun to "glow" at its present rate? See previous Problem.

62. Some stars, in a later stage of evolution, may begin to fuse two ${}^{12}_{6}\text{C}$ nuclei into one ${}^{24}_{12}\text{Mg}$ nucleus. (*a*) How much energy would be released in such a reaction? (*b*) What kinetic energy must two carbon nuclei each have when far apart, if they can then approach each other to within 6.0 fm, center-to-center? (*c*) Approximately what temperature would this require?

63. An average adult body contains about 0.10 $\mu$Ci of ${}^{40}_{19}\text{K}$, which comes from food. (*a*) How many decays occur per second? (*b*) The potassium decays produce beta particles with energies of around 1.4 MeV. Calculate the dose per year in sieverts for a 50-kg adult. Is this a significant fraction of the 3.6 mSv/year background rate?

64. When the nuclear reactor accident occurred at Chernobyl in 1986, $2.0 \times 10^7$ Ci were released into the atmosphere. Assuming that this radiation was distributed uniformly over the surface of the Earth, what was the activity per square meter? (The actual activity was not uniform; even within Europe wet areas received more radioactivity from rainfall).

65. A star with a large helium abundance can burn helium in the reaction ${}^{4}_{2}\text{He} + {}^{4}_{2}\text{He} + {}^{4}_{2}\text{He} \rightarrow {}^{12}_{6}\text{C}$. What is the $Q$-value for this reaction?

66. A 1.0-$\mu$Ci ${}^{137}_{55}\text{Cs}$ source is used for 2.0 hours by a 75-kg student in a physics lab. Radioactive ${}^{137}_{55}\text{Cs}$ decays by $\beta^-$ decay with a half-life of 30 years. The average energy of the emitted betas is about 190 keV per decay. The $\beta$ decay is quickly followed by a $\gamma$ with an energy of 660 keV. Assuming the student absorbs *all* emitted energy, what effective dose (in rem) is received during lab?

67. A large amount of ${}^{90}_{38}\text{Sr}$ was released during the Chernobyl nuclear reactor accident in 1986. The ${}^{90}_{38}\text{Sr}$ enters the body through the food chain. How long will it take for 90% of the ${}^{90}_{38}\text{Sr}$ released during the accident to decay? See Appendix B.

68. Three radioactive sources have the same activity, 25 mCi. Source A emits 1.0-MeV $\gamma$ rays, source B emits 2.0-MeV $\gamma$ rays, and source C emits 2.0-MeV alphas. What is the relative danger of these sources?

69. A 70-kg patient is to be given a medical test involving the ingestion of ${}^{99\text{m}}_{43}\text{Tc}$ (Section 31–7) which decays by emitting a 140-keV gamma. The half-life for this decay is 6 hours. Assuming that about half the gamma photons exit the body without interacting with anything, what must be the initial activity of the Tc sample if the whole-body dose cannot exceed 50 mrem? Make the rough approximation that biological elimination of Tc can be ignored.

## Answers to Exercises

**A:** ${}^{138}_{56}\text{Ba}$.

**B:** 3 neutrons.

**C:** $2 \times 10^{17}$.

This computer-generated reconstruction of a proton–antiproton collision at Fermilab (Fig. 32–3) occurred at a combined energy of nearly 2 TeV. It is one of the events that provided evidence for the top quark (1995). The wire drift chamber (Section 30–13) is in a magnetic field, and the radius of curvature of the charged particle tracks is a measure of each particle's momentum (Chapter 20).

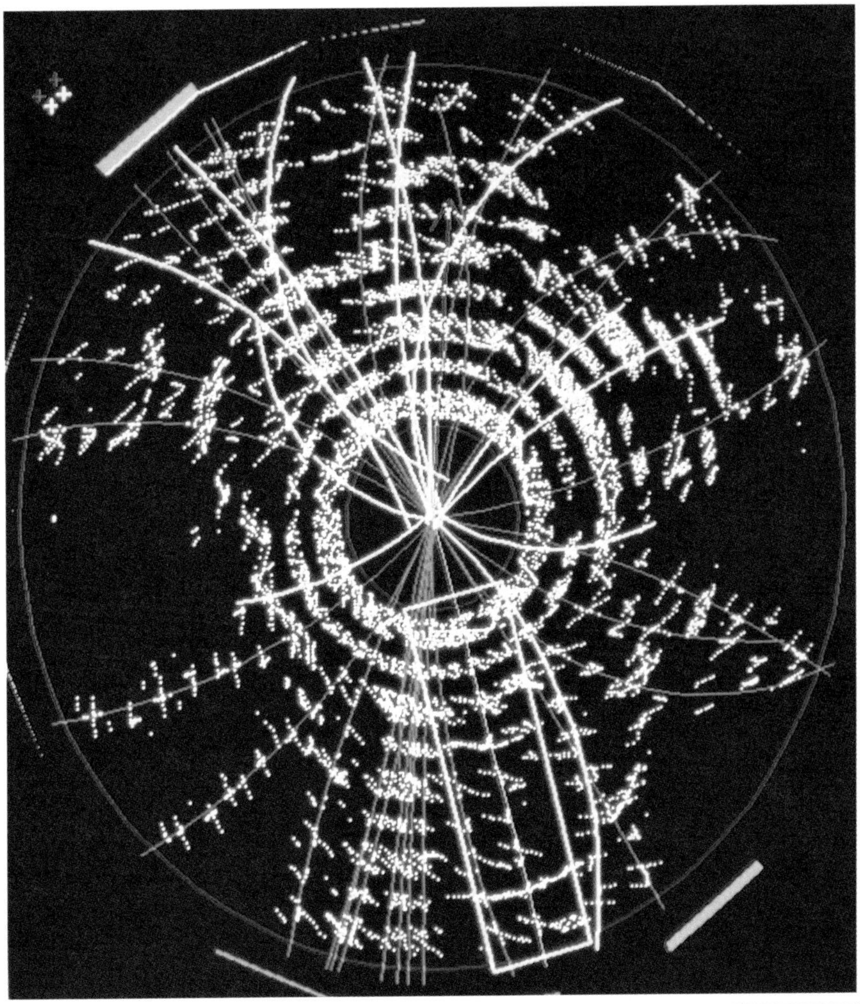

The white dots are the electric wires of the drift chamber (Fig. 30–16). The colored lines are the particle paths.

The top quark (t) has too brief a lifetime $(\approx 10^{-23}\,\mathrm{s})$ to be detected itself, so we look for its possible decay products. Analysis indicates the following interaction and subsequent decays:

$$
\begin{aligned}
p + \bar{p} &\longrightarrow t + \bar{t} \\
\bar{t} &\to W^- + \bar{b}, \quad \bar{b} \to \text{jet}, \quad W^- \to \mu^- + \bar{\nu}_\mu \\
t &\to W^+ + b, \quad b \to \text{jet}, \quad W^+ \to u + \bar{d}, \quad u \to \text{jet}, \quad \bar{d} \to \text{jet}
\end{aligned}
$$

The tracks in the photo include jets (groups of particles moving in roughly the same direction), and a muon $(\mu^-)$ whose track is the pink one enclosed by a yellow rectangle to make it stand out. After reading this Chapter, try to name each symbol above and comment on whether all conservation laws hold.

CHAPTER 32

# Elementary Particles

In the final two Chapters of this book we discuss two of the most exciting areas of contemporary physics: elementary particles in this Chapter, and cosmology and astrophysics in Chapter 33. These are subjects at the forefront of knowledge—elementary particles treats the smallest objects in the universe; cosmology treats the largest (and oldest) aspects of the universe. The reader who wants an understanding of the great beauties of present-day science—and/or wants to be a good citizen—will want to read these Chapters, even if there is not time to cover them in a physics course.

In this penultimate Chapter we discuss *elementary particle* physics, which represents the human endeavor to understand the basic building blocks of all matter. By the mid-1930s, it was recognized that all atoms can be considered to be made up of neutrons, protons, and electrons. The basic constituents of the universe were no longer considered to be atoms but rather the proton, neutron, and electron. Besides these three "elementary particles," several others were also known: the positron (a positive electron), the neutrino, and the $\gamma$ particle (or photon), for a total of six elementary particles.

By the 1950s and 1960s many new types of particles similar to the neutron and proton were discovered, as well as many "midsized" particles called *mesons* whose masses were mostly less than nucleon masses but more than the electron mass. Physicists felt that all of these particles could not be fundamental, and must be made up of even smaller constituents, which were given the name *quarks*.

Today, the basic constituents of matter are considered to be **quarks** (they make up the protons and neutrons of atomic nuclei as well as mesons) and **leptons** (a class that includes electrons, positrons, and neutrinos); in addition there are the "carriers of force" including *gluons* and the photon. The theory that describes our present view is called the **standard model**. How we came to our present understanding of elementary particles is the subject of this Chapter.

One of the exciting recent developments of the last few years is an emerging synthesis between the study of elementary particles and astrophysics (Chapter 33). In fact, very recent observations in astrophysics have led to the conclusion that the greater part of the mass–energy content of the universe is not ordinary matter but two mysterious and invisible forms known as "dark matter" and "dark energy" which cannot be explained by the standard model in its present form.

## 32–1 High-Energy Particles and Accelerators

In the years after World War II, it was found that if the incoming particle in a nuclear reaction has sufficient energy, new types of particles can be produced. The earliest experiments used **cosmic rays**—particles that impinge on the Earth from space. In the laboratory, various types of particle accelerators have been constructed to accelerate protons or electrons, although heavy ions can also be accelerated. These **high-energy accelerators** have been used to probe the nucleus more deeply, to produce and study new particles, and to give us information about the basic forces and constituents of nature. Because the projectile particles are at high energy, this field is sometimes called **high-energy physics**.

### Wavelength and Resolution

Particles accelerated to high energy can probe the interior of nuclei and nucleons that they strike. An important factor is that faster-moving projectiles can reveal more detail. The wavelength of projectile particles is given by de Broglie's wavelength formula (Eq. 27–8),

*de Broglie wavelength*

$$\lambda = \frac{h}{p}, \tag{32–1}$$

showing that the greater the momentum $p$ of the bombarding particle, the shorter its wavelength. As discussed in Chapter 25 on optical instruments, resolution of details in images is limited by the wavelength: the shorter the wavelength, the finer the detail that can be obtained. This is one reason why particle accelerators of higher and higher energy have been built in recent years: to probe ever deeper into the structure of matter, to smaller and smaller size.

**EXAMPLE 32–1 High resolution with electrons.** What is the wavelength, and hence the expected resolution, for a beam of 1.3-GeV electrons?

**APPROACH** Because 1.3 GeV is much larger than the electron rest mass, we must be dealing with relativistic speeds. The momentum of the electrons is found from Eq. 26–10, and the wavelength $\lambda = h/p$.

**SOLUTION** Each electron has KE $= 1.3\,\text{GeV} = 1300\,\text{MeV}$, which is about 2500 times the rest mass energy of the electron $(0.51\,\text{MeV}/c^2)$. Thus we can ignore the term $(m_0c^2)^2$ in Eq. 26–10, $E^2 = p^2c^2 + m_0^2c^4$, and we solve for $p$:

$$p = \sqrt{\frac{E^2 - m_0^2c^4}{c^2}} \approx \sqrt{\frac{E^2}{c^2}} = \frac{E}{c}.$$

Therefore the de Broglie wavelength is

$$\lambda = \frac{h}{p} = \frac{hc}{E},$$

where $E = 1.3\,\text{GeV}$. Hence

$$\lambda = \frac{(6.63 \times 10^{-34}\,\text{J}\cdot\text{s})(3.0 \times 10^8\,\text{m/s})}{(1.3 \times 10^9\,\text{eV})(1.6 \times 10^{-19}\,\text{J/eV})} = 0.96 \times 10^{-15}\,\text{m},$$

or 0.96 fm. This resolution of about 1 fm is on the order of the size of nuclei (see Eq. 30–1).

**NOTE** The maximum possible resolution of this beam of electrons is far greater than for a light beam in a light microscope ($\lambda \approx 500\,\text{nm}$).

**EXERCISE A** What is the wavelength of a proton with KE $= 1.00\,\text{TeV}$?

Another major reason for building high-energy accelerators is that new particles of greater mass can be produced at higher energies, transforming the KE of the colliding particles into massive particles by $E = mc^2$, as we will discuss shortly. Now we look at particle accelerators.

## Cyclotron

The cyclotron was developed in 1930 by E. O. Lawrence (1901–1958; Fig. 32–1) at the University of California, Berkeley. It uses a magnetic field to maintain charged ions—usually protons—in nearly circular paths. Although particle physicists no longer use simple cyclotrons, they are used widely in medicine for treating cancer, and their operating principles are useful for understanding modern accelerators. The protons move in a vacuum inside two D-shaped cavities, as shown in Fig. 32–2. Each time they pass into the gap between the "dees," a voltage accelerates them (the electric force), increasing their speed and increasing the radius of curvature of their path in the magnetic field. After many revolutions, the protons acquire high kinetic energy and reach the outer edge of the cyclotron where they strike a target. The protons speed up only when they are in the gap *between* the dees, and the voltage must be alternating. When protons are moving to the right across the gap in Fig. 32–2, the right dee must be electrically negative and the left one positive. A half-cycle later, the protons are moving to the left, so the left dee must be negative in order to accelerate them.

**FIGURE 32–1** Ernest O. Lawrence, around 1930, holding the first cyclotron (we see the vacuum chamber enclosing it).

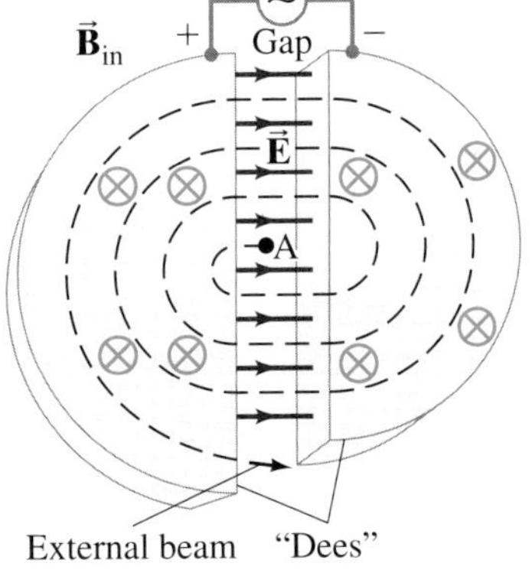


**FIGURE 32–2** Diagram of a cyclotron. The magnetic field, applied by a large electromagnet, points into the page. The protons start at A, the ion source. The field lines shown are for the alternating electric field in the gap at a certain moment.

Cyclotron frequency

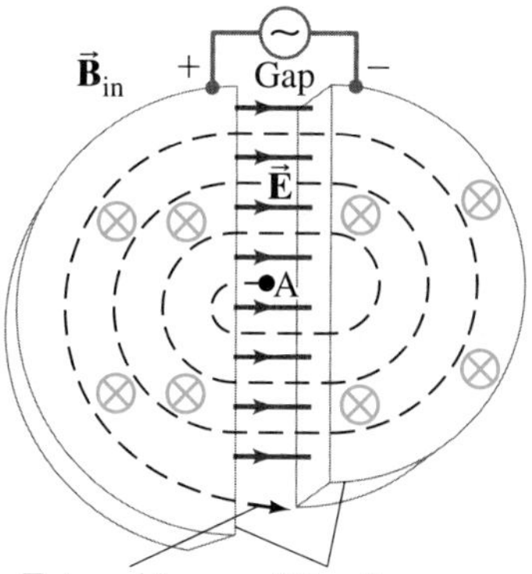


**FIGURE 32–2** (repeated) Diagram of a cyclotron.

The frequency, $f$, of the applied voltage must be equal to that of the circulating protons. When ions of charge $q$ are circulating *within* the hollow dees, the net force $F$ on each is due to the magnetic field $B$, so $F = qvB$, where $v$ is the speed of the ion at a given moment (Eq. 20–4). The magnetic force is perpendicular to both $\vec{\mathbf{v}}$ and $\vec{\mathbf{B}}$ and causes the ions to move in circles; the acceleration inside the dees is thus centripetal and equals $v^2/r$, where $r$ is the radius of the ion's path at a given moment. We use Newton's second law, $F = ma$, and find that

$$F = ma$$
$$qvB = \frac{mv^2}{r}$$

when the protons are within the dees (not the gap), so

$$v = \frac{qBr}{m}.$$

The time required for a complete revolution is the period $T$ and is equal to

$$T = \frac{\text{distance}}{\text{speed}} = \frac{2\pi r}{qBr/m} = \frac{2\pi m}{qB}.$$

Hence the frequency of revolution $f$ is

$$f = \frac{1}{T} = \frac{qB}{2\pi m}. \qquad \textbf{(32–2)}$$

This is known as the **cyclotron frequency**.

**EXAMPLE 32–2** **Cyclotron.** A small cyclotron of maximum radius $R = 0.25\,\text{m}$ accelerates protons in a 1.7-T magnetic field. Calculate (*a*) the frequency needed for the applied alternating voltage, and (*b*) the kinetic energy of protons when they leave the cyclotron.

**APPROACH** The frequency of the protons revolving within the dees (Eq. 32–2) must equal the frequency of the voltage applied across the gap if the protons are going to increase in speed.

**SOLUTION** (*a*) From Eq. 32–2,

$$f = \frac{qB}{2\pi m}$$
$$= \frac{(1.6 \times 10^{-19}\,\text{C})(1.7\,\text{T})}{(6.28)(1.67 \times 10^{-27}\,\text{kg})} = 2.6 \times 10^7\,\text{Hz} = 26\,\text{MHz},$$

which is in the radio-wave region of the EM spectrum (Fig. 22–8).

(*b*) The protons leave the cyclotron at $r = R = 0.25\,\text{m}$. From $qvB = mv^2/r$ (see above), we have $v = qBr/m$, so

$$\text{KE} = \frac{1}{2}mv^2 = \frac{1}{2}m\frac{q^2B^2R^2}{m^2} = \frac{q^2B^2R^2}{2m}$$
$$= \frac{(1.6 \times 10^{-19}\,\text{C})^2(1.7\,\text{T})^2(0.25\,\text{m})^2}{(2)(1.67 \times 10^{-27}\,\text{kg})} = 1.4 \times 10^{-12}\,\text{J} = 8.7\,\text{MeV}.$$

The KE is much less than the rest energy of the proton (938 MeV), so relativity is not needed.

**NOTE** The magnitude of the voltage applied to the dees does not affect the final energy. But the higher this voltage, the fewer the revolutions required to bring the protons to full energy.

An important aspect of the cyclotron is that the frequency of the applied voltage, as given by Eq. 32–2, does not depend on the radius $r$ of the particle's path. Thus the frequency does not have to be changed as the protons or ions start from the source and are accelerated to paths of larger and larger radii. But this is only true at nonrelativistic energies. At higher speeds, the momentum (Eq. 26–4) is $p = m_0 v/\sqrt{1 - v^2/c^2}$, so $m$ in Eq. 32–2 has to be replaced by $\gamma m_0$ and the cyclotron frequency $f$ (Eq. 32–2) depends on speed $v$. To keep the particles in synch, machines called **synchrocyclotrons** reduce the frequency in time, in parallel with the mass increase, as a packet of charged particles increases in speed and mass at larger orbits.

## Synchrotron

*Synchrotron*

Another way to accelerate relativistic particles is to increase the magnetic field $B$ in time so as to keep $f$ (Eq. 32–2) constant as the particles speed up. Such devices are called **synchrotrons**, and today they can be enormous. At the European Center for Nuclear Research (CERN) in Geneva, Switzerland, the new (2007) Large Hadron Collider (LHC) will be 4.3 km in radius and accelerate protons to 7 TeV. The *Tevatron* accelerator at Fermilab (the Fermi National Accelerator Laboratory) at Batavia, Illinois, has a radius of 1.0 km. The Tevatron uses superconducting magnets to accelerate protons to about 1000 GeV = 1 TeV (hence its name); 1 TeV = $10^{12}$ eV. These large synchrotrons use a narrow ring of magnets (see Fig. 32–3) with each magnet placed at the same radius from the center of the circle. The magnets are interrupted by gaps where high voltage accelerates the particles; another way to describe the acceleration is to say the particles "surf" on a traveling electromagnetic wave within radiofrequency (RF) cavities.

**FIGURE 32–3** (a) Aerial view of Fermilab at Batavia, Illinois; the main accelerator is a circular ring 1.0 km in radius. (b) The interior of the tunnel of the main accelerator at Fermilab. The upper (rectangular-shaped) ring of magnets is for the older 500-GeV accelerator. Below it is the ring of superconducting magnets for the 1-TeV Tevatron.

(a)

(b)

Once charged particles are injected, they must move in a circle of constant radius. This is accomplished by giving them considerable energy initially in a smaller accelerator (the injector), and then slowly increasing the magnetic field as they speed up in the large synchrotron.

One problem of any accelerator is that accelerating electric charges radiate electromagnetic energy (see Chapter 22). Since ions or electrons are accelerated in an accelerator, we can expect considerable energy to be lost by radiation. The effect increases with energy and is especially important in circular machines where centripetal acceleration is present, such as synchrotrons, and hence is called **synchrotron radiation**. Synchrotron radiation can be useful, however. Intense beams of photons are sometimes needed, and they are usually obtained from an electron synchrotron.

*Synchrotron radiation*

## Linear Accelerators

Linac

In a **linear accelerator** (linac), electrons or ions are accelerated along a straight-line path, Fig. 32–4a, passing through a series of tubular conductors. Voltage applied to the tubes is alternating so that when electrons (say) reach a gap, the tube in front of them is positive and the one they just left is negative. At low speeds, the particles cover less distance in the same amount of time, so the tubes are shorter at first. Electrons, with their small mass, get close to the speed of light quickly, $v \approx c$, and the tubes are nearly equal in length. Linear accelerators are particularly important for accelerating electrons because of the absence of synchrotron radiation. The largest electron linear accelerator is at Stanford (Stanford Linear Accelerator Center, or SLAC), Fig. 32–4b. It is about 3 km (2 mi) long and can accelerate electrons to 50 GeV. Many hospitals have 10-MeV electron linacs that strike a metal foil to produce $\gamma$ ray photons to irradiate tumors.

**FIGURE 32–4** (a) Diagram of a simple linear accelerator. (b) Photo of the Stanford Linear Accelerator (SLAC) in California.

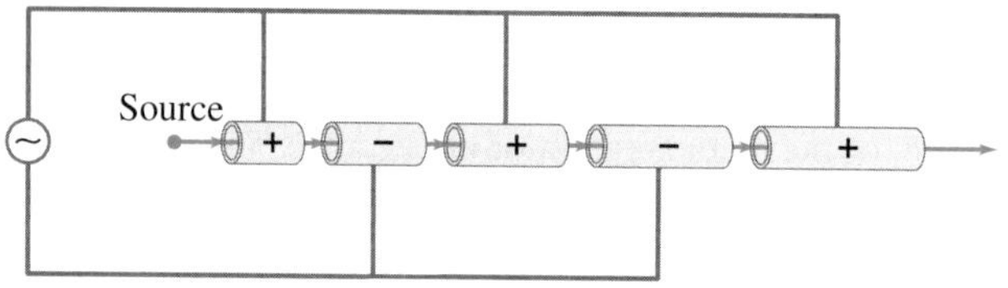


(a)

(b)

## Colliding Beams

Colliders

High-energy physics experiments can be done by allowing a beam of particles from an accelerator to strike a stationary target. But to obtain the maximum possible collision energy from a given accelerator, two beams of particles are accelerated to very high energy and are steered so that they collide head-on. One way to accomplish such **colliding beams** with a single accelerator is through the use of **storage rings**, in which oppositely revolving beams can be repeatedly brought into collision with one another at particular points. For example, in the experiments that provided strong evidence for the top quark (see Chapter opening photo and Section 32–9), the Fermilab Tevatron accelerated protons and antiprotons each to 900 GeV, so that the combined energy of head-on collisions was 1.8 TeV.

The largest collider will soon be the Large Hadron Collider (LHC) at CERN, with a circumference of 26.7 km (Fig. 32–5), scheduled to be completed about 2007. The two colliding beams will each carry 7-TeV protons for a total interaction energy of 14 TeV.

**FIGURE 32–5** The large circle represents the position of the tunnel, about 100 m below the ground at CERN (near Geneva) on the French-Swiss border, which will house the LHC. The smaller circle shows the position of the Super Proton Synchrotron that will be used for accelerating protons prior to injection into the LHC.

**EXAMPLE 32–3** **Speed of a 1.0-TeV proton.** What is the speed of a 1.0-TeV proton produced at Fermilab?

**APPROACH** KE $= 1.0\,\text{TeV} = 1.0 \times 10^{12}\,\text{eV}$ is much greater than the rest mass of the proton, $0.938 \times 10^{9}\,\text{eV}$, so relativistic calculations must be used. In particular, we use Eq. 26–6:

$$\text{KE} = (\gamma - 1)m_0c^2 = \frac{m_0c^2}{\sqrt{1 - v^2/c^2}} - m_0c^2.$$

**SOLUTION** Compared to the KE of $1.0 \times 10^{12}\,\text{eV}$, the rest energy ($\approx 10^{-3}\,\text{TeV}$) can be neglected, so we write

$$\text{KE} = \frac{m_0c^2}{\sqrt{1 - v^2/c^2}}.$$

Then

$$1 - \frac{v^2}{c^2} = \left(\frac{m_0c^2}{\text{KE}}\right)^2$$

or

$$\frac{v}{c} = \sqrt{1 - \left(\frac{m_0c^2}{\text{KE}}\right)^2} = \sqrt{1 - \left(\frac{938 \times 10^6\,\text{eV}}{1.0 \times 10^{12}\,\text{eV}}\right)^2}$$

$$v = 0.9999996c.$$

The proton is traveling at a speed extremely close to $c$, the speed of light.

## 32–2 Beginnings of Elementary Particle Physics—Particle Exchange

The accepted model for elementary particles today views *quarks* and *leptons* as the basic constituents of ordinary matter. To understand our present-day view we need to begin with the ideas leading up to its formulation.†

Elementary particle physics might be said to have begun in 1935 when the Japanese physicist Hideki Yukawa (1907–1981) predicted the existence of a new particle that would in some way mediate the strong nuclear force. To understand Yukawa's idea, we first consider the electromagnetic force. When we first discussed electricity, we saw that the electric force acts over a distance, without contact. To better perceive how a force can act over a distance, we used the idea of a **field**. The force that one charged particle exerts on a second can be said to be due to the electric field set up by the first. Similarly, the magnetic field can be said to carry the magnetic force. Later (Chapter 22), we saw that electromagnetic (EM) fields can travel through space as waves. Finally, in Chapter 27, we saw that electromagnetic radiation (light) can be considered as either a wave or as a collection of particles called *photons*. Because of this wave–particle duality, it is possible to imagine that the electromagnetic force between charged particles is due to

(1) the EM field set up by one charged particle and felt by the other, or
(2) an exchange of photons ($\gamma$ particles) between them.

It is (2) that we want to concentrate on here, and a crude analogy for how an exchange of particles could give rise to a force is suggested in Fig. 32–6. In part (a), two children start throwing heavy pillows at each other; each throw and each catch results in the child being pushed backward by the impulse. This is the equivalent of a repulsive force. On the other hand, if the two children exchange pillows by grabbing them out of the other person's hand, they will be pulled toward each other, as when an attractive force acts.

**FIGURE 32–6** Forces equivalent to particle exchange. (a) Repulsive force (children throwing pillows at each other). (b) Attractive force (children grabbing pillows from each other's hands).

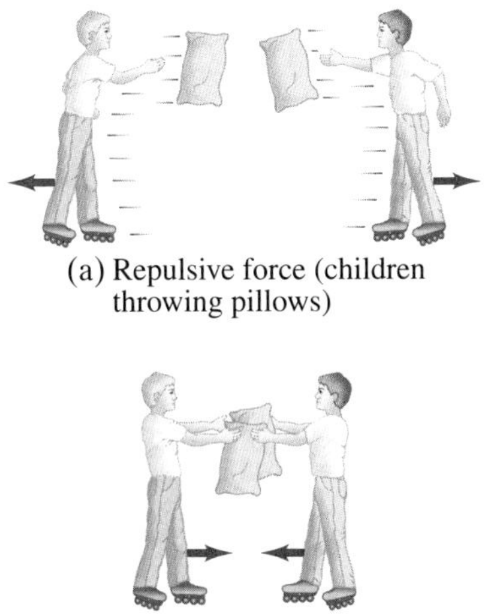

(a) Repulsive force (children throwing pillows)

(b) Attractive force (children grabbing pillows from each other's hands)

†Just telling you how it is today would not be a scientific discussion; nor would it give understanding—see footnote on page 769.

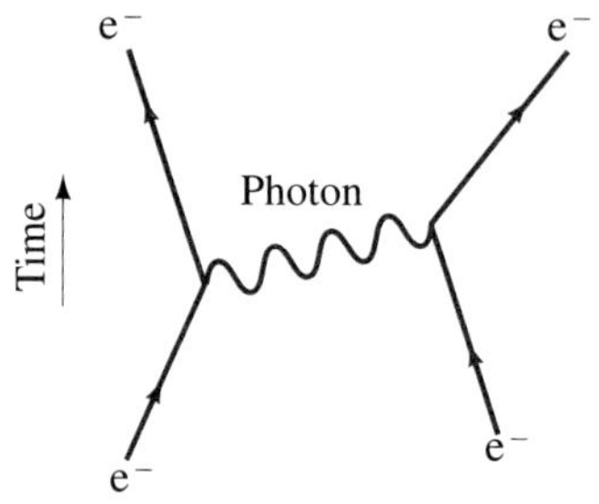


**FIGURE 32–7** Feynman diagram showing a photon acting as the carrier of the electromagnetic force between two electrons. This is sort of an $x$ vs. $t$ graph, with $t$ increasing upward. Starting at the bottom, two electrons approach each other (the distance between them decreases in time). As they get close, momentum and energy get transferred from one to the other, carried by a photon (or, perhaps, by more than one), and the two electrons bounce apart.

For the electromagnetic force, it is photons that are exchanged between two charged particles that give rise to the force between them. A simple diagram describing this photon exchange is shown in Fig. 32–7. Such a diagram, called a **Feynman diagram** after its inventor, the American physicist Richard Feynman (1918–1988), is based on the theory of **quantum electrodynamics** (QED).

Figure 32–7 represents the simplest case in QED, in which a single photon is exchanged. One of the charged particles emits the photon and recoils somewhat as a result; and the second particle absorbs the photon. In any collision or *interaction*, energy and momentum are transferred from one charged particle to the other, carried by the photon. The photon is absorbed by the second particle very shortly after it is emitted by the first and is not observable; hence it is referred to as a *virtual* photon, in contrast to one that is free and can be detected by instruments. The photon is said to *mediate*, or *carry*, the electromagnetic force.

*Particles that mediate or "carry" forces*

By analogy with photon exchange that mediates the electromagnetic force, Yukawa argued in this early theory that there ought to be a particle that mediates the strong nuclear force—the force that holds nucleons together in the nucleus. Yukawa called this predicted particle a **meson** (meaning "medium mass"). Figure 32–8 is a Feynman diagram showing meson exchange: a meson carrying the strong force between a neutron and a proton.

*Mass estimate of exchange particle*

**FIGURE 32–8** Meson exchange when a proton and neutron interact via the strong nuclear force.

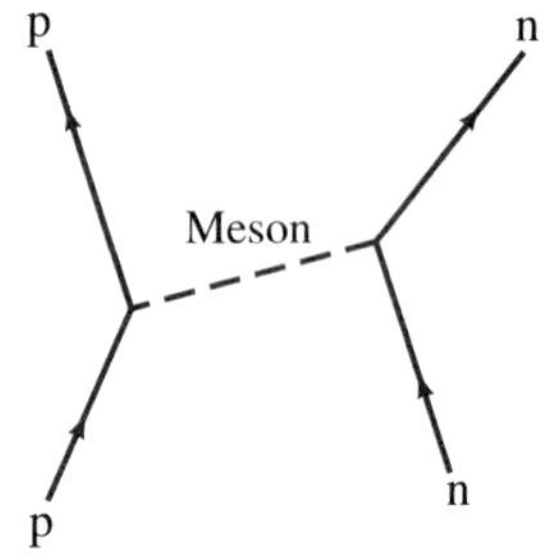


We can make a rough estimate of the mass of the meson as follows. Suppose the proton on the left in Fig. 32–8 is at rest. For it to emit a meson would require energy (to make the meson's mass) which, coming from nowhere, would violate conservation of energy. But the uncertainty principle allows nonconservation of energy by an amount $\Delta E$ if it occurs only for a time $\Delta t$ given by $(\Delta E)(\Delta t) \approx h/2\pi$. We set $\Delta E$ equal to the energy needed to create the mass $m$ of the meson: $\Delta E = mc^2$. Conservation of energy is violated only as long as the meson exists, which is the time $\Delta t$ required for the meson to pass from one nucleon to the other, where it is absorbed and disappears. If we assume the meson travels at relativistic speed, close to the speed of light $c$, then $\Delta t$ need be at most about $\Delta t = d/c$, where $d$ is the maximum distance that can separate the interacting nucleons. Thus we can write

$$\Delta E\, \Delta t \approx \frac{h}{2\pi}$$

$$mc^2\left(\frac{d}{c}\right) \approx \frac{h}{2\pi}$$

or

*Mass of exchange particle*

$$mc^2 \approx \frac{hc}{2\pi d}. \tag{32–3}$$

The range of the strong nuclear force (the maximum distance away it can be felt), is small—not much more than the size of a nucleon or small nucleus (see Eq. 30–1)—so let us take $d \approx 1.5 \times 10^{-15}$ m. Then from Eq. 32–3,

$$mc^2 \approx \frac{hc}{2\pi d} = \frac{(6.6 \times 10^{-34}\,\mathrm{J\cdot s})(3.0 \times 10^8\,\mathrm{m/s})}{(6.28)(1.5 \times 10^{-15}\,\mathrm{m})} \approx 2.1 \times 10^{-11}\,\mathrm{J} = 130\,\mathrm{MeV}.$$

The mass of the predicted meson, roughly $130\,\mathrm{MeV}/c^2$, is about 250 times the electron mass of $0.51\,\mathrm{MeV}/c^2$.†

†Note that since the electromagnetic force has infinite range, Eq. 32–3 with $d = \infty$ tells us that the exchanged particle for the electromagnetic force, the photon, will have zero rest mass, which it does.

The particle predicted by Yukawa was discovered in cosmic rays by C. F. Powell and G. Occhialini in 1947, and is called the "$\pi$" or pi meson, or simply the **pion**. It comes in three charge states: $+$, $-$, or 0. The $\pi^+$ and $\pi^-$ have mass of 139.6 MeV/$c^2$ and the $\pi^0$ a mass of 135.0 MeV/$c^2$, all close to Yukawa's prediction. All three interact strongly with matter. Reactions observed in the laboratory, using a particle accelerator, include

*Pion*

$$\begin{aligned} p + p &\rightarrow p + p + \pi^0, \\ p + p &\rightarrow p + n + \pi^+. \end{aligned} \qquad \textbf{(32–4)}$$

The incident proton from the accelerator must have sufficient energy to produce the additional mass of the free pion.

Yukawa's theory of pion exchange as carrier of the strong force is now out of date, and has been replaced by *quantum chromodynamics* in which the basic entities are *quarks*, and the basic carriers of the strong force are *gluons*, as we shall discuss shortly. But the basic idea of the earlier theory, that forces can be understood as the exchange of particles, remains valid.

*Forces carried by particles even in standard model*

There are four known types of force—or interaction—in nature. The electromagnetic force is carried by the photon, the strong nuclear force by gluons. What about the other two: the weak nuclear force and gravity? These too are believed to be mediated by particles. The particles that transmit the weak force are referred to as the $W^+$, $W^-$, and $Z^0$, and were detected in 1983 (Fig. 32–9).

**FIGURE 32–9** (a) Computer reconstruction of a Z-particle decay into an electron and a positron ($Z^0 \rightarrow e^+ + e^-$) whose tracks are shown in white, which took place in the UA1 detector at CERN. (b) Photo of the UA1 detector at CERN as it was being built.

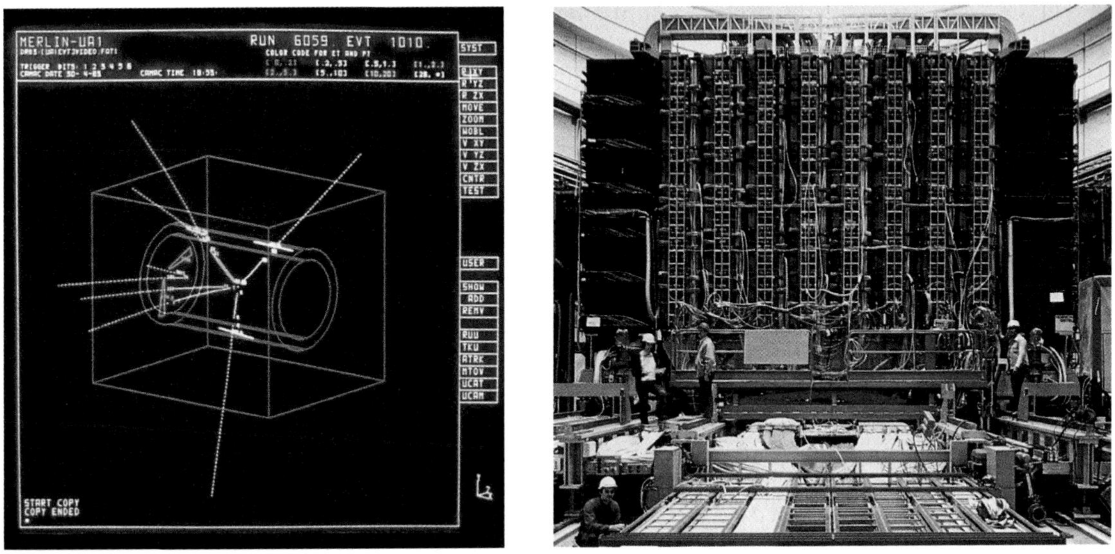


(a) (b)

The quantum (or carrier) of the gravitational force is called the **graviton**, and if it exists it has not yet been observed. A comparison of the four forces is given in Table 32–1, where they are listed according to their (approximate) relative strengths. Notice that although gravity may be the most obvious force in daily life (because of the huge mass of the Earth), on a nuclear scale it is the weakest of the four forces, and its effect at the particle level can nearly always be ignored.

*Graviton*

**TABLE 32–1 The Four Forces in Nature**

| Type | Relative Strength (approx., for 2 protons in nucleus) | Field Particle |
|---|---|---|
| Strong nuclear | 1 | Gluons† (mesons) |
| Electromagnetic | $10^{-2}$ | Photon |
| Weak nuclear | $10^{-6}$ | $W^{\pm}$ and $Z^0$ |
| Gravitational | $10^{-38}$ | Graviton (?) |

† Until the 1970s, thought to be mesons, but now gluons (see Section 32–10).

## 32–3 Particles and Antiparticles

The positron, as we saw in Chapters 27 and 30, is basically a positive electron. That is, many of its properties are the same as for the electron, such as mass, but it has the opposite charge. Other quantum numbers that we discuss shortly are also reversed for antiparticles. The positron is said to be the **antiparticle** to the electron. After the positron was discovered in 1932, it was predicted that other particles also ought to have antiparticles. In 1955 the antiparticle to the proton was found, the **antiproton** ($\overline{\mathrm{p}}$), which carries a negative charge; see Fig. 32–10. (The bar over the p is used to indicate antiparticle.) Soon after, the antineutron ($\overline{\mathrm{n}}$) was found. All particles have antiparticles. But a few, like the photon and the $\pi^0$, do not have distinct antiparticles—we say that they are their own antiparticles.†

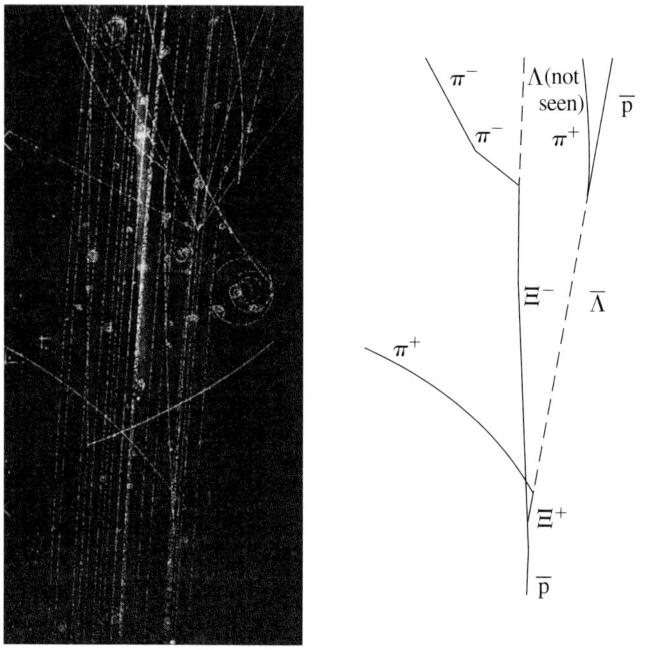


**FIGURE 32–10** Liquid-hydrogen bubble-chamber photograph of an antiproton ($\overline{\mathrm{p}}$) colliding with a proton at rest, producing a Xi–anti-Xi pair ($\overline{\mathrm{p}} + \mathrm{p} \rightarrow \Xi^- + \Xi^+$) that subsequently decay into other particles. The drawing indicates the assignment of particles to each track, which is based on how or if that particle decays, and on mass values estimated from measurement of momentum (curvature of track in magnetic field) and energy (thickness of track, for example). Neutral particle paths are shown by dashed lines since neutral particles produce no bubbles and hence no tracks.

Antiparticles are produced in nuclear reactions when there is sufficient energy available, and they do not live very long in the presence of matter. For example, a positron is stable when by itself; but if it encounters an electron, the two annihilate each other. The energy of their vanished mass, plus any kinetic energy they possessed, is converted into the energy of $\gamma$ rays or of other particles. Annihilation also occurs for all other particle–antiparticle pairs.

## 32–4 Particle Interactions and Conservation Laws

One of the important uses of high-energy accelerators is to study the interactions of elementary particles with each other. As a means of ordering this subnuclear world, the conservation laws are indispensable. The laws of conservation of energy, of momentum, of angular momentum, and of electric charge are found to hold precisely in all particle interactions.

A study of particle interactions has revealed a number of new conservation laws which (just like the old ones) are ordering principles: they help to explain why some reactions occur and others do not. For example, the following reaction has never been found to occur:

$$\mathrm{p} + \mathrm{n} \not\rightarrow \mathrm{p} + \mathrm{p} + \overline{\mathrm{p}}$$

even though charge, energy, and so on, are conserved ($\overline{\mathrm{p}}$ means an antiproton and $\not\rightarrow$ means the reaction does not occur). To understand why such a reaction

†Note, for example, that the opposite charge to $Q = 0$ is still zero.

does not occur, physicists hypothesized a new conservation law, the conservation of **baryon number**. (Baryon number is a generalization of nucleon number, which we saw earlier is conserved in nuclear reactions and decays.) All nucleons are defined to have baryon number $B = +1$, and all antinucleons (antiprotons, antineutrons) have $B = -1$. All other types of particles, such as photons, mesons, and electrons and other leptons, have $B = 0$. The reaction shown at the start of this paragraph does not conserve baryon number since the left side has $B = (+1) + (+1) = +2$, and the right has $B = (+1) + (+1) + (-1) = +1$. On the other hand, the following reaction does conserve $B$ and *does* occur if the incoming proton has sufficient energy:

*Baryon number*

$$\begin{aligned} \mathrm{p} + \mathrm{p} &\rightarrow \mathrm{p} + \mathrm{p} + \overline{\mathrm{p}} + \mathrm{p}, \\ B = +1 + 1 &= +1 + 1 - 1 + 1. \end{aligned}$$

As indicated, $B = +2$ on both sides of this equation. From these and other reactions, the **conservation of baryon number** has been established as a basic principle of physics.

*Conservation of baryon number*

Also useful are the conservation laws for the three **lepton numbers**, associated with weak interactions including decays. In ordinary $\beta$ decay, an electron or positron is emitted along with a neutrino or antineutrino. In a similar type of decay, a particle known as a "$\mu$" or mu meson, or **muon**, can be emitted instead of an electron. The muon (discovered in 1937) seems to be much like an electron, except its mass is 207 times larger $(106\,\mathrm{MeV}/c^2)$. The neutrino $(\nu_\mathrm{e})$ that accompanies an emitted electron is found to be different from the neutrino $(\nu_\mu)$ that accompanies an emitted muon. Each of these neutrinos has an antiparticle: $\overline{\nu}_\mathrm{e}$ and $\overline{\nu}_\mu$. In ordinary $\beta$ decay we have, for example,

*Lepton numbers*

**CAUTION**
*The different types of neutrinos are not identical*

$$\mathrm{n} \rightarrow \mathrm{p} + \mathrm{e}^- + \overline{\nu}_\mathrm{e}$$

but not $\mathrm{n} \not\rightarrow \mathrm{p} + \mathrm{e}^- + \overline{\nu}_\mu$. To explain why these do not occur, the concept of **electron lepton number**, $L_\mathrm{e}$, was invented. If the electron $(\mathrm{e}^-)$ and the electron neutrino $(\nu_\mathrm{e})$ are assigned $L_\mathrm{e} = +1$, and $\mathrm{e}^+$ and $\overline{\nu}_\mathrm{e}$ are assigned $L_\mathrm{e} = -1$, whereas all other particles have $L_\mathrm{e} = 0$, then all observed decays conserve $L_\mathrm{e}$. For example, in $\mathrm{n} \rightarrow \mathrm{p} + \mathrm{e}^- + \overline{\nu}_\mathrm{e}$, $L_\mathrm{e} = 0$ initially, and $L_\mathrm{e} = 0 + (+1) + (-1) = 0$ after the decay. Decays that do not conserve $L_\mathrm{e}$, even though they would obey the other conservation laws, are not observed to occur.

*Lepton numbers conservation*

In a decay involving muons, such as

$$\pi^+ \rightarrow \mu^+ + \nu_\mu,$$

a second quantum number, **muon lepton number** $(L_\mu)$, is conserved. The $\mu^-$ and $\nu_\mu$ are assigned $L_\mu = +1$, and $\mu^+$ and $\overline{\nu}_\mu$ have $L_\mu = -1$, whereas other particles have $L_\mu = 0$. $L_\mu$ too is conserved in interactions and decays. Similar assignments can be made for the **tau lepton number**, $L_\tau$, associated with the $\tau$ lepton (discovered in 1976 with mass more than 3000 times the electron mass) and its neutrino, $\nu_\tau$.

Keep in mind that antiparticles have not only opposite electric charge from their particles, but also opposite $B$, $L_\mathrm{e}$, $L_\mu$, and $L_\tau$. For example, a neutron has $B = +1$, an antineutron has $B = -1$ (and all the $L$'s are zero).

*Antiparticles have opposite Q, B, L*

**CONCEPTUAL EXAMPLE 32–4 Lepton number in muon decay.** Which of the following decay schemes is possible for muon decay: (*a*) $\mu^- \rightarrow \mathrm{e}^- + \overline{\nu}_\mathrm{e}$; (*b*) $\mu^- \rightarrow \mathrm{e}^- + \overline{\nu}_\mathrm{e} + \nu_\mu$; (*c*) $\mu^- \rightarrow \mathrm{e}^- + \nu_\mathrm{e}$? All of these particles have $L_\tau = 0$.

**RESPONSE** A $\mu^-$ has $L_\mu = +1$ and $L_\mathrm{e} = 0$. This is the initial state, and the final state (after decay) must also have $L_\mu = +1$, $L_\mathrm{e} = 0$. In (*a*), the final state has $L_\mu = 0 + 0 = 0$, and $L_\mathrm{e} = +1 - 1 = 0$; $L_\mu$ would not be conserved and indeed this decay is not observed to occur. The final state of (*b*) has $L_\mu = 0 + 0 + 1 = +1$ and $L_\mathrm{e} = +1 - 1 + 0 = 0$, so both $L_\mu$ and $L_\mathrm{e}$ are conserved. This is in fact the most common decay mode of the $\mu^-$. Finally, (*c*) does not occur because $L_\mathrm{e}$ (= +2 in the final state) is not conserved, nor is $L_\mu$.

## Additional Example

**EXAMPLE 32–5** **Energy and momentum are conserved.** In addition to the "number" conservation laws which help explain the decay schemes of particles, we can also apply the laws of conservation of energy and momentum. The decay of a $\Sigma^+$ particle at rest with a rest mass of 1189 MeV/$c^2$ (Table 32–2 on the next page) commonly yields a proton (rest mass of 938 MeV/$c^2$) and a neutral pion, $\pi^0$ (rest mass of 135 MeV/$c^2$):

$$\Sigma^+ \rightarrow \mathrm{p} + \pi^0.$$

What are the kinetic energies of the decay products, assuming the $\Sigma^+$ parent particle was at rest?

**APPROACH** We find the energy release from the change in mass $(E = mc^2)$ as we did for nuclear processes (Eq. 30–2 or 31–1), and apply conservation of energy and momentum.

**SOLUTION** The energy released, or $Q$-value, is the change in mass times $c^2$:

$$Q = \left[m_{\Sigma^+} - (m_{\mathrm{p}} + m_{\pi^0})\right]c^2 = \left[1189 - (938 + 135)\right]\,\mathrm{MeV} = 116\,\mathrm{MeV}.$$

This energy $Q$ becomes the kinetic energy of the resulting decay particles, p and $\pi^0$:

$$Q = \mathrm{KE}_{\mathrm{p}} + \mathrm{KE}_{\pi^0}$$

with each particle's kinetic energy related to its momentum by (Eqs. 26–7 and 26–10):

$$\mathrm{KE}_{\mathrm{p}} = E_{\mathrm{p}} - m_{\mathrm{p}}c^2 = \sqrt{(p_{\mathrm{p}}c)^2 + (m_{\mathrm{p}}c^2)^2} - m_{\mathrm{p}}c^2,$$

and similarly for the pion. From momentum conservation, the proton and pion have the same magnitude of momentum since the original particle was at rest: $p_{\mathrm{p}} = p_{\pi^0} = p$. Then

$$Q = 116\,\mathrm{MeV} = \left[\sqrt{(pc)^2 + (938\,\mathrm{MeV})^2} - 938\,\mathrm{MeV}\right] + \left[\sqrt{(pc)^2 + (135\,\mathrm{MeV})^2} - 135\,\mathrm{MeV}\right].$$

We solved this for $pc$, which gives $pc = 189$ MeV. Substituting into the expression for the kinetic energy, first for the proton, then for the pion we obtain $\mathrm{KE}_{\mathrm{p}} = 19$ MeV and $\mathrm{KE}_{\pi^0} = 97$ MeV.

## 32–5 Neutrinos—Recent Results

The study of neutrinos is a "hot" subject today. Experiments are being carried out in deep underground laboratories, sometimes in deep mine shafts. The thick layer of earth above is meant to filter out all other "background" particles, leaving mainly the very weakly interacting neutrinos to arrive at the detectors.

Two very important results have come to the fore in our young twenty-first century. One result is that the three neutrinos, $\nu_e$, $\nu_\mu$, $\nu_\tau$, can occasionally change into one another in certain circumstances, a phenomenon called **neutrino flavor oscillation** (each of the three types being called, whimsically, a different "flavor"). This result suggests that the lepton numbers $L_e$, $L_\mu$, and $L_\tau$ are not perfectly conserved. But the sum, $L_e + L_\mu + L_\tau$, is believed to be always conserved.

*Neutrino oscillations*

The second exceptional result has long been speculated on: are neutrinos massless as originally thought, or do they have a nonzero rest mass? Rough upper limits on the masses have been made. But in 2002, astrophysical experiments showed that the sum of all three neutrino masses must be less than about 1 eV/$c^2$. But can the masses be zero? Not if there are the flavor oscillations discussed above. It seems likely that at least one neutrino type has rest mass of at least 0.05 eV, a remarkable result.

## 32–6 Particle Classification

In the decades following the discovery of the $\pi$ meson in the late 1940s, hundreds of other subnuclear particles were discovered. One way of arranging the particles in categories is according to their interactions, since not all particles interact by means of all four of the forces known in nature (though all interact via gravity). Table 32–2 lists some of the more common particles classified in this way along with many of their properties. The particles listed are those that are stable, and many that are unstable. At the top of the Table are the **gauge bosons** (so-named after the theory that describes them, "gauge theory"), which include the gluons, the photon, and the W and Z particles; these are the particles that mediate the strong, electromagnetic, and weak interactions, respectively.

*Gauge bosons*

Next in Table 32–2 are the **leptons**, which are particles that do not interact via the strong force but do interact via the weak nuclear force. Leptons that carry electric charge also interact via the electromagnetic force. The leptons include the electron, the muon, and the tau, and three types of neutrino: the electron neutrino ($\nu_e$), the muon neutrino ($\nu_\mu$), and the tau neutrino ($\nu_\tau$). Each has an antiparticle.

*Leptons*

The third category of particle in Table 32–2 is the **hadron**. Hadrons are those particles that interact via the strong nuclear force. Hence they are said to be **strongly interacting particles**. They also interact via the other forces, but the strong force predominates at short distances. The hadrons include the proton, neutron, pion, and a large number of other particles. They are divided into two subgroups: **baryons**, which are those particles that have baryon number +1 (or −1 in the case of their antiparticles); and **mesons**, which have baryon number = 0.

*Hadrons*

*Baryons*

*Mesons*

**TABLE 32–2 Particles (stable under strong decay)†**

| Category | Forces involved | Particle name | Symbol | Anti-particle | Spin | Rest Mass ($\mathrm{MeV}/c^2$) | $B$ | $L_e$ | $L_\mu$ | $L_\tau$ | $S$ | Lifetime (s) | Principal Decay Modes |
|---|---|---|---|---|---|---|---|---|---|---|---|---|---|
| | | | | | | | [antiparticles have opposite sign] | | | | | | |
| Gauge bosons (force carriers) | g | Gluons | g | Self | 1 | 0 | 0 | 0 | 0 | 0 | 0 | Stable | |
| | em | Photon | $\gamma$ | Self | 1 | 0 | 0 | 0 | 0 | 0 | 0 | Stable | |
| | w, em | W | $W^+$ | $W^-$ | 1 | $80.41 \times 10^3$ | 0 | 0 | 0 | 0 | 0 | $3 \times 10^{-25}$ | $e\nu_e$, $\mu\nu_\mu$, $\tau\nu_\tau$, hadrons |
| | w | Z | $Z^0$ | Self | 1 | $91.19 \times 10^3$ | 0 | 0 | 0 | 0 | 0 | $3 \times 10^{-25}$ | $e^+e^-$, $\mu^+\mu^-$, $\tau^+\tau^-$, hadrons |
| Leptons | w, em‡ | Electron | $e^-$ | $e^+$ | $\frac{1}{2}$ | 0.511 | 0 | +1 | 0 | 0 | 0 | Stable | |
| | | Neutrino (e) | $\nu_e$ | $\bar{\nu}_e$ | $\frac{1}{2}$ | 0 (<0.6 eV)‡ | 0 | +1 | 0 | 0 | 0 | Stable | |
| | | Muon | $\mu^-$ | $\mu^+$ | $\frac{1}{2}$ | 105.7 | 0 | 0 | +1 | 0 | 0 | $2.20 \times 10^{-6}$ | $e^-\bar{\nu}_e\nu_\mu$ |
| | | Neutrino ($\mu$) | $\nu_\mu$ | $\bar{\nu}_\mu$ | $\frac{1}{2}$ | 0 (<0.6 eV)‡ | 0 | 0 | +1 | 0 | 0 | Stable | |
| | | Tau | $\tau^-$ | $\tau^+$ | $\frac{1}{2}$ | 1777 | 0 | 0 | 0 | +1 | 0 | $2.91 \times 10^{-13}$ | $\mu^-\bar{\nu}_\mu\nu_\tau$, $e^-\bar{\nu}_e\nu_\tau$, hadrons + $\nu_\tau$ |
| | | Neutrino ($\tau$) | $\nu_\tau$ | $\bar{\nu}_\tau$ | $\frac{1}{2}$ | 0 (<0.6 eV)‡ | 0 | 0 | 0 | +1 | 0 | Stable | |
| Hadrons (selected) | | | | | | | | | | | | | |
| Mesons | s, em, w | Pion | $\pi^+$ | $\pi^-$ | 0 | 139.6 | 0 | 0 | 0 | 0 | 0 | $2.60 \times 10^{-8}$ | $\mu^+\nu_\mu$ |
| | | | $\pi^0$ | Self | 0 | 135.0 | 0 | 0 | 0 | 0 | 0 | $0.84 \times 10^{-16}$ | $2\gamma$ |
| | | Kaon | $K^+$ | $K^-$ | 0 | 493.7 | 0 | 0 | 0 | 0 | +1 | $1.24 \times 10^{-8}$ | $\mu^+\nu_\mu$, $\pi^+\pi^0$ |
| | | | $K^0_S$ | $\bar{K}^0_S$ | 0 | 497.7 | 0 | 0 | 0 | 0 | +1 | $0.89 \times 10^{-10}$ | $\pi^+\pi^-$, $2\pi^0$ |
| | | | $K^0_L$ | $\bar{K}^0_L$ | 0 | 497.7 | 0 | 0 | 0 | 0 | +1 | $5.17 \times 10^{-8}$ | $\pi^\pm e^\mp \overset{(-)}{\nu}_e$, $\pi^\pm\mu^\mp\overset{(-)}{\nu}_\mu$, $3\pi$ |
| | | Eta and others | $\eta^0$ | Self | 0 | 547.3 | 0 | 0 | 0 | 0 | 0 | $5 \times 10^{-19}$ | $2\gamma$, $3\pi^0$, $\pi^+\pi^-\pi^0$ |
| Baryons | s, em, w | Proton | p | $\bar{p}$ | $\frac{1}{2}$ | 938.3 | +1 | 0 | 0 | 0 | 0 | Stable | |
| | | Neutron | n | $\bar{n}$ | $\frac{1}{2}$ | 939.6 | +1 | 0 | 0 | 0 | 0 | 887 | $pe^-\bar{\nu}_e$ |
| | | Lambda | $\Lambda^0$ | $\bar{\Lambda}^0$ | $\frac{1}{2}$ | 1115.7 | +1 | 0 | 0 | 0 | −1 | $2.63 \times 10^{-10}$ | $p\pi^-$, $n\pi^0$ |
| | | Sigma | $\Sigma^+$ | $\bar{\Sigma}^-$ | $\frac{1}{2}$ | 1189.4 | +1 | 0 | 0 | 0 | −1 | $0.80 \times 10^{-10}$ | $p\pi^0$, $n\pi^+$ |
| | | | $\Sigma^0$ | $\bar{\Sigma}^0$ | $\frac{1}{2}$ | 1192.6 | +1 | 0 | 0 | 0 | −1 | $7.4 \times 10^{-20}$ | $\Lambda^0\gamma$ |
| | | | $\Sigma^-$ | $\bar{\Sigma}^+$ | $\frac{1}{2}$ | 1197.4 | +1 | 0 | 0 | 0 | −1 | $1.48 \times 10^{-10}$ | $n\pi^-$ |
| | | Xi | $\Xi^0$ | $\bar{\Xi}^0$ | $\frac{1}{2}$ | 1314.9 | +1 | 0 | 0 | 0 | −2 | $2.90 \times 10^{-10}$ | $\Lambda^0\pi^0$ |
| | | | $\Xi^-$ | $\bar{\Xi}^+$ | $\frac{1}{2}$ | 1321.3 | +1 | 0 | 0 | 0 | −2 | $1.64 \times 10^{-10}$ | $\Lambda^0\pi^-$ |
| | | Omega and others | $\Omega^-$ | $\Omega^+$ | $\frac{3}{2}$ | 1672.5 | +1 | 0 | 0 | 0 | −3 | $0.82 \times 10^{-10}$ | $\Xi^0\pi^-$, $\Lambda^0K^-$, $\Xi^-\pi^0$ |

† See also Table 32–4 for particles with charm and bottomness.

‡ Neutrinos partake only in the weak interaction. Experimental upper limits on neutrino masses are given in parentheses, as obtained from the WMAP survey (Chapter 33). Detection of neutrinos being transformed into one another suggests that at least one of the neutrinos has a nonzero mass greater than 0.05 eV.

Only a few of the hundreds of hadrons discovered are included in Table 32–2. Notice that the baryons $\Lambda$, $\Sigma$, $\Xi$, and $\Omega$ all decay to lighter-mass baryons, and eventually to a proton or neutron. All these processes conserve baryon number. Since there is no lighter particle than the proton with $B = +1$, if baryon number is strictly conserved, the proton itself cannot decay and is stable. (But see Section 32–11.)

The baryon and lepton numbers $(B, L_e, L_\mu, L_\tau)$, as well as strangeness $S$ (Section 32–8), as given in Table 32–2 are for particles; their antiparticles have opposite sign for these numbers.

## 32–7 Particle Stability and Resonances

*Lifetime depends on which force is acting*

Many particles listed in Table 32–2 are unstable. The lifetime of an unstable particle depends on which force is most active in causing the decay. When a stronger force influences a decay, that decay occurs more quickly. Decays caused by the weak force typically have lifetimes of $10^{-13}$ s or longer (W and Z are exceptions). Decays via the electromagnetic force have much shorter lifetimes, typically about $10^{-16}$ to $10^{-19}$ s, and normally involve a $\gamma$ (photon). The unstable particles listed in Table 32–2 decay either via the weak or the electromagnetic interaction.

*Very short-lived particles are inferred from their decay products*

Many particles have been found that decay via the strong interaction, with very short lifetimes, typically about $10^{-23}$ s, and these are not listed in Table 32–2. Their lifetimes are so short they do not travel far enough to be detected before decaying. The existence of such short-lived particles is inferred from their decay products. Consider the first such particle discovered (by Fermi), using a beam of $\pi^+$ directed through a hydrogen target (protons) with varying amounts of energy. The number of interactions ($\pi^+$ scattered) plotted versus the pion's kinetic energy is shown in Fig. 32–11. The large number of interactions around 200 MeV led Fermi to conclude that the $\pi^+$ and proton combined momentarily to form a short-lived particle before coming apart again, or at least that they resonated together for a short time. Indeed, the large peak in Fig. 32–11 resembles a resonance curve (see Figs. 11–18 and 21–42), and this new "particle"—now called the $\Delta$—is referred to as a **resonance**. Hundreds of other resonances have been found, and are regarded as excited states of lighter mass particles such as the nucleon.

*Resonance*

*Uncertainty principle relates lifetime and mass width*

The width of a resonance—in Fig. 32–11 the width of the $\Delta$ peak is on the order of 100 MeV—is an interesting application of the uncertainty principle. If a particle lives only $10^{-23}$ s, then its mass (i.e., its rest energy) will be uncertain by an amount $\Delta E \approx h/(2\pi\ \Delta t) \approx (6.6 \times 10^{-34}\,\mathrm{J\cdot s})/(6)(10^{-23}\,\mathrm{s}) \approx 10^{-11}\,\mathrm{J} \approx$ 100 MeV, which is what is observed. Actually, the lifetimes of $\approx 10^{-23}$ s for such resonances are inferred by the reverse process: from the measured width being $\approx 100$ MeV.

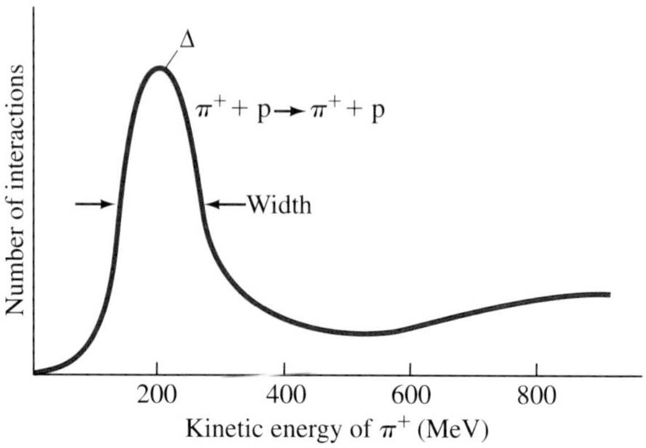


**FIGURE 32–11** Number of $\pi^+$ particles scattered by a proton target as a function of the incident $\pi^+$ kinetic energy. The resonance shape represents the formation of a short-lived particle, the $\Delta$, which has a charge in this case of $+2e$ $(\Delta^{++})$.

## 32–8 Strange Particles? Charm? Maybe a New Model Is Needed!

In the early 1950s, the newly found particles K, $\Lambda$, and $\Sigma$ were found to behave rather strangely in two ways. First, they were always produced in pairs. For example, the reaction

$$\pi^- + p \rightarrow K^0 + \Lambda^0$$

occurred with high probability, but the similar reaction $\pi^- + p \rightarrow K^0 + n$ was never observed to occur even though it did not violate any known conservation law. The second feature of these **strange particles** (as they came to be called) was that they were produced via the strong interaction (that is, at a high rate), but did not decay at a fast rate characteristic of the strong interaction (even though they decayed into strongly interacting particles).

*Strangeness and its conservation*

To explain these observations, a new quantum number, **strangeness**, and a new conservation law, **conservation of strangeness**, were introduced. By assigning the strangeness numbers ($S$) indicated in Table 32–2, the production of strange particles in pairs was explained. Antiparticles were assigned opposite strangeness from their particles. For example, in the reaction $\pi^- + p \rightarrow K^0 + \Lambda^0$, the initial state has strangeness $S = 0 + 0 = 0$, and the final state has $S = +1 - 1 = 0$, so strangeness is conserved. But for $\pi^- + p \rightarrow K^0 + n$, the initial state has $S = 0$ and the final state has $S = +1 + 0 = +1$, so strangeness would not be conserved; and this reaction is not observed.

*Strangeness is conserved in strong interactions but not in weak*

To explain the decay of strange particles, it is assumed that strangeness is conserved in the strong interaction but is *not conserved in the weak interaction*. Thus, strange particles were forbidden by strangeness conservation to decay to nonstrange particles of lower mass via the strong interaction, but could decay by means of the weak interaction at the observed longer lifetimes of $10^{-10}$ to $10^{-8}$ s.

The conservation of strangeness was the first example of a *partially conserved* quantity. In this case, the quantity strangeness is conserved by strong interactions but not by weak.

CONCEPTUAL EXAMPLE 32–6 **Guess the missing particle.** Using the conservation laws for particle interactions, determine the possibilities for the missing particle in the reaction

$$\pi^- + p \rightarrow K^0 + ?,$$

in addition to $K^0 + \Lambda^0$.

**RESPONSE** We write equations for the conserved numbers in this reaction, with $B$, $L_e$, $S$, and $Q$ as unknowns whose determination will reveal what the possible particle might be:

| | |
|---|---|
| Baryon number: | $0 + 1 = 0 + B$ |
| Lepton number: | $0 + 0 = 0 + L_e$ |
| Charge: | $-1 + 1 = 0 + Q$ |
| Strangeness: | $0 + 0 = 1 + S.$ |

The unknown product particle would have to have these characteristics:

$$B = +1 \qquad L_e = 0 \qquad Q = 0 \qquad S = -1.$$

In addition to $\Lambda^0$, a neutral sigma particle, $\Sigma^0$, is also consistent with these numbers.

In the next Section we will discuss another partially conserved quantity which was given the name **charm**. The discovery in 1974 of a particle with charm helped solidify a new theory involving quarks, which we now discuss.

## 32–9 Quarks

All particles, except the gauge bosons, are either leptons or hadrons. The principal difference between these two groups is that the hadrons interact via the strong interaction, whereas the leptons do not.

The six leptons $(e^-, \mu^-, \tau, \nu_e, \nu_\mu, \nu_\tau)$ are considered to be truly elementary particles because they do not show any internal structure, and have no measurable size. (Attempts to determine the size of leptons have put an upper limit of about $10^{-18}$ m.)

There are hundreds of hadrons, on the other hand, and experiments indicate they do have an internal structure. In 1963, M. Gell-Mann and G. Zweig proposed that none of the hadrons, not even the proton and neutron, are truly elementary, but instead are made up of combinations of three, more fundamental, pointlike entities called, somewhat whimsically, **quarks**.† Today, the quark theory is well-accepted, and quarks are considered the truly elementary particles, like leptons. The three quarks originally proposed were labeled u, d, s, and have the names *up*, *down*, and *strange*. The theory today has six quarks, just as there are six leptons—based on a presumed symmetry in nature. The other three quarks are called *charmed*, *bottom*, and *top*. The names apply also to new properties of each (quantum numbers c, t, b) that distinguish the new quarks from the old quarks (see Table 32–3), and which (like strangeness) are conserved in strong, but not weak, interactions. All quarks have spin $\frac{1}{2}$ and an electric charge of either $+\frac{2}{3}e$ or $-\frac{1}{3}e$ (that is, a fraction of the previously thought smallest charge $e$). Antiquarks have opposite sign of electric charge $Q$, baryon number $B$, strangeness $S$, charm $c$, bottomness $b$, and topness $t$. Other properties of quarks are shown in Table 32–3.

*Quarks*

**FIGURE 32–12** Quark compositions for several particles.

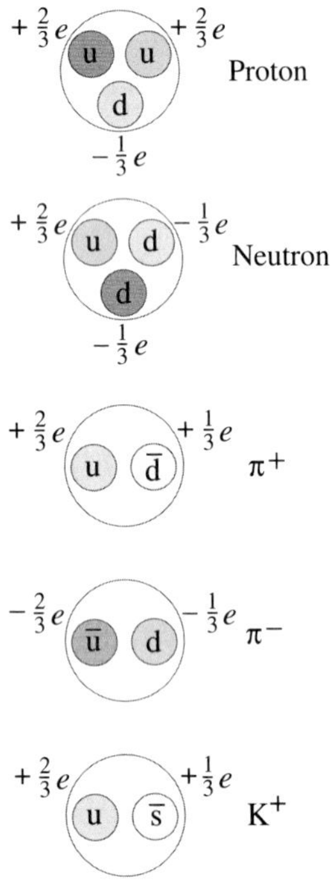


**TABLE 32–3 Properties of Quarks** (Antiquarks have opposite sign $Q$, $B$, $S$, $c$, $t$, $b$)

| Quarks | | | | | | | |
|---|---|---|---|---|---|---|---|
| Name | Symbol | Charge $Q$ | Baryon Number $B$ | Strangeness $S$ | Charm $c$ | Bottomness $b$ | Topness $t$ |
| Up | u | $+\frac{2}{3}e$ | $\frac{1}{3}$ | 0 | 0 | 0 | 0 |
| Down | d | $-\frac{1}{3}e$ | $\frac{1}{3}$ | 0 | 0 | 0 | 0 |
| Strange | s | $-\frac{1}{3}e$ | $\frac{1}{3}$ | −1 | 0 | 0 | 0 |
| Charmed | c | $+\frac{2}{3}e$ | $\frac{1}{3}$ | 0 | +1 | 0 | 0 |
| Bottom | b | $-\frac{1}{3}e$ | $\frac{1}{3}$ | 0 | 0 | −1 | 0 |
| Top | t | $+\frac{2}{3}e$ | $\frac{1}{3}$ | 0 | 0 | 0 | +1 |

All hadrons are considered to be made up of combinations of quarks, and their properties are described by looking at their quark content. Mesons consist of a quark–antiquark pair. For example, a $\pi^+$ meson is a $u\bar{d}$ combination: note that for the $u\bar{d}$ pair, $Q = \frac{2}{3}e + \frac{1}{3}e = +1e$, $B = \frac{1}{3} - \frac{1}{3} = 0$, $S = 0 + 0 = 0$, as they must for a $\pi^+$; and a $K^+ = u\bar{s}$, with $Q = +1$, $B = 0$, $S = +1$. Baryons, on the other hand, consist of three quarks. For example, a neutron is $n = ddu$, whereas an antiproton is $\bar{p} = \bar{u}\bar{u}\bar{d}$. See Fig. 32–12. Strange particles all contain an s or $\bar{s}$ quark, whereas charmed particles contain a c or $\bar{c}$ quark. A few of these hadrons are listed in Table 32–4.

*Mesons = quark + an antiquark*

*Baryons = 3 quarks*

After the quark theory was proposed, physicists began looking for these fractionally charged particles, but direct detection has not been successful. Current models suggest that quarks may be so tightly bound together that they may not ever exist singly in the free state. But observations of very high energy electrons scattered off protons suggest that protons are indeed made up of constituents.

†Gell-Mann chose the word from a phrase in James Joyce's *Finnegans Wake*.

**TABLE 32–4 Partial List of Heavy Hadrons, with Charm and Bottomness ($L_e = L_\mu = L_\tau = 0$)**

| Category | Particle | Anti-particle | Spin | Rest Mass (MeV/$c^2$) | Baryon Number $B$ | Strangeness $S$ | Charm $c$ | Bottomness $b$ | Lifetime (s) | Principal Decay Modes |
|---|---|---|---|---|---|---|---|---|---|---|
| Mesons | $D^+$ | $D^-$ | 0 | 1869.4 | 0 | 0 | +1 | 0 | $10.6 \times 10^{-13}$ | K + others, e + others |
| | $D^0$ | $\overline{D}^0$ | 0 | 1864.6 | 0 | 0 | +1 | 0 | $4.2 \times 10^{-13}$ | K + others, $\mu$ or e + others |
| | $D_S^+$ | $D_S^-$ | 0 | 1969 | 0 | +1 | +1 | 0 | $4.7 \times 10^{-13}$ | K + others |
| | $J/\psi$ (3097) | Self | 1 | 3096.9 | 0 | 0 | 0 | 0 | $0.8 \times 10^{-20}$ | Hadrons, $e^+e^-$, $\mu^+\mu^-$ |
| | $\Upsilon$ (9460) | Self | 1 | 9460.4 | 0 | 0 | 0 | 0 | $1.3 \times 10^{-20}$ | Hadrons, $\mu^+\mu^-$, $e^+e^-$, $\tau^+\tau^-$ |
| | $B^-$ | $B^+$ | 0 | 5279 | 0 | 0 | 0 | −1 | $1.5 \times 10^{-12}$ | $D^0$ + others |
| | $B^0$ | $\overline{B}^0$ | 0 | 5279 | 0 | 0 | 0 | −1 | $1.5 \times 10^{-12}$ | $D^0$ + others |
| Baryons | $\Lambda_c^+$ | $\Lambda_c^-$ | $\frac{1}{2}$ | 2285 | +1 | 0 | +1 | 0 | $2.0 \times 10^{-13}$ | Hadrons (e.g., $\Lambda$ + others) |
| | $\Sigma_c^{++}$ | $\Sigma_c^{--}$ | $\frac{1}{2}$ | 2453 | +1 | 0 | +1 | 0 | ? | $\Lambda_c^+\pi^+$ |
| | $\Sigma_c^+$ | $\Sigma_c^-$ | $\frac{1}{2}$ | 2454 | +1 | 0 | +1 | 0 | ? | $\Lambda_c^+\pi^0$ |
| | $\Sigma_c^0$ | $\overline{\Sigma}_c^0$ | $\frac{1}{2}$ | 2452 | +1 | 0 | +1 | 0 | ? | $\Lambda_c^+\pi^-$ |
| | $\Lambda_b^0$ | $\overline{\Lambda}_b^0$ | $\frac{1}{2}$ | 5640 | +1 | 0 | 0 | −1 | $1.1 \times 10^{-12}$ | $J/\psi\Lambda^0$, $pD^0\pi^-$, $\Lambda_c^+\pi^+\pi^-\pi^-$ |

Today, the truly elementary particles are considered to be the six quarks, the six leptons, and the gauge bosons that carry the fundamental forces. See Table 32–5, where the quarks and leptons are arranged in three "generations." Ordinary matter—atoms made of protons, neutrons, and electrons—is contained in the "first generation." The others are thought to have existed in the very early universe, but are seen by us today only at powerful accelerators or in cosmic rays. All of the hundreds of hadrons can be accounted for by combinations of the six quarks and six antiquarks.

*The elementary particles are quarks, leptons, gauge bosons*

**TABLE 32–5 The Elementary Particles† as Seen Today**

| Gauge bosons | Force | | First generation | Second generation | Third generation |
|---|---|---|---|---|---|
| Gluons | Strong | Quarks | u, d | s, c | b, t |
| $W^\pm$, $Z_0$ | Weak | Leptons | e, $\nu_e$ | $\mu$, $\nu_\mu$ | $\tau$, $\nu_\tau$ |
| $\gamma$ (photon) | EM | | | | |

† Note that the quarks and leptons are arranged into three generations each.

**CONCEPTUAL EXAMPLE 32–7** **Quark combinations.** Find the baryon number, charge, and strangeness for the following quark combinations, and identify the hadron particle that is made up of these quark combinations: (*a*) udd, (*b*) u$\overline{\text{u}}$, (*c*) uss, (*d*) sdd, and (*e*) b$\overline{\text{u}}$.

**RESPONSE** We use Table 32–3 to get the properties of the quarks, then Table 32–2 or 32–4 to find the particle that has these properties.

(*a*) udd has

$$Q = +\tfrac{2}{3}e - \tfrac{1}{3}e - \tfrac{1}{3}e = 0,$$
$$B = \tfrac{1}{3} + \tfrac{1}{3} + \tfrac{1}{3} = 1,$$
$$S = 0 + 0 + 0 = 0,$$

as well as $c = 0$, bottomness $= 0$, topness $= 0$. The only baryon ($B = +1$) that has $Q = 0$, $S = 0$, etc., is the neutron (Table 32–2).

(*b*) u$\overline{\text{u}}$ has $Q = \tfrac{2}{3}e - \tfrac{2}{3}e = 0$, $B = 0$, and all other quantum numbers $= 0$. Sounds like a $\pi^0$ (d$\overline{\text{d}}$ also gives a $\pi^0$, and we say a $\pi^0$ is u$\overline{\text{u}}$ + d$\overline{\text{d}}$).

(*c*) uss has $Q = 0$, $B = +1$, $S = -2$, others $= 0$. This is a $\Xi^0$.

(*d*) sdd has $Q = -1$, $B = +1$, $S = -1$, so must be a $\Sigma^-$.

(*e*) b$\overline{\text{u}}$ has $Q = -1$, $B = 0$, $S = 0$, $c = 0$, bottomness $= -1$, topness $= 0$. This must be a $B^-$ meson (Table 32–4).

**EXERCISE B** What is the quark composition of a $K^-$ meson?

## 32–10 The "Standard Model": Quantum Chromodynamics (QCD) and the Electroweak Theory

Not long after the quark theory was proposed, it was suggested that quarks have another property (or quality) called **color**, or "color charge" (analogous to electric charge). The distinction between the six quarks (u, d, s, c, b, t) was referred to as **flavor**. According to theory, each of the flavors of quark can have three colors, usually designated red, green, and blue. (These are the three primary colors which, when added together in equal amounts, as on a TV screen, produce white.) Note that the names "color" and "flavor" have nothing to do with our senses, but are purely whimsical—as are other names, such as charm, in this new field. (We did, however, "color" the quarks in Fig. 32–12.) The antiquarks are colored antired, antigreen, and antiblue. Baryons are made up of three quarks, one of each color. Mesons consist of a quark–antiquark pair of a particular color and its anticolor. Both baryons and mesons are thus colorless or white.

Originally, the idea of quark color was proposed to preserve the Pauli exclusion principle (Section 28–7). Not all particles obey the exclusion principle. *Fermions* Those that do, such as electrons, protons, and neutrons, are called **fermions**. *Bosons* Those that don't are called **bosons**. These two categories are distinguished also in their spin (Section 28–6): bosons have integer spin (0, 1, 2, etc.) whereas fermions have half-integer spin, usually $\frac{1}{2}$ as for electrons and nucleons, but other fermions have spin $\frac{3}{2}, \frac{5}{2}$, etc. Matter is made up mainly of fermions, but the carriers of the forces ($\gamma$, W, Z, and gluons) are all bosons. Quarks are fermions (they have spin $\frac{1}{2}$) and therefore should obey the exclusion principle. Yet for three particular baryons (uuu, ddd, and sss), all three quarks would have the same quantum numbers, and at least two quarks have their spin in the same direction (since there are only two choices, spin up $[m_s = +\frac{1}{2}]$ or spin down $[m_s = -\frac{1}{2}]$). This would seem to violate the exclusion principle; but if quarks have an additional quantum number (color), which is different for each quark, it would serve to distinguish them and allow the exclusion principle to hold. Although quark color, and the resulting threefold increase in the number of quarks, was originally an *ad hoc* idea, it also served to bring the theory into better agreement with experiment, such as predicting the correct lifetime of the $\pi^0$ meson. The idea of color soon became a central feature of the theory as determining the force binding quarks together in a hadron.

Each quark is assumed to carry a *color charge*, analogous to electric charge, and the strong force between quarks is referred to as the **color force**. This *QCD* theory of the strong force is called **quantum chromodynamics** (*chroma* = color in Greek), or **QCD**, to indicate that the force acts between color charges (and not between, say, electric charges). The strong force between two hadrons is considered to be a force between the quarks that make them up, as suggested in Fig. 32–13. The particles that transmit the color force (analogous to photons for *Gluons* the EM force) are called **gluons** (a play on "glue"). They are included in Table 32–5. There are eight gluons, according to the theory, all massless and all have color charge.† Thus gluons have replaced mesons (Table 32–1) as the particles responsible for the strong (color) force.

You might ask what would happen if we try to see a single quark with color by reaching deep inside a hadron and extracting a single quark. Quarks are so tightly bound to other quarks that extracting one would require a tremendous amount of energy, so much that it would be sufficient to create more quarks $(E = mc^2)$. Indeed, such experiments are done at modern particle colliders and all we get is more hadrons (quark–antiquark pairs, or triplets), not an isolated quark. This property of quarks, that they are always bound in groups that are *Confinement* colorless, is called **confinement**.

†Compare to the EM interaction, where the photon has no electric charge. Because gluons have color charge, they could attract each other and form composite particles (photons cannot). Such "glueballs" are being searched for.

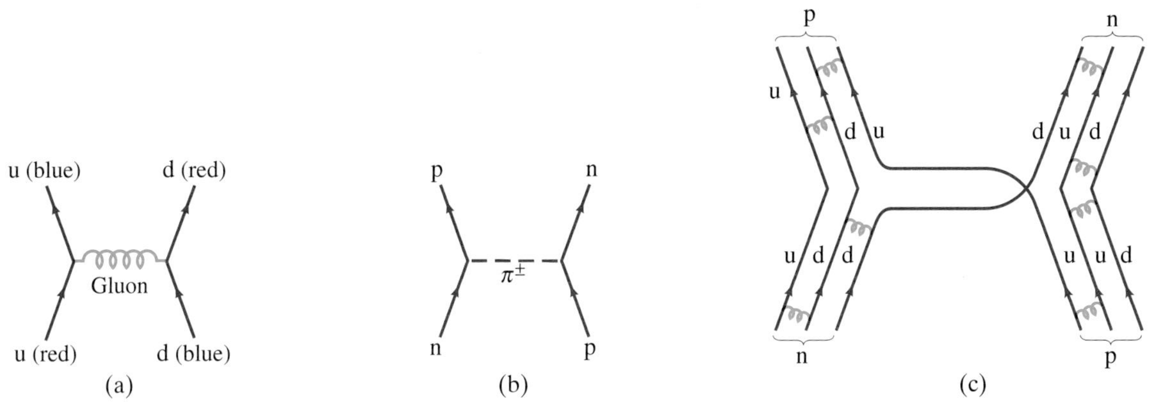


**FIGURE 32–13** (a) The force between two quarks holding them together as part of a proton, for example, is carried by a gluon, which in this case involves a change in color. (b) Strong interaction n + p → n + p with the exchange of a charged $\pi$ meson (+ or −, depending on whether it is considered moving to the left or to the right). (c) Quark representation of the same interaction n + p → n + p. The blue coiled lines between quarks represent gluon exchanges holding the hadrons together.

The color force has the interesting property that, as two quarks approach each other very closely (equivalently, have high energy), the force between them becomes small. This aspect is referred to as **asymptotic freedom**.

*Leptons and the weak force*

The weak force, as we have seen, is thought to be mediated by the $W^+$, $W^-$, and $Z^0$ particles. It acts between the "weak charges" that each particle has. Each elementary particle can thus have electric charge, weak charge, color charge, and gravitational mass, although one or more of these could be zero. For example, all leptons have color charge of zero, so they do not interact via the strong force.

**CONCEPTUAL EXAMPLE 32–8** **Beta decay.** Draw a Feynman diagram, showing what happens in beta decay using quarks.

**RESPONSE** Beta decay is a result of the weak interaction, and the mediator is either a $W^{\pm}$ or $Z^0$ particle. What happens, in part, is that a neutron (udd quarks) decays into a proton (uud). Apparently a d quark (charge $-\frac{1}{3}e$) has turned into a u quark (charge $+\frac{2}{3}e$). Charge conservation means that a negatively charged particle, namely a $W^-$, was emitted by the d quark. Since an electron and an antineutrino appear in the final state, they must have come from the decay of the virtual $W^-$, as shown in Fig. 32–14.

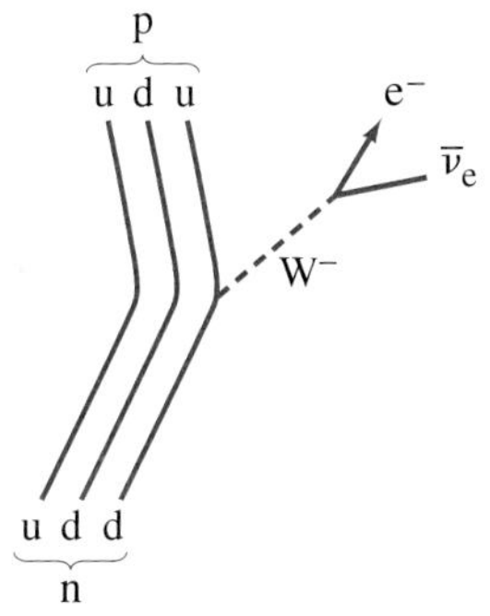


**FIGURE 32–14** Quark representation of the Feynman diagram for $\beta$ decay of a neutron into a proton.

To summarize, the standard model says that the truly elementary particles (Table 32–5) are the leptons, the quarks, and the gauge bosons (photon, W and Z, and the gluons). Some theories suggest there may be other bosons as well. The photon, leptons, $W^+$, $W^-$, and $Z^0$ have all been observed in experiments. But so far only combinations of quarks (baryons and mesons) have been observed, and it seems likely that free quarks and gluons are unobservable.

*Unification*

One important aspect of new theoretical work is the attempt to find a **unified** basis for the different forces in nature. This was a long-held hope of Einstein, which he was never able to fulfill. A so-called **gauge theory** that unifies the weak and electromagnetic interactions was put forward in the 1960s by S. Weinberg, S. Glashow, and A. Salam. In this **electroweak theory**, the weak and electromagnetic forces are seen as two different manifestations of a single, more fundamental, *electroweak* interaction. The electroweak theory has had many successes, including the prediction of the $W^{\pm}$ particles as carriers of the weak force, with masses of $81 \pm 2\,\mathrm{GeV}/c^2$ in excellent agreement with the measured values of $80.41 \pm 0.10\,\mathrm{GeV}/c^2$ (and similar accuracy for the $Z^0$).

*Electroweak theory*

*Standard Model*

The combination of electroweak theory plus QCD for the strong interaction is often referred to today as the **Standard Model**.

Theoreticians have wondered why the W and Z have large masses rather than being massless like the photon. Electroweak theory suggests an explanation by means of a new **Higgs field** and its particle, the **Higgs boson**, which interact with the W and Z to "slow them down." In being forced to go slower than the speed of light, they must acquire mass. The search for the Higgs boson will be a priority for experimental particle physicists when CERN's Large Hadron Collider (Section 32–1) starts running. So far, searches have excluded a Higgs lighter than $115\,\text{GeV}/c^2$. Yet it is expected to have a mass no larger than $200\,\text{GeV}/c^2$. We are narrowing in on it.

*Higgs*

## 32–11 Grand Unified Theories

*GUT*

*Unification of forces*

With the success of the unified electroweak theory, attempts are being made to incorporate it and QCD for the strong (color) force into a so-called **grand unified theory** (GUT). One type of such a grand unified theory of the electromagnetic, weak, and strong forces has been worked out in which there is only one class of particle—leptons and quarks belong to the same family and are able to change freely from one type to the other—and the three forces are different aspects of a single underlying force. The unity is predicted to occur, however, only on a scale of less than about $10^{-32}$ m corresponding to an extremely high energy of about $10^{16}$ GeV. If two elementary particles (leptons or quarks) approach each other to within this **unification scale**, the apparently fundamental distinction between them would not exist at this level, and a quark could readily change to a lepton, or vice versa. Baryon and lepton numbers would not be conserved. The weak, electromagnetic, and strong (color) force would blend to a force of a single strength.

*Symmetry breaking*

What happens between the unification distance of $10^{-32}$ m and more normal (larger) distances is referred to as **symmetry breaking**. As an analogy, consider an atom in a crystal. Deep within the atom, there is much symmetry—in the innermost regions the electron cloud is spherically symmetric (Chapter 28). Farther out, this symmetry breaks down—the electron clouds are distributed preferentially along the lines (bonds) joining the atoms in the crystal. In a similar way, at $10^{-32}$ m the force between elementary particles is theorized to be a single force—it is symmetrical and does not single out one type of "charge" over another. But at larger distances, that symmetry is broken and we see three distinct forces. (In the "standard model" of electroweak interactions, Section 32–10, the symmetry breaking between the electromagnetic and the weak interactions occurs at about $10^{-18}$ m.)

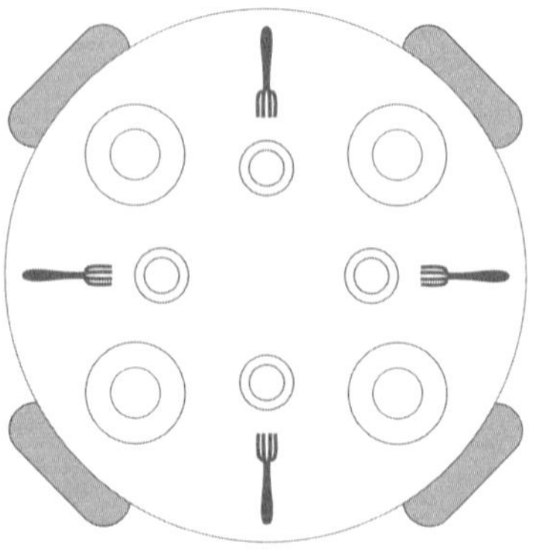

**FIGURE 32–15** Symmetry around a table. Example 32–9.

**CONCEPTUAL EXAMPLE 32–9** **Symmetry.** The table in Fig. 32–15 has four identical place settings. Four people sit down to eat. Describe the symmetry of this table and what happens to it when someone starts the meal.

**RESPONSE** The table has several kinds of symmetry. It is symmetric to rotations of 90°: that is, the table will look the same if everyone moved one chair to the left or to the right. It is also north–south symmetric and east–west symmetric, so that swaps across the table don't affect the way the table looks. It also doesn't matter whether any person picks up the fork to the left of the plate or the fork to the right. But once that first person picks up either fork, the choice is set for all the rest at the table as well. The symmetry has been *broken*. The underlying symmetry is still there—the blue glasses could still be chosen either way—but some choice must get made and at that moment the symmetry of the diners is broken.

Since unification occurs at such tiny distances and huge energies, the theory is difficult to test experimentally. But it is not completely impossible. One testable prediction is the idea that the proton might decay (via, for example, $p \rightarrow \pi^0 + e^+$) and violate conservation of baryon number. This could happen if two quarks approached to within $10^{-31}$ m of each other. But it is very unlikely at normal temperature and energy, so the decay of a proton can only be an unlikely process. In the simplest form of GUT, the theoretical estimate of the proton lifetime for the decay mode $p \rightarrow \pi^0 + e^+$ is about $10^{31}$ yr, and this has just come within the realm of testability.† Proton decays have still not been seen, and experiments put the lower limit on the proton lifetime for the above mode to be about $10^{33}$ yr, somewhat greater than this prediction. This may seem a disappointment, but on the other hand, it presents a challenge. Indeed more complex GUTs are not affected by this result.

*Proton decay?*

**EXAMPLE 32–10 ESTIMATE Proton decay.** An experiment uses 3300 tons of water waiting to see a proton decay of the type $p \rightarrow \pi^0 + e^+$. If the experiment is run for 4 years without detecting a decay, estimate the lower limit on the proton half-life.

**APPROACH** As with radioactive decay, the number of decays is proportional to the number of parent species ($N$), the time interval ($\Delta t$), and the decay constant ($\lambda$) which is related to the half-life $T_{\frac{1}{2}}$ by (see Eqs. 30–3 and 30–6):

$$\Delta N = -\lambda N \, \Delta t = -\frac{\ln 2}{T_{\frac{1}{2}}} N \, \Delta t.$$

**SOLUTION** Dealing only with magnitudes, we solve for $T_{\frac{1}{2}}$:

$$T_{\frac{1}{2}} = \frac{N}{\Delta N} \Delta t \ln 2.$$

Thus for $\Delta N < 1$ over the four-year trial,

$$T_{\frac{1}{2}} > N(4\,\text{yr})(0.693),$$

where $N$ is the number of protons in 3300 tons of water. To determine $N$, we note that each molecule of $H_2O$ contains $(2 + 8 =)10$ protons. So one mole of water (18 g, $6 \times 10^{23}$ molecules) contains $10 \times 6 \times 10^{23}$ protons in 18 g of water, or about $3 \times 10^{26}$ protons per kilogram. One ton is $10^3$ kg, so the chamber contains $(3.3 \times 10^6\,\text{kg})(3 \times 10^{26}\,\text{protons/kg}) \approx 1 \times 10^{33}$ protons. Then our very rough estimate for a lower limit on the proton half-life is $T_{\frac{1}{2}} > (10^{33})(4\,\text{yr})(0.7) \approx 3 \times 10^{33}$ yr.

An interesting prediction of unified theories relates to cosmology (Chapter 33). It is thought that during the first $10^{-35}$ s after the theorized Big Bang that created the universe, the temperature was so extremely high that particles had energies corresponding to the unification scale. Baryon number would not have been conserved then, perhaps allowing an imbalance that might account for the observed predominance of matter ($B > 0$) over antimatter ($B < 0$) in the universe.

*Connection with cosmology*

This last example is interesting, for it illustrates a deep connection between investigations at either end of the size scale: theories about the tiniest objects (elementary particles) have a strong bearing on the understanding of the universe on a large scale. We will look at this more in the next Chapter.

†This is much larger than the age of the universe ($\approx 14 \times 10^9$ yr). But we don't have to wait $10^{31}$ yr to see. Instead we can wait for one decay among $10^{31}$ protons over a year (see Eqs. 30–3 and 30–6, $\Delta N = \lambda N \, \Delta t = 0.693 N \, \Delta t / T_{\frac{1}{2}}$).

## 32–12 Strings and Supersymmetry

Even more ambitious than grand unified theories are attempts to also incorporate gravity, and thus unify all four forces in nature into a single theory. (Such theories are sometimes referred to misleadingly as **theories of everything**.) There are consistent theories that attempt to unify all four forces called **string theories**, in which the elementary particles (Table 32–5) are imagined not as points but as one-dimensional strings perhaps $10^{-35}$ m long.

*String theory*

*Supersymmetry*

A related idea is **supersymmetry**, which applied to strings is known as **superstring theory**. Supersymmetry predicts that interactions exist that would change fermions into bosons and vice versa, and that all known fermions have supersymmetric boson partners. Thus, for each quark we know (a fermion), there would be a *squark* (a *boson*) or "supersymmetric" quark. For every lepton there would be a *slepton*. Likewise, for every known boson (photons and gluons, for example), there would be a supersymmetric fermion (*photinos* and *gluinos*). Supersymmetry predicts also that a *graviton*, which transmits the gravity force, has a partner, the gravitino. Supersymmetric particles are sometimes called "SUSYs" for short, and may be a candidate for the "dark matter" of the universe (discussed in Chapter 33). But why hasn't this "missing part" of the universe ever been detected? The best guess is that supersymmetric particles might be heavier than their conventional counterparts, perhaps too heavy to have been produced in today's accelerators. Until a supersymmetric particle is found, and it may be possible at CERN's new LHC, supersymmetry is just an elegant guess.

The world of elementary particles is opening new vistas. What happens in the future is bound to be exciting.

## Summary

**Particle accelerators** are used to accelerate charged particles, such as electrons and protons, to very high energy. High-energy particles have short wavelength and so can be used to probe the structure of matter at very small distances in great detail. High kinetic energy also allows the creation of new particles through collision (via $E = mc^2$).

**Cyclotrons** and **synchrotrons** use a magnetic field to keep the particles in a circular path and accelerate them at intervals by high voltage. **Linear accelerators** accelerate particles along a line. **Colliding beams** allow higher interaction energy.

An **antiparticle** has the same mass as a particle but opposite charge. Certain other properties may also be opposite: for example, the antiproton has **baryon number** (nucleon number) opposite to that for the proton.

In all nuclear and particle reactions, the following conservation laws hold: momentum, angular momentum, mass–energy, electric charge, baryon number, and **lepton numbers**.

Certain particles have a property called **strangeness**, which is conserved by the strong force but not by the weak force. The properties **charm**, **bottomness**, and **topness** also are conserved by the strong force but not by the weak.

Just as the electromagnetic force can be said to be due to an exchange of photons, the strong nuclear force was first thought to be carried by *mesons* that have rest mass, but recent theory says the force is carried by massless **gluons**. The W and Z particles carry the weak force. These fundamental force carriers (photon, W and Z, gluons) are called **gauge bosons**.

Other particles can be classified as either *leptons* or *hadrons*. **Leptons** participate in the weak and electrically charged electromagnetic interactions. **Hadrons**, which today are considered to be made up of **quarks**, participate in the strong interaction as well. The hadrons can be classified as **mesons**, with baryon number zero, and **baryons**, with nonzero baryon number.

All particles, except for the photon, electron, neutrinos, and proton, decay with measurable half-lives varying from $10^{-25}$ s to $10^{3}$ s. The half-life depends on which force is predominant. Weak decays usually have half-lives greater than about $10^{-13}$ s. Electromagnetic decays have half-lives on the order of $10^{-16}$ to $10^{-19}$ s. The shortest lived particles, called **resonances**, decay via the strong interaction and live typically for only about $10^{-23}$ s.

Today's standard model of elementary particles considers **quarks** as the basic building blocks of the hadrons. The six quark "flavors" are called **up**, **down**, **strange**, **charmed**, **bottom**, and **top**. It is expected that there are the same number of quarks as leptons (six of each), and that quarks and leptons are the truly elementary particles along with the gauge bosons ($\gamma$, W, Z, gluons). Quarks are said to have **color**, and, according to **quantum chromodynamics** (QCD), the strong color force acts between their color charges and is transmitted by **gluons**. **Electroweak theory** views the weak and electromagnetic forces as two aspects of a single underlying interaction. QCD plus the electroweak theory are referred to as the **Standard Model**.

**Grand unified theories** of forces suggest that at very short distances $\left(10^{-32}\text{ m}\right)$ and very high energy, the weak, electromagnetic, and strong forces appear as a single force, and the fundamental difference between quarks and leptons disappears.

# Questions

1. Give a reaction between two nucleons, similar to Eq. 32–4, that could produce a $\pi^-$.
2. If a proton is moving at very high speed, so that its kinetic energy is much greater than its rest energy $(m_0c^2)$, can it then decay via $p \rightarrow n + \pi^+$?
3. What would an "antiatom," made up of the antiparticles to the constituents of normal atoms, consist of? What might happen if *antimatter*, made of such antiatoms, came in contact with our normal world of matter?
4. What particle in a decay signals the electromagnetic interaction?
5. Does the presence of a neutrino among the decay products of a particle necessarily mean that the decay occurs via the weak interaction? Do all decays via the weak interaction produce a neutrino? Explain.
6. Why is it that a neutron decays via the weak interaction even though the neutron and one of its decay products (proton) are strongly interacting?
7. Which of the four interactions (strong, electromagnetic, weak, gravitational) does an electron take part in? A neutrino? A proton?
8. Check that charge and baryon number are conserved in each of the decays in Table 32–2.
9. Which of the particle decays in Table 32–2 occur via the electromagnetic interaction?
10. Which of the particle decays in Table 32–2 occur by the weak interaction?
11. By what interaction, and why, does $\Sigma^{\pm}$ decay to $\Lambda^0$? What about $\Sigma^0$ decaying to $\Lambda^0$?
12. The $\Delta$ baryon has spin $\frac{3}{2}$, baryon number 1, and charge $Q = +2,\ +1,\ 0,$ or $-1$. Why is there no charge state $Q = -2$?
13. Which of the particle decays in Table 32–4 occur via the electromagnetic interaction?
14. Which of the particle decays in Table 32–4 occur by the weak interaction?
15. Quarks have spin $\frac{1}{2}$. How do you account for the fact that baryons have spin $\frac{1}{2}$ or $\frac{3}{2}$, and mesons have spin 0 or 1?
16. Suppose there were a kind of "neutrinolet" that was massless, had no color charge or electrical charge, and did not feel the weak force. Could you say that this particle even exists?
17. Is it possible for a particle to be both (*a*) a lepton and a baryon? (*b*) a baryon and a hadron? (*c*) a meson and a quark? (*d*) a hadron and a lepton? Explain.
18. Using the ideas of quantum chromodynamics, would it be possible to find particles made up of two quarks and no antiquarks? What about two quarks and two antiquarks?
19. Why do neutrons decay when they are free but not when they are inside the nucleus?
20. Is the reaction $e^- + p \rightarrow n + \bar{\nu}_e$ possible? Explain.
21. Occasionally, the $\Lambda$ will decay by the following reaction: $\Lambda^0 \rightarrow p^+ + e^- + \bar{\nu}_e$. Which of the four forces in nature is responsible for this decay? How do you know?

# Problems

### 32–1 Particles and Accelerators

1. (I) What is the total energy of a proton whose kinetic energy is 6.35 GeV?
2. (I) Calculate the wavelength of 35-GeV electrons.
3. (I) What strength of magnetic field is used in a cyclotron in which protons make $2.8 \times 10^7$ revolutions per second?
4. (I) What is the time for one complete revolution for a very high-energy proton in the 1.0-km-radius Fermilab accelerator?
5. (I) If $\alpha$ particles are accelerated by the cyclotron of Example 32–2, what must be the frequency of the voltage applied to the dees?
6. (II) (*a*) If the cyclotron of Example 32–2 accelerated $\alpha$ particles, what maximum energy could they attain? What would their speed be? (*b*) Repeat for deuterons $({}^2_1H)$. (*c*) In each case, what frequency of voltage is required?
7. (II) Which is better for picking out details of the nucleus: 30-MeV alpha particles or 30-MeV protons? Compare each of their wavelengths with the size of a nucleon in a nucleus.
8. (II) The voltage across the dees of a cyclotron is 55 kV. How many revolutions do protons make to reach a kinetic energy of 25 MeV?
9. (II) What is the wavelength (= maximum resolvable distance) of 7.0-TeV protons?
10. (II) A cyclotron with a radius of 1.0 m is to accelerate deuterons $({}^2_1H)$ to an energy of 12 MeV. (*a*) What is the required magnetic field? (*b*) What frequency is needed for the voltage between the dees? (*c*) If the potential difference between the dees averages 22 kV, how many revolutions will the particles make before exiting? (*d*) How much time does it take for one deuteron to go from start to exit. (*e*) Estimate how far it travels during this time.
11. (II) The 4.25-km-radius tunnel that will be used to house the magnets for the Large Hadron Collider (LHC) calls for proton beams of energy 7.0 TeV. What magnetic field will be required?
12. (II) The 1.0-km radius Fermilab Tevatron takes about 20 seconds to bring the energies of the stored protons from 150 GeV to 1.0 TeV. The acceleration is done once per turn. Estimate the energy given to the protons on each turn. (You can assume that the speed of the protons is essentially *c* the whole time.)
13. (III) Show that the energy of a particle (charge *e*) in a synchrotron, in the relativistic limit ($v \approx c$), is given by $E$ (in eV) $= Brc$, where $B$ is magnetic field strength and $r$ the radius of the orbit (SI units).
14. (III) What magnetic field intensity is needed at the 1.0-km-radius Fermilab synchrotron for 1.0-TeV protons?

### 32–2 to 32–6 Particle Interactions, Particle Exchange

15. (I) How much energy is released in the decay
$$\pi^+ \rightarrow \mu^+ + \nu_\mu?$$
See Table 32–2.

16. (I) About how much energy is released when a $\Lambda^0$ decays to $n + \pi^0$? (See Table 32–2.)

17. (I) How much energy is required to produce a neutron–antineutron pair?

18. (I) Estimate the range of the strong force if the mediating particle were the kaon instead of the pion.

19. (II) Two protons are heading toward each other with equal speeds. What minimum kinetic energy must each have if a $\pi^0$ meson is to be created in the process? (See Table 32–2.)

20. (II) What minimum kinetic energy must two neutrons each have if they are traveling at the same speed toward each other, collide, and produce a $K^+K^-$pair in addition to themselves? (See Table 32–2.)

21. (II) Estimate the range of the weak force using Eq. 32–3, given the masses of the W and Z particles as about 80 to 90 $\mathrm{GeV}/c^2$.

22. (II) What are the wavelengths of the two photons produced when a proton and antiproton at rest annihilate?

23. (II) The $\Lambda$ cannot decay by the following reactions. What conservation law is violated in each of the reactions?
(*a*) $\Lambda^0 \rightarrow n + \pi^-$
(*b*) $\Lambda^0 \rightarrow p + K^-$
(*c*) $\Lambda^0 \rightarrow \pi^+ + \pi^-$

24. (II) For the decay $\Lambda^0 \rightarrow p + \pi^-$, calculate (*a*) the $Q$-value (energy released), and (*b*) the kinetic energy of the p and $\pi^-$, assuming the $\Lambda^0$ decays from rest. (Use relativistic formulas.)

25. (II) (*a*) Show, by conserving momentum and energy, that it is impossible for an isolated electron to radiate only a single photon. (*b*) With this result in mind, how can you defend the photon exchange diagram in Fig. 32–7?

26. (II) What would be the wavelengths of the two photons produced when an electron and a positron, each with 420 keV of kinetic energy, annihilate head on?

27. (II) In the rare decay $\pi^+ \rightarrow e^+ + \nu_e$, what is the kinetic energy of the positron? Assume the $\pi^+$ decays from rest.

28. (II) Which of the following reactions and decays are possible? For those forbidden, explain what laws are violated.
(*a*) $\pi^- + p \rightarrow n + \eta^0$
(*b*) $\pi^+ + p \rightarrow n + \pi^0$
(*c*) $\pi^+ + p \rightarrow p + e^+$
(*d*) $p \rightarrow e^+ + \nu_e$
(*e*) $\mu^+ \rightarrow e^+ + \bar{\nu}_\mu$
(*f*) $p \rightarrow n + e^+ + \nu_e$

29. (II) Calculate the kinetic energy of each of the two products in the decay $\Xi^- \rightarrow \Lambda^0 + \pi^-$. Assume the $\Xi^-$ decays from rest.

30. (III) Could a $\pi^+$ meson be produced if a 100-MeV proton struck a proton at rest? What minimum kinetic energy must the incoming proton have?

31. (III) Calculate the maximum kinetic energy of the electron in the decay $\mu^- \rightarrow e^- + \bar{\nu}_e + \nu_\mu$. [*Hint*: in what direction do the two neutrinos move relative to the electron in order to give the latter the maximum kinetic energy? Both energy and momentum are conserved; use relativistic formulas.]

### 32–7 to 32–11 Resonances, Standard Model, Quarks, QCD, GUT

32. (I) Use Fig. 32–11 to estimate the energy width and then the lifetime of the $\Delta$ resonance using the uncertainty principle.

33. (I) The measured width of the $J/\psi$ meson is 88 keV. Estimate its lifetime.

34. (I) The measured width of the $\psi$ (3685) meson is 277 keV. Estimate its lifetime.

35. (I) What is the energy width (or uncertainty) of (*a*) $\eta^0$, and (*b*) $\Sigma^0$? See Table 32–2.

36. (I) The $B^-$ meson is a $b\bar{u}$ quark combination. (*a*) Show that this is consistent for all quantum numbers. (*b*) What are the quark combinations for $B^+$, $B^0$, $\bar{B}^0$?

37. (II) Which of the following decays are possible? For those that are forbidden, explain which laws are violated.
(*a*) $\Xi^0 \rightarrow \Sigma^+ + \pi^-$
(*b*) $\Omega^- \rightarrow \Sigma^0 + \pi^- + \nu$
(*c*) $\Sigma^0 \rightarrow \Lambda^0 + \gamma + \gamma$

38. (II) What are the quark combinations that can form (*a*) a neutron, (*b*) an antineutron, (*c*) a $\Lambda^0$, (*d*) a $\bar{\Sigma}^0$?

39. (II) What particles do the following quark combinations produce: (*a*) uud, (*b*) $\bar{u}\bar{u}\bar{s}$, (*c*) $\bar{u}s$, (*d*) $d\bar{u}$, (*e*) $\bar{c}s$?

40. (II) What is the quark combination needed to produce a $D^0$ meson ($Q = B = S = 0, c = +1$)?

41. (II) The $D_S^+$ meson has $S = c = +1,\ B = 0$. What quark combination would produce it?

42. (II) Draw a possible Feynman diagram using quarks (as in Fig. 32–13c) for the reaction $\pi^- + p \rightarrow \pi^0 + n$.

43. (II) Draw a Feynman diagram for the reaction $n + \nu_\mu \rightarrow p + \mu^-$.

## General Problems

44. What is the total energy of a proton whose kinetic energy is 25 GeV? What is its wavelength?

45. Assume there are $5.0 \times 10^{13}$ protons at 1.0 TeV stored in the 1.0-km-radius ring of the Tevatron. (*a*) How much current (amperes) is carried by this beam? (*b*) How fast would a 1500-kg car have to move to carry the same kinetic energy as this beam?

46. Protons are injected into the 1.0-km-radius Fermilab Tevatron with an energy of 150 GeV. If they are accelerated by 2.5 MV each revolution, how far do they travel and approximately how long does it take for them to reach 1.0 TeV?

47. (*a*) How much energy is released when an electron and a positron annihilate each other? (*b*) How much energy is released when a proton and an antiproton annihilate each other? (All particles KE $\approx 0$.)

48. Which of the following reactions are possible, and by what interaction could they occur? For those forbidden, explain why.
(*a*) $\pi^- + \mathrm{p} \rightarrow \mathrm{K}^+ + \Sigma^-$
(*b*) $\pi^+ + \mathrm{p} \rightarrow \mathrm{K}^+ + \Sigma^+$
(*c*) $\pi^- + \mathrm{p} \rightarrow \Lambda^0 + \mathrm{K}^0 + \pi^0$
(*d*) $\pi^+ + \mathrm{p} \rightarrow \Sigma^0 + \pi^0$
(*e*) $\pi^- + \mathrm{p} \rightarrow \mathrm{p} + \mathrm{e}^- + \bar{\nu}_\mathrm{e}$

49. Which of the following reactions are possible, and by what interaction could they occur? For those forbidden, explain why.
(*a*) $\pi^- + \mathrm{p} \rightarrow \mathrm{K}^0 + \mathrm{p} + \pi^0$
(*b*) $\mathrm{K}^- + \mathrm{p} \rightarrow \Lambda^0 + \pi^0$
(*c*) $\mathrm{K}^+ + \mathrm{n} \rightarrow \Sigma^+ + \pi^0 + \gamma$
(*d*) $\mathrm{K}^+ \rightarrow \pi^0 + \pi^0 + \pi^+$
(*e*) $\pi^+ \rightarrow \mathrm{e}^+ + \nu_\mathrm{e}$

50. One decay mode for a $\pi^+$ is $\pi^+ \rightarrow \mu^+ + \nu_\mu$. What would be the equivalent decay for a $\pi^-$? Check conservation rules.

51. Symmetry breaking occurs in the electroweak theory at about $10^{-18}$ m. Show that this corresponds to an energy that is on the order of the mass of the $\mathrm{W}^\pm$.

52. The mass of a $\pi^0$ can be measured by observing the reaction $\pi^- + \mathrm{p} \rightarrow \pi^0 + \mathrm{n}$ at very low incident $\pi^-$ kinetic energy (assume it is zero). The neutron is observed to be emitted with a kinetic energy of 0.60 MeV. Use conservation of energy and momentum to determine the $\pi^0$ mass.

53. Calculate the $Q$-value for each of the reactions, Eq. 32–4, for producing a pion.

54. Calculate the $Q$-value for the reaction $\pi^- + \mathrm{p} \rightarrow \Lambda^0 + \mathrm{K}^0$, when negative pions strike stationary protons. Estimate the minimum pion kinetic energy needed to produce this reaction. [*Hint*: assume $\Lambda^0$ and $\mathrm{K}^0$ move off with the same velocity.]

55. How many fundamental fermions are there in a water molecule?

56. A proton and an antiproton annihilate each other at rest and produce two pions, $\pi^-$ and $\pi^+$. What is the kinetic energy of each pion?

57. (*a*) Show that the so-called unification distance of $10^{-32}$ m in grand unified theory is equivalent to an energy of about $10^{16}$ GeV. Use the uncertainty principle, and also de Broglie's wavelength formula, and explain how they apply. (*b*) Calculate the temperature corresponding to $10^{16}$ GeV.

58. For the reaction $\mathrm{p} + \mathrm{p} \rightarrow 3\mathrm{p} + \bar{\mathrm{p}}$, where one of the initial protons is at rest, use relativistic formulas to show that the threshold energy is $6m_\mathrm{p}c^2$, equal to three times the magnitude of the $Q$-value of the reaction, where $m_\mathrm{p}$ is the proton mass. [*Hint*: assume all final particles have the same velocity.]

59. The lifetimes listed in Table 32–2 are in terms of *proper time*, measured in a reference frame where the particle is at rest. If a tau lepton is created with a kinetic energy of 450 MeV, how long would its track be as measured in the lab, on average, ignoring any collisions?

60. Identify the missing particle in the following reactions.
(*a*) $\mathrm{p} + \mathrm{p} \rightarrow \mathrm{p} + \mathrm{n} + \pi^+ + ?$
(*b*) $\mathrm{p} + ? \rightarrow \mathrm{n} + \mu^+$

61. Use the quark model to describe the reaction
$$\bar{\mathrm{p}} + \mathrm{n} \rightarrow \pi^- + \pi^0.$$

62. What fraction of the speed of light $c$ is the speed of a 7.0-TeV proton?

## Answers to Exercises

**A:** $1.24 \times 10^{-18}$ m.

**B:** $\mathrm{s}\bar{\mathrm{u}}$.

This map of the entire sky (WMAP) is color-coded to represent slight temperature variations in the almost perfectly uniform 2.7-kelvin microwave background radiation that reaches us from all directions in the sky. Produced in 2003, it is providing detailed information on the origins of our universe and its structures. The red stripe across the middle is our own Galaxy, the Milky Way, showing up in the foreground. (It has been chosen as the "equator" for this projection of the full sky.)

To discuss the nature of the universe as we understand it today, we examine the latest theories on how stars and galaxies form and evolve, including the role of nucleosynthesis. We briefly discuss Einstein's general theory of relativity, which deals with gravity and curvature of space. We take a thorough look at the evidence for the expansion of the universe, and the standard model of the universe evolving from an initial Big Bang. Finally we point out some unsolved problems, including the nature of dark matter and dark energy that make up most of our universe.

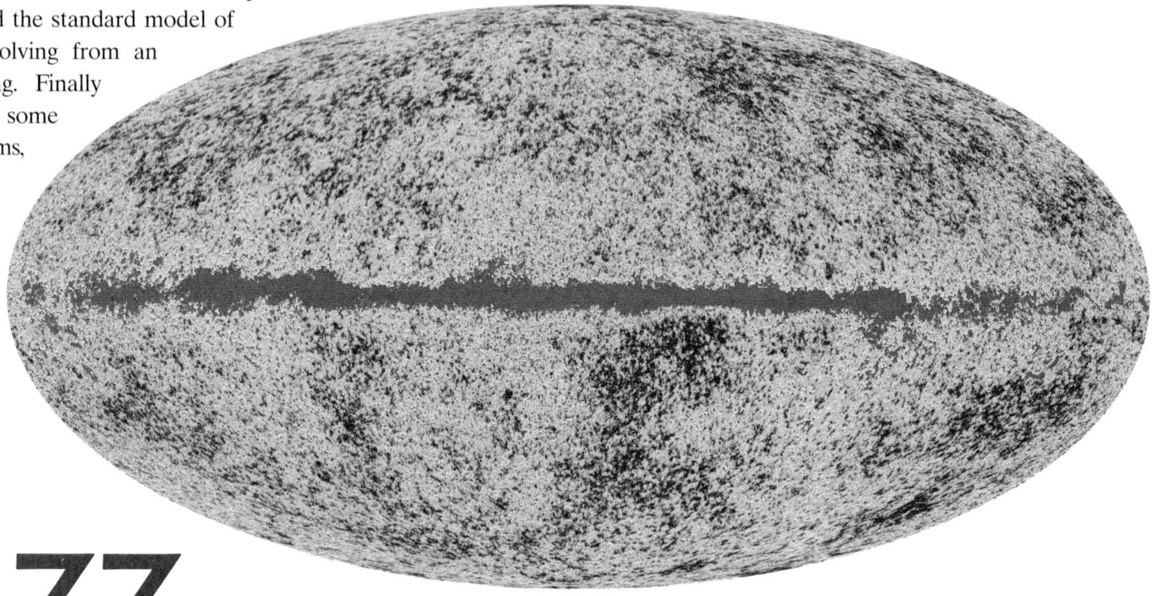

CHAPTER 33

# Astrophysics and Cosmology

In the previous Chapter, we studied the tiniest objects in the universe—the elementary particles. Now we leap to the largest—stars and galaxies. These two extreme realms, elementary particles and the cosmos, are among the most intriguing and exciting subjects in science. And, surprisingly, these two extreme realms are related in a fundamental way, as already hinted in Chapter 32.

Use of the techniques and ideas of physics to study the heavens is often referred to as **astrophysics**. Central to our present theoretical understanding of the universe (or cosmos) is Einstein's *general theory of relativity* and the modern theory of gravitation. Many other aspects of physics are involved, from electromagnetism and thermodynamics to atomic and nuclear physics as well as elementary particles. General Relativity serves also as the foundation for modern **cosmology**, which is the study of the universe as a whole. Cosmology deals especially with the search for a theoretical framework to understand the observed universe, its origin, and its future. The questions posed by cosmology are profound and difficult; the possible answers are often unimaginable. They are questions like "Has the universe always existed, or did it have a beginning in time?" Either alternative is difficult to imagine: time going back indefinitely into the past, or an actual moment when the universe began (but, then, what was there before?). And what about the size of the universe? Is it infinite in size? It is hard to imagine infinity. Or is it finite in size? This is also hard to imagine, for if the universe is finite, it does not make sense to ask what is beyond it, because the universe is all there is.

In the last few years, so much progress has occurred in astrophysics and cosmology that many scientists are calling recent work a "Golden Age" for cosmology. Our survey will be qualitative, but we will nonetheless touch on the major ideas. We begin with a look at what can be seen beyond the Earth.

## 33–1 Stars and Galaxies

According to the ancients, the stars, except for the few that seemed to move (the planets), were fixed on a sphere beyond the last planet. The universe was neatly self-contained, and we on Earth were at or near its center. But in the centuries following Galileo's first telescopic observations of the heavens in 1610, our view of the universe has changed dramatically. We no longer place ourselves at the center, and we view the universe as vastly larger. The distances involved are so great that we specify them in terms of the time it takes light to travel the given distance: for example, 1 light-second $= (3.0 \times 10^8\,\mathrm{m/s})(1.0\,\mathrm{s}) = 3.0 \times 10^8\,\mathrm{m} = 300{,}000\,\mathrm{km}$; 1 light-minute $= 18 \times 10^6\,\mathrm{km}$; and 1 **light-year** (ly) is

$$\begin{aligned} 1\,\mathrm{ly} &= (2.998 \times 10^8\,\mathrm{m/s})(3.156 \times 10^7\,\mathrm{s/yr}) \\ &= 9.46 \times 10^{15}\,\mathrm{m} \approx 10^{13}\,\mathrm{km}. \end{aligned}$$

*Light-year (unit)*

For specifying distances to the Sun and Moon, we usually use meters or kilometers, but we could specify them in terms of light. The Earth–Moon distance is 384,000 km, which is 1.28 light-seconds. The Earth–Sun distance is $1.50 \times 10^{11}$ m, or 150,000,000 km; this is equal to 8.3 light-minutes. Far out in our solar system, the ninth planet, Pluto, is about $6 \times 10^9$ km from the Sun, or $6 \times 10^{-4}$ ly. The nearest star to us, other than the Sun, is Proxima Centauri, about 4.3 ly away. (Note that the nearest star is about 10,000 times farther from us than the outer reaches of our solar system.)

On a clear moonless night, thousands of stars of varying degrees of brightness can be seen, as well as the long cloudy stripe known as the Milky Way (Fig. 33–1). Galileo first observed, with his telescope, that the Milky Way is comprised of countless individual stars. A century and a half later (about 1750), Thomas Wright suggested that the Milky Way was a flat disc of stars extending to great distances in a plane, which we call the **Galaxy** (Greek for "milky way").

**FIGURE 33–1** A section of the Milky Way. The thin line is the trail of an artificial Earth satellite.

**FIGURE 33–2** Our Galaxy, as it would appear from the outside: (a) "edge view," in the plane of the disc; (b) "top view," looking down on the disc. (If only we could see it like this—from the outside!) (c) Infrared photograph of the inner reaches of the Milky Way, showing the central bulge of our Galaxy. This very wide angle photo extends over 180° of sky, and to be viewed properly it should be wrapped in a semicircle with your eyes at the center. The white dots are nearby stars.

(a)

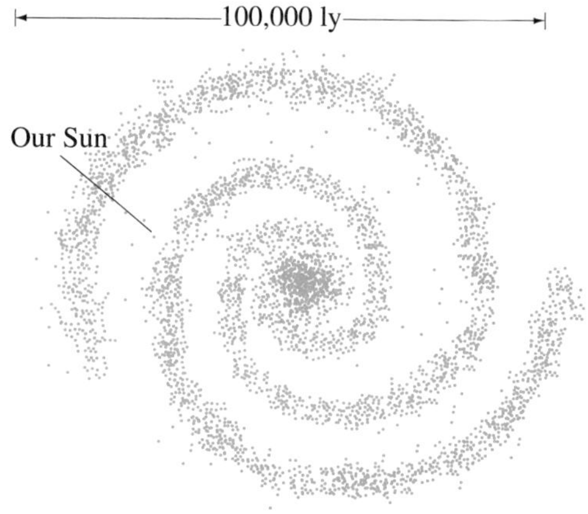

(b)

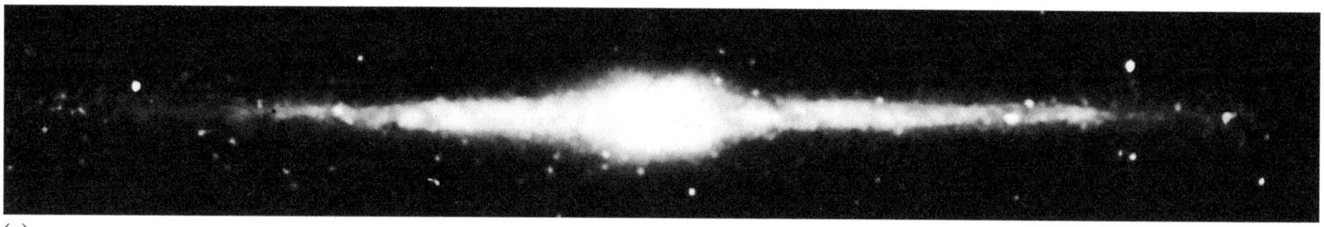
(c)

Our Galaxy has a diameter of almost 100,000 light-years and a thickness of roughly 2000 ly. It has a bulging central "nucleus" and spiral arms (Fig. 33–2). Our Sun, which seems to be just another star, is located about halfway from the galactic center to the edge, some 26,000 ly from the center. Our Galaxy contains roughly 100 billion $(10^{11})$ stars. The Sun orbits the galactic center approximately once every 250 million years or so, so its speed is about 200 km/s relative to the center of the Galaxy. The total mass of all the stars in our Galaxy is estimated to be about $3 \times 10^{41}$ kg, which is ordinary matter. In addition, there is strong evidence that our Galaxy is surrounded by an invisible "halo" of "dark matter," which we discuss in Section 33–8.

**EXAMPLE 33–1 ESTIMATE Our Galaxy's mass.** Estimate the total mass of our Galaxy using the orbital data of the Sun (including our solar system) about the center of the Galaxy. Assume that most of the mass of the Galaxy is concentrated near the center of the Galaxy.

**APPROACH** We assume that the Sun and the solar system (total mass $m$) move in a circular orbit about the center of the Galaxy (total mass $M$), and that the mass $M$ can be considered as being located at the center of the Galaxy. We then apply Newton's second law, $F = ma$, with $a$ being the centripetal acceleration, $a = v^2/r$, and $F$ being the universal law of gravitation (Chapter 5).

**SOLUTION** Our Sun and solar system orbit the center of the Galaxy, according to the best measurements as mentioned above, with a speed of about $v = 200\text{ km/s}$ at a distance from the Galaxy center of about $r = 26{,}000\text{ ly}$. We use Newton's second law:

$$F = ma$$

$$G\frac{Mm}{r^2} = m\frac{v^2}{r}$$

where $M$ is the mass of the Galaxy and $m$ is the mass of our Sun and solar system. Solving this, we find

$$M = \frac{rv^2}{G} \approx \frac{(26{,}000\text{ ly})(10^{16}\text{ m/ly})(2 \times 10^5\text{ m/s})^2}{6.67 \times 10^{-11}\text{ N}\cdot\text{m}^2/\text{kg}^2} \approx 2 \times 10^{41}\text{ kg}.$$

**NOTE** In terms of *numbers* of stars, if they are like our Sun $(m = 2.0 \times 10^{30}\text{ kg})$, there would be about $(2 \times 10^{41}\text{ kg})/(2 \times 10^{30}\text{ kg}) \approx 10^{11}$ or about 100 billion stars.

In addition to stars both within and outside the Milky Way, we can see by telescope many faint cloudy patches in the sky which were all referred to once as "nebulae" (Latin for "clouds"). A few of these, such as those in the constellations Andromeda and Orion, can actually be discerned with the naked eye on a clear night. Some are **star clusters** (Fig. 33–3), groups of stars that are so numerous they appear to be a cloud. Others are glowing clouds of gas or dust (Fig. 33–4), and it is for these that we now mainly reserve the word **nebula**. Most fascinating are those that belong to a third category: they often have fairly regular elliptical shapes and seem to be a great distance beyond our Galaxy. Immanuel Kant (about 1755) seems to have been the first to suggest that these latter might be circular discs, but appear elliptical because we see them at an angle, and are faint because they are so distant. At first it was not universally accepted that these objects were **extragalactic**—that is, outside our Galaxy. The very large telescopes constructed in the twentieth century revealed that individual stars could be resolved within these extragalactic objects and that many contain spiral arms. Edwin Hubble (1889–1953) did much of this observational work in the 1920s using the 2.5-m (100-inch) telescope† on Mt. Wilson near Los Angeles, California, then the world's largest. Hubble demonstrated that these objects were indeed extragalactic because of their great distances. The distance to our nearest large galaxy,‡ Andromeda, is over 2 million light-years, a distance 20 times greater than the diameter of our Galaxy. It seemed logical that these nebulae must be **galaxies** similar to ours. (Note that it is usual to capitalize the word "galaxy" only when it refers to our own.) Today it is thought there are roughly $40 \times 10^9$ galaxies in the observable universe—that is, roughly as many galaxies as there are stars in a galaxy. See Fig. 33–5.

Many galaxies tend to be grouped in **galaxy clusters** held together by their mutual gravitational attraction. There may be anywhere from a few to many thousands

**FIGURE 33–3** This globular star cluster is located in the constellation Hercules.

**FIGURE 33–4** This gaseous nebula, found in the constellation Carina, is about 9000 light-years from us.

†2.5 m (= 100 inches) refers to the diameter of the curved objective mirror. The bigger the mirror, the more light it collects (greater intensity) and the less diffraction there is (better resolution), so more and fainter stars can be seen. See Chapter 25. Until recently, photographic films or plates were used to take long time exposures. Now large solid-state CCD sensors (Section 25–1) are available containing 100 million pixels (compared to 5 or 6 megapixels in a good-quality digital camera).

‡The *Magellanic clouds* are much closer than Andromeda, but are small and are usually considered small satellite galaxies of our own Galaxy.

**FIGURE 33–5** Photographs of galaxies. (a) Spiral galaxy in the constellation Hydra. (b) Two galaxies: the larger and more dramatic one is known as the Whirlpool galaxy. (c) A false-color infrared image of the same galaxies as in (b), here showing the arms of the spiral as being more regular than in the visible light photo (b); the different colors correspond to different light intensities. Visible light is scattered and absorbed by interstellar dust much more than infrared is, so the latter gives us a clearer image.

(a) (b) (c)

**TABLE 33–1 Heavenly Distances**

| Object | Approx. Distance from Earth (ly) |
|---|---|
| Moon | $4 \times 10^{-8}$ |
| Sun | $1.6 \times 10^{-5}$ |
| Size of solar system (distance to Pluto) | $6 \times 10^{-4}$ |
| Nearest star (Proxima Centauri) | 4.3 |
| Center of our Galaxy | $2.6 \times 10^{4}$ |
| Nearest large galaxy | $2.4 \times 10^{6}$ |
| Farthest galaxies | $10^{10}$ |

of galaxies in each cluster. Furthermore, clusters themselves seem to be organized into even larger aggregates: clusters of clusters of galaxies, or **superclusters**. The farthest detectable galaxies are on the order of $10^{10}$ ly distant. See Table 33–1.

CONCEPTUAL EXAMPLE 33–2 **Looking back in time.** Astronomers often think of their telescopes as time machines, looking back toward the origin of the universe. How far back do they look?

**RESPONSE** The distance in light-years measures precisely how long in years the light has been traveling to reach us, so Table 33–1 tells us also how far back in time we are looking. For example, if we saw Proxima Centauri explode into a supernova today, then the event would have really occurred 4.3 years ago. The most distant galaxies, $10^{10}$ ly away, emitted the light we see now $10^{10}$ years ago; so what we see was how they were then, $10^{10}$ yr ago, close to the beginning of the universe.

**EXERCISE A** Suppose we could place a huge mirror 1 light-year away from us. What would we see in this mirror if it is facing us on Earth? When did it take place? (This might be called a "time machine.")

Besides the usual stars, clusters of stars, galaxies, and clusters and superclusters of galaxies, the universe contains a number of other interesting objects. Among these are stars known as *red giants*, *white dwarfs*, *neutron stars*, exploding stars called *novae* and *supernovae*, and *black holes* (very probably) whose gravity is so strong even light can not escape them. In addition, there is electromagnetic radiation that reaches the Earth but does not emanate from the bright pointlike objects we call stars: particularly important is the microwave background radiation that arrives nearly uniformly from all directions in the universe. We will discuss all these phenomena.

Finally, there are "active galactic nuclei" (AGN), which are very luminous pointlike sources of light in the centers of distant galaxies. The most dramatic examples of AGN are *quasars* ("quasistellar objects" or QSOs), which are so luminous that the surrounding starlight of the galaxy is drowned out. Their luminosity is thought to come from matter starting to fall into a giant black hole at a galaxy's center.

*Quasar (QSO)*

## 33–2 Stellar Evolution: The Birth and Death of Stars

The stars appear unchanging. Night after night the heavens reveal no significant variations. Indeed, on a human time scale, the vast majority of stars change very little (except for novae, supernovae, and certain variable stars). Although stars *seem* fixed in relation to each other, many move sufficiently for the motion to be detected. Speeds of stars relative to neighboring stars can be hundreds of km/s, but at their great distance from us, this motion is detectable only by careful measurement. Furthermore, there is a great range of brightness among stars. The differences in brightness are due to differences in the amount of light stars emit as well as to their different distances from us.

### Luminosity and Brightness of Stars

A useful parameter for a star or galaxy is its **luminosity** (or "absolute luminosity"), $L$, by which we mean the total power radiated in watts. Also important is the **apparent brightness**, $l$, defined as the power crossing unit area at the Earth perpendicular to the path of the light. Given that energy is conserved, and ignoring any absorption in space, the total emitted power $L$ when it reaches a distance $d$ from the star will be spread over a sphere of surface area $4\pi d^2$. If $d$ is the distance from the star to the Earth, then $L$ must be equal to $4\pi d^2$ times $l$ (power per unit area at Earth). That is,

$$l = \frac{L}{4\pi d^2}. \qquad \textbf{(33–1)}$$

**EXAMPLE 33–3 Apparent brightness.** Suppose a particular star has absolute luminosity equal to that of the Sun but is 10 ly away from Earth. By what factor will it appear dimmer than the Sun?

**APPROACH** The luminosity $L$ is the same for both stars, so the apparent brightness depends only on their relative distances. We use the inverse square law as stated in Eq. 33–1 to determine the relative brightness.

**SOLUTION** Using Eq. 33–1, we find that the star appears dimmer by a factor

$$\frac{l_{\text{star}}}{l_{\text{Sun}}} = \frac{d_{\text{Sun}}^2}{d_{\text{star}}^2} = \frac{(1.5 \times 10^8\,\text{km})^2}{(10\,\text{ly})^2(10^{13}\,\text{km/ly})^2} \approx 2 \times 10^{-12}.$$

Careful study of nearby stars has shown that the absolute luminosity for most stars depends on the mass:† *the more massive the star, the greater its luminosity.* Another important parameter of a star is its surface temperature, which can be determined from the spectrum of electromagnetic frequencies it emits, just as for a blackbody (Section 27–2). As we saw in Chapter 27, as the temperature of a body increases, the spectrum shifts from predominantly lower frequencies (and longer wavelengths, such as red) to higher frequencies (and shorter wavelengths such as blue). Quantitatively, the relation is given by Wien's law (Eq. 27–2): the peak wavelength $\lambda_P$ in the spectrum of light emitted by a blackbody (and stars are fairly good approximations to blackbodies) is inversely proportional to its kelvin temperature $T$; that is, $\lambda_P T = 2.90 \times 10^{-3}\,\text{m}\cdot\text{K}$. The surface temperatures of stars typically range from about 3500 K (reddish) to perhaps 50,000 K (UV).

*Luminosity increases with star's mass*

**EXAMPLE 33–4 Determining star temperature and star size.** Suppose that the distances from Earth to two nearby stars can be reasonably estimated, and that their measured apparent brightnesses suggest the two stars have about the same absolute luminosity, $L$. The spectrum of one of the stars peaks at about 700 nm (so it is reddish). The spectrum of the other peaks at about 350 nm (bluish). Use Wien's law (Eq. 27–2) and the Stefan-Boltzmann equation (Section 14–8) to determine (*a*) the surface temperature of each star, and (*b*) how much larger one star is than the other.

**APPROACH** We determine the surface temperature $T$ for each star using Wien's law and each star's peak wavelength. Then, using the Stefan-Boltzmann equation (power output or luminosity $\propto AT^4$), we can find the surface area ratio and relative sizes of the two stars.

**SOLUTION** (*a*) Wien's law (Eq. 27–2) states that $\lambda_P T = 2.90 \times 10^{-3}\,\text{m}\cdot\text{K}$. So the temperature of the reddish star is

$$T_{\text{r}} = \frac{2.90 \times 10^{-3}\,\text{m}\cdot\text{K}}{700 \times 10^{-9}\,\text{m}} = 4140\,\text{K}.$$

The temperature of the bluish star will be double this since its peak wavelength is half (350 nm vs. 700 nm); just to check:

$$T_{\text{b}} = \frac{2.90 \times 10^{-3}\,\text{m}\cdot\text{K}}{350 \times 10^{-9}\,\text{m}} = 8280\,\text{K}.$$

(*b*) The Stefan-Boltzmann equation, which we discussed in Chapter 14 (see Eq. 14–5), states that the power radiated *per unit area* of surface from a body is proportional to the fourth power of the kelvin temperature, $T^4$. Now the temperature of the bluish star is double that of the reddish star, so the bluish one must radiate $(2^4) = 16$ times as much energy per unit area. But we are given that they have the same luminosity (the same total power output); so the surface area of the blue star must be $\frac{1}{16}$ that of the red one. Since the surface area of a sphere is $4\pi r^2$, we conclude that the radius of the reddish star is $\sqrt{16} = 4$ times larger than the radius of the bluish star (or $4^3 = 64$ times the volume).

† Applies to "main-sequence" stars (see next page). The mass of a star can be determined by observing its gravitational effects. Many stars are part of a cluster, the simplest being a binary star in which two stars orbit around each other, allowing their masses to be determined using rotational mechanics.

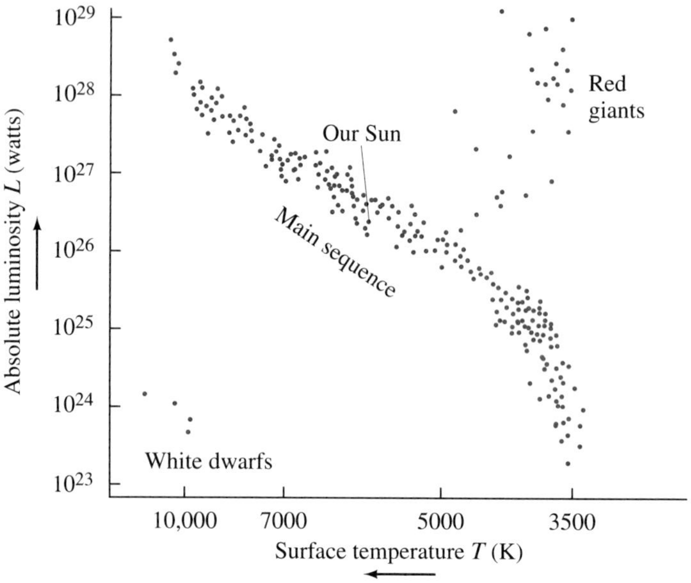


**FIGURE 33–6** Hertzsprung–Russell (H–R) diagram. Note that the temperature $T$ increases to the left.

## H–R Diagram

*H–R diagram*

*Main-sequence stars*

*Red giants*

*White dwarfs*

An important astronomical discovery, made around 1900, was that for most stars, the color is related to the absolute luminosity and therefore to the mass. A useful way to present this relationship is by the so-called Hertzsprung–Russell (H–R) diagram. On the H–R diagram, the horizontal axis shows the temperature $T$ whereas the vertical axis is the luminosity $L$; each star is represented by a point on the diagram, Fig. 33–6. Most stars fall along the diagonal band termed the **main sequence**. Starting at the lower right we find the coolest stars, reddish in color; they are the least luminous and therefore of low mass. Farther up toward the left we find hotter and more luminous stars that are whitish, like our Sun. Still farther up we find still more massive and more luminous stars, bluish in color. Stars that fall on this diagonal band are called *main-sequence stars*. There are also stars that fall outside the main sequence. Above and to the right we find extremely large stars, with high luminosities but with low (reddish) color temperature: these are called **red giants**. At the lower left, there are a few stars of low luminosity but with high temperature: these are the **white dwarfs**.

**EXAMPLE 33–5 ESTIMATE Distance to a star using H–R and color.** Suppose that detailed study of a certain star suggests that it most likely fits on the main sequence of an H–R diagram. Its measured apparent brightness is $l = 1.0 \times 10^{-12}\,\mathrm{W/m^2}$, and the peak wavelength of its spectrum is $\lambda_P \approx 600\,\mathrm{nm}$. Estimate its distance from us.

**APPROACH** We find the temperature using Wien's law, Eq. 27–2. The absolute luminosity is estimated for a main sequence star on the H–R diagram of Fig. 33–6, and then the distance is found using Eq. 33–1.

**SOLUTION** The star's temperature, from Wien's law (Eq. 27–2), is

$$T \approx \frac{2.90 \times 10^{-3}\,\mathrm{m \cdot K}}{600 \times 10^{-9}\,\mathrm{m}} \approx 4800\,\mathrm{K}.$$

A star on the main sequence of an H–R diagram at this temperature has absolute luminosity of about $L \approx 1 \times 10^{26}\,\mathrm{W}$, read off of Fig. 33–6. Then, from Eq. 33–1,

$$d = \sqrt{\frac{L}{4\pi l}} \approx \sqrt{\frac{1 \times 10^{26}\,\mathrm{W}}{4(3.14)(1.0 \times 10^{-12}\,\mathrm{W/m^2})}} \approx 3 \times 10^{18}\,\mathrm{m}.$$

Its distance from us in light-years is

$$d = \frac{3 \times 10^{18}\,\mathrm{m}}{10^{16}\,\mathrm{m/ly}} \approx 300\,\mathrm{ly}.$$

**EXERCISE B** Estimate the distance to a 6000 K star with an apparent brightness of $2.0 \times 10^{-12}\,\mathrm{W/m^2}$.

## Stellar Evolution; Nucleosynthesis

Why are there different types of stars, such as red giants and white dwarfs, as well as main-sequence stars? Were they all born this way, in the beginning? Or might each different type represent a different age in the life cycle of a star? Astronomers and astrophysicists today believe the latter is the case. Note, however, that we cannot actually follow any but the tiniest part of the life cycle of any given star since they live for ages vastly greater than ours, on the order of millions or billions of years. Nonetheless, let us follow the process of **stellar evolution** from the birth to the death of a star, as astrophysicists have theoretically reconstructed it today.

*Birth of a star*

Stars are born, it is believed, when gaseous clouds (mostly hydrogen) contract due to the pull of gravity. A huge gas cloud might fragment into numerous contracting masses, each mass centered in an area where the density was only slightly greater than that at nearby points. Once such "globules" formed, gravity would cause each to contract in toward its center of mass. As the particles of such a *protostar* accelerate inward, their kinetic energy increases. When the kinetic energy is sufficiently high, the Coulomb repulsion between the positive charges is not strong enough to keep the hydrogen nuclei apart, and nuclear fusion can take place. In a star like our Sun, the "burning" of hydrogen[†] (that is, fusion) occurs via the *proton–proton cycle* (Section 31–3, Eqs. 31–6), in which four protons fuse to form a $^4_2\mathrm{He}$ nucleus with the release of $\gamma$ rays, positrons, and neutrinos: $4\,^1_1\mathrm{H} \rightarrow {}^4_2\mathrm{He} + 2\,\mathrm{e}^+ + 2\,\nu_\mathrm{e} + 2\,\gamma$. These reactions require a temperature of about $10^7\,\mathrm{K}$, corresponding to an average kinetic energy ($kT$) of about 1 keV (Eq. 13–8). In more massive stars, the carbon cycle produces the same net effect: Four $^1_1\mathrm{H}$ produce a $^4_2\mathrm{He}$—see Section 31–3. The fusion reactions take place primarily in the core of a star, where $T$ is sufficiently high. (The surface temperature is, of course, much lower—on the order of a few thousand kelvins.) The tremendous release of energy in these fusion reactions produces an outward pressure sufficient to halt the inward gravitational contraction; and our protostar, now really a young *star*, stabilizes on the main sequence. Exactly where the star falls along the main sequence depends on its mass. The more massive the star, the farther up (and to the left) it falls on the H–R diagram of Fig. 33–6. To reach the main sequence requires perhaps 30 million years, if it is a star like our Sun, and it is expected to remain there[‡] about 10 billion years ($10^{10}$ yr). Although most stars are billions of years old, there is evidence that stars are actually being born at this moment.

*Contraction due to gravity*

*Fusion begins when $T$ (and $\overline{\mathrm{KE}}$) is large enough*

*Proton–proton cycle*

*Carbon cycle*

*Reaching the main sequence*

As hydrogen fuses to form helium, the helium that is formed is denser and tends to accumulate in the central core where it was formed. As the core of helium grows, hydrogen continues to fuse in a shell around it: see Fig. 33–7. When much of the hydrogen within the core has been consumed, the production of energy decreases at the center and is no longer sufficient to prevent the huge gravitational forces from once again causing the core to contract and heat up. The hydrogen in the shell around the core then fuses even more fiercely because of this rise in temperature, causing the outer envelope of the star to expand and to cool. The surface temperature, thus reduced, produces a spectrum of light that peaks at longer wavelength (reddish).

**FIGURE 33–7** A shell of "burning" hydrogen (fusing to become helium) surrounds the core where the newly formed helium gravitates.

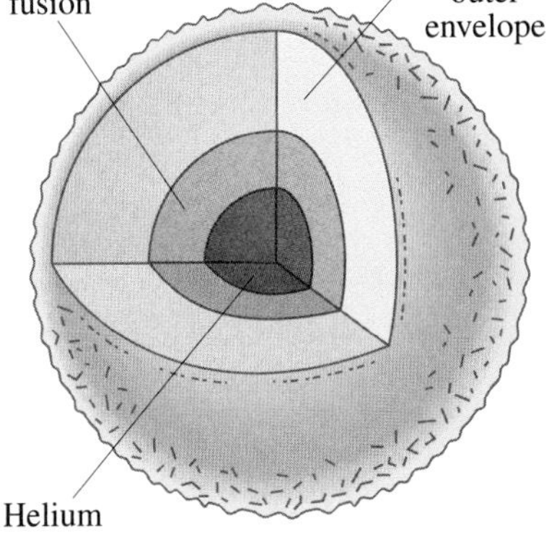


[†] The word "burn" is put in quotation marks because these high-temperature fusion reactions occur via a *nuclear* process, and must not be confused with ordinary burning (of, say, paper, wood, or coal) in air, which is a *chemical* reaction, occurring at the *atomic* level (and at a much lower temperature).

[‡] More massive stars, since they are hotter and the Coulomb repulsion is more easily overcome, "burn" much more quickly, and so use up their fuel faster, resulting in shorter lives. A star 10 times more massive than our Sun, for example, will remain on the main sequence only for about $10^7$ years. Stars less massive than our Sun live much longer than our Sun's $10^{10}$ yr.

By this time the star has left the main sequence. It has become redder, and as it has grown in size, it has become more luminous. So it will have moved to the right and upward on the H–R diagram, as shown in Fig. 33–8. As it moves upward, it enters the **red giant** stage. Thus, theory explains the origin of red giants as a natural step in a star's evolution. Our Sun, for example, has been on the main sequence for about $4\frac{1}{2}$ billion years. It will probably remain there another 4 or 5 billion years. When our Sun leaves the main sequence, it is expected to grow in diameter (as it becomes a red giant) by a factor of 100 or more, swallowing up one or more of the inner planets (Mercury, Venus, maybe Earth).

*Red giants*

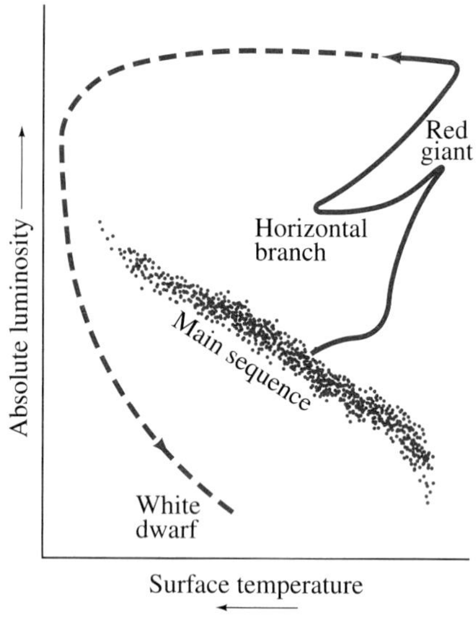


**FIGURE 33–8** Evolutionary "track" of a star like our Sun represented on an H–R diagram.

If the star is like our Sun, or larger, further fusion can occur. As the star's outer envelope expands, its core is shrinking and heating up. When the temperature reaches about $10^8$ K, even helium nuclei, in spite of their greater charge and hence greater electrical repulsion, can then reach each other and undergo fusion. The reactions are

$$\begin{aligned} {}^{4}_{2}\mathrm{He} + {}^{4}_{2}\mathrm{He} &\longrightarrow {}^{8}_{4}\mathrm{Be} \\ {}^{4}_{2}\mathrm{He} + {}^{8}_{4}\mathrm{Be} &\longrightarrow {}^{12}_{6}\mathrm{C} \end{aligned} \qquad \textbf{(33–2)}$$

with the emission of two $\gamma$ rays. These two reactions must occur in quick succession (because ${}^{8}_{4}\mathrm{Be}$ is very unstable), and the net effect is

$$3\,{}^{4}_{2}\mathrm{He} \longrightarrow {}^{12}_{6}\mathrm{C}. \qquad (Q = 7.3\ \mathrm{MeV})$$

This fusion of helium causes a change in the star which moves rapidly to the "horizontal branch" on the H–R diagram (Fig. 33–8). Further fusion reactions are possible, with ${}^{4}_{2}\mathrm{He}$ fusing with ${}^{12}_{6}\mathrm{C}$ to form ${}^{16}_{8}\mathrm{O}$. In more massive stars, higher $Z$ elements like ${}^{20}_{10}\mathrm{Ne}$ or ${}^{24}_{12}\mathrm{Mg}$ can be made. This process of creating heavier nuclei from lighter ones (or by absorption of neutrons which tends to occur at higher $Z$) is called **nucleosynthesis**.

*Nucleosynthesis*

The final fate of a star depends on its mass. Stars can lose mass as parts of their envelope drift off into space. Stars born with a mass less than about 8 (or perhaps 10) solar masses eventually end up with a residual mass less than about 1.4 solar masses, which is known as the *Chandrasekhar limit*. For them, no further fusion energy can be obtained. The core of such a "low mass" star (original mass $\lesssim$ 8 solar masses) contracts under gravity; the outer envelope expands again and the star becomes an even larger red giant. Eventually the outer layers escape into space, the core shrinks, the star cools, and typically follows the dashed route shown in Fig. 33–8, descending downward, becoming a **white dwarf**. A white dwarf with a mass equal to that of the Sun would be about the size of the Earth. A white dwarf contracts to the point at which the electron clouds start to overlap, but collapses no further because, as the Pauli exclusion principle claims, no two electrons can be in the same quantum state. Arriving at this point is called *electron degeneracy*. A white dwarf continues to lose internal energy by radiation, decreasing in temperature and becoming dimmer until its light goes out. It has then become a cold dark chunk of ash.

*White dwarfs*

Stars whose residual mass is greater than the Chandrasekhar limit of 1.4 solar masses (original mass greater than about 8 or 10 solar masses) are thought to follow a quite different scenario. A star with this great a mass can contract under gravity and heat up even further. In the range $T = 2.5\text{–}5 \times 10^9$ K, nuclei as heavy as ${}^{56}_{26}\mathrm{Fe}$ and ${}^{56}_{28}\mathrm{Ni}$ can be made. But here the formation of heavy nuclei from lighter ones, by fusion, ends. As we saw in Fig. 30–1, the average binding energy per nucleon begins to decrease for $A$ greater than about 60. Further fusions would *require* energy, rather than release it.

*Production of heavy elements*

Elements heavier than Ni are thought to form mainly by neutron capture, particularly in supernova explosions. Large numbers of free neutrons, resulting from nuclear reactions, are present inside highly evolved stars and they can readily combine with, say, a ${}^{56}_{26}\mathrm{Fe}$ nucleus to form (if three are captured) ${}^{59}_{26}\mathrm{Fe}$, which decays to ${}^{59}_{27}\mathrm{Co}$. The ${}^{59}_{27}\mathrm{Co}$ can capture neutrons, also becoming neutron rich and decaying by $\beta^-$ to the next higher $Z$ element, and so on. The highest $Z$ elements are thought to form by such neutron capture during supernova explosions when hordes of neutrons are available.

Yet at these extremely high temperatures, well above $10^9$ K, the kinetic energy of the nuclei is so high that fusion of elements heavier than iron is still possible even though the reactions require energy input. But the high-energy collisions can also cause the breaking apart of iron and nickel nuclei into He nuclei, and eventually into protons and neutrons:

$$^{56}_{26}\text{Fe} \rightarrow 13\,^{4}_{2}\text{He} + 4\text{n}$$

$$^{4}_{2}\text{He} \rightarrow 2\text{p} + 2\text{n}.$$

These are energy-requiring (endothermic) reactions, but at such extremely high temperature and pressure there is plenty of energy available, enough even to force electrons and protons together to form neutrons in inverse $\beta$ decay:

$$\text{e}^- + \text{p} \rightarrow \text{n} + \nu.$$

As the core collapses under the huge gravitational forces, the tremendous mass becomes essentially an enormous nucleus made up almost exclusively of neutrons. The size of the star is no longer limited by the exclusion principle applied to electrons, but rather applied to neutrons (*neutron degeneracy*), and the star begins to contract rapidly toward forming an enormously dense **neutron star**. The contraction of the core would mean a great reduction in gravitational potential energy. Somehow this energy would have to be released. Indeed, it was suggested in the 1930s that the final core collapse to a neutron star may be accompanied by a catastrophic explosion whose tremendous energy could form virtually all elements of the periodic table and blow away the entire outer envelope of the star (Fig. 33–9), spreading its contents into interstellar space. Such explosions are believed to produce some of the observed *supernovae*. The presence of heavy elements on Earth and in our solar system suggests that our solar system formed from the debris of supernovae.

*Neutron stars*

*Supernovae*

**FIGURE 33–9** These glowing filaments, observed by the Hubble Space Telescope, are remnants of a supernova whose light would have reached Earth thousands of years ago. Inside is a powerful rotating neutron star called a *pulsar*.

The core of a neutron star contracts to the point at which all neutrons are as close together as they are in a nucleus. That is, the density of a neutron star is on the order of $10^{14}$ times greater than normal solids and liquids on Earth. A cupful of such dense matter would weigh billion of tons. A neutron star that has a mass 1.5 times that of our Sun would have a diameter of only about 20 km.

If the final mass of a neutron star is less than about two or three solar masses, its subsequent evolution is thought to be similar to that of a white dwarf. If the mass is greater than this, the star collapses under gravity, overcoming even the neutron exclusion principle. Gravity would then be so strong that even light emitted from it could not escape—it would be pulled back in by the force of gravity. Since no radiation could escape from such a star, we could not see it—it would be black. An object may pass by it and be deflected by its gravitational field, but if it came too close it would be swallowed up, never to escape. This is a **black hole**.

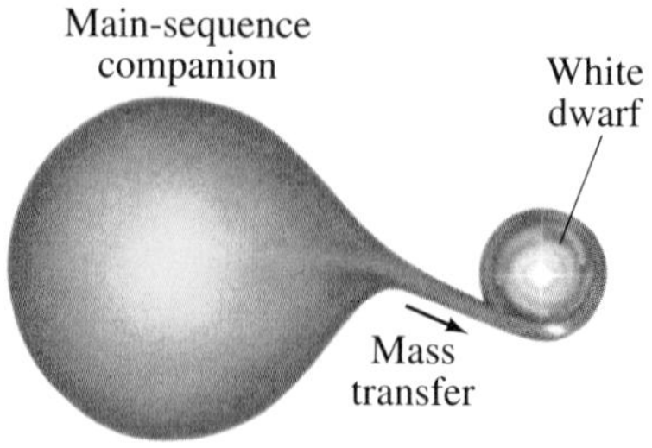


**FIGURE 33–10** Hypothetical model for novae and type Ia supernovae, showing how a white dwarf could pull mass from its normal companion.

## Novae and Supernovae

**Novae** (singular is *nova*, meaning "new" in Latin) are faint stars that have suddenly increased in brightness by as much as a factor of $10^4$ and last for a month or two before fading. Novae are thought to be faint white dwarfs that have pulled mass from a nearby companion (they make up a *binary* system), as illustrated in Fig. 33–10. The captured mass of hydrogen fuses into helium at a high rate for a few weeks. Many novae (maybe all) are *recurrent*—they repeat their bright glow years later.

**Supernovae** are also brief explosive events, but release millions of times more energy than novae, up to $10^{10}$ times more luminous than our Sun. The peak of brightness may equal that of the entire galaxy in which they are located, but lasts only a few days. They remain bright but slowly fade over a few months. Many supernovae form by core collapse to a neutron star as described above.

*Type Ia supernovae*

**Type Ia supernovae** are different. They all seem to have very nearly the same luminosity. They are believed to be binary stars, one of which is a white dwarf that pulls mass from its companion, much like for a nova, Fig. 33–10. The mass is higher, and as mass is captured and the total mass reaches the Chandrasekhar limit of 1.4 solar masses, the star begins to collapse and then explodes as a supernova.

# 33–3 Distance Measurements

*How astronomical distances are measured*

We have talked about the vast distances of objects in the universe. But how do we measure these distances? One basic technique employs simple geometry to measure the **parallax** of a star. By parallax we mean the apparent motion of a star, against the background of more distant stars, due to the Earth's motion about the Sun. As shown in Fig. 33–11, the sighting angle of a star relative to the plane of Earth's orbit (angle $\theta$) can be determined at different times of the year. Since we know the distance $d$ from Earth to Sun, we can reconstruct the right triangles shown in Fig. 33–11 and can determine† the distance $D$ to the star.

†This is essentially the way the heights of mountains are determined, by "triangulation." See Example 1–9.

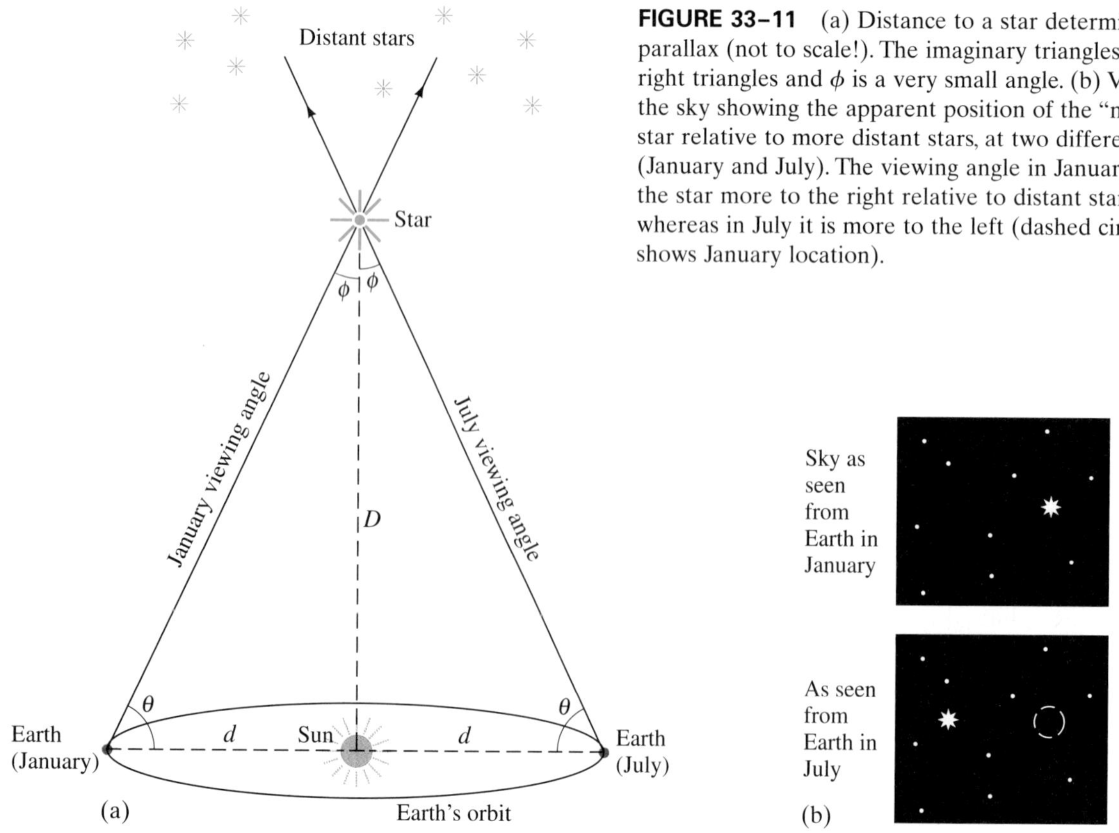


**FIGURE 33–11** (a) Distance to a star determined by parallax (not to scale!). The imaginary triangles are right triangles and $\phi$ is a very small angle. (b) View of the sky showing the apparent position of the "nearby" star relative to more distant stars, at two different times (January and July). The viewing angle in January puts the star more to the right relative to distant stars, whereas in July it is more to the left (dashed circle shows January location).

**EXAMPLE 33–6 ESTIMATE Distance to a star using parallax.** Estimate the distance $D$ to a star if the angle $\theta$ in Fig. 33–11 is measured to be 89.99994°.

**APPROACH** From trigonometry, $\tan\phi = d/D$ in Fig. 33–11. The Sun–Earth distance is $d = 1.5 \times 10^8$ km.

**SOLUTION** The angle $\phi = 90° - 89.99994° = 0.00006°$, or about $1.0 \times 10^{-6}$ radians. We can use $\tan\phi \approx \phi$ since $\phi$ is very small. We solve for $D$ in $\tan\phi = d/D$. The distance $D$ to the star is

$$D = \frac{d}{\tan\phi} \approx \frac{d}{\phi} = \frac{1.5 \times 10^8\,\text{km}}{1.0 \times 10^{-6}\,\text{rad}} = 1.5 \times 10^{14}\,\text{km},$$

or about 15 ly.

Distances to stars are often specified in terms of parallax angle given in seconds of arc: 1 second (1″) is $\frac{1}{60}$ of a minute (′) of arc, which is $\frac{1}{60}$ of a degree, so $1'' = \frac{1}{3600}$ of a degree. The distance is then specified in parsecs (meaning *par*allax angle in *sec*onds of arc), where the **parsec** (pc) is defined as $1/\phi$ with $\phi$ in seconds. In Example 33–6, $\phi = (6 \times 10^{-5})°(3600) = 0.22''$ of arc, so we would say the star is at a distance of $1/0.22'' = 4.5$ pc. It is easy to show that the parsec is given by

$$\begin{aligned} 1\,\text{pc} &= 3.26\,\text{ly} \\ &= (3.26\,\text{ly})(9.46 \times 10^{15}\,\text{m/ly}) = 3.08 \times 10^{16}\,\text{m}. \end{aligned}$$

*Parsec (unit)*

Parallax can be used to determine the distance to stars as far away as about 100 light-years (≈ 30 parsecs) from Earth, and from an orbiting satellite perhaps 5 to 10 times farther. Beyond that distance, parallax angles are too small to measure. For greater distances, more subtle techniques must be employed. We might compare the apparent brightnesses of two galaxies and use the inverse square law (intensity drops off as the square of the distance) to roughly estimate their relative distances. We can't expect this technique to be very precise because we don't expect all galaxies to have the same intrinsic luminosity. A perhaps better estimate assumes the brightest stars in all galaxies (or the brightest galaxies in galaxy clusters) are similar and have about the same absolute luminosity. Consequently, their *apparent* brightness would be a measure of how far away they were.

Another technique makes use of the H–R diagram. Measurement of a star's surface temperature (from its spectra) places it at a certain point (within 20%) on the H–R diagram, assuming it is a main-sequence star, and then its luminosity can be estimated off the vertical axis (Fig. 33–6). Its apparent brightness and Eq. 33–1 give its approximate distance; see Example 33–5.

*Cepheid variables*

A better estimate comes from comparing *variable stars*, such as *Cepheid variables* whose averaged intrinsic luminosity (varying in time) has been found to be correlated to their periods.

*SNIa as standard candles*

The largest distances are estimated by comparing the apparent brightnesses of type Ia supernovae (SNIa). Type Ia supernovae all have a similar origin (they collapse to a neutron star at 1.4 solar masses, as described on the previous page and Fig. 33–10), and their brief explosive burst of light is expected to be of nearly the same total luminosity. They are thus sometimes referred to as "standard candles."

Another important technique for estimating distance is from the "redshift" in the line spectra of elements and compounds. The redshift is related to the expansion of the universe, as discussed in Section 33–5. It is useful for objects further than $10^7$ to $10^8$ ly away.

As we look farther and farther away, the measurement techniques are less and less reliable, so there is more and more uncertainty in the measurements of large distances.

## 33–4 General Relativity: Gravity and the Curvature of Space

We have seen that the force of gravity plays an important role in the processes that occur in stars. Gravity too is important for the evolution of the universe as a whole. The reasons gravity plays the dominant role in the universe, and not one of the other of the four forces in nature, are (1) it is long-range and (2) it is always attractive. The strong and weak nuclear forces act over very short distances only, on the order of the size of a nucleus; hence they do not act over astronomical distances (they do act between nuclei and nucleons in stars to produce nuclear reactions). The electromagnetic force, like gravity, acts over great distances. But it can be either attractive or repulsive. And since the universe does not seem to contain large areas of net electric charge, a large net force does not occur. But gravity acts as an attractive force between *all* masses, and there are large accumulations in the universe of only the one "sign" of mass (not + and − as with electric charge). However, the force of gravity as Newton described it in his law of universal gravitation shows discrepancies on a cosmological scale. Einstein, in his general theory of relativity, developed a theory of gravity that now forms the basis of cosmological dynamics.

**FIGURE 33–12** A freely falling elevator. The released book hovers next to the owner's hand; (b) is a few moments after (a).

(a)

(b)

In the *special theory of relativity* (Chapter 26), Einstein concluded that there is no way for an observer to determine whether a given frame of reference is at rest or is moving at constant velocity in a straight line. Thus the laws of physics must be the same in different inertial reference frames. But what about the more general case of motion where reference frames can be *accelerating*?

Einstein tackled the problem of accelerating reference frames in his **general theory of relativity** and in it also developed a theory of gravity. The mathematics of General Relativity is complex, so our discussion will be mainly qualitative.

We begin with Einstein's **principle of equivalence**, which states that

*Principle of equivalence*

**no experiment can be performed that could distinguish between a uniform gravitational field and an equivalent uniform acceleration.**

If observers sensed that they were accelerating (as in a vehicle speeding around a sharp curve), they could not prove by any experiment that in fact they weren't simply experiencing the pull of a gravitational field. Conversely, we might think we are being pulled by gravity when in fact we are undergoing an "inertial" acceleration having nothing to do with gravity.

As a thought experiment, consider a person in a freely falling elevator near the Earth's surface. If our observer held out a book and let go of it, what would happen? Gravity would pull it downward toward the Earth, but at the same rate ($g = 9.8\,\mathrm{m/s^2}$) at which the person and elevator were falling. So the book would hover right next to the person's hand (Fig. 33–12). The effect is exactly the same as if this reference frame was at rest and *no* forces were acting. On the other hand, if the elevator was out in space where the gravitational field is essentially zero, the released book would float, just as it does in Fig. 33–12. Next, if the elevator (out in space) is accelerating upward at an acceleration of $9.8\,\mathrm{m/s^2}$, the book as seen by our observer would fall to the floor with an acceleration of $9.8\,\mathrm{m/s^2}$, just as if it were falling due to gravity at the surface of the Earth. According to the principle of equivalence, the observer could not determine whether the book fell because the elevator was accelerating upward, or because a gravitational field was acting downward and the elevator was at rest. The two descriptions are equivalent.

The principle of equivalence is related to the concept that there are two types of mass. Newton's second law, $F = ma$, uses **inertial mass**. We might say that inertial mass represents "resistance" to any type of force. The second type of mass is **gravitational mass**. When one body attracts another by the gravitational force (Newton's law of universal gravitation, $F = Gm_1 m_2/r^2$, Chapter 5), the strength of the force is proportional to the product of the *gravitational masses* of the two bodies. This is much like the electric force

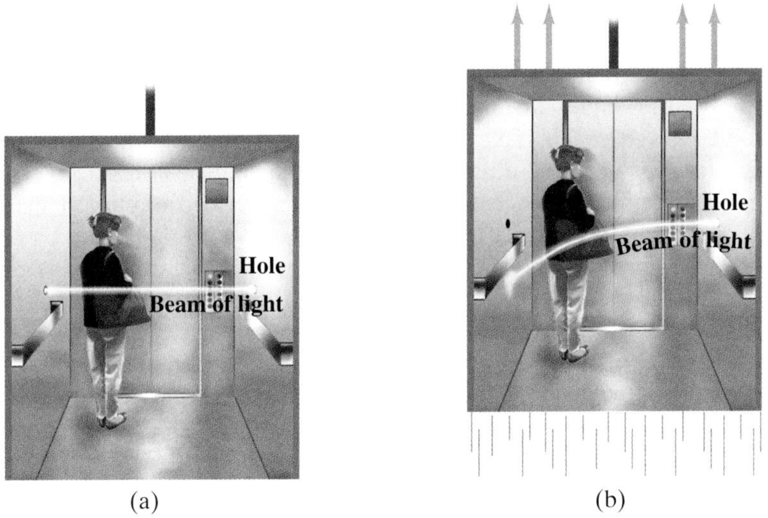


**FIGURE 33–13** (a) Light beam goes straight across an elevator not accelerating. (b) The light beam bends (exaggerated) in an elevator accelerating in an upward direction.

between two bodies which is proportional to the product of their electric charges. The electric charge of a body is not related to its inertial mass; so why should we expect that a body's gravitational mass (call it gravitational charge if you like) be related to its inertial mass? All along we have assumed they were the same. Why? Because no experiment—not even of high precision—has been able to discern any measurable difference between inertial mass and gravitational mass. This is another way to state the equivalence principle: *gravitational mass is equivalent to inertial mass.*

The principle of equivalence can be used to show that light ought to be deflected due to the gravitational force of a massive body. Consider another thought experiment, in which an elevator is in free space where virtually no gravity acts. If a light beam enters a hole in the side of the elevator, the beam travels straight across the elevator and makes a spot on the opposite side if the elevator is at rest (Fig. 33–13a). If the elevator is accelerating upward, as in Fig. 33–13b, the light beam still travels straight across in a reference frame at rest. In the upwardly accelerating elevator, however, the beam is observed to curve downward. Why? Because during the time the light travels from one side of the elevator to the other, the elevator is moving upward at ever-increasing speed. Next we note that according to the equivalence principle, an upwardly accelerating reference frame is equivalent to a downward gravitational field. Hence, we can picture the curved light path in Fig. 33–13b as being the effect of a gravitational field. Thus, from the principle of equivalence, we expect gravity to exert a force on a beam of light and to bend it out of a straight-line path!

**FIGURE 33–14** (a) Three stars in the sky. (b) If the light from one of these stars passes very near the Sun, whose gravity bends the rays, the star will appear higher than it actually is.

*Gravity bends light*

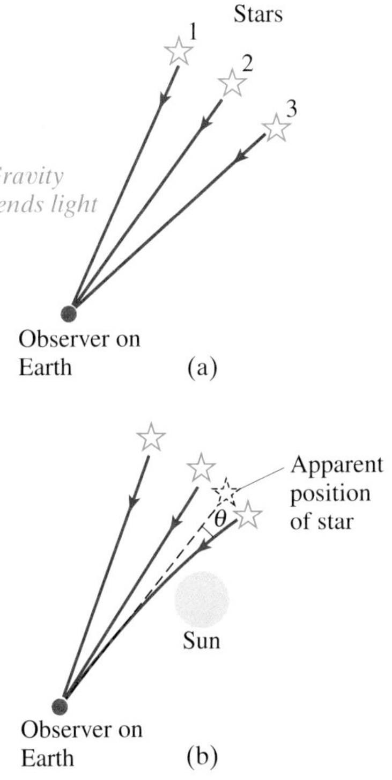


*Space is curved*

That light is affected by gravity is an important prediction of Einstein's general theory of relativity. And it can be tested. The amount a light beam would be deflected from a straight-line path must be small even when passing a massive body. (For example, light near the Earth's surface after traveling 1 km is predicted to drop only about $10^{-10}$ m, which is equal to the diameter of a small atom and not detectable.) The most massive body near us is the Sun, and it was calculated that light from a distant star would be deflected by 1.75″ of arc (tiny but detectable) as it passed near the Sun (Fig. 33–14). However, such a measurement could be made only during a total eclipse of the Sun, so that the Sun's tremendous brightness would not overwhelm the starlight passing near its edge. An opportune eclipse occurred in 1919, and scientists journeyed to the South Atlantic to observe it. Their photos of stars around the Sun revealed shifts in accordance with Einstein's prediction.

If a light beam can follow a curved path, as discussed above, then perhaps we can say that *space itself is curved* and that it is the gravitational mass that causes the curvature. Indeed, the curvature of space—or rather, of four-dimensional space-time—is a basic aspect of Einstein's General Relativity (GR).

What is meant by **curved space**? To understand, recall that our normal method of viewing the world is via Euclidean plane geometry. In Euclidean geometry, there are many axioms and theorems we take for granted, such as that the sum of the angles of any triangle is 180°. Non-Euclidean geometries, which involve curved space, have also been imagined by mathematicians. It is hard enough to imagine three-dimensional curved space, much less curved four-dimensional space-time. So let us try to understand the idea of curved space by using two-dimensional surfaces.

Consider, for example, the two-dimensional surface of a sphere. It is clearly curved, Fig. 33–15, at least to us who view it from the outside—from our three-dimensional world. But how would hypothetical two-dimensional creatures determine whether their two-dimensional space were flat (a plane) or curved? One way would be to measure the sum of the angles of a triangle. If the surface is a plane, the sum of the angles is 180°, as we learn in plane geometry. But if the space is curved, and a sufficiently large triangle is constructed, the sum of the angles will *not* be 180°. To construct a triangle on a curved surface, say the sphere of Fig. 33–15, we must use the equivalent of a straight line: that is, the shortest distance between two points, which is called a **geodesic**. On a sphere, a geodesic is an arc of a great circle (an arc in a plane passing through the center of the sphere) such as the Earth's equator and the Earth's longitude lines. Consider, for example, the large triangle of Fig. 33–15: its sides are two longitude lines passing from the north pole to the equator, and the third side is a section of the equator as shown. The two longitude lines make 90° angles with the equator (look at a world globe to see this more clearly). They make an angle with each other at the north pole, which could be, say, 90° as shown; the sum of these angles is $90° + 90° + 90° = 270°$. This is clearly *not* a Euclidean space. Note, however, that if the triangle is small in comparison to the radius of the sphere, the angles will add up to nearly 180°, and the triangle (and space) will seem flat.

*Geodesic*

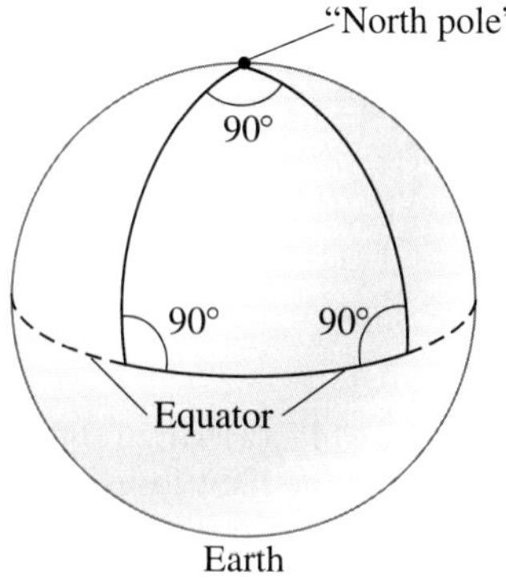


**FIGURE 33–15** On a two-dimensional curved surface, the sum of the angles of a triangle may not be 180°.

Another way to test the curvature of space is to measure the radius $r$ and circumference $C$ of a large circle. On a plane surface, $C = 2\pi r$. But on a two-dimensional spherical surface, $C$ is *less* than $2\pi r$, as can be seen in Fig. 33–16. The proportionality between $C$ and $r$ is *less* than $2\pi$. Such a surface is said to have *positive curvature*. On the saddlelike surface of Fig. 33–17, the circumference of a circle is greater than $2\pi r$, and the sum of the angles of a triangle is less than 180°. Such a surface is said to have a *negative curvature*.

**FIGURE 33–16** On a spherical surface (a two-dimensional world) a circle of circumference $C$ is drawn about point O as the center. The radius of the circle (not the sphere) is the distance $r$ along the surface. (Note that in our three-dimensional view, we can tell that $2\pi a = C$; since $r > a$, then $2\pi r > C$.)

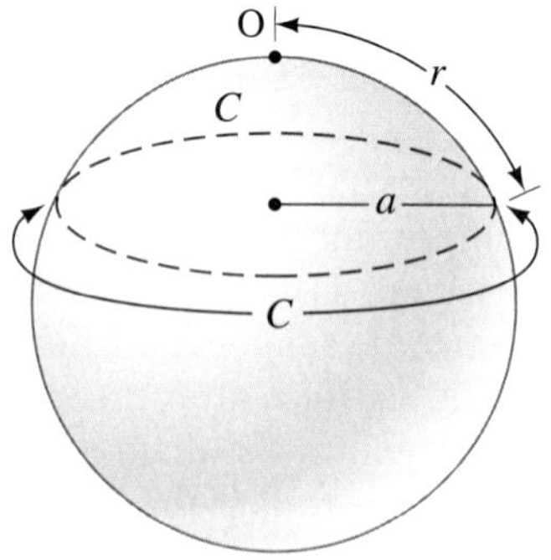


**FIGURE 33–17** Example of a two-dimensional surface with negative curvature.

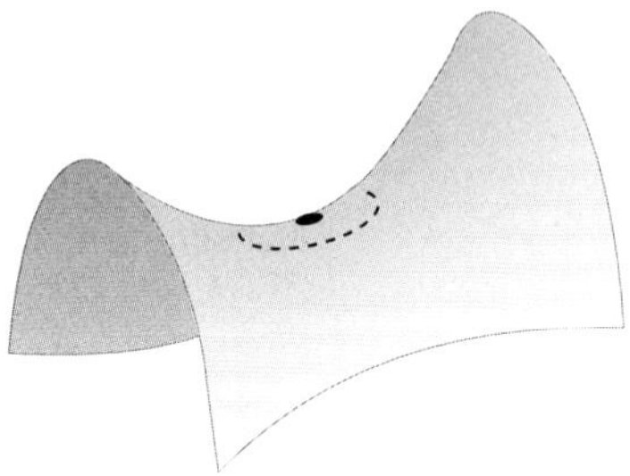

## Curvature of the Universe

Now, what about our universe? On a large scale (not just near a large mass), what is the overall curvature of the universe? Does it have positive curvature, negative curvature, or is it flat (zero curvature)?

*The universe: open or closed?*

If the universe had a positive curvature, the universe would be *closed*, or *finite* in volume. This would *not* mean that the stars and galaxies extended out to a certain boundary, beyond which there is empty space. There is no boundary or edge in such a universe. If a particle were to move in a straight line in a particular direction, it would eventually return to the starting point—perhaps eons of time later.

On the other hand, if the curvature of space was zero or negative, the universe would be *open*. It could just go on forever. An open universe could be *infinite*, but not necessarily according to recent research.

Today the evidence is very strong that the universe on a large scale is very close to being flat. Indeed, it is so close to being flat that we can't tell if it might be very slightly positive or very slightly negative.

## Black Holes

According to Einstein's theory, space-time is curved near massive bodies. We might think of space as being like a thin rubber sheet: if a heavy weight is hung from it, it curves as shown in Fig. 33–18. The weight corresponds to a huge mass that causes space (space itself!) to curve. Thus, in Einstein's theory† we do not speak of the "force" of gravity acting on bodies. Instead we say that bodies and light rays move as they do because space-time is curved. A body at rest or moving slowly near the great mass of Fig. 33–18 would follow a geodesic (the equivalent of a straight line in plane geometry) toward that body.

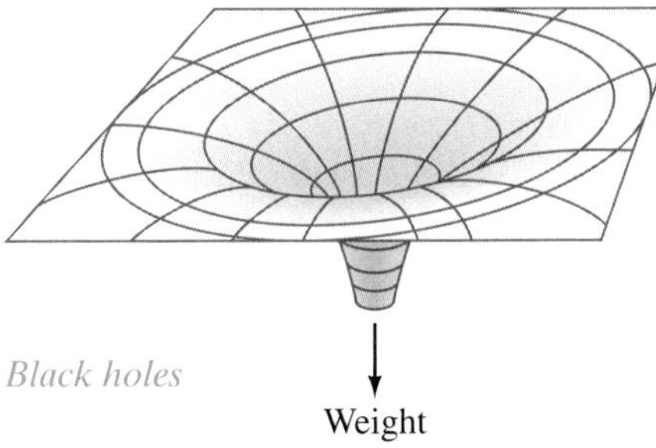


**FIGURE 33–18** Rubber-sheet analogy for space-time curved by matter.

*Black holes*

The extreme curvature of space-time shown in Fig. 33–18 could be produced by a **black hole**. A black hole, as we saw in the Section 33–2, is so dense that even light cannot escape from it. To become a black hole, a body of mass $M$ must undergo **gravitational collapse**, contracting by gravitational self-attraction to within a radius called the **Schwarzschild radius**:

$$R = \frac{2GM}{c^2},$$

where $G$ is the gravitational constant and $c$ the speed of light.

*Event horizon*

The Schwarzschild radius also represents the event horizon of a black hole. By **event horizon** we mean the surface beyond which no signals can ever reach us, and thus inform us of events that happen. As a star collapses toward a black hole, the light it emits is pulled harder and harder by gravity, but we can still see it. Once the matter passes within the event horizon the emitted light cannot escape, but is pulled back in by gravity.

All we can know about a black hole is its mass, its angular momentum (there could be rotating black holes), and its electric charge. No other information, no details of its structure or the kind of matter it was formed of, can be known because no information can escape.

How might we observe black holes? We cannot see them because no light can escape from them. They would be black objects against a black sky. But they do exert a gravitational force on nearby bodies. The black hole believed to be at the center of our Galaxy was discovered by examining the motion of matter in its vicinity. Another technique is to examine stars which appear to be rotating as if they were members of a *binary system* (two stars rotating about their common center of mass), although the companion is invisible. If the unseen star is a black hole, it might be expected to pull off gaseous material from its visible companion (as in Fig. 33–10). As this matter approached the black hole, it would be highly accelerated and should emit X-rays of a characteristic type before plunging inside the event horizon. Such X-rays, plus a sufficiently high mass estimate from the rotational motion, can provide evidence for a black hole. One of the many candidates for a black hole is in the binary-star system Cygnus X-1.

† Alexander Pope (1688–1744) wrote an epitaph for Newton:

> "Nature, and Nature's laws lay hid in night:
> God said, *Let Newton be!* and all was light."

Sir John Squire (1884–1958), perhaps uncomfortable with Einstein's profound thoughts, added:

> "It did not last: the Devil howling '*Ho!*
> *Let Einstein be!*' restored the status quo."

## 33–5 The Expanding Universe: Redshift and Hubble's Law

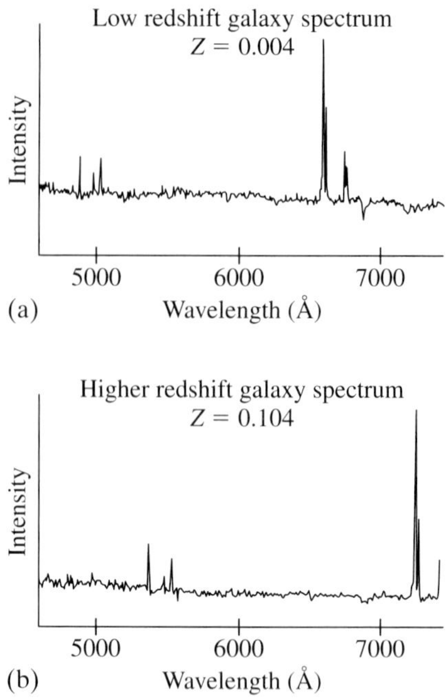


**FIGURE 33–19** Atoms and molecules emit and absorb light of particular frequencies depending on the spacing of their energy levels, as we saw in Chapters 27, 28, and 29. (a) The spectrum of light received from a relatively slow-moving galaxy, where $Z = (\lambda - \lambda_0)/\lambda_0$. (b) Spectrum of a galaxy moving away from us at a much higher speed. Note how the peaks (or lines) in the spectrum have moved to longer wavelengths (the redshift).

We discussed in Section 33–2 how individual stars evolve from their birth to their death as white dwarfs, neutron stars, and black holes. But what about the universe as a whole: is it static, or does it change? One of the most important scientific results of the twentieth century was that distant galaxies are racing away from us, and that the farther they are from us, the faster they are moving away. How astronomers arrived at this astonishing idea, and what it means for the past history of the universe as well as its future, will occupy us for the remainder of the book.

That the universe is expanding was first put forth by Edwin Hubble in 1929. This idea was based on distance measurements of galaxies (Section 33–3), and determination of their velocities by the Doppler shift of spectra lines in the light received from them (Fig. 33–19). In Chapter 12 we saw how the frequency and wavelength of sound are altered if the source is moving toward or away from an observer. If the source moves toward us, the frequency is higher and the wavelength is shorter. If the source moves away from us, the frequency is lower and the wavelength is longer. The **Doppler effect** occurs also for light, but the shifted wavelength or frequency is given by a formula slightly different[†] from that for sound. According to special relativity, the Doppler shift is given by

$$\lambda = \lambda_0\sqrt{\frac{1 + v/c}{1 - v/c}}, \qquad \left[\begin{array}{l}\text{source and observer moving}\\ \text{away from each other}\end{array}\right] \qquad \textbf{(33–3)}$$

where $\lambda_0$ is the emitted wavelength as seen in a reference frame at rest with respect to the source, and $\lambda$ is the wavelength measured in a frame moving with velocity $v$ away from the source along the line of sight. (For relative motion *toward* each other, $v < 0$ in this formula.) When a distant source emits light of a particular wavelength, and the source is moving away from us, the wavelength appears longer to us: the color of the light (if it is visible) is shifted toward the red end of the visible spectrum, an effect known as a **redshift**. (If the source moves toward us, the color shifts toward the blue or shorter wavelength.) The amount of a redshift is specified by the *redshift parameter*, $z$, defined as

*Redshift parameter (defined)*

$$z = \frac{\lambda}{\lambda_0} - 1 = \frac{\lambda - \lambda_0}{\lambda_0} = \frac{\Delta\lambda}{\lambda_0}. \qquad \textbf{(33–4)}$$

We can combine Eqs. 33–4 and 33–3 to obtain[‡]

$$z = \sqrt{\frac{1 + v/c}{1 - v/c}} - 1. \qquad \textbf{(33–5a)}$$

For speeds not too close to the speed of light, it is easy to show (Problem 29) that $z$ is proportional to the speed of the source to or away from us (as was the case for sound):

$$z = \frac{\lambda - \lambda_0}{\lambda_0} \approx \frac{v}{c}. \qquad [v \ll c] \quad \textbf{(33–5b)}$$

But redshifts are not always small, in which case the approximation of Eq. 33–5b would not be valid. Modern telescopes regularly observe galaxies with $z \approx 5$.

[†] For light there is no medium and we can make no distinction between motion of the source and motion of the observer (special relativity), as we did for sound which travels in a medium (Chapter 12).

[‡] Equation 33–5a for $z$ is not precisely correct because, strictly speaking, the redshift is due to the expansion of space, not motion through space (Doppler effect, Eq. 33–3).

**EXAMPLE 33–7** **Given $z$, what is $v$?** What is the speed of a galaxy whose redshift parameter is measured to be $z = 5$?

**APPROACH** We make an approximation by using the Doppler formula, Eq. 33–5a (see footnote ‡ on previous page), and solve for $v$.

**SOLUTION** We add 1 to both sides of Eq. 33–5a:

$$z + 1 = \sqrt{\frac{1 + v/c}{1 - v/c}}.$$

We set $z = 5$ and square both sides of this equation, and then solve for $v$:

$$6^2 = \frac{1 + v/c}{1 - v/c}$$

$$36\left(1 - \frac{v}{c}\right) = 1 + \frac{v}{c}.$$

We collect terms in $v/c$ on one side:

$$35 = 37\frac{v}{c},$$

so

$$v = \frac{35}{37}c = 0.95c.$$

**NOTE** This speed represents how fast the universe (and space itself) is expanding at the position of this galaxy as viewed from Earth.

**EXERCISE C** If $v = 0.70c$, what is $z$?

In the spectra of stars in other galaxies, lines are observed that correspond to lines in the known spectra of particular atoms (see Section 27–11). What Hubble found was that the lines seen in the spectra from distant galaxies were generally *redshifted*, and that the amount of shift seemed to be approximately proportional to the distance of the galaxy from us. That is, the velocity, $v$, of a galaxy moving away from us is proportional to its distance, $d$, from us:

$$v = Hd. \qquad \textbf{(33–6)}$$

*HUBBLE'S LAW*

This is **Hubble's law**, one of the most fundamental astronomical ideas. The constant $H$ is called the **Hubble parameter**. Hubble's law does not work well for nearby galaxies—in fact nearby galaxies can even be "blueshifted" (moving toward us) which merely represents random local motion. For more distant galaxies, the velocity of recession (Hubble's law) is much greater than that of random motion, and so is dominant. We then say it is a **cosmological redshift**, and we have come to view it as due to the expansion of space itself. Indeed, we can think of the originally emitted wavelength $\lambda_0$ as being stretched out (becoming longer) along with the expanding space around it.

The value of $H$ until recently was uncertain by over 20%, and thought to be between 50 and 80 km/s/Mpc. But recent (2003) measurements now put its value more precisely at

$$H = 71\ \text{km/s/Mpc}$$

*Hubble parameter*

(that is, 71 km/s per megaparsec of distance). The uncertainty is about 5%, or $\pm 4$ km/s/Mpc. If we use light-years for distance, then $H = 22$ km/s per million light-years of distance:

$$H \approx 22\ \text{km/s/Mly}$$

with an estimated uncertainty of $\pm 1$ km/s/Mly.

What does it mean that distant galaxies are all moving away from us, and with ever greater speed the farther they are from us? It seems to suggest some kind of explosive expansion that started at some very distant time in the past. And at first sight we seem to be in the middle of it all. But we aren't. The expansion appears the same from any other point in the universe. To understand why, see Fig. 33–20. In Fig. 33–20a we have the view from Earth (or from our Galaxy). The velocities of surrounding galaxies are indicated by arrows, pointing away from us, and the arrows are longer for galaxies more distant from us. Now, what if we were on the galaxy labeled A in Fig. 33–20a? From Earth, galaxy A appears to be moving to the right at a velocity, call it $\vec{\mathbf{v}}_A$, represented by the arrow pointing to the right. If we were *on* galaxy A, Earth would appear to be moving to the left at velocity $-\vec{\mathbf{v}}_A$. To determine the velocities of other galaxies relative to A, we vectorially add the velocity vector, $-\vec{\mathbf{v}}_A$, to all the velocity arrows shown in Fig. 33–20a. This yields Fig. 33–20b, where we see clearly that the universe is expanding away from galaxy A as well; and the velocities of galaxies receding from A are proportional to their distance from A.

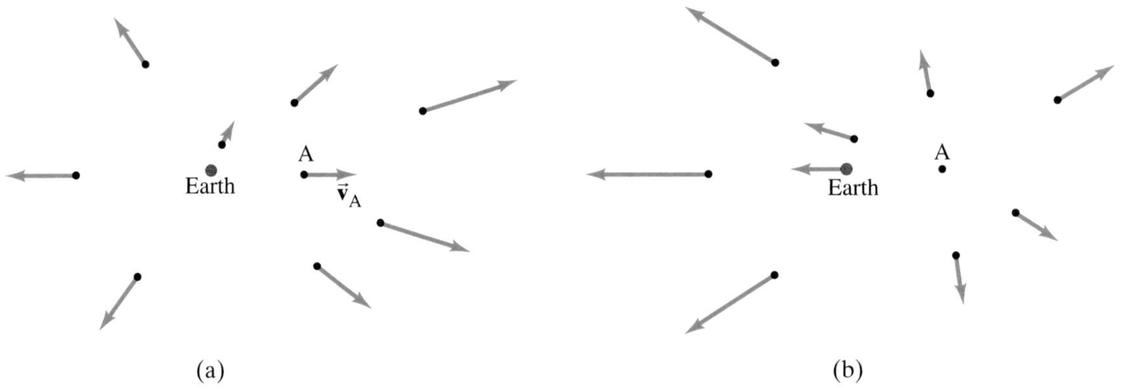


**FIGURE 33–20** Expansion of the universe looks the same from any point in the universe.

Thus the expansion of the universe can be stated as follows: All galaxies are racing away from *each other* at an average rate of about 71 km/s per megaparsec of distance between them. The ramifications of this idea are profound, and we discuss them in a moment.

*Cosmological principle*

A basic assumption in cosmology has been that on a large scale, the universe would look the same to observers at different places at the same time. In other words, the universe is both *isotropic* (looks the same in all directions) and *homogeneous* (would look the same if we were located elsewhere, say in another galaxy). This assumption is called the **cosmological principle**. On a local scale, say in our solar system or within our Galaxy, it clearly does not apply (the sky looks different in different directions). But it has long been thought to be valid if we look on a large enough scale, so that the average population density of galaxies and clusters of galaxies ought to be the same in different areas of the sky. This seems to be valid on distances greater than about 200 Mpc (700 Mly). The expansion of the universe (Fig. 33–20) is consistent with the cosmological principle; and the near uniformity of the cosmic microwave background radiation (discussed in Section 33–6) supports it.

The expansion of the universe, as described by Hubble's law, strongly suggests that galaxies must have been closer together in the past than they are now. This is, in fact, the basis of the *Big Bang* theory of the origin of the universe, which pictures the universe as a relentless expansion starting from a very hot and compressed beginning. We discuss the Big Bang in detail shortly, but first let us see what can be said about the age of the universe.

One way to estimate the age of the universe uses the Hubble parameter. With $H \approx 22\,\text{km/s}$ per $10^6$ light-years, the time required for the galaxies to arrive at their present separations would be approximately (starting with $v = d/t$ and using Hubble's law, Eq. 33–6),

$$t = \frac{d}{v} = \frac{d}{Hd} = \frac{1}{H} \approx \frac{(10^6\,\text{ly})(0.95 \times 10^{13}\,\text{km/ly})}{(22\,\text{km/s})(3.16 \times 10^7\,\text{s/yr})} \approx 13.7 \times 10^9\,\text{yr},$$

or 13.7 billion years. The age of the universe calculated in this way is called the *characteristic expansion time* or "Hubble age." It is a rough estimate and assumes the rate of expansion of the universe was constant (which today we are quite sure is not true). Recent precise measurements (2003) give the age as $13.7 \times 10^9\,\text{yr}$, in remarkable agreement with the rough Hubble age estimate.

*Age of the universe*

## * Steady-State Model

Before discussing the Big Bang in detail, we mention one alternative to the Big Bang—the **steady-state model**—which assumed that the universe is infinitely old and on average looks the same now as it always has. (This assumed uniformity in time as well as space was called the *perfect cosmological principle*.) According to the steady-state model, no large-scale changes have taken place in the universe as a whole, particularly no Big Bang. To maintain this view in the face of the recession of galaxies away from each other, mass–energy conservation must be violated. That is, matter must be created continuously to maintain the assumption of uniformity. The rate of mass creation required is very small—about one nucleon per cubic meter every $10^9$ years.

The steady-state model provided the Big Bang model with healthy competition in the mid-twentieth century. But the discovery of the cosmic microwave background radiation (next Section), as well as the observed expansion of the universe, has made the Big Bang model almost universally accepted.

# 33–6 The Big Bang and the Cosmic Microwave Background

The expansion of the universe seems to suggest that typical objects in the universe were once much closer together than they are now. This is the basis for the idea that the universe began about 13.7 billion years ago as an expansion from a state of very high density and temperature known affectionately as the **Big Bang**.

*The Big Bang*

The Big Bang was not an explosion, because an explosion blows pieces out into the surrounding space. Instead, the Big Bang was the start of an expansion of space itself. The volume of the observable universe was very small at the start and has been expanding ever since. The initial tiny volume of extremely dense matter is not to be thought of as a concentrated mass in the midst of a much larger space around it. The initial tiny but dense volume *was* the universe—the entire universe. There wouldn't have been anything else. When we say that the universe was once smaller than it is now, we mean that the average separation between galaxies (or other objects) was less. Thus, it is the *size of the universe itself* that has increased since the Big Bang.

**FIGURE 33–21** Robert Wilson (left) and Arno Penzias, and behind them their "horn antenna."

A major piece of evidence supporting the Big Bang is the **cosmic microwave background** radiation (or CMB) whose discovery came about as follows.

In 1964, Arno Penzias and Robert Wilson were experiencing difficulty with what they assumed to be background noise, or "static," in their radio telescope (a large antenna device for detecting radio waves from the heavens, Fig. 33–21). Eventually, they became convinced that it was real and that it was coming from outside our Galaxy. They made precise measurements at a wavelength $\lambda = 7.35\,\text{cm}$, in the microwave region of the electromagnetic spectrum (Fig. 22–8). The intensity of this radiation was found initially not to vary by day or night or time of year, nor to depend on direction. It came from all directions in the universe with equal intensity, to a precision of better than 1%. It could only be concluded that this radiation came from the universe as a whole.

*The 2.73-K cosmic microwave background radiation*

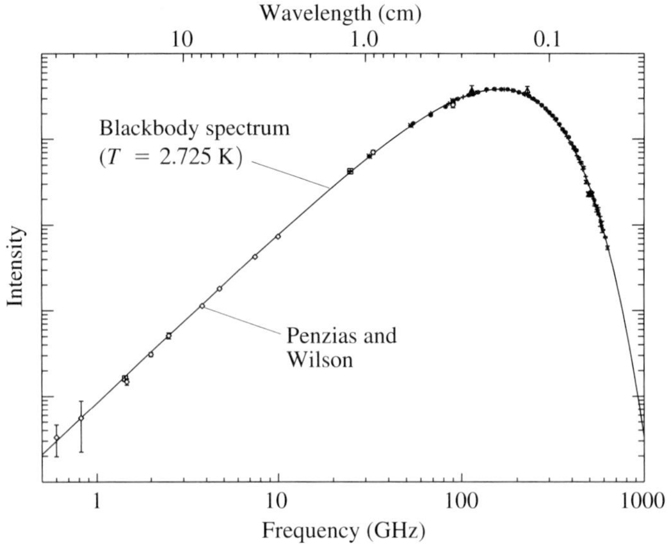


**FIGURE 33–22** Spectrum of cosmic microwave background radiation, showing blackbody curve and experimental measurements including that of Penzias and Wilson. (Thanks to G. F. Smoot and D. Scott. The vertical bars represent the experimental uncertainty in a measurement.)

The intensity of this cosmic microwave background radiation as measured at $\lambda = 7.35\,\mathrm{cm}$ corresponds to blackbody radiation (see Section 27–2) at a temperature of about 3 K. When radiation at other wavelengths was measured, the intensities were found to fall on a blackbody curve as shown in Fig. 33–22, corresponding to a temperature of 2.725 K.

The remarkable uniformity of the cosmic microwave background radiation was in accordance with the cosmological principle. But theorists felt that there needed to be some small inhomogeneities, or "anisotropies," in the CMB that would have provided "seeds" around which galaxy formation could have started. Small areas of slightly higher density and temperature, which could have contracted under gravity to form stars and galaxies, were indeed found. These tiny inhomogeneities were detected first by the COBE (Cosmic Background Explorer) satellite experiment (1992) and by subsequent experiments with greater detail, culminating in 2003 with the WMAP (Wilkinson Microwave Anisotropy Probe) results. See Fig. 33–23. WMAP gives the CMB temperature as $2.725 \pm 0.002\,\mathrm{K}$.

*Importance of CMB: the Big Bang*

The CMB provides strong evidence in support of the Big Bang, and gives us information about conditions in the very early universe. In fact, in the late 1940s, George Gamow and his collaborators calculated that a Big Bang origin of the universe should have generated just such a microwave background radiation.

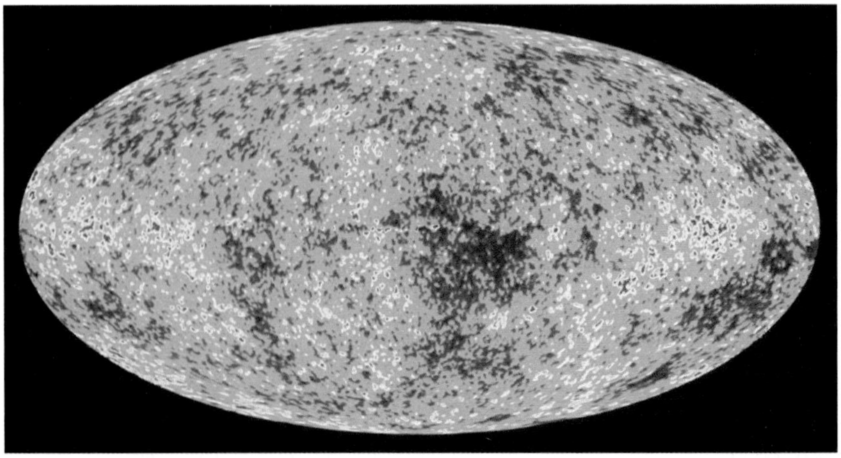

**FIGURE 33–23** The cosmic microwave background radiation over the entire sky, color-coded to represent differences in temperature from the average 2.725 K: the color scale ranges from $+200\,\mu\mathrm{K}$ (red) to $-200\,\mu\mathrm{K}$ (dark blue), representing slightly hotter and colder spots (and also variations in density). Results are from the WMAP satellite in 2003: the angular resolution is 0.2°. The larger version of WMAP at the start of this Chapter was done at a specific frequency band and includes our Galaxy in the foreground (red stripe) which here has been subtracted out.

To understand why, let us look at what a Big Bang might have been like. The temperature must have been extremely high at the start, so high that there could not have been any atoms in the very early stages of the universe. Instead, the universe would have consisted solely of radiation (photons) and a plasma of charged electrons and other elementary particles. The universe would have been opaque—the photons in a sense "trapped," traveling very short distances before being scattered again, primarily by electrons. Indeed, the details of the microwave background radiation is strong evidence that matter and radiation were once in equilibrium at a very high temperature. As the universe expanded, the energy spread out over an increasingly larger volume and the temperature dropped. Only when the temperature had fallen to about 3000 K, some 380,000 years later, could nuclei and electrons combine together as atoms. With the disappearance of free electrons, as they combined with nuclei to form atoms, the radiation would have been freed—**decoupled** from matter, we say. The universe became *transparent* because photons were now free to travel nearly unimpeded straight through the universe.

*Photons decoupled*

As the universe expanded, so too the wavelengths of the radiation lengthened (you might think of standing waves, Section 11–13), thus redshifting to longer wavelengths that correspond to lower temperature (recall Wien's law, $\lambda_P T$ = constant, Section 27–2), until they would have reached the 2.7-K background radiation we observe today.

## * Looking Back toward the Big Bang—Lookback Time

Figure 33–24 shows our Earth point of view, looking out in all directions back toward the Big Bang and the brief (380,000 year long) period when radiation was trapped in the early plasma (yellow band). The time it takes light to reach us from an event (say $5 \times 10^9$ yr ago) is called its **lookback time**. The "close-up" insert in Fig. 33–24 shows a photon scattering repeatedly inside the plasma and then exiting the plasma in a straight line. No matter what direction we look, our view of the very early universe is blocked by this wall of plasma—we can see only as far as its surface, called the "surface of last scattering," but not into it. Wavelengths from there are redshifted by $z \approx 1000$. Time $\Delta t'$ in Fig. 33–24 is the lookback time (not real time that goes forward).

*Lookback time*

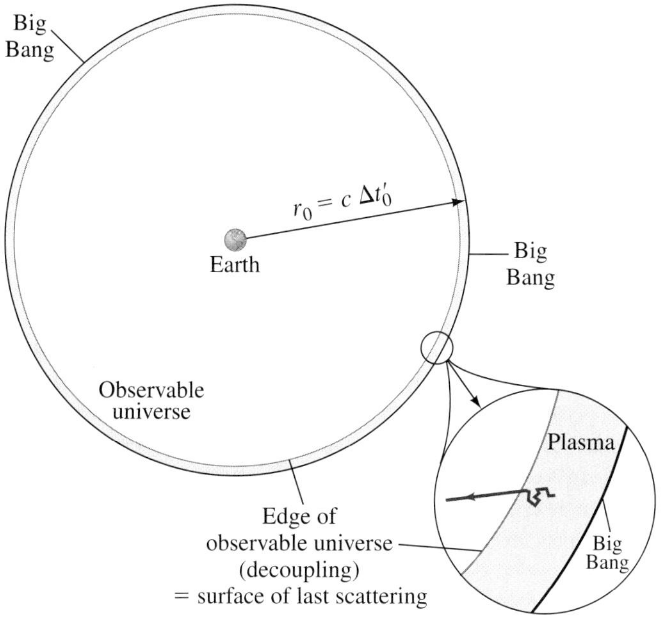


**FIGURE 33–24** When we look out from the Earth, we look back in time. Any other observer in the universe would see the same thing. The farther an object is from us, the earlier in time the light we see left it. We cannot see quite as far as the Big Bang; we can see only as far as the "surface of last scattering," which represents the CMB. The blowup shows the earliest 380,000 years of the universe when it was opaque: a photon is shown scattering many times and then (at decoupling, 380,000 yr after the Big Bang) becoming free to travel in a straight line. If this photon wasn't heading our way when "liberated," many others were. Galaxies are not shown, but would be concentrated close to Earth in this diagram. *Note:* This diagram is not a normal map. Maps show a section of the world as might be seen all *at a given time*. This diagram shows space (like a map), but each point is *not* at the same time. The light coming from a point a distance $r$ from Earth took a time $\Delta t' = r/c$ to reach Earth, and thus shows an event that took place long ago, a time $\Delta t' = r/c$ in the past, which we call its "lookback time." The Big Bang happened $\Delta t_0' = 13.7$ Gyr ago.

# 33–7 The Standard Cosmological Model: the Early History of the Universe

In the last decade or two, a convincing theory of the origin and evolution of the universe has developed, now called the **standard cosmological model**, or (sometimes) the *concordance model*. Part of this theory is based on recent theoretical and experimental advances in elementary particle physics. Indeed, cosmology and elementary particle physics have cross-fertilized to a surprising extent.

Let us go back to the earliest of times—as close as possible to the Big Bang—and follow a standard model scenario of events as the universe expanded and cooled after the Big Bang. Initially we talk of extremely small time intervals as well as extremely high temperatures, far beyond anything in the universe today. Figure 33–25 is a compressed graphical representation of the events, and it may be helpful to consult it as we go along.

**FIGURE 33–25** Compressed graphical representation of the development of the universe after the Big Bang, according to modern cosmology. [The time scale is mostly logarithmic (each factor of 10 in time gets equal treatment), except at the start (there can be no $t = 0$ on a log scale), and just after $t = 10^{-35}$ (to save space). The vertical height is a rough idea of the size of the universe, mainly to suggest expansion of the universe.]

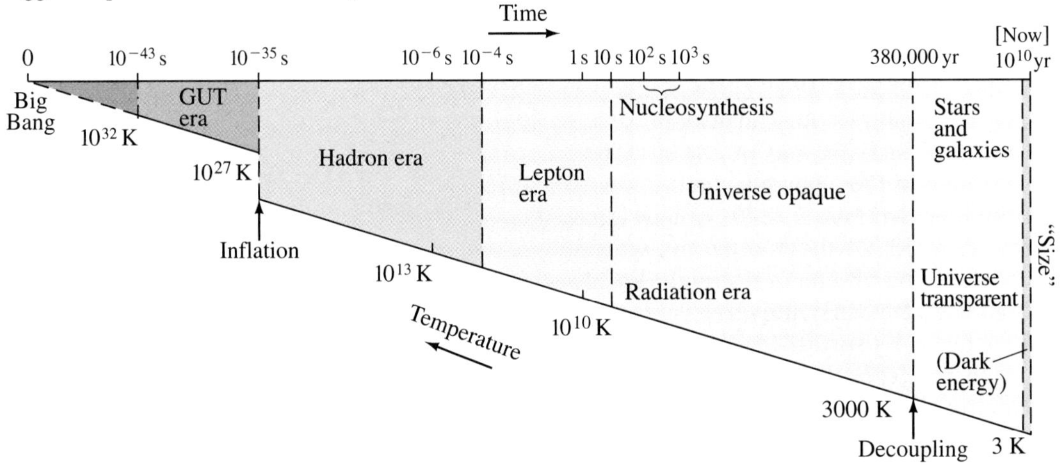


## The History

*Modern cosmology "scenario" of the history of the universe after the Big Bang*

We begin at a time only a minuscule fraction of a second after the Big Bang, $10^{-43}$ s. This is an unimaginably short time, and predictions can be only speculative. Earlier, we can say nothing because we do not yet have a theory of quantum effects on gravity which would be needed for the incredibly high densities and temperatures then. It is thought that prior to $10^{-35}$ s, perhaps as early as $10^{-43}$ s, the four forces in nature were unified—there was only one force. The temperature would have been about $10^{32}$ K, corresponding to particles moving about every which way with an average kinetic energy KE of $10^{19}$ GeV (see Eq. 13–8):

*All four forces unified*

$$\text{KE} \approx kT \approx \frac{\left(1.4 \times 10^{-23}\,\text{J/K}\right)\left(10^{32}\,\text{K}\right)}{1.6 \times 10^{-19}\,\text{J/eV}} \approx 10^{28}\,\text{eV} = 10^{19}\,\text{GeV}.$$

(Note that the factor $\frac{3}{2}$ in Eq. 13–8 is usually ignored in such order of magnitude calculations.) At $t = 10^{-43}$ s, a kind of "phase transition" is believed to have occurred during which the gravitational force, in effect, "condensed out" as a separate force. This, and subsequent phase transitions, are analogous to the phase transitions water undergoes as it cools from a gas, condenses into a liquid, and with further cooling freezes into ice.† The symmetry of the four forces was broken, but the strong, weak, and electromagnetic forces were still unified, and the

*Symmetry broken (gravity condensed out)*

†It may be fun to note that our story of origins here bears some resemblance to ancient accounts that mention the "void," "formless wasteland," "abyss," "divide the waters" (possibly a phase transition?), not to mention the sudden appearance of light.

universe entered the **grand unified era** (see Chapter 32). There was no distinction between quarks and leptons; baryon and lepton numbers were not conserved. Very shortly thereafter, as the universe expanded considerably and the temperature had dropped to about $10^{27}$ K, there was another phase transition and the strong force condensed out at about $10^{-35}$ s after the Big Bang. Now the universe was filled with a "soup" of leptons and quarks. The quarks were initially free, but soon began to "condense" into more normal particles: nucleons and the other hadrons and their antiparticles. With this **confinement of quarks**, the universe entered the **hadron era**.

*Quark confinement*

About this time, when the universe was only $10^{-35}$ s old, a strange thing may have happened, according to theorists. A brilliant idea, proposed around 1980, suggests that the universe underwent an incredible exponential expansion, increasing in size by a factor of $10^{40}$ or $10^{50}$ in a tiny fraction of a second, perhaps $10^{-34}$ s. The usefulness of this **inflationary scenario** is that it solved major problems with earlier Big Bang models, such as explaining why the universe is flat, as well as the thermal equilibrium to provide the nearly uniform CMB.† Inflation is now a generally accepted aspect of Big Bang theory.

*Inflation*

After the very brief inflationary period, the universe would have settled back into its more regular expansion. The universe was now a "soup" of leptons and hadrons. We can think of this "soup" as a grand mixture of particles and antiparticles, as well as photons—all in roughly equal numbers—colliding with one another frequently and exchanging energy.

By the time the universe was only about a microsecond $(10^{-6}\,\mathrm{s})$ old, it had cooled to about $10^{13}$ K, corresponding to an average kinetic energy of 1 GeV, and the vast majority of hadrons disappeared. To see why, let us focus on the most familiar hadrons: nucleons and their antiparticles. When the average kinetic energy of particles was somewhat higher than 1 GeV, protons, neutrons, and their antiparticles were continually being created out of the energies of collisions involving photons and other particles, such as

*Most hadrons disappear*

$$\begin{aligned}\text{photons} &\rightarrow \mathrm{p} + \overline{\mathrm{p}}\\ &\rightarrow \mathrm{n} + \overline{\mathrm{n}}.\end{aligned}$$

But just as quickly, particles and antiparticles would annihilate: for example

$$\mathrm{p} + \overline{\mathrm{p}} \rightarrow \text{photons or leptons}.$$

So the processes of creation and annihilation of nucleons were in equilibrium. The numbers of nucleons and antinucleons were high—roughly as many as there were electrons, positrons, or photons. But as the universe expanded and cooled, and the average kinetic energy of particles dropped below about 1 GeV, which is the minimum energy needed in a typical collision to create nucleons and antinucleons (about 940 MeV each), the process of nucleon creation could not continue. The process of annihilation could continue, however, with antinucleons annihilating nucleons, until there were almost no nucleons left. But not quite zero. To explain our present world, which consists mainly of matter (nucleons and electrons) with very little antimatter in sight, we must suppose that earlier in the universe, perhaps around $10^{-35}$ s after the Big Bang, a slight excess of quarks over antiquarks was formed. This would

*Why is there matter now?*

†How inflation explains flatness might be understood by thinking of a sphere. If the sphere of Fig. 33–15, with obvious curvature of its surface, were to increase vastly in size, the surface would seem essentially flat to an observer on it. Inflation also explains why the CMB is so uniform. Without inflation, the tiny universe at $10^{-35}$ s was still too large for all parts of it to have been in contact so as to reach the same temperature (information cannot travel faster than $c$). Suppose the universe was about 1 cm in diameter at $t \approx 10^{-36}$ s, as per original Big Bang theory. In that $10^{-36}$ s light could have traveled $d = ct = (3 \times 10^8\,\mathrm{m/s})(10^{-36}/\mathrm{s}) \approx 10^{-27}$ m, way too small for opposite sides of a 1-cm-wide universe to have been in communication. But if the universe had been $10^{40}$ or $10^{50}$ times smaller, there could have been contact and thermal equilibrium to produce the observed nearly uniform CMB. Thus inflation allows the very early universe before inflation to have been so small that all parts could have been in thermal equilibrium, and after inflation large enough to give us today's universe.

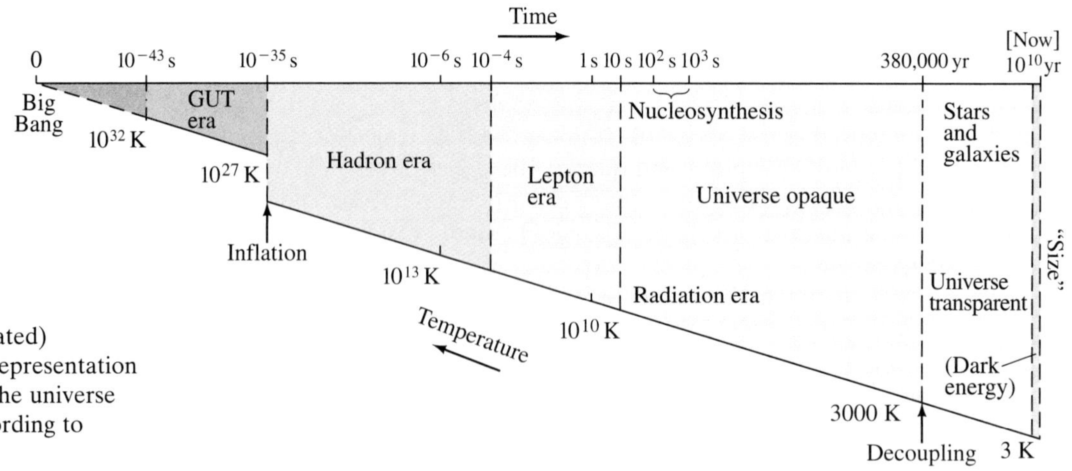


**FIGURE 33–25** (repeated) Compressed graphical representation of the development of the universe after the Big Bang, according to modern cosmology.

have resulted in a slight excess of nucleons over antinucleons. And it is these "leftover" nucleons that we are made of today. The excess of nucleons over antinucleons was about one part in $10^9$. Earlier, during the hadron era, there should have been about as many nucleons as photons. After it ended, the "left-over" nucleons thus numbered only about one nucleon per $10^9$ photons, and this ratio has persisted to this day. Protons, neutrons, and all other heavier particles were thus tremendously reduced in number by about $10^{-6}$ s after the Big Bang. The lightest hadrons, the pions, disappeared as the nucleons had; because they are the lightest mass hadrons (140 MeV), they were the last hadrons to go, about $10^{-4}$ s after the Big Bang. Lighter particles, including electrons and neutrinos, were the dominant form of matter, and the universe entered the **lepton era**.

*Lepton era*

By the time the first full second had passed (clearly the most eventful second in history!), the universe had cooled to about 10 billion degrees, $10^{10}$ K. The average kinetic energy was about 1 MeV. This was still sufficient energy to create electrons and positrons and balance their annihilation reactions, since their masses correspond to about 0.5 MeV. So there were about as many $e^+$ and $e^-$ as there were photons. But within a few more seconds, the temperature had dropped sufficiently so that $e^+$ and $e^-$ could no longer be formed. Annihilation ($e^+ + e^- \rightarrow$ photons) continued. And, like nucleons before them, electrons and positrons all but disappeared from the universe—except for a slight excess of electrons over positrons (later to join with nuclei to form atoms). Thus, about $t = 10\,\text{s}$ after the Big Bang, the universe entered the **radiation era**. Its major constituents were photons and neutrinos. But the neutrinos, partaking only in the weak force, rarely interacted. So the universe, until then experiencing significant amounts of energy in matter and in radiation, now became **radiation-dominated**: much more energy was contained in radiation than in matter, a situation that would last tens of thousands of years (Fig. 33–25).

*Radiation-dominated universe*

*Making He nuclei*

Meanwhile, during the next few minutes, crucial events were taking place. Beginning about 2 or 3 minutes after the Big Bang, nuclear fusion began to occur. The temperature had dropped to about $10^9$ K, corresponding to an average kinetic energy $\overline{\text{KE}} \approx 100\,\text{keV}$, where nucleons could strike each other and be able to fuse (Section 31–3), but now cool enough so newly formed nuclei would not be immediately broken apart by subsequent collisions. Deuterium, helium, and very tiny amounts of lithium nuclei were probably made. But the universe was cooling too quickly, and larger nuclei were not made. After only a few minutes, probably not even a quarter of an hour after the Big Bang, the temperature dropped far enough that nucleosynthesis stopped, not to start again for millions of years (in stars). Thus, after the first hour or so of the universe, matter consisted mainly of bare nuclei of hydrogen (about 75%) and helium (about 25%)[†] and electrons. But radiation (photons) continued to dominate.

Our story is almost complete. The next important event is presumed to have occurred 380,000 years later. The universe had expanded to about $\frac{1}{1000}$ of its present size, and the temperature had cooled to about 3000 K. The average kinetic energy of nuclei, electrons, and photons was less than an electron volt. Since ionization energies of atoms are on the order of eV, then as the temperature dropped below this point, electrons could orbit the bare nuclei and remain there (without being ejected by collisions), thus forming atoms. With the birth of atoms, the photons—which had been continually scattering from the free electrons—now became free to spread nearly unhindered throughout the universe. As mentioned in the previous Section, the photons became **decoupled** from matter. The total energy contained in radiation had been decreasing (lengthening in wavelength as the universe expanded), and even before decoupling (at about $t = 56{,}000\,\text{yr}$) the total energy contained in matter became dominant. The universe was said to have become **matter-dominated**. As the universe continued to expand, the electromagnetic radiation cooled further, to 2.7 K today, forming the cosmic microwave background radiation we detect from everywhere in the universe.

*Birth of stable atoms*

*Matter-dominated universe*

After the birth of atoms, then stars and galaxies could begin to form—presumably by self-gravitation around mass concentrations (inhomogeneities). Stars began to form about 200 million years after the Big Bang, galaxies after almost $10^9$ years. The universe continued to evolve until today, some 13.7 billion years later.

* * *

This scenario is by no means "proven." But it does provide a workable picture, for the first time, of how the universe may have begun and evolved.

A major event, and something only discovered very recently, is that when the universe was about half as old as it is now (5–7 Gyr ago), its expansion began to accelerate. This was a big surprise because it was assumed the expansion of the universe would slow down due to gravitational attraction of all objects to each other. Indeed, another major recent discovery is that ordinary matter makes up very little of the total mass–energy of the universe ($\approx 4\%$). Instead, as we discuss in the next Section, the major contributors to the energy density of the universe are *dark matter* and *dark energy*. On the right in Fig. 33–25 is a narrow vertical strip that represents the most recent 5 to 7 billion years of the universe, during which *dark energy* seems to have dominated.

## 33–8 Dark Matter and Dark Energy

According to the standard Big Bang model, the universe is evolving and changing. Individual stars are being created, evolving, and dying as white dwarfs, neutron stars, black holes. At the same time, the universe as a whole is expanding. One important question is whether the universe will continue to expand forever. Until the late 1990s, the universe was thought to be dominated by matter which interacts by gravity, and this question was connected to the curvature of space-time (Section 33–4). If the universe had *negative* curvature, the expansion of the universe would never stop, although the rate of expansion would decrease due to the gravitational attraction of its parts. Such a universe would be *open* and infinite. If the universe is *flat* (no curvature), it would still be open and infinite but its expansion would slowly approach a zero rate. Finally, if the universe had *positive* curvature, it would be *closed* and finite; the effect of gravity would be strong enough that the expansion would eventually stop and the universe would begin to contract, collapsing back onto itself in a **big crunch**.

[†] This standard model prediction of a 25% primordial production of helium agrees with what we observe today—the universe *does* contain about 25% He—and it is strong evidence in support of the standard Big Bang model. Furthermore, the theory says that 25% He abundance is fully consistent with there being three neutrino types, which is the number we observe. And it sets an upper limit of four to the maximum number of possible neutrino types. Here we have a situation where cosmology actually makes a specific prediction about fundamental physics.

## Critical Density

According to the above scenario (which does not include the recently discovered acceleration of the universe), the fate of the universe would depend on the average mass density in the universe. For an average mass density greater than a critical value known as the **critical density**, estimated to be about

*Critical density of the universe*

$$\rho_c \approx 10^{-26}\,\mathrm{kg/m^3}$$

(i.e., a few nucleons/$\mathrm{m^3}$ on average throughout the universe), gravity would prevent expansion from continuing forever. Eventually (if $\rho > \rho_c$) gravity would pull the universe back into a big crunch and space-time would have a positive curvature. If instead the actual density was equal to the critical density, $\rho = \rho_c$, the universe would be flat and open. If the actual density was less than the critical density, $\rho < \rho_c$, the universe would have negative curvature. See Fig. 33–26. Today we believe the universe is very close to flat. But recent evidence suggests the universe is expanding at an *accelerating* rate, as discussed below.

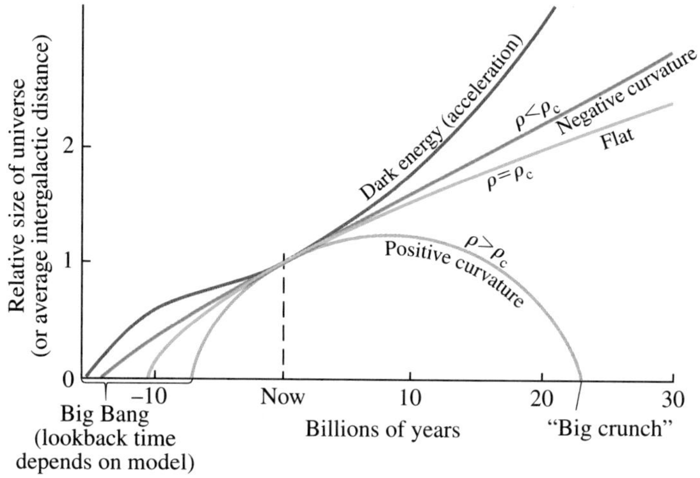


**FIGURE 33–26** Three future possibilities for the universe, depending on the density $\rho$ of ordinary matter, plus a fourth possibility that includes dark energy. Note that all curves have been chosen to have the same slope (= $H$, the Hubble parameter) right now. Looking back in time, the Big Bang occurs where each curve touches the horizontal (time) axis.

## Dark Matter

WMAP and other experiments have convinced scientists that the universe is flat and $\rho = \rho_c$. But this $\rho$ cannot be only normal baryonic matter (atoms are 99.9% baryons—protons and neutrons—by weight). These recent experiments put the amount of normal baryonic matter in the universe at only 4% of the critical density. What is the other 96%? There is strong evidence for a significant amount of nonluminous matter in the universe referred to as **dark matter**. For example, observations of the rotation of galaxies suggest that they rotate as if they had considerably more mass than we can see. Recall from Chapter 5, Example 5–14 (p. 123), that for a satellite revolving around Earth (mass $M$)

*Dark matter*

$$m\frac{v^2}{r} = G\frac{mM}{r^2}$$

and hence $v = \sqrt{GM/r}$. If we apply this equation to stars in a galaxy, we see that their speed depends on galactic mass. Observations show that stars farther from the galactic center revolve much faster than expected from visible matter, suggesting a great deal of invisible matter. Similarly, observations of the motion of galaxies within clusters also suggest that they have considerably more mass than can be seen. What might this nonluminous matter in the universe be? We don't know yet. It cannot be made of ordinary (baryonic) matter, so it must consist of some other sort of elementary particle.

Dark matter makes up about 23% of the mass–energy of the universe, according to the latest experiments. Thus the total mass–energy is 23% dark matter plus 4% baryons for a total of 27%, which does not bring $\rho$ up to $\rho_c$. What is the other 73%? We are not sure about that either, but we have given it the name "dark energy."

## Dark Energy—Cosmic Acceleration

Just before the year 2000, cosmologists received a surprise. Gravity was assumed to be the predominant force on a large scale in the universe, and it was thought that the expansion of the universe ought to be slowing down in time because gravity acts as an attractive force between objects. But measurements on type Ia supernovae (SNIa, our best standard candles—see Section 33–3) unexpectedly showed that very distant (high $z$) SNIa's were dimmer than expected. That is, given their great distance $d$ as determined from their low brightness, their speed $v$ determined from the measured $z$ was less than expected according to Hubble's law. This result suggests that nearer galaxies are moving away from us relatively faster than those very distant ones, meaning the expansion of the universe in more recent epochs has sped up. This **acceleration** in the expansion of the universe (in place of the expected deceleration due to gravitational attraction between masses) seems to have begun roughly 5 billion years ago (8 to 9 Gyr after the Big Bang).

*Acceleration*

What could be causing the universe to accelerate in its expansion, against the attractive force of gravity? Does our understanding of gravity need to be revised? We don't know the answers to these questions; many scientists say dark energy is the biggest mystery facing science today. There are several speculations. But somehow it seems to have a long-range *repulsive* effect on matter, causing objects to speed away from each other ever faster. Whatever it is, it has been given the name **dark energy**.

*Dark energy*

One idea is a sort of quantum field given the name "quintessence." Another possibility suggests an energy latent in space itself (vacuum energy) and relates to an aspect of General Relativity known as the **cosmological constant** (symbol $\Lambda$). When Einstein developed his equations, he found that they offered no solutions for a static universe. In those days (1917) it was thought the universe was static—unchanging and everlasting. Einstein added an arbitrary constant to his equations to provide solutions for a static universe. A decade later, when Hubble showed us an expanding universe, Einstein discarded his cosmological constant as no longer needed $(\Lambda = 0)$. But now it is being reconsidered: perhaps $\Lambda$ is not zero. Theoretical attempts to calculate $\Lambda$ have so far given unreal values.

*Cosmological constant*

There is increasing evidence that the effects of some form of dark energy are very real. The data from the WMAP survey and other recent experiments agree well with theories and computer models when they input dark energy as providing 73% of the mass–energy in the universe, and when the total mass–energy density equals the critical density $\rho_c$.

Today's best estimate of how the mass–energy in the universe is distributed is as follows:

*Mass–energy types in the universe as % of total*

73% dark energy

27% matter, subject to the known gravitational force.

Of this 27%:

23% is dark matter

4% is baryons (what atoms are made of) and only $\frac{1}{10}$ of this 4% is visible matter: stars, and galaxies (that is, 0.4% of the total).

It is remarkable that only 0.4% of all the mass–energy in the universe is visible as stars and galaxies.

The idea that the universe is dominated by a completely unknown form of energy seems bizarre. Nonetheless, the exquisite agreement between theory and the measured CMB anisotropy observations plus other experimental data (clustering of galaxies—see next Section) appears to be meaningful.

**FIGURE 33–27** Distribution of some 50,000 galaxies in a 2.5° slice through almost half of the sky above the equator, as measured by the Sloan Digital Sky Survey (SDSS). Each dot represents a galaxy. The distance from us is obtained from the redshift and Hubble's law, and is given in units of $10^9$ light-years (Gly). At greater distances, fewer galaxies are bright enough to be detected, thus resulting in an apparent thinning out of galaxies. The point 0 represents us, our observation point. Note the "walls" and "voids" of galaxies.

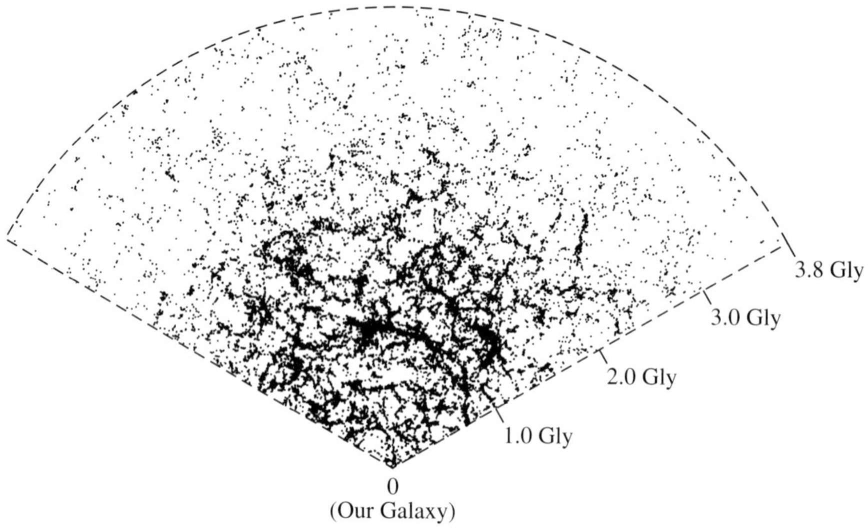


## 33–9 Large-Scale Structure of the Universe

The beautiful WMAP pictures of the sky (Fig. 33–23 and Chapter opening photo) show small but significant inhomogeneities in the temperature of the CMB. These anisotropies reflect compressions and expansions in the primordial plasma just before decoupling, from which stars, galaxies, and clusters of galaxies formed. Analysis of the irregularities in WMAP by mammoth computer simulations predict the distribution of clusters of galaxies and superclusters of galaxies very similar to what is seen today (Fig. 33–27). These simulations are very successful if they contain dark energy and dark matter; and the dark matter needs to be *cold* (slow speed—think of Eq. 13–8, $\frac{1}{2}m\overline{v}^2 = \frac{3}{2}kT$ where $T$ is temperature), rather than "hot" dark matter such as neutrinos which move at or very near the speed of light. Indeed, the modern cosmological model is called the **ΛCDM** model, where lambda (Λ) stands for the cosmological constant, and CDM is **cold dark matter**.

ΛCDM *cosmological model*

Cosmologists have gained substantial confidence in this cosmological model from such a precise fit between observations and theory. They can also extract very precise values for cosmological parameters which previously were only known with low accuracy. The CMB is such an important cosmological observable that every effort is being made to extract all of the information it contains. More space missions are being prepared to observe even finer details. They could provide experimental evidence for inflation, perhaps detecting **gravity waves** as predicted by inflation models (detectable by their effect on the CMB) and also provide information about elementary particle physics at energies far beyond the reach of man-made accelerators.

## 33–10 Finally . . .

When we look up into the night sky, we see stars; and with the best telescopes, we see galaxies and the exotic objects we discussed earlier, including rare supernovae. But even with our best instruments we do not see the processes going on inside stars or supernovae that we hypothesized (and believe). We are dependent on brilliant theorists who come up with viable theories and ideas and verifiable models. We depend on complicated computer models whose parameters are varied until the outputs compare favorably with our observables and analyses of WMAP and other experiments. And we now have a surprisingly precise idea about some aspects of our universe: it is flat, it is 13.7 billion years old, it contains only 4% "normal" baryonic matter (for atoms), and so on. These precise results might suggest that we live at a very interesting time.

The questions raised by cosmology are difficult and profound, and may seem removed from everyday "reality." We can always say, "the Sun is shining, it's going to burn on for an unimaginably long time, all is well." Nonetheless, the questions of cosmology are deep ones that fascinate the human intellect. One aspect that is especially intriguing is this: calculations on the formation and evolution of the universe have been performed that deliberately varied the values—just slightly—of certain fundamental physical constants. The result? A universe in which life as we know it could not exist. [For example, if the difference in mass between proton and neutron were zero, or small (less than the mass of the electron, $0.511 \text{ MeV}/c^2$), there would be no atoms: electrons would be captured by protons never to be freed again.] Such results have given rise to a philosophical idea called the **Anthropic principle**, which says that if the universe were even a little different than it is, we could not be here. It might even seem that the universe is exquisitely tuned, almost as if to accommodate us.

*Anthropic principle*

## Summary

The night sky contains myriads of stars including those in the Milky Way, which is a "side view" of our **Galaxy** looking along the plane of the disc. Our Galaxy includes about $10^{11}$ stars. Beyond our Galaxy are billions of other galaxies.

Astronomical distances are measured in **light-years** ($1 \text{ ly} \approx 10^{13} \text{ km}$). The nearest star is about 4 ly away and the nearest large galaxy is 2 million ly away. Our Galactic disc has a diameter of about 100,000 ly. Distances are often specified in **parsecs**, where $1 \text{ parsec} = 3.26 \text{ ly}$.

Stars are believed to begin life as collapsing masses of hydrogen gas (protostars). As they contract, they heat up (potential energy is transformed to kinetic energy). When the temperature reaches about 10 million degrees, nuclear fusion begins and forms heavier elements (**nucleosynthesis**), mainly helium at first. The energy released during these reactions heats the gas so its outward pressure balances the inward gravitational force, and the young star stabilizes as a **main-sequence** star. The tremendous luminosity of stars comes from the energy released during these thermonuclear reactions. After billions of years, as helium is collected in the core and hydrogen is used up, the core contracts and heats further. The envelope expands and cools, and the star becomes a **red giant** (larger diameter, redder color). The next stage of stellar evolution depends on the mass of the star, which may have lost much of its original mass as its outer envelope escaped into space. Stars of residual mass less than about 1.4 solar masses cool further and become **white dwarfs**, eventually fading and going out altogether. Heavier stars contract further due to their greater gravity: the density approaches nuclear density, the huge pressure forces electrons to combine with protons to form neutrons, and the star becomes essentially a huge nucleus of neutrons. This is a **neutron star**, and the energy released from its final core collapse is believed to produce **supernovae** explosions. If the star is very massive, it may contract even further and form a **black hole**, which is so dense that no matter or light can escape from it.

In the **general theory of relativity**, the **equivalence principle** states that an observer cannot distinguish acceleration from a gravitational field. Said another way, gravitational and inertial masses are the same. The theory predicts gravitational bending of light rays to a degree consistent with experiment. Gravity is treated as a curvature in space and time, the curvature being greater near massive bodies. The universe as a whole may be curved. With sufficient mass, the curvature of the universe would be positive, and the universe is *closed* and *finite*; otherwise, it would be *open* and *infinite*.

Distant galaxies display a **redshift** in their spectral lines, interpreted as a Doppler shift. The universe seems to be **expanding**, its galaxies racing away from each other at speeds ($v$) proportional to the distance ($d$) between them:

$$v = Hd, \qquad \textbf{(33–6)}$$

which is known as **Hubble's law** ($H$ is the **Hubble parameter**). This expansion of the universe suggests an explosive origin, the **Big Bang**, which occurred about 13.7 billion years ago.

The **cosmological principle** assumes that the universe, on a large scale, is homogeneous and isotropic.

Important evidence for the Big Bang model of the universe was the discovery of the **cosmic microwave background** radiation (CMB), which conforms to a blackbody radiation curve at a temperature of 2.725 K.

The **standard model** of the Big Bang provides a possible scenario as to how the universe developed as it expanded and cooled after the Big Bang. Starting at $10^{-43}$ seconds after the Big Bang, according to this model, there was a series of **phase transitions** during which previously unified forces of nature "condensed out" one by one. The **inflationary scenario** assumes that during one of these phase transitions, the universe underwent a brief but rapid exponential expansion. Until about $10^{-35}$ s, there was no distinction between quarks and leptons. Shortly thereafter, quarks were **confined** into hadrons (the **hadron era**). About $10^{-4}$ s after the Big Bang, the majority of hadrons disappeared, having combined with anti-hadrons, producing photons, leptons and energy, leaving mainly photons and leptons to freely move, thus introducing the **lepton era**. By the time the universe was about 10 s old, the electrons too had mostly disappeared, having combined with their antiparticles; the universe was **radiation-dominated**. A couple of minutes later, nucleosynthesis began, but lasted only a few minutes.

It then took several hundred thousand years before the universe was cool enough for electrons to combine with nuclei to form atoms. The background radiation had expanded and cooled so much that its total energy became less than the energy in matter, and matter dominated increasingly over radiation. Then stars and galaxies formed, producing a universe not much different than it is today—some 13 billion years later.

Recent observations indicate that the universe is flat, that it contains an as-yet unknown type of **dark matter**, and that it is dominated by a mysterious **dark energy** which exerts a sort of negative gravity causing the expansion of the universe to accelerate.

Today the evidence suggests that the universe is flat and will continue to expand indefinitely. The total contributions of baryonic (normal) matter, dark matter, and dark energy sum up to the **critical density**.

## Questions

1. The Milky Way was once thought to be "murky" or "milky" but is now considered to be made up of point sources. Explain.
2. A star is in equilibrium when it radiates at its surface all the energy generated at its core. What happens when it begins to generate more energy than it radiates? Less energy? Explain.
3. Describe a red giant star. List some of its properties.
4. Select a point on the H–R diagram. Mark several directions away from this point. Now describe the changes that would take place in a star moving in each of these directions.
5. Does the H–R diagram reveal anything about the core of a star?
6. Why do some stars end up as white dwarfs, and others as neutron stars or black holes?
7. Can we tell, by looking at the population on the H–R diagram, that hotter main-sequence stars have shorter lives? Explain.
8. If you were measuring star parallaxes from the Moon instead of Earth, what corrections would you have to make? What changes would occur if you were measuring parallaxes from Mars?
9. *Cepheid variable* stars change in luminosity with a typical period of several days. The period has been found to have a definite relationship with the absolute luminosity of the star. How could these stars be used to measure the distance to galaxies?
10. What is a geodesic? What is its role in General Relativity?
11. If it were discovered that the redshift of spectral lines of galaxies was due to something other than expansion, how might our view of the universe change? Would there be conflicting evidence? Discuss.
12. All galaxies appear to be moving away from us. Are we therefore at the center of the universe? Explain.
13. If you were located in a galaxy near the boundary of our observable universe, would galaxies in the direction of the Milky Way appear to be approaching you or receding from you? Explain.
14. Compare an explosion on Earth to the Big Bang. Consider such questions as: Would the debris spread at a higher speed for more distant particles, as in the Big Bang? Would the debris come to rest? What type of universe would this correspond to, open or closed?
15. If nothing, not even light, escapes from a black hole, then how can we tell if one is there?
16. What mass will give a Schwarzschild radius equal to that of the hydrogen atom in its ground state?
17. The Earth's age is often given as about 4 billion years. Find that time on Fig. 33–25. People have lived on Earth on the order of a million years. Where is that on Fig. 33–25?
18. Explain what the 2.7-K cosmic microwave background radiation is. Where does it come from? Why is its temperature now so low?
19. Why were atoms, as opposed to bare nuclei, unable to exist until hundreds of thousands of years after the Big Bang?
20. Under what circumstances would the universe eventually collapse in on itself?

## Problems

### 33–1 to 33–3 Stars, Galaxies, Stellar Evolution, Distances

1. (I) Using the definitions of the parsec and the light-year, show that $1\text{ pc} = 3.26\text{ ly}$.
2. (I) A star exhibits a parallax of 0.38 seconds of arc. How far away is it?
3. (I) The parallax angle of a star is 0.00019°. How far away is the star?
4. (I) A star is 36 pc away. What is its parallax angle? State (*a*) in seconds of arc, and (*b*) in degrees.
5. (I) What is the parallax angle for a star that is 55 ly away? How many parsecs is this?
6. (I) If one star is twice as far away from us as a second star, will the parallax angle of the farther star be greater or less than that of the nearer star? By what factor?
7. (II) A star is 35 pc away. How long does it take for its light to reach us?
8. (II) We saw earlier (Chapter 14) that the rate energy reaches the Earth from the Sun (the "solar constant") is about $1.3 \times 10^3\text{ W/m}^2$. What is (*a*) the apparent brightness $l$ of the Sun, and (*b*) the absolute luminosity $L$ of the Sun?
9. (II) What is the relative brightness of the Sun as seen from Jupiter as compared to its brightness from Earth? (Jupiter is 5.2 times farther from the Sun than the Earth.)
10. (II) Estimate the angular width that our Galaxy would subtend if observed from the nearest galaxy to us (Table 33–1). Compare to the angular width of the Moon from Earth.
11. (II) When our Sun becomes a red giant, what will be its average density if it expands out to the orbit of Earth ($1.5 \times 10^{11}$ m from the Sun)?

12. (II) When our Sun becomes a white dwarf, it is expected to be about the size of the Moon. What angular width will it subtend from the present distance to Earth?

13. (II) Calculate the density of a white dwarf whose mass is equal to the Sun's and whose radius is equal to the Earth's. How many times larger than Earth's density is this?

14. (II) A neutron star whose mass is 1.5 solar masses has a radius of about 11 km. Calculate its average density and compare to that for a white dwarf (Problem 13) and to that of nuclear matter.

15. (II) Calculate the $Q$-values for the He burning reactions of Eq. 33–2. (The mass of the very unstable ${}^{8}_{4}\mathrm{Be}$ is 8.005305 u.)

16. (II) Suppose two stars of the same apparent brightness $l$ are also believed to be the same size. The spectrum of one star peaks at 800 nm whereas that of the other peaks at 400 nm. Use Wien's law (Section 27–2) and the Stefan-Boltzmann equation (Eq. 14–5) to estimate their relative distances from us. [*Hint*: see Examples 33–4 and 33–5.]

17. (III) Stars located in a certain cluster are assumed to be about the same distance from us. Two such stars have spectra that peak at $\lambda_1 = 500\,\mathrm{nm}$ and $\lambda_2 = 700\,\mathrm{nm}$, and the ratio of their apparent brightness is $l_1/l_2 = 0.091$. Estimate their relative sizes (give ratio of their diameters). [*Hint*: use the Stefan-Boltzmann equation, Eq. 14–5.]

### 33–4 General Relativity, Gravity and Curved Space

18. (I) Show that the Schwarzschild radius for a star with mass equal to that (*a*) of our Sun is 2.95 km, and (*b*) of Earth is 8.9 mm.

19. (II) What is the Schwarzschild radius for a typical galaxy (like ours)?

20. (II) Describe a triangle, drawn on the surface of a sphere, for which the sum of the angles is (*a*) 359°, and (*b*) 180°.

21. (II) What is the maximum sum-of-the-angles for a triangle on a sphere?

### 33–5 Redshift, Hubble's Law

22. (I) If a galaxy is traveling away from us at 1.0% of the speed of light, roughly how far away is it?

23. (I) The redshift of a galaxy indicates a velocity of 3500 km/s. How far away is it?

24. (I) Estimate the speed of a galaxy (relative to us) that is near the observable "edge" of the universe, say 12 billion light-years away.

25. (II) Estimate the observed wavelength for the 656-nm line in the Balmer series of hydrogen in the spectrum of a galaxy whose distance from us is (*a*) $1.0 \times 10^6$ ly, (*b*) $1.0 \times 10^8$ ly, (*c*) $1.0 \times 10^{10}$ ly.

26. (II) Estimate the speed of a galaxy, and its distance from us, if the wavelength for the hydrogen line at 434 nm is measured on Earth as being 610 nm.

27. (II) What is the speed of a galaxy with $z = 0.60$?

28. (II) What would be the redshift parameter $z$ for a galaxy traveling away from us at $v = 0.50c$?

29. (II) Starting from Eq. 33–3, show that the Doppler shift in wavelength is $\Delta\lambda/\lambda_0 \approx v/c$ (Eq. 33–5b) for $v \ll c$. [*Hint*: use the binomial expansion.]

### 33–6 to 33–8 The Big Bang, CMB, Universe Expansion

30. (I) Calculate the wavelength at the peak of the blackbody radiation distribution at 2.7 K using Wien's law.

31. (II) The critical density for closure of the universe is $\rho_c \approx 10^{-26}\,\mathrm{kg/m^3}$. State $\rho_c$ in terms of the average number of nucleons per cubic meter.

32. (II) The scale of the universe (the average distance between galaxies) at any one moment is believed to have been inversely proportional to the absolute temperature. Estimate the size of the universe, compared to today, at (*a*) $t = 10^6$ yr, (*b*) $t = 1$ s, (*c*) $t = 10^{-6}$ s, and (*d*) $t = 10^{-35}$ s.

33. (II) At approximately what time had the universe cooled below the threshold temperature for producing (*a*) kaons $(M \approx 500\,\mathrm{MeV}/c^2)$, (*b*) $\Upsilon$ $(M \approx 9500\,\mathrm{MeV}/c^2)$, and (*c*) muons $(M \approx 100\,\mathrm{MeV}/c^2)$?

## General Problems

34. Suppose that three main-sequence stars could undergo the three changes represented by the three arrows, A, B, and C, in the H–R diagram of Fig. 33–28. For each case, describe the changes in temperature, luminosity, and size.

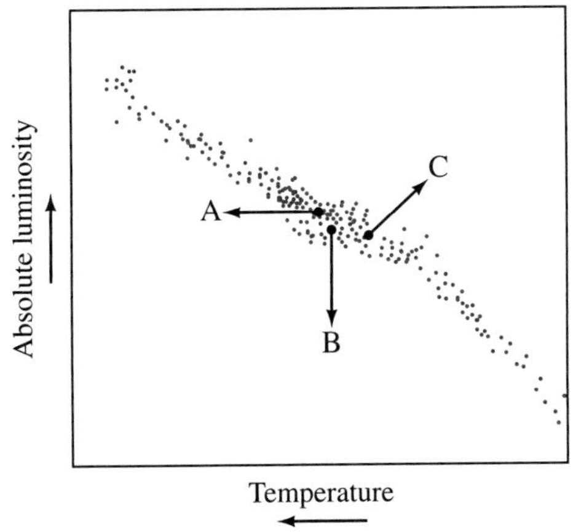


**FIGURE 33–28** Problem 34.

35. Assume that the nearest stars to us have an absolute luminosity about the same as the Sun's. Their apparent brightness, however, is about $10^{11}$ times fainter than the Sun. From this, estimate the distance to the nearest stars. (Newton did this calculation, although he made a numerical error of a factor of 100.)

36. Use conservation of angular momentum to estimate the angular velocity of a neutron star which has collapsed to a diameter of 20 km, from a star whose radius was equal to that of our Sun $(7 \times 10^8\,\mathrm{m})$, of mass 1.5 times that of the Sun, and which rotated (like our Sun) about once a month.

37. By what factor does the rotational kinetic energy change when the star in Problem 36 collapses to a neutron star?

38. A certain pulsar, believed to be a neutron star of mass 1.5 times that of the Sun, with diameter 20 km, is observed to have a rotation speed of 1.0 rev/s. If it loses rotational kinetic energy at the rate of 1 part in $10^9$ per day, which is all transformed into radiation, what is the power output of the star?

39. The nearest large galaxy to our Galaxy is about $2 \times 10^6$ ly away. If both galaxies have a mass of $3 \times 10^{41}$ kg, with what gravitational force does each galaxy attract the other?

40. Estimate what neutrino rest mass (in eV) would provide the critical density to close the universe. Assume the neutrino density is, like photons, about $10^9$ times that of nucleons, and that nucleons make up only (*a*) 2% of the mass needed, or (*b*) 5% of the mass needed.

41. Two stars, whose spectra peak at 600 nm and 400 nm, respectively, both lie on the main sequence. Use Wien's law, the Stefan-Boltzmann equation, and the H–R diagram (Fig. 33–6) to estimate the ratio of their diameters. [*Hint*: see Examples 33–4 and 33–5.]

42. Suppose we can measure distances with parallax at 100 parsecs. What is our minimum angular resolution (in degrees), based on this information?

43. Through some coincidence, the Balmer lines from singly ionized helium in a distant star happen to overlap with the Balmer lines from hydrogen (Fig. 27–22) in the Sun. How fast is the star receding from us?

44. What is the temperature that corresponds to 1.8-TeV collisions at the Fermilab collider? To what era in cosmological history does this correspond? [*Hint*: see Fig. 33–25.]

45. Astronomers have recently measured the rotation of gas around what might be a supermassive black hole of about 2 billion solar masses at the center of a galaxy. If the radius from the galactic center to the gas clouds is 60 light-years, what Doppler shift $\Delta\lambda/\lambda_0$ do you estimate they saw?

46. A galaxy is moving away from Earth. The "blue" hydrogen line at 434 nm emitted from the galaxy is measured on Earth to be 650 nm. (*a*) How fast is the galaxy moving? (*b*) How far is it from Earth?

47. In the later stages of stellar evolution, a star (if massive enough) will begin fusing carbon nuclei to form, for example, magnesium:

$$^{12}_{6}C + ^{12}_{6}C \rightarrow ^{24}_{12}Mg + \gamma.$$

(*a*) How much energy is released in this reaction (see Appendix B). (*b*) How much kinetic energy must each carbon nucleus have (assume equal) in a head-on collision if they are just to touch (use Eq. 30–1) so that the strong force can come into play? (*c*) What temperature does this kinetic energy correspond to?

48. Consider the reaction

$$^{16}_{8}O + ^{16}_{8}O \rightarrow ^{28}_{14}Si + ^{4}_{2}He,$$

and answer the same questions as in Problem 47.

49. How large would the Sun be if its density equaled the critical density of the universe, $\rho_c \approx 10^{-26}\,kg/m^3$? Express your answer in light-years and compare with the Earth–Sun distance and the size of our Galaxy.

## Answers to Exercises

**A:** Ourselves; 2 years ago.

**B:** 600 ly (estimating $L$ from Fig. 33–6 as $L \approx 8 \times 10^{26}$ W; note that on a log scale, 6000 K is closer to 7000 K than it is to 5000 K).

**C:** 1.4.

APPENDIX A

# Mathematical Review

## A–1 Relationships, Proportionality, and Equations

One of the important aspects of physics is the search for relationships between different quantities—that is, determining how one quantity affects another. For example, how does temperature affect the air pressure in a tire? Or how does the net force on an object affect its acceleration? Sometimes a given quantity is affected by two or more quantities; for instance, the acceleration of an object is related to both its mass and the applied force. If you suspect that a relationship exists between two or more quantities, you can try to determine the precise nature of this relationship. This is done by varying one of the quantities and measuring how the other varies as a result. If it is likely that a particular quantity will be affected by more than one factor or quantity, only one quantity is varied at a time, while the others are held constant.†

As a simple example, the ancients found that if one circle has twice the diameter of a second circle, the first also has twice the circumference. If the diameter is three times as large, the circumference is also three times as large. In other words, an increase in the diameter results in a proportional increase in the circumference. We say that the circumference is *directly proportional to* the diameter. This can be written in symbols as $C \propto D$, where "$\propto$" means "is proportional to," and $C$ and $D$ refer to the circumference and diameter of a circle, respectively. The next step is to change this proportionality to an equation, which will make it possible to link the two quantities numerically. This merely entails inserting a proportionality constant, which in many cases is determined by measurement. (In some cases it can be chosen arbitrarily, if it involves only the definition of a new unit.) The ancients found that the ratio of the circumference to the diameter of any circle was 3.1416 (to keep only the first few decimal places). This number is designated by the Greek letter $\pi$. It is the constant of proportionality for the relationship $C \propto D$. To obtain an equation, we insert $\pi$ into the proportion and change the $\propto$ to $=$. Thus, $C = \pi D$.

*Direct proportion*

Other kinds of proportionality occur as well. For example, the area of a circle is proportional to the *square* of its radius. That is, if the radius is doubled, the area becomes four times as large; and so on. In this case we can write $A \propto r^2$, where $A$ stands for the area and $r$ for the radius of the circle.

Sometimes two quantities are related in such a way that an increase in one leads to a proportional *decrease* in the other. This is called *inverse proportion.* For example, the time required to travel a given distance is inversely proportional to the speed of travel. The greater the speed, the less time it takes. We can write this inverse proportion as time $\propto$ 1/speed. The larger the denominator of a fraction, the lower the value of the fraction is as a whole. For example, $\frac{1}{4}$ is less than $\frac{1}{2}$. Thus, if the speed is doubled, the time is halved, which is what we want to express by this inverse proportionality relationship.

*Inverse proportion*

† When one quantity affects another, we often use the expression "is a function of" to indicate this dependence; for example, we say that the pressure in a tire is a function of the temperature.

Whatever kind of proportion is found to hold, it can be changed to an equality by insertion of the proper proportionality constant. Quantitative statements or predictions about the physical world can then be made with the equation.

## A–2 Exponents

When we write $10^4$, we mean that you multiply 10 by itself four times: $10^4 = 10 \times 10 \times 10 \times 10 = 10{,}000$. The superscript 4 is called an *exponent*, and 10 is said to be raised to the fourth power. Any number or symbol can be raised to a power; special names are used when the exponent is 2 ($a^2$ is "$a$ squared") or 3 ($a^3$ is "$a$ cubed"). For any other power, we say $a^n$ is "$a$ to the $n$th power." If the exponent is 1, it is usually dropped: $a^1 = a$, since no multiplication is involved.

The rules for multiplying numbers expressed as powers are as follows:

$$(a^n)(a^m) = a^{n+m}. \qquad \textbf{(A–1)}$$

That is, the exponents are added. To see why, consider the result of the multiplication of $3^3$ by $3^4$:

$$(3^3)(3^4) = (3)(3)(3) \times (3)(3)(3)(3) = (3)^7.$$

Here the sum of the exponents is $3 + 4 = 7$, so rule A–1 works. Notice that this rule works only if the base numbers ($a$ in Eq. A–1) are the same. Thus we *cannot* use the rule of summing exponents for $(6^3)(5^2)$; these numbers would have to be written out. However, if the base numbers are different but the exponents are the same, we can write a second rule:

$$(a^n)(b^n) = (ab)^n. \qquad \textbf{(A–2)}$$

For example, $(5^3)(6^3) = (30)^3$ since

$$(5)(5)(5)(6)(6)(6) = (30)(30)(30).$$

The third rule involves a power raised to another power: $(a^3)^2$ means $(a^3)(a^3)$, which is equal to $a^{3+3} = a^6$. The general rule is then

$$(a^n)^m = a^{nm}. \qquad \textbf{(A–3)}$$

In this case, the exponents are multiplied.

*Negative exponents* are used for reciprocals. Thus,

$$\frac{1}{a} = a^{-1}, \qquad \frac{1}{a^3} = a^{-3},$$

and so on. The reason for using negative exponents is to allow us to use the multiplication rules given above. For example, $(a^5)(a^{-3})$ means

$$\frac{(a)(a)(a)(a)(a)}{(a)(a)(a)} = a^2.$$

Rule A–1 gives us the same result:

$$(a^5)(a^{-3}) = a^{5-3} = a^2.$$

What does an exponent of zero mean? That is, what is $a^0$? Any number raised to the zeroth power is defined as being equal to 1:

$$a^0 = 1.$$

This definition is used because it follows from the rules for adding exponents. For example,

$$a^3 a^{-3} = a^{3-3} = a^0 = 1.$$

But *does* $a^3 a^{-3}$ actually equal 1? Yes, because

$$a^3 a^{-3} = \frac{a^3}{a^3} = 1.$$

*Fractional exponents* are used to represent *roots*. For example, $a^{\frac{1}{2}}$ means the square root of $a$; that is, $a^{\frac{1}{2}} = \sqrt{a}$. Similarly, $a^{\frac{1}{3}}$ means the cube root of $a$, and so on. The fourth root of $a$ means that if you multiply the fourth root of $a$ by itself four times, you again get $a$:

$$\left(a^{\frac{1}{4}}\right)^4 = a.$$

This is consistent with rule A–3 since $\left(a^{\frac{1}{4}}\right)^4 = a^{\frac{4}{4}} = a^1 = a.$

## A–3 Powers of 10, or Exponential Notation

Writing out very large and very small numbers such as the distance of Neptune from the Sun, 4,500,000,000 km, or the diameter of a typical atom, 0.00000001 cm, is inconvenient and prone to error. It also leaves in question (see Section 1–4) the number of significant figures. (How many of the zeros are significant in the number 4,500,000,000 km?) We therefore make use of the "powers of 10," or exponential notation. The distance from Neptune to the Sun is then expressed as $4.50 \times 10^9$ km (assuming that the value is significant to three digits), and the diameter of an atom $1.0 \times 10^{-8}$ cm. This way of writing numbers is based on the use of exponents, where $a^n$ signifies $a$ multiplied by itself $n$ times. For example, $10^4 = 10 \times 10 \times 10 \times 10 = 10{,}000$. Thus, $4.50 \times 10^9 = 4.50 \times 1{,}000{,}000{,}000 = 4{,}500{,}000{,}000$. Notice that the exponent (9 in this case) is just the number of places the decimal point is moved to the right to obtain the fully written-out number (4.500,000,000.)

When two numbers are multiplied (or divided), you first multiply (or divide) the simple parts and then the powers of 10. Thus, $2.0 \times 10^3$ multiplied by $5.5 \times 10^4$ equals $(2.0 \times 5.5) \times \left(10^3 \times 10^4\right) = 11 \times 10^7$, where we have used the rule for adding exponents (Appendix A–2). Similarly, $8.2 \times 10^5$ divided by $2.0 \times 10^2$ equals

$$\frac{8.2 \times 10^5}{2.0 \times 10^2} = \frac{8.2}{2.0} \times \frac{10^5}{10^2} = 4.1 \times 10^3.$$

For numbers less than 1, say 0.01, the exponent power of 10 is written with a negative sign: $0.01 = 1/100 = 1/10^2 = 1 \times 10^{-2}$. Similarly, $0.002 = 2 \times 10^{-3}$. The decimal point has again been moved the number of places expressed in the exponent. Thus, $0.020 \times 3600 = 72$; in exponential notation $\left(2.0 \times 10^{-2}\right) \times \left(3.6 \times 10^3\right) = 7.2 \times 10^1 = 72$.

Notice also that $10^1 \times 10^{-1} = 10 \times 0.1 = 1$, and by the law of exponents, $10^1 \times 10^{-1} = 10^0$. Therefore, $10^0 = 1$.

When writing a number in exponential notation, it is usual to make the simple number be between 1 and 10. Thus it is conventional to write $4.5 \times 10^9$ rather than $45 \times 10^8$, although they are the same number.† This notation also allows the number of *significant figures* to be clearly expressed. We write $4.50 \times 10^9$ if this value is accurate to three significant figures, but $4.5 \times 10^9$ if it is accurate to only two.

## A–4 Algebra

Physical relationships between quantities can be represented as equations involving symbols (usually letters of the alphabet) that represent the quantities. The manipulation of such equations is the field of algebra, and it is used a great deal in physics. An equation involves an equals sign, which tells us that the quantities on either side of the equals sign have the same value. Examples of equations are

$$3 + 8 = 11$$
$$2x + 7 = 15$$
$$a^2 b + c = 6.$$

The first equation involves only numbers, so is called an arithmetic equation. The other two equations are algebraic since they involve symbols. In the third equation, the quantity $a^2 b$ means the product of $a$ times $a$ times $b$: $a^2 b = a \times a \times b$.

†Another convention used, particularly with computers, is that the simple number be between 0.1 and 1. Thus we could write 4,500,000,000 as $0.450 \times 10^{10}$.

## Solving for an Unknown

Often we wish to solve for one (or more) symbols, and we treat it as an *unknown*. For example, in the equation $2x + 7 = 15$, $x$ is the unknown; this equation is true, however, only when $x = 4$. Determining what value (or values) the unknown(s) can have to satisfy the equation(s) is called *solving the equation*. To solve an equation, the following rule can be used:

> *An equation will remain true if any operation performed on one side is also performed on the other side:* for example, ($a$) addition or subtraction of a number or symbol; ($b$) multiplication or division by a number or symbol; ($c$) raising each side of the equation to the same power, or taking the same root (such as square root).

**EXAMPLE A–1** Solve for $x$ in the equation

$$2x + 7 = 15.$$

**APPROACH** We perform the same operations on both sides of the equation to isolate $x$ as the only variable on the left side of the equals sign.

**SOLUTION** We first subtract 7 from both sides:

$$2x + 7 - 7 = 15 - 7$$

or

$$2x = 8.$$

Then we divide both sides by 2 to get

$$\frac{2x}{2} = \frac{8}{2},$$

or, carrying out the divisions,

$$x = 4,$$

and this solves the equation.

**EXAMPLE A–2** ($a$) Solve the equation

$$a^2b + c = 24$$

for the unknown $a$ in terms of $b$ and $c$. ($b$) Solve for $a$ assuming that $b = 2$ and $c = 6$.

**APPROACH** We perform operations to isolate $a$ as the only variable on the left side of the equals sign.

**SOLUTION** ($a$) We are trying to solve for $a$, so we first subtract $c$ from both sides:

$$a^2b = 24 - c,$$

then divide by $b$:

$$a^2 = \frac{24 - c}{b},$$

and finally take square roots:

$$a = \sqrt{\frac{24 - c}{b}}.$$

($b$) If we are given that $b = 2$ and $c = 6$, then

$$a = \sqrt{\frac{24 - 6}{2}} = 3.$$

**NOTE** Whenever we take a square root, the number can be either positive or negative. Thus $a = -3$ is also a solution. Why? Because $(-3)^2 = 9$, just as $(+3)^2 = 9$. So we actually get two solutions: $a = +3$ and $a = -3$.

To check a solution, we put it back into the original equation (this is really a check that we did all the manipulations correctly). In the equation

$$a^2b + c = 24,$$

we put in $a = 3, b = 2, c = 6$ and find

$$(3)^2(2) + (6) \stackrel{?}{=} 24$$
$$24 = 24,$$

which checks.

**EXERCISE A** Put $a = -3$ into the equation of Example A–2 and show that it works too.

## Two or More Unknowns

If we have two or more unknowns, one equation is not sufficient to find them. In general, if there are $n$ unknowns, $n$ independent equations are needed. For example, if there are two unknowns, we need two equations. If the unknowns are called $x$ and $y$, a typical procedure is to solve one equation for $x$ in terms of $y$, and substitute this into the second equation.

**EXAMPLE A–3** Solve the following pair of equations for $x$ and $y$.

$$3x - 2y = 19$$
$$x + 4y = -3.$$

**APPROACH** We have two unknowns and two equations; we can start by solving the second equation for $x$ in terms of $y$. Then we substitute this result for $x$ into the first equation.

**SOLUTION** We subtract $4y$ from both sides of the second equation:

$$x = -3 - 4y.$$

We substitute this expression for $x$ into the first equation, and simplify:

$$3(-3 - 4y) - 2y = 19$$
$$-9 - 12y - 2y = 19 \qquad \text{(carried out the multiplication by 3)}$$
$$-14y = 28 \qquad \text{(added 9 to both sides)}$$
$$y = -2. \qquad \text{(divided both sides by } -14\text{)}$$

Now that we know $y = -2$, we substitute this into the expression for $x$:

$$x = -3 - 4y$$
$$= -3 - 4(-2) = -3 + 8 = 5.$$

Our solution is $x = 5, y = -2$. We check this solution by putting these values back into the original equations:

$$3x - 2y \stackrel{?}{=} 19$$
$$3(5) - 2(-2) \stackrel{?}{=} 19$$
$$15 + 4 \stackrel{?}{=} 19$$
$$19 = 19 \qquad \text{(it checks)}$$

and

$$x + 4y \stackrel{?}{=} -3$$
$$5 + 4(-2) \stackrel{?}{=} -3$$
$$-3 = -3. \qquad \text{(it checks)}$$

Other methods for solving two or more equations, such as the method of determinants, can be found in an algebra textbook.

### The Quadratic Formula

We sometimes encounter equations that involve an unknown, say $x$, that appears not only to the first power, but squared as well. Such a *quadratic equation* can be written in the form

$$ax^2 + bx + c = 0.$$

The quantities $a$, $b$, and $c$ are typically numbers or constants that are given.† The general solutions to such an equation are given by the *quadratic formula*:

*Quadratic formula*

$$x = \frac{-b \pm \sqrt{b^2 - 4ac}}{2a}. \quad \textbf{(A–4)}$$

The $\pm$ sign indicates that there are two solutions for $x$: one where the plus sign is used, the other where the minus sign is used.

**EXAMPLE A–4** Find the solutions for $x$ in the equation

$$3x^2 - 5x = 2.$$

**APPROACH** Here $x$ appears both to the first power and squared, so we use the quadratic equation.

**SOLUTION** First we write this equation in the standard form

$$ax^2 + bx + c = 0$$

by subtracting 2 from both sides:

$$3x^2 - 5x - 2 = 0.$$

In this case, $a$, $b$, and $c$ in the standard formula take the values $a = 3, b = -5$, and $c = -2$. The two solutions for $x$ are

$$x = \frac{+5 + \sqrt{25 - (4)(3)(-2)}}{(2)(3)} = \frac{5 + 7}{6} = 2$$

and

$$x = \frac{+5 - \sqrt{25 - (4)(3)(-2)}}{(2)(3)} = \frac{5 - 7}{6} = -\frac{1}{3}.$$

In this Example, the two solutions are $x = 2$ and $x = -\frac{1}{3}$. In physics problems, it sometimes happens that only one of the solutions corresponds to a real-life situation; in this case, the other solution is discarded. In other cases, both solutions may correspond to physical reality.

Notice, incidentally, that $b^2$ must be greater than $4ac$, so that $\sqrt{b^2 - 4ac}$ yields a real number. If $(b^2 - 4ac)$ is less than zero (negative), there is no real solution. The square root of a negative number is called *imaginary*.

A second-order equation—one in which the highest power of $x$ is 2—has two solutions; a third-order equation—involving $x^3$—has three solutions; and so on.

## A–5 The Binomial Expansion

Sometimes we end up with a quantity of the form $(1 + x)^n$. That is, the quantity $(1 + x)$ is raised to the $n$th power. This can be written as an infinite sum of terms, known as a *series expansion*, as follows:

$$(1 + x)^n = 1 + nx + \frac{n(n-1)}{2!}x^2 + \cdots. \quad \textbf{(A–5)}$$

This formula is useful for us mainly when $x$ is very small compared to one $(x \ll 1)$. In this case, each successive term is much smaller than the preceding

† Or one or more of them could be variables, in which case additional equations are needed.

term. For example, if $x = 0.01$, and $n = 2$, say, then whereas the first term equals 1, the second term is $nx = (2)(0.01) = 0.02$, and the third term is $[(2)(1)/2](0.01)^2 = 0.0001$, and so on. Thus, when $x$ is small, we can ignore all but the first two (or three) terms and can write

$$(1 + x)^n \approx 1 + nx. \tag{A–6}$$

This approximation often allows us to solve an equation easily that otherwise might be very difficult. Some examples are

$$(1 + x)^2 \approx 1 + 2x,$$
$$\frac{1}{1 + x} = (1 + x)^{-1} \approx 1 - x,$$
$$\sqrt{1 + x} = (1 + x)^{\frac{1}{2}} \approx 1 + \tfrac{1}{2}x,$$
$$\frac{1}{\sqrt{1 + x}} = (1 + x)^{-\frac{1}{2}} \approx 1 - \tfrac{1}{2}x,$$

where $x \ll 1$.

As a numerical example, let us evaluate $\sqrt{1.02}$ using the binomial expansion since $x = 0.02$ is much smaller than 1:

$$\sqrt{1.02} = (1.02)^{\frac{1}{2}} = (1 + 0.02)^{\frac{1}{2}} \approx 1 + \tfrac{1}{2}(0.02) = 1.01.$$

You can check with a calculator (and maybe not even more quickly) that $\sqrt{1.02} \approx 1.01$.

## A–6 Plane Geometry

We review here a number of theorems involving angles and triangles that are useful in physics.

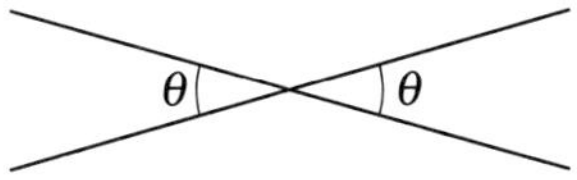


FIGURE A–1

FIGURE A–2

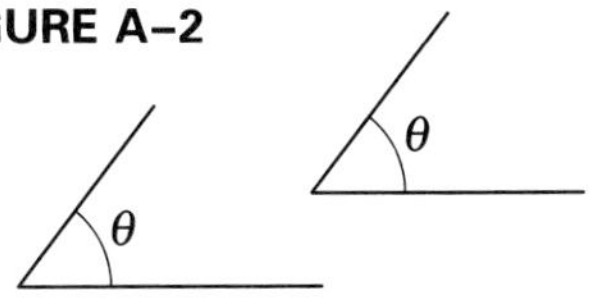


1. *Equal angles.* Two angles are equal if any of the following conditions are true:
   (*a*) They are vertical angles (Fig. A–1); *or*
   (*b*) the left side of one is parallel to the left side of the other, and the right side of one is parallel to the right side of the other (the left and right sides are as seen from the vertex, where the two sides meet; Fig. A–2); *or*
   (*c*) the left side of one is perpendicular to the left side of the other, and the right sides are likewise perpendicular (Fig. A–3).

FIGURE A–3

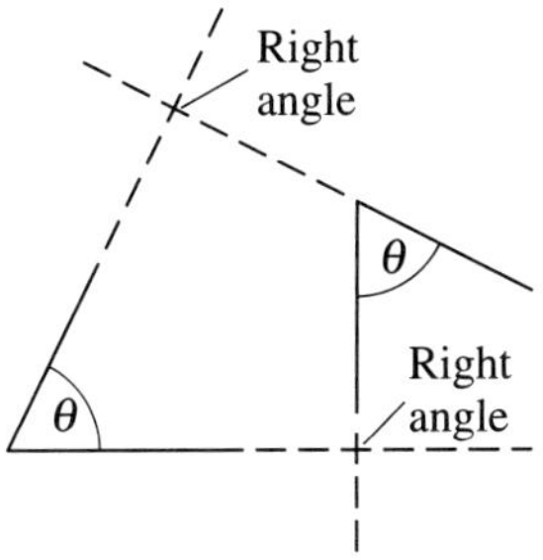


2. *The sum of the angles* in any plane triangle is 180°.

3. *Similar triangles.* Two triangles are said to be similar if all three of their angles are equal (in Fig. A–4, $\theta_1 = \phi_1$, $\theta_2 = \phi_2$, and $\theta_3 = \phi_3$). Similar triangles thus have the same basic shape but may be different sizes and have different orientations. Two useful theorems about similar triangles are:
   (*a*) Two triangles are similar if any two of their angles are equal. (This follows because the third angles must also be equal since the sum of the angles of a triangle is 180°.)
   (*b*) The ratios of corresponding sides of two similar triangles are equal. That is (Fig. A–4),

$$\frac{a_1}{b_1} = \frac{a_2}{b_2} = \frac{a_3}{b_3}.$$

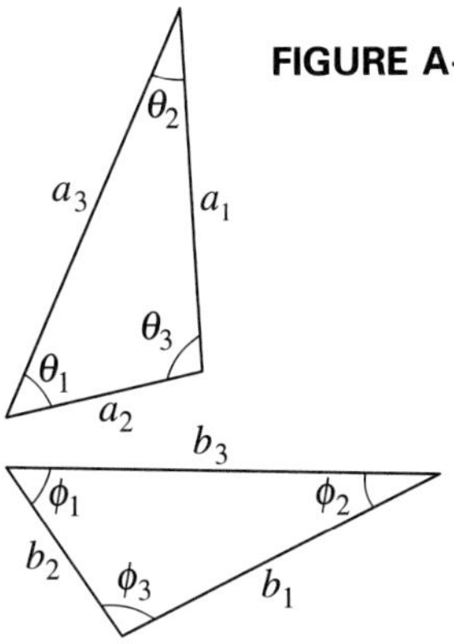


FIGURE A–4

4. *Congruent triangles.* Two triangles are congruent if one can be placed precisely on top of the other. That is, they are similar triangles and they have the same size. Two triangles are congruent if any of the following holds:
   (*a*) The three corresponding sides are equal.
   (*b*) Two sides and the enclosed angle are equal ("side-angle-side").
   (*c*) Two angles and the enclosed side are equal ("angle-side-angle").

FIGURE A–5

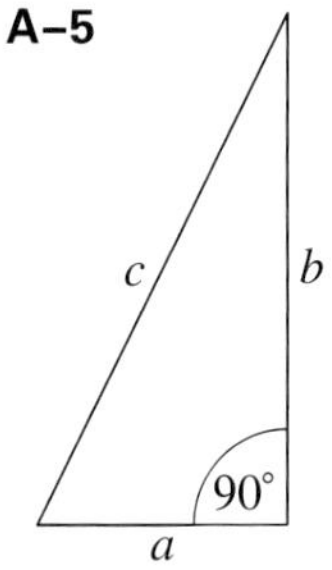


5. *Right triangles.* A right triangle has one angle that is 90° (a *right angle*); that is, the two sides that meet at the right angle are perpendicular (Fig. A–5). The two other (acute) angles in the right triangle add up to 90°.
6. *Pythagorean theorem.* In any right triangle, the square of the length of the hypotenuse (the side opposite the right angle) is equal to the sum of the squares of the lengths of the other two sides. In Fig. A–5,

$$c^2 = a^2 + b^2.$$

## A–7 Trigonometric Functions and Identities

FIGURE A–6

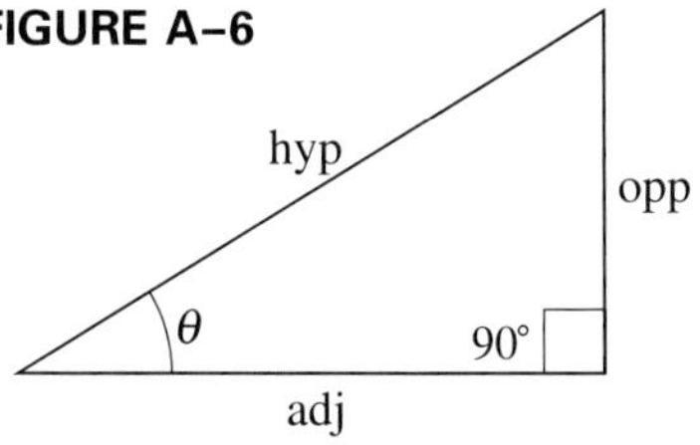


Trigonometric functions for any angle $\theta$ are defined by constructing a right triangle about that angle as shown in Fig. A–6; opp and adj are the lengths of the sides opposite and adjacent to the angle $\theta$, and hyp is the length of the hypotenuse:

$$\sin\theta = \frac{\text{opp}}{\text{hyp}} \qquad \csc\theta = \frac{1}{\sin\theta} = \frac{\text{hyp}}{\text{opp}}$$

$$\cos\theta = \frac{\text{adj}}{\text{hyp}} \qquad \sec\theta = \frac{1}{\cos\theta} = \frac{\text{hyp}}{\text{adj}}$$

$$\tan\theta = \frac{\text{opp}}{\text{adj}} = \frac{\sin\theta}{\cos\theta} \qquad \cot\theta = \frac{1}{\tan\theta} = \frac{\text{adj}}{\text{opp}}$$

$$\text{adj}^2 + \text{opp}^2 = \text{hyp}^2 \qquad \text{(Pythagorean theorem).}$$

FIGURE A–7

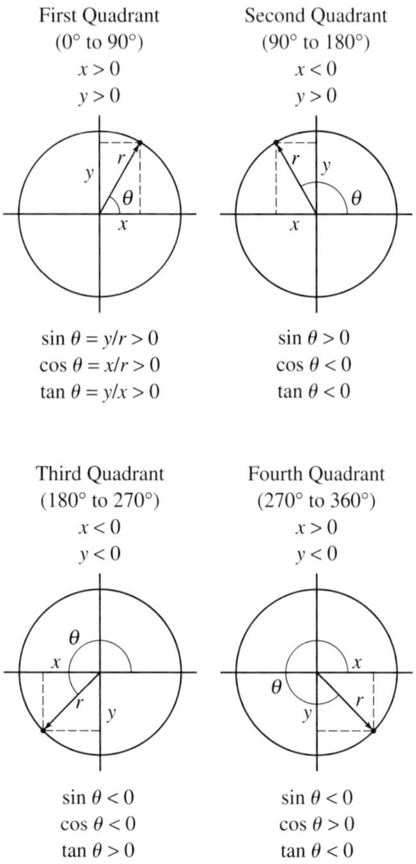


Figure A–7 shows the signs (+ or −) that cosine, sine, and tangent take on for angles $\theta$ in the four quadrants (0° to 360°). Note that angles are measured counterclockwise from the $x$ axis as shown; negative angles are measured from *below* the $x$ axis, clockwise: for example, $-30° = +330°$, and so on.

The following are some useful identities among the trigonometric functions:

$$\sin^2\theta + \cos^2\theta = 1$$

$$\sin 2\theta = 2\sin\theta\cos\theta$$

$$\cos 2\theta = \cos^2\theta - \sin^2\theta = 2\cos^2\theta - 1 = 1 - 2\sin^2\theta$$

$$\tan 2\theta = \frac{2\tan\theta}{1 - \tan^2\theta}$$

$$\sin(A \pm B) = \sin A\cos B \pm \cos A\sin B$$

$$\cos(A \pm B) = \cos A\cos B \mp \sin A\sin B$$

$$\tan(A \pm B) = \frac{\tan A \pm \tan B}{1 \mp \tan A\tan B}$$

$$\sin(180° - \theta) = \sin\theta$$

$$\cos(180° - \theta) = -\cos\theta$$

$$\sin(90° - \theta) = \cos\theta$$

$$\cos(90° - \theta) = \sin\theta$$

$$\sin\tfrac{1}{2}\theta = \sqrt{\frac{1 - \cos\theta}{2}}$$

$$\cos\tfrac{1}{2}\theta = \sqrt{\frac{1 + \cos\theta}{2}}$$

$$\tan\tfrac{1}{2}\theta = \sqrt{\frac{1 - \cos\theta}{1 + \cos\theta}}$$

$$\sin A \pm \sin B = 2\sin\left(\frac{A \pm B}{2}\right)\cos\left(\frac{A \mp B}{2}\right).$$

FIGURE A–8

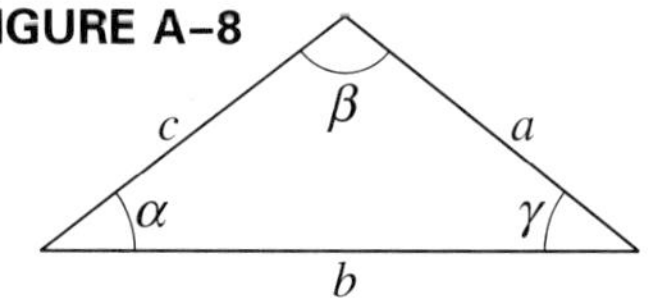


For any triangle (see Fig. A–8):

$$\frac{\sin\alpha}{a} = \frac{\sin\beta}{b} = \frac{\sin\gamma}{c} \qquad \text{(law of sines)}$$

$$c^2 = a^2 + b^2 - 2ab\cos\gamma. \qquad \text{(law of cosines)}$$

## Trigonometric Table: Numerical Values of Sin, Cos, Tan

| Angle in Degrees | Angle in Radians | Sine | Cosine | Tangent | Angle in Degrees | Angle in Radians | Sine | Cosine | Tangent |
|---|---|---|---|---|---|---|---|---|---|
| 0° | 0.000 | 0.000 | 1.000 | 0.000 | | | | | |
| 1° | 0.017 | 0.017 | 1.000 | 0.017 | 46° | 0.803 | 0.719 | 0.695 | 1.036 |
| 2° | 0.035 | 0.035 | 0.999 | 0.035 | 47° | 0.820 | 0.731 | 0.682 | 1.072 |
| 3° | 0.052 | 0.052 | 0.999 | 0.052 | 48° | 0.838 | 0.743 | 0.669 | 1.111 |
| 4° | 0.070 | 0.070 | 0.998 | 0.070 | 49° | 0.855 | 0.755 | 0.656 | 1.150 |
| 5° | 0.087 | 0.087 | 0.996 | 0.087 | 50° | 0.873 | 0.766 | 0.643 | 1.192 |
| 6° | 0.105 | 0.105 | 0.995 | 0.105 | 51° | 0.890 | 0.777 | 0.629 | 1.235 |
| 7° | 0.122 | 0.122 | 0.993 | 0.123 | 52° | 0.908 | 0.788 | 0.616 | 1.280 |
| 8° | 0.140 | 0.139 | 0.990 | 0.141 | 53° | 0.925 | 0.799 | 0.602 | 1.327 |
| 9° | 0.157 | 0.156 | 0.988 | 0.158 | 54° | 0.942 | 0.809 | 0.588 | 1.376 |
| 10° | 0.175 | 0.174 | 0.985 | 0.176 | 55° | 0.960 | 0.819 | 0.574 | 1.428 |
| 11° | 0.192 | 0.191 | 0.982 | 0.194 | 56° | 0.977 | 0.829 | 0.559 | 1.483 |
| 12° | 0.209 | 0.208 | 0.978 | 0.213 | 57° | 0.995 | 0.839 | 0.545 | 1.540 |
| 13° | 0.227 | 0.225 | 0.974 | 0.231 | 58° | 1.012 | 0.848 | 0.530 | 1.600 |
| 14° | 0.244 | 0.242 | 0.970 | 0.249 | 59° | 1.030 | 0.857 | 0.515 | 1.664 |
| 15° | 0.262 | 0.259 | 0.966 | 0.268 | 60° | 1.047 | 0.866 | 0.500 | 1.732 |
| 16° | 0.279 | 0.276 | 0.961 | 0.287 | 61° | 1.065 | 0.875 | 0.485 | 1.804 |
| 17° | 0.297 | 0.292 | 0.956 | 0.306 | 62° | 1.082 | 0.883 | 0.469 | 1.881 |
| 18° | 0.314 | 0.309 | 0.951 | 0.325 | 63° | 1.100 | 0.891 | 0.454 | 1.963 |
| 19° | 0.332 | 0.326 | 0.946 | 0.344 | 64° | 1.117 | 0.899 | 0.438 | 2.050 |
| 20° | 0.349 | 0.342 | 0.940 | 0.364 | 65° | 1.134 | 0.906 | 0.423 | 2.145 |
| 21° | 0.367 | 0.358 | 0.934 | 0.384 | 66° | 1.152 | 0.914 | 0.407 | 2.246 |
| 22° | 0.384 | 0.375 | 0.927 | 0.404 | 67° | 1.169 | 0.921 | 0.391 | 2.356 |
| 23° | 0.401 | 0.391 | 0.921 | 0.424 | 68° | 1.187 | 0.927 | 0.375 | 2.475 |
| 24° | 0.419 | 0.407 | 0.914 | 0.445 | 69° | 1.204 | 0.934 | 0.358 | 2.605 |
| 25° | 0.436 | 0.423 | 0.906 | 0.466 | 70° | 1.222 | 0.940 | 0.342 | 2.747 |
| 26° | 0.454 | 0.438 | 0.899 | 0.488 | 71° | 1.239 | 0.946 | 0.326 | 2.904 |
| 27° | 0.471 | 0.454 | 0.891 | 0.510 | 72° | 1.257 | 0.951 | 0.309 | 3.078 |
| 28° | 0.489 | 0.469 | 0.883 | 0.532 | 73° | 1.274 | 0.956 | 0.292 | 3.271 |
| 29° | 0.506 | 0.485 | 0.875 | 0.554 | 74° | 1.292 | 0.961 | 0.276 | 3.487 |
| 30° | 0.524 | 0.500 | 0.866 | 0.577 | 75° | 1.309 | 0.966 | 0.259 | 3.732 |
| 31° | 0.541 | 0.515 | 0.857 | 0.601 | 76° | 1.326 | 0.970 | 0.242 | 4.011 |
| 32° | 0.559 | 0.530 | 0.848 | 0.625 | 77° | 1.344 | 0.974 | 0.225 | 4.331 |
| 33° | 0.576 | 0.545 | 0.839 | 0.649 | 78° | 1.361 | 0.978 | 0.208 | 4.705 |
| 34° | 0.593 | 0.559 | 0.829 | 0.675 | 79° | 1.379 | 0.982 | 0.191 | 5.145 |
| 35° | 0.611 | 0.574 | 0.819 | 0.700 | 80° | 1.396 | 0.985 | 0.174 | 5.671 |
| 36° | 0.628 | 0.588 | 0.809 | 0.727 | 81° | 1.414 | 0.988 | 0.156 | 6.314 |
| 37° | 0.646 | 0.602 | 0.799 | 0.754 | 82° | 1.431 | 0.990 | 0.139 | 7.115 |
| 38° | 0.663 | 0.616 | 0.788 | 0.781 | 83° | 1.449 | 0.993 | 0.122 | 8.144 |
| 39° | 0.681 | 0.629 | 0.777 | 0.810 | 84° | 1.466 | 0.995 | 0.105 | 9.514 |
| 40° | 0.698 | 0.643 | 0.766 | 0.839 | 85° | 1.484 | 0.996 | 0.087 | 11.43 |
| 41° | 0.716 | 0.656 | 0.755 | 0.869 | 86° | 1.501 | 0.998 | 0.070 | 14.301 |
| 42° | 0.733 | 0.669 | 0.743 | 0.900 | 87° | 1.518 | 0.999 | 0.052 | 19.081 |
| 43° | 0.750 | 0.682 | 0.731 | 0.933 | 88° | 1.536 | 0.999 | 0.035 | 28.636 |
| 44° | 0.768 | 0.695 | 0.719 | 0.966 | 89° | 1.553 | 1.000 | 0.017 | 57.290 |
| 45° | 0.785 | 0.707 | 0.707 | 1.000 | 90° | 1.571 | 1.000 | 0.000 | $\infty$ |

## A–8 Logarithms

Logarithms are defined in the following way:

$$\text{if } y = A^x, \qquad \text{then } x = \log_A y.$$

That is, the logarithm of a number $y$ to the base $A$ is that number which, as the exponent of $A$, gives back the number $y$. For *common logarithms*, the base is 10, so

*Common logs*

$$\text{if } y = 10^x, \qquad \text{then } x = \log y.$$

The subscript 10 on $\log_{10}$ is usually omitted when dealing with common logs. Another base sometimes used is the exponential base $e = 2.718\cdots$, a natural number.† Such logarithms are called *natural logarithms* and are written ln. Thus,

*Natural logs*

$$\text{if } y = e^x, \qquad \text{then } x = \ln y.$$

For any number $y$, the two types of logarithm are related by

$$\ln y = 2.3026 \log y.$$

Some simple rules for logarithms are as follows:

$$\log(ab) = \log a + \log b. \qquad \textbf{(A–7)}$$

This is true because if $a = 10^n$ and $b = 10^m$, then $ab = 10^{n+m}$. From the definition of logarithm, $\log a = n$, $\log b = m$, and $\log(ab) = n + m$; hence, $\log(ab) = n + m = \log a + \log b$. In a similar way, we can show that

$$\log\left(\frac{a}{b}\right) = \log a - \log b \qquad \textbf{(A–8)}$$

and

$$\log a^n = n \log a. \qquad \textbf{(A–9)}$$

These three rules apply not only to common logs but to natural or any other kind of logarithm.

Logs were once used as a technique for simplifying certain types of calculation. Because of the advent of electronic calculators and computers, they are not often used any more for this purpose. However, logs do appear in certain physical equations, so it is helpful to know how to deal with them. If you do not have a calculator that calculates logs, you can easily use a *log table*, such as the small one shown here (Table A–1). The number $N$ is given to two digits (some tables give $N$ to three or more digits); the first digit is in the vertical column to the left, the second digit is in the horizontal row across the top. For example, the Table tells us that $\log 1.0 = 0.000$, $\log 1.1 = 0.041$, and $\log 4.1 = 0.613$. Table A–1 does not include the decimal point—it is understood. The Table gives logs for numbers between 1.0 and 9.9; for larger or smaller numbers, we use rule A–7:

$$\log(ab) = \log a + \log b.$$

For example,

$$\log(380) = \log(3.8 \times 10^2) = \log(3.8) + \log(10^2).$$

From the Table, $\log 3.8 = 0.580$; and from rule A–9,

$$\log(10^2) = 2 \log(10) = 2,$$

since $\log(10) = 1$. [This follows from the definition of the logarithm: if

†The exponential base $e$ can be written as an infinite series:

$$e = 1 + \frac{1}{1} + \frac{1}{1\cdot 2} + \frac{1}{1\cdot 2\cdot 3} + \frac{1}{1\cdot 2\cdot 3\cdot 4} + \cdots.$$

**TABLE A–1 Short Table of Common Logarithms**

| $N$ | 0.0 | 0.1 | 0.2 | 0.3 | 0.4 | 0.5 | 0.6 | 0.7 | 0.8 | 0.9 |
|---|---|---|---|---|---|---|---|---|---|---|
| 1 | 000 | 041 | 079 | 114 | 146 | 176 | 204 | 230 | 255 | 279 |
| 2 | 301 | 322 | 342 | 362 | 380 | 398 | 415 | 431 | 447 | 462 |
| 3 | 477 | 491 | 505 | 519 | 531 | 544 | 556 | 568 | 580 | 591 |
| 4 | 602 | 613 | 623 | 633 | 643 | 653 | 663 | 672 | 681 | 690 |
| 5 | 699 | 708 | 716 | 724 | 732 | 740 | 748 | 756 | 763 | 771 |
| 6 | 778 | 785 | 792 | 799 | 806 | 813 | 820 | 826 | 833 | 839 |
| 7 | 845 | 851 | 857 | 863 | 869 | 875 | 881 | 886 | 892 | 898 |
| 8 | 903 | 908 | 914 | 919 | 924 | 929 | 935 | 940 | 944 | 949 |
| 9 | 954 | 959 | 964 | 968 | 973 | 978 | 982 | 987 | 991 | 996 |

$10 = 10^1$, then $1 = \log(10)$.] Thus,

$$\begin{aligned}\log(380) &= \log(3.8) + \log(10^2)\\ &= 0.580 + 2\\ &= 2.580.\end{aligned}$$

Similarly,

$$\begin{aligned}\log(0.081) &= \log(8.1) + \log(10^{-2})\\ &= 0.908 - 2 = -1.092.\end{aligned}$$

Sometimes we need to do the reverse process: find the number $N$ whose log is, say, 2.670. This is called "taking the antilogarithm." To do so, we separate our number 2.670 into two parts, making the separation at the decimal point:

*Antilogs*

$$\begin{aligned}\log N = 2.670 &= 2 + 0.670\\ &= \log 10^2 + 0.670.\end{aligned}$$

We now look at Table A–1 to see what number has its log equal to 0.670; none does, so we must *interpolate*: we see that $\log 4.6 = 0.663$ and $\log 4.7 = 0.672$. So the number we want is between 4.6 and 4.7, and closer to the latter by $\frac{7}{9}$. Approximately we can say that $\log 4.68 = 0.670$. Thus

*Interpolation*

$$\begin{aligned}\log N &= 2 + 0.670\\ &= \log(10^2) + \log(4.68) = \log(4.68 \times 10^2),\end{aligned}$$

so $N = 4.68 \times 10^2 = 468$.

If the given logarithm is negative, say, $-2.180$, we proceed as follows:

$$\begin{aligned}\log N = -2.180 &= -3 + 0.820\\ &= \log 10^{-3} + \log 6.6 = \log 6.6 \times 10^{-3},\end{aligned}$$

so $N = 6.6 \times 10^{-3}$. Notice that we added to our given logarithm the next largest integer (3 in this case) so that we have an integer, plus a decimal number between 0 and 1.0 whose antilogarithm can be looked up in the Table.

APPENDIX **B**

# Selected Isotopes

| (1) Atomic Number Z | (2) Element | (3) Symbol | (4) Mass Number A | (5) Atomic Mass† | (6) % Abundance (or Radioactive Decay‡ Mode) | (7) Half-life (if radioactive) |
|---|---|---|---|---|---|---|
| 0 | (Neutron) | *n* | 1 | 1.008665 | $\beta^-$ | 10.24 min |
| 1 | Hydrogen | H | 1 | 1.007825 | 99.9885% | |
| | Deuterium | d or D | 2 | 2.014102 | 0.0115% | |
| | Tritium | t or T | 3 | 3.016049 | $\beta^-$ | 12.33 yr |
| 2 | Helium | He | 3 | 3.016029 | 0.000137% | |
| | | | 4 | 4.002603 | 99.999863% | |
| 3 | Lithium | Li | 6 | 6.015122 | 7.59% | |
| | | | 7 | 7.016004 | 92.41% | |
| 4 | Beryllium | Be | 7 | 7.016929 | EC, $\gamma$ | 53.29 days |
| | | | 9 | 9.012182 | 100% | |
| 5 | Boron | B | 10 | 10.012937 | 19.9% | |
| | | | 11 | 11.009306 | 80.1% | |
| 6 | Carbon | C | 11 | 11.011434 | $\beta^+$, EC | 20.39 min |
| | | | 12 | 12.000000 | 98.93% | |
| | | | 13 | 13.003355 | 1.07% | |
| | | | 14 | 14.003242 | $\beta^-$ | 5730 yr |
| 7 | Nitrogen | N | 13 | 13.005739 | $\beta^+$, EC | 9.965 min |
| | | | 14 | 14.003074 | 99.632% | |
| | | | 15 | 15.000109 | 0.368% | |
| 8 | Oxygen | O | 15 | 15.003065 | $\beta^+$, EC | 122.24 s |
| | | | 16 | 15.994915 | 99.757% | |
| | | | 18 | 17.999160 | 0.205% | |
| 9 | Fluorine | F | 19 | 18.998403 | 100% | |
| 10 | Neon | Ne | 20 | 19.992440 | 90.48% | |
| | | | 22 | 21.991386 | 9.25% | |
| 11 | Sodium | Na | 22 | 21.994437 | $\beta^+$, EC, $\gamma$ | 2.6019 yr |
| | | | 23 | 22.989770 | 100% | |
| | | | 24 | 23.990963 | $\beta^-$, $\gamma$ | 14.951 h |
| 12 | Magnesium | Mg | 24 | 23.985042 | 78.99% | |
| 13 | Aluminum | Al | 27 | 26.981538 | 100% | |
| 14 | Silicon | Si | 28 | 27.976927 | 92.2297% | |
| | | | 31 | 30.975363 | $\beta^-$, $\gamma$ | 157.3 min |

† The masses given in column (5) are those for the neutral atom, including the *Z* electrons.
‡ Chapter 30; EC = electron capture.

| (1) Atomic Number $Z$ | (2) Element | (3) Symbol | (4) Mass Number $A$ | (5) Atomic Mass | (6) % Abundance (or Radioactive Decay Mode) | (7) Half-life (if radioactive) |
|---|---|---|---|---|---|---|
| 15 | Phosphorus | P | 31 | 30.973762 | 100% | |
| | | | 32 | 31.973907 | $\beta^-$ | 14.262 days |
| 16 | Sulfur | S | 32 | 31.972071 | 94.9% | |
| | | | 35 | 34.969032 | $\beta^-$ | 87.38 days |
| 17 | Chlorine | Cl | 35 | 34.968853 | 75.78% | |
| | | | 37 | 36.965903 | 24.22% | |
| 18 | Argon | Ar | 40 | 39.962383 | 99.600% | |
| 19 | Potassium | K | 39 | 38.963707 | 93.258% | |
| | | | 40 | 39.963999 | 0.0117% | |
| | | | | | $\beta^-$, EC, $\gamma$, $\beta^+$ | $1.277 \times 10^9$ yr |
| 20 | Calcium | Ca | 40 | 39.962591 | 96.94% | |
| 21 | Scandium | Sc | 45 | 44.955910 | 100% | |
| 22 | Titanium | Ti | 48 | 47.947947 | 73.72% | |
| 23 | Vanadium | V | 51 | 50.943964 | 99.750% | |
| 24 | Chromium | Cr | 52 | 51.940512 | 83.789% | |
| 25 | Manganese | Mn | 55 | 54.940363 | 100% | |
| 26 | Iron | Fe | 56 | 55.934942 | 91.75% | |
| 27 | Cobalt | Co | 59 | 58.933200 | 100% | |
| | | | 60 | 59.933822 | $\beta^-$, $\gamma$ | 5.2708 yr |
| 28 | Nickel | Ni | 58 | 57.935348 | 68.077% | |
| | | | 60 | 59.930791 | 26.223% | |
| 29 | Copper | Cu | 63 | 62.929601 | 69.17% | |
| | | | 65 | 64.927794 | 30.83% | |
| 30 | Zinc | Zn | 64 | 63.929147 | 48.6% | |
| | | | 66 | 65.926037 | 27.9% | |
| 31 | Gallium | Ga | 69 | 68.925581 | 60.108% | |
| 32 | Germanium | Ge | 72 | 71.922076 | 27.5% | |
| | | | 74 | 73.921178 | 36.3% | |
| 33 | Arsenic | As | 75 | 74.921596 | 100% | |
| 34 | Selenium | Se | 80 | 79.916522 | 49.6% | |
| 35 | Bromine | Br | 79 | 78.918338 | 50.69% | |
| 36 | Krypton | Kr | 84 | 83.911507 | 57.00% | |
| 37 | Rubidium | Rb | 85 | 84.911789 | 72.17% | |
| 38 | Strontium | Sr | 86 | 85.909262 | 9.86% | |
| | | | 88 | 87.905614 | 82.58% | |
| | | | 90 | 89.907738 | $\beta^-$ | 28.79 yr |
| 39 | Yttrium | Y | 89 | 88.905848 | 100% | |
| 40 | Zirconium | Zr | 90 | 89.904704 | 51.4% | |
| 41 | Niobium | Nb | 93 | 92.906378 | 100% | |
| 42 | Molybdenum | Mo | 98 | 97.905408 | 24.1% | |
| 43 | Technetium | Tc | 98 | 97.907216 | $\beta^-$, $\gamma$ | $4.2 \times 10^6$ yr |
| 44 | Ruthenium | Ru | 102 | 101.904350 | 31.55% | |
| 45 | Rhodium | Rh | 103 | 102.905504 | 100% | |
| 46 | Palladium | Pd | 106 | 105.903483 | 27.33% | |
| 47 | Silver | Ag | 107 | 106.905093 | 51.839% | |
| | | | 109 | 108.904756 | 48.161% | |

| (1) Atomic Number $Z$ | (2) Element | (3) Symbol | (4) Mass Number $A$ | (5) Atomic Mass | (6) % Abundance (or Radioactive Decay Mode) | (7) Half-life (if radioactive) |
|---|---|---|---|---|---|---|
| 48 | Cadmium | Cd | 114 | 113.903358 | 28.7% | |
| 49 | Indium | In | 115 | 114.903878 | 95.71%; $\beta^-$ | $4.41 \times 10^{14}$ yr |
| 50 | Tin | Sn | 120 | 119.902197 | 32.58% | |
| 51 | Antimony | Sb | 121 | 120.903818 | 57.21% | |
| 52 | Tellurium | Te | 130 | 129.906223 | 34.1%; $\beta^-\beta^-$ | $> 5.6 \times 10^{22}$ yr |
| 53 | Iodine | I | 127 | 126.904468 | 100% | |
| | | | 131 | 130.906124 | $\beta^-, \gamma$ | 8.0207 days |
| 54 | Xenon | Xe | 132 | 131.904155 | 26.89% | |
| | | | 136 | 135.907220 | 8.87%; $\beta^-\beta^-$ | $> 3.6 \times 10^{20}$ yr |
| 55 | Cesium | Cs | 133 | 132.905447 | 100% | |
| 56 | Barium | Ba | 137 | 136.905821 | 11.232% | |
| | | | 138 | 137.905241 | 71.70% | |
| 57 | Lanthanum | La | 139 | 138.906348 | 99.910% | |
| 58 | Cerium | Ce | 140 | 139.905434 | 88.45% | |
| 59 | Praseodymium | Pr | 141 | 140.907648 | 100% | |
| 60 | Neodymium | Nd | 142 | 141.907719 | 27.2% | |
| 61 | Promethium | Pm | 145 | 144.912744 | EC, $\alpha$ | 17.7 yr |
| 62 | Samarium | Sm | 152 | 151.919728 | 26.75% | |
| 63 | Europium | Eu | 153 | 152.921226 | 52.19% | |
| 64 | Gadolinium | Gd | 158 | 157.924101 | 24.84% | |
| 65 | Terbium | Tb | 159 | 158.925343 | 100% | |
| 66 | Dysprosium | Dy | 164 | 163.929171 | 28.2% | |
| 67 | Holmium | Ho | 165 | 164.930319 | 100% | |
| 68 | Erbium | Er | 166 | 165.930290 | 33.6% | |
| 69 | Thulium | Tm | 169 | 168.934211 | 100% | |
| 70 | Ytterbium | Yb | 174 | 173.938858 | 31.8% | |
| 71 | Lutetium | Lu | 175 | 174.940768 | 97.41% | |
| 72 | Hafnium | Hf | 180 | 179.946549 | 35.08% | |
| 73 | Tantalum | Ta | 181 | 180.947996 | 99.988% | |
| 74 | Tungsten (wolfram) | W | 184 | 183.950933 | 30.64%; $\alpha$ | $> 4 \times 10^{18}$ yr |
| 75 | Rhenium | Re | 187 | 186.955751 | 62.60%; $\beta^-$ | $4.35 \times 10^{10}$ yr |
| 76 | Osmium | Os | 191 | 190.960928 | $\beta^-, \gamma$ | 15.4 days |
| | | | 192 | 191.961479 | 40.78% | |
| 77 | Iridium | Ir | 191 | 190.960591 | 37.3% | |
| | | | 193 | 192.962924 | 62.7% | |
| 78 | Platinum | Pt | 195 | 194.964774 | 33.832% | |
| 79 | Gold | Au | 197 | 196.966552 | 100% | |
| 80 | Mercury | Hg | 199 | 198.968262 | 16.87% | |
| | | | 202 | 201.970626 | 29.9% | |
| 81 | Thallium | Tl | 205 | 204.974412 | 70.476% | |
| 82 | Lead | Pb | 206 | 205.974449 | 24.1% | |
| | | | 207 | 206.975881 | 22.1% | |
| | | | 208 | 207.976636 | 52.4% | |
| | | | 210 | 209.984173 | $\beta^-, \gamma, \alpha$ | 22.3 yr |
| | | | 211 | 210.988731 | $\beta^-, \gamma$ | 36.1 min |
| | | | 212 | 211.991887 | $\beta^-, \gamma$ | 10.64 h |
| | | | 214 | 213.999798 | $\beta^-, \gamma$ | 26.8 min |

| (1) Atomic Number $Z$ | (2) Element | (3) Symbol | (4) Mass Number $A$ | (5) Atomic Mass | (6) % Abundance (or Radioactive Decay Mode) | (7) Half-life (if radioactive) |
|---|---|---|---|---|---|---|
| 83 | Bismuth | Bi | 209 | 208.980383 | 100% | |
| | | | 211 | 210.987258 | $\alpha, \gamma, \beta^-$ | 2.14 min |
| 84 | Polonium | Po | 210 | 209.982416 | $\alpha, \gamma$, EC | 138.376 days |
| | | | 214 | 213.995186 | $\alpha, \gamma$ | 164.3 $\mu$s |
| 85 | Astatine | At | 218 | 218.008681 | $\alpha, \beta^-$ | 1.5 s |
| 86 | Radon | Rn | 222 | 222.017570 | $\alpha, \gamma$ | 3.8235 days |
| 87 | Francium | Fr | 223 | 223.019731 | $\beta^-, \gamma, \alpha$ | 22.00 min |
| 88 | Radium | Ra | 226 | 226.025403 | $\alpha, \gamma$ | 1600 yr |
| 89 | Actinium | Ac | 227 | 227.027747 | $\beta^-, \gamma, \alpha$ | 21.773 yr |
| 90 | Thorium | Th | 228 | 228.028731 | $\alpha, \gamma$ | 1.9116 yr |
| | | | 232 | 232.038050 | 100%; $\alpha, \gamma$ | $1.405 \times 10^{10}$ yr |
| 91 | Protactinium | Pa | 231 | 231.035879 | $\alpha, \gamma$ | $3.276 \times 10^4$ yr |
| 92 | Uranium | U | 232 | 232.037146 | $\alpha, \gamma$ | 68.9 yr |
| | | | 233 | 233.039628 | $\alpha, \gamma$ | $1.592 \times 10^5$ yr |
| | | | 235 | 235.043923 | 0.720%; $\alpha, \gamma$ | $7.038 \times 10^8$ yr |
| | | | 236 | 236.045562 | $\alpha, \gamma$ | $2.342 \times 10^7$ yr |
| | | | 238 | 238.050783 | 99.274%; $\alpha, \gamma$ | $4.468 \times 10^9$ yr |
| | | | 239 | 239.054288 | $\beta^-, \gamma$ | 23.45 min |
| 93 | Neptunium | Np | 237 | 237.048167 | $\alpha, \gamma$ | $2.144 \times 10^6$ yr |
| | | | 239 | 239.052931 | $\beta^-, \gamma$ | 2.3565 days |
| 94 | Plutonium | Pu | 239 | 239.052157 | $\alpha, \gamma$ | 24,110 yr |
| | | | 244 | 244.064198 | $\alpha$ | $8.00 \times 10^7$ yr |
| 95 | Americium | Am | 243 | 243.061373 | $\alpha, \gamma$ | 7370 yr |
| 96 | Curium | Cm | 247 | 247.070347 | $\alpha, \gamma$ | $1.56 \times 10^7$ yr |
| 97 | Berkelium | Bk | 247 | 247.070299 | $\alpha, \gamma$ | 1380 yr |
| 98 | Californium | Cf | 251 | 251.079580 | $\alpha, \gamma$ | 898 yr |
| 99 | Einsteinium | Es | 252 | 252.082970 | $\alpha$, EC, $\gamma$ | 471.7 days |
| 100 | Fermium | Fm | 257 | 257.095099 | $\alpha, \gamma$ | 100.5 days |
| 101 | Mendelevium | Md | 258 | 258.098425 | $\alpha, \gamma$ | 51.5 days |
| 102 | Nobelium | No | 259 | 259.10102 | $\alpha$, EC | 58 min |
| 103 | Lawrencium | Lr | 262 | 262.1097 | $\alpha$, EC, fission | 3.6 h |
| 104 | Rutherfordium | Rf | 263 | 263.11831 | fission | 10 min |
| 105 | Dubnium | Db | 262 | 262.11415 | $\alpha$, fission, EC | 34 s |
| 106 | Seaborgium | Sg | 266 | 266.1219 | $\alpha$, fission | 21 s |
| 107 | Bohrium | Bh | 264 | 264.1247 | $\alpha$ | 0.44 s |
| 108 | Hassium | Hs | 269 | 269.1341 | $\alpha$ | 9 s |
| 109 | Meitnerium | Mt | 268 | 268.1388 | $\alpha$ | 0.07 s |
| 110 | Darmstadtium | Ds | 271 | 271.14608 | $\alpha$ | 0.06 ms |
| 111 | | Uuu | 272 | 272.1535 | $\alpha$ | 1.5 ms |
| 112 | | Uub | 277 | 277 | $\alpha$ | 0.24 ms |

APPENDIX C

# Rotating Frames of Reference; Inertial Forces; Coriolis Effect

## Inertial and Noninertial Reference Frames

In Chapters 5 and 8 we examined the motion of objects, including circular and rotational motion, from the outside, as observers fixed on the Earth. Sometimes it is convenient to place ourselves (in theory, if not physically) into a reference frame that is rotating. Let us examine the motion of objects from the point of view, or frame of reference, of persons seated on a rotating platform such as a merry-go-round. It looks to them as if the rest of the world is going around *them*. But let us focus on what they observe when they place a tennis ball on the floor of the rotating platform, which we assume is frictionless. If they put the ball down gently, without giving it any push, they will observe that it accelerates from rest and moves outward as shown in Fig. C–1a. According to Newton's first law, an object initially at rest should stay at rest if no force

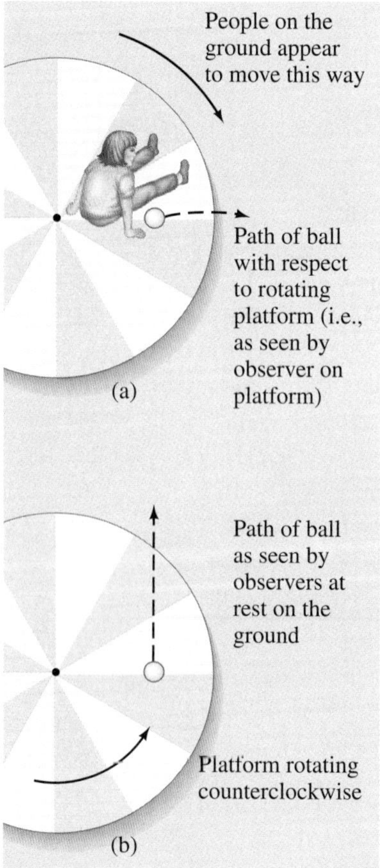


**FIGURE C–1** Path of a ball released on a rotating merry-go-round as seen (a) in the reference frame of the merry-go-round, and (b) in a reference frame fixed on the ground.

acts on it. But, according to the observers on the rotating platform, the ball starts moving even though there is no force applied to it. To observers on the ground, this is all very clear: the ball has an initial velocity when it is released (because the platform is moving), and it simply continues moving in a straight-line path as shown in Fig. C–1b, in accordance with Newton's first law.

But what shall we do about the frame of reference of the observers on the rotating platform? Clearly, Newton's first law, the law of inertia, does not hold in this rotating frame of reference. For this reason, such a frame is called a **noninertial reference frame**. An **inertial reference frame** (as discussed in Chapter 4) is one in which the law of inertia—Newton's first law—does hold, and so do Newton's second and third laws. In a noninertial reference frame, such as our rotating platform, Newton's second law also does not hold. For instance in the situation described above, there is no net force on the ball; yet, with respect to the rotating platform, the ball accelerates.

## Fictitious (Inertial) Forces

Because Newton's laws do not hold when observations are made with respect to a rotating frame of reference, calculation of motion can be complicated. However, we can still apply Newton's laws in such a reference frame if we make use of a trick. The ball on the rotating platform of Fig. C–1a flies outward when released (as if a force were acting on it—though as we saw above, no force actually does act on it); so the trick we use is to write down the equation $\Sigma F = ma$ as if a force equal to $mv^2/r$ (or $m\omega^2 r$) were acting radially outward on the object in addition to any other forces that may be acting. This extra force, which might be designated as "centrifugal force" since it *seems* to act outward, is called a **fictitious force** or **pseudoforce**. It is a pseudoforce ("pseudo" means "false") because there is no object that exerts this force. Furthermore, when viewed from an inertial reference frame, the effect doesn't exist at all. We have made up this pseudoforce so that we can make calculations in a noninertial frame using Newton's second law, $\Sigma F = ma$. Thus the observer in the noninertial frame of Fig. C–1a uses Newton's second law for the ball's outward motion by assuming that a force equal to $mv^2/r$ acts on it. Such pseudoforces are also called **inertial forces** since they arise only because the reference frame is not an inertial one.

*Fictitious force (pseudoforce)*

*Inertial force*

We can examine the motion of a particle in a centrifuge (Section 5–5) from the frame of reference of the rotating test tube. In this frame of reference, the particles move in a more-or-less straight path down the tube. (From the reference frame of the Earth, the particles go round and round.) The acceleration of a particle with respect to the rotating tube can then be calculated using $F = ma$ if we include a pseudoforce, "$F$," equal to $m\omega^2 r = m(v^2/r)$ acting down the tube, in addition to the drag force $F_D$ exerted by the fluid on the particle (Fig. C–2) up the tube.

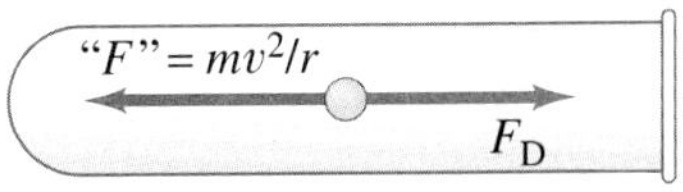


**FIGURE C–2** The forces on a particle in a test tube rotating in a centrifuge, seen in the reference frame of the test tube.

In Section 5–3 we discussed the forces on a person in a car going around a curve (Fig. 5–11) from the point of view of an inertial frame. The car, on the other hand, is not an inertial frame. Passengers in such a car could interpret this being pressed outward as the effect of a "centrifugal" force. But they need to recognize that it is a pseudoforce because there is no identifiable object exerting it. It is an effect of being in a noninertial frame of reference.

The Earth itself is rotating on its axis. Thus, strictly speaking, Newton's laws are not valid on the Earth. However, the effect of the Earth's rotation is usually so small that it can be ignored, although it does influence the movement of large air masses and ocean currents. Because of the Earth's rotation, the material of the Earth is concentrated slightly more at the equator. The Earth is thus not a perfect sphere but is slightly fatter at the equator than at the poles.

## Coriolis Effect

In a reference frame that rotates at a constant angular speed $\omega$ (relative to an inertial frame), there exists another pseudoforce known as the *Coriolis force*. It appears to act on a body in a rotating reference frame only if the body is moving relative to that reference frame, and it acts to deflect the body sideways. It, too, is an effect of the reference frame being noninertial and hence is referred to as an *inertial force*. To see how the Coriolis force arises, consider two people, A and B, at rest on a platform rotating with angular speed $\omega$, as shown in Fig. C–3a. They are situated at distances $r_A$ and $r_B$, respectively, from the axis of rotation (at O). The woman at A throws a ball with a horizontal velocity $\vec{\mathbf{v}}$ (in her reference frame) radially outward toward the man at B on the outer edge of the platform. In Fig. C–3a, we view the situation from an inertial reference frame. The ball initially has not only the velocity $\vec{\mathbf{v}}$ radially outward, but also a tangential velocity $\vec{\mathbf{v}}_A$ due to the rotation of the platform. Now Eq. 8–4 tells us that $v_A = r_A\omega$, where $r_A$ is the woman's radial distance from the axis of rotation at O. If the man at B had this same velocity $v_A$, the ball would reach him perfectly. But his speed is greater than $v_A$ (Fig. C–3a) since he is farther from the axis of rotation. His speed is $v_B = r_B\omega$, which is greater than $v_A$ because $r_B > r_A$. Thus, when the ball reaches the outer edge of the platform, it passes a point that the man at B has already passed because his speed in that direction is greater than the ball's. So the ball passes behind him.

Figure C–3b shows the situation as seen from the rotating platform as frame of reference. Both A and B are at rest, and the ball is thrown with velocity $\vec{\mathbf{v}}$ toward B, but the ball deflects to the right as shown and passes behind B as previously described. This is not a centrifugal-force effect, for the latter acts radially outward. Instead, this effect acts sideways, perpendicular to $\vec{\mathbf{v}}$, and is called a **Coriolis acceleration**; it is said to be due to the Coriolis force, which is a fictitious inertial force. Its explanation as seen from an inertial system was given above: it is an effect of being in a rotating system, wherein points that are farther from the rotation axis have higher linear speeds. On the other hand, when viewed from the rotating system, we can describe the motion using Newton's second law, $\Sigma\vec{\mathbf{F}} = m\vec{\mathbf{a}}$, if we add a "pseudoforce" term corresponding to this Coriolis effect.

Let us determine the magnitude of the Coriolis acceleration for the simple case described above. (We assume $v$ is large and distances are short, so we can ignore

**FIGURE C–3** The origin of the Coriolis effect. Looking down on a rotating platform, (a) as seen from a nonrotating inertial system, and (b) as seen from the rotating platform as frame of reference.

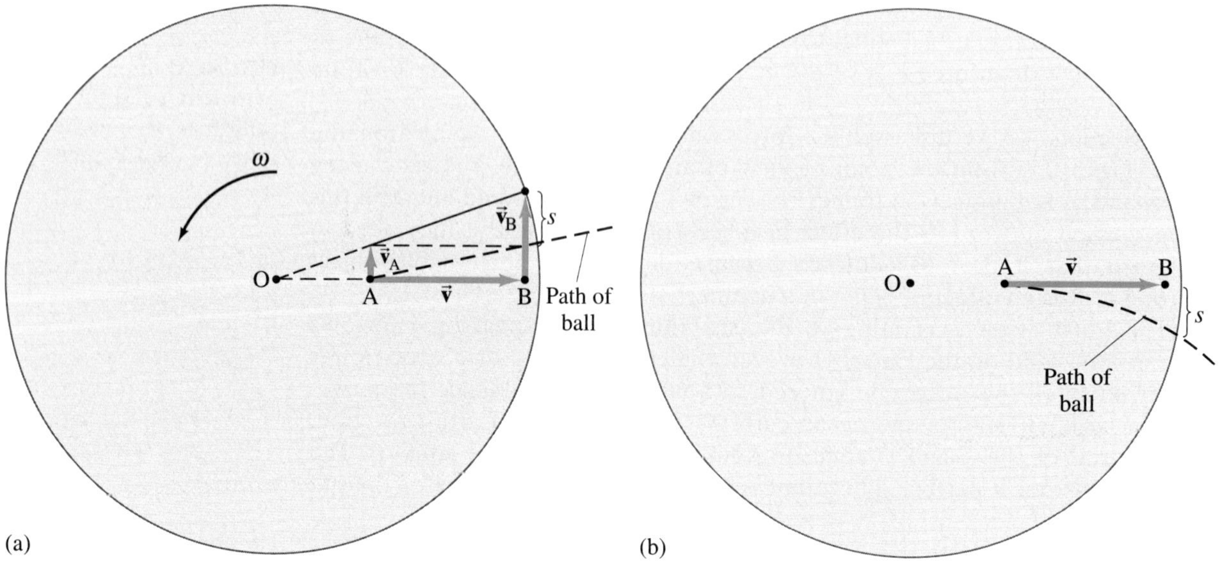

gravity.) We do the calculation from the inertial reference frame (Fig. C–3a). The ball moves radially outward a distance $r_B - r_A$ at speed $v$ in a time $t$ given by

$$r_B - r_A = vt.$$

During this time, the ball moves to the side a distance $s_A$ given by

$$s_A = v_A t.$$

The man at B, in this time $t$, moves a distance

$$s_B = v_B t.$$

The ball therefore passes behind him a distance $s$ (Fig. C–3a) given by

$$s = s_B - s_A = (v_B - v_A)t.$$

We saw earlier that $v_A = r_A\omega$ and $v_B = r_B\omega$, so

$$s = (r_B - r_A)\omega t.$$

We substitute $r_B - r_A = vt$ (see above) and get

$$s = \omega v t^2. \qquad \textbf{(C–1)}$$

This same $s$ equals the sideways displacement as seen from the noninertial rotating system (Fig. C–3b).

We see immediately that Eq. C–1 corresponds to motion at constant acceleration. For as we saw in Chapter 2 (see Eq. 2–11b), $y = \frac{1}{2}at^2$ for a constant acceleration (with zero initial velocity in the $y$ direction). Thus, if we write Eq. C–1 in the form $s = \frac{1}{2}a_{Cor}t^2$, we see that the Coriolis acceleration $a_{Cor}$ is

$$a_{Cor} = 2\omega v. \qquad \textbf{(C–2)}$$

This relation is valid for any velocity in the plane of rotation—that is, in the plane perpendicular to the axis of rotation (in Fig. C–3, the axis through point O perpendicular to the page).

Because the Earth rotates, the Coriolis effect has some interesting manifestations on the Earth. It affects the movement of air masses and thus has an influence on weather. In the absence of the Coriolis effect, air would rush directly into a region of low pressure, as shown in Fig. C–4a. But because of the Coriolis effect, the winds are deflected to the right in the Northern Hemisphere (Fig. C–4b), since the Earth rotates from west to east. So there tends to be a counterclockwise wind pattern around a low-pressure area. The reverse is true in the Southern Hemisphere. Thus cyclones rotate counterclockwise in the Northern Hemisphere and clockwise in the Southern Hemisphere. The same effect explains the easterly trade winds near the equator: any winds heading south toward the equator will be deflected toward the west (that is, as if coming from the east).

The Coriolis effect also acts on a falling body. A body released from the top of a high tower will not hit the ground directly below the release point, but will be deflected slightly to the east. Viewed from an inertial frame, this is because the top of the tower revolves with a slightly higher speed than does the bottom of the tower.

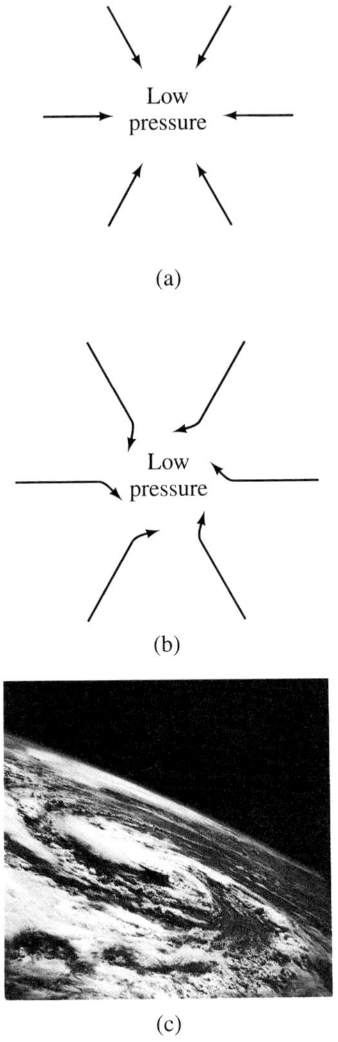


**FIGURE C–4** (a) Winds (moving air masses) would flow directly toward a low-pressure area if the Earth did not rotate; (b) and (c): because of the Earth's rotation, the winds are deflected to the right in the Northern Hemisphere (as in Fig. C–3) as if a fictitious (Coriolis) force were acting.

APPENDIX D

# Molar Specific Heats for Gases, and the Equipartition of Energy

## Molar Specific Heats for Gases

The values of the specific heats for gases depend on how the thermodynamic process is carried out. Two important processes are those in which either the volume or the pressure is kept constant, and Table D–1 shows how different they can be.

The difference in specific heats for gases is nicely explained in terms of the first law of thermodynamics and kinetic theory. For gases we usually use **molar specific heats**, $C_V$ and $C_P$, which are defined as the heat required to raise 1 mol of a gas by 1 C° at constant volume and at constant pressure, respectively. In analogy to Eq. 14–2, the heat $Q$ needed to raise the temperature of $n$ moles of gas by $\Delta T$ is

*Molar specific heats*

$$Q = nC_V\,\Delta T \qquad \text{[volume constant]} \qquad \textbf{(D–1a)}$$

$$Q = nC_P\,\Delta T. \qquad \text{[pressure constant]} \qquad \textbf{(D–1b)}$$

It is clear from the definition of molar specific heat (compare Eqs. 14–2 and D–1) that

$$C_V = Mc_V \quad \text{and} \quad C_P = Mc_P,$$

where $M$ is the molecular mass of the gas ($M = m/n$ in grams/mol). The values for molar specific heats are included in Table D–1. These values are nearly the same for different gases that have the same number of atoms per molecule.

Now we use kinetic theory of gases to see, first, why the specific heats of gases are higher for constant-pressure processes than for constant-volume processes.

**TABLE D–1 Specific Heats of Gases at 15°C**

| Gas | Specific Heats (kcal/kg · K) | | Molar Specific Heats (cal/mol · K) | | $C_P - C_V$ (cal/mol · K) |
|---|---|---|---|---|---|
| | $c_V$ | $c_P$ | $C_V$ | $C_P$ | |
| Monatomic | | | | | |
| He | 0.75 | 1.15 | 2.98 | 4.97 | 1.99 |
| Ne | 0.148 | 0.246 | 2.98 | 4.97 | 1.99 |
| Diatomic | | | | | |
| $N_2$ | 0.177 | 0.248 | 4.96 | 6.95 | 1.99 |
| $O_2$ | 0.155 | 0.218 | 5.03 | 7.03 | 2.00 |
| Triatomic | | | | | |
| $CO_2$ | 0.153 | 0.199 | 6.80 | 8.83 | 2.03 |
| $H_2O$ (100°C) | 0.350 | 0.482 | 6.20 | 8.20 | 2.00 |
| Polyatomic | | | | | |
| $C_2H_6$ | 0.343 | 0.412 | 10.30 | 12.35 | 2.05 |

Imagine that an ideal gas is slowly heated via these two processes—first at constant volume, and then at constant pressure. In both processes, we let the temperature increase by the same amount, $\Delta T$. In the constant-volume process, no work is done since $\Delta V = 0$. Thus, according to the first law of thermodynamics, the heat added (denoted by $Q_V$) all goes into increasing the internal energy of the gas:

$$Q_V = \Delta U.$$

In the constant-pressure process, work *is* done. Hence the heat added, $Q_P$, must not only increase the internal energy but also is used to do work $W = P\,\Delta V$. Thus, for the same $\Delta T$, more heat must be added in the process at constant pressure than at constant volume. For the process at constant pressure, the first law of thermodynamics gives

$$Q_P = \Delta U + P\,\Delta V.$$

Since $\Delta U$ is the same in the two processes (we chose $\Delta T$ to be the same), we can combine the two above equations:

$$Q_P - Q_V = P\,\Delta V.$$

From the ideal gas law, $V = nRT/P$, so for a process at constant pressure $\Delta V = nR\,\Delta T/P$. Putting this into the above equation and using Eqs. D–1, we find

$$nC_P\,\Delta T - nC_V\,\Delta T = P\left(\frac{nR\,\Delta T}{P}\right)$$

or, after cancellations,

$$C_P - C_V = R. \qquad \textbf{(D–2)}$$

Since the gas constant $R = 8.315\,\mathrm{J/mol\cdot K} = 1.99\,\mathrm{cal/mol\cdot K}$, we predict that $C_P$ will be larger than $C_V$ by about $1.99\,\mathrm{cal/mol\cdot K}$. Indeed, this is very close to what is obtained experimentally, as the last column in Table D–1 shows.

Now we calculate the molar specific heat of a monatomic gas using the kinetic theory. For a process carried out at constant volume, no work is done, so the first law of thermodynamics tells us that

$$\Delta U = Q_V.$$

For an ideal monatomic gas, the internal energy, $U$, is the total kinetic energy of all the molecules,

$$U = N\left(\tfrac{1}{2}m\overline{v^2}\right) = \tfrac{3}{2}nRT$$

as we saw in Section 14–2. Then, using Eq. D–1a, we write $\Delta U = Q_V$ as

$$\Delta U = \tfrac{3}{2}nR\,\Delta T = nC_V\,\Delta T \qquad \textbf{(D–3)}$$

or

$$C_V = \tfrac{3}{2}R. \qquad \textbf{(D–4)}$$

Since $R = 8.315\,\mathrm{J/mol\cdot K} = 1.99\,\mathrm{cal/mol\cdot K}$, kinetic theory predicts that $C_V = 2.98\,\mathrm{cal/mol\cdot K}$ for an ideal monatomic gas. This is very close to the experimental values for monatomic gases such as helium and neon (Table D–1). From Eq. D–2, $C_P$ is predicted to be about $4.97\,\mathrm{cal/mol\cdot K}$, also in agreement with experiment (Table D–1).

## Equipartition of Energy

The measured molar specific heats for more complex gases (Table D–1), such as diatomic (two-atom) and triatomic (three-atom) gases, increase with the increased number of atoms per molecule. We can explain this by assuming that the internal energy includes not only translational kinetic energy but other forms of energy as well. For example, in a diatomic gas (Fig. D–1), the two atoms can rotate about two different axes (but rotation about a third axis passing through the two atoms would give rise to neglible energy, since the moment of inertia is so small). The molecules can have rotational as well as translational kinetic energy.

**FIGURE D–1** A diatomic molecule can rotate about two different axes.

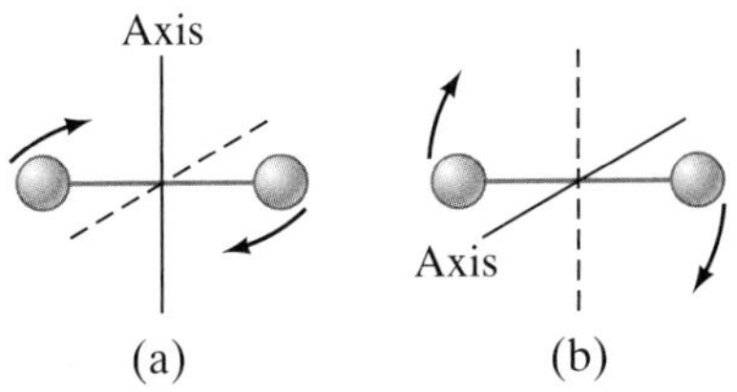

*Degrees of freedom*

It is useful to introduce the idea of **degrees of freedom**, by which we mean the number of independent ways molecules can possess energy. For example, a monatomic gas has three degrees of freedom, because an atom can have velocity along the $x$, $y$, and $z$ axes. These are considered to be three independent motions because a change in any one of the components would not affect the others. A diatomic molecule has the same three degrees of freedom associated with translational kinetic energy plus two more degrees of freedom associated with rotational kinetic energy (Fig. D–1), for a total of five degrees of freedom.

Table D–1 indicates that the $C_V$ for diatomic gases is about $\frac{5}{3}$ times as great as for a monatomic gas—that is, in the same ratio as their degrees of freedom.

*Equipartition of energy*

This led nineteenth-century physicists to the **principle of equipartition of energy**. This principle states that energy is shared equally among the active degrees of freedom, and each active degree of freedom of a molecule has on the average an energy equal to $\frac{1}{2}kT$. Thus, the average energy for a molecule of a monatomic gas would be $\frac{3}{2}kT$ (which we already knew) and of a diatomic gas $\frac{5}{2}kT$. Hence the internal energy of a diatomic gas would be $U = N\left(\frac{5}{2}kT\right) = \frac{5}{2}nRT$, where $n$ is the number of moles. Using the same argument we did for monatomic gases, we see that for diatomic gases the molar specific heat at constant volume would be $\frac{5}{2}R = 4.97\ \text{cal/mol}\cdot\text{K}$, in accordance with measured values. More complex molecules have even more degrees of freedom and thus greater molar specific heats.

However, measurements showed that for diatomic gases at very low temperatures, $C_V$ has a value of only $\frac{3}{2}R$, as if there were only three degrees of freedom. And at very high temperatures, $C_V$ was about $\frac{7}{2}R$, as if there were seven degrees of freedom. The explanation is that at low temperatures, nearly all molecules have only translational kinetic energy, so, no energy goes into rotational energy and only three degrees of freedom are "active." At very high temperatures, all five degrees of freedom are active plus two additional ones. We interpret the two new degrees of freedom as being associated with the two atoms vibrating, as if they were connected by a spring (Fig. D–2). One degree of freedom comes from the kinetic energy of the vibrational motion, and the second from the potential energy of vibrational motion $\left(\frac{1}{2}kx^2\right)$. At room temperature, these two degrees of freedom are apparently not active. Why fewer degrees of freedom are "active" at lower temperatures was eventually explained by Einstein using the quantum theory.

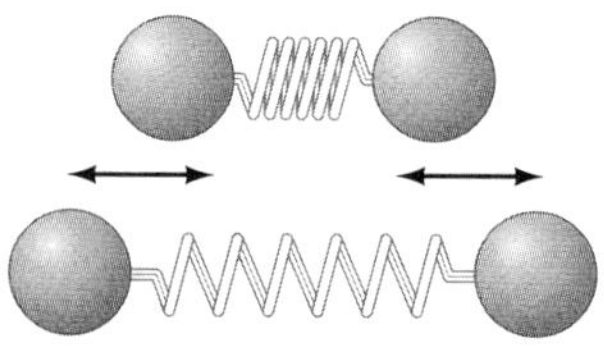

**FIGURE D–2** A diatomic molecule can vibrate, as if the two atoms were connected by a spring. Of course they are not, but rather they exert forces on each other that are electrical in nature—of a form that resembles a spring force.

## Solids

The principle of equipartition of energy can be applied to solids as well. The molar specific heat of any solid at high temperature is close to $3R$ ($6.0\ \text{cal/mol}\cdot\text{K}$), Fig. D–3. This is called the *Dulong and Petit value* after the scientists who first measured it in 1819. (Note that Table 14–1 gave the specific heats per kilogram, not per mole.) At high temperatures, each atom apparently has six degrees of freedom, although some are not active at low temperatures. Each atom in a crystalline solid can vibrate about its equilibrium position as if it were connected by springs to each of its neighbors (Fig. D–4). Thus it can have three degrees of freedom for kinetic energy and three more associated with potential energy of vibration in each of the $x$, $y$, and $z$ directions, which is in accord with measured values.

**FIGURE D–3** Molar specific heats of solids as a function of temperature.

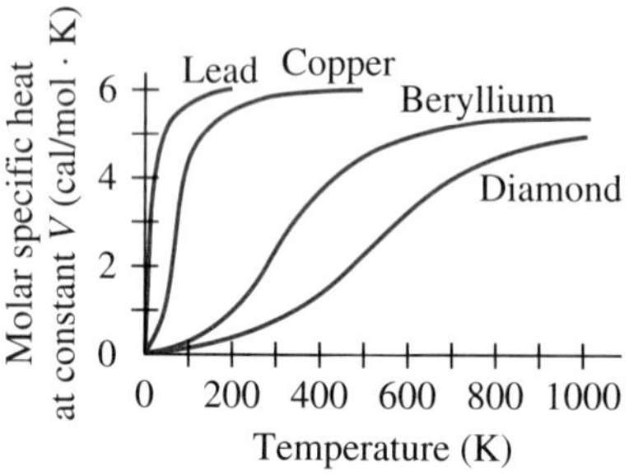


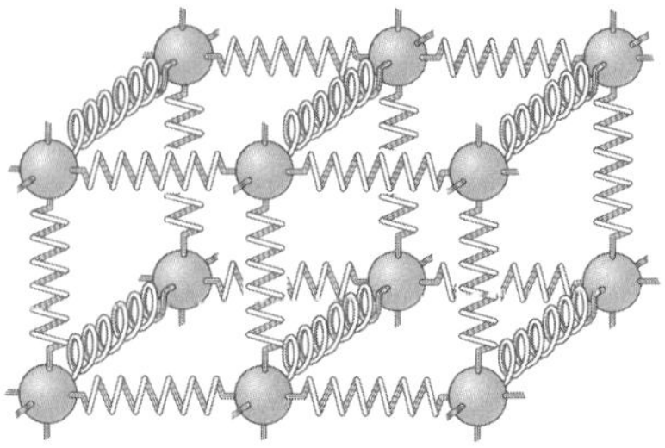

**FIGURE D–4** The atoms in a crystalline solid can vibrate about their equilibrium positions as if they were connected to their neighbors by springs. (The forces between atoms are actually electrical in nature.)

APPENDIX E

# Galilean and Lorentz Transformations

We now examine in detail the mathematics of relating quantities in one inertial reference frame to the equivalent quantities in another. In particular, we will see how positions and velocities *transform* (that is, change) as we go from one frame of reference to another.

We begin with the classical, or Galilean, viewpoint. Consider two reference frames S and S′ which are each characterized by a set of coordinate axes, Fig. E–1. The axes $x$ and $y$ ($z$ is not shown) refer to S, and $x'$ and $y'$ refer to S′. The $x'$ and $x$ axes overlap one another, and we assume that frame S′ moves to the right (in the $x$ direction) at speed $v$ with respect to S. For simplicity let us assume the origins O and O′ of the two reference frames are superimposed at time $t = 0$.

Now consider an event that occurs at some point P (Fig. E–1) represented by the coordinates $x'$, $y'$, $z'$ in reference frame S′ at the time $t'$. What will be the coordinates of P in S? Since S and S′ overlap precisely initially, after a time $t$, S′ will have moved a distance $vt'$. Therefore, at time $t'$, $x = x' + vt'$. The $y$ and $z$ coordinates, on the other hand, are not altered by motion along the $x$ axis; thus $y = y'$ and $z = z'$. Finally, since time is assumed to be absolute in Galilean–Newtonian physics, clocks in the two frames will agree with each other; so $t = t'$. We summarize these in the following **Galilean transformation** equations:

$$\begin{aligned} x &= x' + vt' \\ y &= y' \\ z &= z' \\ t &= t'. \end{aligned} \qquad \text{(E–1)}$$

*Galilean transformations*

These equations give the coordinates of an event in the S frame when those in the S′ frame are known. If those in the S system are known, then the S′ coordinates are obtained from

$$x' = x - vt, \qquad y' = y, \qquad z' = z, \qquad t' = t.$$

These four equations are the "inverse" transformation and are very easily obtained from Eqs. E–1. Notice that the effect is merely to exchange primed and unprimed quantities and replace $v$ by $-v$. This makes sense because from the S′ frame, S moves to the left (negative $x$ direction) with speed $v$.

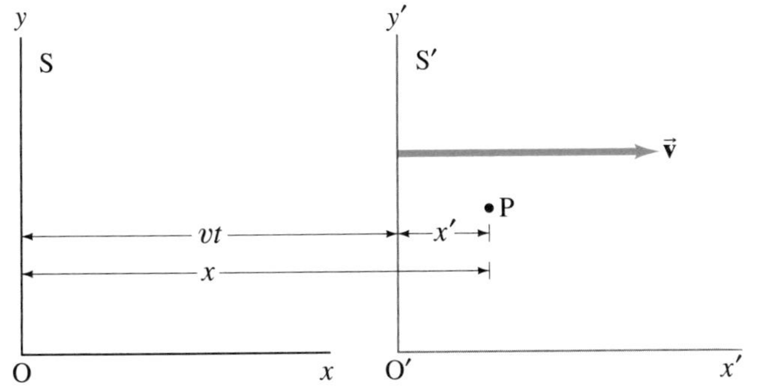


**FIGURE E–1** Inertial reference frame S′ moves to the right at speed $v$ with respect to inertial frame S.

Now suppose that the point P in Fig. E–1 represents an object that is moving. Let the components of its velocity vector in S′ be $u'_x$, $u'_y$, and $u'_z$ (we use $u$ to distinguish it from the relative velocity of the two frames, $v$). Now $u'_x = \Delta x'/\Delta t'$, $u'_y = \Delta y'/\Delta t'$, and $u'_z = \Delta z'/\Delta t'$, where all quantities are as measured in the S′ frame. For example, if at time $t'_1$ the particle is at $x'_1$ and a short time later, $t'_2$, it is at $x'_2$, then

$$u'_x = \frac{x'_2 - x'_1}{t'_2 - t'_1} = \frac{\Delta x'}{\Delta t'}.$$

Now the velocity of P as seen from S will have components $u_x$, $u_y$, and $u_z$. We can show how these are related to the velocity components in S′ by using Eqs. E–1. For example,

$$\begin{aligned} u_x &= \frac{\Delta x}{\Delta t} = \frac{x_2 - x_1}{t_2 - t_1} = \frac{(x'_2 + vt'_2) - (x'_1 + vt'_1)}{t'_2 - t'_1} \\ &= \frac{(x'_2 - x'_1) + v(t'_2 - t'_1)}{t'_2 - t'_1} \\ &= \frac{\Delta x'}{\Delta t'} + v = u'_x + v. \end{aligned}$$

For the other components, $u'_y = u_y$ and $u'_z = u_z$, so we have

*Galilean velocity transformations*

$$\begin{aligned} u_x &= u'_x + v, \\ u_y &= u'_y, \\ u_z &= u'_z. \end{aligned} \qquad \textbf{(E–2)}$$

These are known as the **Galilean velocity transformation** equations. We see that the $y$ and $z$ components of velocity are unchanged, but the $x$ components differ by $v$. This is just what we have used before when dealing with relative velocity. For example, if S′ is a train and S the Earth, and the train moves with speed $v$ with respect to Earth, a person walking toward the front of the train with speed $u'_x$ will have a speed with respect to the Earth of $u_x = u'_x + v$.

*Relativity theory*

The Galilean transformations, Eqs. E–1 and E–2, are valid only when the velocities involved are not relativistic (Chapter 26)—that is, much less than the speed of light, $c$. We can see, for example, that the first of Eqs. E–2 will not work for the speed of light, $c$, which is the same in all inertial reference frames (a basic postulate in the theory of relativity). That is, light traveling in S′ with speed $u'_x = c$ will have speed $c + v$ in S, according to Eq. E–2, whereas the theory of relativity insists it must be $c$ in S. Clearly, then, a new set of transformation equations is needed to deal with relativistic velocities.

We will derive the required equations in a simple way, again looking at Fig. E–1. We assume the transformation is linear and of the form

$$x = \gamma(x' + vt'), \qquad y = y', \qquad z = z'.$$

That is, we modify the first of Eqs. E–1 by multiplying by a factor $\gamma$ which is yet to be determined. But we assume the $y$ and $z$ equations are unchanged because we expect no length contraction in these directions. We won't assume a form for $t$, but will derive it. The inverse equations must have the same form with $v$ replaced by $-v$. (The principle of relativity demands it, since S′ moving to the right with respect to S is equivalent to S moving to the left with respect to S′.) Therefore

$$x' = \gamma(x - vt).$$

Now if a light pulse leaves the common origin of S and S′ at time $t = t' = 0$, after a time $t$ it will have traveled along the $x$ axis a distance

$x = ct$ (in S), or $x' = ct'$ (in S′). Therefore, from the equations for $x$ and $x'$ above,

$$ct = \gamma(ct' + vt') = \gamma(c + v)t',$$
$$ct' = \gamma(ct - vt) = \gamma(c - v)t.$$

We substitute $t'$ from the second equation into the first and find $ct = \gamma(c + v)\gamma(c - v)(t/c) = \gamma^2(c^2 - v^2)t/c$. We cancel out the $t$ on each side and solve for $\gamma$ to find

$$\gamma = \frac{1}{\sqrt{1 - v^2/c^2}}.$$

Now that we have found $\gamma$, we need only find the relation between $t$ and $t'$. To do so, we combine $x' = \gamma(x - vt)$ with $x = \gamma(x' + vt')$:

$$x' = \gamma(x - vt) = \gamma\left[\gamma(x' + vt') - vt\right].$$

We solve for $t$ and find $t = \gamma(t' + vx'/c^2)$. In summary,

$$\begin{aligned} x &= \frac{1}{\sqrt{1 - v^2/c^2}}(x' + vt'), \\ y &= y', \\ z &= z', \\ t &= \frac{1}{\sqrt{1 - v^2/c^2}}\left(t' + \frac{vx'}{c^2}\right). \end{aligned} \qquad \textbf{(E–3)}$$

*Lorentz transformations*

These are called the **Lorentz transformation** equations. They were first proposed, in a slightly different form, by Lorentz in 1904 to explain the null result of the Michelson–Morley experiment and to make Maxwell's equations take the same form in all inertial systems. A year later, Einstein derived them independently based on his theory of relativity. Notice that not only is the $x$ equation modified as compared to the Galilean transformation but so is the $t$ equation. Indeed, we see directly in this last equation, as well as in the first, how the space and time coordinates mix.

The relativistically correct velocity equations are readily obtained. For example, using Eqs. E–3 (we let $\gamma = 1/\sqrt{1 - v^2/c^2}$),

$$\begin{aligned} u_x = \frac{\Delta x}{\Delta t} &= \frac{\gamma(\Delta x' + v\,\Delta t')}{\gamma(\Delta t' + v\,\Delta x'/c^2)} = \frac{(\Delta x'/\Delta t') + v}{1 + (v/c^2)(\Delta x'/\Delta t')} \\ &= \frac{u'_x + v}{1 + vu'_x/c^2}. \end{aligned}$$

The others are obtained in the same way, and we collect them here:

$$\begin{aligned} u_x &= \frac{u'_x + v}{1 + vu'_x/c^2}, \\ u_y &= \frac{u'_y\sqrt{1 - v^2/c^2}}{1 + vu'_x/c^2}, \\ u_z &= \frac{u'_z\sqrt{1 - v^2/c^2}}{1 + vu'_x/c^2}. \end{aligned} \qquad \textbf{(E–4)}$$

*Relativistic velocity transformations*

The first of these equations is Eq. 26–9, which we used in Section 26–11 where we discussed how velocities do not add in our commonsense (Galilean) way, because of the denominator $(1 + vu'_x/c^2)$. We can now also see that the $y$ and $z$ components of velocity are also altered and that they depend on the $x'$ component of velocity.

**EXAMPLE E–1** **Length contraction.** Derive the length contraction formula, Eq. 26–2, from the Lorentz transformation equations.

**SOLUTION** Let an object of length $L_0$ be at rest on the $x$ axis in S. The coordinates of its two end points are $x_1$ and $x_2$, so that $x_2 - x_1 = L_0$. At any instant in S′, the end points will be at $x_1'$ and $x_2'$ as given by the Lorentz transformation equations. The length measured in S′ is $L = x_2' - x_1'$. An observer in S′ measures this length by measuring $x_2'$ and $x_1'$ at the same time (in the S′ frame), so $t_2' = t_1'$. Then, from the first of Eqs. E–3,

$$L_0 = x_2 - x_1 = \frac{1}{\sqrt{1 - v^2/c^2}}\left(x_2' + vt_2' - x_1' - vt_1'\right).$$

Since $t_2' = t_1'$, we have

$$L_0 = \frac{1}{\sqrt{1 - v^2/c^2}}\left(x_2' - x_1'\right) = \frac{L}{\sqrt{1 - v^2/c^2}},$$

or

$$L = L_0\sqrt{1 - \frac{v^2}{c^2}},$$

which is Eq. 26–2.

**EXAMPLE E–2** **Time dilation.** Derive the time dilation formula, Eq. 26–1, from the Lorentz transformation equations.

**SOLUTION** The time $\Delta t_0$ between two events that occur at the same place $\left(x_2' = x_1'\right)$ in S′ is measured to be $\Delta t_0 = t_2' - t_1'$. Since $x_2' = x_1'$, then from the last of Eqs. E–3, the time $\Delta t$ between the events as measured in S is

$$\begin{aligned}\Delta t = t_2 - t_1 &= \frac{1}{\sqrt{1 - v^2/c^2}}\left(t_2' + \frac{vx_2'}{c^2} - t_1' - \frac{vx_1'}{c^2}\right)\\ &= \frac{1}{\sqrt{1 - v^2/c^2}}\left(t_2' - t_1'\right)\\ &= \frac{\Delta t_0}{\sqrt{1 - v^2/c^2}},\end{aligned}$$

which is Eq. 26–1. Notice that we chose S′ to be the frame in which the two events occur at the same place, so that $x_1' = x_2'$, and the terms containing $x_1'$ and $x_2'$ cancel out.

# Answers to Odd-Numbered Problems

## CHAPTER 1

**1.** (*a*) $1.4 \times 10^{10}$ years;
(*b*) $4.4 \times 10^{17}$ s.

**3.** (*a*) $1.156 \times 10^{0}$;
(*b*) $2.18 \times 10^{1}$;
(*c*) $6.8 \times 10^{-3}$;
(*d*) $2.7635 \times 10^{1}$;
(*e*) $2.19 \times 10^{-1}$;
(*f*) $4.44 \times 10^{2}$.

**5.** 1%.

**7.** (*a*) 4%;
(*b*) 0.4%;
(*c*) 0.07%.

**9.** 1.7 m.

**11.** 9%.

**13.** (*a*) 1 megavolt;
(*b*) 2 micrometers;
(*c*) 6 kilodays;
(*d*) 18 hectobucks;
(*e*) 8 nanopieces.

**15.** (*a*) $1.5 \times 10^{11}$ m;
(*b*) 150 gigameters.

**17.** 3.8 s.

**19.** 3.76 m.

**21.** 7.3%.

**23.** (*a*) $3.80 \times 10^{13}\ m^2$;
(*b*) 13.4.

**25.** $\approx 7 \times 10^5$ books.

**27.** $\approx$ 11 hr.

**29.** $8 \times 10^4\ cm^3$.

**31.** $4 \times 10^8$ kg/yr.

**33.** (*a*) Cannot be correct;
(*b*) can be correct;
(*c*) can be correct.

**35.** 50,000 chips.

**37.** $2 \times 10^{-4}$ m.

**39.** (*a*) $10^{12}$ protons or neutrons;
(*b*) $10^{10}$ protons or neutrons;
(*c*) $10^{29}$ protons or neutrons;
(*d*) $10^{68}$ protons or neutrons.

**41.** 1500 gumballs.

**43.** $\approx$ 3 ft.

**45.** $\approx$ 3500 km.

**47.** 150 m long, 25 m wide, 15 m high; $6 \times 10^4\ m^3$.

**49.** 210 yd, 190 m.

**51.** $2.21 \times 10^{19}\ m^3$, 49.3 Moons.

**53.** (*a*) 3%, 3%;
(*b*) 0.7%, 0.2%.

## CHAPTER 2

**1.** 72.3 km/h.

**3.** 61 m.

**5.** −2.5 cm/s.

**7.** (*a*) $2.6 \times 10^2$ km;
(*b*) 77 km/h.

**9.** (*a*) 4.3 m/s;
(*b*) 0 m/s.

**11.** 2.7 min.

**13.** 6.8 h, $8.7 \times 10^2$ km/h.

**15.** 6.73 m/s.

**17.** (*a*) $7.41\ m/s^2$;
(*b*) $9.60 \times 10^4\ km/h^2$.

**19.** $-5.5\ m/s^2$, −0.56 *g*'s.

**21.** $2.0\ m/s^2$, 114 m.

**23.** $1.8 \times 10^2$ m.

**25.** 63.0 m.

**27.** −36 *g*'s.

**31.** 3.1 s.

**33.** 51.8 m.

**35.** (*a*) 8.8 s;
(*b*) 86 m/s.

**37.** 15 m/s, 11 m.

**39.** 5.61 s.

**43.** $4.1 \times 10^{-2}$ s.

**45.** 46 m.

**47.** (*a*) 5.20 s;
(*b*) 38.9 m/s;
(*c*) 84.7 m.

**49.** (*a*) 48 s;
(*b*) 90 s to 108 s;
(*c*) 0 s to 38 s, 65 s to 83 s, 90 s to 108 s;
(*d*) 65 s to 83 s.

**51.** (*a*) 0 s to 18 s;
(*b*) 27 s;
(*c*) 38 s;
(*d*) both directions.

**53.** (*a*) $4\ m/s^2$;
(*b*) $3\ m/s^2$;
(*c*) $0.35\ m/s^2$;
(*d*) $1.6\ m/s^2$.

**55.**

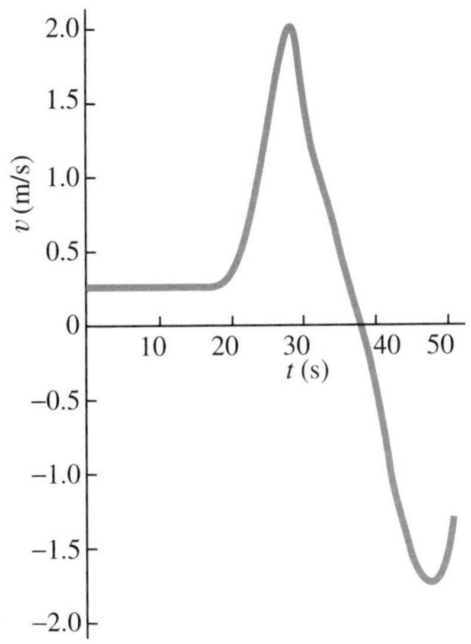


**57.** (*a*) $-150\ m/s^2$;
(*b*) loosen.

**59.** 1.3 m.

**61.** (*b*) 14 m;
(*c*) 39.4 m.

**63.** 31 m/s.

**65.** (*a*) 8.8 min;
(*b*) 7.5 min.

**67.** 4.9 m/s to 5.7 m/s, 6.0 m/s to 6.9 m/s, smaller range of initial velocities.

**69.** 29.0 m.

**71.** $5.1 \times 10^{-2}\ m/s^2$.

**73.** 3.3 min; 5.2 km; 23.3 s, 0.61 km.

**75.** (*a*) 88 m/s;
(*b*) 27 s;
(*c*) 1590 m;
(*d*) 36 s;
(*e*) −177 m/s;
(*f*) 54 s.

**77.**

(*a*)

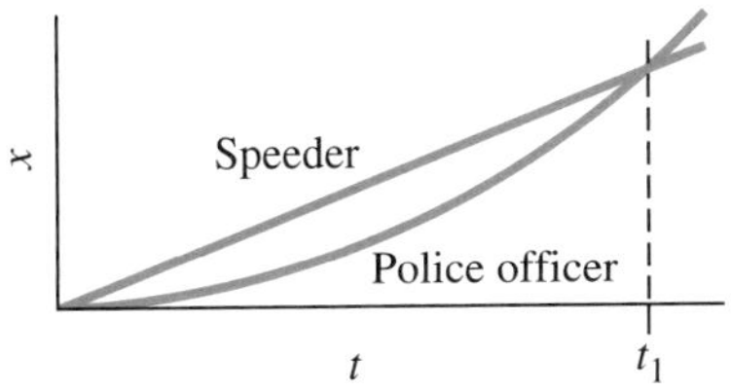


(*b*) 23 s;
(*c*) $3.0\ m/s^2$;
(*d*) 67 m/s.

**79.** 18 m/s.

**81.** 0.44 m/min, 2.9 burgers/min.

**83.** 12 m/s.

**85.** (*a*) Near the midpoint of the time interval;
(*b*) A;
(*c*) at the times when the two graphs cross; at the first crossing, bicycle B is passing bicycle A; at the second crossing, bicycle A is passing bicycle B;
(*d*) A;
(*e*) they have the same average velocity.

## CHAPTER 3

**1.** 282 km, 12° south of west.

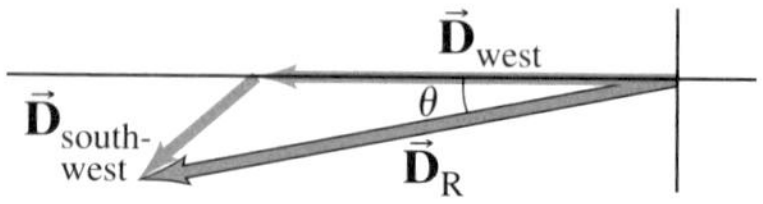


**3.** $\vec{V}_2 - \vec{V}_1$.

**5.** 58 m, 48°.

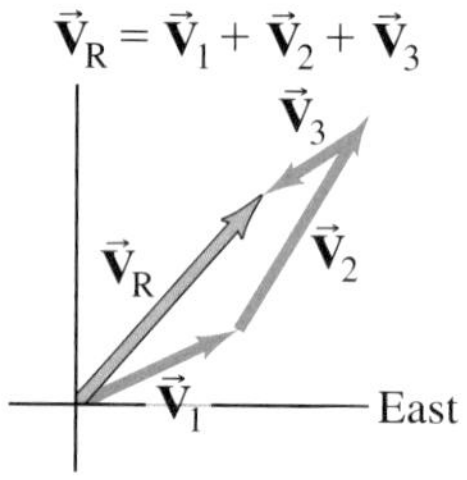


**7.** (*a*)

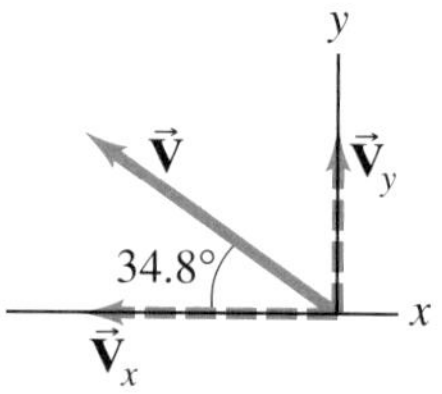


(*b*) −11.7 units, 8.16 units;
(*c*) 14.3 units, 34.8° above the $-x$ axis.

**9.** (*a*) 550 km/h, 487 km/h;
(*b*) 1650 km, 1460 km.

**11.** 64.6, 53.1°.

**13.** (*a*) 62.6, 329°;
(*b*) 77.5, 71.9°;
(*c*) 77.5, 251.9°.

**15.** −2450 m, 3870 m, 2450 m; 5190 m.

**17.** 4.0 m.

**19.** 13° and 77°.

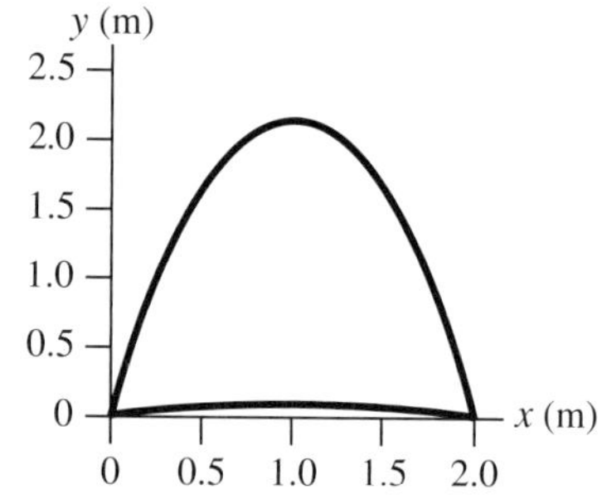


**21.** 7.92 m/s.

**23.** 12.9 m.

**25.** 6 times farther.

**27.** 5.71 s.

**29.** The football will not clear the bar. It is 0.76 m too low when it reaches the goal post.

**31.** (*a*) 10.4 s;
(*b*) 541 m;
(*c*) 51.9 m/s, −63.1 m/s;
(*d*) 81.7 m/s;
(*e*) 50.6° below the horizon;
(*f*) 78.1 m.

**33.** 76°.

**35.** (*a*) 481 m;
(*b*) 8.37 m/s down;
(*c*) 97.4 m/s.

**37.** 1.80 m/s, 19° to the river bank.

**39.** (*a*) 2.59 m/s, 62° from the shore;
(*b*) 3.60 m downstream, 6.90 m across the river.

**41.** (*a*) 543 km/h, 7.61° east of south;
(*b*) 17 km.

**43.** 1.41 m/s.

**45.** (*a*) 1.24 m/s;
(*b*) 2.28 m/s.

**47.** (*a*) 67 m;
(*b*) 170 s.

**49.** 42.2° north of east.

**51.** 114 km/h.

**53.** 6.2°.

**55.** 4.7 m/s² left (opposite to the truck's motion), 2.8 m/s² down.

**57.** $v_T/\tan\theta$.

**59.** 180 s, 4.8 km; 21.2 s, 0.56 km.

**61.** 1.9 m/s².

**63.** 1.9 m/s, 2.7 s.

**65.** 49.6°.

**67.** 63 m/s, 66° above the horizontal.

**69.** 10.8 m/s to 11.0 m/s.

**71.** (*a*) 36 m/s;
(*b*) 20 m/s.

**73.** 7.0 m/s, 97°.

**75.** 39 m.

## CHAPTER 4

**1.** 75.0 N.

**3.** $1.15 \times 10^3$ N.

**5.** (*a*) 196 N, 196 N;
(*b*) 294 N, 98.0 N.

**7.** 68.4 N.

**9.** 780 N, backward.

**11.** 2.00 *g*'s, $9.51 \times 10^3$ N.

**13.** $5.08 \times 10^4$ N, $4.43 \times 10^4$ N.

**15.** 2.5 m/s², down.

**17.** (*a*) 7.4 m/s², down;
(*b*) $1.29 \times 10^3$ N.

**19.** (*a*) 47.0 N;
(*b*) 17.0 N;
(*c*) 0 N.

**21.**

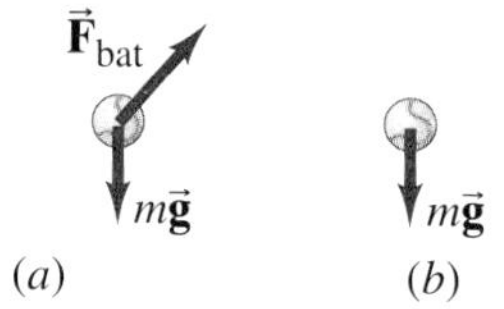


**23.** $1.41 \times 10^3$ N.

**25.** (*a*) 63 N, 31 N;
(*b*) 73 N, 36 N.

**27.** $6.9 \times 10^3$ N, $8.9 \times 10^3$ N.

**29.** (*a*) 320 N;
(*b*) 1.5 m/s².

**31.** (*a*)

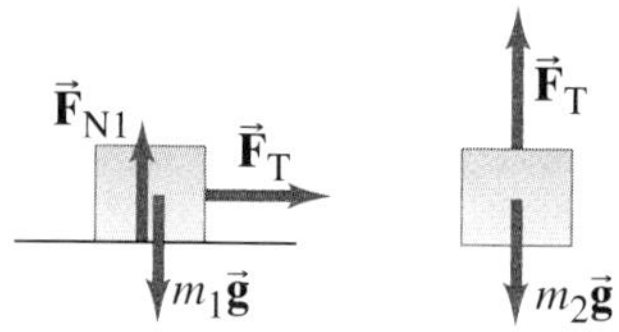


(*b*) $a = g\dfrac{m_2}{m_1 + m_2}$,

$$F_T = m_1 a = g\frac{m_1 m_2}{m_1 + m_2}.$$

**33.** (*a*)

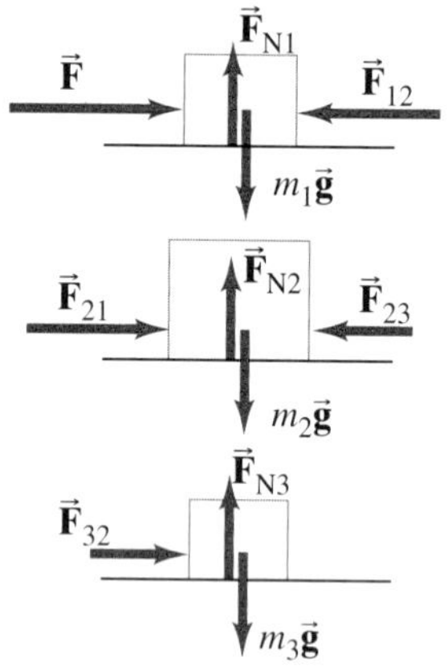


(*b*) $a = \dfrac{F}{m_1 + m_2 + m_3}$;

(*c*) $F_{1\,net} = \dfrac{m_1 F}{m_1 + m_2 + m_3}$,

$$F_{2\,net} = \frac{m_2 F}{m_1 + m_2 + m_3},$$

$$F_{3\,net} = \frac{m_3 F}{m_1 + m_2 + m_3};$$

(*d*) $F_{12} = F_{21} = \dfrac{(m_2 + m_3)F}{m_1 + m_2 + m_3}$,

$$F_{23} = F_{32} = \frac{m_3 F}{m_1 + m_2 + m_3};$$

(*e*) 2.67 m/s²; 32.0 N, 64.0 N, 32.0 N.

**35.** $1.74\ \text{m/s}^2$, 22.6 N, 20.9 N.

**37.** (*a*) 0.98;
(*b*) 0.91.

**39.** $7.8\ \text{m/s}^2$.

**41.** 73 N, 0.59.

**43.** (*a*)

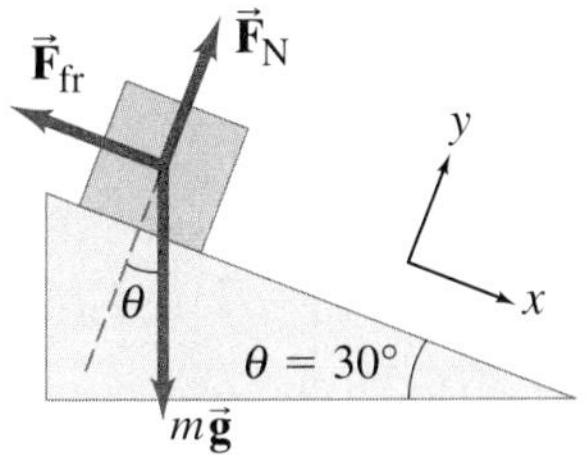


(*b*) No change;
(*c*) friction force direction would be reversed.

**45.** 40 N.

**47.** 4.1 m.

**49.** $-7.4\ \text{m/s}^2$.

**51.** 0.40.

**53.** (*a*) 1.2 m;
(*b*) 1.6 s.

**55.** 101 N, 0.719.

**57.** (*a*) 0.58;
(*b*) 5.7 m/s;
(*c*) 15 m/s.

**59.** 0.36.

**61.** $5.3 \times 10^2$ N.

**63.** (*a*) $g\dfrac{(m_1 \sin\theta - m_2)}{(m_1 + m_2)}$;
(*b*) $m_1 \sin\theta > m_2$ (down the plane), $m_1 \sin\theta < m_2$ (up the plane).

**65.** $1.3 \times 10^2$ N.

**67.** 1.3 m.

**69.** $1.54 \times 10^3$ N.

**71.** (*a*) 16 m/s;
(*b*) 13 m/s.

**73.** Yes, 3.8 m/s.

**75.** 82 m/s.

**77.** 5.9°.

**79.** 940 N, 79° above the horizontal.

**81.** (*a*) $9.43 \times 10^4$ N;
(*b*) $1.33 \times 10^4$ N;
(*c*) $1.33 \times 10^4$ N.

**83.** 12 m/s.

**85.** (*a*) 45 N (10 lb);
(*b*) 37 N (8.4 lb);
(*c*) not when pulled vertically.

**87.** (*a*) $4.1\ \text{m/s}^2$, $3.2\ \text{m/s}^2$;
(*b*) $4.1\ \text{m/s}^2$, $3.2\ \text{m/s}^2$;
(*c*) $3.5\ \text{m/s}^2$.

**89.** $5.3 \times 10^2$ N, $2.6 \times 10^2$ N.

## CHAPTER 5

**1.** (*a*) $1.42\ \text{m/s}^2$;
(*b*) 35.5 N.

**3.** $5.97 \times 10^{-3}\ \text{m/s}^2$, $3.56 \times 10^{22}$ N, the Sun.

**5.** 0.9 *g*'s.

**7.** (*a*) 3.73 N;
(*b*) 9.61 N.

**9.** 25 m/s, yes.

**11.** 30.4 m/s, 0.403 rev/s.

**13.** 8.5 m/s.

**15.** 11 rpm.

**17.** $3.38 \times 10^4$ rpm.

**21.** 0.22.

**23.** $4\pi^2 f^2(m_1 r_1 + m_2 r_2)$, $4\pi^2 m_2 r_2 f^2$.

**25.** $3.5 \times 10^3$ N, $5.0 \times 10^2$ N.

**27.** (*a*) 1.27 m/s;
(*b*) 3.05 m/s.

**29.** (*a*) 21.0 kg, 21.0 kg;
(*b*) 206 N, 252 N.

**31.** $4.4\ \text{m/s}^2$.

**33.** 3.9 kg, 0.1 kg.

**35.** $2.02 \times 10^7$ m.

**37.** $4.38 \times 10^7\ \text{m/s}^2$.

**39.** $3.2 \times 10^{-8}$ N toward center of square.

**41.** $6.4 \times 10^{23}$ kg.

**43.** $6.32 \times 10^3$ m/s.

**45.** 10 s/rev.

**47.** $7.90 \times 10^3$ m/s.

**49.** $2.0 \times 10^4$ s, $7.1 \times 10^4$ s.

**51.** (*a*) 21 N, toward the Moon;
(*b*) $2.0 \times 10^2$ N, away from Moon.

**53.** (*a*) $5.4 \times 10^2$ N;
(*b*) $5.4 \times 10^2$ N;
(*c*) $7.2 \times 10^2$ N;
(*d*) $3.6 \times 10^2$ N;
(*e*) 0 N.

**55.** (*b*) $5.4 \times 10^3\ \text{kg/m}^3$.

**57.** $1.62 \times 10^{11}$ m.

**59.** $2690 \times 10^6$ km, yes, Pluto.

**61.** (*a*) $1.90 \times 10^{27}$ kg;
(*b*) $1.90 \times 10^{27}$ kg, $1.89 \times 10^{27}$ kg, $1.90 \times 10^{27}$ kg, yes.

**63.** $671 \times 10^3$ km, $1070 \times 10^3$ km, $1880 \times 10^3$ km.

**65.** 9.0 d.

**67.** $2.64 \times 10^6$ m.

**69.** 0.344%.

**71.** $2.6\ \text{m/s}^2$ upward.

**73.** (*a*) $2.2 \times 10^3$ m;
(*b*) $5.4 \times 10^3$ N;
(*c*) $3.8 \times 10^3$ N.

**75.** (*a*) $\theta = \tan^{-1} m_M R_{Earth}^2 / M_{Earth} D_M^2$;
(*b*) $5 \times 10^{13}$ kg;
(*c*) $(8 \times 10^{-4})^\circ$.

**77.** $5.07 \times 10^3$ s.

**79.** 26.9 m/s.

**81.** $5.2 \times 10^{39}$ kg, $2.6 \times 10^9$ solar masses.

**83.** (*a*) $3.86 \times 10^3$ m/s;
(*b*) $4.36 \times 10^4$ s.

**85.** (*a*) ≈12 h;
(*b*) $1.8 \times 10^3$ m.

**87.** $5 \times 10^{-5}\ \text{N}\cdot\text{m}^2/\text{kg}^2$.

**89.** $3.8 \times 10^{-10}$ N, upward.

**91.** $1.6 \times 10^{-4}\ \text{m/s}^2$.

**93.** $v_{min} = v_0\sqrt{\dfrac{(1 - \mu_s Rg/v_0^2)}{(1 + \mu_s v_0^2/Rg)}}$,

$v_{max} = v_0\sqrt{\dfrac{(1 + Rg\mu_s/v_0^2)}{(1 - \mu_s v_0^2/Rg)}}$.

## CHAPTER 6

**1.** $7.27 \times 10^3$ J.

**3.** (*a*) $9.2 \times 10^2$ J;
(*b*) $5.2 \times 10^3$ J.

**5.** $4.9 \times 10^2$ J.

**9.** (*a*) 1.10*Mg*;
(*b*) 1.10*Mgh*.

**11.** $5.0 \times 10^3$ J.

**13.** $8.4 \times 10^{-2}$ J.

**15.** 484 m/s.

**17.** $-1.64 \times 10^{-18}$ J.

**19.** 44 m/s.

**21.** 2.25.

**23.** 1.1 N.

**25.** (*a*) $3.24 \times 10^3$ N;
(*b*) $9.83 \times 10^3$ J;
(*c*) $7.13 \times 10^4$ J;
(*d*) $-6.14 \times 10^4$ J;
(*e*) 8.31 m/s.

**27.** 82 J.

**29.** $8.1 \times 10^4$ N/m.

**31.** (*a*) $9.2 \times 10^5$ J;
(*b*) $9.2 \times 10^5$ J;
(*c*) yes.

**33.** 1.4 m, no unless length <0.7 m.

**35.** 5.14 m/s.

**37.** (*a*) 9.2 m/s;
(*b*) −0.31 m.

39. (*a*) 8.3 m/s;
(*b*) 3.64 m.

41. $\frac{1}{2}mv^2 + \frac{1}{2}kx^2 = \frac{1}{2}kx_0^2$.

43. 26 m/s, 12 m/s, 20 m/s.

45. 12 $Mg/h$.

47. $5.3 \times 10^6$ J.

49. (*a*) 21 m/s;
(*b*) $2.4 \times 10^2$ m.

51. (*a*) 25%;
(*b*) 5.4 m/s;
(*c*) heat, sound, non-elastic deformation.

53. 23 m/s.

55. 0.40.

57. (*a*) $1.1 \times 10^3$ km/h;
(*b*) $2 \times 10^3$ N.

59. $5.5 \times 10^2$ N.

61. (*b*) 0.10 hp.

63. $2.2 \times 10^4$ W, $3.0 \times 10^1$ hp.

65. 480 W.

67. $1.0 \times 10^3$ W.

69. 18°.

71. $9.0 \times 10^2$ W.

73. $1.5 \times 10^3$ J.

75. (*a*) $2.5r$;
(*b*) $11mg$;
(*c*) $5mg$;
(*d*) $mg$.

77. (*a*) $\sqrt{2gL}$;
(*b*) $\sqrt{1.2gL}$.

79. (*a*) $2.5 \times 10^5$ J;
(*b*) 23 m/s;
(*c*) −1.56 m.

81. (*a*) $4.0 \times 10^1$ m/s;
(*b*) $3.0 \times 10^5$ W.

83. (*a*) $1.4 \times 10^3$ m;
(*b*) $1.6 \times 10^2$ m/s.

85. $4.2 \times 10^4$ N.

87. $3.9 \times 10^2$ W.

89. $2k$.

91. 4.6 s.

93. (*a*) $1 \times 10^2$ m/s;
(*b*) $4 \times 10^7$ W.

## CHAPTER 7

1. 0.24 kg·m/s.

3. $4.40 \times 10^3$ N toward the pitcher.

5. $6.0 \times 10^7$ N upward.

7. 12.6 m/s.

9. $8 \times 10^2$ N, $F_{\text{wind}} > F_{\text{fr}} \approx 7 \times 10^2$ N.

11. $4.2 \times 10^3$ m/s.

13. (*a*) $6.9 \times 10^3$ m/s away from Earth, $4.7 \times 10^3$ m/s away from Earth;
(*b*) $5.9 \times 10^8$ J.

15. (*a*) 2.0 kg·m/s;
(*b*) $5.8 \times 10^2$ N.

17. 2.1 kg·m/s to the left.

19. (*a*) $3.8 \times 10^2$ kg·m/s;
(*b*) $-3.8 \times 10^2$ kg·m/s;
(*c*) $3.8 \times 10^2$ kg·m/s;
(*d*) $5.1 \times 10^2$ N.

21. 69 m.

23. 1.00 m/s west, 2.00 m/s east.

25. 0.88 m/s and 2.23 m/s, both in direction of tennis ball's initial motion.

27. (*a*) 3.62 m/s, 4.42 m/s;
(*b*) $-4.0 \times 10^2$ kg·m/s, $4.0 \times 10^2$ kg·m/s.

29. 0.35 m, 1.4 m.

31. $v_2 = \sqrt{2}\, v_1$.

33. (*a*) $-M/(m + M)$;
(*b*) −0.96.

35. 23 m/s.

37. (*b*) $e = \sqrt{h'/h}$.

39. (*a*) 1.7 m/s for both;
(*b*) −2.1 m/s, 7.4 m/s;
(*c*) 0, 4.3 m/s, reasonable;
(*d*) 2.8 m/s, 0, not reasonable;
(*e*) −4.0 m/s, 10.3 m/s, not reasonable.

41. 60° relative to eagle A, 6.7 m/s.

43. 141°.

45. 39.9 u.

47. $6.5 \times 10^{-11}$ m.

49. (1.04 m, −1.04 m) relative to raft's center.

51. ($1.2l$, $0.9l$) relative to back left corner.

53. 17% of the whole body mass.

55. 21.7 cm horizontal, 7.6 cm vertical.

57. (*a*) $4.66 \times 10^6$ m from center of Earth.

59. 24.8 cm.

61. $vm/(m + M)$ upward, the balloon stops.

63. $v'_x = \frac{3}{2}v_0$, $v'_y = -v_0$.

65. (*a*) 0.194 m/s;
(*b*) $8.8 \times 10^2$ N.

67. $m_{\text{B}} = \frac{5}{3}m$.

69. 4.00 m.

71. $3.8 \times 10^2$ m/s.

73. (*a*) $2.5 \times 10^{-13}$ m/s;
(*b*) $1.7 \times 10^{-17}$;
(*c*) 0.19 J.

75. (*a*)

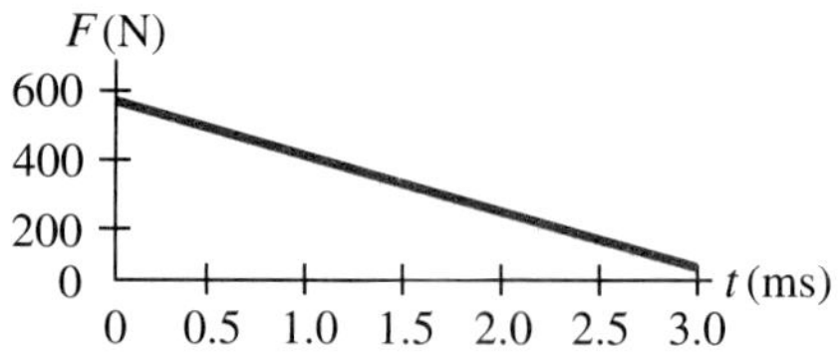


(*b*) 0.93 N·s;
(*c*) $4.2 \times 10^{-3}$ kg.

77. $6.7 \times 10^3$ m/s.

79. (*a*) −4.4 m/s, 4.0 m/s;
(*b*) 2.0 m.

81. −29.6 km/s.

## CHAPTER 8

1. (*a*) 0.52 rad, $\pi/6$ rad;
(*b*) 0.99 rad, $19\pi/60$ rad;
(*c*) 1.57 rad, $\pi/2$ rad;
(*d*) 6.28 rad, $2\pi$ rad;
(*e*) 7.33 rad, $7\pi/3$ rad.

3. $5.3 \times 10^3$ m.

5. $7.4 \times 10^{-2}$ m.

7. (*a*) $2.6 \times 10^2$ rad/s;
(*b*) 46 m/s, $1.2 \times 10^4$ m/s$^2$.

9. (*a*) $1.99 \times 10^{-7}$ rad/s;
(*b*) $7.27 \times 10^{-5}$ rad/s.

11. $3.6 \times 10^4$ rpm.

13. $\omega_1/\omega_2 = R_2/R_1$.

15. $2.8 \times 10^4$ rev.

17. (*a*) $4.0 \times 10^1$ rev/min$^2$;
(*b*) $4.0 \times 10^1$ rpm.

19. (*a*) −0.42 rad/s$^2$;
(*b*) 210 s.

21. (*a*) −4.1 rad/s$^2$;
(*b*) 7.6 s.

23. (*a*) 41 m·N;
(*b*) 29 m·N.

25. $mg(L_2 - L_1)$, clockwise.

27. 1.81 kg·m$^2$.

29. (*a*) 0.94 kg·m$^2$;
(*b*) $2.4 \times 10^{-2}$ m·N.

31. (*a*) 6.1 kg·m$^2$;
(*b*) 0.61 kg·m$^2$;
(*c*) vertical axis.

33. 20 N.

35. 62 m·N.

37. 993 rev, 10.9 s.

39. (*a*) 92 rad/s$^2$;
(*b*) $7.9 \times 10^2$ N.

**41.** $a = \dfrac{(m_2 - m_1)}{(m_1 + m_2 + I/r^2)}\, g < a_{I=0}$,

$a_{I=0} = \dfrac{(m_2 - m_1)}{(m_1 + m_2)}\, g$.

**43.** $1.40 \times 10^4$ J.

**45.** 56 J.

**47.** $1.42 \times 10^4$ J.

**49.** 3.22 m/s.

**51.** $2.64\ \text{kg}\cdot\text{m}^2/\text{s}$.

**53.** (*a*) His rotational inertia increases;
(*b*) 1.6.

**55.** $0.77\ \text{kg}\cdot\text{m}^2$, by pulling her arms in toward the center of her body.

**57.** (*a*) $14\ \text{kg}\cdot\text{m}^2/\text{s}$;
(*b*) $-2.7\ \text{m}\cdot\text{N}$.

**59.** $\omega/2$.

**61.** (*a*) 1.2 rad/s;
(*b*) $1.8 \times 10^3$ J, $1.1 \times 10^3$ J.

**63.** $5 \times 10^{-2}$ rad/s, $2 \times 10^4\ \text{KE}_\text{i}$.

**65.** $(2.7 \times 10^{-16})\%$.

**67.** $-0.30$ rad/s.

**69.** $8.21 \times 10^{-6}$.

**71.** $53\ \text{m}\cdot\text{N}$.

**73.** (*a*) $\omega_\text{R}/\omega_\text{F} = N_\text{F}/N_\text{R}$.
(*b*) 4.0;
(*c*) 1.5.

**75.** (*b*) $2.2 \times 10^3$ rad/s; (*c*) 25 min.

**77.** (*a*) 4.3 m;
(*b*) 5.2 s.

**79.** $Mg\sqrt{2Rh - h^2}/(R - h)$.

**81.** $2.8\ \text{m}\cdot\text{N}$, from his arm muscles.

**83.** (*a*) $7.8\ \text{kg}\cdot\text{m}^2/\text{s}$;
(*b*) $3.9\ \text{m}\cdot\text{N}$;
(*c*) 2.9 rad/s.

**85.** $2.7(R - r)$.

## CHAPTER 9

**1.** 430 N, 112° clockwise from $\vec{\mathbf{F}}_\text{A}$.

**3.** 6.52 kg.

**5.** $1.1 \times 10^3$ N.

**7.** $5.8 \times 10^3$ N, $8.1 \times 10^3$ N.

**9.** (*a*) 2.3 m from adult;
(*b*) 2.5 m from adult.

**11.** $2.6 \times 10^3$ N, $3.1 \times 10^3$ N.

**13.** 0.32 m.

**15.** $6.1 \times 10^3$ N, $5.9 \times 10^3$ N.

**17.** 34.6 N.

**19.** $9.05 \times 10^{-1}$ m.

**21.** (*a*) $4.25 \times 10^2$ N;
(*b*) $4.25 \times 10^2$ N, $3.28 \times 10^2$ N.

**23.** (*a*) 0.78 N;
(*b*) 0.98 N.

**25.** 55.2 N, 63.7 N.

**27.** 0.50.

**29.** $1.0 \times 10^2$ N.

**31.** $9.9 \times 10^2$ N.

**33.** $2.7 \times 10^3$ N.

**35.** $2.4w$.

**37.** (*b*) Yes, by 1/24 of a brick length;
(*c*) $D = \sum_{i=1}^{n} \dfrac{L}{2i}$;
(*d*) 35 bricks.

**39.** (*a*) $2.0 \times 10^5\ \text{N/m}^2$;
(*b*) $4.1 \times 10^{-6}$.

**41.** (*a*) $1.4 \times 10^5\ \text{N/m}^2$;
(*b*) $6.9 \times 10^{-7}$;
(*c*) $6.5 \times 10^{-6}$ m.

**43.** $9.6 \times 10^6\ \text{N/m}^2$.

**45.** $(-2 \times 10^{-2})\%$.

**47.** (*a*) $1.1 \times 10^2\ \text{m}\cdot\text{N}$, clockwise;
(*b*) the wall.

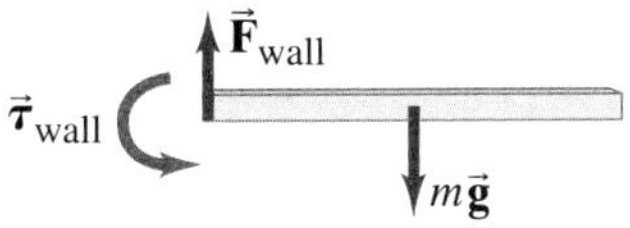


**49.** (*a*) 393 N;
(*b*) thicker.

**51.** (*a*) $4.4 \times 10^{-5}\ \text{m}^2$;
(*b*) $2.7 \times 10^{-3}$ m.

**53.** $1.2 \times 10^{-2}$ m.

**55.** 12 m.

**57.** $2.94 \times 10^{-1}$ kg, $2.29 \times 10^{-1}$ kg, $6.56 \times 10^{-2}$ kg.

**59.** (*a*) $Mg\sqrt{h/(2R - h)}$;
(*b*) $Mg\sqrt{h(2R - h)}/(R - h)$.

**61.** (*a*)

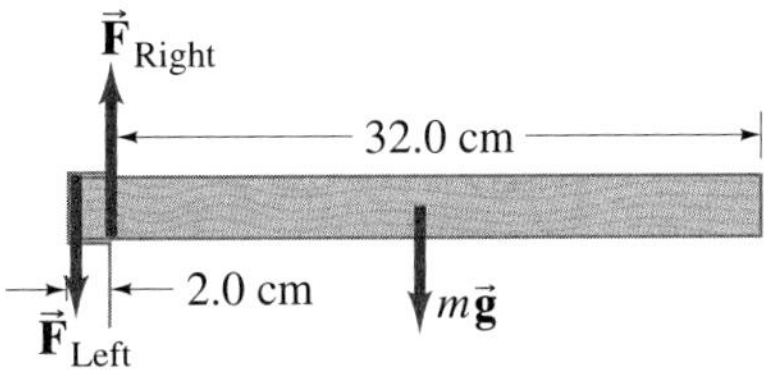


(*b*) $F_\text{Left} = 3.7 \times 10^2$ N,
$F_\text{Right} = 4.2 \times 10^2$ N,
$mg = 49$ N;
(*c*) $8.3\ \text{m}\cdot\text{N}$.

**63.** 29°.

**65.** $3.5 \times 10^{-4}$ m.

**67.** (*a*) $0.29mg$;
(*b*) $0.58mg$;
(*c*) horizontal at lowest point, 60° above the horizontal at points of attachment.

**69.** (*a*) $\mu_\text{s} < l/2h$;
(*b*) $\mu_\text{s} > l/2h$.

**71.** (*a*) $F_\text{Left} = 3.3 \times 10^2$ N up,
$F_\text{Right} = 2.3 \times 10^2$ N down;
(*b*) 0.65 m;
(*c*) 1.2 m.

**73.** $F_\text{Left} = 1.0 \times 10^2$ N,
$F_\text{Right} = 1.9 \times 10^2$ N.

**75.** Average force per area $= 4.5 \times 10^5\ \text{N/m}^2$.

**77.** (*a*) $3.5 \times 10^8\ \text{N/m}^2$;
(*b*) the bone will break;
(*c*) $8.2 \times 10^6\ \text{N/m}^2$, the bone will not break.

**79.** 2.34 m.

## CHAPTER 10

**1.** $3 \times 10^{11}$ kg.

**3.** $5.8 \times 10^2$ kg.

**5.** 0.8477.

**7.** (*a*) $7 \times 10^7\ \text{N/m}^2$;
(*b*) $2 \times 10^5\ \text{N/m}^2$.

**9.** (*a*) $4.7 \times 10^5$ N;
(*b*) $4.7 \times 10^5$ N.

**11.** $2.2 \times 10^3$ kg.

**13.** 13 m.

**15.** $1.60 \times 10^4$ m.

**17.** (*a*) $9.6 \times 10^5\ \text{N/m}^2$;
(*b*) 98 m.

**19.** (*a*) $1.41 \times 10^5$ Pa;
(*b*) $9.8 \times 10^4$ Pa.

**21.** $1.06 \times 10^3\ \text{kg/m}^3$, 3% higher.

**23.** 0.199.

**25.** 920 kg.

**27.** Iron or steel.

**29.** (*a*) $7.4 \times 10^5$ N;
(*b*) $1.0 \times 10^4$ N.

**31.** (*a*) $1.03 \times 10^3\ \text{kg/m}^3$;
(*b*) $\rho_\text{liquid} = \rho_\text{object}(m_\text{object} - m_\text{apparent})/m_\text{object}$.

**33.** 0.105.

**35.** 0.90 m/s.

**39.** $4.4 \times 10^5$ s (5.1 days).

**41.** $5.6 \times 10^{-3}\ \text{m}^3/\text{s}$.

**43.** $1.9 \times 10^5$ N.

**45.** $9.7 \times 10^4$ Pa ($\approx$0.96 atm).

**47.** (*b*) 0.24 m/s.

**49.** (*a*) $2\sqrt{h_1(h_2 - h_1)}$;
(*b*) $h_1' = h_2 - h_1$.

51. new time = 0.13 (previous time).
53. $9.9 \times 10^2$ Pa.
55. 0.9 Pa/cm.
57. (*a*) $Re = 2500$, so turbulent;
(*b*) $Re = 5000$, so turbulent.
59. $3.6 \times 10^{-2}$ N/m.
61. No, $8.3 \times 10^{-6}$ kg is the maximum mass that could be supported.
63. (*a*) 0.75 m;
(*b*) 0.65 m;
(*c*) 0.24 m.
65. 150 N to 220 N.
67. 0.047 atm.
69. 0.6 atm.
71. 0.142 m.
73. $1.3 \times 10^2$ N.
75. 1.1 m.
77. 0.33 kg.
79. 1.1 W.
81. 4.6 m.
83. (*a*) 9.1 m/s;
(*b*) 0.26 L/s;
(*c*) 0.91 m/s.
85. $4.0 \times 10^{-4}$ m$^3$/s.
87. $4.2 \times 10^{-3}$ Pa·s.

## CHAPTER 11

1. 0.72 m.
3. 1.5 Hz.
5. 3.8 Hz.
7. (*a*) 0.16 N/m;
(*b*) 2.8 Hz.
9. (*a*) 2.5 m/s;
(*b*) $\pm 1.6$ m/s;
(*c*) 1.8 J;
(*d*) $x = (0.13 \text{ m}) \cos(6.0\pi t)$.
11. $\pm \frac{1}{2} x_0$.
13. (*a*) $6.0 \times 10^{-2}$ m;
(*b*) 0.58 m/s.
15. (*a*) $4.2 \times 10^2$ N/m;
(*b*) 3.3 kg.
17. $\pm 0.707A$.
19. (*a*) $y = (0.18 \text{ m}) \cos(2\pi t/0.65 \text{ s})$;
(*b*) 0.16 s;
(*c*) 1.7 m/s;
(*d*) 17 m/s$^2$, at the release point.
21. (*a*) 0.38 m;
(*b*) 1.03 Hz;
(*c*) 0.967 s;
(*d*) 0.92 J;
(*e*) $5.1 \times 10^{-7}$ J, 0.86 J.
(*f*)

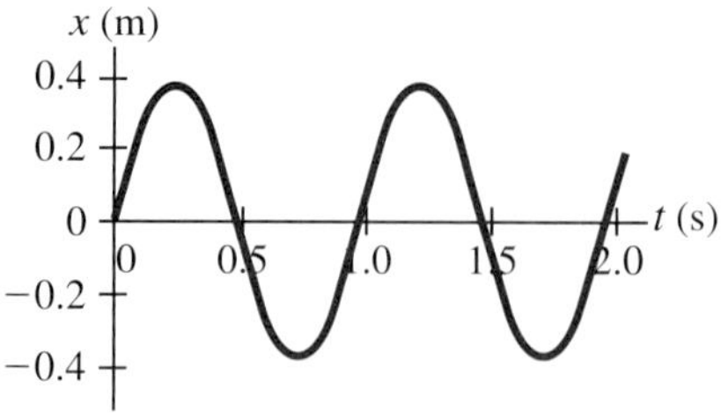


23. (*a*) 0.490 s, 2.04 Hz;
(*b*) 0.231 m;
(*c*) 37.9 m/s$^2$;
(*d*) $y = (0.231 \text{ m}) \sin(4.08\pi t)$;
(*e*) 3.31 J.
27. 114 N/m, 19.4 m.
29. 0.99 m.
31. (*a*) 1.8 s;
(*b*) the pendulum will not oscillate.
33. Shorten the pendulum by 0.7 mm.
35. (*a*) $-11°$;
(*b*) 15°;
(*c*) 15°.
37. 1.31 m.
39. (*a*) $1.4 \times 10^3$ m/s;
(*b*) $4.1 \times 10^3$ m/s;
(*c*) $5.1 \times 10^3$ m/s.
41. 0.35 s.
43. $2.1 \times 10^3$ m.
45. 0.99 m.
47. (*a*) $4.6 \times 10^9$ W/m$^2$;
(*b*) $2.3 \times 10^{10}$ W.
49. 1.73.
51. (a)

(b)

(*c*) All the energy is kinetic energy.
53. 441 Hz.
55. $9.7 \times 10^{-2}$ m.
57. 290 Hz, 580 Hz, 870 Hz.
59. (*a*) 1.3 kg;
(*b*) 0.32 kg;
(*c*) $5.2 \times 10^{-2}$ kg.
61. 1.1 m/s.
63. 25°.
65. 44°.
67. 10 min.
69. (*a*) $3.2 \times 10^{-2}$ m;
(*b*) 1.5 m.
71. (*a*) $1.8 \times 10^4$ N/m;
(*b*) 0.71 s.
73. 220 Hz.
75. (*a*) $1.22f$;
(*b*) $0.71f$.
77. (*a*) G: 784 Hz, 1180 Hz; A: 880 Hz, 1320 Hz;
(*b*) 1.26;
(*c*) 1.12;
(*d*) 0.794.
79. (*a*) 3.0 m/s;
(*b*) $5.0 \times 10^3$ m/s$^2$.
81. $\lambda = 4L/(2n - 1), n = 1, 2, 3, \cdots$.
83. Horizontal period is longer by a factor of $\sqrt{1 + l_0 k/mg}$.
85. 6.44 m from the origin of the first pulse.
87. 0.40 s.

## CHAPTER 12

1. $3.4 \times 10^2$ m.
3. (*a*) 17 cm to 17 m;
(*b*) $3.4 \times 10^{-5}$ m.
5. 55 m.
7. (*a*) 8%;
(*b*) 4%.
9. 63 dB.
11. 114 dB.
13. (*a*) $9 \times 10^{-6}$ W;
(*b*) $1 \times 10^7$ people.
15. (*a*) 122 dB, 114 dB;
(*b*) no.
17. 1.3.
19. 4.
21. 25 dB.
23. (*a*) $10^9$;
(*b*) $10^{12}$.
25. (*a*) 76.6 Hz, 230 Hz, 383 Hz, 536 Hz;
(*b*) 153 Hz, 306 Hz, 459 Hz, 613 Hz.
27. 8.6 mm to 8.6 m.
29. (*a*) 0.18 m;
(*b*) 1.1 m;
(*c*) 440 Hz, 0.78 m.
31. −2.6%.
33. (*a*) 0.583 m;
(*b*) 862 Hz.
35. (*a*) 55 Hz;
(*b*) $2.0 \times 10^2$ m/s.
37. (*a*) 248 overtones;
(*b*) 249 overtones.

**39.** $\pm 0.50$ Hz.

**41.** 28.5 kHz.

**43.** 3.0 Hz.

**45.** $f_A = 438$ Hz or 444 Hz,
$f_C = 437$ Hz or 445 Hz,
$f_{beat} = 1$ Hz or 7 Hz.

**47.** (*a*) 130.5 Hz, 133.5 Hz;
(*b*) increase by 2.3%, decrease by 2.2%.

**49.** (*a*) 1690 Hz;
(*b*) 1410 Hz.

**51.** (*a*) 2091 Hz and 2087 Hz;
(*b*) 3550 Hz and 2870 Hz;
(*c*) 16,000 Hz and 3750 Hz.

**53.** $4.32 \times 10^4$ Hz.

**55.** 2 Hz.

**57.** 0.171 m/s.

**59.** (*a*) 110 m/s;
(*b*) 260 m/s.

**61.** (*a*) 120;
(*b*) 0.48°.

**65.** 0.3 s.

**67.** (*a*) 57 Hz, 69 Hz, 86 Hz, 110 Hz, 170 Hz.

**69.** 88 dB.

**71.** 15 W.

**73.** 50 dB.

**75.** (*a*) $2.8 \times 10^2$ m/s, 48 N;
(*b*) 0.195 m;
(*c*) 880 Hz, 1320 Hz.

**77.** $7.4 \times 10^2$ N.

**79.** 504 Hz.

**81.** 17 m/s.

**83.** 2.84 m.

**85.** $2.29 \times 10^3$ Hz.

**87.** 11.5 m.

**89.** 34 Hz, 43 Hz, 61 Hz.

**91.** $10^6$.

**93.** 17 km/h.

## CHAPTER 13

**1.** $3.3 \times 10^{22}$ atoms.

**3.** (*a*) 20°C;
(*b*) 3300°F.

**5.** (*a*) 5°F;
(*b*) −26°C.

**7.** $4.3 \times 10^{-3}$ m.

**9.** $8 \times 10^{-2}$ m.

**11.** 981 kg/m³.

**13.** 5.12 mL.

**15.** (*a*) −140°C;
(*b*) 180°C.

**17.** (*b*) $5.7 \times 10^{-3}$ (0.57% increase).

**21.** (*a*) 6.1 cm;
(*b*) $\delta L = \dfrac{V_{0\,\text{bulb}}}{\pi r_0^2}(\beta_{\text{Hg}} - \beta_{\text{glass}})\,\Delta T$.

**23.** $3.5 \times 10^7$ N/m².

**25.** (*a*) 27°C;
(*b*) $4.3 \times 10^3$ N.

**27.** −459.67°F.

**29.** 1.07 m³.

**31.** 1.43 kg/m³.

**33.** (*a*) 14.8 m³;
(*b*) $1.83 \times 10^5$ Pa.

**35.** $2.40 \times 10^8$ Pa.

**37.** 37°C.

**39.** 3.43 atm.

**41.** $2.69 \times 10^{25}$ molecules/m³.

**43.** (*a*) $7 \times 10^{22}$ moles;
(*b*) $4 \times 10^{46}$ molecules.

**45.** 19 molecules/breath.

**47.** $6 \times 10^3$ m/s.

**49.** 899°C.

**51.** 25.9°C.

**55.** $3.9 \times 10^2$ m/s.

**57.** $3.34 \times 10^{-9}$ m.

**61.** (*a*) solid or vapor;
(*b*) 5.11 atm $\leq P \leq$ 73 atm,
−56.6°C $\leq T \leq$ 31°C.

**63.** 14°C.

**65.** 91°C.

**67.** $1.1 \times 10^3$ Pa.

**69.** 3.1 kg.

**71.** 0.28 s, $v_{\text{diffuse}} = 5.4 \times 10^{-5}$ m/s,
$v_{\text{rms}} = 3.1 \times 10^2$ m/s,
$v_{\text{diffuse}}/v_{\text{rms}} = 1.7 \times 10^{-7}$.

**73.** (*a*) low;
(*b*) $(1.7 \times 10^{-2})$%.

**75.** 0.21.

**77.** 260 m/s, $4 \times 10^{-22}$ atm.

**79.** 11 L, not advisable.

**81.** 1.65, 1.29.

**83.** $1.1 \times 10^{44}$ molecules.

**85.** 15 hours.

**87.** $0.66 \times 10^3$ kg/m³, −3.5%.

**89.** $1.6 \times 10^{-3}$ cm.

**91.** (*a*) $2.20 \times 10^3$ L;
(*b*) 92 min;
(*c*) 30 min.

**93.** 6.8 balls/s.

**95.** (*a*) $1.7 \times 10^3$ Pa;
(*b*) $7.0 \times 10^2$ Pa.

**97.** 6% decrease.

**99.** 3.0 kg.

## CHAPTER 14

**1.** $1.0 \times 10^7$ J.

**3.** (*a*) $1.0 \times 10^7$ J;
(*b*) 2.9 kWh;
(*c*) $0.29 per day, no.

**5.** 220 kg/h.

**7.** 100 kcal.

**9.** $2.0 \times 10^3$ J/kg·C°.

**11.** 40.1°C.

**13.** $(1.9 \times 10^2)$°C.

**15.** 425 s.

**17.** $2.3 \times 10^3$ J/kg·C°.

**19.** 0.32 C°.

**21.** $5.0 \times 10^6$ J.

**23.** 1.3 kg.

**25.** $9.90 \times 10^{-3}$ kg.

**27.** $4.7 \times 10^3$ kcal.

**29.** $1.12 \times 10^4$ J/kg.

**31.** 1.7 g.

**33.** 83 W.

**35.** (*a*) 95 W;
(*b*) 33 W.

**37.** 23 bulbs.

**39.** $(1.6 \times 10^2)$°C.

**41.** 10 C°.

**43.** (*b*) $\dfrac{Q}{t} = A\dfrac{(T_1 - T_2)}{\sum_{i=1}^{n} l_i/k_i}$.

**45.** 6.4 Calories.

**47.** $4 \times 10^{15}$ J.

**49.** (*a*) $3.2 \times 10^{26}$ W;
(*b*) $1.1 \times 10^3$ W/m².

**51.** 0.80 C°.

**53.** (*a*) 46 W;
(*b*) $7.3 \times 10^3$ W.

**55.** 20 W, only about 9% of the required heat loss rate.

**57.** (*a*) 44 C°;
(*b*) none of the bullet will melt.

**59.** 4.1 g/h.

**61.** (*a*) $1.2 \times 10^{18}$ J;
(*b*) $Q_{\text{Sun}} = 1.3 \times 10^4\, Q_{\text{interior}}$.

**63.** A mixture of liquid water and steam at 100°C, with the mass of liquid water equal to twice the mass of the steam.

65. (*a*) $3.1 \times 10^7$ J;
(*b*) $3.3 \times 10^3$ s.

## CHAPTER 15

1. (*a*) 0 J;
(*b*) $3.40 \times 10^3$ J.

3.
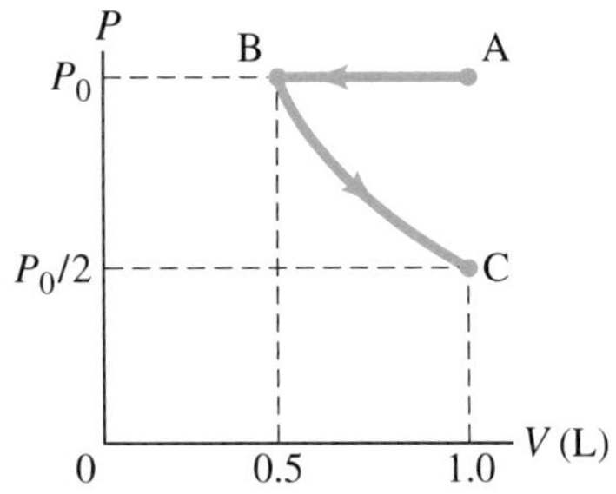


5.
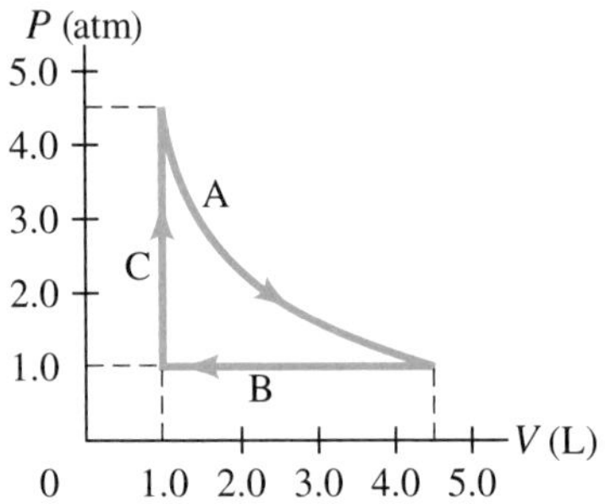


7. (*a*) 0 J;
(*b*) 1850 J;
(*c*) rise.

9. $-4.0 \times 10^2$ K.

11. (*a*, *c*)

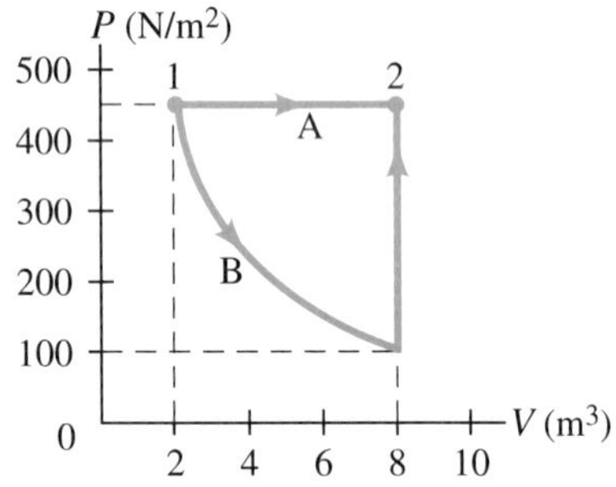


(*b*) $2.73 \times 10^3$ J, $4.10 \times 10^3$ J;
(*d*) $4.10 \times 10^3$ J.

13. (*a*) 25 J;
(*b*) 63 J;
(*c*) −95 J;
(*d*) −120 J;
(*e*) −15 J.

15. 162 W.

17. 0.28.

19. 0.23.

21. $1.6 \times 10^{13}$ J/h.

23. 440°C.

25. $9.0 \times 10^2$ MW (MJ/s).

27. 250°C.

29. 5.7.

31. −21°C.

33. 76 L.

35. $-1.5 \times 10^3$ J/K.

37. $-1.22 \times 10^6$ J/K.

39. 0.15 J/K.

41. $4.35 \times 10^{-2} \dfrac{\text{J/K}}{\text{s}}$.

43. 1.1 J/K.

45. (*a*) 1/9;
(*b*) 1/18.

47. (*a*) 5/16;
(*b*) 1/64.

49. (*a*) $1.32 \times 10^6$ kWh;
(*b*) $7.09 \times 10^4$ kW.

51. Yes, the proposed engine operates at a higher than ideal efficiency.

53. (*a*) $4.0 \times 10^4$ J/s;
(*b*) $1.6 \times 10^5$ J/s;
(*c*) 220 s.

55. (*a*) 0.077.

57. (*a*) 45°C;
(*b*) 0.58 J/K.

59. 0.24.

61. (*a*) $P_A(V_C - V_A)$;
(*b*) $P_C(V_C - V_A)$;
(*c*) $\frac{1}{2}(P_C + P_A)(V_C - V_A)$.

63. (*a*) 5.3C°;
(*b*) 77 J/kg·K.

65. 200 J.

67. 180 W.

## CHAPTER 16

1. 13 N.

3. $2.7 \times 10^{-3}$ N.

5. $5.5 \times 10^3$ N.

7. 4.88 cm.

9. $-5.4 \times 10^7$ C.

11. (*a*) $q_1 = q_2 = 0.5Q_T$;
(*b*) $q_1 = 0, q_2 = Q_T$.

13. top charge: 83.7 N, 90°; lower left charge: 83.7 N, 210°; lower right charge: 83.7 N, 330°.

15. $2.96 \times 10^7$ N, toward center of square.

17. $\vec{\mathbf{F}}_1 = 0.30$ N at 265°, $\vec{\mathbf{F}}_2 = 0.26$ N at 139°, $\vec{\mathbf{F}}_3 = 0.26$ N at 30°.

19. $0.40Q_0$, $0.37l$ from $-Q_0$ toward $-3Q_0$.

21. (*a*) $69.9 \times 10^{6}$ C, $22.1 \times 10^{-6}$ C;
(*b*) $104.4 \times 10^{-6}$ C, $-14.4 \times 10^{-6}$ C.

23. $3.78 \times 10^{-16}$ N, west.

25. $9.5 \times 10^5$ N/C, up.

27. $1.32 \times 10^{14}$ m/s², the direction of the acceleration is opposite to the direction of the field.

29.
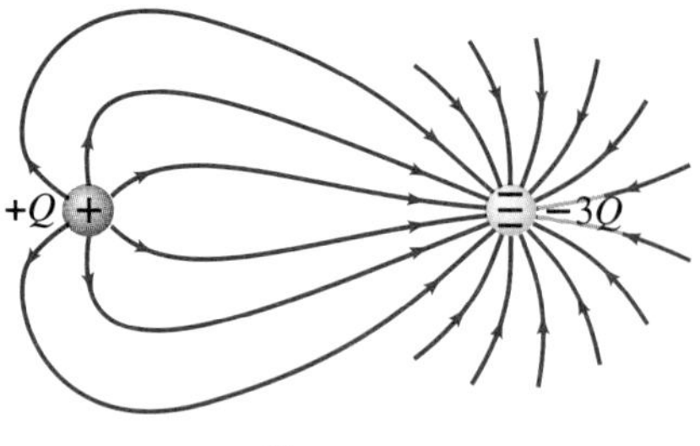


31. $6.54 \times 10^{-10}$ N/C, south.

33. $4.70 \times 10^6$ N/C at 45°.

35. $\dfrac{4kQxa}{(x^2 - a^2)^2}$, to the left.

37. (*a*) $\dfrac{\sqrt{3}\,kQ}{l^2}$, 240°;
(*b*) $\dfrac{kQ}{l^2}$, 330°.

39. 1/4.

41. (*a*) $7.49 \times 10^6$ m/s.

43. $1.28 \times 10^{-8}$ C.

45. (*a*) $-1.1 \times 10^5$ N·m²/C;
(*b*) 0.

47. $1.15 \times 10^{-9}$ C.

49. (*a*) 0;
(*b*) 0;
(*c*) $3.27 \times 10^3$ N/C;
(*d*) $8.74 \times 10^2$ N/C;
(*e*) no difference.

51. (*a*) $4.6 \times 10^{-10}$ N;
(*b*) $7.1 \times 10^{-10}$ N;
(*c*) $6 \times 10^{-5}$ N.

53. $1/(3.5 \times 10^9)$.

55. $6.8 \times 10^5$ C, negative.

57. $1.0 \times 10^7$ electron charges.

59. $2.1 \times 10^{-10}$ m.

61. (*a*) 0.115 m;
(*b*) $2.14 \times 10^{-8}$ s.

63. $\dfrac{1.08 \times 10^7}{[3.00 - \cos(12.5t)]^2}$ N/C (upward).

65. $5 \times 10^{-9}$ C.

67. $7.8 \times 10^{-7}$ C, positive.

69. $-7.0 \times 10^8$ C, 0 C.

71. $x = \dfrac{d}{\sqrt{2} - 1} \approx 2.41d$, no.

73. $-7.66 \times 10^{-6}$ C, unstable.

## CHAPTER 17

**1.** $4.2 \times 10^{-4}$ J.
**3.** $3.7 \times 10^{-15}$ J, $2.3 \times 10^{4}$ eV.
**5.** $3.8 \times 10^{4}$ V/m.
**7.** $3.0 \times 10^{-2}$ m.
**9.** $7 \times 10^{-5}$ m.
**11.** (*a*) $1.6 \times 10^{7}$ m/s;
(*b*) $3.4 \times 10^{7}$ m/s.
**13.** $1.63 \times 10^{7}$ m/s.
**15.** $2.1 \times 10^{-9}$ C.
**17.**

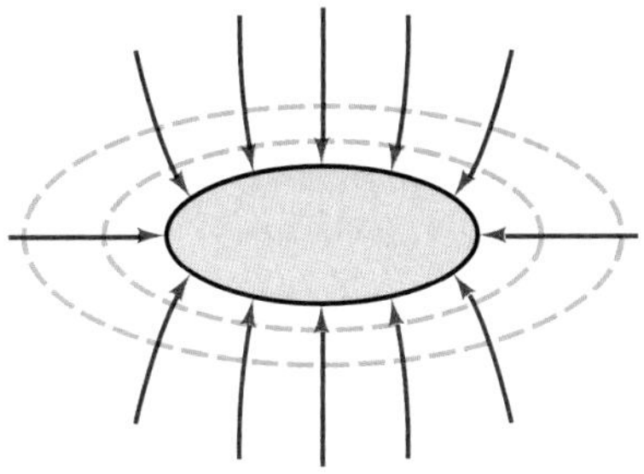

**19.** $\frac{\sqrt{2}kQ}{2L}(\sqrt{2}+1)$.
**21.** $4.8 \times 10^{3}$ m/s.
**23.** $6.9 \times 10^{-18}$ J.
**25.** $4.2 \times 10^{6}$ V.
**27.** (*a*) 27 V;
(*b*) $2.2 \times 10^{-18}$ J, 14 eV;
(*c*) $-2.2 \times 10^{-18}$ J, $-14$ eV;
(*d*) $2.2 \times 10^{-18}$ J, 14 eV.
**29.** (*a*) $3.6 \times 10^{-2}$ V;
(*b*) $2.5 \times 10^{-2}$ V;
(*c*) $-2.5 \times 10^{-2}$ V.
**31.** $2.9 \times 10^{-6}$ F.
**33.** $7.9 \times 10^{-13}$ F.
**35.** $5.0 \times 10^{7}$ m$^2$.
**37.** $2.63 \times 10^{-8}$ C.
**39.** $4.5 \times 10^{4}$ V/m.
**41.** $C_{2.50}$: 712 V, $1.78 \times 10^{-3}$ C;
$C_{6.80}$: 712 V, $4.84 \times 10^{-3}$ C.
**43.** $1.5 \times 10^{-10}$ F.
**45.** $4.82 \times 10^{-9}$ F, 0.283 m$^2$.
**47.** $9.6 \times 10^{-5}$ F.
**49.** (*a*) $7 \times 10^{-12}$ F;
(*b*) $7 \times 10^{-11}$ C;
(*c*) 200 V/m;
(*d*) $3 \times 10^{-10}$ J;
(*e*) capacitance, charge, energy.
**51.** (*a*) quadrupled;
(*b*) doubled.
**53.** $2.9 \times 10^{5}$ V/m.
**55.** (*a*) 6.3 KeV;
(*b*) 42.8 : 1.
**57.** $1.0 \times 10^{-7}$ J/m$^3$.
**59.** 620 V.
**61.** $1.5 \times 10^{-7}$ C.
**63.** (*a*) 11 cm from $-$ charge, on opposite side of $-$ charge from $+$ charge;
(*b*) 0.7 cm from $-$ charge, on same side of $-$ charge as $+$ charge; 5.2 cm from $-$ charge, on opposite side of $-$ charge from $+$ charge.
**65.** 6.5°.
**67.** $9 \times 10^{-16}$ m, no.
**69.** (*a*) 23 J;
(*b*) $3.4 \times 10^{5}$ W.
**71.** $1.03 \times 10^{6}$ m/s.
**73.** $2.5 \times 10^{-10}$ C.
**75.** (*a*) $4.2 \times 10^{-11}$ C;
(*b*) $4.2 \times 10^{-11}$ C;
(*c*) 18 V;
(*d*) $1.3 \times 10^{-10}$ J.
**77.** (*a*) $2.7 \times 10^{3}$ m/s;
(*b*) $2.2 \times 10^{3}$ m/s.

## CHAPTER 18

**1.** $8.13 \times 10^{18}$ electrons/s.
**3.** $5.5 \times 10^{-11}$ A.
**5.** 950 V.
**7.** (*a*) 25 A;
(*b*) $7.5 \times 10^{4}$ C.
**9.** $2.8 \times 10^{-3}$ V.
**11.** (*a*) 20 Ω;
(*b*) 430 J.
**13.** $3.3 \times 10^{-2}$ Ω.
**15.** yes, tungsten diameter = 4.6 mm.
**17.** 22 C°.
**19.** 1800°C.
**21.** (*a*) $3.8 \times 10^{-4}$ Ω;
(*b*) $1.5 \times 10^{-3}$ Ω;
(*c*) $6.0 \times 10^{-3}$ Ω.
**23.** 58.3°C.
**25.** $R_{\text{carbon}} = 2090$ Ω;
$R_{\text{Nichrome}} = 2610$ Ω.
**27.** 0.96 W.
**29.** (*a*) 190 Ω, 0.63 A;
(*b*) 33 Ω, 3.7 A.
**31.** (*a*) 850 W;
(*b*) 17 Ω;
(*c*) 12 Ω.
**33.** 0.14 kWh, 20 cents/month.
**35.** (*a*) 6.7 Ω, 1.4 W;
(*b*) 4.
**37.** 18 bulbs.
**39.** 7500 W.
**41.** (*a*) 10 A;
(*b*) 1.2 Ω.
**43.** 0.39 A, 0.55 A.
**45.** 390 V.
**47.** (*a*) 4500 W;
(*b*) 13 A.
**49.** $5.1 \times 10^{-10}$ m/s.
**51.** 2.6 A/m$^2$, north.
**53.** 35 m/s.
**55.** $5.4 \times 10^{-9}$ W.
**57.** 6.2 A.
**59.** $2.9 \times 10^{-4}$ m.
**61.** $1200 per hour per meter.
**63.** 1/4.
**65.** $3.8 \times 10^{-3}$ m.
**67.** (*a*) 1500 W;
(*b*) 12 A.
**69.** 2 : 1.
**71.** (*a*) 26 Ω;
(*b*) 26 s;
(*c*) 0.17 cents.
**73.** $2.58 \times 10^{-4}$ m, 38.8 m.
**75.** $1.4 \times 10^{12}$ protons.
**77.** $1.8 \times 10^{-4}$ m.
**79.** (*a*) $I_A = 0.33$ A, $I_B = 3.3$ A;
(*b*) $R_A = 360$ Ω, $R_B = 3.6$ Ω;
(*c*) $Q_A = 1.2 \times 10^{3}$ C,
$Q_B = 1.2 \times 10^{4}$ C;
(*d*) $E_A = E_B = 1.4 \times 10^{5}$ J;
(*e*) B.
**81.** $1.34 \times 10^{-4}$ Ω.
**83.** 2200°C.

## CHAPTER 19

**1.** (*a*) 8.41 V;
(*b*) 8.49 V.
**3.** 0.048 Ω, 0.11 Ω.
**5.** 960 Ω, 60 Ω.
**7.** 9.3 V.
**9.** (*a*) 2820 Ω;
(*b*) 300 Ω.
**11.** 720 Ω (all in series), 80 Ω (all in parallel), 360 Ω (two in parallel, in series with third), 160 Ω (two in series, in parallel with third).
**13.** (*a*) 14 V;
(*b*) 28 Ω, 6.9 W.
**15.** 27 Ω.
**17.** (*a*) 840 Ω;
(*b*) $V_{470} = 6.7$ V;
$V_{680} = V_{820} = 5.3$ V.
**19.** (*a*) $V_1$, $V_2$ increase;
$V_3$, $V_4$ decrease;
(*b*) $I_1$, $I_2$ increase;
$I_3$, $I_4$ decrease;
(*c*) increases;
(*d*) before: $I_1 = 0.117$ A, $I_2 = 0$,
$I_3 = I_4 = 0.059$ A;
after: $I_1 = 0.132$ A,
$I_2 = I_3 = I_4 = 0.044$ A; yes.

21. (*a*) $V_{left}$ decreases, $V_{middle}$ increases, $V_{right}$ goes to 0;
(*b*) $I_{left}$ decreases, $I_{middle}$ increases, $I_{right}$ goes to 0;
(*c*) increases;
(*d*) 14.1 V;
(*e*) 14.3 V.

23. 0.41 A.

25. (*a*) −25.7 V;
(*b*) $V_{80} = 77.4$ V, $V_{45} = 43.3$ V.

27. $I_1 = 0.68$ A, left; $I_2 = 0.40$ A, left.

29. $I_1 = 0.13$ A, right; $I_2 = 0.31$ A, left; $I_3 = 0.18$ A, up.

31. 2 Ω: 0.26 A, 6 Ω: 0.028 A, 8 Ω: 0.29 A, 10 Ω: 0.26 A, 12 Ω: 0.29 A.

33. 1.30 A.

35. (*a*) 28.2 μF;
(*b*) 0.78 μF.

37. 3.71 μF.

39. 7300 pF, yes.

41. $C_1 + \frac{C_2 C_3}{C_2 + C_3}$.

43. $Q_1 = 48.0\ \mu C$, $Q_3 = 24.0\ \mu C$; $V_1 = 3.00$ V, $V_2 = 1.50$ V, $V_3 = 1.50$ V; $V = 3.00$ V.

45. (*a*) $V_{0.40} = 5.4$ V, $V_{0.60} = 3.6$ V;
(*b*) $Q_{0.40} = Q_{0.60} = 2.2 \times 10^{-6}$ C;
(*c*) $V_{0.40} = V_{0.60} = 9.0$ V, $Q_{0.40} = 3.6 \times 10^{-6}$ C, $Q_{0.60} = 5.4 \times 10^{-6}$ C.

47. in parallel, 500 pF.

49. $1.0 \times 10^6\ \Omega$.

51. $9.3 \times 10^{-2}$ s.

53. $7.5 \times 10^6\ \Omega$.

55. (*a*) $5.0 \times 10^{-5}\ \Omega$ in parallel;
(*b*) $5.0 \times 10^6$ A in series.

57. 1000 Ω in series, 100 Ω/V.

59. $5.52 \times 10^{-3}$ A.

61. 10 V.

63. 10.4 V, 2.6 Ω.

65. (*b*) 290 Ω, 140 Ω.

67. $7 \times 10^{-3}$ A.

69. $1.1 \times 10^{-5}\ \Omega$.

71. (*a*) $R_x = R_2 R_3 / R_1$;
(*b*) 65.7 Ω.

73. $\frac{1}{4}C, \frac{2}{5}C, \frac{3}{5}C, \frac{3}{4}C, C, \frac{4}{3}C, \frac{5}{2}C, 4C$.

75. 50.1 V, 1.25 Ω.

77. 52.3 V, −28.3 V (two answers because current direction through 4.0-kΩ resistor is unknown.)

79. (*a*) $6.7 \times 10^{-5}$ A, upward;
(*b*) −16 V.

81. (*a*) 3.3 Ω;
(*b*) 2.2 V.

83. 100 Ω.

85. (*a*) 7.6 Ω;
(*b*) 0.33 A;
(*c*) 0.33 A;
(*d*) 0.95 W.

87. 7.2 Ω.

## CHAPTER 20

1. (*a*) 7.6 N/m;
(*b*) 5.3 N/m.

3. 1.95 A.

5. 0.264 T.

7. (*a*) south pole;
(*b*) 4.1 A;
(*c*) $6.4 \times 10^{-2}$ N.

9. 1.3 T.

11. (*a*) left;
(*b*) left;
(*c*) upward;
(*d*) inward;
(*e*) no force;
(*f*) downward.

13. clockwise circular motion of radius $2.77 \times 10^{-5}$ m.

15. 1.6 T, east.

17. (*a*) $2.7 \times 10^{-2}$ m;
(*b*) $3.8 \times 10^{-7}$ s.

23. $6.20 \times 10^{-7}$ m.

25. (*a*) 45°;
(*b*) $3.5 \times 10^{-3}$ m.

27. 69 A.

29. 13 A, upward.

31. 2.5 A.

33. $1.1 \times 10^{-4}$ T up.

35. $4.1 \times 10^{-5}$ T, 11° below horizontal.

37. (*a*) $(2.0 \times 10^{-5}\ \mathrm{T/A})(I - 15\ \mathrm{A})$;
(*b*) $(2.0 \times 10^{-5}\ \mathrm{T/A})(I + 15\ \mathrm{A})$.

39. near wire: $4.5 \times 10^{-2}$ N, attract; far wire: $2.2 \times 10^{-2}$ N, repel.

41. $2.6 \times 10^{-6}$ N, toward straight wire.

43. $4.1 \times 10^{-5}$ T.

45. M: $5.8 \times 10^{-4}$ N/m, 90°; N: $3.4 \times 10^{-4}$ N/m, 300°; P: $3.4 \times 10^{-4}$ N/m, 240°.

47. $\frac{\mu_0 I}{2\pi}\left(\frac{1}{x} - \frac{1}{d - x}\right)$, $y$ direction.

49. 94.3 A.

51. short and fat.

55. 61.6 μA.

57. 0.88.

59. (*a*) $4.01 \times 10^{-5}$ m·N;
(*b*) north.

61. 70 u, 72 u, 73 u, 74 u.

63. 2.5 m.

65. 41 T.

67. 3.0 T, upward.

69. 0.25 N, northerly, 68° above horizontal.

71. $1.12 \times 10^{-6}$ m/s, west.

73. 1.6 A, down.

75. (*a*) $\frac{IlB}{m}t$;
(*b*) $\left(\frac{IlB}{m} - \mu_k g\right)t$;
(*c*) east.

77. (*c*) 48 MeV.

79. They will miss second tube, 9.1°.

81. $1 \times 10^9$ A.

83. (*a*) $2.1 \times 10^{-3}$ T;
(*b*) out of plane formed by velocity and electric field directions;
(*c*) $5.8 \times 10^7$ Hz.

85. $1.3 \times 10^4$ turns.

87. $5.3 \times 10^{-5}$ m, $3.3 \times 10^{-4}$ m.

## CHAPTER 21

1. −420 V.

3. to the left.

5. $8.5 \times 10^{-2}$ V.

7. (*a*) $8.8 \times 10^{-3}$ Wb;
(*b*) 55°;
(*c*) $5.1 \times 10^{-3}$ Wb.

9. (*a*) clockwise;
(*b*) counterclockwise;
(*c*) clockwise;
(*d*) no induced current.

11. (*a*) $6.1 \times 10^{-2}$ V;
(*b*) clockwise.

13. (*a*) clockwise;
(*b*) $4.3 \times 10^{-2}$ V;
(*c*) $1.7 \times 10^{-2}$ A.

15. 0.548 N.

17. (*a*) 0.17 V;
(*b*) $6.1 \times 10^{-3}$ A;
(*c*) $6.4 \times 10^{-4}$ N.

19. 5.86 C.

21. 28V.

23. 2.08 rev/s.

25. (*a*) 99.0 A;
(*b*) $1.3 \times 10^{-2}\ \mathrm{m}^2$.

27. 100 V.

29. 13 A.

31. step down, 0.375, 2.67.

33. 50, 4.8 V.

35. (*a*) step up;
(*b*) 2.8.

37. (*a*) 48 kV (rms);
(*b*) 0.056.

39. 7.7 V.

41. 0.14 H.

43. (*a*) $1.7 \times 10^{-2}$ H,
(*b*) 81 turns.

45. $\mu_0 N_1 N_2 A/l$.

47. 29 J.

49. $5.1 \times 10^{15}$ J.

51. (*a*) 2.3;
(*b*) 4.6;
(*c*) 6.9.

53. (*a*) 368 Ω;
(*b*) $2.21 \times 10^{-2}$ Ω.

55. 9.90 Hz.

57.

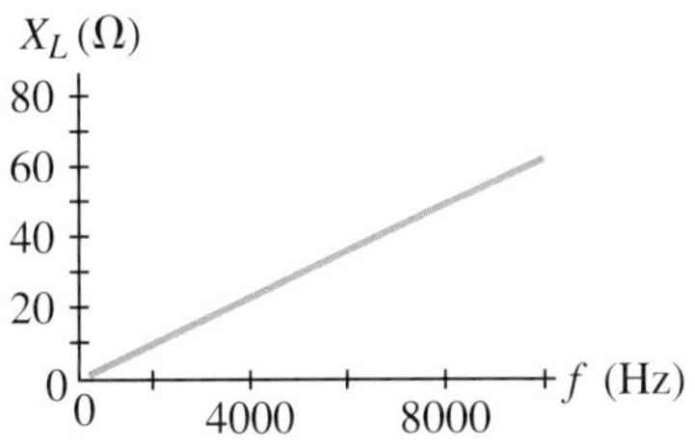


59. $4.97 \times 10^{-2}$ H.

61. (*a*) 30 kΩ;
(*b*) 31 kΩ.

63. 1700 Ω.

65. 8.78 kΩ, −7.62°, $8.26 \times 10^{-2}$ A.

67. (*a*) $6.65 \times 10^{-2}$ A;
(*b*) 4.19°;
(*c*) 119.7 V, 8.77 V.

69. $3.63 \times 10^{5}$ Hz.

71. (*a*) $1.32 \times 10^{-7}$ F;
(*b*) 34.1 A.

73. $7.05 \times 10^{-3}$ J.

75. 280 kV.

77. (*a*) 41 kV;
(*b*) $3.1 \times 10^{7}$ W;
(*c*) $8.8 \times 10^{5}$ W;
(*d*) $3.0 \times 10^{7}$ W.

81. Put a 120-mH inductor in series with the device.

83. 102 V.

85. 0.10 H.

87. $7.5 \times 10^{-2}$ H, 14 Ω.

89. (*b*) $2.5 \times 10^{-6}$ H, $2.9 \times 10^{-2}$ Ω.

## CHAPTER 22

1. $7.9 \times 10^{14}$ V/m/s.

3. 5.25 V/m.

5. $1.88 \times 10^{10}$ Hz.

7. $3.11 \times 10^{-7}$ m, ultraviolet.

9. 499 s (8.31 min).

11. $4.0 \times 10^{16}$ m.

13. (*a*) 261 s;
(*b*) 1260 s.

15. $2.1 \times 10^{6}$ rev/s.

17. 9040 wavelengths, $3.54 \times 10^{-15}$ s.

19. $1.21 \times 10^{7}$ s ($\approx$ 140 days).

21. 0.95 W/m$^2$, 19 V/m.

23. $3.80 \times 10^{26}$ W.

25. (*a*) 280 J;
(*b*) $2.6 \times 10^{9}$ V/m.

27. (*a*) 2.78 m to 3.41 m;
(*b*) 176 m to 561 m.

29. AM is longer, by a factor of 100.

31. 330 pF.

33. $2.6 \times 10^{-9}$ H to $3.9 \times 10^{-9}$ H.

35. 1.5 V/m.

37. 499 s (8.31 min).

39. (*a*) 1.28 s;
(*b*) 260 s (4.3 min).

41. (*a*) 0.07 V/m;
(*b*) 8 km.

43. 469 V/m.

45. (*a*) 150 m;
(*b*) 75 m.

47. (*a*) $1.8 \times 10^{-10}$ J;
(*b*) $8.7 \times 10^{-6}$ V/m, $2.9 \times 10^{-14}$ T.

49. (*a*) parallel;
(*b*) 8.9 pF to 11 pF;
(*c*) 1.1 mH.

53. (*a*) $4.0 \times 10^{-7}$ J;
(*b*) $1.2 \times 10^{-2}$ V/m;
(*c*) $1.2 \times 10^{-2}$ V.

## CHAPTER 23

1. 5.0 m.

3. 5°.

5. $5.9 \times 10^{-6}$ m$^2$.

7. 36.0 cm.

9. 2.09 cm behind the front surface of the ball, virtual, upright.

11. concave, 5.66 cm.

13. (*b*) −6.7 cm; (*c*) 1.0 mm.

15. (*a*) at the center of curvature;
(*b*) real;
(*c*) inverted;
(*d*) −1.

21. (*a*) convex;
(*b*) 22 cm behind the mirror;
(*c*) −98 cm;
(*d*) −196 cm.

23. (*a*) $1.97 \times 10^{8}$ m/s;
(*b*) $1.99 \times 10^{8}$ m/s;
(*c*) $2.21 \times 10^{8}$ m/s.

25. 1.49.

27. 64.0°.

29. 46.8°.

31. 4.6 m.

33. 81.1°.

37. 1.35.

39. $n \geq 1.5$.

43. (*a*)

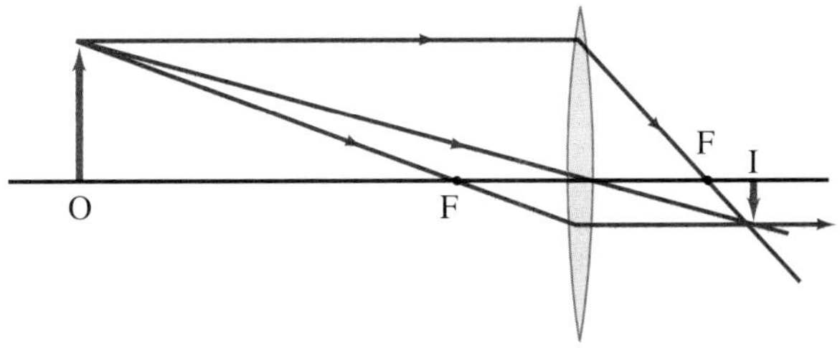


(*b*) 390 mm.

45. converging, 41.1 cm, real.

47. (*a*) −72 cm;
(*b*) 4.0.

49. (*a*) 80.6 mm;
(*b*) 82.2 mm;
(*c*) 87.0 mm;
(*d*) one at 24 cm.

51. (*a*) 3.0 cm away from lens;
(*b*) 0.5 cm toward lens.

53. (*a*) 75.0 mm;
(*b*) 25.0 mm.

55. (*a*) 15.2 cm, −2.54 mm, real and inverted;
(*b*) −12.1 cm, 2.02 mm, virtual and upright.

57. 49.2 cm, 16.8 cm.

59. 7.41 cm behind diverging lens.

61. (*a*) 7.14 cm to right of lens B;
(*b*) −0.357.
(*c*)

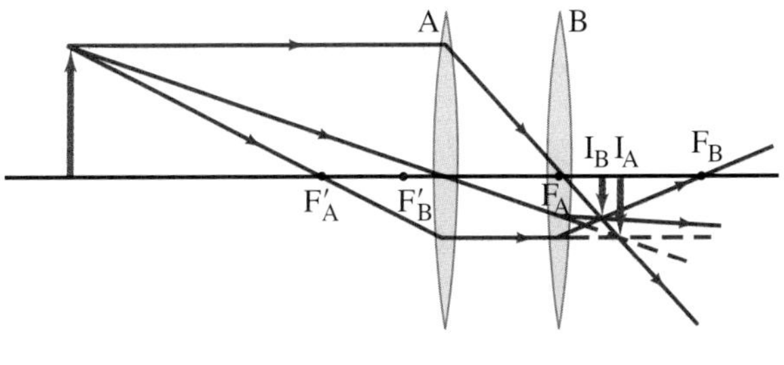

63. (*a*) 16 cm to the left of the converging lens;
(*b*) 1.8 cm to the right of the diverging lens.
67. 1.54.
69. −36.1 cm.
71. 5.6 m.
73. 5.16 m.
75. (*a*) $r = \infty$;
(*b*) $d_o = -d_i$;
(*c*) +1;
(*d*) yes.
77. The object is virtual and is closer to the lens than the focal point.
79. 49°.
81. (*a*)

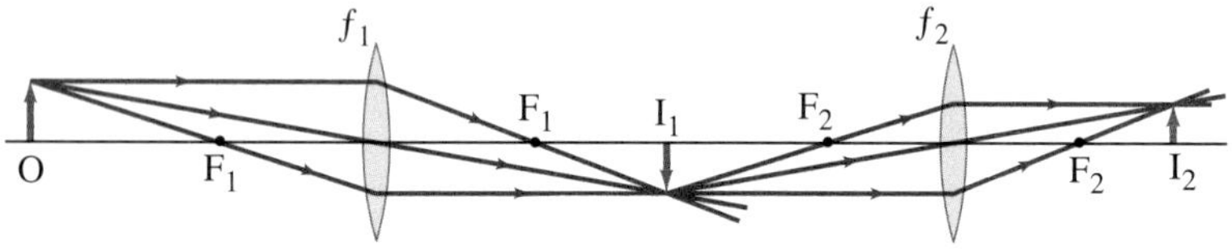


(*b*) 21 cm to the right of the second lens, 0.65.
83. 0.106 m, 2.7 m.
85. real and upright, real and upright.
87. (*a*) 0.26 mm in diameter;
(*b*) 0.47 mm in diameter;
(*c*) 1.3 mm in diameter;
(*d*) 0.56, 2.7.
89. 20.0 cm.
91. 7.5 cm, 10 cm.
93. 20.0 cm, converging.

## CHAPTER 24

1. $4.9 \times 10^{-7}$ m.
3. $6.2 \times 10^{-7}$ m, $4.8 \times 10^{14}$ Hz.
5. $1.4 \times 10^{-4}$ m.
7. 610 nm.
9. reverse of the usual double-slit pattern.
11. $2.7 \times 10^{-3}$ m.
13. 533 nm.
15. 0.22°.
17. 1.51°.
19. 2.51 m.
21. $3.6 \times 10^{-6}$ m.
23. $9.53 \times 10^{-7}$ m.
25. 2.6 cm.
27. 4.43°.
29. 1640 lines/cm.
31. $2.20 \times 10^{-6}$ m, 53.3°.
33. 534 nm, 612 nm, 760 nm.
35. 7140 lines/cm.
37. $5.79 \times 10^5$ lines/m.
39. 643 nm.
41. 169 nm.
43. $8.5 \times 10^{-6}$ m.
45. 113 nm, 225 nm.
47. 471 nm.
49. 699 nm.
51. $2.50 \times 10^{-4}$ m.
53. 0.089.
55. 61.2°.
57. (*a*) 35.3°;
(*b*) 63.4°.
59. 44.5%.
61. $0.031 I_0$.
63. (*a*) constructive;
(*b*) destructive.
65. 360 nm.
67. 31°.
69. 590 nm.
71. 600 nm to 700 nm of second-order spectrum overlaps 400 nm to 467 nm of third-order spectrum.
73. 0.7 m.
75. 810 nm.
77. 320 nm, 160 nm.
79. 36.9°.
81. (*a*) 0.086;
(*b*) none.
83. 48 km.
85. 240 nm.
87. (*a*) 4.8°;
(*b*) 8.7°.

## CHAPTER 25

1. 2.5 mm to 39 mm.
3. 1/62.5 s ≈ 1/60 s.
5. 17 mm.
7. 50 mm.
9. 0.16 s.
11. Glasses would be better.
13. −8.3 D, −7.1 D.
15. (*a*) nearsighted; (*b*) 20.6 cm.
17. 0.2 cm.
19. (*a*) 2.0 cm; (*b*) 1.9 cm.
21. 2.1.
23. (*a*) 17 cm; (*b*) 10 cm.
25. (*a*) 3.63; (*b*) 12.0 mm; (*c*) 6.88 cm.
27. (*a*) −64 cm; (*b*) 3.3×.
29. −27, 79 cm.
31. 22 cm.
33. −110×.
35. −94×.
37. $f_e = 0.73$ cm, $f_o = 124$ cm.
39. 480×.
41. 610×.
43. (*a*) 0.85 cm; (*b*) 230×.
45. (*a*) 14.4 cm; (*b*) 137×.
47. (*a*) 16.0 cm; (*b*) 14.3 cm;
(*c*) 1.7 cm; (*d*) 0.71 mm.
49. 9.1 cm, $6.1 \times 10^{-6}$ rad.
51. $1.7 \times 10^{11}$ m.
53. yes.
55. 0.245 nm.
57. (*a*) 1;
(*b*) 1 to 2.7.
59. 16.
61. 100 mm, 200 mm.
63. 2.9×, 4.1×, the person with the normal eye.
65. (*a*) −2.3×;
(*b*) +4.5 D.
67. 34 cm.
69. −19×.
71. (*a*) 48 cm, −11×, 4.0-cm lens;
(*b*) 180 cm.
73. 1.7 m.

## CHAPTER 26

1. 42.6 m.
3. (*a*) $1 - 2.2 \times 10^{-9}$;
(*b*) 0.9998;
(*c*) 0.980;
(*d*) 0.31;
(*e*) 0.20;
(*f*) 0.0447.
5. $2.32 \times 10^8$ m/s.
7. 26 years.
9. $7 \times 10^{-8}$ %.
11. (*a*) 2.7 years;
(*b*) 9.2 years.
13. (*a*) 6.39 m, 1.25 m;
(*b*) 15.0 s;
(*c*) 0.660*c*;
(*d*) 15.0 s.
15. $8.1 \times 10^{-19}$ kg·m/s.
17. 0.38*c*.
19. (*a*) 310%;
(*b*) 140%.
21. $4 \times 10^{-28}$ kg.
23. 938 MeV/$c^2$.
25. $9.0 \times 10^{13}$ J, $3.7 \times 10^{10}$ kg.
27. 0.60*c*.
29. 942 MeV, 1630 MeV/*c*.
31. 0.437*c*.
33. 0.30*c*.
35. (*a*) 0.866*c*;
(*b*) 0.745*c*.
37. (*a*) $5.5 \times 10^{19}$ J;
(*b*) 3.3%.
39. 237.0483 u.

**41.**

(*a*)
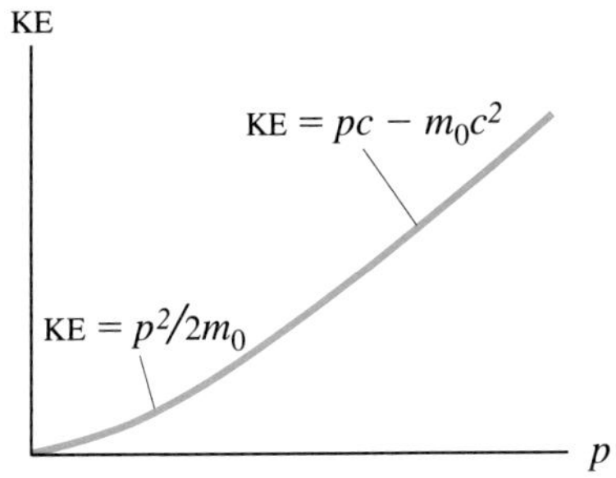


(*b*)
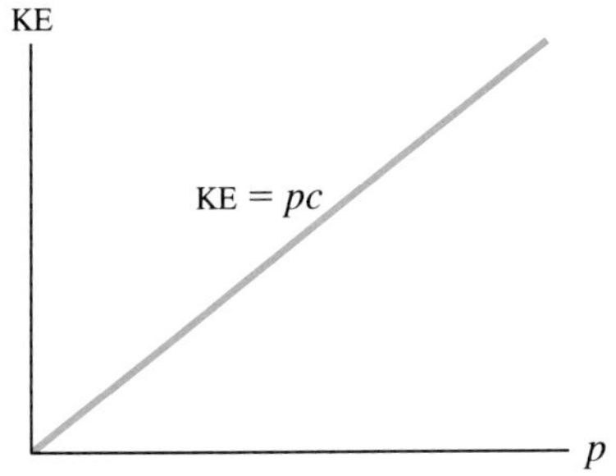


**43.** $0.80c$.

**45.** (*a*) $0.98c$;
(*b*) $0.42c$.

**47.** $0.92c$.

**49.** (*a*) $0.73c$;
(*b*) 5.9 years.

**51.** (*a*) $c - v = 0.77$ m/s;
(*b*) 0.21 m.

**53.** 1.02 MeV (or $1.64 \times 10^{-13}$ J).

**55.** 234 MeV.

**57.** (*a*) $4 \times 10^{9}$ kg/s;
(*b*) $4 \times 10^{7}$ years;
(*c*) $1 \times 10^{13}$ years.

**59.** 28.3 MeV (or $4.53 \times 10^{-12}$ J).

**61.** (*a*) 2470 MeV/$c$;
(*b*) 0;
(*c*) $1.40 \times 10^{4}$ MeV/$c$.

**63.** $2.5 \times 10^{7}$ kg.

**65.** yes in the barn's frame of reference, but no in the boy's frame of reference.

**67.** $0.96c$.

**69.** $c$.

**71.** $6.8 \times 10^{21}$ J, 68× larger.

**73.** (*a*) 1.17 s;
(*b*) 2.68 s.

## CHAPTER 27

**1.** $6.2 \times 10^{4}$ C/kg.

**3.** 5 electrons.

**5.** (*a*) $1.06 \times 10^{-5}$ m, infrared;
(*b*) $8.29 \times 10^{-7}$ m, infrared;
(*c*) $7.25 \times 10^{-4}$ m, microwave;
(*d*) $1.06 \times 10^{-3}$ m, microwave.

**7.** $5.4 \times 10^{-20}$ J, 0.34 eV.

**9.** $9.35 \times 10^{-6}$ m.

**11.** $2.7 \times 10^{-19}$ J to $5.0 \times 10^{-19}$ J, 1.7 eV to 3.1 eV.

**13.** $2.4 \times 10^{-13}$ Hz, $1.2 \times 10^{-5}$ m.

**15.** $6.6 \times 10^{-23}$ kg·m/s (or 0.12 MeV/$c$).

**17.** $6.5 \times 10^{14}$ Hz.

**19.** copper and iron.

**21.** 0.63 eV.

**23.** 2.95 eV.

**25.** 1.9 eV, 43 kcal/mol.

**27.**
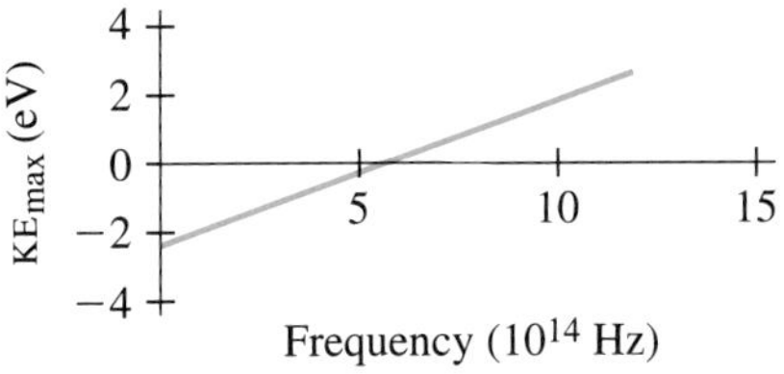


(*a*) $6.7 \times 10^{-34}$ J·s;
(*b*) $5.5 \times 10^{14}$ Hz;
(*c*) 2.30 eV.

**29.** (*a*) $2.42 \times 10^{-12}$ m;
(*b*) $1.32 \times 10^{-15}$ m.

**31.** (*a*) 55 eV;
(*b*) 0.105 nm.

**33.** $6.61 \times 10^{-16}$ m.

**35.** 0.51 MeV, 0.51 MeV/$c$.

**37.** $2.9 \times 10^{-32}$ m.

**39.** 26 V.

**41.** (*a*) $1.3 \times 10^{-24}$ kg·m/s;
(*b*) $1.5 \times 10^{6}$ m/s;
(*c*) 6.0 V.

**45.** $4.7 \times 10^{-38}$ m/s, $6.3 \times 10^{38}$ times smaller.

**47.** $2.48 \times 10^{-11}$ m.

**49.** 3.40 eV.

**51.** 122 eV.

**55.** $5.26 \times 10^{-8}$ m.

**57.**
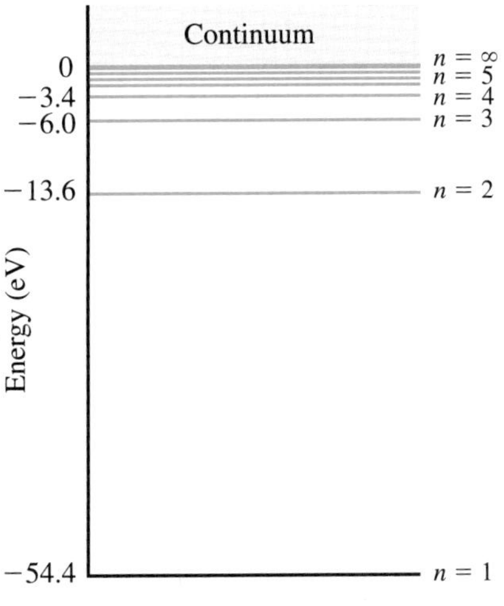


**59.** −27.2 eV, −13.6 eV.

**61.** yes, $7.3 \times 10^{-3}c$, 0.999973.

**63.** (*a*)
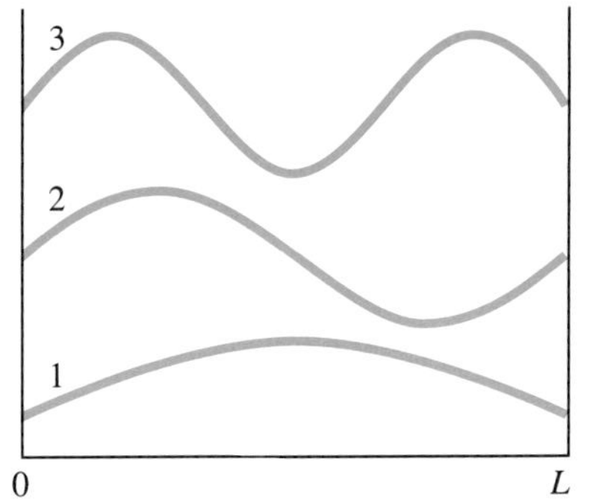


(*c*) $2.4 \times 10^{-17}$ J, 150 eV;
(*d*) $1.6 \times 10^{-66}$ J, $4.7 \times 10^{-33}$ m/s;
(*e*) $1.3 \times 10^{-10}$ m.

**65.** $3.27 \times 10^{15}$ Hz.

**67.** $4.7 \times 10^{26}$ photons/s.

**69.** $5.3 \times 10^{18}$ photons/s.

**71.** 0.39 MeV each.

**73.** $4.7 \times 10^{-14}$ m.

**75.** $(4.4 \times 10^{-40})$:1, yes.

**77.** 0.64 V.

**79.** 6.7 N.

**81.** 1.0 eV, no current would flow.

**83.** (*a*)
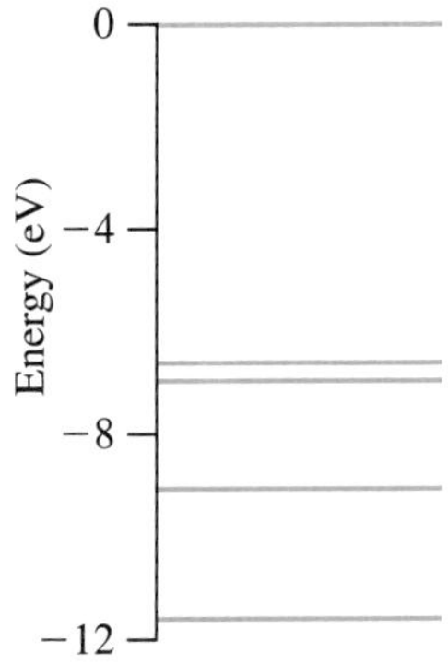


(*b*) ground state, 0.4 eV, 2.2 eV, 2.5 eV, 2.6 eV, 4.7 eV, 5.1 eV.

**85.** $1.8 \times 10^{11}$ C/kg.

**87.** $E_n = -\dfrac{3 \times 10^{165}\ \text{J}}{n^2}$,
$r_n = n^2(5 \times 10^{-129})$ m, no.

## CHAPTER 28

**1.** $3.6 \times 10^{-7}$ m.

**3.** $5.3 \times 10^{-11}$ m.

**5.** $10^{-7}$ eV.

**7.** $3.00 \times 10^{-10}$ eV/$c^2$.

**9.** $\Delta x_{\text{electron}} = 1.4 \times 10^{-3}$ m,
$\Delta x_{\text{baseball}} = 9.1 \times 10^{-33}$ m,
$\Delta x_{\text{electron}} \approx (1.5 \times 10^{29})\Delta x_{\text{baseball}}$.

**13.** 0, 1, 2, 3, 4, 5.

**15.** 14 electrons.

17. (*a*)

| $n$ | $l$ | $m_l$ | $m_s$ |
|---|---|---|---|
| 1 | 0 | 0 | $\frac{1}{2}$ |
| 1 | 0 | 0 | $-\frac{1}{2}$ |
| 2 | 0 | 0 | $\frac{1}{2}$ |
| 2 | 0 | 0 | $-\frac{1}{2}$ |
| 2 | 1 | 1 | $\frac{1}{2}$ |
| 2 | 1 | 1 | $-\frac{1}{2}$ |

Other combinations of quantum numbers are possible for the last two electrons.

(*b*)

| $n$ | $l$ | $m_l$ | $m_s$ |
|---|---|---|---|
| 1 | 0 | 0 | $\frac{1}{2}$ |
| 1 | 0 | 0 | $-\frac{1}{2}$ |
| 2 | 0 | 0 | $\frac{1}{2}$ |
| 2 | 0 | 0 | $-\frac{1}{2}$ |
| 2 | 1 | 1 | $\frac{1}{2}$ |
| 2 | 1 | 1 | $-\frac{1}{2}$ |
| 2 | 1 | 0 | $\frac{1}{2}$ |
| 2 | 1 | 0 | $-\frac{1}{2}$ |
| 2 | 1 | −1 | $\frac{1}{2}$ |
| 2 | 1 | −1 | $-\frac{1}{2}$ |
| 3 | 0 | 0 | $\frac{1}{2}$ |
| 3 | 0 | 0 | $-\frac{1}{2}$ |

**19.** $n \geq 5$; $m_l = 4, 3, 2, 1, 0, -1, -2, -3, -4$; $m_s = +\frac{1}{2}, -\frac{1}{2}$.
**21.** $n \geq 4$; $l \geq 3$; $m_s = +\frac{1}{2}, -\frac{1}{2}$.
**23.** (*a*) $1s^2 2s^2 2p^6 3s^2 3p^6 3d^7 4s^2$;
(*b*) $1s^2 2s^2 2p^6 3s^2 3p^6 3d^{10} 4s^2 4p^6$;
(*c*) $1s^2 2s^2 2p^6 3s^2 3p^6 3d^{10} 4s^2 4p^6 5s^2$.
**25.** (*a*) $n = 6$;
(*b*) −0.378 eV;
(*c*) $L = 0, l = 0$;
(*d*) $m_l = 0$.
**29.** (*a*) $5f, 5p, 4f, 4p, 3p, 2p$;
(*b*) four wavelengths.
**31.** 41 kV.
**33.** 0.18 nm.
**35.** 0.061 nm, partial shielding of the nucleus by the $n = 2$ shell.
**37.** $1.9 \times 10^{-2}$ J, $6.1 \times 10^{16}$ photons.
**39.** $5.64 \times 10^{-4}$ rad;
(*a*) 170 m;
(*b*) $2.2 \times 10^5$ m.
**41.** $5.3 \times 10^{-11}$ m, same as Bohr radius.
**43.** $L_{min} = 0$,
$L_{max} = 4.72 \times 10^{-34}$ kg·m²/s.
**45.** (*a*) $3.1 \times 10^{-34}$ m;
(*b*) $1.8 \times 10^{-32}$ kg·m²/s.
**47.** 3600 C°/min.
**49.** $2870\ \mathrm{m}^{-1/2}$.
**53.** $L_{Bohr} = 2\hbar$, $L_{QM} = 0$ or $\sqrt{2}\,\hbar$.
**55.** $6.3 \times 10^{-14}$ s.
**57.** $\Delta p_{proton} : \Delta p_{electron} = 43:1$.
**59.** $1.8 \times 10^{-35}$ m/s, yes, $10^{34}$ s.
**61.** copper.

## CHAPTER 29

**1.** 5.1 eV.
**3.** 4.6 eV.
**7.** $1.10 \times 10^{-10}$ m.
**9.** (*a*) $1.5 \times 10^{-2}$ eV, $8.2 \times 10^{-5}$ m;
(*b*) $3.0 \times 10^{-2}$ eV, $4.1 \times 10^{-5}$ m;
(*c*) $4.6 \times 10^{-2}$ eV, $2.7 \times 10^{-5}$ m.
**11.** (*a*) 720 N/m;
(*b*) $2.0 \times 10^{-6}$ m.
**13.** $2.82 \times 10^{-10}$ m.
**17.** $1.1 \times 10^{-6}$ m.
**19.** $1.1 \times 10^6$ electrons.
**21.** $5 \times 10^6$.
**23.** 1.9 eV.
**25.** 13 mA.
**27.** (*a*) 2.4 mA;
(*b*) 4.8 mA.
**29.** (*a*) 8.1 mA;
(*b*) 5.7 mA.
**31.** 13 eV.
**33.** (*a*) −5.3 eV;
(*b*) 5.1 eV.
**35.** $1.94 \times 10^{-46}$ kg·m².
**37.** 5.50 eV.
**39.** (*a*) $9.4 \times 10^{-2}$ eV;
(*b*) $6.3 \times 10^{-10}$ m.
**41.** $6.47 \times 10^{-4}$ eV.
**43.** (*a*) $146\ \mathrm{V} \leq V_{supply} \leq 362\ \mathrm{V}$;
(*b*) $3.34\ \mathrm{k\Omega} \leq R_{load} < \infty$.

## CHAPTER 30

**1.** 0.149 u.
**3.** 3726 MeV/$c^2$.
**5.** (*b*) 180 m; (*c*) $2.58 \times 10^{-10}$ m.
**7.** $6 \times 10^{26}$, no, nucleon density is essentially the same for all nuclei.
**9.** 340 MeV.
**11.** 2.224 MeV.
**13.** 7.799 MeV.
**15.** ${}^{23}_{11}\mathrm{Na}$: 8.11 MeV/ nucleon,
${}^{24}_{11}\mathrm{Na}$: 8.06 MeV/ nucelon.
**17.** (*b*) stable.
**19.** 0.783 MeV.
**21.** (*a*) $\beta^+$;
(*b*) ${}^{22}_{11}\mathrm{Na} \rightarrow {}^{22}_{10}\mathrm{Ne} + e^+ + \nu$, 1.819 MeV.
**23.** (*a*) ${}^{234}_{90}\mathrm{Th}$;
(*b*) 234.04367 u.
**25.** 0.0855 MeV.
**27.** (*a*) ${}^{32}_{16}\mathrm{S}$;
(*b*) 31.97152 u.
**29.** 0.862 MeV.
**31.** 0.9602 MeV, 0.9602 MeV, 0 MeV.
**33.** 5.31 MeV.
**37.** (*a*) $1.5 \times 10^{-10}\ \mathrm{yr}^{-1}$;
(*b*) 2.3 h.
**39.** 1/16 (or 0.0625).
**41.** $1.31 \times 10^{-20}$ nuclei.
**43.** (*a*) $3.13 \times 10^{12}$ decays/s;
(*b*) $3.12 \times 10^{12}$ decays/s;
(*c*) $4.26 \times 10^5$ decays/s.
**45.** 0.77 g.
**47.** $1.68 \times 10^{-13}$ kg.
**49.** 2.6 min.
**51.** $2.58 \times 10^{-3}$ g.
**53.** $T_{\frac{1}{2}}({}^{218}_{84}\mathrm{Po}) : T_{\frac{1}{2}}({}^{214}_{84}\mathrm{Po}) = (1.2 \times 10^6):1$.
**55.** ${}^{232}_{90}\mathrm{Th} \rightarrow {}^{228}_{88}\mathrm{Ra} \rightarrow {}^{228}_{89}\mathrm{Ac} \rightarrow {}^{228}_{90}\mathrm{Th} \rightarrow {}^{224}_{88}\mathrm{Ra} \rightarrow {}^{220}_{86}\mathrm{Rn}$,
${}^{235}_{92}\mathrm{U} \rightarrow {}^{231}_{90}\mathrm{Th} \rightarrow {}^{231}_{91}\mathrm{Pa} \rightarrow {}^{227}_{89}\mathrm{Ac} \rightarrow {}^{227}_{90}\mathrm{Th} \rightarrow {}^{223}_{88}\mathrm{Ra}$.
**57.** $N_D = N_0(1 - e^{-\lambda t})$.
**59.** $2.3 \times 10^4$ yr.
**61.** 41 yr.
**63.** 6.64 half-lives.
**65.** (*b*) 98%.
**67.** (*a*) ${}^{191}_{77}\mathrm{Ir}$;
(*b*)

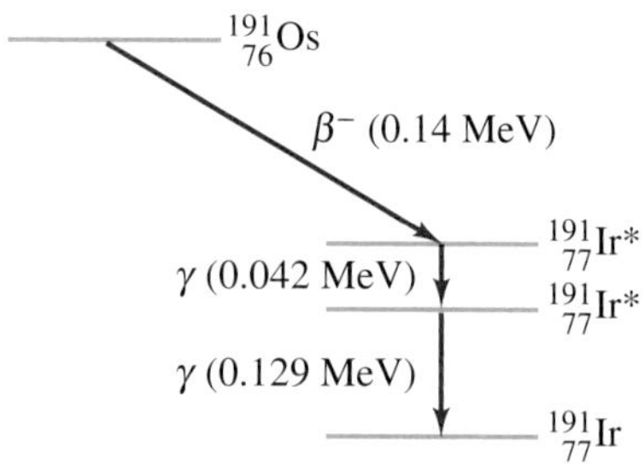


to the higher excited state.
**69.** 550 MeV, $2.5 \times 10^{12}$ J.
**71.** (*a*) $2.4 \times 10^5$ yr;
(*b*) $2.5 \times 10^5$ yr, carbon dating is not useful for times on the order of $10^5$ yr or longer.
**73.** (*a*) $\mathrm{KE}_\alpha : \mathrm{KE}_\beta = 5.48 \times 10^{-4}:1$.
**75.** (*a*) 1.6%;
(*b*) 0.67%.
**77.** 0.18 decays/s or 11 decays/min.

## CHAPTER 31

**1.** ${}^{28}_{13}\mathrm{Al}$, $\beta^-$, ${}^{28}_{14}\mathrm{Si}$.
**3.** possible.
**5.** 5.701 MeV is released.
**7.** (*a*) yes;
(*b*) 19.85 MeV.
**9.** 4.730 MeV.
**11.** $\mathrm{n} + {}^{14}_{7}\mathrm{N} \rightarrow {}^{14}_{6}\mathrm{C} + \mathrm{p}$, 0.626 MeV.
**13.** (*a*) ${}^{3}_{2}\mathrm{He}$ picks up a neutron;
(*b*) ${}^{11}_{6}\mathrm{C}$;
(*c*) 1.856 MeV, exothermic.
**15.** 18.000953 u.
**17.** 173.3 MeV.

19. 1/1100.
21. $3.7 \times 10^{-7}$ kg.
23. 630 kg.
25. $2.1 \times 10^{-16}$ J or 1.3 keV.
29. $6.0 \times 10^{23}$ MeV/g,
$4.9 \times 10^{23}$ MeV/g,
$2.1 \times 10^{24}$ MeV/g,
$5.1 \times 10^{23}$ MeV/g.
31. 0.38 g.
33. $5.3 \times 10^{3}$ kg/h.
35. (*b*) 26.73 MeV;
(*c*) 1.94 MeV, 2.22 MeV, 7.55 MeV, 7.30 MeV, 2.75 MeV, 4.97 MeV;
(*d*) greater repulsion from higher-$Z$ nuclei.
37. 4.0 Gy.
39. 250 rads.
41. 200 counts/s.
43. 2.5 days.
45. $8.25 \times 10^{-7}$ Gy/day.
47. (*a*) ${}^{131}_{53}\mathrm{I} \rightarrow {}^{131}_{54}\mathrm{Xe} + e^{-} + \bar{\nu}$;
(*b*) 27 days;
(*c*) $8 \times 10^{-12}$ kg.
49. (*a*) ${}^{218}_{84}\mathrm{Po}$;
(*b*) radioactive,
$\alpha$ decay: ${}^{218}_{84}\mathrm{Po} \rightarrow {}^{214}_{82}\mathrm{Pb} + {}^{4}_{2}\mathrm{He}$,
$\beta$ decay: ${}^{218}_{84}\mathrm{Po} \rightarrow {}^{218}_{85}\mathrm{At} + e^{-}$,
3.1 min for both;
(*c*) chemically reacting;
(*d*) $5.7 \times 10^{6}$ decays/s, $2.5 \times 10^{4}$ decays/s.
51. (*a*) ${}^{12}_{6}\mathrm{C}$;
(*b*) 5.701 MeV.
53. $v_{235} : v_{238} = 1.0043 : 1$.
55. $5.1 \times 10^{-2}$ rem/yr.
57. 4.7 m.
59. (*a*) 1300 kg;
(*b*) $4.1 \times 10^{6}$ Ci.
61. (*a*) $4.0 \times 10^{26}$ W;
(*b*) $3.7 \times 10^{38}$ protons/s;
(*c*) $1.0 \times 10^{11}$ yr.
63. (*a*) 3700 decays/s;
(*b*) $5.2 \times 10^{-4}$ Sv/yr, about 15% of background.
65. 7.274 MeV.
67. 96 yr.
69. 3 mCi.

## CHAPTER 32

1. 7.29 GeV.
3. 1.8 T.
5. 13 MHz.
7. alpha particles;
$\lambda_{\text{alpha}} = 2.2\times$ nucleon size,
$\lambda_{\text{proton}} = 4.4\times$ nucleon size.
9. $1.8 \times 10^{-19}$ m.
11. 5.5 T.
15. 33.9 MeV.
17. 1879.2 MeV.
19. 67.5 MeV.
21. $2.3 \times 10^{-18}$ m.
23. (*a*) charge (and strangeness);
(*b*) energy;
(*c*) baryon number (and strangeness).
27. 69.3 MeV.
29. $\mathrm{KE}_{\Lambda^{0}} = 8.6$ MeV, $\mathrm{KE}_{\pi} = 57.4$ MeV.
31. 52.3 MeV.
33. $7.5 \times 10^{-21}$ s.
35. (*a*) 1.3 keV;
(*b*) 8.9 keV.
37. (*a*) forbidden, energy is not conserved;
(*b*) forbidden, lepton number is not conserved;
(*c*) possible.
39. (*a*) p;
(*b*) $\overline{\Sigma^{-}}$;
(*c*) $K^{-}$;
(*d*) $\pi^{-}$;
(*e*) $D_S^{-}$.
41. $D_S^{+} = c\bar{s}$.
43.

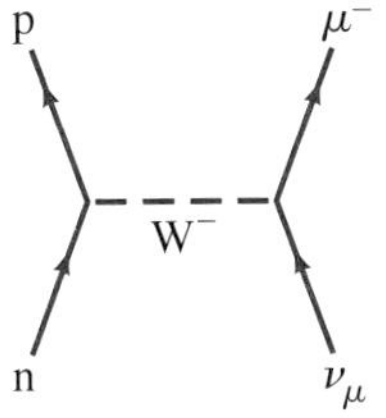


45. (*a*) 0.38 A;
(*b*) $1.0 \times 10^{2}$ m/s.
47. (*a*) 1.022 MeV;
(*b*) 1876.6 MeV.
49. (*a*) forbidden by charge conservation;
(*b*) possible by the strong interaction;
(*c*) forbidden by strangeness conservation for the strong interaction, possible by the weak interaction;
(*d*) forbidden by strangeness conservation for the strong interaction, possible by the weak interaction;
(*e*) possible by weak interaction.
53. −135.0 MeV, −140.9 MeV.
55. 64 fundamental fermions.
57. (*b*) $10^{29}$ K.
59. $6.59 \times 10^{-5}$ m.
61.

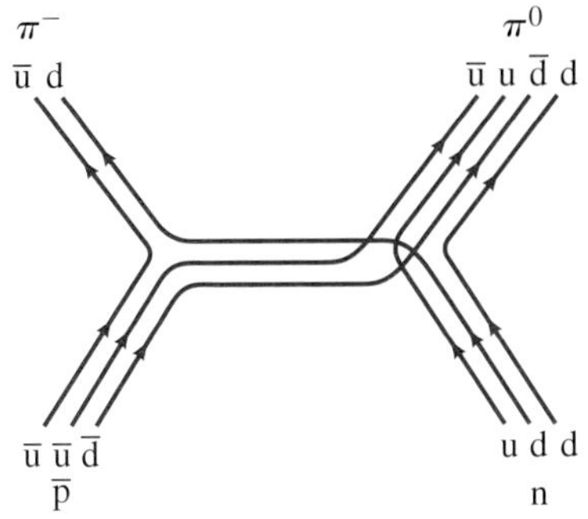


## CHAPTER 33

3. 4.8 ly.
5. 0.059″, 17 pc.
7. 110 yr.
9. $3.7 \times 10^{-2}$.
11. $1.4 \times 10^{-4}$ kg/m³.
13. $1.83 \times 10^{9}$ kg/m³, $3.33 \times 10^{5}$ times larger.
15. −0.092 MeV, 7.366 MeV.
17. $d_1/d_2 = 0.15$.
19. $4 \times 10^{14}$ m.
21. 540°.
23. $1.6 \times 10^{8}$ ly.
25. (*a*) 656 nm;
(*b*) 661 nm;
(*c*) 1670 nm.
27. 0.44$c$.
31. 6 nucleons/m³.
33. (*a*) $10^{-5}$ s;
(*b*) $10^{-7}$ s;
(*c*) $10^{-4}$ s.
35. 5 ly.
37. $5 \times 10^{9}$.
39. $2 \times 10^{28}$ N.
41. $d_{400\,\text{nm}}/d_{600\,\text{nm}} \approx 1.4$.
43. 0.88$c$.
45. $2 \times 10^{-3}$.
47. (*a*) 13.933 MeV;
(*b*) 4.7 MeV;
(*c*) $3.7 \times 10^{10}$ K.
49. ≈400 ly, $2 \times 10^{7}$ times bigger, 100 times smaller.

# INDEX

Note: the abbreviation *defn* means the page cited gives the definition of the term; *fn* means the reference is in a footnote; *pr* means it is found in a Problem or Question; *ff* means also the following pages.

# PHOTO CREDITS

**Title page** Art Wolfe/Getty Images, Inc. **CO-1** NOAA/Phil Degginger/Color-Pic, Inc. **1-01** Erich Lessing/Art Resource, N.Y. **1-02a, 1-02b** Franca Principe/Istituto e Museo di Storia della Scienza **1-03** Franca Principe/Istituto e Museo di Storia della Scienza **1-04a** Philip H. Coblentz/Getty Images, Inc.–Stone Allstock **1-04b** Antranig M. Ouzoonian, P.E./Weidlinger Associates, Inc. **1-05** Mary Teresa Giancoli **1-06a, 1-06b** Douglas C. Giancoli **1-07** Paul Silverman/Fundamental Photographs **1-08a** Oliver Meckes/Eye of Science/Max-Planck-Institut-Tubingen/Photo Researchers, Inc. **1-08b** Douglas C. Giancoli **1-09** Adolfo Viansson **1-10a** Douglas C. Giancoli **1-11** Larry Voight/Photo Researchers, Inc. **1-14** David Parker/Science Photo Library/Photo Researchers, Inc. **1-15** The Image Works **CO-2** George D. Lepp/CORBIS BETTMANN **2-08** John E. Gilmore, III **2-16** SuperStock, Inc. **2-17** Nimatallah/Art Resource, N.Y. **2-18** Harold E. Edgerton/Palm Press, Inc. **CO-3** Michel Hans/Vandystadt/Getty Images, Inc.–Allsport Photography **3-17** Berenice Abbott/Commerce Graphics Ltd., Inc. **3-19** Richard Megna/Fundamental Photographs **3-27a** Dave Wilhemi/Corbis/Stock Market **3-27b** Guy Vanderelst/Taxi/Getty Images, Inc.–Taxi **3-27c** Douglas C. Giancoli **CO-4** Mark Wagner/Aviation-images.com **4-01** Daly & Newton/Getty Images, Inc.–Stone Allstock **4-04** Bettmann/Corbis **4-05** Gerard Vandystadt/Agence Vandystadt/Photo Researchers, Inc. **4-07** David Jones/Photo Researchers, Inc. **4-10** Tsado/NASA/Tom Stack & Associates, Inc. **4-37** Lars Ternblad/Getty Images, Inc.–Image Bank **4-39** Kathleen Schiaparelli **4-41** AP/Wide World Photos **4-63** Tyler Stableford/The Image Bank/Getty Images, Inc. **CO-5** Earth Imaging/Getty Images Inc.–Stone Allstock **5-06c** Jay Brousseau/Getty Images, Inc.–Image Bank **5-12** Guido Alberto Rossi/Getty Images, Inc.–Image Bank **5-23** NASA/Johnson Space Center **5-27a** AP/Wide World Photos **5-27b** Mickey Pfleger/Photo 20-20/PictureQuest **5-27c** Dave Cannon/Getty Images, Inc.–Stone Allstock **5-34** C. Grzimek/Okapia **5-35** Daniel L. Feicht/Cedar Fair L.P. **CO-6** Ben Margot/AP Wide World Photos **6-21** Harold E. Edgerton/Palm Press, Inc. **6-22** David Madison/David Madison Sports Images, Inc. **6-25** AP/Wide World Photos **6-28** Nick Rowe/Getty Images, Inc.–Photodisc **6-42** CORBIS BETTMANN **6-46** R. Maisonneuve/Publiphoto/Photo Researchers, Inc. **CO-7** Richard Megna/Fundamental Photographs **7-01** Stephen Dunn/Getty Images, Inc.–Liaison **7-08** Loren M. Winters/Visuals Unlimited **7-15** D.J. Johnson **7-18** Science Photo Library/Photo Researchers, Inc. **7-22** Berenice Abbott/Photo Researchers, Inc. **7-28** John McDermott Photography **CO-8** Tom Stewart/CORBIS BETTMANN **8-07a** Jeff Greenberg/Photo Researchers, Inc. **8-11a** Richard Megna/Fundamental Photographs **8-11b** Photoquest, Inc. **8-34** Tim Davis/Photo Researchers, Inc. **8-35** Regis Bossu/Corbis/Sygma **8-36** AP/Wide World Photos **8-38** Karl Weatherly/Getty Images, Inc.–Photodisc. **8-42** Tom Stewart/CORBIS BETTMANN **8-56a** Michael Kevin Daly/Corbis/Stock Market **CO-9** John Kelly/Getty Images, Inc.–Image Bank **9-01** AP/Wide World Photos **9-21** Douglas C. Giancoli **9-23a, 9-23b** Mary Teresa Giancoli **9-26** Fabricius & Taylor/Getty Images, Inc.–Liaison **9-28a** Douglas C. Giancoli **9-28b** Galen Rowell/Mountain Light Photography, Inc. **9-30** Douglas C. Giancoli **9-32** Giovanni Paolo Panini (Roman, 1691–1765), "Interior of the Pantheon, Rome," c. 1734. Oil on canvas, 1.280 × .990 (50 1/2 × 39); framed, 1.441 × 1.143 (56 3/4 × 45). Samuel H. Kress Collection. Photograph © 2001 Board of Trustees, National Gallery of Art, Washington. 1939.1.24.(135)/PA. Photo by Richard Carafelli **9-33** Douglas C. Giancoli **9-34a** Italian Government Tourist Board **9-56** Peter LaMastro/Getty Images, Inc. **CO-10** Verlinden, Vic/Getty Images, Inc.–Image Bank **10-10** CORBIS BETTMANN **10-19a-R, 10-19b-R,** David Hazen **10-33a** Lester V. Bergman/CORBIS BETTMANN **10-33b** Biophoto Associates/Photo Researchers, Inc. **10-34** Rod Planck/Tom Stack & Associates, Inc. **10-36** Alan Blank/Bruce Coleman, Inc. **10-46** Douglas C. Giancoli **10-48** Adam Jones/Photo Researchers, Inc. **10-52** NASA Goddard Space Flight Center/Science Source/Photo Researchers, Inc. **CO-11L** Fundamental Photographs **CO-11R** Jonathan Nourok/PhotoEdit **11-04** Robert Reiff/Getty Images, Inc.–Taxi **11-07** Gary Carter/Visuals Unlimited **11-11** Photo Researchers, Inc. **11-13** Douglas C. Giancoli **11-17** Taylor Devices, Inc. **11-19a** AP/Wide World Photos **11-19b** Corbis/Sygma **11-20** Douglas C. Giancoli **11-27** Art Wolfe/Getty Images, Inc.–Stone Allstock **11-37** Douglas C. Giancoli **11-42** Visuals Unlimited **11-48** Gallant, Andre/Getty Images, Inc.–Image Bank **11-55** Richard Megna/Fundamental Photographs **CO-12** Fra Angelico, Linaioli Altarpiece, detail. Museo di San Marco, Florence, Italy. Scala/Art Resource, N.Y. **12-04** Yoav Levy/Phototake NYC **12-09a** Andy Sacks/Getty Images, Inc.–Stone Allstock **12-09b** Getty Images, Inc.–Liaison **12-10** Bob Daemmrich/The Image Works **12-24** Norman Owen Tomalin/Bruce Coleman, Inc. **12-25b** SETTLES, GARY S./Photo Researchers, Inc. **12-28a** P. Saada/Eurelios/Science Photo Library/Photo Researchers, Inc. **12-28b** Howard Sochurek/Medical Images, Inc. **12-38** Dallas & John Heaton/CORBIS BETTMANN **CO-13** Johner/Amana America, Inc. **13-03** Bob Daemmrich/Stock Boston **13-04a, 13-04b, 13-04c** Franca Principe/Istituto e Museo di Storia della Scienza **13-06** Leonard Lessin/Peter Arnold, Inc. **13-14** Leonard Lessin/Peter Arnold, Inc. **13-15** Michael Newman/PhotoEdit **13-23** Paul Silverman/Fundamental Photographs **13-24** JACK DANIELS/Getty Images, Inc.–Taxi **13-25a, 13-25b, 13-25c** Mary Teresa Giancoli **13-28** Kennan Harvey/Getty Images, Inc.–Stone Allstock **13-29** Brian Yarvin/Photo Researchers, Inc. **CO-14** Bill Losh/Getty Images, Inc.–Taxi **14-11** Getty Images, Inc.–Hulton Archive Photos **14-14a, 14-14b** Science Photo Library/Photo Researchers, Inc. **14-16** Phil Degginger/Color-Pic, Inc. **14-22** Taxi/Getty Images, Inc. **CO-15L** David Woodfall/Getty Images, Inc.–Stone Allstock **CO-15R** AP/Wide World Photos **15-09** Will Hart **15-10a, 15-10b, 15-10c** Leonard Lessin/Peter Arnold, Inc. **15-20a** Sandia National Laboratories **15-20b** Martin Bond/Science Photo Library/Photo Researschers, Inc. **15-20c** Lionel Delevingne/Stock Boston **Table 15-4** (clockwise from top right) Ed Degginger/Color-Pic, Inc; Michael Collier; Malcolm Fife/Getty Images, Inc.–Photodisc; Inga Spence/Visuals Unlimited **15-25** Geoff Tompkinson/Science Photo Library/Photo Researchers, Inc. **15-26** Inga Spence/Visuals Unlimited **15-27** Michael Collier **CO-16** Fundamental Photographs **16-36** Michael

J. Lutch/Boston Museum of Science **16-43** Dr. Gopal Murti/Science Photo Library/Photo Researchers, Inc. **CO-17** Gene Moore/Phototake NYC **17-13c** Tom Pantages/Tom Pantages **17-17** Tom Pantages/Tom Pantages **17-18** Custom Medical Stock Photo, Inc. **17-22** Jon Feingersh/Jon Feingersh **CO-18** Mahaux Photography/Getty Images Inc.—Image Bank **18-01** J. L. Charmet/Science Photo Library/Photo Researchers **18-06b** Dave King/Dorling Kindersley Media Library **18-11** T. J. Florian/Rainbow **18-15** Richard Megna/Fundamental Photographs **18-16** Tony Freeman/PhotoEdit **18-18** Barbara Filet/Tony Stone Images **18-32** Jerry Marshall/Jerry Marshall **18-34** Scott T. Smith/Corbis/Bettmann; www.corbis.com/Scott T. Smith/Corbis Images **18-36** Jim Wehtje/Getty Images, Inc.—Photodisc. **CO-19** Courtesy of iRiver **19-24** Dept. Clinical Radiology, Salisbury District Hospital/SPL/Photo Researchers, Inc.; Department of Clinical Radiology, Salisbury District Hospital/Science Photo Library/Photo Researchers, Inc. **19-27a** Getty Images, Inc.—Photodisc. **19-27b** William E. Ferguson/William E. Ferguson **19-27c** Ed Degginger/Color-Pic, Inc. **19-29a** Paul Silverman/Fundamental Photographs **19-29b** Paul Silverman/Fundamental Photographs **CO-20** Chris Rogers/Rainbow; © 2000 Chris Rogers/Rainbow **20-01** Unidentified/Dorling Kindersley Media Library; © Dorling Kindersley **20-04a** Stephen Oliver/Dorling Kindersley Media Library; Stephen Oliver © Dorling Kindersley **20-06** Mary Teresa Giancoli **20-08a** Richard Megna/Fundamental Photographs **20-18** Pekka Parviainen/Science Photo Library/Photo Researchers, Inc. **20-50** Clive Streeter/Dorling Kindersley Media Library; Clive Streeter © Dorling Kindersley **CO-21** Richard Megna/Fundamental Photographs **21-08** Diva de Provence **21-13** Werner H. Muller/Peter Arnold, Inc. **21-21** Joe Raedle/Getty Images, Inc—Liaison **21-27b** Pete Saloutos/Corbis/Bettmann **21-30a** Richard Megna/Fundamental Photographs **CO-22** Jeremy Woodhouse/Getty Images, Inc.—Photodisc. **22-01** American Institute of Physics/Niels Bohr Library/AIP Emilio Segrè Visual Archives **22-09** Image Works **22-18** Larry Mulvehill/The Image Works; © Larry Mulvehill/The Image Works **22-21** World Perspectives/Getty Images, Inc.—Stone Allstock **CO-23** Mulvehill/The Photo Works **23-05** Douglas C. Giancoli **23-9a** Mary Teresa Giancoli/Mary Teresa Giancoli; Mary Teresa Giancoli and Suzanne Saylor **23-9b** Paul Silverman/Fundamental Photographs **23-18** Travel Pix Ltd./SuperStock, Inc. **23-21** Mary Teresa Giancoli **23-28b** S. Elleringmann/Bilderberg/Aurora & Quanta Productions, Inc. **23-30** Douglas C. Giancoli and Howard Shugat **23-46** Mary Teresa Giancoli **CO-24** Dave King/Dorling Kindersley Media Library; Dave King © Dorling Kindersley **24-04a** John M. Dunay IV/Fundamental Photographs **24-13** Science Photo Library/David Parker/Photo Researchers **24-17** George B. Diebold/Corbis/Bettmann **24-31b** Ken Kay/Fundamental Photographs **24-33** Bausch & Lomb Incorporated **24-35** Kristen Brochmann/Fundamental Photographs **24-51** Texas Instruments Incorporated **24-52b** Dan Rutter/Daniel Rutter; © Daniel Rutter/Dan's Data **24-55** Pekka Parviainen/Science Photo Library/Photo Researchers, Inc. **24-56** Spike Mafford/Getty Images, Inc.—Photodisc. **CO-25** Richard Megna/Fundamental Photographs **25-04** Mary Teresa Giancoli **25-07** Leonard Lessin/Peter Arnold **25-18** Franca Principe/Istituto e Museo di Storia della Scienza, Florence, Italy **25-20** Yerkes Observatory **25-21c** Palomar/Caltech **25-21d** Roger Ressmeyer/Starlight **25-23b** Olympus America Inc. **25-28** Reproduced by permission from M. Cagnet, M. Francon, and J. Thrier, *The Atlas of Optical Phenomena*. Berlin: Springer-Verlag, 1962. **25-31** Space Telescope Science Institute **25-32** National Astronomy & Ionosphere Center, Cornell University, Arecibo, Puerto Rico **25-36** Photo by W. Friedrich/Max von Laue. Burndy Library, Dibner Institute for the History of Science and Technology, Cambridge, Massachusetts. **25-40** Rosalind Franklin/Photo Researchers **25-44a** Martin M. Rotker/Martin M. Rotker **25-44b** Simon Fraser/Science Photo Library/Photo Researchers, Inc. **25-47** Ron Chapple/Getty Images, Inc.—Taxi **CO-26** Cambridge University Press; "The City Blocks Became Still Shorter" from page 4 of the book, "Mr Tompkins in Paperback" by George Gamow. Reprinted with the permission of Cambridge University Press. **26-01** Corbis/Bettmann **26-11** Cambridge University Press; "Unbelievably Shortened" from page 3 of "Mr Tompkins in Paperback" by George Gamow. Reprinted with the permission of Cambridge University Press. **CO-27** P. M. Motta and F. M. Magliocca/Science Photo Library/Photo Researchers, Inc. **27-11** S. A. Goudsmit/American Institute of Physics/Niels Bohr Library/AIP Emilio Segrè Visual Archives **27-12** Education Development Center, Inc. **27-15a** Lee D. Simon/Science Source/Photo Researchers, Inc. **27-15b** Oliver Meckes/Max-Planck-Institut-Tubingen/Photo Researchers, Inc. **CO-28** Richard Cummins/Corbis/Bettmann; © Richard Cummins/Corbis **28-01** American Institute of Physics/Emilio Segrè Visual Archives **28-02** ED. Rosetti/American Institute of Physics/Emilio Segrè Visual Archives **28-04** Advanced Research Lab, Hitachi, Ltd. **28-15** Mark Schneider/Visuals Unlimited **28-21** Yoav Levy/Phototake NYC **28-23** Philippe Plaily/Photo Researchers, Inc. **CO-29** Intel Corporation Pressroom Photo Archives **CO-30** Reuters Newsmedia Inc./Corbis **30-03** Center for the History of Chemistry **30-07** University of Chicago/American Institute of Physics/Niels Bohr Library/Courtesy of AIP Emilio Segrè Visual Archives **30-16** Fermilab Visual Media Services **CO-31** Peter Beck/Corbis/Bettmann; © Peter Beck/CORBIS **31-05** Gary Sheahan, "Birth of the Atomic Age," Chicago (Illinois); 1957. Chicago Historical Society, ICHi-33305. **31-08** LeRoy N. Sanchez/Los Alamos National Laboratory **31-10** Corbis **31-13** Lawrence Livermore National Laboratory/Science Source/Photo Researchers, Inc. **31-16** J. Van't Hof. **31-21** Southern Illinois University/Peter Arnold, Inc. **31-23** Mehau Kulyk/Science Photo Library/Photo Researchers, Inc. **CO-32** Fermilab/Science Photo Library/Photo Researchers, Inc. **32-01** Science Service/Watson Davis/American Institute of Physics/Niels Bohr Library/AIP Emilio Segrè Visual Archives/Physics Today Collection **32-03a** Fermilab Visual Media Services **32-03b** Fermilab Visual Media Services **32-04b** Barrie Rokeach/Aerial/Terrestrial Photography **32-05** CERN/Science Photo Library/Photo Researchers, Inc. **32-09** Science Photo Library/Photo Researchers **32-10** Brookhaven National Laboratory **CO-33** NASA/WMAP Science Team/NASA Headquarters **33-01** NASA Headquarters **33-02** Photo Researchers **33-03** U.S. Naval Observatory Photo/NASA Headquarters **33-04** National Optical Astronomy Observatories **33-09** Hubble Space Telescope/NASA/NASA Headquarters; Courtesy of NASA and the Hubble Heritage Team **33-11** National Optical Astronomy Observatories **33-22** Bell Photographers, Inc. **33-24** NASA Headquarters; GSFC/NASA **33-28** Dr. Wes Colley

# Periodic Table of the Elements§

Symbol — Cl 17 — Atomic Number
Atomic Mass§ — 35.4527
$3p^5$ — Electron Configuration (outer shells only)

| Group I | Group II | Transition Elements | | | | | | | | | | Group III | Group IV | Group V | Group VI | Group VII | Group VIII |
|---|---|---|---|---|---|---|---|---|---|---|---|---|---|---|---|---|---|
| **H** 1<br>1.00794<br>$1s^1$ | | | | | | | | | | | | | | | | | **He** 2<br>4.002602<br>$1s^2$ |
| **Li** 3<br>6.941<br>$2s^1$ | **Be** 4<br>9.012182<br>$2s^2$ | | | | | | | | | | | **B** 5<br>10.811<br>$2p^1$ | **C** 6<br>12.0107<br>$2p^2$ | **N** 7<br>14.00674<br>$2p^3$ | **O** 8<br>15.9994<br>$2p^4$ | **F** 9<br>18.9984032<br>$2p^5$ | **Ne** 10<br>20.1797<br>$2p^6$ |
| **Na** 11<br>22.989770<br>$3s^1$ | **Mg** 12<br>24.3050<br>$3s^2$ | | | | | | | | | | | **Al** 13<br>26.981538<br>$3p^1$ | **Si** 14<br>28.0855<br>$3p^2$ | **P** 15<br>30.973761<br>$3p^3$ | **S** 16<br>32.066<br>$3p^4$ | **Cl** 17<br>35.4527<br>$3p^5$ | **Ar** 18<br>39.948<br>$3p^6$ |
| **K** 19<br>39.0983<br>$4s^1$ | **Ca** 20<br>40.078<br>$4s^2$ | **Sc** 21<br>44.955910<br>$3d^14s^2$ | **Ti** 22<br>47.867<br>$3d^24s^2$ | **V** 23<br>50.9415<br>$3d^34s^2$ | **Cr** 24<br>51.9961<br>$3d^54s^1$ | **Mn** 25<br>54.938049<br>$3d^54s^2$ | **Fe** 26<br>55.845<br>$3d^64s^2$ | **Co** 27<br>58.933200<br>$3d^74s^2$ | **Ni** 28<br>58.6934<br>$3d^84s^2$ | **Cu** 29<br>63.546<br>$3d^{10}4s^1$ | **Zn** 30<br>65.39<br>$3d^{10}4s^2$ | **Ga** 31<br>69.723<br>$4p^1$ | **Ge** 32<br>72.61<br>$4p^2$ | **As** 33<br>74.92160<br>$4p^3$ | **Se** 34<br>78.96<br>$4p^4$ | **Br** 35<br>79.904<br>$4p^5$ | **Kr** 36<br>83.80<br>$4p^6$ |
| **Rb** 37<br>85.4678<br>$5s^1$ | **Sr** 38<br>87.62<br>$5s^2$ | **Y** 39<br>88.90585<br>$4d^15s^2$ | **Zr** 40<br>91.224<br>$4d^25s^2$ | **Nb** 41<br>92.90638<br>$4d^45s^1$ | **Mo** 42<br>95.94<br>$4d^55s^1$ | **Tc** 43<br>(98)<br>$4d^55s^2$ | **Ru** 44<br>101.07<br>$4d^75s^1$ | **Rh** 45<br>102.90550<br>$4d^85s^1$ | **Pd** 46<br>106.42<br>$4d^{10}5s^0$ | **Ag** 47<br>107.8682<br>$4d^{10}5s^1$ | **Cd** 48<br>112.411<br>$4d^{10}5s^2$ | **In** 49<br>114.818<br>$5p^1$ | **Sn** 50<br>118.710<br>$5p^2$ | **Sb** 51<br>121.760<br>$5p^3$ | **Te** 52<br>127.60<br>$5p^4$ | **I** 53<br>126.90447<br>$5p^5$ | **Xe** 54<br>131.29<br>$5p^6$ |
| **Cs** 55<br>132.90545<br>$6s^1$ | **Ba** 56<br>137.327<br>$6s^2$ | 57–71† | **Hf** 72<br>178.49<br>$5d^26s^2$ | **Ta** 73<br>180.9479<br>$5d^36s^2$ | **W** 74<br>183.84<br>$5d^46s^2$ | **Re** 75<br>186.207<br>$5d^56s^2$ | **Os** 76<br>190.23<br>$5d^66s^2$ | **Ir** 77<br>192.217<br>$5d^76s^2$ | **Pt** 78<br>195.078<br>$5d^96s^1$ | **Au** 79<br>196.96655<br>$5d^{10}6s^1$ | **Hg** 80<br>200.59<br>$5d^{10}6s^2$ | **Tl** 81<br>204.3833<br>$6p^1$ | **Pb** 82<br>207.2<br>$6p^2$ | **Bi** 83<br>208.98038<br>$6p^3$ | **Po** 84<br>(209)<br>$6p^4$ | **At** 85<br>(210)<br>$6p^5$ | **Rn** 86<br>(222)<br>$6p^6$ |
| **Fr** 87<br>(223)<br>$7s^1$ | **Ra** 88<br>(226)<br>$7s^2$ | 89–103‡ | **Rf** 104<br>(261)<br>$6d^27s^2$ | **Db** 105<br>(262)<br>$6d^37s^2$ | **Sg** 106<br>(266)<br>$6d^47s^2$ | **Bh** 107<br>(264)<br>$6d^57s^2$ | **Hs** 108<br>(269)<br>$6d^67s^2$ | **Mt** 109<br>(268)<br>$6d^77s^2$ | **Ds** 110<br>(271)<br>$6d^97s^1$ | 111<br>(272)<br>$6d^{10}7s^1$ | 112<br>(277)<br>$6d^{10}7s^2$ | | | | | | |

| | | | | | | | | | | | | | | | |
|---|---|---|---|---|---|---|---|---|---|---|---|---|---|---|---|
| †Lanthanide Series | **La** 57<br>138.9055<br>$5d^16s^2$ | **Ce** 58<br>140.115<br>$4f^15d^16s^2$ | **Pr** 59<br>140.90765<br>$4f^35d^06s^2$ | **Nd** 60<br>144.24<br>$4f^45d^06s^2$ | **Pm** 61<br>(145)<br>$4f^55d^06s^2$ | **Sm** 62<br>150.36<br>$4f^65d^06s^2$ | **Eu** 63<br>151.964<br>$4f^75d^06s^2$ | **Gd** 64<br>157.25<br>$4f^75d^16s^2$ | **Tb** 65<br>158.92534<br>$4f^95d^06s^2$ | **Dy** 66<br>162.50<br>$4f^{10}5d^06s^2$ | **Ho** 67<br>164.93032<br>$4f^{11}5d^06s^2$ | **Er** 68<br>167.26<br>$4f^{12}5d^06s^2$ | **Tm** 69<br>168.93421<br>$4f^{13}5d^06s^2$ | **Yb** 70<br>173.04<br>$4f^{14}5d^06s^2$ | **Lu** 71<br>174.967<br>$4f^{14}5d^16s^2$ |
| ‡Actinide Series | **Ac** 89<br>(227.02775)<br>$6d^17s^2$ | **Th** 90<br>232.0381<br>$6d^27s^2$ | **Pa** 91<br>(231)<br>$5f^26d^17s^2$ | **U** 92<br>238.0289<br>$5f^36d^17s^2$ | **Np** 93<br>(237)<br>$5f^46d^17s^2$ | **Pu** 94<br>(244)<br>$5f^66d^07s^2$ | **Am** 95<br>(243)<br>$5f^76d^07s^2$ | **Cm** 96<br>(247)<br>$5f^76d^17s^2$ | **Bk** 97<br>(247)<br>$5f^96d^07s^2$ | **Cf** 98<br>(251)<br>$5f^{10}6d^07s^2$ | **Es** 99<br>(252)<br>$5f^{11}6d^07s^2$ | **Fm** 100<br>(257)<br>$5f^{12}6d^07s^2$ | **Md** 101<br>(258)<br>$5f^{13}6d^07s^2$ | **No** 102<br>(259)<br>$5f^{14}6d^07s^2$ | **Lr** 103<br>(262)<br>$5f^{14}6d^17s^2$ |

§ Atomic mass values averaged over isotopes in the percentages they occur on Earth's surface. For unstable elements, mass of the longest-lived known isotope is given in parentheses. 2003 revisions. (See also Appendix B.)